One method of reducing a part of the earth's surface is by aerial photography. The two photographs on this page are semi-controlled mosaics and are made by matching together a series of vertical aerial photographs. Although an accurate map cannot be made directly from such a mosaic, it does illustrate one way that a map can be made. Each of the mosaics is approximately the scale of its corresponding map. On a map, cultural and physical features are represented by means of signs, symbols, and certain conventions. By comparing the mosaic with the map in each case, one can ascertain how various features on the earth have been represented on the map and how they, and other features, appear from the air. For example, the darkest areas on the Pittsburgh mosaic are wooded areas which are shown in green on the map. The heavily built-up area of Pittsburgh is depicted by a red screen on the map. The major buildings, roads, and bridges are easily recognized.

The part of the Strasburg, Virginia, Quadrangle selected lies in the folded Appalachians just east of Woodstock, Virginia, and across the "Great Valley" of the Shenandoah River. The valley, occupied by the meanders of both forks of the Shenandoah River, is divided at this point by Massanutten Mountain. The latter is a complex synclinal mass, made mostly of sandstone. The three northeast trending parallel ridges of the mountain can be readily recognized and compared. Notice that the shading on the map and the shadows on the mosaic do not agree. The photographs were taken in the morning, placing the western slopes of the ridges in shadow. The general practice of the cartographer, however, is to render the relief as if the light source was from the northwest. The comparison, nevertheless, facilitates an understanding of how contours and relief shading are used to represent surface configuration.

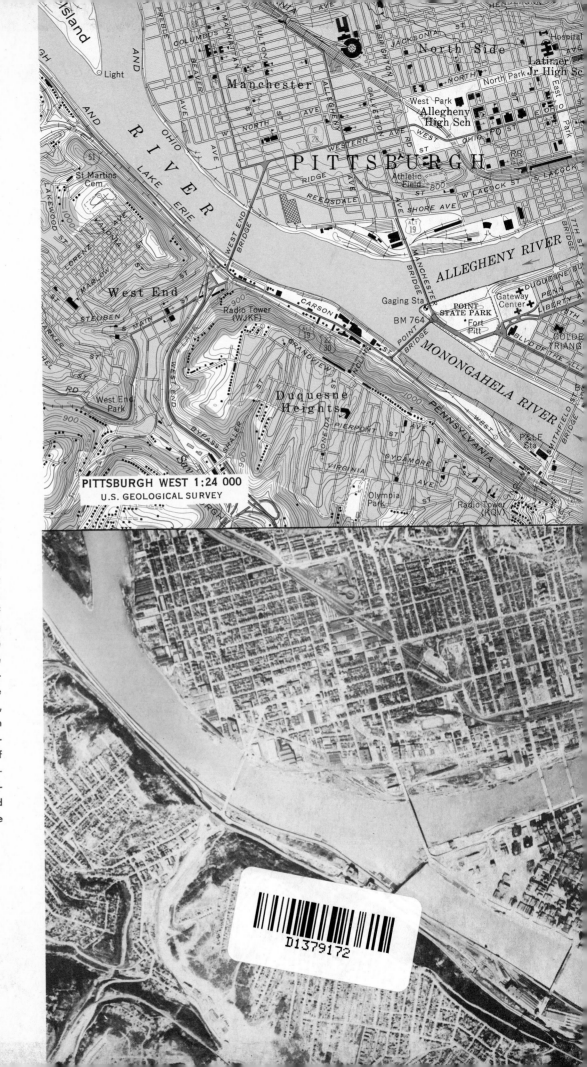

PITTSBURGH WEST 1:24 000
U.S. GEOLOGICAL SURVEY

This book
belongs to the
Smith family
1719 Springview
Drive "69"

GOODE'S

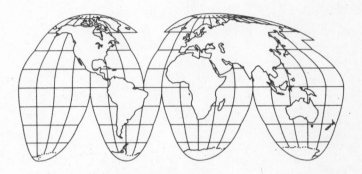

WORLD ATLAS

ELEVENTH EDITION

edited by
Edward B. Espenshade, Jr.
Professor of Geography, Northwestern University

RAND McNALLY & COMPANY · CHICAGO

CONTENTS

Europe

Asia

ACKNOWLEDGMENTS

Sources. Every effort has been made to assemble the latest and most authentic source materials for use in compiling the atlas. For the general physical-political maps, national and state surveys, recent military maps, and hydrographic charts have been utilized. For the specialized maps, the source materials are even more varied. They include both published and unpublished items in the form of maps, descriptions in articles and books, statistics, and correspondence with geographers and others. To the various agencies and organizations, official and unofficial, who have cooperated, appreciation and thanks are expressed. Noteworthy among these organizations and agencies are: Food and Agriculture Organization of The United Nations for production statistics on livestock, crop and forest products, and statistics on world trade; the Office of the Geographer, The Department of State, for the map of Surface Transport Facilities, and other items; the Office of Foreign Agricultural Relations, Department of Agriculture, for information on crop and livestock production and distribution; the Bureau of Mines, Department of the Interior, for information on mineral production; various branches of the National Military Establishment and the Weather Bureau, Department of Commerce, for information on temperature, wind, pressure, and ocean currents; the Maritime Commission and the Department of Commerce, for statistics on ocean trade; the American Geographical Society, for use of its library and permission to use the Miller cylindrical projection; The University of Chicago Press, owners of the copyright, for permission to use Goode's Homolosine equal-area projection; and McGraw-Hill Book Company, for cooperation in permitting the use of Glenn Trewartha's map of climatic regions and Petterson's diagram of zones of precipitation.

Other acknowledgments. The variety and complexity of the problems involved in the preparation of a world atlas make highly desirable the participation of specialists in some of the problems. In the preparation of the new edition of *Goode's World Atlas* the editor has been ably assisted by several such experts. He expresses his deep appreciation and thanks to all of them. He is particularly indebted to the experts listed below who have assumed primary responsibility for certain maps.

The editor's grateful thanks are due to the staff of Rand McNally & Company. It is not possible to cite individual contributions, but the varied skills of geographers, cartographers, and many others are involved. Their faithful and careful work has contributed much to the final result.

Corrigenda. Any completely new series of maps such as that incorporated in this eleventh edition inevitably contains some mistakes and misspellings. It is hoped that users of the atlas will inform us of any errors, so that the atlas may be maintained as accurately as possible.

EDWARD B. ESPENSHADE, JR.
Northwestern University
June, 1960

Cooperating Experts

R. G. HAINSWORTH
Office of Foreign Agricultural Relations
United States Department of Agriculture

A. W. KÜCHLER
Department of Geography
University of Kansas

THOBURN C. LYON
Consultant
Cartography and Air Navigation

A. C. ORVEDAL
Soil Scientist
Division of Soil Survey
United States Department of Agriculture

ERWIN RAISZ
Cartographer
Cambridge, Massachusetts

GLENN T. TREWARTHA
Department of Geography
University of Wisconsin

J. PARKER VAN ZANDT
President
Aviation Research Institute

WALTER H. VOSKUIL
Mineral Economist
Illinois Geological Survey

DERWENT WHITTLESEY
Late Professor of Geography
Harvard University

BOGDAN ZABORSKI
Professor of Geography
University of Ottawa

INTRODUCTION

Utility of maps. There are many kinds of maps, and they are useful in countless ways. It would be difficult to list all the ways in which even a simple road map, for example, is or may be useful. A knowledge of location, relative size, direction, distance, or of other facts which are set down in an atlas is necessary to an understanding of much about which one reads today. The changing world and the widespread commitments of the United States place new emphasis on map study. An atlas has become a prime necessity for understanding the course of world events. Three outstanding attributes may be noted in connection with the maps of this atlas. They are characteristics common to maps of the most varied kinds and utilities.

(1) The maps show facts of areal distribution, both qualitative and quantitative. For example, the world vegetation map (pp. 16-17) is based on observations made by many hundreds of individuals. The map shows hundreds of varied vegetative units and thirty-two types of vegetation. Thousands of words would be required to state the facts portrayed by the map. These facts can be presented best on a map and can be grasped quickly from a map. The information embodied in the world vegetation map is chiefly qualitative. It was reduced from a general, undefined form to a particular, classified form, and so its utility was greatly enhanced. The world rainfall map (pp. 14-15) provides quantitative facts concerning annual precipitation, by means of isohyets (lines connecting points of equal rainfall). Here again, a single map conveys factual information far better than could be done by volumes of words and tables.

(2) The maps in *Goode's World Atlas* also serve to illustrate innumerable facts of significance that are associated with location and areal distribution. For example, the climatic-regions map (pp. 8-9) shows the areal distribution of types of climate which are determined from a synthesis of thousands of rainfall and temperature statistics.

(3) Finally, many useful comparisons may be made between different maps, between two maps in some instances, between three or more in others, with a view to establishing relationships between the various types of information entered on the maps. Useful comparisons may also be made, of course, between different places on the same map as well as between different aspects of the same place as shown on two or more maps. For example, compare the areas of dense population (pp. 20-21) with areas which have an intensive subsistence rice or non-rice agriculture (pp. 24-25). There are few agricultural areas in the world, with the exception of those in Europe, which have similar population densities. Note also on the agricultural-regions map the absence of nomadic herding in the Western Hemisphere, whereas extensive areas exist in Asia and Africa.

Reading maps. An ability to read maps is acquired through practice, in the same manner as the ability to read a written text. The effectiveness of any written text depends both on the skill of the writer and on that of the reader. Similarly, the value of a particular map depends both on the effectiveness of the cartography and on the map-reading ability of the user. Of particular importance in reading maps is a knowledge of map scales, projections, and symbolism.

Understanding scales. A function of all maps is to provide a reduced representation of the earth's surface. Since part or all of the earth's surface is depicted on a single page of this atlas, the question arises, "What is the relation of map size to earth size?" This proportional relationship is the scale of a map. The scale is given in three forms on most maps of this atlas to facilitate answering this question.

To aid further in understanding scales, a comparison of scale is given in a series of maps on the next page. A comparison of diagrams A, B, C, and D illustrates how progressively smaller-scale maps (of constant page size) increase the size of the area covered but reduce the detail which can be expressed. On the second map and on each later map, the area covered by the previous map is outlined within the map, to provide a direct comparison of the areas covered. On the first map, individual buildings are shown. On the final map, even many cities are omitted.

To aid the student in acquiring accurate concepts of the relative size of continents and of some countries and regions, uniform scales for comparable areas are used as far as possible. Continental maps are given on a uniform scale of 1:40,000,000 (one inch to 640 miles). In similar fashion, series of regions comparable in area appear in groups of maps on uniform scales of 1:16,000,000 (one inch to 250 miles), 1:12,000,000 (one inch to 190 miles), 1:4,000,000 (one inch to 64 miles), and on larger scales. The maximum size of the scale utilized for any

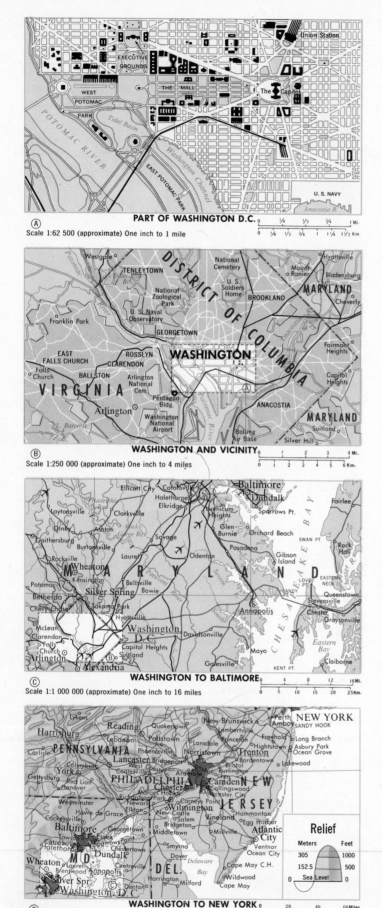

PART OF WASHINGTON D.C.
(A)
Scale 1:62 500 (approximate) One inch to 1 mile

WASHINGTON AND VICINITY
(B)
Scale 1:250 000 (approximate) One inch to 4 miles

WASHINGTON TO BALTIMORE
(C)
Scale 1:1 000 000 (approximate) One inch to 16 miles

WASHINGTON TO NEW YORK
(D)
Scale 1:4 000 000, one inch to 64 miles. Conic Projection

given region is a partial measure of the importance of the region and of interest in it.

Understanding projections. There is no way of representing the curved surface of the globe on a flat surface without some distortion of the useful features desired on flat maps. On large-scale maps covering areas of only a few square miles, this distortion is negligible. In maps representing large areas, as in maps of a large country, a continent, or the whole world, the distortion inevitably is considerable, and, unless understood, it may result in serious misconceptions. The distortion may involve distances, directions, or the shapes and sizes of areas.

A map projection is an orderly system of parallels and meridians on which a map can be drawn. There are hundreds of map projections in use, but none avoids distortion of the spatial relationships that only a globe map can show truthfully. It is not possible to have truth of area, shape, angle, and scale all in the same flat map. It is possible, however, to select from the many types of projections one which is accurate for a particular property or which is a compromise (limiting the distortion of one or more elements at the expense of the others) that is relatively satisfactory for a particular need.

Truth of area is of prime importance in many maps. Most of the maps made for geographical study, particularly those used to show the areal distribution of an item, are drawn on equal-area projections. In an equal-area projection any square inch on the map represents the same number of square miles on the earth's surface as any other square inch on the map. Continents, oceans, islands, states, all are shown in their true relative size. Close to the importance of equality of area is truth of shape. This characteristic is to some extent an esthetic quality, but it is also a practical one. The student becomes familiar with the true shape of a continent or an island or a body of water as it appears on a globe map. Distortion of these shapes almost beyond recognition on a flat map is incongruous and a source of bewilderment to the student. Truth of direction is especially important in the study of the distribution of factors of significance in world relations. To show the latitudinal or zonal distribution of such factors, it is obviously desirable that lines of latitude be parallel, or better, straight lines parallel with the equator.

Most of the maps used in this atlas are drawn on projections that give equality of area, good land and ocean shapes, and parallel latitudinal directions. To provide these and other qualities desired for particular maps, some distortion of other elements is inevitable. The student should make himself aware of the nature of such distortions and make allowances for them in his use of the maps. One of the more practical procedures is to compare the projection grid of the flat map with the grid of the globe map. He should first verify the fundamental characteristics of the globe grid as listed here:

(1) On the globe map all longitude lines are equal in length and meet at the poles.

(2) All latitude lines are parallel.

(3) The length of the latitude lines, that is, the circumference of latitude circles, decreases from the equator to the points representing the poles. At latitude 60°, the circumference of the latitude circle is one-half the circumference of the equatorial circle.

(4) Distances along lines of longitude between any two latitude lines are equal.

(5) All latitude and longitude lines meet at right angles. With item (1) in mind, the student will observe that the projection used on pages 44-45 has latitude lines of equal length. This results in considerable exaggeration of areas in the higher latitudes. With item (5) in mind, he will note that the projection used on pages 6-7 has oblique angles at the junction of latitude and longitude lines in the higher latitudes, and that this partly causes distortion of land shapes in such areas as Alaska and Greenland. In this projection, however, truth of area has been maintained.

Some illustration of the construction of the more commonly used projections and indication of their properties are helpful in making clear the nature of inherent distortions. Pages 2 and 3 are designed to provide this help. They also illustrate the seven projections used in this atlas.

Few of the several hundred projections in use can be constructed graphically by methods of descriptive geometry. Most of them are derived from mathematical formulas designed to afford the properties desired. In some cases it is easier to visualize the general form and characteristics of a projection if the earth's surface is considered to be projected upon a plane, a cone, or a cylinder. The last two surfaces, when they are cut and unrolled, form a plane surface. These surfaces provide one general classification of projections: azimuthal (on a plane), conic, or cylindrical (fig. 1, 2, and 5, pp. 2 and 3). In each class the characteristics of the projections may be changed by varying the systematic arrangement or spacing of the latitude and longitude lines.

Figure 1, A (p. 2) is a true plane projection with the point of projection at the center of the globe. This geometrical projection of the earth grid on a tangent plane is called a gnomonic projection. In the illustration the plane is tangent to the equator, but it could be placed tangent to the poles, or to any other point on the earth's surface. Several other distinctive map projections can be obtained by changing the origin point of the projection. For example, the projection obtained from an origin point on the surface of the globe diametrically opposite the point of contact of the tangent plane is called a stereographic projection, and the projection from an origin point at infinity is called an orthographic projection. None of these perspective projections obtained from projection on a plane is used in this atlas, but the mathematically derived Lambert azimuthal equal-area projection (fig. 1, B, p. 2) may be considered in this general class. The polar aspect of the Lambert azimuthal equal-area projection is used for the map of the Northern Lands and Seas (p. 48); the oblique aspect is used for the series of continental maps. Besides its equal-area quality, the projection gives relatively good shapes to continental areas as a whole.

Conic projections may be thought of as derived from a tangent cone (fig. 2) or from an intersecting cone (fig. 3). In the latter case, the resulting projection is said to have "two standard parallels" along which the scale is exact (since the cone and the sphere coincide throughout the length of the parallels). In maps of areas covering a wide range of longitude, the projection used in this atlas is a modified conic of the latter type

(De Lisle's). In this projection, as here used, the shapes are excellent, and the departure from the equal-area quality is almost negligible. (See Canada, pp. 86-87, and Siberia, pp. 134-135). The scale between the two standard parallels is too small along the parallels, and outside the standard parallels is too great along the parallels. The use of two standard parallels, however, provides a much better opportunity of extending the area within which the scale is reasonably accurate than the use of a single standard parallel, as in the simple conic.

Another modification of the conic principle is the Bonne projection (fig. 3, C, p. 2), used on pages 114-115 for the map of the Mediterranean lands. It has a selected standard parallel, and other parallels are arcs of concentric circles truly divided for points of intersection with the meridians. The scale along all the parallels is true everywhere, but the central meridian is the only one along which it is true. By construction, however, it is equal-area, and reasonably correct representation of shape is obtained in narrow zones along the standard parallel and central meridian, where the intersections are at right angles, or nearly so.

The polyconic projection (fig. 4, p. 2) is used for the United States and some other areas of similar position and size. In the case of the polyconic projection, the earth may be considered as made up of a series of tangent cones. As each base is developed, the result is as shown, somewhat exaggerated, in figure 4, B, page 2. The area of the projection used for the map of the United States (fig. 4, C, page 2) is the central portion of figure 4, B, beneath the word "Pole." In this projection the central meridian crosses all parallels at right angles, as on the globe; other intersections become noticeably oblique only at considerable distance from the central meridian. The scale is true on the central meridian and on each parallel. Shapes, as a result, are very good. Meridian-scale errors, however, increase rapidly with increasing distance from the central meridian. The projection is thus not well adapted to areas of wide longitudinal extent. The departure, however, from equality of area is slight where it has been used for maps in this atlas.

The cylindrical class of projections may be visualized as perspective projections on a tangent or intersecting cylinder (fig. 5, page 3). Many of the cylindrical projections in use, however, are mathematical modifications of the true perspective forms. As a general class, the cylindrical projections have the following characteristics: (1) latitude lines which are straight, parallel, and equal in length; (2) longitude lines which are straight, parallel, equal in length, and equally spaced; (3) meridians and parallels which intersect at right angles (fig. 5, page 3). Since the latitude lines are all drawn equal in length, an increasing distortion of scale occurs along the parallels with increasing distance from the standard parallel or parallels of tangency.

Mercator's projection (fig. 5, C, page 3), which belongs to this general class, is one of the better-known projections. For nearly four hundred years it has been used widely for world distributional maps, in spite of the facts (1) that it is impossible with this projection to show the entire surface of the earth, the poles being at infinity; and (2) that distances and areas grow rapidly larger with increase of latitude, until the distortion becomes enormous in higher latitudes. This is made apparent by

a comparison of the relative size of areas in figures 5, C, and 6. The distortion of area is so great that the use of the Mercator projection for world maps showing areal distributions of most kinds is pedagogically unsound and misleading. The projection was designed by Mercator primarily for use of navigators, and for that use it is incomparable. On it, the navigator can draw a straight line (called a rhumb line) between any two points, read the angle between the rhumb line and any meridian that it crosses, set his compass on that angle, and go direct to his destination without change of compass. This advantage is so great that no other projection has yet taken the place of the Mercator in marine navigation.

A variation of the Mercator is the transverse or oblique Mercator. The grid is derived from a cylinder tangent along a selected great circle (fig. 7). The resulting projection is conformal, but its grid bears no resemblance to that of the ordinary Mercator and may be mistaken for that of a conic projection. Although the tranverse Mercator projection is not used in this atlas, it illustrates a special-purpose projection which is being used more and more because of its value in air navigation for maps of great-circle strips.

Miller's projection (fig. 5, D) is a recent "compromise projection." It has been used in the atlas (with permission of the American Geographical Society) for climatic maps showing barometric pressures, winds, and temperatures, and for the map of ocean communications. A continuous grid without interruptions, and straight-line parallels were desirable for the best presentation of the features listed above. Miller's projection meets these requirements and provides a compromise between the distortion of areas and shapes. Mercator's projection was not suitable because of its excessive area distortion, although shapes of areas are excellent. Use of continuous grids for the whole world which were strictly equal-area would result in considerable distortion of shapes. The student will note, however, that even on the Miller projection there is still considerable distortion of areas and shapes in the higher latitudes (cf. fig. 5, D, 5, C, and 6). Changes in scale according to latitude are indicated in the legend of the map and should be carefully noted. For example, compare on the graphic scale (page 45) a distance of one thousand miles at the equator with the same distance at latitude 60° or 80°.

Figure 6 illustrates three projections which are purely conventional in design. They cannot be readily related to the three general classes just discussed. They are not projections in the sense of being projected on a plane, a cone, or a cylinder; rather, they all are based on mathematical formulas. The sinusoidal projection (fig. 6, C, page 3) is used for the large-scale sectional maps of South America and Africa and for the map showing world surface transport facilities. It is an equal-area projection. On these continental maps it is most accurate along the equator where the two continents are widest. The placement of the central meridian through the center of the continents results in relatively little distortion of scale or shapes in the narrower southern parts of the continents. The scale is true along all parallels and the central meridian, but it increases on other meridians in conformity with their increasing obliquity. On the world map (pp. 42-43) the extent of the distortion is reduced by the technique of interrupting the pro-

jection and of using a separate central meridian for different land masses.

Mollweide's equal-area projection (fig. 6, A, page 3), designed to show the entire globe as an uninterrupted unit, gives an elliptical picture of the earth. The ellipse is drawn to enclose an area equal to that of a globe on the same scale. The central meridian is divided so that the areas of the bands between the parallels are truthfully proportional. Mollweide's projection is thus an equal-area projection, but there is little uniformity in linear scale. So that the areas of greater distortion in the outer parts of the projection will be eliminated, it, like the sinusoidal projection, may be interrupted and a new central meridian established through each continent (cf. the two forms, fig. 6, A and B, page 3).

Most of the world distribution maps in this atlas are drawn on Goode's homolosine equal-area projection (fig. 6, D, page 3). This projection is derived by combining the sinusoidal projection for latitudes up to 40° north and south with the homolographic projection (Mollweide) for areas poleward of these latitudes. In this manner an equal-area projection is obtained which has some of the better qualities of both the sinusoidal and homolographic. Further improvement of shapes is obtained by application of the principle of interruption, so that extremely oblique intersections are eliminated. The result has a number of distinct advantages: (1) It presents the entire surface of the earth, which Mercator's projection cannot do. (2) It is strictly an equal-area projection, with no distortion of the size of areas. (3) On it the parallels of latitude are represented by straight lines trending with the equator, a real advantage in the study of comparative latitudes. (4) On it the grid is interrupted in the oceans so as to give each continent in turn the advantage of being in the center of the projection, thus providing better shapes for the continents than any uninterrupted world map can give. No map projection has been devised which displays to better advantage the distribution of most world phenomena which are studied best from the equatorial aspect.

Symbolism. The signs, symbols, and conventions shown on maps are a form of "shorthand" indicating a variety of phenomena (page xii). Many of them are self-explanatory. Compare also the aerial mosaics with the adjacent topographic maps of Pittsburgh and Strasburg areas (inside cover). A complete legend (page xii) provides a key to the physical-political reference maps.

Two systems of measurement are used in connection with the maps in this atlas. The English system of measures, which is conventional in this country, is utilized, although admittedly it is somewhat irrational and cumbersome. Since much of the world uses the metric system of measurement and the centigrade thermometer, most measures are given also in these scientific terms, or conversion scales are provided. A linear scale in miles is placed alongside a linear scale in kilometers, with the zero points together. Heights and depths may be read in feet or in meters from opposite scales. Comparative scales in the margins permit ready conversion of temperature and precipitation values from one system to another.

Surface configuration on the continental and regional maps is shown in a different manner from previous editions of this

atlas. A combination of two techniques is utilized which gives a striking three-dimensional effect. General elevation above sea level is indicated as previously by layer-tints, altitudinal zones, each of which has a different hue and is defined by a generalized contour line. The hues for the zones, however, have been selected so that their value increases with elevation in preference to the more conventional layer-tint colors. Thus, although shades of green are still used for the lowlands below 1,000 feet, hues of light tan, buff, and yellow are used for successively higher elevations and areas of more than 10,000 feet are left white. Each of the hues increases in value with increasing elevation and thus visually appears closer to the observer.

An oblique shading in gray has been utilized to indicate local relief and the steepness of slopes. This has been superimposed over the layer tints and a much more realistic and readily visualized impression of the surface configuration is obtained. The three-dimensional effect is more noticeable where it is important in the higher mountainous areas whose slopes are steepest, because the shadow contrast is greatest in the very areas where the color values are highest.

This new presentation of relief is designed to overcome some of the serious weaknesses of the layer-tints system used previously. Steepness of slope, the ruggedness of the terrain, and significant relief features which have differences in elevation with a value less than the layer-tint interval are distinguished and can be visualized. No longer should the nearly level high plateau area be confused with an adjacent mountain area. The improved symbolism for representation of surface configuration should facilitate the reading of the maps and should reduce some of the misconceptions obtained when layer-tints alone were utilized.

Place Names. Place names are used to distinguish particular places and features—cities, towns, bays, peninsulas—from other similar features. Many place names consist of two parts—a specific and a generic part. For example, Lake Michigan consists of the specific term "Michigan" modifying the generic term "lake."

If the world used one alphabet and one language, no particular difficulty would arise in the use of place names. Unfortunately, people use many languages and various alphabets. Moreover, some of the people of the world, the Chinese and the Japanese, for example, use non-alphabet languages. In order to make some languages intelligible to American readers, their letters and symbols must be converted into the Roman alphabet. It has been the practice of many people to transform place names further by transcribing or translating part or all of them into English. The recent war, which brought far corners of the earth to our attention, and the increasing facilities for communication in recent years make this practice no longer desirable. In this atlas, a "local-name policy" has been used for the cities and towns and for all local topographic and water features. A short glossary of "geographical equivalents" is given on pages 6 and 7, and a more complete one on page 171.

A distinctive feature of *Goode's World Atlas* is the pronouncing index which has been completely revised. The variable vowel sounds of English and the differences among other languages make the correct pronunciation of place names difficult. The correct pronunciation of many names differs from the pronunciation that may seem natural. Under these circumstances, the pronouncing index of more than thirty thousand names should be very helpful to the student.

Economic maps and statistics. The statistics presented in this atlas are not intended to take the place of statistical reference works. Instead of having been planned to present an absolute index to production and trade, they were planned to give a picture of the relative importance of countries and regions in the particulars involved. The maps have been reserved to present facts of distribution. Marginal graphs show the relative importance of different areas by percentage values of world totals.

No single year affords, for this purpose, a satisfactory base for production and trade statistics. For this reason, the percentages and world totals used have been computed with few exceptions, from averages of a period of three or four years. The base period of years varies, but the latest year for which data are available at time of publication has been used. Few realize that there is a necessary gap of several years between the date of a publication such as this and the date of the statistics used. Organizations issuing statistical data of the sort used in the atlas require two or three years to gather, tabulate, and publish their materials. An additional year is required to incorporate and publish the data within this atlas. Publishers often are reluctant to date their statistical materials, since few users understand the reason for the gap in time. The dates of the base period used are indicated on each graph. In general the averages and percentages will provide the student with a sufficiently accurate picture of the relative importance of areas, despite the fact they are not for the current year. An exception occurs in the case of a product which is subject to major or rapid expansion or contraction of production either nationally, regionally, or on a world wide basis. This occurs more commonly in mineral products than in agricultural products. An important example is petroleum where notable shifts in proven reserves, production, and trade movements have occurred within the last five years.

EDWARD B. ESPENSHADE, JR.
Northwestern University
June, 1960

MAP SYMBOLS

CULTURAL FEATURES

Political Boundaries

------- International

------- Intercolonial

------- Secondary: State, Provincial, etc.

------- Disputed or Indefinite

Parks, Indian Reservations

City Limits

Cities, Towns and Villages
(Except for scales of 1:20,000,000 or smaller)

PARIS — 1,000,000 and over

Ufa — 500,000 to 1,000,000

Győr — 50,000 to 500,000

Agadir — 25,000 to 50,000

Moreno — 0 to 25,000

TŌKYŌ — National Capitals

Boise — Secondary Capitals

Transportation

——— Railroads

------- Railroad Ferries

——— Roads

········· Caravan Routes

✈ Airports

Other Cultural Features

Dams

Pipelines

▲ Pyramids

Ruins

WATER FEATURES

Lakes and Reservoirs

Fresh Water

Fresh Water: Intermittent

Salt Water

Salt Water: Intermittent

Other Water Features

Salt Basins, Flats

Swamps

Glaciers

Rivers

Canals

Aqueducts

Ship Channels

Falls

Rapids

Springs

Water Depths

Fishing Banks

Sand Bars

Reefs

LAND FEATURES

△ Peaks, Spot Heights

= Passes

Sand

Contours

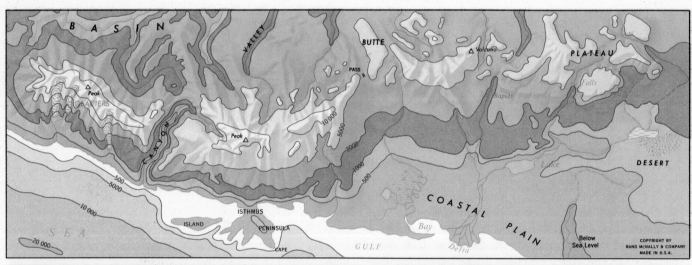

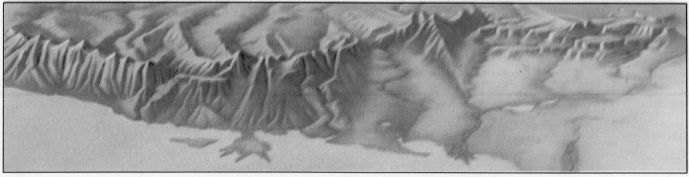

THE SEASONS

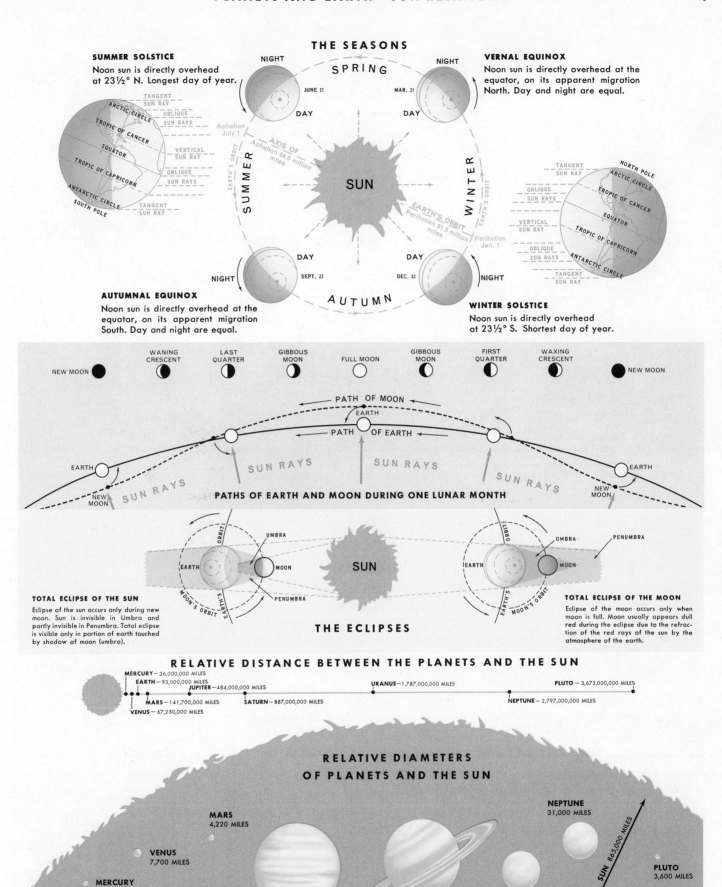

SUMMER SOLSTICE
Noon sun is directly overhead at 23½° N. Longest day of year.

SPRING

JUNE 21

MAR. 21

VERNAL EQUINOX
Noon sun is directly overhead at the equator, on its apparent migration North. Day and night are equal.

NIGHT
DAY

TANGENT SUN RAY
ARCTIC CIRCLE
OBLIQUE SUN RAYS
TROPIC OF CANCER
EQUATOR
VERTICAL SUN RAY
TROPIC OF CAPRICORN
OBLIQUE SUN RAYS
ANTARCTIC CIRCLE
SOUTH POLE
TANGENT SUN RAY

SUMMER

Aphelion July 1
AXIS OF
Aphelion 94.5 million miles
EARTH'S ORBIT

SUN

WINTER

EARTH'S ORBIT
EARTH'S ORBIT
Perihelion 91.5 million miles
Perihelion Jan. 1

TANGENT SUN RAY
NORTH POLE
ARCTIC CIRCLE
TROPIC OF CANCER
OBLIQUE SUN RAYS
EQUATOR
VERTICAL SUN RAY
TROPIC OF CAPRICORN
OBLIQUE SUN RAYS
ANTARCTIC CIRCLE
TANGENT SUN RAY

DAY
SEPT. 23

DAY
DEC. 22

NIGHT
NIGHT

AUTUMN

AUTUMNAL EQUINOX
Noon sun is directly overhead at the equator, on its apparent migration South. Day and night are equal.

WINTER SOLSTICE
Noon sun is directly overhead at 23½° S. Shortest day of year.

NEW MOON

WANING CRESCENT

LAST QUARTER

GIBBOUS MOON

FULL MOON

GIBBOUS MOON

FIRST QUARTER

WAXING CRESCENT

NEW MOON

PATH OF MOON
EARTH
PATH OF EARTH
SUN RAYS
SUN RAYS
SUN RAYS
EARTH
NEW MOON
EARTH
NEW MOON

PATHS OF EARTH AND MOON DURING ONE LUNAR MONTH

ORBIT
UMBRA
EARTH
MOON
SUN
MOON'S ORBIT
EARTH'S
PENUMBRA

ORBIT
UMBRA
PENUMBRA
EARTH
MOON
MOON'S ORBIT
EARTH'S

TOTAL ECLIPSE OF THE SUN
Eclipse of the sun occurs only during new moon. Sun is invisible in Umbra and partly invisible in Penumbra. Total eclipse is visible only in portion of earth touched by shadow of moon (umbra).

THE ECLIPSES

TOTAL ECLIPSE OF THE MOON
Eclipse of the moon occurs only when moon is full. Moon usually appears dull red during the eclipse due to the refraction of the red rays of the sun by the atmosphere of the earth.

RELATIVE DISTANCE BETWEEN THE PLANETS AND THE SUN

MERCURY—36,000,000 MILES
EARTH—93,000,000 MILES
JUPITER—484,000,000 MILES
URANUS—1,787,000,000 MILES
PLUTO—3,675,000,000 MILES
MARS—141,700,000 MILES
SATURN—887,000,000 MILES
NEPTUNE—2,797,000,000 MILES
VENUS—67,250,000 MILES

RELATIVE DIAMETERS OF PLANETS AND THE SUN

MARS
4,220 MILES

NEPTUNE
31,000 MILES

VENUS
7,700 MILES

SUN 865,000 MILES

MERCURY
3,100 MILES

PLUTO
3,600 MILES

EARTH
7,918 MILES

URANUS
32,000 MILES

MOON
2,160 MILES

JUPITER
88,700 MILES

SATURN
71,600 MILES

PROJECTIONS

A map projection is merely an orderly system of parallels and meridians on which a flat map can be drawn. There are hundreds of projections, but no one represents the earth's spherical surface without some distortion. The distortion is relatively small for most practical purposes when a small part of the sphere is projected. For larger areas, a sacrifice of some property is necessary.

Most projections are designed to preserve on the flat map some particular property of the sphere. By varying the systematic arrangement or spacing of the latitude and longitude lines, a projection may be made either equal-area or conformal. Although most projections are derived from mathematical formulas, some are easier to visualize if thought of as projected upon a plane, or upon a cone or cylinder which is then unrolled into a plane surface. Thus, many projections are classified as plane (azimuthal), conic, or cylindrical.

For a fuller discussion of map projections, see Preface. Figures with asterisks indicate projections used in this atlas.

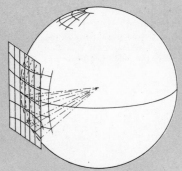
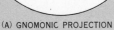

(A) GNOMONIC PROJECTION

A geometric or perspective projection on a tangent plane with the origin point at the center of the globe. Shapes and distances rapidly become increasingly distorted away from the center of the projection. Important in navigation, because all straight lines are great circles.

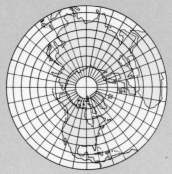

(B) LAMBERT EQUAL AREA PROJECTION*

A mathematically designed azimuthal equal-area projection. Excellent for continental areas. For larger areas away from the center, distortion of distances and shapes is appreciable.

FIGURE 1.–TYPICAL PLANE PROJECTIONS

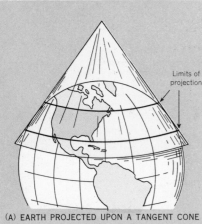

(A) EARTH PROJECTED UPON A TANGENT CONE

(B) CONE CUT FROM BASE TO APEX

A perspective projection on a tangent cone with the origin point at the center of the globe. At the parallel of tangency, all elements of the map are

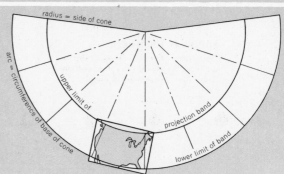

(C) CONE DEVELOPED INTO A PLANE SURFACE

true- angles,distances,shapes,areas. Away from the tangent parallel, distances increase rapidly, giving bad distortion of shapes and areas.

FIGURE 2.–SIMPLE CONIC PROJECTIONS

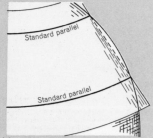

(A) EARTH PROJECTED UPON AN INTERSECTING CONE

This modification of the conic has two standard parallels, or lines of intersection. It is not an equal-area projection, the space being reduced in size between the standard parallels and

(B) CONIC PROJECTION WITH TWO STANDARD PARALLELS*

progressively enlarged beyond the standard parallels. Careful selection of the standard parallels provides, however, good representation for areas of limited latitudinal extent.

(C) BONNE PROJECTION*

An equal-area modification of the conic principle. Distances are true along all parallels and the central meridian; but away from it, increasing obliqueness of intersections and longitudinal distances, with their attendant distortion of shapes, limits the satisfactory area.

FIGURE 3.–MODIFIED CONIC PROJECTIONS

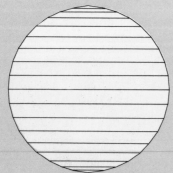

(A) EARTH CONSIDERED AS FORMED BY BASES OF CONES

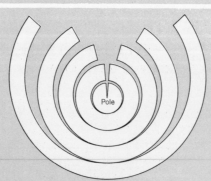

(B) DEVELOPMENT OF THE CONICAL BASES

This variation is not equal-area. Parallels are non-concentric circles truly divided. Distances along the straight central meridian are also true, but

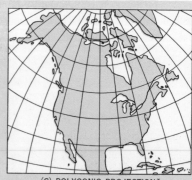

(C) POLYCONIC PROJECTION*

along the curving meridians are increasingly exaggerated. Representation is good near the central meridian, but away from it there is marked distortion.

FIGURE 4.–POLYCONIC PROJECTION

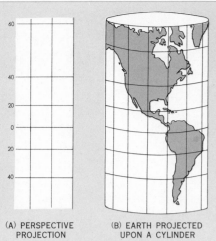

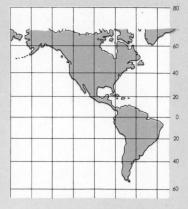

(A) PERSPECTIVE PROJECTION

A perspective projection on a tangent cylinder. Because of rapidly increasing distortion away from the line of tangency and the lack of any special advantage, it is rarely used.

(B) EARTH PROJECTED UPON A CYLINDER

(C) MERCATOR CONFORMAL PROJECTION

Mercator's modification increases the longitudinal distances in the same proportion as latitudinal distances are increased. Thus, at any point shapes are true, but areas become increasingly exaggerated. Of value in navigation, because a line connecting any two points gives the true direction between them.

(D) MILLER PROJECTION*

This recent modification is neither conformal nor equal-area. Whereas shapes are less accurate than on the Mercator, the exaggeration of areas has been reduced somewhat.

FIGURE 5.—CYLINDRICAL PROJECTIONS

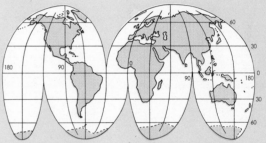

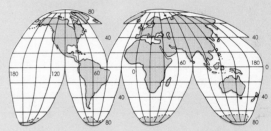

(A) MOLLWEIDE'S HOMOLOGRAPHIC PROJECTION

(B) GOODE'S INTERRUPTED HOMOLOGRAPHIC PROJECTION

(C) SINUSOIDAL PROJECTION*

(D) GOODE'S INTERRUPTED HOMOLOSINE PROJECTION*

Although each of these projections is equal-area, differences in the spacing and arrangement of latitude and longitude lines result in differences in the distribution and relative degree of the shape and distance distortion within each grid. On the homolographic, there is no uniformity in scale. It is different on each parallel and each meridian. On the sinusoidal, only distances along all latitudes and the central meridian are true. The homolosine combines the homolographic, for areas poleward of 40°, with the sinusoidal. The principle of interruption permits each continent in turn the advantage of being in the center of the projection, resulting in better shapes.

FIGURE 6.—EQUAL AREA PROJECTIONS OF THE WORLD

A conformal projection in which a selected great circle of the globe is considered as the "equator" of the ordinary Mercator projection, with the cylinder tangent along the great circle. It is used chiefly for charts of great-circle air routes between distant cities.

FIGURE 7.—TRANSVERSE MERCATOR PROJECTION

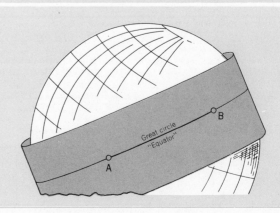

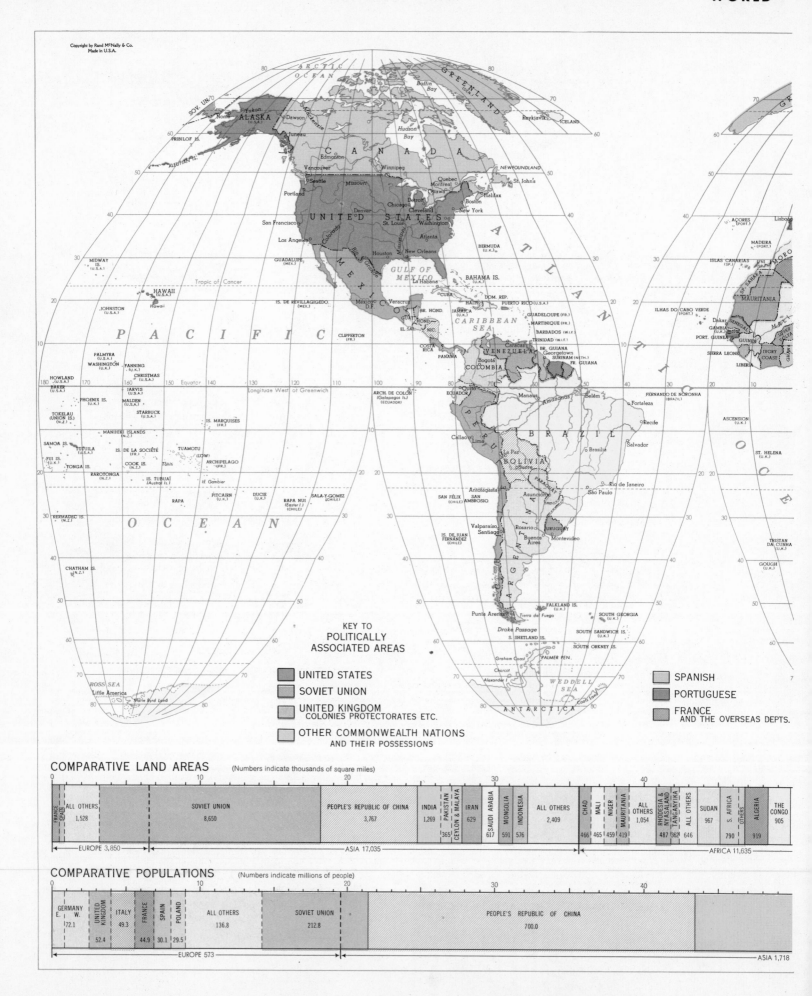

Copyright by Rand McNally & Co.
Made in U.S.A.

KEY TO POLITICALLY ASSOCIATED AREAS

- UNITED STATES
- SOVIET UNION
- UNITED KINGDOM COLONIES PROTECTORATES ETC.
- OTHER COMMONWEALTH NATIONS AND THEIR POSSESSIONS
- SPANISH
- PORTUGUESE
- FRANCE AND THE OVERSEAS DEPTS.

COMPARATIVE LAND AREAS   (Numbers indicate thousands of square miles)

| FRANCE | SPAIN | ALL OTHERS 1,528 | SOVIET UNION 8,650 | PEOPLE'S REPUBLIC OF CHINA 3,767 | INDIA 1,269 | PAKISTAN | CEYLON & MALAYA 365 | IRAN 629 | SAUDI ARABIA 617 | MONGOLIA 591 | INDONESIA 576 | ALL OTHERS 2,409 | CHAD 466 | MALI 465 | NIGER 459 | MAURITANIA 419 | ALL OTHERS 1,054 | RHODESIA & NYASALAND 487 | TANGANYIKA 362 | ALL OTHERS 646 | SUDAN 967 | S. AFRICA 790 | OTHERS | ALGERIA 919 | THE CONGO 905 |

⟵ EUROPE 3,850 ⟶   ⟵ ASIA 17,035 ⟶   ⟵ AFRICA 11,635 ⟶

COMPARATIVE POPULATIONS   (Numbers indicate millions of people)

| GERMANY E. W. 72.1 | UNITED KINGDOM 52.4 | ITALY 49.3 | FRANCE 44.9 | SPAIN 30.1 | POLAND 29.5 | ALL OTHERS 136.8 | SOVIET UNION 212.8 | PEOPLE'S REPUBLIC OF CHINA 700.0 | |

⟵ EUROPE 573 ⟶   ⟵ ASIA 1,718 ⟶

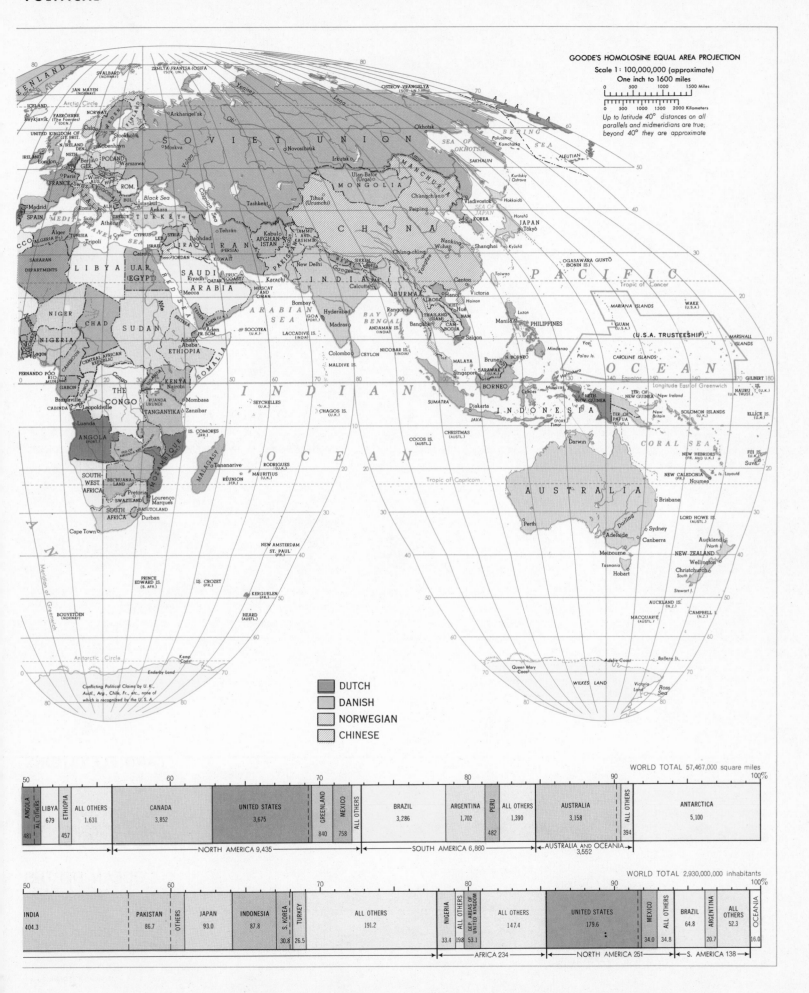

GOODE'S HOMOLOSINE EQUAL AREA PROJECTION
Scale 1 : 100,000,000 (approximate)
One inch to 1600 miles

Up to latitude 40° distances on all
parallels and midmeridians are true;
beyond 40° they are approximate

DUTCH
DANISH
NORWEGIAN
CHINESE

WORLD TOTAL 57,467,000 square miles

| ANGOLA 481 | ALL OTHERS | LIBYA 679 | ETHIOPIA 457 | ALL OTHERS 1,631 | CANADA 3,852 | UNITED STATES 3,675 | GREENLAND 840 | MEXICO 758 | ALL OTHERS | BRAZIL 3,286 | ARGENTINA 1,702 | PERU 482 | ALL OTHERS 1,390 | AUSTRALIA 3,158 | ALL OTHERS 394 | ANTARCTICA 5,100 |

NORTH AMERICA 9,435 — SOUTH AMERICA 6,860 — AUSTRALIA AND OCEANIA 3,552

WORLD TOTAL 2,930,000,000 inhabitants

| INDIA 404.3 | PAKISTAN 86.7 | OTHERS | JAPAN 93.0 | INDONESIA 87.8 | S. KOREA 30.8 | TURKEY 26.5 | ALL OTHERS 191.2 | NIGERIA 33.4 | DEP. AREAS OF UNITED KINGDOM 53.1 | ALL OTHERS 147.4 | UNITED STATES 179.6 | MEXICO 34.0 | ALL OTHERS 34.8 | BRAZIL 64.8 | ARGENTINA 20.7 | ALL OTHERS 52.3 | OCEANIA 16.0 |

AFRICA 234 — NORTH AMERICA 251 — S. AMERICA 138

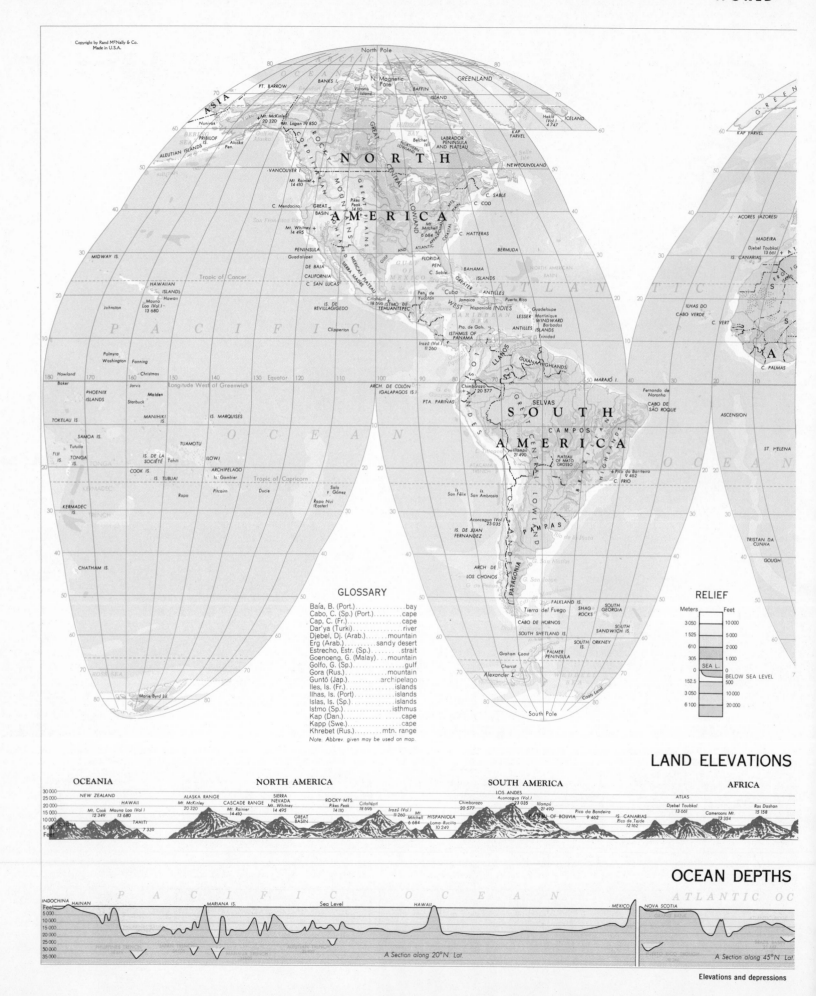

LAND ELEVATIONS

OCEAN DEPTHS

Elevations and depressions

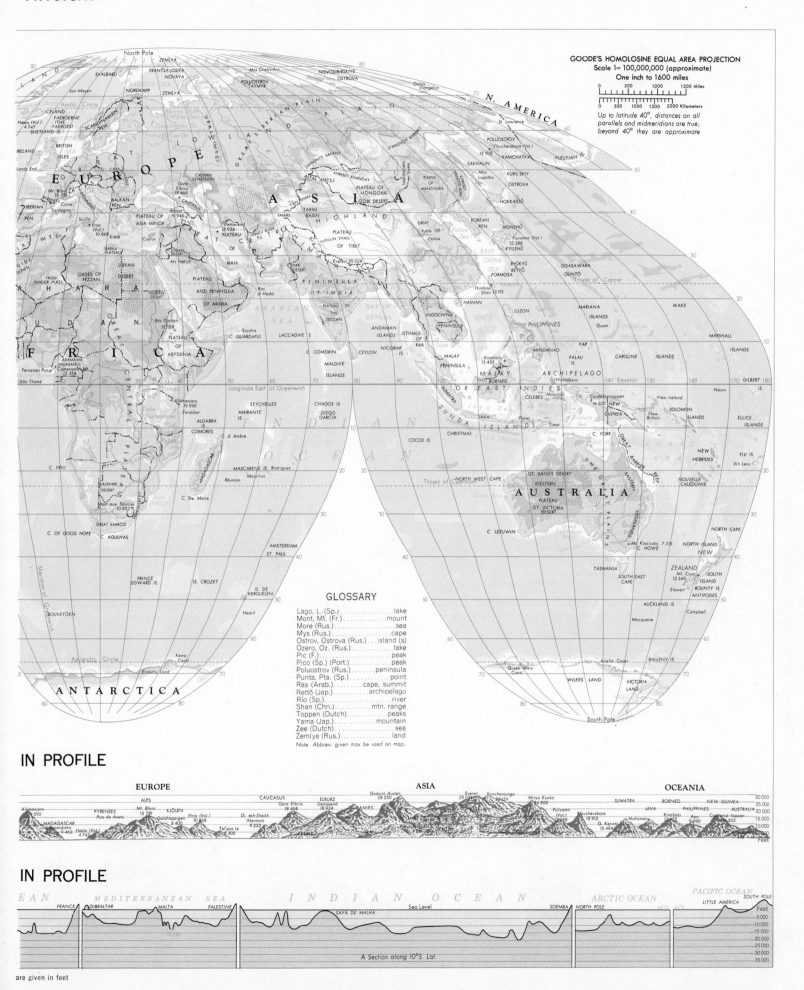

GOODE'S HOMOLOSINE EQUAL AREA PROJECTION
Scale 1= 100,000,000 (approximate)
One inch to 1600 miles

Up to latitude 40°, distances on all
parallels and midmeridians are true;
beyond 40° they are approximate

GLOSSARY

Lago, L. (Sp.)	lake
Mont, Mt. (Fr.)	mount
More (Rus.)	sea
Mys (Rus.)	cape
Ostrov, Ostrova (Rus.)	island (s)
Ozero, Oz. (Rus.)	lake
Pic (F.)	peak
Pico (Sp.) (Port.)	peak
Poluostrov (Rus.)	peninsula
Punta, Pta. (Sp.)	point
Ras (Arab.)	cape, summit
Rettō (Jap.)	archipelago
Río (Sp.)	river
Shan (Chn.)	mtn. range
Toppen (Dutch)	peaks
Yama (Jap.)	mountain
Zee (Dutch)	sea
Zemlya (Rus.)	land

Note. Abbrev. given may be used on map.

IN PROFILE

IN PROFILE

A Section along 10°S Lat.

are given in feet

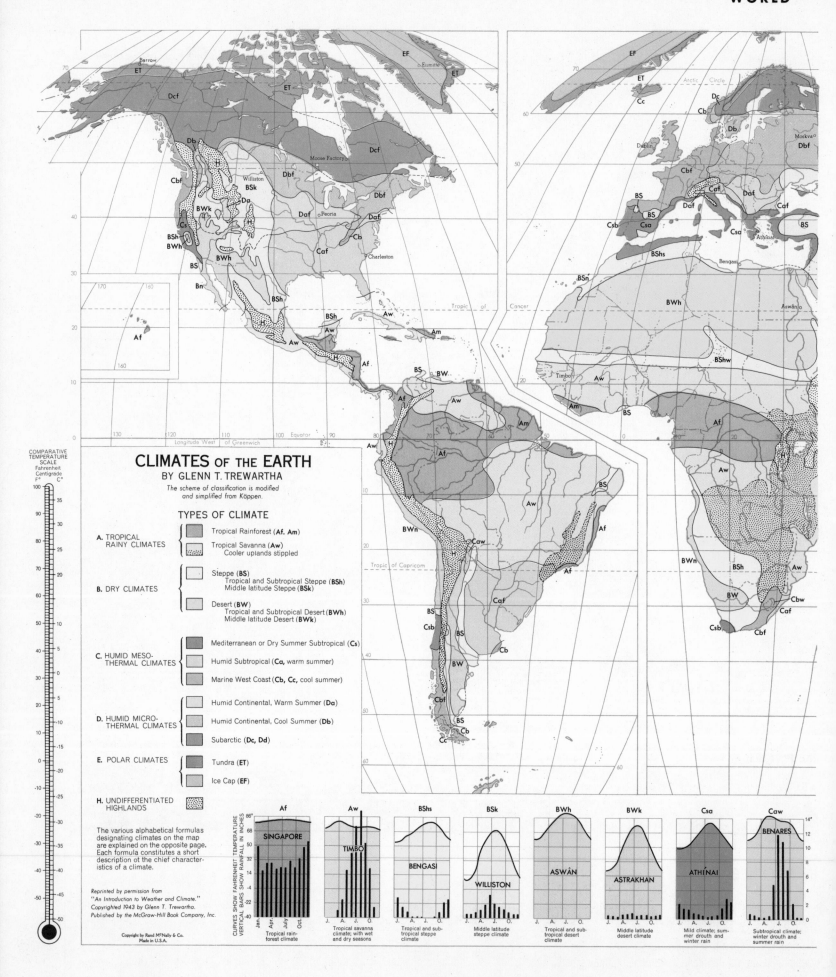

COMPARATIVE
TEMPERATURE
SCALE
Fahrenheit
Centigrade
F°   C°

CLIMATES OF THE EARTH
BY GLENN T. TREWARTHA

*The scheme of classification is modified
and simplified from Köppen.*

TYPES OF CLIMATE

**A. TROPICAL
RAINY CLIMATES**
- Tropical Rainforest (**Af. Am**)
- Tropical Savanna (**Aw**)
  Cooler uplands stippled

B. DRY CLIMATES
- Steppe (**BS**)
  Tropical and Subtropical Steppe (**BSh**)
  Middle latitude Steppe (**BSk**)
- Desert (**BW**)
  Tropical and Subtropical Desert (**BWh**)
  Middle latitude Desert (**BWk**)

**C. HUMID MESO-
THERMAL CLIMATES**
- Mediterranean or Dry Summer Subtropical (**Cs**)
- Humid Subtropical (**Ca**, warm summer)
- Marine West Coast (**Cb, Cc**, cool summer)

**D. HUMID MICRO-
THERMAL CLIMATES**
- Humid Continental, Warm Summer (**Da**)
- Humid Continental, Cool Summer (**Db**)
- Subarctic (**Dc, Dd**)

E. POLAR CLIMATES
- Tundra (**ET**)
- Ice Cap (**EF**)

**H. UNDIFFERENTIATED
HIGHLANDS**

The various alphabetical formulas
designating climates on the map
are explained on the opposite page.
Each formula constitutes a short
description ot the chief characteristics of a climate.

*Reprinted by permission from
"An Introduction to Weather and Climate."
Copyrighted 1943 by Glenn T. Trewartha.
Published by the McGraw-Hill Book Company, Inc.*

Copyright by Rand McNally & Co.
Made in U.S.A.

CURVES SHOW FAHRENHEIT TEMPERATURE
VERTICAL BARS SHOW RAINFALL IN INCHES

Af
SINGAPORE
Tropical rain-
forest climate

Aw
TIMBO
Tropical savanna
climate; with wet
and dry seasons

BShs
BENGASI
Tropical and sub-
tropical steppe
climate

BSk
WILLISTON
Middle latitude
steppe climate

BWh
ASWÂN
Tropical and sub-
tropical desert
climate

BWk
ASTRAKHAN
Middle latitude
desert climate

Csa
ATHÍNAI
Mild climate; sum-
mer drouth and
winter rain

Caw
BENARES
Subtropical climate;
winter drouth and
summer rain

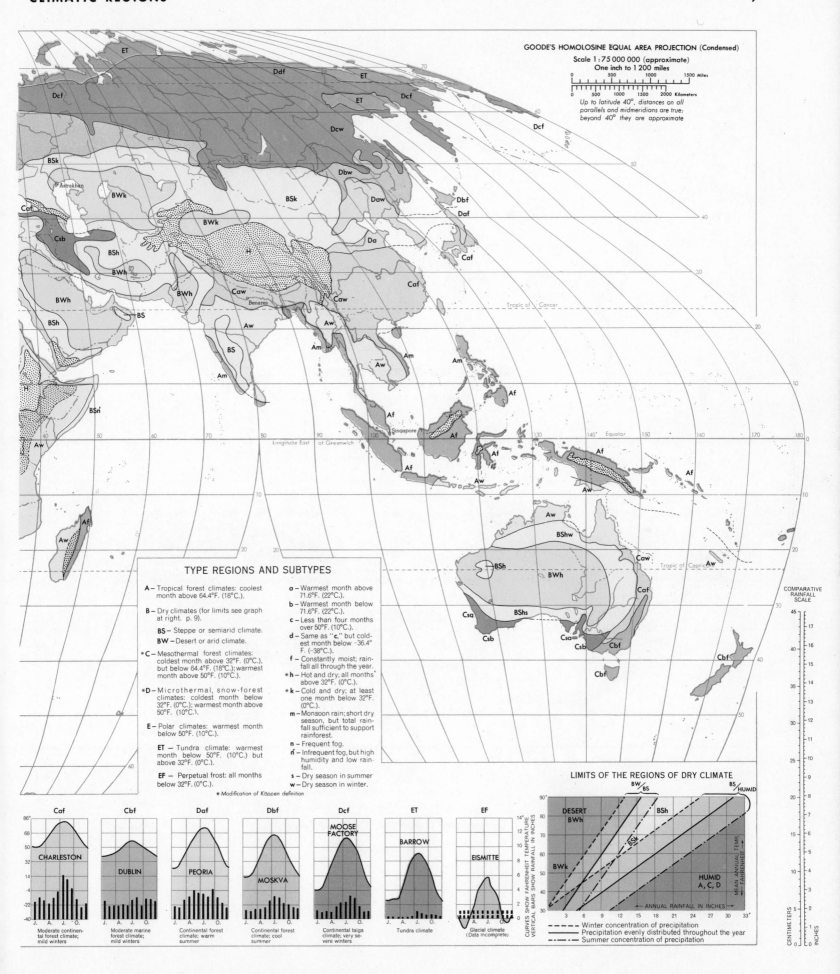

GOODE'S HOMOLOSINE EQUAL AREA PROJECTION (Condensed)
Scale 1 : 75 000 000 (approximate)
One inch to 1 200 miles

Up to latitude 40°, distances on all
parallels and midmeridians are true;
beyond 40° they are approximate

TYPE REGIONS AND SUBTYPES

A – Tropical forest climates: coolest month above 64.4°F. (18°C.).

B – Dry climates (for limits see graph at right. p. 9).

   BS – Steppe or semiarid climate.
   BW – Desert or arid climate.

*C – Mesothermal forest climates: coldest month above 32°F. (0°C.), but below 64.4°F. (18°C.); warmest month above 50°F. (10°C.).

*D – Microthermal, snow-forest climates: coldest month below 32°F. (0°C.); warmest month above 50°F. (10°C.).

E – Polar climates: warmest month below 50°F. (10°C.).

   ET – Tundra climate: warmest month below 50°F. (10°C.) but above 32°F. (0°C.).

   EF – Perpetual frost: all months below 32°F. (0°C.).

* Modification of Köppen definition

a – Warmest month above 71.6°F. (22°C.).
b – Warmest month below 71.6°F. (22°C.).
c – Less than four months over 50°F. (10°C.).
d – Same as "c," but coldest month below –36.4° F. (–38°C.).
f – Constantly moist; rainfall all through the year.
*h – Hot and dry; all months above 32°F. (0°C.).
*k – Cold and dry; at least one month below 32°F. (0°C.).
m – Monsoon rain; short dry season, but total rainfall sufficient to support rainforest.
n – Frequent fog.
ñ – Infrequent fog, but high humidity and low rainfall.
s – Dry season in summer
w – Dry season in winter.

LIMITS OF THE REGIONS OF DRY CLIMATE

CURVES SHOW FAHRENHEIT TEMPERATURE
VERTICAL BARS SHOW RAINFALL IN INCHES

MEAN ANNUAL TEMP., FAHRENHEIT

DESERT BWh   BSh

BWk   BSk

HUMID A, C, D

ANNUAL RAINFALL IN INCHES

- - - Winter concentration of precipitation
——— Precipitation evenly distributed throughout the year
–·–·– Summer concentration of precipitation

COMPARATIVE RAINFALL SCALE

CENTIMETERS / INCHES

Climate graphs

Caf — CHARLESTON — Moderate continental forest climate; mild winters

Cbf — DUBLIN — Moderate marine forest climate; mild winters

Daf — PEORIA — Continental forest climate; warm summer

Dbf — MOSKVA — Continental forest climate; cool summer

Dcf — MOOSE FACTORY — Continental taiga climate; very severe winters

ET — BARROW — Tundra climate

EF — EISMITTE — Glacial climate (Data incomplete)

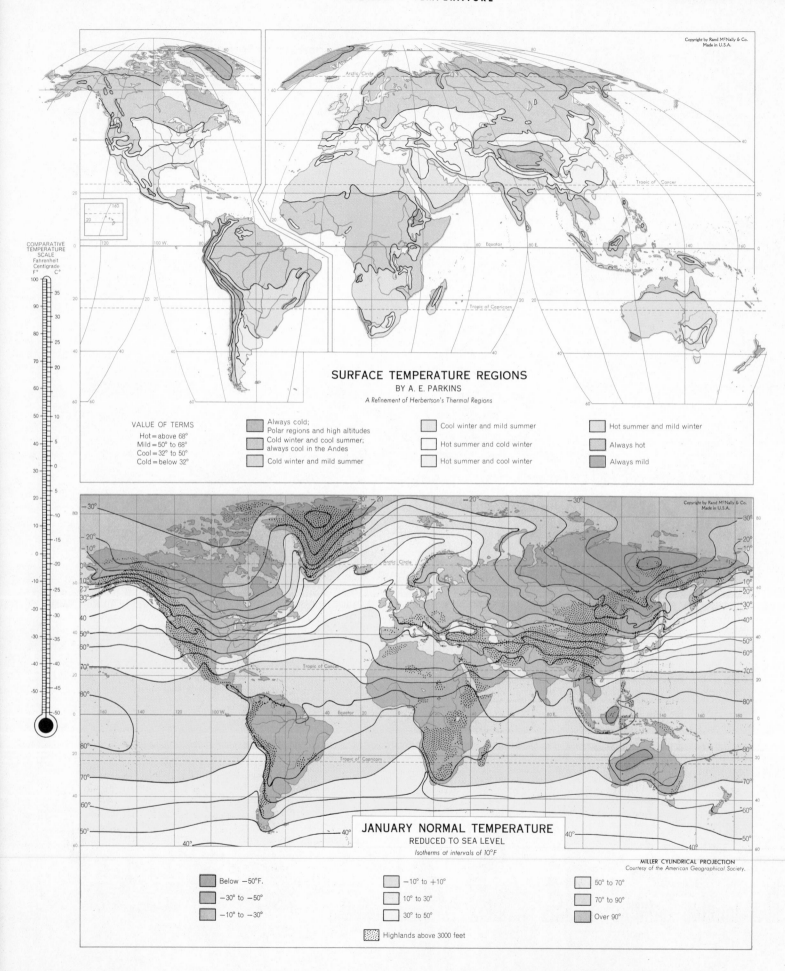

Copyright by Rand McNally & Co.
Made in U.S.A.

SURFACE TEMPERATURE REGIONS
BY A. E. PARKINS
A Refinement of Herbertson's Thermal Regions

VALUE OF TERMS

Hot = above 68°
Mild = 50° to 68°
Cool = 32° to 50°
Cold = below 32°

Always cold;
Polar regions and high altitudes

Cold winter and cool summer;
always cool in the Andes

Cold winter and mild summer

Cool winter and mild summer

Hot summer and cold winter

Hot summer and cool winter

Hot summer and mild winter

Always hot

Always mild

COMPARATIVE
TEMPERATURE
SCALE
Fahrenheit
Centigrade
F°   C°

JANUARY NORMAL TEMPERATURE
REDUCED TO SEA LEVEL
Isotherms at intervals of 10°F

Copyright by Rand McNally & Co.
Made in U.S.A.

MILLER CYLINDRICAL PROJECTION
Courtesy of the American Geographical Society.

Below −50°F.

−30° to −50°

−10° to −30°

−10° to +10°

10° to 30°

30° to 50°

50° to 70°

70° to 90°

Over 90°

Highlands above 3000 feet

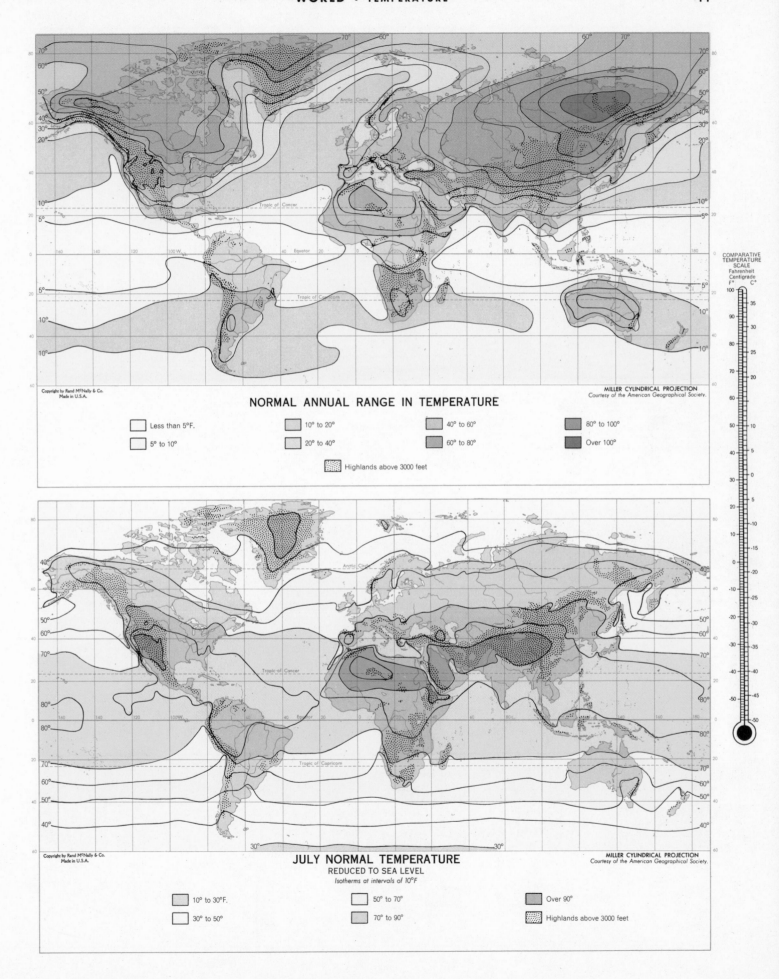

NORMAL ANNUAL RANGE IN TEMPERATURE

MILLER CYLINDRICAL PROJECTION
Courtesy of the American Geographical Society.

Copyright by Rand McNally & Co.
Made in U.S.A.

Less than 5°F.   10° to 20°   40° to 60°   80° to 100°

5° to 10°   20° to 40°   60° to 80°   Over 100°

Highlands above 3000 feet

COMPARATIVE
TEMPERATURE
SCALE
Fahrenheit
Centigrade
F°   C°

JULY NORMAL TEMPERATURE
REDUCED TO SEA LEVEL
Isotherms at intervals of 10°F

MILLER CYLINDRICAL PROJECTION
Courtesy of the American Geographical Society.

Copyright by Rand McNally & Co.
Made in U.S.A.

10° to 30°F.   50° to 70°   Over 90°

30° to 50°   70° to 90°   Highlands above 3000 feet

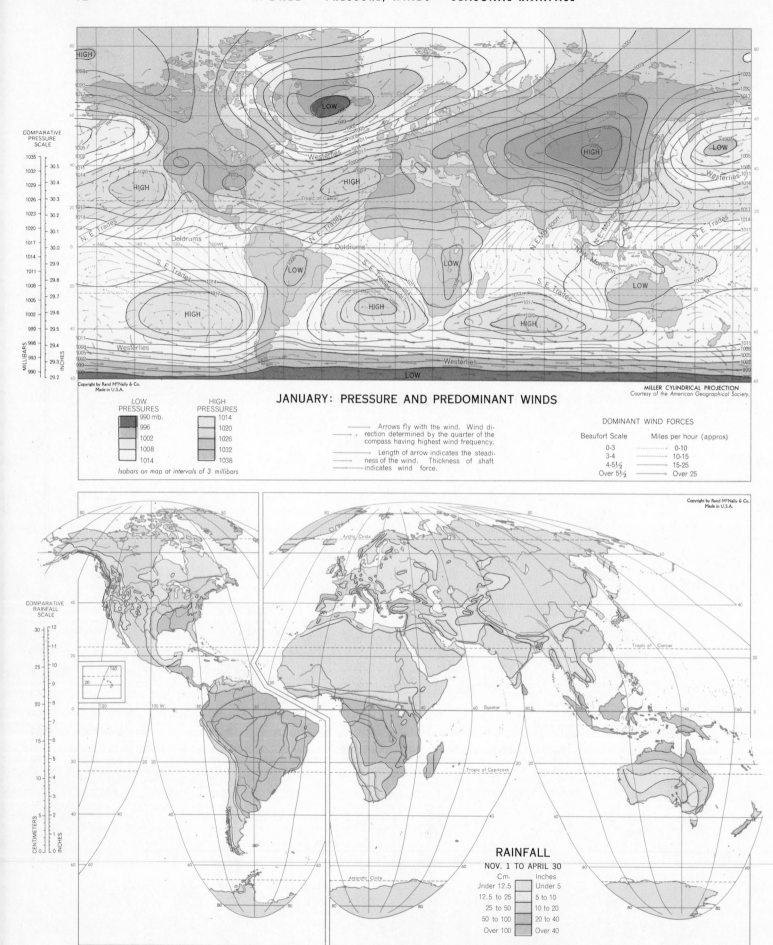

MILLER CYLINDRICAL PROJECTION
Courtesy of the American Geographical Society.

JANUARY: PRESSURE AND PREDOMINANT WINDS

COMPARATIVE PRESSURE SCALE

LOW PRESSURES	HIGH PRESSURES
990 mb.	1014
996	1020
1002	1026
1008	1032
1014	1038

Isobars on map at intervals of 3 millibars

Arrows fly with the wind. Wind direction determined by the quarter of the compass having highest wind frequency.

Length of arrow indicates the steadiness of the wind. Thickness of shaft indicates wind force.

DOMINANT WIND FORCES

Beaufort Scale	Miles per hour (approx)
0-3	0-10
3-4	10-15
4-5½	15-25
Over 5½	Over 25

COMPARATIVE RAINFALL SCALE

RAINFALL

NOV. 1 TO APRIL 30

Cm.	Inches
Under 12.5	Under 5
12.5 to 25	5 to 10
25 to 50	10 to 20
50 to 100	20 to 40
Over 100	Over 40

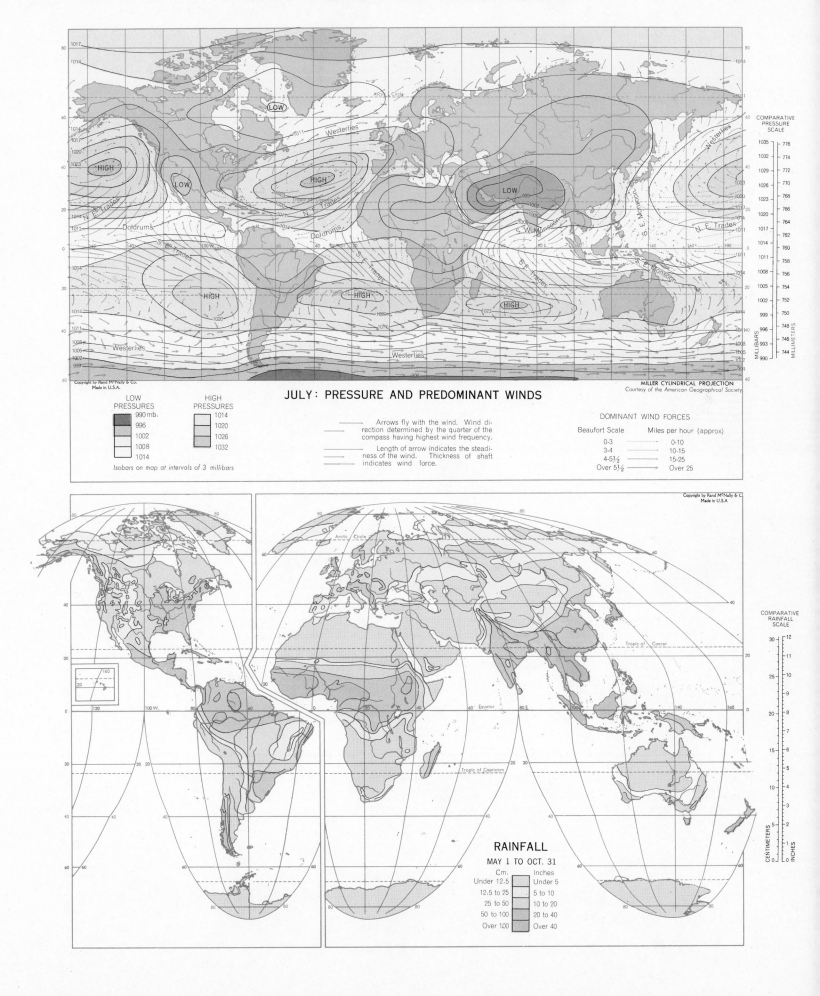

JULY: PRESSURE AND PREDOMINANT WINDS

MILLER CYLINDRICAL PROJECTION
Courtesy of the American Geographical Society

Copyright by Rand McNally & Co.
Made in U.S.A.

COMPARATIVE PRESSURE SCALE

MILLIBARS	MILLIMETERS
1035	776
1032	774
1029	772
1026	770
1023	768
1020	766
1017	762
1014	760
1011	758
1008	756
1005	754
1002	752
999	750
996	748
993	746
990	744

LOW PRESSURES
990 mb.
996
1002
1008
1014

HIGH PRESSURES
1014
1020
1026
1032

Isobars on map at intervals of 3 millibars

Arrows fly with the wind. Wind direction determined by the quarter of the compass having highest wind frequency.

Length of arrow indicates the steadiness of the wind. Thickness of shaft indicates wind force.

DOMINANT WIND FORCES

Beaufort Scale	Miles per hour (approx)
0-3	0-10
3-4	10-15
4-5½	15-25
Over 5½	Over 25

Copyright by Rand McNally & Co.
Made in U.S.A

RAINFALL
MAY 1 TO OCT. 31

Cm.	Inches
Under 12.5	Under 5
12.5 to 25	5 to 10
25 to 50	10 to 20
50 to 100	20 to 40
Over 100	Over 40

COMPARATIVE RAINFALL SCALE

CENTIMETERS	INCHES
30	12
25	11
20	10
15	9
10	8
5	7
1	6
0	5
	4
	3
	2
	1
	0

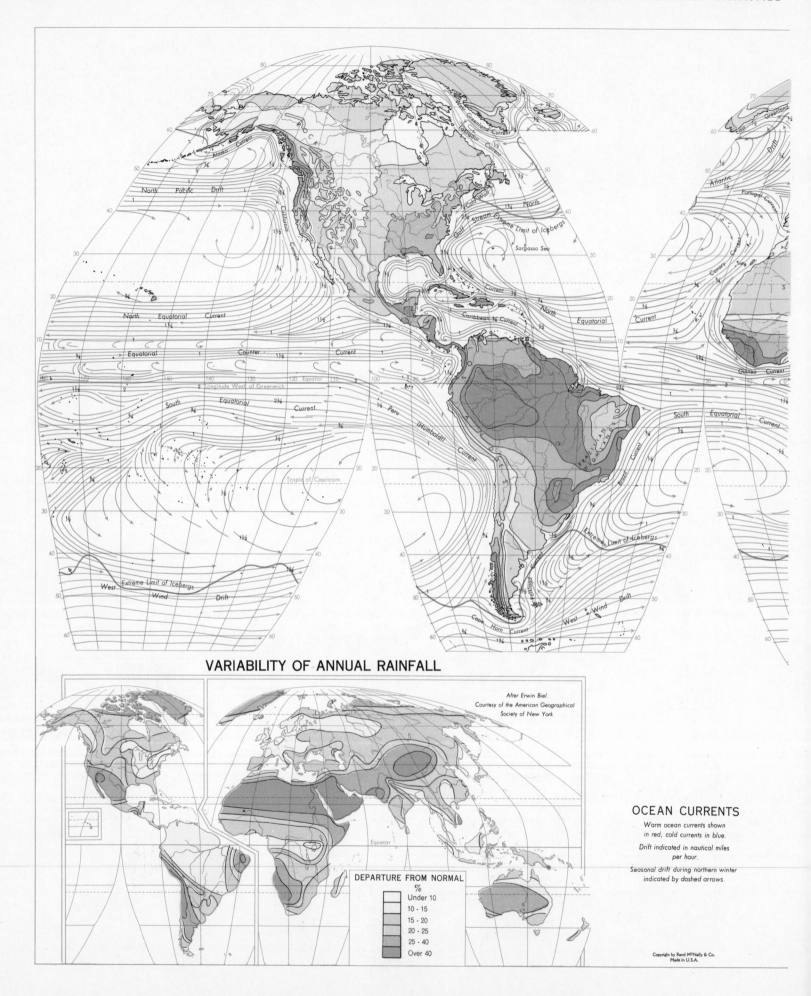

VARIABILITY OF ANNUAL RAINFALL

After Erwin Biel.
Courtesy of the American Geographical
Society of New York

OCEAN CURRENTS

*Warm ocean currents shown
in red, cold currents in blue.*

*Drift indicated in nautical miles
per hour.*

*Seasonal drift during northern winter
indicated by dashed arrows.*

DEPARTURE FROM NORMAL
%
Under 10
10 - 15
15 - 20
20 - 25
25 - 40
Over 40

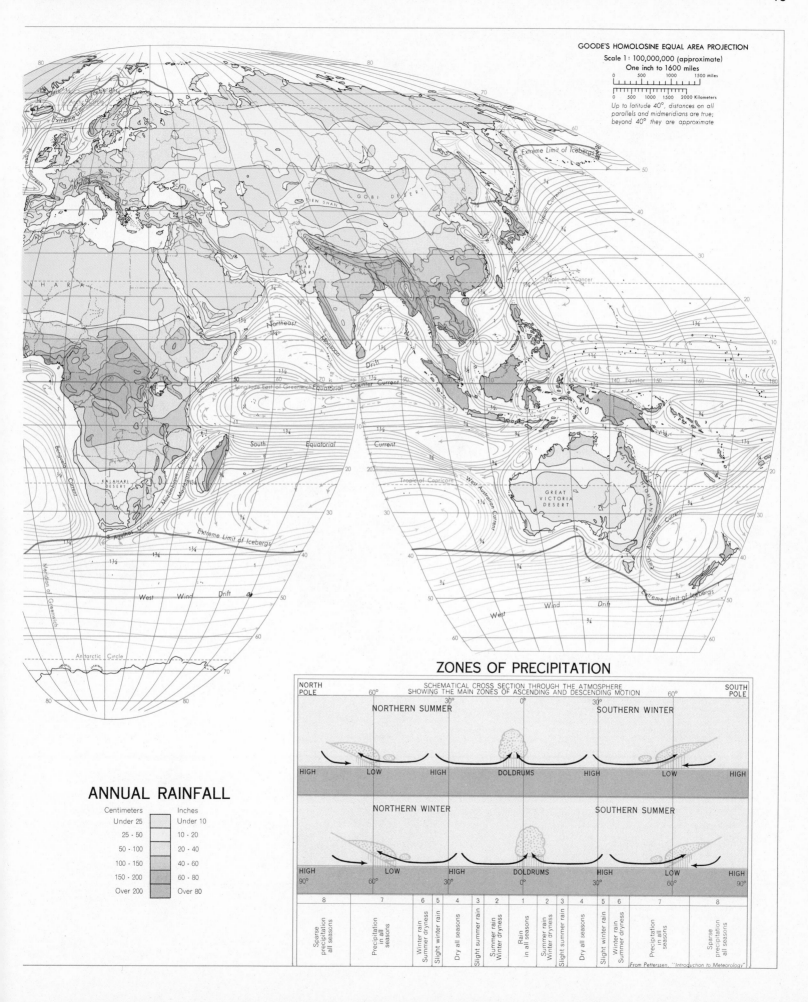

GOODE'S HOMOLOSINE EQUAL AREA PROJECTION

Scale 1 : 100,000,000 (approximate)

One inch to 1600 miles

Up to latitude 40°, distances on all
parallels and midmeridians are true;
beyond 40° they are approximate

ANNUAL RAINFALL

Centimeters	Inches
Under 25	Under 10
25 - 50	10 - 20
50 - 100	20 - 40
100 - 150	40 - 60
150 - 200	60 - 80
Over 200	Over 80

ZONES OF PRECIPITATION

SCHEMATICAL CROSS SECTION THROUGH THE ATMOSPHERE
SHOWING THE MAIN ZONES OF ASCENDING AND DESCENDING MOTION

| NORTH POLE | 60° | 30° | 0° | 30° | 60° | SOUTH POLE |

NORTHERN SUMMER SOUTHERN WINTER

| HIGH | LOW | HIGH | DOLDRUMS | HIGH | LOW | HIGH |

NORTHERN WINTER SOUTHERN SUMMER

| HIGH | LOW | HIGH | DOLDRUMS | HIGH | LOW | HIGH |
| 90° | 60° | 30° | 0° | 30° | 60° | 90° |

8	7	6	5	4	3	2	1	2	3	4	5	6	7	8
Sparse precipitation all seasons	Precipitation in all seasons	Winter rain Summer dryness	Slight winter rain	Dry all seasons	Slight summer rain	Summer rain Winter dryness	Rain in all seasons	Summer rain Winter dryness	Slight summer rain	Dry all seasons	Slight winter rain	Winter rain Summer dryness	Precipitation in all seasons	Sparse precipitation all seasons

From Petterssen, "Introduction to Meteorology"

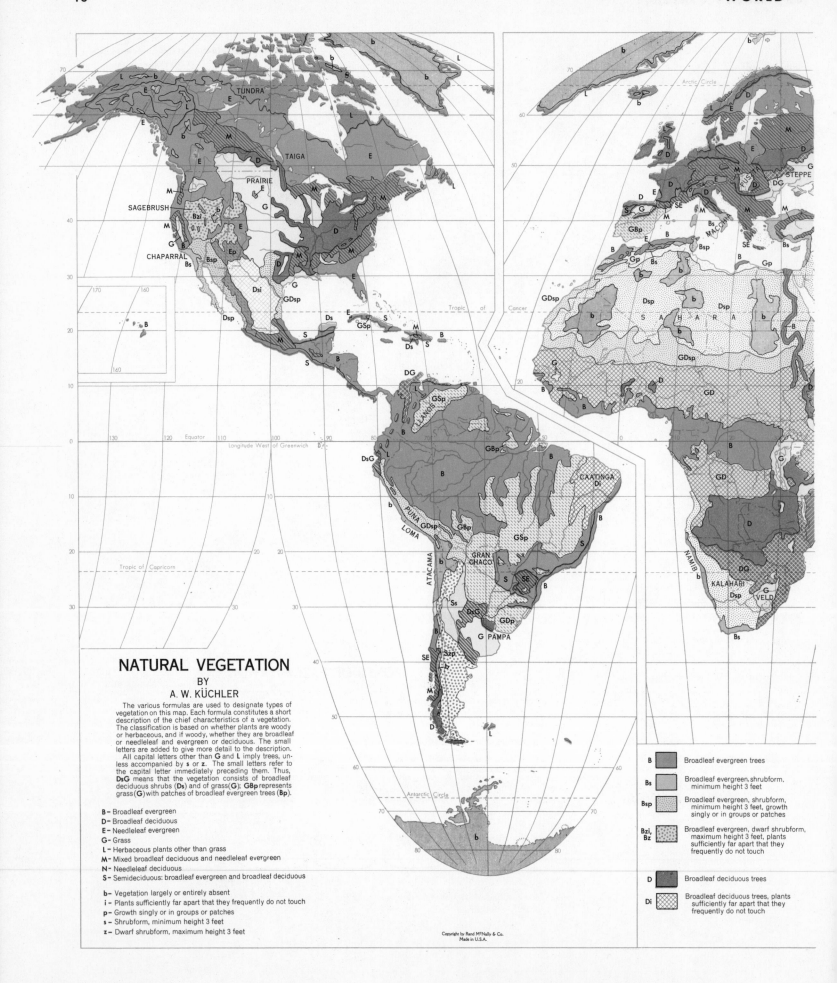

NATURAL VEGETATION

BY
A. W. KÜCHLER

The various formulas are used to designate types of vegetation on this map. Each formula constitutes a short description of the chief characteristics of a vegetation. The classification is based on whether plants are woody or herbaceous, and if woody, whether they are broadleaf or needleleaf and evergreen or deciduous. The small letters are added to give more detail to the description.

All capital letters other than **G** and **L** imply trees, unless accompanied by **s** or **z**. The small letters refer to the capital letter immediately preceding them. Thus, **DsG** means that the vegetation consists of broadleaf deciduous shrubs (**Ds**) and of grass (**G**); **GBp** represents grass (**G**) with patches of broadleaf evergreen trees (**Bp**).

B – Broadleaf evergreen
D – Broadleaf deciduous
E – Needleleaf evergreen
G – Grass
L – Herbaceous plants other than grass
M – Mixed broadleaf deciduous and needleleaf evergreen
N – Needleleaf deciduous
S – Semideciduous: broadleaf evergreen and broadleaf deciduous

b – Vegetation largely or entirely absent
i – Plants sufficiently far apart that they frequently do not touch
p – Growth singly or in groups or patches
s – Shrubform, minimum height 3 feet
z – Dwarf shrubform, maximum height 3 feet

B	Broadleaf evergreen trees
Bs	Broadleaf evergreen, shrubform, minimum height 3 feet
Bsp	Broadleaf evergreen, shrubform, minimum height 3 feet, growth singly or in groups or patches
Bzi, Bz	Broadleaf evergreen, dwarf shrubform, maximum height 3 feet, plants sufficiently far apart that they frequently do not touch
D	Broadleaf deciduous trees
Di	Broadleaf deciduous trees, plants sufficiently far apart that they frequently do not touch

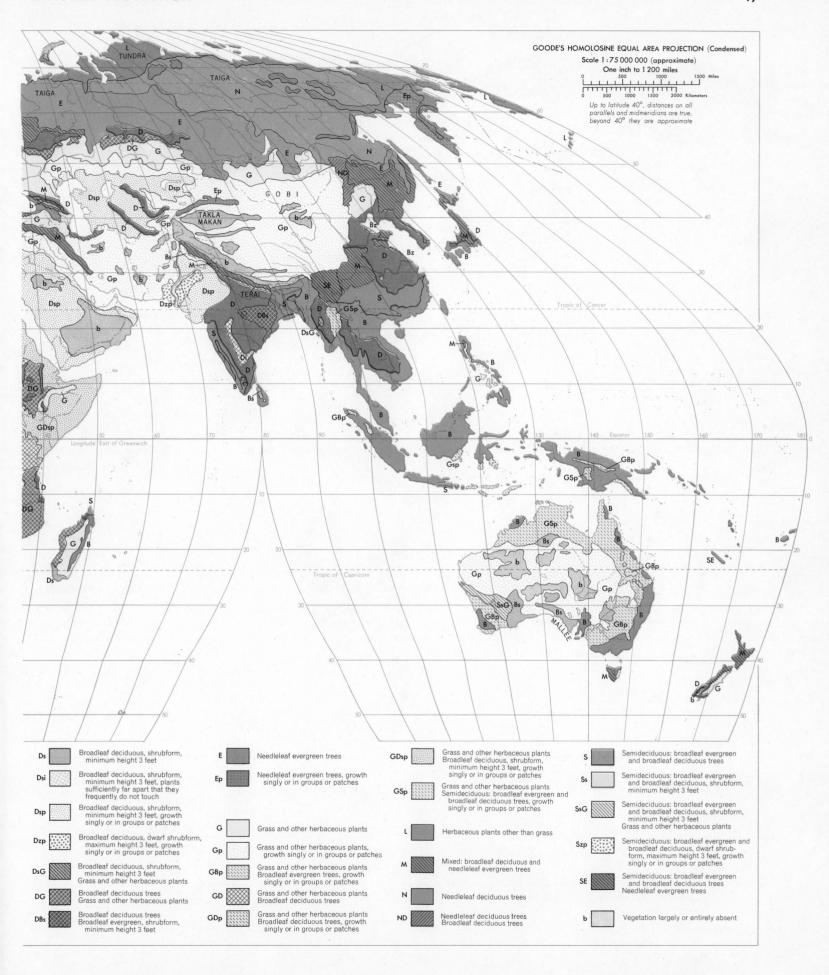

GOODE'S HOMOLOSINE EQUAL AREA PROJECTION (Condensed)
Scale 1:75 000 000 (approximate)
One inch to 1 200 miles

*Up to latitude 40°, distances on all
parallels and midmeridians are true;
beyond 40° they are approximate*

Ds	Broadleaf deciduous, shrubform, minimum height 3 feet
Dsi	Broadleaf deciduous, shrubform, minimum height 3 feet, plants sufficiently far apart that they frequently do not touch
Dsp	Broadleaf deciduous, shrubform, minimum height 3 feet, growth singly or in groups or patches
Dzp	Broadleaf deciduous, dwarf shrubform, maximum height 3 feet, growth singly or in groups or patches
DsG	Broadleaf deciduous, shrubform, minimum height 3 feet Grass and other herbaceous plants
DG	Broadleaf deciduous trees Grass and other herbaceous plants
DBs	Broadleaf deciduous trees Broadleaf evergreen, shrubform, minimum height 3 feet

E	Needleleaf evergreen trees
Ep	Needleleaf evergreen trees, growth singly or in groups or patches
G	Grass and other herbaceous plants
Gp	Grass and other herbaceous plants, growth singly or in groups or patches
GBp	Grass and other herbaceous plants Broadleaf evergreen trees, growth singly or in groups or patches
GD	Grass and other herbaceous plants Broadleaf deciduous trees
GDp	Grass and other herbaceous plants Broadleaf deciduous trees, growth singly or in groups or patches

GDsp	Grass and other herbaceous plants Broadleaf deciduous, shrubform, minimum height 3 feet, growth singly or in groups or patches
GSp	Grass and other herbaceous plants Semideciduous: broadleaf evergreen and broadleaf deciduous trees, growth singly or in groups or patches
L	Herbaceous plants other than grass
M	Mixed: broadleaf deciduous and needleleaf evergreen trees
N	Needleleaf deciduous trees
ND	Needleleaf deciduous trees Broadleaf deciduous trees

S	Semideciduous: broadleaf evergreen and broadleaf deciduous trees
Ss	Semideciduous: broadleaf evergreen and broadleaf deciduous, shrubform, minimum height 3 feet
SsG	Semideciduous: broadleaf evergreen and broadleaf deciduous, shrubform, minimum height 3 feet Grass and other herbaceous plants
Szp	Semideciduous: broadleaf evergreen and broadleaf deciduous, dwarf shrubform, maximum height 3 feet, growth singly or in groups or patches
SE	Semideciduous: broadleaf evergreen and broadleaf deciduous trees Needleleaf evergreen trees
b	Vegetation largely or entirely absent

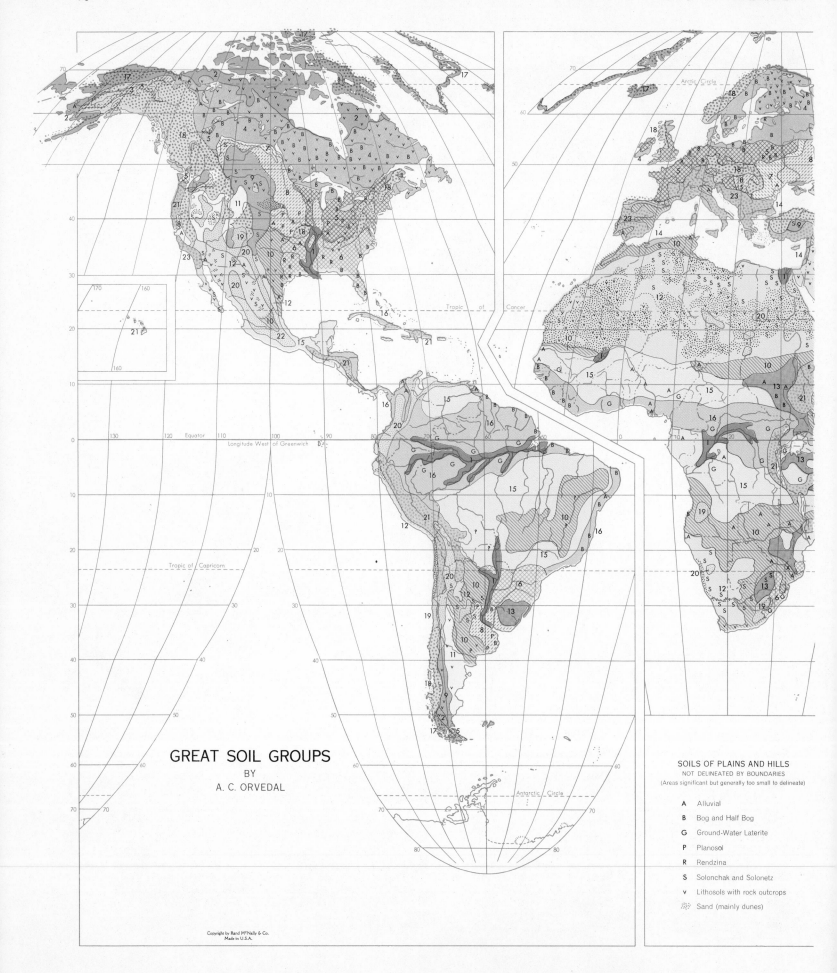

GREAT SOIL GROUPS
BY
A. C. ORVEDAL

SOILS OF PLAINS AND HILLS
NOT DELINEATED BY BOUNDARIES
(Areas significant but generally too small to delineate)

A   Alluvial

B   Bog and Half Bog

G   Ground-Water Laterite

P   Planosol

R   Rendzina

S   Solonchak and Solonetz

v   Lithosols with rock outcrops

⠿   Sand (mainly dunes)

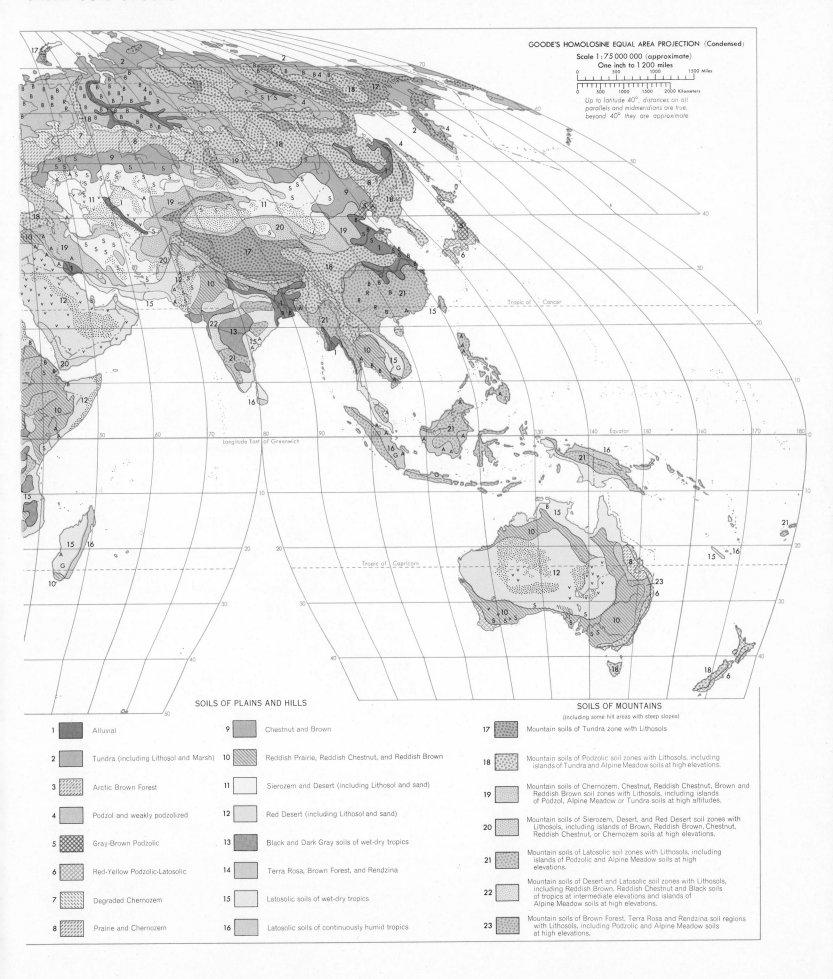

GOODE'S HOMOLOSINE EQUAL AREA PROJECTION (Condensed)

Scale 1:75 000 000 (approximate)

One inch to 1 200 miles

0   500   1000   1500 Miles

0   500   1000   1500   2000 Kilometers

*Up to latitude 40°, distances on all
parallels and midmeridians are true;
beyond 40° they are approximate*

Tropic of Cancer

Longitude East of Greenwich

Equator

Tropic of Capricorn

SOILS OF PLAINS AND HILLS

1 — Alluvial

2 — Tundra (including Lithosol and Marsh)

3 — Arctic Brown Forest

4 — Podzol and weakly podzolized

5 — Gray-Brown Podzolic

6 — Red-Yellow Podzolic-Latosolic

7 — Degraded Chernozem

8 — Prairie and Chernozem

9 — Chestnut and Brown

10 — Reddish Prairie, Reddish Chestnut, and Reddish Brown

11 — Sierozem and Desert (including Lithosol and sand)

12 — Red Desert (including Lithosol and sand)

13 — Black and Dark Gray soils of wet-dry tropics

14 — Terra Rosa, Brown Forest, and Rendzina

15 — Latosolic soils of wet-dry tropics

16 — Latosolic soils of continuously humid tropics

SOILS OF MOUNTAINS
(Including some hill areas with steep slopes)

17 — Mountain soils of Tundra zone with Lithosols

18 — Mountain soils of Podzolic soil zones with Lithosols, including
islands of Tundra and Alpine Meadow soils at high elevations.

19 — Mountain soils of Chernozem, Chestnut, Reddish Chestnut, Brown and
Reddish Brown soil zones with Lithosols, including islands
of Podzol, Alpine Meadow or Tundra soils at high altitudes.

20 — Mountain soils of Sierozem, Desert, and Red Desert soil zones with
Lithosols, including islands of Brown, Reddish Brown, Chestnut,
Reddish Chestnut, or Chernozem soils at high elevations.

21 — Mountain soils of Latosolic soil zones with Lithosols, including
islands of Podzolic and Alpine Meadow soils at high
elevations.

22 — Mountain soils of Desert and Latosolic soil zones with Lithosols,
including Reddish Brown, Reddish Chestnut and Black soils
of tropics at intermediate elevations and islands of
Alpine Meadow soils at high elevations.

23 — Mountain soils of Brown Forest, Terra Rosa and Rendzina soil regions
with Lithosols, including Podzolic and Alpine Meadow soils
at high elevations.

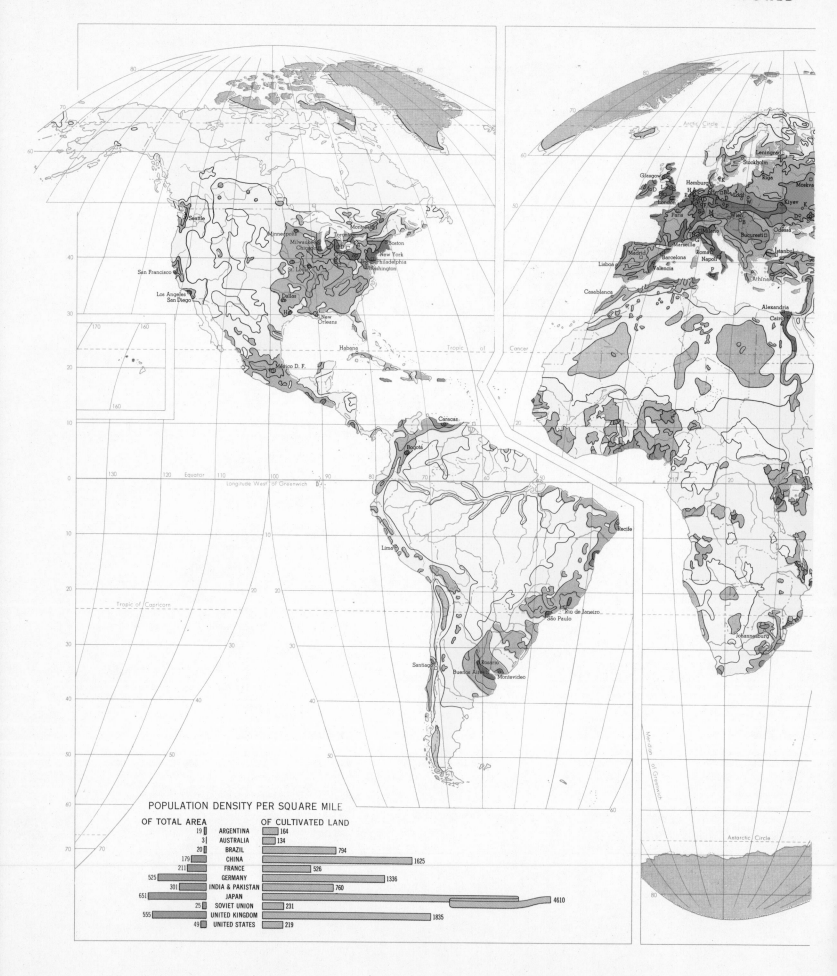

POPULATION DENSITY PER SQUARE MILE

OF TOTAL AREA		OF CULTIVATED LAND
19	ARGENTINA	164
3	AUSTRALIA	134
20	BRAZIL	794
179	CHINA	1625
211	FRANCE	526
525	GERMANY	1336
301	INDIA & PAKISTAN	760
651	JAPAN	4610
25	SOVIET UNION	231
555	UNITED KINGDOM	1835
49	UNITED STATES	219

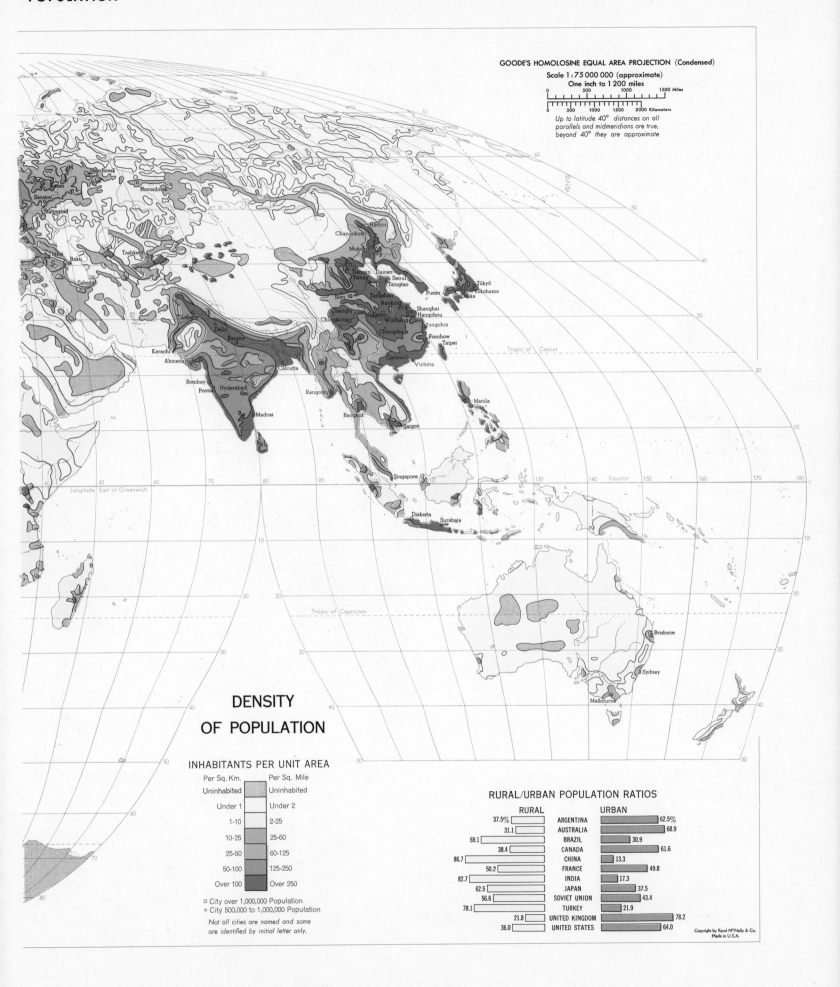

GOODE'S HOMOLOSINE EQUAL AREA PROJECTION (Condensed)

Scale 1 : 75 000 000 (approximate)

One inch to 1 200 miles

*Up to latitude 40° distances on all
parallels and midmeridians are true;
beyond 40° they are approximate*

DENSITY
OF POPULATION

INHABITANTS PER UNIT AREA

Per Sq. Km.		Per Sq. Mile
Uninhabited		Uninhabited
Under 1		Under 2
1-10		2-25
10-25		25-60
25-50		60-125
50-100		125-250
Over 100		Over 250

□ City over 1,000,000 Population
○ City 500,000 to 1,000,000 Population

*Not all cities are named and some
are identified by initial letter only.*

RURAL/URBAN POPULATION RATIOS

RURAL		URBAN
37.5%	ARGENTINA	62.5%
31.1	AUSTRALIA	68.9
69.1	BRAZIL	30.9
38.4	CANADA	61.6
86.7	CHINA	13.3
50.2	FRANCE	49.8
82.7	INDIA	17.3
62.5	JAPAN	37.5
56.6	SOVIET UNION	43.4
78.1	TURKEY	21.9
21.8	UNITED KINGDOM	78.2
36.0	UNITED STATES	64.0

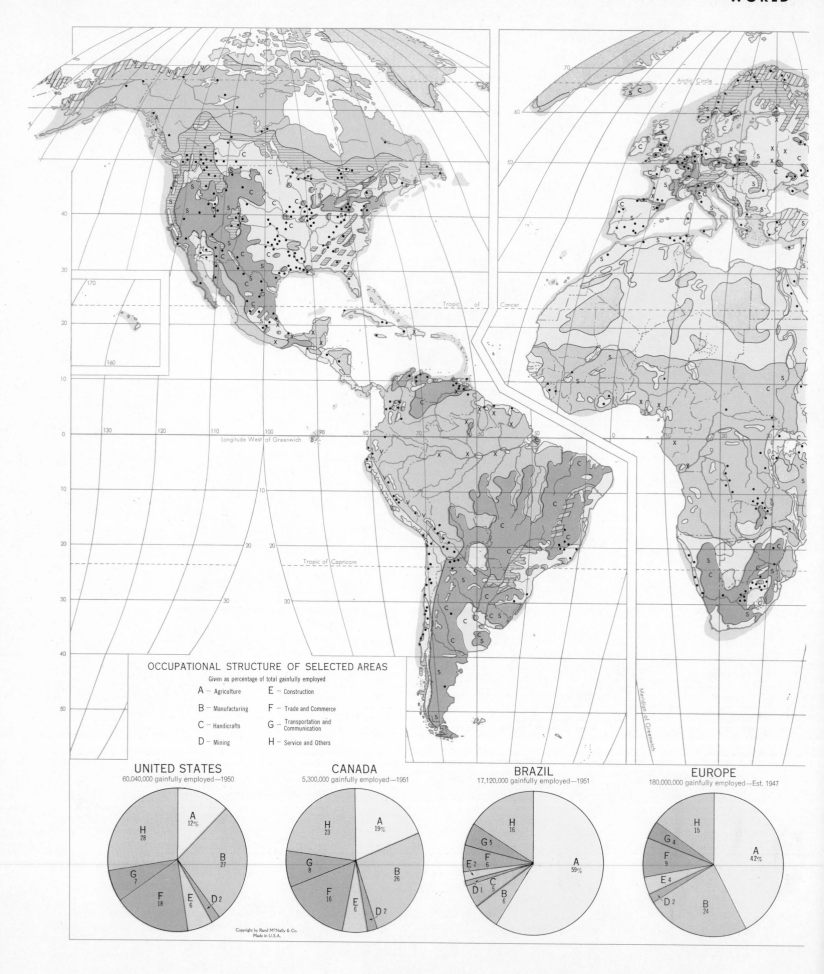

OCCUPATIONAL STRUCTURE OF SELECTED AREAS

Given as percentage of total gainfully employed

A – Agriculture   E – Construction

B – Manufacturing   F – Trade and Commerce

C – Handicrafts   G – Transportation and
                             Communication

D – Mining   H – Service and Others

UNITED STATES
60,040,000 gainfully employed—1950

CANADA
5,300,000 gainfully employed—1951

BRAZIL
17,120,000 gainfully employed—1951

EUROPE
180,000,000 gainfully employed—Est. 1947

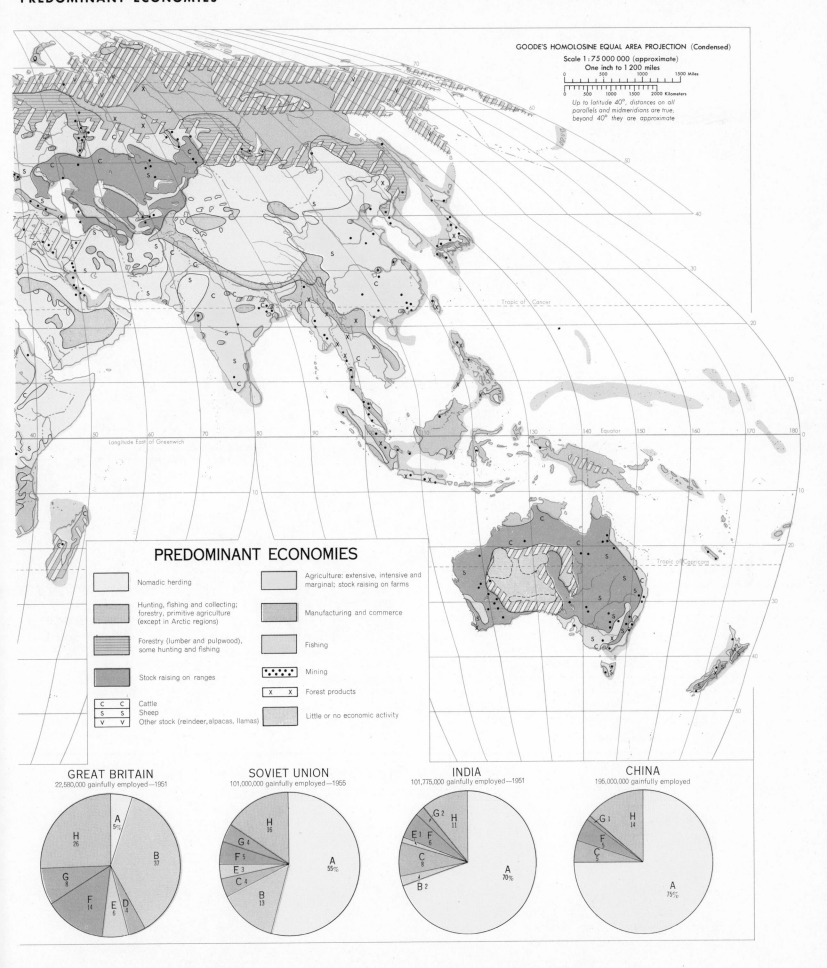

GOODE'S HOMOLOSINE EQUAL AREA PROJECTION (Condensed)
Scale 1 : 75 000 000 (approximate)
One inch to 1 200 miles

Up to latitude 40°, distances on all
parallels and midmeridians are true;
beyond 40° they are approximate

PREDOMINANT ECONOMIES

Nomadic herding

Hunting, fishing and collecting;
forestry, primitive agriculture
(except in Arctic regions)

Forestry (lumber and pulpwood),
some hunting and fishing

Stock raising on ranges

C   C   Cattle
S   S   Sheep
V   V   Other stock (reindeer, alpacas, llamas)

Agriculture: extensive, intensive and
marginal; stock raising on farms

Manufacturing and commerce

Fishing

Mining

X   X   Forest products

Little or no economic activity

GREAT BRITAIN
22,580,000 gainfully employed—1951

A 5%
B 37
D 4
E 6
F 14
G 8
H 26

SOVIET UNION
101,000,000 gainfully employed—1955

A 55%
B 13
C 4
E 3
F 5
G 4
H 16

INDIA
101,775,000 gainfully employed—1951

A 70%
B 2
C 8
E 1
F 6
G 2
H 11

CHINA
195,000,000 gainfully employed

A 75%
C 5
F 5
G 1
H 14

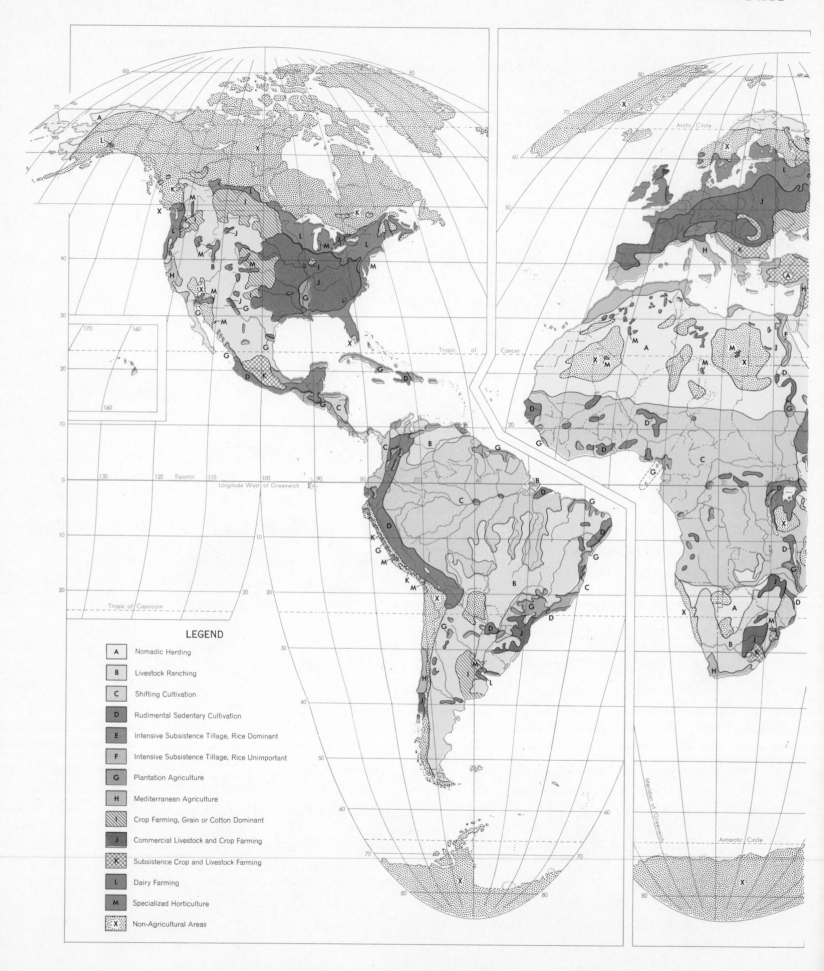

LEGEND

A	Nomadic Herding
B	Livestock Ranching
C	Shifting Cultivation
D	Rudimental Sedentary Cultivation
E	Intensive Subsistence Tillage, Rice Dominant
F	Intensive Subsistence Tillage, Rice Unimportant
G	Plantation Agriculture
H	Mediterranean Agriculture
I	Crop Farming, Grain or Cotton Dominant
J	Commercial Livestock and Crop Farming
K	Subsistence Crop and Livestock Farming
L	Dairy Farming
M	Specialized Horticulture
X	Non-Agricultural Areas

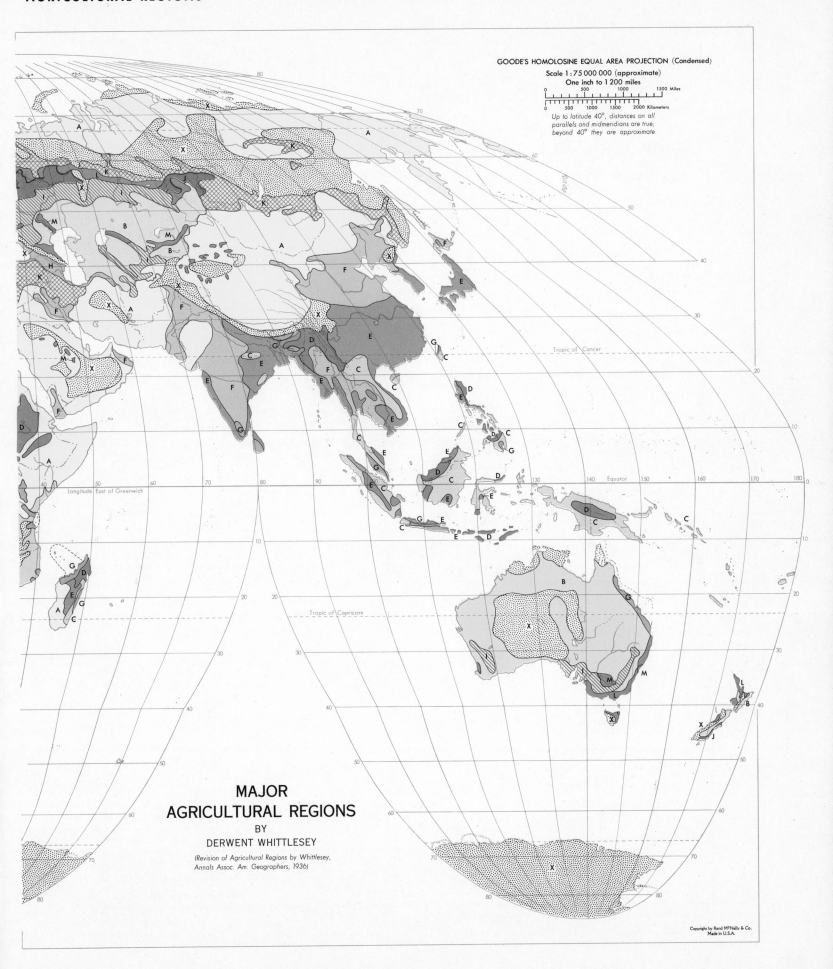

GOODE'S HOMOLOSINE EQUAL AREA PROJECTION (Condensed)

Scale 1:75 000 000 (approximate)

One inch to 1 200 miles

Up to latitude 40°, distances on all
parallels and midmeridians are true;
beyond 40° they are approximate

MAJOR
AGRICULTURAL REGIONS
BY
DERWENT WHITTLESEY

(Revision of Agricultural Regions by Whittlesey,
Annals Assoc. Am. Geographers, 1936)

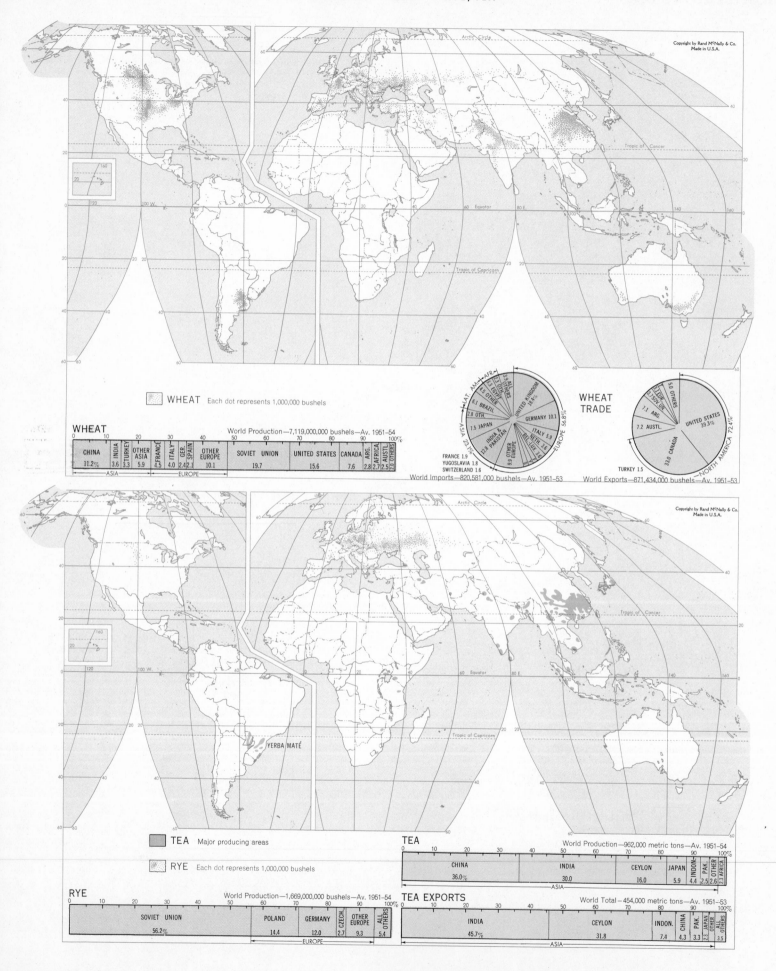

Copyright by Rand McNally & Co.
Made in U.S.A.

WHEAT   Each dot represents 1,000,000 bushels

WHEAT TRADE

| FRANCE 1.9 |
| YUGOSLAVIA 1.8 |
| SWITZERLAND 1.6 |

World Imports—820,581,000 bushels—Av. 1951–53

TURKEY 1.5

World Exports—871,434,000 bushels—Av. 1951–53

WHEAT
World Production—7,119,000,000 bushels—Av. 1951–54

0	10	20	30	40	50	60	70	80	90	100%

| CHINA 11.2% | INDIA 3.6 | TURKEY 3.3 | OTHER ASIA 5.9 | FRANCE 4.5 | ITALY 4.0 | GER. 2.4 | SPAIN 2.1 | OTHER EUROPE 10.1 | SOVIET UNION 19.7 | UNITED STATES 15.6 | CANADA 7.6 | ARG. 2.8 | AFRICA 2.7 | AUSTL. 2.5 | OTHERS |

ASIA   EUROPE

TEA   Major producing areas

RYE   Each dot represents 1,000,000 bushels

TEA
World Production—962,000 metric tons—Av. 1951–54

0	10	20	30	40	50	60	70	80	90	100%

| CHINA 36.0% | INDIA 30.0 | CEYLON 16.0 | JAPAN 5.9 | INDON. 4.4 | PAK. 2.5 | OTHER 2.6 | AFRICA 2.3 |

ASIA

RYE
World Production—1,669,000,000 bushels—Av. 1951–54

0	10	20	30	40	50	60	70	80	90	100%

| SOVIET UNION 56.2% | POLAND 14.4 | GERMANY 12.0 | CZECH. 2.7 | OTHER EUROPE 9.3 | ALL OTHERS 5.4 |

EUROPE

TEA EXPORTS
World Total—454,000 metric tons—Av. 1951–53

0	10	20	30	40	50	60	70	80	90	100%

| INDIA 45.7% | CEYLON 31.8 | INDON. 7.4 | CHINA 4.3 | PAK. 3.3 | JAPAN 2.3 | OTHER | ALL OTHERS 3.5 |

ASIA

YERBA MATÉ

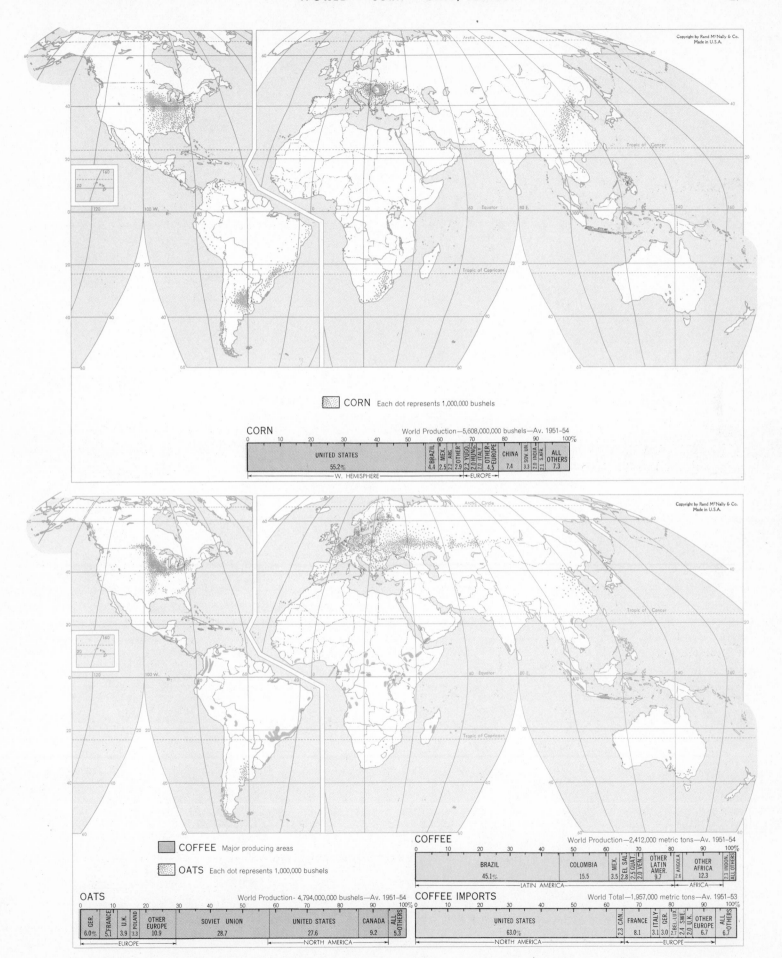

Copyright by Rand M<Nally & Co.
Made in U.S.A.

CORN Each dot represents 1,000,000 bushels

CORN
World Production—5,608,000,000 bushels—Av. 1951–54

UNITED STATES 55.2%	BRAZIL 4.4	MEX. 2.5	ARG. 2.2	OTHER 2.9	YUGO. 2.0	HUNG. 2.0	ITALY 2.0	OTHER EUROPE 4.5	CHINA 7.4	SOV. UN. 3.3	INDIA 2.0	S. AFR. 2.1	ALL OTHERS 7.3

← W. HEMISPHERE → ← EUROPE →

COFFEE Major producing areas

OATS Each dot represents 1,000,000 bushels

COFFEE
World Production—2,412,000 metric tons—Av. 1951–54

BRAZIL 45.1%	COLOMBIA 15.5	MEX. 3.5	EL SAL. 2.8	GUAT. 2.5	VEN. 2.0	OTHER LATIN AMER. 9.7	ANGOLA 2.6	OTHER AFRICA 12.3	INDON. 2.3	ALL OTHERS

← LATIN AMERICA → ← AFRICA →

OATS
World Production– 4,794,000,000 bushels–Av. 1951–54

GER. 6.0%	FRANCE 5.1	U.K. 3.9	POLAND 3.3	OTHER EUROPE 10.9	SOVIET UNION 28.7	UNITED STATES 27.6	CANADA 9.2	ALL OTHERS 5.3

← EUROPE → ← NORTH AMERICA →

COFFEE IMPORTS
World Total—1,957,000 metric tons—Av. 1951–53

UNITED STATES 63.0%	CAN. 2.3	FRANCE 8.1	ITALY 3.1	GER. 3.0	BEL-LUX 2.7	SWE. 2.4	U.K. 2.0	OTHER EUROPE 6.7	ALL OTHERS 6.7

← NORTH AMERICA → ← EUROPE →

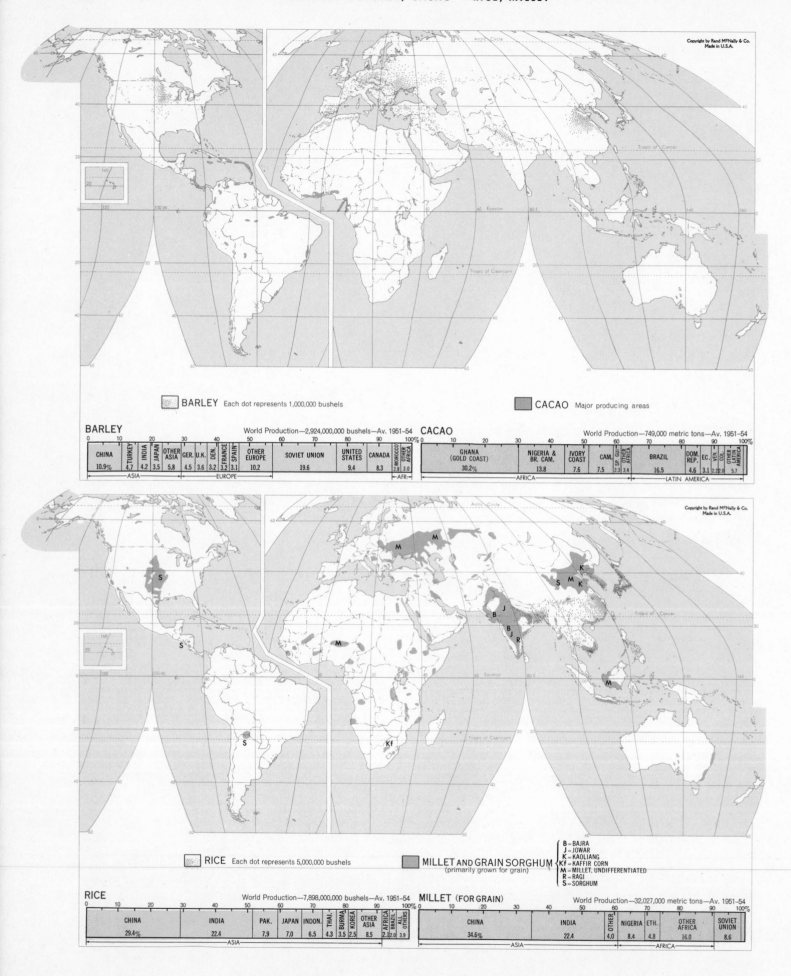

BARLEY Each dot represents 1,000,000 bushels

CACAO Major producing areas

BARLEY

World Production—2,924,000,000 bushels—Av. 1951–54

CHINA	TURKEY	INDIA	JAPAN	OTHER ASIA	GER.	U.K.	DEN.	FRANCE	SPAIN	OTHER EUROPE	SOVIET UNION	UNITED STATES	CANADA	MOROCCO	OTHER AFRICA		
10.9%	4.7	4.2	3.5	5.8	4.5	3.6	3.2	3.2	3.1	10.2	19.6	9.4	8.3	2.8	3.0		

—ASIA—   —EUROPE—   ←AFR.→

CACAO

World Production—749,000 metric tons—Av. 1951–54

GHANA (GOLD COAST)	NIGERIA & BR. CAM.	IVORY COAST	CAM.	SP. GUI.	OTHER AFRICA	BRAZIL	DOM. REP.	EC.	VEN.	COL.	OTHER LATIN AMERICA
30.2%	13.8	7.6	7.5	2.3	3.4	16.5	4.6	3.1	2.2	2.0	5.7

——————————————AFRICA——————————————   ——————————LATIN AMERICA——————————

RICE Each dot represents 5,000,000 bushels

MILLET AND GRAIN SORGHUM
(primarily grown for grain)

B = BAJRA
J = JOWAR
K = KAOLIANG
Kf = KAFFIR CORN
M = MILLET, UNDIFFERENTIATED
R = RAGI
S = SORGHUM

RICE

World Production—7,898,000,000 bushels—Av. 1951–54

CHINA	INDIA	PAK.	JAPAN	INDON.	THAI.	BURMA	KOREA	OTHER ASIA	AFRICA	BRAZIL	ALL OTHERS
29.4%	22.4	7.9	7.0	6.5	4.3	3.5	2.5	8.5	2.1	2.0	3.9

————————————————————————————ASIA————————————————————————————

MILLET (FOR GRAIN)

World Production—32,027,000 metric tons—Av. 1951–54

CHINA	INDIA	OTHER	NIGERIA	ETH.	OTHER AFRICA	SOVIET UNION
34.6%	22.4	4.0	8.4	4.8	16.0	8.6

————————————ASIA————————————   ——————————AFRICA——————————

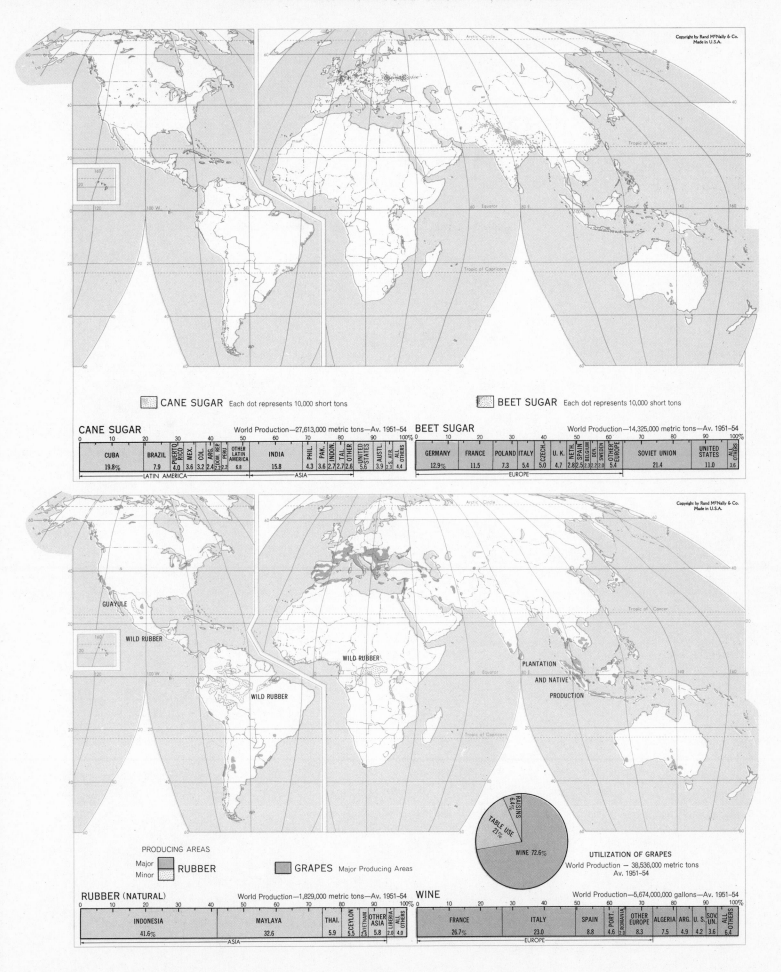

Copyright by Rand McNally & Co.
Made in U.S.A.

CANE SUGAR Each dot represents 10,000 short tons

BEET SUGAR Each dot represents 10,000 short tons

CANE SUGAR
World Production—27,613,000 metric tons—Av. 1951-54

CUBA 19.8%	BRAZIL 7.9	PUERTO RICO 4.0	MEX. 3.6	COL. 3.2	ARG. 2.4	DOM. REP. 2.2	PERU 2.2	OTHER LATIN AMERICA 6.8	INDIA 15.8	PHIL. 4.3	PAK. 3.6	INDON. 2.7	TAI. 2.7	OTHER 2.6	UNITED STATES 5.6	AUSTL. 3.9	S. AFR. 2.3	ALL OTHERS 4.4	

←—— LATIN AMERICA ——→ ←—— ASIA ——→

BEET SUGAR
World Production—14,325,000 metric tons—Av. 1951-54

GERMANY 12.9%	FRANCE 11.5	POLAND 7.3	ITALY 5.4	CZECH. 5.0	U.K. 4.7	NETH. 2.8	SPAIN 2.5	BELGIUM 2.3	DEN. 2.2	SWEDEN 2.0	OTHER EUROPE 5.4	SOVIET UNION 21.4	UNITED STATES 11.0	ALL OTHERS 3.6

←—————————————— EUROPE ——————————————→

Copyright by Rand McNally & Co.
Made in U.S.A.

GUAYULE

WILD RUBBER

WILD RUBBER

WILD RUBBER

WILD RUBBER

PLANTATION

AND NATIVE

PRODUCTION

PRODUCING AREAS

Major
Minor   **RUBBER**

GRAPES Major Producing Areas

RAISINS 6.4%

TABLE USE 21%

WINE 72.6%

UTILIZATION OF GRAPES
World Production — 38,536,000 metric tons
Av. 1951-54

RUBBER (NATURAL)
World Production—1,829,000 metric tons—Av. 1951-54

INDONESIA 41.6%	MAYLAYA 32.6	THAI. 5.9	CEYLON 5.5	VIETNAM 2.6	OTHER ASIA 5.8	LIBERIA 2.0	ALL OTHERS 4.0

←————————————— ASIA —————————————→

WINE
World Production—5,674,000,000 gallons—Av. 1951-54

FRANCE 26.7%	ITALY 23.0	SPAIN 8.8	PORT. 4.6	ROMANIA 2.0	OTHER EUROPE 8.3	ALGERIA 7.5	ARG. 4.9	U.S. 4.2	SOV. UN. 3.6	ALL OTHERS 6.4

←————————————— EUROPE —————————————→

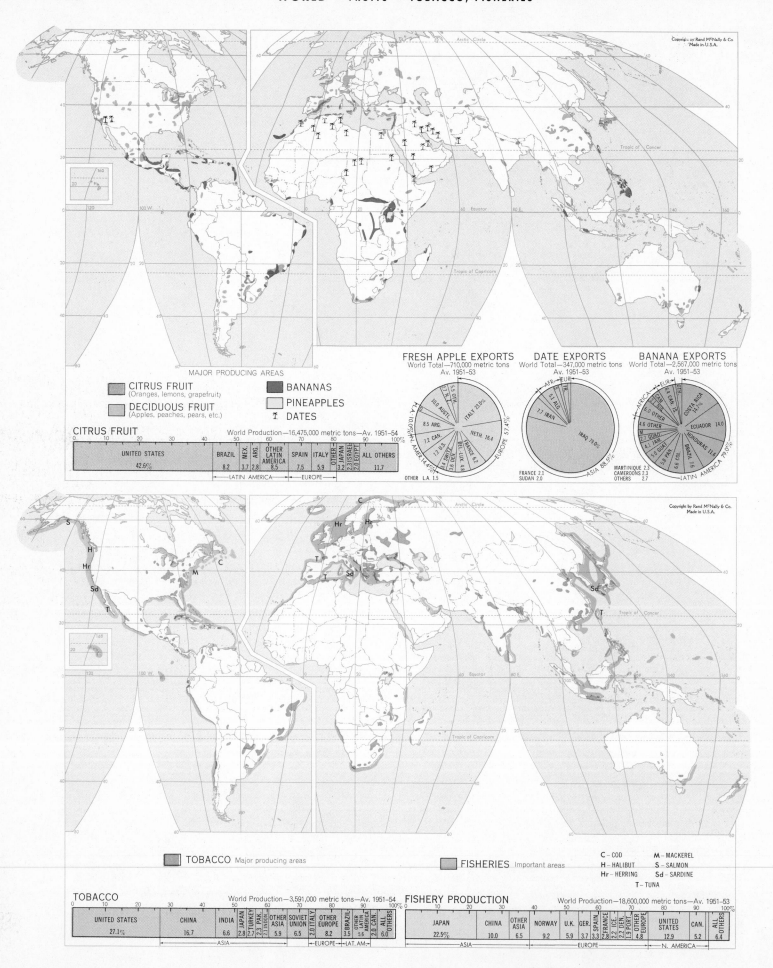

MAJOR PRODUCING AREAS

CITRUS FRUIT (Oranges, lemons, grapefruit)

DECIDUOUS FRUIT (Apples, peaches, pears, etc.)

BANANAS

PINEAPPLES

⌠ DATES

FRESH APPLE EXPORTS
World Total—710,000 metric tons
Av. 1951–53

ITALY 23.0% NETH. 16.4 FRANCE 6.2 BEL.-LUX. 4.8 SWITZ. U.S. EUROPE 57.4% 7.2 CAN. 8.5 ARG. 10.0 AUSTL. 5.5 OTH. N. AMERICA 14.4% LA 10.0%
OTHER L.A. 1.5

DATE EXPORTS
World Total—347,000 metric tons
Av. 1951–53

IRAQ 79.0% 7.7 IRAN 5.1 ALG. TUR. AFR. EUR. ASIA 88.5%
FRANCE 2.1 SUDAN 2.0

BANANA EXPORTS
World Total—2,567,000 metric tons
Av. 1951–53

ECUADOR 14.0 HONDURAS 11.6 BRAZIL 7.6 COL. PAN. GUAT. JAM. GUAD. OTHER CAN. IS. COSTA RICA AFRICA EUR. OTH. LATIN AMERICA 79.0%
MARTINIQUE 2.3 CAMEROONS 2.3 OTHERS 2.7

CITRUS FRUIT
World Production—16,475,000 metric tons—Av. 1951–54

0	10	20	30	40	50	60	70	80	90	100%

| UNITED STATES 42.6% | BRAZIL 8.2 | MEX. 3.7 | ARG. 2.8 | OTHER LATIN AMERICA 8.5 | SPAIN 7.5 | ITALY 5.9 | OTHER | JAPAN 3.2 | ISRAEL 2.3 | EGYPT 2.0 | ALL OTHERS 11.7 |

— LATIN AMERICA —   — EUROPE —

TOBACCO Major producing areas

FISHERIES Important areas

C — COD   M — MACKEREL
H — HALIBUT   S — SALMON
Hr — HERRING   Sd — SARDINE
T — TUNA

TOBACCO
World Production—3,591,000 metric tons—Av. 1951–54

0	10	20	30	40	50	60	70	80	90	100%

| UNITED STATES 27.1% | CHINA 16.7 | INDIA 6.6 | JAPAN 2.8 | TURKEY 2.7 | PAK. 2.3 | INDON. 2.1 | OTHER ASIA 5.9 | SOVIET UNION 6.5 | ITALY 2.0 | OTHER EUROPE 8.2 | BRAZIL 3.5 | OTHER LATIN AMERICA | CAN. 2.0 | ALL OTHERS 6.0 |

— ASIA —   — EUROPE —   — LAT. AM. —

FISHERY PRODUCTION
World Production—18,600,000 metric tons—Av. 1951–53

0	10	20	30	40	50	60	70	80	90	100%

| JAPAN 22.5% | CHINA 10.0 | OTHER ASIA 6.5 | NORWAY 9.2 | U.K. 5.9 | SPAIN 3.7 | FRANCE 2.8 | ICE. 2.2 | DEN. 1.9 | PORT. | OTHER EUROPE 4.8 | UNITED STATES 12.9 | CAN. 5.2 | ALL OTHERS 6.4 |

— ASIA —   — EUROPE —   — N. AMERICA —

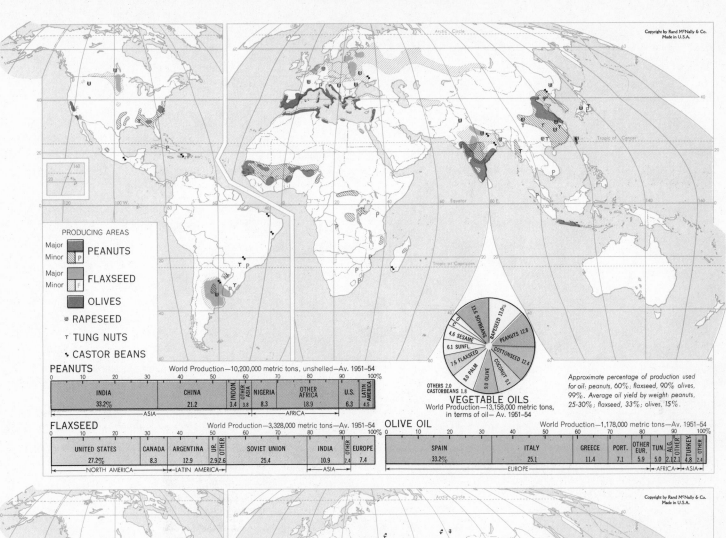

PRODUCING AREAS

Major / Minor	
	PEANUTS
	FLAXSEED
	OLIVES
₩	RAPESEED
т	TUNG NUTS
✦	CASTOR BEANS

VEGETABLE OILS

World Production—13,158,000 metric tons, in terms of oil— Av. 1951–54

Pie chart: SOYBEANS 13.6, RAPESEED 13.0%, PEANUTS 12.8, COTTONSEED 12.4, COCONUT 9.1, OLIVE 9.0, PALM 8.0, FLAXSEED 7.6, SUNFL. 6.1, SESAME 4.6, C, C, OTHERS 2.0, CASTORBEANS 1.8

Approximate percentage of production used for oil: peanuts, 60%; flaxseed, 90%; olives, 99%. Average oil yield by weight: peanuts, 25-30%; flaxseed, 33%; olives, 15%.

PEANUTS
World Production—10,200,000 metric tons, unshelled—Av. 1951–54

INDIA 33.2%	CHINA 21.2	INDON. 3.4	OTHER ASIA 3.8	NIGERIA 8.3	OTHER AFRICA 18.9	U.S. 6.3	LATIN AMERICA 4.5

◄———ASIA———► ◄———AFRICA———►

FLAXSEED
World Production—3,328,000 metric tons—Av. 1951–54

UNITED STATES 27.2%	CANADA 8.3	ARGENTINA 12.9	UR. 2.9	OTHER 2.6	SOVIET UNION 25.4	INDIA 10.9	OTHER 2.4	EUROPE 7.4

◄——NORTH AMERICA——► ◄—LATIN AMERICA—► ◄————ASIA————►

OLIVE OIL
World Production—1,178,000 metric tons—Av. 1951–54

SPAIN 33.2%	ITALY 25.1	GREECE 11.4	PORT. 7.1	OTHER EUR. 5.9	TUN. 5.0	ALG. 2.1	OTHER 2.1	TURKEY 4.8	OTHER 2.4

◄—————————EUROPE—————————► ◄——AFRICA——► ◄ASIA►

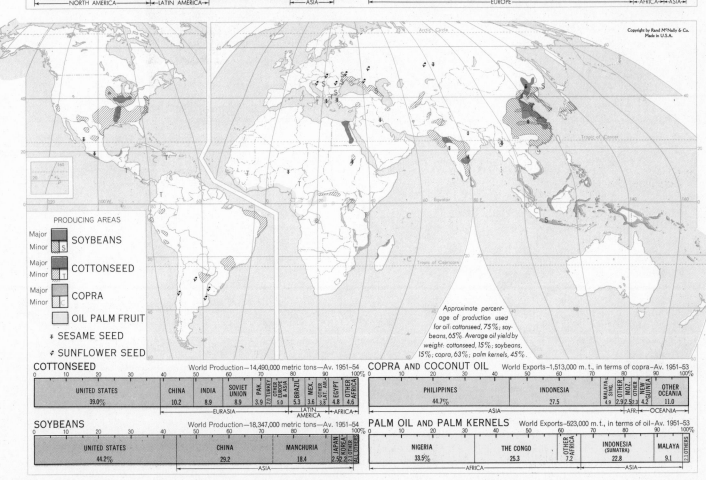

PRODUCING AREAS

Major / Minor	
	SOYBEANS
	COTTONSEED
	COPRA
	OIL PALM FRUIT
⚶	SESAME SEED
⚵	SUNFLOWER SEED

Approximate percentage of production used for oil: cottonseed, 75%; soybeans, 65%. Average oil yield by weight: cottonseed, 15%; soybeans, 15%; copra, 63%; palm kernels, 45%.

COTTONSEED
World Production—14,490,000 metric tons—Av. 1951–54

UNITED STATES 39.0%	CHINA 10.2	INDIA 8.9	SOVIET UNION 8.9	PAK. 3.9	TURKEY 2.0	OTHER EUROPE & ASIA 5.0	BRAZIL 5.3	MEX. 3.6	OTHER LAT. AM. 4.8	EGYPT 4.8	OTHER AFRICA 4.6

◄—————EURASIA—————► ◄—LATIN AMERICA—► ◄—AFRICA—►

COPRA AND COCONUT OIL
World Exports—1,513,000 m. t., in terms of copra–Av. 1951–53

PHILIPPINES 44.7%	INDONESIA 27.5	MALAYA-SING. 4.9	OTHER ASIA 2.9	MOZ. 2.5	NEW GUINEA 2.3	OTHER OCEANIA 11.0

◄—————————ASIA—————————► ◄AFR.► ◄OCEANIA►

SOYBEANS
World Production—18,347,000 metric tons—Av. 1951–54

UNITED STATES 44.2%	CHINA 29.2	MANCHURIA 18.4	JAPAN 2.5	KOREA 2.2	OTHER ALL OTHERS

◄—————————————ASIA—————————————►

PALM OIL AND PALM KERNELS
World Exports—523,000 m. t., in terms of oil–Av. 1951–53

NIGERIA 33.5%	THE CONGO 25.3	OTHER AFRICA 7.2	INDONESIA (SUMATRA) 22.8	MALAYA 9.1	OTHERS 2.1

◄—————AFRICA—————► ◄—————ASIA—————►

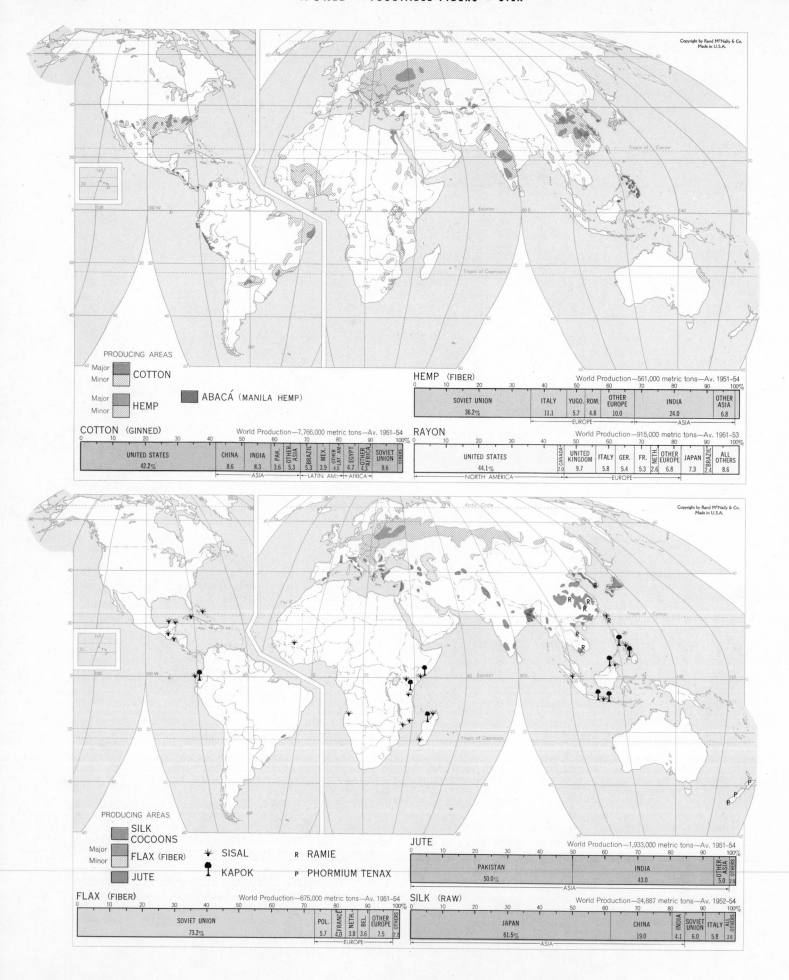

PRODUCING AREAS

Major / Minor　COTTON

Major / Minor　HEMP　　ABACÁ (MANILA HEMP)

COTTON (GINNED)

World Production—7,766,000 metric tons—Av. 1951–54

	10	20	30	40	50	60	70	80	90	100%

| UNITED STATES 42.2% | CHINA 8.6 | INDIA 8.3 | PAK. 3.6 | OTHER ASIA 5.3 | BRAZIL 5.3 | MEX. 3.9 | OTHER LAT. AM. 4.0 | EGYPT 4.7 | OTHER AFRICA 4.3 | SOVIET UNION 8.6 | OTHERS |

←——ASIA——→ ←—LATIN AM.—→ ←AFRICA→

HEMP (FIBER)

World Production—561,000 metric tons—Av. 1951–54

	10	20	30	40	50	60	70	80	90	100%

| SOVIET UNION 36.2% | ITALY 11.1 | YUGO. 5.7 | ROM. 4.8 | OTHER EUROPE 10.0 | INDIA 24.0 | OTHER ASIA 6.8 |

←————EUROPE————→ ←——ASIA——→

RAYON

World Production—915,000 metric tons—Av. 1951–53

	10	20	30	40	50	60	70	80	90	100%

| UNITED STATES 44.1% | CANADA 2.0 | UNITED KINGDOM 9.7 | ITALY 5.8 | GER. 5.4 | FR. 5.3 | NETH. 2.6 | OTHER EUROPE 6.8 | JAPAN 7.3 | BRAZIL 2.4 | ALL OTHERS 8.6 |

←—NORTH AMERICA—→ ←————EUROPE————→

PRODUCING AREAS

SILK COCOONS

Major / Minor　FLAX (FIBER)

JUTE

✳ SISAL　　R RAMIE

🌳 KAPOK　　P PHORMIUM TENAX

JUTE

World Production—1,933,000 metric tons—Av. 1951–54

	10	20	30	40	50	60	70	80	90	100%

| PAKISTAN 50.0% | INDIA 43.0 | OTHER ASIA 5.0 | OTHERS 2.0 |

←————————ASIA————————→

FLAX (FIBER)

World Production—875,000 metric tons—Av. 1951–54

	10	20	30	40	50	60	70	80	90	100%

| SOVIET UNION 73.2% | POL. 5.7 | FRANCE 4.0 | NETH. 3.8 | BEL. 3.6 | OTHER EUROPE 7.5 | OTHERS 2.2 |

←————————EUROPE————————→

SILK (RAW)

World Production—24,887 metric tons—Av. 1952–54

	10	20	30	40	50	60	70	80	90	100%

| JAPAN 61.5% | CHINA 19.0 | INDIA 4.1 | SOVIET UNION 6.0 | ITALY 5.8 | ALL OTHERS 3.6 |

←————————ASIA————————→

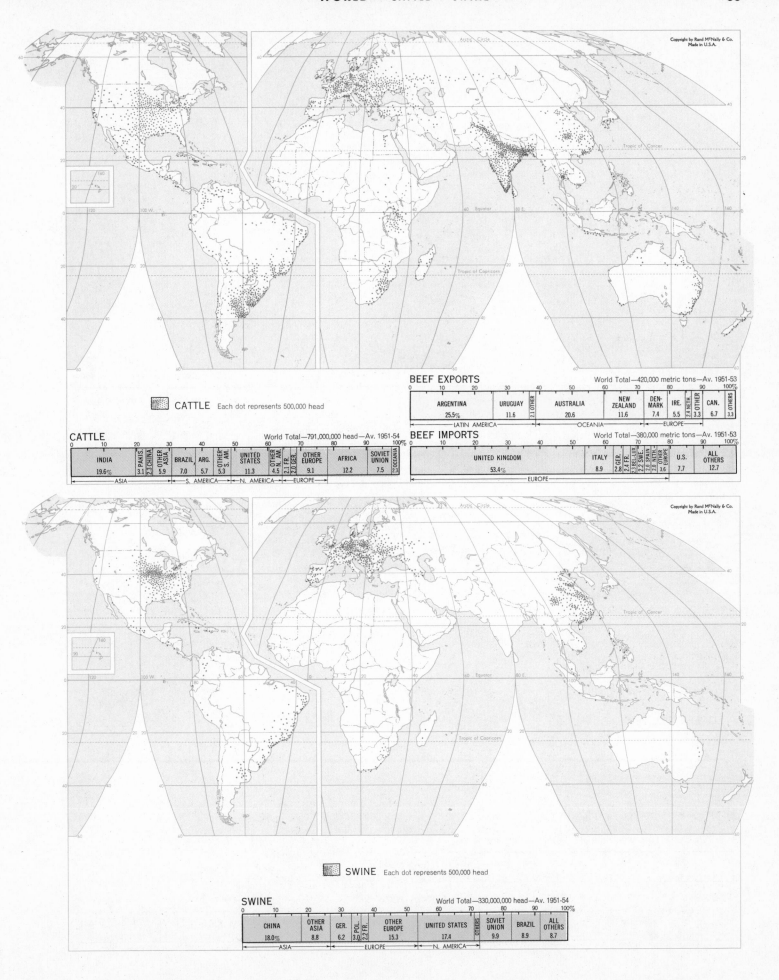

CATTLE Each dot represents 500,000 head

CATTLE

World Total—791,000,000 head—Av. 1951-54

INDIA	PAKIS.	CHINA	OTHER ASIA	BRAZIL	ARG.	OTHER S. AM.	UNITED STATES	OTHER N. AM.	FR.	GER.	OTHER EUROPE	AFRICA	SOVIET UNION	OCEANIA
19.6%	3.1	2.3	5.9	7.0	5.7	5.3	11.3	4.5	2.1	2.0	9.1	12.2	7.5	2.3

ASIA — S. AMERICA — N. AMERICA — EUROPE

BEEF EXPORTS

World Total—420,000 metric tons—Av. 1951-53

ARGENTINA	URUGUAY	OTHER	AUSTRALIA	NEW ZEALAND	DEN-MARK	IRE.	NETH.	OTHER	CAN.	OTHERS
25.5%	11.6	2.1	20.6	11.6	7.4	5.5	2.4	3.3	6.7	3.3

LATIN AMERICA — OCEANIA — EUROPE

BEEF IMPORTS

World Total—380,000 metric tons—Av. 1951-53

UNITED KINGDOM	ITALY	GER.	FR.	BEL.-LUX.	SWE.	SPAIN	NETH.	OTHER EUROPE	U.S.	ALL OTHERS
53.4%	8.9	2.8	2.1	2.3	2.2	2.0	2.0	3.6	7.7	12.7

EUROPE

SWINE Each dot represents 500,000 head

SWINE

World Total—330,000,000 head—Av. 1951-54

CHINA	OTHER ASIA	GER.	POL.	FR.	OTHER EUROPE	UNITED STATES	OTHERS	SOVIET UNION	BRAZIL	ALL OTHERS
18.0%	8.8	6.2	3.0	2.2	15.3	17.4		9.9	8.9	8.7

ASIA — EUROPE — N. AMERICA

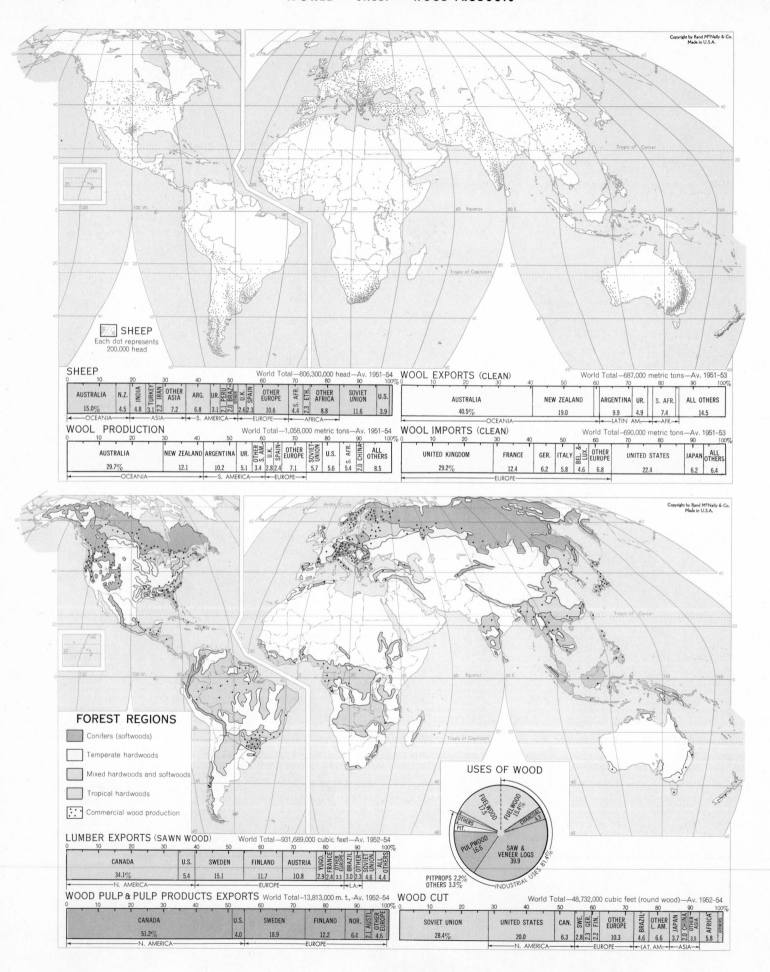

Copyright by Rand McNally & Co.
Made in U.S.A.

SHEEP
Each dot represents
200,000 head

SHEEP
World Total—806,300,000 head—Av. 1951–54

0	10	20	30	40	50	60	70	80	90	100%

| AUSTRALIA 15.0% | N.Z. 4.5 | INDIA 4.8 | TURKEY 3.1 | IRAN 2.2 | OTHER ASIA 7.2 | ARG. 6.8 | PERU 2.1 | BRAZ. 2.0 | OTHER 2.6 | U.K. 2.3 | SPAIN | OTHER EUROPE 10.6 | S. AFR. 4.4 | ETH. 2.3 | OTHER AFRICA 8.8 | SOVIET UNION 11.6 | U.S. 3.9 |

—OCEANIA— · —ASIA— · —S. AMERICA— · —EUROPE→ · —AFRICA—

WOOL EXPORTS (CLEAN)
World Total—687,000 metric tons—Av. 1951–53

0	10	20	30	40	50	60	70	80	90	100%

| AUSTRALIA 40.5% | NEW ZEALAND 19.0 | ARGENTINA 9.9 | UR. 4.9 | S. AFR. 7.4 | ALL OTHERS 14.5 |

—OCEANIA— · —LATIN AM.— · AFR.→

WOOL PRODUCTION
World Total—1,058,000 metric tons—Av. 1951–54

0	10	20	30	40	50	60	70	80	90	100%

| AUSTRALIA 29.7% | NEW ZEALAND 12.1 | ARGENTINA 10.2 | UR. 5.1 | OTHER S. AM. 3.4 | U.K. 2.8 | SPAIN 2.4 | OTHER EUROPE 7.1 | SOVIET UNION 5.7 | U.S. 5.6 | S. AFR. 5.4 | CHINA 2.0 | ALL OTHERS 8.5 |

—OCEANIA— · —S. AMERICA— · —EUROPE→

WOOL IMPORTS (CLEAN)
World Total—690,000 metric tons—Av. 1951–53

0	10	20	30	40	50	60	70	80	90	100%

| UNITED KINGDOM 29.2% | FRANCE 12.4 | GER. 6.2 | ITALY 5.8 | BEL. & LUX. 4.6 | OTHER EUROPE 6.8 | UNITED STATES 22.4 | JAPAN 6.2 | ALL OTHERS 6.4 |

—EUROPE—

Copyright by Rand McNally & Co.
Made in U.S.A.

FOREST REGIONS

- Conifers (softwoods)
- Temperate hardwoods
- Mixed hardwoods and softwoods
- Tropical hardwoods
- Commercial wood production

USES OF WOOD

- FUELWOOD 15.4%
- CHARCOAL 3.3
- SAW & VENEER LOGS 39.9
- PULPWOOD 16.5
- PIT.
- OTHERS
- FUELWOOD
- PITPROPS 2.2%
- OTHERS 3.3%
- INDUSTRIAL USES 81.4%

LUMBER EXPORTS (SAWN WOOD)
World Total—931,689,000 cubic feet—Av. 1952–54

0	10	20	30	40	50	60	70	80	90	100%

| CANADA 34.1% | U.S. 5.4 | SWEDEN 15.1 | FINLAND 11.7 | AUSTRIA 10.8 | YUGO. 2.9 | FRANCE 2.4 | OTHER EUROPE 3.3 | BRAZIL 3.0 | OTHER L.A. 2.3 | SOVIET UNION 4.6 | ALL OTHERS 4.4 |

—N. AMERICA— · —EUROPE— · —L.A.—

WOOD PULP & PULP PRODUCTS EXPORTS
World Total—13,813,000 m. t.—Av. 1952–54

0	10	20	30	40	50	60	70	80	90	100%

| CANADA 51.2% | U.S. 4.0 | SWEDEN 18.9 | FINLAND 12.2 | NOR. 6.4 | AUSTL. 2.1 | OTHER EUROPE 4.6 |

—N. AMERICA— · —EUROPE—

WOOD CUT
World Total—48,732,000 cubic feet (round wood)—Av. 1952–54

0	10	20	30	40	50	60	70	80	90	100%

| SOVIET UNION 28.4% | UNITED STATES 20.0 | CAN. 6.3 | SWE. 2.8 | GER. 2.3 | FIN. 2.2 | OTHER EUROPE 10.3 | BRAZIL 4.6 | OTHER L. AM. 6.6 | JAPAN 3.7 | CHINA 2.0 | OTHER ASIA 3.5 | AFRICA 5.8 | OTHERS |

—N. AMERICA— · —EUROPE— · —LAT. AM.— · —ASIA—

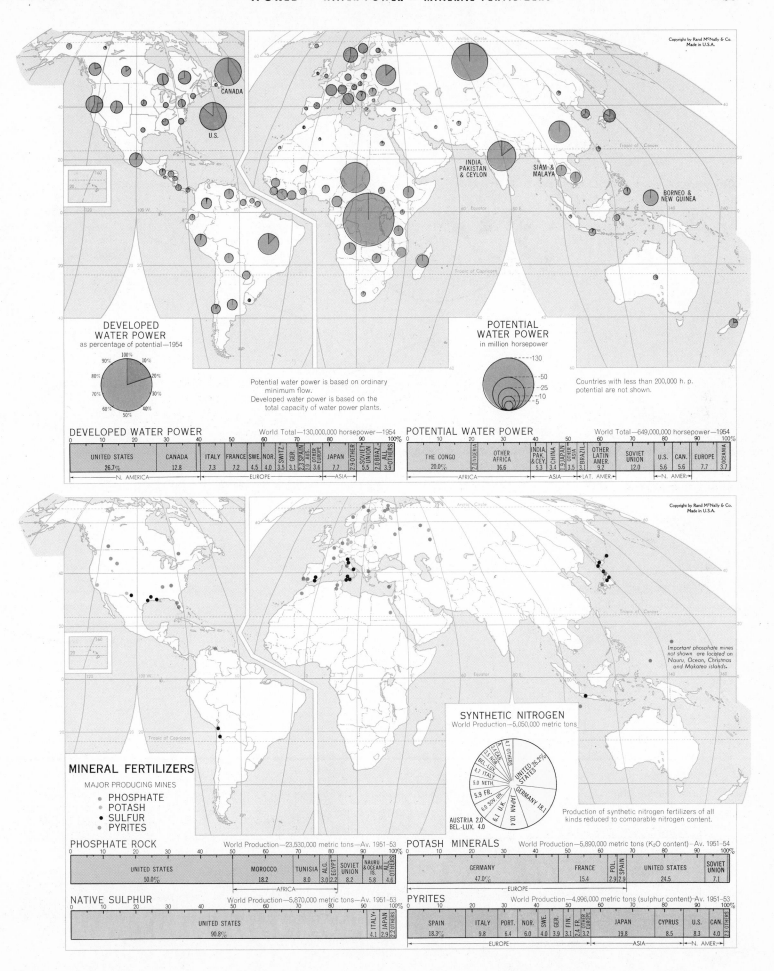

Copyright by Rand McNally & Co.
Made in U.S.A.

CANADA

U.S.

INDIA, PAKISTAN & CEYLON

SIAM & MALAYA

BORNEO & NEW GUINEA

DEVELOPED WATER POWER
as percentage of potential—1954

100%
90%   10%
80%   20%
70%   30%
60%   40%
50%

Potential water power is based on ordinary minimum flow.
Developed water power is based on the total capacity of water power plants.

POTENTIAL WATER POWER
in million horsepower

—130
—50
—25
—10
—5

Countries with less than 200,000 h. p. potential are not shown.

DEVELOPED WATER POWER
World Total—130,000,000 horsepower—1954

UNITED STATES 26.7%	CANADA 12.8	ITALY 7.3	FRANCE 7.2	SWE. 4.5	NOR. 4.0	SWITZ. 3.5	GER. 3.1	SPAIN 2.0	AUS. 2.3	OTHER EUROPE 3.6	JAPAN 7.7	OTHER 2.9	SOVIET UNION 5.5	BRAZ. 2.0	ALL OTHERS 3.9

N. AMERICA — EUROPE — ASIA —

POTENTIAL WATER POWER
World Total—649,000,000 horsepower—1954

THE CONGO 20.0%	NIGERIA 2.0	OTHER AFRICA 16.6	INDIA, PAK. & CEY. 5.3	CHINA 3.4	JAPAN 1.9	OTHER ASIA 3.5	BRAZIL 3.1	OTHER LATIN AMER. 9.2	SOVIET UNION 12.0	U.S. 5.6	CAN. 5.6	EUROPE 7.7	OCEANIA 3.7

AFRICA — ASIA — LAT. AMER. — N. AMER. —

Copyright by Rand McNally & Co.
Made in U.S.A.

Important phosphate mines not shown are located on Nauru, Ocean, Christmas and Makatea islands.

MINERAL FERTILIZERS
MAJOR PRODUCING MINES

- PHOSPHATE
- POTASH
- SULFUR
- PYRITES

SYNTHETIC NITROGEN
World Production—5,050,000 metric tons

UNITED STATES 26.2%
GERMANY 18.1
JAPAN 10.4
U. K. 6.1
SOV. UN. 6.0
FR. 5.9
NETH. 5.0
ITALY 4.7
BEL.-LUX. 4.3
CAN. 3.3
OTHERS 4.7
AUSTRIA 2.0
BEL.-LUX. 4.0

Production of synthetic nitrogen fertilizers of all kinds reduced to comparable nitrogen content.

PHOSPHATE ROCK
World Production—23,530,000 metric tons—Av. 1951-53

UNITED STATES 50.0%	MOROCCO 18.2	TUNISIA 8.0	ALG. 3.0	EGYPT 2.2	SOVIET UNION 8.2	NAURU & OCEAN IS. 5.8	ALL OTHERS 4.6

AFRICA —

POTASH MINERALS
World Production—5,890,000 metric tons (K₂O content)—Av. 1951-54

GERMANY 47.0%	FRANCE 15.4	POL. 2.9	SPAIN 2.9	UNITED STATES 24.5	SOVIET UNION 7.1

EUROPE —

NATIVE SULPHUR
World Production—5,870,000 metric tons—Av. 1951-53

UNITED STATES 90.8%	ITALY 4.1	JAPAN 2.9	2 OTHERS 2.2

PYRITES
World Production—4,996,000 metric tons (sulphur content)—Av. 1951-53

SPAIN 18.3%	ITALY 9.8	PORT. 6.4	NOR. 6.0	SWE. 4.0	GER. 3.9	FIN. 3.1	FR. 2.4	OTHER EUROPE 3.2	JAPAN 19.8	CYPRUS 8.5	U.S. 8.3	CAN. 4.0	2 OTHERS 2.3

EUROPE — ASIA — N. AMER. —

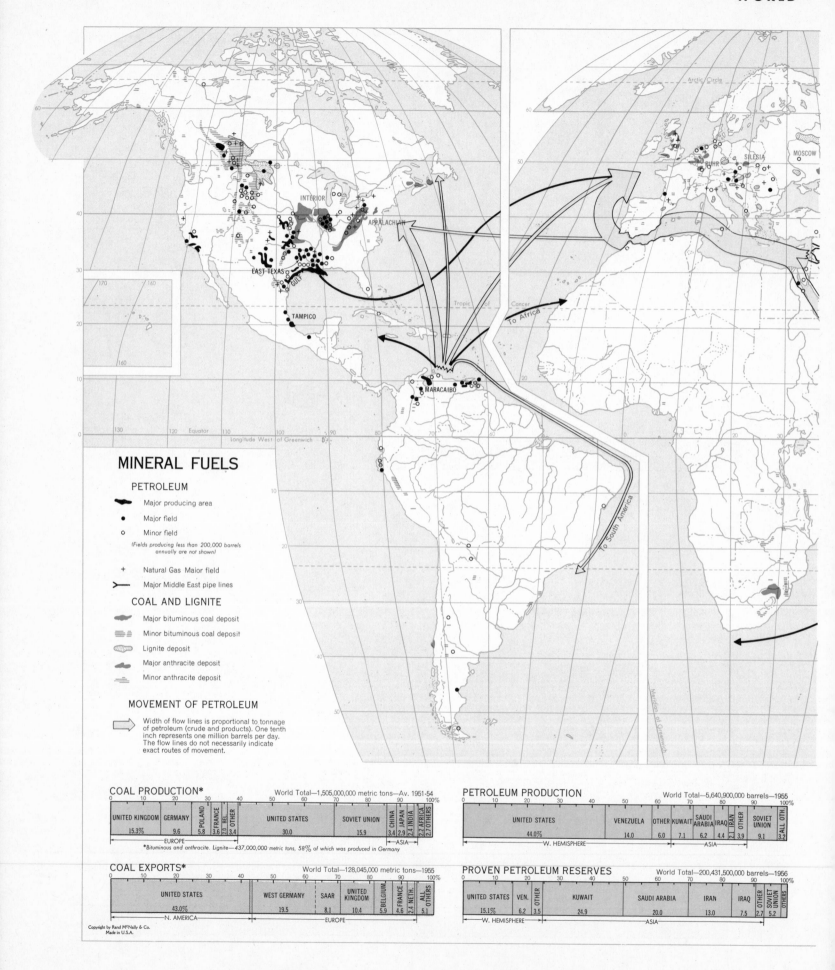

MINERAL FUELS

PETROLEUM

- 〰 Major producing area
- ● Major field
- ○ Minor field

(Fields producing less than 200,000 barrels annually are not shown)

- **+** Natural Gas Major field
- ⪼— Major Middle East pipe lines

COAL AND LIGNITE

- 〰 Major bituminous coal deposit
- ≡ Minor bituminous coal deposit
- ▨ Lignite deposit
- ◆ Major anthracite deposit
- ≡ Minor anthracite deposit

MOVEMENT OF PETROLEUM

⟹ Width of flow lines is proportional to tonnage of petroleum (crude and products). One tenth inch represents one million barrels per day. The flow lines do not necessarily indicate exact routes of movement.

COAL PRODUCTION*   World Total—1,505,000,000 metric tons—Av. 1951-54

0	10	20	30	40	50	60	70	80	90	100%

UNITED KINGDOM	GERMANY	POLAND	FRANCE	BEL	OTHER	UNITED STATES	SOVIET UNION	CHINA	JAPAN	INDIA	AFRICA	OTHERS
15.3%	9.6	5.8	3.6	1.7	3.4	30.0	15.9	3.4	2.9	2.4	2.2	2.7

←—————EUROPE—————→   ←————ASIA————→

*Bituminous and anthracite. Lignite—437,000,000 metric tons, 58% of which was produced in Germany

COAL EXPORTS*   World Total—128,045,000 metric tons—1955

0	10	20	30	40	50	60	70	80	90	100%

UNITED STATES	WEST GERMANY	SAAR	UNITED KINGDOM	BELGIUM	FRANCE	NETH.	ALL OTHERS
43.0%	19.5	8.1	10.4	5.9	4.6	2.4	5.1

←———N. AMERICA———→   ←——————————EUROPE——————————→

PETROLEUM PRODUCTION   World Total—5,640,900,000 barrels—1955

0	10	20	30	40	50	60	70	80	90	100%

UNITED STATES	VENEZUELA	OTHER	KUWAIT	SAUDI ARABIA	IRAQ	IRAN	OTHER	SOVIET UNION	ALL OTH.
44.0%	14.0	6.0	7.1	6.2	4.4	2.1	3.9	9.1	3.2

←————————W. HEMISPHERE————————→   ←————————ASIA————————→

PROVEN PETROLEUM RESERVES   World Total—200,431,500,000 barrels—1956

0	10	20	30	40	50	60	70	80	90	100%

UNITED STATES	VEN.	OTHER	KUWAIT	SAUDI ARABIA	IRAN	IRAQ	OTHER	SOVIET UNION	OTHERS
15.1%	6.2	3.5	24.9	20.0	13.0	7.5	2.7	5.2	

←——W. HEMISPHERE——→   ←————————————ASIA————————————→

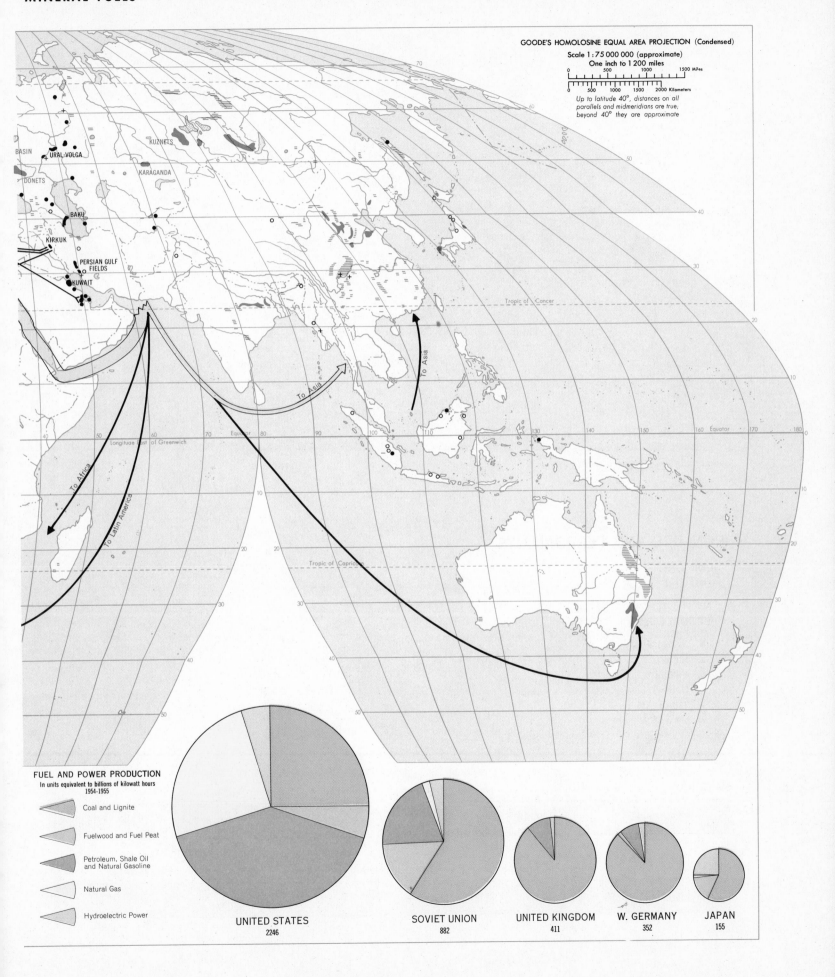

GOODE'S HOMOLOSINE EQUAL AREA PROJECTION (Condensed)
Scale 1:75 000 000 (approximate)
One inch to 1 200 miles

Up to latitude 40°, distances on all
parallels and midmeridians are true;
beyond 40° they are approximate

BASIN

URAL-VOLGA

KUZNETS

KARAGANDA

DONETS

BAKU

KIRKUK

PERSIAN GULF
FIELDS

KUWAIT

To Asia

To Asia

To Africa

To Latin America

Tropic of Cancer

Longitude East of Greenwich

Equator

Tropic of Capricorn

Equator

FUEL AND POWER PRODUCTION
In units equivalent to billions of kilowatt hours
1954-1955

Coal and Lignite

Fuelwood and Fuel Peat

Petroleum, Shale Oil
and Natural Gasoline

Natural Gas

Hydroelectric Power

UNITED STATES
2246

SOVIET UNION
882

UNITED KINGDOM
411

W. GERMANY
352

JAPAN
155

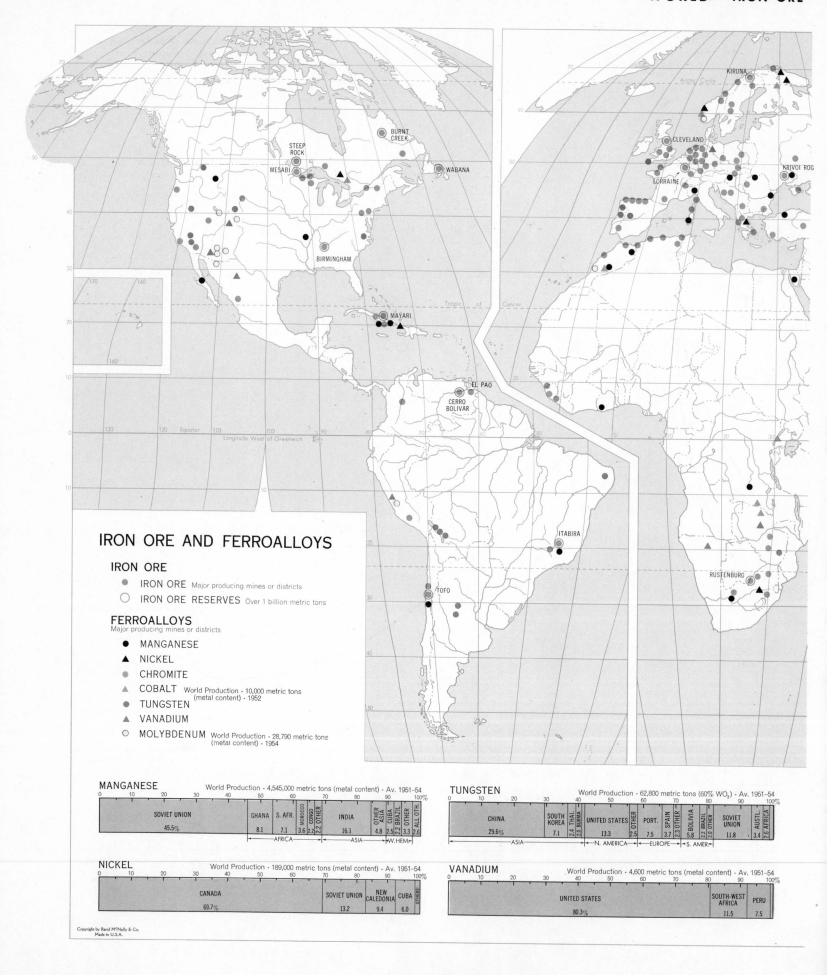

IRON ORE AND FERROALLOYS

IRON ORE

● IRON ORE Major producing mines or districts

○ IRON ORE RESERVES Over 1 billion metric tons

FERROALLOYS
Major producing mines or districts

● MANGANESE

▲ NICKEL

● CHROMITE

▲ COBALT World Production - 10,000 metric tons
(metal content) - 1952

● TUNGSTEN

▲ VANADIUM

○ MOLYBDENUM World Production - 28,790 metric tons
(metal content) - 1954

MANGANESE World Production - 4,545,000 metric tons (metal content) - Av. 1951-54

| SOVIET UNION 45.5% | GHANA 8.1 | S. AFR. 7.1 | MOROCCO 3.6 | CONGO 2.2 | OTHER | INDIA 16.1 | OTHER ASIA 4.8 | CUBA 2.5 | BRAZIL 2.2 | OTHER 3.3 | ALL OTH. 2.6 |

AFRICA — ASIA — W.HEM.

TUNGSTEN World Production - 62,800 metric tons (60% WO₃) - Av. 1951-54

| CHINA 29.6% | SOUTH KOREA 7.1 | THAI. 2.4 | BURMA 2.0 | UNITED STATES 13.3 | OTHER 2.5 | PORT. 7.5 | SPAIN 3.7 | OTHER 2.3 | BOLIVIA 5.8 | BRAZIL 2.2 | OTHER 2.0 | SOVIET UNION 11.8 | AUSTL. 3.4 | AFRICA 2.6 |

ASIA — N. AMERICA — EUROPE — S. AMER.

NICKEL World Production - 189,000 metric tons (metal content) - Av. 1951-54

| CANADA 69.7% | SOVIET UNION 13.2 | NEW CALEDONIA 9.4 | CUBA 6.0 | OTHERS |

VANADIUM World Production - 4,600 metric tons (metal content) - Av. 1951-54

| UNITED STATES 80.3% | SOUTH-WEST AFRICA 11.5 | PERU 7.5 |

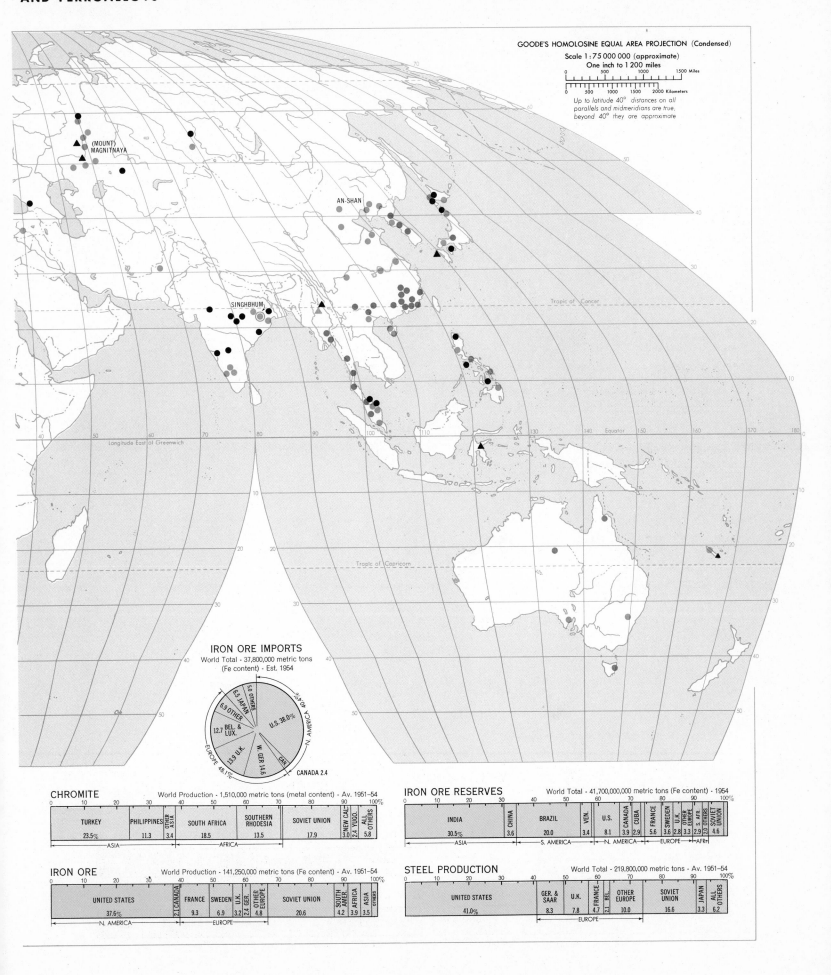

GOODE'S HOMOLOSINE EQUAL AREA PROJECTION (Condensed)
Scale 1 : 75 000 000 (approximate)
One inch to 1 200 miles

Up to latitude 40° distances on all
parallels and midmeridians are true,
beyond 40° they are approximate

(MOUNT) MAGNITNAYA

AN-SHAN

SINGHBHUM

Tropic of Cancer

Longitude East of Greenwich

Equator

Tropic of Capricorn

IRON ORE IMPORTS
World Total - 37,800,000 metric tons
(Fe content) - Est. 1954

- U.S. 38.0%
- N. AMERICA 40.4%
- CANADA 2.4
- CAN.
- W. GER 14.6
- 13.9 U.K.
- 12.7 BEL. & LUX.
- EUROPE 48.1%
- 6.9 OTHER
- 6.5 JAPAN
- 5.0 OTHERS
- 6.4 ASIA

CHROMITE
World Production - 1,510,000 metric tons (metal content) - Av. 1951–54

0	10	20	30	40	50	60	70	80	90	100%

TURKEY	PHILIPPINES	OTHER ASIA	SOUTH AFRICA	SOUTHERN RHODESIA	SOVIET UNION	NEW CAL.	YUGO.	ALL OTHERS
23.5%	11.3	3.4	18.5	13.5	17.9	3.0	2.4	5.8

ASIA — AFRICA

IRON ORE
World Production - 141,250,000 metric tons (Fe content) - Av. 1951–54

0	10	20	30	40	50	60	70	80	90	100%

UNITED STATES	CANADA	FRANCE	SWEDEN	U.K.	GER.	OTHER EUROPE	SOVIET UNION	SOUTH AMER.	AFRICA	ASIA	OTHERS
37.6%	2.1	9.3	6.9	3.2	2.4	4.8	20.6	4.2	3.9	3.5	

N. AMERICA — EUROPE

IRON ORE RESERVES
World Total - 41,700,000,000 metric tons (Fe content) - 1954

0	10	20	30	40	50	60	70	80	90	100%

INDIA	CHINA	BRAZIL	VEN.	U.S.	CANADA	CUBA	FRANCE	SWEDEN	U.K.	OTHER EUROPE	S. AFR.	SOVIET UNION
30.5%	3.6	20.0	3.4	8.1	3.9	2.9	5.6	3.6	2.8	3.3	2.9	2.0	4.6

ASIA — S. AMERICA — N. AMERICA — EUROPE — AFR.

STEEL PRODUCTION
World Total - 219,800,000 metric tons - Av. 1951–54

0	10	20	30	40	50	60	70	80	90	100%

UNITED STATES	GER. & SAAR	U.K.	FRANCE	BEL.	OTHER EUROPE	SOVIET UNION	JAPAN	ALL OTHERS
41.0%	8.3	7.8	4.7	2.1	10.0	16.6	3.3	6.2

EUROPE

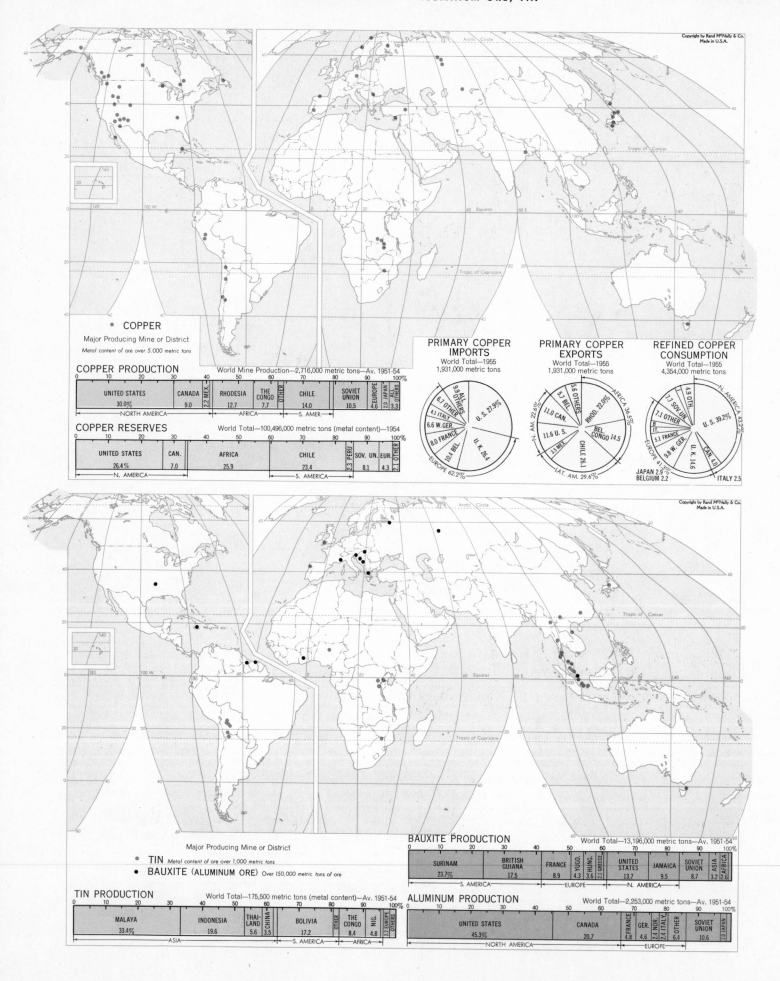

COPPER
Major Producing Mine or District
Metal content of ore over 5,000 metric tons

COPPER PRODUCTION
World Mine Production—2,716,000 metric tons—Av. 1951-54

0	10	20	30	40	50	60	70	80	90	100%

| UNITED STATES 30.0% | CANADA 9.0 | MEX. 2.2 | RHODESIA 12.7 | THE CONGO 7.7 | OTHER | CHILE 14.0 | SOVIET UNION 10.5 | EUROPE 4.6 | JAPAN 2.0 | ALL OTHERS 3.3 |

NORTH AMERICA — AFRICA — S. AMER.

COPPER RESERVES
World Total—100,496,000 metric tons (metal content)—1954

0	10	20	30	40	50	60	70	80	90	100%

| UNITED STATES 26.4% | CAN. 7.0 | AFRICA 25.9 | CHILE 23.4 | PERU 2.3 | SOV. UN. 8.1 | EUR. 4.3 | OTHER 2.1 |

N. AMERICA — S. AMERICA

PRIMARY COPPER IMPORTS
World Total—1955
1,931,000 metric tons

9.9 ALL OTHERS
6.7 OTHER
4.1 ITALY
6.6 W. GER.
8.0 FRANCE
10.4 BEL.
U. S. 27.9%
U. K. 26.4
N. AM. 22.6%
EUROPE 62.2%

PRIMARY COPPER EXPORTS
World Total—1955
1,931,000 metric tons

5.6 OTHERS
5.7 BEL.
11.0 CAN.
11.6 U. S.
3.5 MEX.
AFRICA 36.5%
RHOD. 22.0%
BEL. CONGO 14.5
CHILE 26.1
N. AM. 22.6%
LAT. AM. 29.6%

REFINED COPPER CONSUMPTION
World Total—1955
4,354,000 metric tons

4.9 ALL OTH.
7.1 SOV. UN.
7.1 OTHER
B. IT.
5.1 FRANCE
9.8 W. GER.
N. AMER. 43.2%
U. S. 39.2%
CAN. 4.0
U. K. 14.6
EUROPE 41.3%
JAPAN 2.9
BELGIUM 2.2
ITALY 2.5

Major Producing Mine or District

● **TIN** *Metal content of ore over 1,000 metric tons*
● **BAUXITE (ALUMINUM ORE)** *Over 150,000 metric tons of ore*

BAUXITE PRODUCTION
World Total—13,196,000 metric tons—Av. 1951-54

0	10	20	30	40	50	60	70	80	90	100%

| SURINAM 23.7% | BRITISH GUIANA 17.5 | FRANCE 8.9 | YUGO. 4.3 | HUNG. 3.6 | GREECE 2.1 | UNITED STATES 13.7 | JAMAICA 9.5 | SOVIET UNION 8.7 | ASIA 3.2 | AFRICA 2.6 |

S. AMERICA — EUROPE — N. AMERICA

TIN PRODUCTION
World Total—175,500 metric tons (metal content)—Av. 1951-54

0	10	20	30	40	50	60	70	80	90	100%

| MALAYA 33.4% | INDONESIA 19.6 | THAILAND 5.6 | CHINA 3.5 | BOLIVIA 17.2 | OTHER | THE CONGO 8.4 | NIG. 4.8 | EUROPE 2.2 | OTHERS |

ASIA — S. AMERICA — AFRICA

ALUMINUM PRODUCTION
World Total—2,253,000 metric tons—Av. 1951-54

0	10	20	30	40	50	60	70	80	90	100%

| UNITED STATES 45.3% | CANADA 20.7 | FRANCE 4.8 | GER. 4.6 | NOR. 2.4 | ITALY 2.4 | OTHER 6.4 | SOVIET UNION 10.6 | JAPAN 2.0 |

NORTH AMERICA — EUROPE

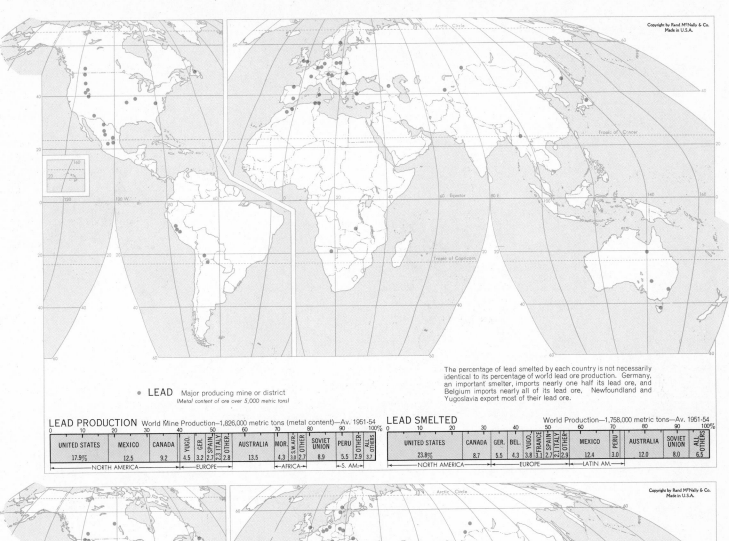

● **LEAD** Major producing mine or district
(Metal content of ore over 5,000 metric tons)

The percentage of lead smelted by each country is not necessarily identical to its percentage of world lead ore production. Germany, an important smelter, imports nearly one half its lead ore, and Belgium imports nearly all of its lead ore, Newfoundland and Yugoslavia export most of their lead ore.

LEAD PRODUCTION World Mine Production—1,826,000 metric tons (metal content)—Av. 1951-54

UNITED STATES	MEXICO	CANADA	YUGO.	GER.	SPAIN	ITALY	OTHER	AUSTRALIA	MOR.	S.W. AFR.	OTHER	SOVIET UNION	PERU	OTHER	ALL OTHERS
17.9%	12.5	9.2	4.5	3.2	2.7	2.3	2.8	13.5	4.3	3.0	2.7	8.9	5.5	2.9	3.7

NORTH AMERICA — EUROPE — AFRICA — S. AM.

LEAD SMELTED World Production—1,758,000 metric tons—Av. 1951-54

UNITED STATES	CANADA	GER.	BEL.	YUGO.	FRANCE	SPAIN	ITALY	OTHER	MEXICO	PERU	AUSTRALIA	SOVIET UNION	ALL OTHERS
23.8%	8.7	5.5	4.3	3.8	3.1	2.7	2.1	2.9	12.4	3.0	12.0	8.0	6.5

NORTH AMERICA — EUROPE — LATIN AM.

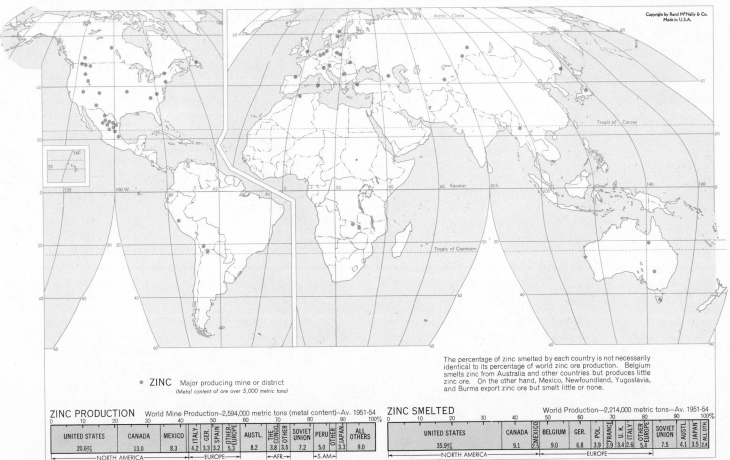

● **ZINC** Major producing mine or district
(Metal content of ore over 5,000 metric tons)

The percentage of zinc smelted by each country is not necessarily identical to its percentage of world zinc ore production. Belgium smelts zinc from Australia and other countries but produces little zinc ore. On the other hand, Mexico, Newfoundland, Yugoslavia, and Burma export zinc ore but smelt little or none.

ZINC PRODUCTION World Mine Production—2,594,000 metric tons (metal content)—Av. 1951-54

UNITED STATES	CANADA	MEXICO	ITALY	GER.	SPAIN	OTHER EUROPE	AUSTL.	THE CONGO	OTHER	SOVIET UNION	PERU	OTHER	JAPAN	ALL OTHERS
20.6%	13.0	8.3	4.2	3.2	3.2	5.3	8.2	3.8	3.5	7.2	5.0	3.3	3.3	9.0

NORTH AMERICA — EUROPE — AFR. — S. AM.

ZINC SMELTED World Production—2,214,000 metric tons—Av. 1951-54

UNITED STATES	CANADA	MEXICO	BELGIUM	GER.	POL.	FRANCE	U. K.	ITALY	OTHER EUROPE	SOVIET UNION	AUSTL.	JAPAN	ALL OTH.
35.9%	9.1	2.5	9.0	6.8	3.9	3.9	3.4	2.6	5.4	7.5	4.1	3.5	2.4

NORTH AMERICA — EUROPE

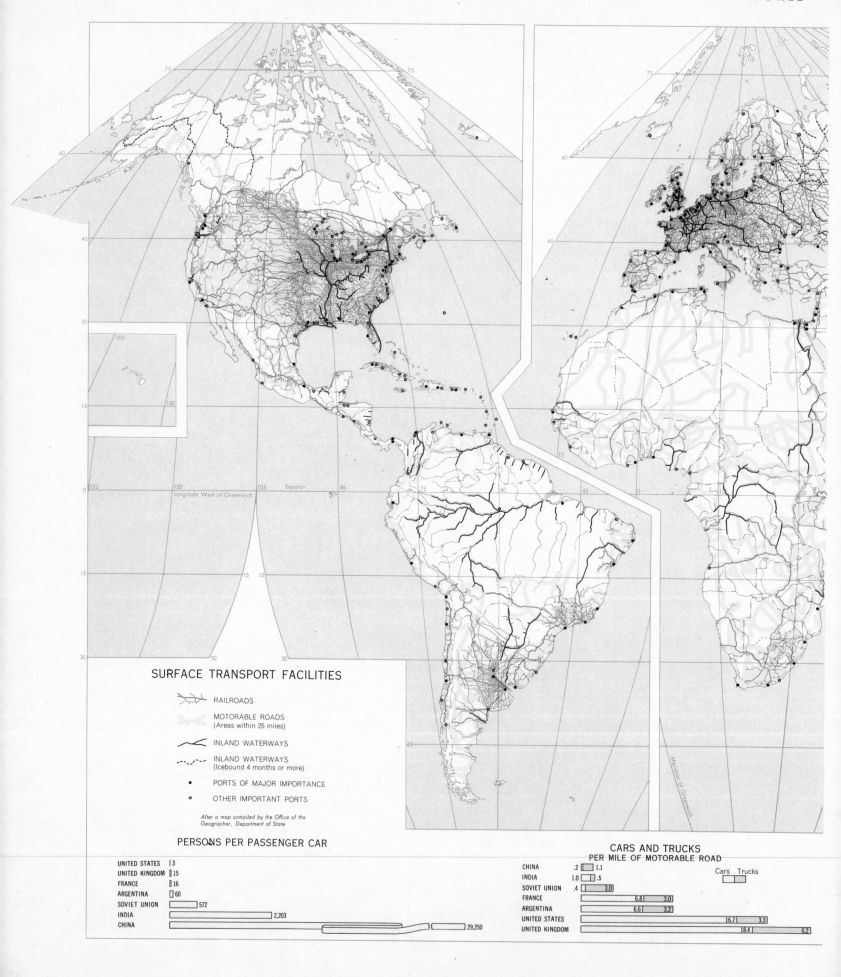

SURFACE TRANSPORT FACILITIES

RAILROADS

MOTORABLE ROADS
(Areas within 25 miles)

INLAND WATERWAYS

INLAND WATERWAYS
(Icebound 4 months or more)

● PORTS OF MAJOR IMPORTANCE

○ OTHER IMPORTANT PORTS

*After a map compiled by the Office of the
Geographer, Department of State*

PERSONS PER PASSENGER CAR

UNITED STATES	3
UNITED KINGDOM	15
FRANCE	16
ARGENTINA	60
SOVIET UNION	572
INDIA	2,203
CHINA	29,250

CARS AND TRUCKS
PER MILE OF MOTORABLE ROAD

Cars   Trucks

	Cars	Trucks
CHINA	.2	1.1
INDIA	1.0	.5
SOVIET UNION	.4	3.0
FRANCE	6.8	3.0
ARGENTINA	6.6	3.2
UNITED STATES	16.7	3.3
UNITED KINGDOM	18.4	6.2

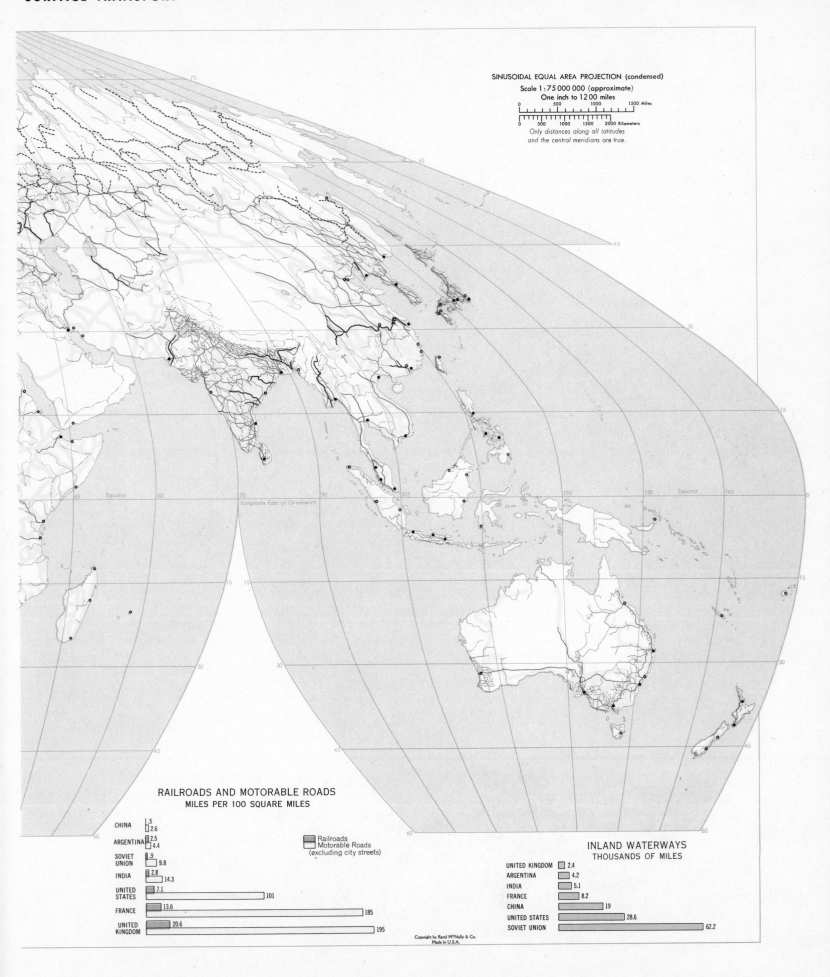

SINUSOIDAL EQUAL AREA PROJECTION (condensed)

Scale 1:75 000 000 (approximate)

One inch to 1200 miles

0 500 1000 1500 Miles

0 500 1000 1500 2000 Kilometers

*Only distances along all latitudes
and the central meridians are true.*

RAILROADS AND MOTORABLE ROADS
MILES PER 100 SQUARE MILES

	Railroads	Motorable Roads
CHINA	.5	2.6
ARGENTINA	2.5	4.4
SOVIET UNION	.9	9.8
INDIA	2.8	14.3
UNITED STATES	7.1	101
FRANCE	13.6	185
UNITED KINGDOM	20.6	195

Railroads
Motorable Roads
(excluding city streets)

INLAND WATERWAYS
THOUSANDS OF MILES

UNITED KINGDOM	2.4
ARGENTINA	4.2
INDIA	5.1
FRANCE	8.2
CHINA	19
UNITED STATES	28.6
SOVIET UNION	62.2

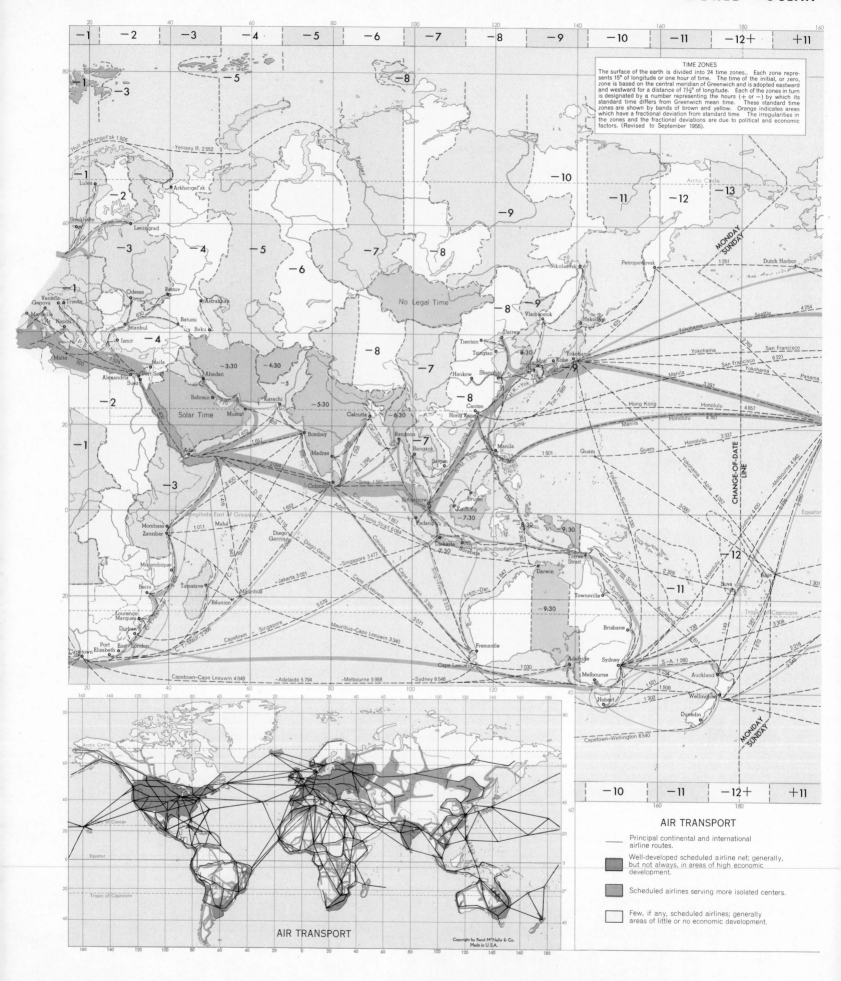

−10 −11 −12+ +11

TIME ZONES

The surface of the earth is divided into 24 time zones.. Each zone represents 15° of longitude or one hour of time. The time of the initial, or zero, zone is based on the central meridian of Greenwich and is adopted eastward and westward for a distance of 7½° of longitude. Each of the zones in turn is designated by a number representing the hours (+ or −) by which its standard time differs from Greenwich mean time. These standard time zones are shown by bands of brown and yellow. Orange indicates areas which have a fractional deviation from standard time. The irregularities in the zones and the fractional deviations are due to political and economic factors. (Revised to September 1956).

AIR TRANSPORT

Copyright by Rand M°Nally & Co.
Made in U.S.A.

AIR TRANSPORT

Principal continental and international airline routes.

Well-developed scheduled airline net; generally, but not always, in areas of high economic development.

Scheduled airlines serving more isolated centers.

Few, if any, scheduled airlines; generally areas of little or no economic development.

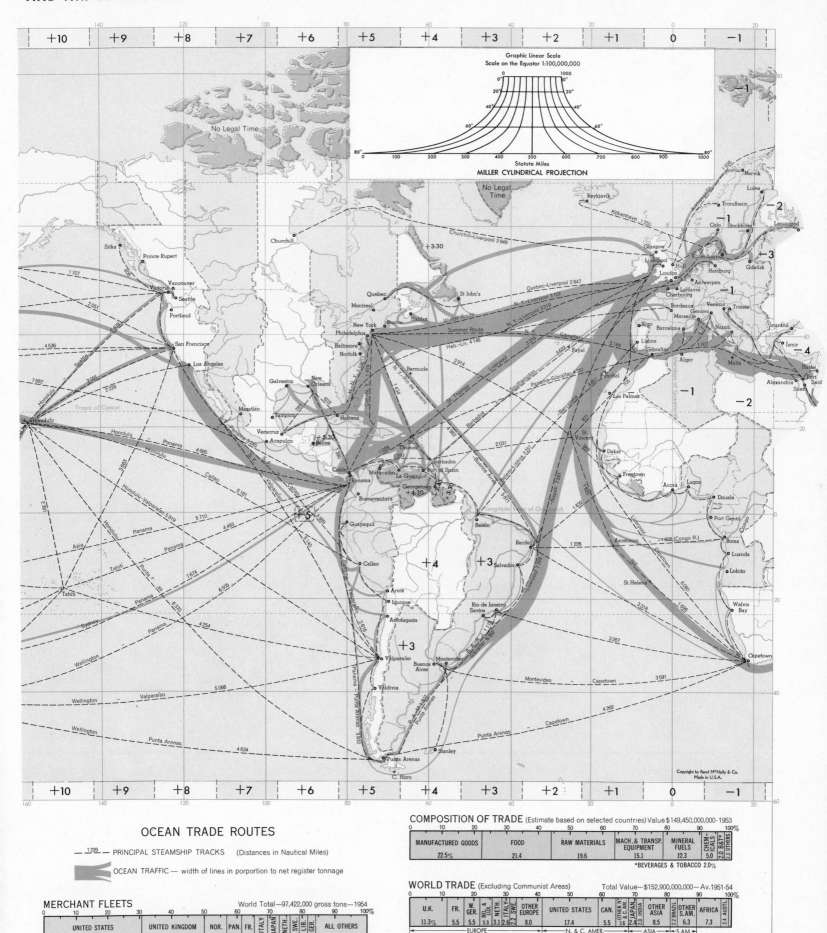

Graphic Linear Scale
Scale on the Equator 1:100,000,000

Statute Miles
MILLER CYLINDRICAL PROJECTION

OCEAN TRADE ROUTES

— 1226 — PRINCIPAL STEAMSHIP TRACKS (Distances in Nautical Miles)

OCEAN TRAFFIC — width of lines in porportion to net register tonnage

MERCHANT FLEETS
World Total—97,422,000 gross tons—1954

0	10	20	30	40	50	60	70	80	90	100%

UNITED STATES	UNITED KINGDOM	NOR.	PAN.	FR.	ITALY	JAPAN	NETH.	SWE.	LIB.	GER.	ALL OTHERS
30.4%	19.6	7.0	4.2	4.0	3.9	3.7	3.5	2.8	2.5	2.3	16.1

COMPOSITION OF TRADE (Estimate based on selected countries) Value $149,450,000,000-1953

0	10	20	30	40	50	60	70	80	90	100%

MANUFACTURED GOODS	FOOD	RAW MATERIALS	MACH. & TRANSP. EQUIPMENT	MINERAL FUELS	CHEM- ICALS	B&T*	OTHERS
22.5%	21.4	19.6	15.1	12.3	5.0	2.0	2.1

*BEVERAGES & TOBACCO 2.0%

WORLD TRADE (Excluding Communist Areas) Total Value—$152,900,000,000—Av.1951-54

0	10	20	30	40	50	60	70	80	90	100%

U.K.	FR.	W. GER.	BEL. & LUX.	NETH.	ITALY	SWE.	OTHER EUROPE	UNITED STATES	CAN.	OTHER N. & C. AM.	JAPAN	INDIA	OTHER ASIA	BRAZIL	OTHER S.AM.	AFRICA	AUSTL.
11.3%	5.5	5.5	3.3	3.1	2.6	2.2	8.0	17.4	5.5	3.6	2.0	2.0	8.5	2.2	6.3	7.3	2.4

EUROPE — N. & C. AMER. — ASIA — S.AM.

Copyright by Rand McNally & Co.
Made in U.S.A.

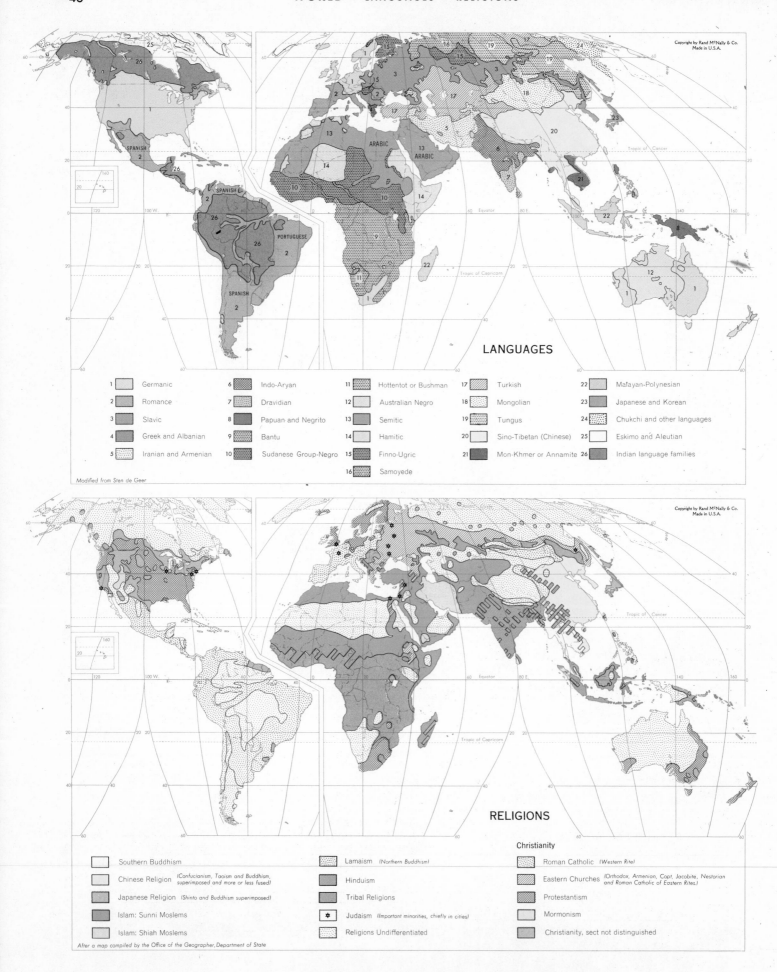

LANGUAGES

1	Germanic	6	Indo-Aryan	11	Hottentot or Bushman	17	Turkish	22	Malayan-Polynesian
2	Romance	7	Dravidian	12	Australian Negro	18	Mongolian	23	Japanese and Korean
3	Slavic	8	Papuan and Negrito	13	Semitic	19	Tungus	24	Chukchi and other languages
4	Greek and Albanian	9	Bantu	14	Hamitic	20	Sino-Tibetan (Chinese)	25	Eskimo and Aleutian
5	Iranian and Armenian	10	Sudanese Group-Negro	15	Finno-Ugric	21	Mon-Khmer or Annamite	26	Indian language families
				16	Samoyede				

Modified from Sten de Geer

RELIGIONS

Christianity

Southern Buddhism	Lamaism *(Northern Buddhism)*	Roman Catholic *(Western Rite)*
Chinese Religion *(Confucianism, Taoism and Buddhism, superimposed and more or less fused)*	Hinduism	Eastern Churches *(Orthodox, Armenian, Copt, Jacobite, Nestorian and Roman Catholic of Eastern Rites.)*
Japanese Religion *(Shinto and Buddhism superimposed)*	Tribal Religions	Protestantism
Islam: Sunni Moslems	✿ Judaism *(Important minorities, chiefly in cities)*	Mormonism
Islam: Shiah Moslems	Religions Undifferentiated	Christianity, sect not distinguished

After a map compiled by the Office of the Geographer, Department of State

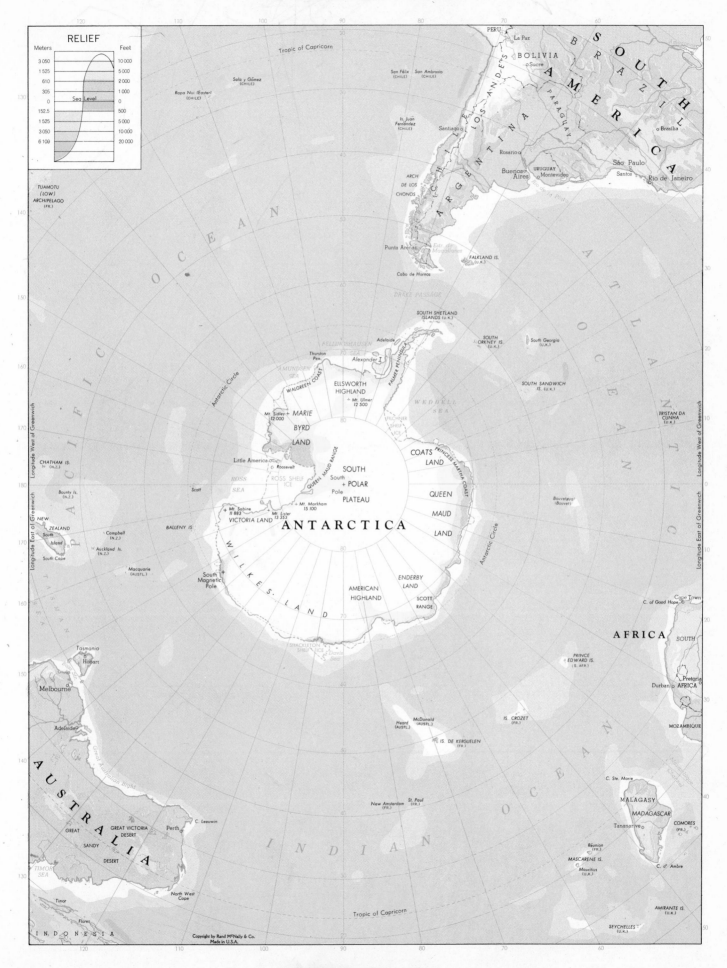

RELIEF

Meters		Feet
3 050		10 000
1 525		5 000
610		2 000
305		1 000
0	Sea Level	0
152.5		500
1 525		5 000
3 050		10 000
6 100		20 000

SOUTH AMERICA

PERU
La Paz
BOLIVIA
Sucre
BRAZIL
Brasilia
PARAGUAY
San Félix (CHILE) · San Ambrosio (CHILE)
Sala y Gómez (CHILE)
Rapa Nui (Easter) (CHILE)
Is. Juan Fernández (CHILE)
Santiago
Rosario
Buenos Aires
URUGUAY
Montevideo
São Paulo
Santos
Rio de Janeiro
ARCH. DE LOS CHONOS
ARGENTINA
CHILE
LOS ANDES
Rio de la Plata

TUAMOTU (LOW) ARCHIPELAGO (FR.)

Punta Arenas
Estr. de Magallanes
FALKLAND IS. (U.K.)
Cabo de Hornos

P A C I F I C   O C E A N

DRAKE PASSAGE

Antarctic Circle

SOUTH SHETLAND ISLANDS (U.K.)
BELLINGSHAUSEN SEA
Thurston Pen.
Adelaide
Alexander I
PALMER PENINSULA
SOUTH ORKNEY IS. (U.K.)
South Georgia (U.K.)
SOUTH SANDWICH IS. (U.K.)

AMUNDSEN SEA
WALGREEN COAST
ELLSWORTH HIGHLAND
+ Mt. Ulmer 12 500
WEDDELL SEA
TRISTAN DA CUNHA (U.K.)

Mt. Sidley 12 000
MARIE BYRD LAND
FILCHNER SHELF ICE
COATS LAND
PRINCESS MARTHA COAST

Little America
Roosevelt
ROSS SHELF ICE
QUEEN MAUD RANGE
SOUTH POLAR PLATEAU
South Pole +
QUEEN MAUD LAND
Bouvetøya (Bouvet)
Longitude West of Greenwich
Longitude East of Greenwich

ROSS SEA
Scott

CHATHAM IS. (N.Z.)
Bounty Is. (N.Z.)
NEW ZEALAND
South Island
South Cape
Campbell (N.Z.)
Auckland Is. (N.Z.)
Macquarie (AUSTL.)

+ Mt. Sabine 11 883
Mt. Lister 13 353
VICTORIA LAND
+ Mt. Markham 15 100
ANTARCTICA
WILKES LAND
South Magnetic Pole
AMERICAN HIGHLAND
ENDERBY LAND
SCOTT RANGE
C. of Good Hope
Cape Town
AFRICA
SOUTH
Pretoria
Durban
AFRICA

BALLENY IS.

TASMAN SEA
Tasmania
Hobart
Melbourne
Adelaide

SHACKLETON SHELF ICE
Davis Sea
PRINCE EDWARD IS. (S. AFR.)
MOZAMBIQUE

A U S T R A L I A
Great Australian Bight
GREAT VICTORIA DESERT
GREAT SANDY DESERT
Perth
C. Leeuwin

I N D I A N   O C E A N

Heard (AUSTL.)
McDonald (AUSTL.)
IS. CROZET (FR.)
IS. DE KERGUELEN (FR.)

C. Ste. Marie
MALAGASY
MADAGASCAR
Tananarive
COMORES (FR.)

New Amsterdam (FR.)
St. Paul (FR.)
Réunion (FR.)
MASCARENE IS.
Mauritius (U.K.)
C. d' Ambre

TIMOR SEA
Timor
Flores
I N D O N E S I A
North West Cape

Tropic of Capricorn

AMIRANTE IS. (U.K.)
SEYCHELLES (U.K.)

A T L A N T I C   O C E A N

Tropic of Capricorn

Elevations and depressions are given in feet
LAMBERTS AZIMUTHAL EQUAL-AREA PROJECTION
Scale 1:60,000,000 (approximate)

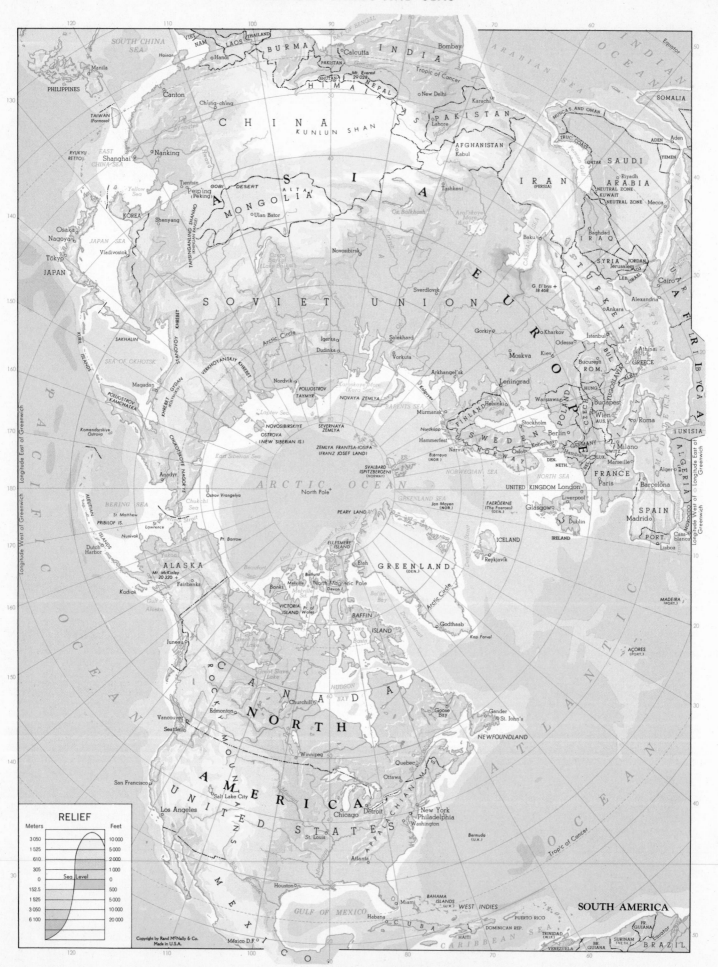

Elevations and depressions are given in feet
LAMBERT AZIMUTHAL EQUAL-AREA PROJECTION
Scale 1:60,000,000 (approximate)

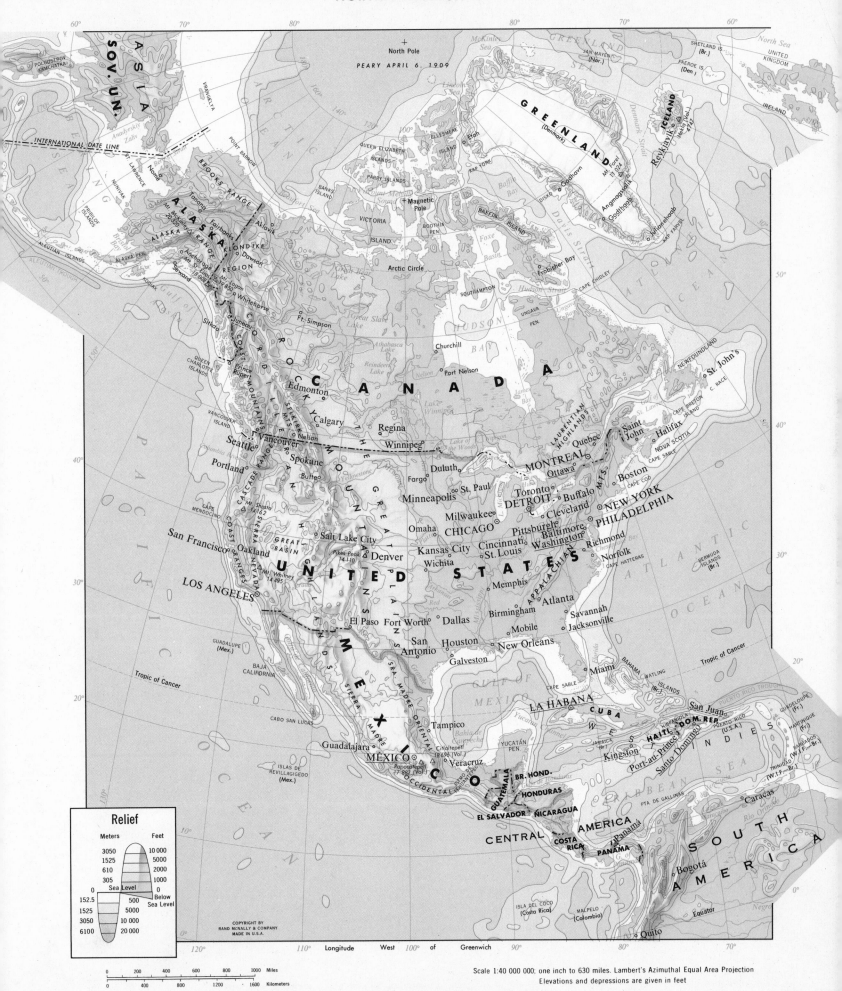

Relief

Meters		Feet
3050		10 000
1525		5000
610		2000
305		1000
0	Sea Level	0
		Below
152.5		500 Sea Level
1525		5000
3050		10 000
6100		20 000

COPYRIGHT BY
RAND McNALLY & COMPANY
MADE IN U.S.A.

| | 200 | 400 | 600 | 800 | 1000 Miles |
| | 400 | 800 | 1200 | 1600 Kilometers |

Longitude   West   of   Greenwich

Scale 1:40 000 000; one inch to 630 miles. Lambert's Azimuthal Equal Area Projection
Elevations and depressions are given in feet

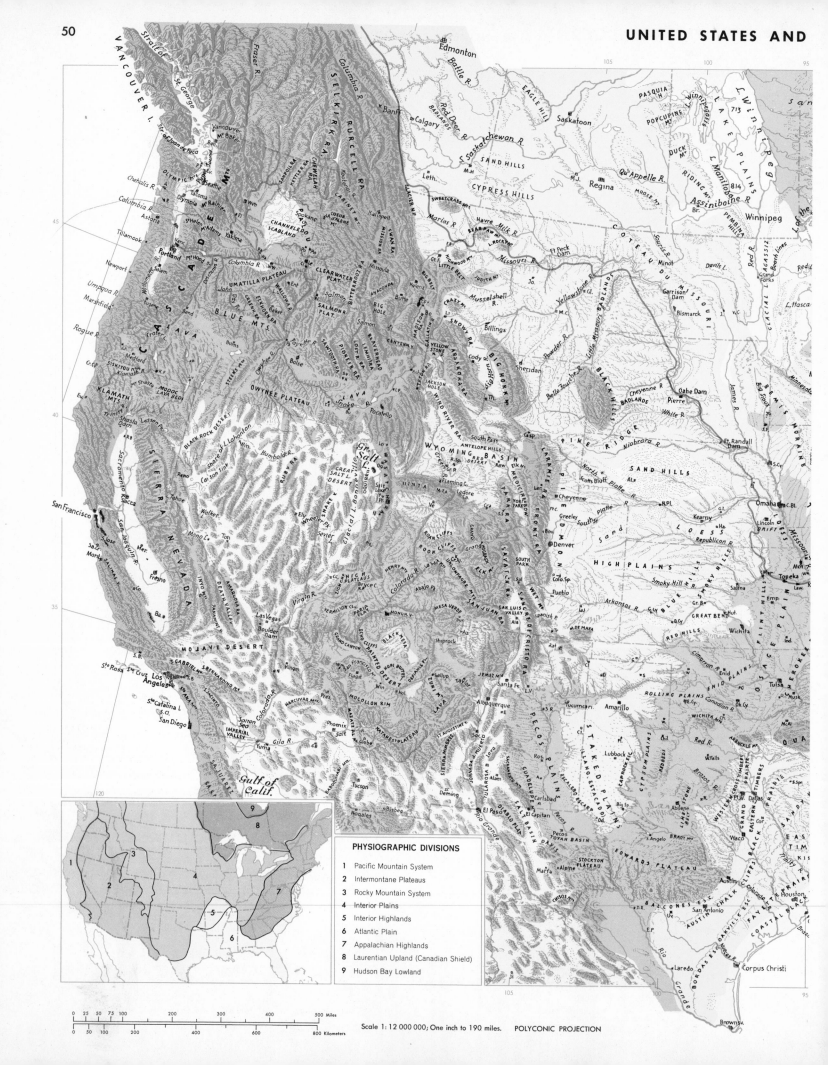

PHYSIOGRAPHIC DIVISIONS

1 Pacific Mountain System
2 Intermontane Plateaus
3 Rocky Mountain System
4 Interior Plains
5 Interior Highlands
6 Atlantic Plain
7 Appalachian Highlands
8 Laurentian Upland (Canadian Shield)
9 Hudson Bay Lowland

0 25 50 75 100   200   300   400   500 Miles

0   50 100   200   400   600   800 Kilometers

Scale 1 : 12 000 000; One inch to 190 miles.   POLYCONIC PROJECTION

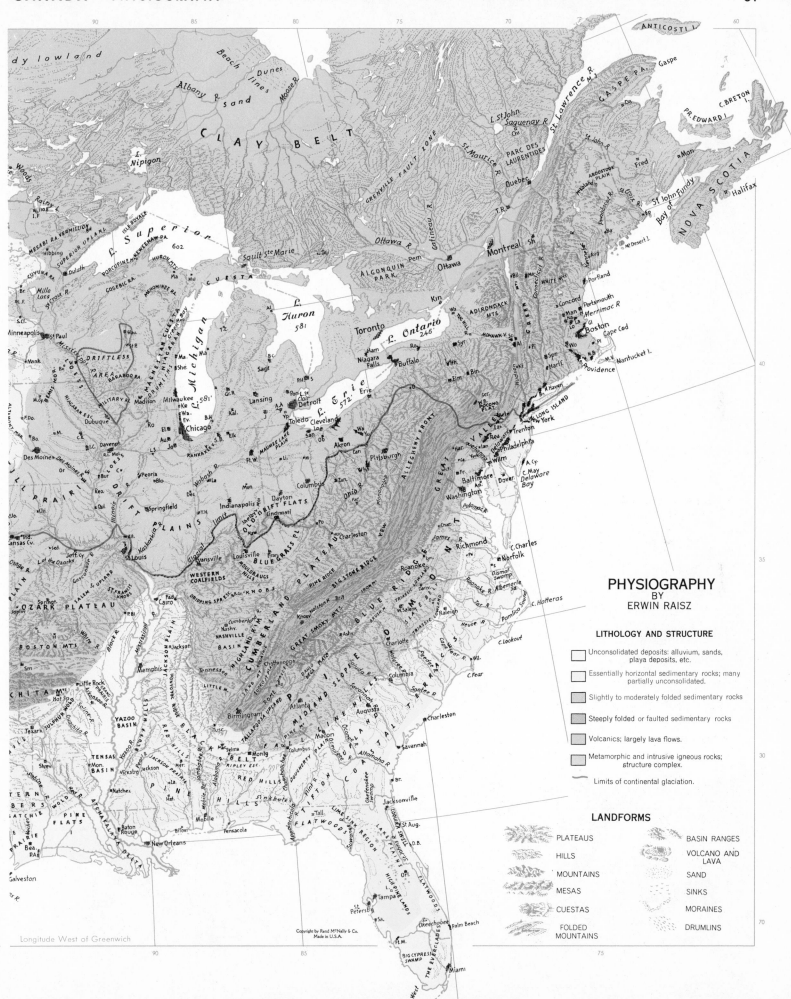

PHYSIOGRAPHY
BY
ERWIN RAISZ

LITHOLOGY AND STRUCTURE

Unconsolidated deposits: alluvium, sands, playa deposits, etc.

Essentially horizontal sedimentary rocks; many partially unconsolidated.

Slightly to moderately folded sedimentary rocks

Steeply folded or faulted sedimentary rocks

Volcanics; largely lava flows.

Metamorphic and intrusive igneous rocks; structure complex.

Limits of continental glaciation.

LANDFORMS

PLATEAUS

HILLS

MOUNTAINS

MESAS

CUESTAS

FOLDED MOUNTAINS

BASIN RANGES

VOLCANO AND LAVA

SAND

SINKS

MORAINES

DRUMLINS

Copyright by Rand McNally & Co.
Made in U.S.A.

Longitude West of Greenwich

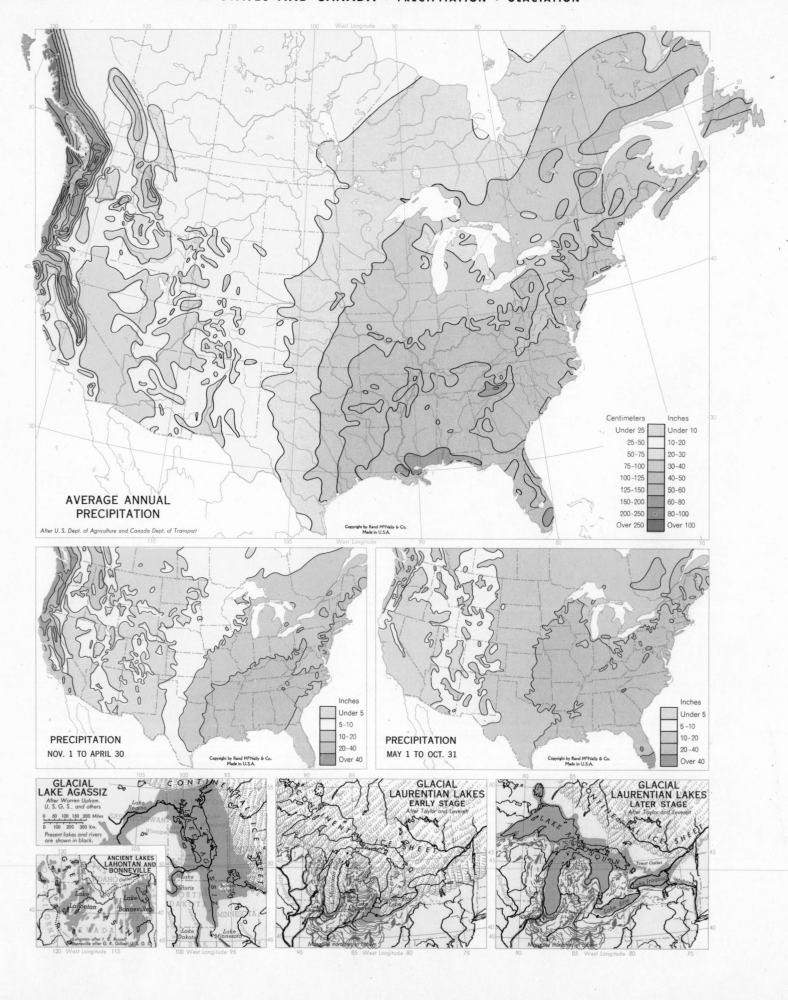

AVERAGE ANNUAL PRECIPITATION

After U. S. Dept. of Agriculture and Canada Dept. of Transport

Copyright by Rand McNally & Co.
Made in U.S.A.

Centimeters	Inches
Under 25	Under 10
25-50	10-20
50-75	20-30
75-100	30-40
100-125	40-50
125-150	50-60
150-200	60-80
200-250	80-100
Over 250	Over 100

PRECIPITATION
NOV. 1 TO APRIL 30

Copyright by Rand McNally & Co.
Made in U.S.A.

Inches
Under 5
5-10
10-20
20-40
Over 40

PRECIPITATION
MAY 1 TO OCT. 31

Copyright by Rand McNally & Co.
Made in U.S.A.

Inches
Under 5
5-10
10-20
20-40
Over 40

GLACIAL LAKE AGASSIZ
After Warren Upham, U. S. G. S., and others

0 50 100 150 200 Miles
0 100 200 300 Km.

Present lakes and rivers are shown in black.

ANCIENT LAKES LAHONTAN AND BONNEVILLE
Lahontan after I. C. Russell
Bonneville after G. K. Gilbert, U. S. G. S.

GLACIAL LAURENTIAN LAKES
EARLY STAGE
After Taylor and Leverett

Moraines in brown

GLACIAL LAURENTIAN LAKES
LATER STAGE
After Taylor and Leverett

Moraines in brown

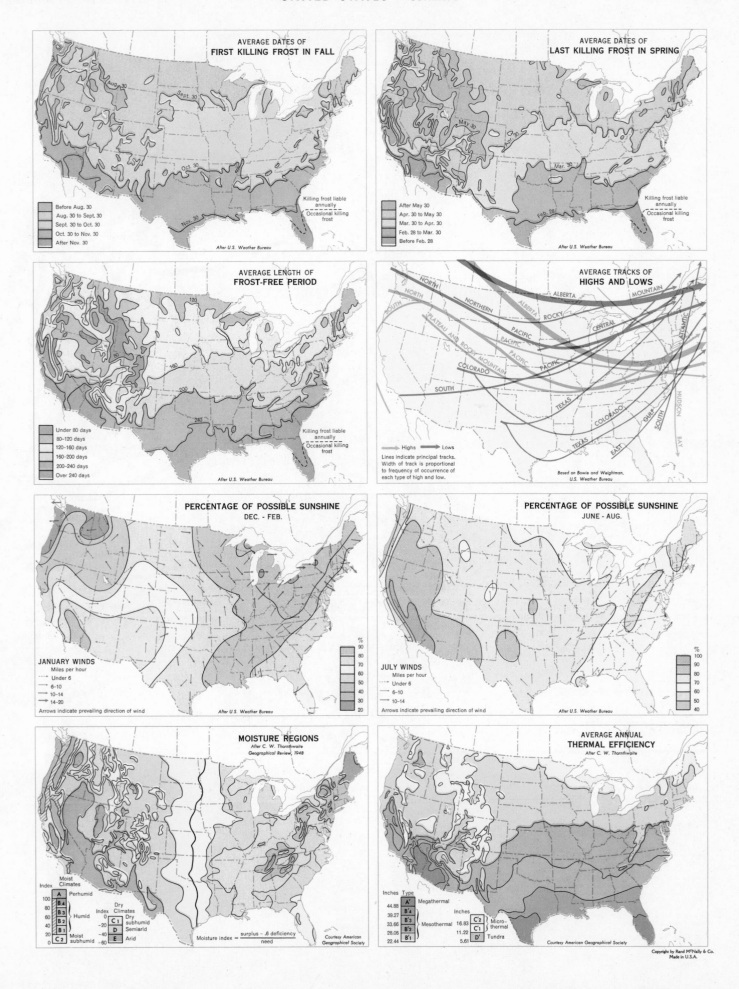

AVERAGE DATES OF FIRST KILLING FROST IN FALL

Before Aug. 30
Aug. 30 to Sept. 30
Sept. 30 to Oct. 30
Oct. 30 to Nov. 30
After Nov. 30

Killing frost liable annually
Occasional killing frost

After U.S. Weather Bureau

AVERAGE DATES OF LAST KILLING FROST IN SPRING

After May 30
Apr. 30 to May 30
Mar. 30 to Apr. 30
Feb. 28 to Mar. 30
Before Feb. 28

Killing frost liable annually
Occasional killing frost

After U.S. Weather Bureau

AVERAGE LENGTH OF FROST-FREE PERIOD

Under 80 days
80–120 days
120–160 days
160–200 days
200–240 days
Over 240 days

Killing frost liable annually
Occasional killing frost

After U.S. Weather Bureau

AVERAGE TRACKS OF HIGHS AND LOWS

Highs   Lows

Lines indicate principal tracks. Width of track is proportional to frequency of occurrence of each type of high and low.

Based on Bowie and Weightman, U.S. Weather Bureau

PERCENTAGE OF POSSIBLE SUNSHINE DEC. - FEB.

JANUARY WINDS
Miles per hour
Under 6
6–10
10–14
14–20
Arrows indicate prevailing direction of wind

%
90
80
70
60
50
40
30
20

After U.S. Weather Bureau

PERCENTAGE OF POSSIBLE SUNSHINE JUNE - AUG.

JULY WINDS
Miles per hour
Under 6
6–10
10–14
Arrows indicate prevailing direction of wind

%
100
90
80
70
60
50
40

After U.S. Weather Bureau

MOISTURE REGIONS
After C. W. Thornthwaite Geographical Review, 1948

Index	Moist Climates	
100	A	Perhumid
80	B4	
60	B3	Humid
40	B2	
20	B1	
0	C2	Moist subhumid

Index	Dry Climates	
0	C1	Dry subhumid
-20	D	Semiarid
-40	E	Arid
-60		

Moisture index = surplus − .6 deficiency / need

Courtesy American Geographical Society

AVERAGE ANNUAL THERMAL EFFICIENCY
After C. W. Thornthwaite

Inches	Type	
44.88	A'	Megathermal
39.27	B'4	
33.66	B'3	Mesothermal
28.05	B'2	
22.44	B'1	

Inches		
16.83	C'2	Microthermal
11.22	C'1	
5.61	D'	Tundra

Courtesy American Geographical Society

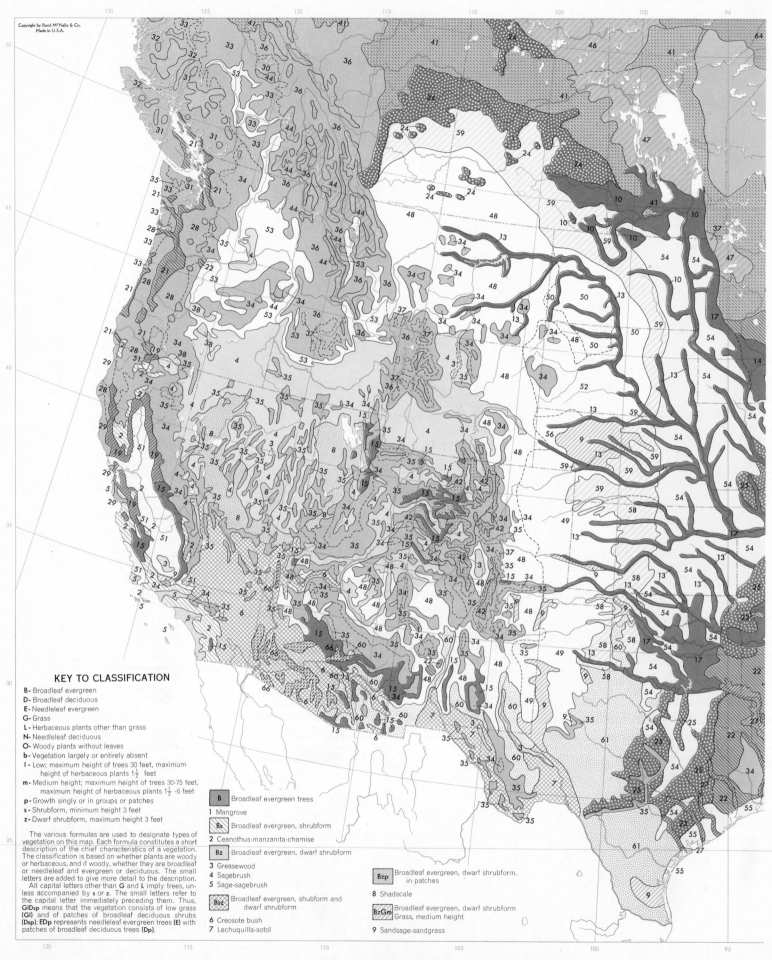

Copyright by Rand McNally & Co.
Made in U.S.A.

KEY TO CLASSIFICATION

B- Broadleaf evergreen
D- Broadleaf deciduous
E- Needleleaf evergreen
G- Grass
L- Herbaceous plants other than grass
N- Needleleaf deciduous
O- Woody plants without leaves
b- Vegetation largely or entirely absent
l - Low; maximum height of trees 30 feet, maximum
    height of herbaceous plants 1½ feet
m- Medium height; maximum height of trees 30-75 feet,
    maximum height of herbaceous plants 1½ -6 feet
p- Growth singly or in groups or patches
s - Shrubform, minimum height 3 feet
z- Dwarf shrubform, maximum height 3 feet

The various formulas are used to designate types of
vegetation on this map. Each formula constitutes a short
description of the chief characteristics of a vegetation.
The classification is based on whether plants are woody
or herbaceous, and if woody, whether they are broadleaf
or needleleaf and evergreen or deciduous. The small
letters are added to give more detail to the description.
    All capital letters other than G and L imply trees, un-
less accompanied by s or z. The small letters refer to
the capital letter immediately preceding them. Thus,
GlDsp means that the vegetation consists of low grass
(Gl) and of patches of broadleaf deciduous shrubs
(Dsp); EDp represents needleleaf evergreen trees (E) with
patches of broadleaf deciduous trees (Dp).

B Broadleaf evergreen trees
1 Mangrove
Bs Broadleaf evergreen, shrubform
2 Ceanothus-manzanita-chamise
Bz Broadleaf evergreen, dwarf shrubform
3 Greasewood
4 Sagebrush
5 Sage-sagebrush
Bsz Broadleaf evergreen, shubform and
    dwarf shrubform
6 Creosote bush
7 Lechuquilla-sotol

Bzp Broadleaf evergreen, dwarf shrubform,
    in patches
8 Shadscale
BzGm Broadleaf evergreen, dwarf shrubform
    Grass, medium height
9 Sandsage-sandgrass

0 25 50 75 100   200   300   400   500 Miles

0 50 100   200   400   600   800 Kilometers

Scale 1:14 000 000; One inch to 220 miles.

NATURAL VEGETATION

BY A. W. KÜCHLER

Based on "A Physiognomic Classification of Vegetation"
Annals of the Assoc. of American Geographers, Vol. 39, September, 1949

Longitude West of Greenwich

LAMBERT CONFORMAL CONIC PROJECTION

D Broadleaf deciduous trees

10 Aspen-oak
11 Beech-maple
12 Beech-tulip tree-maple-basswood
13 Cottonwood-willow
14 Maple-basswood
15 Oak
16 Oak-ash-maple
17 Oak-hickory
18 Oak-tulip tree

DB Broadleaf deciduous trees
Broadleaf evergreen trees

19 Oak-madrone

DE Broadleaf deciduous trees
Needleleaf evergreen trees

20 Maple-yellow birch-hemlock-pine
21 Oak-Douglas fir
22 Oak-pine
23 Maple-beech-hemlock

D / Gmp Broadleaf deciduous trees
Grass, medium height, in patches

24 Aspen-needle grass-wheat grass
25 Oak-hickory-bluestem

DN Broadleaf deciduous trees
Needleleaf deciduous trees

26 Bay trees-bald cypress
27 Tupelo-gum-bald cypress

E Needleleaf evergreen trees

28 Douglas fir
29 Douglas fir-redwood
30 Hemlock-arbor vitae
31 Hemlock-arbor vitae-Douglas fir
32 Hemlock-arbor vitae-fir
33 Hemlock-spruce
34 Pine
35 Pine-juniper
36 Pine-spruce
37 Spruce-fir

Esp Needleleaf evergreen, shrubform, in patches

38 Juniper

EDp Needleleaf evergreen trees
Broadleaf deciduous trees, in patches

39 Douglas fir-pine-aspen
40 Pine-spruce-birch
41 Spruce-aspen
42 Spruce-fir-aspen
43 Spruce-poplar-birch

EN Needleleaf evergreen trees
Needleleaf deciduous trees

44 Hemlock-arbor vitae-Douglas fir-larch
45 Pine-bald cypress
46 Pine-spruce-larch
47 Spruce-larch

Gl Grass, low

48 Grama grass
49 Grama grass-buffalo grass
50 Grama grass-needle grass
51 Needle grass-blue grass
52 Wheat grass
53 Wheat grass-blue grass

Gm Grass, medium height

54 Bluestem
55 Broom grass-water grass
56 Marsh grass
57 Saw grass

Gml Grass, medium and low height

58 Bluestem-bunch grass
59 Needle grass-wheat grass

Gl / Dsp Grass, low
Broadleaf deciduous, shrubform, in patches

60 Bunch grass-oak

Gm / Dsp Grass, medium height
Broadleaf deciduous, shrubform, in patches

61 Mesquite grass-mesquite

L Herbaceous plants other than grass

62 Lichens, etc.

LEp Herbaceous plants other than grass
Needleleaf evergreen trees, in patches

63 Lichens-spruce

LEp / Np Herbaceous plants other than grass
Needleleaf evergreen trees, in patches
Needleleaf deciduous trees, in patches

64 Lichens-spruce-larch

N Needleleaf deciduous trees

65 Bald cypress

Op Woody plants without leaves, in patches

66 Palo verde-cacti-ocotillo

b Vegetation largely or entirely absent

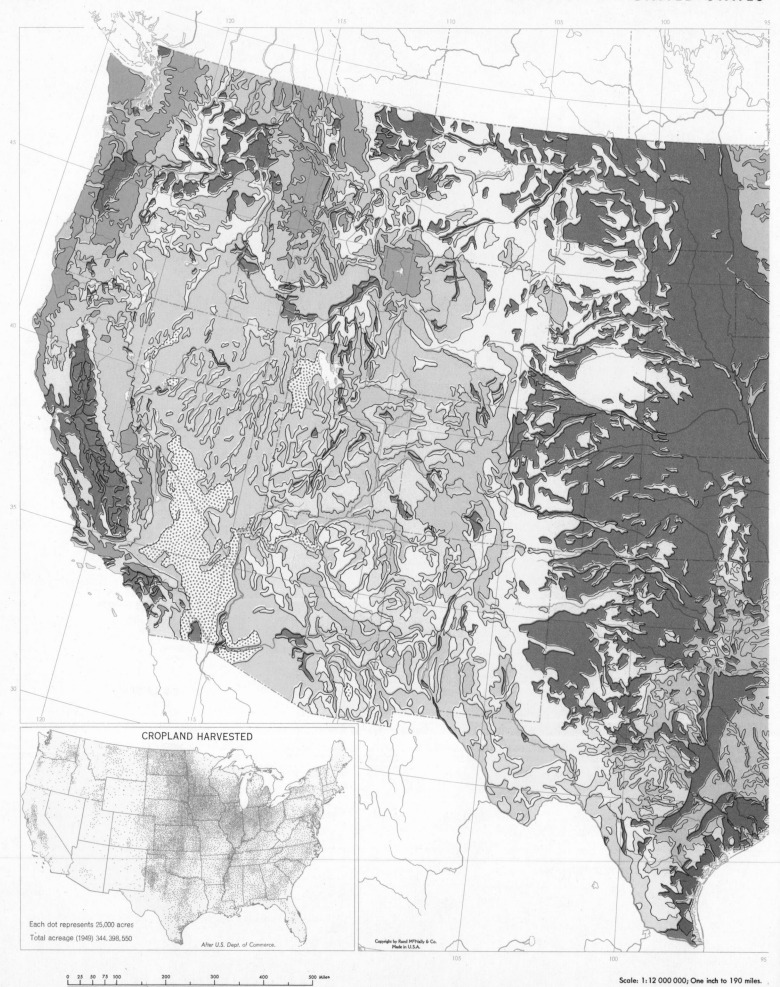

CROPLAND HARVESTED

Each dot represents 25,000 acres

Total acreage (1949) 344,398,550

After U.S. Dept. of Commerce.

Copyright by Rand McNally & Co.
Made in U.S.A.

0   25 50 75 100   200   300   400   500 Miles

0 50 100   200   400   600   800 Kilometers

Scale: 1:12 000 000; One inch to 190 miles.

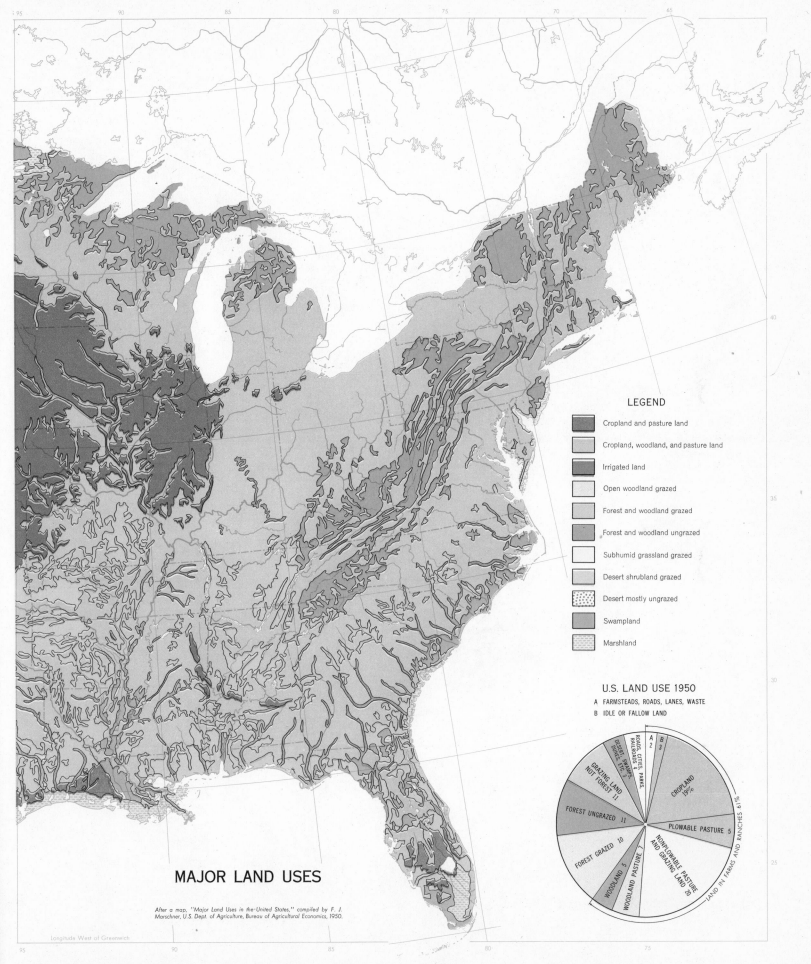

LEGEND

Cropland and pasture land

Cropland, woodland, and pasture land

Irrigated land

Open woodland grazed

Forest and woodland grazed

Forest and woodland ungrazed

Subhumid grassland grazed

Desert shrubland grazed

Desert mostly ungrazed

Swampland

Marshland

U.S. LAND USE 1950

A FARMSTEADS, ROADS, LANES, WASTE
B IDLE OR FALLOW LAND

MAJOR LAND USES

After a map, "Major Land Uses in the United States," compiled by F. J.
Marschner, U.S. Dept. of Agriculture, Bureau of Agricultural Economics, 1950.

Longitude West of Greenwich

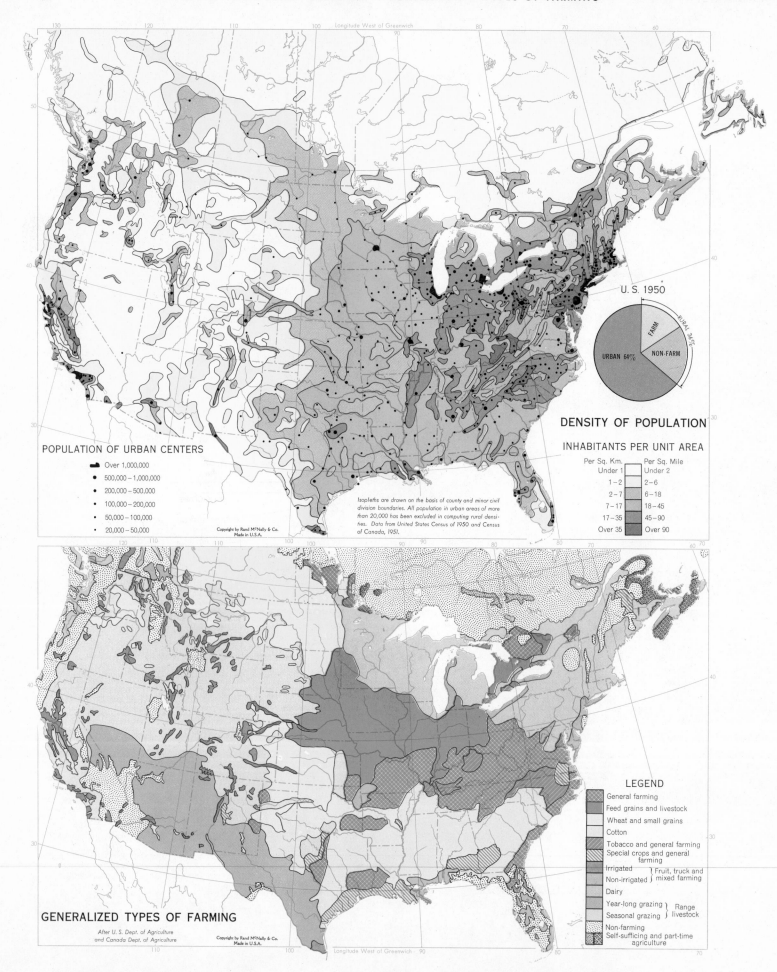

POPULATION OF URBAN CENTERS

- Over 1,000,000
- 500,000 – 1,000,000
- 200,000 – 500,000
- 100,000 – 200,000
- 50,000 – 100,000
- 20,000 – 50,000

U. S. 1950

URBAN 64%　FARM　RURAL 36%　NON-FARM

DENSITY OF POPULATION

INHABITANTS PER UNIT AREA

Per Sq. Km.	Per Sq. Mile
Under 1	Under 2
1 – 2	2 – 6
2 – 7	6 – 18
7 – 17	18 – 45
17 – 35	45 – 90
Over 35	Over 90

Isopleths are drawn on the basis of county and minor civil division boundaries. All population in urban areas of more than 20,000 has been excluded in computing rural densities. Data from United States Census of 1950 and Census of Canada, 1951.

Copyright by Rand McNally & Co.
Made in U.S.A.

GENERALIZED TYPES OF FARMING

After U. S. Dept. of Agriculture and Canada Dept. of Agriculture

Copyright by Rand McNally & Co.
Made in U.S.A.

LEGEND

- General farming
- Feed grains and livestock
- Wheat and small grains
- Cotton
- Tobacco and general farming
- Special crops and general farming
- Irrigated } Fruit, truck and
- Non-irrigated } mixed farming
- Dairy
- Year-long grazing } Range
- Seasonal grazing } livestock
- Non-farming
- Self-sufficing and part-time agriculture

Scale 1: 28 000 000; One inch to 440 miles.　LAMBERT CONFORMAL CONIC PROJECTION

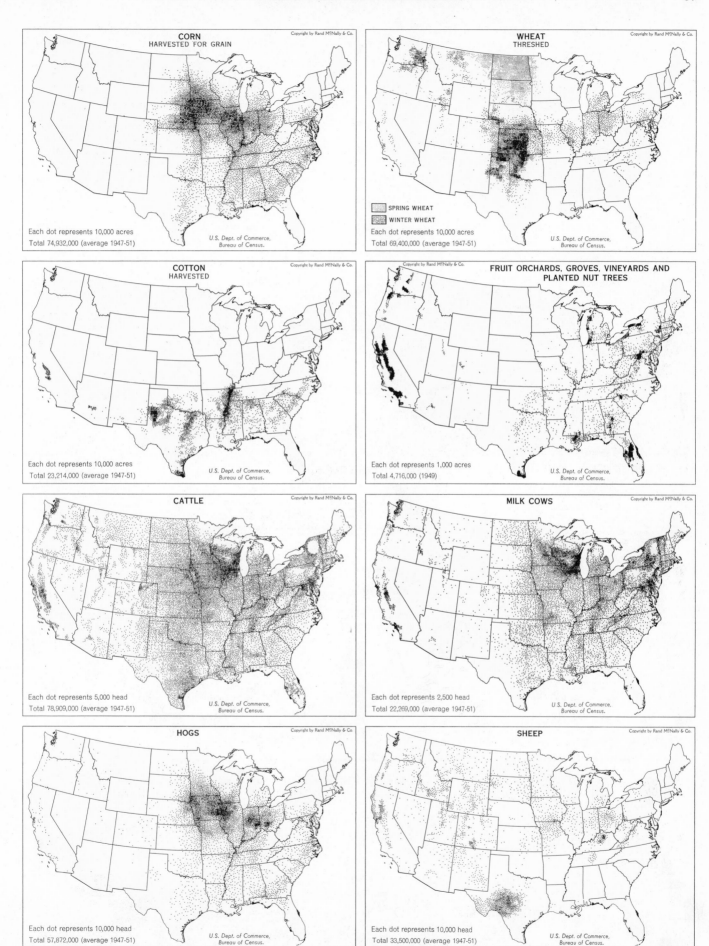

CORN
HARVESTED FOR GRAIN

Copyright by Rand McNally & Co.

Each dot represents 10,000 acres
Total 74,932,000 (average 1947-51)

U.S. Dept. of Commerce,
Bureau of Census.

WHEAT
THRESHED

Copyright by Rand McNally & Co.

SPRING WHEAT
WINTER WHEAT

Each dot represents 10,000 acres
Total 69,400,000 (average 1947-51)

U.S. Dept. of Commerce,
Bureau of Census.

COTTON
HARVESTED

Copyright by Rand McNally & Co.

Each dot represents 10,000 acres
Total 23,214,000 (average 1947-51)

U.S. Dept. of Commerce,
Bureau of Census.

**FRUIT ORCHARDS, GROVES, VINEYARDS AND
PLANTED NUT TREES**

Copyright by Rand McNally & Co.

Each dot represents 1,000 acres
Total 4,716,000 (1949)

U.S. Dept. of Commerce,
Bureau of Census.

CATTLE

Copyright by Rand McNally & Co.

Each dot represents 5,000 head
Total 78,909,000 (average 1947-51)

U.S. Dept. of Commerce,
Bureau of Census.

MILK COWS

Copyright by Rand McNally & Co.

Each dot represents 2,500 head
Total 22,269,000 (average 1947-51)

U.S. Dept. of Commerce,
Bureau of Census.

HOGS

Copyright by Rand McNally & Co.

Each dot represents 10,000 head
Total 57,872,000 (average 1947-51)

U.S. Dept. of Commerce,
Bureau of Census.

SHEEP

Copyright by Rand McNally & Co.

Each dot represents 10,000 head
Total 33,500,000 (average 1947-51)

U.S. Dept. of Commerce,
Bureau of Census.

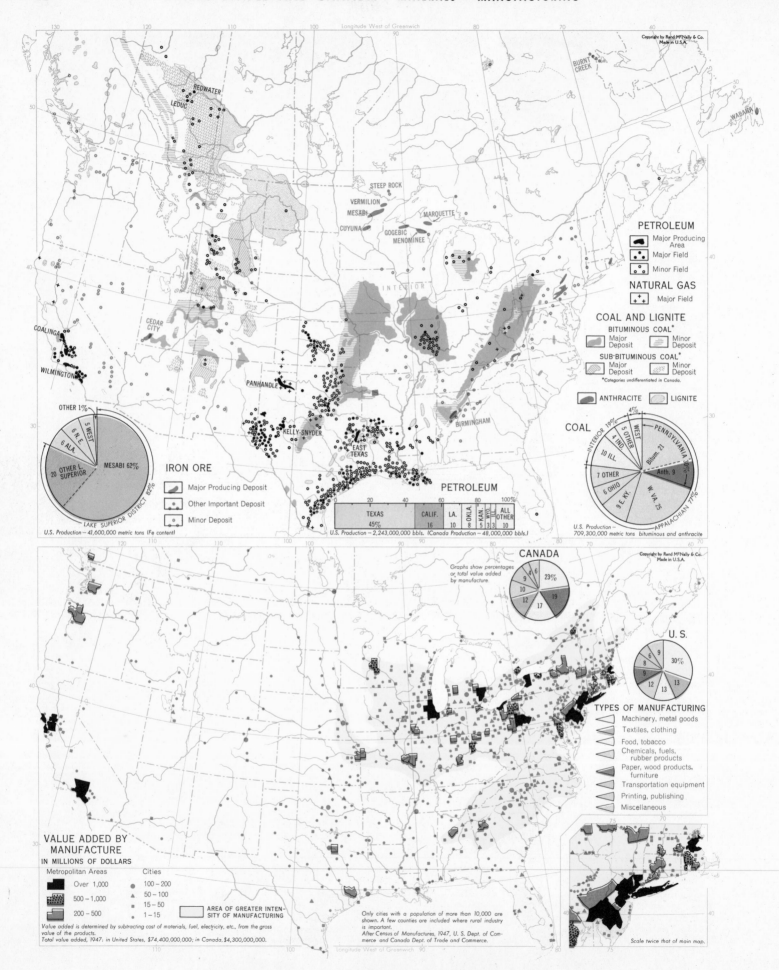

PETROLEUM

Major Producing Area

Major Field

Minor Field

NATURAL GAS

Major Field

COAL AND LIGNITE

BITUMINOUS COAL*

Major Deposit   Minor Deposit

SUB-BITUMINOUS COAL*

Major Deposit   Minor Deposit

*Categories undifferentiated in Canada.

ANTHRACITE   LIGNITE

COAL

U.S. Production — 709,300,000 metric tons bituminous and anthracite

IRON ORE

Major Producing Deposit

Other Important Deposit

Minor Deposit

U.S. Production — 41,600,000 metric tons (Fe content)

PETROLEUM

| TEXAS 45% | CALIF. 16 | LA. 10 | OKLA. 8 | KAN. 5 | WYO. 3 | ILL. 3 | ALL OTHER 10 |

U.S. Production — 2,243,000,000 bbls. (Canada Production — 48,000,000 bbls.)

CANADA

Graphs show percentages of total value added by manufacture.

U.S.

TYPES OF MANUFACTURING

Machinery, metal goods

Textiles, clothing

Food, tobacco

Chemicals, fuels, rubber products

Paper, wood products, furniture

Transportation equipment

Printing, publishing

Miscellaneous

VALUE ADDED BY MANUFACTURE

IN MILLIONS OF DOLLARS

Metropolitan Areas

Over 1,000

500 – 1,000

200 – 500

Cities

100 – 200

50 – 100

15 – 50

1 – 15

AREA OF GREATER INTENSITY OF MANUFACTURING

Value added is determined by subtracting cost of materials, fuel, electricity, etc., from the gross value of the products.
Total value added, 1947: in United States, $74,400,000,000; in Canada, $4,300,000,000.

Only cities with a population of more than 10,000 are shown. A few counties are included where rural industry is important.
After Census of Manufactures, 1947, U. S. Dept. of Commerce and Canada Dept. of Trade and Commerce.

Scale twice that of main map.

Scale 1: 28 000 000; One inch to 440 miles.   LAMBERT CONFORMAL CONIC PROJECTION

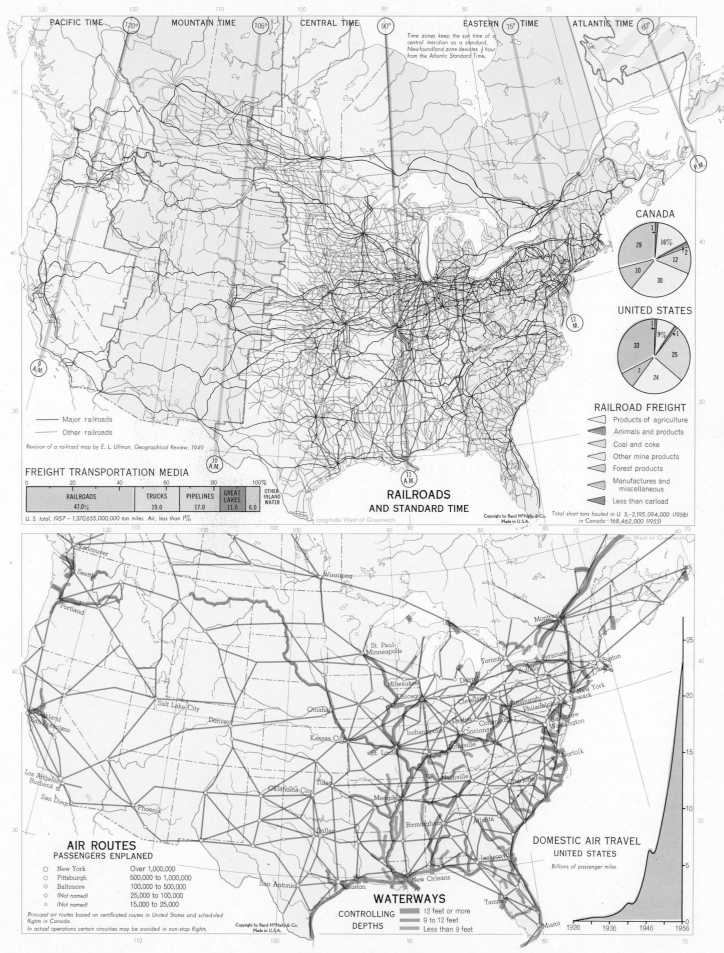

PACIFIC TIME   MOUNTAIN TIME   CENTRAL TIME   EASTERN TIME   ATLANTIC TIME

Time zones keep the sun time of a central meridian as a standard. Newfoundland zone deviates ½ hour from the Atlantic Standard Time.

CANADA

UNITED STATES

RAILROAD FREIGHT
- Products of agriculture
- Animals and products
- Coal and coke
- Other mine products
- Forest products
- Manufactures and miscellaneous
- Less than carload

—— Major railroads
—— Other railroads

Revision of a railroad map by E. L. Ullman, Geographical Review, 1949

FREIGHT TRANSPORTATION MEDIA

					OTHER INLAND WATER
RAILROADS 47.0%	TRUCKS 19.0	PIPELINES 17.0	GREAT LAKES 11.0	6.0	

U. S. total, 1957 – 1,370,655,000,000 ton miles. Air, less than 1%

RAILROADS
AND STANDARD TIME

Copyright by Rand McNally & Co.
Made in U.S.A.

Longitude West of Greenwich

Total short tons hauled in U. S.–2,195,094,000 (1958) in Canada–168,462,000 (1955)

Vancouver
Seattle
Portland
Winnipeg
Montreal
St. Paul-Minneapolis
Toronto
Syracuse
Boston
Buffalo
Salt Lake City
Milwaukee
Detroit
Oakland
San Francisco
Denver
Chicago
Cleveland
Pittsburgh
New York
Newark
Philadelphia
Baltimore
Washington
Omaha
Columbus
Dayton
Cincinnati
Kansas City
Indianapolis
St. Louis
Louisville
Norfolk
Los Angeles
Burbank
Nashville
Charlotte
San Diego
Phoenix
Oklahoma City
Tulsa
Memphis
Birmingham
Atlanta
Dallas
San Antonio
Houston
New Orleans
Jacksonville
Tampa
Miami

AIR ROUTES
PASSENGERS ENPLANED

○	New York	Over 1,000,000
○	Pittsburgh	500,000 to 1,000,000
○	Baltimore	100,000 to 500,000
○	(Not named)	25,000 to 100,000
○	(Not named)	15,000 to 25,000

Principal air routes based on certificated routes in United States and scheduled flights in Canada.
In actual operations certain circuities may be avoided in non-stop flights.

Copyright by Rand McNally & Co.
Made in U.S.A.

WATERWAYS

CONTROLLING DEPTHS
- 12 feet or more
- 9 to 12 feet
- Less than 9 feet

DOMESTIC AIR TRAVEL
UNITED STATES

Billions of passenger miles

1926   1936   1946   1956

Scale 1: 28 000 000; One inch to 440 miles.   LAMBERT CONFORMAL CONIC PROJECTION

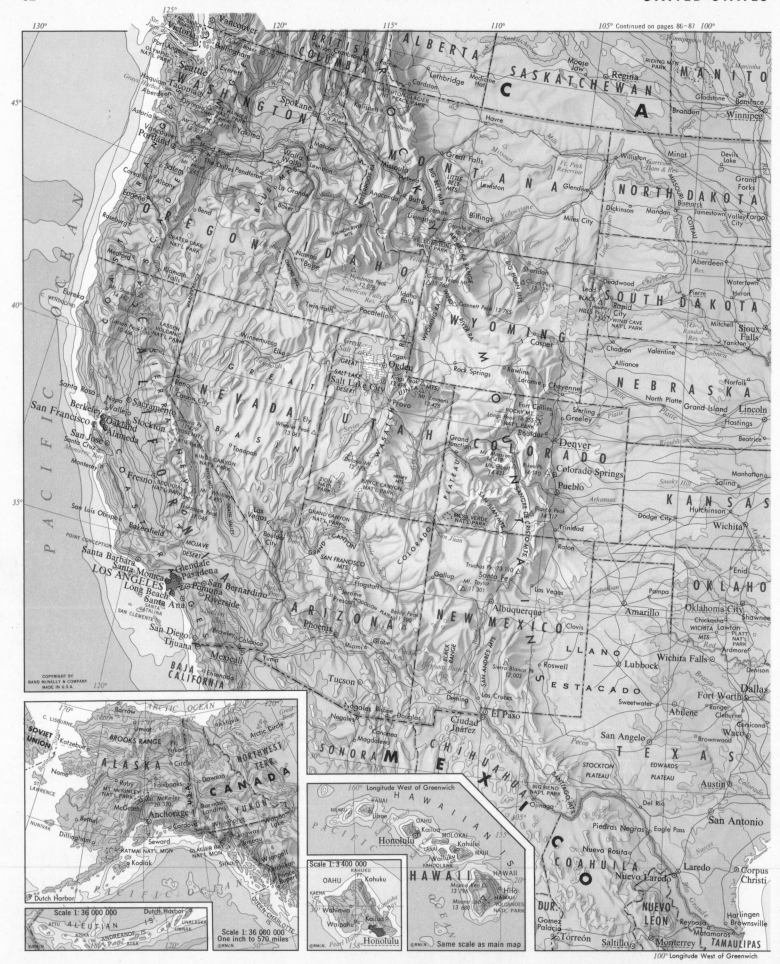

Continued on pages 86–87

COPYRIGHT BY
RAND McNALLY & COMPANY
MADE IN U.S.A.

Scale 1: 36 000 000

Scale 1: 36 000 000
One inch to 570 miles

Scale 1: 3 400 000

HAWAII

Same scale as main map

100° Longitude West of Greenwich

Scale 1:12 000 000; one inch to 190 miles. Polyconic Projection
Elevations and depressions are given in feet

STATE OF ALASKA

Relief
Meters
Feet
3050 1525 610 305 152.5 0 Sea Level
10 000 5000 2000 1000 500 0
152.5 1525 3050 6100
500 5000 10 000 20 000
ARCTIC OCEAN
Beaufort Sea
Chukchi Sea
Bering Sea
Gulf of Alaska
PACIFIC OCEAN
Bristol Bay
Norton Sound
Kotzebue Sound
Bering Strait
Amundsen Gulf
ALASKA
BROOKS RANGE
DELONG MTS.
BAIRD MTS.
ENDICOTT MTS.
RAY MTS.
KAIYUH MTS.
KUSKOKWIM MTS.
KILBUCK MTS.
ALASKA RANGE
KENAI MTS.
WRANGELL MTS.
RICHARDSON MTS.
ROCKY MOUNTAINS
MACKENZIE MTS.
PELLY MTS.
COAST MOUNTAINS
SEWARD PENINSULA
ALASKA PENINSULA
KLONDIKE REGION
YUKON
NORTHWEST TERRITORIES
BRITISH COLUMBIA
CANADA
U.S.A.
U.S.S.R.
INTERNATIONAL DATE LINE
Barrow
POINT BARROW
Wainwright
ICY CAPE
PITT POINT
Kaktovik
GRIFFIN POINT
CAPE LISBURNE
Point Hope
Umiat
Mt. Michelson 9239
Mt. Doonerak 8800
Noatak
Kotzebue
Selawik
Shungnak
Bettles Field
Arctic Circle
Fort Yukon
Circle
Candle
Wales
CAPE PRINCE OF WALES
Teller
Mt. Bendeleben 3730
Council
Koyuk
Nome
Gambell
ST. LAWRENCE
NORTHEAST CAPE
STUART
Nulato
Rampart
Tanana
Livengood
Hot Springs
Fairbanks
Ruby
Nenana
Eagle
Dawson
Big Delta
Tanacross
Unalakleet
St. Michael
Blackburn
MOUNT McKINLEY NAT'L PARK
Ophir
McGrath
Mt. McKinley 20 320
Mt. Foraker 17 395
Mt. Hayes 13 700
Hurricane
Holy Cross
CAPE ROMANZOF
Hooper Bay
ST. MATTHEW
NUNIVAK
NELSON
Aniak
Akiak
Bethel
Kuskovak
Kuskokwim Bay
Kaskanak
Platinum
Dillingham
CAPE NEWENHAM
Talkeetna
Susitna
Palmer
Matanuska
Anchorage
Copper Center
Mt. Wrangell 14 005
Mt. Blackburn 16 523
Chitina
Valdez
Cordova
Hope
Kenai
Seward
Homer
Seldovia
Iliamna Vol. 10 016
Iliamna
Cook Inlet
Prince William Sound
MONTAGUE
MIDDLETON
Mt. Logan 19 850
Mt. Hubbard 14 950
Mt. St. Elias 18 008
Yakutat
Mt. Fairweather 15 300
GLACIER BAY NAT'L MONUMENT
Skagway
Haines
Juneau
Douglas
Hoonah
Cross Sound
CHICHAGOF
ADMIRALTY
SITKA NAT'L MONUMENT
Sitka
BARANOF
Petersburg
Wrangell
ALEXANDER ARCHIPELAGO
PRINCE OF WALES
Klawak
Hydaburg
Ketchikan
Metlakatla
Mt. Stewart 7600
DALL
Dixon Entrance
Prince Rupert
Hecate Strait
Masset
GRAHAM
QUEEN CHARLOTTE ISLANDS
MORESBY
Telegraph Creek
Whitehorse
Carcross
WHITE PASS
Burwash Landing
HIGHWAY
Snag
Fort Selkirk
Mayo Landing
Aklavik
Ft. McPherson
Ft. Good Hope
Norman Wells
Tuktoyaktuk
RICHARDS ISLAND
Mackenzie Bay
CAPE BATHURST
CAPE PARRY
Liverpool Bay
BANKS ISLAND
Kvichak
KATMAI NAT'L MONUMENT
Egegik
AFOGNAK
Marmot Bay
Karluk
KODIAK
Kodiak
Kanatak
Old Harbor
TRINITY ISLANDS
Mt. Veniaminof 8225
Chignik
Perryville
Port Moller
CHIRIKOF
SHUMAGIN ISLANDS
Fort Randall
Shishaldin Vol. 9387
UNIMAK
Unimak Pass
Dutch Harbor
Makushin
Tulik Vol. 4111
UMNAK
UNALASKA
ST. PAUL
PRIBILOF ISLANDS
ST. GEORGE
M. DEZHNEVA (EAST CAPE)
Uellen
Nunyama
CHUKOTSKIY P-OV.
Provideniya
COPYRIGHT BY RAND McNALLY & COMPANY MADE IN U.S.A.
Longitude West of Greenwich
ALEUTIAN ISLANDS
ATTU
NEAR ISLANDS
SEMICHI IS.
AGATTU
BULDIR
KISKA
SEGULA
SEMISOPOCHNOI
RAT ISLANDS
AMCHITKA
Constantine Harbor
GARELOI
TANAGA
AMATIGNAK
GT. SITKIN
KANAGA
Adak
ADAK
Atka
ATKA
AMLIA
SEGUAM
ANDREANOF ISLANDS
ISLANDS OF THE FOUR MTS.
FOX ISLANDS
AKUTAN
Aleutian Trench
25 184
24 170
Longitude East of Greenwich
Same scale as main map
©RMcN.
0 50 100 200 300 400 Miles
0 100 200 300 400 500 600 Kilometers

Scale 1: 12 000 000; one inch to 190 miles. Conic Projection

Elevations and depressions are given in feet

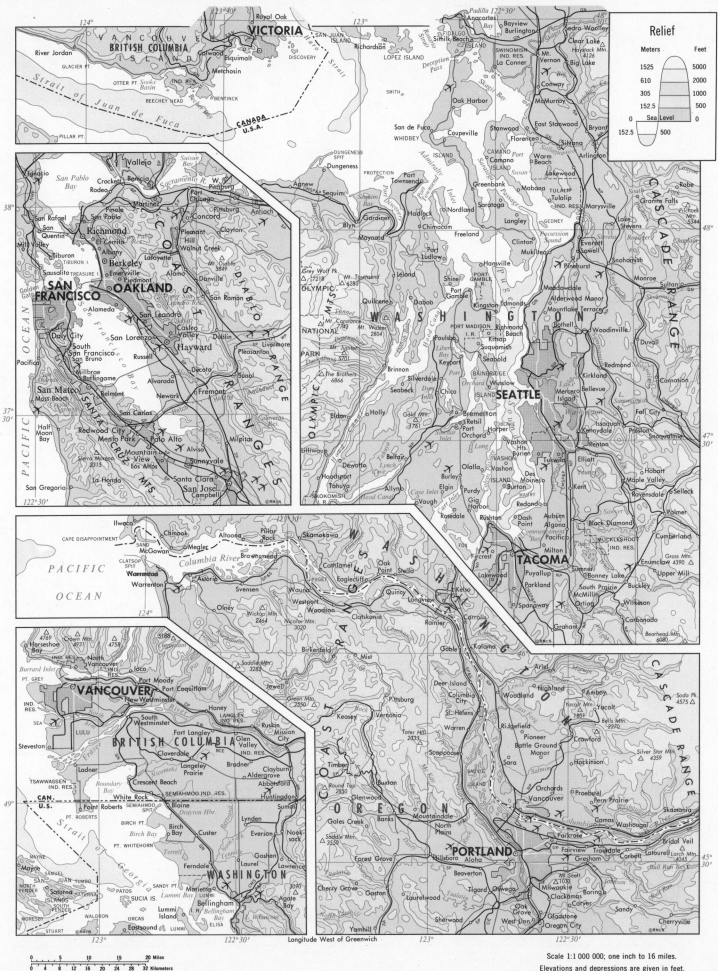

Relief

Meters		Feet
1525		5000
610		2000
305		1000
152.5		500
0	Sea Level	0
152.5		500

Scale 1:1 000 000; one inch to 16 miles.
Elevations and depressions are given in feet.

0 5 10 15 20 Miles
0 4 8 12 16 24 28 32 Kilometers

Longitude West of Greenwich

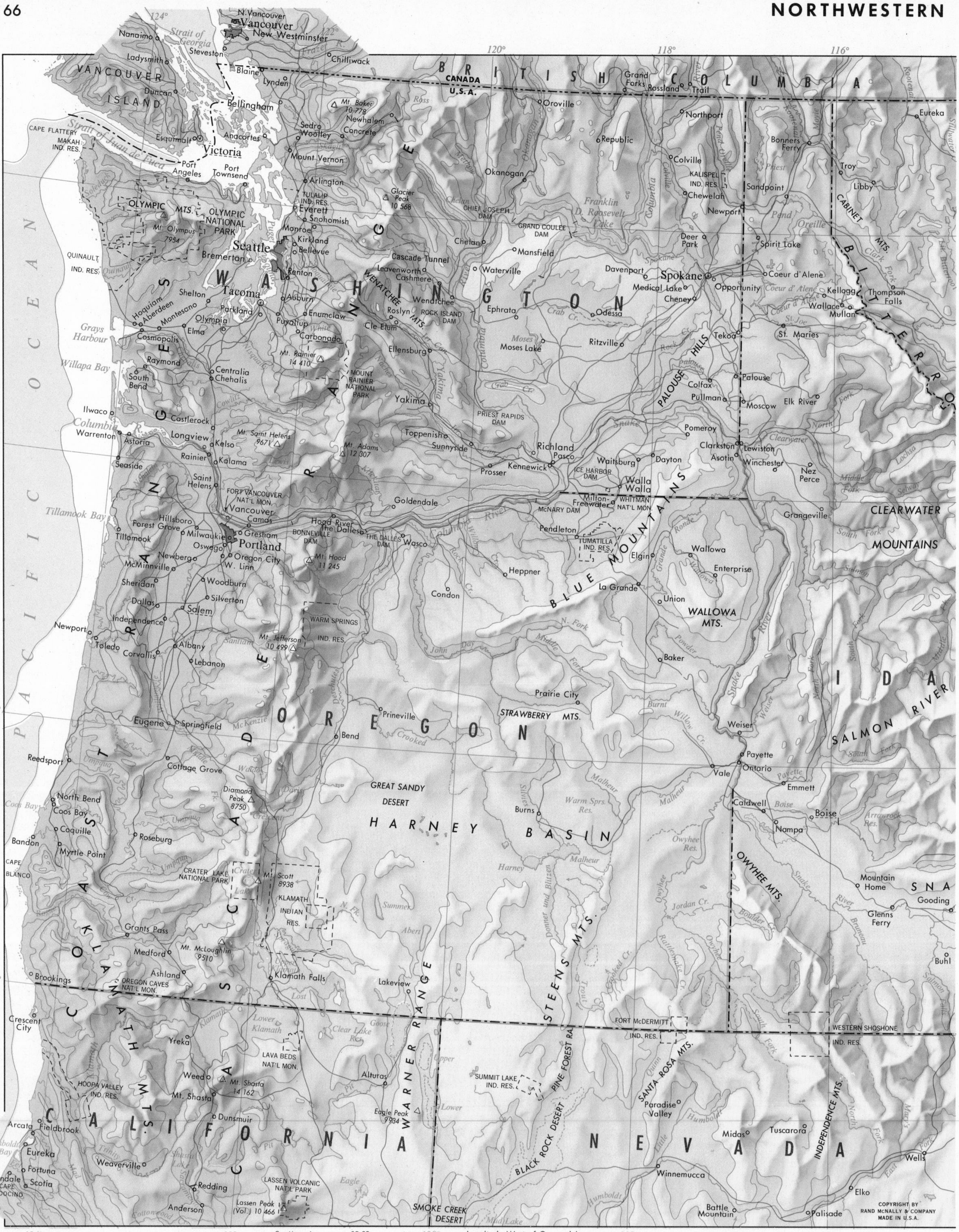

BRITISH COLUMBIA

CANADA
U.S.A.

VANCOUVER ISLAND

Nanaimo
Ladysmith
Duncan
Esquimalt
Victoria
Port Angeles
Cape Flattery
MAKAH IND. RES.

N. Vancouver
Vancouver
New Westminster
Steveston
Blaine
Lynden
Chilliwack
Bellingham
Sedro Woolley
Anacortes
Mount Vernon
Arlington
Port Townsend

△ Mt. Baker 10,778
Newhalem
Concrete
Oroville
Grand Forks
Rossland
Trail
Northport
Eureka

OLYMPIC MTS.
OLYMPIC NATIONAL PARK
Mt. Olympus 7954 △

QUINAULT IND. RES.

Seattle
Bremerton
Everett
Snohomish
Monroe
Kirkland
Bellevue
Renton
Tacoma
Parkland
Auburn
Enumclaw
Puyallup
Carbonado

Glacier Peak 10,568 △

CASCADE TUNNEL
Leavenworth
Cashmere
Wenatchee
Roslyn
Cle Elum
Ellensburg
Rock Island Dam

Colville
KALISPEL IND. RES.
Chewelah
Newport
Sandpoint
Bonners Ferry
Troy
Libby
CABINET MTS.

Okanogan
Chelan
Mansfield
Waterville
Moses Lake
Ritzville

CHIEF JOSEPH DAM
GRAND COULEE DAM

Davenport
Spokane
Medical Lake
Cheney
Odessa

Deer Park
Spirit Lake
Coeur d'Alene
Kellogg
Wallace
Mullan
Thompson Falls

WASHINGTON

Shelton
Hoquiam
Aberdeen
Montesano
Olympia
Cosmopolis
Elma
Raymond
South Bend
Centralia
Chehalis
Castlerock
Warrenton
Astoria
Longview
Kelso
Rainier
Kalama
Seaside
Saint Helens

Grays Harbour
Willapa Bay
Columbia

Mt. Rainier 14,410 △
MOUNT RAINIER NATIONAL PARK

Yakima
Toppenish
Sunnyside
Prosser
Kennewick
Pasco
Richland

Mt. Saint Helens 9671 △
Mt. Adams 12,307 △

PRIEST RAPIDS DAM

St. Maries
Tekoa
Palouse
Colfax
Pullman
Moscow
Elk River

PALOUSE HILLS

Pomeroy
Clarkston
Lewiston
Asotin
Winchester
Nez Perce

Waitsburg
Dayton
Walla Walla
Milton-Freewater
WHITMAN NAT'L MON.
Pendleton
ICE HARBOR DAM
McNARY DAM

Grangeville

CLEARWATER MOUNTAINS

FORT VANCOUVER NAT'L MON.
Vancouver
Camas
Hood River
The Dalles
BONNEVILLE DAM
THE DALLES DAM
Wasco
Goldendale

Hillsboro
Forest Grove
Tillamook
Milwaukie
Gresham
Portland
Oswego
Oregon City
W. Linn
McMinnville
Newberg
Sheridan
Woodburn
Dallas
Silverton
Independence
Salem
Albany
Lebanon
Corvallis
Toledo
Newport

Mt. Hood 11,245 △

Heppner
Condon

TUMATILLA IND. RES.
Elgin
La Grande
Union
Wallowa
Enterprise
WALLOWA MTS.
Baker

Blue Mountains

CLEARWATER MOUNTAINS

OREGON

Mt. Jefferson 10,499 △
WARM SPRINGS IND. RES.

Prineville
Bend
Eugene
Springfield
McKenzie
Reedsport
Cottage Grove

Prairie City
STRAWBERRY MTS.

IDAHO
SALMON RIVER

Weiser
Payette
Vale
Ontario
Emmett
Caldwell
Boise
Nampa

North Bend
Coos Bay
Coquille
Bandon
Myrtle Point
Roseburg

Diamond Peak 8750 △

GREAT SANDY DESERT

HARNEY BASIN

Burns
Warm Sprs. Res.

Owyhee Res.

OWYHEE MTS.
Mountain Home
SNAKE
Glenns Ferry
Gooding

CAPE BLANCO

CRATER LAKE NATIONAL PARK
Mt. Scott 8938 △
KLAMATH INDIAN RES.

Grants Pass

Mt. McLoughlin 9510 △
Medford
Ashland
OREGON CAVES NAT'L MON.
Klamath Falls

Lakeview

STEENS MTS.

FORT McDERMITT IND. RES.
WESTERN SHOSHONE IND. RES.
Buhl

KLAMATH MTS.
Brookings
Crescent City
Yreka

LAVA BEDS NAT'L MON.
Weed
Mt. Shasta 14,162 △
Dunsmuir

Alturas
Eagle Peak 9934 △
WARNER RANGE

SUMMIT LAKE IND. RES.
PINE FOREST RANGE
SANTA ROSA MTS.
Paradise Valley

INDEPENDENCE MTS.
Midas
Tuscarora
Wells

HOOPA VALLEY IND. RES.

CALIFORNIA

Arcata
Fieldbrook
Eureka
Fortuna
Scotia
Ferndale
CAPE MENDOCINO
Weaverville
Redding
Anderson

LASSEN VOLCANIC NAT'L PARK
Lassen Peak (Vol.) 10,466 △

SMOKE CREEK DESERT

BLACK ROCK DESERT

NEVADA
Winnemucca
Battle Mountain
Palisade
Elko

PACIFIC OCEAN

Continued on pages 68-69   Longitude West of Greenwich

COPYRIGHT BY
RAND McNALLY & COMPANY
MADE IN U.S.A.

Scale 1: 4 000 000; one inch to 64 miles. Conic Projection
Elevations and depressions are given in feet

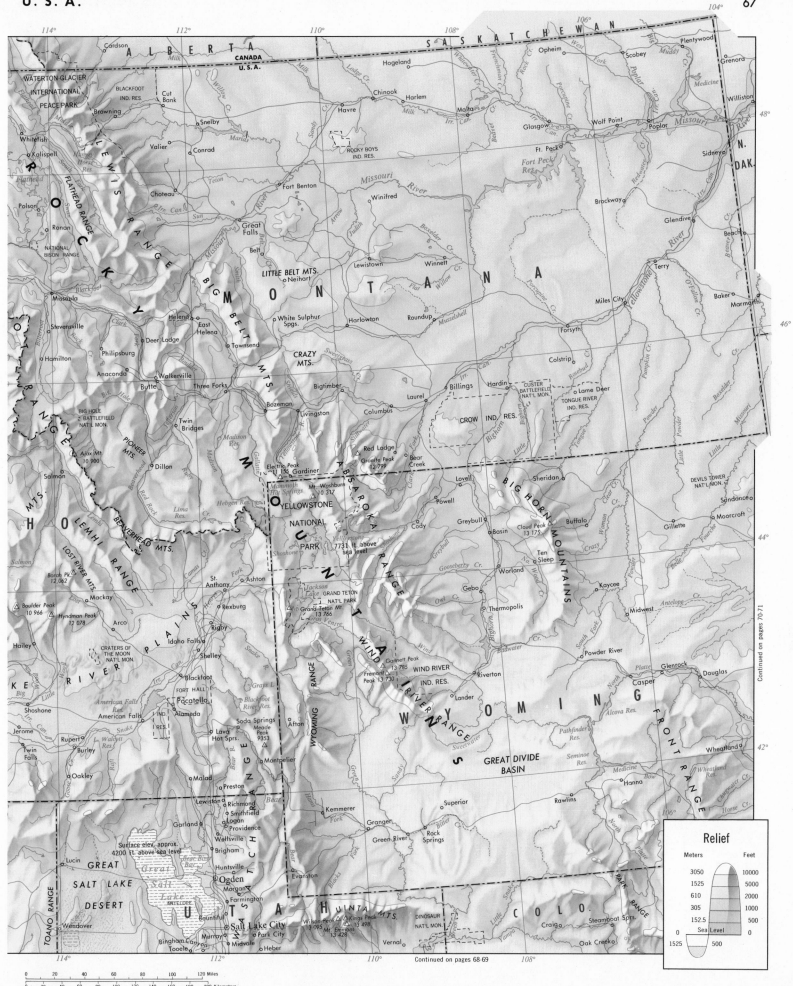

Continued on pages 70-71

Continued on pages 68-69

Relief

Meters		Feet
3050		10000
1525		5000
610		2000
305		1000
152.5		500
Sea Level		0
1525		500

0 20 40 60 80 100 120 Miles

0 20 40 60 80 100 120 140 160 180 200 Kilometers

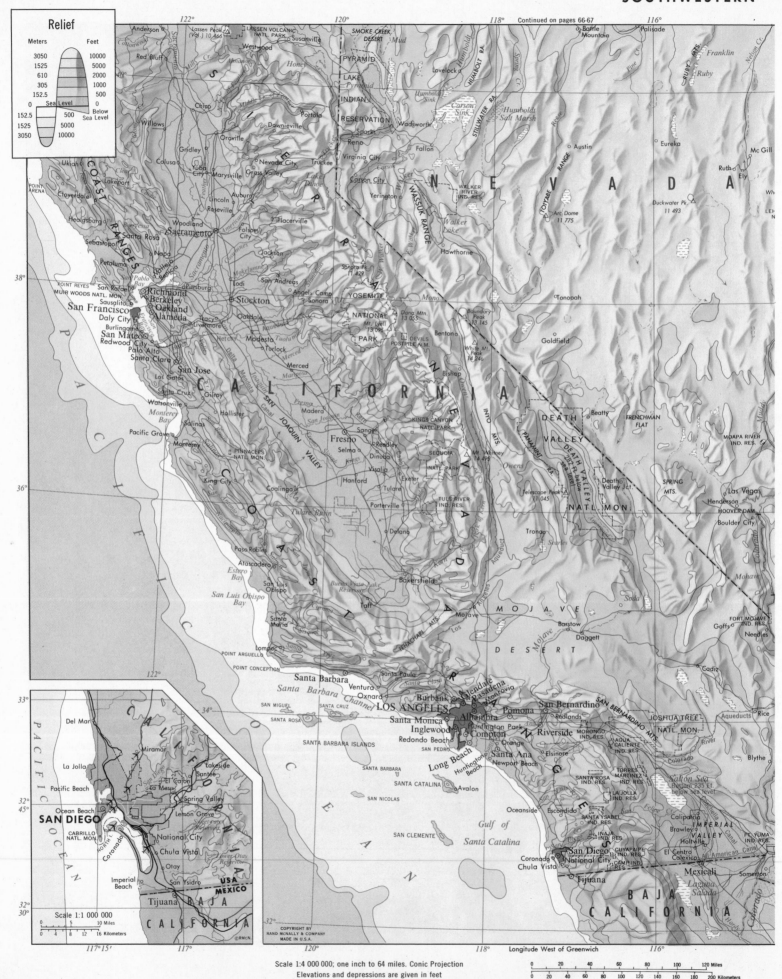

Relief

Meters	Feet
3050	10000
1525	5000
610	2000
305	1000
152.5	500
0 Sea Level	0
	Below Sea Level
152.5	500
1525	5000
3050	10000

Continued on pages 66-67

Scale 1:4 000 000; one inch to 64 miles. Conic Projection
Elevations and depressions are given in feet

Longitude West of Greenwich

Scale 1:1 000 000

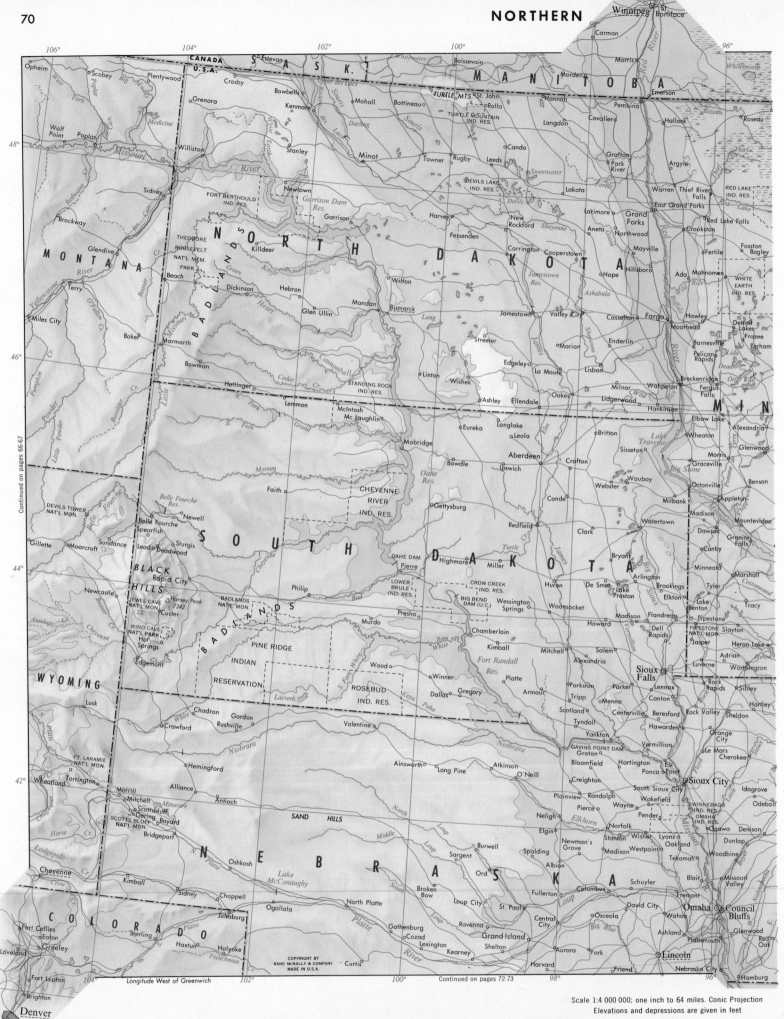

Continued on pages 66-67

Continued on pages 72-73

Longitude West of Greenwich

COPYRIGHT BY
RAND McNALLY & COMPANY
MADE IN U.S.A.

Scale 1:4 000 000; one inch to 64 miles. Conic Projection
Elevations and depressions are given in feet

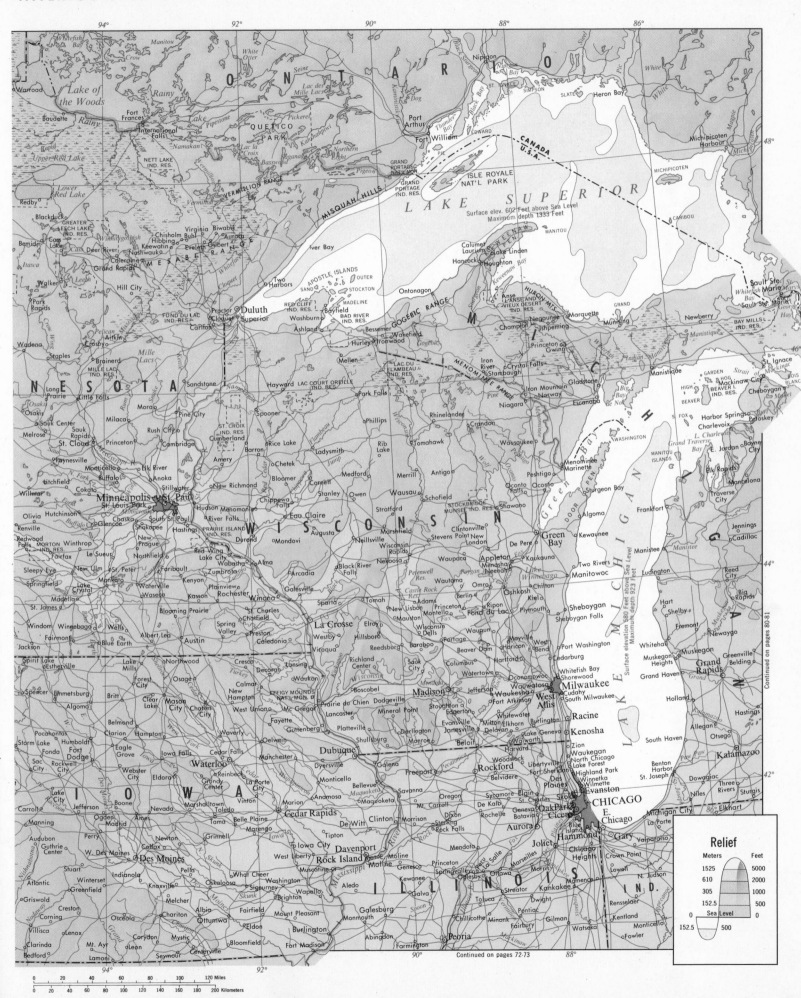

Continued on pages 80-81

Continued on pages 72-73

Relief

Meters	Feet
1525	5000
610	2000
305	1000
152.5	500
Sea Level	0
152.5	500

0 20 40 60 80 100 120 Miles

0 20 40 60 80 100 120 140 160 180 200 Kilometers

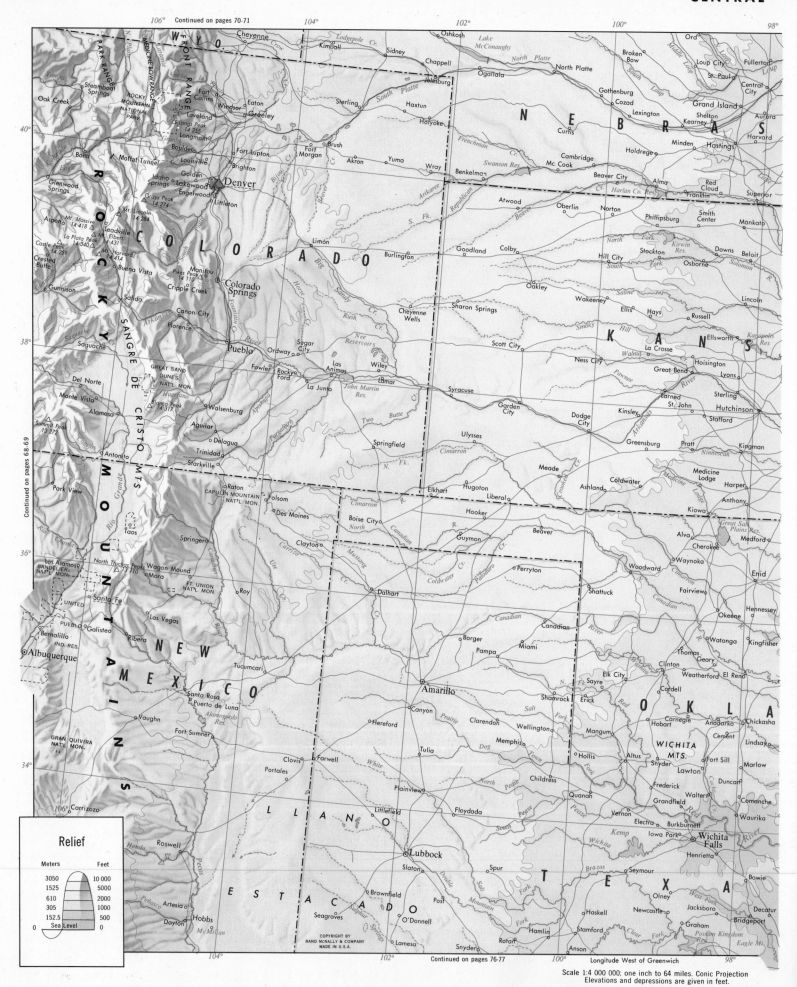

Continued on pages 70-71
Continued on pages 68-69
Continued on pages 76-77

Relief

Meters	Feet
3050	10 000
1525	5000
610	2000
305	1000
152.5	500
0	Sea Level	0

Longitude West of Greenwich

Scale 1:4 000 000; one inch to 64 miles. Conic Projection
Elevations and depressions are given in feet.

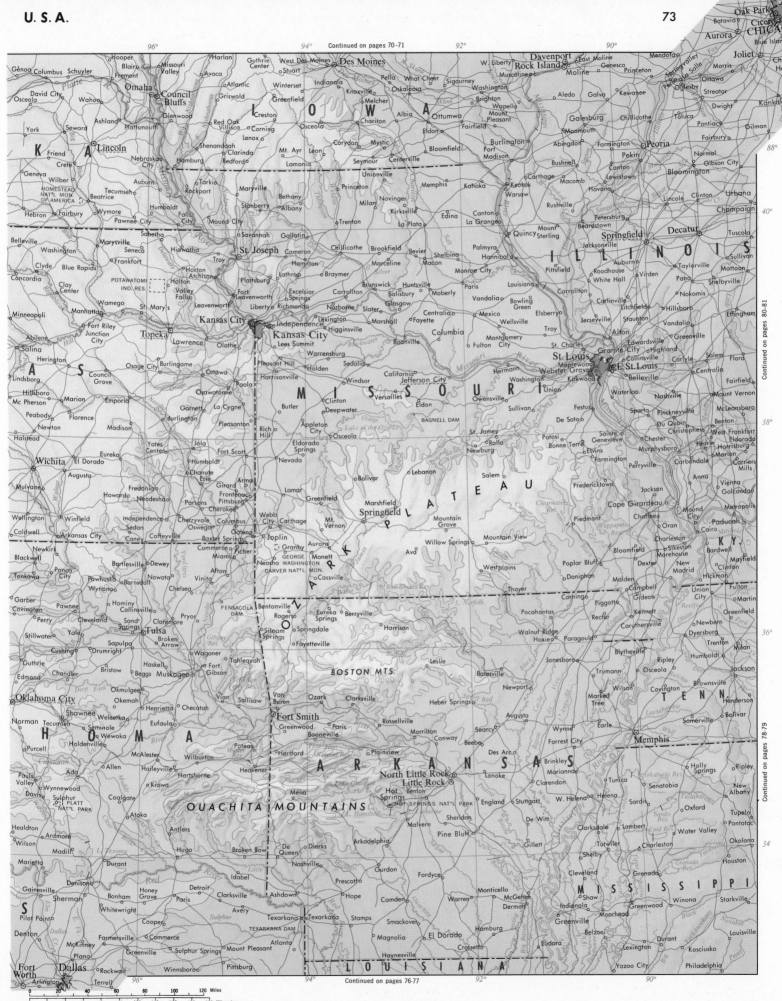

Continued on pages 70-71
Continued on pages 80-81
Continued on pages 78-79
Continued on pages 76-77

MISSOURI

ILLINOIS

IOWA

OKLAHOMA

ARKANSAS

LOUISIANA

MISSISSIPPI

TENN.

KY.

OZARK PLATEAU

BOSTON MTS.

OUACHITA MOUNTAINS

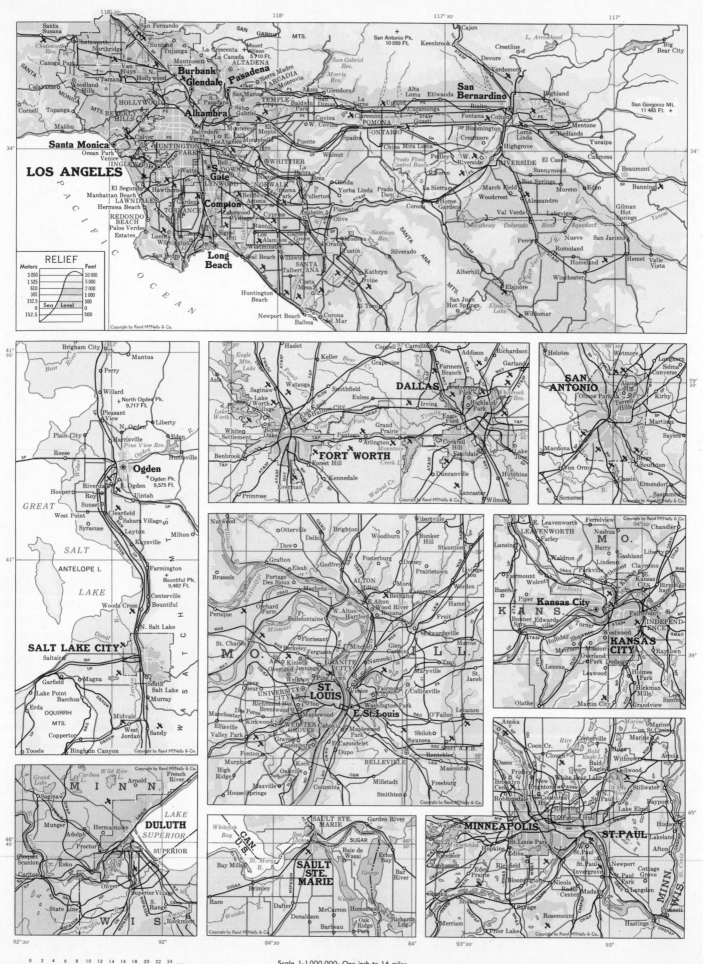

Scale 1:1 000 000; One inch to 16 miles
Elevations and depressions are given in feet

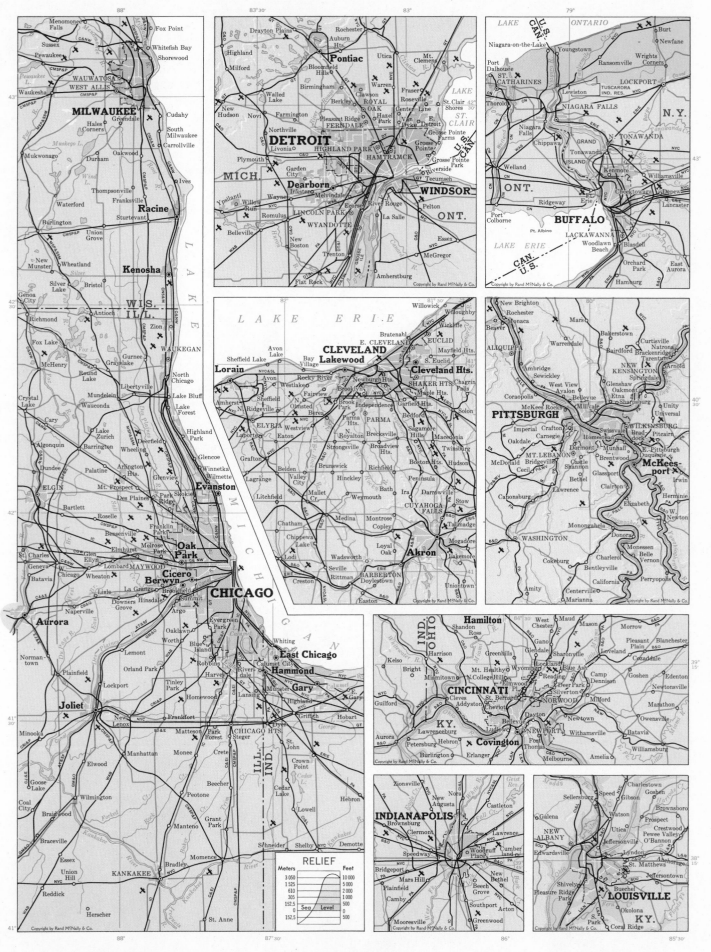

RELIEF

Meters		Feet
3 050		10 000
1 525		5 000
610		2 000
305		1 000
152.5		500
0	Sea Level	0
152.5		500

0 2 4 6 8 10 12 14 16 18 20 22 24 Miles
0 4 8 12 16 20 24 28 32 36 40 Kilometers

Scale 1:1 000 000; One inch to 16 miles.
Elevations and depressions are given in feet.

Copyright by Rand McNally & Co.

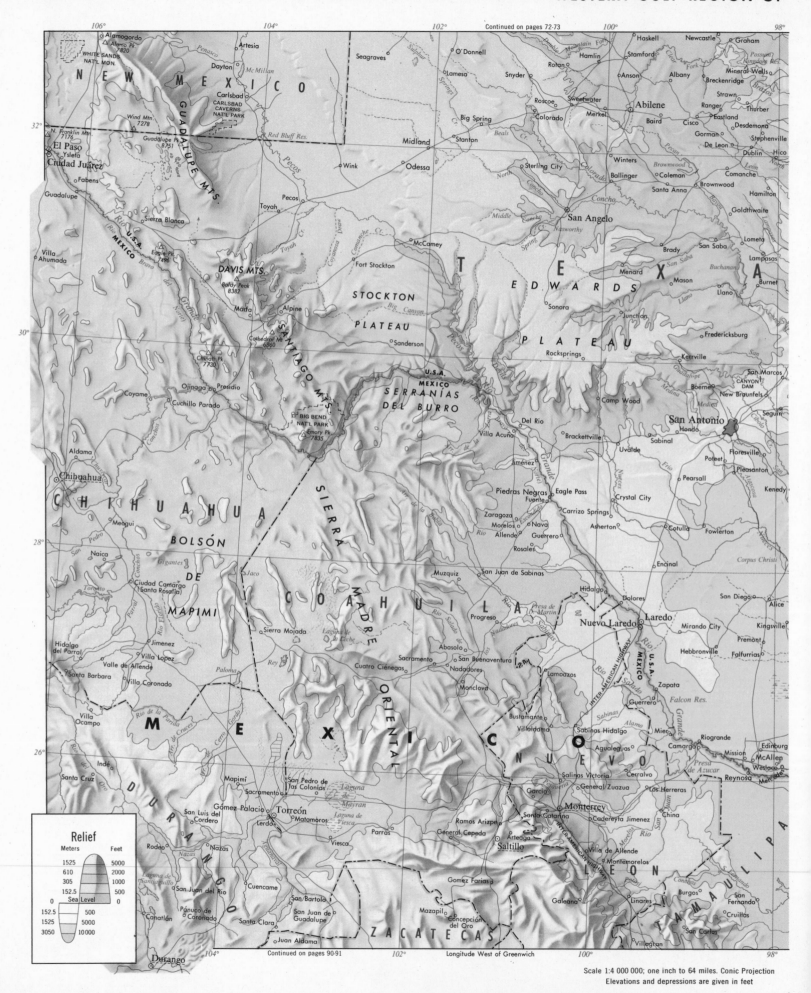

Continued on pages 72-73

NEW MEXICO

WHITE SANDS NAT'L MON.

△ Alamo Pk. 7820

Alamogordo

Artesia

Dayton

McMillan

Seagraves

O'Donnell

Haskell · Newcastle · Graham

Lamesa

Snyder

Rotan

Hamlin · Stamford · Mineral Wells

Carlsbad

CARLSBAD CAVERNS NAT'L PARK

Wind Mtn. 7278

32°

N. Franklin Mtn. 7176

Red Bluff Res.

Big Spring

Roscoe · Sweetwater · Colorado

Abilene

Anson · Albany

Baird · Cisco · Eastland · Ranger · Strawn

Merkel

Breckenridge · Thurber

El Paso

Ysleta

Guadalupe Pk. 8751

Midland

Stanton

Winters

Gorman · De Leon · Desdemona · Stephenville

Dublin · Hico

Ciudad Juárez

Fabens

Wink

Odessa

Sterling City

Ballinger · Coleman

Comanche

Hamilton

Guadalupe

Toyah

Pecos

Brownwood

Santa Anna

Goldthwaite

Villa Ahumada

Sierra Blanca

Eagle Pk. 7496

Pecos

McCamey

San Angelo

Brady · San Saba

Lometa · Lampasas

DAVIS MTS.

Fort Stockton

Menard

Mason · Llano · Burnet

Baldy Peak 8382

STOCKTON PLATEAU

Sonora

Junction

Marfa · Alpine

Big Canyon

EDWARDS PLATEAU

Fredericksburg

Cathedral Mtn. 6860

Sanderson

Rocksprings

Kerrville

Chinati Pk. 7730

USA MEXICO

SERRANÍAS DEL BURRO

Camp Wood

Boerne

San Marcos

CANYON DAM

New Braunfels

Ojinaga · Presidio

BIG BEND NAT'L PARK

△ Emory Pk. 7835

Del Rio

Brackettville

Uvalde · Sabinal

Seguin

Coyame

Villa Acuña

San Antonio

Hondo

Floresville

Chihuahua

Jiménez

Piedras Negras

Eagle Pass

Crystal City

Pearsall · Poteet · Pleasanton

CHIHUAHUA

Meoqui

Zaragoza

Fuente

Carrizo Springs

Asherton

Kenedy

Morelos · Nava

Allende · Guerrero

Cotulla · Fowlerton

BOLSÓN

Naica

Rosales

Encinal

Corpus Christi

Ciudad Camargo (Santa Rosalia)

Muzquiz

San Juan de Sabinas

San Diego

Alice

MAPIMI

DE

Hidalgo del Parral

Sierra Mojada

Laguna de la Leche

Progreso

Presa de D. Martin

Hidalgo

Dolores

Kingsville

Jiménez

Valle de Allende

Sacramento

San Buenaventura

Nadadores

Lampazos

Nuevo Laredo

Laredo

Mirando City

Premont

Hebbronville

Falfurrias

Santa Barbara

Villa López

Villa Coronado

Cuatro Ciénegas

Monclova

Zapata

MEXICO

Villa Ocampo

Paloma

Rey

COAHUILA

ORIENTAL

Bustamante

Villaldama

Guerrero

Mier

Riogrande

Camargo

Mission

Edinburg

McAllen

Weslaco

Reynosa

Inde

Mapimí

San Pedro de las Colonias

Salinas Victoria

Cerralvo

Santa Cruz

Sacramento

Laguna de Mayran

Garcia

General Zuazua

Los Herreras

Presa de Azucar

Gómez Palacio

Torreón

Laguna de Viesca

Ramos Arizpe

Monterrey

Cadereyta Jiménez

China

San Fernando

Rodeo

Nazas

Lerdo

Matamoros

Viesca

Parras

Santa Catarina

General Cepeda

Artéaga

Villa de Allende

Montemorelos

Cuencamé

Saltillo

Gómez Farías

NUEVO LEÓN

Galeana

San Juan del Rio

San Bartolo

Linares

Burgos

Laguna de Santiaguillo

Pánuco de Coronado

San Juan de Guadalupe

Mazapil

Concepción del Oro

DURANGO

Canatlán

Santa Clara

Juan Aldama

ZACATECAS

Villagran

San Carlos

Cruillas

Durango

Continued on pages 90-91

Longitude West of Greenwich

Scale 1:4 000 000; one inch to 64 miles. Conic Projection
Elevations and depressions are given in feet

Relief

Meters	Feet
1525	5000
610	2000
305	1000
152.5	500
0	Sea Level	0
152.5	500
1525	5000
3050	10000

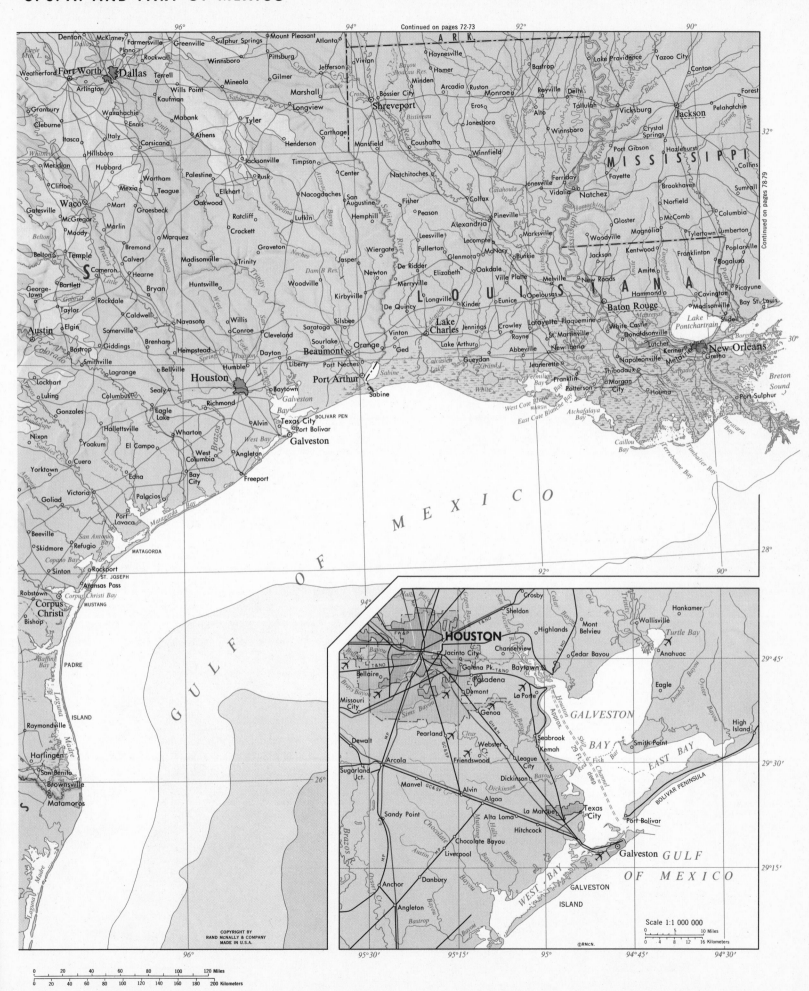

Continued on pages 72-73

Continued on pages 78-79

GULF OF MEXICO

MISSISSIPPI

LOUISIANA

Scale 1:1 000 000

GALVESTON BAY

GALVESTON ISLAND

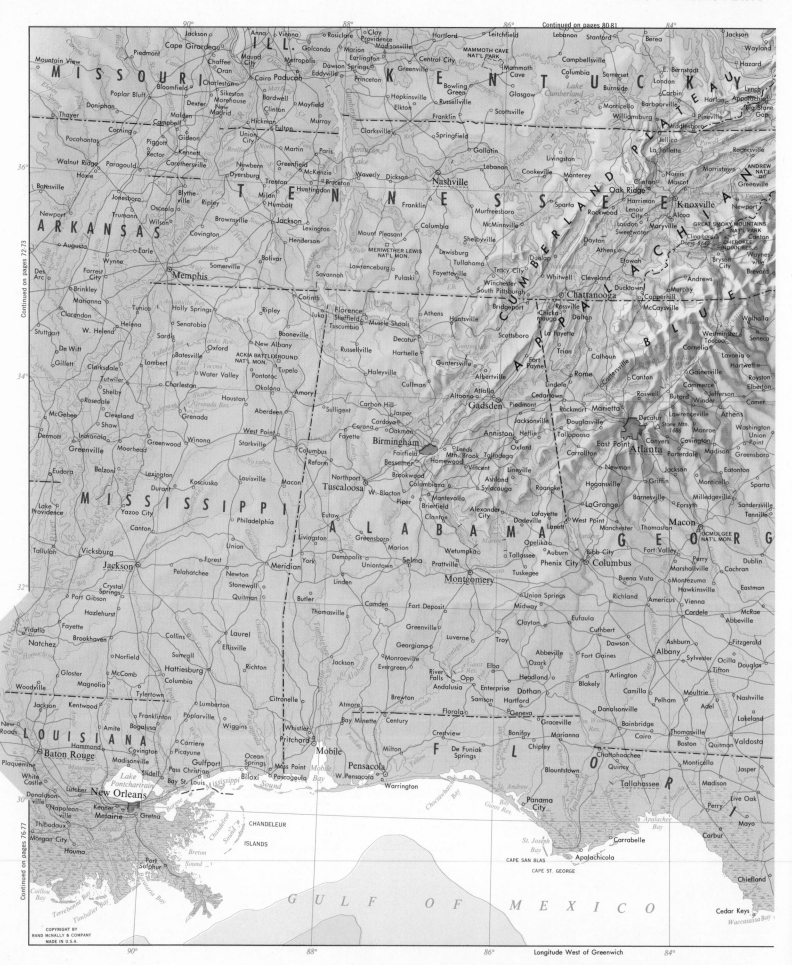

Continued on pages 80-81

Continued on pages 72-73

Continued on pages 76-77

COPYRIGHT BY
RAND MCNALLY & COMPANY
MADE IN U.S.A.

Longitude West of Greenwich

Scale 1:4 000 000; one inch to 64 miles. Conic Projection
Elevations and depressions are given in feet

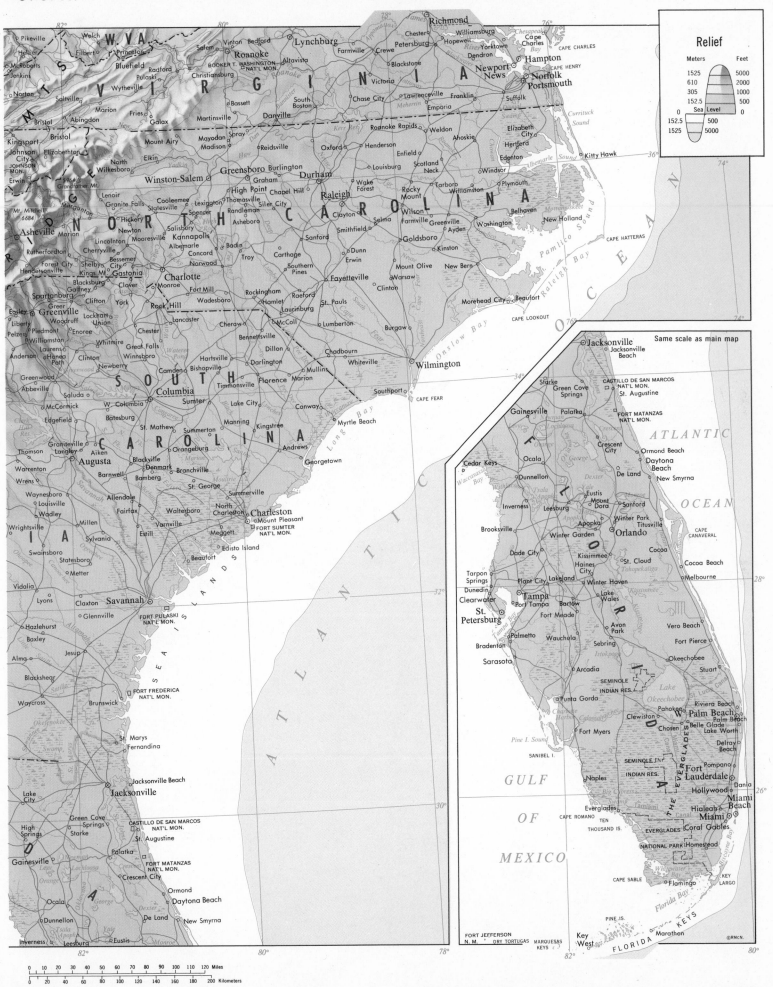

Relief

Meters		Feet
1525		5000
610		2000
305		1000
152.5		500
0	Sea Level	0
152.5		500
1525		5000

Same scale as main map

0 10 20 30 40 50 60 70 80 90 100 110 120 Miles
0 20 40 60 80 100 120 140 160 180 200 Kilometers

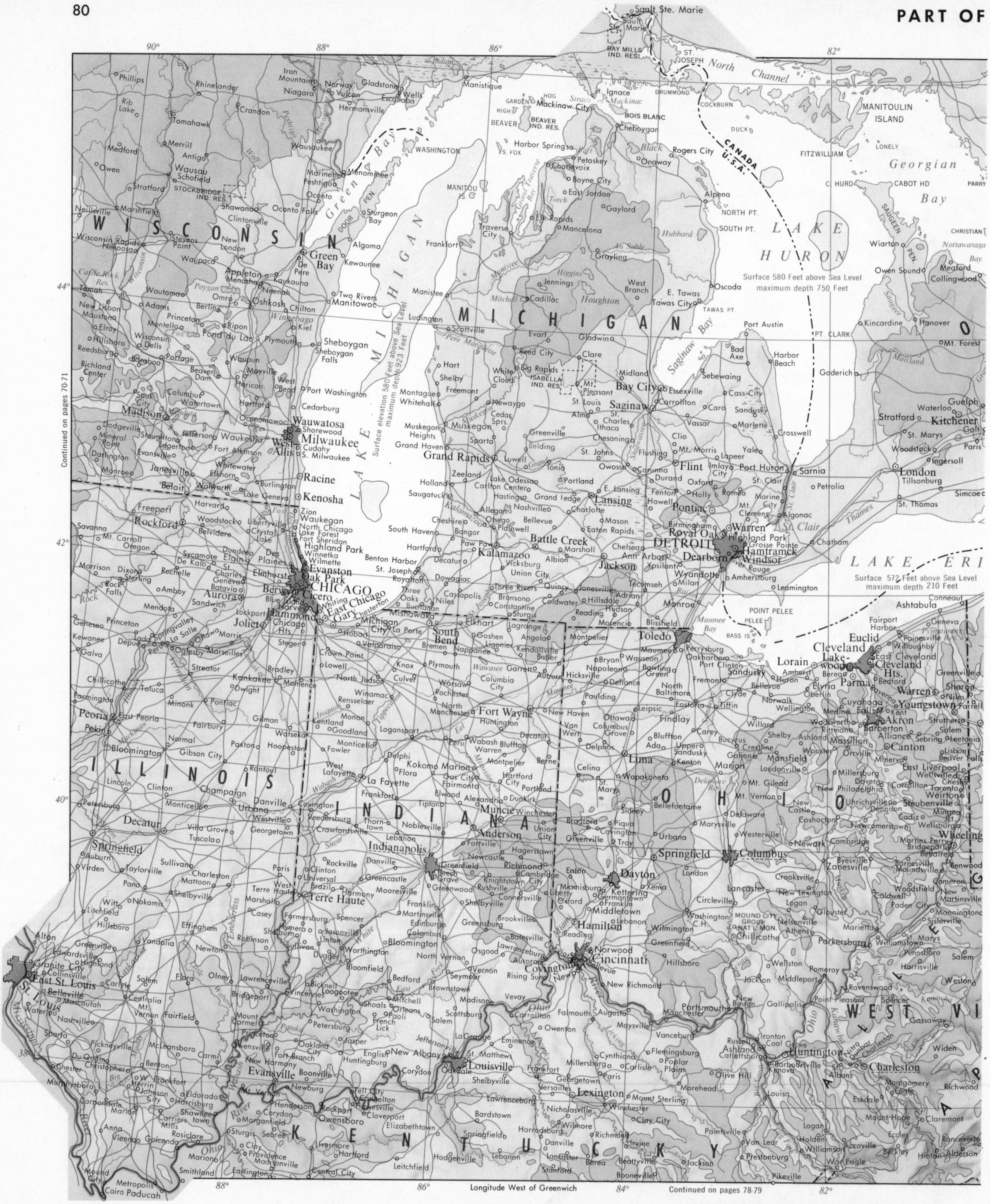

WISCONSIN

MICHIGAN

LAKE MICHIGAN
Surface elevation 580 Feet above Sea Level
maximum depth 923 Feet

LAKE HURON
Surface 580 Feet above Sea Level
maximum depth 750 Feet

LAKE ERIE
Surface 572 Feet above Sea Level
maximum depth 210 Feet

ILLINOIS

INDIANA

OHIO

KENTUCKY

WEST VIRGINIA

CANADA
U.S.A.

Georgian Bay

MANITOULIN ISLAND

North Channel

Sault Ste. Marie

Green Bay

Saginaw Bay

DETROIT

CHICAGO

Milwaukee

Madison

Grand Rapids

Lansing

Indianapolis

Cincinnati

Columbus

Dayton

Cleveland

Toledo

Akron

Youngstown

Louisville

Evansville

St. Louis

East St. Louis

Springfield

Peoria

Fort Wayne

South Bend

Gary

Flint

Saginaw

Bay City

Continued on pages 70-71

Continued on pages 78-79

Longitude West of Greenwich

Scale 1:4 000 000; one inch to 64 miles.   Conic Projection
Elevations and depressions are given in feet

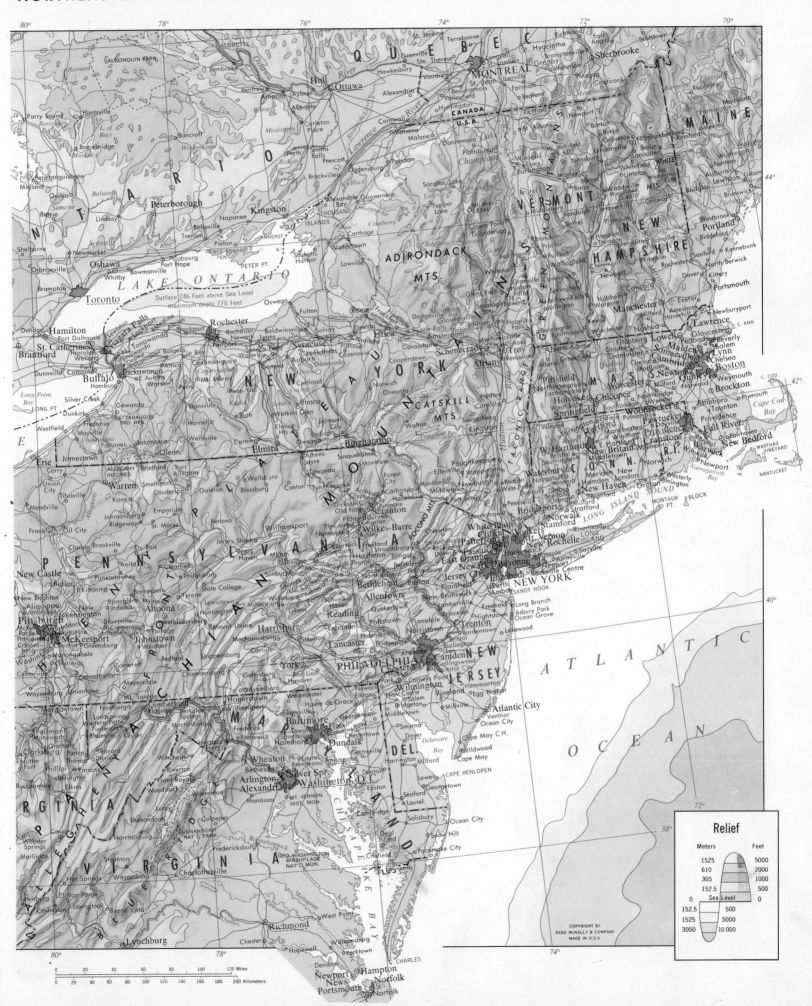

Relief

Meters	Feet
1525	5000
610	2000
305	1000
152.5	500
0	Sea Level 0
152.5	500
1525	5000
3050	10 000

COPYRIGHT BY
RAND McNALLY & COMPANY
MADE IN U.S.A.

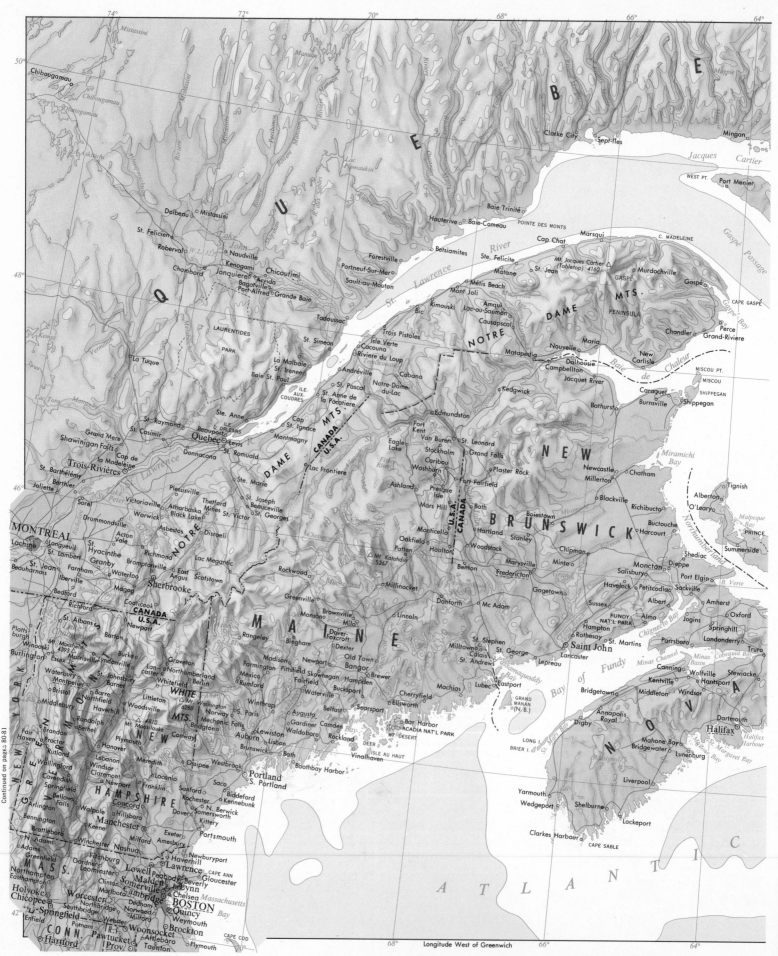

Continued on pages 80-81

Scale 1:4 000 000; one inch to 64 miles. Conic Projection
Elevations and depressions are given in feet.

Longitude West of Greenwich

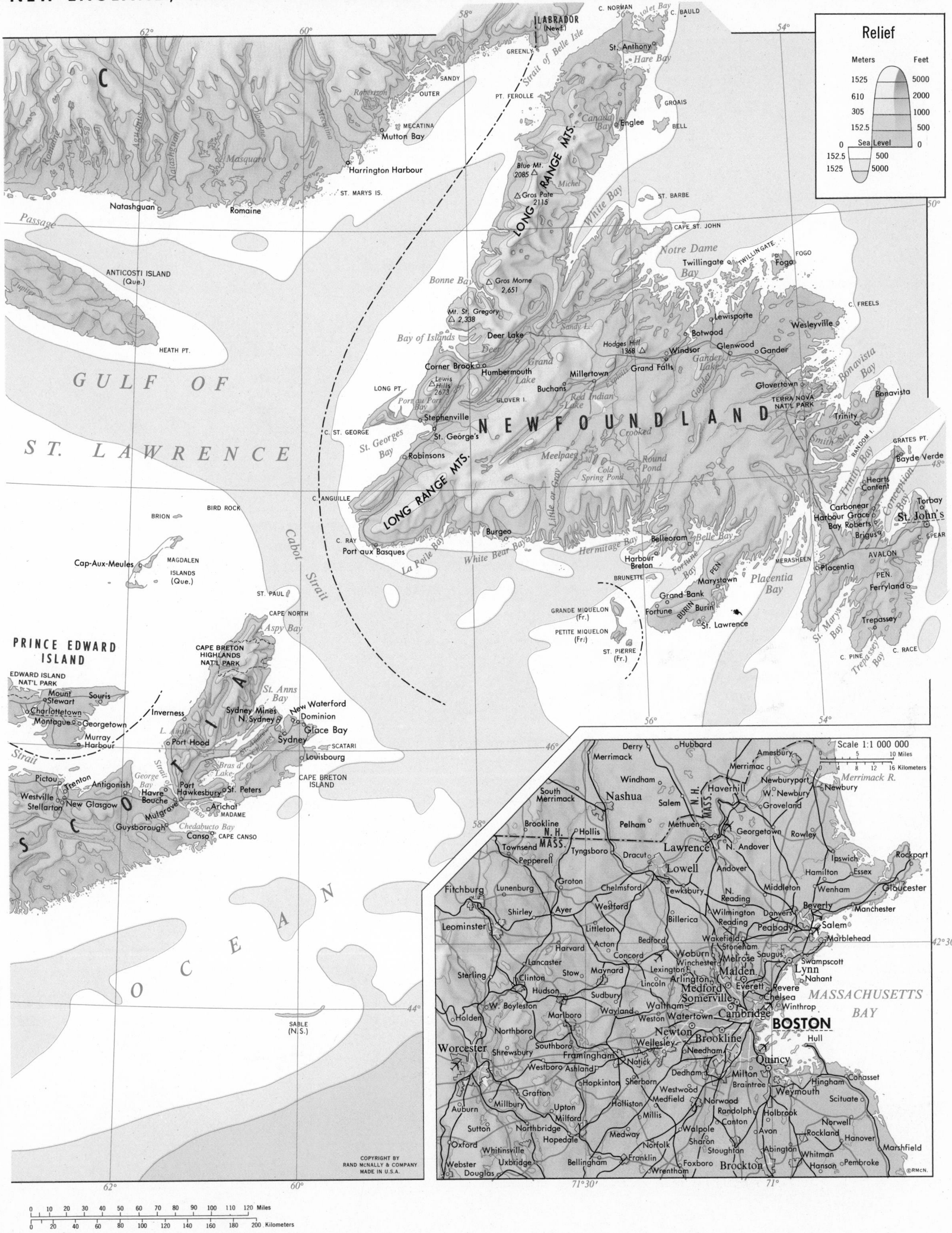

Relief

Meters		Feet
1525		5000
610		2000
305		1000
152.5		500
0	Sea Level	0
152.5		500
1525		5000

C. NORMAN
Quirpon Bay
C. BAULD
LABRADOR (Newf.)
GREENLY
St. Anthony
Hare Bay
SANDY
Strait of Belle Isle
OUTER
PT. FEROLLE
GROAIS
Canada Bay
Englee
BELL
C

Rabertson
MECATINA
Mutton Bay
Harrington Harbour
ST. MARYS IS.
Masquaro
Blue Mt. 2085
LONG RANGE MTS.
Michel
White Bay
ST. BARBE

Natashguan
Romaine
Gros Pate 2115
CAPE ST. JOHN

Passage
Notre Dame Bay
Twillingate
TWILLINGATE
Foga
FOGO

ANTICOSTI ISLAND (Que.)
Bonne Bay
Gros Morne 2,651
Lewisporte
Botwood
Wesleyville

HEATH PT.
Mt. St. Gregory 2,338
Deer Lake
Hodges Hill 1368
Windsor
Glenwood
Gander
C. FREELS

GULF OF
Bay of Islands
Deer Lake
Grand Lake
Gander Lake
Glovertown
Bonavista Bay

ST. LAWRENCE
Corner Brook
Humbermouth
Millertown
Grand Falls
TERRA NOVA NAT'L PARK
Bonavista

LONG PT.
Lewis Hills 2673
Buchans
Red Indian Lake
Grand
Trinity

Port au Port Bay
GLOVER I.
Stephenville
Crooked
Round Pond
Smith Sd.
GRATES PT.

C. ST. GEORGE
St. George's
Meelpaeg
RANDOM I.
Bayde Verde
Trinity Bay

St. Georges Bay
Robinsons
Cold Spring Pond
Hearts Content

NEWFOUNDLAND
Torbay
C. SPEAR

C. ANGUILLE
LONG RANGE MTS.
Carbonear
Harbour Grace
Brigus
St. John's

C. RAY
Port aux Basques
Burgeo
White Bear Bay
Hermitage Bay
Belleoram
Belle Bay
AVALON PEN.
Placentia

La Poile Bay
Harbour Breton
MERASHEEN
Placentia
Ferryland

Cabot Strait
BRUNETTE
Marystown
Placentia Bay
St. Marys Bay

GRANDE MIQUELON (Fr.)
Grand Bank
BURIN
Burin
Trepassey

PETITE MIQUELON (Fr.)
Fortune
St. Lawrence
C. PINE
Trepassey Bay
C. RACE

ST. PIERRE (Fr.)

BRION
BIRD ROCK
MAGDALEN ISLANDS (Que.)
Cap-Aux-Meules
ST. PAUL
CAPE NORTH
Aspy Bay

PRINCE EDWARD ISLAND
EDWARD ISLAND NAT'L PARK
CAPE BRETON HIGHLANDS NAT'L PARK
St. Anns Bay

Mount Stewart
Souris
Inverness
Sydney Mines
N. Sydney
New Waterford
Dominion

Charlottetown
Montague
Georgetown
Port Hood
Sydney
Glace Bay
SCATARI

Murray Harbour
NOVA SCOTIA
Louisbourg
CAPE BRETON ISLAND

Strait
Pictou
Antigonish
George Bay
Havre Bouche
Port Hawkesbury
St. Peters

Westville
Trenton
New Glasgow
Mulgrave
Arichat
MADAME
CAPE BRETON

Stellarton
Guysborough
Chedabucto Bay
Canso
CAPE CANSO

SABLE (N.S.)

GULF OF ST. LAWRENCE
Bras d'Or Lake
Bras d'Or Lake

OCEAN

Inset map (Boston area)

Scale 1:1 000 000

Derry
Hubbard
Amesbury
Merrimack

Merrimack
Merrimac
Newburyport
Newbury
Merrimack R.

Windham
Haverhill
W. Newbury

South Merrimack
Nashua
Salem
N.H.
MASS.

Brookline
Hollis
Pelham
Methuen
Georgetown
Rowley

N.H.
MASS.
Townsend
Lawrence
N. Andover
Ipswich
Rockport

Pepperell
Tyngsboro
Dracut
Andover
Hamilton
Essex

Fitchburg
Lunenburg
Groton
Chelmsford
Lowell
Tewksbury
N. Reading
Middleton
Wenham
Gloucester

Shirley
Ayer
Westford
Billerica
Wilmington
Danvers
Beverly
Manchester

Leominster
Littleton
Acton
Bedford
Reading
Peabody
Salem

Sterling
Harvard
Lancaster
Maynard
Concord
Lexington
Winchester
Stoneham
Melrose
Saugus
Marblehead

Clinton
Stow
Lincoln
Arlington
Malden
Revere
Swampscott
Lynn
Nahant

W. Boylston
Hudson
Sudbury
Wayland
Medford
Somerville
Everett
Chelsea
Winthrop

Holden
Marlboro
Weston
Watertown
Cambridge
MASSACHUSETTS BAY

Northboro
Newton
Brookline
BOSTON
Hull

Worcester
Shrewsbury
Southboro
Framingham
Wellesley
Needham
Milton
Quincy

Westboro
Ashland
Natick
Dedham
Braintree
Weymouth
Cohasset

Grafton
Hopkinton
Sherborn
Westwood
Norwood
Hingham
Scituate

Auburn
Millbury
Upton
Milford
Holliston
Medfield
Randolph
Canton
Holbrook
Norwell

Sutton
Northbridge
Medway
Millis
Walpole
Sharon
Avon
Rockland
Hanover
Marshfield

Oxford
Whitinsville
Hopedale
Norfolk
Stoughton
Foxboro
Abington
Whitman
Pembroke

Webster
Uxbridge
Bellingham
Franklin
Wrentham
Brockton
Hanson

Douglas

©RMcN.

Scale bars

0 10 20 30 40 50 60 70 80 90 100 110 120 Miles

0 20 40 60 80 100 120 140 160 180 200 Kilometers

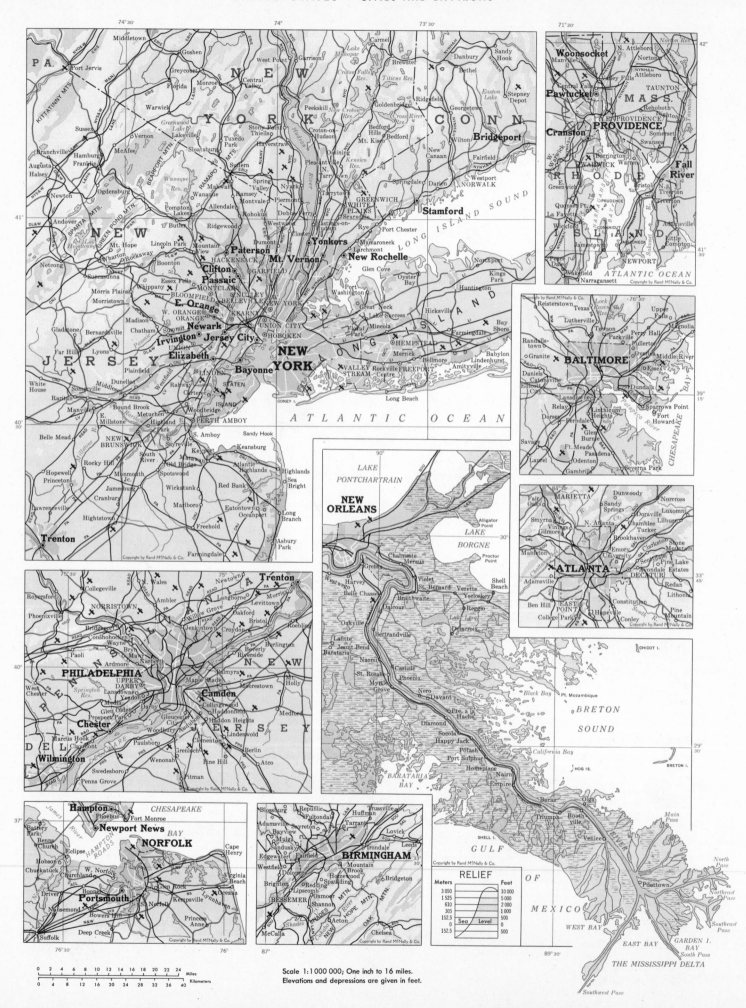

Scale 1:1 000 000; One inch to 16 miles.
Elevations and depressions are given in feet.

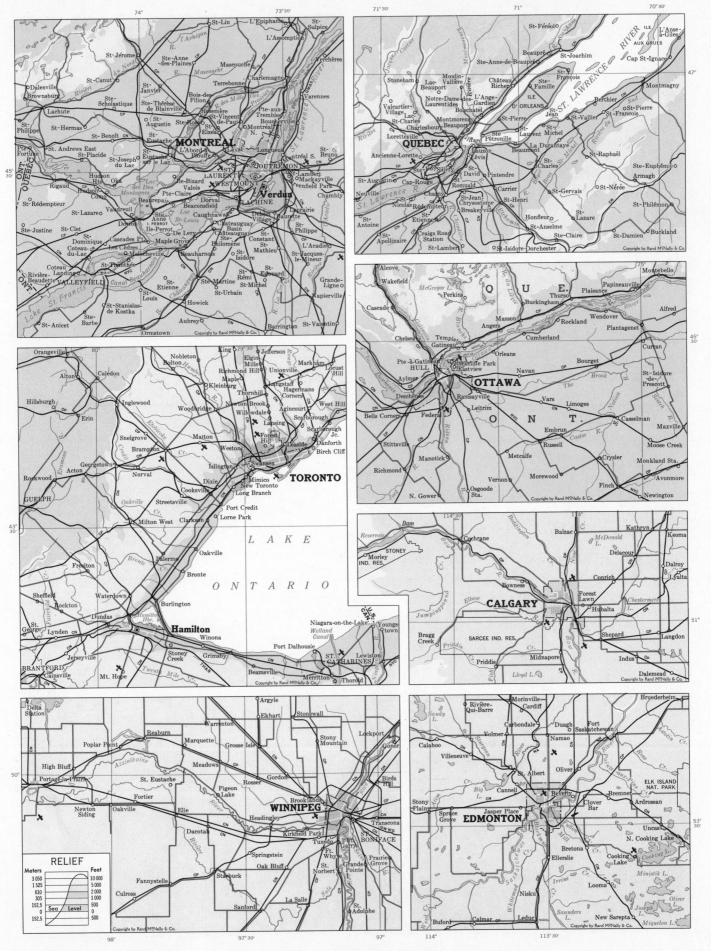

RELIEF

Meters		Feet
3 050		10 000
1 525		5 000
610		2 000
305		1 000
152.5		500
0	Sea Level	0
152.5		500

Scale 1:1 000 000; One inch to 16 miles.
Elevations and depressions are given in feet.

Miles
0 2 4 6 8 10 12 14 16 18 20 22 24

Kilometers
0 4 8 12 16 20 24 28 32 36 40

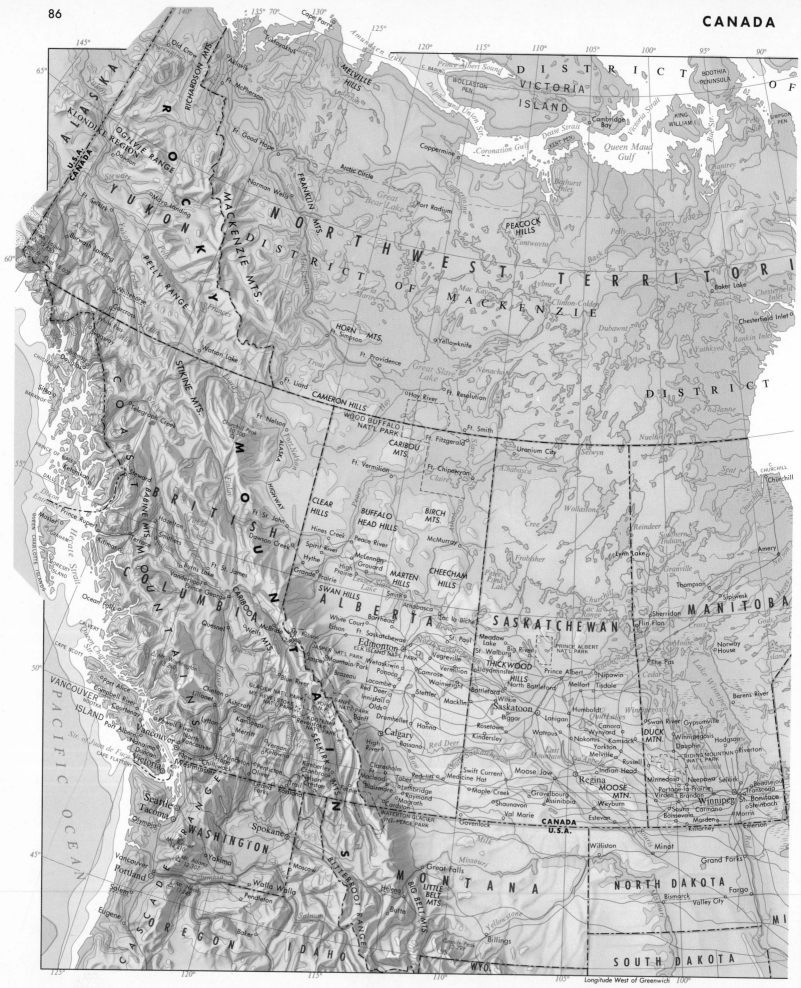

Scale 1: 12 000 000; one inch to 190 miles. Conic Projection
Elevations and depressions are given in feet

Longitude West of Greenwich

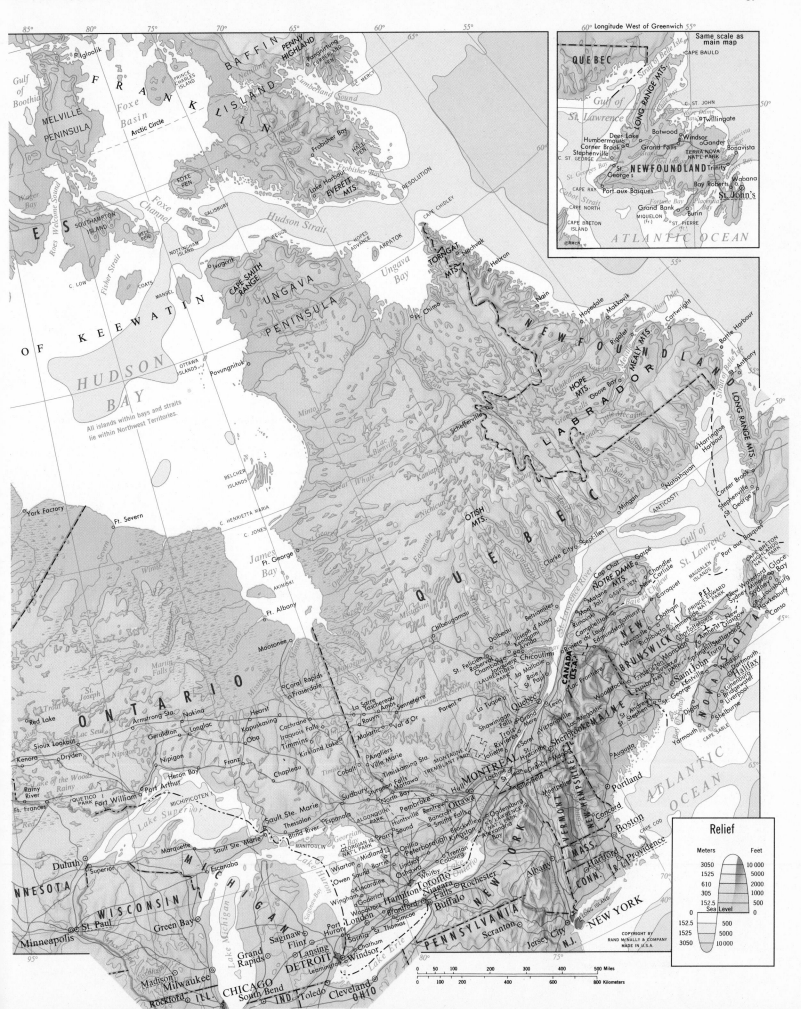

Longitude West of Greenwich

QUEBEC

Same scale as main map

CAPE BAULD

St John

Twillingate

Botwood Windsor Gander

Deer Lake

Humbermouth Grand Falls Bonavista

Corner Brook

Stephenville

TERRA NOVA NAT'L PARK

C. ST. GEORGE

NEWFOUNDLAND Trinity

St. George's

Bay Roberts Wabana

CAPE RAY Port aux Basques St. John's

CAPE NORTH Grand Bank Burin

MIQUELON (Fr.)

CAPE BRETON ISLAND St. Pierre

ATLANTIC OCEAN

©RMCN.

MELVILLE PENINSULA

Gulf of Boothia

Igloolik

FRANKLIN

BAFFIN ISLAND

PENNY HIGHLAND

Foxe Basin

Arctic Circle

Frobisher Bay

HALL PEN.

Lake Harbour

EVERETT MTS.

RESOLUTION

Roes Welcome Sound

SOUTHAMPTON ISLAND

BELL PEN.

Foxe Channel

Foxe Basin

SALISBURY

Hudson Strait

NOTTINGHAM ISLAND

COATS

MANSEL

Ivugivik

CAPE SMITH RANGE

UNGAVA

Ungava Bay

C. CHIDLEY

TORNGAT MTS.

Nachvak

Hebron

Nain

OF KEEWATIN

HUDSON BAY

All islands within bays and straits lie within Northwest Territories.

OTTAWA ISLANDS

Povungnituk

UNGAVA PENINSULA

Ft. Chimo

Hopedale

Makkovik

NEWFOUNDLAND

LABRADOR

BELCHER ISLANDS

Great Whale

HOPE MTS.

MEALY MTS.

Rigolet

Cartwright

York Factory

Ft. Severn

C. HENRIETTA MARIA

Lac Bienville

Schefferville

Goose Bay

Harrington Harbour

Battle Harbour

LONG RANGE MTS.

C. JONES

Fort George

OTISH MTS.

Natashquan

Corner Brook

Stephenville

St. George's

Ft. George

James Bay

Nichicun

QUEBEC

ANTICOSTI

Sept-Iles

AKIMISKI

Ft. Albany

Clarke City

Mingan

Gulf of St. Lawrence

Port aux Basques

Moosonee

ONTARIO

Chibougamau

Betsiamites

CAPE BRETON HIGHLANDS NAT'L PARK

Cap Chat

NOTRE DAME MTS.

Gaspé

Chandler

New Carlisle

Sydney

Glace Bay

Louisbourg

Dolbeau

St. Joseph d'Alma

Matane

GASPÉ PEN.

MAGDALEN ISLANDS

Martin Falls

St. Felicien

Chicoutimi

Rimouski

Baie des Chaleur

Caraquet

P.E.I.

New Glasgow

Coral Rapids

Roberval

Chambord

Jonquiere

Mont Joli

Campbellton

Bathurst

PRINCE EDWARD ISLAND NAT'L PARK

Summerside

Charlottetown

Amherst

Antigonish

Hawkesbury

Fraserdale

La Malbaie

Edmundston

Newcastle

Chatham

Richibucto

Canso

La Sarre

Taschereau

La Tuque

Baie St. Paul

Woodstock

Moncton

NOVA SCOTIA

Hearst

Armstrong Sta.

Nakina

Senneterre

NEW BRUNSWICK

Fredericton

FUNDY NAT'L PARK

Windsor

Geraldton

Longlac

Rouyn

Amos

Shawinigan Falls

Quebec

Levis

Fredericton

Truro

Halifax

Kapuskasing

Cochrane

Malartic

Val d'Or

Trois Rivieres

Grand Mere

MAINE

Saint John

Dartmouth

Red Lake

St. Joseph

Iroquois Falls

Sorel

St. Jean

Lac Megantic

St. Stephen

St. Andrews

Lunenburg

Bridgewater

Sioux Lookout

Lac Seul

Timmins

Kirkland Lake

Angliers

Joliette

St. Hyacinthe

Granby

St. George

Liverpool

Kenora

Dryden

Chapleau

Cobalt

Ville Marie

MONTAGNE TREMBLANT PARK

MONTREAL

Mogog

Sherbrooke

Augusta

Shelburne

CAPE SABLE

Nipigon

Timiskaming Sta.

Lachine

Valleyfield

VERMONT

NEW HAMPSHIRE

Yarmouth

Rainy River

Lake of the Woods

Heron Bay

Sturgeon Falls

North Bay

Ottawa

Hull

St. Jean

Victoriaville

Montpelier

Portland

Franz

Mattawa

ALGONQUIN PARK

Pembroke

Renfrew

Smiths Falls

St. Lawrence

Concord

Boston

Ft. Frances

QUETICO PARK

Fort William

Blind River

Espanola

Sudbury

Huntsville

Bancroft

Brockville

Kingston

Ogdensburg

ST. LAWRENCE ISL.

NAT'L PARK

Alexandria Bay

Hartford

CAPE COD

Port Arthur

Sault Ste. Marie

Thessalon

Parry Sound

ALGONQUIN PARK

GEORGIAN BAY NAT'L PARK

Orillia

Peterborough

Albany

MASS.

Providence

R.I.

Lake Superior

MICHIPICOTEN I.

Sault Ste. Marie

MANITOULIN I.

Georgian Bay

Wiarton

Midland

Barrie

Lindsay

Oshawa

NEW YORK

CONN.

LONG ISLAND

Duluth

Superior

MICHIGAN

Blind River

Owen Sound

Whitby

Marquette

Escanaba

Kincardine

Toronto

Niagara Falls

Rochester

Hamilton

Buffalo

NNESOTA

WISCONSIN

Lake Huron

Wingham

Goderich

Brantford

St. Catharines

Scranton

St. Paul

Green Bay

Stratford

Woodstock

London

Simcoe

NEW YORK

PENNSYLVANIA

Minneapolis

Lake Michigan

Saginaw

Flint

Port Huron

Sarnia

Chatham

St. Thomas

Madison

Milwaukee

Rockford

ILL.

Grand Rapids

Lansing

DETROIT

Windsor

Leamington

Lake Erie

Cleveland

OHIO

St. Paul

CHICAGO

South Bend

IND.

Toledo

Jersey City

N.J.

COPYRIGHT BY RAND McNALLY & COMPANY MADE IN U.S.A.

Relief

Meters		Feet
3050		10 000
1525		5000
610		2000
305		1000
152.5		500
0	Sea Level	0
152.5		500
1525		5000
3050		10 000

0 50 100 200 300 400 500 Miles

0 100 200 400 600 800 Kilometers

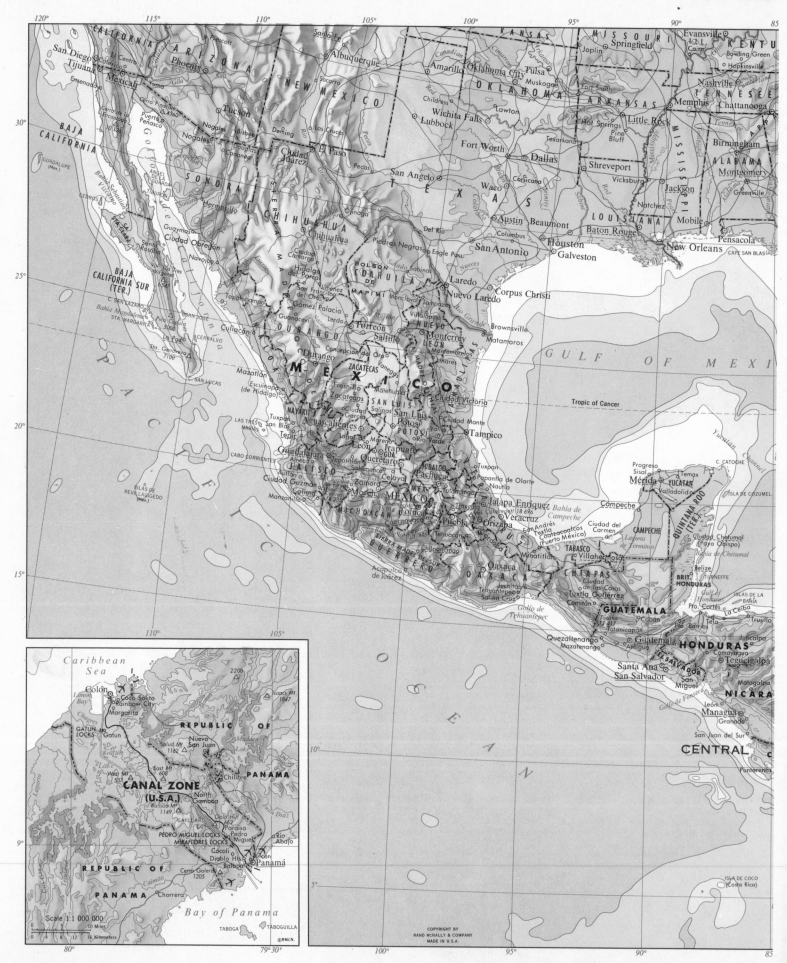

Scale 1:16 000 000; one inch to 250 miles. Polyconic Projection
Elevations and depressions are given in feet

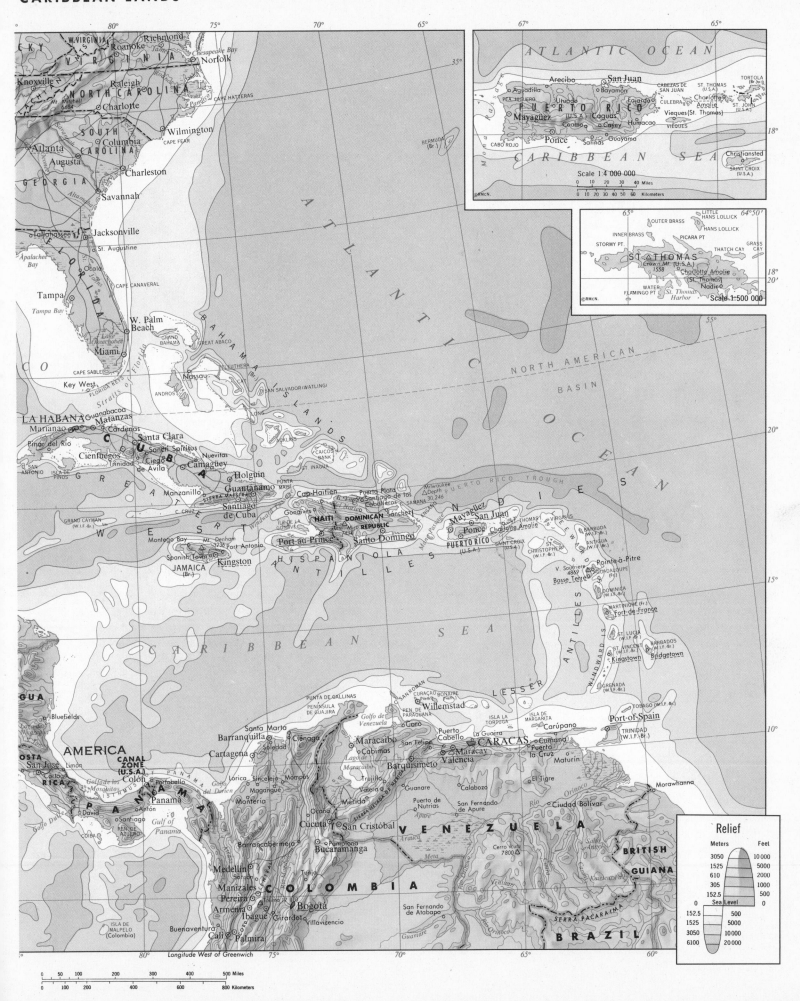

Inset map 1 (Puerto Rico)

ATLANTIC OCEAN

Arecibo · San Juan
Aguadilla · Bayamón · CABEZAS DE SAN JUAN · ST. THOMAS (U.S.A.) · TORTOLA (Br.) ·
PTA. HIGÜERO · Utuado · Carolina · Fajardo · Charlotte Amalie · ST. JOHN (U.S.A.)
PUERTO RICO · CULEBRA
Mayagüez (U.S.A.) · Caguas · Vieques (St. Thomas)
Caamo · Cayey · Humacao · VIEQUES
CABO ROJO · Ponce · Salinas · Guayama · Christiansted
CARIBBEAN SEA · SAINT CROIX (U.S.A.)

Scale 1:4 000 000

0 10 20 30 40 Miles
0 10 20 30 40 50 60 Kilometers
©RMcN.

Inset map 2 (St. Thomas)

LITTLE HANS LOLLICK
INNER BRASS · OUTER BRASS · HANS LOLLICK
STORMY PT. · PICARA PT. · GRASS CAY
THATCH CAY
ST. THOMAS · Crown Mt. (U.S.A.) 1558 · Charlotte Amalie (St. Thomas)
WATER · Nadir
FLAMINGO PT. · St. Thomas Harbor

Scale 1:500 000
©RMcN.

Relief

Meters	Feet
3050	10 000
1525	5000
610	2000
305	1000
152.5	500
0	Sea Level 0
152.5	500
1525	5000
3050	10 000
6100	20 000

0 50 100 200 400 500 Miles
0 100 200 400 600 800 Kilometers

Longitude West of Greenwich

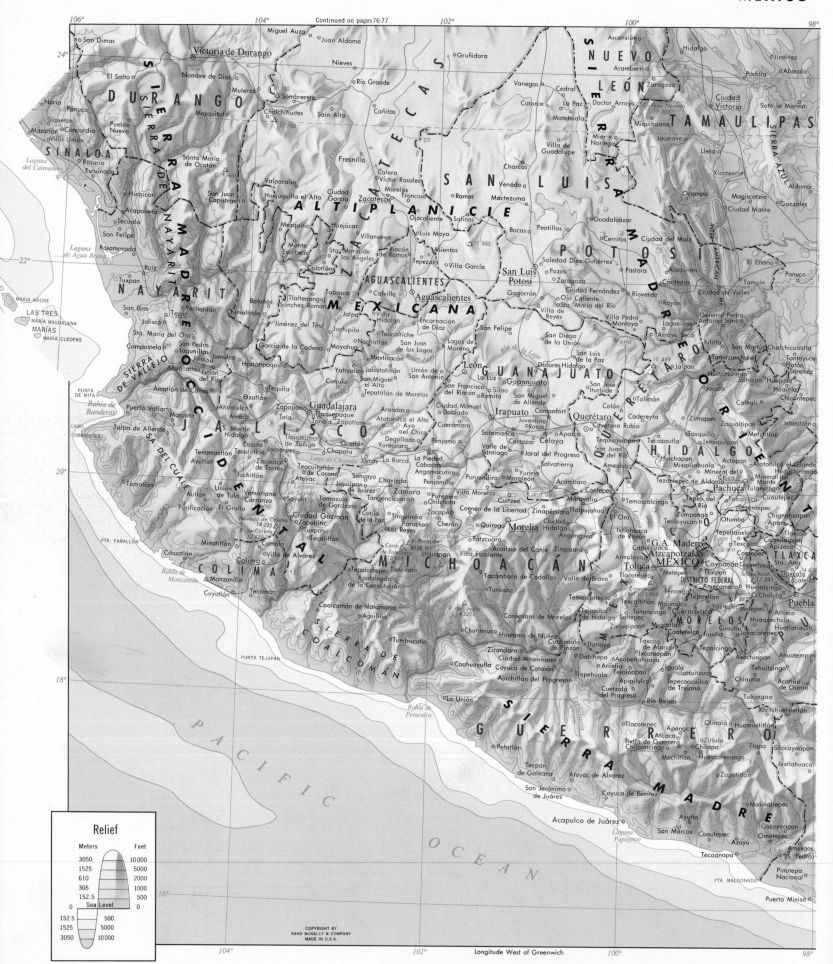

Continued on pages 76-77

Relief

Meters		Feet
3050		10 000
1525		5000
610		2000
305		1000
152.5		500
0	Sea Level	0
152.5		500
1525		5000
3050		10 000

COPYRIGHT BY
RAND McNALLY & COMPANY
MADE IN U.S.A.

Longitude West of Greenwich

Scale 1:4 000 000; one inch to 64 miles. Conic Projection
Elevations and depressions are given in feet

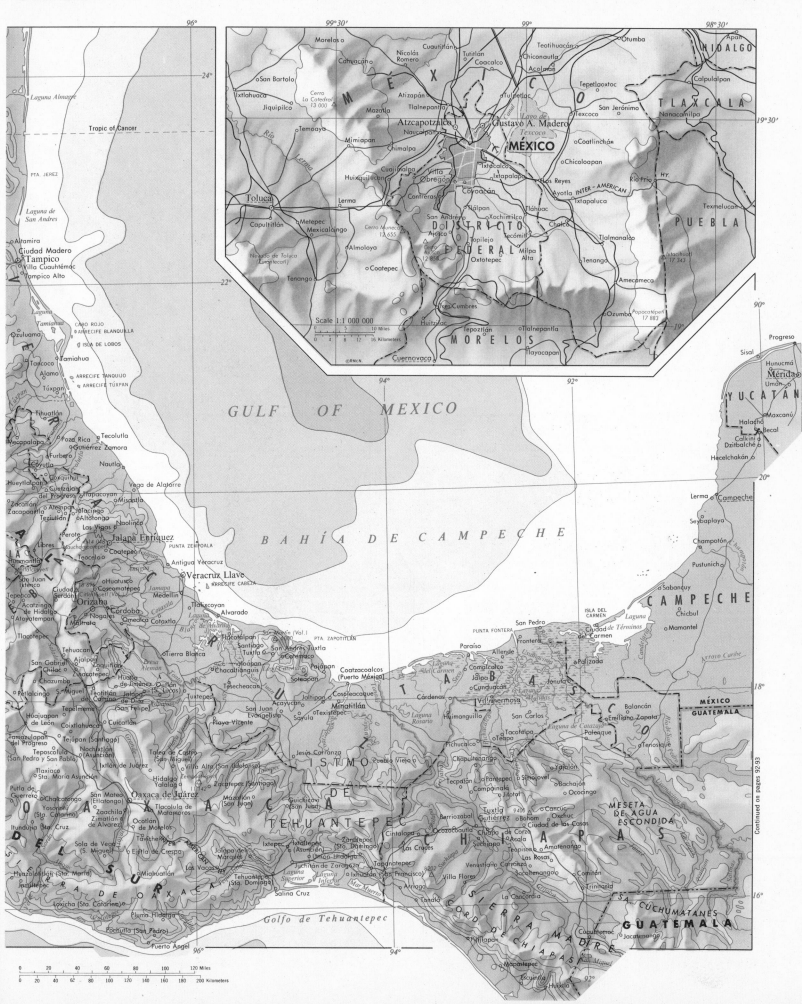

GULF OF MEXICO

BAHÍA DE CAMPECHE

Golfo de Tehuantepec

Continued on pages 92-93

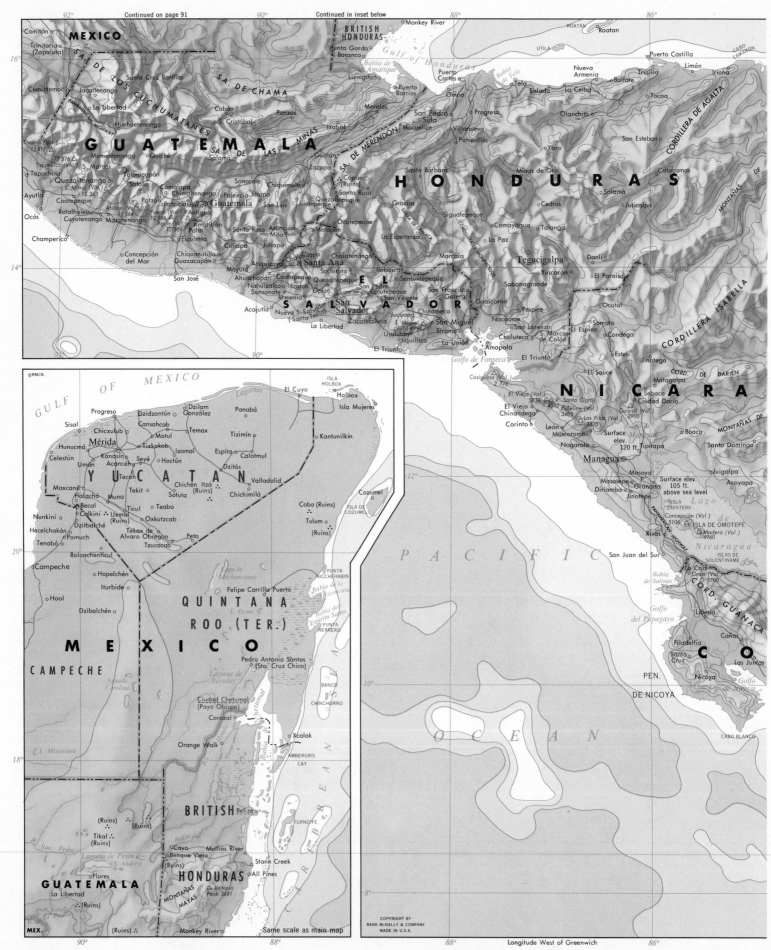

Continued on page 91
Continued in inset below

MEXICO

GUATEMALA

HONDURAS

EL SALVADOR

NICARA

CO

GULF OF MEXICO

YUCATAN

QUINTANA ROO (TER.)

MEXICO

CAMPECHE

BRITISH HONDURAS

GUATEMALA

PACIFIC

OCEAN

Same scale as main map

Longitude West of Greenwich

Scale 1:4 000 000; one inch to 64 miles. Sinusoidal Projection

Elevations and depressions are given in feet

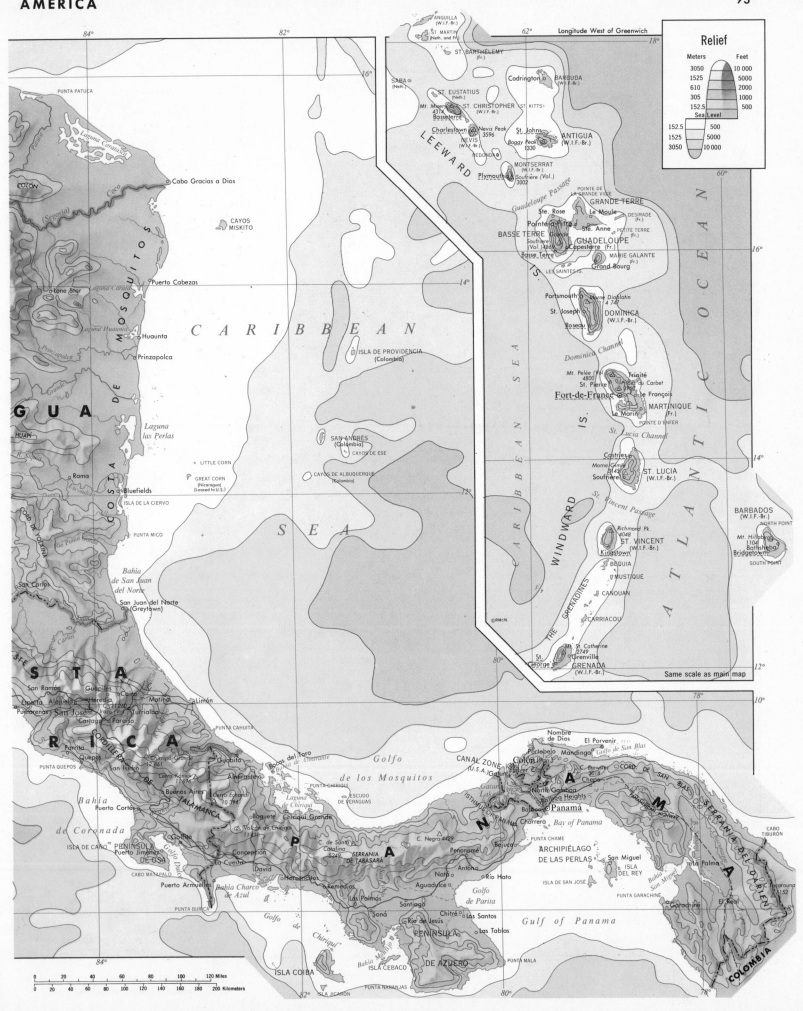

Relief

Meters	Feet
3050	10 000
1525	5000
610	2000
305	1000
152.5	500
Sea Level	
152.5	500
1525	5000
3050	10 000

PUNTA PATUCA

COLÓN

Laguna Caratasca

Cabo Gracias a Dios

CAYOS MISKITO

Lone Star

Puerto Cabezas

Laguna Carata

Huaunta

Laguna Huaunta

Prinzapolca

Prinzapolca

HUAPÍ

C A R I B B E A N

ISLA DE PROVIDENCIA
(Colombia)

Laguna
las Perlas

Rama

LITTLE CORN

SAN ANDRÉS
(Colombia)
CAYOS DE ESE

GREAT CORN
(Nicaragua)
(Leased to U.S.)

CAYOS DE ALBUQUERQUE
(Colombia)

Bluefields

ISLA DE LA CIERVO

PUNTA MICO

S E A

San Carlos

Bahía
de San Juan
del Norte

San Juan del Norte
(Greytown)

Longitude West of Greenwich

ANGUILLA
(W.I.F.-Br.)

ST. MARTIN
(Neth. and Fr.)

ST. BARTHÉLEMY
(Fr.)

SABA
(Neth.)

Codrington   BARBUDA
(W.I.F.-Br.)

ST. EUSTATIUS
(Neth.)

Mt. Misery   ST. CHRISTOPHER (ST. KITTS)
4314   (W.I.F.-Br.)
Basseterre

Charlestown   Nevis Peak
3596   St. Johns   ANTIGUA
(W.I.F.-Br.)

NEVIS
(W.I.F.-Br.)   Boggy Peak
1330

REDONDA

MONTSERRAT
(W.I.F.-Br.)

Plymouth   Soufrière (Vol.)
3002

POINTE DE
LA GRANDE VIGIE

GRANDE TERRE

Ste. Rose   Le Moule   DÉSIRADE
(Fr.)

Pointe-à-Pitre   Ste. Anne   PETITE TERRE

BASSE TERRE   Grande   GUADELOUPE
Soufrière   Capesterre   (Fr.)
(Vol.) 4869

Basse Terre   MARIE GALANTE
(Fr.)

LES SAINTES IS.   Grand Bourg

Portsmouth   Morne Diablotin
4747

St. Joseph   DOMINICA
(W.I.F.-Br.)

Roseau

Dominica Channel

Mt. Pelée (Vol.)   Trinité
4800   Piton du Carbet
St. Pierre   3940

Fort-de-France   Ste. François

MARTINIQUE
Le Marin   (Fr.)

POINTE D'ENFER

St. Lucia Channel

Castries
Morne Gimie
3145   ST. LUCIA
Soufrière   (W.I.F.-Br.)

St. Vincent Passage

Richmond Pk.
4048   ST. VINCENT
(W.I.F.-Br.)
Kingstown

BEQUIA

MUSTIQUE

CANOUAN

CARRIACOU

Mt. St. Catherine
2749   Grenville
St.
George's   GRENADA
(W.I.F.-Br.)

LEEWARD   IS.

C A R I B B E A N   S E A

WINDWARD   IS.

THE   GRENADINES

A T L A N T I C   O C E A N

BARBADOS
(W.I.F.-Br.)
NORTH POINT

Mt. Hillaby
1104   Bathsheba
Bridgetown
SOUTH POINT

Same scale as main map

Nombre
de Dios   El Porvenir

Portobelo   Mandinga   Golfo de San Blas

CANAL ZONE   Colón (Pan.)
(U.S.A.)   Gatún   Silver City   C. Brewster
2018   CORD. DE SAN BLAS

North Gamboa   Chepo

Balboa Heights   Balboa   Panamá

Chorrera   Bay of Panama

PUNTA CHAME

Bejuco

ARCHIPIÉLAGO   San Miguel
DE LAS PERLAS

ISLA
DEL REY

Bahía   ta Palma
San Miguel

CABO
TIBURÓN

Yaviza   4152

El Real

Garachiné

P   A   N   A   M   Á

SERRANIA DEL DARIEN

INTER-AMERICAN HIGHWAY

COLOMBIA

San Ramón   Guápiles
Esparta   Alajuela   Heredia   Cairo   Matina
Puntarenas   San José   Turrialba   Limón
Cartago   Paraíso
PUNTA CAHUITA

Parrita
Quepos

Chirripó Grande
12 861

Cerro Kámuk
11 696   Guyabito

San Isidro   Almirante
Cerro Echandi
10 394

Puerto Cortés

Golfito

Boquete   Chiriquí Grande

ISLA DE CAÑO   PENÍNSULA   Volcán de Chiriquí
Puerto Jiménez   11 410
DE OSA

CABO MATAPALO   Concepción   David
La Cuesta

Horconcitos

Puerto Armuelles   Remedios

PUNTA BURICA

San Miguelito

Gulf of Panama

PUNTA QUEPOS

COSTA   RICA

CORDILLERA   DE   TALAMANCA

Bahía
de Coronada

Golfo Dulce

Bahía Charco
de Azul

Golfo de
Chiriquí

ISLA COIBA

ISLA CEBACO

Bahía Montijo

C A R I B B E A N

Bocas del Toro   Golfo
Bahía de Almirante   de los Mosquitos

PUNTA CHIRIQUÍ

ESCUDO
DE VERAGUAS

Laguna
de Chiriquí

Almirante

C. de Santa
Catalina   Serrania
5249   DE TABASARA
SERRANÍA

C. Negro 4429

Las Palmas

Peñonomé

Natá   Antón   Río Hato

Aguadulce

Santiago

Soná   Río de Jesús   Chitré
Las Santos

Las Tablas

PENÍNSULA

DE AZUERO

PUNTA MALA

Golfo
de
Chiriquí

Golfo de Parita

Gulf of Panama

PUNTA NARANJAS

ISLA JICARON

Bahía
San Miguel

ISLA DE SAN JOSÉ

PUNTA GARACHINE

| 0 | 20 | 40 | 60 | 80 | 100 | 120 Miles |
| 0 | 20 | 40 | 60 | 80 | 100 | 120 | 140 | 160 | 180 | 200 Kilometers |

©RMcN

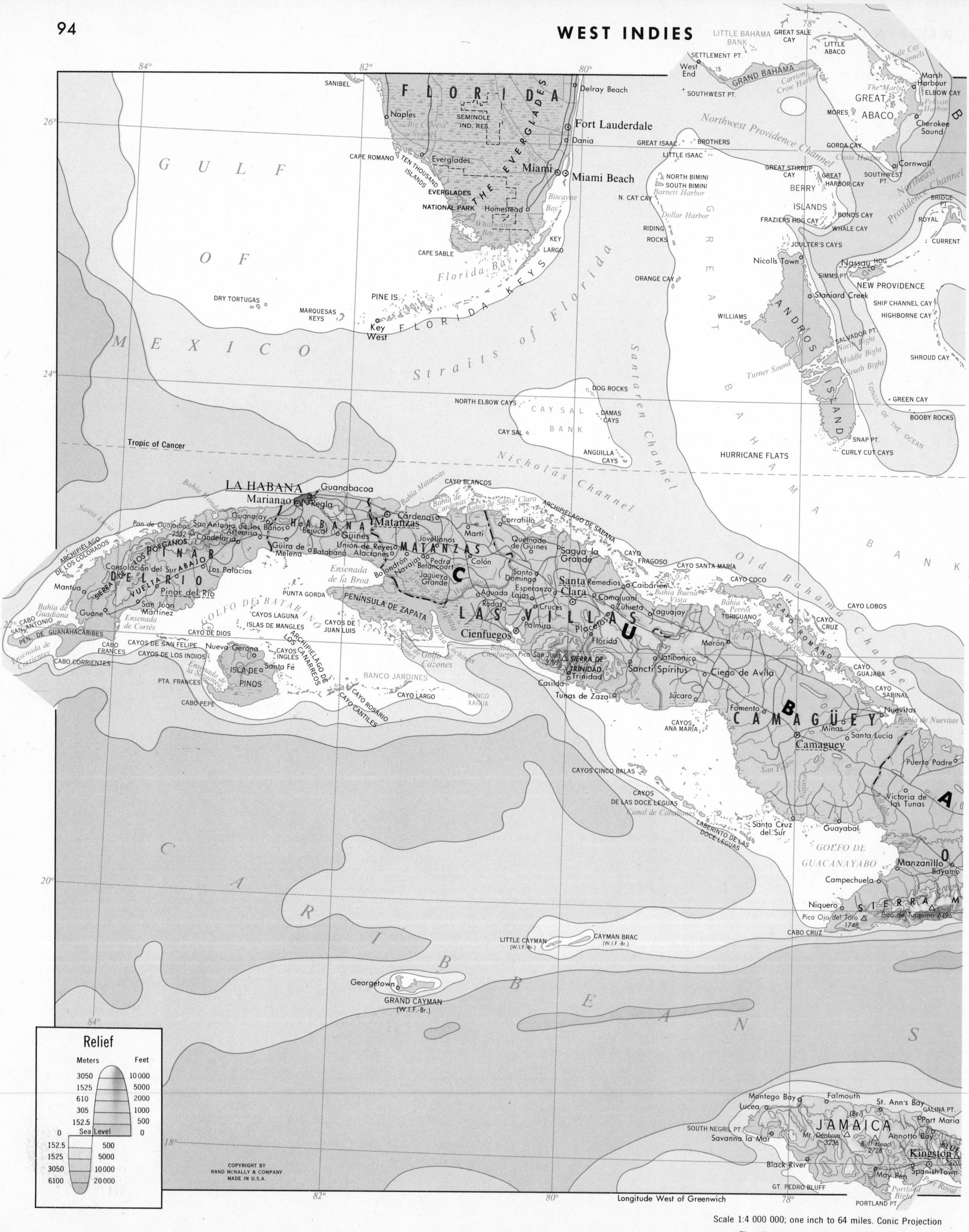

FLORIDA

GULF OF MEXICO

SANIBEL

Naples
Big Cypress Swamp
SEMINOLE IND. RES.
Delray Beach
Fort Lauderdale
Dania
CAPE ROMANO
TEN THOUSAND ISLANDS
Everglades
EVERGLADES
Miami
Miami Beach
NATIONAL PARK
Homestead
Biscayne Bay
THE EVERGLADES
Whitewater Bay
CAPE SABLE
Florida Bay
KEY LARGO
FLORIDA KEYS
DRY TORTUGAS
PINE IS.
MARQUESAS KEYS
Key West
Straits of Florida

LITTLE BAHAMA BANK
GREAT SALE CAY
LITTLE ABACO
SETTLEMENT PT.
West End
GRAND BAHAMA
SOUTHWEST PT.
Northwest Providence Channel
Marsh Harbour
ELBOW CAY
GREAT ABACO
Cherokee Sound
Cornwall
SOUTHWEST PT.
GORDA CAY
GREAT ISAAC
BROTHERS
LITTLE ISAAC
BERRY ISLANDS
GREAT STIRRUP CAY
GREAT HARBOR CAY
BONDS CAY
WHALE CAY
ROYAL
CURRENT
NORTH BIMINI
SOUTH BIMINI
Barnett Harbor
N. CAT CAY
Dollar Harbor
RIDING ROCKS
FRAZIERS HOG CAY
HOG
Nassau
NEW PROVIDENCE
SIMMS PT.
SHIP CHANNEL CAY
HIGHBORNE CAY
Nicolls Town
Staniard Creek
ANDROS ISLAND
WILLIAMS
ORANGE CAY
North Bight
Middle Bight
South Bight
Turner Sound
SHROUD CAY
GREEN CAY
BOOBY ROCKS
Tropic of Cancer
DOG ROCKS
NORTH ELBOW CAYS
CAY SAL BANK
DAMAS CAYS
CAY SAL
ANGUILLA CAYS
HURRICANE FLATS
SNAP PT.
CURLY CUT CAYS
TONGUE OF THE OCEAN
Santaren Channel
Nicholas Channel
Old Bahama Channel

LA HABANA
Guanabacoa
Marianao
Regla
HABANA
CAYO BLANCOS
ARCHIPIELAGO DE SABANA
Guanajay
Cárdenas
San Antonio de los Baños
Artemisa
Güines
Matanzas
Jovellanos
Martí
Corralillo
Quemado de Güines
CAYO
FRAGOSO
CAYO SANTA MARÍA
Pan de Guajaibón 2532
Candelaria
Güira de Melena
Unión de Reyes
Pedro Betancourt
MATANZAS
Santa Domingo
Sagua la Grande
CAYO COCO
Batabanó
Alacranes
Esperanza
Remedios
Caibarién
Bahía Buena Vista
CAYO LOBOS
Consolación del Sur
ABAJOR
Los Palacios
Bolondrón
Navajas
Jagüey Grande
Aguada
Rodas
Lajas
Cruces
Santa Clara
Camajuaní
Zulueta
Yaguajay
TURIGUANO
Bahía Perros
Mantua
SIERRA
VUELTA
Pinar del Río
PUNTA GORDA
PENÍNSULA DE ZAPATA
Palmira
Placetas
Florida
CAYO CRUZ
Guane
San Juan Martínez
Ensenada de Cortés
Cienfuegos
Pico San Juan 1760
Morón
Jatibonica
CAYO GUAJABA
CABO FRANCÉS
CAYOS DE SAN FELIPE
CAYO DE DIOS
GOLFO DE BATABANÓ
CAYOS LAGUNA
ISLAS DE MANGLES
Nueva Gerona
SIERRA DE TRINIDAD
Trinidad
Sancti Spíritus
Ciego de Avila
CAYO SABINAL
Nuevitas
CABO CORRIENTES
CAYOS DE LOS INDIOS
CAYOS INGLES
ARCHIPIELAGO DE LOS CANARREOS
Santa Fé
BANCO JARDINES
Casilda
Tunas de Zaza
Júcaro
CAMAGÜEY
Minas
Santa Lucía
Bahía de Nuevitas
ISLA DE PINOS
CAYO ROSARIO
CAYO LARGO
BANCO XAGUA
CAYOS ANA MARÍA
Fomento
Camagüey
Puerto Padre
PTA. FRANCES
CAYO CANTILES
CAYOS CINCO BALAS
Victoria de las Tunas
CABO PEPE
CAYOS DE LAS DOCE LEGUAS
Santa Cruz del Sur
Guayabal
GOLFO DE GUACANAYABO
Manzanillo
Bayamo
LABERINTO DE LAS DOCE LEGUAS
Campechuela
Niquero
Pico Ojo del Toro 1748
SIERRA
Pico de Turquino 6496
CABO CRUZ

LAS VILLAS
LA HABANA
MATANZAS
C
B
A
O

Canal de Caballones

C A R I B B E A N   S E A

LITTLE CAYMAN (W.I.F.-Br.)
CAYMAN BRAC (W.I.F.-Br.)
Georgetown
GRAND CAYMAN (W.I.F.-Br.)

Montego Bay
Falmouth
St. Ann's Bay
GALINA PT.
Lucea
Port Maria
SOUTH NEGRIL PT.
JAMAICA
(Br.)
Annotto Bay
Savanna la Mar
Mt. Denham 3236
BLUE
Kingston
Black River
May Pen
Spanish Town
GT. PEDRO BLUFF
PORTLAND PT.
Port Royal
Portland Bight

Relief

Meters	Feet
3050	10 000
1525	5000
610	2000
305	1000
152.5	500
0 Sea Level	0
152.5	500
1525	5000
3050	10 000
6100	20 000

Longitude West of Greenwich

Scale 1:4 000 000; one inch to 64 miles. Conic Projection
Elevations and depressions are given in feet.

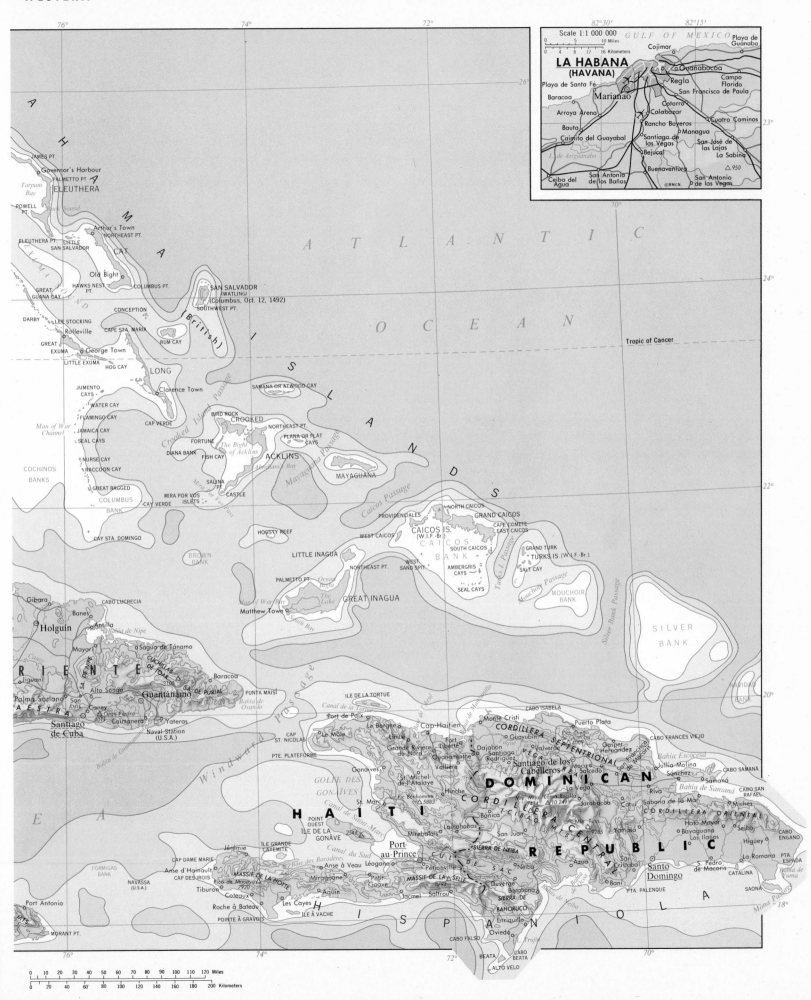

GULF OF MEXICO

Playa de
Guanabo

Cojimar

Guanabocoa

Playa de Santa Fé   Regla   Campo
                                                        Florido
Baracoa   Marianao   San Francisco de Paula

Arroya Arena   Cotorro   Cuatro Caminos
                    Colabazar
Bauta   Rancho Boyeros   Managua
        Caimito del Guayabal   San José de
                            Santiago de   las Lajas   La Sabina
                            las Vegas
                        Bejucal

L. de Arigianabo   Buenaventura   △ 950
Ceiba del   San Antonio
Agua   de los Baños   San Antonio   San Antonio
                                de las Vegas

©RMCN

A   T   L   A   N   T   I   C

O   C   E   A   N

JAMES PT.
Governor's Harbour
PALMETTO PT.
ELEUTHERA
POWELL
PT.
Tarpum
Bay
Rock Sound

Arthur's Town
NORTHEAST PT.
ELEUTHERA PT.
LITTLE
SAN SALVADOR
CAT

Old Bight

HAWKS NEST
PT.
COLUMBUS PT.
SAN SALVADOR
(WATLING)
(Columbus, Oct. 12, 1492)
SOUTHWEST PT.

CONCEPTIÓN

GREAT
GUANA CAY

DARBY
LEE STOCKING
Rolleville
CAPE STA. MARIA

[British]

GREAT
EXUMA
George Town
LITTLE EXUMA
HOG CAY

RUM CAY

Tropic of Cancer

LONG

JUMENTO
CAYS
WATER CAY
FLAMINGO CAY
CAP VERDE
JAMAICA CAY
SEAL CAYS
Man of War
Channel

Clarence Town

SAMANA OR ATWOOD CAY

BIRD ROCK
CROOKED
NORTHEAST PT.
PLANA OR FLAT
CAYS

FORTUNE
DIANA BANK   The Bight
FISH CAY   of Acklins
NURSE CAY
RACCOON CAY

COCHINOS
BANKS

GREAT RAGGED

COLUMBUS
BANK

CAY VERDE

CAY STA. DOMINGO

ACKLINS
Abraham's Bay

MIRA POR VOS
ISLETS
CASTLE
SALINA
PT.

BROWN
BANK

HOGSTY REEF

LITTLE INAGUA

PALMETTO PT.
Ocean
Bight
NORTHEAST PT.
WEST
SAND SPIT

MAYAGUANA

I   S   L   A   N   D   S

Caicos Passage

NORTH CAICOS
GRAND CAICOS
PROVIDENCIALES
CAICOS IS.
(W.I.F.-Br.)
WEST CAICOS
SOUTH CAICOS
CAICOS
BANK
AMBERGRIS
CAYS
SEAL CAYS

CAPE COMETE
EAST CAICOS

GRAND TURK
TURKS IS. (W.I.F.-Br.)
SALT CAY

Gibara
CABO LUCRECIA
Banes
Antilla
Bahía de Nipe
Holguín
Mayarí
Sagua de Tánamo
CUCHILLAS
DE TOAR
SA. DE NIPE
Baracoa
SA. DE PURIAL
PUNTA MAISÍ
Bahía de
Ovando

Matthew Town
GREAT INAGUA
The
Lake

Man of War Bay

South Bay

SILVER
BANK

O   R   I   E   N   T   E

Jiguaní
Alto Songo
Palma Soriano
San
Luis
Caney
Gran Piedra
MAESTRA
**Santiago
de Cuba**
Caimanera
Guantánamo
Yateras
Naval Station
(U.S.A.)

ILE DE LA TORTUE

Canal de la Tortue

CABO ISABELA

NAVIDAD
BANK

Port de Paix
Le Borgne
CAP
ST. NICOLAS
PTE. PLATEFORME

Monte Cristi
Puerto Plata
CORDILLERA SEPTENTRIONAL
Cap-Haïtien
Le Môle
Limbé
Fort
Liberté
Grande Rivière
du Nord
Ouanaminthe
Guayubin
Dajabón
Valverde
Gasper
Hernández
CABO FRANCÉS VIEJO
Santiago
Rodríguez
Salcedo
San Francisco de Macorís
Bahía Escosesa
Julia Molina
Sánchez
CABO SAMANA

Golfe de Guantánamo

St. Michel-
de-l'Atalaye

Gonaïves
Pic Bonhomme
△ 5883
Hinche
La Vega
Bahía de Samaná

GOLFE DES
GONAÎVES
St. Marc
DOMINICAN
Moca
Loma Tucila
△10 249
Jarabacoa
Catui
CABO SAN
RAFAEL
Sabana de la Mar
CORDILLERA ORIENTAL
Samaná
Riva

Port Antonio

FORMIGAS
BANK

NAVASSA
(U.S.A.)

CAP DAME MARIE
Jérémie
ILE GRANDE
CAYEMITE
CAP DES IROIS
Tiburon
Pico de Macaya
1720
MASSIF DE LA HOTTE
Cateaux
Roche à Bateau
POINTE À GRAVOIS

Anse d'Hainault
Miragoâne
Les Cayes
ILE À VACHE

ILE DE LA
GONÂVE

POINT
OUEST
2548 △

Canal du Sud
Port-
au-Prince

△ 2285
Mirebalais
Lascahobas
San Juan
Pétionville
Pétit
Goave
Léogâne
Anse à Veau
Baie des Baradères

MASSIF DE LA
SELLE
△ 8/vd
Jacmel
Saltrou
Duvergé
Bánica

Azua
San Cristóbal
**Santo
Domingo**
PTA.
ESPADA
S. Pedro
de Macoris
La Romana
CATALINA
Bani
PTA. PALENQUE
SOANA
Mona Passage

SIERRA DE NEIBA
REPUBLIC
CORDILLERA CENTRAL
CIBAO
Mte. Mijo
△ 7434
Yamasá
Hato Mayor
Bayaguana
Los Llanos
Seibo
Higüey
CABO
ENGANO
Bahía de
Yuma

Bahoruco
Barahona
SIERRA DE
BAHORUCO
Neiba
CUL
DE
SAC

Enriquillo
Oviedo
L. Trijjl
Bahía de Neiba

CABO FALSO
BEATA
CABO
BEATA
ALTO VELO

MORANT PT.

HAITI

C   A   R   I   B   B   E   A   N   S   E   A

Windward Passage

HISPANIOLA

SOUTH AMERICA

ATLANTIC OCEAN

PACIFIC OCEAN

CARIBBEAN SEA

CENTRAL AMERICA

VENEZUELA

COLOMBIA

ECUADOR

PERU

BRAZIL

GUIANA

BOLIVIA

PARAGUAY

CHACO

ARGENTINA

CHILE

URUGUAY

PAMPAS

TIERRA DEL FUEGO

Drake Passage

Relief

Meters		Feet
3050		10 000
1525		5000
610		2000
305		1000
	Sea Level	0
152.5		500
1525		5000
3050		10 000
6100		20 000

Longitude West of Greenwich

Scale 1:40 000 000; one inch to 630 miles. Lambert's Azimuthal, Equal Area Projection
Elevations and depressions are given in feet

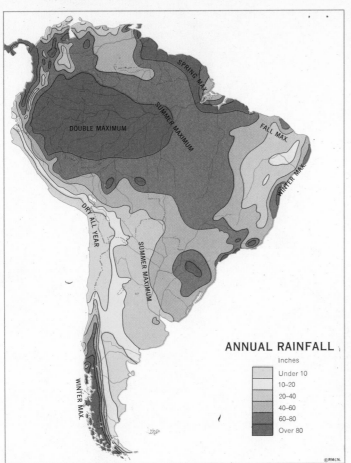

DOUBLE MAXIMUM

SPRING MAX.

SUMMER MAXIMUM

FALL MAX.

WINTER MAX.

DRY ALL YEAR

SUMMER MAXIMUM

WINTER MAX.

ANNUAL RAINFALL

Inches

Under 10
10–20
20–40
40–60
60–80
Over 80

©RMcN.

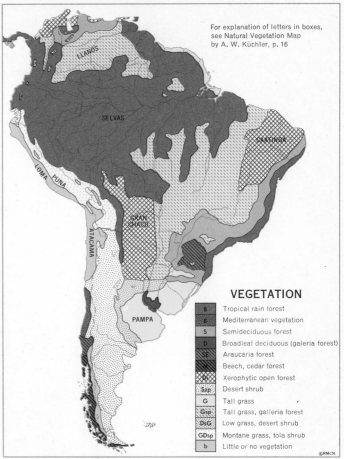

For explanation of letters in boxes,
see Natural Vegetation Map
by A. W. Küchler, p. 16

LLANOS

SELVAS

CAATINGA

LOMA

PUNA

ATACAMA

GRAN CHACO

PAMPA

VEGETATION

B	Tropical rain forest
B	Mediterranean vegetation
S	Semideciduous forest
D	Broadleaf deciduous (galeria forest)
SE	Araucaria forest
K	Beech, cedar forest
D:	Xerophytic open forest
Szp	Desert shrub
G	Tall grass
Gsp	Tall grass, galleria forest
DsG	Low grass, desert shrub
GDsp	Montane grass, tola shrub
b	Little or no vegetation

©RMcN.

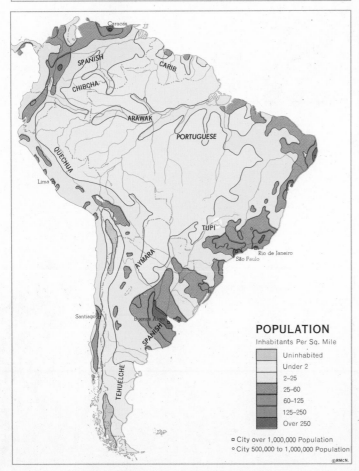

Caracas

SPANISH

CARIB

CHIBCHA

ARAWAK

PORTUGUESE

QUECHUA

Lima

TUPI

Rio de Janeiro
São Paulo

AYMARA

Santiago

Buenos Aires

SPANISH

TEHUELCHE

POPULATION

Inhabitants Per Sq. Mile

Uninhabited
Under 2
2–25
25–60
60–125
125–250
Over 250

□ City over 1,000,000 Population
○ City 500,000 to 1,000,000 Population

©RMcN.

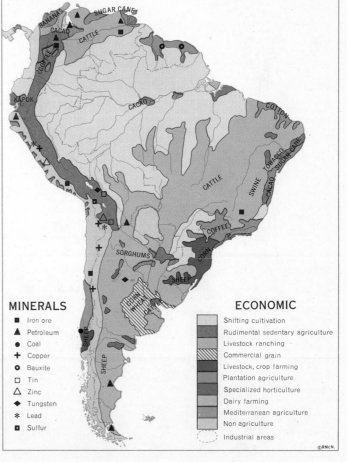

BANANAS
CACAO
SUGAR CANE
CATTLE
COFFEE

KAPOK

CACAO

COTTON

CATTLE

SWINE
TOBACCO
CACAO SUGAR CANE

COFFEE

SORGHUMS

CORN
WHEAT
CATTLE

CORN

SHEEP

SHEEP

SHEEP

MINERALS

■ Iron ore
▲ Petroleum
● Coal
+ Copper
○ Bauxite
□ Tin
△ Zinc
◆ Tungsten
✳ Lead
▣ Sulfur

ECONOMIC

Shifting cultivation
Rudimental sedentary agriculture
Livestock ranching
Commercial grain
Livestock, crop farming
Plantation agriculture
Specialized horticulture
Dairy farming
Mediterranean agriculture
Non agriculture

Industrial areas

©RMcN.

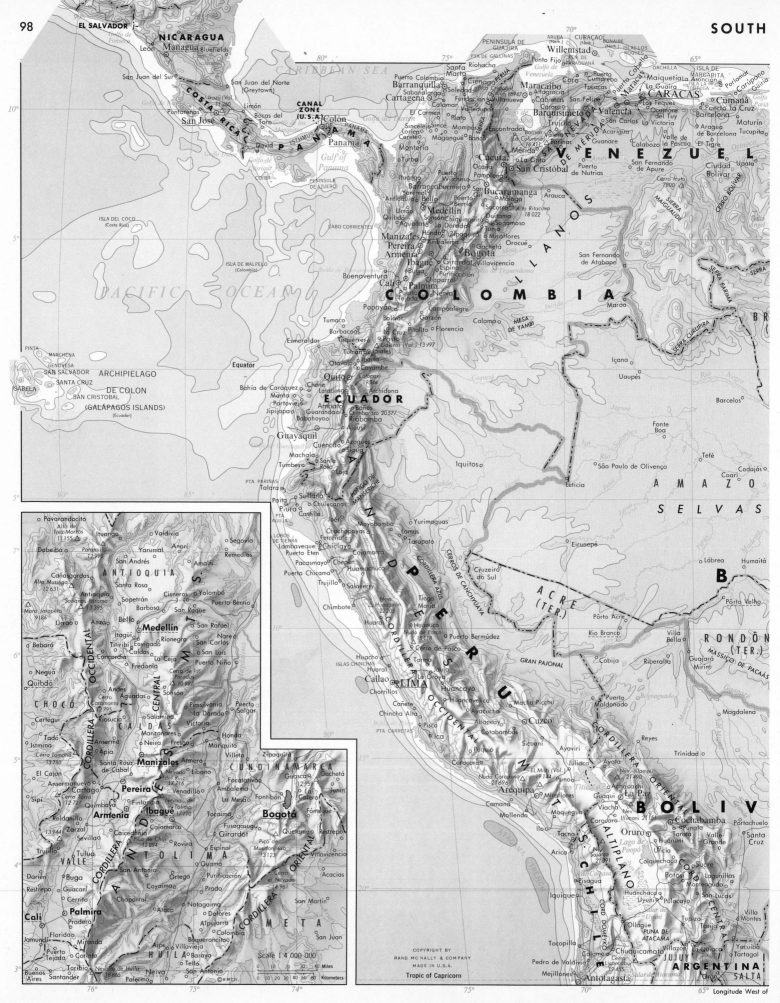

EL SALVADOR

NICARAGUA

CARIBBEAN SEA

PENINSULA DE GUAJIRA

ARUBA (Neth.) CURAÇAO (Neth.) BONAIRE (Neth.) ISLAS LOS ROQUES

70°

Willemstad

ORCHILLA

ISLA DE MARGARITA

Managua
León
Bluefields

PTA. DE GALLINAS

Santa Riohacha

Maiquetía La Guaira

Asunción Porlamar

Golfo de Fonseca

San Juan del Sur

Puerto Colombia
Barranquilla
Cartagena

Ciénaga
Santa Marta

Coro Cumarebo Puerto Cabello
Maracaibo

Cumaná
Carúpano

Guiria

San Juan del Norte (Greytown)

75°

Maracaibo

Curaçao

65°

San Juan del Sur

Limón

COSTA RICA

CANAL ZONE (U.S.A.)

Colón

Bocas del Toro

PANAMA

Panamá

Gulf of Panama

PENINSULA DE AZUERO

CABO CORRIENTES

ISLA DEL COCO (Costa Rica)

ISLA DE MALPELO (Colombia)

PACIFIC OCEAN

ARCHIPIELAGO DE COLON (GALAPAGOS ISLANDS) (Ecuador)

PINTA MARCHENA GENOVESA
SAN SALVADOR
SANTA CRUZ
SAN CRISTOBAL
ISABELA

Equator

COLOMBIA

ECUADOR

Quito

Guayaquil

VENEZUEL

CARACAS

Valencia

Barquisimeto

PERU

BOLIV

ARGENTINA

AMAZO SELVAS

Scale 1:16 000 000; one inch to 250 miles. Sinusoidal Projection
Elevations and depressions are given in feet

Scale 1:4 000 000

0 10 20 30 40 Miles
0 10 20 30 40 50 60 Kilometers

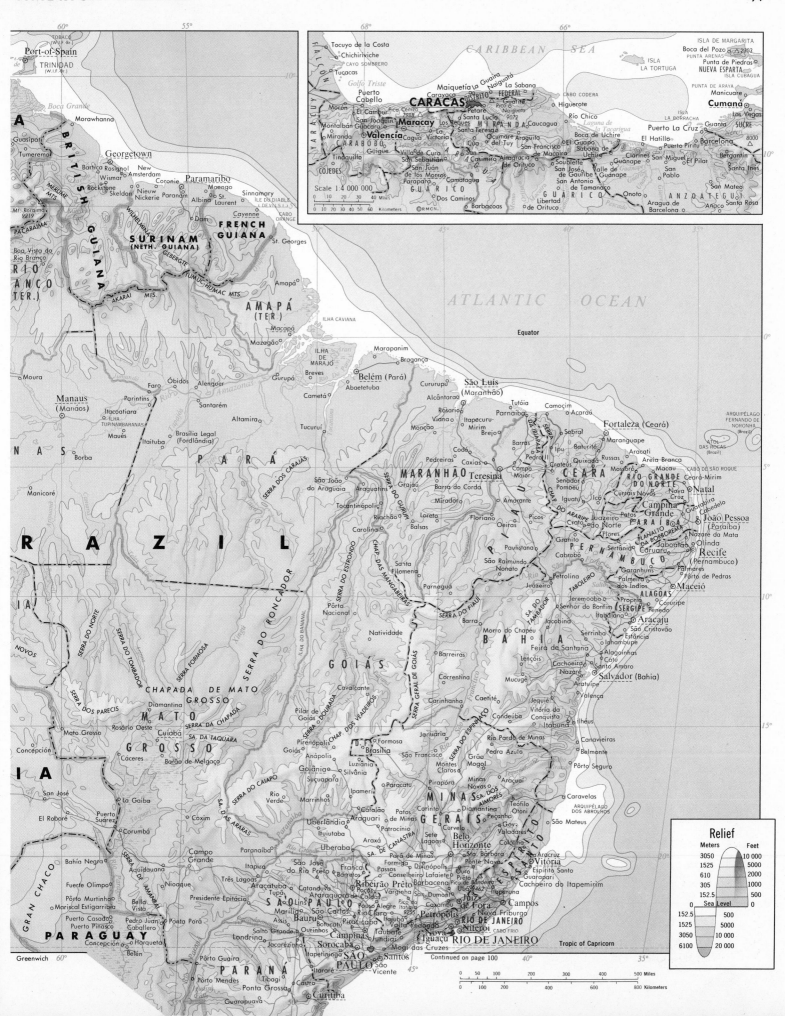

Continued on page 100

Relief

Meters		Feet
3050		10 000
1525		5000
610		2000
305		1000
152.5		500
0	Sea Level	0
152.5		500
1525		5000
3050		10 000
6100		20 000

CARACAS inset — Scale 1:4 000 000

| 0 | 10 | 20 | 30 | 40 Miles |
| 0 | 10 20 30 40 50 | 60 Kilometers |

©RMCN.

Scale bar (main map):
0 50 100 200 300 400 500 Miles
0 100 200 400 600 800 Kilometers

Continued on pages 98-99

BOLIVIA

PARAGUAY

CHACO

GRAN CHACO

EL CHACO

BRAZIL

MATO GROSSO

MINAS GERAIS

SÃO PAULO

PARANÁ

SANTA CATARINA

RIO GRANDE DO SUL

URUGUAY

ARGENTINA

CHILE

PATAGONIA

SANTA CRUZ

CHUBUT

RIO NEGRO

LA PAMPA

BUENOS AIRES

MENDOZA

SAN LUIS

CÓRDOBA

SANTA FE

ENTRE RÍOS

CORRIENTES

SANTIAGO DEL ESTERO

TUCUMÁN

CATAMARCA

LA RIOJA

SAN JUAN

JUJUY

SALTA

FORMOSA

MISIONES

PUNA DE ATACAMA

PACIFIC OCEAN

ATLANTIC OCEAN

Belo Horizonte
Rio de Janeiro
RIO DE JANEIRO
São Paulo
Santos
Curitiba
Pôrto Alegre
Asunción
Antofagasta
Santiago
Valparaíso
Viña del Mar
Córdoba
Rosario
Mendoza
San Juan
BUENOS AIRES
Montevideo
La Plata
Mar del Plata
Bahía Blanca
Neuquén
Comodoro Rivadavia
Golfo San Jorge
Golfo San Matías
PENÍNSULA VALDÉS
Río Gallegos
Punta Arenas
Estrecho de Magallanes
TIERRA DEL FUEGO
CABO DE HORNOS (CAPE HORN)
ISLA DE CHILOÉ
Puerto Montt
Valdivia
Temuco
Concepción
Talcahuano
Talca
ISLAS DIEGO RAMÍREZ

FALKLAND ISLANDS (Br.)
Port Stanley

BANCO BURDWOOD

ISLA DE LOS ESTADOS

BUENOS AIRES

Scale 1:1 000 000

Tigre
San Fernando
San Isidro
Olivos
Vicente López
General San Martín
Morón
San Justo
Lanús
Avellaneda
Quilmes
Lomas de Zamora
Bánfield
Adrogué
RIO DE LA PLATA

RIO DE JANEIRO

Scale 1:1 000 000

SERRA DAS ARARAS
Teresópolis
Petrópolis
Nova Iguaçu
Duque de Caxias
Niterói
RIO DE JANEIRO
Baía de Guanabara
GUANABARA
Copacabana
ATLANTIC OCEAN

Relief

Meters	Feet
3050	10 000
1525	5000
610	2000
305	1000
152.5	500
0 Sea Level	0
152.5	500 Below Sea Level
1525	5000
3050	10 000
6100	20 000

0 50 100 200 300 400 500 Miles
0 100 200 400 600 800 Kilometers

Longitude West of Greenwich

COPYRIGHT BY
RAND McNALLY & COMPANY
MADE IN U.S.A.

Scale 1:16 000 000; one inch to 250 miles. Sinusoidal Projection
Elevations and depressions are given in feet

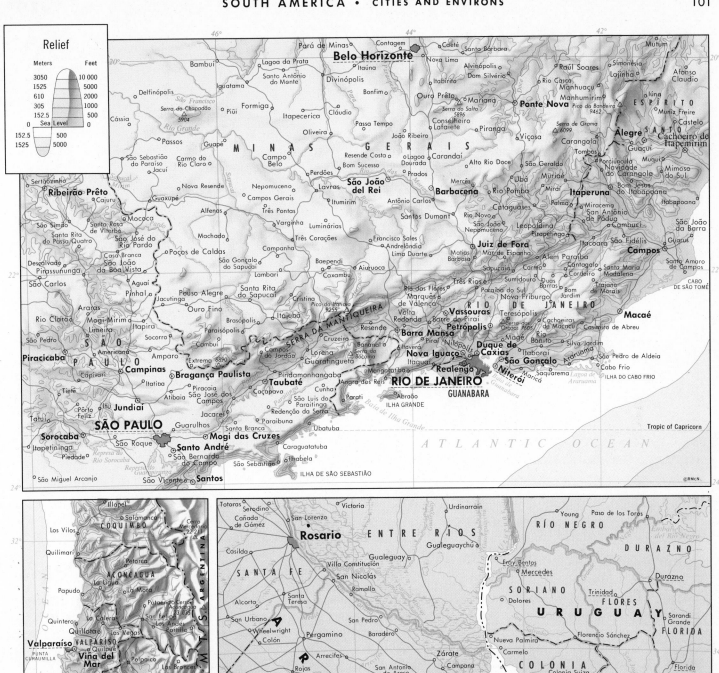

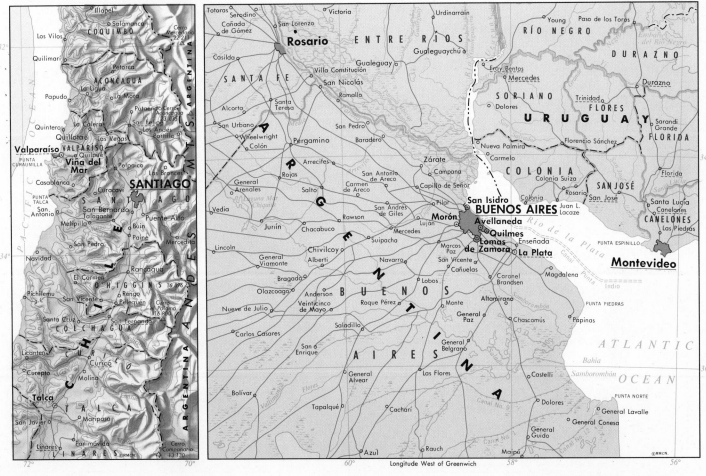

Scale 1:4 000 000; one inch to 64 miles.
Elevations and depressions are given in feet.

Relief

Meters	Feet
3050	10 000
1525	5000
610	2000
305	1000
152.5	500
0 Sea Level	0
152.5	500 Below
1525	5000 Sea Level
3050	10 000

Continued on pages 164-165

Scale 1: 16 000 000; one inch to 250 miles. Conic Projection

Elevations and depressions are given in feet

0	50	100	200	300	400	500 Miles

0	100	200	400	600	800 Kilometers

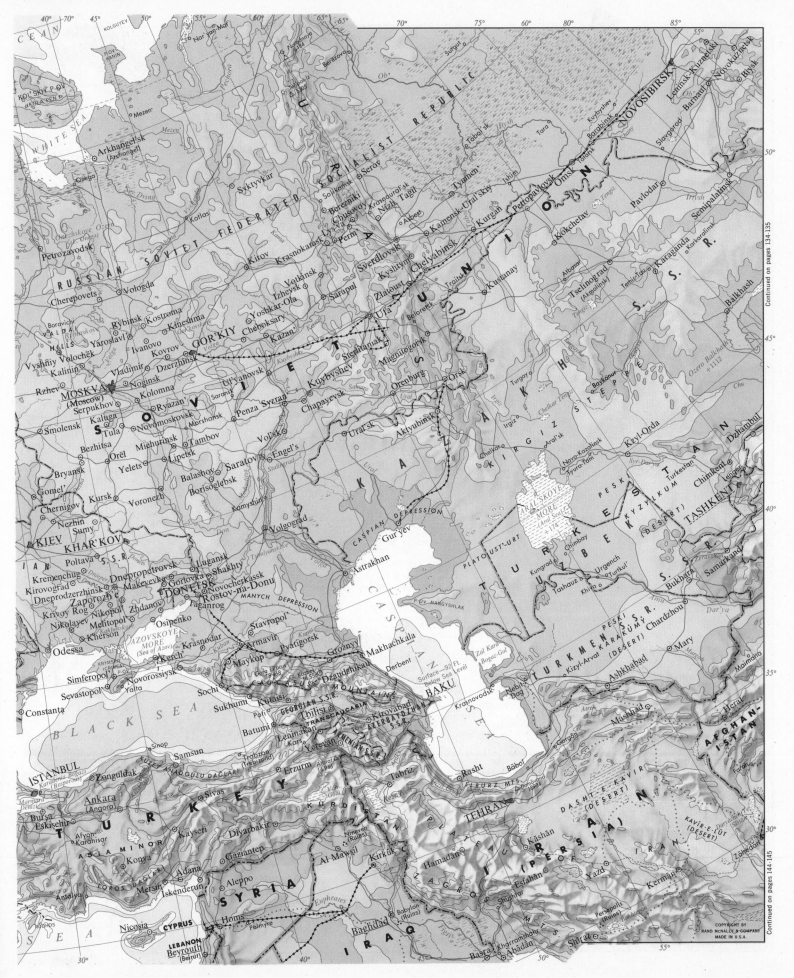

Continued on pages 134-135

Continued on pages 144-145

COPYRIGHT BY
RAND McNALLY & COMPANY
MADE IN U.S.A.

ATLANTIC OCEAN

ICELAND

NORTH SEA

ATLANTIC OCEAN

English Channel

Bay of Biscay

BALTIC SEA

Gulf of Bothnia

Gulf of Finland

LAPPLAND

Arctic Circle

Nord Cape

Murmansk

Limit of Glaciation

656 feet

MEDITERRANEAN

TYRRHENIAN SEA

ADRIATIC SEA

IONIAN SEA

CRETE

Scale 1:16 000 000; one inch to 250 miles. Conic Projection
Elevations and depressions are given in feet.

Longitude West of Greenwich   Longitude East of Greenwich

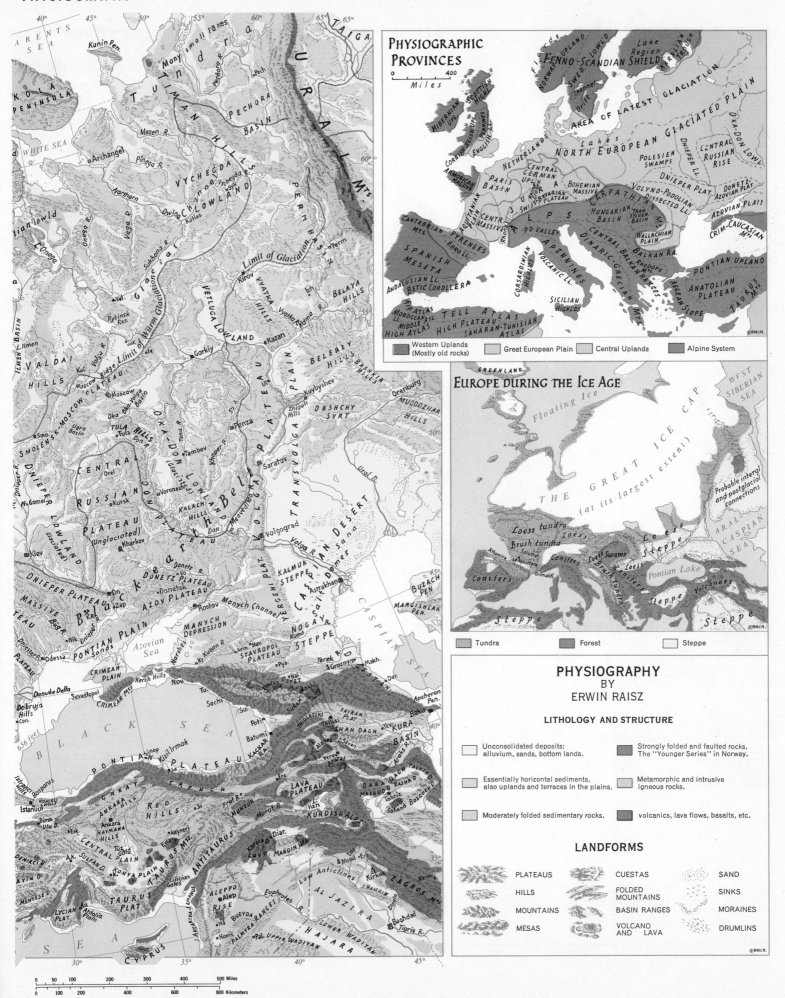

PHYSIOGRAPHIC PROVINCES

0   400
Miles

Western Uplands (Mostly old rocks)   Great European Plain   Central Uplands   Alpine System

EUROPE DURING THE ICE AGE

Tundra   Forest   Steppe

PHYSIOGRAPHY
BY
ERWIN RAISZ

LITHOLOGY AND STRUCTURE

Unconsolidated deposits: alluvium, sands, bottom lands.

Strongly folded and faulted rocks. The "Younger Series" in Norway.

Essentially horizontal sediments, also uplands and terraces in the plains.

Metamorphic and intrusive igneous rocks.

Moderately folded sedimentary rocks.

volcanics, lava flows, basalts, etc.

LANDFORMS

PLATEAUS   CUESTAS   SAND

HILLS   FOLDED MOUNTAINS   SINKS

MOUNTAINS   BASIN RANGES   MORAINES

MESAS   VOLCANO AND LAVA   DRUMLINS

COPYRIGHT BY
RAND MCNALLY & COMPANY
MADE IN U.S.A.

MAJOR LAND USES

- Cropland-wheat important
- Cropland-rye important
- Cropland-corn important
- Cropland-oats and barley important
- Cropland and pasture with some woodland
- Intensive grape culture for wine
- Mediterranean agriculture (including olives, grapes, grains and specialized vegetables)
- Oases and important cotton areas
- Chiefly pasture land (meadow, alpine pastures) with some cropland
- Sparse pasture land (heath, maquis, steppe)
- Sparse grass, desert shrub; seasonally grazed
- Tundra; seasonally grazed
- Forest and woodland
- Waste and unproductive areas

| 0 | 100 | 200 | 300 | 400 | 500 | 600 Miles |
| 0 | 200 | 400 | 600 | 800 | 1000 Kilometers |

Scale 1:20,000,000; one inch to 315 miles Conic Projection

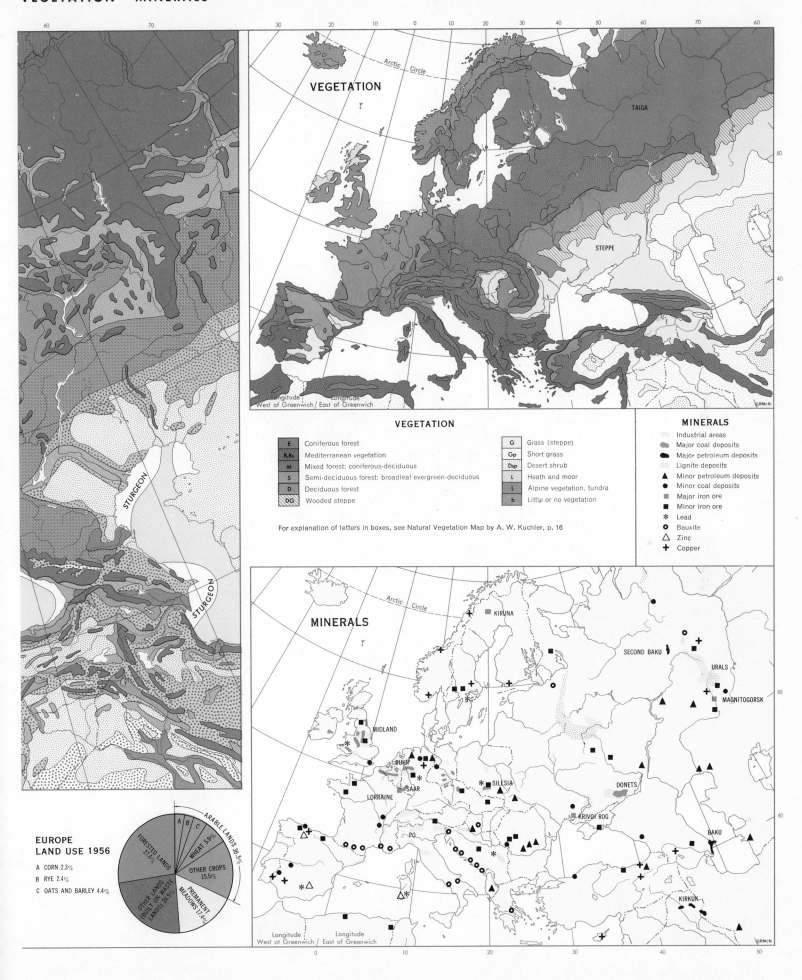

VEGETATION

MINERALS

VEGETATION

E	Coniferous forest
B, Bs	Mediterranean vegetation
M	Mixed forest: coniferous-deciduous
S	Semi-deciduous forest: broadleaf evergreen-deciduous
D	Deciduous forest
DG	Wooded steppe

G	Grass (steppe)
Gp	Short grass
Dsp	Desert shrub
L	Heath and moor
L	Alpine vegetation, tundra
b	Little or no vegetation

For explanation of letters in boxes, see Natural Vegetation Map by A. W. Kuchler, p. 16

MINERALS

Industrial areas
Major coal deposits
Major petroleum deposits
Lignite deposits
▲ Minor petroleum deposits
● Minor coal deposits
■ Major iron ore
■ Minor iron ore
✳ Lead
⊙ Bauxite
△ Zinc
+ Copper

EUROPE
LAND USE 1956

A CORN 2.3%
B RYE 2.4%
C OATS AND BARLEY 4.4%

ARABLE LANDS 30.5%
WHEAT 5.9%
OTHER CROPS 15.5%
FORESTED LANDS 27.6%
OTHER LANDS (BUILT ON WASTE LANDS) 24.5%
PERMANENT MEADOWS 17.4%

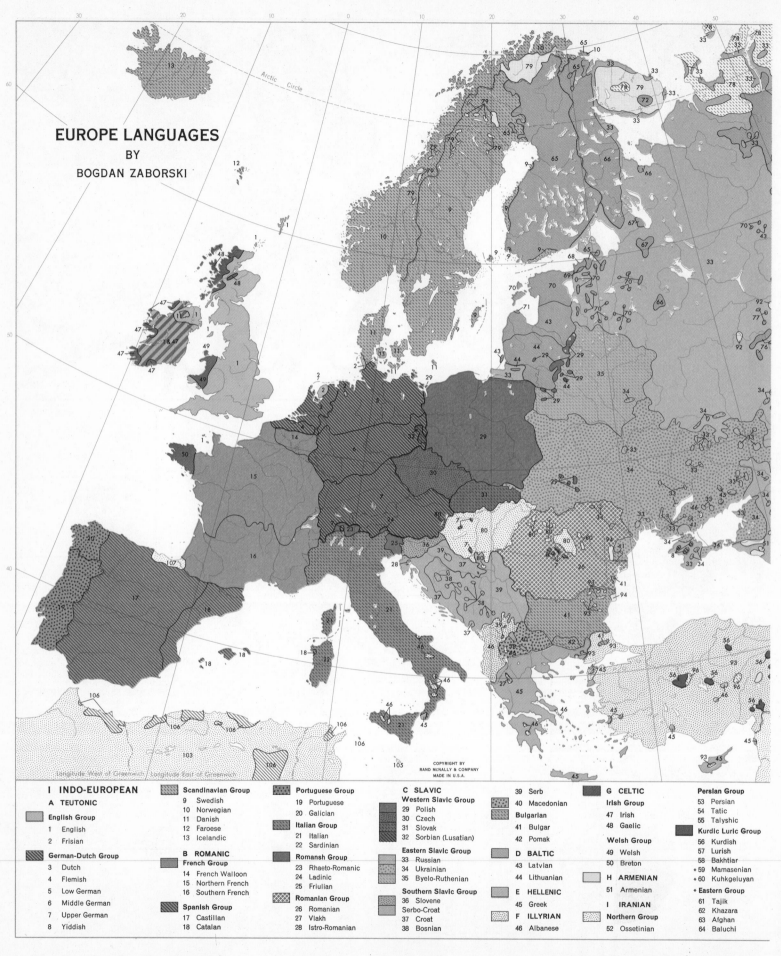

EUROPE LANGUAGES
BY
BOGDAN ZABORSKI

Arctic Circle

Longitude West of Greenwich | Longitude East of Greenwich

COPYRIGHT BY
RAND McNALLY & COMPANY
MADE IN U.S.A.

Scale 1:20,000,000; one inch to 315 miles Conic Projection

| 0 | 100 | 200 | 300 | 400 | 500 | 600 Miles |

| 0 | 200 | 400 | 600 | 800 | 1000 Kilometers |

I INDO-EUROPEAN

A TEUTONIC

English Group
1 English
2 Frisian

German-Dutch Group
3 Dutch
4 Flemish
5 Low German
6 Middle German
7 Upper German
8 Yiddish

Scandinavian Group
9 Swedish
10 Norwegian
11 Danish
12 Faroese
13 Icelandic

B ROMANIC

French Group
14 French Walloon
15 Northern French
16 Southern French

Spanish Group
17 Castilian
18 Catalan

Portuguese Group
19 Portuguese
20 Galician

Italian Group
21 Italian
22 Sardinian

Romansh Group
23 Rhaeto-Romanic
24 Ladinic
25 Friulian

Romanian Group
26 Romanian
27 Vlakh
28 Istro-Romanian

C SLAVIC

Western Slavic Group
29 Polish
30 Czech
31 Slovak
32 Sorbian (Lusatian)

Eastern Slavic Group
33 Russian
34 Ukrainian
35 Byelo-Ruthenian

Southern Slavic Group
36 Slovene
Serbo-Croat
37 Croat
38 Bosnian

39 Serb
40 Macedonian

Bulgarian
41 Bulgar
42 Pomak

D BALTIC
43 Latvian
44 Lithuanian

E HELLENIC
45 Greek

F ILLYRIAN
46 Albanese

G CELTIC

Irish Group
47 Irish
48 Gaelic

Welsh Group
49 Welsh
50 Breton

H ARMENIAN
51 Armenian

I IRANIAN

Northern Group
52 Ossetinian

Persian Group
53 Persian
54 Tatic
55 Talyshic

Kurdic Luric Group
56 Kurdish
57 Lurish
58 Bakhtiar
* 59 Mamasenian
* 60 Kuhkgeluyan

* **Eastern Group**
61 Tajik
62 Khazara
63 Afghan
64 Baluchi

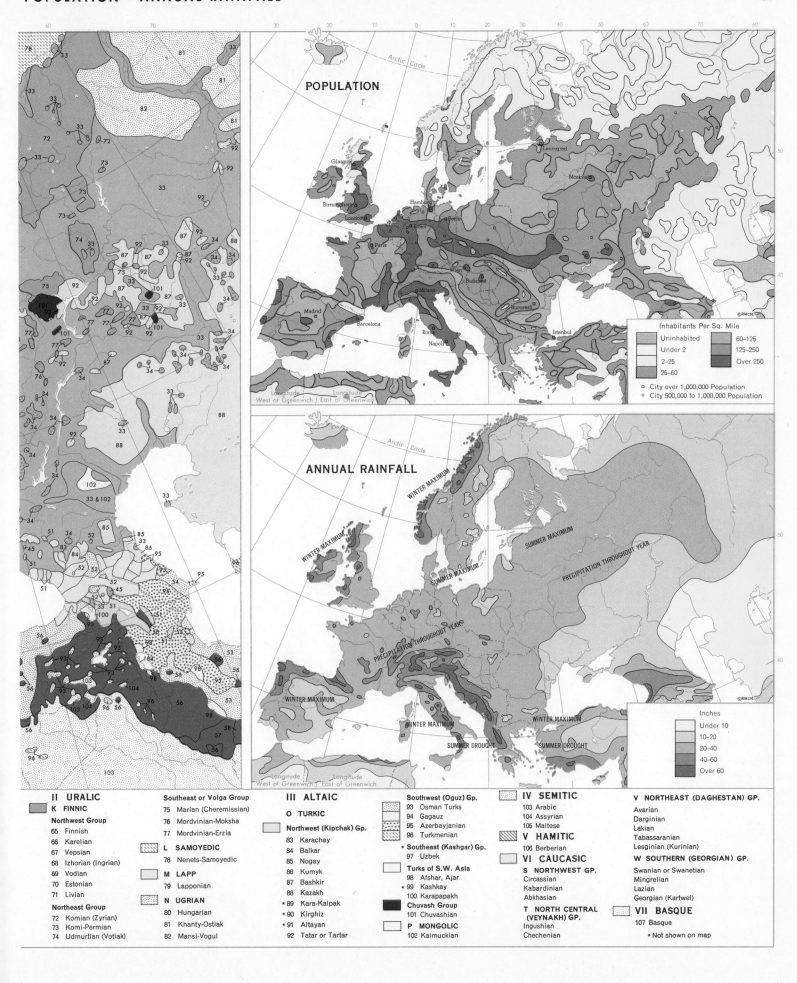

POPULATION

ANNUAL RAINFALL

Inhabitants Per Sq. Mile

Uninhabited	60–125
Under 2	125–250
2–25	Over 250
25–60	

□ City over 1,000,000 Population
○ City 500,000 to 1,000,000 Population

Inches

Under 10
10–20
20–40
40–60
Over 60

II URALIC
K FINNIC

Northwest Group
65 Finnish
66 Karelian
67 Vepsian
68 Izhorian (Ingrian)
69 Vodian
70 Estonian
71 Livian

Northeast Group
72 Komian (Zyrian)
73 Komi-Permian
74 Udmurtian (Votiak)

Southeast or Volga Group
75 Marian (Cheremissian)
76 Mordvinian-Moksha
77 Mordvinian-Erzia

L SAMOYEDIC
78 Nenets-Samoyedic

M LAPP
79 Lapponian

N UGRIAN
80 Hungarian
81 Khanty-Ostiak
82 Mansi-Vogul

III ALTAIC

O TURKIC

Northwest (Kipchak) Gp.
83 Karachay
84 Balkar
85 Nogay
86 Kumyk
87 Bashkir
88 Kazakh
* 89 Kara-Kalpak
* 90 Kirghiz
* 91 Altayan
92 Tatar or Tartar

Southwest (Oguz) Gp.
93 Osman Turks
94 Gagauz
95 Azerbayjanian
96 Turkmenian
* **Southeast (Kashgar) Gp.**
97 Uzbek

Turks of S.W. Asia
98 Afshar, Ajar
* 99 Kashkay
100 Karapapakh
Chuvash Group
101 Chuvashian

P MONGOLIC
102 Kalmuckian

IV SEMITIC
103 Arabic
104 Assyrian
105 Maltese

V HAMITIC
106 Berberian

VI CAUCASIC

S NORTHWEST GP.
Circassian
Kabardinian
Abkhasian

T NORTH CENTRAL (VEYNAKH) GP.
Ingushian
Chechenian

V NORTHEAST (DAGHESTAN) GP.
Avarian
Darginian
Lakian
Tabassaranian
Lesginian (Kurinian)

W SOUTHERN (GEORGIAN) GP.
Swanian or Swanetian
Mingrelian
Lazian
Georgian (Kartwel)

VII BASQUE
107 Basque

* Not shown on map

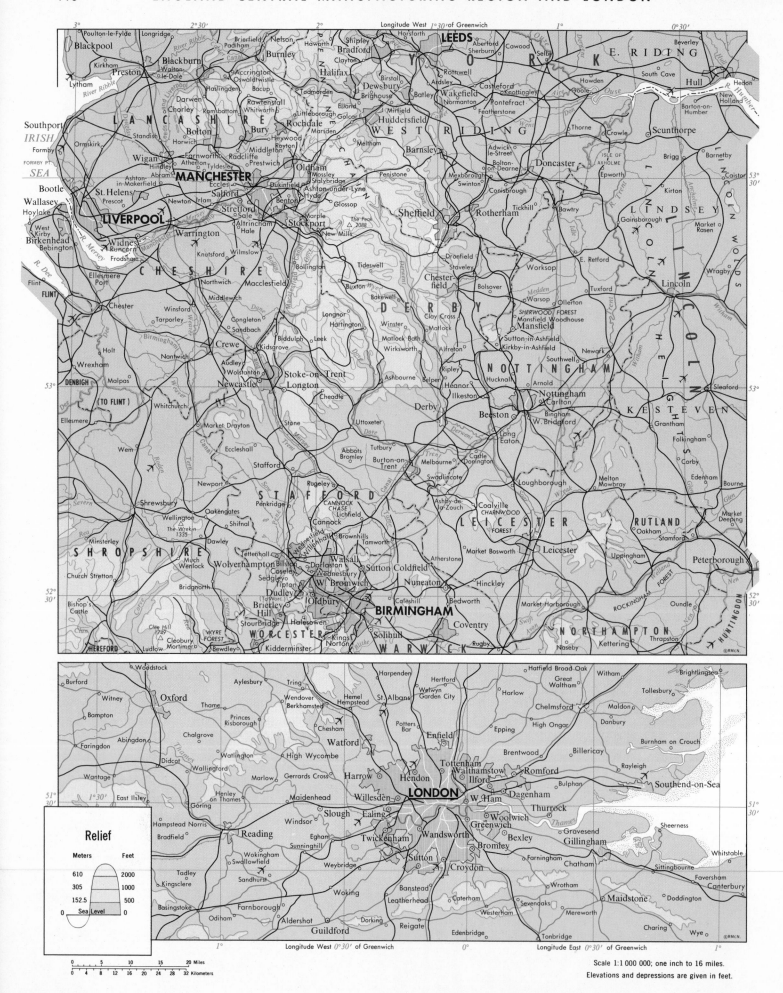

Relief

Meters	Feet
610	2000
305	1000
152.5	500
0	Sea Level	0

Scale 1:1 000 000; one inch to 16 miles.
Elevations and depressions are given in feet.

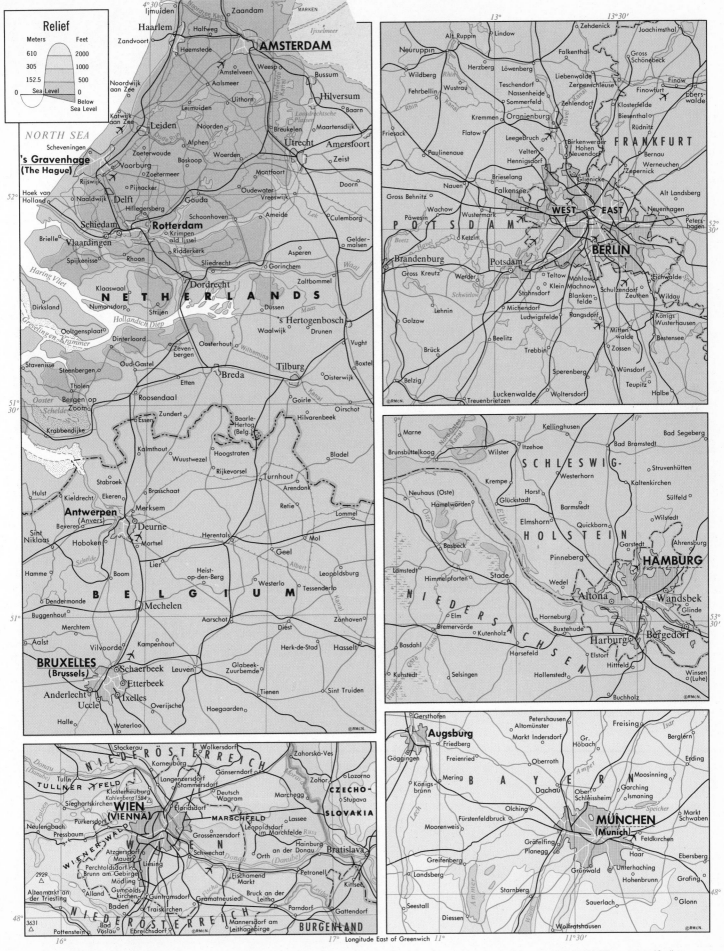

Relief

Meters	Feet
610	2000
305	1000
152.5	500
0 Sea Level	0 Below Sea Level

NORTH SEA

Ijmuiden
Haarlem
Zaandam
Zandvoort
Heemstede
Halfweg
MARKEN
AMSTERDAM
Ijsselmeer
Amstelveen
Weesp
Bussum
Noordwijk aan Zee
Aalsmeer
Uithorn
Hilversum
Baarn
Leimuiden
Noorden
Maartensdijk
Amersfoort
Katwijk aan Zee
Leiden
Alphen
Woerden
Breukelen
Utrecht
Scheveningen
Zoeterwoude
Boskoop
Zeist
's Gravenhage
(The Hague)
Voorburg
Zoetermeer
Montfoort
Doorn
Rijswijk
Pijnacker
Oudewater
Vreeswijk
Delft
Hillegersberg
Gouda
Ameide
Culemborg
Naaldwijk
Schoonhoven
Geldermalsen
Hoek van Holland
Schiedam
Rotterdam
Krimpen ald Ijssel
Sliedrecht
Gorinchem
Waal
Brielle
Vlaardingen
Ridderkerk
Asperen
Zaltbommel
Spijkenisse
Rhoon
Haring Vliet
Klaaswaal
Dordrecht
Maas
Dussen
's Hertogenbosch
Dirksland
Numansdorp
Strijen
NETHERLANDS
Oltgensplaat
Hollandsch Diep
Waalwijk
Drunen
Vught
Greveling en Krammer
Dinterloord
Oosterhout
Wilhemina
Boxtel
Stavenisse
Steenbergen
Oud-Gastel
Zevenbergen
Breda
Tilburg
Oisterwijk
Ooster Schelde
Bergen op Zoom
Roosendaal
Goirle
Oirschot
Krabbendijke
Zundert
Baarle-Hertog (Belg.)
Hilvarenbeek
Hulst
Essen
Kalmthout
Hoogstraten
Bladel
Kieldrecht
Wuustwezel
Stabroek
Rijkevorsel
Turnhout
Arendonk
Lommel
Sint Niklaas
Beveren
Ekeren
Brasschaat
Retie
Antwerpen
(Anvers)
Merksem
Deurne
Herentals
Mol
Hoboken
Mortsel
Geel
Hamme
Lier
Boom
Heist-op-den-Berg
Westerlo
Leopoldsburg
Dendermonde
BELGIUM
Tessenderlo
Mechelen
Zonhoven
Buggenhout
Aarschot
Diest
Hasselt
Merchtem
Kampenhout
Herk-de-Stad
Aalst
Vilvoorde
Leuven
Glabeek-Zuurbemde
Sint Truiden
BRUXELLES
(Brussels)
Schaerbeek
Tienen
Anderlecht
Etterbeek
Ixelles
Overijische
Uccle
Hoegaarden
Halle
Waterloo

NIEDERÖSTERREICH
Stockerau
Wolkersdorf
Zahorska-Ves
Tulln
Korneuburg
Langenzersdorf
Gänserndorf
Lozorno
Donau (Danube)
TULLNER FELD
Klosterneuburg
Kahlenberg 1584
Stammersdorf
Deutsch Wagram
Marchegg
CZECHO-SLOVAKIA
Sieghartskirchen
Floridsdorf
Zohor
Stupava
Neulengbach
WIEN
(VIENNA)
Lassee
Purkersdorf
MARCHFELD
Pressbaum
Grossenzersdorf
Leopoldsdorf im Marchfelde
Russ
Neulengbach
WIENERWALD
WIEN
Bratislava
Atzgersdorf
Mauer
Schwechat
Petronell
2929
Perchtoldsdorf
Liesing
Fischamend Markt
Orth an der Donau (Danube)
Kittsee
Altenmarkt an der Triesting
Brunn am Gebirge
Mödling
Gumpoldskirchen
Guntramsdorf
Bruck an der Leitha
Gattendorf
3631
Alland
Baden
Traiskirchen
Gramatneusiedl
Parndorf
Pottenstein
Bad Vöslau
Ebreichsdorf
Mannersdorf am Leithagebirge
BURGENLAND
NIEDERÖSTERREICH

FRANKFURT
Alt Ruppin
Lindow
Zehdenick
Joachimsthal
Neuruppin
Herzberg
Löwenberg
Falkenthal
Gross Schönebeck
Wildberg
Wustrau
Teschendorf
Liebenwalde
Finow
Fehrbellin
Nassenheide
Zerpenschleuse
Finowfurt
Eberswalde
Rhin
Sommerfeld
Zehlendorf
Klosterfelde
Biesenthal
Rüdnitz
Friesack
Kremmen
Oranienburg
Leegebruch
Birkenwerder
Bernau
Werneuchen
Flatow
Velten
Hohen Neuendorf
Zepernick
Paulinenaue
Hennigsdorf
Brieselang
Glienicke
Alt Landsberg
Gross Behnitz
Nauen
WEST **EAST**
Neuenhagen
Päwesin
Wachow
Wustermark
Falkensee
POTSDAM
Beetz
BERLIN
Peters-hagen
Brandenburg
Ketzin
Havel
Teltow
Mahlow
Eichwalde
Gross Kreutz
Werder
Potsdam
Stahnsdorf
Klein Machnow
Schulzendorf
Zeuthen
Wildau
Schwielow
Blankenfelde
Golzow
Michendorf
Rangsdorf
Königs Wusterhausen
Lehnin
Ludwigsfelde
Mitten-walde
Bestensee
Brück
Beelitz
Trebbin
Zossen
Sperenberg
Wünsdorf
Teupitz
Belzig
Luckenwalde
Woltersdorf
Halbe
Treuenbrietzen

SCHLESWIG-HOLSTEIN
Marne
Kellinghusen
Bad Segeberg
Brunsbüttelkoog
Wilster
Itzehoe
Bad Bramstedt
Struvenhütten
Neuhaus (Oste)
Krempe
Horst
Westerhorn
Kaltenkirchen
Sülfeld
Hamelwörden
Glückstadt
Barmstedt
Quickborn
Wilstedt
Basbeck
Elmshorn
Garstedt
Ahrensburg
Lamstedt
Pinneberg
HAMBURG
Himmelpforten
Stade
Wedel
Wandsbek
NIEDERSACHSEN
Elm
Altona
Glinde
Bremervörde
Horneburg
Kutenholz
Buxtehude
Harburg
Bergedorf
Basdahl
Harsefeld
Elstorf
Hittfeld
Kuhstedt
Selsingen
Hollenstedt
Winsen (Luhe)
Buchholz

Gersthofen
Petershausen
Freising
Augsburg
Altomünster
Isar
Göggingen
Friedberg
Markt Indersdorf
Gr. Höbach
Berglern
Königs-brunn
Freienried
Oberroth
BAYERN
Mering
Moosinning
Erding
Dachau
Ober Schleissheim
Garching
Ismaning
Olching
Speicher
Moorenweis
Fürstenfeldbruck
MÜNCHEN
(Munich)
Markt Schwaben
Landsberg
Greifenberg
Gräfelfing
Planegg
Haar
Feldkirchen
Grünwald
Unterhaching
Ebersberg
Starnberg
Hohenbrunn
Grafing
Seestall
Sauerlach
Glonn
Diessen
Wolfratshausen

0   5   10   15   20 Miles
0 4 8 12 16 20 24 28 32 Kilometers

Scale 1:1 000 000; one inch to 16 miles.
Elevations and depressions are given in feet.

Longitude East of Greenwich

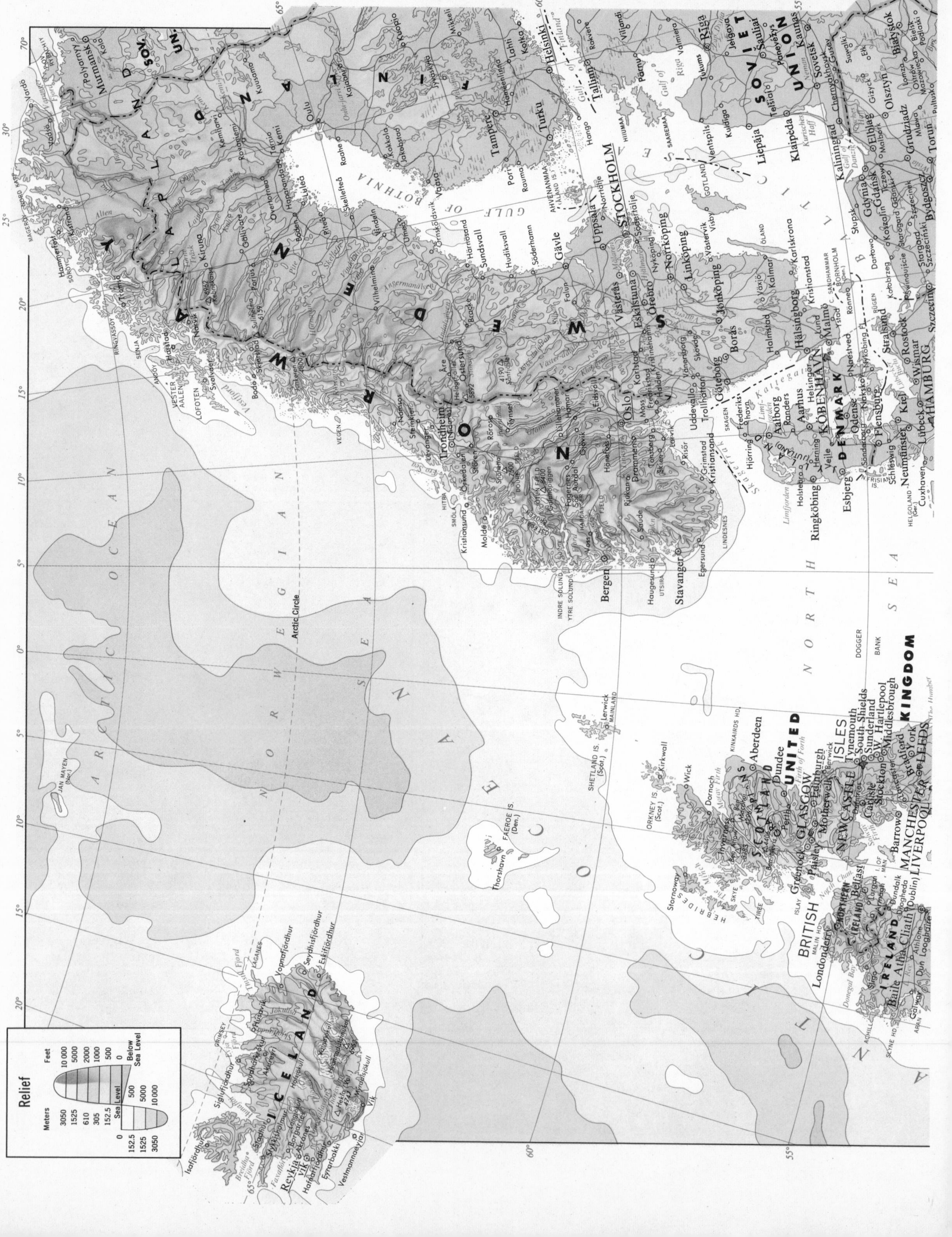

SOVIET UNION

FINLAND

SWEDEN

NORWAY

DENMARK

ICELAND

BRITISH ISLES

UNITED KINGDOM

SCOTLAND

IRELAND

ARCTIC OCEAN

NORWEGIAN SEA

NORTH SEA

GULF OF BOTHNIA

BALTIC SEA

Murmansk · Polyarnyy · Kirkenes · Vardö · Vadsö · Hammerfest

Helsinki · Tampere · Turku · Oulu · Kemi

STOCKHOLM · Uppsala · Gävle · Örebro · Norrköping · Linköping · Jönköping · Göteborg · Borås · Halmstad · Hälsingborg · Malmö

Oslo · Trondheim · Bergen · Stavanger · Kristiansand · Drammen · Hamar · Lillehammer

KÖBENHAVN · Aarhus · Aalborg · Odense · Esbjerg · Randers

Riga · Tallinn · Kaliningrad · Gdansk · Gdynia · Klaipeda · Liepaja · Ventspils

HAMBURG · Lübeck · Kiel · Rostock · Flensburg

GLASGOW · Edinburgh · Aberdeen · Dundee · NEWCASTLE · Sunderland · Middlesbrough · LEEDS · LIVERPOOL · MANCHESTER · Bradford

Dublin · Belfast · Londonderry · Baile Átha Cliath

Reykjavík · Vík · Akureyri

Shetland Is. · Orkney Is. · Hebrides · Faeroe Is. · Jan Mayen

Arctic Circle

113

Scale 1: 10 000 000; one inch to 160 miles. Conic Projection

Elevations and depressions are given in feet

COPYRIGHT BY
RAND M^cNALLY & COMPANY
MADE IN U.S.A.

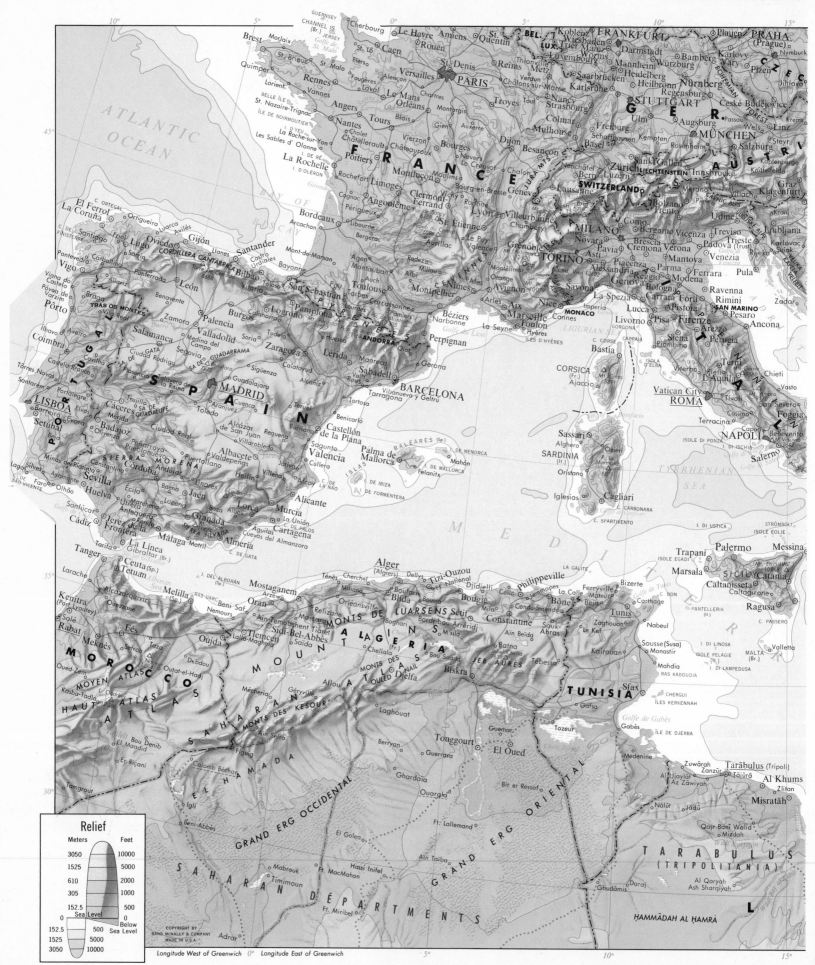

Relief

Meters	Feet
3050	10000
1525	5000
610	2000
305	1000
152.5	500
0 Sea Level	0 Below Sea Level
152.5	500
1525	5000
3050	10000

COPYRIGHT BY
RAND McNALLY & COMPANY
MADE IN U.S.A.

Longitude West of Greenwich 0° Longitude East of Greenwich

Scale 1: 10 000 000; one inch to 160 miles. Bonne's Projection
Elevations and depressions are given in feet

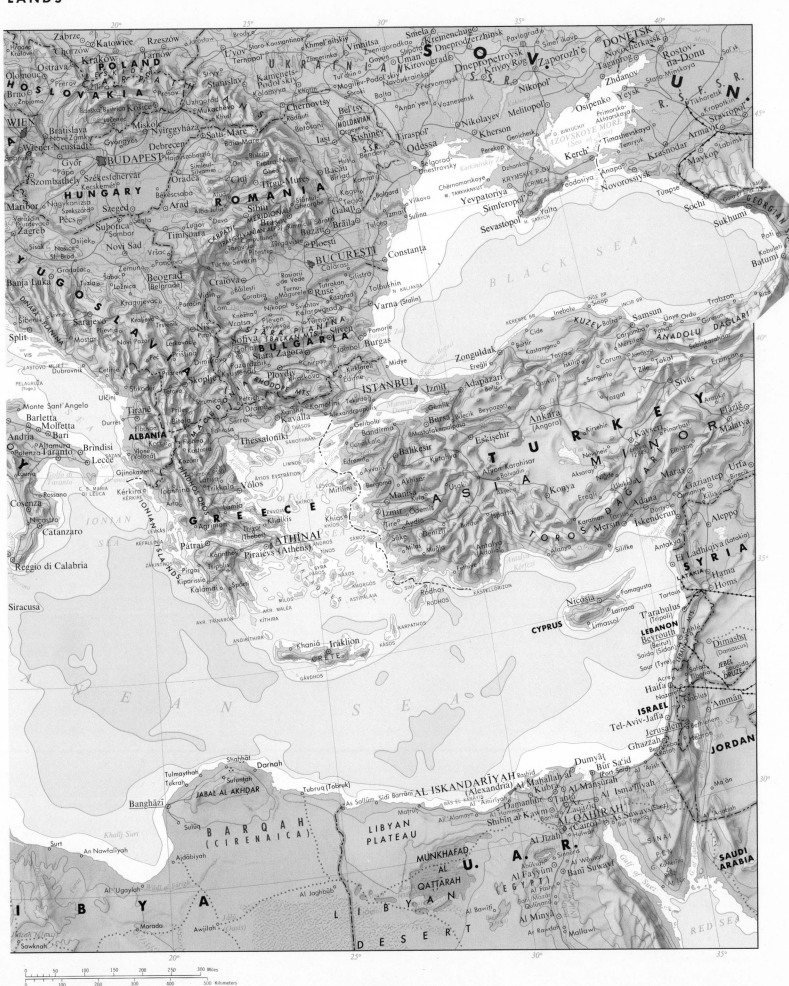

Scale 1: 4 000 000; one inch to 64 miles. Conic Projection
Elevations and depressions are given in feet

0 10 20 30 40 50 60 70 80 90 100 110 120 Miles

0 20 40 60 80 100 120 140 160 180 200 Kilometers

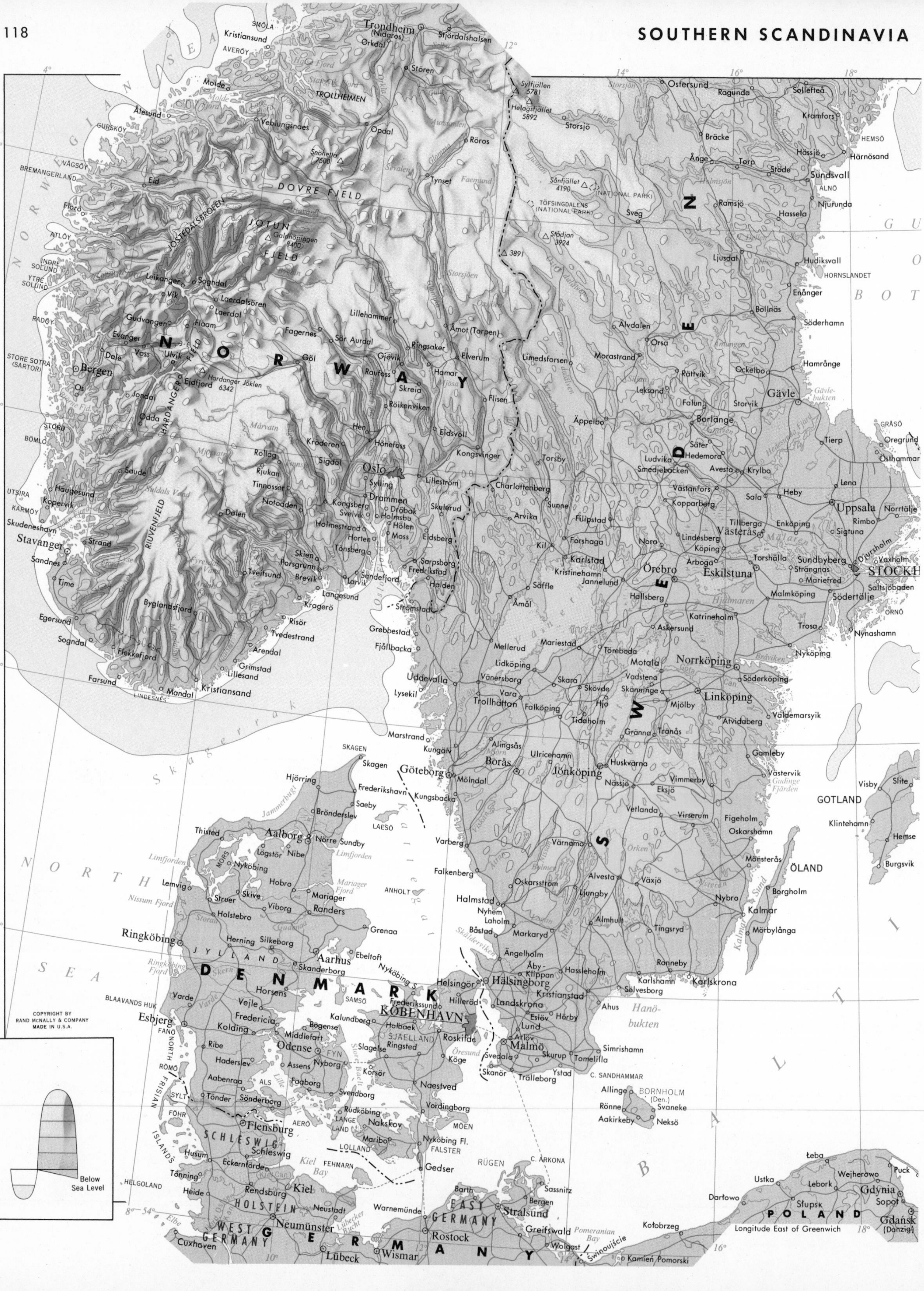

NORWEGIAN SEA

SMÖLA
Kristiansund
Averöy
Trondheim (Nidaros)
Orkdal
Stjördalshalsen
Sylfjällen 5781
Östersund
Ragunda
Sollefteå
Kramfors
Hässjö
Härnösand
HEMSÖ

Molde
Haramöy
Molde Fjord
Stören
Helagsfjället 5892
Storsjö
Bräcke
Torp
Stöde
Sundsvall
ALNÖ
Njurunda

Ålesund
Gursköy
Veblungsnaes
Opdal
Röros
Sånfjället 4190 (NATIONAL PARK)
Svég
Ramsjö
Hassela

Snöhetta 7500
DOVRE FJELD
Tynset
Töfsingdalens (NATIONAL PARK)
Stödjan 3924
Morastrand
Änge

Eid
Floro
JOSTEDALSBROEN
Faemund
3391
Ljusdal
Hudiksvall
HORNSLANDET
Enånger
Bollnäs
Söderhamn

Gudvangen
JOTUN FJELD
Galdhöpiggen 8400
Lillehammer
Sör Aurdal
Åmot (Torpen)
Älvdalen
Orsa
Rättvik
Hamrånge

BREMANGERLAND
VÅGSÖY
ATLÖY
INDRE SOLUND
YTRE SOLUND

Leikanger
Soghdal
Vik
Laerdalsören
Laerdal
Flaam
Fagernes
Gjövik
Ringsaker
Elverum
Limedsforsen
Äppelbo
Ockelbo

NORWAY
Evanger
Dale
Voss
Ulvik
Hardanger Fjord
Eidfjord
Hardanger Jöklen 6342
Göl
Raufoss
Hamar
Skreia
Flisen
Leksand
Falun
Storvik
Gävle
Gävlebukten

Bergen
STORE SOTRA (SARTOR)
Os
Jondal
Odda
Röikenviken
Hönefoss
Torsby
Ludvika
Smedjebäcken
Borlänge
Säter
Hedemora
Tierp
Oregrund
Östhammar
GRÅSÖ

RADÖY
Márvatn
Kröderen
Hen
Eidsvoll
Kongsvinger
Charlottenberg
Västanfors
Avesta
Krylbo
Lena

BÖMLÖ
Rollag
Sigdal
Oslo
Sylling
Lilleström
Arvika
Sunne
Kopparberg
Sala
Heby
Uppsala
Norrtälje
Rimbo

UTSIRA
KARMÖY
Saude
Tinnosset
Rjukan
Notodden
Kongsberg
Svelvik
Drammen
Dröbak
Skulerud
Filipstad
Forshaga
Noro
Lindesberg
Köping
Tillberga
Enköping
Sigtuna

Haugesund
Kopervik
Dalen
Holmestrand
Horten
Moss
Eidsberg
Kil
Karlstad
Örebro
Arboga
Torshälla
Västerås
Sundbyberg
Djursholm
Vaxholm
STOCKHOLM

Skudeneshavn
Strand
Skien
Porsgrunn
Brevik
Tönsberg
Sarpsborg
Fredrikstad
Halden
Säffle
Kristinehamn
Jannelund
Hallsberg
SWEDEN
Eskilstuna
Strängnäs
Mariefred
Saltsjöbaden
ORNÖ

Stavanger
Sandnes
Time
Tveitsund
Larvik
Sandefjord
Åmål
Askersund
Katrineholm
Malmköping
Södertälje
Trosa
Nynäshamn

Egersund
Byglandsfjord
Risör
Grebbestad
Fjällbacka
Strömstad
Mellerud
Mariestad
Töreboda
Motala
Norrköping
Söderköping
Nyköping

Sogndal
Flekkefjord
Tvedestrand
Arendal
Uddevalla
Lidköping
Vänersborg
Skara
Skövde
Skänninge
Vadstena
Bråviken

Farsund
Mandal
Grimstad
Lillesand
Kristiansand
LINDESNES
Lysekil
Vara
Trollhättan
Falköping
Hjo
Tidaholm
Gränna
Tranås
Mjölby
Linköping
Åtvidaberg
Valdemarsvik

SKAGERRAK
Marstrand
Kungälv
Alingsås
Ulricehamn
Huskvarna
Vimmerby
Gamleby
Västervik

SKAGEN
Skagen
Göteborg
Mölndal
Borås
Jönköping
Nässjö
Eksjö
Figeholm
GOTLAND
Visby
Slite

Hjörring
Frederikshavn
Saeby
Kungsbacka
LAESÖ
Varberg
Vetlanda
Virserum
Oskarshamn
Klintehamn
Hemse

Thisted
Aalborg
Norre Sundby
Nörre Sundby
Falkenberg
Värnamo
Alvesta
Mönsterås
ÖLAND
Burgsvik

NORTH SEA
Lemvig
Struer
Skive
Nykøbing
Hobro
Nibe
Logstör
Limfjorden
Mariager Fjord
ANHOLT
Oskarsström
Ljungby
Växjö
Nybro
Borgholm

Ringkøbing
Holstebro
Viborg
Mariager
Randers
Grenaa
Halmstad
Nyhem
Laholm
Almhult
Tingsryd
Mörbylånga
Kalmar

JYLLAND
Herning
Silkeborg
Aarhus
Ebeltoft
Nyköbing
Båstad
Markaryd
Ronneby

DENMARK
Varde
Vejle
Horsens
Skanderborg
Ängelholm
Åby
Klippan
Hässleholm
Karlshamn
Karlskrona

Esbjerg
Kolding
Fredericia
Middelfart
Bogense
Helsingör
Hälsingborg
Kristianstad
Sölvesborg
Ahus

BLAAVANDS HUK
FANÖ
Ribe
Haderslev
Odense
FYN
Kalundborg
Holbaek
Frederikssund
Hillerød
Landskrona
Lund
Härby
Hanöbukten

RÖMÖ
SYLT
Aabenraa
Assens
Nyborg
Slagelse
Ringsted
København
Roskilde
Eslöv
Arlöv
Malmö
Simrishamn

FÖHR
Tönder
Sönderborg
ALS
Faaborg
Korsör
SJAELLAND
Köge
Skanör
Svedala
Skurup
Tomelilla
BORNHOLM (Den.)
Alinge
Svaneke

Husum
Flensburg
AERÖ
Rudkøbing
LANGE
Nakskov
Naestved
Vordingborg
MÖEN
Trälleborg
Ystad
C. Sandhammar
Rönne
Neksö
Aakirkeby

SCHLESWIG
Schleswig
Kiel Bay
LOLLAND
Maribo
Nyköbing Fl. FALSTER
Gedser
RÜGEN
C. Arkona
Sassnitz
Bergen
Leba
Puck
Gdynia

HOLSTEIN
Rendsburg
Kiel
Neustadt
FEHMARN
Lübeck
Warnemünde
Barth
Stralsund
Greifswald
Wolgast
Ustka
Darłowo
Słupsk
Lebork
Wejherowo
Sopot

WEST GERMANY
Neumünster
Heide
Tönning
Cuxhaven
Elbe
Lübecker Bucht
EAST GERMANY
Rostock
Wismar
Pomeranian Bay
Świnoujście
Kamień Pomorski
Kołobrzeg
POLAND
Gdańsk (Danzig)

Longitude East of Greenwich

Below Sea Level

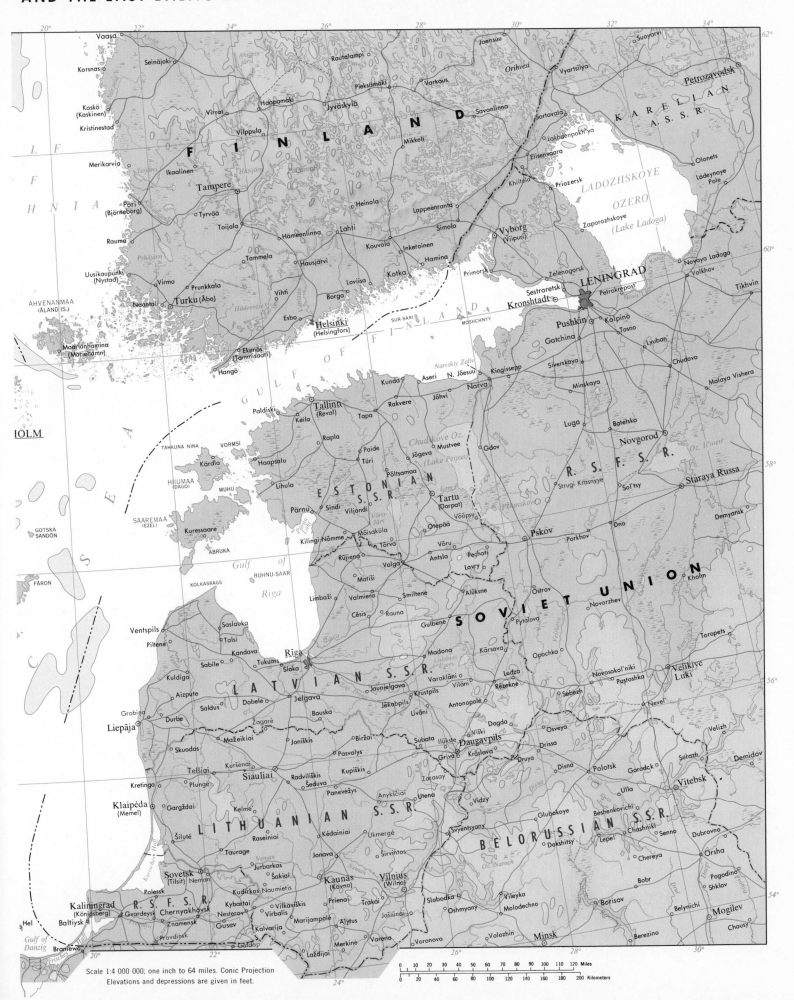

Continued on pp. 122-123

Continued on pp. 126 127

Longitude East of Greenwich

Scale 1:4 000 000; one inch to 64 miles. Conic Projection
Elevations and depressions are given in feet.

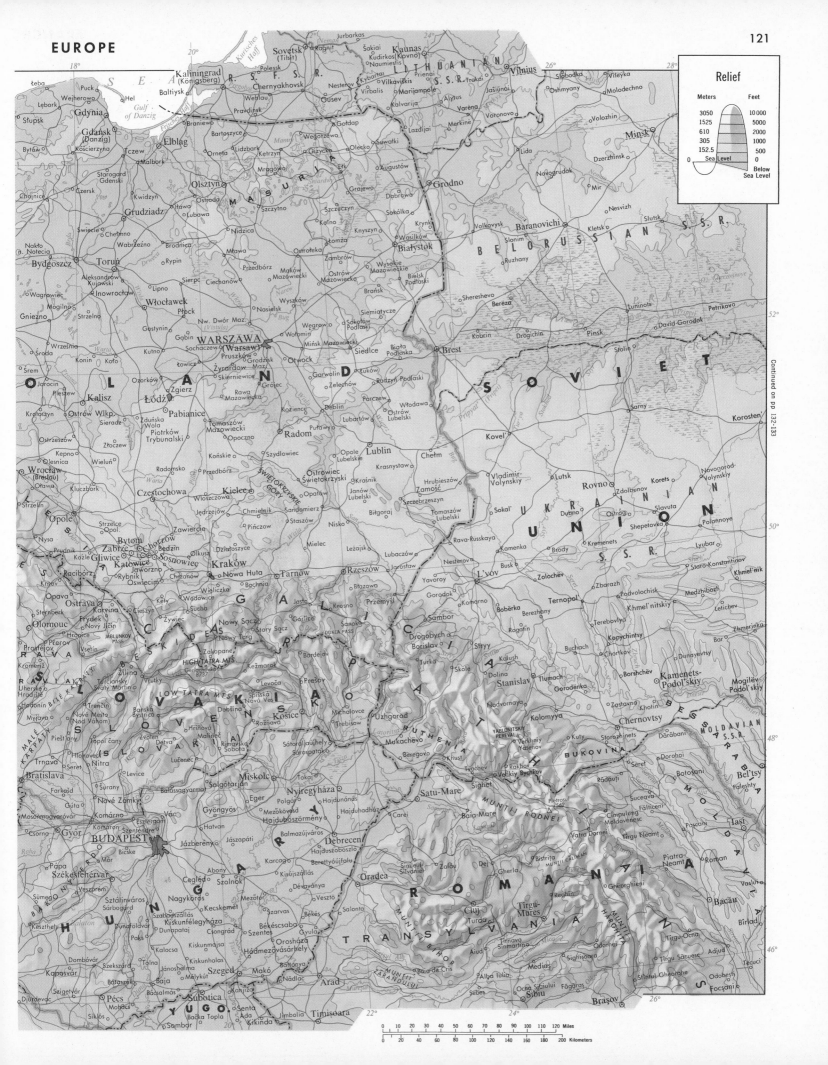

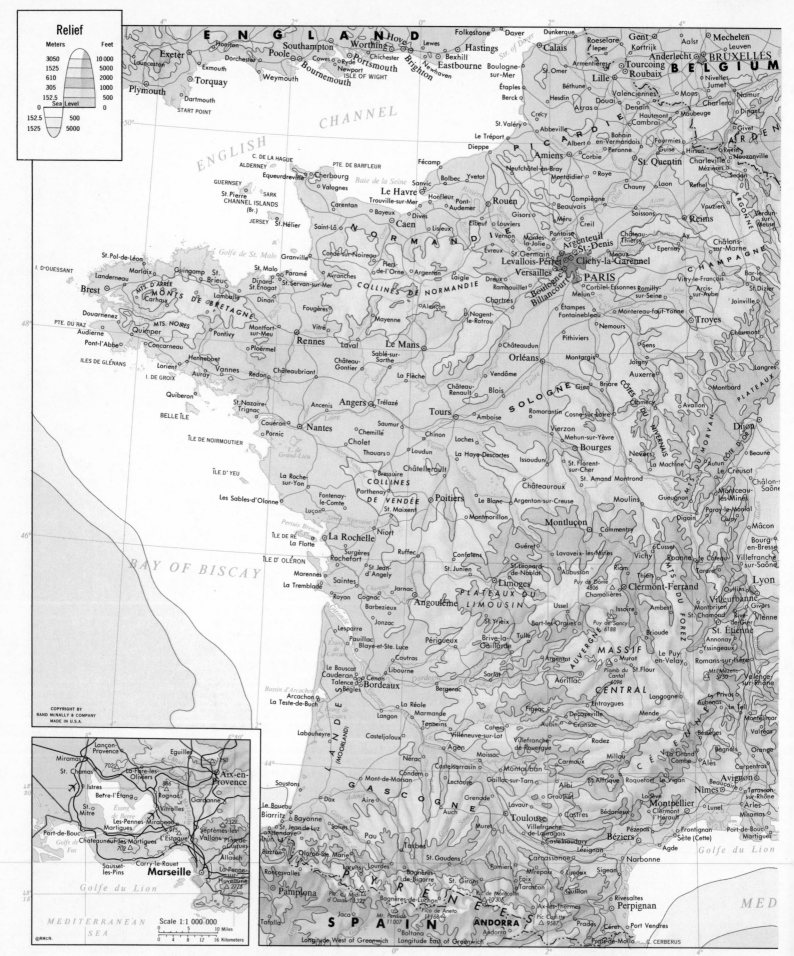

Relief

Meters	Feet
3050	10 000
1525	5000
610	2000
305	1000
152.5	500
0 Sea Level	0
152.5	500
1525	5000

COPYRIGHT BY
RAND McNALLY & COMPANY
MADE IN U.S.A.

Scale 1:1 000 000

Scale 1:4 000 000; one inch to 64 miles. Conic Projection
Elevations and depressions are given in feet

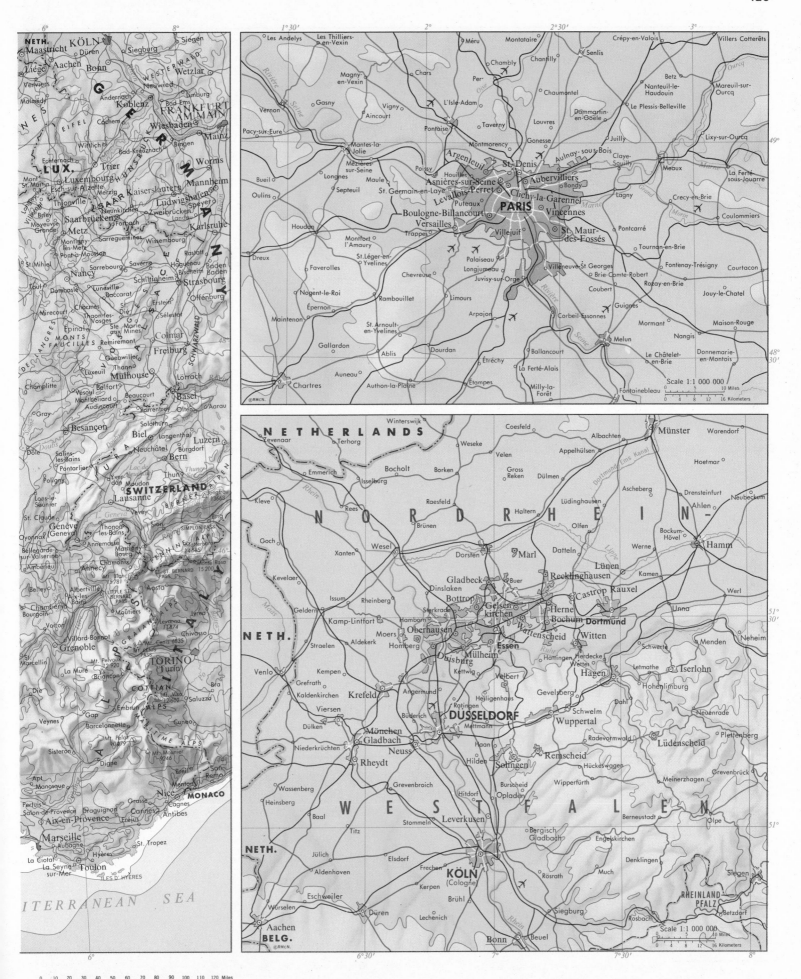

Map 1 (upper left — France/Germany/Switzerland/Italy):

NETH.
KÖLN
Maastricht
Düren
Siegburg
o Siegen
Liège
Aachen
Bonn
Wetzlar
Malmédy
Andernach
Neuwied
Verviers
WESTERWALD
Limburg
Koblenz
FRANKFURT AM MAIN
EIFEL
Cochem
Wiesbaden
Witlich
Bingen
Mainz
Bad-Kreuznach
Echternach
Bad Ems
Worms
LUX.
Trier
Mainz
Mont St. Martin
Luxembourg
Esch-sur-Alzette
Merzig
Kaiserslautern
Mannheim
Briey
Thionville
Neunkirchen
Zweibrücken
Landau
Speyer
Ludwigshafen
Moyeuvre-Grande
Forbach
Karlsruhe
Metz
Sarreguemines
Wissembourg
Rastatt
Baden Baden
Pont-à-Mousson
Sarrebourg
Saverne
Haguenau
Nancy
Lunéville
Schiltigheim
Strasbourg
Toul
Dombasle
Baccarat
Erstein
Offenburg
Mirecourt
St. Dié
Sélestat
Épinal
Ste. Marie aux Mines
Colmar
Remiremont
Freiburg
MONTS FAUCILLES
Guebwiller
SCHWARZWALD
Luxeuil
Mulhouse
Lörrach
Champlitte
Vesoul
Belfort
Basel
Gray
Montbéliard
Audincourt
Aarau
Besançon
Biel
Langenthal
Olten
Salins-les-Bains
Neuchâtel
Luzern
Dôle
Pontarlier
Burgdorf
Poligny
Bern
Lons-le-Saunier
SWITZERLAND
Lausanne
BERNER ALPEN
Jungfrau 13669
St. Claude
Yverdon
Lac de Neuchâtel
Vevey
Oyonnax
Thonon-les-Bains
Sion
Brig
SIMPLON PASS
Bellegarde-sur-Valserine
Annemasse
Martigny
PENNINE ALPS
Matterhorn 14685
Amberieu
Annecy
Chamonix
ST. BERNARD PASS
Monte Rosa 15,200
Belley
Albertville
Mt. Blanc 15781
Aosta
Aix-les-Bains
Moûtiers
Voiron
GRAIAN ALPS
Chambéry
Villard-Bonnot
Iyrea
Levanna 11874
Grenoble
Chivasso
Mt. Pelvoux 12,920
MT. CENIS PASS
Bourgoin
MT. CENIS 6835
La Mure
TORINO (Turin)
St. Marcellin
Briançon
COTTIAN
Embrun
Mt. Viso 12,602
Saluzzo
Gap
ALPS
Bra
Veynes
Barcelonnette
Cuneo
MARITIME ALPS
Sisteron
Mt. Pelat 10,079
Digne
Mt. Mounier 9246
Breil
Apt
Manosque
Mentone
San Remo
Salon-de-Provence
Draguignan
Grasse
Cannes
Antibes
Aix-en-Provence
Fréjus
Nice
MONACO
Marseille
Aubagne
Cagnes
La Ciotat
Hyères
St. Tropez
La Seyne-sur-Mer
Toulon
ÎLES D'HYÈRES
MEDITERRANEAN SEA

Map 2 (upper right — Paris region):

Les Andelys
Les Thilliers-en-Vexin
Méru
Montataire
Crépy-en-Valois
Villers Cotterêts
Magny-en-Vexin
Chars
Chantilly
Senlis
Gasny
Per
Chambly
Nanteuil-le-Haudouin
Mareuil-sur-Ourcq
Vernon
Vigny
L'Isle-Adam
Louvres
Le Plessis-Belleville
Pacy-sur-Eure
Aincourt
Pontoise
Dammartin-en-Goële
Juilly
Lixy-sur-Ourcq
Mantes-la-Jolie
Montmorency
Gonesse
Claye-Souilly
Meaux
Bueil
Mézières-sur-Seine
Maule
Argenteuil
St. Denis
Aulnay-sous-Bois
La Ferté-sous-Jouarre
Longnes
St. Germain-en-Laye
Asnières-sur-Seine
Aubervilliers
Bondy
Lagny
Oulins
Septeuil
Houilles
Levallois-Perret
Clichy-la-Garenne
Crecy-en-Brie
Puteaux
PARIS
Vincennes
Marne
Houdan
Boulogne-Billancourt
Villejuif
St. Maur-des-Fossés
Coulommiers
Versailles
Trappes
Pontcarré
Dreux
Montfort l'Amaury
Chevreuse
Longjumeau
Villeneuve-St. Georges
Tournan-en-Brie
Faverolles
St. Léger-en-Yvelines
Palaiseau
Juvisy-sur-Orge
Brie-Comte-Robert
Fontenay-Trésigny
Courtacon
Nogent-le-Roi
Rambouillet
Limours
Coubert
Rozay-en-Brie
Jouy-le-Chatel
Épernon
Arpajon
Guignes
Maintenon
St. Arnoult-en-Yvelines
Corbeil-Essonnes
Mormant
Maison-Rouge
Gallardon
Dourdan
Melun
Nangis
Ablis
Étréchy
Le Châtelet-en-Brie
Donnemarie-en-Montois
Chartres
Auneau
Authon-la-Plaine
Étampes
La Ferté-Alais
Ballancourt
Milly-la-Forêt
Fontainebleau

Scale 1:1 000 000
0 ... 10 Miles
0 4 8 12 16 Kilometers
©RMcN.

Map 3 (lower right — Ruhr/Netherlands):

NETHERLANDS
Winterswijk
Coesfeld
Albachten
Münster
Warendorf
Zevenaar
Terborg
Weseke
Velen
Appelhülsen
Hoetmar
Emmerich
Bocholt
Borken
Gross Reken
Dülmen
Ascheberg
Drensteinfurt
Neubeckum
Kleve
Rees
Isselburg
Raesfeld
Lüdinghausen
Ahlen
Goch
NORDRHEIN-
Brünen
Haltern
Olfen
Werne
Bockum-Hövel
Hamm
Xanten
Wesel
Dorsten
Marl
Datteln
Lünen
Kamen
Werl
Kevelaer
Recklinghausen
Castrop Rauxel
Unna
Geldern
Issum
Rheinberg
Gladbeck
Buer
Herne
Dinslaken
Bottrop
Gelsenkirchen
Bochum
Dortmund
Kamp-Lintfort
Sterkrade
Hamborn
Wattenscheid
Witten
Schwerte
Straelen
Moers
Oberhausen
Essen
Menden
Neheim
Venlo
Kempen
Homberg
Mülheim
Hattingen
Herdecke
Aldekerk
Duisburg
Kettwig
Wetter
Hagen
Grefrath
Kaldenkirchen
Krefeld
Angermund
Velbert
Heiligenhaus
Gevelsberg
Letmathe
Iserlohn
Viersen
Büderich
Ratingen
Schwelm
Hohenlimburg
Dülken
DÜSSELDORF
Mettmann
Wuppertal
Daht
Neuenrade
Mönchen Gladbach
Haan
Radevormwald
Lüdenscheid
Plettenberg
Niederkrüchten
Neuss
Hilden
Solingen
Remscheid
Hückeswagen
Meinerzhagen
Grevenbrück
Rheydt
Grevenbroich
Burscheid
Wipperfürth
Wassenberg
Hitdorf
Opladen
WESTFALEN
Heinsberg
Baal
Titz
Stommeln
Leverkusen
Bergisch Gladbach
Engelskirchen
Berneustadt
Olpe
NETH.
Jülich
Elsdorf
Frechen
Rösrath
Much
Denklingen
Aldenhoven
Kerpen
KÖLN (Cologne)
Siegen
Aachen
Würselen
Eschweiler
Brühl
Lechenich
Siegburg
Rosbach
BELG.
Düren
Bonn
Beuel
RHEINLAND-PFALZ
Betzdorf

Scale 1:1 000 000
0 ... 10 Miles
0 4 8 12 16 Kilometers
©RMcN.

Bottom scale bar:

0 10 20 30 40 50 60 70 80 90 100 110 120 Miles
0 20 40 60 80 100 120 140 160 180 200 Kilometers

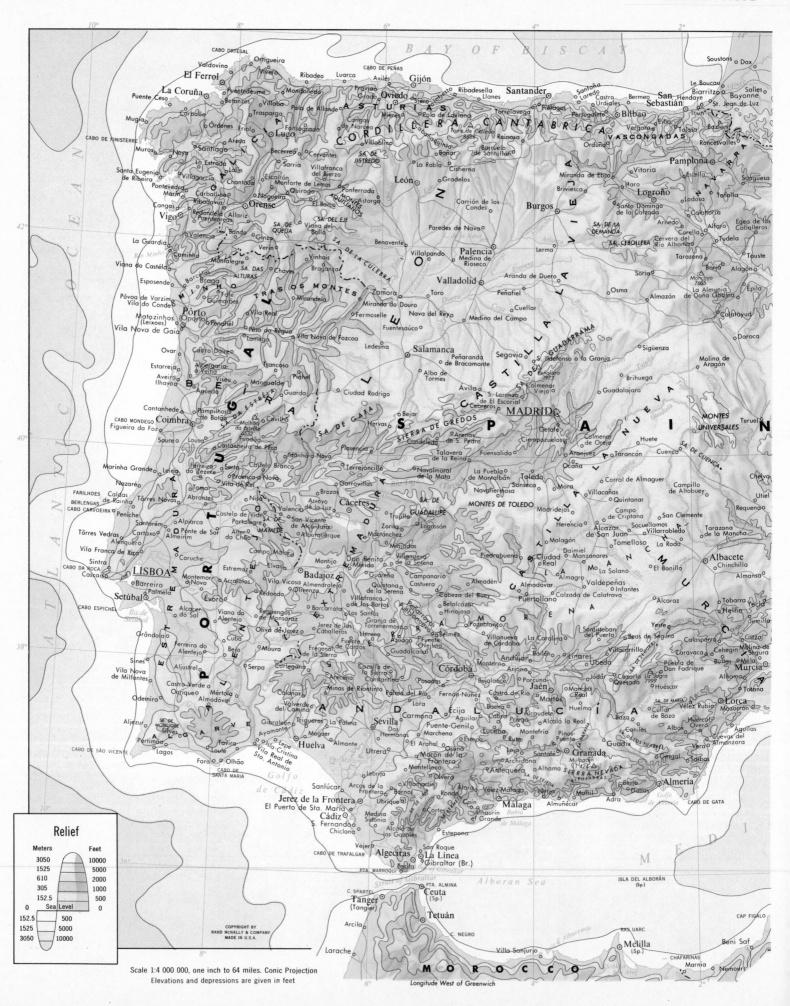

Relief

Meters		Feet
3050		10000
1525		5000
610		2000
305		1000
152.5		500
0	Sea Level	0
152.5		500
1525		5000
3050		10000

COPYRIGHT BY
RAND McNALLY & COMPANY
MADE IN U.S.A.

Scale 1:4 000 000, one inch to 64 miles. Conic Projection
Elevations and depressions are given in feet

Longitude West of Greenwich

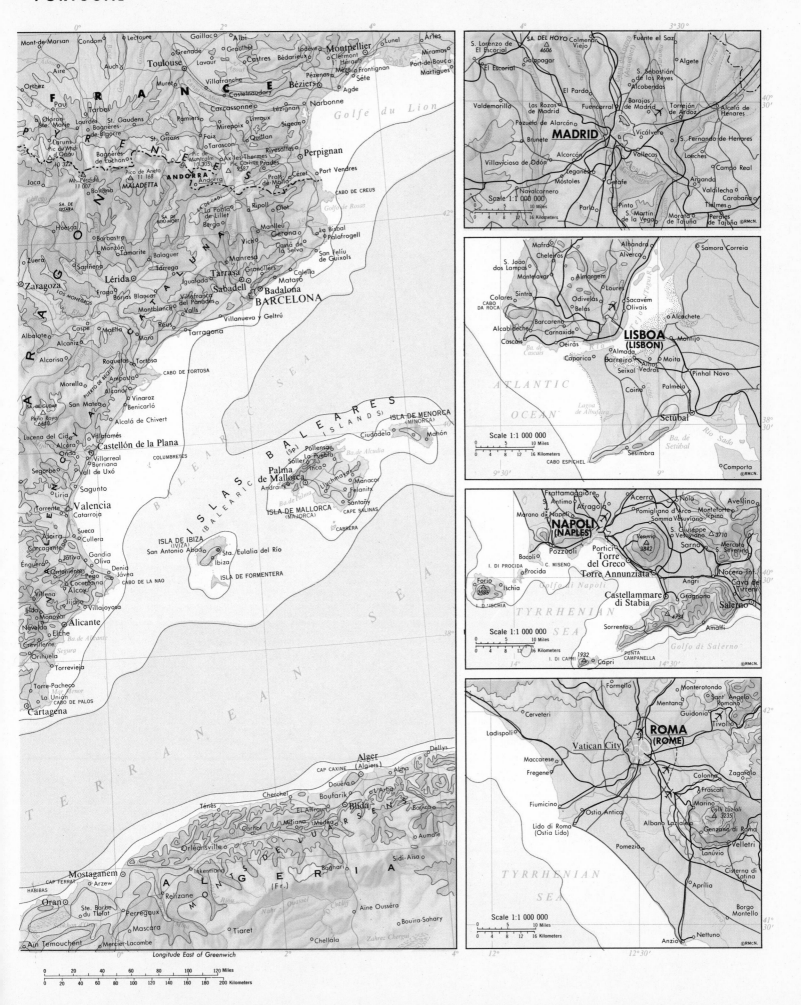

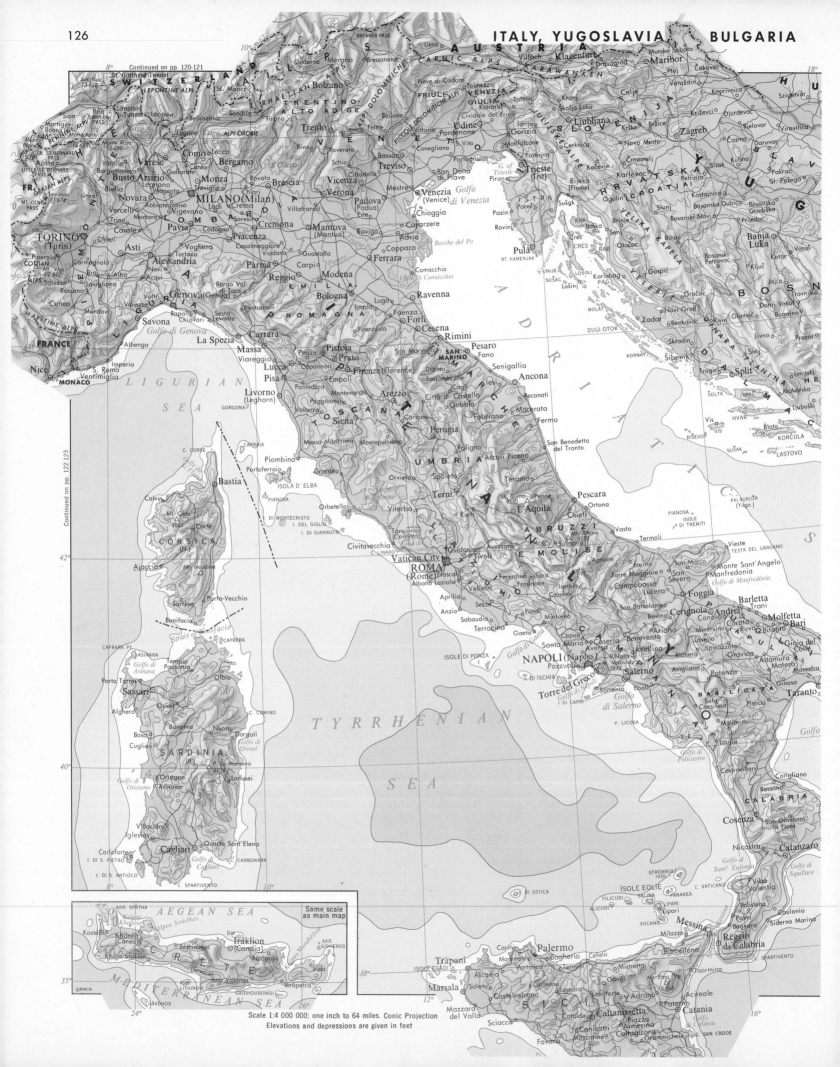

Scale 1:4 000 000; one inch to 64 miles. Conic Projection
Elevations and depressions are given in feet

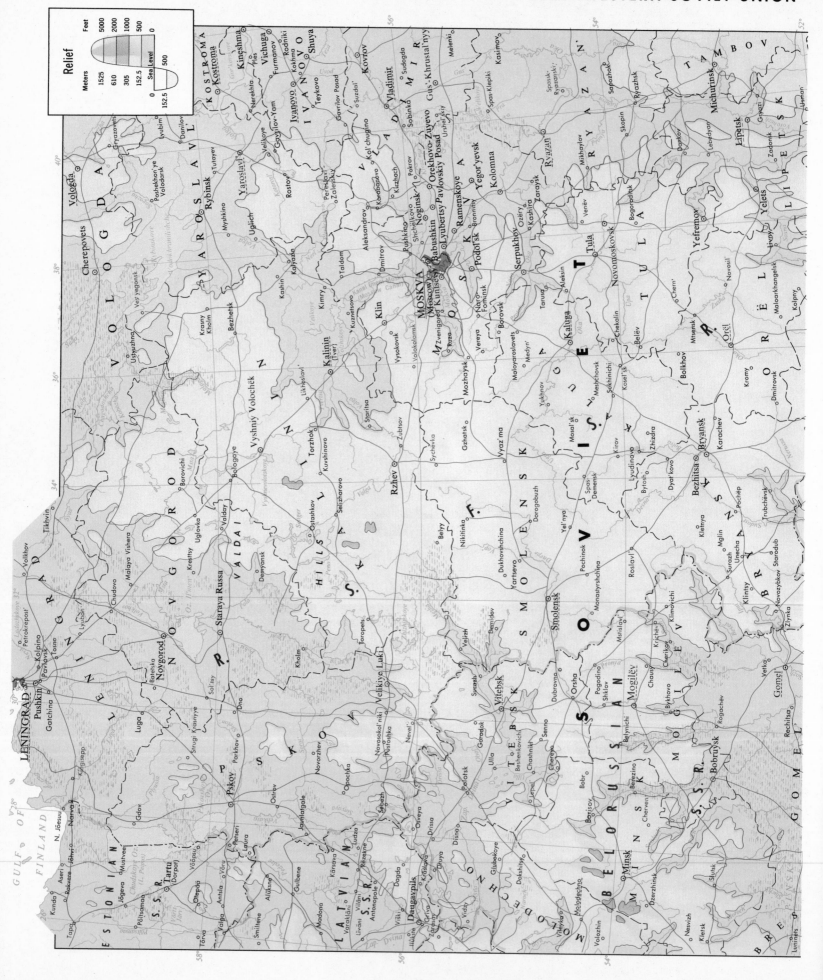

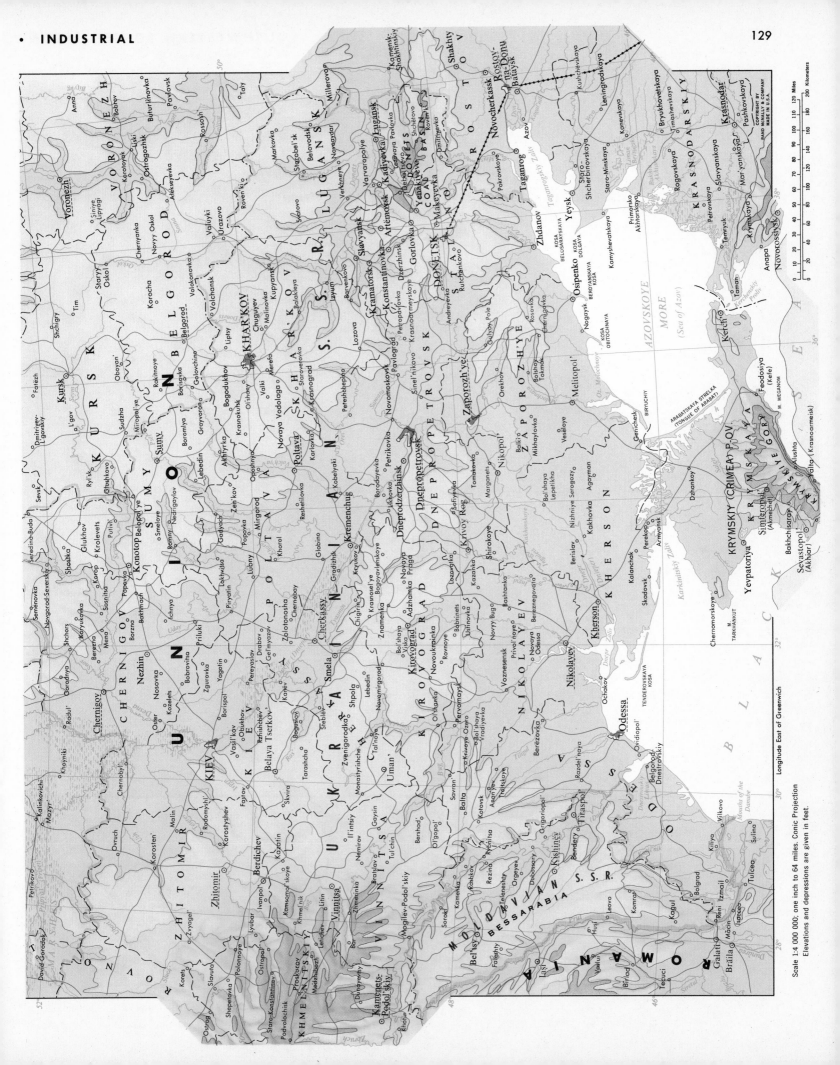

Scale 1:4 000 000; one inch to 64 miles. Conic Projection
Elevations and depressions are given in feet.

Scale 1:20 000 000; one inch to 315 miles.
Lambert's Azimuthal, Equal Area Projection
Elevations and depressions are given in feet

Relief

Meters	Feet
3050	10000
1525	5000
610	2000
305	1000
152.5	500
0	Sea Level
	Below Sea Level
Sea Level	
152.5	500
1525	5000
3050	10000

Continued on pages 112-113

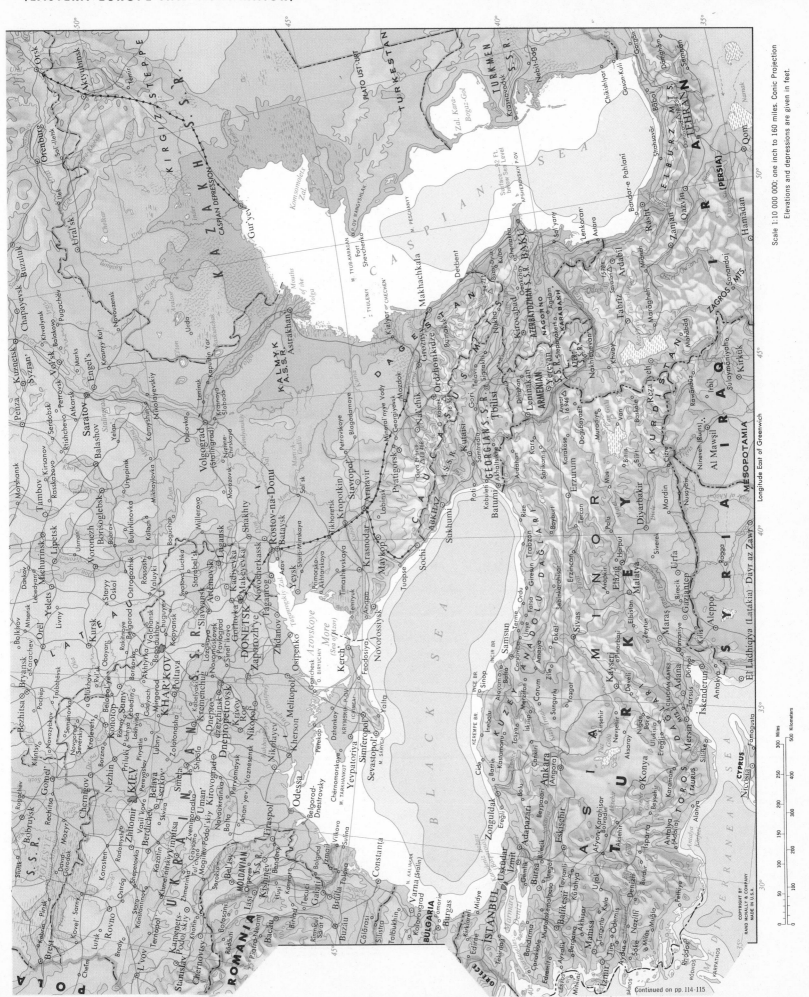

Scale 1:10 000 000; one inch to 160 miles. Conic Projection
Elevations and depressions are given in feet.

Longitude East of Greenwich

COPYRIGHT BY
RAND M^cNALLY & COMPANY
MADE IN U.S.A.

Continued on pp. 114-115

Continued on pp. 102-103

SOVIET

RUSSIAN

WESTERN

SIBERIAN

LOWLAND

SOVIET FEDERA

BARENTS SEA

NOVAYA ZEMLYA

KARSKOYE MORE
(Kara Sea)

ARCTIC

SERGEYA
KIROVA

KARELIAN A.S.S.R.

KOMI A.S.S.R.

PECHORA
BASIN

TUNDRA

GORY PUTORANA

P-OV
YAMAL

P-OV
GYDANSKIY

LENINGRAD
(Leningrad)

MOSKVA
(Moscow)

GORKIY

UDMURT
A.S.S.R.

TATAR A.S.S.R.

BASH. KIR.
A.S.S.R.

K A Z A K H

S T E P P E

ARAL'SKOYE
MORE

PESKI
KYZYL KUM

TURKESTAN

TASHKENT

PESKI MUYUN-KUM

K I R G I Z

PESKI SARY ISHIKOTRAU
(DESERT)

KAZAKH S.S.R.

GORNO-ALTAY
AUT. OBLAST

KHAKASS

TUVA AUT. OB.

TANNU-OLA

SAYAN KHREBET

HANGAYN (KHANGAI) NURUU

M O N G O

C H I N A

TURKESTAN

KIRGIZ S.S.R.

TADZHIK S.S.R.

GORNO-BADAKHSHAN
AUT. OBLAST

PAMIRS

AFGHANISTAN

AN-SHAN (TIEN SHAN)

NOVOSIBIRSK

Novosibirsk

Murmansk

Leningrad

Moskva

Gor'kiy

Kazan'

Sverdlovsk

Chelyabinsk

Magnitogorsk

Omsk

Tomsk

Krasnoyarsk

Irkutsk

Bratsk

Alma-Ata

Tashkent

Samarkand

Arkhangel'sk
(Archangel)

Vorkuta

Noril'sk

Dikson

ZHELANIYA

Belukha
15 157

Munku Sardyk
12 821

Bogda Uula
13 865

85° Longitude East of Greenwich 90°

Scale 1:16 000 000; one inch to 250 miles Conic Projection
Elevations and depressions are given in feet.

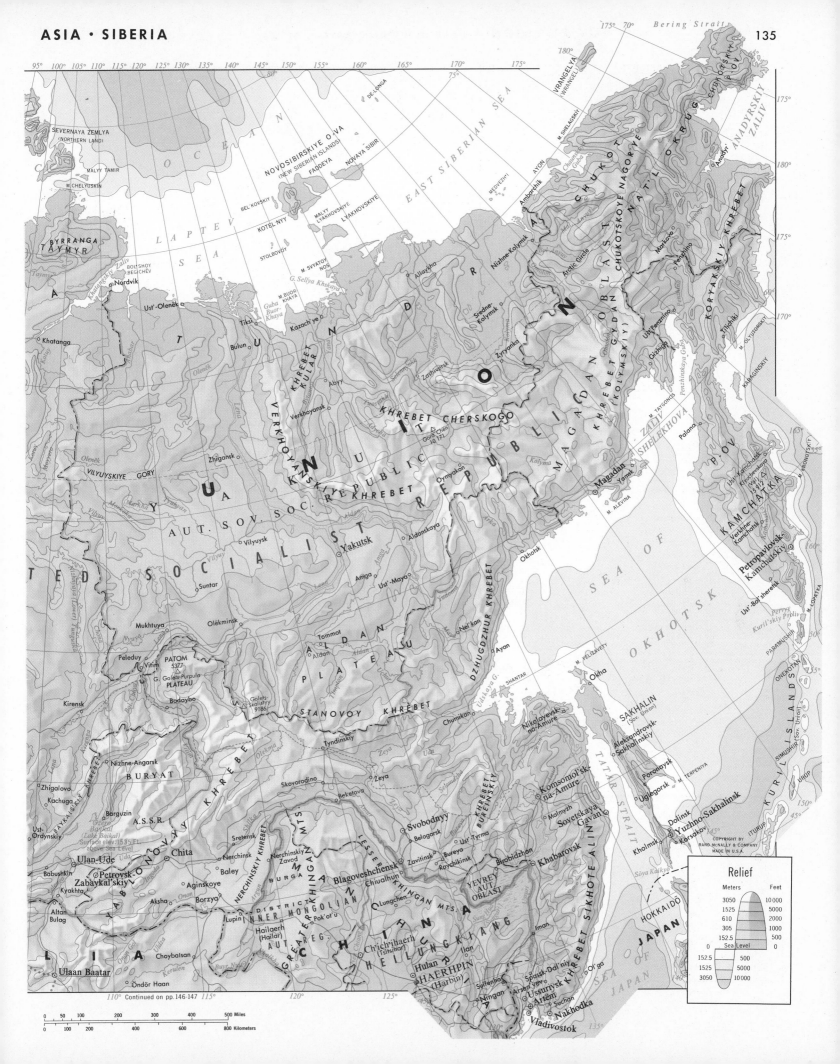

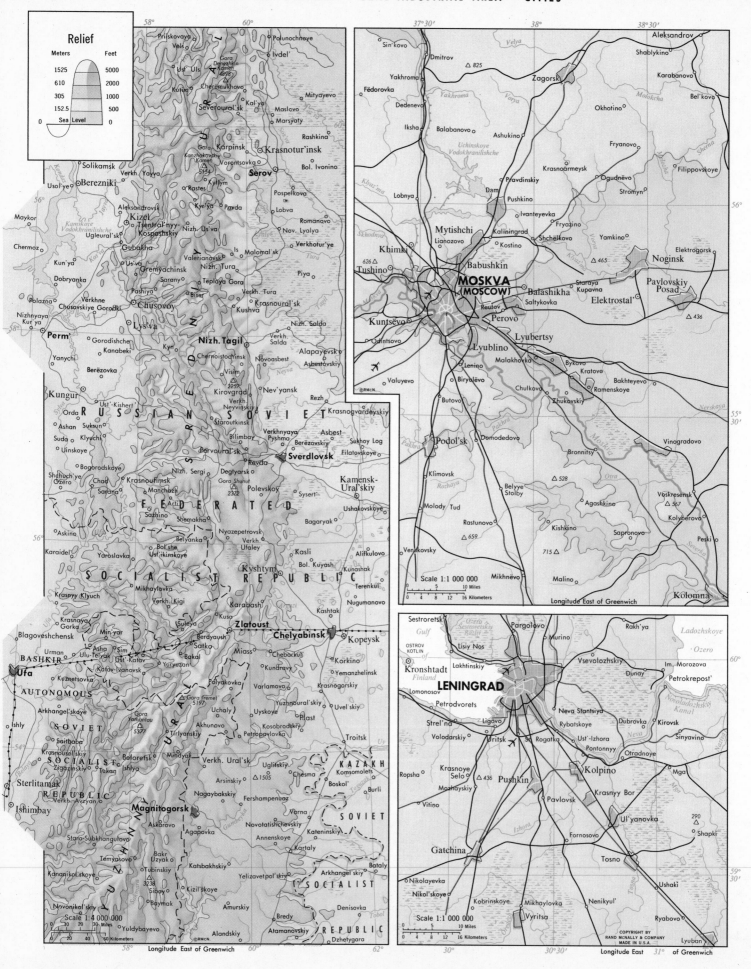

Relief

Meters		Feet
1525		5000
610		2000
305		1000
152.5		500
0	Sea Level	0

Scale 1:1 000 000

Scale 1:4 000 000

Scale 1:1 000 000

Longitude East of Greenwich

Longitude East of Greenwich

COPYRIGHT BY
RAND McNALLY & COMPANY
MADE IN U.S.A.

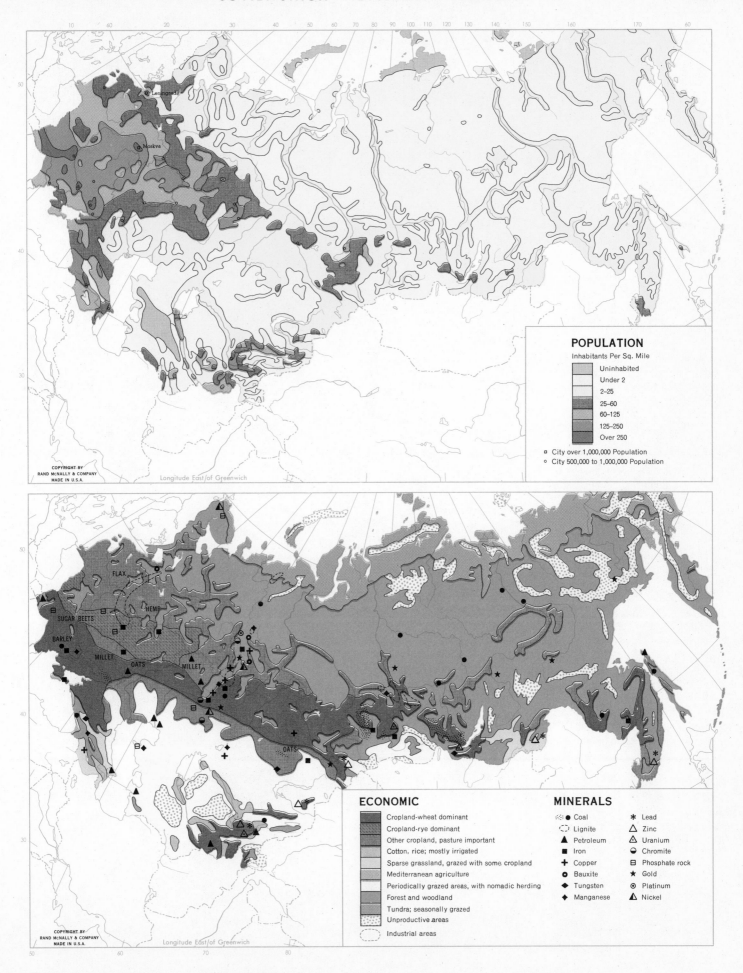

POPULATION

Inhabitants Per Sq. Mile

Uninhabited
Under 2
2–25
25–60
60–125
125–250
Over 250

▫ City over 1,000,000 Population
○ City 500,000 to 1,000,000 Population

COPYRIGHT BY
RAND McNALLY & COMPANY
MADE IN U.S.A.

Longitude East/of Greenwich

ECONOMIC

Cropland-wheat dominant
Cropland-rye dominant
Other cropland, pasture important
Cotton, rice; mostly irrigated
Sparse grassland, grazed with some cropland
Mediterranean agriculture
Periodically grazed areas, with nomadic herding
Forest and woodland
Tundra; seasonally grazed
Unproductive areas
Industrial areas

MINERALS

● Coal   ✳ Lead
Lignite   △ Zinc
▲ Petroleum   △ Uranium
■ Iron   Chromite
✛ Copper   Phosphate rock
● Bauxite   ★ Gold
◆ Tungsten   ◉ Platinum
◆ Manganese   △ Nickel

COPYRIGHT BY
RAND McNALLY & COMPANY
MADE IN U.S.A.

Longitude East/of Greenwich

North Pole
PEARY APRIL 6, 1909

Continued on page 163

Relief

Meters		Feet
3050		10 000
1525		5000
610		2000
305		1000
0	Sea Level	0
152.5	500	Below Sea Level
1525	5000	
3050	10 000	
6100	20 000	

COPYRIGHT BY
RAND McNALLY & COMPANY
MADE IN U.S.A.

Scale 1:40 000 000; one inch to 630 miles. Lambert's Azimuthal, Equal Area Projection
Elevations and depressions are given in feet

Longitude East of Greenwich

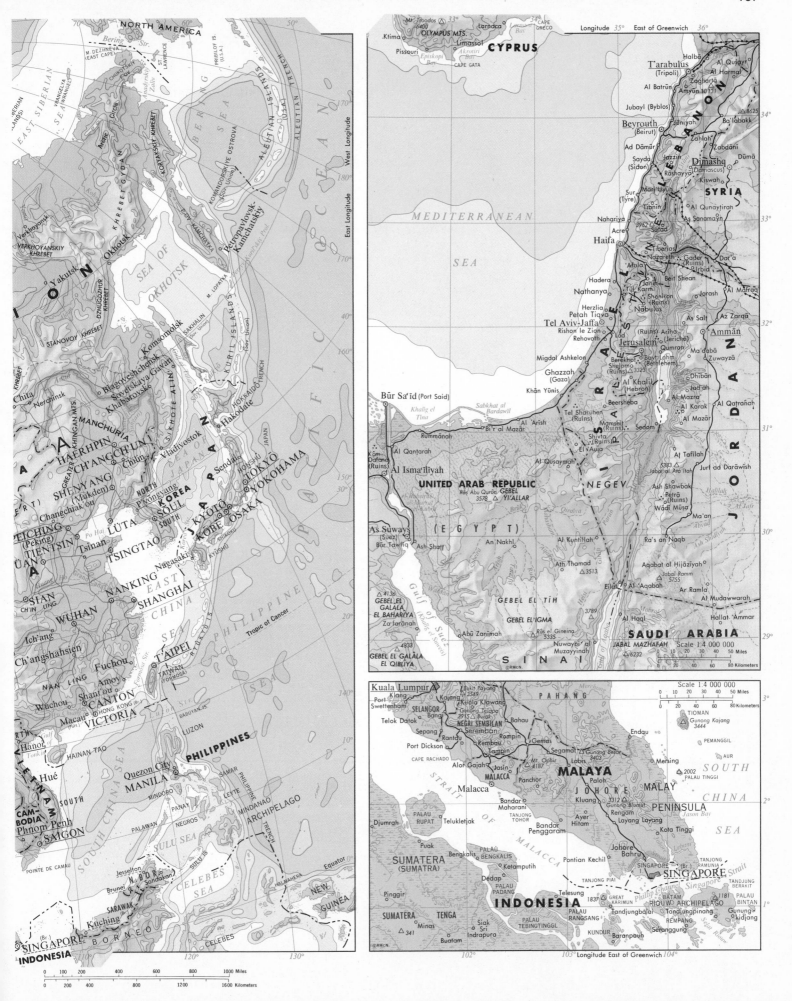

Left map — East Asia and Pacific

NORTH AMERICA

Bering Str.
M. DEZHNEVA (EAST CAPE)
CHUKOTSKIY POLUOSTROV
Arctic Circle
ST. LAWRENCE
PRIBILOF IS. (U.S.A.)
WRANGELYA
VRANGELYA
WEST SIBERIAN SEA
EAST SIBERIAN SEA
NEW SIBERIAN ISLANDS

KOMANDORSKIYE OSTROVA (Sov. Union)
ALEUTIAN ISLANDS (U.S.A.)
ALEUTIAN TRENCH

West Longitude
East Longitude

Verhoyansk
VERKHOYANSKIY KHREBET
Yakutsk
STANOVOY KHREBET
KHREBET GYDAN
KOLYMSKIY KHREBET
OKHOTSK
M. KAMCHATKA
Petropavlovsk-Kamchatskiy
M. LOPATKA
KURIL ISLANDS (Sov. Union)

SEA OF OKHOTSK

Chita
Nerchinsk
DZHUGDZHUR KHREBET
Blagoveshchensk
Sovetskaya Gavan
Khabarovsk
SAKHALIN

GREATER KHINGAN MTS.
MANCHURIA
HAERHPIN
CH'ANGCH'UN (Mukden)
Chilin
Vladivostok
SIKHOTE ALIN
HOKKAIDO
Hakodate
HOKKAIDO TRENCH

PEICHING (Peking)
SHENYANG
Chanchiak'ou
Po Hai
NORTH KOREA
P'yongyang
SOUL
SEOUL
KOREA
SOUTH
HONSHU
TOKYO
YOKOHAMA
KYOTO
KOBE OSAKA
Shikoku

TIENTSIN
LÜTA
Tsinan
TSINGTAO
Nagasaki
KYUSHU

SIAN
CH'IN LING
NANKING
SHANGHAI
WUHAN
CHINA
Ich'ang
Ch'angshahsien
NAN LING
Fuchou
Amoy
Shant'ou
CANTON
Macau
VICTORIA
HONG KONG (Br.)

EAST CHINA SEA
RYUKYU IS.
T'AIPEI
TAIWAN (FORMOSA)
Formosa Str.
Babuyan Is.
Tropic of Cancer

NAN TING
Hanoi
HAINAN TAO
Gulf of Tonkin
Hué
VIET-NAM
SOUTH
CAMBODIA
Phnom Penh
SAIGON
Pointe de Camau

LUZON
PHILIPPINES
Quezon City
MANILA
MINDORO
SAMAR
LEYTE
PANAY
NEGROS
PALAWAN
PHILIPPINE TRENCH
SULU SEA
MINDANAO
ARCHIPELAGO
SULU IS.

PHILIPPINE SEA

PACIFIC OCEAN

SOUTH CHINA SEA
CELEBES SEA
HALMAHERA
NEW GUINEA
Equator

Jesselton
Brunei
Sandakan
SARAWAK
Kuching
BORNEO
CELEBES

SINGAPORE
INDONESIA

0 100 200 400 600 800 1000 Miles
0 200 400 800 1200 1600 Kilometers

Top-right map — Eastern Mediterranean / Israel

Mt. Troodos
OLYMPUS MTS.
Ktima
Pissouri
Episkopi Bay
CAPE GATA
Akrotiri Bay
Larnaca
Limassol
CAPE GRECO
CYPRUS

Longitude 35° East of Greenwich 36°

T'arabulus (Tripoli)
Halba
Al Qusayr
Al Harmal
Al Batrun
Zagharta
Amyun
Jubayl (Byblos)
LEBANON
Ba'labakk
Beyrouth (Beirut)
Juniyah
Zahlah
Zabdani
Ad Damur
Sayda (Sidon)
Jazzin
Dimashq (Damascus)
Duma
Rashayya
Marj 'Uyun
Kiswah
Sur (Tyre)
Tibnin
Al Qunaytirah
SYRIA
Nahariya
As Sanamayn
Acre
Safad
Haifa
Tiberias
Nazareth
Gader (Ruins)
Dar'a
Afula
Irbid
Hadera
Beit Shean
Janin
Jarash
Nathanya
Tul Karm
Al Mafraq
Herzlia
Shomron (Ruins)
Petah Tiqva
Nabulus
As Salt
Tel Aviv-Jaffa
Az Zarqa
Rishon le Zion
Amman
Rehovoth
(Ruins) Ariha (Jericho)
Jerusalem
Qumran
Ma'daba
Migdal Ashkelon
Berekhot Shlomo (Ruins)
Bayt Lahm (Bethlehem)
Zuwayza
Ghazzah (Gaza)
Dhiban
Jad'ah
Al Khalil (Hebron)
Khan Yunis
Al Mazra
Beersheba
Al Karak
Al Qatranah
ISRAEL
Bur Sa'id (Port Said)
Sabkhat al Bardawil
Tel Sharuhen (Ruins)
Al Mazar
Khalig el Tina
Al 'Arish
Shivta (Ruins)
Sedom
Rummanah
Bi'r al Mazar
El 'Auja
Kom Dafane (Ruins)
Al Qantarah
Al Qusaymah
At Tafilah
Al Isma'iliyah
Jurf ad Darawish
UNITED ARAB REPUBLIC
NEGEV
Ash Shawbak
Petra
Ras Abu Qurun GEBEL YI'ALLAR
Wadi Musa
As Suways (Suez)
Ma'an
Bur Tawfiq
An Nakhl
Al Kuntillah
Ash Shatt
Ra's an Naqb
(EGYPT)
Qiralya
Ath Thamad
Aqabat al Hijaziyah
Ar Ramla
GEBEL EL TIH
Eilat
Al 'Aqaba
Jabal Ramm
JORDAN
GEBEL GALALA EL BAHARIYA
Za'faranah
GEBEL EL IGMA
Al Haql
Al Mudawwarah
Abu Zanimah
Ras el Gineina
GEBEL EL GALALA EL QIBLIYA
Nuwaybi' al Muzayyinah
Hallat 'Ammar
SINAI
JABAL MAZHAFAH
SAUDI ARABIA

Scale 1:4 000 000
0 10 20 30 40 50 Miles
0 20 40 60 80 Kilometers

Bottom-right map — Malaya, Singapore, Sumatra

Scale 1:4 000 000
0 10 20 30 40 50 Miles
0 20 40 60 80 Kilometers

Kuala Lumpur
Klang
Port Swettenham
Bukit Payong
PAHANG
Kuala Klawang
SELANGOR
Bangi
Bahau
NEGRI SEMBILAN
Seremban
Rompin
Telok Datok
Sepang
Rantau
Gemas
Rembau
Endau
Port Dickson
Tampin
TIOMAN
Gunong Kajang
Segamat
Mt. Ophir
PEMANGGIL
Alor Gajah
Jasin
Labis
MALAYA
Mersing
MALACCA
Panchor
Gunong Besar
AUR
Malacca
Paloh
PALAU TINGGI
Bandar Maharani
JOHORE
MALAY
TANJONG TOHOR
Kluang
Gunong Blumut
PENINSULA
Djumrah
Ayer Hitam
Jason Bay
PALAU RUPAT
Telukletjak
Rengam
Layang Layang
Puak
Bandar Penggaram
Kota Tinggi
SOUTH CHINA SEA
Pinggir
Bengkalis
Pontian Kechil
Johore Bahru
Dedap
PALAU BENGKALIS
Ketamputih
STRAIT OF MALACCA
Tanjong Piai
SINGAPORE (Br.)
SINGAPORE
PALAU PADANG
Telesung
Phillip Channel
BATAM
TANJONG BERAKIT
SUMATERA (SUMATRA)
Great Karimun
RIOUW ARCHIPELAGO
PALAU BINTAN
SUMATERA TENGA
Siak Sri Indrapura
Tandjungbalai
Tandjungpinang
REMPANG
Gunung kidjang
Minas
Buatan
PALAU RANGSANG
KUNDUR
Baranpauh
Seranggung
INDONESIA

102° Longitude East of Greenwich 103° 104°

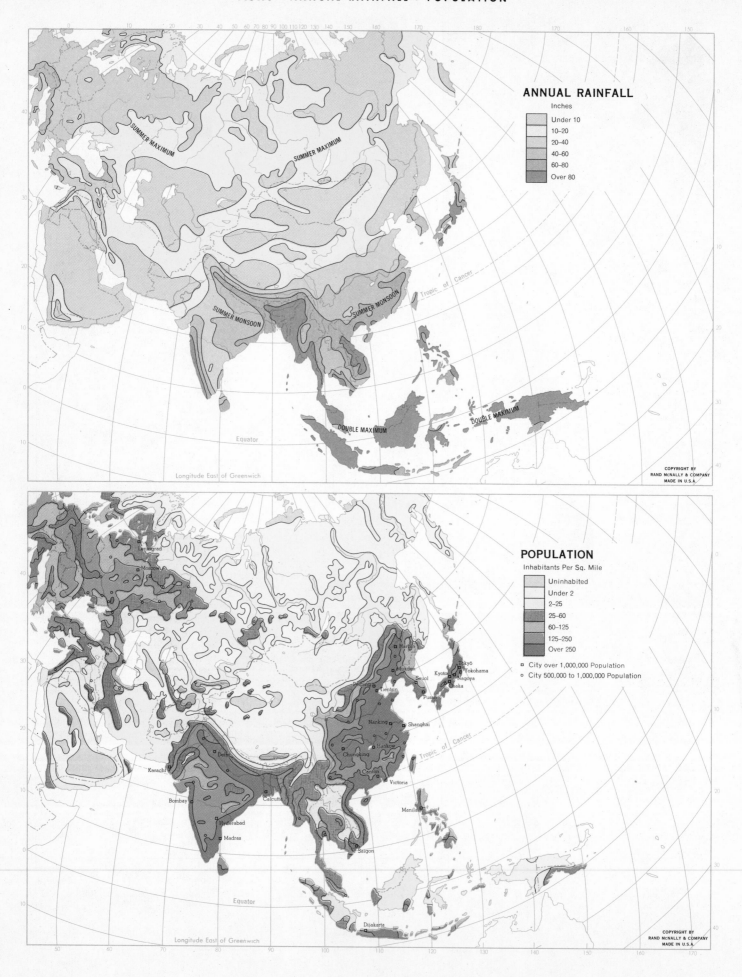

ANNUAL RAINFALL

Inches

Under 10
10–20
20–40
40–60
60–80
Over 80

SUMMER MAXIMUM

SUMMER MAXIMUM

SUMMER MONSOON

SUMMER MONSOON

SUMMER MONSOON

Tropic of Cancer

DOUBLE MAXIMUM

DOUBLE MAXIMUM

Equator

Longitude East of Greenwich

COPYRIGHT BY
RAND McNALLY & COMPANY
MADE IN U.S.A.

POPULATION

Inhabitants Per Sq. Mile

Uninhabited
Under 2
2–25
25–60
60–125
125–250
Over 250

□ City over 1,000,000 Population
○ City 500,000 to 1,000,000 Population

Leningrad
Moscow
Harbin
Mukden
Tōkyō
Yokohama
Kyoto
Nagoya
Seoul
Ōsaka
Peiping
Tientsin
Pusan
Nanking
Shanghai
Hankow
Chungking
Delhi
Karachi
Canton
Victoria
Bombay
Calcutta
Manila
Hyderabad
Madras
Saigon
Tropic of Cancer
Equator
Longitude East of Greenwich
Djakarta

COPYRIGHT BY
RAND McNALLY & COMPANY
MADE IN U.S.A.

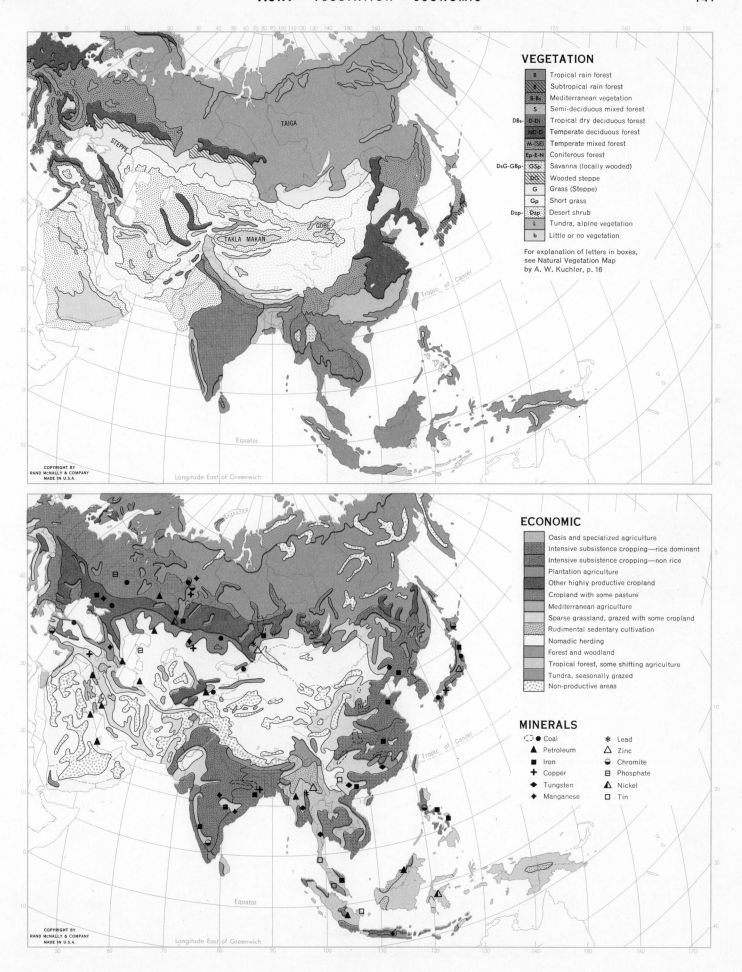

VEGETATION

B	Tropical rain forest
ß	Subtropical rain forest
ß-ßs	Mediterranean vegetation
S	Semi-deciduous mixed forest
DBs- D-Di	Tropical dry deciduous forest
ND-D	Temperate deciduous forest
M-ISEt	Temperate mixed forest
Ep-E-N	Coniferous forest
DsG-GBp- GSp	Savanna (locally wooded)
DG	Wooded steppe
G	Grass (Steppe)
Gp	Short grass
Dzp- Dzp	Desert shrub
L	Tundra, alpine vegetation
b	Little or no vegetation

For explanation of letters in boxes,
see Natural Vegetation Map
by A. W. Kuchler, p. 16

Longitude East of Greenwich

ECONOMIC

	Oasis and specialized agriculture
	Intensive subsistence cropping—rice dominant
	Intensive subsistence cropping—non rice
	Plantation agriculture
	Other highly productive cropland
	Cropland with some pasture
	Mediterranean agriculture
	Sparse grassland, grazed with some cropland
	Rudimental sedentary cultivation
	Nomadic herding
	Forest and woodland
	Tropical forest, some shifting agriculture
	Tundra, seasonally grazed
	Non-productive areas

MINERALS

●	Coal	✳	Lead
▲	Petroleum	△	Zinc
■	Iron	◒	Chromite
✛	Copper	⊟	Phosphate
◆	Tungsten	◮	Nickel
◆	Manganese	☐	Tin

Longitude East of Greenwich

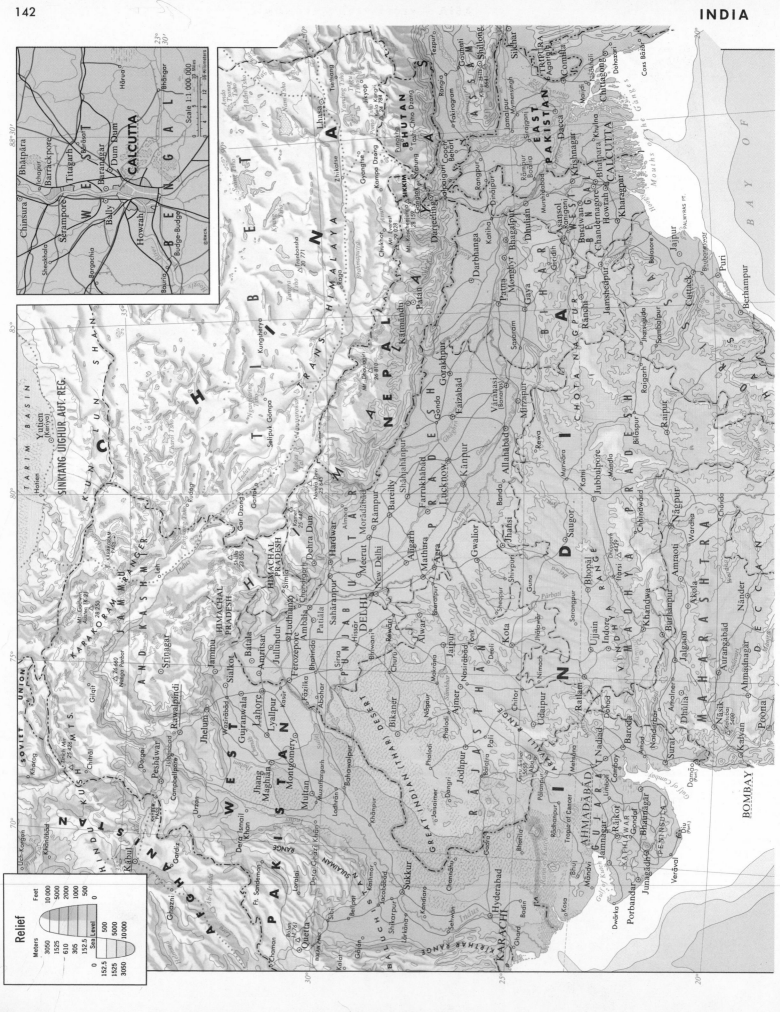

Scale 1:1 000 000

CALCUTTA

Relief

Meters	Feet
3050	10 000
1525	5000
610	2000
305	1000
152.5	500
0	Sea Level 0
152.5	500
1525	5000
3050	10000

BAY OF

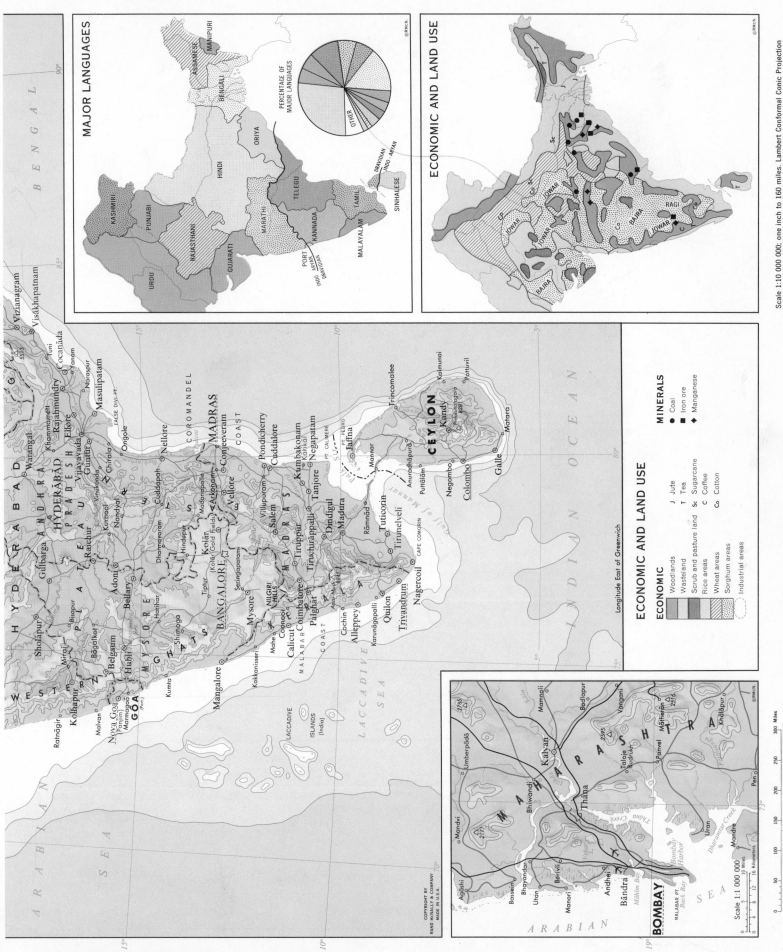

MAJOR LANGUAGES

B E N G A L

KASHMIRI
PUNJABI
ASSAMESE
MANIPURI
BENGALI
RAJASTHANI
HINDI
ORIYA
URDU
GUJARATI
MARATHI
TELEGU
KANNADA
TAMIL
MALAYALAM
SINHALESE

PERCENTAGE OF MAJOR LANGUAGES

OTHER

PORT
INDO ARYAN
DRAVIDIAN

DRAVIDIAN
INDO-ARYAN

ECONOMIC AND LAND USE

Scale 1:10 000 000; one inch to 160 miles. Lambert Conformal Conic Projection
Elevations and depressions are given in feet

JOWAR
BAJRA
RAGI

ECONOMIC AND LAND USE

ECONOMIC

Woodlands
Wasteland
Scrub and pasture land
Rice areas
Wheat areas
Sorghum areas
Industrial areas

J Jute
T Tea
Sc Sugarcane
C Coffee
Co Cotton

MINERALS

● Coal
■ Iron ore
◆ Manganese

Longitude East of Greenwich

COPYRIGHT BY
RAND McNALLY & COMPANY
MADE IN U.S.A.

B E N G A L

Vizianagram
Visākhapatnam
5513
Uni
Cocanāda
Yanam
Narsapur
Masulipatam
FALSE DIVI PT.
Ongole
Nellore

HYDERABAD
Warangal
Khammamett
Rajahmundry
Ellore
Vijayawada
Guntūr
Chirala

ANDHRA
PRADESH
Nandyal
Cuddapah
Nandyāl

Gulbarga
Raichur
Adoni
Kurnool
Vinukonda

Sholāpur
Bisapur
Bellary
Hindupur

MYSORE
Bāgalkot
Hotihar
Shimoga
Dharmavaram
Tiptur
Kolār
(Kolar Gold Fields)
Seringapatam

Bijāpur
Belgaum
Hubli
BANGALORE
Mysore
NILGIRI
HILLS
Coonoor
Coimbatore
Palghāt

Mirai
Kolhāpur
Kumta
Mangalore
Kokkanisseri
Mahe
Calicut

Ratnāgiri
Malvan
Nova Goa
(Panjim)
Mormagāo
GOA
(Port.)

WESTERN
GHATS
MYSORE
COAST
MALABAR

MADRAS
COROMANDEL
COAST
Conjeeveram
Vellore
Arkonam
Madanapalle
Viluppuram
Salem
Tiruppur
Tiruchirappalli
Dindigul
Madura
Rāmnād
Tuticorin
Tirunelveli
Nāgercoil
CAPE COMORIN

Pondicherry
Cuddalore
Kumbakonam
Negapatam
PT. CALIMERE
Kārikāl
Tanjore
PK. PEDRO
Jaffna
Mannar
PALK STRAIT

Cochin
Alleppey
Quilon
Trivandrum
Karunāgapalli

CEYLON
Trincomalee
Kandy
Pidurutalagala
8281
Anurādhapura
Negombo
Puttalam
Colombo
Galle
Matara
Kalmunai
Pottuvil

LACCADIVE
LACCADIVE
ISLANDS
(India)

LACCADIVE SEA

ARABIAN
SEA

INDIAN OCEAN

BOMBAY

MAHARASHTRA

Mamnoli
Badlapur
Vangani
Khalāpur
Mātherān
2516
2785
Umberpāda
Kalyan
Bhiwandi
Thāna
Talojā
Budrukh
Pānvel
Pen

2277
Mandvi
Thāna Creek
Uran
Mondre

Agāshi
Bassein
Bhayandar
Uhan
Manori
Andheri
Bāndra
Māhim Bay
BOMBAY
MALABAR PT.
Back Bay
Bombay
Harbor
Dharamtar Creek

ARABIAN SEA

Scale 1:1 000 000

Miles
Kilometers

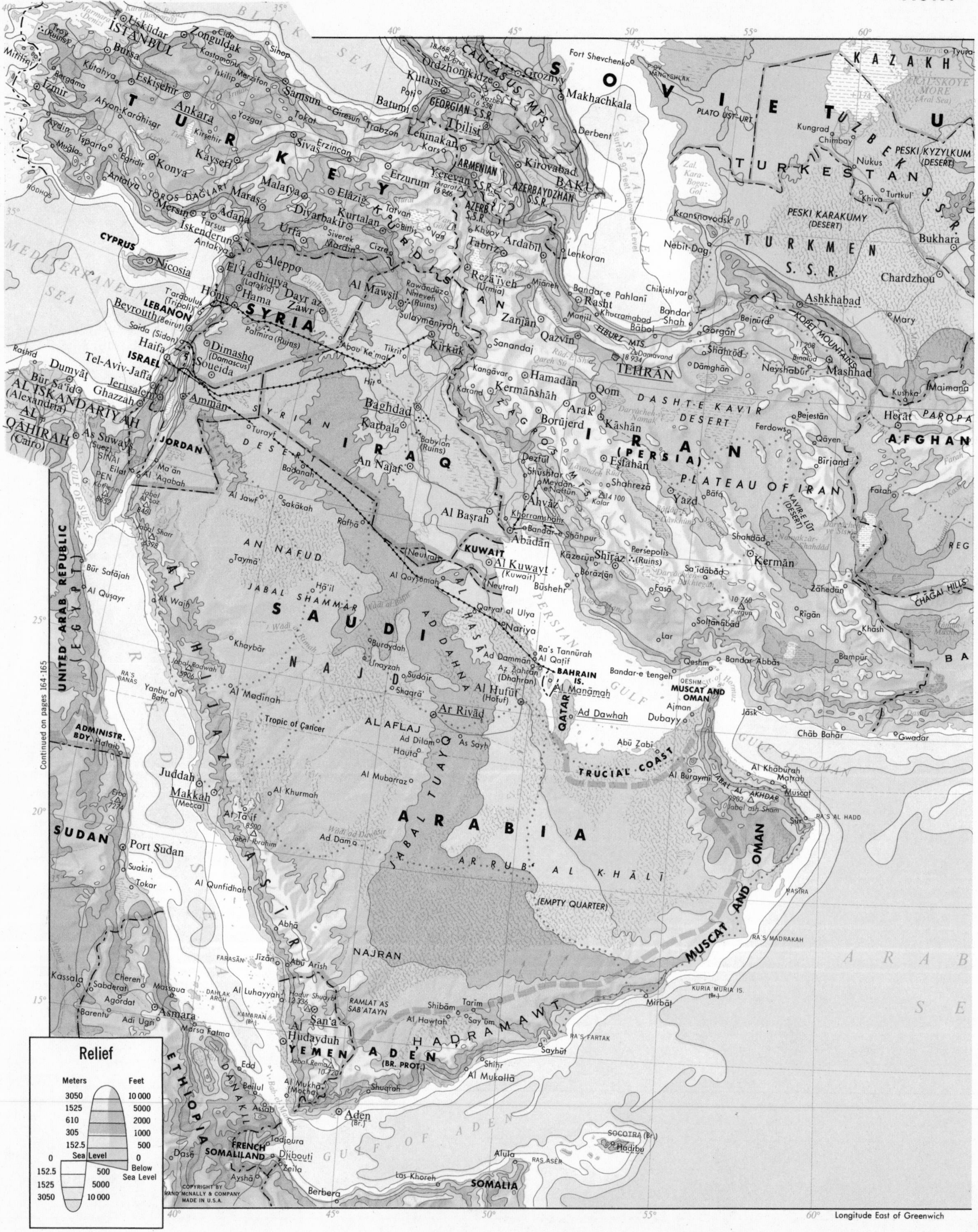

SOVIET
KAZAKH
TUZBEK
TURKESTAN S.S.R.
PESKI KYZYLKUM (DESERT)
PESKI KARAKUMY (DESERT)
TURKMEN S.S.R.

BLACK SEA
İSTANBUL
Bursa
Ankara
Eskişehir
İzmir
T U R K E Y
Kayseri
Konya
Adana
CYPRUS
Nicosia

CAUCASUS MTS.
Grozny
Fort Shevchenko
Ordzhonikidze
GEORGIAN S.S.R.
Tbilisi
Batumi
ARMENIAN S.S.R.
Yerevan
AZERBAYDZHAN
BAKU
AZERB. S.S.R.
Tabriz
CASPIAN SEA
Derbent
Makhachkala
Krasnovodsk
Nebit-Dag
Ashkhabad
Mashhad
Herat

MEDITERRANEAN SEA
Beyrouth (Beirut)
LEBANON
Aleppo
Homs
Hama
SYRIA
Dimashq (Damascus)
ISRAEL
Tel-Aviv-Jaffa
Jerusalem
Amman
JORDAN
AL ISKANDARIYAH (Alexandria)
AL QAHIRAH (Cairo)
UNITED ARAB REPUBLIC (EGYPT)
SINAI

Baghdad
I R A Q
Karbala
An Najaf
Al Başrah
KUWAIT
Al Kuwayt (Kuwait)
(Neutral)
TEHRAN
Hamadan
Qom
I R A N (PERSIA)
Eşfahān
Shīrāz
PLATEAU OF IRAN
DASHT-E KAVIR DESERT
KAVIR-E LUT (DESERT)
Kermān
Yazd
AFGHAN

SYRIAN DESERT
AN NAFUD
S A U D I   A R A B I A
NAJD
AL HASA
AD DAHNA
Ar Riyad
Al Madinah
Makkah (Mecca)
Juddah
Tropic of Cancer
AL HIJAZ
ASIR
BAHRAIN IS.
Al Manāmah
QATAR
Ad Dawhah
TRUCIAL COAST
Abū Zabī
Dubayy
MUSCAT AND OMAN
Muscat
JABAL AL AKHDAR

AR RUB' AL KHALI
(EMPTY QUARTER)

SUDAN
Port Sudan
NAJRAN
YEMEN
San'a
Al Hudaydah
ADEN (BR. PROT.)
HADRAMAWT
Al Mukalla
Aden (Br.)

ETHIOPIA
FRENCH SOMALILAND
Djibouti
SOMALIA
Berbera

GULF OF ADEN
SOCOTRA (Br.)

ARABIAN SEA

PERSIAN GULF
GULF OF OMAN

Continued on pages 164-165

Continued on pages 164-165

Relief

Meters		Feet
3050		10 000
1525		5000
610		2000
305		1000
152.5		500
0	Sea Level	0
		Below Sea Level
152.5		500
1525		5000
3050		10 000

COPYRIGHT BY
RAND McNALLY & COMPANY
MADE IN U.S.A.

Longitude East of Greenwich

Scale 1:16 000 000; one inch to 250 miles. Polyconic Projection
Elevations and depressions are given in feet

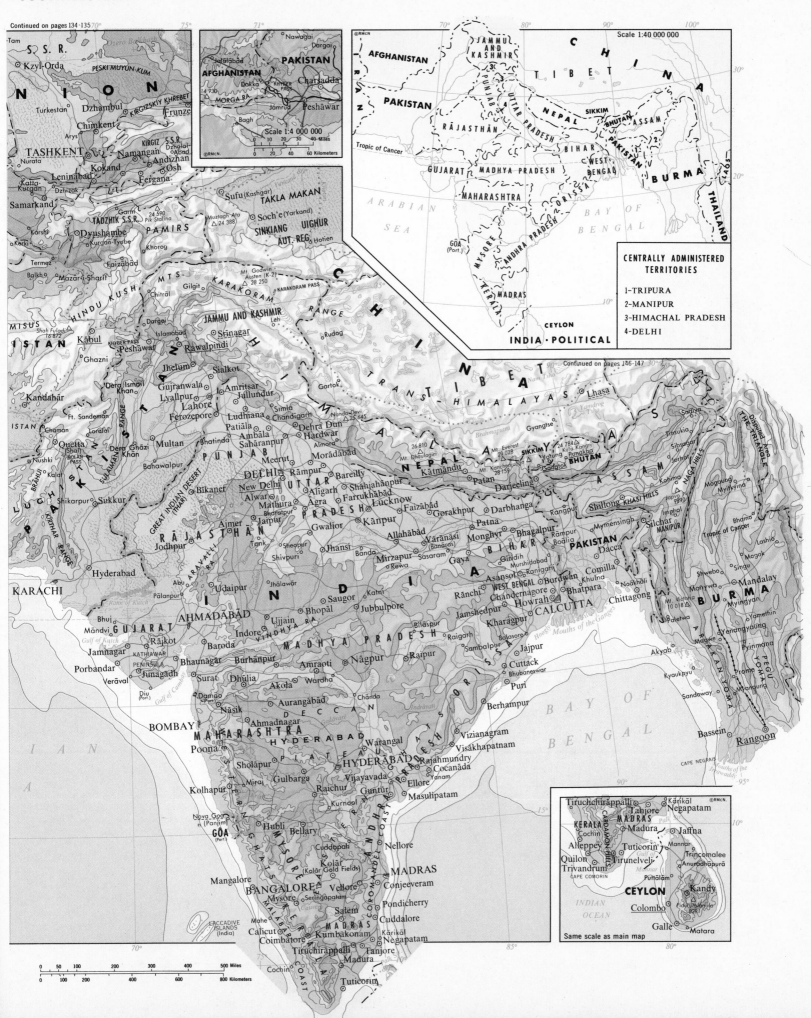

Continued on pages 134-135

Scale 1:40 000 000

AFGHANISTAN

PAKISTAN

JAMMU AND KASHMIR

CHINA

TIBET

NEPAL

SIKKIM

BHUTAN

ASSAM

PAKISTAN

BURMA

PUNJAB

UTTAR PRADESH

RAJASTHAN

BIHAR

WEST BENGAL

ORISSA

THAILAND

Tropic of Cancer

GUJARAT

MADHYA PRADESH

MAHARASHTRA

ARABIAN SEA

BAY OF BENGAL

GÔA (Port.)

MYSORE

ANDHRA PRADESH

KERALA

MADRAS

CEYLON

INDIA · POLITICAL

CENTRALLY ADMINISTERED TERRITORIES

1 – TRIPURA
2 – MANIPUR
3 – HIMACHAL PRADESH
4 – DELHI

PAKISTAN

AFGHANISTAN

MORGA RA.

14 930

Dokka

Dargai

Nawagai

Charsadda

Peshawar

Jámrud

Bagh

KHYBER PASS

Scale 1:4 000 000

0 10 20 30 40 Miles
0 20 40 60 Kilometers

Continued on pages 146-147

S. S. R.

Kzyl-Orda

PESKI MUYUN-KUM

U N I O N

Tam

Turkestan

Chimkent

Arys

Dzhambul

KIRGIZSKIY KHREBET

Frunze

KIRGIZ S.S.R.

Dzhalal-Abad

Osh

TASHKENT

Namangan

Andizhan

Nurata

Kokand

Fergana

Leninabad

Katta-Kurgan

Dzhizak

Samarkand

Garm

Pik Stalina 24 590

Muztagh Ata 24 388

TADZHIK S.S.R.

Karshi

Dyushambe

Kerki

Kurgan-Tyube

PAMIRS

Khorog

Termez

Faizabad

Balkh

Mazar-Sharif

HINDU KUSH

MTS.

Chitral

Dargai

Gilgit

KARAKORAM

RANGE

Mt. Godwin Austen (K-2) 28 250

KARAKORAM PASS

Sufu (Kashgar)

TAKLA MAKAN

Soch'e (Yarkand)

SINKIANG UIGHUR AUT. REG.

Hotien

Yarkand

Khotan

Rudog

Gartok

C H I N A

MISUS

Shah Fuladi 16 872

Kábul

Ghazni

Peshawar

Khyber Pass

Rawalpindi

Jhelum

Sialkot

Srinagar

Leh

JAMMU AND KASHMIR

Islamabad

Dargai

TRANS-HIMALAYAS

Lhasa

Yamdrog Tsho

Nam Tsho

Gyangtse

Gartok

I S T A N

Kandahár

Ft. Sandeman

Chaman

Loralai

Dera Ismail Khan

Gujranwala

Lyallpur

Lahore

Amritsar

Jullundur

Ferozepore

Ludhiana

Chandigarh

Simla

Nanda Devi 25 645

HIMALAYAS

26 810

Mt. Dhaulagiri 26 028

Mt. Everest 29 028

Mt. Kanchenjunga 28 159

24 784

Kula Kangri

Gyangtse

ISTAN

Quetta (Shal)

BOLAN PASS

Kalat

Dera Ghazi Khan

Multan

Bhatinda

Patiala

Ambala

Saháranpur

Dehra Dun

Hardwar

Almora

Morádábád

Káthmandu

Patan

NEPAL

Darjeeling

SIKKIM

Gangtok

Yatung

Punakha

BHUTAN

Nushki

BRAHUI

Shikarpur

Sukkur

PUNJAB

Bikaner

DELHI

New Delhi

Meerut

Rampur

Bareilly

Shahjahanpur

Aligarh

UTTAR

Mathura

Alwar

Bharatpur

Jaipur

Agra

Farrukhabad

Lucknow

Faizabad

Gorakhpur

Darbhanga

Rangpur

Mymensingh

Shillong

KHASI HILLS

Silchar

MANIPUR

Imphal

NAGA HILLS

Kohima

Mogaung

Myitkyina

KIRTHAR RANGE

Hyderabad

PRADESH

Kánpur

Gwalior

Jhansi

Allahabad

Banda

Varanasi (Banáras)

Mirzapur

Sásaram

Patna

Monghyr

Bhagalpur

Giridih

Murshidabad

Ranigonj

Bogra

Rampur

Boalia

DACCA

Comilla

Lashio

Mogok

Shwebo

Singu

Monywa

Mandalay

Myingyan

BURMA

KARACHI

Hyderabad

RÁJASTHÁN

Ajmer

Jodhpur

Abu

GREAT INDIAN DESERT (THAR)

ARAVALLI RA.

Udaipur

Tonk

Sheopur

Shivpuri

Jhálawár

Kátni

Rewa

Sásaram

Gaya

BIHAR

Ránchí

Asansol

Burdwan

WEST BENGAL

Chandernagore

Howrah

Bhatpara

Khulna

Noakháli

Chittagong

Mt. Victoria 10 018

Páletwa

Bhuj

Mándvi

Rann of Kutch

GUJARAT

AHMADÁBÁD

Rájkot

Jamnagar

Jamshedpur

Kharagpur

Balasore

CALCUTTA

Mouths of the Ganges

Hooghly

Akyab

Kyaukpyu

Sandoway

PROME

PEGU YOMA

Yenangyaung

Magwe

Minbu

Paletwa

Porbandar

KATHIAWAR

Junágadh

Bhaunagar

Surat

Dhúlia

Akola

Wardha

Chánda

Indore

Ujjain

Bhopál

Saugor

Jubbulpore

VINDHYA RA.

MADHYA PRADESH

Raigarh

Bilaspur

Raipur

Sambalpur

Jájpur

Cuttack

Bhubaneswar

Puri

Berhampur

BAY OF BENGAL

Bassein

Rangoon

PAKISTAN

YENANGYAUNG

Pyinmana

Yamethin

Toungoo

CAPE NEGRAIS

Mouths of the Irrawaddy

Diu (Port.)

Damáo (Port.)

Gulf of Cambay

Násik

Aurangábád

DECCAN

Amraoti

Nágpur

Indrávati

ORISSA

Vizianagram

Visakhapatnam

Rajahmundry

Cocanáda

Yanam

Ellore

Masulipatam

BOMBAY

MAHARASHTRA

Ahmadnagar

HYDERABAD

Poona

Sholápur

Warangal

HYDERABAD

Gulbarga

Mirai

ANDHRA

Vijayavada

Guntúr

PRADESH

Kolhapur

Raichur

Kurnool

Nellore

COROMANDEL COAST

Mangalore

Nova Goa (Panjim)

GÔA (Port.)

Hubli

Bellary

MYSORE

Cuddapah

Kolar (Kolar Gold Fields)

MADRAS

Conjeeveram

Pondicherry

Cuddalore

Karikal

Negapatam

I N D I A

INDIAN OCEAN

BANGALORE

Mysore

Seringapatam

Vellore

Salem

Mahé

Calicut

Coimbatore

Tiruchirappalli

Madura

Tuticorin

Cochin

LACCADIVE ISLANDS (India)

MALABAR COAST

WESTERN GHATS

NILGIRI HILLS

CEYLON

Tiruchirappalli

Tanjore

Karikal

Negapatam

MADRAS

Madura

Jaffna

Mannar

Trincomalee

Anuradhápura

Pulam

KERALA

Cochin

Alleppey

Quilon

Trivandrum

Tuticorin

Tirunelveli

CAPE COMORIN

CARDAMON HILLS

Kandy

8 281

Colombo

Galle

Matara

Pidurutalagala

Palk Strait

Gulf of Mannar

Same scale as main map

0 50 100 200 300 400 500 Miles
0 100 200 400 600 800 Kilometers

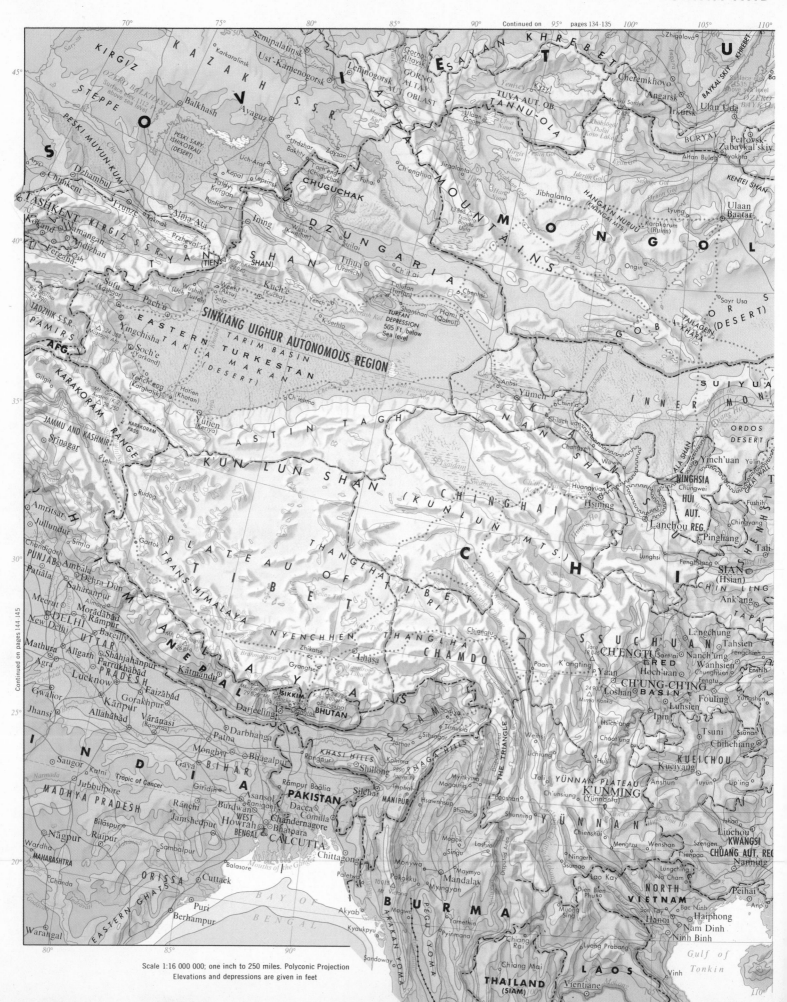

Continued on pages 134-135

Continued on pages 144-145

Scale 1:16 000 000; one inch to 250 miles. Polyconic Projection
Elevations and depressions are given in feet

JAPAN

Relief

Meters		Feet
3050		10 000
1525		5000
610		2000
305		1000
152.5		500
Sea Level		0
152.5		Below Sea Level
	500	
1525	5000	
3050	10 000	
6100	20 000	

COPYRIGHT BY
RAND McNALLY & COMPANY
MADE IN U.S.A.

Longitude East of Greenwich   Continued on pages 154-155

0   50   100   200   300   400   500 Miles
0   100   200   400   600   800 Kilometers

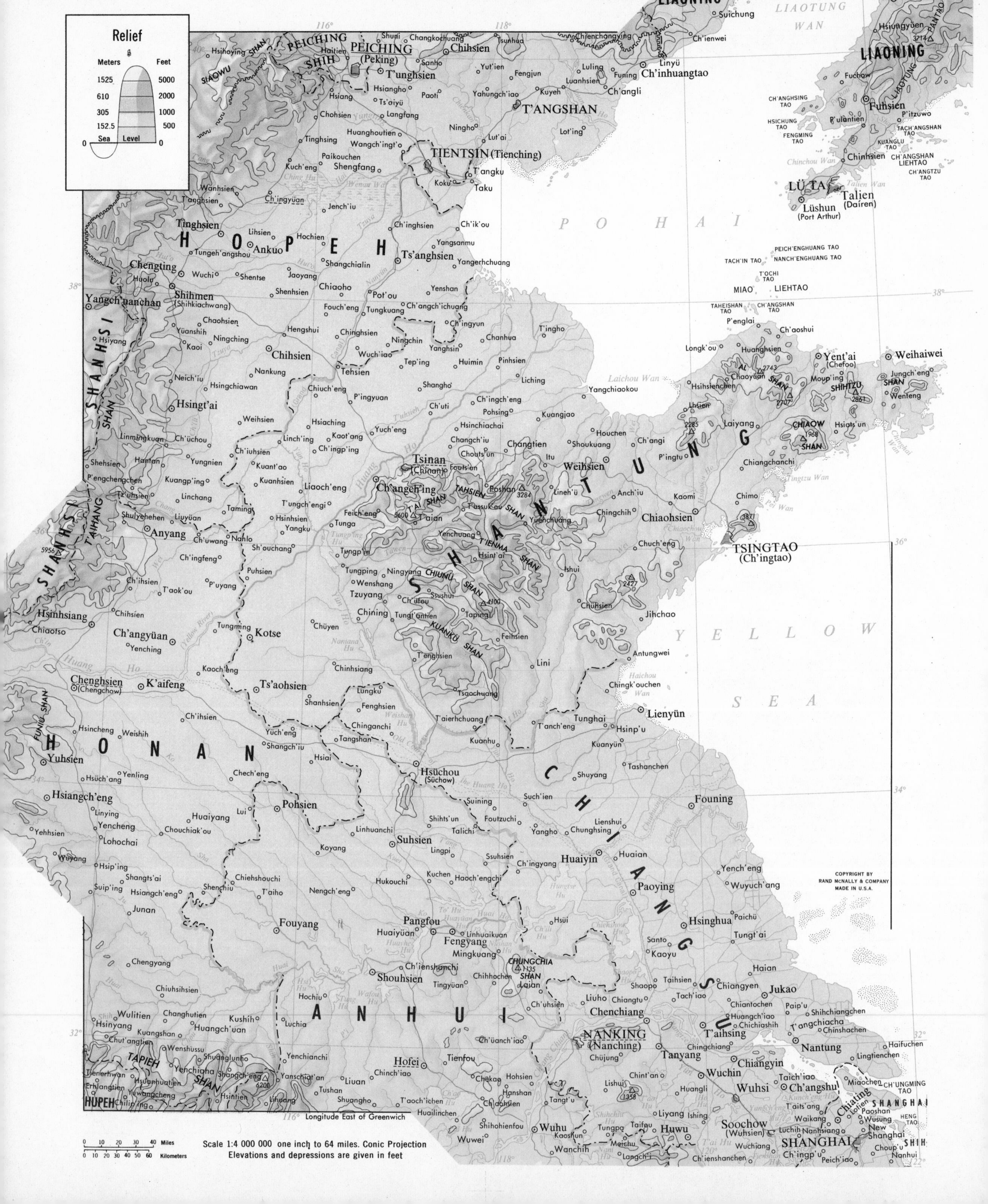

Relief

Meters	Feet
1525	5000
610	2000
305	1000
152.5	500
Sea Level	0
0	0

LIAONING

LIAONING

Hsingch'eng   CHÜHUA TAO   Kaip'ing

Suichung   Ch'ienchangying   Hsiungyüen

PEICHING SHIH   PEICHING (Peking)   T'unghsien   Chihsien   Tsunhua   Ch'ienwei   Ch'ienwei   3214

Hsihoying SHAN   Shuni   Changkochuang   Linyü   Ch'inhuangtao   Fuchow

SIAOWU   Haitien   Sanho   Yut'ien   Luling   Funing   Ch'ienwei   Pitzuwo

Hsiangho   Paoti   Yahungch'iao   Kuyeh   Luanhsien   Ch'angli   P'ulantien   Fuhsien

Chohsien   Langfang   Ningho   Lot'ing   Lut'ai

Huanghoutien   T'ANGSHAN

Tinghsing   Wangch'ingt'o   Lut'ai

TIENTSIN (Tienching)   T'angku   Koku   Taku

POHAI   LÜ TA   Talien (Dairen)

Lüshun (Port Arthur)

HOPEH   Tinghsien   Lihsien   Hochien   Ch'inghsien   Ch'ik'ou   Yangsanmu   Yangerhchuang   Chengting   Wuchi   Ankuo   Shangchialin   Ts'anghsien   Yenshan

Shihmen (Shihkiachwang)   Shentse   Jaoyang   Chiaoho   Pot'ou   Ch'angch'ichuang

Yangch'uanchan   Chaohsien   Shenhsien   Yenshan   Huimin   Pinhsien

Chihsien   Yüanshih   Ningching   Hengshui   Chinghsien   Ningchin   Yanghsin   Liching

SHANSI   SHAN   Hsiang   Kaoi   Nankung   Wuch'iao   Tehsien   Tep'ing   Shangho   Yangchiaokou

Hsingt'ai   Neich'iu   Hsingchiawan   Weihsien   Kaot'ang   Yüch'eng   Ch'uti   Ch'ingch'eng   Pohsing   Kuangjao

Linmingkuan   Ch'üchou   Ch'iuhsien   Linch'ing   Ch'ingp'ing   Hsinchiachai   Houchen   Ch'angi

Shehsien   Hantan   Yungnien   Kuant'ao   Liaoch'eng   Changch'iu   Chouts'un   Itu   Changtien   Shoukuang

P'engchengchen   Kuangp'ing   Kuanhsien   Tsinan (Chinan)   Fouts'un   Poshan   Lineh'u   Anch'iu   Kaomi

T'AIHANG   Ch'iuhsien   Taming   T'ungch'engi   Hsinhsien   Ch'angch'ing   TAHSIEN   TAI SHAN   3284   SHANTUNG

Liuyüan   Nahlo   Yangku   Feich'eng   T'ussuk'ou   Yüehchuang   Chingchih   Chiaohsien

Anyang   Ch'uwang   Sh'ouchang   3600   T'aian   TIENMA SHAN   Chuch'eng

5956   Ch'ihsien   Ch'ingfeng   Tungp'ing   Yenchuang   Hsini'an   Ishui   TSINGTAO (Ch'ingtao)

Hsinhsiang   T'aok'ou   Puhsien   Ningyang   CHIUNÜ SHAN   2427

Chiaotso   Chihsien   P'uyang   Tungp'ing Hu   Wenshang   Ch'üfou   4100   Chühsien

Ch'angyüan   Kotse   Tungming   Chüyen   Chining   Tungt'ientien   Tapingi   Feihsien   Jihchao

Chenghsien (Chengchow)   Yenching   Kaoch'eng   Chinhsiang   KUANKÜ SHAN   T'enghsien   Lini   Antungwei

K'aifeng   Ts'aohsien   Lungku   Fenghsien   Tsaochuang   Chingk'ouchen

FUNIU SHAN   Ch'ihsien   Shanhsien   Chinganchi   T'aierhchuang   SEA

HONAN   Yühsien   Hsincheng   Weishih   Yüch'eng   Tangshan   Kuanhu   T'anch'eng   Tunghai   Lienyün

Yuhsien   Hsüch'ang   Yenling   Chech'eng   Hsiai   Hsüchou (Süchow)   Suining   Such'ien   Shuyang   Tashanchen   Founing

YELLOW

Hsiangch'eng   Linying   Huaiyang   Lui   Pohsien   Shihts'un   Foutzuchi   Yangho   Lienshui

Yehhsien   Yencheng   Chouchiak'ou   Linhuanchi   Talichi   Lingpi   Ssuhsien   Chunghsing   Huaian   Yench'eng

Lohochai   Koyang   Kuchen   Haoch'engchi   Ch'ingyang   Huaiyin   Wuyuch'ang

Wuyang   Hsip'ing   Shangts'ai   Chiehshouchi   Shenchiu   T'aiho   Hukouchi   Nengch'eng   Paoying   Paichü

Suip'ing   Hsiangch'eng   Junan   Fouyang   Pangfou   Hsinghua   Tungt'ai

Chengyang   Huaiyüan   Linhuaikuan   Hsüi   Santo   Haian

Chiuhsihsien   Fengyang   CHUNGCHIA SHAN   H35   Kaoyu   Taihsien   Jukao

Wulitien   Changhutien   Kushih   Luchia   Mingkuang   Laian   Shaopo   Tach'iao   Chiangyen   Paip'u   Shihchiangchen

TAPIEH SHAN   Ch'ienshanchi   Shouhsien   Liuho   Chiangtu   Chiantochen   Huangch'iao   T'angchiacha   Chinshachen

HUPEH   Yenchiaha   Shangch'eng   6200   Hochiu   Tingyüan   Chihhochen   Ch'uhsien   Chenchiang   Chichiashih   Taihsing   Nantung

Tienerhwan   Hsüanhuatien   Yanschiat'an   Tienfou   Tushan   NANKING (Nanching)   Chüjung   Tanyang   Chingchiang   Lingtienchen

Erhlangchen   Wangcheng   Hsintien   Hofei   Livan   Chinch'iao   Chekao   Hohsien   T'ai'ang   Chiangyin   Ch'ungming Tao

Chilip'ing   Shanghao   T'aoch'ichen   Hanshan   Lishui   1358   Liyang   Ishing   Wuhsi   Taich'iao   Ch'angshul   Miaochen

Huailichen   T'aoch'ichen   Ch'aohsien   Tangt'u   Wuchin   T'ai's'ang   Loiten   Paoshan   HENG TAO

Shihhienfou   Wuhu   Kaoshun   Taifau   Meichu   Soochow (Wuhsien)   Luchih   Nanhsiang   New   Shanghai

Wuwei   Wanchih   SHANGHAI SHIH   Ch'ingp'u   Choup'u   Nanhui

0 10 20 30 40 Miles   0 10 20 30 40 50 60 Kilometers

Longitude East of Greenwich

COPYRIGHT BY RAND McNALLY & COMPANY MADE IN U.S.A.

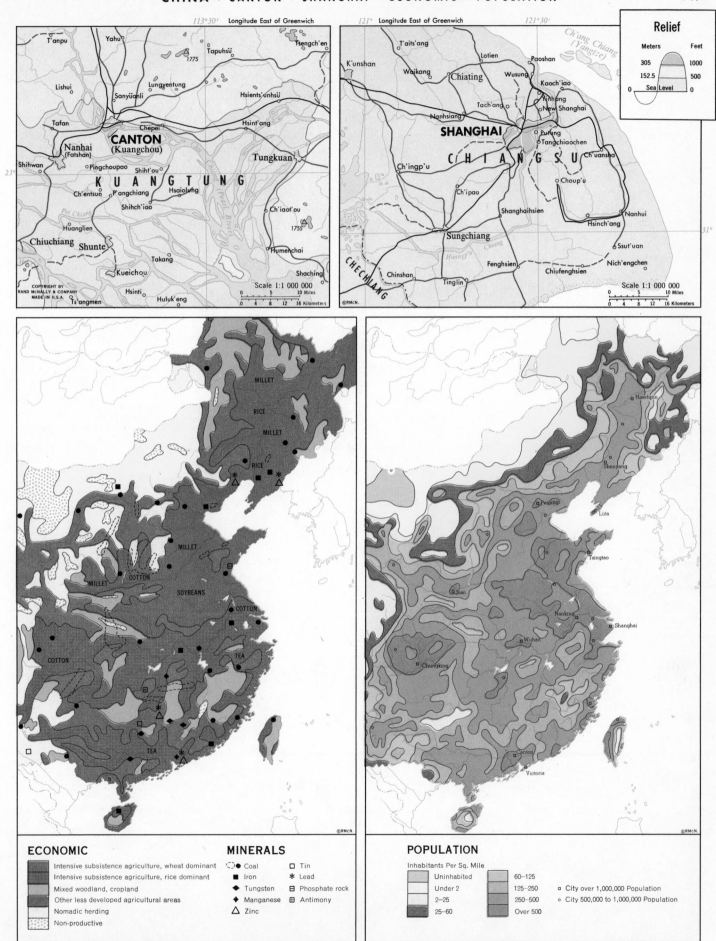

T'anpu · Yahu · Tapuhsü · Tsengch'en
1775
Lishui · Lungyentung · Hsients'unhsü
Sanyüanli · Hsint'ang
Tafan · Chepei
CANTON
(Kuangchou)
Nanhai · Tungkuan
(Fatshan)
Shihwan · Pingchoupao · Shiht'ou · **KUANGTUNG**
Ch'entsun · P'angchiang · Hsaiolung
Shihch'iao · Ch'iaot'ou
1755
Huanglien
Chiuchiang · **Shunte** · Humenchai
Takang
Kueichou · Shaching
Hsinti · Huluk'eng
Ts'angmen

COPYRIGHT BY
RAND McNALLY & COMPANY
MADE IN U.S.A.

Scale 1:1 000 000
0   2   5   10 Miles
0 4 8 12 16 Kilometers

Ch'ang Chiang
(Yangtze)

T'aits'ang · Lotien · Paoshan
K'unshan · Wukang · Chiating · Wusung
Kaoch'iao
Nanhsiang · Tach'ang · Hinhang · New Shanghai
SHANGHAI · Putung
CHIANGSU · Tangchiaochen
Ch'uansha
Ch'ingp'u · Choup'u
Ch'ipao · Nanhui
Shanghaihsien · Hsinch'ang
Sungchiang · Ssut'uan
CHECHIANG · Huangp'u · Nich'engchen
Chinshan · Fenghsien · Chiufenghsien
Tinglin

©RMCN.

Scale 1:1 000 000
0   2   5   10 Miles
0 4 8 12 16 Kilometers

Relief

Meters		Feet
305		1000
152.5		500
0	Sea Level	0

ECONOMIC

- Intensive subsistence agriculture, wheat dominant
- Intensive subsistence agriculture, rice dominant
- Mixed woodland, cropland
- Other less developed agricultural areas
- Nomadic herding
- Non-productive

MINERALS

- ⬤ Coal
- ■ Iron
- ◆ Tungsten
- ◆ Manganese
- △ Zinc
- □ Tin
- ✳ Lead
- ⊟ Phosphate rock
- ⊞ Antimony

POPULATION

Inhabitants Per Sq. Mile
- Uninhabited
- Under 2
- 2–25
- 25–60
- 60–125
- 125–250
- 250–500
- Over 500
- ▫ City over 1,000,000 Population
- ◦ City 500,000 to 1,000,000 Population

MILLET
RICE
MILLET
RICE
MILLET
COTTON
MILLET
SOYBEANS
COTTON
COTTON
TEA
COTTON
TEA

Haerhpin
Shenyang
Peiping · Lüta
Sian
Tsingtao
Nanking
Wuhan · Shanghai
Chungking
Canton
Victoria

©RMcN.
©RMcN.

Continued on page 152

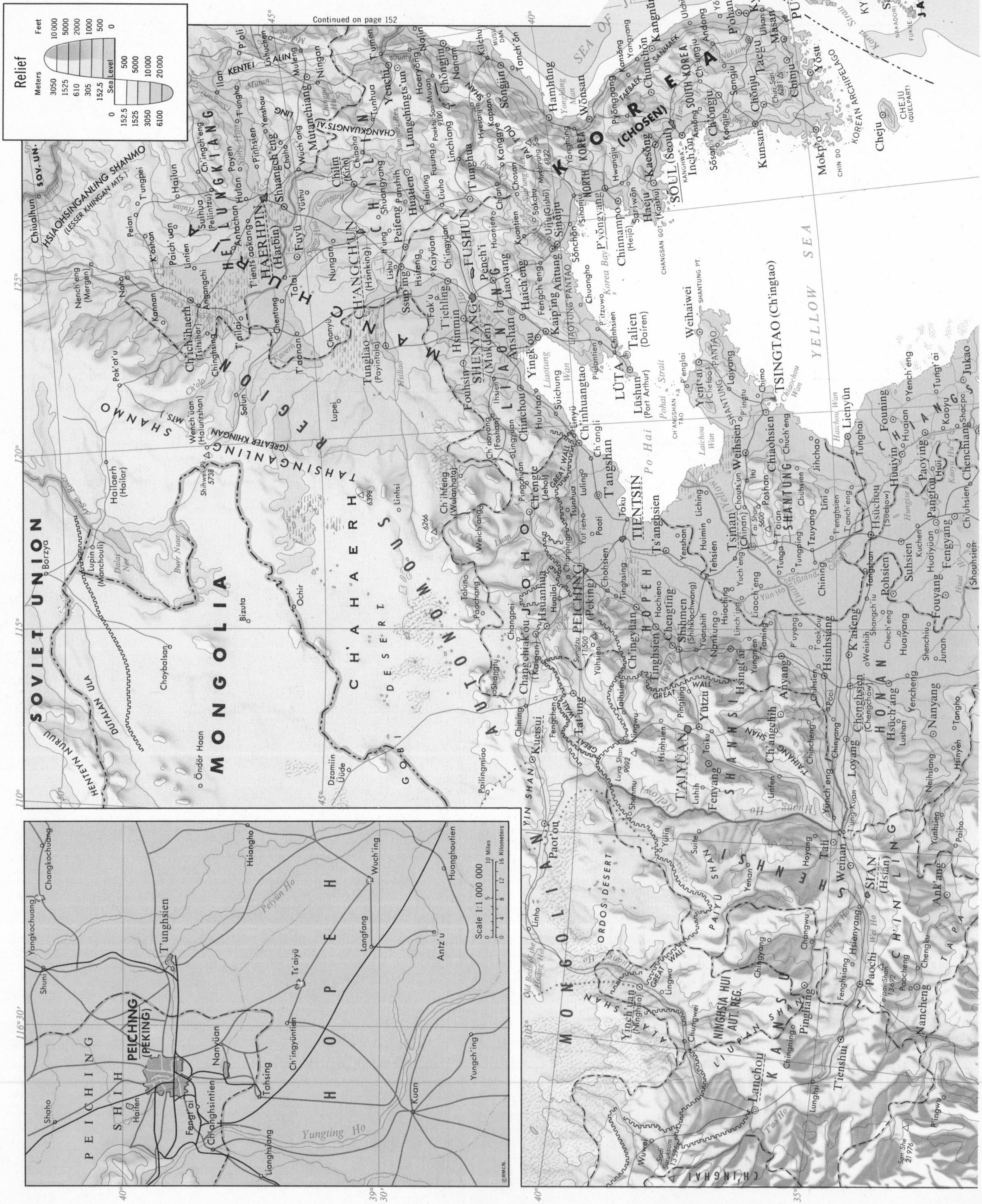

Relief

Meters	Feet
3050	10000
1525	5000
610	2000
305	1000
152.5	500
0	Sea Level 0
152.5	500
1525	5000
3050	10000
6100	20000

SEA OF JAPAN

TSU SHIMA
IKI SHIMA
KYŪSHŪ
Sasebo
JAPAN
NIKADORI
FUKIE
KOREA STRAIT
PUSAN
Masan
Chinju
Yōsu
Mokp'o
KOREAN ARCHIPELAGO
CHEJU (QUELPART)
Cheju
CHIN DO
CHEJU DO

SOVIET UNION

HSIAOHSINGANLING SHANMO (LESSER KHINGAN MTS.)

HEILUNGKIANG
HAERHPIN (Harbin)
Ch'ichihaerh (Tsitsihar)
Hailun
Nench'eng (Mergen)
Hailar (Hailaerh)

KIRIN
CHANGCHUN (Hsinking)
Ssup'ing

MANCHURIA

SHENYANG (Mukden)
FUSHUN
Penhsi
LIAONING
Anshan
Yingkou
LÜTA
Lüshun (Port Arthur)
Talien (Dairen)

KOREA (CHOSEN)
Hamhŭng
Hŭngnam
Wŏnsan
NORTH KOREA
P'yŏngyang (Heijō)
Chinnampo
SOUTH KOREA
Inch'ŏn
SŎUL (Seoul)
Kaesŏng
Sariwŏn
Kunsan
Taegu
Taejŏn

YELLOW SEA

Weihaiwei
Chefoo (Yent'ai)
TSINGTAO (Ch'ingtao)
SHANTUNG
Tsinan
Weihsien
Po Hai

SOVIET UNION
Borzya
MONGOLIA
Choybalsan
Öndör Haan
GOBI
SHAMO DESERT

CH'AERH DESERT

MONGOLIA
Paotou
ORDOS DESERT
NINGHSIA HUI AUT. REG.
Yinch'uan (Ninghsia)

PEICHING (Peking)
HOPEH
TIENTSIN
Tangshan
Chinhuangtao
GREAT WALL
Chengte (Jehol)

SHANSI
TAIYÜAN
SHENSI
SIAN (Hsian)
SZECHWAN
KANSU
Lanchou
Tienshui

HONAN
Kaifeng
Loyang
CHINLING

KIANGSU
Hsüchou

CHINGHAI

Inset: Peiching (Peking) area

PEICHING SHIH
PEICHING (PEKING)
HOPEH
Tunghsien
Wuch'ing
Nanyüan
Langfang
Shaho
Yungting Ho
Paiyün Ho
Kuan
Huanghouhsien

Scale 1:1 000 000
0 10 Miles
0 16 Kilometers

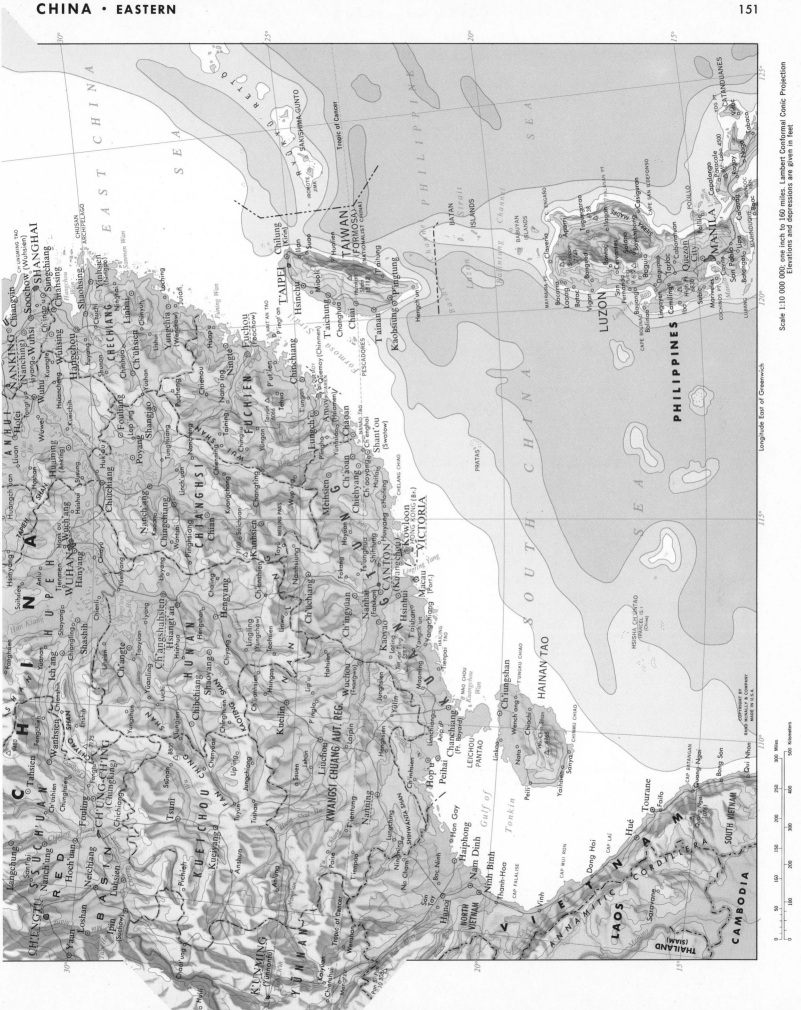

Scale 1:10 000 000; one inch to 160 miles. Lambert Conformal Conic Projection
Elevations and depressions are given in feet

COPYRIGHT BY
RAND McNALLY & COMPANY
MADE IN U.S.A.

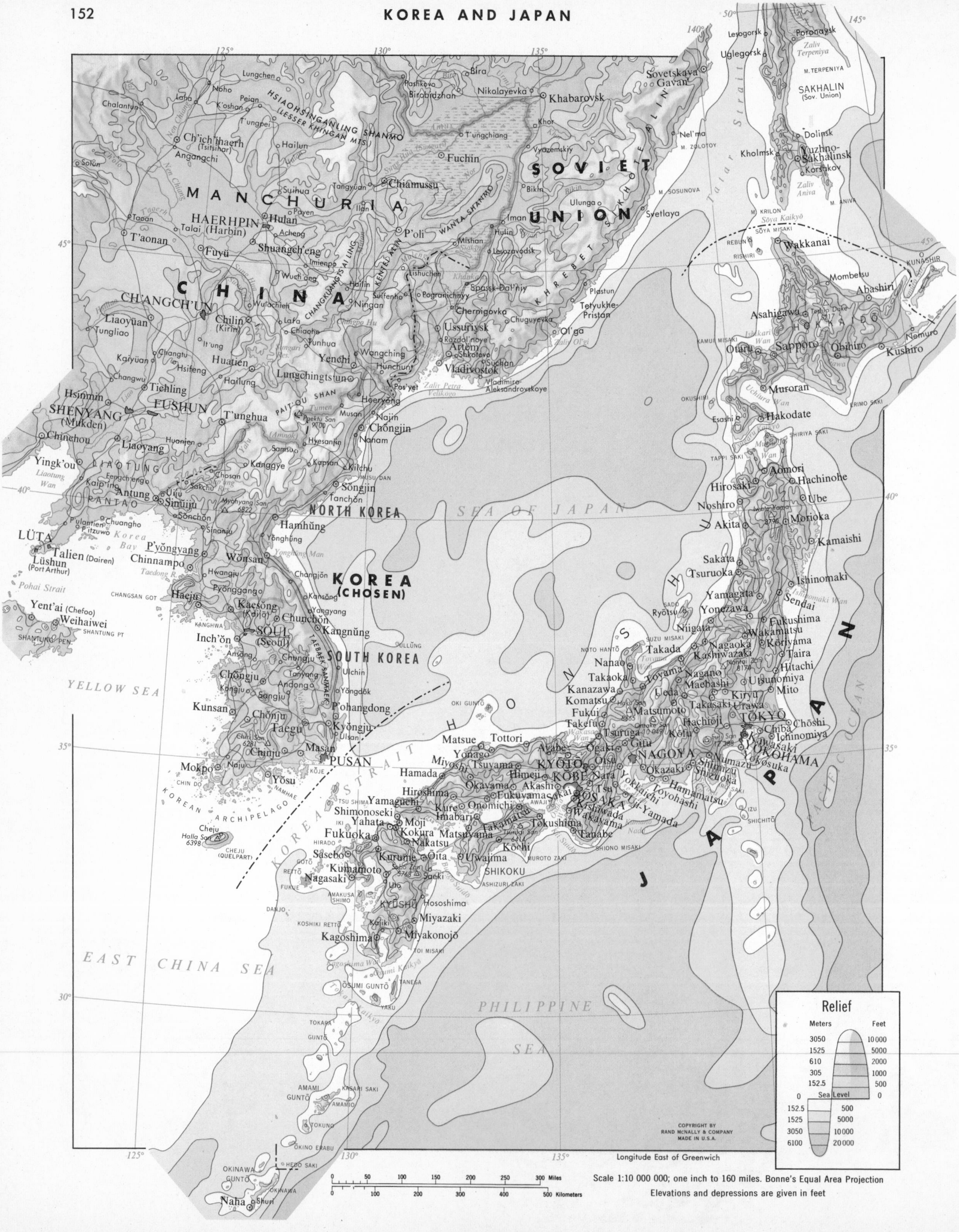

SOVIET UNION

MANCHURIA

CHINA

HAERHPIN (Harbin)

Talai (Harbin)

T'aonan

CH'ANGCH'UN

Liaoyüan

Tungliao

Kaiyüan

Changwu

Tiehling

FUSHUN

SHENYANG (Mukden)

Chinchou

Liaoyang

Yingk'ou

LIAOTUNG

LÜTA

Talien (Dairen)

Lüshun (Port Arthur)

Yent'ai (Chefoo)

Weihaiwei

SHANTUNG PEN.

Pohai Strait

HSIAOHSINGANLING SHANMO (LESSER KHINGAN MTS.)

Khabarovsk

Chiamussu

Fuchin

Ussuriysk

Vladivostok

SAKHALIN (Sov. Union)

Dolinsk

Yuzhno-Sakhalinsk

Korsakov

Wakkanai

Abashiri

Asahigawa

HOKKAIDO

Sapporo

Obihiro

Kushiro

Nemuro

Muroran

Hakodate

Esashi

NORTH KOREA

P'yŏngyang

Chinnampo

Wŏnsan

Hŭngnam

Hamhŭng

Chŏngjin

Najin

Nanam

KOREA (CHOSEN)

SŎUL (Seoul)

Inch'ŏn

Haeju

Kaesŏng (Kaijo)

Chunch'ŏn

Kangnŭng

SOUTH KOREA

Taejŏn

Chŏnju

Taegu

Chinju

Masan

PUSAN

Mokpo

Yŏsu

Cheju (Quelpart)

Halla San 6398

YELLOW SEA

SEA OF JAPAN

HONSHU

Niigata

Nagaoka

Kanazawa

Komatsu

Fukui

Takefu

Matsue

Tottori

Yonago

Hiroshima

Yamaguchi

Shimonoseki

Moji

Kokura

Yahata

Fukuoka

Sasebo

Nagasaki

Kumamoto

Kagoshima

Miyazaki

Miyakonojo

KYUSHU

SHIKOKU

Matsuyama

Takamatsu

Tokushima

Kōchi

Uwajima

Ōita

Nakatsu

Kurume

NAGOYA

KYOTO

KOBE

OSAKA

Nara

Wakayama

TOKYO

YOKOHAMA

Chiba

Nagano

Matsumoto

Gifu

Hamamatsu

Shizuoka

Sendai

Morioka

Akita

Aomori

Hachinohe

Hirosaki

Yamagata

Fukushima

Utsunomiya

Mito

EAST CHINA SEA

PHILIPPINE SEA

PACIFIC OCEAN

JAPAN

KOREA STRAIT

KOREAN ARCHIPELAGO

AMAMI GUNTO

OKINAWA

Naha

COPYRIGHT BY
RAND McNALLY & COMPANY
MADE IN U.S.A.

Relief

Meters		Feet
3050		10 000
1525		5000
610		2000
305		1000
152.5		500
Sea Level		0
152.5		500
1525		5000
3050		10 000
6100		20 000

Scale 1:10 000 000; one inch to 160 miles. Bonne's Equal Area Projection

Elevations and depressions are given in feet

Longitude East of Greenwich

0 50 100 150 200 250 300 Miles

0 100 200 300 400 500 Kilometers

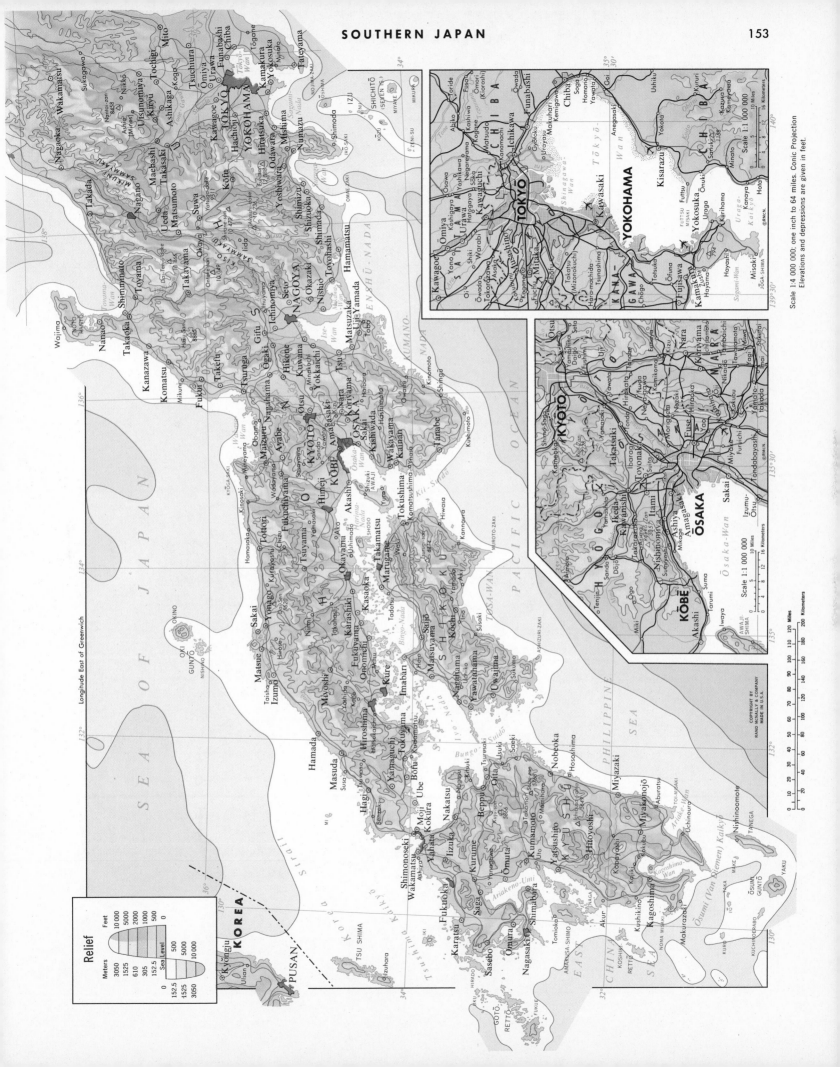

Scale 1:4 000 000; one inch to 64 miles. Conic Projection
Elevations and depressions are given in feet.

Scale 1:1 000 000

TŌKYŌ

YOKOHAMA

KYŌTO

ŌSAKA

KŌBE

Scale 1:1 000 000

KOREA

PUSAN

KYŪSHŪ

SHIKOKU

NAGOYA

TŌKYŌ

YOKOHAMA

KYŌTO

ŌSAKA

KŌBE

SEA OF JAPAN

PACIFIC OCEAN

PHILIPPINE SEA

EAST CHINA SEA

Relief

Meters	Feet
3050	10 000
1525	5000
610	2000
305	1000
152.5	500
0	Sea Level
152.5	500
1525	5000
3050	10 000

COPYRIGHT BY
RAND McNALLY & COMPANY
MADE IN U.S.A.

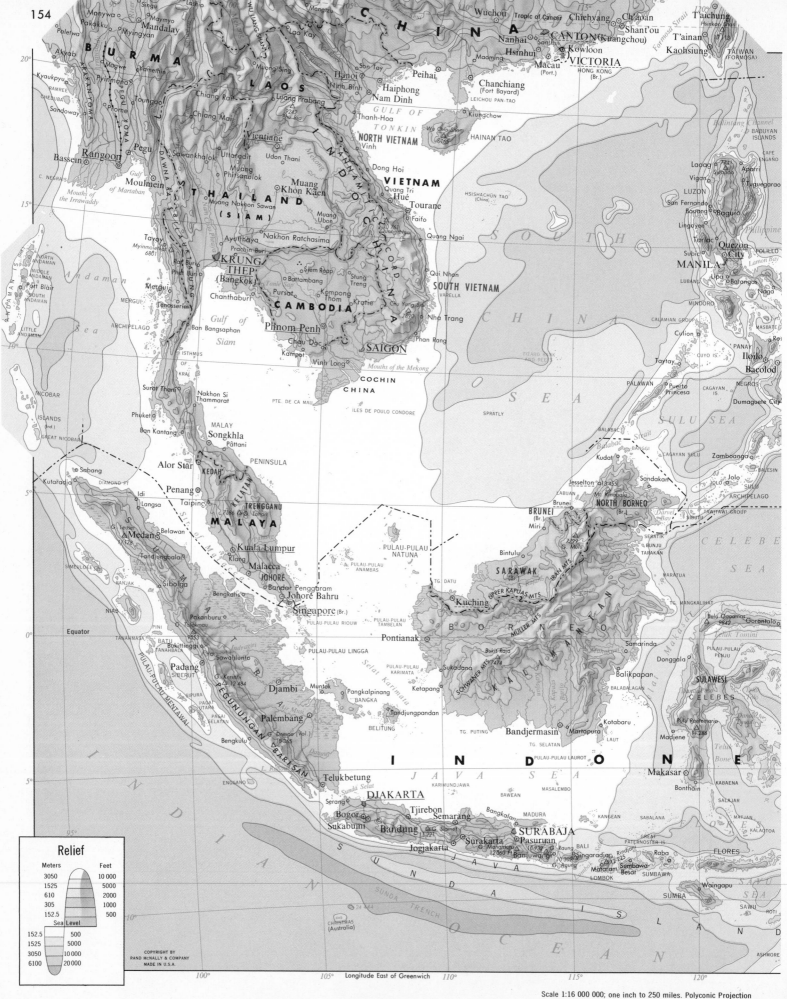

Scale 1:16 000 000; one inch to 250 miles. Polyconic Projection
Elevations and depressions are given in feet

Relief

Meters		Feet
3050		10 000
1525		5000
610		2000
305		1000
152.5		500
	Sea Level	
152.5		500
1525		5000
3050		10 000
6100		20 000

COPYRIGHT BY
RAND McNALLY & COMPANY
MADE IN U.S.A.

Longitude East of Greenwich

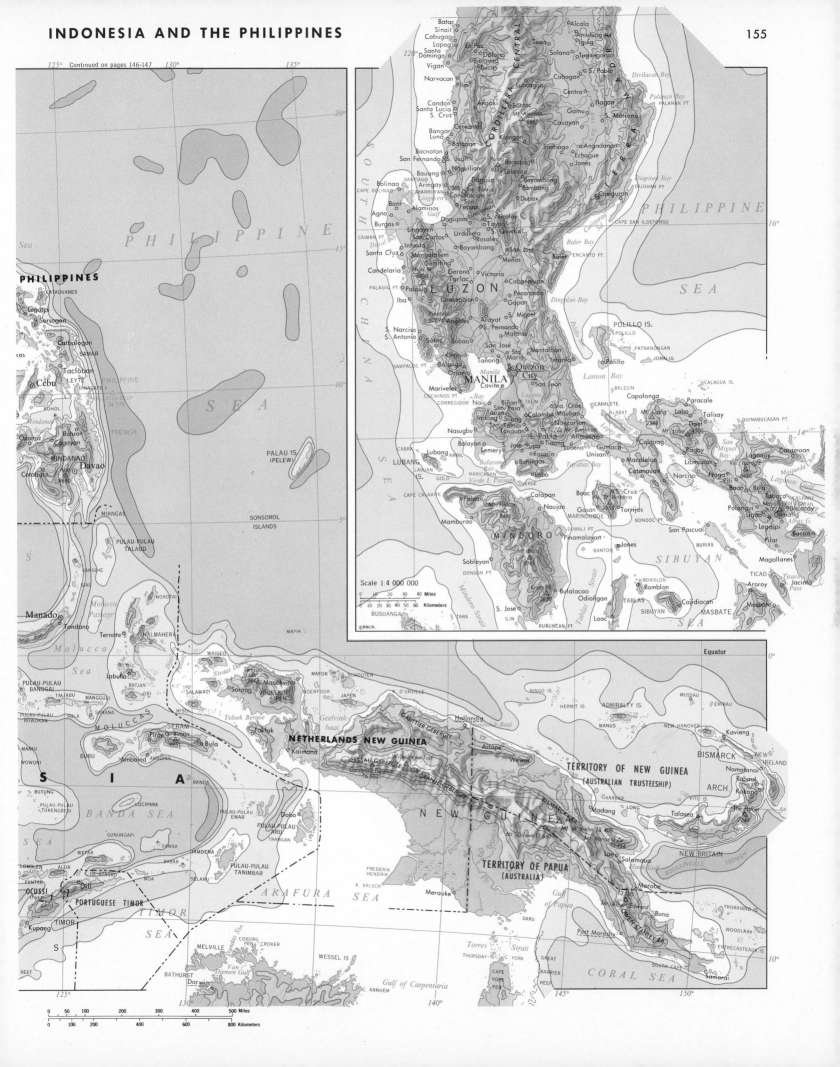

INDONESIA AND THE PHILIPPINES

Continued on pages 146-147

PHILIPPINE

Sea

PHILIPPINES

PHILIPPINE

SEA

SOUTH CHINA SEA

LUZON

MANILA

MINDORO

SIBUYAN

SEA

Scale 1:4 000 000

0 10 20 30 40 Miles

0 10 20 30 40 50 60 Kilometers

©RMcN.

PHILIPPINE

SEA

A   S   I   A

MOLUCCA
Sea

BANDA SEA

MOLUCCAS

Equator

NETHERLANDS NEW GUINEA

NEW   GUINEA

TERRITORY OF NEW GUINEA
(AUSTRALIAN TRUSTEESHIP)

BISMARCK
ARCH.

NEW
IRELAND

NEW BRITAIN

TERRITORY OF PAPUA
(AUSTRALIA)

TIMOR

PORTUGUESE TIMOR

OCUSSI
(Port.)

TIMOR
SEA

ARAFURA
SEA

CORAL SEA

Gulf of Carpentaria

0   50 100   200   300   400   500 Miles

0   100   200   400   600   800 Kilometers

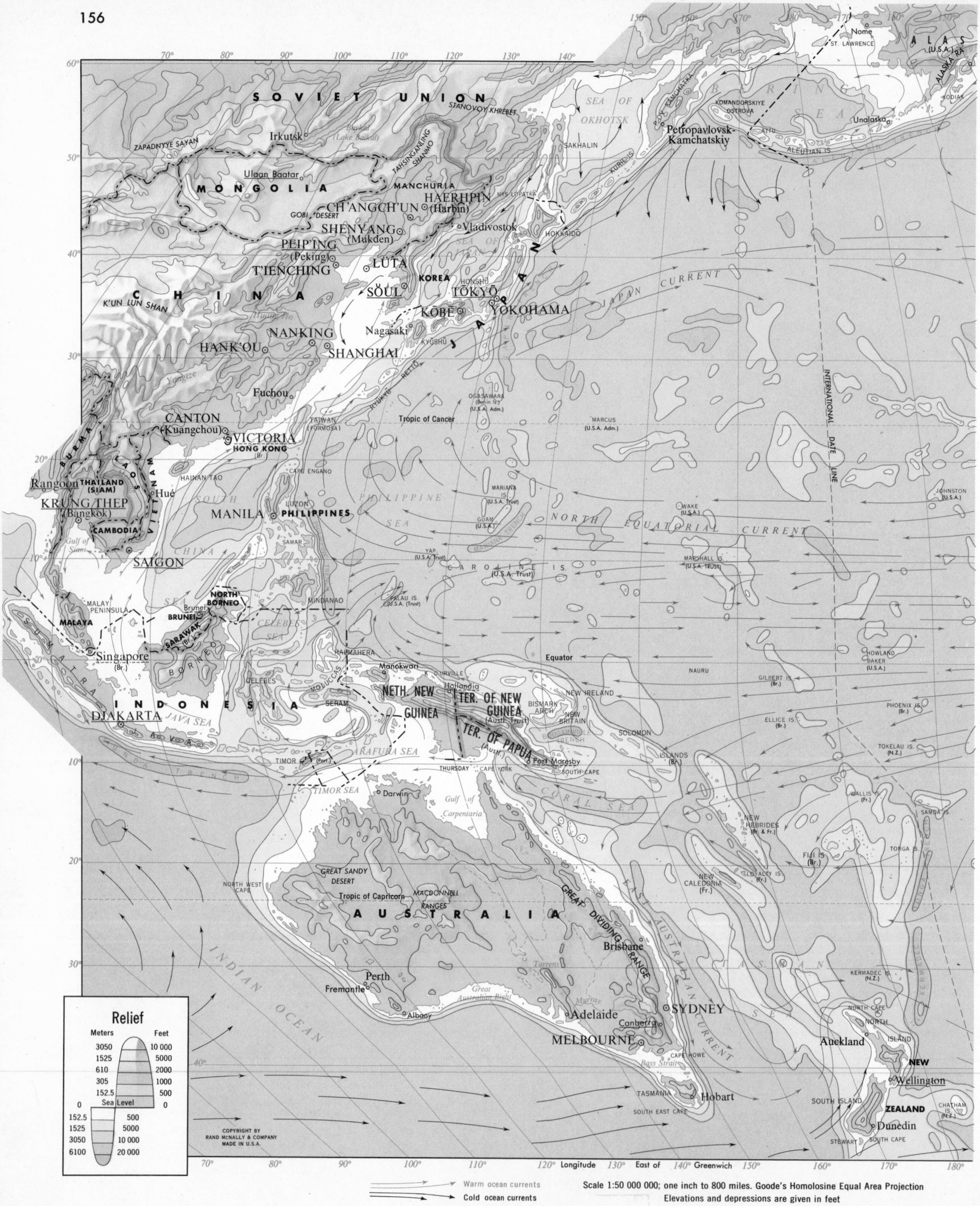

SOVIET UNION

SEA OF OKHOTSK

STANOVOY KHREBÉT

MYS LOPATKA

Irkutsk

Baykal (Lake Baikal)

ZAPADNYYE SAYAN

Petropavlovsk-Kamchatskiy

KOMANDORSKIYE OSTROVA

B E R I N G   S E A

Nome

ST. LAWRENCE

A L A S K A (U.S.A.)

ALASKA RA

KODIAK

Unalaska

TAHSINGANLING SHANMO

MONGOLIA

Ulaan Baatar

MANCHURIA

HAERHPIN (Harbin)

CH'ANGCH'UN

SHENYANG (Mukden)

Vladivostok

SAKHALIN

K U R I L I S

GOBI DESERT

PEIP'ING (Peking)

LÜTA

T'IENCHING

KOREA

SÖUL

HOKKAIDO

J   A   P   A   N

TOKYO

HONSHU

KOBE

YOKOHAMA

JAPAN CURRENT

C H I N A

K'UN LUN SHAN

NANKING

Hwang Ho

Nagasaki

KYUSHU

HANK'OU

SHANGHAI

Yangtze

RYUKYU RETTO

Fuchou

OGASAWARA (Bonin Is.) (U.S.A. Adm.)

Tropic of Cancer

MARCUS (U.S.A. Adm.)

INTERNATIONAL DATE LINE

CANTON (Kuangchou)

VICTORIA HONG KONG (Br.)

TAIWAN (FORMOSA)

BURMA

Rangoon

THAILAND (SIAM)

LAOS

VIETNAM

HAINAN TAO

CAPE ENGANO

MARIANA IS. (U.S.A. Trust)

WAKE (U.S.A.)

JOHNSTON (U.S.A.)

Hué

SOUTH CHINA SEA

LUZON

PHILIPPINE SEA

GUAM (U.S.A.)

KRUNG THEP (Bangkok)

CAMBODIA

MANILA

PHILIPPINES

N O R T H   E Q U A T O R I A L   C U R R E N T

Gulf of Siam

SAIGON

SAMAR

YAP (U.S.A. Trust)

C A R O L I N E   I S.

MARSHALL (U.S.A. Trust)

MINDANAO

PALAU IS. (U.S.A. Trust)

MALAY PENINSULA

NORTH BORNEO

Brunei

MARIANA TRENCH

MALAYA

BRUNEI

SARAWAK (Br.)

CELEBES SEA

SUMATRA

Singapore (Br.)

BORNEO

CELEBES

HALMAHERA

K DURVILLE

Equator

NAURU

GILBERT IS. (Br.)

HOWLAND BAKER (U.S.A.)

MOLUCCOS

Manokwari

NEW IRELAND

PHOENIX IS. (Br.)

SERAM

NETH. NEW GUINEA

Hollandia

TER. OF NEW GUINEA (Austl. Trust)

BISMARK ARCH

NEW BRITAIN

INDONESIA

DJAKARTA

JAVA SEA

JAVA

BOUGAINVILLE TRENCH

SOLOMON

ELLICE IS. (Br.)

TOKELAU IS. (N.Z.)

TER. OF PAPUA (Austl.)

ISLANDS (Br.)

TIMOR (Port.)

ARAFURA SEA

Port Moresby

SOUTH CAPE

WALLIS (Fr.)

SAMOA IS.

SUNDA TRENCH

THURSDAY

CAPE YORK

CORAL SEA

TIMOR SEA

Darwin

Gulf of Carpentaria

NEW HEBRIDES (Br. & Fr.)

NORTH WEST CAPE

GREAT SANDY DESERT

MACDONNELL RANGES

Tropic of Capricorn

GREAT DIVIDING RANGE

NEW CALEDONIA (Fr.)

LOYALTY IS. (Fr.)

FIJI IS. (Br.)

TONGA IS.

A U S T R A L I A

Brisbane

EAST AUSTRALIAN CURRENT

KERMADEC IS. (N.Z.)

Perth

Torrens

Murray

Fremantle

Great Australian Bight

SYDNEY

Adelaide

Canberra

T A S M A N   S E A

NORTH CAPE

NORTH ISLAND

MELBOURNE

CAPE HOWE

Auckland

NEW

Bass Strait

Wellington

TASMANIA

Hobart

SOUTH EAST CAPE

SOUTH ISLAND

ZEALAND

CHATHAM IS. (N.Z.)

STEWART

SOUTH CAPE

Dunedin

I N D I A N   O C E A N

Albany

Relief

Meters		Feet
3050		10 000
1525		5000
610		2000
305		1000
152.5		500
0	Sea Level	0
152.5		500
1525		5000
3050		10 000
6100		20 000

COPYRIGHT BY RAND McNALLY & COMPANY MADE IN U.S.A.

70° 80° 90° 100° 110° 120° Longitude 130° East of 140° Greenwich 150° 160° 170° 180°

→ Warm ocean currents

→ Cold ocean currents

Scale 1:50 000 000; one inch to 800 miles. Goode's Homolosine Equal Area Projection

Elevations and depressions are given in feet

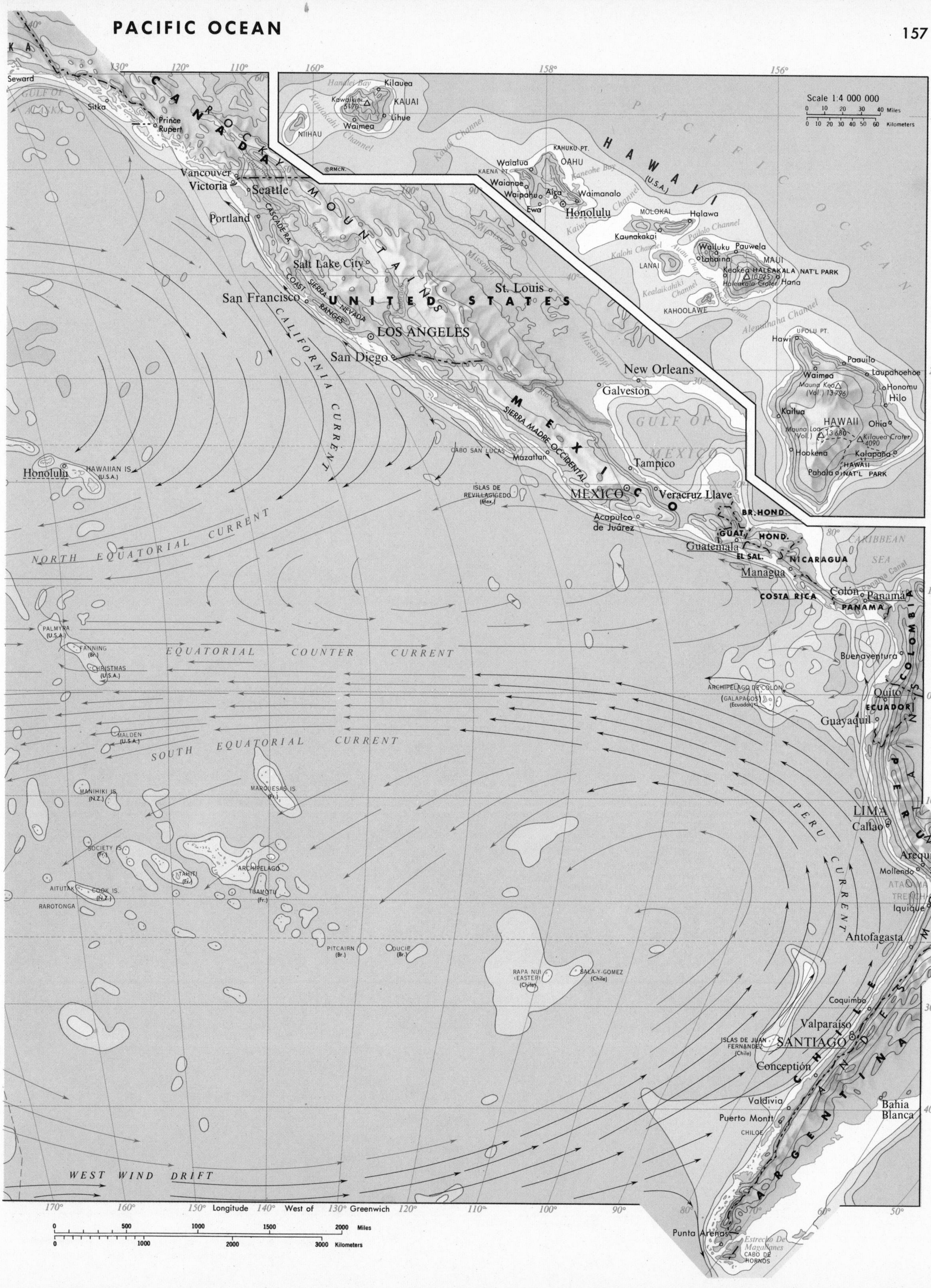

Seward

GULF OF ALASKA

Sitka

Prince Rupert

CANADA

ROCKY MOUNTAINS

Vancouver
Victoria • Seattle

Portland

CASCADE RA.

Salt Lake City

COAST RANGES

San Francisco

SIERRA NEVADA

UNITED STATES

Los Angeles

San Diego

CALIFORNIA CURRENT

St. Louis

Missouri

Mississippi

New Orleans

Galveston

SIERRA MADRE OCCIDENTAL

CABO SAN LUCAS

Mazatlan

MEXICO

GULF OF MEXICO

Tampico

ISLAS DE REVILLAGIGEDO (Mex.)

MEXICO

Veracruz Llave

Acapulco de Juárez

BR. HOND.

GUAT. HOND.

Guatemala
EL SAL. NICARAGUA

Managua

COSTA RICA

Colón Panama

PANAMA

CARIBBEAN SEA

Buenaventura

COLOMBIA

ARCHIPELAGO DE COLON
(GALAPAGOS)
(Ecuador)

Quito
ECUADOR

Guayaquil

PERU

LIMA
Callao

Arequipa

Mollendo

ATACAMA TRENCH

Iquique

Antofagasta

Coquimbo

Valparaíso

ISLAS DE JUAN FERNANDEZ (Chile)

SANTIAGO

Conception

ANDES

ARGENTINA

CHILE

Valdivia

Puerto Montt

CHILOE

Bahia Blanca

Punta Arenas

Estrecho De Magallanes
CABO DE HORNOS

HAWAII inset

Hanalei Bay
Kilauea

Kawaikini 5170

KAUAI

Waimea
Lihue

NIIHAU

Kauakahi Channel

Kaua Channel

KAHUKU PT.

OAHU

KAENA PT.

Waialua

Kaneohe Bay

Waianae

Waipahu
Aiea

Waimanalo

Ewa

Honolulu

MOLOKAI

Halawa

Kaunakakai

Kalohi Channel

Pailolo Channel

LANAI

Wailuku Pauwela
Lahaina

MAUI

Keokea HALEAKALA NAT'L PARK
10,025

Haleakala Crater 4090 Hana

Kealaikahiki Channel

KAHOOLAWE

Alenuihaha Channel

UPOLU PT.

Hawi

Waimea
Mauna Kea △ (Vol.) 13,796

Paauilo
Laupahoehoe

Kailua

Honomu

HAWAII

Hilo

Hookena

Mauna Loa (Vol.) △ 13,680

Kilauea Crater 4090

Ohia

Kalapana

Pahala HAWAII NAT'L PARK

HAWAII (U.S.A.)

PACIFIC OCEAN

Scale 1:4 000 000
0 10 20 30 40 Miles
0 10 20 30 40 50 60 Kilometers

Main ocean area

PACIFIC OCEAN

Honolulu
HAWAIIAN IS. (U.S.A.)

NORTH EQUATORIAL CURRENT

PALMYRA (U.S.A.)

FANNING (Br.)

CHRISTMAS (U.S.A.)

EQUATORIAL COUNTER CURRENT

MALDEN (U.S.A.)

SOUTH EQUATORIAL CURRENT

MANIHIKI IS. (N.Z.)

MARQUESAS IS. (Fr.)

SOCIETY IS. (Fr.)

TAHITI (Fr.)

ARCHIPELAGO

AITUTAKI

COOK IS. (N.Z.)

RAROTONGA

TUAMOTU (Fr.)

PITCAIRN (Br.)

DUCIE (Br.)

RAPA NUI (EASTER) (Chile)

SALA-Y-GOMEZ (Chile)

PERU CURRENT

CHILE

WEST WIND DRIFT

©RMCN

©RMCN

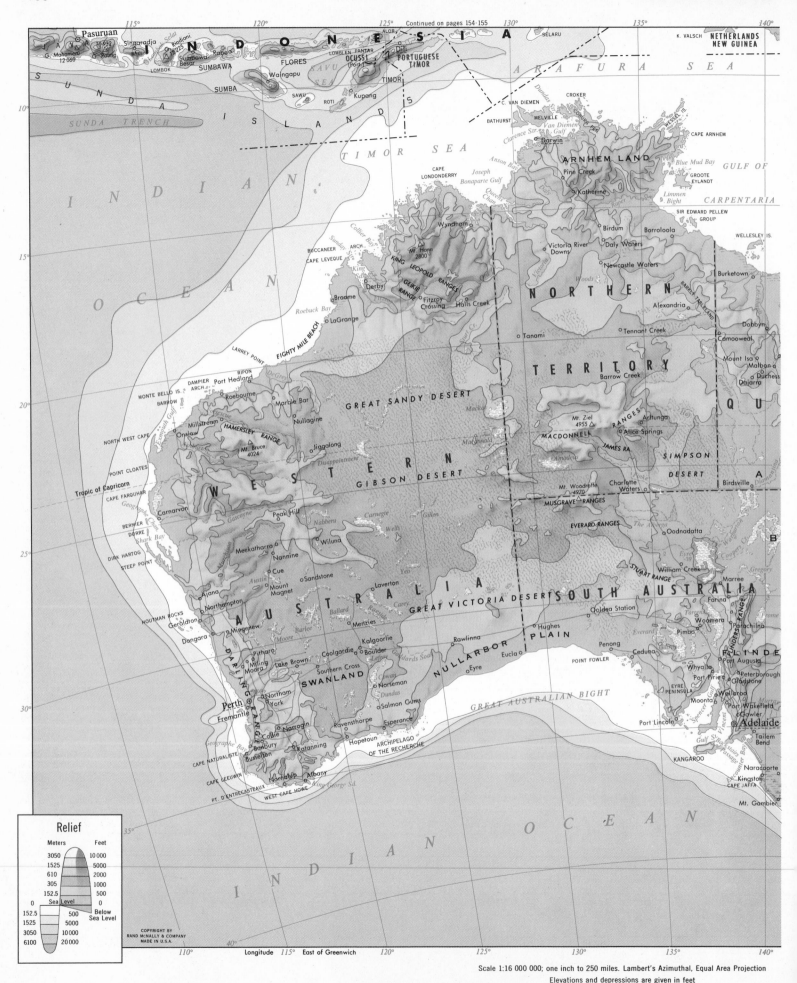

Continued on pages 154·155

Relief

Meters	Feet
3050	10 000
1525	5000
610	2000
305	1000
152.5	500
0 Sea Level	Sea Level
152.5	500 Below Sea Level
1525	5000
3050	10 000
6100	20 000

Longitude 115° East of Greenwich

Scale 1:16 000 000; one inch to 250 miles. Lambert's Azimuthal, Equal Area Projection
Elevations and depressions are given in feet

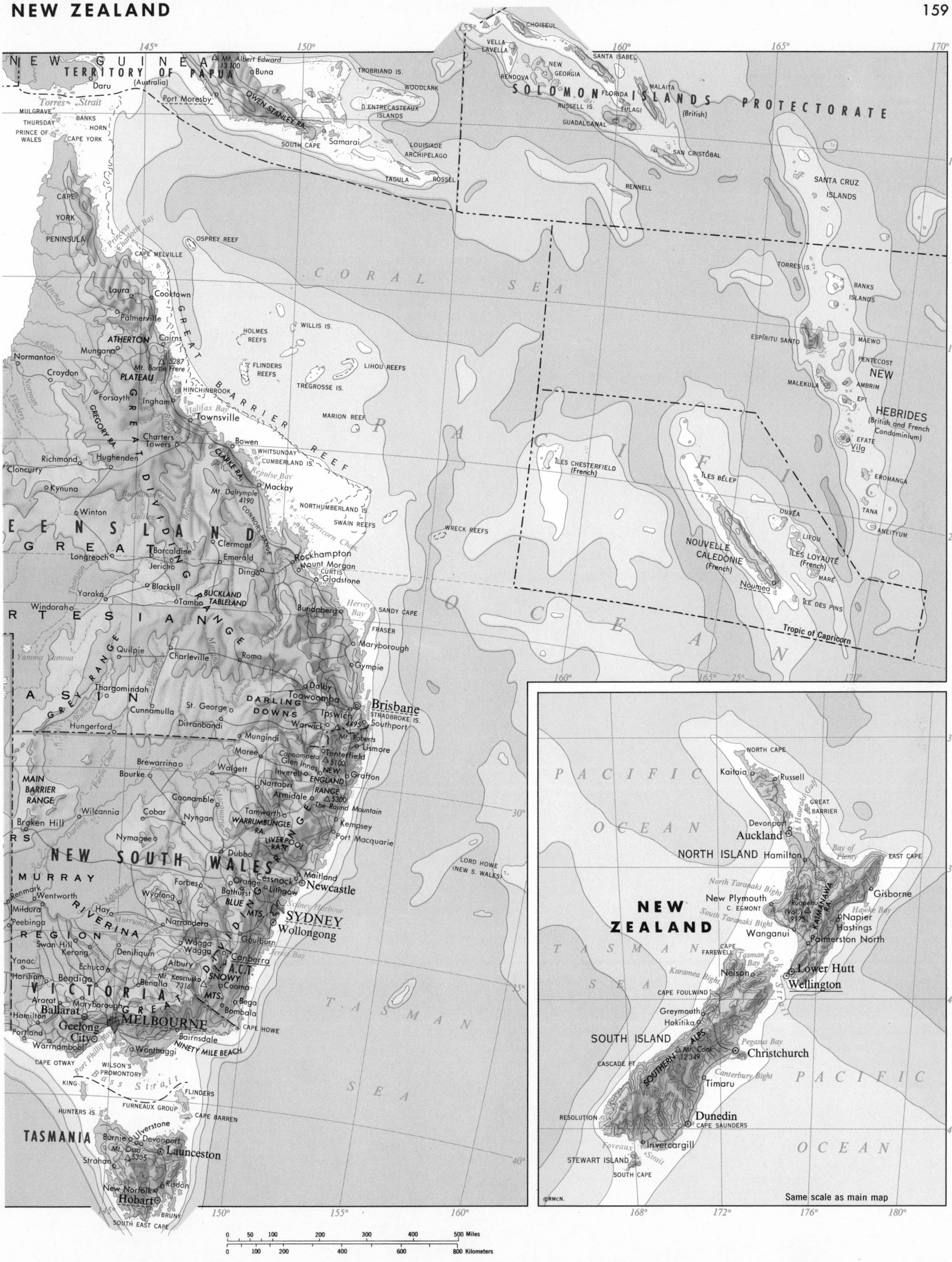

NEW GUINEA
TERRITORY OF PAPUA
(Australia)
Mt. Albert Edward 13,100
Buna
Daru
Port Moresby
Torres Strait
OWEN STANLEY RA.
MULGRAVE
THURSDAY
BANKS
PRINCE OF WALES
HORN
CAPE YORK
TROBRIAND IS.
WOODLARK
D'ENTRECASTEAUX ISLANDS
SOUTH CAPE
Samarai
LOUISIADE ARCHIPELAGO
TAGULA
ROSSEL
CHOISEUL
VELLA LAVELLA
NEW GEORGIA
RENDOVA
SANTA ISABEL
SOLOMON ISLANDS PROTECTORATE
(British)
FLORIDA
MALAITA
RUSSELL IS.
TULAGI
GUADALCANAL
SAN CRISTÓBAL
RENNELL
SANTA CRUZ ISLANDS
CAPE YORK PENINSULA
Princess Charlotte Bay
OSPREY REEF
CAPE MELVILLE
CORAL SEA
Laura
Cooktown
Palmerville
ATHERTON
Cairns
Mungana
Normanton
Croydon
Mt. Bartle Frere 5287
PLATEAU
Forsayth
Ingham
HINCHINBROOK
Halifax Bay
Townsville
GREAT BARRIER REEF
HOLMES REEFS
WILLIS IS.
FLINDERS REEFS
LIHOU REEFS
TREGROSSE IS.
MARION REEF
Mitchell
Gilbert
Norman
Flinders
GREGORY RA.
Charters Towers
Bowen
WHITSUNDAY
CUMBERLAND IS.
Richmond
Hughenden
Cloncurry
CLARKE RA.
Repulse Bay
Mackay
Mt. Dalrymple 4190
Kynuna
GREAT DIVIDING RANGE
CONNORS RANGE
NORTHUMBERLAND IS.
SWAIN REEFS
Winton
Capricorn Chan.
QUEENSLAND
Clermont
Barcaldine
Emerald
Longreach
Jericho
Rockhampton
Mount Morgan
Dingo
CURTIS
Gladstone
Blackall
Yaraka
Tambo
BUCKLAND TABLELAND
Windorah
GREAT ARTESIAN BASIN
Bundaberg
Hervey Bay
SANDY CAPE
FRASER
Maryborough
Quilpie
Charleville
Roma
Gympie
GREAT RANGE
Thargomindah
Dalby
Toowoomba
Brisbane
DARLING DOWNS
Ipswich
STRADBROKE IS.
Cunnamulla
St. George
Warwick
Southport
Hungerford
Dirranbandi
Mungindi
Mt. Roberts 4495
Lismore
Moree
Tenterfield
Capoompeta 5100
Glen Innes
NEW ENGLAND RANGE
Inverell
Grafton
Brewarrina
Walgett
Bourke
Narrabri
MAIN BARRIER RANGE
Armidale
5300
The Round Mountain
Coonamble
Wilcannia
Cobar
Tamworth
Kempsey
Broken Hill
Nyngan
WARRUMBUNGLE RA.
Port Macquarie
Nymagee
LIVERPOOL RA.
NEW SOUTH WALES
Dubbo
LORD HOWE (NEW S. WALES)
MURRAY
Forbes
Cessnock
Maitland
Orange
Newcastle
Renmark
Wentworth
Bathurst
Lithgow
Mildura
Wyalong
BLUE MTS.
Sydney Harbour
Hay
SYDNEY
Peebinga
RIVERINA
Narrandera
Wollongong
REGION
Swan Hill
Goulburn
Kerang
Wagga Wagga
Jervis Bay
Yanac
Echuca
Deniliquin
Albury
Canberra
A.C.T.
Horsham
Bendigo
Benalla
Mt. Kosciusko 7316
SNOWY MTS.
Cooma
VICTORIA
Ararat
Maryborough
Bega
Ballarat
GREAT
Bombala
Hamilton
Geelong
MELBOURNE
CAPE HOWE
Portland
City
Bairnsdale
Warrnambool
Port Phillip Bay
Wonthaggi
NINETY MILE BEACH
CAPE OTWAY
WILSON'S PROMONTORY
KING
Bass Strait
FLINDERS
HUNTERS IS.
FURNEAUX GROUP
CAPE BARREN
TASMANIA
Burnie
Ulverstone
Devonport
Mt. Ossa 5305
Launceston
Strahan
New Norfolk
Risdon
Hobart
BRUNY
SOUTH EAST CAPE
TASMAN SEA
PACIFIC OCEAN
WRECK REEFS
TORRES IS.
BANKS ISLANDS
ESPÍRITU SANTO
MAEWO
PENTECOST
MALEKULA
AMBRIM
EPI
NEW HEBRIDES
(British and French Condominium)
EFATE
Vila
ÎLES CHESTERFIELD (French)
ÎLES BÉLEP
EROMANGA
TANA
OUVÉA
ANEITYUM
LIFOU
NOUVELLE CALEDONIE (French)
ÎLES LOYAUTÉ (French)
MARÉ
Nouméa
ÎLE DES PINS
Tropic of Capricorn
0 50 100 200 300 400 500 Miles
0 100 200 400 600 800 Kilometers
NEW ZEALAND
NORTH CAPE
Kaitaia
Russell
Hauraki Gulf
GREAT BARRIER
Devonport
Auckland
NORTH ISLAND
Hamilton
Bay of Plenty
EAST CAPE
North Taranaki Bight
New Plymouth
C. EGMONT
Ruapehu (Vol.) 9175
KAIMANAWA RA.
Gisborne
South Taranaki Bight
Hawke Bay
Napier
Hastings
Wanganui
Palmerston North
CAPE FAREWELL
Tasman Bay
Nelson
Lower Hutt
Wellington
Karamea Bight
Cook Strait
CAPE FOULWIND
Greymouth
Hokitika
SOUTHERN ALPS
Mt. Cook 12,349
Pegasus Bay
Christchurch
SOUTH ISLAND
CASCADE PT.
Canterbury Bight
Timaru
RESOLUTION
Dunedin
CAPE SAUNDERS
Foveaux Strait
Invercargill
STEWART ISLAND
SOUTH CAPE
Same scale as main map
©RMcN.

QUEENSLAND

GREAT ARTESIAN BASIN

GREAT DIVIDING RANGE

NEW SOUTH WALES

SOUTH AUSTRALIA

VICTORIA

TASMANIA

SIMPSON DESERT

DARLING DOWNS

FLINDERS RANGE

NORTH FLINDERS RANGES

GAWLER RANGES

MAIN BARRIER RANGE

MURRAY

REGION RIVERINA

WARRUMBUNGLE RANGE

NEW ENGLAND

BLUE MTS.

SNOWY MTS.

AUSTRALIAN ALPS

LIVERPOOL RANGE

Cities and towns:

Birdsville, Innamincka, Durham Downs, Welford, Windorah, Yaraka, Yarka, Tambo, Augathella, Charleville, Quilpie, Injune, Roma, Wandoan, Chinchilla, Surat, Meandarra, Dalby, Toowoomba, Warwick, St. George, Dirranbandi, Mungindi, Thargomindah, Cunnamulla, Hungerford, Naryilco, Marree, Farina, Lightning Ridge, Moree, Brewarrina, Bourke, Walgett, Narrabri, Inverell, Glen Innes, Grafton, Tenterfield, Ballina, Lismore, Capoompeta, Armidale, Woomera, Pimba, Parachilna, Hawker, Quorn, Port Augusta, Peterborough, Iron Knob, Whyalla, Kimba, Port Pirie, Gladstone, Kooringa, Port Lincoln, Wallaroo, Moonta, Port Wakefield, Gawler, Adelaide, Peebinga, Renmark, Waikerie, Wentworth, Mildura, Robinvale, Balranald, Hay, Griffith, Narrandera, Wilcannia, Menindee, Broken Hill, Ivanhoe, Cobar, Nymagee, Roto, Nyngan, Dubbo, Wellington, Mudgee, Parkes, Forbes, Orange, Lithgow, Bathurst, Wyalong, Temora, Young, Cootamundra, Wagga Wagga, Canberra, A.C.T., Goulburn, Nowra, Wollongong, Sydney, Newcastle, Maitland, Cessnock, Taree, Port Macquarie, Kempsey, Tamworth, Coonamble, Binnaway, Coonabarabran, Mt. Kaputar, Mt. Banda Banda, Barrington Tops, The Round Mountain,

Kingston, Naracoorte, Millicent, Mount Gambier, Portland, Warrnambool, Colac, Geelong City, Ballarat, Melbourne, Dandenong, Hamilton, Ararat, Maryborough, Castlemaine, Bendigo, Horsham, Warracknabeal, Yanac, Swan Hill, Kerang, Echuca, Deniliquin, Corowa, Albury, Wangaratta, Benalla, Bombala, Bega, Cooma, Orbost, Bairnsdale, Sale, Traralgon, Woodside, Wonthaggi, Ouyen, Tyrell, Tailem Bend, Peterborough, Kingscote,

Smithton, Burnie, Ulverstone, Devonport, Scottsdale, Launceston, St. Marys, Queenstown, Strahan, New Norfolk, Bridgewater, Hobart

Mountains (elevations in feet):

Mt. Fort William 2420, Mt. Mowbullan 3611, Mt. Roberts 4495, Capoompeta 5100, Mt. Kaputar 4999, Ben Lomond (The Round Mountain) 5300, Barrington Tops 5200, Mt. Banda Banda 4144, Mt. Reeves 4470, Bimberi Pk. 6274, Mt. Kosciusko 7316, Mt. Cobberas 6025, Mt. Torbreck 4495, Mt. Baw Baw 5127, Mt. Ossa 5305, Legge Pk. 5160

Water features:

Lake Eyre, Lake Torrens, Lake Frome, Lake Gairdner, Lake Macfarlane, Spencer Gulf, Gulf St. Vincent, Murray River, Darling, Cooper's Creek, Diamantina R., Warrego R., Paroo, Lachlan, Murrumbidgee, Macquarie, Namoi, Gwydir, Barwon (Macintyre), Condamine, Maranoa, Balonne, Nebine Cr., Cowal, Yamma Yamma, Blanche, Callabonna, Gregory,

Encounter Bay, Investigator Strait, Bass Strait, Banks Strait, Tasman Sea, Indian Ocean, Sydney Harbour, Moreton Bay, Hervey Bay, Port Phillip Bay, Western Port, Corner Inlet, Ninety Mile Beach, Port Stephens, Corangamite,

Capes and points:

Sandy Cape, Fraser (Great Sandy), Cape Byron, Sugarloaf Pt., Beecroft Head, Cape Howe, Wilson's Promontory, Cape Otway, Cape Nelson, Cape Jaffa, Thistle, Cape Grim, Cape Barren, Cape Sorell, Freycinet Peninsula, Tasman Peninsula, Furneaux Group, Flinders, King, Hunters Is., Phillip Is., Kangaroo I., Yorke Peninsula,

Relief legend:

Meters		Feet
1525		5000
610		2000
305		1000
152.5		500
0	Sea Level	0
152.5		500
1525	Below Sea Level	5000
3050		10 000

Relief

0   50   100   150   200 Miles

0   50   100   150   200   250   300 Kilometers

140° Longitude East of Greenwich

Scale 1:8 000 000; one inch to 126 miles.
Lambert's Azimuthal, Equal Area Projection.
Elevations and depressions are given in feet.

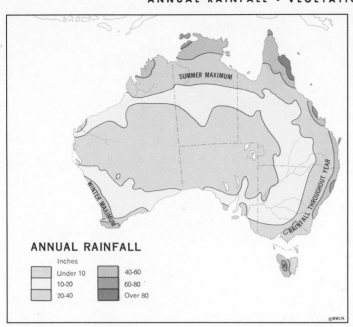

ANNUAL RAINFALL

Inches

Under 10	40-60
10-20	60-80
20-40	Over 80

©RMcN.

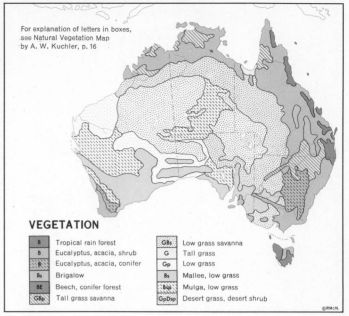

For explanation of letters in boxes,
see Natural Vegetation Map
by A. W. Kuchler, p. 16

VEGETATION

B	Tropical rain forest	GBs	Low grass savanna
B	Eucalyptus, acacia, shrub	G	Tall grass
B	Eucalyptus, acacia, conifer	Gp	Low grass
Bs	Brigalow	Bs	Mallee, low grass
BE	Beech, conifer forest	Bsp	Mulga, low grass
GBp	Tall grass savanna	GpDsp	Desert grass, desert shrub

©RMcN.

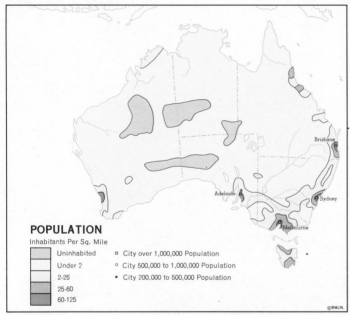

POPULATION

Inhabitants Per Sq. Mile

Uninhabited	▫ City over 1,000,000 Population
Under 2	○ City 500,000 to 1,000,000 Population
2-25	● City 200,000 to 500,000 Population
25-60	
60-125	

©RMcN.

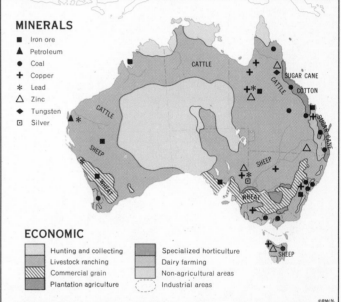

MINERALS

- ■ Iron ore
- ▲ Petroleum
- ● Coal
- ✚ Copper
- ✳ Lead
- △ Zinc
- ◆ Tungsten
- ⊡ Silver

ECONOMIC

	Hunting and collecting	Specialized horticulture
	Livestock ranching	Dairy farming
	Commercial grain	Non-agricultural areas
	Plantation agriculture	Industrial areas

©RMcN.

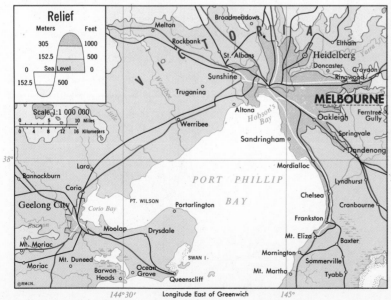

Relief

Meters		Feet
305		1000
152.5		500
0	Sea Level	0
152.5		500

Scale 1:1 000 000

0 4 8 12 16 Kilometers
0 10 Miles

©RMcN.

144°30'   Longitude East of Greenwich   145°

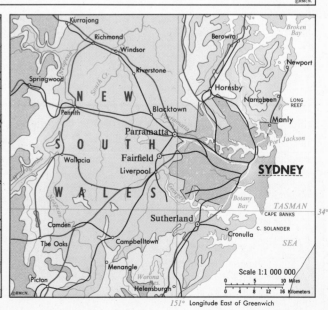

Scale 1:1 000 000

0 5 10 Miles
0 4 8 12 16 Kilometers

©RMcN.

151° Longitude East of Greenwich

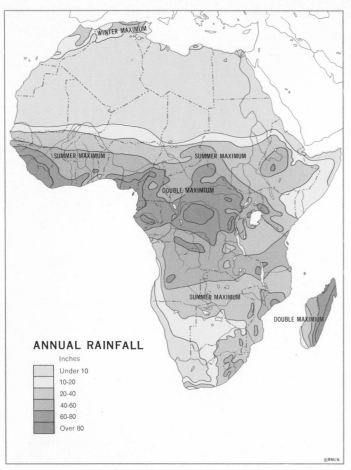

ANNUAL RAINFALL

Inches

- Under 10
- 10-20
- 20-40
- 40-60
- 60-80
- Over 80

©RMcN.

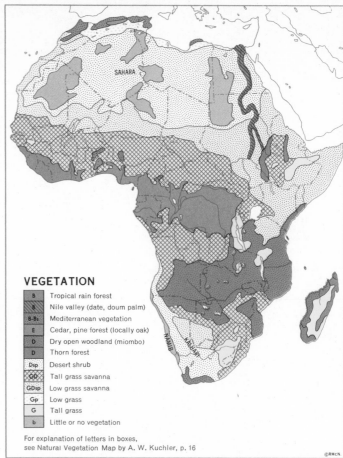

VEGETATION

B	Tropical rain forest
B	Nile valley (date, doum palm)
B-B₂	Mediterranean vegetation
E	Cedar, pine forest (locally oak)
D	Dry open woodland (miombo)
D	Thorn forest
Dsp	Desert shrub
GD	Tall grass savanna
GDsp	Low grass savanna
Gp	Low grass
G	Tall grass
b	Little or no vegetation

For explanation of letters in boxes,
see Natural Vegetation Map by A. W. Kuchler, p. 16

©RMcN.

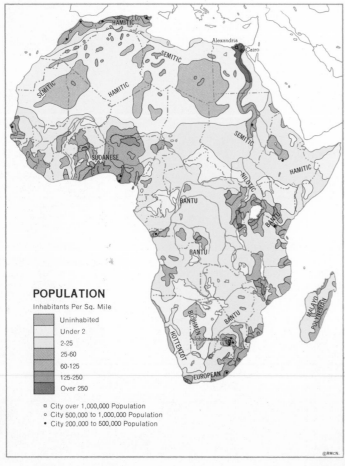

POPULATION

Inhabitants Per Sq. Mile

- Uninhabited
- Under 2
- 2-25
- 25-60
- 60-125
- 125-250
- Over 250

□ City over 1,000,000 Population
○ City 500,000 to 1,000,000 Population
● City 200,000 to 500,000 Population

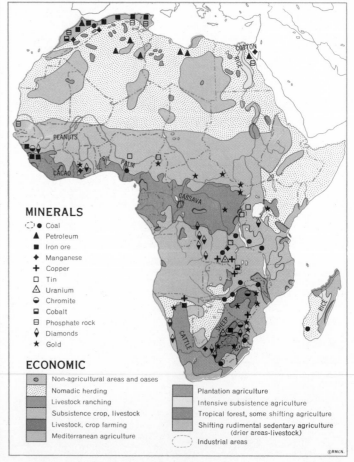

MINERALS

- ⬭ ● Coal
- ▲ Petroleum
- ■ Iron ore
- ◆ Manganese
- + Copper
- □ Tin
- △ Uranium
- ○ Chromite
- ▱ Cobalt
- ⊟ Phosphate rock
- ◈ Diamonds
- ★ Gold

ECONOMIC

- Non-agricultural areas and oases
- Nomadic herding
- Livestock ranching
- Subsistence crop, livestock
- Livestock, crop farming
- Mediterranean agriculture
- Plantation agriculture
- Intensive subsistence agriculture
- Tropical forest, some shifting agriculture
- Shifting rudimental sedentary agriculture (drier areas-livestock)
- Industrial areas

©RMcN.

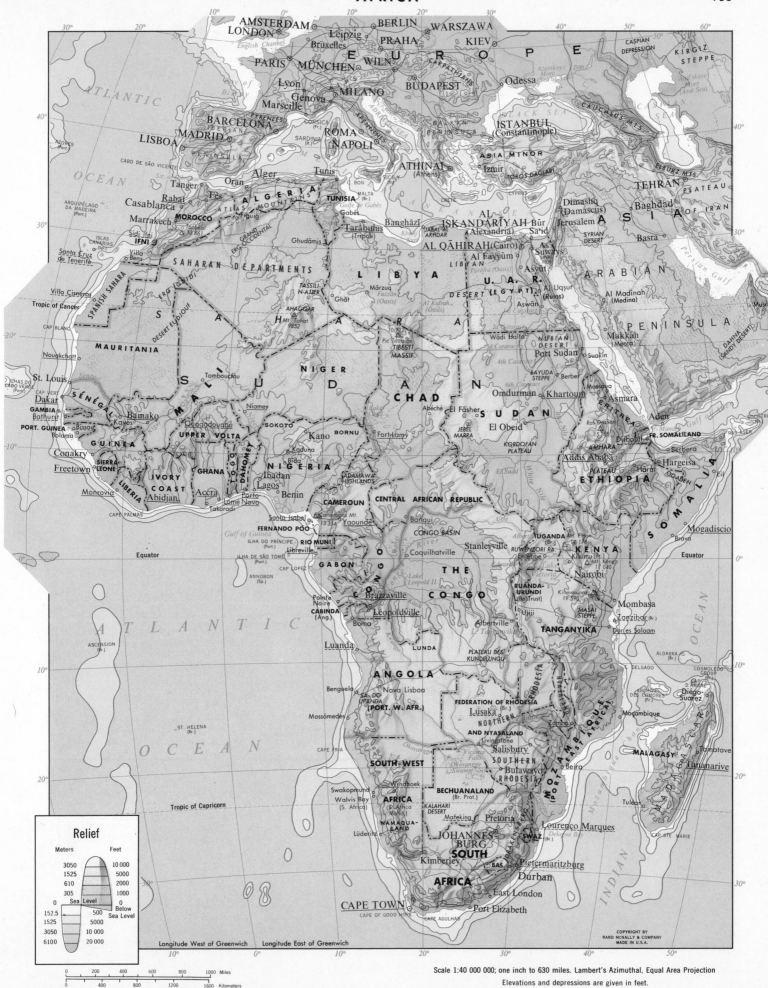

Relief

Meters | Feet
3050 | 10 000
1525 | 5000
610 | 2000
305 | 1000
Sea Level | 0
152.5 | 500 | Below
1525 | 5000 | Sea Level
3050 | 10 000
6100 | 20 000

Longitude West of Greenwich | Longitude East of Greenwich

0   200   400   600   800   1000 Miles

0   400   800   1200   1600 Kilometers

Scale 1:40 000 000; one inch to 630 miles. Lambert's Azimuthal, Equal Area Projection

Elevations and depressions are given in feet.

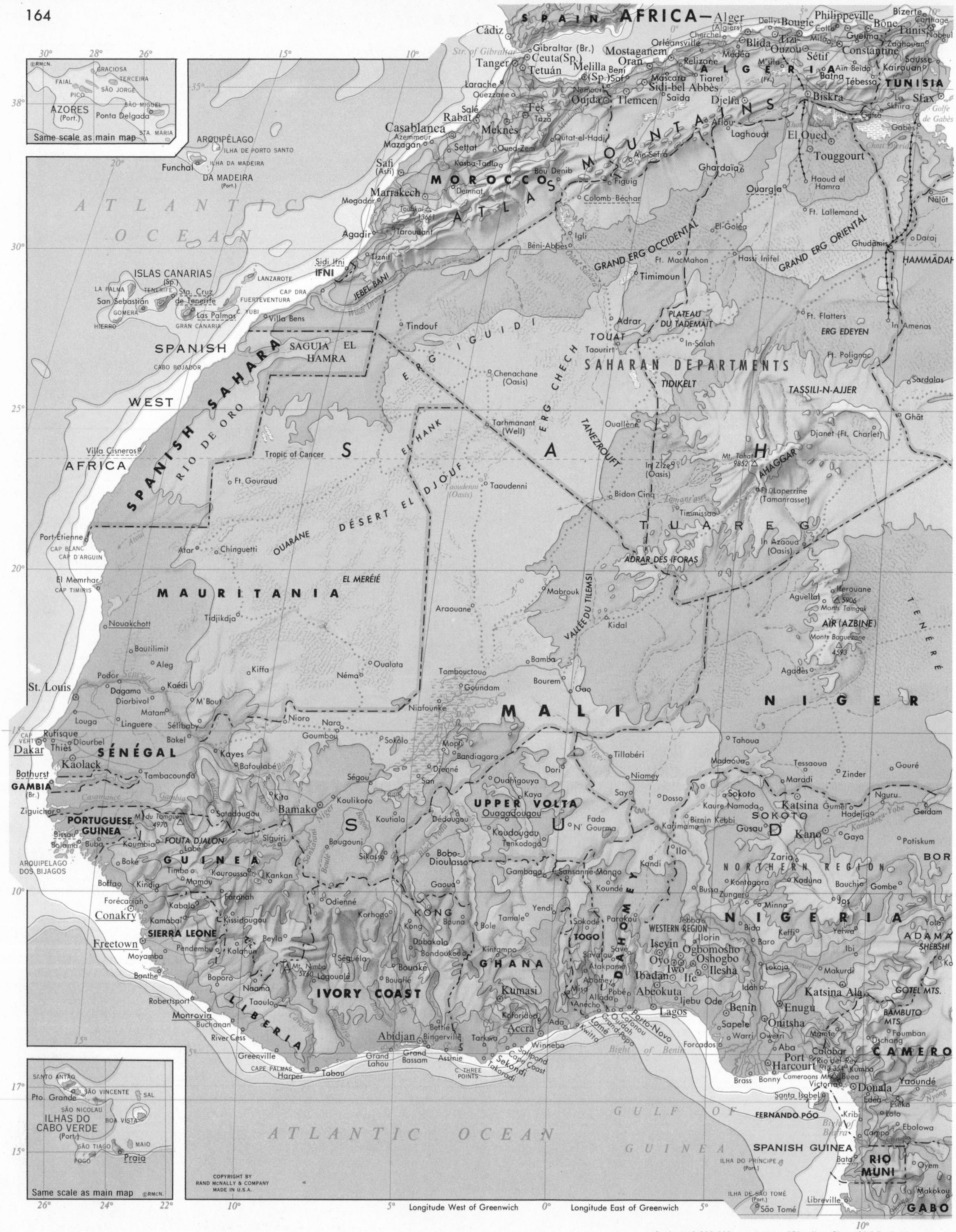

SPAIN AFRICA—Alger (Algiers)

AZORES (Port.)
GRACIOSA
TERCEIRA
FAIAL · SÃO JORGE
PICO
SÃO MIGUEL
STA. MARIA
Ponta Delgada
Same scale as main map

Philippeville · Bizerte
Bône · Carthage
Bougie · Tunis
Dellys · Collo · Guelma · Nabeul
Cherchel · Milla
Bougie · Sousse
Constantine
Blida · Médéa · Sétif · Aïn Beïda · Kairouan
Relizane · Batna · Tébessa
Oran · Mascara · Tiaret · Biskra · TUNISIA
Sidi-bel-Abbès · Saïda · Sfax
Tlemcen · Djelfa · Shira
Aflou · El Oued · Golfe de Gabès
Laghouat · Gabès
Touggourt
Ghardaïa · Ouargla · Haoud el Hamra
Colomb-Béchar · Nālūt
Ft. MacMahon · Hassi Inifel · Ghudāmis · HAMMĀDAH
GRAND ERG OCCIDENTAL · El-Goléa · GRAND ERG ORIENTAL
Timimoun · ERG EDEYEN
Adrar · PLATEAU DU TADEMAÏT · In-Salah · Ft. Flatters
TOUAT · Taourirt · Ft. Polignac · In Amenas
SAHARAN DEPARTMENTS
Ouallène · TIDIKELT · TASSILI-N-AJJER
Chenachane (Oasis) · Sardalas
Tarhmanant (Well) · In Zize (Oasis) · Ghât
ERG CHECH · TANEZROUFT · Mt. Tahat 9852 · Djanet (Ft. Charlet)
Taoudenni (Oasis) · HAGGAR
Taoudenni · Bidon Cinq · Ft. Laperrine (Tamanrasset)
DÉSERT EL DJOUF · Timimissao
EL HANK · Iherouane 5906 · Monts Tamgak
TUAREG · Monts Baguezane 4593
ADRAR DES IFORAS · In Azaoua (Oasis) · AÏR (AZBINE)
Mabrouk · TENERE
EL MERÉIÉ · VALLÉE DU TILEMSI · Aguelal · Agadès

SPANISH SAHARA · SAGUIA EL HAMRA
CAP DRA · YUBI · Villa Bens
ISLAS CANARIAS (Sp.)
LA PALMA · TENERIFE · Sta. Cruz de Tenerife · FUERTEVENTURA
San Sebastián · LANZAROTE · CAP DRA
GOMERA · Las Palmas · GRAN CANARIA
HIERRO

Cádiz · Gibraltar (Br.) · Ceuta (Sp.)
Tanger · Tetuán · Melilla (Sp.)·S of
Larache · Ouezzane · Oujda · Nemours
Rabat · Salé · Fès · Taza
Casablanca · Meknès
Mazagan · Oued-Zem
Safi (Asfi) · Kasba-Tadla
Marrakech · Demnat · Béni-Abbès · Igli
Mogador · Toubkal 13661
Agadir · Taroudant
Sidi Ifni · IFNI · Tiznit · JEBEL BANI
Wadi Dra · Tindouf

ATLANTIC OCEAN

Funchal · ILHA DE PORTO SANTO
ILHA DA MADEIRA (Port.) · ARQUIPÉLAGO DA MADEIRA

ATLAS MOUNTAINS

MOROCCO

SPANISH WEST AFRICA
CABO BOJADOR
RÍO DE ORO
Villa Cisneros
Port-Étienne · CAP BLANC · CAP D'ARGUIN

ERG IGUIDI

EL HANK

Tropic of Cancer

S · A · H · A · R · A

EL MEMRHAR · CAP TIMIRIS
Atar · Chinguetti · OUARANE
Ouâdane
MAURITANIA · Araouane · Kidal
Tidjikdja · Tombouctou
Nouakchott · Bamba · Bourem · Gao
Boutilimit · Oualata · Goundam
Aleg · Kiffa · Néma · Niafounké
St. Louis · Podor · Kaédi · M'Bout
Dagama · Matam · Nioro · Nara
Diorbivol · Séllibaby · Goumbou · Sokolo
Louga · Linguère · Bakel · Tahoua · Madaoua
Rufisque · Dakar · Thiès · Bakel · Mopti · Tessaoua · Zinder · Gouré
CAP VERT · Kaolack · Kayes · Ségou · Niamey · Sokoto · Maradi
SÉNÉGAL · Bafoulabé · Bandiagara · Dori · Dosso · Katsina · Guséi · Geidam
Bathurst · Tambacounda · Djenné · San · Say · Tillabéri
GAMBIA (Br.) · Kita · Koulikoro · Niamey · Kaure Namoda · Hadejia
Ziguinchor · M. du Tamgue 4970 · Bamako · Dédougou · UPPER VOLTA · Birnin Kebbi · Gusau · Gumel · Nguru
PORTUGUESE GUINEA · Satadougou · Ouagadougou · Karimama · Kano · Gaya
Bissau · FOUTA DJALON · Sikasso · Bobo-Dioulasso · Fada N'Gourma · Ilo · SOKOTO · Potiskum
Bolama · Buba · Labé · Siguiri · Koutiala · Koudougou · Tenkodogo · Kandi · Zario · NORTHERN REGION · BOR
ARQUIPÉLAGO DOS BIJAGOS · Boké · Kouroussa · Gaoua · Gambaga · Bussa · Kontagora · Kaduna · Bauchi · Gombe
GUINEA · Kindia · Kankan · Odienné · Sansanné-Mango · Zungeru · Minna · NIGERIA
Boffao · Timbo · Mamou · Séguéla · Bouna · TOGO · Bida · Keffi · Ibi
Forécariah · Mamou · Dabakala · Bole · WESTERN REGION · Baro · Makurdi
Conakry · Kamabai · Kissidougou · Bondoukou · Yendi · Iseyin · Ilorin · Lokoja · Katsina Ala
SIERRA LEONE · Beyla · Korhogo · Kong · Tamale · Sokodé · Oyo · Oshogbo · Idah · ADAMAWA · SHEBSHI
Freetown · Pendembu · Dabakala · Bouna · Save · Iwo · Ilesha · Enugu · GOTEL MTS.
Moyamba · Kolahun · Séguéla · Bouaké · Atakpamé · Ibadan · Ife · Onitsha · BAMBUTO MTS.
Bonthe · Bopora · Mt. Nimba 5760 · Lagouala · Bouaflé · Abomey · Abeokuta · Benin · Foumban · Dschang
Naama · Taoulo · GHANA · Allada · Ijebu Ode · Sapele · Aba · CAMEROONS
Robertsport · IVORY COAST · Kumasi · Lagos · Warri · Owerri · Calabar
Monrovia · Buchanan · Koforidua · Porto-Novo · Forcados · Port Harcourt
LIBERIA · Bettié · Bingerville · Accra · Cotonou · Brass · Bonny · Victoria
River Cess · Grand Lahou · Ada · Winneba · SPANISH GUINEA
Greenville · CAPE PALMAS · Grand Bassam · Assinie · Sekondi · RIO MUNI
Harper · Tabou · C. THREE POINTS · FERNANDO PÓO · Santa Isabel · Douala · Yaoundé
Bight of Benin · ILHA DO PRINCIPE (Port.) · Kribi · Eboéwa
GULF OF GUINEA · ILHA DE SÃO TOMÉ (Port.) · São Tomé · Campo · Libreville
GABO · Makokou · Oyem

MALI · NIGER

Gourma · Gambaga

KONG

SUDAN

ILHAS DO CABO VERDE (Port.)
SANTO ANTÃO
Pto. Grande · SÃO VICENTE · SAL
SÃO NICOLAU · BOA VISTA
SÃO TIAGO · MAIO
FOGO · Praia
Same scale as main map

ATLANTIC OCEAN

30° · 28° · 26° · 15° · 10° · 5°
Longitude West of Greenwich · Longitude East of Greenwich · 5°

38° · 35° · 30° · 25° · Tropic of Cancer · 20° · 15° · 10°

26° · 24° · 22° · 10° · 5°

Scale 1:16 000 000; one inch to 250 miles. Sinusoidal Projection
Elevations and depressions are given in feet

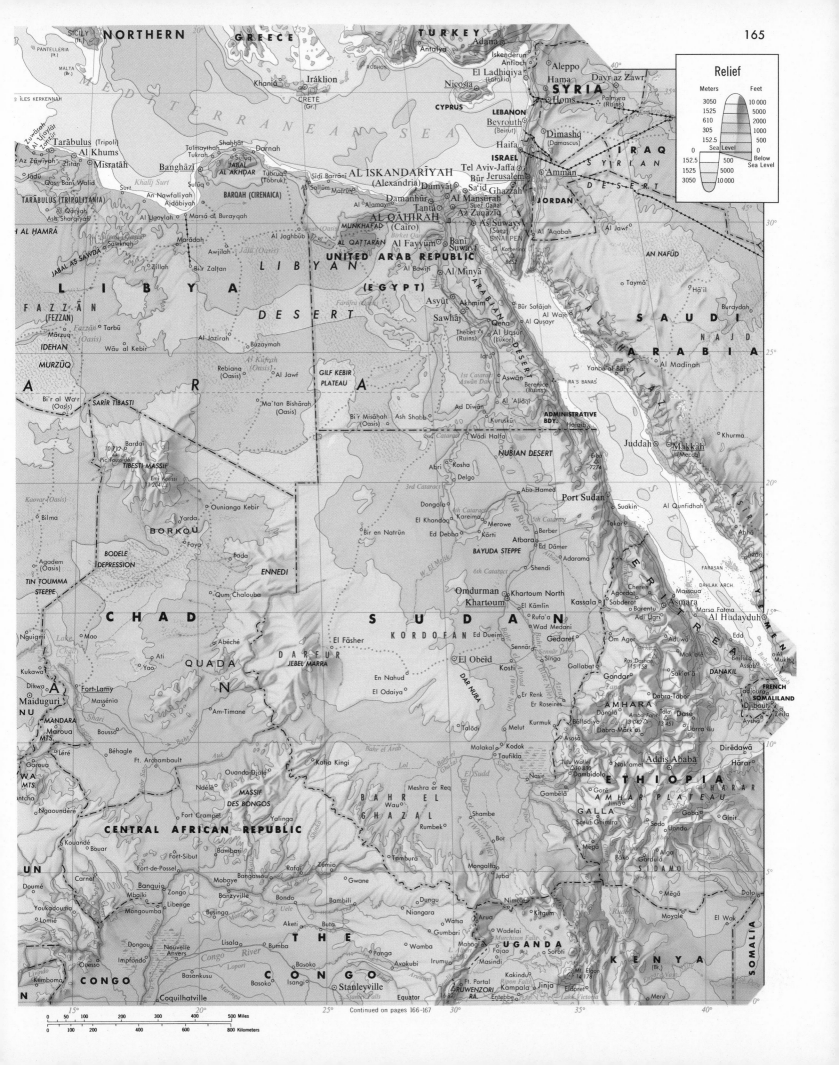

Relief

Meters		Feet
3050		10 000
1525		5000
610		2000
305		1000
152.5		500
0	Sea Level	0
152.5		500 Below Sea Level
1525		5000
3050		10 000

NORTHERN

SICILY (It.)

PANTELLERIA (It.)

MALTA (Br.)

ÎLES KERKENNAH

GREECE

Khaniá
Iráklion
CRETE (Gr.)

TURKEY
Antalya
Adana
Iskenderun
Antioch
El Ladhiqiya (Latakia)
Aleppo
Hama
Dayr az Zawr
Homs
SYRIA
Palmyra (Ruins)
LEBANON
Beyrouth (Beirut)
Dimashq (Damascus)
CYPRUS
Nicosia
Haifa
ISRAEL
Tel Aviv-Jaffa
Jerusalem
Amman
JORDAN
IRAQ
SYRIAN DESERT
Al Jawf
AN NAFŪD

MEDITERRANEAN SEA

Zuwārah
Al 'Uqaylāt
Lanṭur
Tarābulus (Tripoli)
Al Khums
Az Zāwiyah
Zlitan
Misrātāh
Jādū
Qaṣr Bani Walid
TARĀBULUS (TRIPOLITANIA)
Al Qaryah
Ash Shariqīyah

Tulmaythah
Shahhāt
Darnah
Suluq
Banghāzī
JABAL AL AKHDAR
Tukrah
BARQAH (CIRENAICA)
An Nawfaliyah
Ajdābiyah
Al Ugaylah
Marsā al Burayqah

Sīdī Barrānī
Sollum
Matrūḥ
Al Alamayn
AL ISKANDARĪYAH (Alexandria)
Damanhūr
Dumyāt
Būr Sa'īd
Tanta
Al Mansūrah
Az Zaqāzīq
Suez Canal
Ghazzah

As Suways (Suez)
Al 'Aqabah
SINAI PEN.
St. Katharina 8652

RAH HAMRĀ

JĀLŪ (Oasis)
Awjilah
Marādah
Sawknah
Zillah
Bi'r Zalṭan
JABAL AS SAWDĀ

MUNKHAFAD
AL QAṬṬĀRAH
Al Jaghbūb
Birket Qarūn
AL QĀHIRAH (Cairo)
Al Fayyūm
Bani Suwayf
Al Bawīṭī
Al Minyā
Taymā
Hā'il
SAUDI ARABIA
Buraydah
NAJD

LIBYA
FAZZĀN (FEZZAN)
IDEHAN MURZŪQ

Marzuq
Tarbū
Wāu al Kebir

LIBYAN DESERT

Farāfra (Oasis)

Asyūṭ
Akhmīm
Sawhāj
Būr Safājah
Qena
Al Quṣayr
Thebes (Ruins)
Al Uqsur (Luxor)
Al Wajh
Yanbu' al Baḥr
Al Madīnah

Bi'r al Wa'r (Oasis)
SARĪR TIBASTI

Al Jazīrah
Buzaymah
Al Kufrah (Oasis)
Rebiana (Oasis)
Al Jawf
GILF KEBIR PLATEAU
Ma'tan Bishārah (Oasis)

Idfū
Aswān
1st Cataract
Aswān Dam
Berenice (Ruins)
RA'S BANAS
RED SEA

S A H A R A

Bi'r Misāhah (Oasis)
Ash Shabb
Ad Dīwān
Al 'Allāqī
Kuruskū
ADMINISTRATIVE BDY.
Halaib

10 712
Bardaï
Pic Toussidé
TIBESTI MASSIF
Emi Koussi 11 204

2nd Cataract
Wādi Halfa
Abri
Kosha
Delgo
NUBIAN DESERT
Erba 7274

Juddah
Makkah (Mecca)
Khurma

Kaovar (Oasis)
Bilma
Ounianga Kebir
Yarda
BORKOU
Faya
Fada
ENNEDI
Qum Chalouba

3rd Cataract
Dongola
4th Cataract
El Khandaq
Kareima
Merowe
Korti
Ed Debba
Abū Hamed
Berber
5th Cataract
Atbara
Ed Dāmer
Adarama
Port Sudan
Suakin
Tokar
Al Qunfidhah
Abha

BODELE DEPRESSION
BAYUDA STEPPE
Bir en Natrūn
W. EL Melik

Agadem (Oasis)
TIN TOUMMA STEPPE

6th Cataract
Shendi
Omdurman
Khartoum North
Khartoum
El Kāmlin
Kassala
Cheren
Agordat
Sabderat
Barentu
Massaua
DAHLAK ARCH.
Asmara
Marsa Fatma
FARASAN
Jizan
YEMEN

Nguigmi
Mao
Lake Chad
Abéché
Ati
Yao

CHAD
QUADAÏ

Bir el War

SUDAN
KORDOFAN
DARFUR
Jebel Marra
Ed Dueim
Rufa'a
Wad Medani
Gedaref
Om Ager
Adi Ugri
ERITREA
Adwa
Mak'ale
Al Hudayduh
Edd

Kukawa
Dikwa
Maiduguri
MANDARA MTS.
Maroua

En Nahud
El Obeïd
Kosti
Sennār
Sennār Dam
Singa
Gallabat
Gondar
Ras Dashan 4620 15 158
DANAKIL
Sak'ota
Beilula
Assab
Al Mukta

Léré
Bongor
Béhagle
Fort-Lamy
Massénia
Bousso
Shari

Am-Timane
Talōdi
DAR NUBA
Melut
Kurmuk
Er Renk
Er Roseires
Dānglä
Belfodiyo
Dambidolo
Dabra-Tabor
Amba Farit 13 042
Tola 13 451
AMHARA
Dase
Worra Ilu
Aysha
Djibouti
FRENCH SOMALILAND
Zeila

Garoua
Maroua
Ft. Archambault
Ouanda-Djalé
Ndélé
MASSIF DES BONGOS

Auk
Kafia Kingi
Bahr el Arab
Lol
El Sudd
Malakal
Kodok
Taufikia
Nasir
Asosa
Gore
Dabra-Mārk'os
GALLA
Jima
Tulu Wallel 10 830
Nak'amet
Addis Ababa
Dirēdawa
Hārar
HARAR

Ngaoundéré
Bouar
Fort Grampel
Yalinga
Bambari
Fort-Sibut
CENTRAL AFRICAN REPUBLIC
Bouca

Wau
Shambe
Rumbek
BAHR EL GHAZAL
Bor
Meshra er Req
Gambela
Goré
Sodo
Ginir
Mega
AMHAR PLATEAU
Uondo
Gidole
Bako
Alga
SIDAMO

Kouandé
Bouar
Fort-de-Possel
Carnot
Doumé
Rafai
Zémio
Gwane
Tamburā
Mongalla
Juba
Mega
Dolo
SOMALIA

Youkadouma
Lomié
Mbaiki
Banqui
Zongo
Libenge
Mobaye
Banzyville
Bondo
Bambili
Dungu
Niangara
Watsa
Wadelai
Arua
Kitgum
Moyale
El Wak

Ouesso
Kembroma
Dongou
Nouvelle Anvers
Lisala
Bumba
Panga
Wamba
UGANDA
Gulu
Soroti
Meru
KENYA

Impfondo
Impondo
Basankusu
Isangi
Basoko
Aketi
Buta
Gumbari
Avakubi
Irumu
Masindi
Ft. Portal
RUWENZORI RA.
Mahagi
Fajao
Murchison Falls
Kakindu
Mt. Elgon 14 178
Eldoret
Jinja
Kampala
Entebbe
Lake Victoria

CONGO
THE CONGO
Stanleyville
Coquilhatville
Stanley Falls
Equator

Continued on pages 166-167

0 50 100   200   300   400   500 Miles
0 100   200   400   600   800 Kilometers

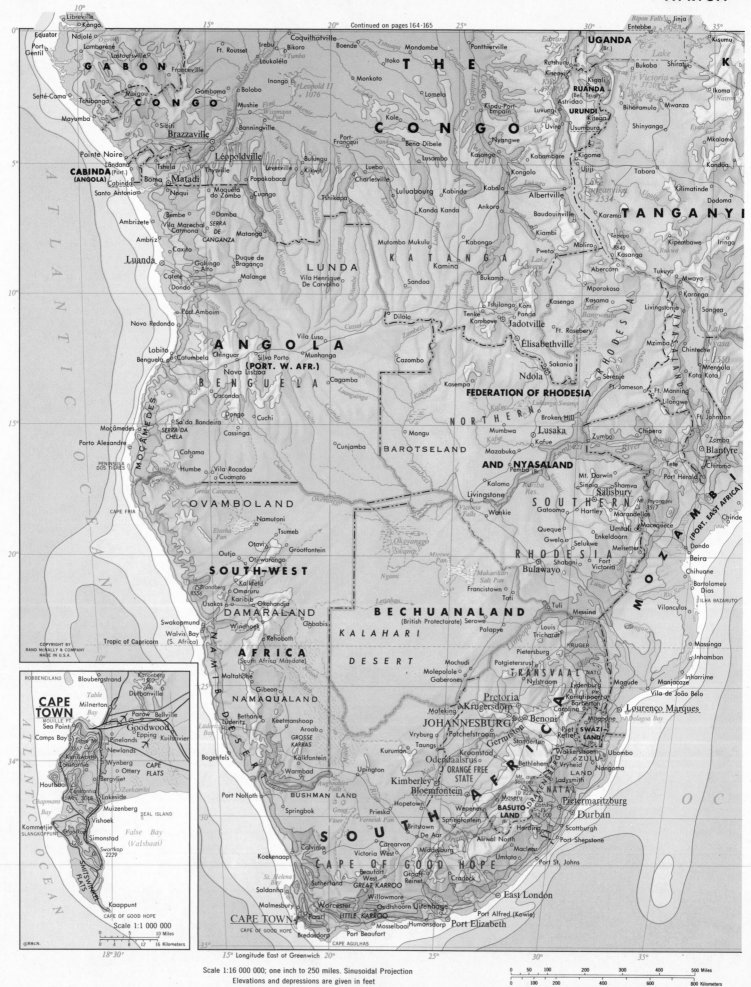

CAPE TOWN

Scale 1:1 000 000

0   5   10 Miles
0 4   8 12 16 Kilometers

©RMcN.

18°30'

Scale 1:16 000 000; one inch to 250 miles. Sinusoidal Projection
Elevations and depressions are given in feet

0 50 100   200   300   400   500 Miles

0 100 200   400   600   800 Kilometers

COPYRIGHT BY
RAND McNALLY & COMPANY
MADE IN U.S.A.

Continued on pages 164·165

15° Longitude East of Greenwich 20°

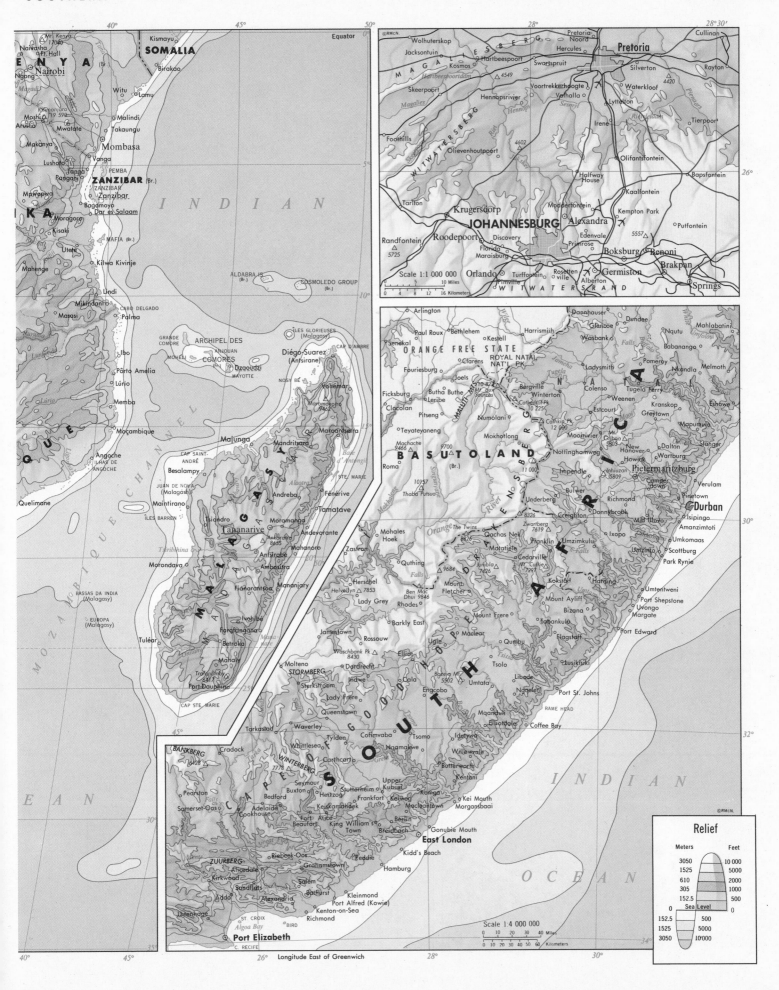

Relief

Meters		Feet
3050		10 000
1525		5000
610		2000
305		1000
152.5		500
0	Sea Level	0
152.5		500
1525		5000
3050		10 000

Scale 1:1 000 000

Scale 1:4 000 000

Longitude East of Greenwich

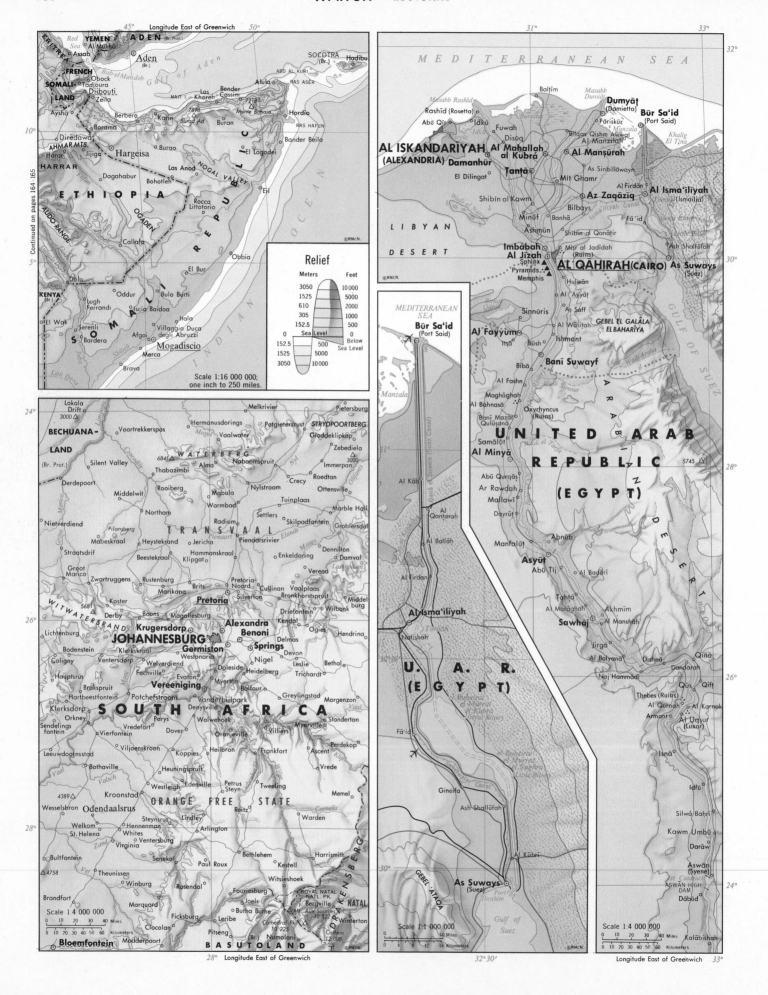

Continued on pages 164-165

Longitude East of Greenwich

Inset 1 (Horn of Africa):

YEMEN — ADEN (Br. Prot.)
Al Mukhā
Assab
ERITREA
FRENCH SOMALI-LAND
Obock
Tadjoura
Djibouti
Zeila
Aysha
Borama
Berbera
Karin
Surud Ad
Monte Bahaja 7898
7218
Bender Cassim
Alula
RAS ASÈR
SOCOTRA (Br.)
Hadibu
ABD AL KURI
Hordio
RAS HAFUN
Bander Beila
Diredawa
AHMAR MTS.
Harar
Jijiga
Hargeisa
Dagahabur
Bohotleh
Las Anod
HARRAR
El Lagodei
ETHIOPIA
OGADEN
NOGAL VALLEY
El
Rocca Littotorio
Callafo
Dolo
KENYA (Br.)
El Wak
Lugh Ferrandi
Oddur
Iscia Baidoa
Itala
Serenli
Bardera
Afgoi
Villaggio Duca degli Abruzzi
Merca
Brava
Lak Dera
Shibeli
Mogadiscio
SOMALI REPUBLIC
INDIAN OCEAN
Red Sea
Gulf of Aden
Bab-el-Mandeb
MATT I.
Las Khoreh
Burao
El Bur
Obbia
Bulo Burti
AUDO RANGE

Relief legend:

Relief

Meters	Feet
3050	10 000
1525	5000
610	2000
305	1000
152.5	500
0 Sea Level	0 Sea Level
152.5	500
1525	5000
3050	10 000

Below Sea Level

Scale 1:16 000 000;
one inch to 250 miles

Inset 2 (South Africa):

Lokala Drift
3000 △
Melkrivier
Pietersburg
BECHUANA-LAND (Br. Prot.)
Hermanusdorings
Potgietersrust
STRYDPOORTBERG
Voortrekkerspos
Vaalwater
Gladdeklipkop
Silent Valley
WATERBERG
6841 △
Alma
Zebediela
Derdepoort
Thabazimbi
Naboomspruit
Immerpan
Middelwit
Rooiberg
Mabula
Nylstroom
3000 △
Crecy
Roedtan
Ottensville
Nietverdiend
Northam
Warmbad
Tuinplaas
Marble Hall
Mabeskraal
Radium
Settlers
Skilpadfontein
Groblersdal
Pilansberg
Jericho
TRANSVAAL
Piendarsrivier
Dennilton
Damval
Straatdrif
Heystekrand
Hammanskraal
Klipgat
Enkeldoring
Verena
Groot Marico
Zwartruggens
Rustenburg
Brits
Pretoria-Noord
Vaalplaas
Bronkhorstspruit
Middelburg
Koster
Marikana
Pretoria
Silverton
Witbank
Derby
Magaliesburg
Boons
Cullinan
Driefontein
Kendal
Lichtenburg
Krugersdorp
Alexandra
Benoni
Ogies
Hendrina
Bodenstein
Klerkskraal
JOHANNESBURG
Germiston
Springs
Delmas
Coligny
Ventersdorp
Welverdiend
Westonaria
Nigel
Devon
Leslie
Bethal
Hauptrus
Brakspruit
Fochville
Evaton
Daleside
Myerton
Heidelberg
Trichardt
Hartbeestfontein
Potchefstroom
Vereeniging
Balfour
Greylingstad
Morgenzon
Klerksdorp
Orkney
Vanderbijlpark
Denysville
Wolwehoek
Standerton
Sendelingsfontein
Vredefort
Parys
Villiers
Myerville
Leeuwdoornsstad
Vierfontein
Oranjeville
Perdekop
Viljoenskroon
Koppies
Frankfort
Ascent
Vrede
Bothaville
Heilbron
Memel
Welkom
Westleigh
Edenville
Petrus Steyn
Tweeling
St. Helena
Virginia
Senekal
Bethlehem
Kestell
Harrismith
Bultfontein
Paul Roux
Theunissen
Steynsrus
Lindley
Arlington
Warden
Hennenman
Whites
Ventersburg
Odendaalsrus
Bloemfontein
Brandfort
Winburg
Rosendal
Fouriesburg
Witsieshoek
ROYAL NATAL NATL. PK.
Bergville
NATAL
Marquard
Ficksburg
Leribe
Cathedral Pk.
Aux Sources
Mt. 10 225
Clocolan
Modderpoort
Winterton
Catkin Pk. 12 000
Numolani
Butha Buthe
Pitseng
BASUTOLAND
DRAKENSBERG
SOUTH AFRICA
ORANGE FREE STATE
WITWATERSRAND
5681 △
4389 △
4758 △
Scale 1:4 000 000
0 10 20 30 40 Miles
0 10 20 30 40 60 Kilometers

Inset 3 (Suez Canal):

MEDITERRANEAN SEA
Būr Sa'id (Port Said)
Manzala
Qanā el Suweis (Suez Canal)
Al Kāb
Al Qantarah
Al Ballāḥ
Al Firdan
Al Ismā'īlīyah
Nafishah
Tūsūn
Lake Timsāh
Buheirat Murrat el Kubra (Great Bitter Lake)
Fā'id
Buheirat Murrat Sughra (Little Bitter Lake)
Geneifa
Ash Shallūfah
Al Kūbrī
As Suways (Suez)
GEBEL ATAQA
Gulf of Suez
Port Ibrahim
Ismail Canal
Scale 1:1 000 000
0 4 8 12 Miles
0 4 8 12 16 Kilometers

Main map (Egypt / United Arab Republic):

MEDITERRANEAN SEA
Masabb Rashid
Masabb Dumiāt
Baltīm
Burullus
Manzala
Dumyāt (Damietta)
Būr Sa'id (Port Said)
Rashīd (Rosetta)
Idkū
Fuwah
Biltqas Qishm Awwal
Al Manzilah
Khalig El Tina
Abū Qīr
Fāriskūr
AL ISKANDARIYAH (ALEXANDRIA)
Disūq
Al Maḥallah al Kubrā
As Sinbillāwayn
Damanhūr
Mīt Ghamr
Al Firdān
Al Ismā'īlīyah (Ismailia)
Tanṭā
El Dilingat
Shibīn al Kawm
Az Zaqāzīq
Minūf
Banhā
Bilbays
Fā'id
Ismā'īlīya Canal
LIBYAN DESERT
Ashmūn
Shibīn al Qanāṭir
Ash Shallūfah
Imbābah
Al Jīzah
Misr al Jadīdah (Ruins)
AL QAHIRAH (CAIRO)
As Suways (Suez)
Sphinx
Pyramids
Memphis
Ḥulwān
Al 'Ayyāt
Sinnūris
Aṣ Ṣaff
GEBEL EL GALĀLA EL BAHARĪYA
Al Fayyūm
Al Wāsiṭah
Ishmant
Itsā
Būsh
Banī Suwayf
Biba
Wadi Araba
Bibā
Al Fashn
Maghāghah
Al Bahnasā
Banī Mazār
Qulūsanā
Oxyrhyncus (Ruins)
Samālūṭ
UNITED ARAB REPUBLIC (EGYPT)
Al Minyā
5745 △
Abū Qurqāṣ
Ar Rawdah
Mallawī
Dayrūṭ
Manfalūṭ
Abnūb
Asyūṭ
Abū Tīj
Al Badārī
Ṭahṭā
Al Marāghah
Akhmīm
Sawhāj
Al Manshāh
Jirgā
Al Balyanā
Dishnā
Naj Ḥammādi
Qinā
Dandarah
Thebes (Ruins)
Qūṣ
Qifṭ
Al Qurnah
Armant
Al Karnak
Al Uqṣur (Luxor)
Isnā
Idfū
Silwā Baḥrī
Kawm Umbū
Darāw
Aswān (Syene)
1st Cataract
ASWĀN HIGH DAM
Dābūd
Kalābishah
ARABIAN DESERT
GULF OF SUEZ
Wadi en Natrūn
Wādi el Tarfa

Scale 1:4 000 000
0 10 20 30 40 Miles
0 10 20 30 40 60 Kilometers

Longitude East of Greenwich

WORLD COMPARISONS

General Information

Equatorial diameter of the earth, 7,926.68 miles
Polar diameter of the earth, 7,899.99 miles
Diameter of the mean sphere of the earth, 7,917.78 miles
Equatorial circumference of the earth, 24,902.45 miles
Polar circumference of the earth, 24,818.60 miles
Mean distance from the earth to the sun, 92,900,000 miles
Mean distance from the earth to the moon, 238,857 miles
Total area of the earth, 196,940,400 square miles
Highest elevation on the earth's surface, Mt. Everest, Asia, 29,028 feet
Lowest elevation on the earth's land surface, shores of the Dead Sea, Asia.—1,286 feet
Greatest known depth of the ocean, south of the Mariana Islands, Pacific Ocean, 35,640 feet
Total land area of the earth, including inland water but excluding Antarctica, 52,195,000 square miles
Area of Africa, 11,700,000 square miles
Area of Antarctica, 5,100,000 square miles
Area of Asia, 17,075,000 square miles
Area of Australia, 2,971,081 square miles
Area of Europe, 3,835,000 square miles
Area of North America, 9,420,000 square miles
Area of South America, 6,870,000 square miles
Population of the earth (est. 1/1/1962), 3,072,000,000

Principal Islands and Their Areas

Island	Area Sq. Miles
Baffin, Arctic Region	183,810
Banks, Arctic Region	23,230
Borneo, East Indies	208,286
Bougainville, Oceania	3,880
Celebes, East Indies	72,986
Ceylon, Indian Ocean	25,332
Corsica, Mediterranean Sea	3,367
Crete, Mediterranean Sea	3,238
Cuba, West Indies	44,217
Cyprus, Mediterranean Sea	3,572
Devon, Arctic Region	20,861
Ellesmere, Arctic Region	82,119
Formosa, China Sea	13,885
Great Britain, North Atlantic O.	88,756
Greenland, Arctic Region	840,000
Hainan, South China Sea	13,127
Hawaii, Pacific O.	4,030
Hispaniola, West Indies	29,522
Hokkaido, Japan	29,950
Honshu, Japan	88,930
Iceland, Arctic Region	39,768
Ireland, North Atlantic O.	32,596
Jamaica, West Indies	4,411
Java, East Indies	50,745
Kyūshū, Japan	16,215
Luzon, Philippines	40,814
Madagascar, Indian Ocean	228,000
Melville, Arctic Region	16,141
Mindanao, Philippines	36,906
Mindoro, Philippines	3,794
Negros, Philippines	4,903
New Britain, East Indies	14,592
New Caledonia, South Pacific O.	7,202
Newfoundland, North Atlantic O.	42,734
New Guinea, East Indies	343,232
North East Island, Arctic Region	6,350
North Island (New Zealand), South Pacific O.	44,281
Novaya Zemlya, Arctic Region	31,390
Palawan, Philippines	4,500
Panay, Philippines	4,448
Prince of Wales, Arctic Region	12,830
Puerto Rico, West Indies	3,435
Sakhalin, Soviet Union	29,344
Samar, Philippines	5,124
Sardinia, Mediterranean Sea	9,301
Seram, East Indies	6,046
Sicily, Mediterranean Sea	9,925
Shikoku, Japan	7,245
Somerset, Arctic Region	9,370
Southampton, Hudson Bay	15,700
South Island (New Zealand) South Pacific O.	58,897
Sumatra, East Indies	182,859
Tasmania, Australia	26,215
Tierra del Fuego	18,600
Timor, East Indies	13,094
Vancouver, Canada	12,408
Victoria, Arctic Region	81,930
Vrangelya, Arctic Region	2,819
West Spitsbergen, Arctic Region	15,260

Principal Lakes, Oceans, Seas, and Their Areas

Lake Country	Area Sq. Miles
Aral'skoye More (Sea), Sov. Un.	26,525
Arctic O.	5,541,000
Athabasca, L., Can.	3,058
Atlantic O.	31,529,000
Balkhash, Ozero (L.), Sov. Un.	6,680
Baltic Sea, Eur.	158,000
Baykal, Ozero (L.), Sov. Un.	12,162
Bering Sea, Pac. O.	878,000
Black Sea, Eur.-Asia	168,500
Caribbean Sea, Cen. Am.	750,000
Caspian Sea, Sov. Un.	152,123
Chad, L., Chad	8,000
Ch'Ing Hai (L.), China	2,300
East China Sea, Pac. O.	480,000
Erie, L., U. S.-Can.	9,940
Eyre, L., Austl.	3,700
Gairdner, L., Austl.	1,500
Great Bear, L., Can.	12,000
Great Salt, L., U. S.	1,700
Great Slave, L., Can.	11,170
Hudson Bay, Can.	472,000
Huron, L., U. S.-Can.	23,010
Indian O.	28,357,000
Japan Sea, Asia	405,000
Ladozhskoye Ozero (L.), Sov. Un.	7,104
Leopold II, L., Bel. Congo	1,700
Manitoba, L., Can.	1,817
Mediterranean Sea, Eur.	1,145,000
Mexico, G. of, N. A.	700,000
Michigan, L., U. S.	22,400
Nicaragua, Lago de (L.), Nic.	3,060
North Sea, Atl. O.	221,000
Nyasa, L., Tan.-Moz.	10,900
Okhotsk, Sea of, Pac. O.	582,000
Onezhskoye Ozero (L.), Sov. Un.	3,822
Ontario, L., U. S.-Can.	7,540
Pacific O.	63,985,000
Red Sea, Afr.-Asia	178,000
Rudolf, L., Ken.-Eth.	3,500
Superior, L., U. S.-Can.	31,820
Tanganyika, L., Tan.	12,355
Titicaca, Lago (L.), Bol.-Peru	3,261
Torrens, L., Austl.	2,400
Vanern, L., Swe.	2,150
Van Gölü (L.), Tur.	1,450
Victoria, L., Tan.	26,828
Winnipeg, L., Can.	9,094
Winnipegosis, L., Can.	2,086
Yellow Sea, China	480,000

Principal Mountains and Their Heights

Mountain Country	Height in Feet
Aconcagua, Argentina	22,834
Albert Edward, Papua	13,100
Altar, Ecuador	17,457
Annapurna, Nepal-India	26,504
Antisana, Ecuador	18,714
Antofalla, Argentina	21,129
Apo, Philippines	9,690
Ararat, Turkey	16,946
Azufre, Chile	20,300
Balbi, Solomon I.	9,000
Bandeira, Brazil	9,462
Barriere Juliana, Neth. New Guinea	15,420
Bejeda, Ethiopia	15,158
Belukha, Soviet Union	15,157
Blanc, France-Italy	15,781
Blanca, Colorado, U. S.	14,317
Bolivar, Venezuela	16,411
Bona, Alaska, U. S.	16,421
Borah, Idaho, U. S.	12,662
Cameroons, Nigeria	13,353
Cano, Cape Verde Is.	9,760
Carstensz, Neth. New Guinea	16,503
Cayambe, Ecuador	19,170
Chimborazo, Ecuador	20,577
Citlaltépetl, Mexico	18,696
Colima, Mexico	14,235
Cook, New Zealand	12,349
Cotopaxi, Ecuador	19,344
Cristobal Colon, Colombia	18,947
Damavand, Iran	18,934
Dhaulagiri, Nepal	28,810
Dos Conos, Argentina	22,507
Dykh-Tau, Soviet Union	17,054
Elbert, Colorado, U. S.	14,431
Elbrus, Soviet Union	18,468
Elgon, Kenya-Uganda	14,178
Emi Koussi, Chad	11,204
Erebus, Antarctica	13,350
Etna, Italy	10,868
Everest, Nepal	29,028
Finsteraarhorn, Switzerland	14,026
Foraker, Alaska, U. S.	17,395
Fuji-san, Japan	12,388
Galdhōpigen, Norway	8,400
Gasherbrum, India	26,470
Godwin Austen (K-2), India	28,250
Gosainthan, China	26,291
Gran Paradiso, Italy	13,323
Gunnbjorn, Greenland	12,139
Gurla Mandhata, China	25,355
Hekla, Iceland	4,747
Hood, Oregon, U. S.	11,245
Hsinkao Shan, Formosa	13,113
Huascarán, Peru	22,205
Huila, Colombia	18,865
Hvannadalshnukur, Iceland	6,952
Illampu, Bolivia	21,490
Illimani, Bolivia	21,151
Incahuasi, Argentina-Chile	21,719
Ixtacihuatl, Mexico	17,343
Jabal Al Loz, Saudi Arabia	8,461
Jabal Razih, Saudi Arabia	11,999
Jungfrau, Switzerland	13,668
Kailas, China (Tibet)	22,028
Kámet, India	25,447
Kanchenjunga, Nepal-Sikkim	28,168
Karisimbi, Belgian Congo	14,787
Kazbek, Soviet Union	16,558
Kenya, Kenya	17,040
Kerintji, Indonesia	12,484
Kilimanjaro, Tanganyika	19,590
Kinabalu, North Borneo	13,455
Klyuchevskaya, Soviet Union	15,912
Korab, Albania	9,068
Koscuisko, Australia	7,328
Krakatoa (Rakata), Indonesia	2,667
Kwanmo, Korea	8,336
Lassen, California, U. S.	10,466
Lenina, Soviet Union	23,382
Leuser, Indonesia	11,178
Llullaillaco, Argentina-Chile	22,146
Logan, Canada	19,850
McKinley, Alaska, U. S.	20,320
Makalu, China-Nepal	27,790
Markham, Antarctica	15,100
Maromokotro, Malagash	9,468
Matterhorn, Switz.-Italy	14,685
Mauna Kea, Hawaii, U. S.	13,796
Mauna Loa, Hawaii, U. S.	13,680
Mercedario, Argentina-Chile	22,211
Minya Konka, China	24,900
Misti, Peru	19,144
Mitchell, North Carolina, U. S.	6,684
Musala, Bulgaria	9,592
Muztagh Ata, China	24,388
Namcha Barwa, China	25,445
Nanda Devi, India	25,645
Nanga Parbat, India	26,660
Negoi, Romania	8,346
Neiges, Piton des, Reunion I.	10,069
Ojos del Salado, Argentina-Chile	22,590
Olimbos Greece	9,550
Orohena, Tahiti	7,618
Paricutín, Mexico	9,100
Pelée, Martinique	4,800
Pic du Midi, d'Ossau, France	10,322
Pidurutalagala, Ceylon	8,281
Pikes Peak, Colorado, U. S.	14,110
Pissis, Argentina	22,546
Pobeda, China-Soviet Union	24,409
Popocatépetl, Mexico	17,883
Pulog, Philippines	9,612
Qurnet, es Sa'uda, Lebanon	10,131
Rainier, Washington, U. S.	14,410
Rakaposhi, India	25,551
Rendjani, Indonesia	12,225
Rosa, Monte, Italy-Switzerland	15,200
Ruapehu, New Zealand	9,175
Ruwenzori, Belgian Congo-Uganda	16,821
St. Elias, Alaska-Canada	18,008
Sajama, Bolivia	21,391
Sanford, Alaska, U. S.	16,208
Sangay, Ecuador	17,749
Semeroe, Java	12,060
Shasta, California, U. S.	14,162
Shkhara, Soviet Union	17,059
Sources, Mt. aux, Basutoland	10,822
Stalina, Soviet Union	24,590
Tengri Khan, Soviet Union	22,940
Thabantshonyana, Basutoland	11,425
Tina, Dominican Republic	8,399
Tirich Mir, Afghanistan	25,426
Tocorpuri, Bolivia-Chile	22,162
Toubkal, Morocco	13,661
Tupungato, Argentina-Chile	22,310
Ulugh Muztagh, China	25,340
Vesuvia, Italy	3,842
Victoria, Fiji I.	4,341
Weisshorn, Switzerland	14,803
Whitney, California, U. S.	14,495
Wilhelmina, Neth. New Guinea	15,518
Wrangell, Alaska, U. S.	14,005
Yerupaja, Peru	21,758

Principal Rivers and Their Lengths

River Continent	Length in Miles
Albany, North America	610
Aldan, Asia	1,392
Amazonas, South America	3,900
Amu Dar'ya, Asia	1,628
Amur, Asia	2,802
Araguaia, South America	1,630
Arkansas, North America	1,450
Athabasca, North America	765
Back, North America	605
Brahmaputra, Asia	1,800
Branco, South America	580
Brazos, North America	870
Canadian, North America	906
Churchill, North America	1,000
Colorado, North America	1,450
Columbia, North America	1,214
Congo, Africa	2,900
Cumberland, North America	687
Danube, Europe	1,770
Darling, Australia	1,750
Dnepr, Europe	1,420
Dnestr, Europe	876
Don, Europe	1,224
Donets, Europe	735
Elbe, Europe	720
Euphrates, Asia	1,675
Fraser, North America	850
Gambia, Africa	680
Ganges, Asia	1,550
Gila, North America	630
Godāvari, Asia	930
Hsi Chiang, Asia	1,590
Hwang Ho, Asia	2,903
Indus, Asia	1,980
Irrawaddy, Asia	1,425
Japurá, South America	1,400
Juruá, South America	1,200
Kama, Europe	1,261
Kolyma	1,615
Lena, Asia	2,653
Loire, Europe	625
Mackenzie, North America	2,635
Madeira, South America	2,060
Magdalena, South America	950
Marañón, South America	1,000
Mekong, Asia	2,600
Meuse, Europe	575
Mississippi, North America	2,348
Mississippi-Missouri-Red Rock, N. A.	3,860
Missouri-Red Rock, N. A.	2,683
Negro, South America	1,305
Nelson, North America	1,600
Neman, Eur.	582
Niger, Africa	2,590
Nile, Africa	4,132
N. Dvina-Sukhona, Europe	814
Obitsu-Irtysh, Asia	3,461
Oder, Europe	565
Ohio-Allegheny, N. A.	1,306
Oka, Europe	920
Orange, Africa	1,155
Orinoco, South America	1,800
Ottawa, North America	696
Paraná, South America	2,450
Parnaíba, South America	850
Peace, North America	1,195
Pechora, Europe	1,118
Pilcomayo, South America	1,550
Plata-Paraguay, S. America	2,300
Purús, South America	1,900
Red, North America	1,018
Rhein, Europe	820
Rhône, Europe	500
Rio Grande, North America	1,885
Roosevelt, South America	950
St. Lawrence, North America	1,900
Salado, South America	870
Salween, Asia	1,730
São Francisco, South America	1,800
Saskatchewan, North America	1,205
Sava, Europe	585
Senegal, Asia	1,000
Snake, North America	1,038
Sung Hua, Asia	1,140
Syr Darya, Asia	1,653
Tajo, Europe	625
Tennessee-French Broad, N. A.	862
Tigris, Asia	1,150
Tisza, Europe	607
Tobol, Asia	1,093
Tocantins, South America	1,640
Ucayali, South America	1,220
Ural, Europe	1,522
Uruguay, South America	1,025
Verkhnyaya Tunguska, Asia	1,549
Vilyuy, Asia	1,513
Volga, Europe	2,293
White, North America	690
Wisla, Europe	630
Xingú, South America	1,230
Yangtze Kiang, Asia	3,430
Yellowstone, North America	671
Yenisey, Asia	2,566
Yukon, North America	1,800
Zambezi, Africa	1,650

PRINCIPAL COUNTRIES AND REGIONS OF THE WORLD

Political Division or Region	Area in sq. miles	Population 1/1/62 est.	Pop. per sq. mi.
Aden (Colony) . . . (U.K.)	80	157,000	1,963
Aden Protectorate (U.K.)	112,000	665,000	5.9
Afghanistan	251,000	14,000,000	56
Africa	11,700,000	261,000,000	22
Alabama (U.S.)	51,609	3,303,000	64
Alaska (U.S.)	586,400	239,000	0.4
Albania	11,099	1,680,000	151
Alberta (Can.)	255,285	1,340,000	5.2
Algeria (Fr.)	917,537	11,150,000	12
American Samoa (U.S.)	76	21,000	276
Andorra	175	9,000	51
Angola (Port.)	481,351	4,700,000	9.8
Antarctica	5,100,000	....	....
Argentina	1,072,747	20,500,000	19
Arizona (U.S.)	113,909	1,412,000	12
Arkansas (U.S.)	53,104	1,791,000	34
Asia	17,075,000	1,791,000,000	105
Australia (Br. Comm.)	2,971,081	10,675,000	4.0
Austria	32,374	7,090,000	219
Azores Is. (Port.)	890	345,000	388
Bahamas (U.K.)	4,375	108,000	25
Bahrain	231	153,000	552
Basutoland (U.K.)	11,716	700,000	60
Bechuanaland (U.K.)	275,000	345,000	1.3
Belgium	11,778	9,230,000	784
Bermuda (U.K.)	21	53,000	2,524
Bhutan	19,300	675,000	35
Bolivia	424,163	3,530,000	8.3
Bonin Is. (Mil. Govt. U.S.)	40	200	5.0
Brazil	3,287,203	71,900,000	22
British Columbia (Can.)	366,255	1,655,000	4.5
Br. Comm. of Nations	11,187,541	735,533,000	66
British Guiana (U.K.)	83,000	592,000	7.1
British Honduras (U.K.)	8,866	93,000	10
Brunei (U.K.)	2,226	90,000	40
Bulgaria	42,729	7,975,000	187
Burma	261,789	20,975,000	80
California (U.S.)	158,693	16,751,000	106
Cambodia	66,606	5,100,000	77
Cameroun	183,333	4,150,000	23
Canada (Br. Comm.)	3,851,809	18,310,000	4.8
Canal Zone (U.S.)	553	42,000	76
Canary Is. (Sp.)	2,808	940,000	335
Cape Verde Is. (Port.)	1,552	208,000	134
Central African Republic	238,224	1,275,000	5.4
Central America	199,951	12,644,000	63
Ceylon (Br. Comm.)	25,332	10,200,000	403
Chad	495,800	2,750,000	5.5
Channel Is. (U.K.)	75	109,000	1,453
Chile	286,397	7,880,000	28
China (excl. Taiwan)	3,691,500	700,000,000	190
Colombia	439,513	14,625,000	33
Colorado (U.S.)	104,247	1,824,000	17
Congo (Republic of Congo; capital Brazzaville)	132,000	850,000	6.4
Congo, The (Republic of the Congo; capital Léopoldville)	905,381	14,500,000	16
Connecticut (U.S.)	5,009	2,643,000	528
Cook Is. (N.Z.)	90	18,000	200
Costa Rica	19,600	1,254,000	64
Cuba	44,217	7,000,000	158
Cyprus	3,572	586,000	164
Czechoslovakia	49,366	13,800,000	280
Dahomey	44,696	1,960,000	44
Delaware (U.S.)	2,057	467,000	227
Denmark	16,619	4,635,000	279
Denmark and Possessions	857,159	4,702,000	5.5
Dist. of Columbia (U.S.)	69	755,000	10,942
Dominican Republic	18,816	3,150,000	167
Ecuador	104,506	4,500,000	43
El Salvador	8,260	2,750,000	333
England and Wales (U.K.)	58,348	46,250,000	793
Ethiopia (incl. Eritrea)	457,147	20,000,000	44
Europe	3,835,000	583,300,000	152
Faeroe Is. (Den.)	540	35,000	65
Falkland Is. (excl. Deps.) (U.K.)	4,618	2,200	0.5
Fiji (U.K.)	7,055	415,000	59
Finland	130,119	4,517,000	35
Florida (U.S.)	58,560	5,341,000	91
France	212,822	46,200,000	217
France and Possessions	1,194,495	58,780,000	49
French Guiana (Fr.)	35,100	32,000	0.9
French Polynesia (Fr.)	1,550	79,000	51
French Somaliland (Fr.)	8,500	69,000	8.1
Gabon	103,100	450,000	4.4
Gambia (U.K.)	4,003	315,000	79
Georgia (U.S.)	58,876	4,025,000	68
Germany (Entire)	137,557	73,850,000	537
Germany, East	41,634	17,170,000	412
Germany, West (incl. West Berlin)	95,923	56,680,000	591
Ghana (Br. Comm.)	91,843	6,925,000	75
Gibraltar (U.K.)	2	26,000	13,000
Gilbert and Ellice Is. (U.K.)	349	47,000	135
Greece	51,169	8,435,000	165
Greenland (Den.)	840,000	32,000	0.04
Guadeloupe and Deps. (Fr.)	687	280,000	408
Guam (U.S.)	212	70,000	330
Guatemala	42,042	3,930,000	93
Guinea	94,925	3,000,000	32
Haiti	10,714	3,570,000	333
Hawaii (U.S.)	6,424	662,000	103
Honduras	43,277	1,925,000	44
Hong Kong (U.K.)	391	3,225,000	8,248
Hungary	35,919	10,065,000	280
Iceland	39,800	182,000	4.6
Idaho (U.S.)	83,557	682,000	8.2
Ifni (Sp.)	580	58,000	100
Illinois (U.S.)	56,400	10,346,000	183
India (incl. Kashmir) (Br. Comm.)	1,259,991	444,200,000	353
Indiana (U.S.)	36,291	4,746,000	131
Indonesia	575,893	95,800,000	166
Iowa (U.S.)	56,290	2,785,000	49
Iran	636,300	20,925,000	33
Iraq	171,599	7,350,000	43
Ireland	27,136	2,805,000	103
Isle of Man (U.K.)	227	48,000	211
Israel	8,000	2,200,000	275
Italy	116,303	49,700,000	427
Ivory Coast	124,503	3,340,000	27
Jamaica (U.K.)	4,411	1,650,000	374
Japan	142,726	94,500,000	662
Jordan	37,301	1,800,000	48
Kansas (U.S.)	82,264	2,200,000	27
Kentucky (U.S.)	40,395	3,074,000	76
Kenya (U.K.)	224,960	7,400,000	33
Korea, North	47,861	8,200,000	171
Korea, South	37,424	25,700,000	687
Kuwait	5,800	232,000	40
Laos	91,400	1,875,000	21
Lebanon	4,000	1,850,000	463
Liberia	43,000	1,300,000	30
Libya	679,358	1,225,000	1.8
Liechtenstein	61	17,000	279
Louisiana (U.S.)	48,523	3,357,000	69
Luxembourg	998	317,000	318
Macao (Port.)	6	225,000	37,500
Madeira Is. (Port.)	308	280,000	909
Maine (U.S.)	33,215	981,000	30
Malagasy Republic (Madagascar)	227,800	5,625,000	25
Malaya (Br. Comm.)	50,680	7,225,000	143
Maldive Is.	115	89,000	774
Mali	464,874	4,150,000	8.9
Malta (U.K.)	122	330,000	2,705
Manitoba (Can.)	251,000	920,000	3.7
Martinique (Fr.)	425	285,000	671
Maryland (U.S.)	10,577	3,237,000	306
Massachusetts (U.S.)	8,257	5,285,000	640
Mauritania	419,230	740,000	1.8
Mauritius and Deps	808	685,000	848
Mexico	760,375	36,300,000	48
Michigan (U.S.)	58,216	8,000,000	137
Midway Is. (U.S.)	2	2,500	1,250
Minnesota (U.S.)	84,068	3,498,000	42
Mississippi (U.S.)	47,716	2,200,000	46
Missouri (U.S.)	69,686	4,387,000	63
Monaco	0.6	23,000	38,333
Mongolia	591,100	950,000	1.6
Montana (U.S.)	147,138	691,000	4.7
Morocco	171,599	11,950,000	70
Mozambique (Port.)	297,846	6,500,000	22
Muscat and Oman	82,000	575,000	7.0
Nauru (Austl.)	8	4,600	575
Nebraska (U.S.)	77,227	1,429,000	19
Nepal	54,362	9,480,000	174
Netherlands	12,529	11,710,000	935
Netherlands and Poss.	228,643	12,931,000	57
Neth. Antilles (Neth.)	371	197,000	531
Neth. New Guinea (Neth.)	160,606	700,000	4.4
Nevada (U.S.)	110,540	306,000	2.8
New Brunswick (Can.)	28,354	615,000	22
New Caledonia (incl. Deps.) (Fr.)	7,300	80,000	11
Newfoundland (Can.)	156,185	475,000	3.0
New Guinea Ter. (Austl.)	94,430	1,450,000	15
New Hampshire (U.S.)	9,304	622,000	67
New Hebrides (Fr.-U.K.)	5,700	61,000	11
New Jersey (U.S.)	7,836	6,320,000	807
New Mexico (U.S.)	121,666	997,000	8.2
New York (U.S.)	49,576	17,123,000	345
New Zealand (Br. Comm.)	103,736	2,450,000	24
Nicaragua	48,600	1,550,000	31
Niger	458,995	2,900,000	6.3
Nigeria (Br. Comm.)	367,641	36,100,000	98
Niue (N.Z.)	100	5,000	50
Norfolk I. (Austl.)	13	1,000	77
North America	9,420,000	272,800,000	29
North Borneo (U.K.)	29,388	475,000	16
North Carolina (U.S.)	52,712	4,645,000	88
North Dakota (U.S.)	70,665	641,000	9.1
Northern Ireland (U.K.)	5,439	1,425,000	262
Northern Rhodesia (Rh. and Nya.)	288,130	2,525,000	8.8
Northwest Ters. (Can.)	1,304,903	22,000	0.02
Norway	125,064	3,629,000	29
Nova Scotia (Can.)	21,425	735,000	34
Nyasaland (Rh. and Nya.)	46,066	2,920,000	63
Oceania	3,295,000	16,300,000	4.9
Ohio (U.S.)	41,222	9,943,000	241
Oklahoma (U.S.)	69,919	2,371,000	34
Ontario (Can.)	412,582	6,250,000	15
Oregon (U.S.)	96,981	1,811,000	19
Pacific Is. Tr. Ter. (U.S.)	672	80,000	119
Pakistan (excl. Kashmir) (Br. Comm.)	364,737	95,600,000	262
Panama	28,753	1,100,000	38
Papua (excl. N. Gui. Ter.) (Austl.)	90,600	530,000	5.8
Paraguay	157,047	1,835,000	12
Pennsylvania (U.S.)	45,333	11,521,000	254
Peru	496,223	11,400,000	23
Philippines	115,707	28,600,000	247
Pitcairn (excl. Deps.) (U.K.)	2	150	75
Poland	120,359	30,265,000	251
Portugal	36,376	9,000,000	247
Portugal and Possessions	840,407	22,441,000	27
Portuguese Guinea (Port.)	13,948	580,000	42
Portuguese India (Port.)	1,628	650,000	399
Portuguese Timor (Port.)	7,332	510,000	70
Prince Edward I. (Can.)	2,184	105,000	48
Puerto Rico (U.S.)	3,435	2,410,000	702
Qatar	8,000	50,000	6.3
Quebec (Can.)	594,860	5,260,000	8.8
Reunion (Fr.)	969	352,000	363
Rhode Island (U.S.)	1,214	868,000	715
Rhodesia and Nyasaland (U.K.)	484,529	8,625,000	18
Romania	91,698	18,700,000	204
Ruanda-Urundi (Bel.)	20,915	5,025,000	240
St. Helena (excl. Deps.) (U.K.)	47	4,600	98
St. Pierre-Miquelon (Fr.)	93	5,000	54
San Marino	23	17,000	739
Sao Tome and Principe (Port.)	372	68,000	183
Sarawak (U.K.)	47,000	800,000	17
Saskatchewan (Can.)	251,700	919,000	3.7
Saudi Arabia	617,800	6,200,000	10
Scotland (U.K.)	30,411	5,185,000	170
Senegal	76,124	3,200,000	42
Seychelles (U.K.)	156	43,000	276
Sierra Leone (Br. Comm.)	27,925	2,500,000	90
Sikkim	2,744	162,000	59
Singapore (U.K.)	224	1,695,000	7,567
Solomon Is. (Austl.)	4,320	55,000	13
Solomon Is., British (U.K.)	11,500	130,000	11
Somali Republic	246,202	2,035,000	8.3
South Africa	472,733	16,350,000	35
South America	6,870,000	147,600,000	21
South Carolina (U.S.)	31,055	2,421,000	78
South Dakota (U.S.)	77,047	689,000	8.9
Southern Rhodesia (Rh. and Nya.)	150,333	3,180,000	21
S. W. Africa (S. Afr.)	318,099	535,000	1.7
Spain	194,345	30,525,000	157
Spain and Possessions	308,541	30,980,000	100
Spanish Sahara (Sp.)	102,703	25,000	0.24
Sudan	967,500	12,300,000	13
Surinam (Neth.)	55,145	324,000	5.9
Svalbard (Nor.)	24,101	4,000	0.2
Swaziland (U.K.)	6,704	270,000	40
Sweden	173,622	7,520,000	43
Switzerland	15,941	5,520,000	346
Syria	71,227	4,825,000	68
Taiwan (Formosa) (Nationalist China)	13,884	11,150,000	803
Tanganyika (Br. Comm.)	361,800	9,500,000	26
Tennessee (U.S.)	42,244	3,632,000	86
Texas (U.S.)	267,339	9,920,000	37
Thailand	198,500	26,300,000	132
Tibet (incl. Chamdo) (China)	471,660	1,300,000	2.8
Togo	22,000	1,475,000	67
Tokelau (Union Is.) (N.Z.)	4	2,000	500
Tonga (U.K.)	269	67,000	249
Trucial Coast	32,300	88,000	2.7
Tunisia	48,332	4,260,000	88
Turkey	301,381	28,675,000	95
Uganda (U.K.)	93,981	6,925,000	74
Union of Soviet Socialist Republics	8,599,300	220,000,000	26
United Arab Republic (Egypt)	386,000	27,000,000	70
United Kingdom	94,205	52,860,000	561
United Kingdom and Poss.	1,039,705	80,622,000	78
United States	3,675,633	185,200,000	50
United States and Poss.	3,680,752	187,860,000	51
Upper Volta	105,839	3,735,000	35
Uruguay	72,172	2,880,000	40
Utah (U.S.)	84,916	929,000	11
Vatican City	0.2	1,000	5,000
Venezuela	352,143	7,600,000	22
Vermont (U.S.)	9,609	393,000	41
Vietnam, North	59,933	15,400,000	257
Vietnam, South	65,948	14,600,000	221
Virgin Is. (U.S.-U.K.)	192	40,500	375
Virginia (U.S.)	40,815	4,044,000	99
Wales (incl. Monmouthshire) (U.K.)	8,016	2,645,000	330
Washington (U.S.)	68,192	2,937,000	43
Western Samoa	1,130	110,000	97
West Indies, The (Federation) (U.K.)	3,594	1,565,000	435
West Virginia (U.S.)	24,181	1,831,000	76
Wisconsin (U.S.)	56,154	4,047,000	72
World	57,295,000	3,072,000,000	54
Wyoming (U.S.)	97,914	338,000	3.5
Yemen	75,300	5,000,000	66
Yugoslavia	98,776	18,700,000	189
Yukon (Can.)	207,076	14,000	0.06
Zanzibar (U.K.)	1,020	313,000	307

GLOSSARY OF FOREIGN GEOGRAPHICAL TERMS

Annam ... Annamese
Arab ... Arabic
Bantu ... Bantu
Bur ... Burmese
Camb ... Cambodian
Celt ... Celtic
Chn ... Chinese
Czech ... Czech
Dan ... Danish
Du ... Dutch
Fin ... Finnish
Fr ... French
Ger ... German
Gr ... Greek
Hung ... Hungarian
Ice ... Icelandic
India ... India
Indian ... American Indian
Indon ... Indonesian
It ... Italian
Jap ... Japanese
Kor ... Korean
Mal ... Malayan
Mong ... Mongolian
Nor ... Norwegian
Per ... Persian
Pol ... Polish
Port ... Portuguese
Rom ... Romanian
Rus ... Russian
Siam ... Siamese
So. Slav ... Southern Slavonic
Sp ... Spanish
Swe ... Swedish
Tib ... Tibetan
Tur ... Turkish
Yugo ... Yugoslav

å, *Nor., Swe* ... brook, river
aa, *Dan., Nor* ... brook
aas, *Dan., Nor* ... ridge
ab, *Per* ... water, river
abad, *India, Per* ... town, city
ada, *Tur* ... island
adrar, *Arab* ... mountain
air, *Indon* ... stream
akrotírion, *Gr* ... cape
älf, *Swe* ... river
alp, *Ger* ... mountain
altipiano, *It* ... plateau
alto, *Sp* ... height
archipel, *Fr* ... archipelago
archipiélago, *Sp* ... archipelago
arquipélago, *Port* ... archipelago
arroyo, *Sp* ... brook, stream
ås, *Nor., Swe* ... ridge
austral, *Sp* ... southern
baai, *Du* ... bay
bab, *Arab* ... gate, port
bach, *Ger* ... brook, stream
backe, *Swe* ... hill
bad, *Ger* ... bath, spa
bahía, *Sp* ... bay, gulf
bahr, *Arab* ... sea, lake
baia, *It* ... bay, gulf
baía, *Port* ... bay
baie, *Fr* ... bay, gulf
bajo, *Sp* ... depression
bak, *Indon* ... stream
bakke, *Dan., Nor* ... hill
balkan, *Tur* ... mountain range
bana, *Jap* ... point, cape
banco, *Sp* ... bank
bandar, *Mal., Per.* ... town, port, harbor
bang, *Siam* ... village
bassin, *Fr* ... basin
batang, *Indon., Mal* ... river
ben, *Celt* ... mountain, summit
bender, *Arab* ... harbor, port
bereg, *Rus* ... coast, shore
berg, *Du., Ger., Nor., Swe.* ... mountain, hill
bir, *Arab* ... well
birket, *Arab* ... pond, pool
bit, *Arab* ... house
bjaerg, *Dan., Nor* ... mountain
bocche, *It* ... mouth
bogaz, *Tur* ... strait
bois, *Fr* ... forest, wood
boloto, *Rus* ... marsh
bolsón, *Sp* flat-floored desert valley
boreal, *Sp* ... northern
borg, *Dan., Nor., Swe* ... castle, town
borgo, *It* ... town, suburb
bosch, *Du* ... forest, wood
bouche, *Fr* ... river mouth
bourg, *Fr* ... town, borough
bro, *Dan., Nor., Swe* ... bridge
brücke, *Ger* ... bridge
bucht, *Ger* ... bay, bight
bugt, *Dan., Nor., Swe* ... bay, gulf
bulu, *Indon* ... mountain
burg, *Du., Ger* ... castle, town
buri, *Siam* ... town
burun, burnu, *Tur* ... cape
by, *Dan., Nor., Swe* ... village
caatinga, *Port. (Brazil)* ... open brushland
cabezo, *Sp* ... summit
cabo, *Port., Sp* ... cape
campo, *It., Port., Sp* ... field
campos, *Port. (Brazil)* ... plains
cañon, *Sp* ... canyon
cap, *Fr* ... cape
capo, *It* ... cape
casa, *It., Port., Sp* ... house
castello, *It., Port* ... castle, fort
castillo, *Sp* ... castle
càte, *Fr* ... hill
çay, *Tur* ... stream, river
cayo, *Sp* ... rock, shoal, islet
cerro, *Sp* ... hill
champ, *Fr* ... field
chang, *Chn* ... village, middle
château, *Fr* ... castle
chen, *Chn* ... market town
chiang, *Chn* ... river
chott, *Arab* ... salt lake
chou, *Chn* capital of district; island
chu, *Tib* ... water, stream
cidade, *Port* ... town, city
cima, *Sp* ... summit, peak
città, *It* ... town, city
ciudad, *Sp* ... town, city
cochilha, *Port* ... ridge
col, *Fr* ... pass
colina, *Sp* ... hill
cordillera, *Sp* ... mountain chain
costa, *It., Port., Sp* ... coast
côte, *Fr* ... coast
cuchilla, *Sp* ... mountain ridge
dag, *Tur* ... mountain
dake, *Jap* ... peak, summit
dal, *Dan., Du., Nor., Swe* ... valley
dan, *Kor* ... point, cape
danau, *Indon* ... lake
dar, *Arab* ... house, abode, country
darya, *Per* ... river, sea
dasht, *Per* ... plain, desert
deniz, *Tur* ... sea
désert, *Fr* ... desert
deserto, *It* ... desert
desierto, *Sp* ... desert
détroit, *Fr* ... strait
dijk, *Du* ... dam, dike
djebel, *Arab* ... mountain
do, *Kor* ... island
dorf, *Ger* ... village
dorp, *Du* ... village
duin, *Du* ... dune
dzong, *Tib.* ... fort, administrative capital
eau, *Fr* ... water
ecuador, *Sp* ... equator
eiland, *Du* ... island
elv, *Dan., Nor* ... river, stream
embalse, *Sp* ... reservoir
erg, *Arab* ... dune, sandy desert
est, *Fr., It* ... east
estado, *Sp* ... state
este, *Port., Sp* ... east
estrecho, *Sp* ... strait
étang, *Fr* ... pond, lake
état, *Fr* ... state
eyjar, *Ice* ... islands
feld, *Ger* ... field, plain
festung, *Ger* ... fortress
fiume, *It* ... river
fjäll, *Swe* ... mountain
fjärd, *Swe* ... bay, inlet
fjeld, *Nor* ... mountain, hill
fjord, *Dan., Nor* ... fiord, inlet
fjördur, *Ice* ... fiord, inlet
fleuve, *Fr* ... river
flod, *Dan., Swe* ... river
flói, *Ice* ... bay, marshland
fluss, *Ger* ... river
foce, *It* ... river mouth
fontein, *Du* ... a spring
forêt, *Fr* ... forest
fors, *Swe* ... waterfall
forst, *Ger* ... forest
fos, *Dan., Nor* ... waterfall
fu, *Chn* ... town, residence
fuente, *Sp* ... spring, fountain
fuerte, *Sp* ... fort
furt, *Ger* ... ford
gang, *Kor* ... stream, river
gangri, *Tib* ... mountain
gat, *Dan., Nor* ... channel
gàve, *Fr* ... stream
gawa, *Jap* ... river
gebergte, *Du* ... mountain range
gebiet, *Ger* ... district, territory
gebirge, *Ger* ... mountains
ghat, *India* ... pass, mountain range
gobi, *Mong* ... desert
goenoeng, *Mal* ... mountain
gol, *Mong* ... river
göl, gölü, *Tur* ... lake
golf, *Du., Ger* ... gulf, bay
golfe, *Fr* ... gulf, bay
golfo, *It., Port., Sp* ... gulf, bay
gomba, gompa, *Tib* ... monastery
gora, *Rus., So. Slav* ... mountain
góra, *Pol* ... mountain
gorod, *Rus* ... town
grad, *Rus., So. Slav* ... town
guba, *Rus* ... bay, gulf
gundung, *Indon* ... mountain
guntō, *Jap* ... archipelago
haf, *Swe* ... sea, ocean
hafen, *Ger* ... port, harbor
haff, *Ger* ... gulf, inland sea
hai, *Chn* ... sea, lake
hama, *Jap* ... beach, shore
hamada, *Arab* ... rocky plateau
hamn, *Swe* ... harbor
hamun, *Per* ... swampy lake, plain
hantō, *Jap* ... peninsula
hassi, *Arab* ... well, spring
haus, *Ger* ... house
haut, *Fr* ... summit, top
hav, *Dan., Nor* ... sea, ocean
havn, *Dan., Nor* ... harbor, port
havre, *Fr* ... harbor, port
háza, *Hung* ... house, dwelling of
heim, *Ger* ... hamlet, home
hem, *Swe* ... hamlet, home
higashi, *Jap* ... east
hisar, *Tur* ... fortress
hissar, *Arab* ... fort
ho, *Chn* ... river
hoek, *Du* ... cape
hof, *Ger* ... court, farm house
höfn, *Ice* ... harbor
hoku, *Jap* ... north
holm, *Dan., Nor., Swe* ... island
hora, *Czech* ... mountain
horn, *Ger* ... peak
hoved, *Dan., Nor* ... cape
hsien, *Chn* district, district capital
hu, *Chn* ... lake
hügel, *Ger* ... hill
huk, *Dan., Swe* ... point
hus, *Dan., Nor., Swe* ... house
île, *Fr* ... island
ilha, *Port* ... island
indsö, *Dan., Nor* ... lake
insel, *Ger* ... island
insjö, *Swe* ... lake
irmak, irmagi, *Tur* ... river
isla, *Sp* ... island
isola, *It* ... island
istmo, *It., Sp* ... isthmus
istrova, *Rus* ... islands
järvi, jaur, *Fin* ... lake
jebel, *Arab* ... mountain
jima, *Jap* ... island
jökel, *Nor* ... glacier
joki, *Fin* ... river
jökull, *Ice* ... ice-covered mountain
kaap, *Du* ... cape
kai, *Jap* ... bay, gulf, sea
kaikyō, *Jap* ... channel, strait
kalat, *Per* ... castle, fortress
kale, *Tur* ... fort
kali, *Mal* ... river
kand, *Per* ... village
kang, *Chn* mountain ridge; village
kap, *Dan., Ger* ... cape
kapp, *Nor., Swe* ... cape
kasr, *Arab* ... fort, castle
kawa, *Jap* ... river
kefr, *Arab* ... village
kei, *Jap* ... creek, river
ken, *Jap* ... prefecture
khor, *Arab* ... bay, inlet
khrebet, *Rus* ... mountain range
kiang, *Chn* ... large river
king, *Chn* ... capital city, town
kita, *Jap* ... north
ko, *Jap* ... lake
köbstad, *Dan* ... market-town
kol, *Mong* ... lake
kólpos, *Gr* ... gulf
kong, *Chn* ... river
kopf, *Ger* ... head, summit, peak
köpstad, *Swe* ... market-town
korfezi, *Tur* ... gulf
kosa, *Rus* ... cape
kou, *Chn* ... river mouth
köy, *Tur* ... village
kraal, *Du. (Africa)* ... native village
ksar, *Arab* ... fortified village
kuala, *Mal* ... river mouth
kuh, *Per* ... mountain
kum, *Tur* ... sand
kuppe, *Ger* ... summit
küste, *Ger* ... coast
kyo, *Jap* ... town, capital
la, *Tib* ... mountain pass
labuan, *Mal* ... anchorage, port
lac, *Fr* ... lake
lago, *It., Port., Sp* ... lake
lagoa, *Port* ... lake, marsh
laguna, *It., Port., Sp* ... lagoon, lake
lahti, *Fin* ... bay, gulf
län, *Swe* ... county
landsby, *Dan., Nor* ... village
liehtao, *Chn* ... archipelago
liman, *Tur* ... bay, port
ling, *Chn* ... pass, ridge, mountain
llanos, *Sp* ... plains
loch, *Celt. (Scotland)* ... lake, bay
loma, *Sp* ... long, low hill
lough, *Celt. (Ireland)* ... lake, bay
machi, *Jap* ... town
man, *Kor* ... bay
mar, *Port., Sp* ... sea
mare, *It., Rom* ... sea
marisma, *Sp* ... marsh, swamp
mark, *Ger* ... boundary, limit
massif, *Fr* ... block of mountains
mato, *Port* ... forest, thicket
me, *Siam* ... river
meer, *Du., Ger* ... lake, sea
mer, *Fr* ... sea
mesa, *Sp* ... flat-topped mountain
meseta, *Sp* ... plateau
mina, *Port., Sp* ... mine
minami, *Jap* ... south
minato, *Jap* ... harbor, haven
misaki, *Jap* ... cape, headland
mont, *Fr* ... mount, mountain
montagna, *It* ... mountain
montagne, *Fr* ... mountain
montaña, *Sp* ... mountain
monte, *It., Port., Sp.* ... mount, mountain
more, *Rus., So. Slav* ... sea
morro, *Port., Sp* ... hill, bluff
mühle, *Ger* ... mill
mund, *Ger* ... mouth, opening
mündung, *Ger* ... river mouth
mura, *Jap* ... township
myit, *Bur* ... river
mys, *Rus* ... cape
nada, *Jap* ... sea
nadi, *India* ... river, creek
naes, *Dan., Nor* ... cape
nafud, *Arab* ... desert of sand dunes
nagar, *India* ... town, city
nahr, *Arab* ... river
nam, *Siam* ... river, water
nan, *Chn., Jap* ... south
näs, *Nor., Swe* ... cape
nez, *Fr* ... point, cape
nishi, nisi, *Jap* ... west
njarga, *Fin* ... peninsula
nong, *Siam* ... marsh
noord, *Du* ... north
nor, *Mong* ... lake
nord, *Dan., Fr., Ger., It., Nor., Swe* ... north
norte, *Port., Sp* ... north
nos, *Rus* ... cape
nyasa, *Bantu* ... lake
ö, *Dan., Nor., Swe* ... island
occidental, *Sp* ... western
ocna, *Rom* ... salt mine
odde, *Dan., Nor* ... point, cape
oedjoeng, *Mal* ... point, cape
oeste, *Port., Sp* ... west
oka, *Jap* ... hill
oost, *Du* ... east
oriental, *Sp* ... eastern
óros, *Gr* ... mountain
ost, *Ger., Swe* ... east
öster, *Dan., Nor., Swe* ... eastern
ostrov, *Rus* ... island
oued, *Arab* ... river, stream
ouest, *Fr* ... west
ozero, *Rus* ... lake
pää, *Fin* ... mountain
padang, *Mal* ... plain, field
pampas, *Sp. (Argentina)* ... grassy plains
pará, *Indian (Brazil)* ... river
pas, *Fr* ... channel, passage
paso, *Sp* ... passage
passo, *It., Port* ... passage, strait
patam, *India* ... city, town
pei, *Chn* ... north
pélagos, *Gr* ... open sea
pegunungan, *Indon* ... mountains
peña, *Sp* ... rock
peresheyek, *Rus* ... isthmus
pertuis, *Fr* ... strait
peski, *Rus* ... desert
pic, *Fr* ... mountain peak
pico, *Port., Sp* ... mountain peak
piedra, *Sp* ... stone, rock
ping, *Chn* ... plain, flat
planalto, *Port* ... plateau
planina, *Yugo* ... mountains
playa, *Sp* ... shore, beach
pnom, *Camb* ... mountain
poelau, *Mal* ... island
pointe, *Fr* ... point
polder, *Du., Ger* ... reclaimed marsh
polje, *So. Slav* ... field
poluostrov, *Rus* ... peninsula
pont, *Fr* ... bridge
ponta, *Port* ... point, headland
ponte, *It., Port* ... bridge
pore, *India* ... city, town
porthmós, *Gr* ... strait
porto, *It., Port* ... port, harbor
potamós, *Gr* ... river
p'ov, *Rus* ... peninsula
prado, *Sp* ... field, meadow
presqu'île, *Fr* ... peninsula
proliv, *Rus* ... strait
pu, *Chn* ... commercial village
pueblo, *Sp* ... town, village
puerto, *Sp* ... port, harbor
pulau, *Mal* ... island
punkt, *Ger* ... point
punt, *Du* ... point
punta, *It., Sp* ... point
pur, *India* ... city, town
puy, *Fr* ... peak
qal'a, qal'at, *Arab* ... fort, village
qasr, *Arab* ... fort, castle
rann, *India* ... wasteland
ras, *Arab* ... cape, head
reka, *Rus., So. Slav* ... river
represa, *Port* ... reservoir
rettō, *Jap* ... island chain
ría, *Sp* ... estuary
ribeira, *Port* ... stream
riberão, *Port* ... river
rio, *It., Port* ... stream, river
río, *Sp* ... river
rivière, *Fr* ... river
roca, *Sp* ... rock
rt, *Yugo* ... cape
rud, *Per* ... river
saari, *Fin* ... island
sable, *Fr* ... sand
sahara, *Arab* ... desert, plain
saki, *Jap* ... cape
sal, *Sp* ... salt
salar, *Sp* ... salt flat, salt lake
salto, *Sp* ... waterfall
san, *Jap., Kor* ... mountain, hill
sat, satul, *Rom* ... village
schloss, *Ger* ... castle
sebkha, *Arab* ... salt marsh
see, *Ger* ... lake, sea
şehir, *Tur* ... town, city
selat, *Indon* ... stream
selvas, *Port. (Brazil)* ... tropical rain forests
seno, *Sp* ... bay
serra, *Port* ... mountain chain
serranía, *Sp* ... mountain ridge
seto, *Jap* ... strait
severnaya, *Rus* ... northern
shahr, *Per* ... town, city
shan, *Chn* ... mountain, hill, island
shatt, *Arab* ... river
shi, *Jap* ... city
shima, *Jap* ... island
shōtō, *Jap* ... archipelago
si, *Chn* ... west, western
sierra, *Sp* ... mountain range
sjö, *Nor., Swe* ... lake, sea
sö, *Dan., Nor* ... lake, sea
söder, södra, *Swe* ... south
soengai, soengei, *Mal* ... river
song, *Annam* ... river
sopka, *Rus* ... peak, volcano
source, *Fr* ... a spring
spitze, *Ger* ... summit, point
staat, *Ger* ... state
stad, *Dan., Du., Nor., Swe.* ... city, town
stadt, *Ger* ... city, town
stato, *It* ... state
step, *Rus* ... treeless plain, steppe
straat, *Du* ... strait
strand, *Dan., Du., Ger., Nor., Swe* ... shore, beach
stretto, *It* ... strait
strom, *Ger* ... river, stream
ström, *Dan., Nor., Swe* stream, river
stroom, *Du* ... stream, river
su, suyu, *Tur* ... water, river
sud, *Fr., Sp* ... south
süd, *Ger* ... south
suidō, *Jap* ... channel
sul, *Port* ... south
sund, *Dan., Nor., Swe* ... sound
sungai, sungei, *Indon., Mal* ... river
sur, *Sp* ... south
syd, *Dan., Nor., Swe* ... south
tafelland, *Ger* ... plateau
take, *Jap* ... peak, summit
tal, *Ger* ... valley
tandjoeng, tanjong, *Mal* ... cape
tao, *Chn* ... island
târg, târgul, *Rom* ... market, town
tell, *Arab* ... hill
teluk, *Indon* ... bay, gulf
terra, *It* ... land
terre, *Fr* ... earth, land
thal, *Ger* ... valley
tierra, *Sp* ... earth, land
tō, *Jap* ... east; island
tonle, *Camb* ... river, lake
top, *Du* ... peak
torp, *Swe* ... hamlet, cottage
tsangpo, *Tib* ... river
tsi, *Chn* ... village, borough
tso, *Tib* ... lake
tsu, *Jap* ... harbor, port
tundra, *Rus* ... treeless arctic plains
tung, *Chn* ... east
tuz, *Tur* ... salt
udde, *Swe* ... cape
ufer, *Ger* ... shore, river bank
umi, *Jap* ... sea, gulf
ura, *Jap* ... bay, coast, creek
ust'ye, *Rus* ... river mouth
valle, *It., Port., Sp* ... valley
vallée, *Fr* ... valley
valli, *It* ... lake
vár, *Hung* ... fortress
város, *Hung* ... town
varoš, *So. Slav* ... town
veld, *Du* ... open plain, field
verkh, *Rus* ... top, summit
ves, *Czech* ... village
vest, *Dan., Nor., Swe* ... west
vik, *Swe* ... cove, bay
vila, *Port* ... town
villa, *Sp* ... town
villar, *Sp* ... village, hamlet
ville, *Fr* ... town, city
vostok, *Rus* ... east
wad, wadi, *Arab.* ... intermittent stream
wald, *Ger* ... forest, woodland
wan, *Chn., Jap* ... bay, gulf
weiler, *Ger* ... hamlet, village
westersch, *Du* ... western
wüste, *Ger* ... desert
yama, *Jap* ... mountain
yarimada, *Tur* ... peninsula
yug, *Rus* ... south
zaki, *Jap* ... cape
zaliv, *Rus* ... bay, gulf
zapad, *Rus* ... west
zee, *Du* ... sea
zemlya, *Rus* ... land
zuid, *Du* ... south

ABBREVIATIONS OF
GEOGRAPHICAL NAMES AND TERMS

Afg.............Afghanistan
Afr...................Africa
Ala..................Alabama
Alb..................Albania
Alg..................Algeria
And..................Andorra
Ang...................Angola
Ant. O.............Antarctica
Arc. O...........Arctic Ocean
Arch..............Archipelago
Arg................Argentina
Ariz.................Arizona
Ark.................Arkansas
A. S. S. R.
  Autonomous Soviet
  Socialist Republic
Atl. O..........Atlantic Ocean
Aus...................Austria
Austl...............Australia
Aut...............Autonomous

B.................Bay, Bahia
Ba. Is...........Bahama Is.
Barb................Barbados
Bas...............Basutoland
Bdy................Boundary
Bech...........Bechuanaland
Bel..................Belgium
Bg......................Berg
Bhu...................Bhutan
Bk......................Bank
Bol..................Bolivia
Br....................British
Braz..................Brazil
Br. Comm.
  British Commonwealth
  of Nations
Br. Gu........British Guiana
Br. Hond...British Honduras
Brit. Prot...British Protectorate
Bru...................Brunei
Bul.................Bulgaria
Bur....................Burma

C................Cerro, Cape
Calif..............California
Cam................Cameroun
Camb...............Cambodia
Can..........Canal, Canada
Can. Is........Canary Is.
Cen. Afr. Rep.
  Central African Republic
Cen. Am.....Central America
C. H............Court House
Chan................Channel
Co.....................County
Col.................Colombia
Colo................Colorado
Con. B.
  Congo; capital Brazzaville
Con. L....Congo, The; capital;
  Léopoldville
Conn.............Connecticut
Cor...................Corsica
C. R..............Costa Rica
Cr......................Creek
C. V. Is.......Cape Verde Is.
C. Z.............Canal Zone
Czech........Czechoslovakia

D. C.....District of Columbia
Del.................Delaware
Den..................Denmark
Dept..............Department
Des....................Desert
D. F.......Distrito Federal
Dist.................District
Div..................Division
Dom. Rep.
  Dominican Republic

E.......................East
Ec...................Ecuador
Elec.................Electric
Eng..................England
E. Pak..........East Pakistan
Eth.................Ethiopia
Eur...................Europe

Faer............The Faeroes
Falk. Is.........Falkland Is.
Fd.....................Fjord
Fed. of Rh. & Nya.
  Federation of Rhodesia
  & Nyasaland
Fin...................Finland
Fk.......................Fork
Fla...................Florida
For....................Forest
Fr......................France
Fr. Com...French Community
Fr. Gu......French Guiana
Fr. Som....French Somaliland
Ft........................Fort

G........................Gulf
Ga...................Georgia
Gam..................Gambia
Ger..................Germany
Gib................Gibraltar
Grc....................Greece
Grnld..............Greenland

Gt.......................Great
Gt. Brit.........Great Britain
Guad..............Guadeloupe
Guat...............Guatemala
Gui....................Guinea

Hai......................Haiti
Har., Hbr...........Harbor
Hd.......................Head
Hond...............Honduras
Hts..................Heights
Hung................Hungary

I.......................Island
Ice...................Iceland
Ill....................Illinois
In........................Inset
Ind...................Indiana
Ind. O.........Indian Ocean
Indon..............Indonesia
Ind. Res...Indian Reservation
Int., Intl....International
Ire...................Ireland
Is....................Islands
Isr......................Israel
Isth.................Isthmus
It........................Italy

Jam..................Jamaica
Jap.....................Japan
Jc...................Junction

Kans..................Kansas
Ken.....................Kenya
Km...Kilometer, Kilometers
Kor......................Korea
Kur. Is...........Kuril Is.
Kuw...................Kuwait
Ky...................Kentucky

L.......Lake, Loch, Lough
La.................Louisiana
Lat..................Latitude
Leb..................Lebanon
Le. Is...........Leeward Is.
Lib.....................Liberia
Liech...........Liechtenstein
Long................Longitude
Lux...............Luxembourg

M...............Mile, Miles
Mad. Is......Madeira Islands
Mala...................Malaya
Mand................Mandate
Mart..............Martinique
Mass..........Massachusetts
Max.................Maximum
Max. surf. elev.
  Maximum surface
  elevation
Md...................Maryland
Medit..........Mediterranean
Mex..................Mexico
Mi...............Mile, Miles
Mich................Michigan
Minn..............Minnesota
Miss.............Mississippi
Mo...................Missouri
Mong................Mongolia
Mont................Montana
Mor..................Morocco
Moz..............Mozambique
Mt.......................Mount
Mtn.................Mountain
Mts...............Mountains
Mus. & Om...Muscat & Oman

N. A...................North
N. A........North America
Natl.................National
Natl. Mon.
  National Monument
N. Bor.........North Borneo
N. C.........North Carolina
N. Cal.......New Caledonia
N. D.........North Dakota
Nebr................Nebraska
Nep.....................Nepal
Neth.............Netherlands
Neth. N. Gui.
  Netherlands New Guinea
Nev...................Nevada
New Hebr.....New Hebrides
N. Gui. Ter...New Guinea Ter.
N. H..........New Hampshire
Nic.................Nicaragua
Nig....................Nigeria
N. Ire......Northern Ireland
N. J..............New Jersey
N. Mex........New Mexico
Nor....................Norway
N. Y..............New York
N. Z.............New Zealand

O.......................Ocean
Obs...............Observatory
Okla...............Oklahoma
Ore.....................Oregon

P........................Pass
Pa...............Pennsylvania

Pac. O.........Pacific Ocean
Pan...................Panama
Pap. Ter.........Papua Ter.
Par.................Paraguay
Pass.................Passage
Pen................Peninsula
Phil.............Philippines
Pk..............Peak, Park
Plat.................Plateau
Pln.....................Plain
Pol....................Poland
Port.................Portugal
Port. Gui...Portuguese Guinea
Port. Tim...Portuguese Timor
Poss..............Possession
P. R..............Puerto Rico
Prot.............Protectorate
Prov.................Province
Pt.......................Point
Pta.....................Punta
Pte....................Pointe

R..........River, Rio, Rivière
Ra...........Range, Ranges
Reg.....................Region
Rep..................Republic
Res...Reservation, Reservoir
Rf.......................Reef
R. I............Rhode Island
Rom.................Romania
R. R..................Railroad
R. S. F. S. R....Russian Soviet
  Federated Socialist
  Republic
Ry.....................Railway
Rys.................Railways

S.........San, Santo, South
Sa.............Serra, Sierra
S. A..........South America
Sal..................Salvador
Sam....................Samoa
Sar...................Sarawak
Sard.................Sardinia
Sau. Ar........Saudi Arabia
S. C..........South Carolina
Scot................Scotland
S. D........South Dakota
Sd......................Sound
S. L...........Sierra Leone
Sol. Is..........Solomon Is.
Som..................Somalia
Sov. Un........Soviet Union
Sp........................Spain
Sp. Gui......Spanish Guinea
Spr., Sprs......Spring, Springs
Sp. Sah......Spanish Sahara
S. S. R.......Soviet Socialist
  Republic
St.......................Saint
Sta.....................Santa
Ste....................Sainte
Str......................Strait
Strm.................Stream
Sud......................Sudan
Sur...................Surinam
S. Afr..........South Africa
S. W. Afr....Southwest Africa
Swaz..............Swaziland
Swe....................Sweden
Switz............Switzerland
Swp....................Swamp
Syr.......................Syria

Tan..............Tanganyika
Tas................Tasmania
Tenn..............Tennessee
Ter..................Territory
Tex......................Texas
Thai................Thailand
Trin.................Trinidad
Tr. Coast......Trucial Coast
Tun...................Tunisia
Tur......................Turkey

U. A. R.United Arab Republic
Ug......................Uganda
U. K.........United Kingdom
  of Gt. Brit. and N. Ire.
Ur....................Uruguay
U. S., U. S. A.
  United States of America

Va...................Virginia
Val......................Valley
Ven................Venezuela
Viet..................Vietnam
Vir. Is.............Virgin Is.
Vol..................Volcano
Vt...................Vermont

W.........................West
Wash............Washington
W. I...............West Indies
W. I. F.West Indies Federation
Wind. Is....Windward Islands
Wis.................Wisconsin
W. Pak........West Pakistan
W. Va........West Virginia
Wyo.................Wyoming

Yugo.............Yugoslavia

Zan................Zanzibar

PRONUNCIATION OF
GEOGRAPHICAL NAMES

Key to the Sound Values of Letters and Symbols
Used in the Index to Indicate Pronunciation

ă—ăt, căt, băttle
ȧ—ȧppeal, finȧl
ā—rāte, elāte
â—inanimâte, senâte
ä—cälm, ärm
à—àsk, bàth
a̤—ma̤rine, sofa̤ (short neutral or indeterminate sound)
â—fâre, prepâre
ch—church, choose
dh—as th in other, either
ē—bē, ēve
ê—crêate, êvent
ĕ—bĕt, ĕnd
ě—recěnt (short neutral or indeterminate sound)
ẽ—cratẽr, cindẽr
g—gō, gāme
gh—guttural g
ĭ—wĭll, bĭt
ĭ—short neutral or indeterminate sound
ī—rīde, bīte
ᴋ—guttural k as ch in German ich
ng—sing
ŋ—baŋk, liŋger
ɴ—indicates nasalized preceding vowel
ŏ—nŏd, ŏdd
ô—cômmit, cônnect
ō—ōld, bōld
ô—ôbey, hôtel
ô—ôrder, nôrth
oi—boil
oo—food, root
oo—foot, wood
ou—thou, out
s—as in soft, so, sane
sh—dish, finish
th—thin, thick
ū—pūre, cūre
û—ûnite, ûsurp
û—ûrn, fûr
ŭ—stŭd, ŭp
ü—as in French tu or as "y" in study
u̇—circu̇s, su̇bmit
zh—as z in azure
'—indeterminate vowel sound

In many cases the spelling of foreign geographic names does not even remotely indicate the pronunciation to an American, i. e., Slupca in Poland is pronounced swŏŏp'tsȧ; Jujuy in Argentina is pronounced hōō-hwē'; Spezia in Italy is spät'sē-ä.

This condition is hardly surprising, however, when we consider that in our own language Worcester, Massachusetts, is pronounced wŏŏs'tēr; Sioux City, Iowa, sōō sĭ'tĭ; Schuylkill Haven, Pennsylvania, skōōl'kĭl; Poughkeepsie, New York, pŏ-kĭp'sē.

The indication of pronunciation of geographic names presents several peculiar problems:

(1) Many foreign tongues use sounds that are not present in the English language and which an American cannot normally articulate. Thus, though the nearest English equivalent sound has been indicated, only approximate results are possible.

(2) There are several dialects in each foreign tongue which cause variation in the local pronunciation of names. This also occurs in identical names in the various divisions of a great language group, as the Slavic or the Latin.

(3) Within the United States there are marked differences in pronunciation, not only of local geographic names, but also of common words, indicating that the sound and tone values for letters as well as the placing of the emphasis vary considerably from one part of the country to another.

(4) A number of different letter and diacritical combinations could be used to indicate essentially the same or approximate pronunciations.

Some variation in pronunciation other than that indicated in this index may be encountered, but such a difference does not necessarily indicate that either is in error, and in many cases it is a matter of individual choice as to which is preferred. In fact, an exact indication of pronunciation of many foreign names using English letters and diacritical marks is extremely difficult and sometimes impossible.

A PRONOUNCING INDEX

of over 30,000 Geographical Names

This universal index includes in a single alphabetical list all important names that appear on the reference maps. Each place name is preceded by the page number of the map on which it appears. Place names are followed by the pronunciation of the name (see facing page for an explanation of the pronunciation system); the location; and the approximate geographic coordinates.

State locations are listed for all places in the United States. All other place name entries show only country locations. When a name is only shown on an inset map the name of the inset on which it appears is listed.

All minor political divisions are followed by a descriptive term (Dist., Reg., Prov., State, etc.) and by the country in which they are located.

The names of physical features and points of interest that are shown on the maps are listed in the index. Each entry is followed by a descriptive term (Bay, Hill, Mtn., Is., Plat., etc.) to indicate its nature.

The system of alphabetizing used in the index is standard. When more than one name with the same spelling is shown, including both political and physical names, the order of precedence is as follows: *first*, place names, *second*, political divisions, and *third*, physical features.

Page	Name Pronunciation Region	Lat. °′	Long. °′
118	Aabenraa (ô′bĕn-rô)........Den.	55·03 N	9·20 E
123	Aachen (ä′kĕn)...Ger. (Ruhr In.)	50·46 N	6·07 E
118	Aakirkeby (ô-kĭr′kĕ-bü).....Den.	55·04 N	15·00 E
118	Aalborg (ôl′bŏr)...........Den.	57·02 N	9·55 E
120	Aalen (ä′lĕn)...............Ger.	48·49 N	10·08 E
111	Aalsmeer..Neth. (Amsterdam In.)	52·16 N	4·44 E
111	Aalst.........Bel. (Bruxelles In.)	50·58 N	4·00 E
120	Aarau (är′ou)..............Switz.	47·22 N	8·03 E
118	Aarhus (ôr′ho͞os)...........Den.	56·09 N	10·10 E
111	Aarschot......Bel. (Bruxelles In.)	50·59 N	4·51 E
164	Aba........................Nig.	5·13 N	7·14 E
144	Ābādān (ä-bŭ-dän′).........Iran	30·15 N	48·30 E
99	Abaetetuba (ä′bȧĕ-tĕ-to͞o′bȧ) Braz.	1·44 S	48·45 W
69	Abajo Pk. (ä-bȧ′-hŏ)........Utah	38·50 N	109·35 W
134	Abakan (ŭ-bȧ-kän′).....Sov. Un.	53·43 N	91·28 E
134	Abakan (R.)............Sov. Un.	53·00 N	91·06 E
98	Abancay (ä-bän-kă′ē).......Peru	13·44 S	72·46 W
152	Abashiri (ä-bä-shē′rē)........Jap.	44·00 N	144·13 E
90	Abasolo (ä-bä-sō′lô)........Mex.	24·05 N	98·24 W
76	Abasolo....................Mex.	27·13 N	101·25 W
165	Abaya L. (ȧ-bä′yȧ).........Eth.	6·24 N	38·22 E
165	Abbai R. (ȧ-bä′ē)...........Eth.	9·45 N	37·23 E
78	Abbeville (ăb′ē-vĭl).........Ala.	31·35 N	85·15 W
122	Abbeville (ȧb-vēl′)............Fr.	50·08 N	1·49 E
78	Abbeville (ăb′ē-vĭl)..........Ga.	31·53 N	83·23 W
77	Abbeville...................La.	29·59 N	92·07 W
79	Abbeville..................S. C.	34·09 N	82·25 W
126	Abbiategrasso (äb-byä′tȧ-gräs′sō) It.	45·23 N	8·52 E
110	Abbots Bromley (ăb′ŭts brŭm′lē).Eng.	52·49 N	1·52 W
65	Abbotsford (ăb′ŭts-fērd) Can. (Vancouver In.)	49·03 N	122·17 W
168	Abd Al Kuri I. (ăbd-ĕl-ko͞o′rē) Som. (Horn of Afr. In.)	12·21 N	51·00 E
132	Abdulino (äb-do͞o-lē′nō)..Sov. Un.	53·40 N	53·45 E
165	Abéché (ȧ-bĕ-shā′).........Chad	13·48 N	20·39 E
164	Abeokuta (ä-bȧ-ô-ko͞o′tȧ)....Nig.	7·14 N	3·19 E
166	Abercorn (ăb′ēr-kôrn) Fed. of Rh. & Nya.	8·45 S	31·23 E
116	Aberdare (ăb-ēr-dâr′).......Wales	51·45 N	3·35 W
116	Aberdeen (ăb-ēr-dēn′).......Scot.	57·10 N	2·05 W
78	Aberdeen..................Miss.	33·49 N	88·33 W
70	Aberdeen..................S. D.	45·28 N	98·29 W
66	Aberdeen.................Wash.	47·00 N	123·48 W
110	Aberford (ăb′ēr-fērd)........Eng.	53·49 N	1·21 W
116	Abergavenny (ăb′ēr-gȧ-vĕn′ĭ) Wales	51·45 N	3·05 W
66	Abert L. (ā′bērt)............Ore.	42·39 N	120·24 W
116	Aberystwyth (ă-bēr-ĭst′wĭth) Wales	52·25 N	4·04 W
136	Abestovskiy (ä-bĕs′tôv-skĭ) Sov. Un. (Urals In.)	57·46 N	61·23 E
144	Abhā..................Sau. Ar.	17·47 N	42·29 E
164	Abidjan (ä-bēd-zhäN′).Ivory Coast	5·26 N	4·06 W
153	Abiko (ä-bē-kō).Jap. (Tōkyō In.)	35·53 N	140·01 E
73	Abilene (ăb′ĭ-lēn)..........Kans.	38·54 N	97·12 W
76	Abilene....................Tex.	32·25 N	99·45 W
110	Abingdon......Eng. (London In.)	51·38 N	1·17 W
71	Abingdon (ăb′ĭng-dŭn)........Ill.	40·48 N	90·21 W
79	Abingdon...................Va.	36·42 N	81·57 W
83	Abington (ăb′ĭng-tŭn) Mass. (Boston In.)	42·07 N	70·57 W
87	Abitibi (L.) (ăb-ĭ-tĭb′ĭ)......Can.	48·27 N	80·20 W
87	Abitibi (R.)................Can.	49·30 N	81·10 W
133	Abkhaz A.S.S.R.........Sov. Un.	43·10 N	40·45 E
123	Ablis (ȧ-blē′)......Fr. (Paris In.)	48·31 N	1·50 E
168	Abnūb (ȧb-no͞ob′) U. A. R. (Nile In.)	27·18 N	31·11 E
	Åbo, see Turku		
142	Abohar....................India	30·12 N	74·13 E
164	Abomey (ȧb-ô-mā′).....Dahomey	7·13 N	2·04 E
121	Abony (ŏ′bô-ny′)..........Hung.	47·12 N	20·00 E
144	Abou Kemal (ä′bo͞o kĕ′mȧl) U. A. R.	34·27 N	40·46 E
155	Abra (R.) (ä′brä) Phil. (Manila In.)	17·16 N	120·38 E
101	Abraão (äbrȧ-ouN′) Braz. (Rio de Janeiro In.)	23·10 S	44·10 W
95	Abraham's B.............Ba. Is.	22·20 N	73·50 W
110	Abram (ā′brăm)............Eng.	53·31 N	2·36 W
124	Abrantes (ȧ-brän′tĕs).......Port.	39·28 N	8·13 W
165	Abri......................Sud.	20·36 N	29·57 E
99	Abrolhos, Arquipélago dos (Arch.) (ä-ro͞oē-pĕ′lä-gô-dôs-ä-brô′l-yōs) Braz.	17·58 S	38·40 W
119	Abruka (I.) (ȧ-bro͞o′kȧ)..Sov. Un.	58·09 N	22·30 E
126	Abruzzi and Molise (Reg.) (ä-bro͞ot′sē, mô′lē-zā)........It.	42·10 N	13·55 E
67	Absaroka Ra. (Mts.) (ȧb-sȧ-rō′kȧ).Wyo.	44·50 N	109·47 W
142	Abu (ȧ′bo͞o)...............India	24·38 N	72·45 E
144	Abū Arīsh (ä′bo͞o ȧ-rēsh′).Sau. Ar.	16·48 N	43·00 E
165	Abu Hamed (ä′bo͞o hä′mĕd)..Sud.	19·37 N	33·21 E
115	Abūksāh...............U. A. R.	29·29 N	30·40 E
98	Abunã (R.) (ȧ-bo͞o-nä′).Bol-Braz..	10·25 S	67·00 W
168	Abū Qīr (ä′bo͞o kēr′) U. A. R. (Nile In.)	31·18 N	30·06 E
168	Abū Qurqāṣ (ä′bo͞o ko͞or-käs′) U. A. R. (Nile In.)	27·57 N	30·51 E
139	Abu Qurûn, Ras (Mt.) U. A. R. (Palestine In.)	30·22 N	33·32 E
153	Aburatsu (ä′bo͝o-rät′so͞o).....Jap.	31·33 N	131·20 E
168	Abū Tīj.......U. A. R. (Nile In.)	27·03 N	31·19 E
144	Abū Zabī..............Sau. Ar.	24·15 N	54·28 E
139	Abū Zanīmah U. A. R. (Palestine In.)	29·03 N	33·08 E
139	Abyad (R.).Jordan (Palestine In.)	30·07 N	36·01 E
118	Åby-Klippan (ô′bü klĭp′pȧn).Swe.	56·08 N	13·09 E
135	Abyy..................Sov. Un.	68·24 N	145·08 E
98	Acacias (ȧ-kȧ′sēäs).....Col. (In.)	3·59 N	73·44 W
82	Acadia Natl. Park (ȧ-kā′dĭ-ȧ) Maine	44·19 N	68·01 W
92	Acajutla (ä-kä-ho͞ot′lä).......Sal.	13·37 N	89·50 W
91	Acala (ä-kä′-lä)............Mex.	16·38 N	92·49 W
90	Acàmbaro (ä-käm′bä-rō)....Mex.	20·03 N	100·42 W
92	Acancéh (ä-kän-sĕ′) Mex. (Yucatan In.)	20·50 N	89·27 W
90	Acapetlahuaya (ä-kä-pĕt′lä-hwä′yä).Mex.	18·24 N	100·04 W
90	Acaponeta (ä-kä-pô-nā′tȧ)...Mex.	22·31 N	105·25 W
90	Acaponeta (R.).............Mex.	22·47 N	105·23 W
90	Acapulco de Juárez (ä-kä-po͞ol′kō-dĕ-kwä′-rāz).Mex.	16·49 N	99·57 W
99	Acaraú (ä-kȧrhȧ-o͞o′).......Braz.	2·55 S	40·04 W
98	Acarigua (äkȧ-rē′gwä).......Ven.	9·29 N	69·11 W
90	Acatlán de Osorio (ä-kät-län′dā ô-sō′rē-ō).Mex.	18·11 N	98·04 W
91	Acatzingo de Hidalgo (ä-kät-zĭŋ′gō dā ē-dhäl′gō).Mex.	18·58 N	97·47 W
91	Acayucan (ä-kä-yo͞o′kän)....Mex.	17·56 N	94·55 W
80	Accoville (äk′kô-vĭl)......W. Va.	37·45 N	81·50 W
164	Accra (ă′krȧ).............Ghana	5·40 N	0·15 W
110	Accrington (ăk′rĭng-tŭn).....Eng.	53·45 N	2·22 W
125	Acerra (ä-chĕ′r-rä) It. (Napoli In.)	40·42 N	14·22 E
98	Achacachi (ä-chä-kä′chē).....Bol.	16·11 S	68·32 W
152	Acheng (ä′chĕng′).........China	45·32 N	126·59 E
116	Achill (ă-chĭl′)...............Ire.	53·55 N	9·65 W
134	Achinsk (ȧ-chēnsk′).....Sov. Un.	56·13 N	90·32 E
126	Acireale (ä-chē-rā-ä′lā).........It.	37·37 N	15·12 E
78	Ackia Battle Ground Natl. Mon. (ă-kyŭ′).Miss.	34·22 N	89·05 W
95	Acklins (I.) (ăk′lĭns)......Ba. Is.	22·30 N	73·55 W
95	Acklins, The Bight of (B.).Ba. Is.	22·35 N	74·20 W
91	Acolman (ä-kôl-mȧ′n) Mex. (Mexico In.)	19·38 N	98·56 W
101	Aconcagua (ä-kôn-kä′gwä) (Prov.) Chile (Santiago In.)	32·20 S	71·00 W
101	Aconcagua, Cerro (Mtn.) Arg. (Santiago In.)	32·38 S	70·00 W
101	Aconcagua (R.) Chile (Santiago In.)	32·43 S	70·53 W
92	Acoyapa (ä-kô-yä′pä)........Nic.	11·54 N	85·11 W
126	Acqui (äk′kwē)...............It.	44·41 N	8·22 W
139	Acre (ä′kēr)...Isr. (Palestine In.)	32·56 N	35·05 E
98	Acre (Ter.) (ä′krā).........Braz.	8·40 S	70·45 W
98	Acre (R.)................Braz.	10·33 S	68·34 W
84	Acton (ăk′tŭn) Ala. (Birmingham In.)	33·21 N	86·49 W
85	Acton........Can. (Toronto In.)	43·38 N	80·02 W
75	Acton.....Ind. (Indianapolis In.)	39·39 N	85·58 W
83	Acton.......Mass. (Boston In.)	42·29 N	71·26 W
82	Acton Vale................Can.	45·39 N	72·33 W
90	Actopan (äk-tô-pän′).......Mex.	20·16 N	98·57 W
91	Actópan (R.) (äk-tŏ′pän)....Mex.	19·25 N	96·31 W
90	Acuitzio del Canje (ä-kwēt′zē-ō dĕl kän′hȧ).Mex.	19·28 N	101·21 W
95	Acul, Baie de l' (B.) (ä-ko͞ol′).Hai.	19·55 N	72·20 W
164	Ada (ä′dä)................Ghana	5·57 N	0·31 E
70	Ada (ā′dŭ)................Minn.	47·17 N	96·32 W
80	Ada......................Ohio	40·45 N	83·45 W
73	Ada......................Okla.	34·45 N	96·43 W
127	Ada (ä′dä)................Yugo.	45·48 N	20·06 E
64	Adak (ă-dăk′)............Alaska	56·50 N	176·48 W
64	Adak (I.)................Alaska	51·40 N	176·28 W
64	Adak Str.................Alaska	51·42 N	177·16 W
	Adalia, see Antalya		
164	Adamawa (Reg.) (ä-dä-mä′wä) Nig.-Cam.	8·39 N	11·58 E
81	Adams (ăd′ămz)...........Mass.	42·35 N	73·10 W
71	Adams....................Wis.	43·55 N	89·48 W
64	Adams, Mt...............Alaska	55·40 N	130·25 W
66	Adams, Mt...............Wash.	46·15 N	121·19 W
84	Adamsville (ăd′ămz-vĭl) Ala. (Birmingham In.)	33·36 N	86·57 W
84	Adamsville.....Ga. (Atlanta In.)	33·45 N	84·31 W
84	Adamsville, R. I. (Providence In.)	41·33 N	71·04 W
133	Adana (ä′dä-nä)............Tur.	37·05 N	35·20 E
133	Adapazari (ä-dä-pä-zä′rē)....Tur.	40·45 N	30·20 E
165	Adarama (ä-dä-rä′mä).......Sud.	17·11 N	34·56 E
126	Adda (R.) (äd′dä).............It.	45·43 N	9·31 E
144	Ad Dahna (Des.)........Sau. Ar.	26·05 N	47·15 E
144	Ad Dam (äd däm′)......Sau. Ar.	20·45 N	44·12 E
144	Ad Dammān...........Sau. Ar.	26·27 N	49·59 E
139	Ad Damur....Leb. (Palestine In.)	33·44 N	35·27 E
144	Ad Dawhah............Sau. Ar.	20·02 N	51·28 E
144	Ad Dilam.............Sau. Ar.	23·47 N	47·03 E
165	Addis Ababā...............Eth.	9·00 N	38·44 E
74	Addison (ă′dĭ-sŭn) Tex. (Dallas, Fort Worth In.)	32·58 N	96·50 W
165	Ad Dīwān..............U. A. R.	22·44 N	32·15 E
167	Addo (ădō)....S. Afr. (Natal In.)	33·33 S	25·43 E
75	Addyston (ăd′ē-stŭn) Ohio (Cincinnati In.)	39·09 N	84·42 W
78	Adel (ā-dĕl′)................Ga.	31·08 N	83·55 W
167	Adelaide (ăd-ĕl′ād) S. Afr. (Natal In.)	32·41 S	26·07 E
160	Adelaide (ăd′ē-lād)........Austl.	34·46 S	139·08 E
47	Adelaide I.................Ant.	67·15 S	68·40 W
144	Aden (ä′dĕn)..............Aden	12·48 N	45·00 E
138	Aden......................Asia	14·35 N	47·45 E
144	Aden, G. of...............Aden	11·45 N	45·45 E
155	Adi (I.) (ä′dē).....Neth. N. Gui.	4·25 S	133·52 E
114	Adige R. (ä′dē-jā).....Aus.-Switz.	46·34 N	10·51 E
126	Adige, Fiume (R.) (fyo͞o′mĕ-ä′dē-jā).It.	46·38 N	10·43 E
143	Adini.....................India	15·42 N	77·18 E
81	Adirondack, Mts. (ăd-ĭ-rŏn′dăk) N. Y.	43·45 N	74·40 W
165	Adi Ugri (ä-dē o͞o′grē).......Eth.	14·54 N	38·52 E
121	Adjud (äd′zho͝od)..........Rom.	46·05 N	27·12 E
64	Admiralty (I.)............Alaska	57·50 N	133·50 W
65	Admiralty Inlet (ăd′mĭrȧl-tē) Wash. (Seattle In.)	48·10 N	122·45 W
155	Admiralty Is........N. Gui. Ter.	1·40 S	146·45 E
74	Adolph (ā′dolf) Minn. (Duluth In.)	46·47 N	92·17 W
122	Adour (R.) (ȧ-do͞or′).........Fr.	43·43 N	0·38 W
124	Adra (ä′drä).................Sp.	36·45 N	3·02 W
126	Adrano (ä-drä′nō)............It.	37·42 N	14·52 E
164	Adrar des Iforas (Reg.) (ä-drär′) Alg.	20·22 N	1·44 E
126	Adria (ä′drē-ä)...............It.	45·03 N	12·01 E
80	Adrian (ā′drĭ-ăn)..........Mich.	41·55 N	84·00 W
70	Adrian....................Minn.	43·39 N	95·56 W
	Adrianople, see Edirne		
126	Adriatic Sea...............Eur.	41·30 N	14·27 E
164	Adrir......................Alg.	27·53 N	0·15 W
100	Adrogué (ȧdrō-gā′).....Arg. (In.)	34·33 S	58·24 W
165	Aduwā.....................Eth.	14·02 N	38·58 E
110	Adwick-le-Street (ăd′wĭk-lē-strēt′) Eng.	53·35 N	1·11 W
135	Adycha (R.) (ä′dĭ-chȧ)..Sov. Un.	66·11 N	136·45 E
129	Adzhamka (ȧd-zhäm′kȧ).Sov. Un.	48·33 N	32·28 E
132	Adz'va (R.) (ädz′vȧ)....Sov. Un.	67·00 N	59·20 E
115	Aegean Sea (ē-jē′ăn)....Eur.-Asia	39·04 N	24·56 E
118	Aerö (I.) (âr′ö).............Den.	54·52 N	10·22 E
138	Afghanistan (ăf-găn-ĭ-stăn′)..Asia	33·00 N	63·00 E
168	Afgoi (äf-gô′ĭ) Som. (Horn of Afr. In.)	2·08 N	45·08 E
164	Aflou (ä-flo͞o′)..............Alg.	33·59 N	2·04 E
64	Afognak (I.) (ä-fŏg-nȧk′)..Alaska	58·28 N	151·35 W
125	Afragola (ä-frȧ′gō-lä) It. (Napoli In.)	40·40 N	14·19 E
7	Africa (ăf′rĭ-kȧ)		
74	Afton (ăf′tŭn)..............Minn. (Minneapolis, St. Paul In.)	44·54 N	92·47 W
73	Afton.....................Okla.	36·42 N	94·56 W
67	Afton.....................Wyo.	42·42 N	110·52 W

174 'Afula–Alcira PRONOUNCING INDEX

Page	Name Pronunciation Region	Lat. °'	Long. °'
139	'Afula (ä-fōō'lȧ) Isr. (Palestine In.)	32·36 N	35·17 E
133	Afyon-Karahisar (ä-fē-ōn-kä-rȧ-hē-sär'). Tur.	38·45 N	30·20 E
165	Agadem (Oasis) (ä'gà-dĕm). Niger	16·50 N	13·15 E
164	Agadès (ä'gȧ-dĕs)......Niger	17·01 N	7·55 E
164	Agadir (ä-gȧ-dēr)......Mor.	30·30 N	9·37 W
92	Agalta, Cord. de (Mts.) (kôr-dēl-yĕ'rä-dĕ-ä-gä'l-tä)......Hond.	15·15 N	85·42 W
136	Agapovka (ä-gä-pôv'kä) Sov. Un. (Urals In.)	53·18 N	59·10 E
142	Agartala......India	23·53 N	91·22 E
143	Agāshi......India (Bombay In.)	19·28 N	72·46 E
136	Agashkino (ȧ-gäsh'kĭ-nô) Sov. Un. (Moskva In.)	55·18 N	38·13 E
65	Agate Bay (ăg'ĭt) (ăg'ȧt) Wash. (Vancouver In.)	48·45 N	122·20 W
64	Agattu (I.) (ȧ'gä-tōō)....Alaska	52·14 N	173·40 E
129	Agayman (ȧ-gä-ē-män')..Sov. Un.	46·39 N	34·20 E
133	Agdam (äg'däm)......Sov. Un.	40·00 N	47·00 E
122	Agde (ägd)......Fr.	43·19 N	3·30 E
122	Agen (ȧ-zhăɴ')......Fr.	44·13 N	0·31 E
85	Agincourt (ă'zhĕɴ-kōōr') Can. (Toronto In.)	43·47 N	79·16 W
135	Aginskoye (ä-hĭn'skô-yĕ). Sov. Un.	51·15 N	113·15 E
65	Agnew (ăg'nū). Wash. (Seattle In.)	48·06 N	123·15 W
155	Agno (äg'nō)...Phil. (Manila In.)	16·07 N	119·49 E
155	Agno (R.)......Phil. (Manila In.)	15·42 N	120·28 E
126	Agnone (än-yō'nä)......It.	41·49 N	14·23 E
165	Agordat (ä-gōr'dät)......Eth.	15·34 N	37·54 E
142	Agra (ä'grä)......India	27·18 N	78·00 E
126	Agri (R.) (ä'grē)......It.	40·15 N	16·21 E
127	Agrínion (ȧ-grē'nyôn)......Grc.	38·38 N	21·06 E
92	Agua (Vol.) (ä'gwä)......Guat.	14·28 N	90·43 W
90	Agua Blanca, Río (R.) (rē'ō-ä-gwä-blä'n-kä). Mex.	21·46 N	102·54 W
90	Agua Brava, Laguna de (L.) (lä-gōō'nä-dĕ-ä'gwä-brä'vä)...Mex.	22·04 N	105·40 W
68	Agua Caliente Ind. Res. (ä'gwä kal-yĕn'tä). Calif.	33·50 N	116·24 W
94	Aguada (ä-gwä'dȧ)......Cuba	22·25 N	80·50 W
92	Aguada L....Mex. (Yucatan In.)	18·46 N	89·40 W
98	Aguadas (ä-gwä'-däs)...Col. (In.)	5·37 N	75·27 W
89	Aguadilla (ä-gwä-dēl'yä) P. R. (Puerto Rico In.)	18·27 N	67·10 W
93	Aguadulce (ä-gwä-dōōl'sä)...Pan.	8·15 N	80·33 W
91	Agua Escondida, Meseta de (Plat.) (mĕ-sĕ'tä-dĕ-ä'gwä-ĕs-kôn-dē'dä). Mex.	16·54 N	91·35 W
101	Aguai (ägwä-ē') Braz. (Rio de Janeiro In.)	22·04 S	46·57 W
76	Agualeguas (ä-gwä-lä'gwäs). Mex.	26·19 N	99·33 W
76	Aguanaval, R. (ȧ-guä-nä-väl'). Mex.	25·12 N	103·28 W
92	Aguán R. (ä-gwä'n)......Hond.	15·22 N	87·00 W
83	Aguanus (R.) (ä-gwä'nŭs)...Can.	50·45 N	62·03 W
90	Aguascalientes (ä'gwäs-käl-yĕn'täs). Mex.	21·52 N	102·17 W
124	Agueda (ä-gwä'dȧ)......Port.	40·36 N	8·26 W
124	Agueda (R.) (ä-gĕ-dȧ)......Sp.	40·50 N	6·44 W
164	Aguellal (ä-gĕl-yäl)......Niger	19·05 N	8·10 E
72	Aguilar (ä-gē-lär')......Colo.	37·24 N	104·38 W
124	Aguilar......Sp.	37·32 N	4·39 W
124	Aguilas (ä'gē-läs)......Sp.	37·26 N	1·35 W
90	Aguililla (ä-gē-lēl-yä)......Mex.	18·44 N	102·44 W
98	Aguja, Pta. (Pt.) (pŭn'tä ȧ-gōō' hä). Peru	6·00 S	81·15 W
166	Agulhas, C. (ä-gōōl'yäs)...S. Afr.	34·47 S	20·00 E
154	Agung, Gunung (Mtn.) (ä-gōōng'). Indon.	8·41 S	115·07 E
155	Agusan (R.) (ä-gōō'sän)......Phil.	8·12 N	126·07 E
164	Ahaggar (Mts.) (ȧ-hä-gär')...Alg.	23·14 N	6·00 E
123	Ahlen (ä'lĕn)......Ger. (Ruhr In.)	51·45 N	7·52 E
142	Ahmadābād (ŭ-mĕd-ä-bäd'). India	23·04 N	72·38 E
142	Ahmadnagar (ä'mŭd-nŭ-gŭr). India	19·09 N	74·45 E
168	Ahmar Mts. Eth. (Horn of Afr. In.)	9·22 N	42·00 E
165	Ahmara Plat......Eth.	10·09 N	37·21 E
79	Ahoskie (ā-hŏs'kē)......N. C.	36·15 N	77·00 W
111	Ahrensburg (ä'rĕns-bōōrg) Ger. (Hamburg In.)	53·40 N	10·14 E
120	Ahrweiler (är'vī-lĕr)......Ger.	50·34 N	7·05 E
119	Ahtärin-järvi (L.)......Fin.	62·46 N	24·25 E
90	Ahuacatlán (ä-wä-kät-län')...Mex.	21·05 N	104·28 W
92	Ahuachapan (ä-wä-chä-pän')..Sal.	13·57 N	89·53 W
90	Ahualulco (ä-wä-lōōl'kō)....Mex.	20·43 N	103·57 W
90	Ahuatempan (ä-wä-tĕm-pän). Mex.	18·11 N	98·02 W
118	Ahus (ô'hōōs)......Swe.	55·56 N	14·19 E
144	Ahvāz......Iran	31·15 N	48·54 E
118	Ahvenanma (Åland Is.) (ä'vĕ-nän-mô) (ō'länd). Fin.	60·36 N	19·55 E
157	Aica......Hawaii (In.)	21·18 N	157·52 W
79	Aiken (ā'kĕn)......S. C.	33·32 N	81·43 W
99	Aimorés, Serra dos (Mts.) (sĕ'r-rä-dôs-ī-mō-rĕ's). Braz.	17·40 S	42·38 W
153	Aimoto (ī-mô-tō). Jap. (Ōsaka In.)	34·59 N	135·09 E
164	Aïn Beida (ä'ēn bā-dä')......Alg.	35·57 N	7·25 E
123	Aincourt (ăɴ-kōō'r). Fr. (Paris In.)	49·04 N	1·47 E
125	Aïne Oussèra (ĕn ōō-sä-rȧ)....Alg.	35·25 N	2·50 E
164	Aïn Sefra (ä'ēn sĕf'rä)......Alg.	32·49 N	0·39 W
83	Ainsle, L. (ān'slē)......Can.	46·08 N	61·23 W
70	Ainsworth (ānz'wûrth)......Nebr.	42·32 N	99·51 W
114	Aïn Taïba (ä'ēn tä'ē-bä)......Alg.	30·20 N	5·30 E
113	Aïn-Temouchent (ä'ēntĕ-mōō-shaɴ'). Alg.	35·20 N	1·23 W
98	Aipe (ī'-pĕ)......Col. (In.)	3·13 N	75·15 W
122	Aire (âr)......Fr.	43·42 N	0·17 W
110	Aire (R.)......Eng.	53·42 N	1·00 W
139	Airhitam, Selat (Str.) Indon. (Singapore In.)	0·58 N	102·38 E
164	Aïr ou Azbine (Mts.)......Niger	18·28 N	7·51 E
122	Aisne (R.) (ĕn)......Fr.	49·28 N	3·32 E
155	Aitape (ä-ē-tä'pä)....N. Gui. Ter.	3·00 S	142·10 E
71	Aitkin (āt'kĭn)......Minn.	46·32 N	93·43 W
127	Aitolikón (ȧ-tō'lĭ-kôn)......Grc.	38·27 N	21·21 E
127	Aitos (ä-ē'tōs)......Bul.	42·42 N	27·17 E
157	Aitutak (I.)......Cook Is.	19·00 S	162·00 W
121	Aiud (ä'ē-ōōd)......Rom.	46·19 N	23·40 E
101	Aiuruoca (äē'ōō-rōōô'-kȧ) Braz. (Rio de Janeiro In.)	21·57 S	44·36 W
101	Aiuruoca (R.) Braz. (Rio de Janeiro In.)	22·11 S	44·35 W
122	Aix-en-Provence (ĕks-prô-vȧɴs) Fr. (Marseille In.)	43·32 N	5·27 E
123	Aix-les-Bains (ĕks'-lā-baɴ')....Fr.	45·42 N	5·56 E
127	Aiyien......Grc.	37·37 N	22·12 E
127	Aiyina (I.)......Grc.	37·43 N	23·35 E
127	Aiyion......Grc.	38·13 N	22·04 E
119	Aizpute (ä'ēz-pōō-tĕ)....Sov. Un.	56·44 N	21·37 E
126	Ajaccio (ä-yät'chō)......Fr.	41·55 N	8·42 E
91	Ajalpan (ä-häl'pän)......Mex.	18·21 N	97·14 W
158	Ajana (āj-än'ĕr)......Austl.	28·00 S	114·45 E
67	Ajax Mt. (ā'jăks)......Mont.	45·19 N	113·43 W
165	Ajdabiyah......Libya	30·56 N	20·16 E
144	Ajman......Sau. Ar.	25·15 N	54·30 E
142	Ajmer (ŭj-mēr')......India	26·26 N	74·42 E
69	Ajo (ä'hō)......Ariz.	32·20 N	112·55 W
90	Ajuchitlán del Progreso (ä-hōō-chet-lån). Mex.	18·11 N	100·32 W
91	Ajusco (ä-hōō's-kō) Mex. (Mexico In.)	19·13 N	99·12 W
91	Ajusco, Cerro (sĕ'r-rô-ä-hōō's-kō) Mex. (Mexico In.)	19·12 N	99·16 W
153	Akaishi-dake (Mtn.) (ä-kī-shē dä'kä). Jap.	5·30 N	138·00 E
99	Akarai Mts. (ä'kä-rä'ē). Braz.-Sur.	1·30 N	57·40 W
153	Akashi (ä'kä-shē). Jap. (Ōsaka In.)	34·38 N	134·59 E
165	Aketi (ä-kȧ-tē)......Con. L.	2·58 N	23·57 E
133	Akhaltsikhe (äkȧ'l-tsĭ-kĕ) Sov. Un.	41·40 N	42·50 E
165	Akhdar, Jabal al (Mts.)....Libya	32·45 N	21·52 E
144	Akhdar, Jabal al (Mts.) Mus. & Om.-Sau. Ar.	23·30 N	56·43 E
127	Akhelóös (R.) (ä-hĕ'lô-ōs)....Grc.	38·45 N	21·26 E
133	Akhisar (äk-hĭs-sär')......Tur.	38·58 N	27·58 E
129	Akhtarskaya, Bukhta (B.) (bōōk'tä äκ-tär'skȧ-yȧ). Sov. Un.	45·53 N	38·22 E
127	Akhtopol (äκ'tô-pōl)......Bul.	42·08 N	27·54 E
129	Akhtyrka (äκ-tür'kȧ)....Sov. Un.	50·18 N	34·53 E
136	Akhunovo (ä-kŭ'nô-vô) Sov. Un. (Urals In.)	54·13 N	59·36 E
153	Aki (ä'kē)......Jap.	33·31 N	133·51 E
64	Akiak (äk'yȧk)......Alaska	61·00 N	161·02 W
87	Akimiski (I.) (ȧ-kĭ-mĭ'skĭ)...Can.	52·54 N	80·22 W
152	Akita (ä'kē-tä)......Jap.	39·40 N	140·12 E
86	Aklavik (äk'lä-vĭk)......Can.	68·28 N	135·26 W
153	Ako (ä'kō)......Jap.	34·44 N	134·22 E
142	Akola (ȧ-kō'lä)......India	20·47 N	77·00 E
87	Akpatok (I.) (äk'pä-tŏk)....Can.	60·30 N	67·10 W
112	Akranes......Ice.	64·18 N	21·40 W
127	Akrítas, Akr. (C.)......Grc.	37·45 N	23·53 E
72	Akron (äk'rŭn)......Colo.	40·09 N	103·14 W
75	Akron......Ohio (Cleveland In.)	41·05 N	81·30 W
139	Akrotiri B.. Cyprus (Palestine In.)	34·38 N	33·18 E
133	Aksaray (äk-sä-rī')......Tur.	38·30 N	34·05 E
133	Akşehir (äk'shȧ-hĕr)......Tur.	38·20 N	31·20 E
133	Aksehir (L.)......Tur.	38·40 N	31·30 E
135	Aksha (äk'shȧ)......Sov. Un.	50·28 N	113·00 E
	Aksu, see Wensu		
146	Ak Su (R.)......China	40·34 N	77·15 E
133	Aktyubinsk (äk'työō-bĕnsk) Sov. Un.	50·20 N	57·00 E
153	Akune (ä'kōō-nȧ)......Jap.	32·03 N	130·16 E
112	Akureyri (ä-kōō-rȧ'rē)......Ice.	65·39 N	18·01 W
64	Akutan (I.) (ä-kōō-tän')....Alaska	53·58 N	169·54 W
63	Alabama (State) (ăl-ȧ-băm'ȧ). U. S.	32·50 N	87·30 W
78	Alabama (R.)......Ala.	31·20 N	87·39 W
155	Alabat (I.) (ä-lä-bät') Phil. (Manila In.)	14·14 N	122·05 E
155	Alaca (ä-lä-kä). Phil. (Manila In.)	17·56 N	121·39 E
133	Alacam (ä-lä-chäm')......Tur.	41·30 N	35·40 E
94	Alacranes (ä-lä-krä'nås)....Cuba	22·45 N	81·35 W
144	Alaflau (Des.)......Sau. Ar.	24·00 N	44·47 E
99	Alagôas (ä-lä-gō'äzh)......Braz.	9·50 S	36·33 W
99	Alagoinhas (ä-lä-gō-ēn'yäzh). Braz.	12·13 S	38·12 W
124	Alagón (ä-lä-gōn')......Sp.	41·46 N	1·07 W
124	Alagón (R.)......Sp.	39·53 N	6·42 W
90	Alahuatán (R.) (ä-lä-wä-tä'n). Mex.	18·30 N	100·00 W
93	Alajuela (ä-lä-hwä'lä)......C.R.	10·01 N	84·14 W
134	Alakol (L.)......Sov. Un.	45·45 N	81·13 E
157	Alalakeiki Chan. (ä-lä-lä-kā'kē) Hawaii (In.)	20·40 N	156·30 W
165	Al 'Alamayn......U. A. R.	30·53 N	28·52 E
165	Al 'Allāqī......U. A. R.	23·06 N	32·47 E
65	Alameda (ăl-ȧ-mā'dȧ) Calif. (San Francisco In.)	37·46 N	122·15 W
67	Alameda......Idaho	42·51 N	112·29 W
65	Alameda (R.) Calif. (San Francisco In.)	37·36 N	122·02 W
155	Alaminos (ä-lä-mē'nôs) Phil. (Manila In.)	16·09 N	119·58 E
115	Al 'Āmirīyah......U. A. R.	31·01 N	29·52 E
65	Alamo (ă'lȧ-mō) Calif. (San Francisco In.)	37·51 N	122·02 W
91	Alamo (ä'lä-mô)......Mex.	21·07 N	99·35 W
76	Alamo, R. (ä'lä-mô)......Mex.	26·33 N	99·35 W
69	Alamogordo (ăl-ȧ-mō-gôr'dō) N. Mex.	32·55 N	106·00 W
74	Alamo Heights (ă'lȧ-mō) Tex. (San Antonio In.)	29·28 N	98·27 W
76	Alamo Pk. (ă'lȧ-mō pēk)..N. Mex.	32·50 N	105·55 W
69	Alamosa (ăl-ȧ-mō'sȧ)......Colo.	37·25 N	105·50 W
136	Alandskiy (ä-länt'skĭ) Sov. Un. (Urals In.)	52·14 N	59·48 E
133	Alanya......Tur.	36·40 N	32·10 E
167	Alaotra (L.) (ä-lä-ō'trȧ). Malagasy	17·15 S	48·17 E
136	Alapayevsk (ä-lä-pä'yĕfsk) Sov. Un. (Urals In.)	57·50 N	61·35 E
139	Al Aqabah. Jordan (Palestine In.)	29·32 N	35·00 E
90	Alaquines (ä-lȧ-kē'nås)......Mex.	22·07 N	99·35 W
139	Al 'Arīsh (a-rēsh') U. A. R. (Palestine In.)	31·08 N	33·48 E
150	Ala Shan (Mtns.) (ä'lä-shän') China	38·02 N	105·20 E
62	Alaska (State) (ȧ-lăs'kȧ)......U. S.	65·00 N	158·00 W
64	Alaska, G. of......Alaska	57·42 N	147·40 W
64	Alaska Hy......Alaska	63·00 N	142·00 W
64	Alaska Pen......Alaska	55·50 N	162·10 W
64	Alaska Ra......Alaska	62·00 N	152·18 W
132	Alatyr' (ä'lä-tür)......Sov. Un.	54·55 N	46·30 E
98	Alausí (ä-lou-sē')......Ec.	2·15 S	78·45 W
168	Al 'Ayyāţ (ä-ē-yät') U. A. R. (Nile In.)	29·38 N	31·18 E
126	Alba (äl'bä)......It.	44·41 N	8·02 E
124	Albacete (äl-bä-thā'tä)......Sp.	39·00 N	1·49 W
123	Albachten (äl-bä'κ-tĕn) Ger. (Ruhr In.)	51·55 N	7·31 E
168	Al Badārī......U. A. R. (Nile In.)	26·59 N	31·29 E
124	Alba de Tormes (äl-bȧ dā tôr'mās) Sp.	40·48 N	5·28 W
168	Al Bahnasā...U. A. R. (Nile In.)	28·35 N	30·30 E
121	Alba Iulia (äl-bä yōō'lyȧ)...Rom.	46·05 N	23·32 E
125	Albalate (äl-bä-lä'tä)......Sp.	41·07 N	0·34 W
168	Al Ballāḥ (bä'lä) U. A. R. (Suez In.)	30·46 N	32·20 E
168	Al Balyanā....U. A. R. (Nile In.)	26·12 N	32·00 E
102	Albania (ăl-bā'nĭ-ȧ)......Eur.	41·45 N	20·00 E
125	Albano, Lago (L.) (lä'-gō-äl-bä'nō) It. (Roma In.)	41·45 N	12·44 E
125	Albano Laziale (äl-bä'nō lät-zē-ä'lä). It. (Roma In.)	41·44 N	12·43 E
158	Albany (ôl'bȧ-nĭ)......Austl.	35·00 S	118·00 E
65	Albany. Calif. (San Francisco In.)	37·54 N	122·18 W
78	Albany......Ga.	31·35 N	84·10 W
73	Albany......Mo.	40·14 N	94·18 W
81	Albany......N. Y.	42·40 N	73·50 W
66	Albany......Ore.	44·38 N	123·06 W
76	Albany......Tex.	32·43 N	99·17 W
87	Albany (R.)......Can.	51·45 N	83·30 W
144	A'l Basrah......Iraq	30·27 N	47·52 E
139	Al Batrūn (bä-trōōn') Leb. (Palestine In.)	34·16 N	35·39 E
165	Al Bawīţī......U. A. R.	28·19 N	29·00 E
155	Albay G. (äl-bä'ē) Phil. (Manila In.)	13·09 N	123·52 E
79	Albemarle (ăl'bē-märl)......N. C.	35·24 N	80·36 W
79	Albemarle Sd......N. C.	36·00 N	76·17 W
126	Albenga (äl-bĕŋ'gä)......It.	44·04 N	8·13 E
124	Alberche (R.) (äl-bĕr'chä)......Sp.	40·08 N	4·19 W
158	Alberga, The (R.) (ăl-bŭr'gȧ) Austl.	27·15 S	135·00 E
124	Albergaria a-Velha (äl-bĕr-gä-rē'-ȧ-ä-väl'yȧ). Port.	40·47 N	8·31 W
74	Alberhill (ăl'bĕr-hĭl) Calif. (Los Angeles In.)	33·43 N	117·23 W
82	Albert (ăl'bĕrt)......Can.	45·44 N	64·46 W
122	Albert (äl-bâr')......Fr.	50·00 N	2·49 E
86	Alberta (Prov.) (ăl-bûr'tȧ)...Can.	54·33 N	117·10 W
155	Albert Edward, Mt. (ăl'bĕrt ĕd'wērd). Austl.	8·25 S	147·25 E
101	Alberti (äl-bĕ'r-tē) Arg. (Buenos Aires In.)	35·01 S	60·16 W
111	Albert Kanal (can.) Bel. (Bruxelles In.)	51·07 N	5·07 E
165	Albert L. (ăl'bĕrt) (äl-bâr') Con. L.-Ug.	2·00 N	30·16 E
71	Albert Lea (ăl'bĕrt lē')......Minn.	43·38 N	93·24 W
82	Alberton (ăl'bĕr-tŭn)......Can.	46·50 N	64·02 W
167	Alberton......S. Afr. (Johannesburg & Pretoria In.)	26·16 S	28·08 E
78	Albertville (ăl'bĕrt-vĭl)......Ala.	34·15 N	86·10 W
166	Albertville (äl-bĕr-vēl')....Con. L.	5·59 S	29·12 E
123	Albertville......Fr.	45·42 N	6·25 E
122	Albi (äl-bē')......Fr.	43·54 N	2·07 E
71	Albia (ăl bĭ-ȧ)......Iowa	41·01 N	92·44 W
99	Albina (äl-bē'nä)......Fr. Gu.	5·30 N	54·33 W
75	Albino, Pt. (äl-bē'nō) Can. (Buffalo In.)	42·50 N	79·05 W
80	Albion (ăl'bĭ-ŭn)......Mich.	42·15 N	84·50 W
70	Albion......Nebr.	41·42 N	99·00 W
81	Albion......N. Y.	43·15 N	78·10 W
124	Alboran, Isla del (I.) (ē's-lä-dĕl-äl-bō-rä'n). Sp.	35·58 N	3·02 W
124	Alboran Sea......Med.	35·54 N	4·26 W
124	Albox (äl-bōk')......Sp.	37·23 N	2·08 W
69	Albuquerque (ăl-bŭ-kûr'kē) N. Mex.	35·05 N	106·40 W
93	Albuquerque, Cayus de (I.) (ăl-bŭ-kûr'kē). Col.	12·12 N	81·24 W
144	Al Buraymī......Sau. Ar.	23·45 N	55·39 E
124	Alburquerque (äl-bōōr-kĕr'kä). Sp.	39·13 N	6·58 W
160	Albury (ôl'bĕr-ē)......Austl.	36·00 S	147·00 E
125	Alcabideche (äl-kä-bē-dä'chä) Port. (Lisboa In.)	38·43 N	9·24 W
124	Alcacer do Sal (äl-kä'sĕr dōō säl') Port.	38·24 N	8·33 W
125	Alcalá de Chivert (äl-kä-lä'dä chē-vĕrt'). Sp.	40·18 N	0·12 E
125	Alcalá de Henares (äl-kä-lä' dā ä nä'räs). Sp. (Madrid In.)	40·29 N	3·22 W
124	Alcalá de los Gazules (äl-kä-lä' dā lōs gä-thōō'läs). Sp.	36·29 N	5·44 W
124	Alcalá la Real (äl-kä-lä'lä rā-äl'). Sp.	37·27 N	3·57 W
126	Alcamo (äl'kä-mō)......It.	37·58 N	13·03 E
125	Alcanadre (R.) (äl-kä-nä'drā). Sp.	41·41 N	0·18 W
125	Alcanar (äl-kä-när')......Sp.	40·35 N	0·27 E
125	Alcañiz (äl-kän-yēth')......Sp.	41·03 N	0·08 W
99	Alcântara (äl-kän'tȧ-rȧ)......Braz.	2·17 S	44·29 W
124	Alcaraz (äl-kä-räth')......Sp.	38·39 N	2·28 W
124	Alcaudete (äl-kou-dhā'tä)......Sp.	37·38 N	4·05 W
124	Alcázar de San Juan (äl-kä'thär dā sän hwän'). Sp.	39·22 N	3·12 W
114	Alcazarquivir......Mor.	35·01 N	5·48 W
125	Alcira (ä-thē'rä)......Sp.	39·09 N	0·26 W

ăt; finăl; rate; senâte; ärm; ȧsk; sofȧ; fâre; ch-choose; dh-as th in other; bē; ēvent; bĕt; recĕnt; cratẽr; g-go; gh-guttural g; bĭt; ĭ-short neutral; rīde; κ-guttural k as ch in German ich;

Page	Name Pronunciation Region	Lat. °'	Long. °'
78	Alcoa (ăl-kō'ȧ) Tenn.	35·45 N	84·00 W
125	Alcobendas (äl-kō-bĕn'dȧs) Sp. (Madrid In.)	40·32 N	3·39 W
125	Alcochete (äl-kō-chā'ta) Port. (Lisboa In.)	38·45 N	8·58 W
125	Alcora (äl-kō'rä) Sp.	40·05 N	0·12 W
125	Alcorisa (äl-kō-rē'sä) Sp.	40·53 N	0·20 W
125	Alcorón (äl-kô-rô'n) Sp. (Madrid In.)	40·22 N	3·50 W
101	Alcorta (äl-kôr'tä) Arg. (Buenos Aires In.)	33·32 S	61·08 W
67	Alcova Res. (ăl-kō'vȧ) Wyo.	42·31 N	106·33 W
85	Alcove (ăl-kōv')Can. (Ottawa In.)	45·41 N	75·55 W
125	Alcoy (äl-koi') Sp.	38·42 N	0·30 W
125	Alcudia, Ba. de (B.) (bä-ē'ä-dĕ-äl-kōō-dhē'ä).Sp.	39·48 N	3·20 E
167	Aldabra Is. (äl-dä'brä) Afr.	9·16 S	46·17 E
90	Aldama (äl-dä'mä) Mex.	22·54 N	98·04 W
76	Aldama Mex.	28·50 N	105·54 W
135	Aldan Sov. Un.	58·46 N	125·19 E
135	Aldan (R.) Sov. Un.	63·30 N	132·14 E
135	Aldan Plat Sov. Un.	57·42 N	130·28 E
135	Aldanskaya Sov. Un.	61·52 N	135·29 E
123	Aldekerk (äl'dĕ-kĕ'rk) Ger. (Ruhr In.)	51·26 N	6·26 E
123	Aldenhoven (äl'dĕn-hō'vĕn) Ger. (Ruhr In.)	50·54 N	6·18 E
65	Aldergrove (ôl'dēr-grōv) Can. (Vancouver In.)	49·03 N	122·28 W
122	Alderney (I.) (ôl'dēr-nĭ) .Chan. Is.	49·43 N	2·11 W
110	Aldershot (ôl'dēr-shŏt) Eng. (London In.)	51·14 N	0·46 W
80	Alderson (ôl-dēr-sŭn) W. Va.	37·40 N	80·40 W
65	Alderwood Manor (ôl'dēr-wŏŏd măn'ŏr) .Wash. (Seattle In.)	47·49 N	122·18 W
73	Aledo (ȧ-le'dō) Ill.	41·12 N	90·47 W
164	Aleg Mauritania	17·10 N	13·57 W
101	Alegre (àlĕ'-grĕ) Braz. (Rio de Janeiro In.)	20·41 S	41·32 W
100	Alegre (R.) Braz. (In.)	22·22 S	43·34 W
100	Alegrete (ä-lå-grā'tā) Braz.	29·46 S	55·44 W
136	Aleksandrov (ä-lyĕk-sän' drôf) Sov. Un. (Moskva In.)	56·24 N	38·45 E
136	Aleksandrovsk (ä-lyĕk-sän'drôfsk) Sov. Un. (Urals In.)	59·11 N	57·36 E
135	Aleksandrovsk-Sakhalinskiy (ä-lyĕk-sän'drôfsk-sŭ-kŭ-lyēn'skē) Sov. Un.	51·02 N	142·21 E
121	Aleksandrow Kujawski (ä-lĕk-säh'drōōv kōō-yav'skē) Pol.	52·54 N	18·45 E
129	Alekseyevka (ä-lyĕk-sā-yĕf'kȧ) Sov. Un.	50·39 N	38·40 E
128	Aleksin (ä-lyĕk-sēn) Sov. Un.	54·31 N	37·07 E
127	Aleksinac (ȧ-lyĕk-sē-nȧk') . Yugo.	43·33 N	21·42 E
101	Alem Paraíba (ä-lĕ'm-pȧ-räē'bȧ) Braz. (Rio de Janeiro In.)	21·54 S	42·40 W
122	Alençon (ȧ-läN-sôN') Fr.	48·26 N	0·08 E
99	Alenquer (ä-lĕŋ-kĕr') Braz.	1·58 S	54·44 W
124	Alenquer Port.	39·04 N	9·01 W
124	Alentjo (Reg.) (ä-lĕŋ-tā'zhōō) Port.	38·05 N	7·45 W
157	Alenuihaha Chan. (ā'lā-nōō-ē-hā'hä) .Hawaii (In.)	20·20 N	156·05 W
115	Aleppo (ȧ-lĕp-ō) Syria	36·10 N	37·18 E
122	Alès (ä-lĕs') Fr.	44·07 N	4·06 E
126	Alessandria (ä-lĕs-sän'drê-ä) . . .It.	44·53 N	8·35 E
74	Alessandro (ä-lĕs-san'drō) Calif. (Los Angeles In.)	33·52 N	117·16 W
	Alessio, see Lesh		
118	Ålesund (ô'lĕ-sōōn') Nor.	62·28 N	6·14 E
64	Aleutian Is. (ȧ-lu'shăn) Alaska	52·40 N	177·30 E
64	Aleutian Trench Alaska	50·40 N	177·10 E
135	Alevina, Mys (C.) Sov. Un.	58·49 N	151·44 E
64	Alexander Arch. (ăl-ĕg-zăn'dēr) Alaska	57·05 N	138·10 W
78	Alexander City Ala.	32·55 N	85·55 W
47	Alexander I Ant.	71·00 S	71·00 W
167	Alexandra (äl-ex-än'-drȧ) S. Afr. (Johannesburg & Pretoria In.)	26·07 S	28·07 E
158	Alexandria (ăl-ĕg-zăn'drĭ-ȧ) . Austl.	19·00 S	136·56 E
81	Alexandria Can.	45·50 N	74·35 W
80	Alexandria Ind.	40·20 N	85·20 W
77	Alexandria La.	31·18 N	92·28 W
70	Alexandria Minn.	45·53 N	95·23 W
127	Alexandria Rom.	43·55 N	25·21 E
70	Alexandria S. D.	43·39 N	97·45 W
167	Alexandria (ăl-ĕx-än-drĭ-ȧ) S. Afr. (Natal In.)	33·40 S	26·26 E
81	Alexandria (ăl-ĕg-zăn'drĭ-ȧ) . . .Va.	38·50 N	77·05 W
	Alexandria, see Al Iskandarīyah		
81	Alexandria Bay N. Y.	44·20 N	75·55 W
127	Alexandroupolis (Dedeagats) (ä-lĕk-sän-drōō'pō-lĭs) (dé'dĕ-ä-gäts) .Grc.	40·51 N	25·51 E
124	Alfaro (äl-färō) Sp.	42·08 N	1·43 W
168	Al Fashn U. A. R. (Nile In.)	28·47 N	30·53 E
165	Al Fayyūm U. A. R.	29·14 N	30·48 E
101	Alfenas (äl-fĕ'nàs) Braz. (Rio de Janeiro In.)	21·26 S	45·55 W
127	Alfiós (R.) Grc.	37·33 N	21·50 E
168	Al Firdān (fer-dän') U. A. R. (Nile In.)	30·43 N	32·20 E
101	Alfonso Claudio (äl-fōn'sô-klou'dēô) Braz. (Rio de Janeiro In.)	20·05 S	41·05 W
85	Alfred (ăl'frĕd) . Can. (Ottawa In.)	45·34 N	74·52 W
110	Alfreton (ăl'fēr-tŭn) Eng.	53·06 N	1·23 W
165	Alga Eth.	5·56 N	38·09 E
124	Algarve (Reg.) (äl-gär'vĕ) . . .Port	37·15 N	8·12 W
124	Algeciras (äl-hā-thē'räs) Sp.	36·08 N	5·25 W
164	Alger (Algiers) (àl-zhā') (ăl-jēr) Alg.	36·51 N	2·56 E
163	Algeria (ăl-gē'rĭ-ȧ) Afr.	34·58 N	2·00 E
125	Algete (äl-hā'tā) . Sp. (Madrid In.)	40·36 N	3·30 W
126	Alghero (äl-gâ'rō) It.	40·32 N	8·22 E
	Algiers, see Alger		
77	Algoa (ăl-gō'ȧ) Tex. (In.)	29·24 N	95·11 W
167	Algoa B. (ăl'gôȧ) S. Afr. (Natal In.)	33·51 S	24·50 E
71	Algoma (ăl-gō'mȧ) Iowa	43·04 N	94·11 W
65	Algoma Wash. (Seattle In.)	47·17 N	122·15 W
71	Algoma Wis.	44·38 N	87·29 W
80	Algonac (ăl'gô-năk) Mich.	42·35 N	82·30 W
75	Algonquin (ăl-gŏŋ'kwĭn) Ill. (Chicago In.)	42·10 N	88·17 W
81	Algonquin Park Can.	45·50 N	78·20 W
124	Alhama (äl-hä'mä) Sp.	37·00 N	3·59 W
124	Alhama Sp.	37·50 N	1·24 W
74	Alhambra (ăl-hăm'brȧ) Calif. (Los Angeles In.)	34·05 N	118·08 W
115	Al Ḩammām U. A. R.	30·46 N	29·42 E
125	Alhandra (äl-yän'drȧ) Port. (Lisboa In.)	38·55 N	9·01 W
139	Al Haql . . .Sau. Ar. (Palestine In.)	29·15 N	34·57 E
139	Al Harmal . . . .Leb. (Palestine In.)	34·23 N	36·22 E
144	Al Hasā (Plain) Sau. Ar.	27·00 N	47·48 E
124	Alhaurín el Grande (ä-lou-rēn'ĕl-grä'n-dĕ) .Sp.	36·40 N	4·40 W
144	Al Hijaz (Reg.) Sau. Ar.	23·45 N	39·08 E
125	Alhos Vedros (äl'yōs-vā'drōs) Port. (Lisboa In.)	38·39 N	9·02 W
124	Alhucemas, Baie d' (B.) Mor.	35·18 N	5·50 W
144	Al Hudaydub Yemen	14·43 N	43·03 E
144	Al Hufūf (Hofuf) (hô-fōōf') Sau. Ar.	25·15 N	49·43 E
127	Aliákmon (R.) (àl-ê-àk'-mōn) Grc.	40·26 N	22·17 E
125	Alicante (ä-lê-kän'tā) Sp.	38·20 N	0·30 W
125	Alicante, Bahia de (B.) (bä-ē'ä-dĕ-ä-lê-kän'tā) .Sp.	38·12 N	0·22 W
76	Alice (ăl'ĭs) Tex.	27·45 N	98·04 W
167	Alice (ăl-ĭs) S. Afr. (Natal In.)	32·47 S	26·51 E
167	Alicedale (ăl'ĭs-dāl) S. Afr. (Natal In.)	33·18 S	26·04 E
158	Alice Springs (ăl'ĭs) Austl.	23·38 S	133·56 E
126	Alicudi (I.) (ä-lē-kōō'dē) It.	38·34 N	14·21 E
136	Alifkulovo (ä-lĭf-kŭ'lô-vô) Sov. Un. (Urals In.)	55·57 N	62·06 E
142	Alīgarh (ä-lê-gŭr') India	27·58 N	78·08 E
118	Alingsås (ȧ'lĭŋ-sôs) Swe.	57·57 N	12·30 E
75	Aliquippa (ăl-ĭ-kwĭp'ȧ) Pa. (Pittsburgh In.)	40·37 N	80·15 W
168	Al Iskandarīyah (Alexandria) U. A. R. (Nile In.)	31·12 N	29·58 E
168	Al Isma'īlīyah (Ismailia) (ēs-mä-ēl'ē-ä) . U. A. R. (Suez In.)	30·35 N	32·17 E
166	Aliwal North (ä-lē-wäl') S. Afr.	31·09 S	28·26 E
139	Al Jafr (L.) .Jordan (Palestine In.)	30·17 N	36·20 E
165	Al Jaghbūb Libya	29·46 N	24·32 E
165	Al Jawf Libya	24·14 N	23·15 E
144	Al Jawf Sau. Ar.	29·45 N	39·30 E
165	Al Jazirah Libya	25·47 N	21·25 E
124	Aljezur (äl-zhä-zōōr') Port.	37·18 N	8·52 W
168	Al Jīzah U. A. R. (Nile In.)	30·01 N	31·12 E
165	Al Jufrah (Oasis) Libya	29·30 N	15·16 E
124	Aljustrel (äl-zhōō-strĕl') Port.	37·44 N	8·23 W
168	Al Kāb U. A. R. (Suez In.)	30·56 N	32·19 E
139	Al Karak (kĕ-räk') Jordan (Palestine In.)	31·11 N	35·42 E
168	Al Karnak (kär'nak) U. A. R. (Nile In.)	25·42 N	32·43 E
144	Al Khābūrah Mus. & Om.	23·45 N	57·30 E
139	Al Khalīl (Hebron) Jordan (Palestine In.)	31·31 N	35·07 E
165	Al Khums Libya	32·35 N	14·10 E
144	Al Khurmah Sau. Ar.	21·37 N	41·44 E
117	Alkmaar (älk-mär') Neth.	52·39 N	4·42 E
168	Al Kūbrī (kōō'brê) U. A. R. (Suez In.)	30·01 N	32·35 E
165	Al Kufrah (Oasis) Libya	24·45 N	22·45 E
139	Al Kuntillah U. A. R. (Palestine In.)	29·59 N	34·42 E
144	Al Kuwayt (Kuwait) (koō-wit) Kuwait	29·04 N	47·59 E
164	Allada (äl-lä'dä) Dahomey	6·44 N	2·08 E
82	Allagash (R.) (ăl'ȧ-găsh) . . . Maine	46·50 N	69·24 W
142	Allahābād (ŭl-ŭ-hä-băd') India	25·32 N	81·53 E
68	All American can. (âl ȧ-mĕr'ĭ-kăn) Calif.	32·43 N	115·12 W
111	Alland Aus. (Wien In.)	48·04 N	16·05 E
124	Allariz (äl-yä-rēth') Sp.	42·10 N	7·48 W
78	Allatoona (R.) (ăl'ȧ-tōōn'ȧ) . . . Ga.	34·05 N	84·57 W
122	Allauch (ä-lĕ'ōō) Fr. (Marseille In.)	43·21 N	5·30 E
120	Allier R. (ăl'ēr) Ger.	52·43 N	9·50 E
135	Allaykha (ä-lī'kȧ) Sov. Un.	70·32 N	148·53 E
80	Allegan (ăl'ê-găn) Mich.	42·30 N	85·55 W
81	Allegany Ind. Res. (ăl-ê-gā'nĭ) N. Y.	42·05 N	78·55 W
81	Allegheny (R.) Pa.	41·10 N	79·20 W
63	Allegheny Mts U. S.	37·35 N	81·55 W
80	Allegheny Plat U. S.	39·00 N	81·15 W
81	Allegheny Front (Mts.) U. S.	38·12 N	80·03 W
73	Allen (ăl'ĕn) Okla.	34·51 N	96·26 W
116	Allen, Lough (B.) (lŏk ăl'ĕn) . . Ire.	54·07 N	8·09 W
84	Allendale (ăl'ĕn-dāl) N. J. (New York In.)	41·02 N	74·08 W
79	Allendale S. C.	33·00 N	81·19 W
91	Allende (äl-yĕn'dȧ) Mex.	18·23 N	92·49 W
76	Allende Mex.	28·20 N	100·50 W
81	Allentown (ăl'en-toun) Pa.	40·35 N	75·30 W
143	Alleppey (ȧ-lĕp'ē) India	9·33 N	76·22 E
120	Aller R. (äl'ēr) Ger.	52·43 N	9·50 E
70	Alliance (ȧ-lī'ăns) Nebr.	42·06 N	102·53 W
80	Alliance Ohio	40·55 N	81·10 W
122	Allier (R.) (ȧ-lyā') Fr.	46·43 N	3·03 E
84	Alligator Pt. (ăl'ĭ-gā-tēr) La. (New Orleans In.)	30·57 N	89·41 W
118	Allinge (äl'ĭŋ-ĕ) Den.	55·16 N	14·48 E
92	All Pines (ôl pĭnz) Br. Hond. (Yucatan In.)	16·55 N	88·15 W
144	Al Luhayyah Yemen	15·58 N	42·48 E
65	Allyn (ăl'ĭn) . . Wash. (Seattle In.)	47·23 N	122·51 W
125	Alma (ä-mà) Alg.	36·44 N	1·27 E
82	Alma (ăl'mȧ) Can.	45·36 N	65·01 W
79	Alma Ga.	31·33 N	82·31 W
80	Alma Mich.	43·25 N	84·40 W
72	Alma Nebr.	40·08 N	99·21 W
168	Alma . . . .S. Afr. (Johannesburg & Pretoria In.)	24·30 S	28·05 E
71	Alma Wis.	44·21 N	91·57 W
134	Alma-Ata (ăl'mȧ ȧ'tȧ) . . .Sov. Un.	43·19 N	77·08 E
125	Almada (äl-mä'dä) Port. (Lisboa In.)	38·40 N	9·09 W
124	Almadén (äl-mä-dhān') Sp.	38·47 N	4·50 W
144	Al Madīnah Sau. Ar.	24·26 N	39·42 E
139	Al Mafraq .Jordan (Palestine In.)	32·21 N	36·13 E
91	Almagre, Laguna (L.) (lä-gōō'nä-äl-mä'grĕ) Mex.	22·48 N	97·45 W
124	Almagro (äl-mä'grō) Sp.	38·52 N	3·41 W
168	Al Mahallah al Kubrá U. A. R. (Nile In.)	31·00 N	31·10 E
144	Al Manāmah Bahrain	26·01 N	50·33 E
68	Almanor (R.) (ăl-măn'ôr) . . . Calif.	40·11 N	121·20 W
124	Almansa (äl-män'sä) Sp.	38·52 N	1·09 W
168	Al Manshāh . . . U. A. R. (Nile In.)	26·31 N	31·46 E
124	Almansor (R.) (äl-män-sôr) . . Port.	38·41 N	8·27 W
168	Al Manṣūrah . . U. A. R. (Nile In.)	31·02 N	31·25 W
168	Al Manzilah (män'za-la) U. A. R. (Nile In.)	31·09 N	32·05 E
124	Almanzora (R.) (äl-män-thō'rä) Sp.	37·20 N	2·25 W
168	Al Marāghah . . U. A. R. (Nile In.)	26·41 N	31·35 E
125	Almargem (äl-mär-zhĕN) Port. (Lisboa In.)	38·51 N	9·16 W
144	Al Mawsil Iraq	36·00 N	42·53 E
124	Almazán (äl-mä-thän') Sp.	41·30 N	2·33 W
139	Al Mazār . . .Jordan (Palestine In.)	31·04 N	35·41 E
139	Al Mazra' . . Jordan (Palestine In.)	31·17 N	35·33 E
124	Almeirim (äl-māī-rēN') Port.	39·13 N	8·31 W
117	Almelo (äl'mē-lō) Neth.	52·20 N	6·42 E
124	Almendralejo (äl-män-drä-lā'hō) Sp.	38·43 N	6·24 W
124	Almería (äl-mā-rē'ä) Sp.	36·52 N	2·28 W
124	Almeria, Golfo de (G.) (gôl-fô-dĕ-äl-māī-reN') .Sp.	36·45 N	2·26 W
124	Almería (R.) Sp.	37·00 N	2·40 W
118	Almhult (älm'hōōlt) Swe.	56·35 N	14·08 E
124	Almina, Pta. (äl-mē'nä) Mor.	35·58 N	5·17 W
168	Al Minyā . . . . .U. A. R. (Nile In.)	28·04 N	30·45 E
93	Almirante (äl-mē-rän'tā) Pan.	9·18 N	82·24 W
93	Almirante, Bahia de (B.) (bä-ē'ä-dĕ-äl-mē-rän'tā) . Pan.	9·22 N	82·07 W
127	Almirós Grc.	39·13 N	22·47 E
124	Almodóvar (äl-mō-dhō'vär) . . . Sp.	38·43 N	4·10 W
142	Almoi India	29·41 N	79·42 E
90	Almoloya (äl-mō-lō'yä) Mex.	19·32 N	99·44 W
91	Almoloya Mex. (Mexico In.)	19·11 N	99·28 W
81	Almonte (äl-mŏn'tê) Can.	45·15 N	76·15 W
124	Almonte (äl-mōn'tä) Sp.	37·16 N	6·32 W
124	Almonte (R.) Sp.	39·35 N	5·50 W
142	Almora India	29·20 N	79·40 E
144	Al Mubarraz Sau. Ar.	22·31 N	46·27 E
139	Al Mudawwarah Jordan (Palestine In.)	29·20 N	36·01 E
144	Al Mukallā Aden	14·27 N	49·05 E
144	Al Mukhā Yemen	13·43 N	43·27 E
124	Almuñécar (äl-mōōn-yā'kär) . . . Sp.	36·44 N	3·43 W
118	Alnö (I.) Swe.	62·20 N	17·39 E
65	Aloha (ä'lô-hä) Ore. (Portland In.)	45·29 N	122·52 W
155	Alor (I.) (ä'lôr) Indon.	8·07 S	125·00 E
124	Álora (ä'lô-rä) Sp.	36·49 N	4·42 W
139	Alor Gajah . . Mala (Singapore In.)	2·23 N	102·13 E
154	Alor Star (ä'lôr stär) Mala.	6·24 N	100·08 E
65	Alouette (R.) (ä-lōō-ĕt') Can. (Vancouver In.)	49·16 N	122·32 W
80	Alpena (ăl-pē'nȧ) Mich.	45·05 N	83·30 W
111	Alphen . . . .Neth. (Amsterdam In.)	52·07 N	4·38 E
124	Alpiarça (äl-pyär'sȧ) Port.	39·38 N	8·37 W
76	Alpine (ăl'pīn) Tex.	30·21 N	103·41 W
114	Alps (Mts.) (ălps) Eur.	46·18 N	8·42 E
98	Alpujarra (äl-pōō-kä'r'rä) Col. (In.)	3·23 N	74·56 W
124	Alpujarras (Mts.) (äl-pōō-här'räs) Sp.	36·55 N	3·25 W
168	Al Qāhirah (Cairo) U. A. R. (Nile In.)	30·03 N	31·17 E
168	Al Qanṭarah . .U. A. R. (Suez In.)	30·51 N	32·20 E
165	Al Qaryah Libya	30·36 N	13·13 E
144	Al Qaṭīf Sau. Ar.	26·30 N	50·00 E
139	Al Qaṭranah.Jordan (Palestine In.)	31·15 N	36·04 E
144	Al Qaysumah Sau. Ar.	28·30 N	46·27 E
139	Al Quarayyah Sau. Ar. (Palestine In.)	28·43 N	36·11 E
139	Al Qunaytirah .Syr. (Palestine In.)	33·09 N	35·49 E
144	Al Qunfidhah Sau. Ar.	18·48 N	41·28 E
168	Al Qurnah (kōōr'na) U. A. R. (Nile In.)	25·44 N	32·39 E
139	Al Quṣaymah U. A. R. (Palestine In.)	30·40 N	34·23 E
165	Al Quṣayr U. A. R.	26·14 N	34·11 E
139	Al Quṣayr . U. A. R. (Palestine In.)	34·32 N	36·33 E
118	Als (äls) Den.	55·06 N	9·40 E
123	Alsace (Reg.) (äl-sȧ's) Fr.	48·25 N	7·24 E
148	Al Shan (Mts.) (ăĭ'shän) . . . China	37·27 N	120·35 E
118	Alsterån (R.) Swe.	56·54 N	15·50 E
74	Altadena (ăl-tȧ-dē'nä) Calif. (Los Angeles In.)	34·12 N	118·08 W
100	Alta Gracia (äl'tä grä'sē-a) . . . Arg.	31·41 S	64·19 W
98	Altagracia Ven.	10·42 N	71·34 W
99	Altagracia de Orituco (ä'l-tà-grà' sēä-dĕ-ôrē-tōō'kô) . Ven. (In.)	9·53 N	66·22 W
134	Altai Ter Sov. Un.	53·39 N	78·52 E

ng-sing; ŋ-baŋk; N-nasalized n; nŏd; cŏmmit; ōld; ôbey; ôrder; fōōd; fŏŏt; ou-out; s-soft; sh-dish; th-thin; pūre; ûnite; ûrn; stŭd; circŭs; ü-as "y" in study; '-indeterminate vowel.

Page	Name Pronunciation Region	Lat. °′	Long. °′
146	Altai Mts. (äl'tī') ... Asia	49·11 N	87·15 E
74	Alta Loma (ăl'tȧ lō'mä) Calif. (Los Angeles In.)	34·07 N	117·35 W
77	Alta Loma (ăl'tȧ lō-mȧ) Tex. (In.)	29·22 N	95·05 W
79	Altamaha (R.) (ôl-tȧ-mȧ-hô') Ga.	31·50 N	82·00 W
99	Altamira (äl-tä-mē'rä) Braz.	3·13 S	52·14 W
91	Altamira Mex.	22·25 N	97·55 W
100	Altamirano (äl-tä-mê-rä'nō) Arg.	35·26 S	58·12 W
126	Altamura (äl-tä-mōō'rä) It.	40·40 N	16·35 E
135	Altan Bulag Mong.	50·18 N	106·31 E
79	Altavista (ăl-tȧ-vĭs'tȧ) Va.	37·08 N	79·14 W
112	Alten (R.) (äl'tĕn) Nor.	69·40 N	24·09 E
120	Altenburg (äl-tĕn-bŏŏrgh) Ger.	50·59 N	12·27 E
111	Altenmarket an der Triesting Aus. (Wien In.)	48·02 N	16·00 E
124	Alter do Chão (äl-tĕr'dŏŏ shäN'ōN) Port.	39·13 N	7·38 W
90	Altiplanicie Mexicana (Plat.) (äl-tē-plä-nē'syĕ-mĕ-ĸē-kä-nä) Mex.	22·38 N	102·33 W
98	Altiplano (Plat.) (äl-tē-plä'nō) Bol.	18·38 S	68·20 W
111	Alt Landsberg (ält länts'bĕrgh) Ger. (Berlin In.)	52·34 N	13·44 E
77	Alto (ăl'tō) La.	32·21 N	91·52 W
98	Alto Marañón, Rio (R.) (rē'ō-ȧl'tô-mä-rän-yŏ'n) Peru	8·18 S	77·13 W
111	Altomünster (äl'tō-mün'stĕr) Ger. (München In.)	48·24 N	11·16 E
85	Alton (ôl'tŭn) Can. (Toronto In.)	43·52 N	80·05 W
74	Alton Ill. (St. Louis In.)	38·53 N	90·11 W
161	Altona Austl. (Melbourne In.)	37·52 S	144·50 E
111	Altona (äl'tō-nä) Ger. (Hamburg In).	53·33 N	9·54 E
78	Altoona (ăl-tōō'nȧ) Ala.	34·01 N	86·15 W
81	Altoona Pa.	40·25 N	78·25 W
65	Altoona Wash. (Portland In.)	46·16 N	123·39 W
101	Alto Rio Doce (äl'tô-rē'ô-dō'sĕ) Braz. (Rio de Janeiro In.)	21·02 S	43·23 W
95	Alto Songo (äl-fō-sôŋ'gō) Cuba	20·10 N	75·45 W
91	Altotonga (äl-tō-tôŋ'gä) Mex.	19·44 N	97·13 W
95	Alto Velo (I.) (äl-tô-vĕ'lō) Dom. Rep.	17·30 N	71·35 W
110	Altrincham (ôl'trĭng-ăm) Eng.	53·18 N	2·21 W
111	Alt Ruppin (ält rōō'ppēn) Ger. (Berlin In.)	54·56 N	12·48 E
66	Alturas (ăl-tōō'rȧs) Calif.	41·29 N	120·33 W
72	Altus (ăl'tŭs) Okla.	34·38 N	99·20 W
165	Al 'Ugaylah Libya	30·15 N	19·07 E
165	Al Ujaylāt Libya	32·45 N	12·27 E
128	Alūksne (ä'lŏŏks-nĕ) Sov. Un.	57·24 N	27·04 E
168	Alula (ä-lōō'lä) Som. (Horn of Afr. In.)	11·53 N	50·40 E
81	Alumette I. (ȧ-lü-mĕt') Can.	45·50 N	77·00 W
168	Al Uqṣur (Luxor) U. A. R. (Nile In.)	25·38 N	32·59 E
129	Alushta (ä'lŏŏsh-tȧ) Sov. Un.	44·39 N	34·23 E
72	Alva (ăl'vȧ) Okla.	36·46 N	98·41 W
65	Alvarado (ăl-vȧ-rä'dō) Calif (San Francisco In.)	37·35 N	122·05 W
91	Alvarado (äl-vä-rä'dhō) Mex.	18·48 N	95·45 W
91	Alvarado, Luguna de (L.) (lä-gōō'nä-dĕ-äl-vä-rä'dô) Mex.	18·44 N	96·45 W
118	Älvdalen (ĕlv'dä-lĕn) Swe.	61·14 N	14·04 E
125	Alverca (al-vĕr'kȧ) Port. (Lisboa In.)	38·53 N	9·02 W
118	Alvesta (äl-vĕs'tä) Swe.	56·55 N	14·29 E
77	Alvin (ăl'vĭn) Tex. (In.)	29·25 N	95·14 W
101	Alvinópolis (äl-vēnŏ'pō-lēs) Braz. (Rio de Janeiro In.)	20·07 S	43·03 W
65	Alviso (ăl-vī'sō) Calif. (San Francisco In.)	37·26 N	121·59 W
144	Al Wajh Sau. Ar.	26·15 N	36·32 E
142	Alwar (ŭl'wŭr) India	27·39 N	76·39 E
168	Al Wāsiṭah U. A. R. (Nile In.)	29·21 N	31·15 E
119	Alytus (ä'lē-tōōs) Sov. Un.	54·25 N	24·05 E
118	Åmå (ô'môl) Swe.	59·05 N	12·40 E
90	Amacuzac (R.) (ä-mä-kōō-zäk) Mex.	18·00 N	99·03 W
158	Amadeus, (L.) (ăm-ȧ-dē'ŭs) Austl.	24·30 S	131·25 E
87	Amadjuak (L.) (ä-mädj'wăk) Can.	64·50 N	69·20 W
153	Amagasaki (ä'mä-gä-sä'kē) Jap. (Osaka In.)	34·43 N	135·25 E
153	Amakusa-Shimo (I.) (ämä-kōō'sä shē-mō) Jap.	32·24 N	129·35 E
98	Amalfi (ä-mà'l-fē) Col. (In.)	6·55 N	75·04 W
125	Amalfi (ä-mä'l-fê) It. (Napoli In.)	40·23 N	14·36 E
127	Amaliás (ȧ-mäl'yȧs) Grc.	37·48 N	21·23 E
142	Amalner India	21·07 N	75·06 E
99	Amambay, Cordillera de (Mts.) Braz.	20·06 S	57·08 W
152	Amami Guntō (Is.) (ä'mä'mē gōōn'tō') Jap.	28·25 N	129·00 E
152	Amamio (I.) (ä-mä'mē-ō) Jap.	28·10 N	129·55 E
167	Amanzimtoti S. Afr. (Natal In.)	30·02 S	30·54 E
99	Amapá (ä-mä-pà') Braz.	2·14 N	50·48 W
99	Amapá (Ter.) Braz.	1·15 N	52·15 W
92	Amapala (ä-mä-pä'lä) Hond.	13·16 N	87·39 W
99	Amarante (ä-mä-rän'tä) Braz.	6·17 S	42·43 W
68	Amargosa (R.) (ȧ'mär-gō'sȧ) Calif.	35·55 N	116·45 W
72	Amarillo (ăm-ȧ-rĭl'ō) Tex.	35·14 N	101·49 W
126	Amaro, Mt. (ä-mä'rō) It.	42·07 N	14·07 E
133	Amasya (ä-mä'sē-ȧ) Tur.	40·40 N	35·50 E
91	Amatenango (ä-mä-tä-naŋ'gō) Mex.	16·30 N	92·29 W
64	Amatignak (I.) (ä-mȧ'tê-näk) Alaska	51·12 N	178·30 W
92	Amatique, Bahía de (B.) (bä-ē'ä-dĕ-ä-mä-tē'kä) Guat.-Br. Hond.	15·58 N	88·50 W
92	Amatitlán (ä-mä-tê-tlän') Guat.	14·27 N	90·39 W
90	Amatlán de Cañas (ä-mät-län'dā kän-yäs) Mex.	20·50 N	104·22 W

Page	Name Pronunciation Region	Lat. °′	Long. °′
98	Amazonas Selvas (Reg.) (ä-mä-thō'näs) Braz.	4·15 S	64·30 W
99	Amazonas, Rio (R.) (rē'ō-ä-mä-thō'näs) Braz.	2·03 S	53·18 W
142	Ambala (ŭm-bä'lŭ) India	30·31 N	76·48 E
98	Ambalema (äm-bä-lā'mä) Col. (In.)	4·47 N	74·45 W
135	Ambarchik (ŭm-bär'chĭk) Sov. Un.	69·39 N	162·18 E
98	Ambato (äm-bä'tō) Ec.	1·15 S	78·44 W
120	Amberg (äm'bĕrgh) Ger.	49·26 N	11·51 E
95	Ambergris Cays (Is.) (ăm'bēr-grēs kāz) Ba. Is.	21·20 N	71·40 W
92	Ambergris I. Br. Hond. (Yucatan In.)	18·04 N	87·43 W
123	Ambérieu (äN-bā-rê-û') Fr.	45·57 N	5·21 E
122	Ambert (äN-bĕr') Fr.	45·32 N	3·41 E
155	Ambil (I.) (äm'bēl) Phil. (Manila In.)	13·51 N	120·25 E
84	Ambler (ăm'blēr) Pa. (Philadelphia In.)	40·09 N	75·13 W
155	Amboina (ăm-boi'nȧ) Indon.	3·45 S	128·17 E
155	Amboina (I.) Indon.	4·50 S	128·45 E
122	Amboise (äN-bwäz') Fr.	47·25 N	0·56 E
167	Ambositra (äN-bô-sē'trä) Malagasy	20·31 S	47·28 E
80	Amboy (ăm'boi) Ill.	41·45 N	89·15 W
65	Amboy Wash. (Portland In.)	45·55 N	122·27 W
167	Ambre, Cap d' (C.) Malagasy	12·06 S	49·15 E
75	Ambridge (ăm'brĭdj) Pa. (Pittsburgh In.)	40·36 N	80·13 W
159	Ambrim (I.) New Heb.	16·28 S	158·17 E
166	Ambriz Ang.	7·50 S	15·10 E
166	Ambrizete Ang.	7·15 S	12·50 E
64	Amchitka P. (ăm-chĭt'kȧ) Alaska	51·30 N	179·36 W
90	Amealco (ä-mā-äl'kō) Mex.	20·12 N	100·08 W
90	Ameca (ä-mĕ'kä) Mex.	20·34 N	104·02 W
91	Amecameca (ä-mȧ-kä-mä'kä) Mex. (Mexico In.)	19·06 N	98·46 W
111	Ameide Neth. (Amsterdam In.)	51·57 N	4·57 E
117	Ameland (I.) Neth.	53·29 N	5·54 E
75	Amelia (ȧ-mēl'yȧ) Ohio (Cincinnati In.)	39·01 N	84·12 W
68	American (R.) (ȧ-mĕr'ĭ-kăn) Calif.	38·37 N	121·19 W
101	Americana (ä-mĕ-rê-kȧ'nȧ) Braz. (Rio de Janeiro In.)	22·46 S	47·19 W
67	American Falls (ȧ-mĕr-ĭ-kăn) Idaho	42·45 N	112·53 W
67	American Falls Res. Idaho	42·56 N	113·18 W
69	American Fork Utah	40·20 N	111·50 W
47	American Highland Ant.	72·00 S	79·00 E
78	Americus (ȧ-mĕr'ĭ-kŭs) Ga.	32·04 N	84·15 W
111	Amersfoort (ä'mĕrz-fōrt) Neth. (Amsterdam In.)	52·08 N	5·23 E
86	Amery (ā'mēr-ê) Can.	56·32 N	93·58 W
71	Amery Wis.	45·19 N	92·24 W
71	Ames (āmz) Iowa	42·00 N	93·36 W
83	Amesbury (āmz'bēr-ê) Mass. (Boston In.)	42·51 N	70·56 W
127	Amfissa Grc.	38·32 N	22·26 E
135	Amga (ŭm-gä') Sov. Un.	61·08 N	132·09 E
135	Amga (R.) Sov. Un.	61·41 N	133·11 E
135	Amgun' Sov. Un.	53·33 N	137·57 E
165	Amhara (Prov.) (äm-hä'rä) Eth.	11·30 N	36·45 E
82	Amherst (ăm'hērst) Can.	45·49 N	64·14 W
75	Amherst Ohio (Cleveland In.)	41·24 N	82·13 W
81	Amherst (I.) Can.	44·10 N	76·40 W
122	Amiens (ä-myäN') Fr.	49·54 N	2·18 E
142	Amio Tsönag Tsho (L.) China	31·38 N	91·18 E
47	Amirante Is Ind. O.	6·02 S	52·30 E
77	Amite (ȧ-mēt') La.	30·43 N	90·32 W
77	Amite R La.	30·45 N	90·48 W
75	Amity (ăm'ĭ-tĭ) Pa. (Pittsburgh In.)	40·02 N	80·11 W
84	Amityville (ăm'ĭ-tĭ-vĭl) N. Y. (New York In.)	40·41 N	73·24 W
64	Amlia (I.) (ȧ'm-lêȧ) Alaska	52·00 N	173·28 W
139	'Ammān (äm' män) Jordan (Palestine In.)	31·57 N	35·57 E
111	Ammer L. (äm'mĕr) Ger. (München In.)	48·00 N	11·08 E
74	Amnicon R. (ăm'nê-kŏn) Wis. (Duluth In.)	46·35 N	91·56 W
	Amnok, see Yalu		
	Amnok, see Yalu (R.)		
142	Amod India	21·47 N	72·58 E
127	Amorgós (I.) (ä-môr'gōs) Grc.	36·47 N	25·47 E
78	Amory (ăm'o-rē) Miss.	33·58 N	88·27 W
87	Amos (ā'mŭs) Can.	48·31 N	78·04 W
118	Åmot (Torpen) (ô'mōt) (tôr'pĕn) Nor.	61·08 N	11·17 E
151	Amoy (Hsiamen) (I.) (ȧ-moi') China	24·30 N	118·10 E
101	Amparo (äm-pȧ'-rô) Braz. (Rio de Janeiro In.)	22·43 S	46·44 W
111	Amper R. (äm'pĕr) Ger. (München In.)	48·18 N	11·32 E
125	Amposta (äm-pōs'tä) Sp.	40·42 N	0·34 E
82	Amqui Can.	48·27 N	67·27 W
142	Amraoti (ŭm-rŭ-ō'tê) India	20·58 N	77·47 E
142	Amritsar (ŭm-rĭt'sŭr) India	31·43 N	74·52 E
111	Amstelveen Neth. (Amsterdam In.)	52·18 N	4·51 E
111	Amsterdam (äm-stēr-däm') Neth. (Amsterdam In.)	52·21 N	4·52 E
81	Amsterdam (ăm'stēr-dăm) N. Y.	42·55 N	74·10 W
120	Amstetten (äm'stĕt-ĕn) Aus.	48·09 N	14·53 E
165	Am-Timane (äm'tê-män') Chad	11·18 N	20·30 E
144	Amu Dar'ya (Oxus) (R.) (ä-mōō-dä'rēä) Asia	40·40 N	62·47 E
142	Amu Dar'ye (R.) (ä-mōō dä'rēä) Afg.-Sov. Un.	36·50 N	66·58 E
64	Amukta P. (ä-mōōk'tȧ) Alaska	52·30 N	172·00 W
155	Amulung (ä'mōō'lōōng) Phil. (Manila In.)	17·51 N	121·43 E
86	Amundsen G. (ä'mŭn-sĕn) Can.	70·17 N	23·28 W

Page	Name Pronunciation Region	Lat. °′	Long. °′
47	Amundsen Sea Ant.	72·00 S	110·00 W
118	Amungen (L.) Swe.	61·07 N	16·00 E
150	Amur R. (ä-mōōr') China and Sov. Un.	49·38 N	127·25 E
136	Amurskiy (ä-mûr'skĭ) Sov. Un. (Urals In.)	52·35 N	59·36 E
152	Amurskiy, Zaliv (B.) (zä'lĭf ä-mōōr'skĭ) Sov. Un.	43·20 N	131·40 E
90	Amusgos (San Pedro) (ä-mōō's-gôs) (sän-pĕ'drō) Mex.	16·39 N	98·09 W
155	Amuyao, Mt. (ä-mōō-yä'ō) Phil. (Manila In.)	17·04 N	121·09 E
127	Amvrakikos Kólpos (G.) Grc.	39·00 N	21·00 E
139	Amyun Leb. (Palestine In.)	34·18 N	35·48 E
135	Anabar (R.) (ăn-ȧ-bär') Sov. Un.	71·15 N	113·00 E
99	Anaco (ä-nȧ'kô) Ven. (In.)	9·29 N	64·27 W
67	Anaconda (ăn-ȧ-kŏn'dȧ) Mont.	46·07 N	112·55 W
65	Anacortes (ăn-ȧ-kôr'tĕz) Wash. (Seattle In.)	48·30 N	122·37 W
72	Anadarko (ăn-ȧ-där'kō) Okla.	35·05 N	98·14 W
135	Anadyr (ŭ-nȧ-dĭr') Sov. Un.	64·47 N	177·01 E
135	Anadyr (R.) Sov. Un.	65·30 N	172·45 E
139	Anadyrskiy Zaliv (B.) Sov. Un.	64·10 N	178·00 W
74	Anaheim (ăn'ȧ-hīm) Calif. (Los Angeles In.)	33·50 N	117·55 W
77	Anahuac (ä-nä'wăk) Tex. (In.)	29·46 N	94·41 W
143	Anai Mudi Mt India	15·28 N	77·10 E
94	Ana María, Cayos (Is.) (kä'yōs-ä'nȧ mȧ-rē'ȧ) Cuba	21·55 N	78·50 W
154	Anambas, Pulau-Pulau (Is.) (ä-näm-bäs) Indon.	2·41 N	106·38 E
71	Anamosa (ăn-ȧ-mō'sȧ) Iowa	42·06 N	91·18 W
129	Anan'yev (ȧ-nä'nyĕf) Sov. Un.	47·43 N	29·59 E
129	Anapa (ȧ-nä'pä) Sov. Un.	44·54 N	37·19 E
99	Anápolis (ä-nȧ'pō-lēs) Braz.	16·17 S	48·47 W
100	Añatuya (ä-nyä-tōō'yȧ) Arg.	28·22 S	62·45 W
122	Ancenis (äN-sĕ-nē') Fr.	47·24 N	1·12 W
100	Anchieta (än-chyĕ'tä) Braz. (In.)	22·49 S	43·24 W
64	Anchitka (I.) (än-chē't-kä) Alaska	51·25 N	178·10 E
148	Anch' iu (än'chē) China	36·26 N	119·12 E
110	Ancholme (R.) (ăn'chŭm) Eng.	53·28 N	0·27 W
77	Anchor (ăŋ'kēr) Tex. (In.)	29·13 N	95·28 W
64	Anchorage (ăŋ'kēr-āj) Alaska	61·12 N	149·48 W
75	Anchorage Ky. (Louisville In.)	38·16 N	85·32 W
85	Ancienne-Lorette (äN-syĕn' lō-rĕt') Can. (Quebec In.)	46·48 N	71·21 W
88	Ancon (aŋ-kōn') C. Z. (Panama Canal In.)	8·55 N	79·32 W
126	Ancona (än-kō'nä) It.	43·37 N	13·32 E
100	Ancud (äŋ-kōōdh') Chile	41·52 S	73·45 W
100	Ancud, G. de (gôl-fô-dĕ-äŋ-kōōdh') Chile	41·15 S	73·00 W
100	Andalgalá (ȧ'n-däl-gä-lȧ') Arg.	27·35 S	66·14 W
124	Andalucia (Reg.) (än-dä-lōō-sē'ä) Sp.	37·35 N	5·40 W
78	Andalusia (ăn-dȧ-lōō'zhĭȧ) Ala.	31·19 N	86·19 W
154	Andaman Is. (ăn-dȧ-măn') India	11·38 N	92·17 E
154	Andaman Sea Asia	12·44 N	95·45 E
111	Anderlecht (än'dĕr-lĕkt) Bel. (Bruxelles In.)	50·49 N	4·16 E
120	Andernach (än'dĕr-näĸ) Ger.	50·25 N	7·23 E
101	Anderson (ȧ'n-dĕr-sōn) Arg. (Buenos Aires In.)	35·15 S	60·15 W
66	Anderson (ăn'dēr-sŭn) Calif.	40·28 N	122·19 W
80	Anderson Ind.	40·05 N	85·50 W
79	Anderson S. C.	34·30 N	82·40 W
86	Anderson (R.) Can.	68·32 N	125·12 W
98	Andes (ăn'dēz) (än'dās) Col. (In.)	5·40 N	75·54 W
96	Andes Mts. S. A.	13·00 S	75·00 W
167	Andevorante (än-dā-vō-rän'tā) Malagasy	18·53 S	48·13 E
143	Andhei India (Bombay In.)	19·08 N	72·50 E
143	Andhra Pradesh (State) India	22·00 N	78·50 E
115	Andikíthira (I.) Grc.	35·50 N	23·20 E
134	Andizhan (än-dê-zhän') Sov. Un.	40·51 N	72·39 E
152	Andong (än'dŭng') Kor.	36·31 N	128·42 E
125	Andorra (än-dôr'rä) And.	42·38 N	1·30 E
125	Andorra Eur.	42·32 N	1·18 E
83	Andover (ăn'dô-vēr) Mass. (Boston In.)	42·39 N	71·08 W
84	Andover N. J. (New York In.)	40·59 N	74·45 W
112	Andöy (I.) (änd-ûē) Nor.	69·12 N	14·58 E
125	Andraitx (än-drä-ĭtsh') Sp.	39·34 N	2·25 E
64	Andreanof Is. (än-drä-ä'nôf) Alaska	51·10 N	177·00 W
167	Andreba (än-drā'bȧ) Malagasy	17·44 S	48·41 E
101	Andrelândia (än-drĕ-lâ'n-dyȧ) Braz. (Rio de Janeiro In.)	21·45 S	44·18 W
82	Andréville Can.	47·40 N	69·44 W
78	Andrew Johnson Natl Mon. (ăn'drōō jŏn'sŭn) Tenn.	36·15 N	82·55 W
78	Andrews (ăn'drōōz) N. C.	35·12 N	83·48 W
79	Andrews S. C.	33·25 N	79·32 W
129	Andreyevka (än-drä-yĕf'kȧ) Sov. Un.	48·03 N	37·03 E
126	Andria (än'drê-ä) It.	41·17 N	15·55 E
127	Andros (än'dhrōs) Grc.	37·50 N	24·54 E
94	Andros I. (ăn'drŏs) Ba. Is.	24·30 N	78·00 W
127	Andrós (I.) (än'dhrôs) Grc.	37·59 N	24·55 E
82	Androscoggin (R.) (ăn-drŭs-kŏg'ĭn) Maine	44·25 N	70·45 W
124	Andújar (än-dōō'här) Sp.	38·04 N	4·03 W
164	Anécho (ä-nā'chō) Togo	6·25 N	1·36 E
153	Anegasaki (ä'mĕ-gä-sä'kē) Jap. (Tōkyō In.)	35·29 N	140·02 E
159	Aneityum (I.) (ä-nā-ē'tē-ŭm) New Hebr.	20·15 S	169·49 E
70	Aneta (ă-nē'tȧ) N. D.	47·41 N	97·57 W
155	Angadanan (äŋ-gȧ-dä'nȧn) Phil. (Manila In.)	16·45 N	121·45 E
155	Angaki (än-gä'kē) Phil. (Manila In.)	17·10 N	120·40 E
90	Angamacutiro (än'gä-mä-kōō-tē'rō) Mex.	20·08 N	101·44 W
150	Angangchi (än'gäng'kē') China	47·05 N	123·58 E
90	Angangueo (än-gäŋ'gwā-ō) Mex.	19·36 N	100·18 W

ăt: finăl; rāte; senâte; ärm; àsk; sofȧ; fâre; ch-choose; dh-as th in other; bē; êvent; bĕt; recĕnt; cratēr; g-go; gh-guttural g; bĭt; ĭ-short neutral; rīde; ĸ-guttural k as ch in German ich;

PRONOUNCING INDEX   Angara–Ardmore   177

Page	Name Pronunciation Region	Lat. °′	Long. °′
	Angara (R.), see Verkhnyaya Tunguska		
134	Angarsk..........Sov. Un.	52·48 N	104·15 E
118	Ånge (ông′ā)..........Swe.	62·31 N	15·39 E
99	Angel, Salto (Falls) (säl′tō-à′n-hĕl).Ven.	5·44 N	62·27 W
88	Angel De La Guarda (I.) (à′n-hĕl-dĕ-lā-gwà′r-dä).Mex.	29·30 N	113·00 W
155	Angeles (än′hâ-lās) Phil. (Manila In.)	15·09 N	120·35 E
118	Ängelholm (ĕng′ĕl-hôlm).....Swe.	56·14 N	12·50 E
77	Angelina R. (ăn-jê lē′nȧ).....Tex.	31·30 N	94·53 W
68	Angels Camp (ān′jĕls kămp′) Calif.	38·03 N	120·33 W
112	Angermanälven (R.)........Swe.	64·02 N	17·15 E
123	Angermund (ān′ngĕr-münd) Ger. (Ruhr In.)	51·20 N	6·47 E
120	Angermünde (äng′ĕr-mûn-dĕ).Ger.	53·02 N	14·00 E
85	Angers (äɴ-zhā′) Can. (Ottawa In.)	41·31 N	75·29 W
122	Angers..........Fr.	47·29 N	0·36 W
116	Anglesey (I.) (ăŋ′g′l-sê)....Wales	52·28 N	4·35 W
77	Angleton (aŋ′g′l-tŭn)...Tex. (In.)	29·10 N	95·25 W
87	Angliers..........Can.	47·29 N	79·16 W
49	Angmagssalik (àŋ-mà′sà-lĭk) Grnld.	65·40 N	37·40 W
167	Angoche (än-gō′châ)........Moz.	16·13 S	39·58 E
167	Angoche, Ilhas de (Is.) (ê′lās-dĕ-än-gō′châ).Moz.	16·03 S	40·17 E
100	Angol (äŋ-gōl′)..........Chile	37·47 S	72·43 W
80	Angola (ăŋ-gō′lȧ)..........Ind.	41·35 N	85·00 W
163	Angola (Portuguese West Africa) Afr.	14·15 S	16·00 E
	Angora, see Ankara		
122	Angoulême (äŋ-gōō-lâm′)......Fr.	45·42 N	0·09 E
101	Angra dos Reis (aŋ′-grä dōs rā′ēs) Braz. (Rio de Janeiro In.)	23·01 S	44·17 W
125	Angri (ä′n-grê)....It. (Napoli In.)	40·30 N	14·35 E
94	Anguilla, Cays (Is.) (ăŋ-gwĭl′ȧ) Ba. Is.	23·30 N	79·35 W
93	Anguilla I. W. I. F. (Le. & Wind. Is. In.)	18·15 N	62·54 W
83	Anguille, C. (äŋ-gē′yĕ)......Can.	47·58 N	59·35 W
118	Anholt (I.) (än′hŏlt)........Den.	56·43 N	11·34 E
146	Anhsi..........China	40·36 N	95·49 E
147	Anhui (Anhwei) (Prov.)....China	31·23 N	116·53 E
64	Aniak (ă-nyà′k)..........Alaska	61·32 N	159·35 W
125	Aniene (ä-nyĕ′nĕ)..It. (Roma In.)	41·54 N	12·49 E
69	Animas (R.) (ä′nê-màs).....Colo.	37·03 N	107·50 W
127	Anina (ä-nē′nä)..........Rom.	45·03 N	21·50 E
81	Anita (ȧ-nē′ȧ)..........Pa.	41·05 N	79·00 W
152	Aniva, Mys (Pt.) (mĭs à-nē′và) Sov. Un.	46·08 N	143·13 E
152	Aniva, Zaliv (B.) (zä′lĭf à-nē′và) Sov. Un.	46·28 N	143·30 E
167	Anjouan (I.) (äɴ-zhwäɴ) Comores, Arch. des	12·14 S	44·47 E
150	Ank′ang..........China	32·38 N	109·10 E
133	Ankara (Angora) (än′kȧ-rȧ) (ăn-gō′rȧ).Tur.	39·55 N	32·50 E
167	Ankaratra (Mtn.)......Malagasy	19·17 S	47·27 E
151	Anking (Huaining) (än′kĭng′) China	30·32 N	117·00 E
120	Anklam (än′kläm)..........Ger.	53·52 N	13·43 E
166	Ankoro (äŋ-kō′rō)........Con. L.	6·48 S	26·45 E
148	Ankou (an′gōō ŭ)..........China	38·27 N	115·19 E
151	Anlu (än′lōō′)..........China	31·18 N	113·40 E
151	Anlung..........China	25·01 N	105·32 E
81	Ann, C. (ăn)..........Mass.	42·40 N	70·40 W
73	Anna (ăn′ȧ)..........Ill.	37·28 N	89·15 W
129	Anna (än′ä)..........Sov. Un.	51·31 N	40·27 E
120	Annaberg-Buchols (än′ä-bĕrgh).Ger.	50·35 N	13·02 E
144	An Nafud (Des.)........Sau. Ar.	28·23 N	39·30 E
144	An Najaf (än nä-jäf′)..........Iraq	31·30 N	44·31 E
139	An Nakhl.U. A. R. (Palestine In.)	29·55 N	33·45 E
154	Annamitic Cord. Mts. (ă-nȧ-mĭt′ĭk kôr-dĭl-yä′rȧ).Laos-Viet.	17·34 N	105·38 E
81	Annapolis (ă-năp′ô-lĭs)......Md.	39·00 N	76·25 W
82	Annapolis Royal..........Can.	44·44 N	65·32 W
80	Ann Arbor (ăn är′bĕr)......Mich.	42·15 N	83·45 W
165	An Nawfalīyah..........Libya	30·57 N	17·38 E
123	Annecy (ȧn′sē′)..........Fr.	45·54 N	6·07 E
123	Annemasse (än′mäs′)......Switz.	46·09 N	6·13 E
136	Annenskoye (ä-nĕn′skô-yĕ) Sov. Un. (Urals In.)	53·09 N	60·25 E
78	Anniston (ăn′ĭs-tŭn)..........Ala.	33·39 N	85·47 W
163	Annobon (I.) (än-nō-bôn′).Atl. O.	2·00 S	3·30 E
122	Annonay (à-nô-nĕ′)..........Fr.	45·16 N	4·36 E
94	Annotto Bay (än-nō′tō)......Jam.	18·15 N	76·45 W
74	Anoka (ȧ-nō′kȧ) Minn. (Minneapolis, St. Paul In.)	45·12 N	93·24 W
98	Anori (ä-nō′rê)........(Col. In.)	7·01 N	75·09 W
127	Ano Theológos..........Grc.	40·37 N	24·41 E
126	Áno Viánnos........Grc. (Inset)	35·52 N	25·26 E
151	Anp′u..........China	21·28 N	110·00 E
120	Ansbach (äns′bäk)..........Ger.	49·18 N	10·35 E
95	Anse à Veau (äɴs′ ä-vō′).....Hai.	18·30 N	73·25 W
95	Anse d′ Hainault (äɴs′dĕnō)...Hai	18·45 N	74·25 W
98	Anserma (à′n-sĕ′r-mà)...Col. (In.)	5·13 N	75·47 W
98	Ansermanuevo(à′n-sĕ′r-mà-nwĕ′vō) Col. (In.)	4·47 N	75·59 W
150	Anshan..........China	41·00 N	123·00 E
151	Anshun (än-shōōn′)........China	26·12 N	105·50 E
76	Anson (ăn′sŭn)..........Tex.	32·45 N	99·52 W
158	Anson B..........Austl.	13·10 S	34·25 E
152	Ansŏng (än′sŭng′)..........Kor.	37·00 N	127·12 E
81	Ansonia (ăn-sō′nĭ-ȧ)........Conn.	41·20 N	73·05 W
150	Antachan..........China	41·20 N	125·20 E
133	Antakya (än-täk′yä)....U. A. R.	36·20 N	36·10 E
133	Antalya (Adalia) (än-tä′lê-ä) (ä-dä′lê-ä).Tur.	37·00 N	30·50 E
133	Antalya Körfezi (G.)........Tur.	36·40 N	31·20 E
47	Antarctica	80·15 S	127·00 E
67	Antelope Cr. (ăn′tê-lōp).....Wyo.	43·29 N	105·42 W
74	Antelope I. Utah (Salt Lake City In.)	40·39 N	112·07 W
124	Antequera (än-tĕ-kĕ′rä)......Sp.	37·01 N	4·34 W
72	Anthony (ăn′thô-nê).......Kans.	37·08 N	98·01 W
123	Antibes (äɴ-tēb′)..........Fr.	43·36 N	7·12 E
83	Anticosti I. (ăn-tĭ-kŏs′tê)....Can.	49·40 N	62·00 W
71	Antigo (ăn′tĭ-gō)..........Wis.	45·09 N	89·11 W
83	Antigonish (ăn-tĭ-gô-nêsh′)...Can.	45·39 N	61·59 W
92	Antigua (än-tē′gwä)........Guat.	14·32 N	90·43 W
91	Antigua (R.)..........Mex.	19·16 N	96·36 W
93	Antigua I. W. I. F. (Le. & Wind. Is. In.)	17·07 N	61·32 W
91	Antigua Veracruz (än-tē′gwä vā-rä-krōōz′).Mex.	19·18 N	96·17 W
95	Antilla (än-tē′lyä)..........Cuba	20·50 N	75·50 W
89	Antilles, Greater (Is.)......N. A.	20·30 N	79·15 W
89	Antilles, Lesser (Is.)........N. A.	12·15 N	65·00 W
65	Antioch (ăn′tĭ-ŏk) Calif. (San Francisco In.)	38·00 N	121·48 W
75	Antioch........Ill. (Chicago In.)	42·29 N	88·06 W
70	Antioch..........Nebr.	42·05 N	102·36 W
98	Antioquia (än-tê-ō′kēä).Col. (In.)	6·34 N	75·49 W
98	Antioquia (Dept.)......Col. (In.)	6·48 N	75·42 W
73	Antlers (ănt′-lērz)..........Okla.	34·14 N	95·38 W
100	Antofagasta (än-tô-fä-gäs′tä) Chile	23·32 S	70·21 W
100	Antofalla, Salar de (Des.) (sà-lär′de àn′tō-fä′lä).Arg.	26·00 S	67·52 W
93	Antón (än-tōn′)..........Pan.	8·24 N	80·15 W
167	Antongil, Baie d′ (B.) (äɴ-tôɴ-zhēl′).Malagasy	16·15 S	50·15 E
101	Antonio Carlos (än-tō′nēōō-kà′r-lōs) Braz. (Rio de Janeiro In.)	21·19 S	43·45 W
72	Antonito (ăn-tô-nē′tō)......Colo.	37·04 N	106·01 W
128	Antonopole (än′tô-nô-pō lyĕ) Sov. Un.	56·19 N	27·11 E
116	Antrim Mts. (ăn′trĭm).....N. Ire.	54·60 N	6·15 W
167	Antsirabe (ànt-sê-rä′bā).Malagasy	19·49 S	47·16 E
	Antsirane, see Diégo-Suarez		
128	Antsla (änt′slȧ)........Sov. Un.	57·49 N	26·29 E
100	Antuco (Vol.) (än-tōō′kō)...Chile	37·30 S	72·30 W
150	Antung (än′tōōng′)........China	40·10 N	124·30 E
148	Antungwei (ändōōngwā)....China	35·08 N	119·19 E
111	Antwerpen (Anvers) (änt′wĕrpĕn) (äɴ-vârs′).Bel. (Bruxelles In.)	51·13 N	4·24 E
150	Antz′u........China (Peking In.)	39·23 N	116·44 E
142	Anun (R.)..........Nepal	27·18 N	86·51 E
143	Anuradhāpura (ŭ-nōō′rä-dŭ-pōō′rŭ) Ceylon	8·24 N	80·25 E
	Anvers, see Antwerpen		
148	Anyang (än′yäng)........China	36·05 N	114·22 E
119	Anykščiai (anĭksh-chä′ê).Sov. Un.	55·34 N	25·04 E
98	Anzá (än-zà′)..........Col. (In.)	6·19 N	75·51 W
134	Anzhero-Sudzhensk ((än′zhâ-rô-sōōd′zhĕnsk).Sov. Un.	56·08 N	86·08 E
125	Anzio (änt′zê-ō)...It. (Roma In.)	41·28 N	12·39 E
99	Anzoategui (State) (àn-zôà′tĕ-gê) Ven. (In.)	9·38 N	64·45 W
152	Aomori (äô-mō′rê).........Jap.	40·45 N	140·52 E
126	Aosta (ä-ôs′tä)..........It.	45·45 N	7·20 E
78	Apalachicola (ăp-ȧ-lăch-ĭ-kō′lȧ) Fla.	29·43 N	84·59 W
90	Apam (ä-päm′)..........Mex.	19·41 N	98·31 W
91	Apan (ä-pà′n)..Mex. (Mexico In.)	19·43 N	98·27 W
90	Apango (ä-päŋ′gō)..........Mex.	17·41 N	99·22 W
98	Apaporis (R.) (ä-pä-pō′rĭs)...Col.	0·48 N	72·32 W
154	Aparri (ä-pär′rê)..........Phil.	18·15 N	121·40 E
90	Apasco (ä-pà′s-kō)..........Mex.	20·33 N	100·43 W
127	Apatin (ŏ′pŏ-tĭn)..........Yugo.	45·40 N	19·00 E
90	Apatzingán de la Constitución (ä-pät-zĭŋ-gän′dä lä cōn-stĭ-tōō-sê-ōn′).Mex.	19·07 N	102·21 W
117	Apeldoorn (ä′pĕl-dōōrn)....Neth.	52·14 N	5·55 E
98	Apía (ä-pē′ä)..........Col. (In.)	5·07 N	75·58 W
90	Apipilulco (ä-pĭ-pĭ-lōōl′kō)...Mex.	18·09 N	99·40 W
127	Apíranthos..........Grc.	37·07 N	25·32 E
72	Apishapa (R.) (ăp-ĭ-shä′pȧ).Colo.	37·40 N	104·08 W
90	Apizaco (ä-pê-zä′kō)........Mex.	19·18 N	98·11 W
155	Apo (Mtn.) (ä′pō)..........Phil.	6·56 N	125·05 E
79	Apoka (ä-pŏp′kȧ)......Fla. (In.)	28·37 N	81·30 W
79	Apoka (L.)........Fla. (In.)	28·38 N	81·50 W
71	Apostle Is. (ȧ-pŏs′l)........Wis.	97·03 N	90·55 W
78	Appalachia (ăpȧ-lăch′ĭ-ȧ).....Va.	36·54 N	82·49 W
63	Appalachian Mts. (ăp-ȧ-lăch′ĭ-ăn).U. S.	37·20 N	82·00 W
78	Appalachicola R. (ăpȧ-lăch′ĭ-cōlä) Fla.	30·11 N	85·00 W
118	Äppelbo (ĕp-ĕl-bōō)........Swe.	60·30 N	14·02 E
123	Appelhülsen (ä′pĕl-hül′-sĕn) Ger. (Ruhr In.)	51·55 N	7·26 E
126	Appennino (Mts.) (äp-pĕn-nē′nō) It.	43·48 N	11·06 E
120	Appenzell (äp′ĕn-tsĕl)......Switz.	47·19 N	9·22 E
70	Appleton (ăp′ l-tŭn)........Minn.	45·10 N	96·01 W
71	Appleton..........Wis.	44·14 N	88·27 W
73	Appleton City..........Mo.	38·10 N	94·02 W
79	Appomattox (R.) (ăp-ô-măt′ŭks) Va.	37·22 N	78·09 W
125	Aprília (ȧ-prē′lyȧ) .It. (Roma In.)	41·36 N	12·40 E
133	Apsheronskiy, P-Ov. (pen.) Sov. Un.	40·20 N	50·30 E
123	Apt (äpt)..........Fr.	43·54 N	5·19 E
	Apulia (Reg.), see Puglia		
98	Apure (R.) (ä-pōō′rä)........Ven.	8·08 N	68·46 W
98	Apurimac (R.) (ä-pōō-rê-mäk′) Peru	11·39 S	73·48 W
115	Aqaba, G. of (ä′kà-bà).......Asia	28·30 N	34·40 E
139	Aqaba (R.) U. A. R. (Palestine In.)	29·58 N	34·05 E
139	Aqabat al Hijaziyah Jordan (Palestine In.)	29·45 N	35·55 E
69	Aqua (R.) (ä′gwä)..........Ariz.	33·43 N	112·22 W
99	Aquidauana (ä-kē-däwä′nä).Braz.	20·24 S	55·46 W
84	Aquidneck (ȧ-kwĭd′nĭk) R. I. (Providence In.)	41·31 N	71·14 W
124	Aquilianos, Montes (Mts.) (mô′n-tĕs-ä-kē-lyä′nôs).Sp.	42·27 N	6·35 W
95	Aquin (ä-kăn′)..........Hai.	18·20 N	73·25 W
153	Ara (R.) (ä-rä)..Jap. (Tōkyō In.)	35·40 N	139·52 E
	Araba, see Ha′arava (R.)		
168	Araba, Wadi..U. A. R. (Nile In.)	29·02 N	32·10 E
129	Arabatskaya Strelka (Spit) (Tongue of Arabat) (ä-rä-bat′ skà-yȧ strĕl′kȧ) (ă-rȧ-băt′) Sov. Un.	45·50 N	35·05 E
165	Arabian Des. (ȧ-rā′bĭ-ăn).U. A. R.	27·06 N	32·49 E
163	Arabian Pen..........Asia	28·00 N	40·00 E
138	Arabian Sea (ȧ-rā′bĭ-ăn).....Asia	16·00 N	65·15 E
99	Aracaju (ä-rä′kä-zhōō′).....Braz.	11·00 S	37·01 W
99	Aracati (ä-rä′kä-tē′)........Braz.	4·31 S	37·41 W
99	Araçatuba (ä-rä-sà-tōō′bä)..Braz.	21·14 S	50·19 W
99	Aracruz (ä-rä-krōō′s)......Braz.	19·58 S	40·11 W
99	Araçuaí (ä-rä-sōō-ä-ē′)......Braz.	16·57 S	41·56 W
121	Arad (ŏ′rŏd)..........Rom.	46·10 N	21·18 E
156	Arafura Sea (ä-rä-fōō′rä)..Oceania	8·40 S	112·00 E
125	Aragon (Reg.) (ä-rä-gōn′).....Sp.	40·55 N	0·45 W
124	Aragón (R.)..........Sp.	42·35 N	1·10 W
99	Aragua (State) (ä-rä′gwä) Ven. (In.)	10·00 N	67·05 W
99	Aragua de Barcelona (ä-rä′gwä dä bär-thā-lō′nä).Ven. (In.)	9·29 N	64·48 W
99	Araguaía (R.) (ä-rä-gwä′yä).Braz.	8·37 S	49·43 W
99	Araguari (ä-rä-gwä′rê)......Braz.	18·43 S	48·03 W
98	Araguatins (ä-rä-gwä-tēns)..Braz.	5·41 S	48·04 W
99	Aragüita (ärä-gwē′tä)..Ven. (In.)	10·13 N	66·28 W
115	Araj (Oasis) (ä-räj′).....U. A. R.	29·05 N	26·51 E
144	Arak..........Iran	34·08 N	49·57 E
146	Arakanyoma (Mts.) (ŭ-rŭ-kŭn′yō′mȧ).Bur.	19·51 N	94·13 E
127	Arakhthos (R.) (är′äκ-thôs)..Grc.	39·10 N	21·05 E
	Aral Sea, see Aral′skoye More		
134	Aral′sk (ȧ-rälsk′)........Sov. Un.	46·47 N	62·00 E
103	Aral′skoye More (Aral Sea) Sov. Un.	45·17 N	60·02 E
133	Aralsor (L.) (à-räl′sôr′)..Sov. Un.	49·00 N	48·20 E
90	Aramberri (ä-ràm-bĕr-rē′)...Mex.	24·05 N	99·47 W
116	Aran (I.) (ăr′ăn)..........Ire.	53·04 N	9·59 W
116	Aran (I.)..........Ire.	54·60 N	8·25 W
124	Aranda de Duero (ä-rän′dä dā dwā′rō).Sp.	41·43 N	3·45 W
90	Arandas (ä-rän′däs)........Mex.	20·43 N	102·18 W
124	Aranjuez (ä-rän-hwāth′)......Sp.	40·02 N	3·24 W
77	Aransas Pass (ȧ-răn′sȧs pȧs).Tex.	27·55 N	97·09 W
142	Aransol..........India	23·45 N	86·58 E
164	Araouane..........Mali	18·54 N	3·33 W
133	Arapkir (ä-räp-kēr′)........Tur.	39·00 N	38·10 E
99	Araraquara (ä-rä-rä-kwä′rä).Braz.	21·47 S	48·08 W
101	Araras (ä-rä′rȧs) Braz. (Rio de Janeiro In.)	22·21 S	47·22 W
99	Araras, Serra das (Mts.) (sĕ′r-rä-däs-ä-rä′räs).Braz.	18·03 S	53·23 W
100	Araras, Serra das (Mts.)....Braz.	23·30 S	53·00 W
100	Araras, Serra das (Mts.).Braz.(In.)	22·24 S	43·15 W
160	Ararat (ăr′ȧrăt)..........Austl.	37·12 S	38·00 E
133	Ararat (Mtn.)..........Tur.	39·50 N	44·20 E
99	Arari (L.) (ä-rä′rē)........Braz.	0·30 S	48·50 W
99	Araripe, Chapadodo (Plain) (shä-pä′dä-dô-ä-rä-rē′pĕ).Braz.	5·55 S	40·42 W
101	Araruama (ä-rä-rōō-ä′mä) Braz. (Rio de Janeiro In.)	22·53 S	42·19 W
101	Araruama, Lagoa de (L.) (lä-gôä-dĕ-ä-rä-rōō-ä′mä) Braz. (Rio de Janeiro In.)	23·00 S	42·15 W
133	Aras (R.) (ä-räs)...Iran-Sov. Un.	39·15 N	47·10 E
99	Aratuípe (ä-rä-tōō-ē′pĕ).....Braz.	13·12 S	38·58 W
98	Arauca (ä-rou′kä)..........Col.	6·56 N	70·45 W
98	Arauca (R.)..........Ven.	7·13 N	68·43 W
142	Aravalli Ra. (ä-rä′vŭ-lê)....India	29·15 N	72·59 E
99	Araxá (ä-rä-shä′)..........Braz.	19·41 S	46·46 W
99	Araya, Punta de (Pt.) (pŭn′tȧ-dĕ-ä-rä′yȧ).Ven. (In.)	10·40 N	64·15 W
155	Arayat (ä-rä′yät) Phil. (Manila In.)	15·10 N	120·44 E
118	Arboga (är-bō′gä)..........Swe.	59·26 N	15·50 E
126	Arborea (är-bō-rĕ′ä)..........It.	39·50 N	8·36 E
116	Arbroath (är-brōth′)........Scot.	56·36 N	2·25 W
123	Arc (R.) (ärk)..Fr. (Marseille In.)	43·32 N	5·17 E
122	Arcachon (är-κä-shôɴ′).......Fr.	44·39 N	1·12 W
122	Arcachon, Bassin d′ (Basin) (bä-sĕn′ där-kä-shôɴ′).Fr.	44·42 N	1·50 W
74	Arcadia (är-kā′dĭ-ȧ) Calif. (Los Angeles In.)	34·08 N	118·02 W
79	Arcadia..........Fla. (In.)	27·12 N	81·51 W
77	Arcadia..........La.	32·33 N	92·56 W
71	Arcadia..........Wis.	44·15 N	91·30 W
66	Arcata (är-kȧ′tȧ)..........Calif.	40·54 N	124·05 W
68	Arc Dome Mtn. (ärk dōm)..Nev.	38·51 N	117·21 W
90	Arcelia (är-sā′lē-ä)..........Mex.	18·19 N	100·14 W
81	Archbald (ärch′bôld)..........Pa.	41·30 N	75·35 W
69	Arches Natl. Mon. (är′ches).Utah	38·45 N	109·35 W
98	Archidona (är-chê-dō′nä)......Ec.	1·01 S	77·49 W
124	Archidona (är-chē-dō′nä)......Sp.	37·08 N	4·24 W
157	Archipelago (I.)........Oceania	16·50 S	142·00 W
124	Arcila (är-sē′lä)..........Mor.	35·30 N	6·05 W
122	Arcis-sur-Aube (är-sēs′sûr-ōb′).Fr.	48·31 N	4·04 E
67	Arco (är′kô)..........Idaho	43·39 N	113·15 W
74	Arcola (är′kō′lȧ) Minn. (Minneapolis, St. Paul In.)	45·07 N	92·46 W
77	Arcola..........Tex. (In.)	29·30 N	95·28 W
124	Arcos de la Frontera (är′kōs-dĕ-lä-frôn-tĕ′rä).Sp.	36·44 N	5·48 W
48	Arctic Ocean (ärk′tĭk)		
127	Arda (R.) (är′dä)..........Bul.	41·36 N	25·18 E
144	Ardabil..........Iran	38·15 N	48·00 E
133	Ardahan (är-dȧ-hän′)........Tur.	41·10 N	42·40 E
118	Ardals Fd. (är-däls)........Nor.	58·53 N	7·55 E
132	Ardatov (är-dȧ-tôf′)....Sov. Un.	54·58 N	46·10 E
117	Ardennes (Mts.) (är-dĕn′).....Bel.	50·01 N	5·12 E
124	Ardila (R.) (är-dē′lȧ)........Port.	38·12 N	7·15 W
73	Ardmore (ärd′mōr)..........Okla.	34·10 N	97·08 W
84	Ardmore...Pa. (Philadelphia In.)	40·01 N	75·18 W

ng-sing; ŋ-baŋk; ɴ-nasalized n; nŏd; cŏmmit; ōld; ôbey; ôrder; fōōd; fŏŏt; ou-out; s-soft; sh-dish; th-thin; pūre; ûnite; ûrn; stŭd; circŭs; ü-as "y" in study; ′-indeterminate vowel.

Page	Name / Pronunciation / Region	Lat. °′	Long. °′
	Asunción, see Nochixtlán		
92	Asuncion Mita (ä-sōōn-syŏ'n-mē'tä)..Guat.	14·19 N	89·43 W
117	Åsunden (L.) (ô'sōōn-dĕn)...Swe.	57·46 N	13·16 E
168	Aswān (Syene) (ä-swän') (sē-ā'nē).U. A. R. (Nile In.)	24·05 N	32·57 E
165	Aswān Dam...U. A. R.	23·50 N	31·30 E
168	Aswān High Dam U. A. R. (Nile In.)	23·58 N	32·53 E
168	Asyūt (ä-syōōt') U. A. R. (Nile In.)	27·10 N	31·10 E
100	Atacama, Puna de (Reg.) (pōō'nä-dĕ-ätä-kà'mä).Chile	23·15 S	68·45 W
98	Atacama, Puna de (Plat.) (pōō'nä-dĕ-ä-tä-kà'mä).Bol.	21·35 S	66·58 W
96	Atacama, Desierto de (Des.) (dĕ-syĕ'r-tô-dĕ-ä-tä-kà'mä) Chile-Peru	23·50 S	69·00 W
100	Atacama, Salar de (L.) (sä-lär'dĕ-ätä-kà'mä).Chile	23·38 S	68·15 W
98	Ataco (ä-tà'kŏ)...Col. (In.)	3·36 N	75·22 W
139	'Ata'Itah, Jabal al (Mts.) Jordan (Palestine In.)	30·48 N	35·19 E
164	Atakpamé (ä'ták-pà-mā')...Togo	7·37 N	1·09 E
136	Atamanovskiy (ä-tä-mä'nôv-skĭ) Sov. Un. (Urals In.)	52·15 N	60·47 E
168	Ataqa Gebel (Plat.) U. A. R. (Suez In.)	29·59 N	32·20 E
164	Atar (ä-tär')...Mauritania	20·45 N	13·16 W
68	Atascadero (ăt-ăs-kà-dâ'rō).Calif.	35·29 N	120·40 W
76	Atascosa R. (ăt-ăs-kō'sà)...Tex.	28·50 N	98·17 W
165	Atbara (ät'bà-rä)...Sud.	17·45 N	30·01 E
165	Atbara R...Sud.	17·14 N	34·27 E
134	Atbasar (ät'bä-sär')...Sov. Un.	51·42 N	68·28 E
77	Atchafalaya B. (ăch-à-fà-lī'à).La.	29·25 N	91·30 W
77	Atchafalaya R...La.	30·53 N	91·51 W
73	Atchison (ăch'ĭ-sŭn)...Kans.	39·33 N	95·08 W
84	Atco (ăt'kō) N. J. (Philadelphia In.)	39·46 N	74·53 W
91	Atempan (ä-tĕm-pà'n)...Mex.	19·49 N	97·25 W
90	Atenguillo (R.) (ä-tĕn-gē'l-yô) Mex.	20·18 N	104·35 W
86	Athabasca (ăth-à-băs'kà)...Can.	54·41 N	113·11 W
86	Athabasca (L.)...Can.	59·04 N	109·10 W
86	Athabasca (R.)...Can.	57·21 N	112·02 W
82	Atharbaska (ăth-ar-băs'kà)..Can.	46·03 N	71·54 W
78	Athens (ăth'ĕnz)...Ala.	34·47 N	86·58 W
78	Athens...Ga.	33·55 N	83·24 W
80	Athens...Ohio	39·20 N	82·10 W
81	Athens...Pa.	42·00 N	76·30 W
78	Athens...Tenn.	35·26 N	84·36 W
77	Athens...Tex.	32·13 N	95·51 W
	Athens, see Athina		
110	Atherstone (ăth'ēr-stŭn)...Eng.	52·34 N	1·33 W
110	Atherton (ăth'ēr-tŭn)...Eng.	53·32 N	2·29 W
159	Atherton Plat. (ădh-ĕr-tŏn).Austl.	17·00 S	144·30 E
167	Athi (R.) (ä'tē)...Ken.	2·31 S	35·28 E
127	Athina (Athens)...Grc.	38·00 N	23·38 E
116	Athlone (ăth-lōn')...Ire.	53·24 N	7·30 W
127	Athos (Mtn.) (ăth'ŏs)...Grc.	40·10 N	24·15 E
139	Ath Thamad U. A. R. (Palestine In.)	29·41 N	34·17 E
116	Athy (à-thī)...Ire.	52·59 N	7·08 W
165	Ati (ä-tē')...Chad	13·16 N	18·09 E
101	Atibaia (ä-tē-bà'yà) Braz. (Rio de Janeiro In.)	23·08 S	46·32 W
87	Atikonak (L.)...Can.	52·34 N	63·49 W
85	Atim Cr...Can. (Edmonton In.)	53·34 N	113·59 W
155	Atimonan (ä-tē-mō'nän) Phil. (Manila In.)	13·59 N	121·56 E
92	Atiquizaya (ä'tê-kê-zä'yä)...Sal.	14·00 N	89·42 W
92	Atitlan (Vol.) (ä-tê-tlän')..Guat.	14·35 N	91·11 W
92	Atitlan L. (ä-tê-tlän')...Guat.	14·38 N	91·23 W
91	Atizapán (ä'tê-zä-pän') Mex. (Mexico In.)	19·33 N	99·16 W
64	Atka (ăt'kà)...Alaska	52·18 N	174·18 W
64	Atka (I.)...Alaska	51·58 N	174·30 W
133	Atkarsk (ät-kärsk')...Sov. Un.	51·50 N	45·00 E
70	Atkinson (ăt'kĭn-sŭn)...Nebr.	42·32 N	98·58 W
84	Atlanta (ăt-lăn'tà) Ga. (Atlanta In.)	33·45 N	84·23 W
73	Atlanta...Tex.	33·09 N	94·09 W
71	Atlantic (ăt-lăn'tĭk)...Iowa	41·23 N	94·58 W
84	Atlantic Highlands N. J. (New York In.)	40·25 N	74·04 W
81	Atlantic City...N. J.	39·20 N	74·30 W
6	Atlantic Ocean		
164	Atlas Mts. (ăt'lăs)...Alg.-Mor.	31·22 N	4·57 W
90	Atliaca (ät-lê-ä'kä)...Mex.	17·38 N	99·24 W
86	Atlin (L.) (ăt'lĭn)...Can.	59·34 N	133·20 W
90	Atlixco (ät-lēz'kō)...Mex.	18·52 N	98·27 W
118	Atlöy (I.) (ät-lûê)...Nor.	61·24 N	4·46 E
78	Atmore (ăt'mōr)...Ala.	31·01 N	87·31 W
73	Atoka (à-tō'kà)...Okla.	34·23 N	96·07 W
90	Atotonilco el Alto (ä'tô-tô-nēl'kō ĕl äl'tō).Mex.	20·35 N	102·32 W
90	Atotonilco el Grande (ä'tô-tô-nēl-kō ĕl grän'dā).Mex.	20·17 N	98·41 W
164	Atoui R. (à-tōō-ē') Mauritania-Sp. Sah.	21·00 N	15·32 W
90	Atoyac (ä-tô-yäk')...Mex.	20·01 N	103·28 W
91	Atoyac (R.)...Mex.	16·27 N	97·28 W
90	Atoyac (R.)...Mex.	18·35 N	98·16 W
90	Atoyac de Alvarez (ä-tô-yäk'dā äl'vä-räz).Mex.	17·13 N	100·29 W
91	Atoyatempan (ä-tō'yà-tĕm-pän') Mex.	18·47 N	97·54 W
144	Atrak, Rud-e (R.)...Iran	37·42 N	55·30 E
118	Atran (R.)...Swe.	57·02 N	12·43 E
99	Atrato, Rio (R.) (rê'ō-ä-trä'tō).Col.	7·00 N	77·12 W
98	Atrato (R.) (ä-trä'tō)...Col. (In.)	5·48 N	76·19 W
139	Aṭ Tafilah (tä-fē'la) Jordan (Palestine In.)	30·50 N	35·36 E
144	At Tāif...Sau. Ar.	21·03 N	41·00 E
78	Attalla (ă-tăl'yà)...Ala.	34·01 N	86·05 W
87	Attawapiskat (R.) (ăt'à-wà-pĭs'kăt).Can.	52·31 N	86·22 W
120	Atter See (L.) (Kammer)...Aus.	47·57 N	13·25 E
81	Attica (ăt'ĭ-kà)...N. Y.	42·55 N	78·15 W
84	Attleboro (ăt''l-bŭr-ô) Mass. (Providence In.)	41·56 N	71·15 W
116	Attow, Ben (Mtn.) (bĕn ăt'tô) Scot.	57·15 N	5·25 W
77	Attoyac Bay (ă-toi'yăk)...Tex.	31·45 N	94·23 W
64	Attu (I.) (ät-tōō')...Alaska	53·08 N	173·18 E
115	Aṭ Ṭūr...U. A. R.	28·09 N	33·47 E
118	Atvidaberg (ôt-vē'dà-bĕrgh)..Swe.	58·12 N	15·55 E
72	Atwood (ăt'wŏŏd)...Kans.	39·48 N	101·06 W
91	Atzcapotzalco (ät'zkä-pô-tzäl'kō) Mex. (Mexico In.)	19·29 N	99·11 W
111	Atzgersdorf...Aus. (Wien In.)	48·10 N	16·17 E
157	Auau Chan (ä'ōō-ä'ōō) Hawaii (In.)	20·55 N	156·50 W
123	Aubagne (ō-bän'y')...Fr.	43·18 N	5·34 E
122	Aube (R.) (ōb)...Fr.	48·42 N	3·49 E
122	Aubenas (ōb'-nä') Fr.	44·37 N	4·22 E
123	Aubervilliers (ō-bĕr-vē-yā') Fr. (Paris In.)	48·54 N	2·23 E
122	Aubin (ō-băn')...Fr.	44·29 N	2·12 E
85	Aubrey (ô-brē') Can. (Montreal In.)	45·08 N	73·47 W
78	Auburn (ô'bŭrn)...Ala.	32·35 N	85·26 W
68	Auburn...Calif.	38·52 N	121·05 W
73	Auburn...Ill.	39·36 N	89·46 W
80	Auburn...Ind.	41·20 N	85·05 W
82	Auburn...Maine	44·04 N	70·24 W
83	Auburn...Mass. (Boston In.)	42·11 N	71·51 W
73	Auburn...Nebr.	40·23 N	95·50 W
81	Auburn...N. Y.	42·55 N	76·35 W
65	Auburn...Wash. (Seattle In.)	47·18 N	122·14 W
75	Auburn Hts...Mich. (Detroit In.)	42·37 N	83·13 W
122	Aubusson (ō-bü-sôn')...Fr.	45·57 N	2·10 E
122	Auch (ōsh)...Fr.	43·38 N	0·35 E
78	Aucilla (R.) (ô-sĭl'à)...Fla.-Ga.	30·15 N	83·55 W
159	Auckland (ôk'lănd)...N. Z. (In.)	37·43 S	174·53 E
47	Auckland Is...N. Z.	50·30 S	166·30 E
122	Aude (ōd)...Fr.	42·55 N	2·08 E
122	Audierne (ō-dyĕrn')...Fr.	48·02 N	4·31 W
123	Audincourt (ō-dăn-kōōr')...Fr.	47·30 N	6·49 E
110	Audley (ôd'lĭ)...Eng.	53·03 N	2·18 W
168	Audo Ra..Eth. (Horn of Afr. In.)	6·58 N	41·18 E
71	Audubon (ô'dŏŏ-bŏn)...Iowa	41·43 N	94·57 W
84	Audubon..N. J. (Philadelphia In.)	39·54 N	75·04 W
120	Aue (ou'ĕ)...Ger.	50·35 N	12·44 E
160	Augathella (ôr'gà'thĕ-là)...Austl.	25·49 S	146·40 E
166	Aughrabies Falls (ô-grä'bês) S. Afr.	28·30 S	20·00 E
111	Augsburg (ouks'bŏŏrgh) Ger. (München In.)	48·23 N	10·55 E
73	Augusta (ô-gŭs'tà)...Ark.	35·16 N	91·21 W
79	Augusta...Ga.	33·26 N	82·00 W
73	Augusta...Kans.	37·41 N	96·58 W
80	Augusta...Ky.	38·45 N	84·00 W
82	Augusta...Maine	44·19 N	69·42 W
84	Augusta...N. J. (New York In.)	41·07 N	74·44 W
71	Augusta...Wis.	44·40 N	91·09 W
121	Augustow (ou-gŏŏs'tŏŏf)...Pol.	53·52 N	23·00 E
165	Auk R. (ouk)...Chad	9·30 N	20·45 E
123	Aulnay-sous-Bois (ō-nĕ'sōō-bwä') Fr. (Paris In.)	48·56 N	2·30 E
122	Aulne (R.) (ōn)...Fr.	48·08 N	3·53 W
125	Aumale (ō-mäl')...Alg.	36·05 N	3·40 E
123	Auneau (ō-nō')...Fr. (Paris In.)	48·28 N	1·45 E
166	Auob (R.) (ä'wŏb)...S. W. Afr.	25·00 S	19·00 E
139	Aur (I.)...Mala. (Singapore In.)	2·27 N	104·51 E
142	Aurangābād (ou-rŭŋ-gä-bäd') India	19·56 N	75·19 E
122	Auray (ō-rĕ')...Fr.	47·42 N	3·00 W
122	Aurillac (ō-rē-yák')...Fr.	44·57 N	2·27 E
75	Aurora (ô-rō'rà).Ill. (Chicago In.)	41·45 N	88·18 W
75	Aurora...Ind. (Cincinnati In.)	39·04 N	84·55 W
71	Aurora...Minn.	47·31 N	92·17 W
73	Aurora...Mo.	36·58 N	93·42 W
72	Aurora...Nebr.	40·54 N	98·01 W
118	Aursunden (L.) (äûr-sûndĕn).Nor.	62·42 N	11·10 E
80	Au Sable (R.) (ô-sā'b'l)...Mich.	44·40 N	84·25 W
81	Ausable (R.)...N. Y.	44·25 N	73·50 W
	Aussig, see Usti nad Labem		
71	Austin (ôs'tĭn)...Minn.	43·40 N	92·58 W
68	Austin...Nev.	39·30 N	117·05 W
77	Austin...Tex.	30·15 N	97·42 W
158	Austin (L.)...Austl.	27·45 S	117·30 E
77	Austin Bay (ôs'tĭn bī-ōō') Tex. (In.)	29·17 N	95·21 W
7	Australia (ôs-trā'lĭ-à)		
160	Australian Alps (Mts.)...Austl.	37·10 S	147·55 E
160	Australian Capital Ter. (ôs-trā'lĭ-ăn).Austl.	35·30 S	148·40 E
102	Austria (ôs'trĭ-à)...Eur.	47·15 N	11·53 E
123	Authon-la-Plaine (ō-tôn-lä-plĕ'n) Fr. (Paris In.)	48·27 N	1·58 E
90	Autlán (ä-ōōt-län')...Mex.	19·47 N	104·24 W
122	Autun (ō-tŭn')...Fr.	46·58 N	4·14 E
122	Auvergne (Mts.) (ō-vĕrn'y')...Fr.	45·12 N	2·31 E
122	Auxerre (ō-sâr')...Fr.	47·48 N	3·32 E
85	Aux Grues, Ile (I.) (ō grü) Can. (Quebec In.)	47·05 N	70·32 W
73	Ava (ā'và)...Mo.	36·56 N	92·40 W
165	Avakubi (ä-vä-kōō'bê)...Con. L.	1·19 N	27·32 E
122	Avallon (à-và-lôn')...Fr.	47·30 N	3·58 E
75	Avalon (ăv'à-lŏn) Pa. (Pittsburgh In.)	40·31 N	80·05 W
68	Avalon...Calif.	33·21 N	118·22 W
83	Avalon Pen...Can.	47·23 N	53·10 W
124	Aveiro (ä-vā'rōō)...Port.	40·38 N	8·38 W
100	Avelar (ä'vĕ-là'r)...Braz. (In.)	22·20 S	43·25 W
100	Avellaneda (ä-vĕl-yä-nā'dhä) Arg. (In.)	34·25 S	58·23 W
125	Avellino (ä-vĕl-lē'nō) It. (Napoli In.)	40·40 N	14·46 E
118	Averöy (I.) (ävĕr-ûê)...Nor.	63·40 N	7·16 E
126	Aversa (ä-vĕr'sä)...It.	40·58 N	14·13 E
73	Avery (ā'vēr-ĭ)...Tex.	33·34 N	94·46 W
118	Avesta (ä-vĕs'tä)...Swe.	60·16 N	16·09 E
122	Aveyron (R.) (ä-vâ-rôn)...Fr.	44·07 N	1·45 E
126	Avezzano (ä-vât-sä'nō)...It.	42·03 N	13·27 E
126	Avigliano (ä-vēl-yä'nō)...It.	40·45 N	15·44 E
122	Avignon (à-vē-nyôn')...Fr.	43·55 N	4·50 E
124	Avila (ä-vê-lä)...Sp.	40·39 N	4·42 W
124	Avilés (ä-vê-lās')...Sp.	43·33 N	5·55 W
73	Avoca (à-vō'kà)...Iowa	41·29 N	95·16 W
81	Avon (ā'vŏn)...Conn.	41·40 N	72·50 W
116	Avon (ā'vŭn)...Eng.	52·05 N	1·55 W
83	Avon (ā'vŏn)..Mass. (Boston In.)	42·08 N	71·03 W
75	Avon...Ohio (Cleveland In.)	41·27 N	82·02 W
84	Avondale...Ga. (Atlanta In.)	33·47 N	84·16 W
75	Avon Lake..Ohio (Cleveland In.)	41·31 N	82·01 W
85	Avonmore (ā'vŏn-mōr) Can. (Ottawa In.)	45·11 N	74·58 W
79	Avon Park (ā'vŏn pärk').Fla. (In.)	27·35 N	81·29 W
122	Avranches (à-vränsh')...Fr.	48·43 N	1·34 W
153	Awaji (ä'wä-jê)...Jap.	34·23 N	135·00 E
153	Awaji-Shima (I.) (ä'wä-jê shē-mä) Jap. (Osaka In.)	34·32 N	135·02 E
165	Awash R. (à-wäsh')...Eth.	9·19 N	40·30 E
116	Awe, Loch (L.) (lŏk ôr)...Scot.	56·22 N	5·04 W
165	Awjilah...Libya	29·07 N	21·21 E
122	Ax-les-Thermes (äks'lā tĕrm')..Fr.	42·43 N	1·50 E
90	Axochiapan(äks-ō-chyä'pän).Mex.	18·29 N	98·49 W
122	Ay (à'ê)...Fr.	49·05 N	3·58 E
132	Ay (R.)...Sov. Un.	55·55 N	57·55 E
153	Ayabe (ä'yä-bĕ)...Jap.	35·16 N	135·17 E
100	Ayacucho (ä-yä-kōō'chō)...Arg.	37·05 S	58·30 W
98	Ayacucho...Peru	12·12 S	74·03 W
134	Ayaguz (ä-yà-gōōz')...Sov. Un.	48·00 N	80·12 E
124	Ayamonte (ä-yä-mô'n-tĕ)...Port.	37·14 N	7·28 W
135	Ayan (à-yän')...Sov. Un.	56·26 N	138·18 E
98	Ayata (ä-yä'tä)...Bol.	15·17 S	68·43 W
98	Ayaviri (ä-yä-vē'rē)...Peru	14·46 S	70·38 W
129	Aydar (R.) (ī-där')...Sov. Un.	49·15 N	38·48 E
79	Ayden (ā'dĕn)...N. C.	35·27 N	77·25 W
133	Aydin (à'ĭ-dĭn)...Tur.	37·40 N	27·40 E
83	Ayer (âr)...Mass. (Boston In.)	42·33 N	71·36 W
139	Ayer Hitam.Mala. (Singapore In.)	1·55 N	103·11 E
127	Ayiassos...Grc.	39·06 N	26·25 E
127	Áyion Óros (Mount Athos) (Reg.) Grc.	40·20 N	24·15 E
127	Áyios Evstrátion (I.)...Grc.	39·30 N	24·58 E
127	Ayiá...Grc.	39·42 N	22·47 E
110	Aylesbury (ālz'bēr-ĭ) Eng. (London In.)	51·47 N	0·49 W
85	Aylmer (āl'mēr) Can. (Ottawa In.)	45·24 N	75·50 W
86	Aylmer (L.)...Can.	64·27 N	108·22 W
90	Ayo el Chico (ä'yō el chē'kō).Mex.	20·31 N	102·21 W
135	Ayon (I.) (ī-ôn')...Sov. Un.	70·04 N	168·33 E
91	Ayotla (ä-yōt'lä) Mex. (Mexico In.)	19·18 N	98·55 W
116	Ayr (âr)...Scot.	55·27 N	4·40 W
116	Ayr (L.)...Scot.	55·25 N	4·20 W
168	Ayshā...Eth. (Horn of Afr. In.)	10·48 N	42·32 E
92	Ayutla (ä-yōōt'lä)...Guat.	14·44 N	92·11 W
90	Ayutla...Mex.	16·50 N	99·16 W
90	Ayutla...Mex.	20·09 N	104·20 W
154	Ayutthaya (ä-yōōt'hē'ä)...Thai.	14·16 N	100·37 E
127	Ayvalik (aï-vä'lĕk)...Tur.	39·19 N	26·40 E
164	Azemmour (ä-zē-mōōr')...Mor.	33·20 N	8·21 W
130	Azerbaydzhan (Azerbaijan) (S. S. R.) (ä'zĕr-bä-ê-jän') Sov. Un.	40·38 N	47·25 E
82	Aziscoos (L.) (ăz'ĭ kōōs')...Maine	45·03 N	70·50 W
74	Azle (āz'lē) Tex. (Dallas, Fort Worth In.)	35·54 N	97·33 W
98	Azogues (ä-sō'gās)...Ec.	2·47 S	78·45 W
164	Azores Is. (à-zōrz')...Port.	37·44 N	29·25 W
129	Azov (à-zôf') (ä'zôf)...Sov. Un.	47·07 N	39·19 E
	Azov, Sea of, see Azovskoye More		
129	Azovskoye More (Sea of Azov) (à-zôf'skô-yĕ mô'rĕ).Sov. Un.	46·00 N	36·20 E
90	Azoyú (ä-zô-yōō')...Mex.	16·42 N	98·46 W
69	Aztec (ăz'tĕk)...N. Mex.	36·40 N	108·00 W
69	Aztec Ruins Natl. Mon...N. Mex.	36·50 N	108·00 W
95	Azua (ä'swä)...Dom. Rep.	18·30 N	70·45 W
124	Azuaga (ä-thwä'gä)...Sp.	38·15 N	5·42 W
93	Azuero, Peninsula de (Pen.) (ä-swä'rō).Pan.	7·30 N	80·34 W
76	Azucar, Presa de (Res.) (prĕ'sä-dĕ-ä-zōō'kär).Mex.	26·06 N	98·44 W
100	Azufre, Cerro (Copiapó) (Vol.) (sĕr'rō ä-sōō'frā) (kō-pê-äpō') Chile	26·10 S	69·00 W
101	Azul (ä-sōōl') Arg. (Buenos Aires In.)	36·46 S	59·51 W
90	Azul, Sierra (Mts.) (sē-ĕ'r-rä-zōō'l) Mex.	23·20 N	98·28 W
98	Azul, Cordillera (Mts.) (kô'r-dē-lyĕ'rä-zōō'l).Peru	7·15 S	75·30 W
165	Azum, Bahr (R.) (bär à-zōōm') Chad	10·06 N	19·16 E
74	Azusa (à-zōō'sà) Calif. (Los Angeles In.)	34·08 N	117·55 W
144	Az Zahrān (Dhahran) (dà-rän') Sau. Ar.	26·13 N	50·00 E
168	Az Zaqāzīq...U. A. R. (Nile In.)	30·36 N	31·36 E
139	Az Zarqā'..Jordan (Palestine In.)	32·03 N	36·07 E
165	Az Zawiyah...Libya	32·28 N	11·55 E
123	Baal (bäl)...Ger. (Ruhr In.)	51·02 N	6·17 E
155	Baao (bä'ō)...Phil. (Manila In.)	13·27 N	123·22 E
111	Baarle-Hertog Bel. (Bruxelles In.)	51·26 N	4·57 E
111	Baarn...Neth. (Amsterdam In.)	52·12 N	5·18 E
127	Babaeski (bä'bä-ĕs'kĭ)...Tur.	41·25 N	27·05 E
98	Babahoyo (bä-bä-ō'yō)...Ec.	1·56 S	79·24 W
167	Babanango...S. Afr. (Natal In.)	28·24 S	31·11 E
155	Babar (I.) (bä'bàr)...Indon.	7·50 S	129·15 E
144	Bābel...Iran	36·30 N	52·48 E

ng-sing; ŋ-baŋk; n-nasalized n; nŏd; cŏmmit; ōld; ôbey; ôrder; fōōd; fŏŏt; ou-out; s-soft; sh-dish; th-thin; pūre; ûnite; ûrn; stŭd; circŭs; ü-as "y" in study; '-indeterminate vowel.

180 Bab-el-Mandeb–Bandeira PRONOUNCING INDEX

Page	Name Pronunciation Region	Lat. °′	Long. °′
165	Bab-el-Mandeb Str. (băb'ĕl măn-dĕb') . Afr.-Asia	13·17 N	42·49 E
76	Babia, Arroyo de la (är-rō'yō dā lä bä'bê-ȧ) . Mex.	28·26 N	101·50 W
86	Babine (L.) (băb'ēn) . Can.	54·34 N	126·47 W
86	Babine Mts. . Can.	55·35 N	128·26 W
135	Babushkin (bä'bo͝osh-kĭn) Sov. Un.	51·47 N	106·08 E
136	Babushkin . Sov. Un. (Moskva In.)	55·52 N	37·42 E
154	Babuyan Is. (bä-bo͞o-yän') . Phil.	4·30 N	122·38 E
127	Babyak (bäb'zhȧk) . Bul.	41·59 N	23·42 E
84	Babylon (băb'ĭ-lŏn) N. Y. (New York In.)	40·42 N	73·19 W
144	Babylon (Ruins) . Iraq	32·15 N	45·23 E
155	Bacacay (bä-kä-kī') Phil. (Manila In.)	13·17 N	123·48 E
92	Bacalar, Laguna de (L.) (lä-go͞o-nä-dĕ-bȧ-kȧ-lär') Mex. (Yucatan In.)	18·50 N	88·31 W
151	Bacarra (bä-kär'rä) . Phil.	18·22 N	120·40 E
121	Bacău . Rom.	46·34 N	27·00 E
123	Baccarat (bȧ-kȧ-rȧ') . Fr.	48·29 N	6·42 E
74	Bacchus (băk'ŭs) Utah (Salt Lake City In.)	40·40 N	112·06 W
91	Bachajón (bä-chä-hōn') . Mex.	17·08 N	92·18 W
127	Bačka Topola (Bäch'kä Tô'pô-lä') Yugo.	45·48 N	19·38 E
143	Back Bay (băk) India (Bombay In.)	18·55 N	72·45 E
158	Backstairs Pass. (băk-stârs') Austl.	35·50 S	138·15 E
151	Bac Ninh (băk'nēn'') . Viet.	21·10 N	106·02 E
155	Bacnotan (bäk-nô-tän') Phil. (Manila In.)	16·43 N	120·21 E
155	Baco, Mt. (bä'kô) Phil. (Manila In.)	12·50 N	121·11 E
125	Bacoli (bä-kō-lē') It. (Napoli In.)	40·33 N	14·05 E
154	Bacolod (bä-kō'lôd) . Phil.	10·42 N	123·03 E
155	Bacon (bä-kōn') . Phil. (Manila In.)	13·02 N	124·04 E
121	Bácsalmás (bäch'ôl-mäs) . Hung.	46·07 N	19·18 E
110	Bacup (băk'ŭp) . Eng.	53·42 N	2·12 W
70	Bad (R.) (băd) . S. D.	44·04 N	100·58 W
124	Badajoz (bä-dhä-hōth') . Sp.	38·52 N	6·56 W
125	Badalona (bä-dhä-lō'nä) . Sp.	41·27 N	2·15 E
144	Badanah . Sau. Ar.	30·49 N	40·45 E
80	Bad Axe (băd' ăks) . Mich.	43·50 N	82·55 W
111	Bad Bramstedt (bät bräm'shtĕt) Ger. (Hamburg In.)	53·55 N	9·53 E
123	Bad Ems (bät ĕms) . Ger.	50·20 N	7·45 E
111	Baden (bä'dĕn) . Aus. (Wien In.)	48·00 N	16·14 E
120	Baden . Switz.	47·28 N	8·17 E
120	Baden-Baden (bä'dĕn-bä'dĕn) . Ger.	48·46 N	8·11 E
120	Baden Württemberg (State) (bä'dĕn vür'tĕm-bĕrgh) . Ger.	48·38 N	9·00 E
120	Bad Freienwalde (bät frī'ĕn-väl'dĕ) . Ger.	52·47 N	14·00 E
120	Bad Hersfeld (bät hĕrsh'fĕlt) . Ger.	50·53 N	9·43 E
117	Bad Homberg (bät hōm'bĕrgh) Ger.	50·14 N	8·35 E
79	Badin (bă'dĭn) . N. C.	35·23 N	80·08 W
120	Bad Ischl (bät ĭsh''l) . Aus.	47·46 N	13·37 E
120	Bad Kissingen (bät kĭs'ĭng-ĕn) . Ger.	50·12 N	10·05 E
120	Bad Kreuznach (bät kroits'näk) Ger.	49·52 N	7·53 E
70	Badlands (Reg.) (băd' lănds) N. D.	46·43 N	103·22 W
70	Badlands (Reg.) . S. D.	43·43 N	102·36 W
70	Badlands Natl. Mon . S. D.	43·56 N	102·37 W
143	Badlapur . India (Bombay In.)	19·12 N	73·12 E
120	Bad Oldesloe (bät ōl'dĕs-lōē) . Ger.	53·48 N	10·21 E
120	Bad Reichenhall (bät rī'ĸĕn-häl) Ger.	47·43 N	12·53 E
71	Bad River Ind. Res. (băd) . Wis.	46·41 N	90·36 W
111	Bad Segeburg (bät sĕ'gĕ-bo͝orgh) Ger. (Hamburg In.)	53·56 N	10·18 E
120	Bad Tölz (bät tûltz) . Ger.	47·46 N	11·35 E
111	Bad Vöslau . Aus. (Wien In.)	47·58 N	16·13 E
67	Badwater Cr. (băd'wô-tēr) . Wyo.	43·13 N	107·55 W
124	Baena (bä-ā'nä) . Sp.	37·38 N	4·20 W
101	Baependi (bä-å-pĕn'dĭ) Braz. (Rio de Janeiro In.)	21·57 S	44·51 W
49	Baffin B. (băf'ĭn) . Can.	72·00 N	65·00 W
77	Baffin B. . Tex.	27·11 N	97·35 W
49	Baffin I. . Can.	67·20 N	71·00 W
164	Bafoulabe (bä-fo͞o-lä-bā') . Mali	13·58 N	10·51 W
144	Bāfq (bäfk) . Iran	31·48 N	55·23 E
133	Bafra (bäf'rä) . Tur.	41·30 N	35·50 E
155	Bagabag (bä-gä-bäg') Phil. (Manila In.)	16·38 N	121·16 E
143	Bāgalkot . India	16·14 N	75·40 E
167	Bagamoyo (bä-gä-mō'yō) . Tan.	6·28 S	38·49 E
136	Bagaryak (bȧ-gȧr-yäk') Sov. Un. (Urals In.)	56·13 N	61·32 E
100	Bagé (bä-zhā') . Braz.	31·17 S	54·07 W
145	Bagh (bäk) . Afg. (Khyber Pass In.)	33·47 N	70·45 E
144	Baghdad (bȧgh-dȧd') (băg'dăd) Iraq	33·14 N	44·22 E
126	Bagheria (bä-gå-rē'ä) . It.	38·03 N	13·32 E
70	Bagley (băg'lē) . Minn.	47·31 N	95·24 W
126	Bagnara (bän-yä'rä) . It.	38·17 N	15·52 E
73	Bagnell Dam (băg'nĕl) . Mo.	38·13 N	92·40 W
122	Bagnères-de-Bigorre (bän-yâr'dĕ-bê-gor') . Fr.	43·40 N	0·70 E
122	Bagnères-de-Luchon (bän-yâr' dĕ-lü chôɴ') . Fr.	42·46 N	0·36 E
122	Bagnols (bä-nyôl') . Fr.	44·09 N	4·37 E
164	Bagoe R. (bȧ-gō'ȧ) . Mali	12·22 N	6·34 W
82	Bagotville (bȧ-gô-vēl') . Can.	48·20 N	70·58 W
146	Bagrash Köl (L.) . China	42·06 N	88·01 E
164	Baguezane, Monts (Mt.) (bȧ-gē-zän') . Niger	17·45 N	8·40 E
155	Baguio (bä-gē-ō') Phil. (Manila In.)	16·24 N	120·36 E
168	Bahaja, Monte (Mt.) Som. (Horn of Afr. In.)	11·00 N	49·38 E
89	Bahama Is. (bȧ-hā'mȧ) . N. A.	26·15 N	76·00 W
139	Bahau . Mala. (Singapore In.)	2·48 N	102·25 E
142	Bahawalpur (bŭ-hä'wŭl-po͞or) W. Pak.	29·29 N	71·41 E
	Bahia, see Salvador		
88	Bahía, Islas de la (I.) (ē's-läs-dĕ-lä-bä-ē'ä) . Hond.	16·15 N	86·30 W
100	Bahia Blanca (bä-ē'ä bläŋ'kä) Arg.	38·45 S	62·07 W
98	Bahía de Caraquez (bä-e'ä dā kä-rä'kĕz) . Ec.	0·45 S	80·29 W
99	Bahía Negra (bä-ē'ä nā'grä) . Par.	20·11 S	58·05 W
100	Bahias, Cabo dos (C.) (kä'bô-dôs-bä-ē'äs) . Arg.	44·55 S	65·35 W
95	Bahoruco, Sierra de (Mts.) (sē-ĕ'r-rä-dĕ-bä-ō-ro͞o'kô) Dom. Rep.	18·10 N	71·25 W
144	Bahrain Is. (bä-rān') . Asia	26·15 N	51·17 E
165	Bahr el Ghazal (Prov.) (bär ĕl ghä-zäl') . Sud.	7·56 N	27·15 E
115	Baḩrīyah (Oasis) (bȧ-hȧ-rē'yȧ) U. A. R.	28·34 N	29·01 E
121	Baia de Cris (bä'yä dā krēs') Rom.	46·11 N	22·40 E
121	Baia-Mare (bä'yä-mä'rä) . Rom.	47·40 N	23·35 E
82	Baie-Comeau . Can.	49·15 N	68·12 W
74	Baie de Wasai (bā dē wä-sä'ê) Mich. (Sault Ste. Marie In.)	46·27 N	84·15 W
82	Baie St. Paul (bā'sănt-pôl') . Can.	47·26 N	70·33 W
82	Baie Trinite . Can.	49·24 N	67·21 W
	Baikal, see Baykal'skiy Khrebet		
	Baikal, L., see Baykal Ozero		
116	Baile Atha Cliath (Dublin) (bŏ'lĕ ô'hŏ clē'ŏh) (dŭb'lĭn) . Ire.	53·20 N	6·15 W
124	Bailén (bä-ê-lān') . Sp.	38·05 N	3·48 W
127	Băileşti (bŭ-ĭ-lĕsh'tē) . Rom.	44·01 N	23·21 E
78	Bainbridge (bān'brĭj) . Ga.	30·52 N	84·35 W
65	Bainbridge I. . Wash. (Seattle In.)	47·39 N	122·32 W
76	Baird (bârd) . Tex.	32·22 N	99·28 W
75	Bairdford (bârd'fōrd) Pa. (Pittsburgh In.)	40·37 N	79·53 W
64	Baird Mts. . Alaska	67·35 N	160·10 W
160	Bairnsdale (bârnz'dāl) . Austl.	137·50 S	47·39 E
122	Baïse (R.) (bä-ēz') . Fr.	43·52 N	0·23 E
121	Baja (bŏ'yŏ) . Hung.	46·11 N	18·55 E
113	Baja . Tun.	36·52 N	9·20 E
88	Baja California (State) (bä-hä) . Mex.	30·15 N	117·25 W
88	Baja California (Ter.) . Mex.	26·00 N	113·30 W
154	Bajak (I.) . Indon.	2·08 N	97·15 E
136	Bakal (bä'kăl) . Sov. Un. (Urals In.)	54·57 N	58·50 E
164	Bakel (bȧ-kĕl') . Senegal	14·52 N	12·26 W
67	Baker (bā'kēr) . Mont.	46·21 N	104·12 W
66	Baker . Ore.	44·46 N	117·52 W
156	Baker (I.) . Oceania	1·00 N	176·00 W
86	Baker (L.) . Can.	63·51 N	96·10 W
66	Baker, Mt. . Wash.	48·46 N	121·52 W
75	Baker Cr. . Ill. (Chicago In.)	41·13 N	87·47 W
86	Baker Lake . Can.	64·18 N	96·26 W
68	Bakersfield (bā'kērz-fēld) . Calif.	35·23 N	119·00 W
75	Bakerstown (bā'kerz-toun) Pa. (Pittsburgh In.)	40·39 N	79 56 W
110	Bakewell (bāk'wĕl) . Eng.	53·12 N	1·40 W
129	Bakhchisaray (bȧĸ'chê-sȧ-rī') Sov. Un.	44·46 N	33·54 E
129	Bakhmach (bȧĸ-mäch') . Sov. Un.	51·09 N	32·47 E
144	Bakhtegān, Daryachch-ye (L.) Iran	29·29 N	54·31 E
136	Bakhteyevo (bȧk-tyĕ'yĕ-vô) Sov. Un. (Moskva In.)	55·35 N	38·32 E
165	Bāko (bä'kō) . Eth.	5·47 N	36·39 E
121	Bakony-Erdo (Mts.) (bȧ-kōn'y') Hung.	46·57 N	17·30 E
164	Bakoy R. (bȧ-kô'ê) . Mali	12·49 N	9·51 W
136	Bakr Uzyak (bȧkr o͞oz'yȧk) Sov. Un. (Urals In.)	52·59 N	58·43 E
133	Baku (bȧ-ko͞o') . Sov. Un.	40·28 N	49·45 E
154	Balabac (I.) (bä'lä-bäk) . Phil.	8·00 N	116·28 E
154	Balabac Str. . Indon.-Phil.	7·23 N	116·30 E
139	Ba'labakk . Leb. (Palestine In.)	34·00 N	36·13 E
154	Balabalagan (I.) (bä-lȧ-bä'lȧ-gän) Indon.	2·00 S	117·15 E
136	Balabanovo (bȧ-lȧ-bä'nô-vô) Sov. Un. (Moskva In.)	56·10 N	37·44 E
134	Balagansk (bä-lä-gänsk') Sov. Un.	53·58 N	103·09 E
125	Balaguer (bä-lä-gĕr') . Sp.	41·48 N	0·50 E
134	Balakhta (bȧ'lăk-tȧ') . Sov. Un.	55·22 N	91·43 E
129	Balakleya (bȧ'lȧ-klā'yȧ) . Sov. Un.	49·28 N	36·51 E
133	Balakovo (bȧ'lȧ-kô'vô) . Sov. Un.	52·00 N	47·40 E
91	Balancán (bä-läŋ-kän') . Mex.	17·47 N	91·32 W
155	Balanga (bä-läŋ'gä) Phil. (Manila In.)	14·41 N	120·31 E
155	Balaoan (bä-lou'än) Phil. (Manila In.)	16·49 N	120·24 E
136	Balashikha (bȧ-lä'shĭ-kȧ) Sov. Un. (Moskva In.)	55·48 N	37·58 E
133	Balashov (bȧ'lȧ-shôf) . Sov. Un.	51·30 N	43·00 E
142	Balasore (bä-lȧ-sōr') . India	21·38 N	86·59 E
121	Balassagyarmat (bô'lôsh-shô-dyôr'môt) . Hung.	48·04 N	19·19 E
121	Balaton L. (bô'lô-tôn) . Hung.	46·47 N	17·55 E
155	Balayan (bä-lä-yän') Phil. (Manila In.)	13·56 N	120·44 E
155	Balayan B. . Phil. (Manila In.)	13·46 N	120·46 E
74	Balboa (băl-bō'ȧ) Calif. (Los Angeles In.)	33·36 N	117·54 W
88	Balboa (bäl-bô'ä) C. Z. (Panama Canal In.)	8·55 N	79·34 W
93	Balboa Heights . Pan.	8·59 N	79·33 W
88	Balboa Mt. C. Z. (Panama Canal In.)	9·05 N	79·44 W
100	Balcarce (bäl-kär'sä) . Arg.	37·49 S	58·17 W
127	Balchik . Bul.	43·24 N	28·13 E
74	Bald Eagle (bôld ē'g'l) Minn. (Minneapolis, St. Paul In.)	45·06 N	93·01 W
74	Bald Eagle L. Minn. (Minneapolis, St. Paul In.)	45·08 N	93·03 W
142	Baldin . W. Pak.	24·47 N	69·51 E
74	Baldwin Park (bôld'wĭn) Calif. (Los Angeles In.)	34·05 N	117·58 W
81	Baldwinsville (bôld'wĭns-vĭl) . N. Y.	43·10 N	76·20 W
69	Baldy Pk. (bôl'dê) . Ariz.	33·55 N	109·35 W
76	Baldy Pk. (bôl'dē pēk) . Tex.	30·38 N	104·11 W
125	Baleares, Islas (Balearic Is.) (ē's-läs bä-lē-ä'rĕs) . Sp.	39·25 N	1·28 E
	Balearic Is., see Baleares, Islas		
125	Balearic Sea (băl-ê-ăr'ĭk) . Eur.	39·40 N	1·05 E
155	Baler (bä-lär') . Phil. (Manila In.)	15·46 N	121·33 E
155	Baler B. . Phil. (Manila In.)	15·51 N	121·40 E
154	Balesin (I.) (bä-lĕ-sēn') . Phil.	6·37 N	122·07 E
155	Balesin (I.) . Phil. (Manila In.)	14·28 N	122·10 E
135	Baley (bȧl-yā') . Sov. Un.	51·29 N	116·12 E
142	Balfate (bäl-fä'tē) . Hond.	15·48 N	86·24 W
168	Balfour (băl'fo͝or) . S. Afr. (Johannesburg & Pretoria In.)	26·41 S	28·37 E
154	Bali (I.) (bä'lē) . Indon.	8·00 S	115·22 E
133	Balikesir (bä-lĭ-kĕ-sēr') . Tur.	39·40 N	27·50 E
154	Balikpapan (bä'lĕk-pä'pän) . Indon.	1·13 N	116·52 E
154	Balintang Chan. (bā-lĭn-täng') Phil.	19·50 N	121·08 E
	Balkan Mts., see Stara Planina		
142	Balkh (bälk) . Afg.	36·48 N	66·50 E
134	Balkhash (bȧl-kăsh') . Sov. Un.	46·58 N	75·00 E
134	Balkhash, Ozero (L.) . Sov. Un.	45·58 N	72·15 E
129	Balki (bäl'kĭ) . Sov. Un.	47·22 N	34·56 E
123	Ballancourt (bä-äɴ-ko͞or') Fr. (Paris In.)	48·31 N	2·23 E
160	Ballarat (băl'ȧ-răt) . Austl.	37·37 S	144·00 E
158	Ballard (I.) (băl'ȧrd) . Austl.	29·15 S	120·45 E
116	Ballater (băl'ȧ-tēr) . Scot.	57·05 N	3·06 W
47	Balleny Is. (băl'ĕ nê) . Ant.	67·00 S	164·00 E
160	Ballina (băl-ĭ-nä') . Austl.	28·54 S	153·30 E
116	Ballina . Ire.	54·06 N	9·05 W
116	Ballinasloe (băl'ĭ-nȧ-slō') . Ire.	53·20 N	8·09 W
76	Ballinger (băl'ĭn-jēr) . Tex.	31·45 N	99·58 W
81	Ballston Spa (bôls'tŭn spä') . N. Y.	43·05 N	73·50 W
142	Bally . India (Calcutta In.)	22·38 N	88·20 E
121	Balmazújváros (bŏl'mŏz-o͞o'y'vä'rôsh) . Hung.	47·35 N	21·23 E
160	Balonne (R.) (băl-ōn') . Austl.	27·00 S	149·10 E
142	Balotra . India	25·56 N	72·12 E
160	Balranald (băl'-rȧn-ăld) . Austl.	34·42 S	143·30 E
127	Balş (bälsh) . Rom.	44·21 N	24·05 E
81	Balsam (L.) (bôl'sȧm) . Can.	44·30 N	78·50 W
99	Balsas (bäl'säs) . Braz.	7·09 S	46·04 W
90	Balsas (R.) . Mex.	18·15 N	102·08 W
129	Balta (bäl'tȧ) . Sov. Un.	47·57 N	29·38 E
112	Baltic Sea (bôl'tĭk) . Eur.	55·20 N	16·50 E
168	Balṭīm (bȧl-tēm') U. A. R. (Nile In.)	31·33 N	31·04 E
84	Baltimore (bôl'tĭ-môr) Md. (Baltimore In.)	39·20 N	76·38 W
119	Baltiysk (bäl-tēysk') . Sov. Un.	54·40 N	19·55 E
145	Baluchistan (Reg.) (bȧ-lo͞o-chĭ-stän') . W. Pak.	27·45 N	66·58 E
90	Balurte, Río del (rē'ō-dĕl-bä-lo͞o'r-tĕ) . Mex.	23·09 N	105·42 W
85	Balzac (bôl'zăk) . Can. (Calgary In.)	51·13 N	114·00 W
164	Bamako (bä-mä-kō') . Mali	12·45 N	7·50 W
164	Bamba (bäm-bä') . Mali	17·13 N	1·30 W
155	Bambang (bäm-bäng') Phil. (Manila In.)	16·24 N	121·08 E
165	Bambari (bäm-bȧ-rē) Cen. Afr. Rep.	5·44 N	20·40 E
120	Bamberg (bäm'bĕrgh) . Ger.	49·53 N	10·52 E
79	Bamberg (băm'bûrg) . S. C.	33·17 N	81·04 W
165	Bambili (bäm-bē-lē') . Con. L.	3·46 N	26·09 E
101	Bambuí (bä'm-bo͞o'-ê) Braz. (Rio de Janeiro In.)	20·01 S	45·59 W
164	Bambuto Mts. (bäm-bo͞o'tō) Nig.-Cam.	6·22 N	11·14 E
110	Bampton (băm'tŭn) Eng. (London In.)	51·42 N	1·33 W
144	Bampūr (bŭm-po͞or') . Iran	27·15 N	60·22 E
155	Banahao, Mt. (bä-nä-hä'ô) Phil. (Manila In.)	14·04 N	121·45 E
101	Bananal (bä-nä-näl') Braz. (Rio de Janeiro In.)	22·42 S	44·17 W
99	Bananal, Ilha do (I.) (ē'lä-dô-bä-nä-näl') . Braz.	12·09 S	50·27 W
	Banaras, see Vārānasi		
142	Banās (R.) (bän-äs') . India	25·20 N	74·51 E
165	Banas, Ra's (C.) . U. A. R.	23·48 N	36·39 E
127	Banat (Reg.) (bä-nät') Yugo.-Rom.	45·35 N	21·05 E
154	Ban Bangsaphan . Thai.	11·19 N	99·27 E
98	Banco (bän'-kô) . Col.	8·58 N	74·01 W
81	Bancroft (băn'krŏft) . Can.	45·05 N	77·55 W
142	Banda (bän'dä) . India	25·36 N	80·21 E
155	Banda (I.) . Indon.	4·40 S	129·56 E
160	Banda Banda, Mt. (băn'dȧ băn'dȧ) . Austl.	31·09 S	152·15 E
164	Bandama R. (bän-dä'mä) Ivory Coast	6·19 N	5·40 W
144	Bandar Abbās (Hbr.) (bän-där' äb-bäs') . Iran	27·04 N	56·22 E
144	Bandar-e Lengeh (Hbr.) . Iran	26·44 N	54·47 E
133	Bandar-e Pahlanī (bän-där') . Iran	37·30 N	49·30 E
144	Bandar-e-Shāhpūr (Hbr.) . Iran	30·27 N	48·45 E
139	Bandar Maharani (bän-där' mä-hä-rä'nê) Mala. (Singapore In.)	2·02 N	102·34 E
139	Bandar Penggaram Mala. (Singapore In.)	1·51 N	102·56 E
144	Bandar Shah (Hbr.) . Iran	37·00 N	54·08 E
155	Banda Sea (bän'dä) . Indon.	6·05 S	127·28 E
101	Bandeira, Pico da (Pk.) (pē'ko͞o dä bän-dā'rä) . Braz. (Rio de Janeiro In.)	20·27 S	41·47 W

ăt; finȧl; rāte; senȧte; ärm; ȧsk; sofȧ; fâre; ch-choose; dh-as th in other; bē; ėvent; bĕt; recĕnt; cratēr; g-go; gh-guttural g; bĭt; ĭ-short neutral; rīde; ĸ-guttural k as ch in German ich;

Page	Name	Pronunciation	Region	Lat. °'	Long. °'
69	Bandelier Natl. Mon.	(băn-dĕ-lēr') N. Mex.		35·50 N	106·45 W
90	Banderas, Bahía de (B.)	(bä-ē'ä-dĕ-băn-dĕ'räs) . Mex.		20·38 N	103·25 W
168	Bander Beila	Som. (Horn of Afr. In.)		9·40 N	50·45 E
164	Bandiagara	(băn-dĕ-à-gä'rä). Mali		14·19 N	3·39 W
133	Bandirma	(băn-dĭr'mà) . . . . . Tur.		40·25 N	27·50 E
154	Bandjermasin	(băn-jĕr-mä'sĕn) Indon.		3·18 S	114·32 E
124	Bando	(bä'n-dò) . . . . Sp.		42·02 N	7·58 W
66	Bandon	(băn'dŭn) . . . . Ore.		43·06 N	124·25 W
143	Bāndra	. . . . . . India (Bombay In.)		19·04 N	72·49 E
154	Bandung	. . . . Indon.		7·00 S	107·22 E
95	Banes	(bä'nās) . . . . Cuba		21·00 N	75·45 W
86	Banff	(bănf) . . . . Can.		51·17 N	115·30 W
116	Banff	. . . . Scot.		57·39 N	2·37 W
86	Banff Natl. Park	. . . . Can.		51·45 N	116·04 W
100	Bánfield	(bä'n-fyĕ'ld) . . Arg. (In.)		34·30 S	58·24 W
143	Bangalore	(băŋ'gà'lōr) . . . . India		13·03 N	77·39 E
155	Bangar	(băŋ-gär') Phil. (Manila In.)		16·54 N	120·24 E
165	Bangassou	(băN-gà-sōō') Cen. Afr. Rep.		4·47 N	22·49 E
155	Bangeta, Mt.	. . . . N. Gui. Ter.		6·20 S	147·00 E
155	Banggai, Pulau-Palau (Is.)	(băŋ-gī') .Indon.		1·05 S	123·45 E
154	Banggi (I.)	. . . . N. Bor.		7·12 N	117·10 E
165	Banghazī	. . . . Libya		32·08 N	20·06 E
139	Bangi	. . . . . Mala. (Singapore In.)		2·54 N	101·48 E
154	Bangka (I.)	(băŋ'kà) . . . . Indon.		2·24 S	106·55 E
154	Bangkalan	(băŋ-kà-län') . . Indon.		6·07 S	112·50 E
	Bangkok, see Krungthep				
82	Bangor	(băn'gẽr) . . . . Maine		44·47 N	68·47 W
80	Bangor	. . . . Mich.		42·20 N	86·05 W
81	Bangor	. . . . Pa.		40·55 N	75·10 W
116	Bangor	(băŋ'ẽr) (băŋ'ŏr) . . Wales		53·13 N	4·05 W
69	Bangs, Mt.	(băŋs) . . . . Ariz.		36·45 N	113·50 W
155	Bangued	(băn-gād') Phil. (Manila In.)		17·36 N	120·38 E
165	Bangui	(băN-gē'). Cen. Afr. Rep.		4·28 N	18·35 E
166	Bangweulu, L.	(băŋ-wē-ōō'lōō) Fed. of Rh. & Nya.		10·30 S	30·15 E
168	Banhã	. . . . . . U. A. R. (Nile In.)		30·24 N	31·11 E
95	Bani	(bä'-nē) . . . . . . Dom. Rep.		18·15 N	70·25 W
155	Bani	(bä'nē) . . Phil. (Manila In.)		16·11 N	119·51 E
164	Bani (R.)	. . . . Mali		13·00 N	5·36 W
164	Bani, Jebel (Mts.)	(jĕb'ĕl bä'nē) Mor.		28·39 N	9·33 W
95	Bánica	(bä'-nē-kà) . . . . Dom. Rep.		19·00 N	71·35 W
168	Banī Mazār	. . U. A. R. (Nile In.)		28·29 N	30·48 E
168	Banī Suwayf	. . U. A. R. (Nile In.)		29·05 N	31·06 E
126	Banja Luka	(băn-yä-lōō'kà) .Yugo.		44·45 N	17·11 E
154	Banjuwangi	(băn-jōō-wäŋ'gĕ) Indon.		8·15 S	114·15 E
154	Ban Kantang	(băn-kän'täng') Thai.		7·26 N	99·28 E
167	Bankberg (Mts.)	(băŋk'bûrg) S. Afr. (Natal In.)		32·10 S	25·11 E
65	Banks	(băŋks) . Ore. (Portland In.)		45·37 N	123·07 W
159	Banks (Is.)	. . . . Austl.		10·10 S	143·08 E
161	Banks, C.	. . . Austl. (Sydney In.)		34·01 S	151·17 E
49	Banks I.	. . . . Can.		73·00 N	123·00 W
159	Banks Is.	. . . . New Hebr.		13·38 S	168·23 E
160	Banks Str.	. . . . Austl.		40·45 S	148·00 E
116	Bann	(băn) . . . . N. Ire.		54·50 N	6·29 W
74	Banning	(băn'ĭng) Calif. (Los Angeles In.)		33·56 N	116·53 W
166	Banningville	. . . . Con. L.		3·19 S	17·28 E
79	Bannister (R.)	(băn'ĭs-tẽr) . . . . Va.		36·45 N	79·17 W
161	Bannockburn	Austl. (Melbourne In.)		38·03 S	144·11 E
98	Baños	(bä'-nyôs) . . . . Ec.		1·30 S	78·22 W
121	Banská Bystrica	(bän'skä bē'strê-tzä) . Czech.		48·46 N	19·10 E
127	Bansko	(bän'skō) . . . . Bul.		41·51 N	23·33 E
110	Banstead	(băn'stĕd) Eng. (London In.)		51·18 N	0·09 W
164	Banthe	(băn'thê) . . . . S. L.		7·36 N	12·34 W
155	Banton	(băn-tōn') Phil. (Manila In.)		12·54 N	121·55 E
116	Bantry	(băn'trĭ) . . . . Ire.		51·39 N	9·30 W
116	Bantry B.	. . . . Ire.		51·25 N	10·09 W
165	Banzyville	(băn-zē-vēl') . . Con. L.		4·14 N	21·11 E
164	Baoule R.	(bà-ōō-lā') . . . . . . Mali		14·00 N	9·08 W
167	Bapsfontein	(băps-fŏn-tān') S. Afr. (Johannesburg & Pretoria In.)		26·01 S	28·26 E
98	Baqueroncito	(bä-kĕ-rō'n-sē-tö) Col. (In.)		3·18 N	74·40 W
129	Bar	(bär) . . . . Sov. Un.		49·02 N	27·44 E
127	Bar	. . . . Yugo.		42·05 N	19·09 E
134	Barabinsk	(bä'rà-bĭnsk) .Sov. Un.		55·18 N	78·00 E
71	Baraboo	(băr'á-bōō) . . . . Wis.		43·29 N	89·44 W
95	Baracoa	(bä-rä-kō'à) . . . . . . Cuba		20·20 N	74·25 W
95	Baracoa (La Habana In.)	. . . . . Cuba		23·03 N	82·34 W
101	Baradeo	(bä-rä-dĕ'ō) Arg. (Buenos Aires In.)		33·50 S	59·30 W
95	Baradères, Baie des (B.)	(bä-rä-dâr') . Hai.		18·35 N	73·35 W
95	Barahona	(bä-rä-ô'nä) .Dom. Rep.		18·15 N	71·10 W
125	Barajas de Madrid	(bä-rä'häs dä mä-drēdh') .Sp. (Madrid In.)		40·28 N	3·35 W
165	Baraka R.	(bà-rä'kä) . . . . Eth.		16·44 N	37·34 E
142	Baranagar	. . . India (Calcutta In.)		22·38 N	88·25 E
92	Barranco	(bä'rä'kō) . . . Br. Hond.		16·01 N	88·55 W
64	Baranof (I.)	(bä-rä'nôf) . . . . Alaska		56·48 N	136·08 W
121	Baranovichi	(bä'rä-nô-vē'chê) Sov. Un.		53·08 N	25·59 E
139	Baranpauh .Indon. (Singapore In.)			0·40 N	103·28 E
100	Barão de Juperanã	(bä-rou'N-dĕ-zhōō-pe-rá'ná) .Braz. (In.)		22·21 S	43·41 W
99	Barão de Melgaço	(bä-roun-dĕ-mĕl-gä'sò).Braz.		16·12 S	55·48 W
142	Bārāsat	. . . . . . India (Calcutta In.)		22·42 N	88·29 E

Page	Name	Pronunciation	Region	Lat. °'	Long. °'
84	Barataria	(bä-rà-tä'rê-á) La. (New Orleans In.)		29·44 N	90·08 W
77	Barataria B.	. . . . La.		29·13 N	89·90 W
98	Baraya	(bä-rä'yä) . . . . . Col. (In.)		3·10 N	75·04 W
101	Barbacena	Braz. (Rio de Janeiro In.)		21·15 S	43·46 W
98	Barbacoas	(bär-bä-kō'äs) . . . . .Col.		1·39 N	78·12 W
99	Barbacoas	(bär-bä-kô'äs) Ven. (In.)		9·30 N	66·58 W
93	Barbados I.	(bär-bä'dōz) W. I. F. (Le. & Wind. Is. In.)		13·30 N	59·48 W
125	Barbastro	(bär-bäs'trō) . . . . . . .Sp.		42·05 N	0·05 E
74	Barbeau	(bär-bō') Mich. (Sault Ste. Marie In.)		46·17 N	84·16 W
75	Barberton	(bär'bẽr-tŭn) Ohio (Cleveland In.)		41·01 N	81·37 W
166	Barberton	. . . . S. Afr.		25·48 S	31·04 E
122	Barbezieux	(bärb'zyû') . . . . . . Fr.		45·30 N	0·11 W
78	Barbourville	(bär'bẽr-vĭl) . . . Ky.		36·52 N	83·58 W
98	Barbosa	(bär-bō'-sä) . Col. (In.)		6·26 N	75·19 W
80	Barboursville	(bär'bẽrs-vĭl) .W. Va.		38·20 N	82·20 W
93	Barbuda I.	(bär-bōō'dá) W. I. F. (Le. & Wind. Is. In.)		17·40 N	61·37 W
159	Barcaldine	(bär'kôl-dīn) . . . Austl.		28·30 S	145·43 E
125	Barcarena	(bär-kä-rĕ'-nä) Port. (Lisboa In.)		38·29 N	9·17 W
124	Barcarrota	(bär-kär-rō'tä) . . . . .Sp.		38·31 N	6·50 W
126	Barcellona	(bär-chĕl-lō'nä) . . . . It.		38·07 N	15·15 E
125	Barcelona	(bär-thä-lō'nä) . . . . .Sp.		41·25 N	2·08 E
99	Barcelona	(bär-sä-lō'nä) .Ven. (In.)		10·09 N	64·41 W
123	Barcelonnette	(bär-sĕ-lô-nĕt') . Fr.		44·24 N	6·42 E
98	Barcelos	(bär-sĕ'lòs) . . . . . Braz.		1·04 S	63·00 W
124	Barcelos	(bär-thä'lōs) . . . . . Port.		41·34 N	8·39 W
165	Bardaï	(bär-dá'ê) . . . . . . Chad		21·22 N	17·01 E
144	Bardar-e Pahlant	. . . . . . Iran		37·16 N	49·15 E
139	Bardawīl, Sabkhat al (B.)	U. A. R. (Palestine In.)		31·20 N	33·24 E
121	Bardejov	(bär'dyĕ-yôf) . .Czech.		49·18 N	21·18 E
168	Bardera	(bär-dā'rä) Som. (Horn of Afr. In.)		2·13 N	42·24 E
116	Bardsey (I.)	(bärd'sê) . . . . Wales		52·45 N	4·50 W
80	Bardstown	(bärds'toun) . . . . . Ky.		37·50 N	85·30 W
78	Bardwell	(bärd'wĕl) . . . . Ky.		36·51 N	88·57 W
130	Barents Sea	(bä'rĕnts) . .Sov. Un.		72·14 N	37·28 E
165	Barentu	(bä-rĕn'tōō) . . . . . . Eth.		15·06 N	37·39 E
122	Barfleur, Pte. de (Pt.)	(bär-flûr') Fr		49·43 N	1·17 W
142	Bargāchia	. . India (Calcutta In.)		22·39 N	88·07 E
135	Barguzin	(bär'gōō-zĭn).Sov. Un.		53·44 N	109·28 E
82	Bar Harbor	(bär här'bẽr). Maine		44·22 N	68·13 W
126	Bari	(bä'rē) . . . . It.		41·08 N	16·53 E
98	Barinas	(bä-rē'näs) . . . . . . .Ven.		8·36 N	70·14 W
86	Baring, C.	(bâr'ĭng) . . . . Can.		70·07 N	119·48 W
154	Barisan, Pegunungan (Mts.)	(bä-rê-sän') .Indon.		2·38 S	101·45 E
154	Barito (Strm.)	(bä-rē'tō) .Indon.		2·10 S	114·38 E
167	Barkly East	(bärk'lē ēst) S. Afr. (Natal In.)		30·58 S	27·37 E
158	Barkly Tableland (Reg.)	(bär'klê) Austl.		18·15 S	145·55 E
122	Bar-le-Duc	(bär-lē-dük') . . . . . . Fr.		48·47 N	5·05 E
158	Barlee (L.)	(bär-lē') . . . . . . Austl.		29·45 S	119·00 E
126	Barletta	(bär-lĕt'tä) . . . . It.		41·19 N	16·20 E
111	Barmstedt	(bärm'shtĕt) Ger. (Hamburg In.)		53·47 N	9·46 E
134	Barnaul	(bär-nä-ōōl') . . .Sov. Un.		53·18 N	83·23 E
81	Barnesboro	(bärnz'bẽr-ò) . . . . Pa.		40·45 N	78·50 W
78	Barnesville	(bärnz'vĭl) . . . . . . Ga.		33·03 N	84·10 W
70	Barnesville	. . . . Minn.		46·38 N	96·25 W
80	Barnesville	. . . . Ohio		39·55 N	81·10 W
81	Barnet	(bär'nĕt) . . . . Vt.		44·20 N	72·00 W
110	Barnetby	(bär'nĕt-bĭ) . . . . . . Eng.		53·34 N	0·26 W
94	Barnett Hbr.	. . . . Ba.		25·40 N	79·20 W
73	Barnsdall	(bärnz'dôl) . . . . . . Okla.		36·38 N	96·14 W
110	Barnsley	(bärnz'lĭ) . . . . Eng.		53·33 N	1·29 W
116	Barnstaple	(bärn'stä-p'l) . . . . . Eng.		51·06 N	4·05 W
79	Barnwell	(bärn'wĕl) . . . . S. C.		33·14 N	81·23 W
164	Baro	(bä'rō) . . . . Nig.		8·34 N	6·25 E
142	Baroda	(bä-rō'dà) . . . . India		22·21 N	73·12 E
165	Baro R.	(bä'rī) . . . . Eth.		7·40 N	34·17 E
166	Barotseland (Reg.)	(bá-rŏt'sĕ-länd) Fed. of Rh. & Nya.		16·00 S	22·52 E
165	Barqah (Cirenaica) (Prov.) .Libya			31·09 N	21·45 E
98	Barquisimeto	(bär-kē-sē-mä'tō) Ven.		10·04 N	69·16 W
99	Barra	(bär'rä) . . . . Braz.		11·04 S	43·11 W
142	Barrackpore	. India (Calcutta In.)		22·46 N	88·22 E
99	Barra do Corda	(bär'rä dō̄ cōr-dä) Braz.		5·35 S	45·13 W
116	Barra Is.	(bär'rä) . . . . Scot.		56·57 N	6·85 W
101	Barra Mansa	(bär'rä män'sä) Braz. (Rio de Janeiro In.)		22·35 S	44·09 W
98	Barrancabermeja	(bär-räŋ'kä-bẽr-mā'hä) .Col.		7·06 N	73·49 W
98	Barranquilla	(bär-rän-kēl'yä) .Col.		10·57 N	75·00 W
99	Barras	(bä'r-räs) . . . . Braz.		3·45 S	42·14 W
81	Barre	(bär'ê) . . . . .Vt.		44·15 N	72·30 W
101	Barre do Piraí	(bär'rê-dô-pē'rä-ē') Braz. (Rio de Janeiro In.)		22·30 S	43·49 W
99	Barreiras	(bär-rā'-räs) . . . .Braz.		12·13 S	44·59 W
125	Barreiro	(bär-rĕ'-rōō) Port. (Lisboa In.)		38·39 N	9·05 W
160	Barren, C.	(bär'ĕn) . . . . Austl.		38·25 S	149·00 E
167	Barren, Îles (Is.)	. . . Malagasy		18·18 S	43·57 E
78	Barren (R.)	. . . . Ky.		37·00 N	86·20 W
99	Barretos	(bär-rā'tòs) . . . . . .Braz.		20·33 S	48·36 W
86	Barrhead	(bär-hĕd') (bär'ĭd) . Can.		54·10 N	114·20 W
81	Barrie	(băr'ĭ) . . . . Can.		44·25 N	79·45 W
85	Barrington	Can. (Montreal In.)		45·07 N	73·35 W
75	Barrington . Ill. (Chicago In.)			42·09 N	88·08 W
84	Barrington . R. I. (Providence In.)			41·44 N	71·16 W
160	Barrington Tops (Mtn.) .Austl.			32·03 S	151·25 E
74	Bar River	(bär) Can. (Sault Ste. Marie In.)		46·27 N	84·02 W
71	Barron	(băr'ŭn) . . . . Wis.		45·24 N	91·51 W
64	Barrow	(băr'ō) . . . . Alaska		71·20 N	156·00 W

Page	Name	Pronunciation	Region	Lat. °'	Long. °'
116	Barrow	. . . . Eng.		54·10 N	3·15 W
158	Barrow (I.)	. . . . Austl.		21·05 S	11·30 E
64	Barrow, Pt.	. . . . Alaska		71·20 N	156·00 W
158	Barrow Creek	. . . . Austl.		21 23 S	133·55 E
116	Barrow R.	(bá-rä) . . . . Ire.		52 35 N	7·05 W
124	Barruelo de Santullán	(bär-rōō-ä-lō dä sän-tōō-lyän') .Sp.		42·55 N	4·19 W
74	Barry	(băr'rĭ) Mo. (Kansas City In.)		39·14 N	94·36 W
68	Barstow	(bär'stō) . . . . Calif.		34·53 N	117·03 W
120	Barth	(bärt) . . . . Ger.		54·20 N	12·43 E
73	Bartholomew Bay.	(bär-thŏl'ô-mū bī-ōō') .Ark.		33·53 N	91·45 W
82	Barthurst	(bär-thŭrst') . . . . Can.		47·38 N	65·40 W
99	Bartica	(bär'tĭ-kà) . . . . . Br. Gu.		6·23 N	58·32 W
133	Bartin	(bär'tĭn) . . . . Tur.		41·35 N	32·12 E
159	Bartle Frere, Mt.	(bärt'l frẽr') Austl.		17·30 S	145·46 E
73	Bartlesville	(bär'tlz-vĭl) . . . . Okla.		36·44 N	95·58 W
75	Bartlett	(bärt'lĕt) .Ill. (Chicago In.)		41·59 N	88·11 W
77	Bartlett	. . . . Tex.		30·48 N	97·25 W
166	Bartolmeu Dias	(bär-tô-lô-mā'ōō dē'äzh).Moz.		20·44 S	35·13 E
81	Barton	(bär'tŭn) . . . . Vt.		44·22 N	72·11 W
110	Barton-on-Humber	(bär'tŭn-ŏn-hŭm'bẽr) .Eng.		53·41 N	0·26 W
121	Bartoszyce	(bär-tô-shĭ'tsä) . . Pol.		54·15 N	20·50 E
79	Bartow	(bär'tō) . . . . . .Fla. (In.)		27·51 N	81·50 W
129	Barvenkovo	(bär'vĕn-kô'vô) Sov. Un.		48·55 N	36·59 E
160	Barwon (R.)	(bär'wŭn) . . . . Austl.		29·45 S	148·25 E
161	Barwon Heads	Austl. (Melbourne In.)		38·17 S	144·59 E
120	Barycz R.	(bá'rĭch) . . . . Pol.		51·30 N	16·38 E
165	Basankusu	(bä-sän-kōō'sōō) Con. L.		1·14 N	19·45 E
111	Basbeck	(bäs'bĕk) Ger. (Hamburg In.)		53·40 N	9·11 E
111	Basdahl	(bäs'däl) Ger. (Hamburg In.)		53·27 N	9·00 E
74	Basehor	(bäs'hôr) Kans. (Kansas City In.)		39·08 N	94·55 W
120	Basel	(bä'z'l) . . . . Switz.		47·32 N	7·35 E
167	Bashee (R.)	(bä-shē') S. Afr. (Natal In.)		31·47 S	28·25 E
151	Bashi Chan	(bäsh'ê) . . . . . . Phil.		21·20 N	120·22 E
132	Bashkir (A.S.S.R.)	(bäsh-kēr') Sov. Un.		54·12 N	57·15 E
129	Bashtanka	(bäsh-tän'kà) .Sov. Un.		47·32 N	32·31 E
126	Basilicata (Reg.)	(bä-zē-lē-kä'tä) It.		40·30 N	15·55 E
67	Basin	(bä'sĭn) . . . . Wyo.		44·22 N	108·02 W
110	Basingstoke	(bä'zĭng-stōk) Eng. (London In.)		51·14 N	1·06 W
126	Baška	(bäsh'ka) . . . . Yugo.		44·58 N	14·44 E
133	Baskale	(bäsh-kä'lĕ) . . . . . Tur.		38·10 N	44·00 E
133	Baskunchak (L.)	. . . . Sov. Un.		48·10 N	46·40 E
165	Basoko	(nà-sō'kò) . . . . . . Con. L.		0·52 N	23·50 E
165	Basoko	. . . . Con. L.		1·22 N	23·40 E
86	Bassano	(bäs-sän'ō) . . . . . . Can.		50·44 N	112·35 W
126	Bassano	. . . . It.		45·46 N	11·44 E
167	Bassas da India (I.)	(bäs'säs dä ēn'dē-á) .Malagasy		21·23 S	39·42 E
154	Bassein	(bŭ-sēn') . . . . .Bur.		16·46 N	94·47 E
143	Bassein	. . . India (Bombay In.)		19·20 N	72·47 E
79	Basset	(bäs'sĕt) . . . . Va.		36·45 N	81·58 W
93	Basse Terre	(bàs' târ') Guad. (Le. & Wind. Is. In.)		16·00 N	61·43 W
93	Basseterre	W. I. F. (Le. & Wind. Is. In.)		17·20 N	62·42 W
93	Basse Terre I.	Guad. (Le. & Wind. Is. In.)		16·10 N	62·14 W
80	Bass Is.	(bäs) . . . . Ohio		41·40 N	82·50 W
160	Bass Str.	. . . . Austl.		39·40 S	145·40 E
71	Basswood (L.)	(bäs'wōōd) Can.-Minn.		48·10 N	91·36 W
118	Båstad	(bô'stät) . . . . Swe.		56·26 N	12·46 E
126	Bastia	(bäs'tē-ä) . . . . Fr.		42·43 N	9·27 E
117	Bastogne	(bäs-tôn'y') . . . . . . Bel.		50·02 N	5·45 E
77	Bastrop	(băs'trŭp) . . . . La.		32·47 N	91·55 W
77	Bastrop	. . . . Tex.		30·08 N	97·18 W
77	Bastrop Bay	. . . . .Tex.		29·07 N	95·22 W
166	Basutoland	(bá-sōō'tō-länd) . Afr.		29·45 S	28·07 E
164	Bata (I.)	. . . . Rio Muni		1·53 N	9·48 E
94	Batabanó	(bä-tä-bä-nō') . . . . Cuba		22·45 N	82·20 W
94	Batabano, Golfo de (G.)	(gôl-fô-dĕ-bä-tä-bä'nò) .Cuba		22·10 N	83·05 W
155	Batac	. . . . Phil. (Manila In.)		17·56 N	120·29 E
142	Batala	. . . . India		31·54 N	75·18 E
136	Bataly	(bá-tä'lĭ) . . . . Sov. Un. (Urals In.)		52·51 N	62·03 E
139	Batam I.	(bä-täm') Indon. (Singapore In.)		1·03 N	104·00 E
155	Batan	(bä-tän').Phil. (Manila In.)		13·20 N	124·00 E
151	Batan Is.	. . . . Phil.		20·58 N	122·20 E
151	Batangan, C.	. . . . Viet.		15·18 N	109·10 E
155	Batangas	(bä-tän'gäs) Phil. (Manila In.)		13·45 N	121·04 E
121	Bataszék	(bä'tä-sĕk) . . . . . . Hung.		46·07 N	18·40 E
75	Batavia	(bá-tā'vĭ-á) Ill. (Chicago In.)		41·51 N	88·18 W
81	Batavia	. . . . N. Y.		40·30 N	78·15 W
75	Batavia . Ohio (Cincinnati In.)			39·05 N	84·10 W
129	Bataysk	(bá-tīsk') . . . . .Sov. Un.		47·08 N	39·44 E
79	Batesburg	(bāts'bûrg) . . . . . S. C.		33·53 N	81·34 W
73	Batesville	(bāts'vĭl) . . . . Ark.		35·46 N	91·39 W
80	Batesville	. . . . Ind.		39·15 N	85·15 W
78	Batesville	. . . . Miss.		34·17 N	89·55 W
128	Batetska	(bä-tĕ'tskà) .Sov. Un.		58·36 N	30·21 E
82	Bath	(băth) . . . . Can.		46·31 N	67·36 W
116	Bath	. . . . Eng.		51·24 N	2·20 W
82	Bath	. . . . Maine		43·54 N	69·50 W
81	Bath	. . . . N. Y.		42·25 N	77·20 W
75	Bath . . . Ohio (Cleveland In.)			41·11 N	81·38 W
93	Bathsheba	W.I.F. (Le. & Wind. Is. In.)		13·13 N	60·30 W

182 Bathurst–Bellingham PRONOUNCING INDEX

Page	Name Pronunciation	Region	Lat. °′	Long. °′
159	Bathurst (bȧth'ŭrst)	Aust.	33·28 S	149·30 E
164	Bathurst	Gam.	13·23 N	16·45 W
167	Bathurst (băt-hûrst)	S. Afr. (Natal In.)	33·26 S	26·53 E
64	Bathurst, C. (bȧth'ŭrst)	Can.	70·33 N	127·55 W
158	Bathurst (I.)	Austl.	11·19 S	130·13 E
86	Bathurst Inlet	Can.	67·25 N	106·50 W
155	Batian (I.)	Indon.	1·07 S	127·52 E
144	Batin, Wādī al (R.)	Sau. Ar.	27·17 N	44·13 E
155	Batjan (I.) (bät-jän')	Indon.	1·07 S	127.52 E
144	Bātlaq-E Gāvkhūn (L.)	Iran	31·40 N	52·48 E
110	Batley (băt'lĭ)	Eng.	53·43 N	1·37 W
164	Batna (bät'nä)	Alg.	35·41 N	6·12 E
77	Baton Rouge (băt'ŭn ro͞ozh')	La.	30·28 N	91·10 W
154	Battambang (bȧt-tȧm-bäng')	Camb.	13·14 N	103·15 E
84	Battery Park (băt'ēr-ĭ)	Va. (Norfolk In.)	36·59 N	76·36 W
80	Battle Creek (băt''l krēk')	Mich.	42·20 N	85·15 W
86	Battleford (băt''l-fērd)	Can.	52·44 N	108·30 W
65	Battle Ground (băt''l ground)	Wash. (Portland In.)	45·47 N	122·32 W
87	Battle Harbour (băt''l här'bēr)	Can.	52·17 N	55·33 W
66	Battle Mountain	Nev.	40·40 N	116·56 W
121	Battonya (bät-tô'nyä)	Hung.	46·17 N	21·00 E
154	Batu (I.) (bä'to͞o)	Indon.	0·10 S	99·55 E
133	Batumi (bŭ-to͞o'mē)	Sov. Un.	41·40 N	41·30 E
99	Baturité (bä-to͞o-rê-tä')	Braz.	4·16 S	38·47 W
155	Bauang (bä'wäng)	Phil. (Manila In.)	16·31 N	120·19 E
164	Bauchi (bȧ-o͞o'chê)	Nig.	10·19 N	9·51 E
166	Baudouinville (bō-dwăn-vēl')	Con. L.	7·12 S	29·39 E
83	Bauld, C.	Can.	51·38 N	55·10 W
85	Baurette (bō-rĕt')	Can. (Montreal In.)	45·24 N	73·32 W
142	Bāuria	India (Calcutta In.)	22·29 N	88·08 E
99	Bauru (bou-ro͞o')	Braz.	22·21 S	48·57 W
119	Bauska (bou'skȧ)	Sov. Un.	56·24 N	24·12 E
95	Bauta (bä'o͞o-tä)	Cuba (La Habana In.)	22·14 N	82·33 W
120	Bautzen (bout'sĕn)	Ger.	51·11 N	14·27 E
	Bavaria, see Bayern			
160	Baw Baw, Mt. (bô-bȧ)	Austl.	37·50 S	146·17 E
154	Bawean (I.) (bȧ'vē-än)	Indon.	5·50 S	112·40 E
110	Bawtry (bô'trĭ)	Eng.	53·26 N	1·01 W
79	Baxley (băks'lĭ)	Ga.	31·47 N	82·22 W
161	Baxter (băks'tēr)	Austl. (Melbourne In.)	38·12 S	145·10 E
73	Baxter Springs (băks'tēr sprĭngs')	Kans.	37·01 N	94·44 W
95	Bayaguana (bä-yä-gwä'nä)	Dom. Rep.	18·45 N	69·40 W
114	Bay al Kabīr Wadi (R.)	Libya	29·52 N	14·28 E
155	Bayambang (bä-yäm-bäng')	Phil. (Manila In.)	15·50 N	120·26 E
94	Bayamo (bä-yä'mō)	Cuba	20·25 N	76·35 W
89	Bayamón	P. R. (Puerto Rico In.)	18·27 N	66·13 W
134	Bayan-Aul (bä'yän-oul')	Sov. Un.	50·43 N	75·37 E
70	Bayard (bā'ērd)	Nebr.	41·45 N	103·20 W
81	Bayard	W. Va.	39·15 N	79·20 W
133	Bayburt (bä'ī-bo͝ort)	Tur.	40·15 N	40·10 E
80	Bay City (bā)	Mich.	43·35 N	83·55 W
77	Bay City	Tex.	28·59 N	95·58 W
146	Baydarag Gol (R.)	Mong.	46·09 N	98·52 E
132	Baydaratskaya Guba (B.)	Sov. Un.	69·20 N	66·10 E
83	Bayde Verde	Can.	48·06 N	52·50 W
120	Bayern (Bavaria) (State) (bī'ērn) (bȧ-vâ-rĭ-ȧ)	Ger.	49·00 N	11·16 E
122	Bayeux (bȧ-yû')	Fr.	49·19 N	0·41 W
71	Bayfield (bā'fēld)	Wis.	46·48 N	90·51 W
135	Baykal, Ozero (Baikal, L.) (bī'kăl') (bī'kôl)	Sov. Un.	53·00 N	109·28 E
135	Baykals'kiy Khrebet (Baikal Mts.)	Sov. Un.	53·30 N	102·00 E
134	Baykit (bī-kēt')	Sov. Un.	61·43 N	96·39 E
134	Baykonur (bī-kô-no͞or')	Sov. Un.	47·46 N	66·11 E
136	Baymak (bȧy'mäk)	Sov. Un. (Urals In.)	52·35 N	58·21 E
78	Bay Minette (bā'mĭn-ĕt')	Ala.	30·52 N	87·44 W
74	Bay Mills (bā mĭlls)	Mich. (Sault Ste. Marie In.)	46·27 N	84·36 W
71	Bay Mills Ind. Res.	Mich.	46·19 N	85·03 W
155	Bayombong (bä-yôm-bŏng')	Phil. (Manila In.)	16·28 N	121·09 E
122	Bayonne (bȧ-yŏn')	Fr.	43·28 N	1·30 W
84	Bayonne (bā-yōn')	N. J. (New York In.)	40·40 N	74·07 W
77	Bayou Bodcau Res. (bī'yo͞o bŏd'kō)	La.	32·49 N	93·22 W
74	Bayport (bā'pōrt)	Minn. (Minneapolis, St. Paul In.)	45·02 N	92·46 W
127	Bayramiç	Tur.	39·48 N	26·35 E
120	Bayreuth (bī-roit')	Ger.	49·56 N	11·35 E
83	Bay Roberts (bā rŏb'ērts)	Can.	47·36 N	53·12 W
81	Bays, L. of (bās)	Can.	45·15 N	79·00 W
78	Bay St. Louis (bā' sănt lo͞o'ĭs)	Miss.	30·19 N	89·20 W
84	Bay Shore (bā' shôr)	N. Y. (New York In.)	40·44 N	73·15 W
139	Bayt Lahm (Bethlehem) (bĕth'lē-hĕm)	Jordan (Palestine In.)	31·42 N	35·13 E
77	Baytown (bā'town)	Tex. (In.)	29·44 N	95·01 W
165	Bayuda Steppe (bä-yo͞o'dä)	Sud.	17·27 N	31·43 E
84	Bayview (bā'vū)	Ala. (Birmingham In.)	33·34 N	86·59 W
65	Bayview	Wash. (Seattle In.)	48·29 N	122·28 W
75	Bay Village (bā)	Ohio (Cleveland In.)	41·29 N	81·56 W
124	Baza (bä'thä)	Sp.	37·29 N	2·46 W
133	Bazar-Dyuzi, Gora (Mt.) (bä'zär-dyo͞oz'ĕ)	Sov. Un.	41·20 N	47·40 E
166	Bazaruto, Ilha (I.) (ē'lä-bä-zä-ro͞o'tō)	Moz.	21·42 S	36·10 E
167	Bazeia Mt. (bă-zēȧ)	S. Afr. (Natal In.)	31·33 S	28·23 E
124	Baztán (bäth-tän')	Sp.	43·12 N	1·30 W
70	Beach (bēch)	N. D.	46·55 N	104·00 W
81	Beacon (bē'kŭn)	N. Y.	41·30 N	73·55 W
85	Beaconsfield (bē'kŭnz-fēld)	Can. (Montreal In.)	45·26 N	73·51 W
84	Beafort Mtn. (bē'fōrt)	N. J. (New York In.)	41·08 N	74·23 W
76	Beals Cr. (bēls)	Tex.	32·10 N	101·14 W
85	Beamsville	Can. (Toronto In.)	43·10 N	79·29 W
67	Bear Creek (bâr krēk)	Mont.	45·11 N	109·07 W
78	Bear Cr. (bâr)	Ala.	34·27 N	88·00 W
74	Bear Cr.	Tex. (Dallas, Fort Worth In.)	32·56 N	97·09 W
73	Beardstown (bērds'toun)	Ill.	40·01 N	90·26 W
65	Bearhead Mtn. (bâr'hĕd)	Wash. (Seattle In.)	47·01 N	121·49 W
67	Bear L.	Idaho-Utah	41·56 N	111·10 W
67	Bear R.	Idaho	42·17 N	111·42 W
74	Bear R.	Utah (Salt Lake City In.)	41·28 N	112·10 W
67	Bear River B.	Utah	41·25 N	112·20 W
124	Beas de Segura (bā'äs dā sä-go͞o'rä)	Sp.	38·16 N	2·53 W
95	Beata (I.) (bĕ-ä'tä)	Dom. Rep.	17·40 N	71·40 W
95	Beata, Cabo (C.) (kä'bô-bĕ-ä'tä)	Dom. Rep.	17·40 N	71·20 W
73	Beatrice (bē'ȧ-trĭs)	Nebr.	40·16 N	96·45 W
68	Beatty (bēt'ê)	Nev.	36·58 N	116·48 W
80	Beattyville (bēt'ē-vĭl)	Ky.	37·35 N	83·40 W
122	Beaucaire (bō-kâr')	Fr.	43·49 N	4·37 E
82	Beauceville (bōs'vēl)	Can.	46·12 N	70·46 W
123	Beaucourt (bō-ko͞or')	Fr.	47·30 N	6·54 E
79	Beaufort (bō'fērt)	N. C.	34·43 N	76·40 W
79	Beaufort	S. C.	32·25 N	80·40 W
64	Beaufort Sea	Alaska	70·30 N	138·40 W
166	Beaufort West	S. Afr.	32·20 S	22·45 E
85	Beauharnois (bō-är-nwä')	Can. (Montreal In.)	45·23 N	73·52 W
74	Beaumont (bō'mŏnt)	Calif. (Los Angeles In.)	33·57 N	116·57 W
85	Beaumont	Can. (Quebec In.)	46·50 N	71·01 W
77	Beaumont	Tex.	30·05 N	94·06 W
122	Beaune (bōn)	Fr.	47·02 N	4·49 E
85	Beauport (bō-pôr')	Can. (Quebec In.)	46·52 N	71·11 W
85	Beaupré (bō-prā')	Can. (Quebec In.)	47·03 N	70·53 W
85	Beaurepaire (bōr-pĕr')	Can. (Montreal In.)	45·25 N	73·53 W
86	Beausejour	Can.	50·07 N	96·39 W
122	Beauvais (bō-vĕ')	Fr.	49·25 N	2·05 E
72	Beaver (bē'vēr)	Okla.	36·46 N	100·31 W
75	Beaver	Pa. (Pittsburgh In.)	40·42 N	80·18 W
69	Beaver	Utah	38·15 N	112·40 W
80	Beaver (I.)	Mich.	45·40 N	85·30 W
86	Beaver (R.)	Can.	54·21 N	111·50 W
72	Beaver City	Nebr.	40·08 N	99·52 W
72	Beaver Cr.	Colo.	39·42 N	103·37 W
72	Beaver Cr.	Kans.	39·44 N	101·05 W
70	Beaver Cr.	Mont.	46·45 N	104·18 W
70	Beaver Cr.	Wyo.	43·46 N	104·25 W
71	Beaver Dam	Wis.	43·29 N	88·50 W
67	Beaverhead Mts. (bē'vēr-hĕd)	Mont.	44·33 N	112·59 W
67	Beaverhead R.	Mont.	45·05 N	112·50 W
80	Beaver Ind. Res.	Mich.	45·40 N	85·30 W
65	Beaverton (bē'vēr-tŭn)	Ore. (Portland In.)	45·29 N	122·49 W
98	Bebara' (bĕ-bȧ-rȧ')	Col. (In.)	6·07 N	76·39 W
110	Bebington (bē'bĭng-tŭn)	Eng.	53·20 N	2·59 W
91	Becal (bā-käl')	Mex.	20·25 N	90·04 W
127	Bečej (bĕ'chā)	Yugo.	45·36 N	20·03 E
124	Becerreá (bā-thā'rē-ä)	Sp.	42·49 N	7·12 W
64	Becharof (L.) (bĕk ȧ rôf)	Alaska	57·58 N	156·58 W
65	Becher B. (bēch'ēr)	Can. (Seattle In.)	48·18 N	123·37 W
163	Bechuanaland (bĕch-o͞o-ä'nȧ-lănd)	Afr.	22·10 S	23·13 E
80	Beckley (bĕk'lĭ)	W. Va.	37·40 N	81·15 W
122	Bédarieux (bā-dȧ-ryû')	Fr.	43·36 N	3·11 E
85	Beddington Cr. (bĕd'ĕng tŭn)	Can. (Calgary In.)	51·14 N	114·13 W
81	Bedford (bĕd'fērd)	Can.	45·10 N	73·00 W
116	Bedford	Eng.	52·10 N	0·25 W
80	Bedford	Ind.	38·50 N	86·30 W
71	Bedford	Iowa	40·40 N	94·41 W
83	Bedford	Mass. (Boston In.)	42·30 N	71·17 W
84	Bedford	N. Y. (New York In.)	41·12 N	73·38 W
75	Bedford	Ohio (Cleveland In.)	41·23 N	81·32 W
81	Bedford	Pa.	40·05 N	78·20 W
167	Bedford	S. Afr. (Natal In.)	32·43 S	26·19 E
79	Bedford	Va.	37·19 N	79·27 W
84	Bedford Hill	N. Y. (New York In.)	41·14 N	73·41 W
110	Bedworth (bĕd'wērth)	Eng.	52·29 N	1·28 W
121	Bedzin (băn-jēn')	Pol.	50·19 N	19·10 W
73	Beebe (bē'bē)	Ark.	35·04 N	91·54 W
75	Beecher (bē'chûr)	Ill. (Chicago In.)	41·20 N	87·38 W
65	Beechey Hd. (bē'chĭ hĕd)	Can. (Seattle In.)	48·19 N	123·40 W
75	Beech Grove (bēch grōv)	Ind. (Indianapolis In.)	39·43 N	86·05 W
160	Beecroft Hd. (bē'krŏft)	Austl.	35·03 S	151·15 E
111	Beelitz (bĕ'lētz)	Ger. (Berlin In.)	52·14 N	12·59 E
139	Beer (R.)	Isr. (Palestine In.)	31·23 N	34·30 E
139	Beersheba (bēr-shē'bȧ)	Isr. (Palestine In.)	31·15 N	34·48 E
168	Beestekraal	S. Afr. (Johannesburg & Pretoria In.)	25·22 S	27·34 E
110	Beeston (bēs't'n)	Eng.	52·55 N	1·11 W
111	Beetz R. (bĕtz)	Ger. (Berlin In.)	52·28 N	12·37 E
77	Beeville (bē'vĭl)	Tex.	28·24 N	97·44 W
160	Bega (bā'gȧ)	Austl.	36·50 S	149·49 E
73	Beggs (bĕgz)	Okla.	35·46 N	96·06 W
122	Bègles (bĕ'gl')	Fr.	44·47 N	0·34 W
165	Béhagle (bā-ä'gl')	Chad	9·29 N	16·18 E
142	Behampur	India	20·19 N	85·53 E
120	Beilinzona	Switz.	46·11 N	9·00 E
165	Beilul	Eth.	13·15 N	42·21 E
166	Beira (bā'rȧ)	Moz.	19·46 S	34·58 E
124	Beira (Reg.) (bĕ'y-rä)	Port.	40·38 N	8·00 W
	Beirut, see Beyrouth			
139	Beit Shean	Isr. (Palestine In.)	32·30 N	35·30 E
124	Beja (bä'zhä)	Port.	38·03 N	7·53 W
124	Bejar	Sp.	40·25 N	5·43 W
144	Bejestān	Iran	34·30 N	58·22 E
144	Bejnurd	Iran	37·29 N	57·13 E
95	Bejucal (bā-ho͞o-käl')	Cuba (La Habana In.)	22·08 N	82·23 W
93	Bejuco (bĕ-ko͞o'kŏ)	Pan.	8·37 N	79·54 W
121	Békés (bā'kāsh)	Hung.	46·45 N	21·08 E
121	Békéscsaba (bā'kāsh-chô'bô)	Hung.	46·39 N	21·06 E
147	Beketova (bĕk'e-to'vȧ)	Sov. Un.	53·23 N	125·21 E
127	Bela Crkva (bĕ'lä tsĕrk'vä)	Yugo.	44·53 N	21·25 E
124	Belalcázar (bāl-ál-kä'thär)	Sp.	38·35 N	5·12 W
125	Belas (bĕ'-läs)	Port. (Lisboa In.)	38·47 N	9·16 W
127	Bela-Slatina (byä'la slä'tēnä)	Bul.	43·26 N	23·56 E
154	Belawan (bå-lä'wän)	Indon.	3·43 N	98·43 E
132	Belaya (R.) (byĕ'lĭ-yȧ)	Sov. Un.	52·45 N	61·15 E
129	Belaya Tserkov' (byĕ'lĭ-yȧ tsĕr'kôf)	Sov. Un.	49·48 N	30·09 E
87	Belcher Is. (bĕl'chēr)	Can.	56·20 N	80·40 W
75	Belden (bĕl'dĕn)	Ohio (Cleveland In.)	41·14 N	82·01 W
80	Belding (bĕl'dĭng)	Mich.	43·05 N	85·25 W
132	Belebey (byĕ'lĕ-bā'ĭ)	Sov. Un.	54·00 N	54·10 E
159	Belef, Isles	N. Cal.	19·30 S	160·32 E
99	Belém (Pará) (bå-lĕn') (pä-rä')	Braz.	1·18 S	48·27 W
69	Belen (bĕ-lån')	N. Mex.	34·40 N	106·45 W
100	Belén (bā-lān')	Par.	23·30 S	57·09 W
128	Belëv (byĕl'yĕf)	Sov. Un.	53·49 N	36·06 E
65	Belfair (bĕl'fâr)	Wash. (Seattle In.)	47·27 N	122·50 W
116	Belfast (bĕl'fȧst)	N. Ire.	54·36 N	5·45 W
82	Belfast	Maine	44·25 N	69·01 W
116	Belfast, Lough (B.) (lŏk bĕl'fȧst)	Ire.	54·45 N	7·40 W
165	Bēlfodiyo	Eth.	10·45 N	39·27 E
123	Belfort (bā-fôr')	Fr.	47·40 N	7·50 E
143	Belgaum	India	15·57 N	74·32 E
102	Belgium (bĕl'jĭ-ŭm)	Eur.	51·00 N	2·52 E
129	Belgorod (byĕl'gŭ-rut)	Sov. Un.	50·36 N	36·32 E
129	Belgorod (Oblast)	Sov. Un.	50·40 N	36·42 E
129	Belgorod Dnestrovskiy (byĕl'gŭ-rud nyĕs-trôf'skē)	Sov. Un.	46·09 N	30·19 E
	Belgrade, see Beograd			
79	Belhaven (bĕl'hā-vĕn)	N. C.	35·33 N	76·37 W
81	Belington (bĕl'ĭng-tŭn)	W. Va.	39·00 N	79·55 W
127	Beli Timok (R.) (Bĕ'lē Tē'môk)	Yugo.	43·35 N	22·13 E
154	Belitung (I.)	Indon.	3·30 S	107·30 E
92	Belize (bĕ-lēz')	Br. Hond. (Yucatan In.)	17·31 N	88·10 W
92	Belize R.	Br. Hond. (Yucatan In.)	17·16 N	88·56 W
136	Bel'kovo (byĕl'kô-vô)	Sov. Un. (Moskva In.)	56·15 N	38·49 E
135	Bel'kovskiy (I.) (byĕl-kôf'skĭ)	Sov. Un.	75·52 N	133·00 E
74	Bell (bĕl)	Calif. (Los Angeles In.)	33·59 N	118·11 W
83	Bell (I.)	Can.	50·45 N	55·35 W
80	Bellaire (bĕl-âr')	Ohio	40·00 N	80·45 W
77	Bellaire	Tex. (In.)	29·43 N	95·28 W
143	Bellary (bĕl-lä'rē)	India	15·15 N	76·56 E
100	Bella Union (bĕ'l-yä-o͞o-nyô'n)	Ur.	30·18 S	57·26 W
100	Bella Vista (bä'lyä vēs'tä)	Arg.	27·07 S	65·14 W
100	Bella Vista	Arg.	28·35 S	58·53 W
100	Bella Vista	Arg. (In.)	34·18 S	58·41 W
99	Bella Vista	Braz.	22·16 S	56·14 W
83	Belle B. (bĕl)	Can.	47·35 N	55·15 W
84	Belle Chasse (bĕl shäs')	La. (New Orleans In.)	29·52 N	90·00 W
80	Bellefontaine (bĕl-fŏn'tân)	Ohio	40·25 N	83·50 W
70	Belle Fourche (bĕl' fo͞orsh')	S. D.	44·28 N	103·50 W
70	Belle Fourche (R.)	Wyo.	44·29 N	104·40 W
70	Belle Fourche Res.	S. D.	44·51 N	103·44 W
123	Bellegarde-sur-Valserine (bĕl-gärd'sür-väl-sâ-rēn')	Fr.	46·06 N	6·50 E
79	Belle Glade (bĕl glād)	Fla. (In.)	26·39 N	80·37 W
122	Belle Île (I.) (bĕl-ēl')	Fr.	47·15 N	3·30 W
87	Belle Isle, Str. of	Can.	51·21 N	55·56 W
84	Belle Mead (bĕl mēd)	N. J. (New York In.)	40·28 N	74·40 W
83	Belleoram	Can.	47·29 N	55·50 W
71	Belle Plaine (bĕl plān')	Iowa	41·52 N	92·19 W
75	Belle Vernon (bĕl vûr'nŭn)	Pa. (Pittsburgh In.)	40·08 N	79·52 W
81	Belleville (bĕl'vĭl)	Can.	44·15 N	77·25 W
74	Belleville	Ill. (St. Louis In.)	38·31 N	89·59 W
73	Belleville	Kans.	39·49 N	97·37 W
75	Belleville	Mich. (Detroit In.)	42·12 N	83·29 W
84	Belleville	N. J. (New York In.)	40·47 N	74·09 W
71	Bellevue (bĕl'vū)	Iowa	42·14 N	90·26 W
75	Bellevue	Ky. (Cincinnati In.)	39·06 N	84·29 W
80	Bellevue	Mich.	42·30 N	85·00 W
80	Bellevue	Ohio	41·15 N	82·45 W
75	Bellevue	Pa. (Pittsburgh In.)	40·30 N	80·04 W
65	Bellevue	Wash. (Seattle In.)	47·37 N	122·12 W
123	Belley (bĕ-lē')	Fr.	45·46 N	5·41 E
74	Bellflower (bĕl-flou'ēr)	Calif. (Los Angeles In.)	33·53 N	118·08 W
83	Bellingham (bĕl'ĭng-hăm)	Mass. (Boston In.)	42·05 N	71·28 W
65	Bellingham	Wash. (Vancouver In.)	48·46 N	122·29 W
65	Bellingham B.	Wash. (Vancouver In.)	48·44 N	122·34 W

ăt; finăl; rāte; senāte; ärm; ȧsk; sofȧ; fâre; ch-choose; dh-as th in other; bē; ēvent; bĕt; recĕnt; cratēr; g-go; gh-guttural g; bĭt; ĭ-short neutral; rīde: K-guttural k as ch in German ich;

PRONOUNCING INDEX Bellingshausen–Biafra 183

Page	Name Pronunciation Region	Lat. °'	Long. °'
47	Bellingshausen Sea (bĕl'ĭngz houz'n) . Ant.	72·00 S	80·30 W
126	Bellinzona (bĕl-ĭn-tsō'nä) ... Switz.	46·10 N	9·09 E
84	Bellmore (bĕl-mōr) N. Y. (New York In.)	40·40 N	73·31 W
98	Bello (bĕ'l-yô) ... Col. (In.)	6·20 N	75·33 W
81	Bellows Falls (bĕl'ōz fôls) ... Vt.	43·10 N	72·30 W
142	Bellpat ... W. Pak.	29·08 N	68·00 E
87	Bell Pen ... Can.	63·50 N	81·16 W
85	Bells Corners .. Can. (Ottawa In.)	45·20 N	75·49 W
65	Bells Mtn. (bĕls) Wash. (Portland In.)	45·50 N	122·21 W
126	Belluno (bĕl-lōō'nō) ... It.	46·08 N	12·14 E
100	Bell Ville (bĕl vēl') ... Arg.	32·33 S	62·36 W
166	Bellville S. Afr. (Cape Town In.)	33·54 S	18·38 E
77	Bellville (bĕl'vĭl) ... Tex.	29·57 N	96·15 W
124	Bélmez (bĕl'mĕth) ... Sp.	38·17 N	5·17 W
71	Belmond (bĕl'mŏnd) ... Iowa	42·49 N	93·37 W
65	Belmont . Calif. (San Francisco In.)	37·34 N	122·18 W
99	Belmonte (bĕl-mōn'tå) ... Braz.	15·58 S	38·47 W
135	Belogorsk ... Sov. Un.	51·09 N	128·32 E
101	Belo Horizonte (bĕ'lô-re-sô'n-tĕ) Braz. (Rio de Janeiro In.)	19·54 S	43·56 W
72	Beloit (bê-loit') ... Kans.	39·26 N	98·06 W
71	Beloit ... Wis.	42·31 N	89·04 W
132	Belomorsk (byĕl-ô-môrsk') Sov. Un.	64·30 N	34·42 E
129	Belopol'ye (byĕ'lô-pôl'yĕ) . Sov. Un.	51·10 N	34·19 E
136	Beloretsk (byĕ'lō-rĕtsk) Sov. Un. (Urals In.)	53·58 N	58·25 E
130	Belorussian (S. S. R.) ... Sov. Un.	53·30 N	25·33 E
129	Belosarayskaya, Kosa (C.) (kô-sä' byĕ'lô-sä-räy'skå'yä) Sov. Un.	46·43 N	37·18 E
134	Belovo (byĕ'lŭ-vû) ... Sov. Un.	54·17 N	86·23 E
129	Belovodsk (byĕ-lŭ-vôdsk') Sov. Un.	49·12 N	39·36 E
132	Beloye (L.) ... Sov. Un.	60·10 N	38·05 E
132	Belozersk (byĕ-lŭ-zyôrsk') . Sov. Un.	60·00 N	38·00 E
110	Belper (bĕl'pēr) ... Eng.	53·01 N	1·28 W
67	Belt (bĕlt) ... Mont.	47·11 N	110·58 W
67	Belt Cr. ... Mont.	47·19 N	110·58 W
77	Belton (bĕl'tŭn) ... Tex.	31·04 N	97·27 W
77	Belton L. ... Tex.	31·15 N	97·35 W
129	Bel'tsy (bĕl'tsē) ... Sov. Un.	47·47 N	27·57 E
134	Belukha, Gol'tsy (Mtn.) . Sov. Un.	49·47 N	86·23 E
74	Belvedere (bĕl-vĕ-dēr') Calif. (Los Angeles In.)	34·02 N	118·11 W
71	Belvidere ... Ill.	42·14 N	88·52 W
81	Belvidere ... Pa.	40·50 N	75·05 W
159	Belyando (R.) (bĕl-yän'dō) . Austl.	22·09 S	146·48 E
136	Belyanka (byĕl'yan-kå) Sov. Un. (Urals In.)	56·04 N	59·16 E
128	Belynichi (byĕl-ĭ-nĭ'chĭ) .. Sov. Un.	54·02 N	29·42 E
128	Belyy (byĕ'lē) ... Sov. Un.	55·52 N	32·58 E
134	Belyy (I.) ... Sov. Un.	73·19 N	72·00 E
136	Belyye Stolby (byĕl'ĭ-ye stôl'bĭ) Sov. Un. (Moskva In.)	55·20 N	37·52 E
111	Belzig (bĕl'tsēg) .. Ger. (Berlin In.)	52·08 N	12·35 E
78	Belzoni (bĕl-zō'nê) ... Miss.	33·09 N	90·30 W
166	Bembe (bĕN'bĕ) ... Ang.	7·00 S	14·20 E
124	Bembezar (R.) (bĕm-bä-thär') . Sp.	38·00 N	5·18 W
71	Bemidji (bê-mĭj'ĭ) ... Minn.	47·28 N	94·54 W
166	Bena Dibele (bĕn'å dē-bĕ'lĕ) Con. L.	4·00 S	22·49 E
160	Benalla (bĕn-ăl'å) ... Austl.	36·30 S	14·600 E
124	Benavente (bä-nä-vĕn'tä) ... Sp.	42·01 N	5·43 W
74	Benbrook (bĕn'brŏŏk) Tex. (Dallas, Fort Worth In.)	32·41 N	97·27 W
66	Bend (bĕnd) ... Ore.	44·04 N	121·17 W
64	Bendeleben, Mt. (bĕn-dĕl-bĕn) Alaska	65·18 N	163·45 W
168	Bender Cassim Som. (Horn of Afr. In.)	11·19 N	49·10 E
129	Bendery (bĕn-dyĕ're) ... Sov. Un.	46·49 N	29·29 E
160	Bendigo (bĕn'dĭ-gō) ... Austl.	36·39 S	144·20 E
120	Benešov (bĕn'ĕ-shôf) ... Czech.	49·48 N	14·40 E
126	Benevento (bā-nā-vĕn'tō) ... It.	41·08 N	14·46 E
138	Bengal, B. of (bĕn-gôl') ... Asia	17·30 N	87·00 E
139	Bengkalis (bĕng-kä'lĭs) Indon. (Singapore In.)	1·29 N	102·06 E
154	Bengkulu ... Indon.	3·46 S	102·18 E
166	Benguela (bĕn-gĕl'á) ... Ang.	12·35 S	13·28 E
166	Benguela (Reg.) ... Ang.	13·13 S	16·00 E
116	Ben Hope (Mtn.) (bĕn hōp) .. Scot.	58·25 N	4·25 W
84	Ben Hill (bĕn hĭl) Ga. (Atlanta In.)	33·42 N	84·31 W
98	Beni (R.) (bā'nê) ... Bol.	13·41 S	67·30 W
164	Beni-Abbès (bā'nê ä-bĕs') ... Alg.	30·11 N	2·13 W
125	Benicarló (bā-nē-kär-lō') ... Sp.	40·26 N	0·25 E
65	Benicia (bê-nĭsh'ĭ-á) Calif. (San Francisco In.)	38·03 N	122·09 W
164	Benin (bĕn-ēn') ... Nig.	6·21 N	5·34 E
164	Benin, Bight of ... Afr.	5·09 N	2·19 E
164	Beni Saf (bā'nê säf') ... Alg.	35·23 N	1·20 W
72	Benkelman (bĕn-kĕl-mán) ... Nebr.	40·05 N	101·35 W
126	Benkovac (bĕn'kō-váts) ... Yugo.	44·02 N	15·41 E
167	Ben Mac Dhui (Mtn.) (bĕn măk-dōō'ê) . Bas. (Natal In.)	30·38 S	27·54 E
79	Bennettsville (bĕn'ĕts-vĭl) ... S. C.	34·35 N	79·41 W
81	Bennington (bĕn'ĭng-tŭn) ... Vt.	42·55 N	73·15 W
84	Benns Church (bĕnz' chûrch') Va. (Norfolk In.)	36·47 N	76·35 W
167	Benoni (bĕ-nō'nī) ... S. Afr. (Johannesburg & Pretoria In.)	26·11 S	28·19 E
92	Benque Viejo (bĕn-kĕ bĭĕ'hō) Br. Hond. (Yucatan In.)	17·07 N	89·07 W
75	Bensenville (bĕn'sĕn-vĭl) Ill. (Chicago In.)	41·57 N	87·56 W
120	Bensheim (bĕns-hīm) ... Ger.	49·42 N	8·38 E
69	Benson (bĕn-sŭn) ... Ariz.	32·00 N	110·20 W
70	Benson ... Minn.	45·18 N	95·36 W
75	Bentleyville (bent'lē vĭl) Pa. (Pittsburgh In.)	40·07 N	80·01 W
82	Benton (bĕn'tŭn) ... Can.	45·59 N	67·36 W
73	Benton ... Ark.	34·34 N	92·34 W
68	Benton ... Calif.	37·44 N	118·22 W
110	Benton ... Eng.	53·27 N	2·07 W
80	Benton ... Ill.	38·00 N	88·55 W
80	Benton Harbor (bĕn'tŭn här'bēr) Mich.	42·05 N	86·30 W
73	Bentonville (bĕn'tŭn-vĭl) ... Ark.	36·22 N	94·11 W
164	Benue R. (bā'nōō-å) ... Nig.	7·49 N	7·54 E
139	Benut (R.) . Mala. (Singapore In.)	1·43 N	103·20 E
80	Benwood (bĕn-wŏŏd) ... W. Va.	39·55 N	80·45 W
127	Beograd (Belgrade) (bĕ-ō'gråd) (bĕl'gräd) . Yugo.	44·48 N	20·32 E
153	Beppu (bĕ'pōō) ... Jap.	33·16 N	131·30 E
93	Bequia I. (bĕk-ē'ä) W. I. F. (Le. & Wind. Is. In.)	13·00 N	61·08 W
155	Beraoe, Teloek (B.) . Neth. N. Gui.	2·22 S	131·40 E
127	Berat (bĕ-rät') ... Alb.	40·43 N	19·59 E
100	Berazategui (bĕ-rä-zá'tĕ-gē) Arg. (In.)	34·31 S	58·12 W
165	Berber (bûr'bĕr) ... Sud.	18·11 N	34·00 E
168	Berbera (bûr'bûr-á) Som. (Horn of Afr. In.)	10·25 N	45·05 E
122	Berck (bĕrk) ... Fr.	50·26 N	1·36 E
129	Berdichev (bĕ-dē'chĕf) ... Sov. Un.	49·53 N	28·32 E
129	Berdyanskaya, Kosa (C.) (kô-sä' bĕr-dyän'skä-yä) . Sov. Un.	46·38 N	36·42 E
136	Berdyaush (bĕr'dyâûsh) Sov. Un. (Urals In.)	55·10 N	59·12 E
78	Berea (bê-rē'á) ... Ky.	37·30 N	84·19 W
75	Berea ... Ohio (Cleveland In.)	41·22 N	81·51 W
121	Beregovo (bĕ'rĕ-gô-vô) ... Sov. Un.	48·13 N	22·40 E
139	Berekhot Shelmo (Mt) Jordan (Palestine In.)	31·35 N	35·07 E
165	Berenice (Ruins) (bĕr-ê-nī'sê) U. A. R.	23·56 N	35·18 E
86	Berens River (bĕr'ĕnz) ... Can.	52·28 N	97·11 W
70	Beresford (bĕr'ĕs-fērd) ... S. D.	43·05 N	96·46 W
121	Berettyóújfalu (bĕ'rĕt-tyō-ōō'y'fô-lōō) . Hung.	47·14 N	21·33 E
121	Berëza (bĕ-rā'zå) ... Sov. Un.	52·29 N	24·59 E
121	Berezhany (bĕr-yĕ'zhá-nê) Sov. Un.	49·25 N	24·58 E
128	Berezina (R.) (bĕr-yĕ'zē-nà) Sov. Un.	53·20 N	29·05 E
128	Berezino (bĕr-yä'zê-nô) .. Sov. Un.	53·51 N	28·54 E
129	Berezna (bĕr-yôz'nà) ... Sov. Un.	51·32 N	31·47 E
129	Bereznegovata ... Sov. Un.	47·19 N	32·58 E
136	Berezniki (bĕr-yôz'nyê-kê) Sov. Un. (Urals In.)	59·25 N	56·46 E
129	Berezovka (bĕr-yôz'ôf-kå) Sov. Un.	47·12 N	30·56 E
136	Berëzovka ... Sov. Un. (Urals In.)	57·35 N	57·19 E
132	Berëzovo (bĭr-yô'zē-vû) .. Sov. Un.	64·10 N	65·10 E
136	Berëzovskiy (bĕr-yô'zôf-skĭ) Sov. Un. (Urals In.)	56·54 N	60·47 E
125	Berga (bĕr'gä) ... Sp.	42·05 N	1·52 E
127	Bergama (bĕr'gä-mä) ... Tur.	39·08 N	27·09 E
126	Bergamo (bĕr'gä-mō) ... It.	45·43 N	9·41 E
99	Bergantín (bĕr-gän-tē'n) Ven. (In.)	10·04 N	64·23 W
111	Bergedorf (bĕr'gĕ-dôrf) Ger. (Hamburg In.)	53·29 N	10·12 E
120	Bergen (bĕr'gĕn) ... Ger.	54·26 N	13·26 E
118	Bergen ... Nor.	60·24 N	5·20 E
111	Bergen op Zoom Neth. (Amsterdam In.)	51·29 N	3·16 E
122	Bergerac (bĕr-zhē-råk') ... Fr.	44·49 N	0·28 E
123	Bergisch Gladbach (bĕrg'ĭsh-glät'bäk) . Ger. (Ruhr In.)	50·59 N	7·08 E
111	Berglern (bĕrgh'lĕrn) Ger. (München In.)	48·24 N	11·55 E
74	Bergs (bûrgs) Tex. (San Antonio In.)	29·19 N	98·26 W
167	Bergville (bĕrg'vĭl) S. Afr. (Natal In.)	28·46 S	29·22 E
166	Bergvliet . S. Afr. (Cape Town In.)	34·03 S	18·27 E
49	Bering Sea (bē'rĭng) ... Asia-N. A.	58·00 N	175·00 W
64	Bering Str. ... Alaska	64·50 N	169·50 W
129	Berislav (byĕr'ĭ-släf) ... Sov. Un.	46·49 N	33·24 E
124	Berja (bĕr'hä) ... Sp.	36·50 N	2·56 W
65	Berkeley (bûrk'lĭ) Calif. (San Francisco In.)	37·52 N	122·17 W
74	Berkeley ... Mo. (St. Louis In.)	38·45 N	90·20 W
81	Berkeley Springs (bûrk'lĭ sprĭngz) W. Va.	39·40 N	78·10 W
110	Berkhamsted (bĕrk'hăm'stĕd) Eng. (London In.)	51·44 N	0·34 W
75	Berkley (bûrk'lĭ) Mich. (Detroit In.)	42·30 N	83·10 W
127	Berkovitsa (bĕ-kō'vē-tså) ... Bul.	43·14 N	23·08 E
124	Berlengas (Is.) (bĕr-lĕn'gäzh) . Port.	39·25 N	9·33 W
111	Berlin (bĕr-lēn') .. Ger. (Berlin In.)	52·27 N	13·26 E
81	Berlin (bûr-lĭn) ... N. H.	44·25 N	71·10 W
84	Berlin ... N. J. (Philadelphia In.)	39·47 N	74·56 W
167	Berlin (bĕr-lĭn) . S. Afr. (Natal In.)	32·53 S	27·36 E
71	Berlin (bûr-lĭn') ... Wis.	43·58 N	88·58 W
124	Bermeja, Sierra (Mts.) (sē-ĕ'r-rä-bĕr-mĕ'hä) . Sp.	36·35 N	5·03 W
100	Bermejo (R.) (bĕr-mā'hō) ... Arg.	25·05 S	61·00 W
124	Bermeo (bĕr-mā'yō) ... Sp.	43·23 N	2·43 W
89	Bermuda (I.) ... N. A.	32·20 N	65·45 W
120	Bern (bĕrn) ... Switz.	46·55 N	7·25 E
100	Bernal (bĕr-näl') ... Arg. (In.)	34·27 S	58·17 W
69	Bernalillo (bĕr-nä-lē'yō) .. N. Mex.	35·20 N	106·30 W
81	Bernard (L.) (bĕr-närd') ... Can.	45·45 N	79·25 W
84	Bernardsville (bûr nārds'vĭl) N. J. (New York In.)	40·43 N	74·34 W
111	Bernau (bĕr'nou) . Ger. (Berlin In.)	52·40 N	13·35 E
120	Bernburg (bĕrn'bŏŏrgh) ... Ger.	51·48 N	11·43 E
120	Berndorf (bĕrn'dôrf) ... Aus.	47·57 N	16·05 E
80	Berne (bûrn) ... Ind.	40·40 N	84·55 W
120	Berner Alpen (Mts.) ... Switz.	46·29 N	7·30 E
123	Berneustadt (bĕr'noi'shtät) Ger. (Ruhr In.)	51·01 N	7·39 E
158	Bernier (I.) (bĕr-nēr') ... Austl.	24·58 S	113·15 E
120	Bernina Pizzo (Pk.) ... Switz.	46·23 N	9·58 E
120	Beroun (bā'rōn) ... Czech.	49·57 N	14·03 E
120	Berounka R. (bĕ-rōn'kå) ... Czech.	49·53 N	13·40 E
161	Berowra ... Austl. (Sydney In.)	33·36 S	151·10 E
122	Berre, Étang de (L.) (ā-tôN' dĕ bâr') . Fr. (Marseille In.)	43·27 N	5·07 E
122	Berre-l' Étang (bâr'lā-tôN') Fr. (Marseille In.)	43·28 N	5·11 E
91	Berriozabal (bā'rēō-zä-bäl') .. Mex.	16·47 N	93·16 W
114	Berryan (bĕr-ê-äN') ... Alg.	32·50 N	3·49 E
68	Berryessa (R.) (bĕ'rĭ ĕs'á) ... Calif.	38·35 N	122·33 W
94	Berry Is. ... Ba. Is.	25·35 N	3·49 E
73	Berryville (bĕr'ê-vĭl) ... Ark.	36·21 N	93·34 W
129	Bershad' (byĕr'shät) ... Sov. Un.	48·22 N	29·31 E
82	Berthier (bĕr-tyā') ... Can.	46·04 N	73·14 W
85	Berthier ... Can. (Quebec In.)	46·56 N	70·44 W
65	Bertrand (R.) (bûr'trånd) Wash. (Vancouver In.)	48·58 N	122·31 W
84	Bertrandville (bûr'trånd-vĭl) La. (New Orleans In.)	29·47 N	90·01 W
116	Berwick (bûr'ĭk) ... Scot.	55·45 N	2·01 W
81	Berwick (bûr'wĭk) ... Pa.	41·05 N	76·10 W
75	Berwyn (bûr'wĭn) Ill. (Chicago In.)	41·49 N	87·47 W
116	Berwyn Ra. ... Wales	52·45 N	3·41 W
167	Besalampy (bĕz-á-lăm-pē') Malagasy	16·48 S	40·40 E
123	Besançon (bē-säN-sôn) ... Fr.	47·14 N	6·02 E
139	Besar, Gunong (Mt.) Mala. (Singapore In.)	2·31 N	103·09 E
128	Besed (R.) (byĕ'syĕt) . Sov. Un. ..	52·58 N	31·36 E
128	Beshenkovichi (byĕ'shĕn-kō vē'chĭ) . Sov. Un.	55·04 N	29·29 E
121	Beskides (Mts.) (bĕs'kĕdz') Czech.-Pol.	49·23 N	19·00 E
122	Bessèges (bĕ-sĕzh') ... Fr.	44·20 N	4·07 E
84	Bessemer (bĕs'ĕ-mēr) Ala. (Birmingham In.)	33·24 N	86·58 W
71	Bessemer ... Mich.	46·29 N	90·04 W
79	Bessemer City ... N. C.	35·16 N	81·17 W
111	Bestensee (bĕs'tĕn-zā) Ger. (Berlin In.)	52·15 N	13·39 E
124	Betanzos (bĕ-tän'thōs) ... Sp.	43·18 N	8·14 W
69	Betatakin Ruin (bĕt-á-täk'ĭn) Ariz.	36·40 N	110·29 W
168	Bethal (bĕth'ăl) . S. Afr. (Johannesburg & Pretoria In.)	26·27 S	29·28 E
74	Bethalto (bá-thăl'tō) Ill. (St. Louis In.)	38·54 N	90·03 W
166	Bethanie (bĕth'á-nĭ) ... S. W. Afr.	26·20 S	16·10 E
73	Bethany ... Mo.	40·15 N	94·04 W
64	Bethel (bĕth'ĕl) ... Alaska	60·50 N	161·50 W
84	Bethel ... Conn. (New York In.)	41·22 N	73·24 W
75	Bethel ... Pa. (Pittsburgh In.)	40·19 N	80·02 W
81	Bethel ... Vt.	43·50 N	72·40 W
81	Bethesda (bĕ-thĕs'dá) ... Md.	39·00 N	77·10 W
81	Bethlehem (bĕth'lê-hĕm) ... Pa.	40·40 N	75·25 W
168	Bethlehem . S. Afr. (Johannesburg & Pretoria In.)	28·14 S	28·18 E
	Bethlehem, see Bayt Lahm		
122	Béthune (bā-tün') ... Fr.	50·32 N	2·37 E
167	Betroka (bĕ-trōk'å) ... Malagasy	23·13 S	46·17 E
82	Betsiamites ... Can.	48·55 N	68·39 W
82	Betsiamites, R. ... Can.	49·10 N	69·15 W
167	Betsiboka (R.) (bĕt-sĭ-bō'kå) Malagasy	16·47 S	46·45 E
164	Bettié (bĕt-tyā') ... Ivory Coast	6·04 N	3·32 W
64	Bettles Field (bĕt'tŭls) ... Alaska	66·58 N	151·48 W
142	Betwa (R.) (bĕt'wå) ... India	23·56 N	77·37 E
123	Betz (bĕ) ... Fr. (Paris In.)	49·09 N	2·58 E
123	Betzdorf (bĕtz'dōrf) Ger. (Ruhr In.)	50·47 N	7·53 E
123	Beuel (boi'ĕl) ... Ger. (Ruhr In.)	50·44 N	7·08 E
111	Beveren ... Bel. (Bruxelles In.)	51·13 N	4·14 E
85	Beverly (bĕv'ēr-lĭ) Can. (Edmonton In.)	53·34 N	113·23 W
110	Beverly ... Eng.	53·50 N	0·25 W
83	Beverly ... Mass. (Boston In.)	42·34 N	70·53 W
84	Beverly ... N. J. (Philadelphia In.)	40·03 N	74·56 W
74	Beverly Hills Calif. (Los Angeles In.)	34·05 N	118·24 W
73	Bevier (bê-vēr') ... Mo.	39·44 N	92·36 W
110	Bewdley (būd'lĭ) ... Eng.	52·22 N	2·19 W
117	Bexhill (bĕks'hĭl) ... Eng.	50·49 N	0·25 E
110	Bexley (bĕks'ly) Eng. (London In.)	51·26 N	0·09 E
164	Beyla (bā'lå) ... Gui.	8·38 N	8·39 W
133	Beypazari (bā-pá-zá'rĭ) ... Tur.	40·10 N	31·40 E
139	Beyrouth (Beirut) (bā-rōōt') Leb. (Palestine In.)	33·53 N	35·30 E
133	Beyşehir (bā-shĕ'h'r) ... Tur.	38·00 N	31·45 E
133	Beysehir Gölü (L.) ... Tur.	38·00 N	31·30 E
129	Beysugskiy, Liman (B.) (lĭ-män' bĕy-sōōg'skĭ) . Sov. Un.	46·07 N	38·35 E
128	Bezhetsk (byĕ-zhĕtsk') ... Sov. Un.	57·46 N	36·40 E
128	Bezhitsa (byĕ-zhĭ'tså) ... Sov. Un.	53·19 N	34·18 E
122	Béziers (bā-zyā') ... Fr.	43·21 N	3·12 E
142	Bhagalpur (bä'gŭl-pōōr) ... India	25·15 N	86·59 E
142	Bhamo (bŭ-mō') ... Bur.	24·22 N	97·13 E
142	Bhāngar ... India (Calcutta In.)	22·30 N	88·36 E
142	Bharatpur (bĕrt'pōōr) ... India	27·21 N	77·33 E
142	Bhatinda (bŭ-tĭn-dä) ... India	30·19 N	74·56 E
142	Bhatpara (bŭt-pä'rå) ... India	22·53 N	83·30 E
142	Bhātpāra ... India (Calcutta In.)	22·50 N	88·24 E
142	Bhaunāgār (bäv-nŭg'ŭr) ... India	21·45 N	72·58 E
142	Bhayandar ... India (Bombay In.)	19·20 N	72·50 E
142	Bhīma (R.) (bē'må) ... India	17·44 N	75·28 E
142	Bhiwani ... India	28·53 N	76·08 E
143	Bhiwandi ... India (Bombay In.)	19·18 N	73·03 E
142	Bhopāl (bô-pāl) ... India	23·20 N	77·25 E
142	Bhorīla ... W. Pak.	24·48 N	70·11 E
142	Bhubaneswar (bōō-bŭ-năsh'vûr) India	20·21 N	85·53 E
142	Bhuj (bōōj) ... India	23·22 N	69·39 E
138	Bhutan (bōō-tän') ... Asia	28·00 N	90·00 E
164	Biafra, Bight of ... Cam.	2·52 N	9·01 E

184 Biala–Blooming PRONOUNCING INDEX

Page	Name Pronunciation Region	Lat. °′	Long. °′
121	Biała Podlaska (byä'wä pōd-läs'kä) . Pol.	52·01 N	23·08 E
120	Białogard (byä-wō'gärd) . Pol.	54·00 N	16·01 E
121	Białystok (byä-wĭs'tōk) . Pol.	53·08 N	23·12 E
122	Biarritz (byä-rēts') . Fr.	43·27 N	1·39 W
168	Bibā (bē'bä) . U. A. R. (Nile In.)	28·54 N	30·59 E
78	Bibb City (bĭb' sĭ'tē) . Ga.	32·31 N	84·56 W
120	Biberach (bē'bĕräk) . Ger.	48·06 N	9·49 E
82	Bic (bĭk) . Can.	48·21 N	68·44 W
80	Bicknell (bĭk'nĕl) . Ind.	38·45 N	87·20 W
121	Bicske (bĭsh'kē) . Hung.	47·29 N	18·38 E
164	Bida (bē'dä) . Nig.	9·05 N	6·04 E
82	Biddeford (bĭd'ē-fērd) . Maine	43·29 N	70·29 W
110	Biddulph (bĭd'ŭlf) . Eng.	53·07 N	2·10 W
164	Bidon Cing . Alg.	22·22 N	0·33 E
121	Biebrza R. (byĕb'zhä) . Pol.	53·18 N	22·25 E
120	Biel (bēl) . Switz.	47·09 N	7·12 E
120	Bielefeld (bē'lē-fĕlt) . Ger.	52·01 N	8·35 E
127	Bieljina (bē-yĕ'lyē-nä) . Yugo.	44·44 N	19·15 E
126	Biella (byĕl'lä) . It.	45·34 N	8·05 E
121	Bielsk Podlaski (byĕlsk pŭd-lä'skĭ) Pol.	52·47 N	23·14 E
87	Bienville, Lac (L.) . Can.	55·32 N	72·45 W
111	Biesenthal (bē'sĕn-täl) Ger. (Berlin In.)	52·46 N	13·38 E
126	Biferno (R.) (bē-fĕr'nō) . It.	41·49 N	14·46 E
82	Big (L.) (bĭg) . Can.	45·06 N	67·43 W
65	Big (L.) . Wash. (Seattle In.)	48·23 N	122·14 W
78	Big (R.) . Ark.	35·55 N	90·10 W
127	Biğa (bē'ghȧ) . Tur.	40·13 N	27·14 E
73	Big Bay (bĭg' bĭ'yōō) . Ark.	33·04 N	91·28 W
71	Big Bay de Noc (bĭg bā dē nok') Mich.	45·48 N	86·41 W
74	Big Bear City (bĭg bâr) Calif. (Los Angeles In.)	34·16 N	116·51 W
74	Big Bear Lake (bĭg bâr lāk) Calif. (Los Angeles In.)	34·14 N	116·54 W
67	Big Belt Mts. (bĭg bĕlt) . Mont.	46·53 N	111·43 W
70	Big Bend Dam (bĭg bĕnd) . S. D.	44·11 N	99·33 W
76	Big Bend Natl. Park . Tex.	29·15 N	103·15 W
78	Big Black (R.) (bĭg blăk) . Miss.	32·05 N	90·49 W
73	Big Blue (R.) (bĭg blōō) . Nebr.	40·53 N	97·00 W
76	Big Canyon (bĭg kăn'yŭn) . Tex.	30·27 N	102·19 W
79	Big Cypress Swp. (bĭg sī'prĕs) Fla. (In.)	26·02 N	81·20 W
64	Big Delta (bĭg dĕl'tȧ) . Alaska	64·08 N	145·48 W
71	Big Fork (R.) (bĭg fôrk) . Minn.	48·08 N	93·47 W
86	Biggar . Can.	52·09 N	108·10 W
67	Big Hole R. (bĭg 'hōl) . Mont.	45·53 N	113·15 W
67	Big Hole Battlefield Natl. Mon. (bĭg hōl băt''l-fēld) . Mont.	45·44 N	113·35 W
67	Big Horn Mts. (bĭg hôrn) . Wyo.	44·47 N	107·40 W
67	Bighorn R. . Mont.	45·17 N	107·53 W
65	Big Lake (bĭg lāk) Wash. (Seattle In.)	48·24 N	122·14 W
85	Big L. (bĭg lāk) Can. (Edmonton In.)	53·35 N	113·47 W
80	Big Muddy (R.) . Ill.	37·55 N	89·10 W
67	Big Muddy Cr. (bĭg mud'ĭ) . Mont.	48·53 N	105·02 W
80	Big Rapids (bĭg răp'ĭdz) . Mich.	43·40 N	85·30 W
86	Big River . Can.	53·50 N	107·20 W
	Big Sandy, see Fraser I.		
69	Big Sandy (R.) (bĭg sănd'ē) . Ariz.	34·59 N	113·36 W
80	Big Sandy (R.) . Ky.-W. Va.	38·15 N	82·35 W
72	Big Sandy Cr. . Colo.	39·08 N	103·36 W
70	Big Sioux (R.) (bĭg sōō) . S. D.	44·34 N	97·00 W
76	Big Spring (bĭg sprĭng) . Tex.	32·15 N	101·28 W
70	Big Stone (L.) (bĭg stōn) Minn.-S. Dak.	45·29 N	96·40 W
78	Big Stone Gap . Va.	36·50 N	82·50 W
67	Bigtimber (bĭg'tĭm-bēr) . Mont.	45·50 N	109·57 W
67	Big Wood R. (bĭg wōōd) . Idaho	43·02 N	114·30 W
126	Bihać (bē'häch) . Yugo.	44·48 N	15·52 E
142	Bihar (State) (bē-här') . India	23·48 N	84·57 E
166	Biharamulo (bē-hä-rä-mōō'lō) Tan.	2·38 S	31·39 E
121	Bihor, Muntii (Mts.) (bē'hôr) Rom.	46·37 N	22·37 E
164	Bijagos, Arquipelagos dos (Is.) (är-kē-pĕ'-lä-gôs-dôs-bē-zhä'-gôs) Port. Gui.	10·58 N	16·39 W
143	Bijapur . India	16·53 N	75·42 E
127	Bijelo Polje (bē'yĕ-lō pô'lyĕ) Yugo.	43·02 N	19·48 E
72	Bijou Cr. (bē'zhōō) . Colo.	39·41 N	104·13 W
142	Bīkaner (bĭ-kä'nûr) . India	28·07 N	73·19 E
152	Bikin (bē-kēn') . Sov. Un.	46·41 N	134·29 E
152	Bikin (R.) . Sov. Un.	46·37 N	135·55 E
166	Bikoro (bē-kō'rō) . Con. L.	0·45 S	18·51 E
142	Bilāspur (bē-läs'pōōr) . India	22·08 N	82·12 E
154	Bilauktaung Ra. . Thai.	14·27 N	98·53 E
124	Bilbao (bĭl-bä'ō) . Sp.	43·12 N	2·48 W
168	Bilbays . U. A. R. (Nile In.)	30·26 N	31·37 E
127	Bileća (bē'lĕ-chä) . Yugo.	42·52 N	18·26 E
133	Bilecik (bē-lĕd-zhĕk') . Tur.	40·10 N	29·58 E
121	Bilé Karpaty (Mts.) . Czech.	48·53 N	17·35 E
121	Biłgoraj (bēw-gō'rī) . Pol.	50·31 N	22·43 E
136	Bilimbay (bē'lĭm-bāy) Sov. Un. (Urals In.)	56·59 N	59·53 E
160	Billabong (R.) (bĭl'ă-bŏng) . Austl.	35·15 S	145·20 E
83	Billerica (bĭl'rĭk-ȧ) Mass. (Boston In.)	42·33 N	71·46 W
110	Billericay . Eng. (London In.)	51·38 N	0·25 E
67	Billings (bĭl'ĭngz) . Mont.	45·47 N	108·29 W
69	Bill Williams (L.) (bĭl-wĭl'yumz) Ariz.	34·10 N	113·50 W
165	Bilma (bēl'mä) . Niger.	18·41 N	13·20 E
78	Biloxi (bĭ-lŏk'sĭ) . Miss.	30·24 N	88·50 W
168	Bilqas Qishm Awwal U. A. R. (Nile In.)	31·14 N	31·25 E
110	Bilston (bĭl'stŭn) . Eng.	52·34 N	2·04 W
160	Bimberi Pk. (bĭm'bĕrĭ) . Austl.	35·45 S	148·50 W
155	Binaja, Gunung (Mtn.) . Indon.	3·07 S	129·25 E
155	Binalonan (bē-nä-lô'nän) Phil. (Manila In.)	16·03 N	120·35 E
144	Binalud (Mtn.) . Iran	36·32 N	58·34 E
155	Biñan (bē'nän) . Phil. (Manila In.)	14·20 N	121·06 E
120	Bingen (bĭn'gĕn) . Ger.	49·57 N	7·54 E
164	Bingerville (băn-zhä-vēl') Ivory Coast	5·24 N	3·56 W
110	Bingham (bĭng'ăm) . Eng.	52·57 N	0·57 W
82	Bingham . Maine	45·03 N	69·51 W
74	Bingham Canyon Utah (Salt Lake City In.)	40·33 N	112·09 W
81	Binghamton (bĭng'ăm-tŭn) . N. Y.	42·05 N	75·55 W
153	Bingo-Nada (Sea) (bĭn'gō nä-dä) Jap.	34·06 N	133·14 E
160	Binnaway (bĭn'ă-wā) . Austl.	31·42 S	149·22 E
139	Bintan, Palau (I.) (bĭn'tän) Indon. (Singapore In.)	1·09 N	104·43 E
154	Bintulu (bēn'tōō-lōō) . Sar.	3·07 N	113·06 E
152	Bira (bē'rȧ) . Sov. Un.	49·00 N	133·18 E
152	Bira (R.) . Sov. Un.	48·55 N	132·25 E
167	Birakao . Som.	1·14 S	41·47 E
139	Bi'r al Mazār U. A. R. (Palestine In.)	31·03 N	33·24 E
165	Bi'r al Wa'r (Oasis) . Libya	22·51 N	14·22 E
65	Birch Bay . Wash. (Vancouver In.)	48·55 N	122·45 W
65	Birch B. (bûrch) Wash. (Vancouver In.)	48·55 N	122·52 W
85	Birch Cliff (bērch klĭf) Can. (Toronto In.)	43·41 N	79·16 W
86	Birch Mts. . Can.	57·36 N	113·10 W
65	Birch Pt. . Wash. (Vancouver In.)	48·57 N	122·50 W
167	Bird (I.) (bērd) S. Afr. (Natal In.)	33·51 S	26·21 E
95	Bird Rock (I.) (bŭrd) . Ba. Is.	22·50 N	74·20 W
83	Bird Rock (I.) . Can.	47·53 N	61·00 W
85	Birds Hill (bûrds) Can. (Winnipeg In.)	49·58 N	97·00 W
160	Birdsville (bûrdz'vĭl) . Aust.	22·50 S	139·31 E
158	Birdum (bûrd'ŭm) . Austl.	15·45 S	133·25 E
133	Birecik (bē-rĕd-zhĕk') . Tur.	37·10 N	37·50 E
165	Bir en Natrūn . Sud.	18·13 N	26·44 E
114	Bir er Ressof (bēr-ĕr-rĕ-sôf') . Alg.	32·19 N	7·58 E
144	Bīrjand (bēr'jänd) . Iran	33·07 N	59·16 E
65	Birkenfeld . Ore. (Portland In.)	49·59 N	123·20 W
110	Birkenhead (bûr'kĕn-hĕd) . Eng.	53·23 N	3·02 W
111	Birkenwerder (bēr'kĕn-vĕr-dĕr) Ger. (Berlin In.)	52·41 N	13·22 E
121	Bîrlad . Rom.	46·15 N	27·43 E
84	Birmingham (bûr'mĭng-häm) Ala. (Birmingham In.)	33·31 N	86·49 W
110	Birmingham . Eng.	52·29 N	1·53 W
75	Birmingham . Mich. (Detroit In.)	42·32 N	83·13 W
74	Birmingham Mo. (Kansas City In.)	39·10 N	94·22 W
110	Birmingham, Can. . Eng.	53·07 N	2·40 W
165	Bi'r Misāḥah (Oasis) . U. A. R.	22·16 N	28·04 E
164	Birnin Kebbi . Nig.	12·26 N	4·04 E
135	Birobidzhan (bē'rô-bē-jän') Sov. Un.	48·42 N	133·28 E
132	Birsk (bĭrsk) . Sov. Un.	55·25 N	55·30 E
110	Birstall (bûr'stôl) . Eng.	53·44 N	1·39 W
129	Biryuchiy (I.) (bĭr-yōō'chĭ) Sov. Un.	46·07 N	35·12 E
136	Biryulëvo (bēr-yōōl'yô-vô) Sov. Un. (Moskva In.)	55·35 N	37·39 E
134	Biryusa (R.) (bēr-yōō'sä) . Sov. Un.	56·43 N	97·30 E
118	Biržai (bēr-zhä'ē) . Sov. Un.	56·11 N	24·45 E
165	Bi'r Zaltan . Libya	28·20 N	19·40 E
69	Bisbee (bĭz'bē) . Ariz.	31·30 N	109·55 W
113	Biscay, B. of (bĭs'kā') . Eur.	45·19 N	3·51 W
79	Biscayne B. (bĭs-kān') . Fla. (In.)	25·22 N	80·15 W
123	Bischeim (bĭsh'hĭm) . Fr.	48·40 N	7·48 E
136	Biser (bē'sĕr) . Sov. Un. (Urals In.)	58·24 N	58·54 E
126	Biševo (Is.) (bē'shĕ-vō) . Yugo.	43·58 N	15·41 E
68	Bishop (bĭsh'ŭp) . Calif.	37·22 N	118·25 W
77	Bishop . Tex.	27·35 N	97·46 W
110	Bishop's Castle (bĭsh'ŏps käs' l) Eng.	52·29 N	2·57 W
79	Bishopville (bĭsh'ŭp-vĭl) . S. C.	34·11 N	80·13 W
164	Biskra (bēs'krä) . Alg.	34·52 N	5·39 E
70	Bismarck (bĭz'märk) . N. D.	46·48 N	100·46 W
155	Bismarck Arch. . N. Gui. Ter.	3·15 S	150·45 E
155	Bismarck Ra. . N. Gui. Ter.	5·15 S	144·15 E
164	Bissau (bē-sä'ōō) . Port. Gui.	11·52 N	15·47 W
77	Bistineau L. (bĭs-tĭ-nō') . La.	32·19 N	93·45 W
121	Bistrita (bĭs'trĭt-sà) . Rom.	47·09 N	24·29 E
121	Bistrita R. . Rom.	47·08 N	25·47 E
133	Bitlis (bĭt-lēs') . Tur.	38·30 N	42·00 E
127	Bitola (Monastir) (bē'tô-lä) (mô'nä-stēr) . Yugo.	41·02 N	21·22 E
126	Bitonto (bē-tôn'tō) . It.	41·08 N	16·42 E
67	Bitter Cr. (bĭt'ēr) . Wyo.	41·36 N	108·29 W
120	Bitterfeld (bĭt'ēr-fĕlt) . Ger.	51·39 N	12·19 E
66	Bitterroot Ra. (bĭt'ēr-ōōt) . Mont.	47·15 N	115·13 W
67	Bitterroot R. . Mont.	46·28 N	114·10 W
129	Bityug (R.) (bĭt'yōōg) . Sov. Un.	51·23 N	40·33 E
71	Biwabik (bē-wä'bĭk) . Minn.	47·32 N	92·24 W
153	Biwa-ko (L.) (bē-wä'kō) Jap. (Osaka In.)	35·03 N	135·51 E
134	Biya (R.) (bī'yȧ) . Sov. Un.	52·22 N	87·28 E
134	Biysk (bēsk) . Sov. Un.	52·32 N	85·28 E
167	Bizana (bĭz-änä) S. Afr. (Natal In.)	30·51 S	29·54 E
164	Bizerte (bē-zērt') . Tun.	37·23 N	9·52 E
150	Bizuta . Mong.	41·28 N	115·10 E
126	Bjelovar (byĕ-lō'vär) . Yugo.	45·54 N	16·53 E
	Bjorneborg, see Pori		
118	Bjorne Fd. (byûr'nĕ fyôrd) . Nor.	60·11 N	5·26 E
118	Blaavands Huk (C.) . Den.	55·36 N	7·35 E
80	Black (L.) (blăk) . Mich.	45·25 N	84·15 W
81	Black (L.) . N. Y.	44·30 N	75·35 W
73	Black (R.) . Ark.	35·47 N	91·22 W
81	Black (R.) . N. Y.	43·45 N	75·20 W
79	Black (R.) . S. C.	34·55 N	80·08 W
71	Black (R.) . Wis.	44·07 N	90·56 W
159	Blackall (blăk'ŭl) . Austl.	24·23 S	145·37 E
71	Black B. (blăk) . Can.	48·36 N	88·32 W
84	Black B. . La. (New Orleans In.)	29·38 N	89·33 W
64	Blackburn (blăk'bûrn) . Alaska	63·20 N	159·45 W
110	Blackburn . Eng.	53·45 N	2·28 W
64	Blackburn, Mt. . Alaska	61·50 N	143·12 W
69	Black Canyon of the Gunnison Natl. Mon. (blăk kăn'yŭn) . Colo.	38·35 N	107·45 W
65	Black Diamond (dī'mŭnd) Wash. (Seattle In.)	47·19 N	122·00 W
116	Blackdown Hills (blăk'doun) . Eng.	57·58 N	3·19 W
71	Blackduck (blăk'dŭk) . Minn.	47·41 N	94·33 W
67	Blackfoot (blăk'fŏŏt) . Idaho	43·11 N	112·23 W
67	Blackfoot Ind. Res. . Mont.	48·49 N	112·53 W
67	Blackfoot R. . Mont.	46·53 N	113·33 W
67	Blackfoot River Res. . Idaho	42·53 N	111·23 W
70	Black Hills (Reg.) . S. D.	44·08 N	103·47 W
82	Black Lake . Can.	46·02 N	71·24 W
69	Black Mesa (blăk māsȧ) . Ariz.	36·33 N	110·40 W
69	Black Mts. . N. Mex.	33·15 N	107·55 W
85	Blackmud Cr. (blăk'mŭd) Can. (Edmonton In.)	53·28 N	113·34 W
110	Blackpool (blăk'pōōl) . Eng.	53·49 N	3·02 W
94	Black River (blăk') . Jam.	18·00 N	77·50 W
75	Black R. . Ohio (Cleveland In.)	41·26 N	82·08 W
151	Black R. . Viet.	20·56 N	104·30 E
71	Black River Falls . Wis.	44·18 N	90·51 W
66	Black Rock Des. (rŏk) . Nev.	40·55 N	119·00 W
79	Blacksburg (blăks'bûrg) . S. C.	35·09 N	81·30 W
103	Black Sea . Eur.-Asia	43·01 N	32·16 E
79	Blackshear (blăk'shĭr) . Ga.	31·20 N	82·15 W
79	Blackstone (blăk'stōn) . Va.	37·04 N	78·00 W
71	Black Sturgeon (R.) (stû'jŭn) . Can.	49·12 N	88·41 W
161	Blacktown (blăk'toun) Austl. (Sydney In.)	33·47 S	150·55 E
82	Blackville (blăk'vĭl) . Can.	46·44 N	65·50 W
79	Blackville . S. C.	33·21 N	81·19 W
164	Black Volta R. (vōl'tȧ) Upper Volta	11·21 N	4·21 W
78	Black Warrior (R.) (blăk wŏr'ĭ-ēr) Ala.	32·37 N	87·42 W
78	Black Warrior (R.), Locust Fk. Ala.	34·06 N	86·27 W
78	Black Warrior (R.), Mulberry Fk. Ala.	34·06 N	86·32 W
116	Blackwater (blăk-wô'tēr) . Ire.	52·05 N	9·02 W
73	Blackwater (R.) . Mo.	38·53 N	93·22 W
79	Blackwater (R.) . Va.	37·07 N	77·10 W
73	Blackwell (blăk'wĕl) . Okla.	36·47 N	97·19 W
111	Bladel . Neth. (Amsterdam In.)	51·22 N	5·15 E
133	Blagodarnoye (blä'gô-där-nō'yĕ) Sov. Un.	45·00 N	43·30 E
127	Blagoevgrad (Gorna Dzhumaya) Bul.	42·01 N	23·06 E
135	Blagoveshchensk (blä'gŏ-vyĕsh'-chĕnsk) . Sov. Un.	50·16 N	127·47 E
136	Blagoveshchensk Sov. Un. (Urals In.)	55·03 N	56·00 E
65	Blaine (blān) Wash. (Vancouver In.)	48·59 N	122·49 W
81	Blaine . W. Va.	39·25 N	79·10 W
70	Blair (blâr) . Nebr.	41·33 N	96·09 W
86	Blairmore (blâr-mōr) . Can.	49·38 N	114·20 W
81	Blairsville (blârs'vĭl) . Pa.	40·30 N	79·40 W
65	Blake (I.) (blāk) Wash. (Seattle In.)	47·37 N	122·28 W
78	Blakely (blāk'lē) . Ga.	31·22 N	84·55 W
164	Blanc, Cap (C.) . Mauritania	20·39 N	18·08 W
123	Blanc, Mt. (môn blän) . Fr.-It.	45·50 N	6·53 E
100	Blanca, Bahia (B.) (bä-ē'ä-blän'kä) . Arg.	39·30 S	61·00 W
72	Blanca Pk. (blăŋ'kȧ) . Colo.	37·36 N	105·22 W
160	Blanch (L.) (blănch) . Austl.	29·20 S	139·12 E
85	Blanche, R. . Can. (Ottawa In.)	45·34 N	75·38 W
75	Blanchester (blăn'chĕs-tēr) Ohio (Cincinnati In.)	39·18 N	83·58 W
100	Blanco, C. (blăŋ'kō) . Arg.	47·08 S	65·47 W
92	Blanco, Cabo (C.) (kä'bô-blăŋ'kō) C. R.	9·29 N	85·15 W
66	Blanco, C. (blăn'kō) . Ore.	42·53 N	124·38 W
91	Blanco (R.) . Mex.	18·42 N	96·03 W
90	Blanco (R.) . Mex.	24·05 N	99·21 W
94	Blancos, Cayo (I.) (kä'yō-blăŋ'kōs) . Cuba	23·15 N	80·55 W
69	Blanding . Utah	37·40 N	109·31 W
117	Blankenburg (blăŋ'kĕn-bōōrgh) Ger.	51·45 N	13·07 E
111	Blankenfelde (blän'kĕn-fĕl-dĕ) Ger. (Berlin In.)	52·20 N	13·24 E
91	Blanquilla, Arrecife (Reef) (är-rĕ-sē'fĕ-blän-kē'l-yä) . Mex.	21·32 N	97·14 W
166	Blantyre (blăn-tīr') Fed. of Rh. & Nya.	15·48 S	35·07 E
75	Blasdell (blăz'dĕl) N. Y. (Buffalo In.)	42·48 N	78·51 W
126	Blato (blä'tō) . Yugo.	42·55 N	16·47 E
122	Blaye-et-Ste. Luce (blä'ā-sănt-lüs') . Fr.	45·08 N	0·40 W
121	Błażowa (bwä-zhō'vä) . Pol.	49·51 N	22·05 E
164	Blida . Alg.	36·33 N	2·45 E
87	Blind River (blīnd) . Can.	46·10 N	83·09 W
80	Blissfield (blĭs-fēld) . Mich.	41·50 N	83·50 W
110	Blithe (blĭth) . Eng.	52·22 N	1·49 W
81	Block (I.) (blŏk) . R. I.	41·05 N	71·35 W
168	Bloemfontein (blōōm'fŏn-tān) S. Afr. (Johannesburg & Pretoria In.)	29·09 S	26·16 E
122	Blois (blwä) . Fr.	47·36 N	1·21 E
71	Bloomer (blōōm'ēr) . Wis.	45·07 N	91·30 W
80	Bloomfield (blōōm'fēld) . Ind.	39·00 N	86·55 W
71	Bloomfield . Iowa	40·44 N	92·21 W
73	Bloomfield . Mo.	36·54 N	89·55 W
70	Bloomfield . Nebr.	42·36 N	97·40 W
84	Bloomfield . N. J. (New York In.)	40·48 N	74·12 W
75	Bloomfield Hills Mich. (Detroit In.)	42·35 N	83·15 W
71	Blooming Prairie (blōōm'ĭng prâ'rĭ) . Minn.	43·52 N	93·04 W

ăt; finăl; rāte; senâte; ärm; ȧsk; sofȧ; fâre; ch-choose; dh-as th in other; bē; ēvent; bĕt; recĕnt; cratẽr; g-go; gh-guttural g; bĭt; ĭ-short neutral; rīde; ĸ-guttural k as ch in German ich;

Page	Name Pronunciation Region	Lat. °'	Long. °'
74	Bloomington (blōōm'ĭng-tŭn) Calif. (Los Angeles In.)	34·04 N	117·24 W
80	Bloomington Ill.	40·30 N	89·00 W
80	Bloomington Ind.	39·10 N	86·35 W
74	Bloomington Minn. (Minneapolis, St. Paul In.)	44·50 N	93·18 W
81	Bloomsburg (blōōmz'bûrg) Pa.	41·00 N	76·25 W
84	Blossburg (blŏs'bûrg) Ala. (Birmingham In.)	33·38 N	86·57 W
81	Blossburg Pa.	41·45 N	77·00 W
166	Bloubergstrand S. Afr. (Cape Town In.)	33·48 S	18·28 E
78	Blountstown (blŭnts'tun) Fla.	30·24 N	85·02 W
120	Bludenz (blōō-dĕnts') Aus.	47·09 N	9·50 E
83	Blue, Mt Can.	50·28 N	57·11 W
75	Blue Ash (blōō ăsh) Ohio (Cincinnati In.)	39·14 N	84·23 W
71	Blue Earth (blōō ûrth) Minn.	43·38 N	94·05 W
71	Blue Earth (R.) Minn.	43·55 N	94·16 W
79	Bluefield (blōō'fēld) W. Va.	37·15 N	81·11 W
93	Bluefields (blōō'fēldz) Nic.	12·03 N	83·45 W
75	Blue Island Ill. (Chicago In.)	41·39 N	87·41 W
160	Blue Mts Austl.	33·35 S	149·00 E
94	Blue Mts Jam.	18·05 N	76·35 W
66	Blue Mts Ore.	45·15 N	118·50 W
158	Blue Mud B. (blōō mŭd) Austl.	13·20 S	136·45 E
	Blue Nile, see El Azraq, Bahr		
73	Blue Rapids (blōō răp'ĭdz) Kans.	39·40 N	96·41 W
63	Blue Ridge (Mts.) (blōō rĭj) U. S.	35·30 N	82·50 W
86	Blue River Can.	52·09 N	119·21 W
74	Blue R. Mo. (Kansas City In.)	38·55 N	94·33 W
69	Bluff Utah	37·18 N	109·34 W
80	Bluffton (blŭf-tŭn) Ind.	40·40 N	85·15 W
80	Bluffton (blŭf-tŭn) Ohio	40·50 N	83·55 W
100	Blumenau (blōō'mĕn-ou) Braz.	26·53 S	48·58 W
139	Blumut, Gunong (Mt.) Mala. (Singapore In.)	2·03 N	103·34 E
65	Blyn (blĕn) Wash. (Seattle In.)	48·01 N	123·00 W
116	Blyth (blīth) Eng.	55·03 N	1·34 W
68	Blythe Calif.	33·37 N	114·37 W
73	Blytheville (blīth'vĭl) Ark.	35·55 N	89·51 W
155	Boac Phil. (Manila In.)	13·26 N	121·50 E
92	Boaco (bô-ä'kō) Nic.	12·24 N	85·41 W
99	Boa Vista do Rio Branco (bō'a vēsh'tä dōō rē'ōō brän'kōō) Braz.	2·46 N	60·45 W
164	Boa Vista I. (bō-ä-vēsh'tȧ) C. V. Is. (In.)	16·01 N	23·52 W
121	Boberka (bō'bēr-kȧ) Sov. Un.	49·36 N	24·18 E
164	Bobo-Dioulasso (bō'bô-dyōō-làs-sō') Upper Volta	11·13 N	4·13 W
128	Bobr (bô'b'r) Sov. Un.	54·19 N	29·11 E
129	Bobrinets (bô'brē-nyĭts) Sov. Un.	48·04 N	32·10 E
120	Bobr R. (bŭ'br) Pol.	51·44 N	15·13 E
129	Bobrov (bŭb-rôf') Sov. Un.	51·07 N	40·01 E
129	Bobrovitsa (bŭb-rô'vē-tsȧ) Sov. Un.	50·43 N	31·27 E
128	Bobruysk (bŏ-brōō'ĭsk) Sov. Un.	53·07 N	29·13 E
99	Boca del Pozo (bô-kä-dĕl-pô'zō) Ven. (In.)	11·00 N	64·21 W
99	Boca de Uchire (bô-kä-dĕ-ōō-chē'rĕ) Ven. (In.)	10·09 N	65·27 W
101	Bocaina, Serra da (Mtn.) (sĕ'r-rä-dä-bô-kä'ē-nä) Braz. (Rio de Janeiro In.)	22·47 S	44·39 W
93	Bocas (bō'käs) Mex.	22·29 N	101·03 W
93	Bocas del Toro (bō'käs dĕl tō'rō) Pan.	9·24 N	82·15 W
121	Bochnia (bōĸ'nyä) Pol.	49·58 N	20·28 E
123	Bocholt (bō'ĸōlt) Ger. (Ruhr In.)	51·50 N	6·37 E
123	Bochum (bō'ĸōōm) Ger. (Ruhr In.)	51·29 N	7·13 E
123	Bockum-Hövel (bō'kōōm-hû'fĕl) Ger. (Ruhr In.)	51·41 N	7·45 E
135	Bodaybo (bō-dī'bō) Sov. Un.	57·12 N	114·46 E
165	Bodele Depression (bō-dȧ-lā') Chad	17·21 N	16·38 E
112	Boden Swe.	65·51 N	21·29 E
120	Boden See (L.) (bō'dĕn zā) Ger.	47·48 N	9·22 E
168	Bodenstein (bō'dĕn-stān) S. Afr. (Johannesburg & Pretoria In.)	26·20 S	26·27 E
116	Boderg (bō'dûrg) Ire.	53·51 N	8·06 W
116	Bodmin (bŏd'mĭn) Eng.	50·29 N	4·45 W
116	Bodmin Moor (bŏd'mĭn mōōr) Eng.	50·36 N	4·43 W
112	Bodö (bôd'û) Nor.	67·13 N	14·19 E
166	Boende (bō-ĕn'dȧ) Con. L.	0·21 S	21·06 E
76	Boerne (bō'ērn) Tex.	29·49 N	98·44 W
77	Boeuf R. (bĕf) La.	32·23 N	91·57 W
164	Boffa (bôf'ȧ) Gui.	10·13 N	14·06 W
153	Bōfu (bō'fōō) Jap.	34·03 N	131·35 E
77	Bogalusa (bō-gȧ-lōō'sȧ) La.	30·48 N	82·52 W
160	Bogan (R.) (bō'gĕn) Austl.	32·10 S	147·40 E
166	Bogenfels (bō'ghĕn-fĕls) S. W. Afr.	27·35 S	15·30 E
118	Bogense (bô'gĕn-sĕ) Den.	55·34 N	10·09 E
93	Boggy Pk. (bŏg'ĭ-pēk) W. I. F. (Le. & Wind. Is. In.)	17·03 N	61·50 W
125	Boghari (bō-gȧ-rē') Alg.	35·50 N	2·48 E
129	Bogodukhov (bŏ-gŏ-dōō'ĸôf) Sov. Un.	50·10 N	35·31 E
154	Bogor Indon.	6·45 S	106·45 E
128	Bogoroditsk (bŏ-gŏ'rŏ-dĭtsk) Sov. Un.	53·48 N	38·06 E
132	Bogorodsk Sov. Un.	56·02 N	43·40 E
136	Bogorodskoye (bŏ-gô-rôd'skô-yĕ) Sov. Un. (Urals In.)	56·43 N	56·53 E
98	Bogotá (bō-gō-tä') Col. (In.)	4·38 N	74·06 W
98	Bogotá, Rio (R.) (rē'ō-bō-gō-tä') Col. (In.)	4·27 N	74·38 W
134	Bogotol (bŏ'gô-tŏl) Sov. Un.	56·13 N	89·13 E
129	Bogoyavlenskoye (bŏ'gô-yäf'lĕn-skō'yĕ) Sov. Un	48·46 N	33·19 E
133	Boguchar (bō'gōō-chär) Sov. Un.	49·40 N	41·00 E
93	Boguete (bō-gĕ'tĕ) Pan.	8·54 N	82·29 W
129	Boguslav (bō'gōō-släf) Sov. Un.	49·34 N	30·51 E
122	Bohain-en-Vermandois (bô-ăN-ôN-vâr-mäN-dwä') Fr.	49·58 N	3·22 E
	Bohemia, see Ceske		
120	Bohemian For. (bō-hē'mĭ-ăn) Ger.	49·35 N	12·27 E
155	Bohol (I.) (bô-hôl') Phil.	9·28 N	124·35 E
91	Bohom (bŏ-ô'm) Mex.	16·47 N	92·42 W
168	Bohotleh (bō-hŏt'lĕ) Som. (Horn of Afr. In.)	8·15 N	46·20 E
82	Boiestown (boiz'toun) Can.	46·27 N	66·25 W
127	Boin (R.) (bô'ĕn) Yugo.	44·19 N	17·54 E
80	Bois Blanc (I.) (boi' blăŋk) Mich.	45·45 N	84·30 W
85	Boischatel (bwä-shä-tĕl') Can. (Quebec In.)	46·54 N	71·08 W
85	Bois-des-Filion (bōō-ä'dĕ-fē-yōN') Can. (Montreal In.)	45·40 N	73·46 W
66	Boise (boi'zē) Idaho	43·38 N	116·12 W
72	Boise City Okla.	36·42 N	102·30 W
66	Boise R. Idaho	43·43 N	116·30 W
86	Boissevain (bois'vān) Can.	49·11 N	100·01 W
145	Boizabād Afg.	37·13 N	70·38 E
164	Bojador, Cabo (C.) (kä'bô-bō-hä-dōr') (bŏj-ȧ-dōr') Sp. Sah.	26·21 N	16·08 W
164	Boké (bō-kā') Gui.	10·58 N	14·15 W
118	Bokn Fd. (bôk''n fyôrd) Nor.	59·12 N	5·37 E
167	Boksburg (bŏks'bûrgh) S. Afr. (Johannesburg & Pretoria In.)	26·13 S	28·15 E
164	Bolama (bō-lä'mä) Port. Gui.	11·34 N	15·41 W
142	Bolan Mt. (bō-län') W. Pak.	35·13 N	67·09 E
90	Bolaños (bō-län'yōs) Mex.	21·40 N	103·48 W
90	Bolaños (R.) Mex.	21·26 N	103·54 W
142	Bolan P W. Pak.	34·50 N	67·10 E
122	Bolbec (bôl-bĕk') Fr.	49·37 N	0·26 E
164	Bole (bō'lā) Ghana	9·02 N	2·28 W
120	Boleslawiec (bō-lĕ-slä'vyĕts) Pol.	51·15 N	15·35 E
129	Bolgrad (bŏl-grát) Sov. Un.	45·41 N	28·38 E
155	Bolinao (bō-lē-nä'ō) Phil. (Manila In.)	16·24 N	119·53 E
155	Bolinao, C. Phil. (Manila In.)	16·24 N	119·42 E
101	Bolívar (bô-lē'vär) Arg. (Buenos Aires In.)	36·15 S	61·05 W
98	Bolívar Col.	1·46 N	76·58 W
73	Bolivar (bŏl'ĭ-vȧr) Mo.	37·37 N	93·22 W
78	Bolivar Tenn.	35·14 N	88·56 W
98	Bolívar, Cerro (Mts.) (sĕr-rô-bô-lē'vär) Ven.	6·25 N	64·52 W
98	Bolívar (La Columna) (Mtn.) (bô-lē'vär) (lä-kô-lōō'm-nä) Ven.	8·44 N	70·54 W
77	Bolivar Pen. (bŏl'ĭ-vȧr) Tex. (In.)	29·25 N	94·40 W
96	Bolivia (bô-lĭv'ĭ-ȧ) S. A.	17·00 S	64·00 W
128	Bolkhov (bŏl-ĸôf') Sov. Un.	53·27 N	35·59 E
110	Bollin (R.) (bŏl'ĭn) Eng.	53·18 N	2·11 W
110	Bollington (bôl'ĭng-tŭn) Eng.	53·18 N	2·06 W
118	Bollnäs (bôl'nĕs) Swe.	61·22 N	16·20 E
118	Bolmen (L.) (bôl'mĕn) Swe.	56·58 N	13·25 E
166	Bolobo (bō'lō-bō) Con. L.	2·14 S	16·18 E
126	Bologna (bô-lōn'yä) It.	44·30 N	11·18 E
128	Bologoye (bŏ-lŏ-gō'yĕ) Sov. Un.	57·52 N	34·02 E
92	Bolonchenticul (bô-lôn-chĕn-tē-kōō'l) Mex. (Yucatan In.)	20·03 N	89·47 W
94	Bolondrón (bô-lôn-drōn') Cuba	22·45 N	81·25 W
126	Bolseno, Lago di (L.) (lä'gō-dē-bôl-sā'nō) It.	42·35 N	11·40 E
132	Bol'shaya Kinel' (R.) Sov. Un.	53·20 N	52·40 E
129	Bol'shaya Lepetikha (bŏl-shà' yȧ lyĕ'pyĕ-tē'kȧ) Sov. Un.	47·11 N	33·58 E
129	Bol'shaya Viska (vĭs-kä') Sov. Un.	48·34 N	31·54 E
129	Bol'shaya Vradiyevka (vrä-dyĕf'kȧ) Sov. Un.	47·51 N	30·38 E
136	Bol'she Ust'ikinskoye (bŏl'shĕ ōōs-tyĭ-kĕn'skô-yĕ) Sov. Un. (Urals In.)	55·58 N	58·18 E
135	Bolshoy Anyuy (R.) Sov. Un.	67·58 N	161·15 E
135	Bol'shoy Begichëv (I.) Sov. Un.	74·30 N	114·40 E
135	Bolshoy Chuva (R.) Sov. Un.	58·15 N	111·13 E
136	Bol'shoye Ivonino (ĭ-vô'nĭ-nô) Sov. Un. (Urals In.)	59·41 N	61·12 E
136	Bol'shoy Kuyash (bŏl'-shôy kōō'yȧsh) Sov. Un. (Urals In.)	55·52 N	61·07 E
129	Bolshoy Tokmak (bŏl-shôy' tôk-mäk') Sov. Un.	47·17 N	35·48 E
76	Bolson de Mapimi (bôl-sŏ'n-dĕ-mä-pē'mē) Mex.	28·07 N	104·30 W
110	Bolsover (bōl'zō-vēr) Eng.	53·14 N	1·17 W
125	Boltana (bôl-tä'nä) Sp.	42·28 N	0·03 E
85	Bolton (bōl'tŭn) Can. (Toronto In.)	43·53 N	79·44 W
110	Bolton Eng.	53·35 N	2·26 W
110	Bolton-on-Dearne (bōl'tŭn-ŏn-dûrn) Eng.	53·31 N	1·19 W
133	Bolu (bō'lōō) Tur.	40·45 N	31·45 E
128	Bolva (R.) (bôl'vä) Sov. Un.	53·30 N	34·30 E
133	Bolvadin (bŏl-vä-dēn') Tur.	38·50 N	30·50 E
126	Bolzano (bôl-tsä'nō) It.	46·29 N	9·22 E
166	Boma (bō'mä) Con. L.	5·45 S	13·05 E
160	Bombala (bŭm-bä'lȧ) Austl.	36·55 S	149·07 E
143	Bombay (bŏm-bā') India (Bombay In.)	18·58 N	72·50 E
142	Bombay (State) India	27·20 N	72·56 E
143	Bombay Hbr. India (Bombay In.)	18·55 N	72·52 E
101	Bom Jardim (bôn zhär-dēN') Braz. (Rio de Janeiro In.)	22·10 S	42·25 W
101	Bom Jesus do Itabapoana (bôN-zhĕ-sōō's-dô-ē-tá'bä-pô-á'nä) Braz. (Rio de Janeiro In.)	21·08 S	41·51 W
118	Bömlo (I.) (bûmlô) Nor.	59·47 N	4·57 E
101	Bom Sucesso (bôN-sōō-sĕ'sō) Braz. (Rio de Janeiro In.)	21·02 S	44·44 W
113	Bon, C. (bôN) Tun.	37·04 N	11·13 E
98	Bonaire (I.) (bō-nâr') Neth. Antilles	12·10 N	68·15 W
124	Boñar (bō-nyär') Sp.	42·53 N	5·18 W
83	Bonavista (bŏ-nȧ-vĭs'tȧ) Can.	48·38 N	53·09 W
83	Bonavista B Can.	48·48 N	53·20 W
72	Bond (bŏnd) Colo.	39·53 N	106·40 W
165	Bondo (bôn'dô) Con. L.	3·49 N	23·43 E
155	Bondoc Pen. (bôn-dŏk') Phil. (Manila In.)	13·24 N	122·30 E
155	Bondoc Pt. Phil. (Manila In.)	13·11 N	122·20 E
164	Bondoukou (bŏn-dōō'kōō) Ivory Coast	8·06 N	3·47 W
94	Bonds Cay (I.) (bŏnds kē) Ba. Is.	25·30 N	77·45 W
164	Bone (bōn) Alg.	36·57 N	7·39 E
154	Bone, Teluk (L.) Indon.	4·09 S	121·00 E
101	Bonfim (bôN-fē'N) Braz. (Rio de Janeiro In.)	20·20 S	44·15 W
165	Bongos, Massif des (Mts.) Cen. Afr. Rep.	8·04 N	21·59 E
151	Bong Son Viet.	14·20 N	109·10 E
73	Bonham (bŏn'ăm) Tex.	33·35 N	96·09 W
95	Bonhomme, Pic (Pk.) Hai.	19·10 N	72·20 W
126	Bonifacio (bō-nē-fä'chō) Fr.	41·23 N	9·10 E
126	Bonifacio, Str. of Eur.	41·14 N	9·02 E
78	Bonifay (bŏn-ĭ-fā') Fla.	30·46 N	85·40 W
	Bonin Is., see Ogasawara		
123	Bonn (bŏn) Ger. (Ruhr In.)	50·44 N	7·06 E
66	Bonners Ferry (bon'erz fĕr'ĭ) Idaho	48·41 N	116·19 W
74	Bonner Springs (bŏn'ēr sprĭngz) Kans. (Kansas City In.)	39·04 N	94·52 W
73	Bonne Terre (bŏn târ') Mo.	37·55 N	90·32 W
66	Bonneville Dam (bŏn'ē-vĭl) Wash.-Ore.	45·37 N	121·57 W
83	Bonnie B. (bŏn'ē) Can.	49·38 N	58·15 W
164	Bonny (bŏn'ē) Nig.	4·29 N	7·13 E
65	Bonny Lake (bŏn'ē lăk) Wash. (Seattle In.)	47·11 N	122·11 W
126	Bonorva (bô-nôr'vä) It.	40·26 N	8·46 E
154	Bonthain (bôn-tīn') Indon.	5·30 S	119·52 E
155	Bontoc (bôn-tŏk') Phil. (Manila In.)	17·10 N	121·01 E
94	Booby Rocks (I.) (bōō'bĭ rŏks) Ba. Is.	25·55 N	77·00 W
79	Booker T. Washington Natl. Mon. (bŏŏk'ẽr tē wŏsh'ĭng-tŭn) Va.	37·07 N	79·45 W
111	Boom Bel. (Bruxelles In.)	51·05 N	4·22 E
71	Boone (bōōn) Iowa	42·04 N	93·51 W
84	Boone Va. (Norfolk In.)	36·50 N	76·26 W
73	Booneville (bōōn'vĭl) Ark.	35·09 N	93·54 W
80	Booneville Ky.	37·25 N	83·40 W
78	Booneville Miss.	34·37 N	88·35 W
168	Boons S. Afr. (Johannesburg & Pretoria In.)	25·59 S	27·15 E
84	Boonton (bōōn'tŭn) N. J. (New York In.)	40·54 N	74·24 W
80	Boonville Ind.	38·00 N	87·15 W
73	Boonville Mo.	38·57 N	92·44 W
82	Boothbay Harbor (bōōth'bā här'bēr) Maine	43·51 N	69·39 W
87	Boothia, G. of (bōō'thĭ-ȧ) Can.	69·04 N	86·04 W
49	Boothia Pen Can.	73·30 N	95·00 W
84	Boothville (bōōth'vĭl) La. (New Orleans In.)	29·21 N	89·25 W
110	Bootle (bōōt'l) Eng.	53·29 N	3·02 W
164	Boporo (bô-pō'rō) Lib.	7·13 N	10·47 W
120	Boppard (bôp'ärt) Ger.	50·14 N	7·35 E
165	Bor (bôr) Sud.	6·13 N	31·35 E
133	Bor (bōr) Tur.	37·50 N	34·40 E
67	Borah Pk. (bō'rä) Idaho	44·12 N	113·47 W
168	Borama (bôr-á-mȧ) Som. (Horn of Afr. In.)	10·05 N	43·08 E
118	Borås (bōō'rōs) Swe.	57·43 N	12·55 E
144	Borāzjān (bō-räz-jän') Iran	29·13 N	51·13 E
99	Borba (bôr'bä) Braz.	4·23 S	59·31 W
99	Borborema, Planalto da (Plat.) (plä-näl'tô-dä-bôr-bô-rĕ'mä) Braz.	7·35 S	36·40 W
122	Bordeaux (bôr-dō') Fr.	44·50 N	0·37 W
81	Bordentown (bôr'dĕn-toun) N. J.	40·05 N	74·40 W
113	Bordj-bou-Arréridj (bôrj-bōō-à-rä-rēj') Alg.	36·03 N	4·48 E
119	Borga (bôr'gōō) Fin.	60·26 N	25·41 E
112	Borgarnes Ice.	64·31 N	21·40 W
72	Borger (bôr'gēr) Tex.	35·40 N	101·23 W
118	Borgholm (bôrg-hŏlm') Swe.	56·52 N	16·40 E
77	Borgne L. (bôrn'y') La.	30·03 N	89·36 W
126	Borgomanero (bôr'gō-mä-nâ'rō) It.	45·40 N	8·28 E
125	Borgo Montello (bôr'zhō-môn-tĕ'lō) It. (Roma In.)	41·31 N	12·48 E
126	Borgo Val di Taro (bô'r-zhō-väl-dē-tä'rō) It.	44·29 N	9·44 E
65	Boring (bōr ĭng) Ore. (Portland In.)	45·26 N	122·22 W
121	Borislav (bô'rĭs-lôf) Sov. Un.	49·17 N	23·24 E
133	Borisoglebsk (bŏ-rē sô-glyĕpsk') Sov. Un.	51·20 N	42·00 E
128	Borisov (bŏ-rē'sôf) Sov. Un.	54·16 N	28·33 E
129	Borisovka (bŏ-rē-sôf'kȧ) Sov. Un.	50·38 N	36·00 E
129	Borispol' (bŏ-rĭs'pol) Sov. Un.	50·17 N	30·54 E
143	Borivli India (Bombay In.)	19·15 N	72·48 E
124	Borja (bôr'hä) Sp.	41·50 N	1·33 W
125	Borjas Blancas (bô'r-ĸäs-blä'n-käs) Sp.	41·29 N	0·53 E
123	Borken (bôr'kĕn) Ger. (Ruhr In.)	51·50 N	6·51 E
165	Borkou (Reg.) (bôr-kōō') Chad.	18·11 N	18·28 E
120	Borkum I. (bōr'kōōm) Ger.	53·31 N	6·50 E
118	Borlänge (bôr-lĕŋ'gĕ) Swe.	60·30 N	15·24 E
154	Borneo (I.) (bôr'nē-ō) Asia	0·25 N	112·39 E
118	Bornholm (I.) (bôrn-hôlm) Den.	55·16 N	15·15 E
124	Bornos (bôr'nōs) Sp.	36·48 N	5·45 W
164	Bornu (Reg.) Nig.	11·13 N	12·15 E
129	Borodayevka Sov. Un.	48·44 N	34·09 E
129	Boromlya (bŏ-rôm'l-yä) Sov. Un.	50·36 N	34·58 E
127	Borovan (bŏ-rō-vän') Bul.	43·24 N	23·47 E
128	Borovichi (bŏ-rô-vē'chē) Sov. Un.	58·22 N	33·56 E
128	Borovsk (bŏ'rôvsk) Sov. Un.	55·13 N	36·26 E
99	Borracha, Isla la (I.) (ē's-lä-lä-bôr-rä'chä) Ven. (In.)	10·18 N	64·44 W
158	Borroloola (bŏr-rô-lōō'lȧ) Austl.	16·15 S	136·19 E
121	Borshchëv (bôrsh-chyôf') Sov. Un.	48·47 N	26·04 E
122	Bort-les-Orgues (bôr-lä-zôrg) Fr.	45·26 N	2·26 E
144	Borūjerd Iran	33·45 N	48·53 E

186 Borzna–Bridlington PRONOUNCING INDEX

Page	Name Pronunciation Region	Lat. °′	Long. °′
129	Borzna (bôrz'nȧ)........Sov. Un.	51·15 N	32·26 E
135	Borzya (bôrz'yȧ)........Sov. Un.	50·37 N	116·53 E
126	Bosa (bō'sä)................It.	40·18 N	8·34 E
126	Bosanska Dubica (bō'sän-skä dōō'bĭt-sä).Yugo.	45·10 N	16·49 E
126	Bosanska Gradiška (bō'sän-skä grä-dĭsh'kä).Yugo.	45·08 N	17·15 E
126	Bosanski Novi (bō's sän-skĭ nō'vē) Yugo.	45·00 N	16·22 E
126	Bosanski Petrovac (bō'sän-skĭ pĕt'rō-väts).Yugo.	44·33 N	16·23 E
127	Bosanski Šamac (bō'sän-skĭ shä'mȧts).Yugo.	45·03 N	18·30 E
71	Boscobel (bŏs'kō-bĕl)........Wis.	43·08 N	90·44 W
136	Boskol' (bȧs-kôl') Sov. Un. (Urals In.)	53·45 N	61·17 E
111	Boskoop..Neth. (Amsterdam In.)	52·04 N	4·39 E
120	Boskovice (bŏs'kō-vē-tsĕ)..Czech.	49·26 N	16·37 E
127	Bosnia (Reg.) (bŏs'nĭ-ȧ)....Yugo.	44·17 N	16·58 E
	Bosporous, see Karadeniz Boğazi		
77	Bossier City (bŏsh'ēr)........La.	32·31 N	93·42 W
78	Boston (bôs'tŭn).............Ga.	30·47 N	83·47 W
83	Boston........Mass. (Boston In.)	42·15 N	71·07 W
75	Boston Heights Ohio (Cleveland In.)	41·15 N	81·30 W
73	Boston Mts................Ark.	35·46 N	93·32 W
161	Botany B. (bŏt'ȧ-nĭ) Austl. (Sydney In.)	33·58 S	151·11 E
127	Botevgrad.................Bul.	42·54 N	23·41 E
168	Bothaville (bō'tä-vĭl)......S. Afr. (Johannesburg & Pretoria In.)	27·24 S	26·38 E
65	Bothell (bŏth'ĕl) Wash. (Seattle In.)	47·46 N	122·12 W
112	Bothnia, G. of (bŏth'nĭ-ȧ)....Eur.	61·45 N	19·45 E
121	Botosani (bô-tô-shän'ĭ).....Rom.	47·46 N	26·40 E
70	Bottineau (bŏt-ĭ-nō').......N. D.	48·48 N	100·28 W
123	Bottrop (bōt'trōp) Ger. (Ruhr In.)	51·31 N	6·56 E
99	Botucatú (bô-tōō-kä-tōō')...Braz.	22·50 S	48·23 W
83	Botwood (bŏt'wŏŏd)........Can.	49·10 N	55·23 W
164	Bouaflé (bōō-à-flā')..Ivory Coast	7·23 N	5·32 W
164	Bouaké (bōō-à-kā')...Ivory Coast	7·45 N	5·08 W
165	Bouar (bōō-är)....Cen. Afr. Rep.	6·04 N	15·34 E
83	Bouche..................Can.	45·37 N	61·25 W
85	Boucherville (bōō-shä-vēl') Can. (Montreal In.)	45·37 N	73·27 W
164	Bou Denib (bōō-dĕ-nēb')....Mor.	32·14 N	3·04 W
71	Boudette (bōō-dĕt)........Minn.	48·42 N	94·34 W
113	Bou Dia, C. (bōō dē'ȧ)......Tun.	35·18 N	11·17 E
125	Boufarik (bōō-fá-rēk')......Alg.	36·35 N	2·55 E
156	Bougainville Trench (bōō-găN-vēl').Oceania	7·00 S	152·00 E
164	Bougie (bōō-zhē')..........Alg.	36·46 N	5·00 E
164	Bougouni (bōō-gōō-nē')......Mali	11·27 N	7·30 W
114	Bouira (boo-ē'rȧ)...........Alg.	36·25 N	3·55 W
125	Bouïra-Sahary (bwē-rȧ sá'ȧ-rē) Alg.	35·16 N	3·23 E
158	Boulder (bōl'dēr)..........Austl.	31·00 S	121·40 E
72	Boulder..................Colo.	40·02 N	105·19 W
68	Boulder City..............Nev.	35 57 N	114·50 W
66	Boulder Cr................Idaho	42·53 N	116·49 W
67	Boulder Pk................Idaho	43·53 N	114·33 W
67	Boulder R.................Mont.	46·10 N	112·07 W
164	Boulé R. (bōō-lā')..........Mali	10·53 N	7·30 W
123	Boulogne-Billancourt (bōō-lôn'y'-bē-yäN-kōōr').Fr. (Paris In.)	48·50 N	2·14 E
122	Boulogne-sur-Mer (bōō-lôn'y-sür-mâr').Fr.	50·44 N	1·37 E
125	Bou-Mort, Sierra de (Mts.) (sē-ĕ'r-rä-dĕ-bô-ōō-mô'rt).Sp.	42·11 N	1·05 E
164	Bouna (bōō-nä')......Ivory Coast	9·14 N	3·56 W
65	Boundary B. (boun'dȧ-rĭ) Can. (Vancouver In.)	49·03 N	122·59 W
68	Boundary Pk...............Nev.	37·52 N	118·20 W
84	Bound Brook (bound brŏŏk) N. J. (New York In.)	40·34 N	74·32 W
74	Bountiful (boun'tĭ-fŏŏl) Utah (Salt Lake City In.)	40·55 N	111·53 W
75	Bountiful Pk. (boun'tĭ-fŏŏl) Utah (Salt Lake City In.)	40·58 N	111·49 W
47	Bounty Is.................N. Z.	47·42 S	179·05 E
164	Bourem (bōō-rĕm')..........Mali	16·43 N	0·15 W
122	Bourg-en-Bresse (bōōr-gĕN-brĕs') Fr.	46·12 N	5·13 E
122	Bourges (bōōrzh)............Fr.	47·06 N	2·22 E
85	Bourget (bōōr-zhĕ') Can. (Ottawa In.)	45·26 N	75·09 W
123	Bourgoin (bōōr-gwăN')........Fr.	45·46 N	5·17 E
160	Bourke (bûrk)............Austl.	30·10 S	146·00 E
135	Bour Khaya, Guba (B.).Sov. Un.	71·45 N	131·00 E
110	Bourne (bôrn).............Eng.	52·46 N	0·22 W
116	Bournemouth (bôrn'mŭth)...Eng.	50·44 N	1·55 W
114	Bou Saada (bōō-sä'dä).......Alg.	35·13 N	4·17 E
165	Bousso (bōō-sô')............Chad	10·33 N	16·45 E
164	Boutilimit (bōō-tê-lê-mē') Mauritania	17·30 N	14·54 W
	Bouvet (I.), see Bouvetøya		
47	Bouvetøya (Bouvet) (I.)...Atl. O.	54·26 S	3·24 E
126	Bovino (bō-vē'nō)...........It.	41·14 N	15·21 E
86	Bow (R.) (bō)..............Can.	50·33 N	112·25 W
70	Bowbells (bō'bĕls)........N. D.	48·50 N	102·16 W
70	Bowdle (bōd''l)...........S. D.	45·28 N	99·42 W
159	Bowen (bō'ĕn)............Austl.	20·02 S	148·14 E
84	Bowers Hill (bou'ērs) Va. (Norfolk In.)	36·47 N	76·25 W
77	Bowie (bōō'ĭ) (bō'ē).........Tex.	33·34 N	97·50 W
78	Bowling Green (bōlĭng grēn)..Ky.	37·00 N	86·26 W
73	Bowling Green.............Mo.	39·19 N	91·09 W
80	Bowling Green............Ohio	41·25 N	83·40 W
70	Bowman (bō'mȧn).........N. D.	46·11 N	103·23 W
81	Bowmanville (bō'mȧn-vĭl)...Can.	43·50 N	78·40 W
85	Bowness......Can. (Calgary In.)	51·06 N	114·13 W
155	Bowokan, Pulau-Pulau (Is.) Indon.	2·20 S	123·45 E
70	Boxelder Cr. (bŏks'ĕl-dēr)..Mont.	45·35 N	104·28 W
67	Boxelder Cr..............Mont.	47·17 N	108·37 W
74	Box Springs (bŏks sprĭngz) Calif (Los Angeles In.)	33·55 N	117·17 W
111	Boxtel....Neth. (Amsterdam In.)	51·40 N	5·21 E
85	Boyer, R. (boi'ēr) Can. (Quebec In.)	46·46 N	70·56 W
70	Boyer (R.)................Iowa	41·45 N	95·36 W
116	Boyle (boil)................Ire.	53·59 N	8·15 W
80	Boyne City...............Mich.	45·15 N	85·05 W
116	Boyne R. (boin).............Ire.	53·40 N	6·40 W
127	Bozcaada (Tenedos) (bōz-cä'dä) (tĕ'nĕ-dŏs).Tur.	39·50 N	26·05 E
127	Bozcaada (I.) (bōz-cä'dä)....Tur.	39·50 N	26·00 E
67	Bozemen (bōz'mȧn)........Mont.	45·41 N	111·00 W
126	Bra (brä)...................It.	44·41 N	7·52 E
126	Brač (I.) (bräch)..........Yugo.	43·18 N	16·36 E
126	Bracciano, Lago di (L.) (lä'gō-dē-brä-chä'nō).It.	42·05 N	12·00 E
81	Bracebridge (brās'brĭj)......Can.	45·05 N	79·20 W
75	Braceville (brās'vĭl) Ill. (Chicago In.)	41·13 N	88·16 W
118	Bräcke (brĕk'kĕ)...........Swe.	62·44 N	15·28 E
75	Brackenridge (brăk'ĕn-rĭj) Pa. (Pittsburgh In.)	40·37 N	79·44 W
76	Brackettville (brăk'ĕt-vĭl)....Tex.	29·19 N	100·24 W
99	Braço Menor (R.) (brä'zô-mĕ-nō'r).Braz.	13·46 S	50·34 W
126	Brádano (R.) (brä-dä'nō)......It.	40·43 N	16·22 E
75	Braddock (brăd'ŭk) Pa. (Pittsburgh In.)	40·24 N	79·52 W
79	Bradenton (brā'dĕn-tŭn).Fla. (In.)	27·28 N	82·35 W
110	Bradfield (brăd-fēld) Eng. (London In.)	51·25 N	1·08 W
110	Bradford (brăd'fērd)........Eng.	53·47 N	1·44 W
80	Bradford..................Ohio	40·10 N	84·30 W
81	Bradford....................Pa.	42·00 N	78·40 W
75	Bradley (brăd'lĭ).Ill. (Chicago In.)	41·09 N	87·52 W
65	Bradner (brăd'nēr) Can. (Vancouver In.)	49·05 N	122·26 W
76	Brady (brā'dĭ)..............Tex.	31·09 N	99·21 W
124	Braga (brä'gä).............Port.	41·20 N	8·25 W
101	Bragado (brä-gä'dō) Arg. (Buenos Aires In.)	35·07 S	60·28 W
99	Bragança (brä-gän'sä)......Braz.	1·02 S	46·50 W
124	Bragança..................Port.	41·48 N	6·46 W
101	Bragança Paulista (brä-gän'sä-pä'ōō-lē's-tà) Braz. (Rio de Janeiro In.)	22·58 S	46·31 W
85	Bragg Creek (brăg) Can. (Calgary In.)	50·57 N	114·35 W
145	Brahmaputra (R.) (brä'mȧ-pōō'trȧ).India	26·45 N	92·45 E
145	Brahui (Reg.)...........W. Pak.	28·32 N	66·15 E
75	Braidwood (brăd'wŏŏd) Ill. (Chicago In.)	41·16 N	88·13 W
129	Brăila (brē'ēlȧ)............Rom.	45·15 N	27·58 E
71	Brainerd (brān'ērd)........Minn.	46·20 N	94·09 W
83	Braintree (brān'trē) Mass. (Boston In.)	42·14 N	71·00 W
84	Braithwaite (brĭth'wĭt) La. (New Orleans In.)	29·52 N	89·57 W
167	Brakpan (brăk'păn).......S. Afr. (Johannesburg & Pretoria In.)	26·15 S	28·22 E
168	Brakspruit.S. Afr. (Johannesburg & Pretoria In.)	26·41 S	26·34 E
85	Brampton (brămp'tŭn) Can. (Toronto In.)	43·41 N	79·46 W
100	Branca, Pedra (Mtn.) (pĕ'drä-brȧ'N-kä).Braz. (In.)	22·55 S	43·28 W
84	Branchville (brănch'vĭl) N. J. (New York In.)	41·09 N	74·44 W
79	Branchville...............S. C.	33·17 N	80·48 W
99	Branco (R.) (brăŋ'kō)......Braz.	2·21 N	60·38 W
166	Brandberg (Mtn.).......S. W. Afr.	21·15 S	14·15 E
111	Brandenburg (brän'dĕn-bōōrgh) Ger. (Berlin In.)	52·25 N	12·33 E
120	Brandenburg (Reg.).........Ger.	52·12 N	13·31 E
168	Brandfort (brăn'd-fôrt) S. Afr. (Johannesburg & Pretoria In.)	28·42 S	26·29 E
86	Brandon (brăn'dŭn)........Can.	49·42 N	99·53 W
81	Brandon....................Vt.	43·45 N	73·05 W
116	Brandon Hill (brăn-dŏn).....Ire.	52·15 N	10·12 W
81	Branford (Brăn'fērd).......Conn.	41·15 N	72·50 W
121	Braniewo (brä-nyĕ'vô).......Pol.	54·23 N	19·50 E
168	Brankhorstspruit S. Afr. (Johannesburg & Pretoria In.)	24·47 S	28·45 E
121	Brańsk (brän' sk)...........Pol.	52·44 N	22·51 E
85	Brantford (brănt'fērd) Can. (Toronto In.)	43·09 N	80·17 W
83	Bras d'Or L. (brä-dôr')......Can.	45·53 N	60·47 W
99	Brasília (brä-sē'lyä)........Braz.	15·49 S	47·39 W
99	Brasília Legal (Fordlândia) (brä-sē'lyä-lĕ-gäl) (fō'rd-län-dyä) Braz.	3·45 S	55·46 W
101	Brasópolis (brä-sô'pô-lēs) Braz. (Rio de Janeiro In.)	22·30 S	45·36 W
127	Brașov (Orașul-Stalin)......Rom.	45·39 N	25·35 E
164	Brass (brăs)...............Nig.	4·28 N	6·28 E
111	Brasschaat (bräs'kät) Bel. (Bruxelles In.)	51·19 N	5·30 E
75	Bratenahl (bră'tĕn-ôl) Ohio (Cleveland In.)	41·34 N	81·36 W
111	Bratislava (brä'tĭs-lä-vä) Czech (Wien In.)	48·09 N	17·07 E
134	Bratsk (brätsk).........Sov. Un.	56·10 N	102·04 E
129	Bratslav (brät'släf)......Sov. Un.	48·48 N	28·59 E
81	Brattleboro (brăt''l-bŭr-ō)....Vt.	42·50 N	72·35 W
120	Braunau (brou'nou).........Aus.	48·15 N	13·05 E
120	Braunschweig (broun'shvīgh) Ger.	52·16 N	10·32 E
168	Brava (brä'vä) Som. (Horn of Afr. In.)	1·20 N	44·00 E
118	Bråviken (R.)..............Swe.	58·40 N	16·40 E
	Bravo del Norte, Rio, see Grande, Rio		
68	Brawley (brô'lĭ)...........Calif.	32·59 N	115·32 W
116	Bray (brā)..................Ire.	53·10 N	6·05 W
73	Braymer (brā'mēr)..........Mo.	39·34 N	93·47 W
77	Brays Bay. (brās'bĭ'yōō).Tex. (In.)	29·41 N	95.33 W
86	Brazeau....................Can.	52·31 N	116·00 W
80	Brazil (brȧ-zĭl')............Ind.	39·30 N	87·00 W
96	Brazil......................S. A.	9·00 S	53·00 W
96	Brazilian Highlands (Mts.) (brȧ zĭl yȧn hī-lȧndz.Braz.	14·00 S	48·00 W
62	Brazos (R.) (brä'zōs).......U. S.	33·10 N	98·50 W
76	Brazos (R.), Clear Fk.......Tex.	32·56 N	99·14 W
72	Brazos (R.), Double Mountain Fk. Tex.	33·23 N	101·21 W
72	Brazos (R.), Salt Fk. (sôlt fôrk) Tex.	33·20 N	100·57 E
166	Brazzaville (brȧ-zȧ-vēl')...Con. B.	4·10 S	15·18 E
127	Brčko (bĕrch'kô)..........Yugo.	44·54 N	18·46 E
121	Brda R. (bĕr-dȧ')...........Pol.	53·18 N	17·55 E
74	Brea (brē'ȧ) Calif. (Los Angeles In.)	33·55 N	117·54 W
85	Breakeyville....Can. (Quebec In.)	46·40 N	71·13 W
70	Breckenridge (brĕk'ĕn-rĭj)..Minn.	46·17 N	96·35 W
76	Breckenridge...............Tex.	32·46 N	98·53 W
75	Brecksville (brĕks'vĭl) Ohio (Cleveland In.)	41·19 N	81·38 W
120	Breclav (brzhĕl'läf)........Czech.	48·46 N	16·54 E
116	Brecon Beacons (brĕk'ŭn bē kŭns) Wales	52·00 N	3·55 W
111	Breda (brā-dä') Neth. (Amsterdam In.)	51·35 N	4·47 E
166	Bredasdorp (brā'das-dôrp) S. Afr.	34·15 S	20·00 E
136	Bredy (brĕ'dĭ) Sov. Un. (Urals In.)	52·25 N	60·23 E
120	Bregenz (brā'gĕnts).........Aus.	47·30 N	9·46 E
127	Bregovo (brĕ'gô-vô)........Yugo.	44·09 N	22·39 E
167	Breidbach (brēd'băk) S. Afr. (Natal In.)	32·54 S	27·26 E
112	Breidha Fd. (brā'dĭ).........Ice.	65·15 N	22·50 W
123	Breil (brĕ'y')................Fr.	43·57 N	7·36 E
99	Brejo (brā'zhŏŏ)...........Braz.	3·33 S	42·46 W
118	Bremangerland (I.) (brĕ-măngĕr-lănd).Nor.	61·51 N	4·25 E
120	Bremen (brā-mĕn)..........Ger.	53·05 N	8·50 E
80	Bremen (brē'mĕn)...........Ind.	41·25 N	86·05 W
120	Bremerhaven (brām-ēr-hä'fĕn) Ger.	53·33 N	8·38 E
65	Bremerton (brĕm'ēr-tŭn) Wash. (Seattle In.)	47·34 N	122·38 W
111	Bremervörde (brĕ'mĕr-fûr-dĕ) Ger. (Hamburg In.)	53·29 N	9·09 E
85	Bremner (brĕm'nēr) Can (Edmonton In.)	53·34 N	113·14 W
77	Bremond (brĕm'ŭnd).........Tex.	31·11 N	96·40 W
77	Brenham (brĕn'ăm)..........Tex.	30·10 N	96·24 W
120	Brenner P. (brĕn'ēr)......Aus.-It.	47·00 N	11·30 E
110	Brentwood (brĕnt'wŏŏd) Eng. (London In.)	51·37 N	0·18 E
81	Brentwood..................Md.	39·00 N	76·55 W
74	Brentwood....Mo. (St. Louis In.)	38·37 N	90·21 W
75	Brentwood....Pa. (Pittsburgh In.)	40·22 N	79·59 W
126	Brescia (brā'shä).............It.	45·33 N	10·15 E
	Breslau, see Wrocław		
126	Bressanone (brĕs-sä-nō'nā).....It.	46·42 N	11·40 E
122	Bressuire (brĕ-swēr')..........Fr.	46·49 N	0·14 W
122	Brest (brĕst)................Fr.	48·24 N	4·30 W
121	Brest..................Sov. Un.	52·06 N	23·43 E
128	Brest (Oblast)..........Sov. Un.	52·30 N	26·50 E
122	Bretagne, Monts de (Mts.) (mŏN-dĕ-brĕ-tăN'yĕ).Fr.	48·25 N	3·36 W
122	Breton, Pertvis (Str.) (pâr-twē'brĕ-tôN').Fr.	46·18 N	1·43 W
84	Breton I. (brĕt'ŭn) La. (New Orleans In.)	29·27 N	89·10 W
77	Breton Sd. (brĕt'ŭn).........La.	29·38 N	89·15 W
85	Bretona (brĕ-tō'nȧ) Can. (Edmonton In.)	53·27 N	113·20 W
111	Breukelen Neth. (Amsterdam In.)	52·09 N	5·00 E
78	Brevard (brê-värd')........N. C.	35·14 N	82·45 W
99	Breves (brā'vĕzh)..........Braz.	1·32 S	50·13 W
118	Brevik (brĕ'vêk)............Nor.	59·04 N	9·39 E
160	Brewarrina (brōō-ēr-rē'nȧ)..Austl.	29·54 S	146·50 E
82	Brewer (brōō'ēr)..........Maine	44·46 N	68·46 W
84	Brewster (brōō'stēr) N. Y. (New York In.)	41·23 N	73·38 W
93	Brewster, Cerro (Mt.) (sĕ'r-rô-brōō'stēr).Pan.	9·19 N	79·15 W
78	Brewton (brōō'tŭn)..........Ala.	31·06 N	87·04 W
127	Breznik (brĕs'nêk)..........Bul.	42·44 N	22·55 E
123	Briancon (brē-äN-sôN')........Fr.	44·54 N	6·39 E
122	Briare (brē-är')..............Fr.	47·40 N	2·46 E
65	Bridal Veil (brīd'ăl văl) Ore. (Portland In.)	45·33 N	122·10 W
94	Bridge Pt. (brĭj)..........Ba. Is.	25·35 N	76·40 W
78	Bridgeport (brĭj'pôrt)........Ala.	34·55 N	85·42 W
84	Bridgeport.Conn. (New York In.)	41·12 N	73·12 W
80	Bridgeport..................Ill.	38·40 N	87·45 W
75	Bridgeport.Ind. (Indianapolis In.)	39·44 N	86·18 W
70	Bridgeport.................Nebr.	41·40 N	103·06 W
80	Bridgeport.................Ohio	40·00 N	80·45 W
84	Bridgeport.Pa. (Philadelphia In.)	40·06 N	75·21 W
72	Bridgeport..................Tex.	33·13 N	97·46 W
84	Bridgeton (brĭj'tŭn) Ala. (Birmingham In.)	33·27 N	86·39 W
81	Bridgeton..................N. J.	39·30 N	75·15 W
82	Bridgetown.................Can.	44·51 N	65·21 W
93	Bridgetown (brĭj' toun) W. I. F. (Le. & Wind. Is. In.)	13·08 N	59·37 W
75	Bridgeville (brĭj'vĭl) Pa. (Pittsburgh In.)	40·22 N	80·07 W
160	Bridgewater (brĭj'wô-tēr)...Austl.	42·50 S	147·28 E
82	Bridgewater................Can.	44·24 N	64·34 W
110	Bridgnorth (brĭj'nôrth)......Eng.	52·32 N	2·25 W
82	Bridgton (brĭj'tŭn).........Maine	44·04 N	70·45 W
116	Bridlington (brĭd'lĭng-tŭn)...Eng.	54·06 N	0·10 W

ăt: finăl; rāte; senâte; ärm; ȧsk; sofȧ; fâre; ch-choose; dh-as th in other; bē; ēvent: bĕt; recĕnt; cratēr; g-go; gh-guttural g; bĭt; ĭ-short neutral; rīde; K-guttural k as ch in German ich;

PRONOUNCING INDEX

Brie-Comte-Robert—Burdur 187

Page	Name Pronunciation Region	Lat. °'	Long. °'
123	Brie-Comte-Robert (brē-kônt-ĕ-rō-bâr').Fr. (Paris In.)	48·42 N	2·37 E
111	Brielle....Neth. (Amsterdam In.)	51·54 N	4·08 E
82	Brier (I.) (brī'ēr)....Can.	44·16 N	66·24 W
78	Brierfield (brī'ēr-fēld)....Ala.	33·01 N	86·55 W
110	Brierfield (brī'ēr fēld)....Eng.	53·49 N	2·14 W
110	Brierley Hill (brī'ēr-lē hĭl)....Eng.	52·28 N	2·07 W
111	Brieselang (brē'zĕ-läng) Ger. (Berlin In.)	52·36 N	12·59 E
123	Briey (brē-ĕ')....Fr.	49·15 N	5·57 E
120	Brig (brēg)....Switz.	46·17 N	7·59 E
110	Brigg (brĭg)....Eng.	53·33 N	0·29 W
74	Brigham City (brĭg'ăm) Utah (Salt Lake City In.)	41·31 N	112·01 W
110	Brighouse (brĭg'hous)....Eng.	53·42 N	1·47 W
75	Bright (brīt).Ind. (Cincinnati In.)	39·13 N	84·51 W
110	Brightlingsea (brī't-lĭng-sē) Eng. (London In.)	51·50 N	1·00 E
84	Brighton (brīt'ŭn) Ala. (Birmingham In.)	33·27 N	86·56 W
72	Brighton....Colo.	39·58 N	104·49 W
116	Brighton....Eng.	50·47 N	0·07 W
74	Brighton....Ill. (St. Louis In.)	39·03 N	90·08 W
71	Brighton....Iowa	41·11 N	91·47 W
83	Brigus (brĭg'ŭs)....Can.	47·31 N	53·11 W
124	Brihuega (brē-wā'gä)....Sp.	40·32 N	2·52 W
74	Brimley (brĭm lē) Mich. (Sault Ste. Marie In.)	46·24 N	84·34 W
127	Brindisi (brēn'dē-zē)....It.	40·38 N	17·57 E
126	Brinje (brēn'yĕ)....Yugo.	45·00 N	15·08 E
73	Brinkley (brĭŋk'lĭ)....Ark.	34·52 N	91·12 W
65	Brinnon (brĭn'ŭn) Wash. (Seattle In.)	47·41 N	122·54 W
83	Brion (brē-ôN')....Can.	47·47 N	61·26 W
122	Brioude (brē-ōōd')....Fr.	45·18 N	3·22 E
160	Brisbane (brĭz' bân)....Austl.	27·30 S	153·10 E
80	Bristol (brĭs' tŭl)....Conn.	41·40 N	72·55 W
116	Bristol....Eng.	51·29 N	2·39 W
84	Bristol....Pa. (Philadelphia In.)	40·06 N	74·51 W
84	Bristol....R.I. (Providence In.)	41·41 N	71·14 W
79	Bristol....Tenn.	36·35 N	82·10 W
81	Bristol....Vt.	44·10 N	73·00 W
79	Bristol....Va.	36·36 N	82·12 W
75	Bristol....Wis. (Milwaukee In.)	42·32 N	88·04 W
64	Bristol B....Alaska	58·08 N	158·54 W
116	Bristol Chan....Eng.	51·20 N	3·47 E
73	Bristow (brĭs'tō)....Okla.	35·50 N	96·25 W
86	British Columbia (Prov.) (brĭt'ĭsh kŏl'ŭm-bĭ-ȧ).Can.	56·00 N	124·53 W
99	British Guiana (gē-ä'nȧ)....S. A.	7·00 N	59·40 W
88	British Honduras (hĕn-dōō'rȧs) N. A.	17·00 N	88·40 W
168	Brits..S. Afr. (Johannesburg & Pretoria In.)	25·39 S	27·47 E
166	Britstown (brĭts'toun)....S. Afr.	30·30 S	23·40 E
71	Britt (brĭt)....Iowa	43·05 N	93·47 W
70	Britton (brĭt'ŭn)....S. D.	45·47 N	97·44 W
122	Brive-la-Gaillarde (brēv-lä-gī-yärd'ĕ).Fr.	45·10 N	1·31 E
124	Briviesca (brē-vyās'kȧ)....Sp.	42·34 N	3·21 W
120	Brno (b'r'nô)....Czech.	49·18 N	16·37 E
94	Broa, Ensenada de la (B.) (ĕn-sĕ-nä'-dä-dĕ-lä-brō'ä).Cuba	22·30 N	82·00 W
78	Broad (R.) (brôd)....Ga.	34·15 N	83·14 W
79	Broad (R.)....N. C.	35·38 N	82·40 W
161	Broadmeadows (brôd'mĕd-ōz) Austl. (Melbourne In.)	37·40 S	144·53 E
75	Broadview Heights (brôd'vū) Ohio (Cleveland In.)	41·18 N	81·41 W
81	Brockport (brŏk'pōrt)....N. Y.	43·15 N	77·55 W
83	Brockton (brŏk'tŭn) Mass. (Boston In.)	42·04 N	71·01 W
81	Brockville (brŏk'vĭl)....Can.	44·35 N	75·40 W
67	Brockway (brŏk'wā)....Mont.	47·24 N	105·41 W
121	Brodnica (brôd'nĭt-sȧ)....Pol.	53·16 N	19·26 E
121	Brody (brô'dĭ)....Sov. Un.	50·05 N	25·10 E
73	Broken Arrow (brō'kĕn ăr'ō).Okla.	36·03 N	95·48 W
161	Broken B....Austl. (Sydney In.)	33·34 S	151·20 E
70	Broken Bow (brō'kĕn bō)....Nebr.	41·24 N	99·37 W
73	Broken Bow....Okla.	34·02 N	94·43 W
160	Broken Hill (brōk'ĕn)....Austl.	31·55 S	141·35 E
166	Broken Hill...Fed. of Rh. & Nya.	14·18 S	28·28 E
110	Bromley (brŭm'lĭ) Eng. (London In.)	51·23 N	0·01 E
81	Bromptonville (brŭmp'tŭn-vĭl) Can.	45·30 N	72·00 W
118	Brönderslev (brûn'dēr-slĕv)..Den.	57·15 N	9·56 E
136	Bronnitsy (brô-nyĭ'tsĭ) Sov. Un. (Moskva In.)	55·26 N	38·16 E
80	Bronson (brŏn'sŭn)....Mich.	41·55 N	85·15 W
85	Bronte (brŏNt) Can. (Toronto In.)	43·24 N	79·43 W
85	Bronte Cr....Can. (Toronto In.)	43·25 N	79·53 W
79	Brood (R.) (brōōd)....S. C.	34·46 N	81·25 W
85	Brook, The (R.) Can. (Ottawa In.)	45·25 N	75·09 W
75	Brookfield (brŏŏk'fēld) Ill. (Chicago In.)	41·49 N	87·51 W
73	Brookfield....Mo.	39·45 N	93·04 W
84	Brookhaven (brŏŏk'hāv'n) Ga. (Atlanta In.)	33·52 N	84·21 W
78	Brookhaven....Miss.	31·35 N	90·26 W
66	Brookings (brŏŏk'ĭngs)....Ore.	42·04 N	124·16 W
70	Brookings....S. D.	44·18 N	96·47 W
85	Brooklands (brŏŏk'lăndz) Can. (Winnipeg In.)	49·56 N	97·12 W
83	Brookline (brŏŏk'lĭn) Mass. (Boston In.)	42·20 N	71·08 W
83	Brookline....N. H. (Boston In.)	42·44 N	71·37 W
75	Brooklyn (brŏŏk'lĭn) Ohio (Cleveland In.)	41·26 N	81·44 W
74	Brooklyn Center Minn. (Minneapolis, St. Paul In.)	45·05 N	93·21 W
75	Brook Park (brŏŏk) Ohio (Cleveland In.)	41·24 N	81·50 W
64	Brooks Range (brŏŏks)....Alaska	68·20 N	159·00 W
79	Brooksville (brŏŏks'vĭl).Fla. (In.)	28·32 N	82·28 W
80	Brookville (brŏŏk'vĭl)....Ind.	39·20 N	85·00 W
81	Brookville....Pa.	41·10 N	79·00 W
78	Brookwood (brŏŏk'wŏŏd)....Ala.	33·15 N	87·17 W
116	Broom (L.) (brōōm)....Scot.	57·59 N	5·32 W
158	Broome (brōōm)....Austl.	18·00 S	122·15 E
94	Brothers (Is.) (brŭd'hērs)..Ba. Is.	26·05 N	79·00 W
120	Broumov (brōō'mōf)....Czech.	50·33 N	15·55 E
95	Brown Bk....Ba. Is.	21·30 N	74·35 W
72	Brownfield (broun'fēld)....Tex.	33·11 N	102·16 W
110	Brownhills (broun'hĭlz)....Eng.	52·38 N	1·55 W
67	Browning (broun'ĭng)....Mont.	48·37 N	113·05 W
75	Brownsboro (brounz'bô-rô) Ky. (Louisville In.)	38·22 N	85·30 W
85	Brownsburg (brouns'bûrg) Can. (Montreal In.)	45·40 N	74·24 W
75	Brownsburg Ind. (Indianapolis In.)	39·51 N	86·23 W
65	Brownsmead (brounz'-mēd) Ore. (Portland In.)	46·13 N	123·33 W
80	Brownstown (brounz'toun)...Ind.	38·50 N	86·00 W
78	Brownsville (brounz'vĭl)....Tenn.	35·35 N	89·15 W
77	Brownsville....Tex.	25·55 N	97·30 W
82	Brownville (broun'vĭl)....Maine	45·20 N	69·04 W
76	Brownwood (broun'wŏŏd)....Tex.	31·44 N	98·58 W
76	Brownwood L....Tex.	31·55 N	99·15 W
124	Brozas (brō'thäs)....Sp.	39·37 N	6·44 W
158	Bruce, Mt. (brōōs)....Austl.	22·35 S	118·15 E
78	Bruceton (brōōs'tŭn)....Tenn.	36·02 N	88·14 W
120	Bruchsal (brŏŏk'zäl)....Ger.	49·08 N	8·34 E
120	Bruck (brŏŏk)....Aus.	47·25 N	15·14 E
111	Brück (brük)....Ger. (Berlin In.)	52·12 N	12·45 E
111	Bruck an der Leitha Aus. (Wien In.)	48·01 N	16·47 E
85	Bruederheim (brōō'dēr-hīm) Can. (Edmonton In.)	53·47 N	113·56 W
117	Brugge....Bel.	51·13 N	3·05 E
123	Brühl (brül)....Ger. (Ruhr In.)	50·49 N	6·54 E
66	Bruneau R. (brōō-nō')....Idaho	42·47 N	115·43 W
154	Brunei....Asia	4·52 N	113·38 E
154	Brunei (brŏŏ-nī')....Bru.	5·00 N	114·59 E
123	Brünen (brü'nĕn).Ger. (Ruhr In.)	51·43 N	6·41 E
125	Brunete (brōō-nā'tā) Sp. (Madrid In.)	40·24 N	4·00 W
83	Brunette (I.) (brōō-nĕt')....Can.	47·17 N	55·55 W
111	Brunn am Gebirge (brōōn'äm gĕ-bĭr'gĕ) Aus. (Wien In.)	48·07 N	16·18 E
111	Brunsbüttelkoog (brōōns'büt-tĕl-kōg).Ger. (Hamburg In.)	53·58 N	9·10 E
79	Brunswick (brŭnz'wĭk)....Ga.	31·08 N	81·30 W
82	Brunswick....Maine	43·54 N	69·57 W
81	Brunswick....Md.	39·20 N	77·35 W
73	Brunswick....Mo.	39·25 N	93·07 W
175	Brunswick...Ohio (Cleveland In.)	41·14 N	81·50 W
100	Brunswick, Pen. de....Chile	53·25 S	71·15 W
59	Bruny (I.) (brōō'nē)....Austl.	43·30 S	47·50 E
72	Brush (brŭsh)....Colo.	40·14 N	103·40 W
100	Brusque (brōō's-kōōĕ)....Braz.	27·15 S	48·45 W
74	Brussels (brŭs'ĕls) Ill. (St. Louis In.)	38·57 N	90·36 W
	Brussels, see Bruxelles		
111	Bruxelles (Brussels) (brü-sĕl') (brŭs'ĕls).Bel. (Bruxelles In.)	50·51 N	4·21 E
80	Bryan (brī'ăn)....Ohio	41·25 N	84·30 W
77	Bryan....Tex.	30·40 N	96·22 W
128	Bryansk (b'r-yänsk')....Sov. Un.	53·12 N	34·23 E
128	Bryansk (Oblast)....Sov. Un.	52·43 N	32·25 E
70	Bryant (brī'ănt)....S. D.	44·35 N	97·29 E
65	Bryant....Wash. (Seattle In.)	48·14 N	122·10 W
69	Bryce Canyon Natl. Park (brīs) Utah	37·35 N	112·15 W
84	Bryn Mawr (brĭn mȧr') Pa. (Philadelphia In.)	40·02 N	75·20 W
78	Bryson City (brīs'ŭn)....N. C.	35·25 N	83·25 W
129	Bryukhovetskaya (b'ryŭk'ô-vyĕt-skä'yä).Sov. Un.	45·56 N	38·58 E
126	Bržice (br'zhĕ-tsĕ)....Yugo.	45·55 N	15·37 E
139	Buatam....Indon. (Singapore In.)	0·45 N	101·49 E
164	Buba (bōō'bä)....Port. Gui.	11·39 N	14·58 W
98	Bucaramanga (bōō-kä'rä-mäŋ'gä) Col.	7·12 N	73·14 W
155	Bucay (bōō-ki').Phil. (Manila In.)	17·32 N	120·42 E
158	Buccaneer Arch. (bŭk-ȧ-nēr') Austl.	16·05 S	122·00 E
121	Buchach (bŏŏ'chȧch)....Sov. Un.	49·04 N	25·25 E
164	Buchanan (bû-kăn'ăn)....Lib.	6·05 N	10·10 W
80	Buchanan....Mich.	41·50 N	86·25 W
159	Buchanan (L.) (bû-kân'nŏn).Austl.	21·45 S	21·02 E
76	Buchanan L. (bû-kăn'ăn)....Tex.	30·55 N	98·40 W
83	Buchans....Can.	48·49 N	56·54 W
	Bucharest, see Bucureşti		
111	Buchholtz (bŏŏk'hōltz) Ger. (Hamburg In.)	53·19 N	9·53 E
75	Buck Cr. (bŭk) Ind. (Indianapolis In.)	39·43 N	85·58 W
81	Buckhannon (bŭk-hăn'ŭn) W. Va.	39·00 N	80·10 W
116	Buckhaven (bŭk-hā'v'n)....Scot.	56·10 N	3·10 W
116	Buckie (bŭk'ĭ)....Scot.	57·40 N	2·50 W
85	Buckingham (bŭk'ĭng-ăm) Can. (Ottawa In.)	45·35 N	75·25 W
142	Buckingham (R.) (bŭk'ĭng-ăm) India	15·18 N	79·50 E
85	Buckland (bŭk'lănd) Can. (Quebec In.)	46·37 N	70·33 W
159	Buckland Tableland, (Reg.) Austl.	24·31 S	148·00 E
65	Buckley (buk'lē) Wash. (Seattle In.)	47·10 N	122·02 W
82	Bucksport (bŭks'pôrt)....Maine	44·35 N	68·47 W
82	Buctouche (bük-tōōsh')....Can.	46·30 N	64·42 W
127	Bucureşti (Bucharest) (bōō-kȧ-rĕst') (bōō-kŏŏ-rĕsh'tĭ).Rom.	44·23 N	26·10 E
80	Bucyrus (bû-sī'rŭs)....Ohio	40·50 N	82·55 W
121	Budapest (bōō'dȧ-pĕsht')...Hung.	47·30 N	19·05 E
123	Büderich (bü'dĕ-rēk) Ger. (Ruhr In.)	51·15 N	6·41 E
142	Budge-Budge.India (Calcutta In.)	22·28 N	88·08 E
164	Buea (bōō-ā'ä)....Nig.	4·10 N	9·12 E
75	Buechel (bĕ-chûl') Ky. (Louisville In.)	38·12 N	85·38 W
123	Bueil (bwā')....Fr. (Paris In.)	48·55 N	1·27 E
74	Buena Park (bwā'nȧ pärk) Calif. (Los Angeles In.)	33·52 N	118·00 W
98	Buenaventura (bwā'nä-vĕn-tōō'rȧ) Col.	3·46 N	77·09 W
95	Buenaventura Cuba (La Habana In.)	22·08 N	82·22 W
98	Buenaventura, Bahia de (B.) (bä-ē'ä-dĕ-bwā'nä-vĕn-tōō'rȧ) Col.	3·45 N	79·23 W
72	Buena Vista (bū'nȧ vĭs'tȧ)..Colo.	38·51 N	106·07 W
78	Buena Vista....Ga.	32·15 N	84·30 W
81	Buena Vista....Va.	37·45 N	79·20 W
94	Buena Vista, Bahía (B.) (bä-ē'ä-bwĕ-nä-vē's-tä).Cuba	22·30 N	79·10 W
68	Buena Vista Lake Res. (bū'nȧ vĭs'tȧ) Calif.	35·14 N	119·17 W
100	Buenos Aires (bwā'nōs ī'rās) Arg. (In.)	34·20 S	58·30 W
98	Buenos Aires....Col. (In.)	3·01 N	76·34 W
93	Buenos Aires....C. R.	9·10 N	83·21 W
100	Buenos Aires (Prov.)....Arg.	36·15 S	61·45 W
100	Buenos Aires (L.)....Arg.-Chile	46·30 S	72·15 W
123	Buer (bür)....Ger. (Ruhr In.)	51·35 N	7·03 E
71	Buffalo (buf'ȧ lō)....Minn.	45·10 N	93·50 W
75	Buffalo....N. Y. (Buffalo In.)	42·54 N	78·51 W
67	Buffalo....Wyo.	44·19 N	106·42 W
73	Buffalo (R.)....Ark.	35·56 N	92·58 W
167	Buffalo (R.)....S. Afr. (Natal In.)	28·35 S	30·27 E
78	Buffalo (R.)....Tenn.	35·24 N	87·10 W
77	Buffalo Bay....Tex. (In.)	29·46 N	95·32 W
71	Buffalo Cr....Minn.	44·46 N	94·28 W
86	Buffalo Head Hills....Can.	57·16 N	116·18 W
85	Buford (bū'fûrd) Can. (Edmonton In.)	53·15 N	113·55 W
78	Buford (bū'fērd)....Ga.	34·05 N	84·00 W
69	Buford (L.)....N. Mex.	36·37 N	107·12 W
129	Bug (R.) (bŏŏk)....Sov. Un.	48·12 N	30·13 E
98	Buga (bōō'gä)....Col. (In.)	3·54 N	76·17 W
111	Buggenhout...Bel. (Bruxelles In.)	51·01 N	4·10 E
126	Bugojno (bōō-gō ĭ nô)....Yugo.	44·03 N	17·28 E
121	Bug R. (bōōg)....Pol.	52·29 N	21·20 E
132	Bugul'ma (bōō-gōōl'mȧ).Sov. Un.	54·40 N	52·40 E
132	Buguruslan (bōō-gōō-rōōs-lán') Sov. Un.	53·30 N	52·32 E
155	Buhi (bōō'ē)....Phil. (Manila In.)	13·26 N	123·31 E
66	Buhl (būl)....Idaho	42·36 N	114·45 W
71	Buhl....Minn.	47·28 N	92·49 W
101	Buin (bōō-ēn') Chile (Santiago In.)	33·44 S	70·44 W
133	Buinaksk (bōō'ē-näksk)..Sov. Un.	42·40 N	47·20 E
124	Bujalance (bōō-hä-län'thā)....Sp.	37·54 N	4·22 W
166	Bukama (bōō-kä'mä)....Con. L.	9·08 S	26·00 E
103	Bukhara (bōō-kä'rä)....Sov. Un.	39·31 N	64·22 E
154	Bukittingg....Indon.	0·25 S	100·28 E
166	Bukoba....Tan.	1·19 S	31·49 E
121	Bukovina (Reg.) (bōō-kô'vĭ-nȧ) Sov. Un.	48·06 N	25·20 E
155	Bula (bōō'lä)....Indon.	3·17 S	130·27 E
155	Bulalacao (bōō-lä-lä'kä-ô) Phil. (Manila In.)	12·32 N	121·25 E
166	Bulawayo (bōō-lȧ-wä'yō) Fed. of Rh. & Nya.	20·12 S	28·43 E
64	Buldir (I.) (bŭl dĭr)....Alaska	52·22 N	175·50 E
102	Bulgaria (bŏŏl-gā'rĭ-ă)....Eur.	42·12 N	24·13 E
124	Bullaque (R.) (bōō-lä'kå)....Sp.	39·15 N	4·13 W
124	Bullas (bōōl'yäs)....Sp.	38·07 N	1·48 W
69	Bulldog Cr. (bŭl'dŏg')....Utah	37·45 N	110·55 W
94	Bull Head (Mtn.)....Jam.	18·10 N	77·15 W
159	Bulloo (R.) (bŭ-lōō')....Austl.	25·23 S	143·30 E
65	Bull Run (R.) (bŏŏl) Ore. (Portland In.)	45·26 N	122·11 W
65	Bull Run Res. (bŏŏl) Ore. (Portland In.)	45·29 N	122·11 W
73	Bull Shoals Res. (bŏŏl shōlz) Ark.-Mo.	36·35 N	92·57 W
168	Bulo Burti (bōō'lō bŏŏr'tĭ) Som. (Horn of Afr. In.)	3·53 N	45·30 E
110	Bulphan (bŏŏl'făn) Eng. (London In.)	51·33 N	0·21 E
168	Bultfontein (bŏŏlt'fŏn-tān') S. Afr. (Johannesburg & Pretoria In.)	28·18 S	26·10 E
135	Bulun (bōō-lōōn')....Sov. Un.	70·48 N	127·27 E
166	Bulungu (bōō-lōōŋ'gōō)...Con. L.	4·58 S	18·57 E
167	Bulwer (bŏŏl-wēr) S. Afr. (Natal In.)	29·49 S	29·48 E
165	Bumba (bŏŏm'bȧ)....Con. L.	2·15 N	22·32 E
155	Buna (bōō'nȧ)....Pap. Ter.	8·58 S	148·38 E
158	Bunbury (bŭn'bŭrĭ)....Austl.	33·25 S	115·45 E
160	Bundaberg (bŭn'dȧ-bûrg)...Austl.	24·45 S	152·18 E
153	Bungo-Suidō (Chan.) (bōōŋ'gō sōō-ē'dō).Jap.	33·26 N	131·54 E
74	Bunker Hill (bŭnk'ēr hĭl) Ill. (St. Louis In.)	39·03 N	89·57 W
77	Bunkie (bŭŋ'kĭ)....La.	30·55 N	92·10 W
135	Buor Khaya, Mys (C.)..Sov. Un.	71·47 N	133·22 E
168	Buran (bûr'ăn) Som. (Horn of Afr. In.)	10·38 N	48·30 E
168	Burao....Som. (Horn of Afr. In.)	9·20 N	45·45 E
84	Buras (bûr'ȧs) La. (New Orleans In.)	29·22 N	89·33 W
144	Buraydah....Sau. Ar.	26·23 N	44·14 E
74	Burbank (bûr'bănk) Calif. (Los Angeles In.)	34·11 N	118·19 W
159	Burdekin (R.) (bûr'dē-kĭn).Austl.	19·22 S	145·07 E
133	Burdur (bōōr-dōōr')....Tur.	37·50 N	30·15 E

ng-sing; ŋ-baŋk; N-nasalized n; nŏd; cŏmmit; ōld; ôbey; ôrder; fōōd; fŏŏt; ou-out; s-soft; sh-dish; th-thin; pūre; ûnite; ûrn; stŭd; circŭs; ü-as "y" in study; '-indeterminate vowel.

Page	Name	Pronunciation	Region	Lat. °'	Long. °'
142	Burdwan	(bŏŏrd-wän')	India	23·29 N	87·53 E
100	Burdwood, Banco (Bk.)		Atl. O.	54·00 S	60·45 W
135	Bureinskiy, Khrebet (Mts.)		Sov. Un.	51·15 N	133·30 E
135	Bureya	(bŏŏrā'ä)	Sov. Un.	49·55 N	130·00 E
135	Bureya (R.)	(bŏŏ-rā'yä)	Sov. Un.	51·00 N	130·14 E
110	Burford	(bûr-fẽrd)	Eng. (London In.)	51·46 N	1·38 W
147	Burga Dist.		China	50·31 N	120·30 E
127	Burgas	(bŏŏr'gäs)	Bul.	42·29 N	27·30 E
127	Burgaski Zaliv (G.)		Bul.	42·30 N	27·40 E
79	Burgaw	(bûr'gô)	N. C.	34·31 N	77·56 W
120	Burgdorf	(bŏŏrg'dôrf)	Switz.	47·04 N	7·37 E
111	Burgenland (State)		Aus. (Wien In.)	47·58 N	16·57 E
83	Burgeo		Can.	47·36 N	57·39 W
76	Burgos	(bŏŏr'gōs)	Mex.	24·57 N	98·47 W
155	Burgos		Phil. (Manila In.)	16·03 N	119·52 E
124	Burgos	(bŏŏ'r-gōs)	Sp.	42·20 N	3·44 E
118	Burgsvik	(bŏŏrgs'vĭk)	Swe.	57·04 N	18·18 E
142	Burhānpur	(bŏŏr'hän-pŏŏr)	India	21·26 N	76·08 E
155	Burias I.	(bŏŏ'rē-äs)	Phil. (Manila In.)	12·56 N	122·56 E
155	Burias Pass	(bŏŏ'rē-äs)	Phil. (Manila In.)	13·04 N	123·11 E
93	Burica, Punta (Pt.)	(pŏŏ'n-tä-bŏŏ'rē-kä)	Pan.	8·02 N	83·12 W
65	Burien	(bû'rĭ-ĕn)	Wash. (Seattle In.)	47·28 N	122·20 W
83	Burin	(bûr'ĭn)	Can.	47·03 N	55·33 W
83	Burin Pen.		Can.	47·04 N	55·14 W
72	Burkburnett	(bûrk-bûr'nĕt)	Tex.	34·04 N	98·35 W
81	Burke	(bûrk)	Vt.	44·40 N	72·00 W
158	Burketown	(bûrk'toun)	Austl.	17·50 S	139·30 E
67	Burley	(bûr'lĭ)	Idaho	42·31 N	113·48 W
65	Burley		Wash. (Seattle In.)	47·25 N	122·38 W
136	Burli		Sov. Un. (Urals In.)	53·36 N	61·55 E
65	Burlingame	(bûr'lĭn-gām)	Calif. (San Francisco In.)	37·35 N	122·22 W
73	Burlingame		Kans.	38·45 N	95·49 W
85	Burlington	(bûr'lĭng-tŭn)	Can. (Toronto In.)	43·19 N	79·48 W
72	Burlington		Colo.	39·17 N	102·26 W
71	Burlington		Iowa	40·48 N	91·05 W
73	Burlington		Kans.	38·10 N	95·46 W
75	Burlington		Ky. (Cincinnati In.)	39·01 N	84·44 W
84	Burlington		N. J. (Philadelphia In.)	40·04 N	74·52 W
79	Burlington		N. C.	36·05 N	79·26 W
81	Burlington		Vt.	44·30 N	73·15 W
65	Burlington		Wash. (Seattle In.)	48·28 N	122·20 W
75	Burlington		Wis. (Milwaukee In.)	42·41 N	88·16 W
138	Burma	(bûr'má)	Asia	21·00 N	95·15 E
76	Burnet	(bûrn'ĕt)	Tex.	30·46 N	98·14 W
110	Burnham on Crouch	(bûrn'ăm-ŏn-krouch)	Eng. (London In.)	51·38 N	0·48 E
160	Burnie	(bûr'nē)	Austl.	41·15 S	146·05 E
110	Burnley	(bûrn'lē)	Eng.	53·47 N	2·19 W
66	Burns	(bûrnz)	Ore.	43·35 N	119·05 W
78	Burnside	(bûrn'sīd)	Ky.	36·57 N	84·33 W
86	Burns Lake	(bûrnz lāk)	Can.	54·12 N	125·38 W
82	Burnsville	(bûrnz'vĭl)	Can.	47·44 N	65 07 W
66	Burnt R.	(bûrnt)	Ore.	44·26 N	117·53 W
65	Burrard Inlet	(bûr'ård)	Can. (Vancouver In.)	49·19 N	123·15 W
125	Burriana	(bŏŏr-rē-ä'nä)	Sp.	39·53 N	0·05 W
133	Bursa	(bŏŏr'sá)	Tur.	40·10 N	28·10 E
165	Bür Safājah		U. A. R.	26·57 N	33·56 E
168	Bür Sa'īd (Port Said)		U. A. R. (Suez In.)	31·15 N	32·19 E
123	Burscheid	(bŏŏr'shīd)	Ger. (Ruhr In.)	51·05 N	7·07 E
75	Burt	(bûrt)	N. Y. (Buffalo In.)	43·19 N	78·45 W
80	Burt (L.)	(bûrt)	Mich.	45·25 N	84·45 W
139	Bür Tawfīg		U. A. R. (Palestine In.)	29·58 N	32·33 E
65	Burton	(bûr'tŭn)	Wash. (Seattle In.)	47·24 N	122·28 W
110	Burton-on-Trent	(bûr'tŭn-ŏn-trĕnt)	Eng.	52·48 N	1·37 W
78	Burton Res.		Ga.	34·46 N	83·40 W
155	Buru (I.)		Indon.	3·30 S	126·30 E
168	Burullus L.		U. A. R. (Nile In.)	31·20 N	30·58 E
155	Buruncan Pt.	(bŏŏ-rōōn'kän)	Phil. (Manila In.)	12·11 N	121·23 E
86	Burwash Landing	(bûr wäsh)	Can.	61·20 N	139·12 W
70	Burwell	(bûr'wĕl)	Nebr.	41·46 N	99·08 W
110	Bury	(bĕr'ĭ)	Eng.	53·36 N	2·17 W
135	Buryat A.S.S.R.		Sov. Un.	54·15 N	111·22 E
117	Bury St. Edmunds	(bĕr'ĭ-sånt ĕd'mŭndz)	Eng.	52·14 N	0·44 E
100	Burzaco	(bŏŏr-zá'kŏ)	Arg. (In.)	34·35 S	58·23 W
168	Büsh	(bōōsh)	U. A. R. (Nile In.)	29·13 N	31·08 E
144	Büshehr	(bōōsh'ĕhr)	Iran	28·48 N	50·53 E
166	Bushman Land (Reg.)	(bŏŏsh-mǎn länd)	S. Afr.	29·15 S	18·45 E
167	Bushmans (R.)	(bŏŏsh'mǎnz)	S. Afr. (Natal In.)	33·29 S	26·09 E
73	Bushnell	(bŏŏsh'nĕl)	Ill.	40·33 N	90·28 W
165	Businga	(bōō-siŋ'gä)	Con. L.	3·14 N	20·33 E
121	Busk	(bōō'sk)	Sov. Un.	49·58 N	24·39 E
164	Bussa	(bōō'sä)	Nig.	10·11 N	4·20 E
158	Busselton	(bûs'l'tŭn)	Austl.	33·40 S	115·30 E
111	Bussum		Neth. (Amsterdam In.)	52·16 N	5·10 E
76	Bustamante	(bōōs-tä-män'tā)	Mex.	26·34 N	100·30 W
126	Busto Arsizio	(bōōs'tŏ är-sēd'zĕ-ō)	It.	45·47 N	8·51 E
155	Busuanga (I.)	(bōō-swän'gä)	Phil.	12·20 N	119·43 E
165	Buta	(bōō'tä)	Con. L.	2·47 N	24·46 E
167	Butha Buthe	(bōō-thä-bōō'thä)	Bas. (Natal In.)	28·49 S	28·16 E
78	Butler	(bŭt'lĕr)	Ala.	32·05 N	88·10 W
80	Butler		Ind.	41·25 N	84·50 W
73	Butler		Mo.	38·16 N	94·19 W
84	Butler		N. J. (New York In.)	41·00 N	74·20 W
81	Butler		Pa.	40·50 N	79·55 W
136	Butovo	(bōō-tô'vô)	Sov. Un. (Moskva In.)	55·33 N	37·36 E
78	Buttahatchie (R.)	(bŭt-á-hăch'ê)	Ala.-Miss.	34·02 N	88·05 W
67	Butte	(būt)	Mont.	46·00 N	112·31 W
167	Butterworth	(bŭ tēr'wûrth)	S. Afr. (Natal In.)	32·20 S	28·09 E
116	Butt of Lewis	(bŭt ŏv lū'ĭs)	Scot.	58·34 N	6·15 W
155	Butuan	(bōō-tōō'än)	Phil.	8·40 N	125·33 E
155	Butung (I.)		Indon.	5·15 S	124·15 E
129	Buturlinovka	(bōō-tōō'lĕ-nôf'ka)	Sov. Un.	50·47 N	40·35 E
111	Buxtehude	(bŏŏks-tĕ-hōō'dĕ)	Ger. (Hamburg In.)	53·29 N	9·42 E
110	Buxton	(bŭks't'n)	Eng.	53·15 N	1·55 W
65	Buxton		Ore. (Portland In.)	45·41 N	123·11 W
167	Buxton		S. Afr. (Natal In.)	32·36 S	26·39 E
132	Buy	(bwē)	Sov. Un.	58·30 N	41·48 E
150	Buyr Nuur	(bōō'yĕr nôr)	Mong.	47·50 N	117·00 E
127	Buzău	(bōō-zĕ'ōō)	Rom.	45·09 N	26·51 E
129	Buzâu (R.)		Rom.	45·17 N	27·22 E
165	Buzaymah		Libya	25·14 N	22·13 E
133	Buzuluk	(bōō-zōō-lōōk')	Sov. Un.	52·50 N	52·10 E
127	Byala		Bul.	43·26 N	25·44 E
	Byblos, see Jubayl				
121	Bydgoszcz	(bĭd'gôshch)	Pol.	53·07 N	18·00 E
80	Byesville	(bīz'vĭl)	Ohio	39·55 N	81·35 W
118	Bygdin	(bügh-dĕn')	Nor.	61·24 N	8·31 E
118	Byglandsfjord	(bügh'lǎnds-fyôr)	Nor.	58·40 N	7·49 E
136	Bykhovo	(bĭ'-kô'vô)	Sov. Un.	53·32 N	30·15 E
136	Bykovo	(bĭ-kô'vô)	Sov. Un. (Moskva In.)	55·38 N	38·05 E
134	Byrranga, Gory (Mts.)		Sov. Un.	74·15 N	94·28 E
135	Bytantay (R.)	(byän'tāy)	Sov. Un.	68·15 N	132·15 E
121	Bytom	(bī'tŭm)	Pol.	50·21 N	18·55 E
128	Bytosh'	(bī-tôsh')	Sov. Un.	53·48 N	34·06 E
121	Bytow	(bī'tŭf)	Pol.	54·10 N	17·30 E
127	Buziu (R.)		Rom.	45·18 N	26·29 E
100	Caazapa	(kä-zä-pä')	Par.	26·14 S	56·18 W
155	Cabagan	(kä-bä-gän')	Phil. (Manila In.)	17·27 N	12·46 E
155	Cabalete (I.)	(kä-bä-lā'tä)	Phil. (Manila In.)	14·19 N	122·00 E
94	Caballones, Canal de (Chan.)	(kä-nä'l-dĕ-kä-bäl-yō'nĕs)	Cuba	20·45 N	79·20 W
69	Caballo Res.	(kä-bä-lyō')	N. Mex.	33·00 N	107·20 W
124	Cabañaquinta	(kä-bän-yä-kê'n-tä)	Sp.	43·10 N	5·37 W
155	Cabanatuan	(kä-bä-nä-twän')	Phil. (Manila In.)	15·30 N	120·56 E
82	Cabano	(kä-bä-nō')	Can.	47·41 N	68·55 W
160	Cabar	(kä'bēr)	Austl.	31·28 S	145·50 E
155	Cabarruyan (I.)	(kä-bä-rōō'yän)	Phil. (Manila In.)	16·21 N	120·10 E
99	Cabedelo	(kä-bē-dā'lōō)	Braz.	6·58 S	34·49 W
91	Cabeza, Arrecife (Reef)	(är-rĕ-sē'fĕ-kä-bĕ-zä)	Mex.	19·07 N	95·52 W
124	Cabeza del Buey	(kä-bā'thä dĕl bwä')	Sp.	38·43 N	5·18 W
98	Cabimas	(kä-bē'mäs)	Ven.	10·21 N	71·27 W
166	Cabinda	(kä-bĭn'dä)	Ang.	5·45 S	12·10 E
163	Cabinda	(kä-bĭn'dä)	Afr.	5·00 S	10·00 E
66	Cabinet Mts.	(kăb'ĭ-nĕt)	Mont.	48·13 N	115·52 W
101	Cabo Frio	(kä'bŏ-frē'ŏ)	Braz. (Rio de Janeiro In.)	22·53 S	42·02 W
101	Cabo Frio, Ilha do	(ē'lä-dŏ-kä'bŏ frē'ŏ)	Braz. (Rio de Janeiro In.)	23·01 S	42·00 W
80	Cabot Hd.	(kăb'ŭt)	Can.	45·15 N	81·20 W
83	Cabot Str.	(kăb'ŭt)	Can.	47·35 N	60·00 W
164	Cabo Verde, Ilhas do		Afr. (In.)	15·48 N	26·02 W
124	Cabra	(kä'brä)	Sp.	37·28 N	4·29 W
155	Cabra (I.)		Phil. (Manila In.)	13·55 N	119·55 E
125	Cabrera (I.)	(kä-brä'rä)	Sp.	39·08 N	2·57 E
124	Cabriel (R.)	(kä-brē-ĕl')	Sp.	39·41 N	1·32 W
68	Cabrillo Natl. Mon.	(kä-brēl'yō)	Calif. (San Diego In.)	32·41 N	117·03 W
99	Cabrobó	(kä-brō-bô')	Braz.	8·34 S	39·13 W
100	Cabuçu (R.)	(kä-bōō-sōō)	Braz. (In.)	22·57 S	43·36 W
155	Cabugao	(kä-bōō'gä-ô)	Phil. (Manila In.)	17·48 N	120·28 E
127	Čačak	(chä'chäk)	Yugo.	43·51 N	20·22 E
101	Caçapava	(kä'sä-pä'vä)	Braz. (Rio de Janeiro In.)	23·05 S	45·42 W
99	Cáceres	(kä'-sĕ-rĕs)	Braz.	16·11 S	57·32 W
124	Cáceres	(kä'thä-räs)	Sp.	39·28 N	6·20 W
101	Cachapoal (R.)	(kä-chä-pô-ä'l)	Chile (Santiago In.)	34·23 S	70·19 W
101	Cacharí	(kä-chä-rē')	Arg. (Buenos Aires In.)	36·23 S	59·29 W
73	Cache (R.)	(kăsh)	Ark.	35·24 N	91·12 W
68	Cache Cr.	(kăsh)	Calif.	38·53 N	122·24 W
72	Cache la Poudre (R.)	(kăsh lä pōōd'r)	Colo.	40·43 N	105·39 W
100	Cachi, Nevados de (Pk.)	(nĕ-vá'dôs-dĕ-kä'chē)	Arg.	24·35 S	65·59 W
100	Cachinal	(kä-chē-näl')	Chile	25·57 S	69·33 W
99	Cachoeira	(kä-shô-ā'rä)	Braz.	12·32 S	38·47 W
100	Cachoeira do Sul	(kä-shô-ā'rä-dô-sōō'l)	Braz.	30·02 S	52·49 W
101	Cachoeiras de Macacu	(kä-shô-ā'räs-dĕ-mä-kä'kōō)	Braz. (Rio de Janeiro In.)	22·28 S	42·39 W
101	Cachoeiro de Itapemirim	(kä-shô-ā'rô-dĕ-ē'tä-pĕmē-rē'N)	Braz. (Rio de Janeiro In.)	20·51 S	41·06 W
166	Caconda	(kä-kôn'dä)	Ang.	13·40 S	15·05 E
77	Caddo L.	(kăd'ō)	La.-Tex.	32·37 N	94·15 W
90	Cadereyta	(kä-dā-rā'tä)	Mex.	20·42 N	99·47 W
76	Cadereyta Jimenez	(kä-dā-rā'tä hē-mā'nāz)	Mex.	25·36 N	99·59 W
125	Cadi, Sierra de (Mts.)	(sē-ĕ'r-rä-dĕ-kä'dē)	Sp.	42·17 N	1·34 E
155	Cadig, Mt.	(kä'dĕg)	Phil. (Manila In.)	14·11 N	122·26 E
80	Cadillac	(kăd'ĭ-lăk)	Mich.	44·15 N	85·25 W
68	Cadiz	(kä'dĭz)	Calif.	34·33 N	115·30 W
80	Cadiz		Ohio	40·15 N	81·00 W
124	Cádiz	(kä'dēz)	Sp.	36·34 N	6·20 W
124	Cádiz, Golfo de (G.)	(gôl-fô-dĕ-kä'dēz)	Sp.	36·50 N	7·00 W
122	Caen	(kän)	Fr.	49·13 N	0·22 W
101	Caeté	(kä-tĕ')	Braz. (Rio de Janeiro In.)	19·53 S	43·41 W
99	Caetité	(kä-ĕ-tē-tā')	Braz.	14·02 S	42·14 W
166	Cagamba	(kä-gä'm-bä)	Ang.	13·20 S	19·55 E
155	Cagayan	(kä-gä-yän')	Phil.	8·13 N	124·30 E
154	Cagayan (R.)		Phil.	16·45 N	121·55 E
154	Cagayan Is.		Phil.	9·40 N	120·30 E
154	Cagayan Sulu (I.)	(kä-gä-yän sōō'lōō)	Phil.	7·00 N	118·30 E
126	Cagli	(kä'lyē)	It.	42·33 N	12·38 E
126	Cagliari	(käl'yä-rē)	It.	39·16 N	9·08 E
126	Cagliari, Golfo di (G.)	(gôl-fô-dē-käl'yä-rē)	It.	39·08 N	9·12 E
123	Cagnes	(kän'y')	Fr.	43·40 N	7·14 E
99	Cagua	(kä'-gwä)	Ven. (In.)	10·12 N	67·27 W
89	Caguas	(kä'gwäs)	P. R. (Puerto Rico In.)	18·12 N	66·01 W
78	Cahaba (R.)	(kä hä-bä)	Ala.	32·50 N	87·15 W
166	Cahama	(kä-ä'mä)	Ang.	16·15 S	14·15 E
74	Cahokia	(kä-hô'kĭ-ä)	Ill. (St. Louis In.)	38·34 N	90·11 W
122	Cahors	(kä-ôr')	Fr.	44·27 N	1·27 E
91	Cahuacán	(kä-wä-kä'n)	Mex. (Mexico In.)	19·38 N	99·25 W
93	Cahuita, Punta (Pt.)	(pōō'n-tä-kä-wē'tá)	C. R.	9·47 N	82·41 W
99	Caiapó, Serra do (Mts.)	(sē'r-rä-dô-kä-yä-pô')	Braz.	17·52 S	52·37 W
94	Caibarién	(kī-bä-rē-ĕn')	Cuba	22·35 N	79·30 W
98	Caicedonia	(kī-sĕ-dô-nĕä)	Col. (In.)	4·21 N	75·48 W
95	Caicos Bk.	(kī'kōs)	Ba. Is.	21·35 N	72·00 W
95	Caicos Is.		Jam.	21·45 N	71·50 W
95	Caicos Passage (Str.)		Ba. Is.	21·55 N	72·45 W
77	Caillou B.	(kä-yōō')	La.	29·07 N	91·00 W
95	Caimanera	(kä-mä-nä'rä)	Cuba	20·00 N	75·10 W
90	Caimanere, Laguna del	(lä-gōō'nä-dĕl-kä-ē-mä-nĕ-rĕ)	Mex.	22·57 N	106·07 W
155	Caiman Pt.	(kī'mán)	Phil. (Manila In.)	15·56 N	119·33 E
88	Caimito, (R.)	(kä-ē-mē'tô)	Pan. (Panama Canal In.)	8·50 N	79·45 W
95	Caimito del Guayabal	(kä-ē-mē'tô-dĕl-gwä-yä-bä'l)	Cuba (La Habana In.)	22·12 N	82·36 W
85	Cainsville	(kānz'vĭl)	Can. (Toronto In.)	43·09 N	80·13 W
159	Cairns	(kârnz)	Austl.	17·02 S	145·49 E
93	Cairo	(kī'-rô)	C. R.	10·06 N	83·47 W
78	Cairo	(kä'rō)	Ga.	30·48 N	84·12 W
73	Cairo		Ill.	36·59 N	89·11 W
	Cairo, see Al Qāhirah				
110	Caistor	(kās'tēr)	Eng.	53·30 N	0·20 W
98	Cajamarca	(kä-kä-mä'r-kä)	Col. (In.)	4·25 N	75·25 W
98	Cajamarca	(kä-hä-mär'kä)	Peru	7·16 S	78·30 W
155	Cajidiocan	(kä-hē-dyô'kän)	Phil. (Manila In.)	12·22 N	122·41 E
127	Čajniče	(chī'nĭ-chĕ)	Yugo.	43·32 N	19·04 E
74	Cajon	(kä-hōn')	Calif. (Los Angeles In.)	34·18 N	117·28 W
101	Cajuru	(kä-zhōō'-rōō)	Braz. (Rio de Janeiro In.)	21·17 S	47·17 W
126	Čakovec	(chä'kō-vĕts)	Yugo.	46·23 N	16·27 E
167	Cala	(cä-lá)	S. Afr. (Natal In.)	31·33 S	27·41 E
164	Calabar	(kä-lä-bär')	Nig.	4·58 N	8·21 E
74	Calabasas	(kä-lä-bäs'äs)	Calif. (Los Angeles In.)	34·09 N	118·39 W
95	Calabazar	(kä-lä-bä-zä'r)	Cuba (La Habana In.)	23·02 N	82·25 W
98	Calabozo	(kä-lä-bô'zô)	Ven.	8·48 N	67·27 W
126	Calabria (Reg.)	(kä-lä'brĕ-ä)	It.	39·26 N	16·23 E
127	Calafat	(kä-lä-fät')	Rom.	43·59 N	22·56 E
155	Calagua Is.	(kä-läg'wä)	Phil. (Manila In.)	14·30 N	123·06 E
85	Calahoo	(kä-lä-hōō')	Can. (Edmonton In.)	53·42 N	113·58 W
124	Calahorra	(kä-lä-ôr'rä)	Sp.	42·18 N	1·58 W
82	Calais	(kä-lĕ')	Can.	45·11 N	67·15 W
122	Calais		Fr.	50·56 N	1·51 E
100	Calama	(kä-lä'mä)	Chile	22·17 S	68·58 W
98	Calamar	(kä-lä'mär)	Col.	1·55 N	72·33 W
98	Calamar	(kä-lä-mär')	Col.	10·24 N	75·00 W
155	Calamba	(kä-läm'bä)	Phil. (Manila In.)	14·12 N	121·10 E
154	Calamian Group (Is.)	(kä-lä-myän')	Phil.	12·14 S	118·38 E
124	Calañas	(kä-län'yäs)	Sp.	37·41 N	6·52 W
155	Calapan	(kä-lä-pän')	Phil. (Manila In.)	13·25 N	121·11 E
115	Călărasi	(kŭ-lŭ-räsh'ĭ)	Rom.	44·09 N	27·20 E
114	Calasparra	(kä-lä-spär'rä)	Sp.	38·13 N	1·40 W
124	Calatayud	(kä-lä-tä-yōōdh')	Sp.	41·23 N	1·37 W
155	Calauag	(kä-lä-wäg')	Phil. (Manila In.)	13·56 N	122·16 E
155	Calauag B.		Phil. (Manila In.)	14·07 N	122·10 E
155	Calaveras Res. (R.)		Calif. (San Francisco In.)	37·29 N	121·47 W
155	Calavite, C.	(kä-lä-vē'tä)	Phil. (Manila In.)	13·29 N	120·00 E
77	Calcasieu L.	(kăl'kä-shū)	La.	29·58 N	93·08 W
77	Calcasieu R.		La.	30·22 N	93·08 W

ăt; fīnål; rāte; senāte; ärm; ȧsk; sofȧ; fâre; ch-choose; dh-as th in other; bē; ēvent; bĕt; recĕnt; crātēr; g-go; gh-guttural g; bĭt; ĭ-short neutral; rīde; ᴋ-guttural k as ch in German ich;

PRONOUNCING INDEX Calcutta–Cape Flats 189

Page	Name Pronunciation Region	Lat. °′	Long. °′
142	Calcutta (kăl-kŭt'ȧ) India (Calcutta In.)	22·32 N	88·22 E
98	Caldas (kȧ'l-däs) Col. (In.)	6·06 N	75·38 W
98	Caldas (Dept.) Col. (In.)	5·20 N	75·38 W
124	Caldas de Rainha (käl'däs dā rīn'yȧ) Port.	39·25 N	9·08 W
110	Calder (R.) (kôl'dẽr) Eng.	53·39 N	1·30 W
110	Calder (R.) Eng.	53·48 N	2·25 W
100	Caldera (käl-dā'rä) Chile	27·02 S	70·53 W
66	Caldwell (kôld'wĕl) Idaho	43·40 N	116·43 W
73	Caldwell Kans.	37·04 N	97·36 W
80	Caldwell Ohio	39·40 N	81·30 W
77	Caldwell Tex.	30·30 N	96·40 W
85	Caledon (kăl'ē-dŏn) Can. (Toronto In.)	43·52 N	79·59 W
71	Caledonia (kăl-ē-dō'nĭ-ȧ) Minn.	43·38 N	91·31 W
116	Caledonian Can. (kăl-ē-dō'nĭ-ăn) Scot.	56·58 N	4·05 W
125	Calella (kä-lĕl'yä) Sp.	41·37 N	2·39 E
90	Calera Victor Rosales (kä-lā'rä-vē'k-tôr-rō-sä'lĕs) Mex.	22·57 N	102·42 W
68	Calexico (kȧ-lĕk'sĭ-kō) Calif.	32·41 N	115·30 W
85	Calgary (kăl'gȧ-rĭ) Can. (Calgary In.)	51·03 N	114·05 W
78	Calhoun (kăl-ho͞on') Ga.	34·30 N	84·56 W
98	Cali (kä'lē) Col. (In.)	3·26 N	76·30 W
143	Calicut (kăl'ĭ-kŭt) India	11·19 N	75·49 E
69	Caliente (käl-yĕn'tä) Nev.	37·38 N	114·30 W
73	California (kăl-ĭ-fôr'nĭ-ȧ) Mo.	38·38 N	92·38 W
75	California Pa. (Pittsburgh In.)	40·03 N	79·53 W
62	California (State) U. S.	38·10 N	121·20 W
88	California, Golfo de (G.) (gôl-fô-dĕ-kä-lê-fôr-nyä) Mex.	30·30 N	113·45 W
84	California B. La. (New Orleans In.)	29·29 N	89·32 W
121	Căliman, Muntii (Mts.) Rom.	47·05 N	24·47 E
143	Calimere, Pt India	15·25 N	80·05 E
74	Calimesa (kă-lĭ-mā'sȧ) Calif. (Los Angeles In.)	34·00 N	117·04 W
68	Calipatria (kăl-ĭ-pȧt'rĭ-ȧ) Calif.	33·03 N	115·30 W
91	Calkini (käl-kê-nē') Mex.	20·21 N	90·06 W
160	Callabonna (L.) (călă'bŏnȧ) Austl.	29·35 S	140·28 E
168	Callafo Eth. (Horn of Afr. In.)	5·40 N	44·00 E
98	Callao (käl-yä'ô) Peru	12·80 S	77·07 W
85	Calmar (kăl'mär) Can. (Edmonton In.)	53·16 N	113·49 W
71	Calmar Iowa	43·12 N	91·54 W
90	Calnali (käl-nä-lē') Mex.	20·53 N	98·34 W
79	Calooshatchee (R.) (kȧ-loo-sȧ-hăch'ē) Fla. (In.)	26·45 N	81·41 W
92	Calotmul (kä-lôt-mo͞ol) Mex. (Yucatan In.)	20·58 N	88·11 W
90	Calpulálpam (käl-po͞o-läl'päm) Mex.	19·35 N	98·33 W
126	Caltagirone (käl-tä-jē-rō'nȧ) It.	37·14 N	14·32 E
126	Caltanissetta (käl-tä-nē-sĕt'tä) It.	37·30 N	14·02 E
71	Calumet (kă-lū-mĕt') Mich.	47·15 S	88·29 W
75	Calumet, L. Ill. (Chicago In.)	41·43 N	87·36 W
75	Calumet City Ill. (Chicago In.)	41·37 N	87·33 W
77	Calvert (kăl'vẽrt) Tex.	30·59 N	96·41 W
86	Calvert (I.) Can.	51·40 N	129·02 W
126	Calvi (käl'vē) Fr.	42·33 N	8·35 E
90	Calvillo (käl-vēl'yō) Mex.	21·51 N	102·44 W
166	Calvinia (kăl-vĭn'ĭ-ȧ) S. Afr.	31·20 S	19·50 E
124	Calzada de Calatrava (käl-zä'dä-dĕ-kä-lä-trä'vä) Sp.	38·42 N	3·44 W
116	Cam (R.) (kăm) Eng.	52·15 N	0·05 E
94	Camaguey (kä-mä-gwā') Cuba	21·25 N	78·00 W
94	Camaguey (State) Cuba	21·30 N	78·10 W
94	Camajuani (kä-mä-hwä'nê) Cuba	22·25 N	79·50 W
155	Camalig (kä-mä'lĕg) Phil. (Manila In.)	13·11 N	123·36 E
98	Camaná (kä-mä'nä) Peru	16·37 S	72·33 W
65	Camano (kä-mä'no) Wash. (Seattle In.)	48·10 N	122·32 W
65	Camano I. Wash. (Seattle In.)	48·11 N	122·29 W
76	Camargo (kä-mär'gō) Mex.	26·19 N	98·49 W
92	Camaron, Cabo (C.) (kȧ'bô-kä-mä-rōn') Hond.	16·06 N	85·05 W
65	Camas (kăm'ȧs) Wash. (Portland In.)	45·35 N	122·54 W
67	Camas Cr. Idaho	44·10 N	112·09 W
99	Camatagua (kä-mä-tä'gwä) Ven. (In.)	9·49 N	66·55 W
154	Ca Mau, Pte de Viet.	8·42 N	103·11 E
142	Cambay (kăm-bā') India	22·22 N	72·39 E
142	Cambay, G. of India	21·05 N	71·58 E
64	Cambell (kămbĕl') Alaska	63·48 N	171·58 W
139	Cambodia (kăm-bō'dĭ-ȧ) Asia	14·00 N	105·45 E
116	Camborne (kăm'bôrn) Eng.	50·15 N	5·28 W
122	Cambrai (käN-brĕ') Fr.	50·10 N	3·15 E
116	Cambrian (Mts.) (kăm'brĭ-ăn) Wales	52·05 N	4·05 W
116	Cambridge (kām'brĭj) Eng.	52·12 N	0·11 E
81	Cambridge Md.	38·35 N	76·10 W
83	Cambridge Mass. (Boston In.)	42·23 N	71·07 W
71	Cambridge Minn.	45·35 N	93·14 W
72	Cambridge Nebr.	40·17 N	100·10 W
80	Cambridge Ohio	40·00 N	81·35 W
86	Cambridge Bay Can.	69·15 N	105·00 W
80	Cambridge City Ind.	39·45 N	85·15 W
101	Cambuci (käm-bo͞o'sē) Braz. (Rio de Janeiro In.)	21·35 S	41·54 W
101	Cambuí (käm-bo͞o-ē') Braz. (Rio de Janeiro In.)	22·38 S	46·02 W
75	Camby (kăm'bē) Ind. (Indianapolis In.)	39·40 N	86·19 W
78	Camden (kăm'dĕn) Ala.	31·58 N	87·15 W
73	Camden Ark.	33·36 N	92·49 W
161	Camden Austl. (Sydney In.)	34·03 S	150·42 E
82	Camden Maine	44·11 N	69·05 W
84	Camden N. J. (Philadelphia In.)	39·56 N	75·06 W
79	Camden S. C.	34·14 N	80·37 W
73	Cameron (kăm'ẽr-ŭn) Mo.	39·44 N	94·14 W
77	Cameron Tex.	30·52 N	96·57 W
80	Cameron W. Va.	39·40 N	80·35 W
86	Camerons Hills Can.	60·13 N	120·20 W
164	Cameroons Mt. Nig.	4·15 N	9·01 E
163	Cameroun Afr.	5·48 N	11·00 E
99	Cametá (kä-mȧ-tä') Braz.	1·14 S	49·30 W
155	Camiling (kä-mê-lĭng') Phil. (Manila In.)	15·42 N	120·24 E
78	Camilla (kȧ-mĭl'ȧ) Ga.	31·13 N	84·12 W
124	Caminha (kä-mĭn'yȧ) Port.	41·52 N	8·44 W
99	Camoçim (kä-mô-sēN') Braz.	2·56 S	40·55 W
158	Camooweal Austl.	20·00 S	138·13 E
101	Campana (käm-pä'nä) Arg. (Buenos Aires In.)	34·10 S	58·58 W
100	Campana (I.) (käm-pän'yä) Chile	48·20 S	75·15 W
124	Campanario (käm-pä-nä'rê-ō) Sp.	38·51 N	5·36 W
101	Campanha (käm-pän-yäN') Braz. (Rio de Janeiro In.)	21·51 S	45·24 W
126	Campania (Reg.) (käm-pän'yä) It.	43·00 N	14·40 E
125	Campanella, Punta (C.) (po͞o'n-tä-käm-pä-nĕ'lä) It. (Napoli In.)	40·20 N	14·21 E
65	Campbell (kăm'bĕl) Calif. (San Francisco In.)	37·17 N	121·57 W
73	Campbell Mo.	36·29 N	90·04 W
47	Campbell Is. N. Z.	52·30 S	169·00 E
142	Campbellpore W. Pak.	33·49 N	72·24 E
86	Campbell River Can.	50·00 N	125·24 W
78	Campbellsville (kăm'bĕlz-vĭl) Ky.	37·19 N	85·20 W
82	Campbellton (kăm'bĕl-tŭn) Can.	48·00 N	66·43 W
161	Campbelltown (kăm'bĕl-toun) Austl. (Sydney In.)	34·04 S	150·49 E
116	Campbeltown (kăm'b'l-toun) Scot.	55·25 N	5·50 W
75	Camp Dennison (dĕ'nĭ-sŏn) Ohio (Cincinnati In.)	39·12 N	84·17 W
91	Campeche (käm-pā'chȧ) Mex.	19·51 N	90·32 W
88	Campeche (State) Mex.	18·55 N	90·20 W
88	Campeche, Bahía de (B.) (bä-ē'ä-dĕ-käm-pä'chä) Mex.	19·30 N	93·40 W
94	Campechuela (käm-pȧ-chwā'lä) Cuba	20·15 N	77·15 W
167	Camperdown (kăm'pẽr-doun) S. Afr. (Natal In.)	29·14 S	30·33 E
124	Campillo de Altobuey (käm-pēl'yō dā äl-tō-bo͞o'ā) Sp.	39·37 N	1·50 W
99	Campina Grande (käm-pē'nä grän'dĕ) Braz.	7·15 S	35·49 W
101	Campinas (käm-pē'näzh) Braz. (Rio de Janeiro In.)	22·53 S	47·03 W
68	Camp Ind. Res. (kămp) Calif.	32·39 N	116·26 W
164	Campo (käm'pō) Cam.	2·32 N	9·54 E
98	Campoalegre (kä'm-pô-älĕ'grĕ) Col.	2·34 N	75·20 W
126	Campobasso (käm'pô-bäs'sō) It.	41·35 N	14·39 E
100	Campo Belo (kä'm-pô-bĕ'lô) Braz. (In.)	22·54 S	43·33 W
101	Campo Belo Braz. (Rio de Janeiro In.)	20·52 S	45·15 W
124	Campo de Criptana (käm'pō dā krêp-tä'nä) Sp.	39·24 N	3·09 W
95	Campo Florido (kä'm-pō flô-rê'dō) Cuba (La Habana In.)	23·07 N	82·07 W
99	Campo Grande (käm-po͝o grän'dĕ) Braz.	20·28 S	54·32 W
99	Campo Maior (käm-po͝o mä-yôr') Braz.	4·48 S	42·12 W
124	Campo Maior Port.	39·03 N	7·06 W
125	Campo Real (käm'pô rȧ-äl') Sp. (Madrid In.)	40·21 N	3·23 W
164	Campo R. Cam.	2·23 N	11·07 E
101	Campos (kä'm-pôs) Braz. (Rio de Janeiro In.)	21·46 S	41·19 W
101	Campos do Jordão (kä'm-pôs-dô-zhôr-dou'N) Braz. (Rio de Janeiro In.)	22·45 S	45·35 W
101	Campos Gerais (kä'm-pôs-zhĕ-rä'es) Braz. (Rio de Janeiro In.)	21·17 S	45·43 W
166	Camps Bay (kămps) S. Afr. (Cape Town In.)	33·57 S	18·22 E
76	Camp Wood (kămp wo͝od) Tex.	29·39 N	100·02 W
86	Camrose (kăm-rōz) Can.	53·08 N	112·50 W
95	Camu (R.) (kä'mo͞o) Dom. Rep.	19·05 N	70·15 W
82	Canaan (R.) (kā'năn) Can.	45·55 N	65·45 W
49	Canada (kăn'ȧ-dȧ) N. A.	50·00 N	100·00 W
83	Canada B. Can.	50·51 N	56·22 W
101	Cañada de Gomez (kä-nyä'dä-dĕ-gô'mĕz) Arg. (Buenos Aires In.)	32·49 S	61·24 W
72	Canadian (kȧ-nā'dĭ-ăn) Tex.	35·54 N	100·24 W
73	Canadian R. Okla.	34·53 N	97·06 W
81	Canajoharie (kăn-ȧ-jô-här'ē) N. Y.	42·55 N	74·35 W
127	Çanakkale (chä-näk-kä'lĕ) Tur.	40·10 N	26·26 E
127	Çanakkale boğazi (Dardanelles) (Str.) (chä-näk-kä'lĕ) (dár-dȧ-nĕlz') Tur.	40·05 N	25·50 E
88	Canal Zone N. A. (Panama Canal In.)	9·08 N	80·30 W
81	Canandaigua (kăn-ăn-dā'gwȧ) N. Y.	42·55 N	77·20 W
81	Canandaigua (L.) N. Y.	42·45 N	77·20 W
88	Cananea (kä-nä-nĕ'ä) Mex.	31·00 N	110·20 W
75	Canard R. Can. (Detroit In.)	42·10 N	83·04 W
164	Canarias, Islas (Is.) (ê's-läs-kä-nä'ryäs) Sp.	20·09 N	17·30 W
94	Canarreos, Arch. de los (Is.) (är-chē-pyĕ'lä-gô-dĕ-lôs-kä-när-rĕ'ōs) Cuba	21·35 N	82·20 W
92	Cañas (kä'-nyäs) C. R.	10·26 N	85·06 W
98	Cañasgordas (kä'nyäs-gô'r-däs) Col. (In.)	6·44 N	76·01 W
92	Cañas R. C. R.	10·20 N	85·21 W
81	Canastota (kăn-ȧs-tō'tȧ) N. Y.	43·05 N	75·45 W
99	Canastra, Serra de (Mts.) (sĕ'r-rä-dĕ-kä-nä's-trȧ) Braz.	19·53 S	46·57 W
76	Canatlán (kä-nät-län') Mex.	24·30 N	104·45 W
79	Canaveral, C. (kȧ-năv'ẽr-ăl) Fla. (In.)	28·30 N	80·23 W
99	Canavieiras (kä-nȧ-vē-ā'räs) Braz.	15·40 S	38·49 W
160	Canberra (kăn'bĕr-ȧ) Austl.	35·21 S	149·10 E
70	Canby (kăn'bĭ) Minn.	44·43 N	96·15 W
98	Canchuaya, Cerros de (Mts.) (sĕ'r-rôs-dĕ-kän-cho͞o-ȧ'ïä) Peru	7·30 S	74·30 W
91	Cancuc (kän-ko͞ok) Mex.	16·58 N	92·17 W
94	Candelaria (kän-dĕ-lä'ryä) Cuba	22·45 N	82·55 W
155	Candelaria (kän-dȧ-lä'rê-ä) Phil. (Manila In.)	15·39 N	119·55 E
91	Candelaria (R.) (kän-dĕ-lä-ryä) Mex.	18·25 N	91·21 W
124	Candeleda (kän-dhȧ-lā'dhä) Sp.	40·09 N	5·18 W
	Candia, see Kráklion		
64	Candle (kăn'd'l) Alaska	65·00 N	162·04 W
70	Cando (kăn'dō) N. D.	48·27 N	99·13 W
155	Candon (kän-dōn') Phil. (Manila In.)	17·13 N	120·26 E
	Canea, see Khaniá		
101	Canelones (kä-nĕ-lô-nĕs) Ur. (Buenos Aires In.)	34·32 S	56·19 W
101	Canelones (Dept.) Ur. (Buenos Aires In.)	34·34 S	56·15 W
98	Cañete (kän-yā'tȧ) Peru	13·06 S	76·17 W
95	Caney (kä-nā') (kā'nĭ) Cuba	20·05 N	75·45 W
73	Caney (kā'nĭ) Kans.	37·00 N	95·57 W
78	Caney (R.) Tenn.	36·10 N	85·50 W
166	Canganza, Sierra de (Mts.) (sĕr'rȧ dä kän-gän'zȧ) Ang.	7·35 S	15·30 E
124	Cangas (kän'gäs) Sp.	42·15 N	8·43 W
124	Cangas de Narcea (kä'n-gäs-dĕ-när-sĕ-ä) Sp.	43·08 N	6·36 W
126	Canicatti (kä-nê-kät'tē) It.	37·18 N	13·58 E
124	Caniles (kä-nē'lås) Sp.	37·26 N	2·43 W
90	Cañitas (kän-yē'täs) Mex.	23·38 N	102·44 W
133	Cankiri (chän-kē'rē) Tur.	40·40 N	33·40 E
85	Cannell Can. (Edmonton In.)	53·35 N	113·38 W
80	Cannelton (kăn'ĕl-tŭn) Ind.	37·55 N	86·45 W
123	Cannes (kån) Fr.	43·34 N	7·05 E
82	Canning (kăn'ĭng) Can.	45·11 N	64·26 W
110	Cannock (kăn'ŭk) Eng.	52·41 N	2·02 W
110	Cannock Chase (Reg.) (kăn'ŭk chās) Eng.	52·43 N	1·54 W
71	Cannon (R.) (kăn'ŭn) Minn.	44·18 N	93·24 W
70	Cannonball (R.) (kăn'ŭn-bäl) N. D.	46·17 N	101·35 W
93	Caño, Isla de (I.) (ê's-lä-dĕ-kä'nō) C. R.	8·38 N	84·00 W
74	Canoga Park (kȧ-nō'gȧ) Calif. (Los Angeles In.)	34·07 N	118·36 W
72	Canon City (kăn'yŭn) Colo.	38·27 N	105·16 W
75	Canonsburg (kăn'ŭnz-bûrg) Pa. (Pittsburgh In.)	40·16 N	80·11 W
79	Canoochee (R.) (kȧ-no͞o'chē) Ga.	32·25 N	82·11 W
86	Canora (kȧ-nōrȧ) Can.	51·43 N	102·32 W
126	Canosa (kä-nō'sä) It.	41·14 N	16·03 E
93	Canouan I. W. I. F. (Le. & Wind. Is. In.)	12·44 N	61·10 W
92	Cansaheab (kän-sä-ĕ-äb) Mex. (Yucatan In.)	21·11 N	89·05 W
83	Canso (kăn'sō) Can.	45·23 N	60·59 W
83	Canso, C. Can.	45·21 N	60·46 W
83	Canso, Str. of Can.	45·50 N	61·35 W
101	Cantagalo (kän-tä-gá'lo) Braz. (Rio de Janeiro In.)	21·59 S	42·22 W
124	Cantanhede (kän-tän-yā'dȧ) Port.	40·22 N	8·35 W
110	Canterbury (kăn'tẽr-bĕr-ê) Eng. (London In.)	51·17 N	1·06 E
159	Canterbury Bght. N. Z. (In.)	44·17 S	172·38 E
94	Cantiles, Cayo (I.) (ky-ō-kän-tē'lås) Cuba	21·40 N	82·00 W
149	Canton (Kuangchou) (kăn'tŏn') China (Canton In.)	23·07 N	113·15 E
78	Canton Ga.	34·13 N	84·29 W
73	Canton Ill.	40·34 N	90·02 W
83	Canton Mass. (Boston In.)	42·09 N	71·09 W
78	Canton Miss.	32·36 N	90·01 W
73	Canton Mo.	40·08 N	91·33 W
78	Canton N. C.	35·32 N	82·50 W
80	Canton Ohio	40·50 N	81·25 W
81	Canton Pa.	41·50 N	76·45 W
70	Canton S. D.	43·17 N	96·37 W
126	Cantu (kän-to͞o') It.	45·43 N	9·09 E
101	Cañuelas (kä-nyo͞oĕ'-läs) Arg. (Buenos Aires In.)	35·03 S	58·45 W
99	Canumã (R.) (kä-no͞o-mä') Braz.	6·20 S	58·57 W
72	Canyon (kăn'yŭn) Tex.	34·59 N	101·57 W
65	Canyon (R.) Wash. (Seattle In.)	48·09 N	121·48 W
76	Canyon Dam Tex.	29·51 N	98·20 W
69	Canyon De Chelly Natl. Mon. Ariz.	36·14 N	110·00 W
155	Capalonga (kä-pä-lôŋ'gä) Phil. (Manila In.)	14·20 N	122·30 E
126	Capannori (kä-pän'nô-rē) It.	43·50 N	10·30 E
125	Caparica (kä-pä-rē'kä) Port. (Lisboa In.)	38·40 N	9·12 W
83	Cap-Aux-Meules Can.	47·25 N	61·51 W
99	Capaya (R.) (kä-pä-ïä) Ven. (In.)	10·28 N	66·15 W
82	Cap Chat (kȧp shä') Can.	49·07 N	66·42 W
82	Cap de la Madeleine (kȧp dē lȧ mȧ-d'lĕn') Can.	46·23 N	72·30 W
83	Cape Breton (I.) (kāp brĕt'ŭn) Can.	45·48 N	59·53 W
83	Cape Breton Highlands Natl. Park Can.	46·45 N	61·05 W
79	Cape Charles (kāp chärlz) Va.	37·13 N	76·02 W
164	Cape Coast Ghana	5·14 N	1·19 W
81	Cape Cod B. (kāp kŏd) Mass.	41·50 N	70·20 W
79	Cape Fear (R.) (kāp fēr) N. C.	34·43 N	78·41 W
166	Cape Flats (kāp flăts) S. Afr. (Cape Town In.)	34·01 S	18·37 E

190 Cape Girardeau–Castelli PRONOUNCING INDEX

Page	Name Pronunciation Region	Lat. °′	Long. °′
73	Cape Girardeau (jē-rär-dō′) . . Mo.	37·17 N	89·32 W
84	Cape Henry (hĕn′rē) Va. (Norfolk In.)	36·55 N	76·00 W
81	Cape May (kāp mā) . . . . N. J.	38·55 N	74·50 W
81	Cape May C. H. (kāp mā) . . N. J.	39·05 N	75·00 W
166	Cape of Good Hope (Prov.) (kāp ŏv good hōp) . S. Afr.	31·50 S	21·15 E
86	Cape Parry (kāp păr′rē) . . . . . Can.	70·29 N	127·41 W
87	Cape Smith Ra. (kāp smĭth) . Can.	61·23 N	76·32 W
93	Capesterre Guad. (Le. & Wind. Is. In.)	16·02 N	61·37 W
166	Cape Town (kāp toun) S. Afr. (Cape Town In.)	33·48 S	18·28 E
159	Cape York Pen. (kāp yôrk) . Austl.	12·30 S	142·35 E
95	Cap-Haitian (kȧp à-ē-syăn′) . . Hai.	19·45 N	72·15 W
101	Capilla de Señor (kä-pēl′yä dā sän-yôr′) . Arg. (Buenos Aires In.)	34·18 S	59·07 W
69	Capitol Reef Natl. Mon. (kăp′ĭ-tŏl) . Utah	38·15 N	111·10 W
101	Capivari (kä-pē-vä′rē) Braz. (Rio de Janeiro In.)	22·59 S	47·29 W
100	Capivari . . . . Braz. (In.)	22·39 S	43·19 W
160	Capoompeta (Mtn.) (kȧ-pōōm-pē′tȧ) . Austl.	29·15 S	152·12 E
126	Caporetto (kä-pô-rĕt′tō) . . . Yugo.	46·15 N	13·34 E
126	Capraia (I.) (kä-prä′yä) . . . . . . It.	43·02 N	9·51 E
126	Caprara Pt. (kä-prä′rä) . . . . . . It.	41·08 N	8·20 E
126	Caprera (I.) (kä-prā′rä) . . . . . . It.	41·12 N	9·28 E
125	Capri . . . . It. (Napoli In.)	40·18 N	14·16 E
125	Capri, I. di (ē′-sō-lä-dē-kä′prē) It. (Napoli In.)	40·19 N	14·10 E
159	Capricorn Chan. (kăp′rĭ-kôrn) Austl.	22·27 S	151·24 E
85	Cap-Rouge (kȧp rōōzh′) Can. (Quebec In.)	46·45 N	71·21 W
85	Cap St. Ignace (kĭp săN-tē-nyȧs′) Can. (Quebec In.)	47·02 N	70·27 W
126	Capua (kä′pwä) . . . . It.	41·07 N	14·14 E
90	Capulhuaco (kä-pōōl-hwäk′) . Mex.	19·33 N	99·43 W
72	Capulin Mountain Natl. Mon. (kȧ-pū′lĭn) . N. Mex.	36·15 N	103·58 W
91	Capultitlán (kä-pōō′l-tē-tlä′n) Mex. (Mexico In.)	19·15 N	99·40 W
98	Caquetá (R.) (kä-kä-tä′) . . . . . Col.	0·23 S	73·22 W
125	Carabaña (kä-rä-bän′yä) Sp. (Madrid In.)	40·16 N	3·15 W
99	Carabobo (State) (kä-rä-bô′-bô) Ven. (In.)	10·07 N	68·06 W
127	Caracal (kȧ-rȧ-kȧl′) . . . . Rom.	44·06 N	24·22 E
99	Caracas (kä-rä′kȧs) . . . . Ven. (In.)	10·30 N	66·58 W
90	Carácuaro de Morelos (kä-rä′kwä-rō-dĕ-mô-rĕ-lōs) . Mex.	18·44 N	101·04 W
101	Caraguatatuba (kä-rä-gwä-tȧ-tōō′bä) . Braz. (Rio de Janeiro In.)	23·37 S	45·26 W
99	Carajás, Serra dos (Mts.) (sĕ′r-rä-dôs-kä-rä-zhà′s) . Braz.	5·58 S	51·45 W
98	Caramanta, Cerro (Mtn.) (sĕ′r-rô-kä-rä-mà′n-tä) . Col. (In.)	5·29 N	76·01 W
100	Caramarca (kä-rä-mà′r-kä) . . . Arg.	28·29 S	65·45 W
155	Caramoan (kä-rä-mō′än) Phil. (Manila In.)	13·46 N	123·52 E
101	Carandaí (kä-rän-dàē′) Braz. (Rio de Janeiro In.)	20·57 S	43·47 W
101	Carangola (kä-rán′gō′lä) Braz. (Rio de Janeiro In.)	20·46 S	42·02 W
127	Caransebes (kȧ-rȧn-sā′bĕsh) . Rom.	45·24 N	22·13 E
100	Carapeguá (kä-rä-pȧ-gwä′) . . . Arg.	26·01 S	58·13 W
82	Caraquet (kă-rȧ-kĕt′) . . . . . . Can.	47·47 N	64·56 W
93	Carata, Laguna (L.) (lä-gōō′nä-kä-rä′tä) . Nic.	13·59 N	83·41 W
93	Caratasca, Laguna (L.) (lä-gōō′nä-kä-rä-täs′kä) . Hond.	15·20 N	83·45 W
124	Caravaca (kä-rä-vä′kä) . . . . . . Sp.	38·05 N	1·51 W
99	Caravelas (kȧ-rȧ-vĕl′äzh) . . . . Braz.	17·46 S	39·06 W
99	Carayaca (kä-rä-iä′kä) . . Ven. (In.)	10·32 N	67·07 W
100	Caràzinho (kä-rá′zē-nyō) . . . . Braz.	28·22 S	52·33 W
124	Carballino (kär-bäl-yē′nō) . . . . . Sp.	42·26 N	8·04 W
124	Carballo (kär-bäl′yō) . . . . Sp.	43·13 N	8·40 W
65	Carbon (R.) (kär′bŏn) Wash. (Seattle In.)	47·06 N	122·08 W
65	Carbonado (kȧr-bō-nä′dō) Wash. (Seattle In.)	47·05 N	122·03 W
126	Carbonara, C. (kär-bō-nä′rä) . . . It.	39·08 N	9·33 E
85	Carbondale (kär′bŏn-dāl) Can. (Edmonton In.)	53·45 N	113·32 W
73	Carbondale . . . . Ill.	37·42 N	89·12 W
81	Carbondale . . . . Pa.	41·35 N	75·30 W
83	Carbonear (kär-bō-nēr′) . . . . . Can.	47·43 N	53·16 W
78	Carbon Hill (kär′bŏn hĭl) . . . . . Ala.	33·53 N	87·34 W
78	Carbur (kär′bûr) . . . . Fla.	29·55 N	83·25 W
125	Carcagente (kär-kä-hĕn′tä) . . . . Sp.	39·09 N	0·29 W
122	Carcans, Étang de (L.) (ā-taN-dĕ-kär-kaN) . Fr.	45·12 N	1·00 W
122	Carcassonne (kȧr-kȧ-sôn′) . . . . . Fr.	43·12 N	2·23 E
86	Carcross (kär′krôs) . . . . Can.	60·18 N	134·54 W
145	Cardamon Hills (kär′dȧ-mŭm) Ceylon (In.)	9·45 N	77·28 E
94	Cárdenas (kär′dȧ-näs) . . . . . . Cuba	23·00 N	81·10 W
91	Cárdenas (kà′r-dĕ-näs) . . . . . . Mex.	17·59 N	93·23 W
90	Cárdenas . . . . Mex.	22·01 N	99·38 W
95	Cardenas, Bahía de (B.) (bä-ē′ä-dĕ-kär′dȧ-näs) . Cuba	23·10 N	81·10 W
85	Cardiff (kär′dĭf) Can. (Edmonton In.)	53·46 N	113·36 W
116	Cardiff . . . . Wales	51·30 N	3·18 W
116	Cardigan (kär′dĭ-găn) . . . . . . Wales	52·05 N	4·40 W
116	Cardigan B . . . . Wales	52·35 N	4·40 W
86	Cardston (kärds′tŭn) . . . . Can.	49·14 N	113·23 W
121	Carei (kä-rĕ′) . . . . Rom.	47·42 N	22·28 E
122	Carentan (kä-rôN-täN′) . . . . Fr.	49·19 N	1·14 W
80	Carey (kā′rē) . . . . Ohio	40·55 N	83·25 W
158	Carey (I.) (kâr′ē) . . . . Austl.	29·20 S	123·35 E
122	Carhaix (kär-ĕ′) . . . . Fr.	48·17 N	3·37 W
89	Caribbean Sea (kăr-ĭ-bē′ăn) N. A.-S. A.	14·30 N	75·30 W
86	Cariboo Mts. (kă′rĭ-bōō) . . . . Can.	53·51 N	122·13 W
82	Caribou . . . . Maine	46·51 N	68·01 W
71	Caribou (I.) . . . . Can.	47·22 N	85·42 W
74	Caribou L. . . . Minn. (Duluth In.)	46·54 N	92·16 W
86	Caribou Mts . . . . Can.	59·20 N	115·30 W
99	Carinhanha (kä-rĭ-nyän′yä) . Braz.	14·14 S	43·44 W
126	Carini (kä-rē′nē) . . . . It.	38·09 N	13·10 E
	Carinthia, See Kärnten		
81	Carleton Place (kärl′tŭn) . . . . Can.	45·15 N	76·10 W
73	Carlinville (kär′lĭn-vĭl) . . . . Ill.	39·16 N	89·52 W
116	Carlisle (kär-lĭl′) . . . . Eng.	54·54 N	3·03 W
80	Carlisle . . . . Ky.	38·20 N	84·00 W
84	Carlisle . . . . La. (New Orleans In.)	29·41 N	89·57 W
81	Carlisle . . . . Pa.	40·10 N	77·15 W
122	Carlitte, Pic (Pk.) (pēk′-kär-lēt′) Fr.	42·33 N	1·56 E
126	Carloforte (kär′lō-fôr-tā) . . . . . . It.	39·11 N	8·18 E
101	Carlos Casares (kär-lôs-kä-sȧ′rĕs) Arg. (Buenos Aires In.)	35·38 S	61·17 W
116	Carlow (kär′lō) . . . . Ire.	52·50 N	7·00 W
76	Carlsbad (kärlz′băd) . . . . . N. Mex.	32·24 N	104·12 W
76	Carlsbad Caverns Natl. Park N. Mex.	32·08 N	104·30 W
110	Carlton (kärl′tŭn) . . . . Eng.	52·58 N	1·05 W
74	Carlton . . . . . . Minn. (Duluth In.)	46·40 N	92·26 W
80	Carlton Center (kärl′tŭn sĕn′tēr) Mich.	42·45 N	85·20 W
73	Carlyle (kär-lĭl′) . . . . Ill.	38·37 N	89·23 W
126	Carmagnolo (kär-mä-nyô′lä) . . . It.	44·52 N	7·48 E
86	Carman (kär′mȧn) . . . . Can.	49·30 N	98·02 W
116	Carmarthen (kär-mär′thĕn) Wales	51·50 N	4·20 W
116	Carmarthen B. (kär-mär′thĕn) Wales	51·33 N	4·50 W
122	Carmaux (kȧr-mō′) . . . . Fr.	44·05 N	2·09 E
84	Carmel (kär′mĕl) N. Y. (New York In.)	41·25 N	73·42 W
101	Carmelo (kär-mĕ′lo) Ur. (Buenos Aires In.)	33·59 S	58·15 W
90	Carmen, Isla del (I.) (ē′s-lä-dĕl-kà′r-mĕn) . Mex.	18·43 N	91·40 W
91	Carmen, Laguna del (L.) (lä-gōō′nä-dĕl-kà′r-mĕn) . Mex.	18·15 N	93·26 W
101	Carmen de Areco (kär′mĕn′ dā ä-rā′kō) . Arg. (Buenos Aires In.)	34·21 S	59·50 W
100	Carmen de Patagones (kà′r-mĕn-dĕ-pä-tä-gô′-nĕs) Arg.	40·47 S	62·56 W
80	Carmi (kär′mī) . . . . Ill.	38·05 N	88·10 W
101	Carmo (kà′r-mô) Braz. (Rio de Janeiro In.)	21·57 S	42·06 W
101	Carmo do Rio Clara (kà′r-mô-dô-rē′ô-klä′-rȧ) Braz. (Rio de Janeiro In.)	20·57 S	46·04 W
124	Carmona (kär-mō′nä) . . . . Sp.	37·28 N	5·38 W
158	Carnarvon (kär-når′vŭn) . . . . Austl.	24·45 S	113·45 E
166	Carnarvon . . . . S. Afr.	31·00 S	22·15 E
116	Carnarvon . . . . Wales	53·08 N	4·17 W
116	Carnarvon Bay . . . . Wales	53·09 N	4·56 W
65	Carnation (kär-nā′shŭn) Wash. (Seattle In.)	47·39 N	121·55 W
125	Carnaxide (kär-nä-shē′dĕ) Port. (Lisboa In.)	38·44 N	9·15 W
116	Carndonagh (kärn-dō-nä′) . . . . Ire.	54·75 N	6·75 W
72	Carnegie (kär-nĕg′ĭ) . . . . Okla.	35·06 N	98·38 W
75	Carnegie . . . . . Pa. (Pittsburgh In.)	40·24 N	80·06 W
81	Carneys Point (kär′nês) . . . . . N. J.	39·45 N	75·25 W
120	Carnic Alps (Mts.) . . . . Aus.-It.	46·43 N	12·38 E
125	Carnot (kär nō′) . . . . Alg.	36·15 N	1·40 E
165	Carnot . . . . Cen. Afr. Rep.	4·56 N	16·00 E
116	Carnsore Pt. (kärn′sôr) . . . . Ire.	52·10 N	6·16 W
80	Caro (kȧ′rō) . . . . Mich.	43·30 N	83·25 W
99	Carolina (kä-rō-lē′nä) . . . . Braz.	7·26 S	47·16 W
166	Carolina (kăr-ô-lī′nȧ) . . . . . . S. Afr.	26·07 S	30·09 E
92	Carolina L. (kä-rŏ-lē′-nä) Mex. (Yucatan In.)	18·41 N	89·40 W
156	Caroline Is. (kăr′ô-lĭn) Pac. Is. Trust Ter.	9·30 N	143·00 E
98	Caroni (R.) (kä-rō′nē) . . . . Ven.	5·49 N	62·57 W
98	Carora (kä-rō′rä) . . . . Ven.	10·09 N	70·12 W
115	Carpathians Mts. (kär-pā′thĭ-ăn) Eur.	49·23 N	20·14 E
127	Carpatii Meridionali (Transylvanian Alps) (Mts.) . Rom.	45·30 N	23·30 E
158	Carpentaria, G. of (kär-pĕn-târ′ĭȧ) . Austl.	14·45 S	138·50 E
74	Carpenter (kär′pĕn-tēr) Ill. (St. Louis In.)	38·54 N	89·54 W
122	Carpentras (kär-päN-träs′) . . . . Fr.	44·04 N	5·01 E
126	Carpi . . . . It.	44·48 N	10·54 E
78	Carrabelle (kăr′ȧ-bĕl) . . . . Fla.	29·50 N	84·40 W
116	Carrantuohill (kă-răn-tōō′ĭl) . Ire.	52·01 N	9·48 W
126	Carrara (kä-rä′rä) . . . . It.	44·05 N	10·05 E
98	Carretas, Punta (Pt.) (pōō′n-tä-kär-rĕ′tĕ′rȧs) . Peru	13·50 S	76·24 W
93	Carriacou I. (kăr-ē-ȧ-kōō′) W. I. F. (Le. & Wind. Is. In.)	12·28 N	61·20 W
116	Carrick (kăr′ĭk) . . . . Ire.	52·20 N	7·35 W
85	Carrier (kă′rĭ-ēr) Can. (Quebec In.)	46·43 N	71·05 W
78	Carriere (kȧ-rēr′) . . . . Miss.	30·37 N	89·37 W
80	Carriers Mills (kăr′ĭ-ērs) . . . . . . Ill.	37·40 N	88·40 W
70	Carrington (kăr′ĭng-tŭn) . . . . N. D.	47·26 N	99·06 W
65	Carr Inlet (kăr ĭn′lĕt) Wash. (Seattle In.)	47·20 N	122·42 W
124	Carrion (kär-rē-ōn′) . . . . Sp.	42·36 N	6·42 W
94	Carrion Crow Hbr. (kăr′ĭŭn krō) Ba. Is.	26·35 N	77·55 W
124	Carrión de los Condes (kär-rē-ōn′ dā lōs kōn′dȧs) . Sp.	42·20 N	4·35 W
72	Carrizo Cr. (kär-rē′zō) . . . N. Mex.	36·22 N	103·39 W
76	Carrizo Springs . . . . Tex.	28·32 N	99·51 W
69	Carrizozo (kär-rē-zō′zō) . . N. Mex.	33·40 N	105·55 W
71	Carroll (kăr′ŭl) . . . . Iowa	42·03 N	94·51 W
78	Carrollton (kăr-ŭl-tŭn) . . . . Ga.	33·35 N	84·05 W
73	Carrollton . . . . Ill.	39·18 N	90·22 W
80	Carrollton . . . . Ky.	38·45 N	85·15 W
80	Carrollton . . . . Mich.	43·30 N	83·55 W
73	Carrollton . . . . Mo.	39·21 N	93·29 W
80	Carrollton . . . . Ohio	40·35 N	81·10 W
74	Carrollton Tex. (Dallas, Fort Worth In.)	32·58 N	96·53 W
75	Carrollville (kăr′ŭl vĭl) Wis. (Milwaukee In.)	42·53 N	87·52 W
65	Carrols (kăr′ŭlz) Wash. (Portland In.)	46·05 N	122·51 W
116	Carron (L.) (kȧ′rŭn) . . . . Scot.	57·25 N	5·25 W
122	Carry-le-Rouet (kä-rē′lĕ-rōō-ā′) Fr. (Marseille In.)	43·20 N	5·10 E
133	Carsamba (chär-shäm′bä) . . . . Tur.	41·05 N	36·40 E
68	Carson (R.) (kär′sŭn) . . . . Nev.	39·15 N	119·25 W
68	Carson City . . . . Nev.	39·10 N	119·45 W
68	Carson Sink . . . . Nev.	39·51 N	118·25 W
155	Carstensz-Toppen (Pk.) (kärs′tĕns) Neth. N. Gui.	4·00 S	137·10 E
98	Cartagena (kär-tä-hā′nä) . . . . . Col.	10·30 N	75·40 W
125	Cartagena (kär-tä-ĸĕ′nä) . . . . . . Sp.	37·46 N	1·00 W
98	Cartago (kär-tä′gō) . . . . . Col. (In.)	4·44 N	75·54 W
93	Cartago . . . . C. R.	9·52 N	83·56 W
124	Cartaxo (kär-tä′shō) . . . . Port.	39·10 N	8·48 W
84	Carteret (kär′tē-rĕt) N. J. (New York In.)	40·35 N	74·13 W
78	Cartersville (kär′tērs-vĭl) . . . . . Ga.	34·09 N	84·47 W
73	Carthage (kär′thȧj) . . . . Ill.	40·27 N	91·09 W
73	Carthage . . . . Mo.	37·10 N	94·18 W
81	Carthage . . . . N. Y.	44·00 N	75·45 W
79	Carthage . . . . N. C.	35·22 N	79·25 W
77	Carthage . . . . Tex.	32·09 N	94·20 W
164	Carthage . . . . Tun.	37·04 N	10·18 E
167	Carthcart (cärth-cȧ′t) S. Afr. (Natal In.)	32·18 S	27·11 E
87	Cartwright (kärt′rīt) . . . . Can.	53·36 N	57·00 W
99	Caruaru (kä-rōō-ȧ-rōō′) . . . . . Braz.	8·19 S	35·52 W
98	Carúpano (kä-rōō′pä-nō) . . . . Ven.	10·45 N	63·21 W
73	Caruthersville (kȧ-rŭdh′ērz-vĭl) Mo	36·09 N	89·41 W
65	Carver (kärv′ēr) Ore. (Portland In.)	45·24 N	122·30 W
124	Carvoeira, Cabo (C.) (kȧ′bō-kär-vō-ĕ′y-rȧ) . Port.	39·22 N	9·24 W
75	Cary (kă′rē) . . . . Ill. (Chicago In.)	42·13 N	88·14 W
101	Casablanca (kä-sä-blăŋ′kȧ) Chile (Santiago In.)	33·19 S	71·24 W
164	Casablanca . . . . Mor.	33·32 N	7·41 W
101	Casa Branca (kȧ′sȧ-brȧ′N-kȧ) Braz. (Rio de Janeiro In.)	21·47 S	47·04 W
69	Casa Grande (kä′sä grăn′dā) . Ariz.	32·50 N	111·45 W
69	Casa Grande Natl. Mon. . . . . Ariz.	33·00 N	111·33 W
126	Casale (kä-sä′lā) . . . . It.	45·08 N	8·26 E
126	Casalmaggiore (kä-säl-mȧd-jō′rā) . It.	45·00 N	10·24 E
164	Casamance R. (kä-sȧ-mäNs′) Senegal	12·58 N	15·15 W
85	Cascade (kăs-kād′) Can. (Ottawa In.)	45·35 N	75·51 W
159	Cascade Pt. . . . . N. Z. (In.)	43·59 S	168·23 E
62	Cascade Ra . . . . U. S.	42·50 N	122·20 W
85	Cascades Point (kăs-kādz′) Can. (Montreal In.)	45·19 N	73·58 W
66	Cascade Tun . . . . Wash.	47·41 N	120·53 W
125	Cascais (käs-kȧ-ēzh) Port. (Lisboa In.)	38·42 N	9·25 W
125	Cascais, Ba. de (B.) (bä-ē′ä-dĕ-käs-kī′s) Port. (Lisboa In.)	38·41 N	9·24 W
65	Case Inlet (kās) Wash. (Seattle In.)	47·22 N	122·47 W
100	Caseros (kä-sā′rôs) . . . . . Arg. (In.)	34·21 S	58·34 W
126	Caserta (kä-zĕr′tä) . . . . It.	41·04 N	14·21 E
80	Casey (kā′sĭ) . . . . Ill.	39·20 N	88·00 W
66	Cashmere (kăsh′mĭr) . . . . Wash.	47·30 N	120·28 W
155	Casiguran (kä-sē-gōō′rän) Phil. (Manila In.)	16·15 N	122·10 E
155	Casiguran Sd. . . Phil. (Manila In.)	16·02 N	121·51 E
101	Casilda (kä-sē′l-dä) Arg. (Buenos Aires In.)	33·02 S	61·11 W
94	Casilda . . . . Cuba	21·50 N	80·00 W
101	Casimiro de Abreu (kä′sē-mē′ro-dĕ-á-brĕ′ōō) . Braz. (Rio de Janeiro In.)	22·30 S	42·11 W
98	Casiquiare (R.) (kä-sē-kyä′rā) Ven.	2·11 N	66·15 W
125	Caspe (käs′pȧ) . . . . Sp.	41·18 N	0·02 W
67	Casper (kăs′pēr) . . . . Wyo.	42·51 N	106·18 W
132	Caspian Dep. (kăs′pĭ-ăn) . Sov. Un.	47·40 N	51·40 E
130	Caspian Sea . . . . Sov. Un.	39·30 N	52·00 E
81	Cass (kăs) . . . . W. Va.	38·25 N	79·55 W
71	Cass (L.) . . . . Minn.	47·23 N	94·28 W
125	Cassá de la Selva (käs-sä′dĕ-lä-sĕl-vä) . Sp.	41·52 N	2·52 E
166	Cassai (R.) (kä-sä′ē) . . . . Ang.	11·15 S	21·00 E
80	Cass City (kăs) . . . . Mich.	43·35 N	83·10 W
85	Casselman (kăs′′l-mȧn) Can. (Ottawa In.)	45·18 N	75·05 W
70	Casselton (kăs′′l-tŭn) . . . . N. D.	46·53 N	97·14 W
101	Cássia (kà′syä) Braz. (Rio de Janeiro In.)	20·36 S	46·53 W
74	Cassin (kăs′ĭn) Tex. (San Antonio In.)	29·16 N	98·29 W
166	Cassinga (kä-sĭŋ′gȧ) . . . . Ang.	15·05 S	16·15 E
126	Cassino (käs-sē′nō) . . . . It.	41·30 N	13·50 E
71	Cass Lake (kăs) . . . . Minn.	47·23 N	94·37 W
80	Cassopolis (kăs-ŏ′pô-lĭs) . . . . Mich.	41·55 N	86·00 W
73	Cassville (kăs′vĭl) . . . . Mo.	36·41 N	93·52 W
124	Castanheira de Pêra (käs-tän-yä′rä-dĕ-pĕ′rä) . Port.	40·00 N	8·07 W
122	Casteljaloux (käs-tĕl-zhä-lōō′) . Fr.	44·20 N	0·04 E
125	Castellammare di Stabia (käs-tĕl-läm-mä′rä-dē-stä′byä) It. (Napoli In.)	40·26 N	14·29 E
101	Castelli (kȧs-tĕ′zhē) Arg. (Buenos Aires In.)	36·07 S	57·48 W

ăt; finăl; rāte; senâte; ärm; ȧsk; sofȧ; fâre; ch-choose; dh-as th in other; bē; ēvent; bĕt; recĕnt; cratēr; g-go; gh-guttural g; bĭt; ĭ-short neutral; rīde; ĸ-guttural k as ch in German ich;

PRONOUNCING INDEX Castellon–Chalons-sur-Marne 191

Page	Name Pronunciation Region	Lat. °′	Long. °′
125	Castellón de la Plana (käs-těl-yô′n-dě-lä-plä′nä) . Sp.	39·59 N	0·05 W
122	Castelnaudary (kȧs′těl-nō-dȧ-rē′) Fr.	43·20 N	1·57 E
101	Castelo (käs-tě′lô) Braz. (Rio de Janeiro In.)	21·37 S	41·13 W
124	Castelo Branco (käs-tā′lo͞o bräŋ′ko͞o) . Port.	39·48 N	7·37 W
124	Castelo de Vide (käs-tā′lo͞o dĭ vē′dĭ) . Port.	39·25 N	7·25 W
122	Castelsarrasin (kȧs′těl-sȧ-rȧ-zăN′) . Fr.	44·03 N	1·05 E
126	Castelvetrano (käs′těl-vě-trä′nō) It.	37·43 N	12·50 E
98	Castilla (kȧs-tē′l-yä) . . . . Peru	5·18 S	80·40 W
124	Castilla La Nueva (Reg.) (käs-tē′lyä lä nwā′vȧ) . Sp.	39·15 N	3·55 W
124	Castilla La Vieja (Reg.) (käs-tēl′yä lä vyā′hä) . Sp.	40·48 N	4·24 W
79	Castillo De San Marcos Natl. Mon. (käs-tē′lyā de-sän mär-kŏs) Fla.	29·55 N	81·25 W
95	Castle (I.) (kȧs′′l) . . . . Ba. Is.	22·05 N	74·20 W
116	Castlebar (kȧs′′l-bär) . . . . Ire.	53·55 N	9·15 W
69	Castle Dale (kȧs′′l dāl) . . . . . . Utah	39·15 N	111·00 W
110	Castle Donington (dŏn′ĭng-tŭn) Eng.	52·50 N	1·21 W
110	Castleford (kȧs′l-fērd) . . . . Eng.	53·43 N	1·21 W
160	Castlemaine (käs′′l-mān) . . . Austl.	37·05 S	144·14 E
69	Castle Pk. . . . . Colo.	39·00 N	106·50 W
66	Castlerock (kȧs′′l-rŏk) . . . . . Wash.	46·17 N	122·53 W
71	Castle Rock Res. . . . . Wis.	44·03 N	89·48 W
75	Castle Shannon (shăn′ŭn) Pa. (Pittsburgh In.)	40·22 N	80·02 W
75	Castleton (kȧs′′l-tŏn) Ind. (Indianapolis In.)	39·54 N	86·03 W
85	Castor R. (kăs′tôr) Can (Ottawa In.)	45·16 N	75·14 W
73	Castor (R.) . . . . Mo.	36·59 N	89·53 W
122	Castres (kȧs′tr′) . . . . Fr.	43·36 N	2·13 E
93	Castries (kȧs-trē′) W. I. F. (Le. & Wind. Is. In.)	14·01 N	61·00 W
100	Castro (käs′tro͞o) . . . . Braz.	24·56 S	50·00 W
100	Castro (käs′tro) . . . . Chile	42·27 S	73·48 W
124	Castro Daire (käs′tro͞o dīr′ĭ) . Port.	40·56 N	7·57 W
124	Castro de Río (käs-trô-dě-rê′ō) Sp.	37·42 N	4·28 W
123	Castrop Rauxel (käs′trōp rou′ksěl) . Ger. (Ruhr In.)	51·33 N	7·19 E
124	Castro Urdiales (käs′trō o͝or-dyä′lās) . Sp.	43·23 N	3·11 W
65	Castro Valley Calif. (San Francisco In.)	37·42 N	122·05 W
124	Castro Verde (käs-trō věr′dě) . Port.	37·43 N	8·05 W
126	Castrovillari (käs′trō-vēl-lyä′rē) . It.	39·48 N	16·11 E
124	Castuera (käs-to͞o-ā′rä) . . . . Sp.	38·43 N	5·33 W
95	Cat (I.) . . . . Ba. Is.	25·30 N	75·30 W
92	Catacamas (kä-tä-kȧ′mäs) . Hond.	14·52 N	85·55 W
155	Cataduanes (I.) (kä-tä-dwä′něs) Phil.	13·55 N	125·00 E
101	Cataguases (kä-tä-gwȧ′sěs) Braz. (Rio de Janeiro In.)	21·23 S	42·42 W
77	Catahoula L. (kăt-ȧ-ho͞o′lȧ) . . . La.	31·35 N	92·20 W
99	Catalão (kä-tä-louN′) . . . . Braz.	18·09 S	47·42 W
95	Catalina (I.) (kä-tä-lê′nä) Dom. Rep.	18·20 N	69·00 W
125	Cataluma (Reg.) (kä-tä-lo͞o′mä) Sp.	41·23 N	0·50 E
100	Catamarca (Prov.) (kä-tä-mär′kä) Arg.	27·15 S	67·15 W
99	Catanduva (kä-tȧn-do͞o′vä) . . Braz.	21·12 S	48·47 W
126	Catania (kä-tä′nyä) . . . . It.	37·30 N	15·09 E
126	Catania, Golfo di (G.) (gôl-fô-dē-kȧ-tä′nyä) . It.	37·24 N	15·28 E
155	Catanuan (kä-tä-nä′wän) . . . . Phil.	13·36 N	122·20 E
126	Catanzaro (kä-tän-dzä′rō) . . . . . It.	38·53 N	16·34 E
125	Catarroja (kä-tär-rō′hä) . . . . . . Sp.	39·24 N	0·25 W
79	Catawba (L.) . . . . S. C.	35·02 N	81·21 W
79	Catawba (R.) (kȧ-tô′bȧ) . . . . N. C.	35·25 N	80·55 W
91	Catazajá, Laguna de (L.) (lä-go͞o′nä-dě-kä-tä-zä-hȧ′) . Mex.	17·45 N	92·03 W
155	Catbalogan (kät-bä-lō′gän) . . . Phil.	11·45 N	124·52 E
91	Catemaco (kä-tā-mä′kō) . . . . . Mex.	18·26 N	95·06 W
91	Catemaco, Lago (L.) (lä′gô-kä-tā-mä′kō) . Mex.	18·23 N	95·04 W
110	Caterham (kā′tēr-ŭm) Eng. (London In.)	51·16 N	0·04 W
166	Catete (kä-tě′tě) . . . . Ang.	9·05 S	13·38 E
76	Cathedral Mt. (kȧ-thē′drăl) . . Tex.	30·09 N	103·46 W
167	Cathedral Pk. (kă-thê′drăl) S. Afr. (Natal In.)	28·53 S	29·04 E
73	Catherine, L. (kă-thēr-ĭn) . . . . Ark.	34·26 N	92·47 W
167	Cathkin Pk. (kăth′kĭn) S. Afr. (Natal In.)	29·08 S	29·22 E
65	Cathlamet (kăth-lăm′ět) Wash. (Portland In.)	46·12 N	123·53 W
80	Catlettsburg (kăt′lěts-bŭrg) . . . Ky.	38·20 N	82·35 W
88	Catoche, C. (kä-tô′chě) . . . . . Mex.	21·30 N	87·15 W
84	Catonsville (kā′tŭnz-vĭl) Md. (Baltimore In.)	39·16 N	76·45 W
90	Catorce (kä-tôr′sȧ) . . . . Mex.	23·41 N	100·51 W
81	Catskill (kăts′kĭl) . . . . N. Y.	42·15 N	73·50 W
81	Catskill Mts. . . . . N. Y.	42·20 N	74·35 W
81	Cattaraugus Ind. Res. (kăt′tā-rȧ-gŭs) . N. Y.	42·30 N	79·05 W
99	Catu (kȧ-to͞o) . . . . Braz.	12·26 S	38·12 W
166	Catumbela (kä′tŏm-běl′ȧ) . . . . Ang.	12·30 S	13·35 E
155	Cauayan (kou-ä′yän) Phil. (Manila In.)	16·56 N	121·46 E
98	Cauca (R.) (kou′kä) . . . . Col.	7·30 N	75·26 W
99	Caucagua (käo͞o-kȧ′gwä) Ven. (In.)	10·17 N	66·22 W
133	Caucasus Mts. (kô′kȧ-sŭs) Sov. Un.	43·20 N	42·00 E
122	Cauderan (kō-dā-räN′) . . . . Fr.	44·50 N	0·40 W
85	Caughnawaga Can. (Montreal In.)	45·24 N	73·41 W
126	Caulonia (kou-lō′nyä) . . . . It.	38·24 N	16·22 E
100	Cauquenes (kou-kā′nās) . . . . . Chile	35·54 S	72·14 W
98	Caura (R.) (kou′rä) . . . . Ven.	6·48 N	64·40 W
82	Causapscal . . . . Can.	48·19 N	67·18 W
95	Cauto (R.) (kou′tō) . . . . Cuba	18·35 N	76·20 W
142	Cauvery (R.) . . . . India	11·15 N	78·06 E
100	Cava (kȧ′vä) . . . . Braz. (In.)	22·41 S	43·26 W
125	Cava de' Tirreni (kä′vä-dě-tēr-rě′nē) . It. (Napoli In.)	40·27 N	14·43 E
124	Cavado (R.) (kä-vä′dō) . . . . . Port.	41·43 N	8·08 W
99	Cavalcante (kä-väl-kän′tā) . . Braz.	13·45 S	47·33 W
70	Cavalier (kăv-ȧ-lēr′) . . . . N. D.	48·45 N	97·39 W
164	Cavally (R.) . . . . Lib.-Ivory Coast	6·06 N	8·09 W
116	Cavan (kăv′ȧn) . . . . Ire.	54·01 N	7·00 W
126	Cavarzere (kä-vär′dzâ-rā) . . . . . It.	45·08 N	12·06 E
81	Cavendish (kăv′ĕn-dĭsh) . . . . . . Vt.	43·25 N	72·35 W
99	Caviana, Ilha (I.) (kä-vyä′nä) Braz.	0·45 N	49·33 W
155	Cavite (kä-vē′tā) Phil. (Manila In.)	14·30 N	120·54 E
110	Cawood (kā′wo͝od) . . . . Eng.	53·49 N	1·07 W
101	Caxambu (kä-shȧ′m-bo͞o) Braz. (Rio de Janeiro In.)	21·58 S	44·55 W
99	Caxias (kä′shê-äzh) . . . . Braz.	4·48 S	43·16 W
100	Caxias do Sul (kä′shê-äzh-dô-so͞o′l) . Braz.	29·13 S	51·03 W
125	Caxine, Cap (C.) (kăp kăk′sēn) Alg.	36·47 N	2·52 E
166	Caxito (kä-shē′to͞o) . . . . Ang.	8·20 S	13·35 E
98	Cayambe (kȧ-īä′m-bě) . . . . Ec.	0·03 N	79·09 W
99	Cayenne (kā-ĕn′) . . . . Fr. Gu.	4·56 N	52·18 W
90	Cayetano Rubio (kä-yě-tȧ-nô-ro͞o′byô) . Mex.	20·37 N	100·21 W
89	Cayey . . . . P. R. (Puerto Rico In.)	18·05 N	66·12 W
94	Cayman Brac (I.) (kī-män′ brȧk) W. I. F.	19·45 N	79·50 W
92	Cayo (kī′yō) Br. Hond. (Yucatan In.)	17·11 N	89·04 W
94	Cay Sal Bk. (kē-săl) . . . . . . Ba. Is.	23·55 N	80·20 W
81	Cayuga (L.) (kā-yo͞o′gȧ) . . . . N. Y.	42·35 N	76·35 W
124	Cazalla de la Sierra (kä-thäl′yä-dě-lä-sē-ĕ′r-rä) . Sp.	37·55 N	5·48 W
122	Cazaux, Étang de (L.) (ā-täN′ dĕ kä-zō′) . Fr.	44·32 N	0·59 W
81	Cazneovia (kăz-ê-nō′vĭ-ă) . . . N. Y.	42·55 N	75·50 W
75	Cazenovia Cr. . N. Y. (Buffalo In.)	42·49 N	78·45 W
126	Čazma (chäz′mä) . . . . Yugo.	45·44 N	16·39 E
166	Cazombo (kä-zô′m-bŏ) . . . . . . Ang.	12·25 S	22·40 E
91	Cazones (R.) (kä-zô′něs) . . . . Mex.	20·37 N	97·28 W
94	Cazones, Ensenada de (B.) (ĕn-sĕ-nä-dä-dĕ-kä-zō′nâs) . Cuba	22·05 N	81·30 W
94	Cazones, Golfo de (G.) (gôl-fô-dĕ-kä-zō′nâs) . Cuba	23·55 N	81·15 W
124	Cazorla (kä-thôr′lä) . . . . Sp.	37·55 N	2·58 W
124	Cea (R.) (thā′ä) . . . . Sp.	42·18 N	5·10 W
	Ceará, see Fortaleza		
99	Ceará (State) (sā-ä-rä′) . . . . . Braz.	5·13 S	39·43 W
99	Ceará-Mirim (sā-ä-rä′mē-rê′N) Braz.	6·00 S	35·13 W
93	Cebaco, Isla (I.) (ê′s-lä--sȧ-bä′kō) Pan.	7·27 N	81·08 W
69	Cebolla Cr. (sē-bōl′yä) . . . . . . Colo.	38·15 N	107·10 W
124	Cebollera, Sierra (Mts.) (sē-ĕ′r-rä-sĕ-bôl-yĕ-rä) . Sp.	42·03 N	2·53 W
124	Cebreros (sĕ-brĕ′rôs) . . . . Sp.	40·28 N	4·28 W
155	Cebu (sā-bo͞o′) . . . . Phil.	10·22 N	123·49 E
75	Cecil (sē′sĭl) . . Pa. (Pittsburgh In.)	40·20 N	80·10 W
86	Cedar (L.) . . . . Can.	53·18 N	101·08 W
71	Cedar (R.) . . . . Iowa	42·23 N	92·07 W
65	Cedar (R.) . . Wash. (Portland In.)	45·56 N	122·32 W
71	Cedar (R.) West Fk. . . . . Iowa	42·49 N	93·10 W
77	Cedar Bay . . . . Tex. (In.)	29·54 N	94·58 W
77	Cedar Bayou . . . . Tex. (In.)	29·46 N	94·56 W
69	Cedar Breaks Natl. Mon. . . . . Utah	37·35 N	112·55 W
71	Cedarburg (sē′dēr bûrg) . . . . . Wis.	43·23 N	88·00 W
69	Cedar City . . . . Utah	37·40 N	113·10 W
70	Cedar Cr . . . . N. D.	46·05 N	102·10 W
71	Cedar Falls . . . . Iowa	42·31 N	92·29 W
78	Cedar Keys . . . . Fla.	29·06 N	83·03 W
75	Cedar Lake . . . . Ind. (Chicago In.)	41·22 N	87·27 W
75	Cedar L. . . . . . . Ind. (Chicago In.)	41·23 N	87·25 W
71	Cedar Rapids . . . . Iowa	42·00 N	91·43 W
80	Cedar Springs . . . . Mich.	43·15 N	85·40 W
78	Cedartown (sē′dēr-toun) . . . . . . Ga.	34·00 N	85·15 W
167	Cedarville (cê-dȧr′vĭl) S. Afr. (Natal In.)	30·23 S	29·04 E
90	Cedral (sā-dräl′) . . . . Mex.	23·47 N	100·42 W
92	Cedros (sā′drōs) . . . . Hond.	14·36 N	87·07 W
88	Cedros (I.) . . . . Mex.	28·10 N	115·10 W
158	Ceduna (sê-do͞o′nȧ) . . . . Austl.	32·15 S	133·55 E
126	Cefalú (chā-fä-lo͞o′) . . . . It.	38·01 N	14·01 E
124	Cega (R.) (thā′gä) . . . . Sp.	41·25 N	4·27 W
121	Cegléd (tsă′glād) . . . . Hung.	47·10 N	19·49 E
127	Ceglie (chĕ′lyĕ) . . . . It.	40·39 N	17·32 E
124	Cehegín (thā-â-hēn′) . . . . Sp.	38·05 N	1·48 W
95	Ceiba del Agua (sā′-bä-dĕl-ȧ′gwä) Cuba (La Habana In.)	22·08 N	82·38 W
90	Celaya (sā-lä′yä) . . . . Mex.	20·33 N	100·49 W
154	Celebes (Is.) (sĕl′ê-bēz) (sĕl-ā′bĕs) . Indon.	2·15 S	120·30 E
154	Celebes Sea . . . . Indon.	3·45 N	121·52 E
92	Celestún (sĕ-lĕs-to͞o′n) Mex. (Yucatan In.)	20·57 N	90·18 W
80	Celina (sê-lī′na) . . . . Ohio	40·30 N	84·35 W
126	Celje (tsĕl′yĕ) . . . . Yugo.	46·13 N	15·17 E
120	Celle (tsĕl′ē) . . . . Ger.	52·37 N	10·05 E
72	Cement (sê-mĕnt′) . . . . Okla.	34·56 N	98·07 W
99	Ceniza, Pico (Mtn.) (pē′-kô-sĕ-nē′zä) . Ven. (In.)	10·24 N	67·26 W
122	Cenon (sē-nôN′) . . . . Fr.	44·51 N	0·33 W
77	Center (sĕn′tēr) . . . . Tex.	31·50 N	94·10 W
78	Centerhill Res. (sĕn′tēr-hĭl) . Tenn.	36·02 N	86·00 W
75	Center Line (sĕn′tēr līn) Mich. (Detroit In.)	42·29 N	83·01 W
71	Centerville (sĕn′tēr-vĭl) . . . . . . Iowa	40·44 N	92·48 W
74	Centerville . Minn. (Minneapolis, St. Paul In.)	45·10 N	93·03 W
75	Centerville . . . Pa. (Pittsburgh In.)	40·02 N	79·58 W
70	Centerville . . . . S. D.	43·70 N	96·56 W
75	Centerville. Utah (Salt Lake City In.)	40·55 N	111·53 W
98	Central, Cordillera (Mts.) (kôr-dēl-yĕ′-rä-sĕn-trȧ′l) . Bol.	19·18 S	65·29 W
98	Central, Cordillera (Mts.) Col. (In.)	3·58 N	75·55 W
95	Central, Cordillera (Cibao Mts.) (kôr-dēl-yā′rȧ sĕn′träl) (sê-bä′ô) Dom. Rep.	19·05 N	71·30 W
163	Central African Republic . . . . . Afr.	7·50 N	21·00 E
88	Central America (ȧ-mĕr′ĭ-kȧ) N. A.	10·45 N	87·15 W
78	Central City (sĕn′trȧl) . . . . Ky.	37·15 N	87·09 W
70	Central City (sĕn′trȧl sĭ′tĭ) . . Nebr.	41·07 N	98·00 W
84	Central Falls (sĕn′trȧl fôlz) R. I. (Providence In.)	41·54 N	71·23 W
80	Centralia (sĕn-trā′lĭ-ȧ) . . . . Ill.	38·35 N	89·05 W
73	Centralia . . . . Mo.	39·11 N	92·07 W
66	Centralia . . . . Wash.	46·42 N	122·58 W
133	Central Plat . . . . Sov. Un.	55·00 N	33·30 E
84	Central Valley N. Y. (New York In.)	41·19 N	74·07 W
81	Centreville (sĕn′tēr-vĭl) . . . . . . Md.	39·05 N	76·05 W
155	Centro (sĕ′n-trô) Phil. (Manila In.)	17·16 N	121·48 E
78	Century (sĕn′tû-rĭ) . . . . Fla.	30·57 N	87·15 W
	Cephalonia, see Kefallinéa		
122	Céret (sā-rĕ′) . . . . Fr.	42·29 N	2·47 E
98	Cereté (sĕ-rĕ-tĕ′) . . . . Col.	8·56 N	75·58 W
126	Cerignola (chā-rê-nyô′lä) . . . . . . It.	41·16 N	15·55 E
126	Cerknica (tsĕr′knê-tsȧ) . . . . . Yugo.	45·48 N	14·21 E
76	Cerralvo (sĕr-räl′vō) . . . . Mex.	26·05 N	99·37 W
88	Cerralvo (I.) . . . . Mex.	24·00 N	109·59 W
98	Cerrito (sĕr-rē′-tô) . . . . . . Col. (In.)	3·41 N	76·17 W
90	Cerritos (sĕr-rē′tôs) . . . . Mex.	22·26 N	100·16 W
98	Cerro de Pasco (sĕr′rō dā päs′kō) Peru	10·45 S	76·14 W
76	Cerro Gordo, Arroyo de (är-rô-yŏ-dĕ-sĕ′r-rô-gôr-dŏ) Mex.	26·12 N	104·06 W
98	Certegui (sĕr-tĕ′gē) . . . . . Col. (In.)	5·21 N	76·35 W
155	Cervantes (sĕr-vän′tās) Phil. (Manila In.)	16·59 N	120·42 E
124	Cervantes (thĕr-vän′tās) . . . . . . Sp.	42·43 N	7·04 W
124	Cervera del Río Alhama (thĕr-vā′rȧ dĕl rē′ō-äl-ä′mä) Sp.	42·02 N	1·55 W
125	Cerveteri (chĕr-vĕ′tĕ-rē) It. (Roma In.)	42·00 N	12·06 E
126	Cesena (chĕ′sĕ-nä) . . . . It.	44·08 N	12·16 E
119	Cēsis (sā′sĭs) . . . . Sov. Un.	57·19 N	25·17 E
120	Česka Lipa (chĕs′kä lē′pa) . Czech.	50·41 N	14·31 E
120	Ceske (Bohemia) (Prov.) (chĕs′kā) (bô-hē′mĭ-ȧ) . Czech.	49·51 N	13·55 E
120	České Budějovice (chĕs′kā bo͞o′dyĕ-yô-vēt-sĕ) . Czech.	49·00 N	14·30 E
120	Ceskomoravaska Vysočina (Hts.) Czech.	49·21 N	15·40 E
127	Cesme (chĕsh′mĕ) . . . . Tur.	38·20 N	26·20 E
160	Cessnock . . . . Austl.	32·58 S	151·15 E
127	Cetinje (tsĕt′in-yĕ) . . . . Yugo.	42·23 N	18·55 E
	Cette, see Sète		
164	Ceuta (Sp.) (thā-o͞o′tä) . . . . . . Afr.	36·04 N	5·36 W
122	Cévennes (sā-vĕn′) . . . . Fr.	44·20 N	3·48 E
115	Ceyhan (R.) . . . . Tur.	37·19 N	36·06 E
138	Ceylon (sê-lŏn′) . . . . Asia	8·45 N	82·30 E
144	Chāb Bahār . . . . Iran	25·18 N	60·45 E
65	Chabot (L.) (sha′bŏt) Calif. (San Francisco In.)	37·44 N	122·06 W
101	Chacabuco (chä-kä-bo͞o′kō) Arg. ((Buenos Aires In.)	34·37 S	60·27 W
91	Chacaltianguis (chä-käl-tê-äŋ′-gwês) . Mex.	18·18 N	95·50 W
98	Chachapoyas (chä-chä-poi′yäs) Peru	6·16 S	77·48 W
69	Chaco Can. Natl. Mon. (chä′kô) N. Mex.	35·38 N	108·06 W
136	Chad (chäd) . Sov. Un. (Urals In.)	56·33 N	57·11 E
163	Chad . . . . Afr.	17·48 N	19·00 E
165	Chad, L . . . . Chad.	14·00 N	14·28 E
79	Chadbourn (chăd′bŭrn) . . . . . N. C.	34·19 N	78·55 W
70	Chadron (chăd′rŭn) . . . . Nebr.	42·50 N	103·10 W
124	Chafarinas (C.) . . . . Mor.	35·08 N	2·20 W
73	Chaffee (chăf′ê) . . . . Mo.	37·10 N	89·39 W
144	Chāgal Hills . . . . Afg.-Pak.	29·15 N	63·28 E
128	Chagodoshcha (R.) (chä-gō-dôsh-chä) . Sov. Un.	59·08 N	35·13 E
93	Chagres R. (chä′grĕs) . . . . Pan.	9·18 N	79·22 W
75	Chagrin R. (shȧ′grĭn) Ohio (Cleveland In.)	41·34 N	81·24 W
75	Chagrin Falls (shȧ′grĭn fôls) Ohio (Cleveland In.)	41·26 N	81·23 W
150	Ch'ahaerh (Reg.) (chä′här) . China	44·25 N	115·00 E
152	Chalantun (chä′län-to͞on′) . . China	47·59 N	122·56 E
92	Chalatenango (chäl-ä-tĕ-näŋ′gō) Sal.	14·04 N	88·54 W
91	Chalcatongo (chäl-kä-tôŋ′gō) Mex.	17·04 N	97·41 W
90	Chalchihuites (chäl-chê-wē′tâs) Mex.	23·28 N	103·57 W
92	Chalchuapa (chäl-chwä′pä) . . . Sal.	14·01 N	89·39 W
91	Chalco (chäl-kō) Mex. (Mexico In.)	19·15 N	98·54 W
82	Chaleur, B. de (shȧ-lûr′) . . . . . Can.	48·07 N	64·50 W
110	Chalgrove (chăl′grôv) Eng. (London In.)	51·38 N	1·05 W
151	Chaling (chä′lĭng) . . . . China	27·00 N	118·30 E
84	Chalmette (shăl-mĕt′) La. (New Orleans In.)	29·57 N	89·57 W
122	Châlons-sur-Marne (shȧ-lôN′-sür-märn) . Fr.	48·57 N	4·23 E

ng-sing; ŋ-baŋk; N-nasalized n; nŏd; cŏmmit; ōld; ôbey; ôrder; fo͞od; fo͝ot; ou-out; s-soft; sh-dish; th-thin; pūre; ûnite; ûrn; stŭd; circŭs; ü-as "y" in study; '-indeterminate vowel.

192 Chalon-sur-Saone–Chepo PRONOUNCING INDEX

Page	Name Pronunciation	Region	Lat. °′	Long. °′
122	Châlon-sur-Saône	Fr.	46·47 N	4·54 E
100	Chaltel, Cerro (Mtn.) (sě′r-rô-chäl′těl)	Arg.-Chile	48·10 S	73·18 W
69	Chama (R.) (chä′mä)	N. Mex.	36·19 N	106·31 W
92	Chama, Sierra de (Mts.) (sē-ě′r-rä-dě-chä-mä)	Guat.	15·48 N	90·20 W
122	Chamalières (shä-mä-lyår′)	Fr.	45·45 N	2·59 E
142	Chaman (chŭm,-än′)	W. Pak.	30·58 N	66·21 E
142	Chambal (R.) (chŭm-bäl′)	India	26·05 N	76·37 E
70	Chamberlain (chām′bēr-lĭn)	S. D.	43·48 N	99·21 W
82	Chamberlain (L.)	Maine	46·15 N	67·05 W
81	Chambersburg (chām′bērz-bûrg)	Pa.	40·00 N	77·40 W
123	Chambéry (shäm-bā-rē′)	Fr.	45·35 N	5·54 E
84	Chamblee (chăm-blē′)	Ga. (Atlanta In.)	33·53 N	84·18 W
85	Chambly (shäN-blē′)	Can. (Montreal In.)	45·27 N	73·17 W
123	Chambly	Fr. (Paris In.)	49·11 N	2·14 E
87	Chambord	Can.	48·22 N	72·01 W
146	Chamdo (Prov.)	China	30·15 N	95·00 E
93	Chame, Punta (Pt.) (po͝o′n-tä-chä′må)	Pan.	8·41 N	79·27 W
92	Chamelecón R. (chä-mĕ-lĕ-kô′n)	Hond.	15·09 N	88·42 W
165	Chamo L. (chä′mō)	Eth.	5·58 N	37·00 E
123	Chamonix (shå-mô-nē′)	Fr.	45·55 N	6·50 E
122	Champagne (Reg.) (shäm-pän′-yē)	Fr.	48·53 N	4·48 E
80	Champaign (shăm-pān′)	Ill.	40·10 N	88·15 W
92	Champerico (chăm-på-rē′kō)	Guat.	14·18 N	91·55 W
71	Champion (chăm′pĭ-ŭn)	Mich.	46·30 N	87·59 W
81	Champlain, L. (shăm-plān′)	N. Y.-Vt.	44·45 N	73·20 W
123	Champlitte (shäN-plēt′)	Fr.	47·38 N	5·28 E
91	Champotón (chäm-pō-tōn′)	Mex.	19·21 N	90·43 W
91	Champotón (R.)	Mex.	19·19 N	90·15 W
100	Chañaral (chän-yä-räl′)	Chile	26·20 S	70·46 W
124	Chanca (R.) (chäŋ′kä)	Sp.-Port.	38·15 N	7·22 W
151	Chanchiang (Fort Bayard)	China	21·20 N	110·28 E
142	Chanda (chăn′dŭ)	India	19·58 N	79·21 E
78	Chandeleur Is. (shăn-dē-lo͞or′)	La.	29·53 N	88·35 W
78	Chandeleur Sd	La.	29·47 N	89·08 W
142	Chandernagore (chŭn-dēr-nå-gōr′)	India (Calcutta In.)	22·51 N	88·21 E
142	Chandīgarh	India	30·51 N	77·13 E
82	Chandler (chăn′dlēr)	Can.	48·24 N	64·40 W
74	Chandler	Mo. (Kansas City In.)	39·18 N	94·24 W
73	Chandler	Okla.	35·42 N	96·52 W
148	Chang (R.) (jäng)	China	36·17 N	114·31 E
148	Ch′angch′ichuang (chäng′chē′zho͝oäng)	China	37·59 N	116·57 E
150	Ch′angchih	China	35·58 N	112·58 E
148	Ch′angch′ing (chäng′chĭng)	China	36·33 N	116·42 E
148	Changch′iu (zhängchĭû)	China	36·50 N	117·29 E
150	Ch′angch′un (Hsinking) (chäng′cho͞on′) (hsĭn′kĭng)	China	43·55 N	125·25 E
148	Ch′anghsing Tao (I.) (chängsĭng dou)	China	39·38 N	121·10 E
150	Ch′anghsintien	China (Peking In.)	39·49 N	116·12 E
151	Changhua (chäng′hwä′)	China	24·02 N	120·32 E
148	Changhutien (jang′ho͞o′dĭan)	China	32·07 N	114·44 E
148	Ch′angi (jäng′yē)	China	36·51 N	119·23 E
152	Changjōn (chäng′jŭn′)	Kor.	38·38 N	128·02 E
150	Changkochuang	China (Peking In.)	40·09 N	116·56 E
150	Changkuangts′ai Ling (Mts.)	China	43·50 N	127·55 E
148	Ch′angli (chäng′lē′)	China	39·46 N	119·10 E
150	Changpei (chäng′pě′)	China	41·12 N	114·50 E
152	Changsan Cot (I.)	Kor.	38·06 N	124·50 E
148	Ch′angshan Liehtao (Is.) (chäng′shän′ lĭĕdou)	China	39·08 N	122·26 E
148	Ch′angshan Tao (I.) (chäng′shän′ dou)	China	37·56 N	120·42 E
148	Ch′angshu (chäng′sho͞o′)	China	31·40 N	120·45 E
151	Ch′angte (chäng′tě′)	China	29·00 N	111·38 E
148	Changtien (jäng′dĭan)	China	36·48 N	118·04 E
151	Changting	China	25·50 N	116·18 E
146	Ch′angtu (chäng′to͞o′)	China	31·06 N	96·30 E
152	Changtu	China	43·00 N	124·02 E
148	Ch′angtzu Tao (I.) (chäng′zho͞o dou)	China	39·02 N	122·44 E
150	Changwu (chäng′wo͞o′)	China	35·12 N	107·45 E
152	Changwu	China	42·21 N	123·00 E
146	Changyeh	China	38·46 N	101·00 E
148	Ch′angyüan (chäng′yü-än′)	China	35·10 N	114·41 E
74	Chanhassen (shān′hās-sĕn)	Minn. (Minneapolis, St. Paul In.)	44·52 N	93·32 W
148	Chanhua (jän′ho͝oå)	China	37·42 N	117·49 E
122	Channel Is. (chăn′ĕl)	Eur.	49·20 N	2·40 W
77	Channelview (chăn′elvū)	Tex. (In.)	29·46 N	95·07 W
150	Chanping	China	40·12 N	116·10 E
124	Chantada (chän-tä′dä)	Sp.	42·38 N	7·36 W
154	Chanthaburi	Thai.	12·37 N	102·04 E
123	Chantilly (shäN-tē-yē′)	Fr. (Paris In.)	49·12 N	2·30 E
86	Chantrey Inlet (chăn-trē)	Can.	67·49 N	94·30 W
73	Chanute (shȧ-no͞ot′)	Kans.	37·41 N	95·27 W
134	Chany (L.) (chä′nê)	Sov. Un.	54·15 N	77·31 E
150	Chanyü	China	44·30 N	122·30 E
151	Ch′aoan (chä′ō-än′)	China	23·48 N	117·10 E
148	Ch′aohsien (chou′sĭän)	China	31·37 N	117·50 E
148	Chaohsien	China	37·46 N	114·48 E
154	Chao Phraya, Mae Nam (R.)	Thai.	16·13 N	99·33 E
148	Ch′aoshui (jĭouso͞oĭ)	China	37·43 N	120·56 E
151	Chaot′ung (chä′ō-to͝ong)	China	27·18 N	103·50 E
151	Ch′aoyang (chä′ō-yäng′)	China	23·18 N	116 32 E
150	Ch′aoyang (Foshan)	China	41·32 N	120·20 E
148	Chaoyüan (chä′ō-yü-än′)	China	37·22 N	120·23 E
99	Chapada, Serra da (Mts.) (sě′r-rä-dä-shä-pä′dä)	Braz.	14·57 S	54·34 W
101	Chapadão, Serra do (Mtn.) (sě′r-rä-dô-shä-på-dou′N)	Braz. (Rio de Janeiro In.)	20·31 S	46·20 W
90	Chapala, Lago de (L.) (lä′gô-dě-chä-pä′lä)	Mex.	20·14 N	103·02 W
90	Chapalagana (R.) (chä-pä-lä-gå′nä)	Mex.	22·11 N	104·09 W
98	Chaparral (chä-păr-rå′l)	Col. (In.)	3·44 N	75·28 W
90	Chapata (chä-på′tä)	Mex.	20·18 N	103·10 W
133	Chapayevsk (châ-pī′ĕfsk)	Sov. Un.	53·00 N	49·30 E
79	Chapel Hill (chăp′′l hĭl)	N. C.	35·55 N	79·05 W
65	Chaplain (L.) (chăp′lĭn)	Wash. (Seattle In.)	47·58 N	121·50 W
87	Chapleau (chăp-lō′)	Can.	47·43 N	83·28 W
166	Chapmans B. (chăp′mȧns bă)	S. Afr. (Cape Town In.)	34·06 S	18·17 E
70	Chappell (chă-pěl′)	Nebr.	41·06 N	102·29 W
91	Chapultenango (chä-po͝ol-tē-näŋ′gō)	Mex.	17·19 N	93·08 W
90	Charcas (chär′käs)	Mex.	23·09 N	101·09 W
93	Charco de Azul, Bahia (B.) (bä-ē′ä-chä′r-kô-dě-ä-zo͞o′l)	Pan.	8·14 N	82·45 W
103	Chardzhou (chēr-jô′o͝o)	Sov. Un.	38·52 N	63·37 E
122	Charente (shå-räNt′)	Fr.	45·48 N	0·28 W
110	Charing (chă′rĭng)	Eng. (London In.)	51·13 N	0·49 E
71	Chariton (châr′ĭ-tŭn)	Iowa	41·02 N	93·16 W
73	Chariton (R.)	Mo.	40·24 N	92·38 W
85	Charlemagne (shärl-mäny′)	Can. (Montreal In.)	45·43 N	73·29 W
117	Charleroi (shår-lē-rwä′)	Bel.	50·25 N	4·35 E
75	Charleroi (shär′lē-roi)	Pa. (Pittsburgh In.)	40·08 N	79·54 W
79	Charles, C. (chärlz)	Va.	37·05 N	75·48 W
85	Charlesbourg (shårl-bo͞or′)	Can. (Quebec In.)	46·51 N	71·16 W
71	Charles City (chärlz)	Iowa	43·03 N	92·40 W
80	Charleston (chärlz′tŭn)	Ill.	39·30 N	88·10 W
78	Charleston	Miss.	34·00 N	90·02 W
73	Charleston	Mo.	36·53 N	89·20 W
79	Charleston	S. C.	32·47 N	79·56 W
80	Charleston	W. Va.	38·20 N	81·35 W
75	Charlestown (chärlz′toun)	Ind. (Louisville In.)	38·46 N	85·39 W
93	Charlestown	W. I. F. (Le. & Wind. Is. In.)	17·10 N	62·32 W
166	Charlesville	Con. L.	5·19 S	30·59 E
160	Charleville (chär′lê-vĭl)	Austl.	26·16 S	146·28 E
122	Charleville (shärl-vēl′)	Fr.	49·48 N	4·41 E
80	Charlevoix (shär′lē-voi)	Mich.	45·20 N	86·15 W
71	Charlevoix, L	Mich.	45·17 N	85·43 W
80	Charlotte (shär′lŏt)	Mich.	42·35 N	84·50 W
79	Charlotte	N. C.	35·15 N	80·50 W
89	Charlotte Amalie (St. Thomas) (shär-lŏt′ĕ ä-mä′lĭ-å)	Virgin Is. (U. S. A.) (St. Thomas In.)	18·21 N	64·54 W
79	Charlotte Hbr	Fla. (In.)	26·47 N	81·58 W
118	Charlottenberg (shär-lŭt′ĕn-bĕrg)	Swe.	59·53 N	12·17 E
81	Charlottesville (shär′lŏtz-vĭl)	Va.	38·00 N	78·25 W
83	Charlottetown (shär′lŏt-toun)	Can.	46·14 N	63·08 W
158	Charlotte Waters (shär′lŏt)	Austl.	26·00 S	134·50 E
123	Charmes (shärm)	Fr.	48·23 N	6·19 E
110	Charnwood Forest (chärn′wo͝od)	Eng.	52·42 N	1·15 W
85	Charny (shär-nē′)	Can. (Quebec In.)	46·43 N	71·16 W
142	Charol Tsho (L.)	China	34·00 N	81·47 E
123	Chars (shär)	Fr. (Paris In.)	49·09 N	1·57 E
145	Charsadda (chŭr-sä′dä)	W. Pak. (Khyber Pass In.)	34·17 N	71·43 E
159	Charters Towers (chär′tērz)	Austl.	20·03 S	146·20 E
123	Chartres (shärt′r′)	Fr. (Paris In.)	48·26 N	1·29 E
101	Chascomús (chäs-kō-mo͞os′)	Arg. (Buenos Aires In.)	35·32 S	58·01 W
79	Chase City (chās)	Va.	36·45 N	78·27 W
128	Chashniki (chäsh′nyê-kē)	Sov. Un.	54·51 N	29·08 E
74	Chaska (chăs′kå)	Minn. (Minneapolis, St. Paul In.)	44·48 N	93·36 W
122	Châteaubriant (shä-tō-brē-äN′)	Fr.	47·43 N	1·23 W
122	Châteaudun (shä-tō-dåN′)	Fr.	48·04 N	1·23 E
122	Château-Gontier (chå-tō′ gôN′ tyā′)	Fr.	47·48 N	0·43 W
85	Chateauguay (chå-tō-gā′)	Can. (Montreal In.)	45·22 N	73·45 W
85	Châteauguay, R.	Can. (Montreal In.)	45·13 N	73·51 W
85	Chateauguay Basin	Can. (Montreal In.)	45·22 N	73·44 W
122	Chateauneuf-les-Martigues (shä-tō-nûf′lā-mär-tēg′ĕ)	Fr. (Marseille In.)	43·23 N	5·11 E
122	Château-Renault (shå-tō-rē-nō′)	Fr.	47·36 N	0·57 E
85	Château-Richer (shå-tō′rē-shā′)	Can. (Quebec In.)	46·58 N	71·01 W
122	Châteauroux (shå-tō-ro͞o′)	Fr.	46·47 N	1·39 E
122	Château-Thierry (shå-tō′tyĕr-rē′)	Fr.	49·03 N	3·22 E
122	Châtellerault (shä-těl-rō′)	Fr.	46·48 N	0·31 E
71	Chatfield (chăt′fēld)	Minn.	43·50 N	92·10 W
80	Chatham (chăt′ȧm)	Can.	42·25 N	82·10 W
82	Chatham	Can.	47·01 N	65·28 W
110	Chatham (chăt′ŭm)	Eng. (London In.)	51·21 N	0·27 E
84	Chatham (chăt′ȧm)	N. J. (New York In.)	40·44 N	74·23 W
75	Chatham	Ohio (Cleveland In.)	41·06 N	82·01 W
156	Chatham Is	N. Z.	44·00 S	178·00 W
64	Chatham Str	Alaska	57·00 N	134·40 W
74	Chatsworth (chătz′wûrth)	Calif. (Los Angeles In.)	34·16 N	118·36 W
74	Chatsworth Res.	Calif. (Los Angeles In.)	34·15 N	118·41 W
78	Chattahoochee (chăt-tå-ho͞o′ chēē)	Fla.	30·42 N	84·47 W
78	Chattahoochee (R.)	Ala.-Ga.	31·17 N	85·10 W
78	Chattanooga (chăt-ȧ-no͞o′gȧ)	Tenn.	35·01 N	85·15 W
78	Chattooga (R.) (chă-to͞o′gȧ)	Ga.-S. C.	34·47 N	83·13 W
82	Chaudiere (R.) (shō-dyěr′)	Can.	46·26 N	71·10 W
154	Chau Doc (shō-dôk′)	Camb.	10·49 N	104·57 E
122	Chaumont (shō-môN′)	Fr.	48·08 N	5·07 E
123	Chaumontel (shô-mŏN-těl′)	Fr. (Paris In.)	49·07 N	2·26 E
135	Chaunskaya Guba (B.)	Sov. Un.	69·15 N	170·00 E
122	Chauny (shō-nē′)	Fr.	49·40 N	3·09 E
128	Chausy (chou′sĭ)	Sov. Un.	53·57 N	30·58 E
81	Chautauqua (L.) (shȧ-tô′kwȧ)	N. Y.	42·10 N	79·25 W
132	Chavaniga	Sov. Un.	66·02 N	37·50 E
124	Chaves (chä′vězh)	Port.	41·44 N	7·30 W
90	Chavinda (chä-vē′n-dä)	Mex.	20·01 N	102·27 W
91	Chazumba (chä-zo͝om′bä)	Mex.	18·11 N	97·41 W
110	Cheadle (chē′d′l)	Eng.	52·59 N	1·59 W
81	Cheat (R.) (chēt)	W. Va.	39·35 N	79·40 W
120	Cheb (Kěb)	Czech.	50·05 N	12·23 E
136	Chebarkul (chě-bår-kûl′)	Sov. Un. (Urals In.)	54·59 N	60·22 E
132	Cheboksary (chyě-bôk-sä′rê)	Sov. Un.	56·00 N	47·20 E
80	Cheboygan (shê-boi′găn)	Mich.	45·40 N	84·30 W
164	Chech, Erg (Dune)	Alg.	24·45 N	2·07 W
133	Chechen′ (I.) (chyěch′ĕn)	Sov. Un.	44·00 N	48·10 E
148	Chech′eng (jĭŭcheng)	China	34·05 N	115·19 E
147	Chechiang (Chekiang) (Prov.)	China	29·28 N	119·33 E
73	Checotah (chê-kō′tȧ)	Okla.	35·27 N	95·32 W
83	Chedabucto B. (chěd-ȧ-bŭk-tō)	Can.	45·25 N	61·05 W
154	Cheduba (I.)	Bur.	18·45 N	93·01 E
86	Cheecham Hills (chēē′hăm)	Can.	55·56 N	112·06 W
75	Cheektowaga (chēk-tŏ-wä′gȧ)	N. Y. (Buffalo In.)	42·54 N	78·46 W
	Chefoo, see Yent′ai			
66	Chehalis (chê-hā′lĭs)	Wash.	46·39 N	122·58 W
66	Chehalis R	Wash.	46·47 N	123·17 W
152	Cheju (chě′jo͞o′)	Kor.	33·29 N	126·40 E
152	Cheju (Quelpart) (I.)	Kor.	33·20 N	126·25 E
128	Chekalin (chě-kä′lĭn)	Sov. Un.	54·05 N	36·13 E
148	Chekao (jĭŭgou)	China	31·47 N	117·44 E
	Chekiang, see Chechiang			
166	Chela, Serrada (Mts.) (sěr′rȧ dā shā′lȧ)	Ang.	15·30 S	13·30 E
66	Chelan (chê-lăn′)	Wash.	47·51 N	119·59 W
151	Chelang Chiao (Pt.)	China	22·38 N	116·00 E
66	Chelan R	Wash.	48·09 N	120·20 W
125	Cheleiros (shě-la′rōzh)	Port. (Lisboa In.)	38·54 N	9·19 W
113	Chelic (Mt.) (shěl-ĭk)	Alg.	35·22 N	6·47 E
125	Chéliff, Oued (R.) (o͞o-ěd shā-lēf)	Alg.	36·17 N	1·22 E
134	Chelkar (chyěl′kär)	Sov. Un.	47·52 N	59·41 E
133	Chelkar (L.)	Sov. Un.	50·30 N	51·30 E
134	Chelkar Tengiz (L.) (chyěl′kär těn′yēz)	Sov. Un.	47·42 N	61·45 E
125	Chellala (chěl-å′lå)	Alg.	35·12 N	2·20 E
121	Chełm (Kělm)	Pol.	51·08 N	23·30 E
121	Chełmno (Kělm′nō)	Pol.	53·20 N	18·25 E
110	Chelmsford (chělm′s-fērd)	Eng. (London In.)	51·44 N	0·28 E
83	Chelmsford	Mass. (Boston In.)	42·36 N	71·21 W
84	Chelsea (chěl′sê)	Ala. (Birmingham In.)	33·20 N	86·38 W
161	Chelsea	Austl. (Melbourne In.)	38·05 S	145·08 E
85	Chelsea	Can. (Ottawa In.)	45·30 N	75·46 W
83	Chelsea	Mass. (Boston In.)	42·23 N	71·02 W
80	Chelsea	Mich.	42·20 N	84·00 W
73	Chelsea	Okla.	36·32 N	95·23 W
116	Cheltenham (chělt′′nŭm)	Eng.	51·57 N	2·06 W
125	Chelva (chěl′vä)	Sp.	39·43 N	1·00 W
136	Chelyabinsk (chěl-yä-bênsk′)	Sov. Un. (Urals In.)	55·10 N	61·25 E
135	Chelyuskin, Mys (C.) (chěl-yo͝os′-kĭn)	Sov. Un.	77·45 N	104·45 E
122	Chemillé (shē-mê-yā′)	Fr.	47·13 N	0·46 W
	Chemnitz, see Karl-Marx-Stadt			
81	Chemung (R.) (shê-mŭng)	N. Y.	42·20 N	77·25 W
135	Chën, Gora (Mtn.)	Sov. Un.	65·13 N	142·12 E
142	Chenāb (R.) (chê-näb)	W. Pak.	31·33 N	72·28 E
164	Chenachane (Oasis) (shē-nå-shän′)	Alg.	26·14 N	4·14 W
148	Chenchiang (jienjäng)	China	32·13 N	119·24 E
66	Cheney (chē′nå)	Wash.	47·29 N	117·34 W
166	Chengane (R.) (chěn-gä′ně)	Moz.	22·42 S	32·46 E
	Chengchow, see Chenghsien			
151	Ch′enghai	China	23·22 N	116·40 E
148	Chenghsien (Chengchow) (jěngsĭen) (jěngjō)	China	34·46 N	113·42 E
146	Ch′enghua	China	47·52 N	87·50 E
151	Chengku	China	33·05 N	107·25 E
150	Ch′engte (Jehol) (chěng′tě′) (rē-hōl′)	China	40·50 N	117·50 E
148	Chengting (chengding)	China	38·10 N	114·35 E
151	Ch′engtu (chěng′to͞o′)	China	30·30 N	104·10 E
148	Chengyang (chěn′yäng′)	China	32·34 N	114·22 E
146	Chenhsi	China	43·43 N	92·50 E
151	Ch′enshien	China	25·40 N	113·00 E
149	Ch′entsun	China (Canton In.)	22·58 N	113·14 E
150	Chentung	China	45·28 N	123·42 E
151	Chenyüan (chěn′yü-an′)	China	27·08 N	108·30 E
149	Chepei	China (Canton In.)	23·07 N	113·23 E
98	Chepén (chě-pě′n)	Peru	7·17 S	79·24 W
93	Chepo (chā′pō)	Pan.	9·12 N	79·06 W

ăt; finăl; rāte; senâte; ärm; åsk; sofȧ; fâre; ch-choose; dh-as th in other; bē; êvent; bět; recĕnt; cratēr; g-go; gh-guttural g; bĭt; ĭ-short neutral; rīde; K-guttural k as ch in German ich;

PRONOUNCING INDEX Chepo–Chinhsiang 193

Page	Name Pronunciation Region	Lat. °′	Long. °′
93	Chepo R. Pan.	9·10 N	78·36 W
122	Cher (R.) (shâr) Fr.	47·14 N	1·34 E
90	Cheran (chā-rän') Mex.	19·41 N	101·54 W
79	Cheraw (chē'rô) S. C.	34·40 N	79·52 W
122	Cherbourg (shär-bōōr') Fr.	49·39 N	1·43 W
164	Cherchel (shĕr-shĕl') Alg.	36·38 N	2·09 E
146	Cherchen (R.) (chĕr-chĕn') China	39·00 N	87·19 E
132	Cherdyn' (chĕr-dyēn') Sov. Un.	60·25 N	56·32 E
134	Cheremkhovo (chĕr'yĕm-kô-vō) Sov. Un.	52·58 N	103·18 E
136	Cherëmukhovo (chĕr-yĕ-mû-kô-vô) Sov. Un. (Urals In.)	60·20 N	60·00 E
165	Cheren (chĕr'ĕn) Eth.	15·46 N	38·28 E
134	Cherepanovo (chĕr'yĕ pä-nô'vō) Sov. Un.	54·13 N	83·18 E
128	Cherepovets (chĕr-yĕ-pô'vyĕtz) Sov. Un.	59·08 N	35·54 E
128	Chereya (chĕr-ā'yä) Sov. Un.	54·38 N	29·16 E
114	Chergui, Chott ech (L.) (chĕr gē) Alg.	34·12 N	0·10 W
114	Chergui I. Tun.	34·48 N	11·41 E
128	Cherikov (chĕ'rē-kôf) Sov. Un.	53·34 N	31·22 E
129	Cherkassy (chĕr-kà'sĭ) Sov. Un.	49·26 N	32·03 E
129	Cherkassy (Oblast) Sov. Un.	48·58 N	30·55 E
134	Cherlak (chĭr-läk') Sov. Un.	54·04 N	74·28 E
136	Chermoz (chĕr-môz') Sov. Un. (Urals In.)	58·47 N	56·08 E
128	Chern' (chĕrn) Sov. Un.	53·28 N	36·49 E
129	Chërnaya Kalitva (R.) (chôr'nà yà kà-lēt'và) Sov. Un.	50·15 N	39·16 E
129	Chernigov (chĕr-nē'gôf) Sov. Un.	51·28 N	31·18 E
129	Chernigov (Oblast) (chĕr-nē'gôf) Sov. Un.	51·23 N	31·15 E
152	Chernigovka (chĕr-nê-gôf'kà) Sov. Un.	44·16 N	132·13 E
129	Chernobay (chĕr-nō-bī') Sov. Un.	49·41 N	32·24 E
129	Chernobyl' (chĕr-nō-bĭl') Sov. Un.	51·17 N	30·14 E
134	Chernogorsk (chĕr-nŏ-gôrsk') Sov. Un.	54·01 N	91·07 E
129	Chernogovka (chĕr-nô-gôf'kà) Sov. Un.	47·08 N	36·20 E
136	Chernoistochinsk (chĕr-nôy-stô'chĭnsk) Sov. Un. (Urals In.)	57·44 N	59·55 E
129	Chërnomorskoye (chĕr-nô-môr'skô-yĕ) Sov. Un.	45·29 N	32·43 E
121	Chernovtsy (Cernăuti) (chĭr-nôf'tsê) (chĕr-nou'tsê) Sov. Un.	48·18 N	25·56 E
119	Chernyakhovsk (chĕr-nyä'kôfsk) Sov. Un.	55·38 N	21·17 E
129	Chernyanka (chĕrn-yäŋ'kä) Sov. Un.	50·56 N	37·48 E
70	Cherokee (chĕr-ô-kē') Iowa	42·43 N	95·33 W
73	Cherokee Kans.	37·21 N	94·50 W
72	Cherokee Okla.	36·44 N	98·22 W
78	Cherokee (R.) Tenn.	36·22 N	83·22 W
78	Cherokee Indian Res. N. C.	35·33 N	83·12 W
94	Cherokee Sd. Ba. Is.	26·15 N	76·55 W
73	Cherokees, L. of the (chĕr-ô-kēz') Okla.	36·32 N	95·14 W
82	Cherryfield (chĕr'ĭ-fēld) Maine	44·37 N	67·56 W
65	Cherry Grove Ore. (Portland In.)	45·27 N	123·15 W
73	Cherryvale Kans.	37·16 N	95·33 W
79	Cherryville (chĕr'ĭ-vĭl) N. C.	35·32 N	81·22 W
65	Cherryville Ore. (Portland In.)	45·22 N	122·08 W
135	Cherskogo, Khrebet (Mts.) Sov. Un.	66·15 N	138·30 E
128	Cherven' (chĕr'vyĕn) Sov. Un.	53·43 N	28·26 E
128	Chervonoye (L.) (chĕr-vô'nô-yĕ) Sov. Un.	52·24 N	28·12 E
80	Chesaning (chĕs'à-nĭng) Mich.	43·10 N	84·10 W
81	Chesapeake B. (chĕs'à-pēk bā) Md.	38·20 N	76·15 W
110	Chesham (chĕsh'ŭm) Eng. (London In.)	51·41 N	0·37 W
80	Cheshire (chĕsh'ĭr) Mich.	42·25 N	86·00 W
110	Cheshire (Co.) Eng.	53·16 N	2·30 W
132	Chëshskaya Guba (B.) Sov. Un.	67·25 N	46·00 E
136	Chesma (chĕs'mà) Sov. Un. (Urals In.)	53·50 N	60·42 E
134	Chesnokovka (chĕs-nŏ-kôf'kà) Sov. Un.	53·28 N	83·41 E
110	Chester (chĕs'tẽr) Eng.	53·12 N	2·53 W
73	Chester Ill.	37·54 N	89·48 W
84	Chester Pa. (Philadelphia In.)	39·51 N	75·22 W
79	Chester S.C.	34·42 N	81·11 W
79	Chester Va.	37·20 N	77·24 W
80	Chester W. Va.	40·35 N	80·30 W
110	Chesterfield (chĕs'tẽr-fēld) Eng.	53·14 N	1·26 W
159	Chesterfield, Isles N. Cal.	19·38 S	160·08 E
86	Chesterfield (Inlet) Can.	63·59 N	92·09 W
86	Chesterfield Inlet Can.	63·19 N	91·11 W
85	Chestermere L. (chĕs'tẽr-mẽr) Can. (Calgary In.)	51·03 N	113·45 W
80	Chesterton (chĕs'tẽr-tŭn) Ind.	41·35 N	87·05 W
81	Chestertown (chĕs'tẽr-toun) Md.	39·15 N	76·05 W
82	Chesuncook (chĕs'ŭn-kŏŏk) Maine	46·03 N	69·40 W
71	Chetek (chĕ'tĕk) Wis.	45·18 N	91·41 W
92	Chetumal, Bahia de (B.) (bä-ē-ä dĕ chĕt-ōō-mäl') Br. Hond. (Yucatan In.)	18·07 N	88·05 W
69	Chevalon Cr. (shĕv'à-lŏn) Ariz.	34·35 N	111·00 W
75	Cheviot (shĕv'ĭ-ŭt) Ohio (Cincinnati In.)	39·10 N	84·37 W
116	Cheviot Hills Scot., Eng.	55·20 N	2·40 W
123	Chevreuse (shĕ-vrûz') Fr. (Paris In.)	48·42 N	2·02 E
66	Chewelah (chē-wē'lä) Wash.	48·17 N	117·42 W
148	Cheyang (R.) (Sĭyang) China	33·42 N	119·40 E
70	Cheyenne (shī-ĕn') Wyo.	41·10 N	104·49 W
70	Cheyenne (R.) S. D.	44·20 N	102·15 W
70	Cheyenne River Ind. Res. S. D.	45·07 N	100·46 W
72	Cheyenne Wells Colo.	38·46 N	102·21 W
151	Chiachi China	19·10 N	110·28 E
151	Chiahsing China	30·45 N	120·50 E
151	Chiai (chĭ'ī') China	23·28 N	120·28 E
151	Chialing (R.) China	30·30 N	106·20 E
151	Chian China	27·12 N	115·10 E
150	Chian China	41·00 N	126·04 E
148	Chiangchanchi China	36·39 N	120·31 E
83	Chianghsi (Kiangsi) (Prov.) China	28·16 N	115·34 E
151	Chiangling China	30·30 N	112·10 E
146	Chiang Mai Thai.	18·38 N	98·44 E
154	Chiang Rai Thai.	19·53 N	99·48 E
147	Chiangsu (Kiangsu) (Prov.) China	33·51 N	120·09 E
148	Chiangtu (jiang'dōō) China	32·24 N	119·24 E
148	Chiangyen (jĭäng'yĭn) China	32·33 N	120·07 E
148	Chiangyin (jiäng'in) China	31·54 N	120·15 E
148	Chiantochen (jĭäng'tô'jĕn) China	32·23 N	120·14 E
148	Chiaochou Wan (B.) (jĭou'zhĕō wän) China	36·10 N	119·55 E
148	Chiaoho (jēou'hŭ) China	38·03 N	116·18 E
150	Chiaoho China	43·40 N	127·20 E
148	Chiaohsien (jēou'sĭän) China	36·18 N	120·01 E
149	Ch'iaot'ou China (Canton In.)	22·55 N	113·39 E
148	Chiaotso (jēou'zhŏŏ) China	35·17 N	113·11 E
148	Chiaow Shan (Mts.) (jēou shän) China	36·59 N	121·15 E
92	Chiapa, Rio de (R.) (rê-ô-dĕ-chê-ä'pä) Mex.	16·00 N	92·20 W
91	Chiapa de Corzo (chê-ä'pä dā kôr'zō) Mex.	16·44 N	93·01 W
88	Chiapas (State) (chê-ä'päs) Mex.	17·10 N	93·00 W
91	Chiapas, Cordilla de (Mts.) (kôr-dĕl-yĕ'rä-dĕ-chyà'räs) Mex.	15·55 N	93·15 W
126	Chiari (kyä'rē) It.	45·31 N	9·57 E
120	Chiasso Switz.	45·50 N	8·57 E
149	Chiating China (Shanghai In.)	31·23 N	121·15 E
90	Chiautla (chyä-ōōt'lä) Mex.	18·16 N	98·37 W
126	Chiavari (kyä-vä'rē) It.	44·18 N	9·21 E
151	Chiayü China	33·00 N	114·00 E
153	Chiba (chē'bà) Jap. (Tōkyō In.)	35·37 N	140·08 E
153	Chiba (Pref.) Jap. (Tōkyō In.)	35·47 N	140·02 E
87	Chibougamau (chē-bōō'gä-mou) Can.	49·57 N	74·23 W
75	Chicago (shĭ-kô-gō) (chĭ-kà'gō) Ill. (Chicago In.)	41·49 N	87·37 W
75	Chicago Heights (shĭ-kô'gō) (chĭ-kä'gō) Ill. (Chicago In.)	41·30 N	87·38 W
166	Chicapa (R.) (chē-kä'pä) Ang.	8·15 S	20·15 E
91	Chicbul (chēk-bōō'l) Mex.	18·45 N	90·56 W
64	Chichagof (I.) (chê-chä'gôf) Alaska	57·50 N	137·00 W
92	Chichâncanab, Lago de (L.) (lä'-gô-dĕ-chē-chän-kä-nä'b) Mex. (Yucatan In.)	19·50 N	88·28 W
92	Chichen Itzá (Ruins) (chē-chĕ'n-ē-tsä') Mex. (Yucatan In.)	20·38 N	88·35 W
116	Chichester (chĭch'ĕs-tẽr) Eng.	50·50 N	0·55 W
151	Chichiang China	29·05 N	106·40 E
148	Chichiashih (jĭ'jĭä'shē) China	32·10 N	120·17 E
150	Ch'ich'ihaerh (Tsitsihar) China	47·18 N	124·00 E
92	Chichimila (chē-chē-mē'lä) Mex. (Yucatan In.)	20·36 N	88·14 W
99	Chichiriviche (chē-chē-rē-vē-chĕ) Ven. (In.)	10·56 N	68·17 W
78	Chickamauga (chĭk-à-mô'gà) Ga.	34·50 N	85·15 W
79	Chickamauga, (R.) Tenn.	35·18 N	85·22 W
78	Chickasawhay (R.) (chĭk-à-sô'wā) Miss.	31·45 N	88·45 W
72	Chickasha (chĭk'à-shā) Okla.	35·04 N	97·56 W
124	Chiclana (chê-klä'nä) Sp.	36·25 N	6·09 W
98	Chiclayo (chê-klä'yō) Peru	6·46 S	79·50 W
68	Chico (chē'kō) Calif.	39·43 N	121·51 W
65	Chico Wash. (Seattle In.)	47·37 N	122·43 W
100	Chico (R.) Arg.	44·30 S	66·00 W
100	Chico (R.) Arg.	49·15 S	69·30 W
155	Chico (R.) Phil. (Manila In.)	17·33 N	121·24 E
91	Chicoloapan (chê-kō-lwä'pän) Mex. (Mexico In.)	19·24 N	98·54 W
91	Chiconautla (chê-kō-nä-ōō'tlä) Mex. (Mexico In.)	19·39 N	99·01 W
90	Chicontepec (chê-kōn'tĕ-pĕk') Mex.	20·58 N	98·08 W
81	Chicopee (chĭk'ô-pē) Mass.	42·10 N	72·35 W
84	Chicot I. (shē-kō') La. (New Orleans In.)	29·44 N	89·15 W
82	Chicoutimi (shē-kōō'tē-mē') Can.	48·27 N	71·03 W
92	Chicxulub (chēk-sōō-lōō'b) Mex. (Yucatan In.)	21·10 N	89·30 W
87	Chidley, C. (chĭd'lĭ) Can.	60·32 N	63·56 W
66	Chief Joseph Dam Wash.	48·00 N	119·39 W
78	Chiefland (chēf'lănd) Fla.	29·30 N	82·50 W
146	Ch'iehmo China	38·02 N	85·16 E
148	Chiehshou Hu (L.) (jĭeh'shō hōō) China	32·59 N	119·04 E
151	Chiehyang China	23·38 N	116·20 E
120	Chiem See (L.) (Kēm zā) Ger.	47·58 N	12·20 E
148	Chienchangying (jĭan'chang'yĭng) China	40·09 N	118·47 E
148	Chienkan (R.) (jĭan'gän) China	39·35 N	117·34 E
151	Chienli China	29·50 N	112·52 E
151	Chienning China	26·50 N	116·55 E
151	Chienou China	27·10 N	118·18 E
148	Ch'ienshanchen (chĭan'shän'jen) China	31·05 N	120·24 E
148	Ch'ienshanchi (chĭan'shan'jĭ) China	32·38 N	117·02 E
151	Chienshih China	30·40 N	109·45 E
151	Chienshui China	23·32 N	102·50 E
148	Ch'ienwei (chĭan'wā) China	40·11 N	120·05 E
126	Chieri (kyâ'rē) It.	45·03 N	7·48 E
126	Chieti (kyĕ'tē) It.	42·22 N	14·22 E
129	Chigirin (chê-gē'rên) Sov. Un.	49·02 N	32·39 E
90	Chignanuapan (chē'g-nä-nwä-pà'n) Mex.	19·49 N	98·02 W
82	Chignecto B. (shĭg-nĕk'tō) Can.	45·33 N	64·50 W
64	Chignik (chĭg'nĭk) Alaska	56·14 N	158·12 W
64	Chignik B. Alaska	56·18 N	157·22 W
151	Chihchiang China	27·25 N	109·45 E
150	Ch'ihfeng (chĭ'fûng) China	42·18 N	118·52 E
148	Chihhochen (zhĭ'hŭ'jen) China	32·32 N	117·57 E
148	Ch'ihsien (chĭ'hsyĕn') China	34·33 N	114·47 E
148	Chihsien China	35·25 N	114·03 E
148	Ch'ihsien China	35·36 N	114·13 E
148	Chihsien China	37·37 N	115·33 E
148	Chihsien China	40·03 N	117·25 E
76	Chihuahua (chê-wä'wä) Mex.	28·37 N	106·06 W
88	Chihuahua (State) Mex.	29·00 N	107·30 W
166	Chihuane (chē-wà'nâ) Moz.	20·43 S	34·57 E
133	Chikishlyar (chê-kêsh-lyär') Sov. Un.	37·40 N	53·50 E
148	Ch'ik'ou (chē'kō) China	38·37 N	117·33 E
90	Chilapa (chê-lä'pä) Mex.	17·34 N	99·14 W
90	Chilchota (chêl-chō'tä) Mex.	19·40 N	102·04 W
72	Childress (chīld'rĕs) Tex.	34·26 N	100·11 W
96	Chile (chē'lä) S.A.	53·24 N	2·53 W
100	Chilecito (chê-lâ-sē'tō) Arg.	29·06 S	67·25 W
98	Chilí, Pico de (Pk.) (pē'kô-dĕ chē-lê') Col. (In.)	4·14 N	75·38 W
88	Chilibre (chē-lê'brĕ) Pan. (Panama Canal In.)	9·09 N	79·37 W
148	Ch'ili Hu (L.) (chē'lē hōō) China	32·57 N	118·26 E
150	Chilin (Kirin) (chĭl'ĭn') (kĭr'ĭn) China	43·58 N	126·40 E
147	Chilin (Prov.) China	44·36 N	124·23 E
148	Chilip'ing (chē'lē'pĭng) China	31·28 N	114·41 E
142	Chilka (L.) India	19·26 N	85·42 E
100	Chillán (chēl-yän') Chile	36·44 S	72·06 W
80	Chillicothe (chĭl-ĭ-kŏth'ē) Ill.	41·55 N	89·30 W
73	Chillicothe Mo.	39·46 N	93·32 W
80	Chillicothe Ohio	39·20 N	83·00 W
86	Chilliwack (chĭl'ĭ-wăk) Can.	49·09 N	121·59 W
100	Chiloé, Isla de (I.) (ē's-lä-dĕ-chē-lô-ā') Chile	43·00 S	76·30 W
90	Chilpancingo (chēl-pän-sēŋ'gō) Mex.	17·32 N	97·30 W
71	Chilton (chĭl'tŭn) Wis.	44·00 N	88·12 W
151	Chilung (Kirin) (chĭ'lŭng) China	25·02 N	121·48 E
65	Chimacum (chĭm'ä-kŭm) Wash. (Seattle In.)	48·01 N	122·47 W
19	Chimalpa (chē-mäl'pä) Mex. (Mexico In.)	19·26 N	99·22 W
92	Chimaltenango (chê-mäl-tâ-näŋ'gō) Guat.	14·39 N	90·48 W
90	Chimaltitan (chêmäl-tē-tän') Mex.	21·36 N	103·50 W
103	Chimbay (chĭm-bī') Sov. Un.	43·00 N	59·44 E
98	Chimborazo (Mtn.) (chêm-bô-rä'zō) Ec.	1·35 S	78·45 W
98	Chimbote (chêm-bō'tâ) Peru	9·02 S	78·33 W
134	Chimkent (chĭm-kĕnt) Sov. Un.	42·17 N	69·42 E
148	Chimo (gē'mŭ) China	36·22 N	120·28 E
138	China (chī'nà) Asia	36·45 N	93·00 E
76	China (chē'nä) Mex.	25·43 N	99·13 W
92	Chinameca (chē-nä-mā'kä) Sal.	13·31 N	88·18 W
	Chinan, see Tsinan		
92	Chinandega (chē-nän-dā'gä) Nic.	12·38 N	87·08 W
76	Chinati Pk. (chĭ-nä'tē) Tex.	92·56 N	104·29 W
145	Chinawin (R.) Bur.	23·30 N	94·30 E
98	Chincha Alta (chĭn'chä äl'tä) Peru	13·24 S	76·04 W
98	Chinchas, Islas (Is.) (ē's-läs-chē'n-chäs) Peru	11·27 S	79·05 W
150	Chincheng China	35·30 N	112·50 E
151	Chinchiang China	24·58 N	118·40 E
148	Chinch'iao (jĭnchĭou) China	31·46 N	116·46 E
160	Chinchilla (chĭn-chĭl'à) Austl.	26·44 S	150·36 E
124	Chinchilla (chên-chē'lyä) Sp.	38·54 N	1·43 W
92	Chinchorro, Banco (Bk.) (bä'n-kô-chēn-chô'r-rō) Mex. (Yucatan In.)	18·43 N	87·25 W
150	Chinchou China	41·00 N	121·00 E
148	Chinchou Wan (B.) (jĭn'zhō wän) China	39·07 N	121·17 E
166	Chinde (shĕn'dĕ) Moz.	17·39 S	36·34 E
152	Chin Do (I.) Kor.	34·30 N	125·43 E
142	Chindwara India	22·08 N	78·57 E
146	Chindwin R. (chĭn-dwĭn) Bur.	23·30 N	94·34 E
148	Chinganchi (jing'än'jĭ) China	34·30 N	116·55 E
148	Ch'ingcheng (chĭng'cheng) China	37·12 N	117·43 E
150	Ch'ingch'eng China	46·50 N	127·30 E
151	Chingchiang (jĭng'jĭang) China	28·00 N	115·30 E
148	Chingchiang China	32·02 N	120·15 E
148	Chingchih (jing'jē) China	36·19 N	119·23 E
148	Ch'ingfeng (chingfeng) China	35·52 N	115·05 E
146	Chinghai (Tsinghai) (Prov.) China	36·14 N	95·30 E
146	Ch'ing Hai (Koko Nor) (L.) (kō'kō nor) China	37·26 N	98·30 E
148	Chinghai Wan (B.) (jĭng'hăĭ wän) China	36·47 N	122·10 E
150	Ching Ho (R.) (chĭng'hō') China	34·40 N	108·20 E
151	Chinghsien (jĭng'sĭan) China	26·32 N	109·45 E
148	Chinghsien China	37·43 N	116·17 E
148	Ch'inghsien (chingsĭan) China	38·37 N	116·48 E
150	Chingshing China	47·00 N	123·00 E
148	Ching Hu (L.) (chĭng hōō) China	39·00 N	115·45 E
148	Chingk'ouchen (chĭng'kō'jĕn) China	34·52 N	119·07 E
151	Chingliu China	26·15 N	116·50 E
150	Chingning China	35·28 N	105·50 E
148	Ch'ingp'ing (chĭng'pĭng) China	36·46 N	116·03 E
150	Chingpo Hu (L.) China	44·10 N	129·00 E
149	Ch'ingp'u China (Shanghai In.)	31·08 N	121·06 E
	Ch'ingtao, see Tsingtao		
166	Chinguar (chĭng-gär) Ang.	12·35 S	16·15 E
164	Chinguetti (chêŋ-gĕt'ê) Mauritania	20·34 N	12·34 W
148	Ch'ingyang (chĭng'yäng) China	33·25 N	118·13 E
150	Chingyang China	36·02 N	107·42 E
148	Ch'ingyüan (chĭng'yōōän) China	38·52 N	115·31 E
150	Ch'ingyüan China	42·04 N	125·00 E
151	Ch'ingyüang China	23·43 N	113·10 E
148	Ch'ingyun (chĭng'yōōn) China	37·52 N	117·26 E
150	Ch'ingyütien China (Peking In.)	39·41 N	116·31 E
148	Chinhsiang (jĭn'sĭang) China	35·03 N	116·20 E

194 Chinhsien–Ciudad Hidalgo PRONOUNCING INDEX

Page Name Pronunciation Region Lat. °′ Long. °′

148 Chinhsien (jĭn′siän)........China 37·08 N 121·43 E
151 Ch'inhsien................China 22·00 N 108·35 E
151 Chinhua....................China 29·10 N 119·42 E
148 Ch'inhuangtao (chĭnhōōäng′dou) China 39·57 N 119·34 E
148 Chining (jē′nĭng)..........China 35·26 N 116·34 E
150 Chining....................China 41·00 N 113·10 E
152 Chinju (chĭn′jōō)...........Kor. 35·13 N 128·10 E
151 Chinkiang (chĭn′kyăng′)....China 32·05 N 119·25 E
151 Chinmen....................China 24·42 N 118·05 E
Chinmen, see Quemoy
151 Chinmen (I.)...............China 24·40 N 118·38 E
151 Chinmu Chiao (Pt.).........China 18·10 N 109·40 E
152 Chinnampo (chĭn-näm′pō)...Kor. 38·47 N 125·28 E
74 Chino (chē′nō) Calif. (Los Angeles In.) 34·01 N 117·42 W
122 Chinon (shē-nôN′)...........Fr. 47·09 N 0·13 E
67 Chinook (shĭn-ŏŏk′).......Mont. 48·35 N 109·15 W
65 Chinook (shĭn-ŏŏk′) Wash. (Portland In.) 46·17 N 123·57 W
148 Chinshachen (jĭn′shä′jĕn)...China 32·08 N 121·06 E
149 Chinshan...China (Shanghai In.) 30·53 N 121·09 E
142 Chinsura.....India (Calcutta In.) 22·53 N 88·24 E
146 Chint'a....................China 40·11 N 98·45 E
148 Chint'an (jĭn′tän)..........China 31·47 N 119·34 E
166 Chinteche (chĭn-tĕ′chĕ).....Tan. 11·48 S 34·14 E
150 Chinyang (chĭn′yäng′)......China 35·00 N 112·55 E
151 Chinyüh....................China 28·40 N 120·08 E
126 Chioggia (kyôd′jä)..........It. 45·12 N 12·17 E
149 Ch'ipao.....China (Shanghai In.) 31·06 N 121·16 E
166 Chipera (zhê-pĕ′rä)........Moz. 15·16 S 32·30 E
78 Chipley (chĭp′lĭ)............Fla. 30·45 N 85·33 W
82 Chipman (chĭp′măn).........Can. 46·11 N 65·53 W
78 Chipola (R.) (chĭ-pō′lȧ).......Fla. 30·40 N 85·14 W
75 Chippawa (chĭp′ê-wä) Can. (Buffalo In.) 43·03 N 79·03 W
70 Chippewa (R.) (chĭp′ê-wä)..Minn. 45·07 N 95·41 W
71 Chippewa (R.)..............Wis. 45·07 N 91·19 W
71 Chippewa Falls.............Wis. 44·55 N 91·26 W
75 Chippewa Lake Ohio (Cleveland In.) 41·04 N 81·54 W
82 Chiputneticook (L.) (chĭ-pōōt-nĕt′ĭ-kŏŏk).Can. 45·47 N 67·35 W
92 Chiquimula (chē-kê-mōō′lä).Guat. 14·47 N 89·31 W
92 Chiquimulilla (chē-kē-mōō-lē′l-yä) Guat. 14·08 N 90·23 W
98 Chiquinquira (chê-kēŋ′kê-rä′).Col. 5·33 N 73·49 W
101 Chiquita, Laguna Mar (L.) (lä-gōō′nä-mär-chê-kē′tä) Arg. (Buenos Aires In.) 34·25 S 61·10 W
100 Chiquita, Laguna Mar (L.)..Arg. 30·45 S 62·30 W
69 Chiracahua Natl. Mon. (chĭ-rä-cä′hwä).Ariz. 32·02 N 109·18 W
143 Chirald....................India 15·52 N 80·22 E
134 Chirchik (chĭr-chĕk′)....Sov. Un. 41·28 N 69·18 E
64 Chirikof (I.) (chĭ′rĭ-kôf)...Alaska 55·50 N 155·35 W
93 Chiriquí, Golfo de (G.) (gôl-fô-dĕ-chē-rê-kē′).Pan. 7·56 N 82·18 W
93 Chiriquí, Laguna de (L.) (lä-gōō′nä-dĕ-chē-rê-kē′).Pan. 9·06 N 82·02 W
93 Chiriqui, Punta (Pt.) (pōō′n-tä-chē-rê-kē′).Pan. 9·13 N 81·39 W
93 Chiriqui, Volcán de (Vol.) (vôl-kä′n-dĕ-chē-rê-kē′).Pan. 8·48 N 82·37 W
93 Chiriquí Grande (chē-rê-kē′ grän′dä).Pan. 8·57 N 82·08 W
152 Chiri San (Mt.) (chĭ′rĭ-sän′)..Kor. 35·20 N 127·39 E
166 Chiromo....................Tan. 16·34 S 35·13 E
127 Chirpan....................Bul. 42·12 N 25·19 E
93 Chirripo, R. (chêr-rē′pō)....C. R. 9·50 N 83·20 W
93 Chirripo Grande (Mt.) (chêr-rē′pō grän′dä).C. R. 9·30 N 83·31 W
71 Chisholm (chĭz′ŭm)........Minn. 47·28 N 92·53 W
132 Chistopol' (chĭs-tô′pôl-y′) Sov. Un. 55·18 N 50·30 E
135 Chita (chê-tä′)..........Sov. Un. 52·09 N 113·39 E
146 Ch'it'aí....................China 44·07 N 89·04 E
64 Chitina (chĭ-tē′nȧ)........Alaska 61·28 N 144·35 W
142 Chitor.....................India 24·59 N 74·42 E
142 Chitrāl (chē-träl′).......W. Pak. 35·58 N 71·48 E
93 Chitré (chē′trå)............Pan. 7·59 N 80·26 W
142 Chittagong (chĭt-ȧ-gông′).E. Pak. 22·26 N 90·51 E
150 Chiualhun...................China 49·59 N 127·15 E
148 Chiuch'eng (jĭō′chĕng)......China 37·14 N 116·03 E
146 Chiuch'ian.................China 39·46 N 98·26 E
151 Chiuchiang.................China 29·43 N 116·00 E
149 Chiuchiang...China (Canton In.) 23·50 N 113·02 E
147 Chiuchichien...............China 52·23 N 121·04 E
149 Chiufenghsien China (Shanghai In.) 30·55 N 121·38 E
148 Ch'iuhsien (chĭō′siän)......China 36·43 N 115·13 E
148 Chiuhsihsien (jĭo′sē′siän)...China 32·20 N 114·42 E
148 Chiuhuang (R.) (jĭō′hooäng) China 33·48 N 119·30 E
166 Chiumbe (R.) (chê-ŏŏm′bȧ)..Ang. 10·00 S 21·00 E
151 Ch'iungshan................China 20·00 N 110·20 E
148 Chiunü Shan (Mts.) (jĭō′nü′shän).China 35·47 N 117·23 E
126 Chivasso (kê-väs′sō).........It. 45·13 N 7·52 E
101 Chivilcoy (chē-vêl-koi′) Arg. (Buenos Aires In.) 34·51 S 60·03 W
92 Chixoy R. (chē-ĸoi′).......Guat. 15·40 N 90·35 W
151 Chiyang....................China 26·40 N 113·00 E
151 Ch'iyao Shan (Mtn.).......China 30·00 N 108·50 E
153 Chizu (chê-zōō′)...........Jap. 35·16 N 134·15 E
69 Chloride (klō′rīd)..........Ariz. 35·25 N 114·15 W
121 Chmielnik (ĸmyĕl′nêĸ)......Pol. 50·36 N 20·46 E
101 Choapa (chô-ä′pä) (R.) Chile (Santiago In.) 31·56 S 70·48 W
98 Chocó (chô-kô′) (Dept.).Col. (In.) 5·33 N 76·28 W
77 Chocolate Bay (chŏ′ō-lĭt) (chŏk′lĭt).Tex. (In.) 29·21 N 95·19 W
78 Choctawhatchee, B. (chôk-tô-hăch′ê).Fla. 30·15 N 86·32 W
78 Choctawhatchee, R......Fla.-Ga. 30·37 N 85·56 W
120 Chodziez (ĸōj′yĕsh)..........Pol. 52·59 N 16·55 E
100 Choele Choel (chô-ĕ′lĕ-chô ĕ′l) Arg. 39·14 S 66·46 W
153 Chōfu (chō′fōō′).Jap. (Tōkyō In.) 35·39 N 139·33 E
153 Chōgo (chō-gō)..Jap. (Tōkyō In.) 35·25 N 139·28 E
148 Chohsien (jōōŭ′siän)........China 39·30 N 115·59 E
159 Choiseul, (I.) (shwä-zûl′)..Sol. Is. 7·30 S 157·30 E
121 Chojnice (ĸōĭ-nē-tsĕ)........Pol. 53·41 N 17·34 E
122 Cholet (shô-lĕ′).............Fr. 47·06 N 0·54 W
150 Ch'olo (R.)................China 47·20 N 121·40 E
90 Cholua (chō-lōō′lä)..........Mex. 19·04 N 98·19 W
92 Choluteca (chō-lōō-tā′kä)...Hond. 13·18 N 87·12 W
92 Choluteco R................Hond. 13·34 N 86·59 W
120 Chomutov (kō′mōō-tôf)....Czech. 50·27 N 13·23 E
135 Chona (R.) (chō′nä).....Sov. Un. 60·45 N 109·15 E
98 Chone (chô′nĕ)...............Ec. 0·48 S 80·06 W
152 Chŏngjin (chŭng-jĭn′).......Kor. 41·48 N 129·46 E
152 Chŏngju (chŭng-jōō′)........Kor. 36·35 N 127·30 E
152 Chŏnju (chŭn-jōō′)..........Kor. 35·48 N 127·08 E
110 Chorley (chôr′lĭ)............Eng. 53·40 N 2·38 W
88 Chorrera (chôr-rā′rä) Pan. (Panama Canal In.) 8·23 N 79·17 W
98 Chorrillos (chôr-rē′l-yōs).....Peru 12·17 S 76·55 W
121 Chortkov (chôrt′kôf)....Sov. Un. 49·01 N 25·48 E
121 Chorzów (kô-zhōōf′).........Pol. 50·17 N 19·00 E
152 Chosan (chō-sän′)............Kor. 40·44 N 125·48 E
79 Chosen (chō′z′n).......Fla. (In.) 26·41 N 80·41 W
Chosen, see Korea
152 Chōshi (chō′shē).............Jap. 35·40 N 140·55 E
120 Choszczno (chôsh′chnô).......Pol. 53·10 N 15·25 E
142 Chota Nagpur (Reg.).......India 28·20 N 81·40 E
67 Choteau (shō′tō)...........Mont. 47·51 N 112·10 W
113 Chott el Hodna (L.).........Alg. 35·20 N 3·27 E
148 Chou (R.) (jēō)............China 31·59 N 114·57 E
148 Chouchiak'ou (jĕō′jĭä′kō)...China 33·39 N 114·40 E
149 Choup'u...China (Shanghai In.) 31·07 N 121·33 E
148 Chouts'un (jēō′tsōōn).......China 36·49 N 117·52 E
79 Chowan (R.) (chô-wăn′)....N. C. 36·13 N 76·46 W
150 Choybalsan................Mong. 47·50 N 114·15 E
159 Christchurch (krīst′chûrch) N. Z. (In.) 43·30 S 172·38 E
80 Christian (I.) (krĭs′chăn)....Can. 44·50 N 80·00 W
79 Christiansburg (krĭs′chănz-bûrg) Va. 37·08 N 80·25 W
89 Christiansted Vir. Is. (U. S. A.) (Puerto Rico In.) 17·45 N 64·44 W
154 Christmas (I.)...........Ind. O. 10·35 S 105·40 E
157 Christmas (I.) Gilbert & Ellice Is. 2·20 N 157·40 W
73 Christopher (krĭs′tô-fĕr).......Ill. 37·58 N 89·04 W
120 Chrudim (ĸrōō′dyĕm).......Czech. 49·57 N 15·46 E
121 Chrzanów (ĸzhä′nōōf).......Pol. 50·08 N 19·24 E
148 Ch'üanch'iao (chüän′jĭou)..China 32·06 N 118·17 E
150 Chuangho...................China 39·40 N 123·00 E
151 Ch'üanhsien................China 25·58 N 111·02 E
149 Ch'uansha...China (Shanghai In.) 31·12 N 121·41 E
100 Chubut (Prov.) (chōō-bōōt′)..Arg. 44·00 S 69·15 W
100 Chubut (chōō-bōōt′) (R.).....Arg. 43·05 S 69·00 W
148 Chuch'eng (chōō′chĕng′)....China 36·01 N 119·24 E
151 Chuchi.....................China 29·58 N 120·10 E
151 Ch'üchiang.................China 24·58 N 113·42 E
149 Chu Chiang (Pearl R.) China (Canton In.) 23·04 N 113·28 E
148 Ch'üchou (chü′jēō).........China 36·47 N 114·58 E
84 Chuckatuck (chŭck ȧ-tŭck) Va. (Norfolk In.) 36·51 N 76·35 W
93 Chucunague, R. (chōō-kōō-nä′kä) Pan. 8·36 N 77·48 W
128 Chudovo (chōō′dô-vô)...Sov. Un. 59·03 N 31·56 S
128 Chudskoye Oz. (Peipus, L.) (chōōt′skô-yĕ).Sov. Un. 58·43 N 26·45 E
148 Ch'üfou (chü′fōō)..........China 35·37 N 116·59 E
Chuguchak, see T'ach'eng
146 Chuguchak (Reg.) (chōō′gōō-chäk′).China 46·09 N 83·58 E
129 Chuguyev (chōō′gōō-yĕf).Sov. Un. 49·52 N 36·40 E
152 Chuguyevka (chōō-gōō′yĕf-kȧ) Sov. Un. 43·58 N 133·49 E
70 Chugwater Cr. (chŭg′wô-tēr) Wyo. 41·43 N 104·54 W
150 Chuho......................China 45·18 N 127·52 E
151 Ch'ühsien..................China 27·58 N 118·58 E
148 Ch'uhsien (chōō′siän)......China 31·19 N 118·19 E
148 Chühsien (jü′siän)..........China 35·35 N 118·50 E
146 Ch'uhsiung.................China 25·19 N 101·34 E
148 Chühua Tao (I.) (jü′hōōȧ dou) China 40·30 N 120·47 E
148 Chüjung (jü′rōōng)..........China 31·58 N 119·12 E
142 Chukhor....................China 28·22 N 87·28 E
135 Chukot Natl. Okrug (Reg.) Sov. Un. 68·15 N 170·00 E
135 Chukotskiy (Chukot) P-Ov (Pen.) Sov. Un. 66·12 N 174·35 E
135 Chukotskoye Nagor'ye (Mts.) Sov. Un. 66·00 N 166·00 E
68 Chula Vista (chōō′lȧ vĭs′tȧ) Calif. (San Diego In.) 32·38 N 117·05 W
136 Chulkovo (chōōl-kô vô) Sov. Un. (Moskva In.) 55·33 N 38·04 E
98 Chulucanas (chōō-lōō-kä′näs) Peru 5·13 S 80·13 W
134 Chulum (R.).............Sov. Un. 57·52 N 84·45 E
148 Chüma (R.) (jü′mȧ)........China 39·37 N 115·45 E
135 Chumikan (chōō-mē-kän′) Sov. Un. 54·47 N 135·09 E
152 Chunchŏn (chōōn-chŭn′).....Kor. 37·51 N 127·46 E
148 Chungchia Shan (Mts.) (jōōng′jĭä shän).China 32·42 N 118·19 E
151 Ch'ung-Ch'ing (Chungking) (ch′ungch′ing) (chōōng′kĭng′) China 29·38 N 107·30 E
151 Chunghsien.................China 30·20 N 108·00 E
148 Chunghsing (jōōng′sĭng)....China 33·43 N 118·42 E
152 Chungju (chŭng′jōō′)........Kor. 37·00 N 128·19 E
Chungking, see Ch'ung-Ch'ing
151 Ch'ungming Tao (I.).......China 31·40 N 122·30 E
150 Chungwei (chōōng′wā).....China 37·32 N 105·10 E
134 Chunya (R.) (chōōn′yä′).Sov. Un. 61·45 N 101·28 E
100 Chuquicamata (chōō-kê-kä-mä′tä) Chile 22·08 S 68·57 W
120 Chur (kōōr)..............Switz. 46·51 N 9·32 E
86 Churchill (chûrch′ĭl)........Can. 58·48 N 94·10 W
86 Churchill, C...............Can. 59·07 N 93·50 W
86 Churchill (R.)..............Can. 57·00 N 95·21 W
86 Churchill Pk................Can. 58·10 N 125·14 W
84 Churchland (chûrch-lănd) Va. (Norfolk In.) 36·52 N 76·24 W
110 Church Stretton (chûrch strĕt′ŭn).Eng. 52·32 N 2·49 W
142 Churu.....................India 28·22 N 75·00 E
90 Churumuco (chōō-rōō-mōō′kō) Mex. 18·39 N 101·40 W
151 Chusan Archipelago (Is.)...China 30·00 N 123·00 E
151 Ch'ushien.................China 30·40 N 106·48 E
69 Chuska, Mts. (chŭs-kȧ) Ariz.-N. Mex. 36·21 N 109·11 W
136 Chusovaya R. (chōō-sô-vä′yȧ) Sov. Un. (Urals In.) 58·08 N 58·35 E
136 Chusovoy (chōō-sô-vôy′) Sov. Un. (Urals In.) 58·18 N 57·50 E
134 Chust (chōōst)..........Sov. Un. 41·05 N 71·28 E
148 Chut'angtien (jō′däng′dĭän) China 31·59 N 114·13 E
148 Ch'uti (chü′tē)............China 37·07 N 117·17 E
132 Chuvash (A. S. S. R.) (chōō′väsh) Sov. Un. 55·45 N 46·00 E
76 Chuviscar R. (chōō-vês-kär′) Mex. 28·34 N 105·36 W
148 Ch'uwang (chōō′wäng).....China 36·08 N 114·53 E
154 Chu Yang Sin (Pk.)........Viet. 12·22 N 108·20 E
148 Chüyen (jü′yĕ)..............China 35·24 N 116·05 E
Cibao Mts., see Central, Cordillera
76 Cibolo Cr. (sē′bô-lō).........Tex. 29·28 N 98·13 W
75 Cicero (sĭs′ēr-ō) .Ill. (Chicago In.) 41·50 N 87·46 W
133 Cide (jē′dĕ)................Tur. 41·50 N 33·00 E
121 Ciechanów (tsyĕ-kä′nōōf).....Pol. 52·52 N 20·39 E
94 Ciego de Avila (syā′gō dā ä′vê-lä) Cuba 21·50 N 78·45 W
124 Ciempozuelos (thyĕm-pô-thwā′lōs) Sp. 40·09 N 3·36 W
98 Ciénaga (syā′nä-gä).........Col. 11·01 N 74·15 W
94 Cienfuegos (syĕn-fwā′gōs)...Cuba 22·10 N 80·30 W
94 Cienfuegos, Bahía (B.) (bä-ē′ä-syĕn-fwā′gōs).Cuba 22·00 N 80·35 W
93 Ciervo, Isla de la (I.) (ê′s-lä-dĕ-lä-syĕ′r-vô).Nic. 11·56 N 83·20 W
121 Cieszyn (tsyĕ′shĕn)..........Pol. 49·47 N 18·45 E
124 Cieza (thyā′thä).............Sp. 38·13 N 1·25 W
90 Cihuatlán (sē-wä-tlä′n).....Mex. 19·13 N 104·36 W
90 Cihuatlán (R.)..............Mex. 19·11 N 104·30 W
133 Cilician Gates (P.)..........Tur. 37·30 N 35·30 E
116 Cill Mantainn (Wicklow) (kĭl măn′tăn) (wĭk′lō).Ire. 52·59 N 6·06 W
72 Cimarron (R.), North Fk....Colo. 37·13 N 102·30 W
72 Cimarron R. (sĭm-ȧ-rōn′)....Okla. 36·26 N 98·47 W
127 Cîmpina....................Rom. 45·08 N 25·47 E
127 Cîmpulung..................Rom. 45·15 N 25·03 E
121 Cîmpulung Moldovenesc....Rom. 47·31 N 25·36 E
125 Cinca (R.) (thēŋ′kä).........Sp. 42·09 N 0·08 E
75 Cincinnati (sĭn-sĭ-năt′ĭ) Ohio (Cincinnati In.) 39·08 N 84·30 W
94 Cinco Balas, Cayos (Is.) (kä′yōs-thēŋ′kō bä′läs).Cuba 21·05 N 79·25 W
91 Cintalapa (sēn-tä-lä′pä).....Mex. 16·41 N 93·44 W
91 Cintalapa (R.)..............Mex. 16·46 N 93·36 W
126 Cinto, Mt. (chēn′tō)..........Fr. 42·24 N 8·54 E
64 Circle (sûr′k'l)............Alaska 65·49 N 144·22 W
80 Circleville (sûr′k'lvĭl)......Ohio 39·35 N 83·00 W
Cirenica, see Bargah
76 Cisco (sĭs′kō)...............Tex. 32·23 N 98·57 W
98 Cisneros (sês-nĕ′rôs)....Col. (In.) 5.33 N 75·05 W
125 Cisterna di Latina (chēs-tĕ′r-nä-dē-lä-tē′nä).It. (Roma In.) 41·36 N 12·53 E
124 Cistierna (thēs-tyĕr′nä).......Sp. 42·48 N 5·08 W
91 Citlaltépetl (Vol.) (sē-tlȧl-tĕ′pĕtl) Mex. 19·04 N 97·14 W
78 Citronelle (cĭt-rô′nĕl)........Ala. 3·04 N 88·12 W
126 Cittadella (chēt-tä-dĕl′lä)......It. 45·39 N 11·51 E
126 Città di Castello (chēt-tä′dē käs-tĕl′lō).It. 43·27 N 12·17 E
90 Ciudad Altamirano (syōō-dä′d-äl-tä-mē-rä′nô).Mex. 18·24 N 100·38 W
98 Ciudad Bolívar (syōō-dhädh′ bô-lē′vär).Ven. 8·07 N 63·41 W
76 Ciudad Camargo (Santa Rosalia) (syōō-dhädh′ kä-mär′gō) (sän′tȧ rō-sä′lēȧ).Mex. 27·42 N 105·10 W
92 Ciudad Chetumal (Payo Obispo) (syōō-dhädh′ chĕt-ōō-mäl) (pä′yō ō-bēs′pō) Mex. (Yucatan In.) 18·30 N 88·17 W
92 Ciudad Dario (syōō-dhädh′dä′rê-ō).Nic. 12·44 N 86·08 W
91 Ciudad de las Casas (syōō-dä′d-dĕ-läs-kȧ′säs).Mex. 16·44 N 92·39 W
91 Ciudad del Carmen (syōō-dä′d-dĕl-kȧ′r-mĕn).Mex. 18·39 N 91·49 W
90 Ciudad del Maíz (syōō-dhädh′del mä-ēz′).Mex. 22·24 N 99·37 W
90 Ciudad de Valles (syōō-dhädh′dā vä′lyās).Mex. 21·59 N 99·02 W
125 Ciudadela (thyōō-dhä-dhä′lä).Sp. 40·00 N 3·52 E
90 Ciudad Fernández (syōō-dhädh′fĕr-nän′dĕz).Mex. 21·56 N 100·03 W
90 Ciudad Garcia (syōō-dhädh′gär-sē′ä).Mex. 22·39 N 103·02 W
90 Ciudad Guzmán (syōō-dhädh′gōōz-män′).Mex. 19·40 N 103·29 W
90 Ciudad Hidalgo (syōō-dä′d-ê-dä′l-gô).Mex. 19·41 N 100·35 W

Page	Name Pronunciation Region	Lat. °′	Long. °′
76	Ciudad Juárez (syōō-dhädh hwä'räz) . Mex.	31·44 N	106·28 W
91	Ciudad Madero (syōō-dä'd-mä-dĕ'-rô) . Mex.	22·16 N	97·52 W
90	Ciudad Mante (syōō-dä'd-män'tĕ) . Mex.	22·34 N	98·58 W
90	Ciudad Manuel Doblado (syōō-dä'd-män-wäl' dō-blä'dō) Mex.	20·43 N	101·57 W
88	Ciudad Obregon (syōō-dhädh-ô-brĕ-gô'n) . Mex.	27·40 N	109·58 W
124	Ciudad Real (thyōō-dhädh'rā-äl') . Sp.	38·59 N	3·55 W
124	Ciudad Rodrigo (thyōō-dhädh'rô-drē'gō) . Sp.	40·38 N	6·34 W
91	Ciudad Serdán (syōō-dä'd-sĕr-dà'n) . Mex.	18·58 N	97·26 W
90	Ciudad Victoria (syōō-dhädh'vêk-tō'rê-ä) . Mex.	23·43 N	99·09 W
126	Civadale del Friuli (chē-vê-dä'lā-dĕl-frē-ōō'lē) . It.	46·06 N	13·24 E
126	Civitavecchia (chē'vê-tä-vĕk'kyä) It.	42·06 N	11·49 E
65	Clackamas (klăc-kà'măs) Ore. (Portland In.)	42·25 N	122·34 W
86	Claire (L.) (klâr) . Can.	58·33 N	113·16 W
75	Clairton (klârtŭn) Pa. (Pittsburgh In.)	40·17 N	79·53 W
78	Clanton (klăn'tŭn) . Ala.	32·50 N	86·38 W
80	Clare (klâr) . Mich.	43·50 N	84·45 W
116	Clare (I.) . Ire.	53·46 N	9·60 W
74	Claremont (klâr'mŏnt) Calif. (Los Angeles In.)	34·06 N	117·43 W
81	Claremont (klâr'mŏnt) . N. H.	43·20 N	72·20 W
80	Claremont . W. Va.	37·55 N	81·00 W
73	Claremore (klâr'mōr) . Okla.	36·16 N	95·37 W
116	Claremorris (klâr-mŏr'ĭs) . Ire.	53·46 N	9·05 W
158	Clarence Str. (klăr'ĕns) . Austl.	12·15 S	130·05 E
95	Clarence Town . Ba. Is.	23·05 N	75·00 W
73	Clarendon (klâr'ĕn-dŭn) . Ark.	34·42 N	91·17 W
72	Clarendon . Tex.	34·55 N	100·52 W
167	Clarens (clâ-rĕns) S. Afr. (Natal In.)	28·34 S	28·26 E
86	Claresholm (klâr'ĕs-hōlm) . Can.	50·01 N	113·30 W
71	Clarinda (klà-rĭn'dà) . Iowa	40·42 N	95·00 W
99	Clarines (klä-rē'nĕs) . Ven. (In.)	9·57 N	65·10 W
71	Clarion (klăr'i-ŭn) . Iowa	42·43 N	93·45 W
81	Clarion . Pa.	41·10 N	79·25 W
70	Clark (klärk) . S. D.	44·52 N	97·45 W
80	Clark, Pt. . Can.	44·05 N	81·50 W
82	Clark City . Can.	50·12 N	66·38 W
69	Clarkdale (klärk-dāl) . Ariz.	34·45 N	112·05 W
159	Clarke Ra. . Austl.	20·30 S	148·00 E
82	Clarkes Harbour (klärks) . Can.	43·28 N	65·37 W
67	Clark Fork R. . Mont.	47·50 N	115·35 W
79	Clark Hill Res. (klärk-hĭl) Ga.-S. C.	33·50 N	82·35 W
81	Clarksburg (klärkz'bûrg) . W. Va.	39·15 N	80·20 W
78	Clarksdale (klärks-dāl) . Miss.	34·10 N	90·31 W
85	Clarkson . Can. (Toronto In.)	43·31 N	79·38 W
84	Clarkston (klärks'-tŭn) Ga. (Atlanta In.)	33·49 N	84·15 W
66	Clarkston . Wash.	46·24 N	117·01 W
73	Clarksville (klärks-vĭl) . Ark.	35·28 N	93·26 W
78	Clarksville . Tenn.	36·30 N	87·23 W
73	Clarksville . Tex.	33·37 N	95·02 W
65	Clatskanie . Oreg. (Portland In.)	46·06 N	123·11 W
65	Clatskanie (R.) (klăt-skā'nê) Ore. (Portland In.)	46·03 N	123·06 W
65	Clatsop Spit (klăt-sŏp) Ore. (Portland In.)	46·13 N	124·04 W
101	Cláudio (klou'-dēō) Braz. (Rio de Janeiro In.)	20·26 S	44·44 W
151	Claveria (klä-vä-rē'ä) . Phil.	18·38 N	121·08 E
75	Clawson (klô's'n) Mich. (Detroit In.)	42·32 N	83·09 W
79	Claxton (klăks'tŭn) . Ga.	32·07 N	81·54 W
78	Clay (klā) . Ky.	37·28 N	87·50 W
65	Clayburn (klā'bûrn) Can. (Vancouver In.)	49·05 N	122·17 W
73	Clay Center (klā sĕn'tēr) . Kans.	39·23 N	97·08 W
80	Clay City (klā sĭ'tĭ) . Ky.	37·50 N	83·55 W
74	Claycomo (kla-kō'mo) Mo. (Kansas City In.)	39·12 N	94·30 W
110	Clay Cross (klā krŏs) . Eng.	53·10 N	1·25 W
123	Claye-Souilly (klĕ-sōō-yē') Fr. (Paris In.)	48·56 N	2·43 E
84	Claymont (klā-mŏnt) Del. (Philadelphia In.)	39·48 N	75·28 W
78	Clayton (klā'tŭn) . Ala.	31·52 N	85·25 W
65	Clayton . Calif. (San Francisco In.)	37·56 N	122·56 W
110	Clayton . Eng.	53·47 N	1·49 W
74	Clayton . Mo. (St. Louis In.)	38·39 N	90·20 W
72	Clayton . N. Mex.	36·26 N	103·12 W
79	Clayton . N. C.	35·40 N	78·27 W
68	Clear, (L.) . Calif.	39·05 N	122·50 W
116	Clear, C. (klēr) . Ire.	51·24 N	9·15 W
73	Clear Boggy Cr. (klēr bŏg'ĭ krēk) Okla.	34·21 N	96·22 W
69	Clear Cr. . Ariz.	34·40 N	111·05 W
67	Clear Cr. . Wyo.	44·35 N	106·20 W
81	Clearfield (klēr-fēld) . Pa.	41·00 N	78·25 W
74	Clearfield Utah (Salt Lake City In.)	41·07 N	112·01 W
86	Clear Hills . Can.	57·11 N	119·20 W
71	Clear Lake . Iowa	43·09 N	93·23 W
65	Clear Lake . Wash. (Seattle In.)	48·27 N	122·14 W
66	Clear Lake Res. . Calif.	41·53 N	121·00 W
77	Clear R. . Tex. (In.)	29·34 N	95·13 W
79	Clearwater (klēr-wô'tēr) . Fla. (In.)	27·43 N	82·45 W
66	Clearwater Mts. . Idaho	45·56 N	115·15 W
73	Clearwater Res. . Mo.	37·20 N	91·04 W
66	Clearwater R. . Idaho	46·27 N	116·33 W
66	Clearwater R., Middle Fork . Idaho	46·10 N	115·48 W
66	Clearwater R., North Fork . Idaho	46·34 N	116·08 W
66	Clearwater R., South Fork . Idaho	45·46 N	115·53 W
77	Cleburne (klē'bŭrn) . Tex.	32·21 N	97·23 W
110	Clee Hill (klē) . Eng.	52·24 N	2·37 W
66	Cle Elum (klē ĕl'ŭm) . Wash.	47·12 N	120·55 W
84	Clementon (klē'mĕn-tŭn) N. J. (Philadelphia In.)	39·49 N	75·00 W
110	Cleobury Mortimer (klē'ô-bĕr'ĭ môr'tĭ-mĕr) . Eng.	52·22 N	2·29 W
159	Clermont (klĕr'mŏnt) . Austl.	23·02 S	147·46 E
75	Clermont . Ind. (Indianapolis In.)	39·48 N	86·19 W
122	Clermont-Ferrand (klĕr-môN'fĕr-räN') . Fr.	45·47 N	3·03 E
122	Clermont l'Herault (klĕr-mŏN' lā-rō') . Fr.	43·38 N	3·22 E
78	Cleveland (klēv'lănd) . Miss.	33·45 N	90·42 W
75	Cleveland . Ohio (Cleveland In.)	41·30 N	81·42 W
73	Cleveland . Okla.	36·18 N	96·28 W
78	Cleveland . Tenn.	35·09 N	84·52 W
77	Cleveland . Tex.	30·18 N	95·05 W
75	Cleveland Heights Ohio (Cleveland In.)	41·30 N	81·35 W
75	Cleves (klē'vĕs) Ohio (Cincinnati In.)	39·10 N	84·45 W
116	Clew (B.) (klōō) . Ire.	53·47 N	9·45 W
79	Clewiston (klē'wĭs-tŭn) . Fla. (In.)	26·44 N	80·55 W
123	Clichy-la-Garennel (klē-shē'-lā-gä-rĕ-nĕl') Fr. (Paris In.)	48·54 N	2·18 E
116	Clifden (klĭf'dĕn) . Ire.	53·31 N	10·04 W
69	Clifton (klĭf'tŭn) . Ariz.	33·05 N	109·20 W
84	Clifton . N. J. (New York In.)	40·35 N	74·09 W
79	Clifton . S. C.	35·00 N	81·47 W
77	Clifton . Tex.	31·45 N	97·31 W
81	Clifton Forge . Va.	37·50 N	79·50 W
78	Clinch Res. (klĭnch) . Tenn.-Va.	36·30 N	83·19 W
78	Clingmans Dome, (Mtn.) (klĭng'măns dōm) . N. C.	35·37 N	83·26 W
86	Clinton (klĭn-tŭn) . Can.	51·09 N	121·40 W
80	Clinton . Ill.	40·10 N	88·55 W
80	Clinton . Ind.	39·40 N	87·25 W
71	Clinton . Iowa	41·50 N	90·13 W
78	Clinton . Ky.	36·39 N	88·56 W
83	Clinton . Mass. (Boston In.)	42·25 N	71·41 W
73	Clinton . Mo.	38·23 N	93·46 W
79	Clinton . N. C.	35·58 N	78·20 W
72	Clinton . Okla.	35·31 N	98·56 W
79	Clinton . S. C.	34·27 N	81·53 W
78	Clinton . Tenn.	36·05 N	84·08 W
65	Clinton . Wash. (Seattle In.)	47·59 N	122·22 W
86	Clinton-Colden (L.) . Can.	63·58 N	106·34 W
75	Clinton R. . Mich. (Detroit In.)	42·36 N	83·00 W
71	Clintonville (klĭn'tŭn-vĭl) . Wis.	44·37 N	88·46 W
80	Clio (klē'ō) . Mich.	43·10 N	83·45 W
158	Cloates, Pt. (klōts) . Austl.	22·47 S	113·45 E
168	Clocolan S. Afr. (Johannesburg & Pretoria In.)	28·56 S	27·35 E
116	Clonakilty B. (klŏn-à-kĭltē) . Ire.	51·30 N	8·50 W
158	Cloncurry (klŏn-kŭr'ê) . Austl.	20·58 S	140·42 E
116	Clonmel (klŏn-mĕl) . Ire.	52·21 N	7·45 W
74	Cloquet (klô-kā') Minn. (Duluth In.)	46·28 N	92·28 W
71	Cloquet (R.) . Minn.	47·02 N	92·17 W
84	Closter (clōs'tēr) N. J. (New York In.)	40·58 N	74·57 W
67	Cloud Pk. (kloud) . Wyo.	44·23 N	107·11 W
74	Clough (klou'h) Minn. (Minneapolis, St. Paul In.)	45·08 N	93·14 W
79	Clover (klō'vēr) . S. C.	35·08 N	81·08 W
85	Clover Bar (klō'vēr bär) Can. (Edmonton In.)	53·34 N	113·20 W
68	Cloverdale (klō'vēr-dāl) . Calif.	38·47 N	123·03 W
65	Cloverdale . Can. (Vancouver In.)	49·06 N	122·44 W
80	Cloverport (klō'vēr pōrt) . Ky.	37·50 N	86·35 W
72	Clovis (klō'vĭs) . N. Mex.	34·24 N	103·11 W
121	Cluj (klōōzh) . Rom.	46·46 N	23·34 E
110	Clun (R.) (klŭn) . Eng.	52·25 N	2·56 W
122	Cluny (klü-nē') . Fr.	46·27 N	4·40 E
159	Clutha (R.) (klōō'thà) . N. Z. (In.)	45·26 S	169·15 E
73	Clyde (klīd) . Kans.	39·34 N	97·23 W
80	Clyde . Ohio	41·15 N	83·00 W
116	Clyde (L.) . Scot.	55·35 N	3·50 W
116	Clyde, Firth of (fûrth ŏv klīd) Scot.	55·28 N	5·01 W
116	Clydebank . Scot.	55·56 N	4·20 W
124	Côa (R.) (kô'ä) . Port.	40·28 N	6·55 W
91	Coacalco (kō-ä-käl'kō) Mex. (Mexico In.)	19·37 N	99·06 W
68	Coachella, Can. (kō'chĕl-là) . Calif.	30·10 N	115·23 W
90	Coahuayana, Rio de (R.) (rê'ō-dĕ-kô-ä-wä-yà'nä) . Mex.	19·00 N	103·33 W
90	Coahuayutla (kō-ä-wē'lä) . Mex.	18·19 N	101·44 W
88	Coahuila (State) (kō-ä-wē'lä) Mex.	27·30 N	103·00 W
75	Coal City (kōl sĭ'tĭ) Ill. (Chicago In.)	41·17 N	88·17 W
90	Coalcomán, Sierra de (Mts.) (syĕr'rä dā kō-äl-kō-män') . Mex.	18·30 N	102·45 W
90	Coalcomán, Rio de (R.) (rê'ō-dĕ-kō-äl-kō-män') . Mex.	18·30 N	102·48 W
90	Coalcomán de Matamoros (kō-äl-kō-män' dä mä-tä-mō'rôs) Mex.	18·46 N	103·10 W
73	Coalgate (kōl'gāt) . Okla.	34·33 N	96·13 W
80	Coal Grove (kōl grōv) . Ohio	38·20 N	82·40 W
68	Coalinga (kō-à-lĭŋ'gà) . Calif.	36·09 N	120·23 W
110	Coalville (kōl'vĭl) . Eng.	52·43 N	1·21 W
89	Coamo (kō-ä'mō) P. R. (Puerto Rico In.)	18·05 N	66·21 W
98	Coari (kō-är'ê) . Braz.	4·06 S	63·10 W
86	Coast Mts. (kōst) . Can.	57·10 N	131·05 W
62	Coast Ranges, (Mts.) . U. S.	41·28 N	123·30 W
90	Coatepec (kō-ä-tä-pĕk) . Mex.	19·23 N	98·44 W
91	Coatepec . Mex.	19·26 N	96·56 W
91	Coatepec . Mex. (Mexico In.)	19·08 N	99·25 W
92	Coatepeque (kō-ä-tà-pā'kā) . Guat.	14·40 N	91·52 W
92	Coatepeque . Sal.	13·56 N	89·30 W
81	Coatesville (kōts'vĭl) . Pa.	40·00 N	75·50 W
90	Coatetelco (kō-ä-tà-tĕl'kō) . Mex.	18·43 N	99·47 W
81	Coaticook (kō'tĭ-kŏŏk) . Can.	45·10 N	71·55 W
91	Coatlinchán (kô-ä-tlē'n-chä'n) Mex. (Mexico In.)	19·26 N	98·52 W
87	Coats (I.) (kōts) . Can.	62·23 N	82·11 W
47	Coats Land (Reg.) . Ant.	74·00 S	12·00 W
91	Coatzacoalcos (Puerto Mexico) kô-ät'zä-kô-äl'kōs) (pwĕ'r-tô-mĕ'-kē-kô) . Mex.	18·09 N	94·26 W
91	Coatzacoalcos (R.) . Mex.	17·40 N	94·41 W
92	Coba (Ruins) (kô'bä) Mex. (Yucatan In.)	20·23 N	87·23 W
87	Cobalt (kō'bôlt) . Can.	47·21 N	79·40 W
92	Cobán (kō-bän') . Guat.	15·28 N	90·19 W
160	Cobberas, Mt. (cŏ-bēr-ăs) . Austl.	36·45 S	148·15 E
82	Cobequid B. (kŏb'ê-kwĭd) . Can.	45·22 N	63·50 W
116	Cobh (kôv) . Ire.	51·52 N	8·09 W
98	Cobija (kô-bē'hä) . Bol.	11·12 S	68·49 W
81	Cobourg (kō'bŏŏrgh) . Can.	43·55 N	78·05 W
94	Cobre (R.) (kō'brā) . Jam.	18·05 N	77·00 W
120	Coburg (kō'bŏŏrg) . Ger.	50·16 N	10·57 E
143	Cocanāda (kō-kō-nä'dà) . India	16·58 N	82·18 E
125	Cocentaina (kō-thān-tä-ē'nà) . Sp.	38·44 N	0·27 W
98	Cochabamba (kō-chä-bäm'bä) Bol.	17·28 S	65·43 W
123	Cochem (kō'kĕm) . Ger.	50·10 N	7·06 E
143	Cochin (kō-chĭn') . India	9·58 N	76·19 E
154	Cochin (Reg.) . Viet.	9·45 N	107·20 E
94	Cochinos, Bahia (B.) (bä-ē'ä-kô-chê'nōs) . Cuba	22·05 N	81·10 W
95	Cochinos Bks. . Ba. Is.	22·20 N	76·15 W
155	Cochinos Pt. (kô-chē'-nôs) Phil. (Manila In.)	14·25 N	120·15 E
78	Cochran (kŏk'răn) . Ga.	32·23 N	83·23 W
87	Cochrane (kŏk'răn) . Can.	49·01 N	81·06 W
85	Cochrane . Can. (Calgary In.)	51·11 N	114·28 W
80	Cockburn (I.) (kŏk-bûrn) . Can.	45·55 N	83·25 W
81	Cockeysville (kŏk'ĭz-vĭl) . Md.	39·30 N	76·40 W
74	Cockrell Hill (kŏk'rĕl) Tex. (Dallas, Fort Worth In.)	32·44 N	96·53 W
98	Coco, Isla del (I.) (ē's-lä-dĕl-kô-kô) C. R.	5·33 N	87·02 W
94	Coco, Cayo (I.) (kä'yō-kô'kô) Cuba	22·30 N	78·30 W
79	Cocoa (kō'kō) . Fla. (In.)	28·21 N	80·44 W
79	Cocoa Beach . Fla. (In.)	28·09 N	80·37 W
88	Cocoli (kŏ-kô'lē) C. Z. (Panama Canal In.)	8·58 N	79·36 W
69	Coconino, Plat. (kō kō nē'nō) . Ariz.	35·45 N	112·28 W
93	Coco R. (Segovia) (kô-kô) (sĕ-gô'vyä) . Hond.	14·55 N	83·45 W
7	Cocos (Keeling) (kō'kŏs) (kē'lĭng) Is. . Ind. O.	11·50 S	90·50 E
88	Coco Solito (kô-kô-sŏ-lē'tŏ) C. Z. (Panama Canal In.)	9·21 N	79·53 W
82	Cocouna . Can.	47·54 N	69·31 W
90	Cocula (kō-kōō'lä) . Mex.	20·23 N	103·47 W
90	Cocula (R.) . Mex.	18·17 N	99·11 W
98	Codajás (kō-dä-häzh') . Braz.	3·44 S	62·09 W
99	Codera, Cabo (C.) (kà'bô-kô-dĕ'rä) . Ven. (In.)	10·35 N	66·06 W
99	Codó (kō'dō) . Braz.	4·21 S	43·52 W
126	Codogno (kô-dō'nyō) . It.	45·08 N	9·43 E
93	Codrington (kŏd'rĭng-tŭn) W. I. F. (Le. & Wind. Is. In.)	17·39 N	61·49 W
67	Cody (kō'dĭ) . Wyo.	44·31 N	109·02 W
123	Coesfeld (kûs'fĕld) Ger. (Ruhr In.)	51·56 N	7·10 E
66	Coeur d' Alene (kûr dà-lān') Idaho	47·43 N	116·35 W
66	Coeur d' Alene L. . Idaho	47·32 N	116·39 W
66	Coeur d' Alene R. . Idaho	47·26 N	116·35 W
167	Coffee Bay (cŏfē bā) S. Afr. (Natal In.)	31·58 S	29·10 E
73	Coffeyville (kŏf'ĭ-vĭl) . Kans.	37·01 N	95·38 W
167	Cofimvaba (căfĭm'vä-bà) S. Afr. (Natal In.)	32·01 S	27·37 E
126	Coghinas (R.) (kō'gē-nàs) . It.	40·31 N	9·00 E
122	Cognac (kôn-yak') . Fr.	45·41 N	0·22 W
83	Cohasset (kô-hăs'ĕt) Mass. (Boston In.)	42·14 N	70·48 W
81	Cohoes (kô-hōz') . N. Y.	42·50 N	73·40 W
100	Coig (kô'ĕk) (R.) . Arg.	51·15 S	71·00 W
143	Coimbatore (kô-ēm-bà-tōr') . India	11·03 N	76·56 E
124	Coimbra (kô-ēm'brä) . Port.	40·14 N	8·23 W
124	Coín (kô-ēn') . Sp.	36·40 N	4·45 W
125	Coina (kô-ē'nà) . Port. (Lisboa In.)	38·35 N	9·03 W
125	Coina (R.) (kô'y-nä) Port. (Lisboa In.)	38·35 N	9·02 W
98	Coipasa, Salar de (Salt Flat) (sä-lä'r-dĕ-koi-pä'-sä) . Chile	19·12 S	69·13 W
91	Coixtlahuaca (kō-ēks'tlä-wä'kä) Mex.	17·42 N	97·17 W
99	Cojedes (State) (kô-kĕ'dĕs) Ven. (In.)	9·50 N	68·21 W
95	Cojimar (kō-hê-mär') Cuba (La Habana In.)	23·10 N	82·19 W
92	Cojutepeque (kô-hōō-tĕ-pā'kā) Sal.	13·45 N	88·50 W
71	Cokato (kô-kā'tō) . Minn.	45·03 N	94·11 W
75	Cokeburg (kōk bûgh) Pa. (Pittsburgh In.)	40·06 N	80·03 W
160	Colac (kŏ'lăc) . Austl.	38·25 S	143·40 E
125	Colares (kô-lä'rĕs) Port. (Lisboa In.)	38·47 N	9·27 W
99	Colatina (kô-lä-tē'nä) . Braz.	19·33 S	40·42 W
72	Colby (kōl'bĭ) . Kans.	39·23 N	101·04 W
101	Colchagua (Prov.) (kôl-chà'gwä) Chile (Santiago In.)	36·42 S	71·24 W
117	Colchester (kōl'chĕs-tēr) . Eng.	51·52 N	0·50 E
83	Cold Spring Pd. (kōld) . Can.	48·08 N	56·25 W
72	Coldwater (kōld'wô-tēr) . Kans.	37·14 N	99·21 W
80	Coldwater . Mich.	41·55 N	85·00 W
78	Coldwater (R.) . Miss.	34·25 N	90·12 W
72	Coldwater Cr. . Tex.	36·10 N	101·45 W

n-sing ŋ-baŋk; N-nasalized n; nŏd; cŏmmit; ōld; ôbey; ôrder; fōōd; fŏŏt; ou-out; s-soft; sh-dish; th-thin; pūre; ûnite; ûrn; stŭd; circŭs; ü-as "y" in study; '-indeterminate vowel.

196 Coleman–Corabia PRONOUNCING INDEX

Page	Name Pronunciation	Region	Lat. °'	Long. °'
76	Coleman (kōl'măn)	Tex.	31·50 N	99·25 W
167	Colenso (kŏ-lĕnz'ō)	S. Afr. (Natal In.)	28·48 S	29·49 E
116	Coleraine (kōl-rān')	N. Ire.	54·66 N	6·40 W
71	Coleraine	Minn.	47·16 N	93·29 W
110	Coleshill (kōlz'hĭl)	Eng.	52·30 N	1·42 W
71	Colfax (kōl'făks)	Iowa	41·40 N	93·13 W
77	Colfax	La.	31·31 N	92·42 W
66	Colfax	Wash.	46·53 N	117·21 W
100	Colhué Huapi (L.) (kôl-wā'ŏŏă'pê)	Arg.	45·30 S	68·45 W
168	Coligny	S. Afr. (Johannesburg & Pretoria In.)	26·20 S	26·18 E
90	Colima (kōlē'mä)	Mex.	19·13 N	103·45 W
90	Colima, Vol. de (vôl-kȧ'n-dĕ-kō-lē'mä)	Mex.	19·30 N	103·38 W
116	Coll (I.) (kŏl)	Scot.	56·42 N	6·23 W
84	College Park (kŏl'ĕj)	Ga. (Atlanta In.)	33·39 N	84·27 W
84	Collegeville (kŏl'ĕj-vĭl)	Pa. (Philadelphia In.)	40·11 N	75·27 W
158	Collie (kŏl'ê)	Austl.	33·20 S	116·20 E
158	Collier B. (kŏl-yēr)	Austl.	15·30 S	123·30 E
125	Colli Laziali (Mtn.) (kô'lē-lät-zyȧ'lē)	It. (Roma In.)	41·46 N	12·45 E
84	Collingswood (kŏl'ĭngz-wŏŏd)	N. J. (Philadelphia In.)	39·54 N	75·04 W
80	Collingwood	Can.	44·30 N	80·20 W
78	Collins (kŏl'ĭns)	Miss.	31·40 N	89·34 W
74	Collinsville (kŏl'ĭnz-vĭl)	Ill. (St. Louis In.)	38·41 N	89·59 W
73	Collinsville	Okla.	36·21 N	95·50 W
164	Collo (kôl'ō)	Alg.	37·02 N	6·29 E
123	Colmar (kôl'mär)	Fr.	48·40 N	7·22 E
124	Colmenar de Oreja (kôl-mā-när'dāōrā'hä)	Sp.	40·06 N	3·25 W
125	Colmenar Viejo (kôl-mā-när'vyā'hō)	Sp. (Madrid In.)	40·40 N	3·46 W
	Cologne, see Köln			
164	Colomb-Béchar	Alg.	31·39 N	2·14 W
98	Colombia (kô-lôm'bê-ä)	Col. (In.)	3·23 N	74·48 W
96	Colombia	S. A.	3·30 N	72·30 W
143	Colombo (kô-lôm'bō)	Ceylon	6·58 N	79·52 E
101	Colón (kō-lōn')	Arg. (Buenos Aires In.)	33·55 S	61·08 W
88	Colón (kŏ-lô'n)	C. Z. (Panama Canal In.)	9·22 N	79·54 W
94	Colón (kô-lô'n)	Cuba	22·45 N	80·55 W
90	Colón (kō-lōn')	Mex.	20·46 N	100·02 W
98	Colon, Arch. de (Galápagos Is.) (är-chē-pyĕ'l-ägô-dĕ-kō-lōn') (gä-lä'pägôs)	Ec.	0·10 S	87·45 W
93	Colōn, Montañas de (Mts.) (môn-tä'n-yäs-dĕ-kŏ-lô'n)	Hond.	14·58 N	84·39 W
101	Colonia (kō-lō'nê-ä)	Ur. (Buenos Aires In.)	34·27 S	57·50 W
101	Colonia (Dept.)	Ur. (Buenos Aires In.)	34·08 S	57·50 W
101	Colonia Suiza (kô-lô'nêä-sōōē'zä)	Ur. (Buenos Aires In.)	34·17 S	57·15 W
125	Colonna (kô-lô'n-nä)	It. (Roma In.)	41·50 N	12·48 E
127	Colonne, C. di (kô-lō'n-nĕ)	It.	39·02 N	17·15 E
116	Colonsay (I.) (kŏl-ôn-sā')	Scot.	56·08 N	6·08 W
76	Colorado (kŏl-ô-rä'dō)	Tex.	32·24 N	100·50 W
62	Colorado (State)	U. S.	39·30 N	106·55 W
62	Colorado, R.	U. S.	36·25 N	112·00 W
100	Colorado, Rio (R.)	Arg.	38·30 S	66·00 W
69	Colorado Natl. Mon.	Colo.	39·00 N	108·40 W
62	Colorado Plat.	U. S.	36·20 N	109·25 W
77	Colorado R.	Tex.	30·08 N	97·33 W
69	Colorado River Ind. Res.	Ariz.	34·03 N	114·02 W
68	Colorado River Aqueducts	Calif.	33·38 N	115·43 W
100	Colorados, Lomas (Hills) (lô'mäs-kō-lō-rä'däs)	Arg.	43·30 S	68·00 W
94	Colorados, Arch. de los (Is.) (är-chē-pyĕ-lä-gô-dĕ-lôs-kô-lô-rä'dōs)	Cuba	22·25 N	84·25 W
72	Colorado Springs (kŏl-ô-rä'dō)	Colo.	38·49 N	104·48 W
91	Colotepec (R.) (kô-lô'tĕ-pĕk)	Mex.	15·56 N	96·57 W
90	Colotlán (kô-lô-tlän')	Mex.	22·06 N	103·14 W
90	Colotlán (R.)	Mex.	22·09 N	103·17 W
98	Colquechaca (kôl-kā-chä'kä)	Bol.	18·47 S	66·02 W
67	Colstrip (kōl'strĭp)	Mont.	45·54 N	106·38 W
74	Colton (kōl'tŭn)	Calif. (Los Angeles In.)	34·04 N	117·20 W
74	Columbia (kô-lŭm'bĭ-ȧ)	Ill. (St. Louis In.)	38·26 N	90·12 W
78	Columbia	Ky.	37·06 N	85·15 W
78	Columbia	Miss.	31·15 N	89·49 W
73	Columbia	Mo.	38·55 N	92·19 W
81	Columbia	Pa.	40·00 N	76·25 W
79	Columbia	S. C.	34·00 N	81·00 W
78	Columbia	Tenn.	35·36 N	87·02 W
80	Columbia City	Ind.	41·10 N	85·30 W
65	Columbia City	Ore. (Portland In.)	45·53 N	122·49 W
74	Columbia Heights	Minn. (Minneapolis, St. Paul In.)	45·03 N	93·15 W
78	Columbiana (kô-lŭm-bĭ-ă'nȧ)	Ala.	33·10 N	86·35 W
62	Columbia R.	U. S.-Can.	46·20 N	123·00 W
125	Columbretes (I.) (kô-lōōm-brĕ'tĕs)	Sp.	39·54 N	0·54 E
78	Columbus (kô-lŭm'bŭs)	Ga.	32·29 N	84·56 W
80	Columbus	Ind.	39·15 N	85·55 W
73	Columbus	Kans.	37·10 N	94·50 W
78	Columbus	Miss.	33·30 N	88·25 W
67	Columbus	Mont.	45·39 N	109·15 W
70	Columbus	Nebr.	41·25 N	97·25 W
69	Columbus	N. Mex.	31·50 N	107·40 W
80	Columbus	Ohio	40·00 N	83·00 W
77	Columbus	Tex.	29·44 N	96·34 W
71	Columbus	Wis.	43·20 N	89·01 W

Page	Name Pronunciation	Region	Lat. °'	Long. °'
95	Columbus Bk. (kô-lŭm'bŭs)	Ba. Is.	22·05 N	75·30 W
80	Columbus Grove	Ohio	40·55 N	84·00 W
95	Columbus Pt.	Ba. Is.	24·10 N	75·15 W
68	Colusa (kô-lū'sȧ)	Calif.	39·12 N	122·01 W
66	Colville (kŏl'vĭl)	Wash.	48·33 N	117·53 W
64	Colville (R.)	Alaska	69·00 N	156·25 W
66	Colville R.	Wash.	48·25 N	117·58 W
65	Colvos Pass. (kōl'vōs)	Wash. (Seattle In.)	47·24 N	122·32 W
65	Colwood (kŏl'wŏŏd)	Can. (Seattle In.)	48·26 N	123·30 W
126	Comacchio (kô-mäk'kyō)	It.	44·42 N	12·12 E
90	Comala (kō-mä-lä')	Mex.	19·22 N	103·47 W
92	Comalapa (kō-mä-lä'-pä)	Guat.	14·43 N	90·56 W
91	Comalcalco (kō-mäl-käl'kō)	Mex.	18·16 N	93·13 W
72	Comanche (kô-măn'chê)	Okla.	34·20 N	97·58 W
76	Comanche	Tex.	31·54 N	98·37 W
76	Comanche Cr.	Tex.	31·02 N	102·47 W
92	Comayagua (kō-mä-yä'gwä)	Hond.	14·24 N	87·36 W
79	Combahee (R.) (kŏm-bȧ-hē')	S. C.	32·42 N	80·40 W
78	Comer (kŭm'ēr)	Ga.	34·02 N	83·07 W
95	Comete, C. (kô-mā'tȧ)	Ba. Is.	21·45 N	71·25 W
142	Comilla (kô-mĭl'ä)	E. Pak.	23·33 N	91·17 E
126	Comino, C. (kô-mē'nō)	It.	40·30 N	9·48 E
91	Comitán (kô-mē-tän')	Mex.	16·16 N	92·09 W
65	Commencement Bay (kŏ-mĕns'mĕnt bā)	Wash. (Seattle In.)	47·17 N	122·21 W
122	Commentry (kô-mäN-trē')	Fr.	46·16 N	2·44 E
78	Commerce (kŏm'ērs)	Ga.	34·10 N	83·27 W
73	Commerce	Okla.	36·57 N	94·54 W
73	Commerce	Tex.	33·15 N	95·52 W
85	Como (kō'mō)	Can. (Montreal In.)	45·27 N	74·08 W
126	Como	It.	45·48 N	9·03 E
126	Como, Lago di (L.) (lä'gō-dē-kō'mō)	It.	46·00 N	9·30 E
100	Comodoro Rivadavia (kō'mô-dō'rô rē-vä-dä'vê-ä)	Arg.	45·47 S	67·31 W
90	Comonfort (kô-mōn-fô'rt)	Mex.	20·43 N	100·47 W
167	Comores, Archipel des (Is.) (är-chē-pĕ'lä-gô-dĕs-kô-mô'rĕs)	Afr.	11·46 S	44·12 E
143	Comorin C. (kŏ'mô-rĭn)	Ind.	13·18 N	77·16 E
91	Compainalá (kôm-pä-ē-nä-lä')	Mex.	17·05 N	93·11 W
101	Companario, Cerro (Mtn.) (sĕ'r-rô-kôm-pä-nä'ryō)	Arg.-Chile (Santiago In.)	35·54 S	70·23 W
122	Compiègne (kôN-pyĕn'y')	Fr.	49·25 N	2·49 E
125	Comporta (kôm-pôr'tȧ)	Port.	38·24 N	8·48 W
90	Compostela (kōm-pô-stā'lä)	Mex.	21·41 N	104·54 W
74	Compton (kŏmp'tŭn)	Calif. (Los Angeles In.)	33·54 N	118·14 W
78	Cona (R.) (kô-nȧ)	Ga.	34·40 N	84·51 W
164	Conakry (kô-nȧ-krē')	Gui.	9·29 N	13·45 W
84	Conanicut (kŏ'ȧ-nĭ-kŭt)	R. I. (Providence In.)	41·34 N	71·20 W
122	Concarneau (kôN-kär-nō')	Fr.	47·54 N	3·52 W
99	Concepción (kôn-sĕp'syōn')	Bol.	15·47 S	61·08 W
100	Concepción	Chile	36·51 S	72·59 W
93	Concepcion	Pan.	8·31 N	82·38 W
100	Concepción	Par.	23·29 S	57·18 W
155	Concepcion	Phil. (Manila In.)	15·19 N	120·40 E
88	Concepción (R.)	Mex.	30·25 N	112·20 W
92	Concepción (Vol.)	Nic.	11·36 N	85·43 W
92	Concepcion del Mar (kôn-sĕp-syōn' dĕl mär')	Guat.	14·07 N	91·23 W
76	Concepcion del Oro (kôn-sĕp-syōn' dĕl ō'rō)	Mex.	24·39 N	101·24 W
100	Concepción del Uruguay (kôn-sĕp-syô'n-dĕl-ōō-rōō-gwī')	Ur.	32·31 S	53·13 W
95	Conception (I.)	Ba. Is.	23·50 N	75·05 W
68	Conception, Pt.	Calif.	34·27 N	120·28 W
83	Conception B. (kŏn-sĕp'shŭn)	Can.	47·50 N	52·50 W
76	Concho R. (kŏn'chō)	Tex.	31·34 N	100·02 W
76	Conchos R.	Mex.	29·08 N	105·02 W
76	Conchos R. (kōn'chōs)	Mex.	25·03 N	99·00 W
65	Concord (kŏŋ'kŏrd)	Calif. (San Francisco In.)	37·58 N	122·02 W
83	Concord	Mass. (Boston In.)	42·28 N	71·21 W
81	Concord	N. H.	43·10 N	71·30 W
79	Concord	N. C.	35·23 N	80·11 W
100	Concordia (kôn-kôr'dĭ-ä)	Arg.	31·18 S	57·59 W
98	Concordia	Col. (In.)	6·04 N	75·54 W
73	Concordia	Kans.	39·32 N	97·39 W
90	Concordia (kôn-kô'r-dyä)	Mex.	23·17 N	106·06 W
66	Concrete (kŏn'krēt)	Wash.	48·33 N	121·44 W
70	Conde (kŏn-dē')	S. D.	45·10 N	98·06 W
92	Condega (kŏn-dĕ'gä)	Nic.	13·20 N	86·27 W
122	Condem (kôn-dĕN)	Fr.	43·58 N	0·22 E
113	Condé-Smendou (kôN-dā'smäN-dōō')	Alg.	36·34 N	6·51 E
122	Condé-sur-Noireau (kôN-dā'sūr-nwä-rō')	Fr.	48·50 N	0·36 W
99	Condeúba (kōn-dā-ōō'bä)	Braz.	14·47 S	41·44 W
66	Condon (kŏn'dŭn)	Ore.	45·14 N	120·10 W
78	Conecun (R.) (kô-nē'kŭ)	Ala.	31·05 N	86·52 W
126	Conegliano (kō-nål-yä'nō)	It.	45·59 N	12·17 E
69	Conejos (R.) (kô-nā'hōs)	Colo.	37·07 N	106·19 W
81	Conemaugh (kŏn'ē-mô)	Pa.	40·25 N	78·50 W
84	Coney I. (kō'nĭ)	N. Y. (New York In.)	40·34 N	73·27 W
122	Confolens (kôN-fä-läN')	Fr.	46·01 N	0·41 E
79	Congaree (R.) (kŏŋ-gȧ-rē')	S. C.	33·53 N	80·55 W
110	Congleton (kŏŋ'g'l-tŭn)	Eng.	53·10 N	2·13 W
166	Congo (Reg.) (kŏŋ'gō)	Ang.	6·40 S	14·00 E
163	Congo (Republic of Congo)	Afr.	3·00 S	13·48 E
163	Congo, The (Republic of The Congo)	Afr.	1·00 S	22·15 E
163	Congo Basin	Con. L.	2·47 N	20·58 E
163	Congo R.	Afr.	2·00 S	17·01 E
110	Conisbrough (kŏn'ĭs-bŭr-ō)	Eng.	53·29 N	1·13 W
143	Conjeeveram (kŏn'ĭs-bŭr-o)	India	12·55 N	79·43 E
84	Conley (kŏn'lĭ)	Ga. (Atlanta In.)	33·38 N	84·19 W
116	Conn, Lough (B.) (lŏk kŏn)	Ire.	53·56 N	9·25 W

Page	Name Pronunciation	Region	Lat. °'	Long. °'
116	Connacht (cŏn'ȧt)	Ire.	53·50 N	8·45 W
80	Conneaut (kŏn-ê-ôt')	Ohio	41·55 N	80·35 W
63	Connecticut (State) (kŏ-nĕt'ĭ-kŭt)	U. S.	41·40 N	73·10 W
81	Connecticut R.	U. S.	43·55 N	72·15 W
81	Connellsville (kŏn'nĕlz-vĭl)	Pa.	40·00 N	79·40 W
116	Connemara, Mts. (kŏn-nê-mȧ'rȧ)	Ire.	53·30 N	9·54 W
80	Connersville (kŏn'ērz-vĭl)	Ind.	39·35 N	85·10 W
159	Connors Ra. (kŏn'nŏrs)	Austl.	22·15 S	149·00 E
67	Conrad (kŏn'răd)	Mont.	48·11 N	111·56 W
85	Conrich (kŏn'rĭch)	Can. (Calgary In.)	51·06 N	113·51 W
77	Conroe (kŏn'rō)	Tex.	30·18 N	95·23 W
101	Conselheiro Lafaiete (kŏn-sĕ-lā'rô-lȧ-fā'ĕ-tĕ)	Braz. (Rio de Janeiro In.)	20·40 S	43·46 W
84	Conshohocken (kŏn-shô-hŏk'ĕn)	Pa. (Philadelphia In.)	40·04 N	75·18 W
94	Consolación (kōn-sô-lä-syōn')	Cuba	22·30 N	83·55 W
155	Consolacion (kôn-sô-lä-syô'n)	Phil. (Manila In.)	16·20 N	120·21 E
65	Constance, Mt. (kŏn'stăns)	Wash. (Seattle In.)	47·46 N	123·08 W
115	Constanța (kōn-stån'tsȧ)	Bul.	44·12 N	28·36 E
166	Constantia (kŏn-stăn-tĭ-ȧ)	S. Afr. (Cape Town In.)	34·01 S	18·25 E
166	Constantia Mts.	S. Afr. (Cape Town In.)	34·03 S	18·23 E
124	Constantina (kŏn-stän-tē'nä)	Sp.	37·52 N	5·39 W
164	Constantine (kôN-stäN'tēn')	Alg.	36·28 N	6·38 E
80	Constantine (kŏn'stȧn-tēn)	Mich.	41·50 N	85·40 W
64	Constantine Harbor	Alaska	51·22 N	179·20 E
100	Constitución (kōn'stĭ-tōō-syōn')	Chile	35·24 S	72·25 W
84	Constitution (kŏn-stĭ-tū'shŭn)	Ga. (Atlanta In.)	33·41 N	84·20 W
101	Contagem (kōn-tȧ'zhĕm)	Braz. (Rio de Janerio In.)	19·54 S	44·05 W
90	Contepec (kōn-tĕ-pĕk')	Mex.	20·04 N	100·07 W
91	Contreras (kôn-trĕ'räs)	Mex. (Mexico In.)	19·18 N	99·14 W
74	Converse (kŏn'vērs)	Tex. (San Antonio In.)	29·31 N	98·17 W
73	Conway (kŏn'wā)	Ark.	35·06 N	92·27 W
81	Conway	N. H.	44·00 N	71·10 W
79	Conway	S. C.	33·49 N	79·01 W
65	Conway	Wash. (Seattle In.)	48·20 N	122·20 W
78	Conyers (kŏn'yērz)	Ga.	33·41 N	84·01 W
142	Cooch-Bèhar	India	26·25 N	89·34 E
159	Cook, Mt.	N. Z. (In.)	43·27 S	170·13 E
78	Cookeville (kŏŏk'vĭl)	Tenn.	36·07 N	85·30 W
167	Cookhouse (kŏŏk'hous)	S. Afr. (Natal In.)	32·44 S	25·49 E
85	Cooking Lake (kŏŏk'ĭng)	Can. (Edmonton In.)	53·10 N	113·08 W
85	Cooking L. (kŏŏk'ĭng)	Can. (Edmonton In.)	53·26 N	113·03 W
64	Cook Inlet (kŏŏk)	Alaska	60·50 N	151·38 W
157	Cook Is.	Oceania	19·20 S	158·00 W
159	Cook Str.	N. Z. (In.)	40·37 S	174·15 E
85	Cooksville (kŏŏkz'vĭl)	Can. (Toronto In.)	43·34 N	79·37 W
159	Cooktown (kŏŏk'toun)	Austl.	15·40 S	145·20 E
79	Cooleemee (kōō-lē'mē)	N. C.	35·50 N	80·32 W
158	Coolgardie (kōōl-gär'dê)	Austl.	31·00 S	121·25 E
160	Cooma (kōō'mȧ)	Austl.	36·22 S	149·10 E
160	Coonamble (kōō-năm'b'l)	Austl.	30·50 S	144·27 E
74	Coon Creek (kōōn)	Minn. (Minneapolis, St. Paul In.)	45·09 N	93·17 W
143	Coonoort	India	10·22 N	76·15 E
73	Cooper (kōōp'ēr)	Tex.	33·23 N	95·40 W
64	Cooper Center (kōōp'ēr sĕn'tēr)	Alaska	61·54 N	145·30 W
160	Coopers Cr. (kōō'pērz)	Austl.	27·32 S	141·19 E
81	Cooperstown	N. Y.	42·45 N	74·55 W
70	Cooperstown (kōōp'ērs-toun)	N. D.	47·26 N	98·07 W
160	Coorong, The (L.) (kōō'rŏng)	Austl.	36·07 S	139·45 E
78	Coosa (kōō'sȧ)	Ala.	32·43 N	86·25 W
79	Coosa (R.)	Ala.	34·09 N	85·50 W
78	Coosawattee (R.) (kōō-sȧ-wôt'ē)	Ga.	34·37 N	84·45 W
66	Coos Bay (kōōs)	Ore.	43·21 N	124·12 W
66	Coos B. (kōōs)	Ore.	43·19 N	124·40 W
160	Cootamundra (kōōtȧ-mŭnd'rȧ)	Austl.	34·25 S	148·00 E
100	Copacabana (kô'pä-kȧ-bȧ'nȧ)	Braz. (In.)	22·57 S	43·11 W
91	Copalita (R.) (kô-pä-lē'tä)	Mex.	15·55 N	96·06 W
92	Copán (Ruins) (kō-pän')	Hond.	14·50 N	89·10 W
77	Copano B. (kō-pän'ō)	Tex.	28·08 N	97·25 W
	Copenhagen, see København			
100	Copiapó (kō-pyä-pō')	Chile	27·16 S	70·28 W
75	Copley (kŏp'lē)	Ohio (Cleveland In.)	41·06 N	81·38 W
126	Copparo (kôp-pä'rō)	It.	44·53 N	11·50 E
74	Coppell (kŏp'pĕl)	Tex. (Dallas, Fort Worth In.)	32·57 N	97·00 W
64	Copper (R.) (kŏp'ēr)	Alaska	62·38 N	145·00 W
78	Copperhill (kŏp'ēr hĭl)	Tenn.	35·00 N	84·22 W
86	Coppermine (kŏp'ēr-mīn)	Can.	67·46 N	115·19 W
86	Copperinine (R.)	Can.	66·48 N	114·59 W
74	Copperton (kŏp'ēr-tŭn)	Utah (Salt Lake City In.)	40·34 N	112·06 W
165	Coquilhatville (kô-kē'yȧ-vēl')	Con. L.	0·01 N	18·17 E
66	Coquille (kô-kēl')	Ore.	43·11 N	124·11 W
100	Coquimbo (kô-kēm'bō)	Chile	29·58 S	71·31 W
101	Coquimbo (kô-kēm'bō) (Prov.)	Chile (Santiago In.)	31·50 S	71·05 W
65	Coquitlam (Mtn.) (kō-kwĭt-lȧm)	Can. (Vancouver In.)	49·23 N	122·44 W
127	Corabia (kô-rä'bĭ-ȧ)	Rom.	43·45 N	24·29 E

ăt; finȧl; rāte; senāte; ärm; ȧsk; sofȧ; fâre; ch-choose; dh-as th in other; bē; êvent; bĕt; recĕnt; cratēr; g-go; gh-guttural g; bĭt; ĭ-short neutral; rīde; K-guttural k as ch in German ich;

Page	Name	Pronunciation	Region	Lat. °'	Long. °'
98	Coracora	(kō'rä-kō'rä)	Peru	15·12 s	73·42 w
79	Coral Gables		Fla. (In.)	25·43 N	80·14 w
94	Coralillo	(kō-rä-lē-yō)	Cuba	73·00 N	80·40 w
87	Coral Rapids	(kŏr'ăl)	Can.	50·18 N	81·49 w
75	Coral Ridge	(kŏr'ăl)	Ky. (Louisville In.)	38·05 N	85·42 w
156	Coral Sea	(kŏr'ăl)	Oceania	13·30 s	150·00 E
160	Corangamite	(L.) (cŏr-ăng'á-mīt)	Austl.	38·05 s	142·55 E
75	Coraopolis	(kō-rä-ŏp'ŏ-lĭs)	Pa. (Pittsburgh In.)	40·31 N	80·10 w
126	Corato	(kō'rä-tô)	It.	41·08 N	16·28 E
123	Corbeil-Essonnes	(kŏr-bā'yĕ-sŏn')	Fr. (Paris In.)	48·31 N	2·29 E
65	Corbett	(kŏr'bĕt)	Ore. (Portland In.)	45·31 N	122·17 w
122	Corbie	(kŏr-bē')	Fr.	49·55 N	2·27 E
78	Corbin	(kŏr'bĭn)	Ky.	36·55 N	84·06 w
110	Corby	(kŏr'bĭ)	Eng.	52·50 N	0·32 w
100	Corcovado	(Mtn.) (kŏr-kō-vä'dhō)	Braz. (In.)	22·57 s	43·13 w
100	Corcovado, Golfo	(G.) (kŏr-kô-vä'dhō)	Chile	43·40 s	75·00 w
101	Cordeiro	(kŏr-dā'rō)	Braz. (Rio de Janeiro In.)	22·03 s	42·22 w
78	Cordele	(kôr-dēl')	Ga.	31·55 N	83·50 w
72	Cordell	(kŏr-dĕl')	Okla.	35·19 N	98·58 w
124	Cordillera Cantabrica	(Mts.) (kŏr-dēl-yĕ'rä-kän-tä'brē-kä)	Sp.	43·05 N	6·05 w
155	Cordillera Central	(Mts.) (kŏr-dēl-yĕ'rä-sĕn'trāl)	Phil. (Manila In.)	17·05 N	120·55 E
49	Cordilleran Highlands	(Reg.) (kŏr dĭl'lŭr ăn)	N. A.	55·00 N	125·00 w
100	Córdoba	(kŏr'dô-vä)	Arg.	30·20 s	64·03 w
91	Córdoba	(kŏ'r-dô-bä)	Mex.	18·53 N	96·54 w
124	Córdoba	(kŏ'r-dô-bä)	Sp.	37·55 N	4·45 w
100	Córdoba (Prov.)	(kŏr'dô-vä)	Arg.	32·00 s	64·00 w
100	Córdoba, Sa. de	(Mts.)	Arg.	31·15 s	64·30 w
78	Cordova	(kŏr'dô-à)	Ala.	33·45 N	86·11 w
64	Cordova	(kŏr'dô-vä)	Alaska	60·34 N	145·38 w
124	Corella	(kō-rĕl'yä)	Sp.	42·07 N	1·48 w
126	Corigliano	(kō-rē-lyä'nō)	It.	39·35 N	16·30 E
78	Corinth	(kŏr'ĭnth)	Miss.	34·55 N	88·30 w
	Corinth, see Korinthos				
99	Corinto	(kô-rē'n-tō)	Braz.	18·20 s	44·16 w
98	Corinto	(kŏr-ĭn'tō)	Col. (In.)	3·09 N	76·12 w
92	Corinto	(kŏr-ĭn'to)	Nic.	12·30 N	87·12 w
161	Corio	Austl. (Melbourne In.)		38·05 s	144·22 E
161	Corio B.	Austl. (Melbourne In.)		38·07 s	144·25 E
116	Cork	(kôrk)	Ire.	51·54 N	8·25 w
116	Cork Hbr		Ire.	51·50 N	8·15 w
126	Corleone	(kŏr-lâ-ō'nä)	It.	37·48 N	13·18 E
127	Corlu	(chôr'lōō)	Tur.	41·09 N	27·48 E
78	Cornelia	(kŏr-nē'lyá)	Ga.	34·31 N	83·30 w
168	Cornelis R.	S. Afr. (Johannesburg & Pretoria In.)		27·48 s	29·15 E
74	Cornell	(kôr-nĕl')	Calif. (Los Angeles In.)	34·06 N	118·46 w
71	Cornell		Wis.	45·10 N	91·10 w
83	Corner Brook	(kôr'nēr)	Can.	48·58 N	57·49 w
160	Corner Inlet		Austl.	38·55 s	146·45 E
	Corneta, see Targuinia				
73	Corning	(kŏr'nĭng)	Ark.	36·26 N	90·35 w
71	Corning		Iowa	40·58 N	94·40 w
81	Corning		N. Y.	42·10 N	77·05 w
126	Corno, M. (Mtn.)	(kŏr'nō)	It.	42·28 N	13·37 E
94	Cornwall		Ba. Is.	25·35 N	77·15 w
81	Cornwall	(kôrn'wôl)	Can.	45·05 N	74·35 w
116	Cornwall Pen.	(kôrn'wôl)	Eng.	50·25 N	5·04 w
98	Coro		Ven.	11·22 N	69·43 w
98	Corocoro	(kō-rô-kō'rō)	Bol.	17·15 s	68·21 w
143	Coromandel Coast	(kŏr-ô-man'dĕl)	India	17·50 N	80·14 E
78	Corona	(kō-rō'nä)	Ala.	33·42 N	87·28 w
74	Corona	Calif. (Los Angeles In.)		33·52 N	117·34 w
93	Coronada, Bahia de	(B.) (bä-ē'ä-dĕ-kô-rō-nä'dō)	C.R.	8·47 N	84·04 w
74	Corona del Mar	(kō-rō'ná dĕl mǎr)	Calif. (Los Angeles In.)	33·36 N	117·53 w
68	Coronado	(kŏr-ô-nä'dō)	Calif. (San Diego In.)	32·42 N	117·12 w
86	Coronation G.	(kŏr-ô-nä'shŭn)	Can.	68·07 N	112·50 w
100	Coronel	(kō-rô-nĕl')	Chile	37·00 s	73·10 w
101	Coronel Brandsen	(kŏ-rô-nĕl-brä'nd-sĕn)	Arg. (Buenos Aires In.)	35·09 s	58·15 w
100	Coronel Dorrego	(kŏ-rô-nĕl-dôr-rĕ'gô)	Arg.	38·43 s	61·16 w
100	Coronel Oviedo	(kŏ-rô-nĕl-ô-vē̆'dô)	Par.	25·28 s	56·22 w
100	Coronel Pringles	(kŏ-rô-nĕl-prēn'glĕs)	Arg.	37·54 s	61·22 w
100	Coronel Suárez	(kŏ-rô-nĕl-swä'räs)	Arg.	37·24 s	66·49 w
99	Coronie		Sur.	5·51 N	56·17 w
160	Corowa	(cŏr-ōwä)	Austl.	36·05 s	146·20 E
92	Corozal	(cŏr-ŏth-äl')	Br. Hond. (Yucatan In.)	18·25 N	88·23 w
77	Corpus Christi	(kŏr'pŭs krĭs'tē)	Tex.	27·48 N	97·24 w
77	Corpus Christi B.		Tex.	27·47 N	97·14 w
76	Corpus Christi L.		Tex.	28·08 N	98·20 w
100	Corral	(kô-räl')	Chile	39·57 s	73·15 w
124	Corral de Almaguer	(kŏr-räl'dä äl-mä-gâr')	Sp.	39·45 N	3·10 w
155	Corregidor	(I.) (kô-rä-hē-dôr')	Phil. (Manila In.)	14·21 N	120·25 E
99	Correntina	(kô-rĕn-tē-nä')	Braz.	13·18 s	44·33 w
116	Corrib, Lough	(B.) (lŏk kŏr'ĭb)	Ire.	53·56 N	9·19 w
100	Corrientes	(kō-ryĕn'täs)	Arg.	27·25 s	58·39 w
100	Corrientes (Prov.)		Arg.	28·45 s	58·00 w
98	Corrientes, Cabo	(C.) (ká'bô-kō-ryĕn'täs)	Col.	5·34 N	77·35 w

Page	Name	Pronunciation	Region	Lat. °'	Long. °'
94	Corrientes, Cabo	(C.) (ká'bô-kŏr-rē-ĕn'tĕs)	Cuba	21·50 N	84·25 w
94	Corrientes, Ensenada de	(B.) (ĕn-sĕ-nä-dä-dĕ-kō-ryĕn'täs)	Cuba	21·45 N	84·45 w
90	Corrientes, Cabo	(C.)	Mex.	20·25 N	105·41 w
81	Cory	(kŏr'ĭ)	Pa.	41·55 N	79·40 w
126	Corse, C.	(kôrs)	Fr.	42·59 N	9·19 E
77	Corsicana	(kŏr-sĭ-kăn'á)	Tex.	32·06 N	96·28 w
126	Corsica	(I.)	Fr.	42·10 N	8·55 E
90	Cortazar	(kôr-tä-zär')	Mex.	20·30 N	100·57 w
126	Corte	(kôr'tä)	Fr.	42·18 N	9·10 E
124	Cortegana	(kŏr-tà-gä'nä)	Sp.	37·54 N	6·48 w
124	Cortes	(kôr-täs')	Sp.	36·38 N	5·20 w
94	Cortés, Ensenada de	(B.) (ĕn-sĕ-nä-dä-dĕ-kôr-täs')	Cuba	22·05 N	83·45 w
81	Cortland	(kôrt'lănd)	N. Y.	42·35 N	76·10 w
126	Cortona	(kŏr-tō'nä)	It.	43·16 N	12·00 E
124	Coruche	(kō-rōō'she)	Port.	38·58 N	8·34 w
133	Coruh (R.)	(chō-rōōk')	Tur.	40·30 N	41·10 E
133	Corum	(chô-rōōm')	Tur.	39·30 N	34·50 E
99	Corumbá	(kō-rōōm-bä')	Braz.	19·01 s	57·28 w
80	Corunna	(kō-rŭn'á)	Mich.	43·00 N	84·05 w
99	Coruripe	(kō-rōō-rē'pĭ)	Braz.	10·09 s	36·13 w
66	Corvallis	(kŏr-vǎl'ĭs)	Ore.	44·34 N	123·17 w
110	Corve (R.)	(kŏr'vĕ)	Eng.	52·28 N	2·43 w
80	Corydon	(kŏr'ĭ-dŭn)	Ind.	38·10 N	86·05 w
71	Corydon		Iowa	40·45 N	93·20 w
80	Corydon		Ky.	37·45 N	87·40 w
91	Cosamaloápan	(kô-sä-mä-lwä'pän)	Mex.	18·21 N	95·48 w
91	Coscomatepec	(kôs'kōmä-tĕ-pĕk')	Mex.	19·04 N	97·03 w
110	Coseley	(kŏs'lē)	Eng.	52·33 N	2·10 w
126	Cosenza	(kô-zĕnt'sä)	It.	39·18 N	16·15 E
80	Coshocton	(kō-shŏk'tŭn)	Ohio	40·15 N	81·55 w
92	Cosigüina (Vol.)		Nic.	12·59 N	83·35 w
167	Cosmoledo Group	(Is.) (kŏs-mô-lä'dō)	Afr.	9·42 s	47·45 E
66	Cosmopolis	(kŏz-mŏp'ō-lĭs)	Wash.	46·58 N	123·47 w
122	Cosne-sur-Loire	(kōn-sür-lwär')	Fr.	47·25 N	2·57 E
91	Cosoleacaque	(kō sō lā-ä-kä'kē)	Mex.	18·01 N	94·38 w
74	Costa Mesa	(kŏs'tá mā'sá)	Calif. (Los Angeles In.)	33·39 N	118·54 w
89	Costa Rica	(kŏs'tá rē'kä)	N. A.	10·30 N	84·30 w
68	Cosumnes (R.)	(kô-sŭm'nĕz)	Calif.	38·21 N	121·17 w
98	Cotabambas	(kō-tä-bám'bäs)	Peru	13·49 s	72·17 w
155	Cotabato	(kō-tä-bä'tō)	Phil.	7·06 N	124·13 E
91	Cotaxtla	(kō-täs'tlä)	Mex.	18·49 N	96·22 w
91	Cotaxtla (R.)		Mex.	18·54 N	96·21 w
85	Coteau-du-Lac	(cō-tō'dü-lák)	Can. (Montreal In.)	45·17 N	74·11 w
85	Coteau Landing		Can. (Montreal In.)	45·15 N	74·13 w
95	Coteaux		Hai.	18·15 N	74·05 w
122	Côte d'Or	(hill) (kōt-dôr')	Fr.	47·02 N	4·35 E
90	Cotija de la Paz	(kō-tē'-kä-dĕ-lä-pä'z)	Mex.	19·46 N	102·43 w
164	Cotonou	(kō-tô-nōō')	Dahomey	6·26 N	2·19 E
98	Cotopaxi (Mtn.)	(kō-tô-päk'sĕ)	Ec.	0·40 s	78·26 w
95	Cotorro	(kô-tôr-rō)	Cuba (La Habana In.)	23·03 N	82·17 w
116	Cotswold Hills	(kŭtz'wōld)	Eng.	51·35 N	2·16 w
74	Cottage Grove	(kŏt'áj grōv)	Minn. (Minneapolis, St. Paul In.)	44·50 N	92·52 w
66	Cottage Grove		Ore.	43·48 N	123·04 w
120	Cottbus	(kŏtt'bōōs)	Ger.	51·47 N	14·20 E
123	Cottian Alps (Mts.)	(kŏt'tē-ŭn-älps)	Fr.-It.	44·46 N	7·02 E
70	Cottonwood (R.)	(kŏt'ŭn-wŏd)	Minn.	44·25 N	95·35 w
66	Cottonwood Cr.		Calif.	40·24 N	122·50 w
95	Cotui	(kō-tōō'ē)	Dom. Rep.	19·05 N	70·10 w
76	Cotulla	(kō-tŭl'lá)	Tex.	28·26 N	99·14 w
123	Coubert	(kōō-bâr')	Fr. (Paris In.)	48·40 N	2·43 E
81	Coudersport	(kou'dĕrz-port)	Pa.	41·45 N	78·00 w
82	Coudres, Ile-aux-		Can.	47·25 N	70·25 w
122	Couéron	(kōō-â-rôN')	Fr.	47·16 N	1·45 w
123	Coulommiers	(kōō-lô-myä')	Fr. (Paris In.)	48·49 N	3·05 E
100	Coulto, Serra do	(Mts.) (sĕ'r-rä-dō-kô-ōō'tô)	Braz. (In.)	22·33 s	43·27 w
64	Council	(koun'sĭl)	Alaska	64·55 N	163·40 w
70	Council Bluffs	(koun'sĭl blŭf)	Iowa	41·16 N	95·53 w
73	Council Grove	(koun'sĭl grōv)	Kans.	38·39 N	96·30 w
65	Coupeville	(kōōp'vĭl)	Wash. (Seattle In.)	48·13 N	122·41 w
99	Courantyne	(kôr'ăntĭn)	Br. Gu.-Sur.	4·28 N	57·42 w
86	Courtenay	(cōōrt-nā')	Can.	49·51 N	125·07 w
77	Coushatta	(kou-shăt'á)	La.	32·02 N	93·21 w
122	Coutras	(kōō-trä')	Fr.	45·02 N	0·07 w
110	Coventry	(kŭv'ĕn-trĭ)	Eng.	52·25 N	1·29 w
124	Covilhã	(kō-vēl'yăN)	Port.	40·18 N	7·29 w
74	Covina	(kō-vē'ná)	Calif. (Los Angeles In.)	34·06 N	117·54 w
78	Covington	(kŭv'ĭng-tŭn)	Ga.	33·36 N	83·50 w
80	Covington		Ind.	40·10 N	87·15 w
75	Covington	Ky. (Cincinnati In.)		39·05 N	84·31 w
77	Covington		La.	30·30 N	90·06 w
80	Covington		Ohio	40·10 N	84·20 w
73	Covington		Okla.	36·18 N	97·32 w
78	Covington		Tenn.	35·33 N	89·40 w
78	Covington		Va.	37·50 N	80·00 w
160	Cowal (R.)	(kou'ăl)	Austl.	33·30 s	147·10 E
158	Cowan (L.)	(kou'ăn)	Austl.	32·00 s	122·30 E
66	Cow Cr.	(kou)	Ore.	42·45 N	123·35 w
116	Cowes	(kouz)	Eng.	50·43 N	1·15 w
66	Cowlitz R.	(kou'lĭts)	Wash.	46·30 N	122·45 w
99	Coxim	(kō-shēN')	Braz.	18·32 s	54·43 w

Page	Name	Pronunciation	Region	Lat. °'	Long. °'
91	Coxquihui	(kōz-kē-wē')	Mex.	20·10 N	97·34 w
142	Coxs Bazar		E. Pak.	21·32 N	92·00 E
98	Coyaima	(kô-yä'-mä)	Col. (In.)	3·48 N	75·11 w
76	Coyame	(kō-yä'mä)	Mex.	29·26 N	105·05 w
76	Coyanosa Draw	(kŏ yä-nō'sä)	Tex.	30·55 N	103·07 w
91	Coyoacàn	(kō-yô-ä-kän')	Mex. (Mexico In.)	19·21 N	99·10 w
65	Coyote (R.)	(kī'ōt)	Calif. (San Francisco In.)	37·27 N	121·57 w
90	Coyuca de Benítez	(kō-yōō'kä dā bā-nē'täz)	Mex.	17·04 N	100·06 w
90	Coyuca de Catalán	(kō-yōō'kä dā kä-tä-län')	Mex.	18·19 N	100·41 w
91	Coyutla	(kō-yōō'tlä)	Mex.	20·13 N	97·40 w
72	Cozad	(kō'zăd)	Nebr.	40·53 N	99·59 w
75	Cozaddale	(kô-zăd-dāl)	Ohio (Cincinnati In.)	39·16 N	84·09 w
90	Cozoyoapan	(kô-zō-yô-ä-pä'n)	Mex.	16·45 N	98·17 w
92	Cozumel	(kŏ-zōō-mĕ'l)	Mex. (Yucatan In.)	20·31 N	86·55 w
92	Cozumel, Isla de	(I.) (ē's-lä-dĕ-kŏ-zōō-mĕ'l)	Mex. (Yucatan In.)	20·26 N	87·10 w
66	Crab Cr.	(krăb)	Wash.	46·47 N	119·43 w
66	Crab Cr.		Wash.	47·21 N	119·09 w
167	Cradock	(krä'dŭk)	S. Afr. (Natal In.)	32·12 s	25·38 E
75	Crafton	(krăf'tŭn)	Pa. (Pittsburgh In.)	40·26 N	80·04 w
67	Craig	(krāg)	Colo.	40·32 N	107·31 w
85	Craigs Road Station	(krāgz)	Can. (Quebec In.)	46·37 N	71·22 w
127	Craiova	(krà-yō'vä)	Rom.	44·18 N	23·50 E
81	Cranberry (L.)	(krăn'bĕr-ĭ)	N. Y.	44·10 N	74·50 w
161	Cranbourne	Austl. (Melbourne In.)		38·07 s	145·16 E
86	Cranbrook	(krăn'brōōk)	Can.	49·43 N	115·47 w
84	Cranbury	(krăn'bĕ-rĭ)	N. J. (New York In.)	40·19 N	74·31 w
71	Crandon	(krăn'dŭn)	Wis.	45·35 N	88·55 w
122	Cransac	(krän-zäk')	Fr.	44·28 N	2·19 E
84	Cranston	R. I. (Providence In.)		41·46 N	71·25 w
66	Crater L.	(krā'tẽr)	Ore.	42·58 N	122·08 w
66	Crater Lake Natl. Park		Ore.	42·58 N	122·40 w
67	Craters of the Moon Natl. Park		Idaho	43·28 N	113·15 w
99	Crateús	(krä-tä-ōōzh')	Braz.	5·09 s	40·35 w
99	Crato	(krä'tōō)	Braz.	7·19 s	39·13 w
70	Crawford	(krô'fẽrd)	Nebr.	42·41 N	103·25 w
65	Crawford	Wash. (Portland In.)		45·49 N	122·24 w
80	Crawfordsville	(krô'fẽrdz-vĭl)	Ind.	40·00 N	86·55 w
67	Crazy Mts.	(krā'zĭ)	Mont.	46·11 N	110·25 w
67	Crazy Woman Cr.		Wyo.	44·08 N	106·40 w
122	Crécy	(krā-sē')	Fr.	50·13 N	1·48 E
168	Crecy	(krĕ-sè)	S. Afr. (Johannesburg & Pretoria In.)	24·38 s	28·52 E
123	Crecy-en-Brie	(krä-sē'-ĕN-brē')	Fr. (Paris In.)	48·52 N	2·55 E
85	Credit R.	Can. (Toronto In.)		43·41 N	79·55 w
86	Cree (L.)	(krē)	Can.	57·35 N	107·52 w
70	Creighton	(krā'tŭn)	Nebr.	42·27 N	97·54 w
167	Creighton	(cre-tŏn)	S. Afr. (Natal In.)	30·02 s	29·52 E
122	Creil	(krĕ'y)	Fr.	49·18 N	2·28 E
126	Crema	(krā'mä)	It.	45·21 N	9·53 E
126	Cremona	(krā-mō'nä)	It.	45·09 N	10·02 E
123	Crépy-en-Valois	(krä-pē'-ĕN-vä-lwä')	Fr. (Paris In.)	49·14 N	2·53 E
126	Cres (Tsrĕs)		Yugo.	44·58 N	14·21 E
126	Cres (I.)		Yugo.	44·50 N	14·31 E
79	Crescent (R.)	(krĕs'ĕnt)	Fla.	29·33 N	81·30 w
79	Crescent Beach		Can. (Vancouver In.)	49·03 N	122·58 w
79	Crescent City		Fla.	29·26 N	81·35 w
66	Crescent L.		Ore.	43·25 N	121·58 w
71	Cresco	(krĕs'kō)	Iowa	43·23 N	92·07 w
66	Cresent City	(krĕs'ĕnt)	Calif.	41·46 N	124·13 w
69	Crested Butte	(krĕst'ĕd būt)	Colo.	38·50 N	107·00 w
74	Crestline	(krĕst-lĭn)	Calif. (Los Angeles In.)	34·15 N	117·17 w
80	Crestline		Ohio	40·50 N	82·40 w
74	Crestmore	(krĕst'mōr)	Calif. (Los Angeles In.)	34·02 N	117·23 w
86	Creston	(krĕs'tŭn)	Can.	49·09 N	116·32 w
71	Creston		Iowa	41·04 N	94·22 w
75	Creston		Ohio (Cleveland In.)	40·59 N	81·54 w
78	Crestview	(krĕst'vū)	Fla.	30·44 N	86·35 w
75	Crestwood	(krĕst'wŏod)	Ky. (Louisville In.)	38·20 N	85·28 w
75	Crete	(krēt)	Ill. (Chicago In.)	41·26 N	87·38 w
73	Crete		Nebr.	40·38 N	96·56 w
126	Crete (I.)		Grc. (Inset)	35·15 N	24·30 E
125	Creus, Cabo de	(C.) (kā'-bô-dĕ-krĕ-ōōs)	Sp.	42·16 N	3·18 E
122	Creuse (krûz)		Fr.	46·51 N	0·49 E
74	Creve Coeur	(krēv kŏr)	Mo. (St. Louis In.)	38·40 N	90·27 w
125	Crevillente	(krä-vē-lyĕn'tä)	Sp.	38·12 N	0·48 w
110	Crewe	(krōō)	Eng.	53·06 N	2·27 w
79	Crewe		Va.	37·09 N	78·08 w
	Crimea Poluostrov (Pen.), see Krymskiy				
120	Crimmitschau	(krĭm'ĭt-shou)	Ger.	50·49 N	12·22 E
72	Cripple Creek	(krĭp'l)	Colo.	38·44 N	105·12 w
81	Crisfield	(krĭs-fēld)	Md.	38·00 N	75·50 w
101	Cristina	Braz. (Rio de Janeiro In.)		22·13 s	45·15 w
98	Cristobal Colón, Pico	(pē'kô-krēs-tô'bäl-kō-lôn')	Col.	11·00 N	74·00 w
121	Crisul Alb R.	(krē'shōōl älb)	Rom.	46·20 N	22·15 E

Page	Name Pronunciation Region	Lat. °′	Long. °′
127	Crna (R.) (ts'r'nȧ) Yugo.	41·03 N	21·46 E
127	Črna Gora (Montenegro) (Reg.) (ts'r-nȧ-gō'rȧ) (môn-tȧ-nā'grō) (mōn-tê-nē'grō). Yugo.	42·55 N	18·52 E
126	Črnomelj (ch'r'nō-māl') Yugo.	45·35 N	15·11 E
	Croatia, see Hrvatska		
65	Crockett (krŏk'ĕt) Calif. (San Francisco In.)	38·03 N	122·14 W
77	Crockett Tex.	31·19 N	95·28 W
168	Crocodile R. (krŏ'kō-dīl) S. Afr. (Johannesburg & Pretoria In.)	24·25 S	27·08 E
70	Crofton (krŏf'tŭn) S. D.	45·25 N	98·04 W
71	Croix, Lac la (L.) (krōō-ä' läk lä). Can.-Minn.	48·19 N	91·53 W
158	Croker (krō'kẽr) Austl.	10·45 S	132·25 E
161	Cronulla (krō-nŭl'ȧ) Austl. (Sydney In.)	34·03 S	151·09 E
95	Crooked (I.) Ba. Is.	22·45 N	74·10 W
83	Crooked (L.) Can.	48·24 N	56·00 W
73	Crooked Cr. (krŏŏk'ĕd) Ill.	40·21 N	90·49 W
66	Crooked Cr. Ore.	42·23 N	118·14 W
95	Crooked Island Passage (Str.) Ba. Is.	22·40 N	74·50 W
66	Crooked R. Ore.	44·07 N	120·30 W
70	Crookston (krŏŏks'tŭn) Minn.	47·44 N	96·35 W
80	Crooksville (krŏŏks'vĭl) Ohio	39·45 N	82·05 W
71	Crosby (krôz'bĭ) Minn.	46·29 N	93·58 W
70	Crosby N. D.	48·55 N	103·18 W
77	Crosby Tex. (In.)	29·55 N	95·04 W
81	Cross (L.) (krôs) Can.	44·55 N	76·55 W
86	Cross (L.) Can.	54·40 N	98·47 W
73	Crossett (krôs'ĕt) Ark.	33·08 N	91·56 W
94	Cross Hbr. Ba. Is.	25·55 N	77·15 W
77	Cross L. La.	32·33 N	93·58 W
84	Cross River Res. (krôs) N. Y. (New York In.)	41·14 N	73·34 W
64	Cross Sd. (krŏs) Alaska	58·12 N	137·20 W
80	Crosswell (krōz'wĕl) Mich.	43·15 N	82·35 W
127	Crotone (krō-tô'nĕ) It.	39·05 N	17·08 E
84	Croton Falls Res. (krōtŭn) N. Y. (New York In.)	41·22 N	73·44 W
84	Croton-on-Hudson (krō'tŭn-ŏn hŭd'sŭn). N. Y. (New York In.)	41·12 N	73·53 W
71	Crow (L.) Can.	49·13 N	93·29 W
72	Crow Cr. Colo.	41·08 N	104·25 W
70	Crow Creek Ind. Res. S. D.	44·17 N	99·17 W
67	Crow Ind. Res. (krō) Mont.	45·26 N	108·12 W
110	Crowle (kroul) Eng.	53·36 N	0·49 W
77	Crowley (krou'lē) La.	30·13 N	92·22 W
89	Crown, Mt. Vir. Is. (U. S. A.) (St. Thomas In.)	18·22 N	64·58 W
65	Crown Mtn. (kroun) Can. (Vancouver In.)	49·24 N	123·05 W
75	Crown Point (kroun point') Ind. (Chicago In.)	41·25 N	87·22 W
81	Crown Point N. Y.	44·00 N	73·25 W
71	Crow Wing (R.) (krō) Minn.	44·50 N	94·01 W
71	Crow Wing (R.) Minn.	46·42 N	94·48 W
71	Crow Wing (R.), North Fork. Minn.	45·16 N	94·28 W
71	Crow Wing (R.), South Fork Minn.	44·59 N	94·42 W
159	Croydon (kroi'dŭn) Austl.	18·15 S	142·15 E
161	Croydon...Austl. (Melbourne In.)	37·48 S	145·17 E
110	Croydon...Eng. (London In.)	51·22 N	0·06 W
84	Croydon...Pa. (Philadelphia In.)	40·05 N	74·55 W
47	Crozet I. (krō-zĕ') Ind. O.	46·20 S	51·30 E
94	Cruces (krōō'sås) Cuba	22·20 N	80·20 W
76	Cruces, Arroyo de (är-rō'yō-dĕ-krōō'sĕs). Mex.	26·17 N	104·32 W
76	Cruillas (krōō-ēl'yäs) Mex.	24·45 N	98·31 W
94	Cruz, Cabo (C.) (kä'-bô-krōōz) Cuba	19·50 N	77·45 W
94	Cruz, Cayo (I.) (kä'yō-krōōz) Cuba	22·15 N	77·50 W
100	Cruz Alta (krōōz äl'tä) Braz.	28·41 S	54·02 W
100	Cruz del Eje (krōō's-dĕl-ĕ-kĕ). Arg.	30·46 S	64·45 W
101	Cruzeiro (krōō-zä'rōō) Braz. (Rio de Janeiro In.)	22·36 S	44·57 W
98	Cruzeiro do Sul (krōō-zā'rōō dōō sōōl). Braz.	7·34 S	72·40 W
85	Crysler Can. (Ottawa In.)	45·13 N	75·09 W
76	Crystal City (krĭs'tăl sĭ'tĭ) Tex.	28·40 N	99·90 W
71	Crystal Falls (krĭs'tăl fôls) Mich.	46·06 N	88·21 W
75	Crystal Lake (krĭs'tăl lāk) Ill. (Chicago In.)	42·15 N	88·18 W
78	Crystal Springs (krĭs'tăl springz) Miss.	31·58 N	90·20 W
65	Crystal Spr. (krĭs'tăl) Calif. (San Francisco In.)	37·31 N	122·26 W
121	Csongrád (chôn'grād) Hung.	46·42 N	20·09 E
121	Csorna (chôr'nä) Hung.	47·39 N	17·11 E
99	Cúa (kōō'ä) Ven. (In.)	10·10 N	66·54 W
91	Cuajimalpa (kwä-hê-mäl'pä) Mex. (Mexico In.)	19·21 N	99·18 W
90	Cuale, Sierra del (Mts.) (sē-ĕ'r-rä-dĕl-kwä'lĕ). Mex.	20·20 N	104·58 W
166	Cuamato (kwä-mä'tō) Ang.	17·05 S	15·15 E
166	Cuando (R.) (kwän'dō) Ang.	14·15 S	20·00 E
166	Cuango (kwäŋ'gō) Ang.	6·15 S	16·53 E
166	Cuanza (R.) (kwän'zä) Ang.	9·45 S	15·00 E
100	Cuarto Saladillo (R.) (kwär'tō-sä-lä-dē'l-yô). Arg.	33·00 S	63·25 W
95	Cuatro Caminos (kwä'trô-kä-mē'nōs). Cuba. (La Habana In.)	23·01 N	82·13 W
76	Cuatro Ciénegas (kwä'trō syā'nå-gäs). Mex.	26·59 N	102·03 W
92	Cuauhtemoc (kwä-ōō-tĕ-mŏk') Mex.	15·43 N	91·57 W
90	Cuautepec (kwä-ōō-tĕ-pĕk) Mex.	16·41 N	99·04 W
90	Cuautepec Mex.	20·01 N	98·19 W
91	Cuautitlán (kwä-ōō-tēt-län') Mex. (Mexico In.)	19·40 N	99·12 W
90	Cuautla (kwä-ōō'tlä) Mex.	18·47 N	98·57 W
124	Cuba (kōō'bȧ) Port.	38·10 N	7·55 W
89	Cuba (kū'bȧ) N. A.	22·00 N	79·00 W
99	Cubagua, Isla (ē's-lä-kōō-bä'gwä) Ven. (In.)	10·48 N	64·10 W
166	Cubango (R.) (kōō-bäŋ'gō) Ang.	15·45 S	18·00 E
74	Cucamonga (kōō-kȧ-mŏŋ'gȧ) Calif. (Los Angeles In.)	34·05 N	117·35 W
166	Cuchi Ang.	14·40 S	16·50 E
76	Cuchillo Parado (kōō-chē'lyō pä-rä'dō). Mex.	29·26 N	104·52 W
92	Cuchumatanes, Sierra de los (Mts.) Guat.	16·02 N	91·50 W
98	Cúcuta (kōō'kōō-tä) Col.	7·56 N	72·30 W
75	Cudahy (kŭd'ȧ-hī) Wis. (Milwaukee In.)	42·57 N	87·52 W
143	Cuddalore (kŭd ȧ-lōr') India	11·49 N	79·46 E
143	Cuddapah (kŭd'ȧ-pä) India	14·31 N	78·52 E
158	Cue (kū) Austl.	27·30 S	118·10 E
124	Cuellar (kwā'lyär') Sp.	41·24 N	4·15 W
98	Cuenca (kwĕn'kä) Ec.	2·52 S	78·54 W
124	Cuenca Sp.	40·05 N	2·07 W
124	Cuenca, Sierra de (Mts.) (sē-ĕ'r-rä-dĕ-kwĕ'n-kä). Sp.	40·02 N	1·50 W
76	Cuencame (kwĕn-kä-mā') Mex.	24·52 N	103·42 W
90	Cuerámaro (kwā-rä'mä-rō) Mex.	20·39 N	101·44 W
91	Cuernavaca (kwĕr-nä-vä'kä) Mex. (Mexico In.)	18·55 N	99·15 W
77	Cuero (kwā'rō) Tex.	29·05 N	97·16 W
90	Cuetzalá del Progreso (kwĕt-zä-lä dĕl prō-grā'sō). Mex.	18·07 N	99·51 W
91	Cuetzalan del Progreso (kwĕt-zä-län dĕl prō-grā'sō). Mex.	20·02 N	97·33 W
124	Cuevas del Almanzora (kwĕ'väs-dĕl-äl-män-zō-rä). Sp.	37·19 N	1·54 W
126	Cuglieri (kōō-lyâ'rē) It.	40·11 N	8·37 E
99	Cuiabá (kōō-yä-bä') Braz.	15·33 S	56·03 W
91	Cuicatlan (kwē-kä-tlän') Mex.	17·46 N	96·57 W
92	Cuilapa (kōō-ē-lä'pä) Guat.	14·16 N	90·20 W
116	Cuillin Sd. Scot.	57·00 N	6·20 W
166	Cuito (R.) (kōō-ē'tō) Ang.	14·30 S	19·10 E
90	Cuitzeo (kwēt'zā-ō) Mex.	19·57 N	101·11 W
90	Cuitzeo, Laguna de (L.) (lä-ōō'nä-dĕ-kwēt'zā-ō). Mex.	19·58 N	101·05 W
95	Cul de Sac (Val.) (kōō'l-dĕ-sä'k) Dom. Rep.-Hai.	18·35 N	72·05 W
89	Culebra (I.) (kōō-lā'brä) P. R. (Puerto Rico In.)	18·19 N	65·32 W
111	Culemborg Neth. (Amsterdam In.)	51·57 N	5·14 E
159	Culgoa (R.) (kŭl-gō'ȧ) Austl.	29·21 S	147·00 E
88	Culiacán (kōō-lyä-kä'n) Mex.	24·45 N	107·30 W
154	Culion (kōō-lê-ōn') Phil.	11·43 N	119·58 E
124	Cúllar de Baza (kōō'l-yär-dĕ-bä'zä). Sp.	37·36 N	2·35 W
125	Cullera (kōō-lyā'rä) Sp.	39·12 N	0·15 W
167	Cullinan (kŏŏ'lĭ-năn) S. Afr. (Johannesburg & Pretoria In.)	25·41 S	28·32 E
78	Cullman (kŭl'mȧn) Ala.	34·10 N	86·50 W
81	Culpeper (kŭl'pĕp-ẽr) Va.	38·30 N	77·55 W
85	Culross (kŭl'rôs) Can. (Winnipeg In.)	49·43 N	97·54 W
80	Culver (kŭl'vẽr) Ind.	41·15 N	86·25 W
74	Culver City Calif. (Los Angeles In.)	34·00 N	118·23 W
99	Cumaná (kōō-mä-nä') Ven. (In.)	10·28 N	64·10 W
85	Cumberland (kŭm'bẽr-lănd) Can. (Ottawa In.)	45·31 N	75·25 W
75	Cumberland Ind. (Indianapolis In.)	39·46 N	85·57 W
81	Cumberland Md.	39·40 N	78·40 W
65	Cumberland...Wash. (Seattle In.)	47·17 N	121·55 W
71	Cumberland Wis.	45·31 N	92·01 W
78	Cumberland, L. Ky.	36·55 N	85·20 W
63	Cumberland (R.) U. S.	36·30 N	87·40 W
159	Cumberland Is. Austl.	20·29 S	149·46 E
87	Cumberland Pen. Can.	65·59 N	64·05 W
78	Cumberland Plat. Tenn.	35·25 N	85·30 W
87	Cumberland Sd. Can.	65·27 N	65·44 W
98	Cundinamarca (Dept.) (kōōn-dē-nä-mä'r-kä). Col. (In)	4·57 N	74·27 W
91	Cunduacán (kōōn-dōō-ȧ-kän') Mex.	18·04 N	93·23 W
166	Cunene (Kunene) (R.) Ang.-S. W. Afr.	17·00 S	13·00 E
126	Cuneo (kōō'nā-ō) It.	44·24 N	7·31 E
101	Cunha (kōō'nyȧ) Braz. (Rio de Janeiro In.)	23·05 S	44·56 W
166	Cunjamba (kōōn-kä'm-bä) Ang.	15·45 S	20·15 E
160	Cunnamulla (kŭn-ȧ-mŭl-ȧ). Austl.	28·00 S	145·55 E
88	Cupula, Pico (Mtn.) (pē'kō-kōō'pōō-lä). Mex.	24·45 N	111·10 W
90	Cuquío (kōō-kē'ō) Mex.	20·55 N	103·03 W
98	Curaçao (kōō-rä-sä'ō) (I.) Neth. Antilles	12·12 N	68·58 W
100	Curacautín (kä-rä-kä'ōō-tē'n) Chile	38·25 S	71·53 W
101	Curacaví (kōō-rä-kä-vē') Chile (Santiago In.)	33·23 S	71·09 W
101	Curaumilla, Punta (Pt.) (kōō-rou-mē'lyä). Chile (Santiago In.)	33·05 S	71·44 W
101	Curepto (kōō-rĕp-tō) Chile (Santiago In.)	35·06 S	72·02 W
101	Curicó (kōō-rē-kō') Chile (Santiago In.)	34·57 S	71·14 W
101	Curico (Prov.) Chile (Santiago In.)	34·55 S	71·15 W
100	Curitiba (kōō-rē-tē'bä) Braz.	25·20 S	49·15 W
94	Curly Cut Cays (Is.) Ba. Is.	23·40 N	77·40 W
99	Currais Novos (kōōr-rä'ēs nō-vōs). Braz.	6·02 S	36·39 W
85	Curran (kü-räN') Can. (Ottawa In.)	45·30 N	74·00 W
94	Current (I.) (kŭ-rĕnt) Ba. Is.	25·20 N	76·50 W
73	Current (R.) (kûr'ĕnt) Mo.	37·18 N	91·21 W
167	Currie, Mt. (cŭ-rē) S. Afr. (Natal In.)	30·28 S	29·23 E
79	Currituck Sd. (kûr'ĭ-tŭk) N. C.	36·27 N	75·42 W
127	Curtea de Argeş (kōōr'tĕ-ä dĕ är'zhĕsh). Rom.	45·09 N	24·40 E
72	Curtis (kûr'tĭs) Nebr.	40·36 N	100·29 W
159	Curtis (I.) Austl.	23·38 S	151·43 E
75	Curtisville (kûr'tĭs-vĭl) Pa. (Pittsburgh In.)	40·38 N	79·50 W
99	Curuá (R.) (kōō-rōō-ä') Braz.	6·26 S	54·39 W
127	Ćurug (chōō'rōōg) Yugo.	45·27 N	20·06 E
98	Curupira, Serra (Mts.) (sĕr'rȧ kōō-rōō-pē'rȧ) Braz.-Ven.	1·00 N	65·30 W
99	Cururupu (kōō-rōō-rōō-pōō') Braz.	1·40 S	44·56 W
100	Curuzú Cuatiá (kōō-rōō-zōō' kwä-tê-ä'). Arg.	29·45 S	57·58 W
99	Curvelo (kōōr-vĕl'ōō) Braz.	18·47 S	44·14 W
73	Cushing (kŭsh'ĭng) Okla.	35·58 N	96 46 W
122	Cusset (kü-sĕ') Fr.	46·08 N	3·29 E
70	Custer (kŭs'tẽr) S. D.	43·46 N	103·36 W
65	Custer...Wash. (Vancouver In.)	48·55 N	122·39 W
67	Custer Battlefield Nat'l. Mon. (kŭs'tẽr băt''l-fēld). Mont.	45·44 N	107·15 W
67	Cut Bank (kŭt bănk) Mont.	48·38 N	112·19 W
78	Cuthbert (kŭth'bẽrt) Ga.	31·47 N	84·48 W
142	Cuttack (kŭ-tăk') India	20·38 N	85·53 E
90	Cutzamala (R.) (kōō-tzä-mä-lä') Mex.	18·57 N	100·41 W
90	Cutzamalá de Pinzón (kōō-tzä-mä-lä'dĕ-pēn-zô'n). Mex.	18·28 N	100·36 W
166	Cuvo (R.) (kōō'vō) Ang.	11·15 S	14·15 E
120	Cuxhaven (kŏŏks' hä-fĕn) Ger.	53·51 N	8·43 E
75	Cuyahoga Falls Ohio (Cleveland In.)	41·08 N	81·29 W
75	Cuyahoga R. (kī-ȧ-hō'gȧ) Ohio (Cleveland In.)	41·22 N	81·38 W
68	Cuyapaire Ind. Res. (kū-yȧ-pâr) Calif.	32·46 N	116·20 W
154	Cuyo Is. (kōō'yō) Phil.	10·54 N	120·08 E
92	Cuyotenango (kōō-yô-tĕ-näŋ'gô) Guat.	14·30 N	91·35 W
99	Cuyuni (R.) (kōō-yōō'nē) Br. Gu.-Ven.	6·40 N	60·44 W
90	Cuyutlán (kōō-yōō-tlän') Mex.	18·54 N	104·04 W
98	Cuzco Peru	13·36 S	71·52 W
80	Cynthiana (sĭn-thĭ-ăn'ȧ) Ky.	38·20 N	84·20 W
74	Cypress (sī'prĕs) Calif. (Los Angeles In.)	33·50 N	118·03 W
77	Cypress Cr. Tex.	32·49 N	94·35 W
115	Cyprus (sī'prŭs) Asia	34·56 N	31·28 E
102	Czechoslovakia (chĕk'ō-slō-vä'kĭ-ȧ). Eur.	49·28 N	16·00 E
121	Czersk (chĕrsk) Pol.	53·47 N	17·58 E
121	Czestochowa (chĕN-stô Kô'vȧ). Pol.	50·49 N	19·10 E
164	Dabakala (dä-bä-kä'lä) Ivory Coast	8·16 N	4·36 W
98	Dabeiba (dȧ-bā'bä) Col. (In.)	7·01 N	76·16 W
65	Dabob (dā'bŏb) Wash. (Seattle In.)	47·50 N	122·49 W
65	Dabob B. Wash. (Seattle In.)	47·44 N	122·50 W
165	Dabra-Mārk'os Eth.	10·15 N	37·45 E
165	Dabra-Tābor Eth.	11·57 N	38·09 E
121	Dabrowa (dŏN-brō'vä) Pol.	53·37 N	23·18 E
168	Dābūd U. A. R. (Nile In.)	23·55 N	32·50 E
142	Dacca (dă'kȧ) (dăk'ȧ) E. Pak.	23·45 N	90·29 E
111	Dachau (dä'Kou) Ger. (München In.)	48·16 N	11·26 E
85	Dacotah (dȧ-kō'tȧ) Can. (Winnipeg In.)	49·52 N	97·38 W
79	Dade City (dād) Fla. (In.)	28·22 N	82·09 W
78	Dadeville (dād'vĭl) Ala.	32·48 N	85·44 W
155	Daet (Mtn.) (dä'ĕt) Phil. (Manila In.)	14·07 N	122·59 E
74	Dafter (dăf'tẽr) Mich. (Sault Ste. Marie In.)	46·21 N	84·26 W
168	Dagahabur Eth. (Horn of Afr. In.)	8·10 N	43·25 E
164	Dagama (dä-gä'mä) Senegal	16·27 N	15·28 W
128	Dagda (dåg'dȧ) Sov. Un.	56·04 N	27·30 E
110	Dagenham (dăg'ĕn-ăm) Eng. (London In.)	51·32 N	0·09 E
133	Dagestan (Reg.) (dä-gĕs-tän') Sov. Un.	43·40 N	46·10 E
68	Daggett (dăg'ĕt) Calif.	34·50 N	116·52 W
155	Dagupan (dä-gōō'pän) Phil. (Manila In.)	16·02 N	120·20 E
123	Dahl (däl) Ger. (Ruhr In.)	51·18 N	7·33 E
163	Dahomey (dȧ-hō-mā') Afr.	8·48 N	20·00 E
153	Daigo (dī-gō) Jap. (Ōsaka In.)	34·57 N	135·49 E
124	Daimiel Manzanares (dī-myĕl' män-zä-nä'rĕs). Sp.	39·05 N	3·36 W
	Dairen, see Talien		
65	Dairy (R.) (dâr'ĭ) Ore. (Portland In.)	45·33 N	123·04 W
65	Dairy (R.) East Fk. Ore. (Portland In.)	45·40 N	123·03 W
153	Dai-Sen (Mtn.) (dī'sĕn') Jap.	35·22 N	133·35 E
153	Dai-Tenjo-dake (Mtn.) (dī-tĕn'jō dä-Kä). Jap.	36·21 N	137·38 E
95	Dajabón (dä-Kä-bô'n) Dom. Rep.	19·35 N	71·40 W
158	Dajarra (dȧ-jăr'ȧ) Austl.	21·45 S	139·30 E
164	Dakar (dȧ-kär') Senegal	14·39 N	17·28 W
145	Dakka (dăk'ȧ) Afg. (Khyber Pass In.)	34·13 N	71·02 E
127	Dakovica (dyä'kō-vê-tsa) Yugo.	42·23 N	20·28 E
150	Dalai Nor (L.) (dȧ-lī'nōr). China	48·50 N	116·45 E
118	Dalälven Swe.	60·26 N	15·50 E
160	Dalby (dôl'bē) Austl.	27·10 S	151·15 E
84	Dalcour (dăl-kour) La. (New Orleans In.)	29·49 N	89·59 W
118	Dale (dä'lĕ) Nor.	60·34 N	5·46 E
78	Dale Hollow (L.) (dāl hŏl'ō). Tenn.	36·33 N	85·03 W
85	Dalemead (dä'lē-mēd) Can. (Calgary In.)	50·53 N	113·38 W
118	Dalen (dä'lĕn) Nor.	59·28 N	8·01 E
168	Daleside (dāl'sīd) S. Afr. (Johannesburg & Pretoria In.)	26·30 S	28·03 E
85	Dalesville (dālz'vĭl) Can. (Montreal In.)	45·42 N	74·23 W

ăt; finăl; rāte; senâte; ärm; åsk; sofȧ; fâre; ch-choose; dh-as th in other; bē; êvent; bĕt; recĕnt; cratẽr; g-go; gh-guttural g; bĭt; ĭ-short neutral; rīde; K-guttural k as ch in German ich;

Page	Name Pronunciation Region	Lat. °′	Long. °′
158	Daley (L.) (dā'lĭ) Austl.	14·15 S	131·15 E
158	Daley Waters (dā-lė) Austl.	16·15 S	133·30 E
72	Dalhart (dăl'härt) Tex.	36·04 N	102·32 W
82	Dalhousie (dăl-hōō'zė) Can.	48·03 N	66·24 W
124	Dalías (dä-lē'äs) Sp.	36·49 N	2·50 W
64	Dall (I.) (dăl) Alaska	54·50 N	133·10 W
66	Dallas (dăl'lás) Ore.	44·55 N	123·20 W
70	Dallas S. D.	43·13 N	99·34 W
74	Dallas Tex. (Dallas Fort Worth In.)	32·45 N	96·48 W
73	Dallas (L.) Tex.	33·16 N	96·54 W
66	Dalles Dam Ore.	45·36 N	121·08 W
126	Dalmacija (Reg.) (däl-mä'tsē-yä) Yugo.	43·25 N	16·37 E
85	Dalroy (dăl'roi). Can. (Calgary In.)	51·08 N	113·40 W
159	Dalrymple, Mt. (dăl'rĭm-p'l) Austl.	21·14 S	148·46 E
78	Dalton (dôl'tŭn) Ga.	34·46 N	84·58 W
167	Dalton (dŏl'tŏn) S. Afr. (Natal In.)	29·21 S	30·41 E
65	Daly City (dā'lė) Calif. (San Francisco In.)	37·42 N	122·27 W
99	Dam (däm) Sur.	4·36 N	54·54 W
168	Damanhūr (dä-män-hōōr') U. A. R. (Nile In.)	30·59 N	30·31 E
142	Damão (Port.) Asia	20·32 N	75·52 E
155	Damar (I.) Indon.	7·15 S	129·15 E
166	Damaraland (Reg.) (dă'mȧ-rȧ-lănd). S. W. Afr.	22·15 S	16·15 E
94	Damas Cays (Is.) (dä'mäs). Ba. Is.	23·50 N	79·50 W
	Damascus, see Dimashq		
133	Damavand (Mtn.) Iran	36·05 N	52·05 E
166	Damba (däm'bä) Ang.	6·50 S	15·20 E
165	Dambidolo Eth.	8·46 N	34·46 E
77	Dam B Res. (dăm) Tex.	30·52 N	94·30 W
95	Dame Marie, Cap (C.) (dăm mȧrē'). Hai.	18·35 N	74·50 W
144	Dāmghān (dăm-gān') Iran	35·50 N	54·15 E
	Damietta, see Dumyāṭ		
123	Dammartin-en-Goële (däN-mär-tăN-äN-gō-ĕl'). Fr. (Paris In.)	49·03 N	2·40 E
155	Dampier, Straat (Str.) (däm'pēr) Neth. N. Gui.	0·40 N	131·15 E
158	Dampier Arch. (däN-pyâr'). Austl.	20·15 S	116·25 E
79	Dan (R.) (dán) N. C.	36·26 N	79·40 W
165	Danakil Des. Eth.	12·45 N	41·01 E
154	Danau (R.) Indon.	4·17 S	105·00 E
84	Danbury (dăn'bĕr-ĭ) Conn. (New York In.)	41·23 N	73·27 W
110	Danbury Eng. (London In.)	51·42 N	0·34 E
77	Danbury Tex. (In.)	29·14 N	95·22 W
168	Dandarah (dĕn'dȧ-rȧ) U. A. R. (Nile In.)	26·08 N	32·42 E
161	Dandenong (dăn'dė-nông) Austl. (Melbourne In.)	37·59 S	145·13 E
110	Dane (R.) (dān) Eng.	53·11 N	2·14 W
85	Danforth (dăn'fŭrth) Can. (Toronto In.)	43·42 N	79·15 W
82	Danforth Maine	45·38 N	67·53 W
165	Dānglā Eth.	11·17 N	36·69 E
142	Dangri India	26·43 N	71·32 E
79	Dania (dā'nĭ-ȧ) Fla. (In.)	26·01 N	80·10 W
84	Daniels (dă-nĭ-ĕls) Md. (Baltimore In.)	39·19 N	76·49 W
128	Danilov (dä'nē-lôf) Sov. Un.	58·12 N	40·08 E
127	Danilov Grad (dä'nē-lôf'gräd) Yugo.	42·31 N	19·08 E
128	Dankov (däŋ'kôf) Sov. Un.	53·17 N	39·09 E
92	Danlí (dän'lē) Hond.	14·02 N	86·35 W
81	Dannemora (dăn-ė-mō'rȧ). N. Y.	44·45 N	73·45 W
167	Dannhauser (dän'hou-zĕr) S. Afr. (Natal In.)	28·07 S	30·04 E
81	Dansville (dănz'vĭl) N. Y.	42·30 N	77·40 W
129	Danube, Mouths of the (dăn'ub) Rom.	45·13 N	29·37 E
115	Danube R. Eur.	43·41 N	23·35 E
83	Danvers (dăn'vẽrz) Mass. (Boston In.)	42·34 N	70·57 W
65	Danville (dăn'vĭl) Calif. (San Francisco In.)	37·49 N	122·00 W
80	Danville Ill.	40·10 N	87·35 W
80	Danville Ind.	39·45 N	86·30 W
80	Danville Ky.	37·35 N	84·50 W
81	Danville Pa.	41·00 N	76·35 W
79	Danville Va.	36·35 N	79·24 W
	Danzig, see Gdańsk		
112	Danzig, G. of (dán'tsĭk) Pol.	54·41 N	19·01 E
139	Dar'a Syria (Palestine In.)	32·37 N	36·07 E
121	Dărăbani (dă-rä-băn'ĭ) Rom.	48·13 N	26·38 E
164	Daraj Libya	30·12 N	10·14 E
168	Darāw (dȧ-rä'ōō) U. A. R. (Nile In.)	24·24 N	32·56 E
142	Darbhanga (dŭr-bŭŋ'gä) India	26·03 N	85·09 E
84	Darby (där'bĭ) Pa. (Philadelphia In.)	39·55 N	75·16 W
95	Darby (I.) Ba. Is.	23·50 N	76·20 W
	Dardanelles (Str.), see Çanakkale boğazi		
167	Dar es Salaam (där ĕs sȧ-läm') Tan.	6·58 S	39·13 E
165	Darfur (Prov.) (där-fōōr') Sud.	13·21 N	23·46 E
145	Dargai (dŭr-gä'ė) W. Pak. (Khyber Pass In.)	34·32 N	71·55 E
164	D'Arguin, Cap (C.) Mauritania	20·28 N	17·46 W
98	Darien (dā-rĭ-ĕn') Col. (In.)	3·56 N	76·30 W
84	Darien (dâ-rē-ĕn') Conn. (New York In.)	41·04 N	73·28 W
	Daíren, see Talien		
92	Darien, Cordillera de (Mts.). Nic.	13·00 N	85·42 W
98	Darien, Golfo del (G.) (gôl-fô-dĕl-dä-rĭ-ĕn'). N. A.-S. A.	9·36 N	77·54 W
93	Darien, Serrania del (Ra.) (sĕr-ä-nē'ä dĕl dä-rė-ĕn'). Pan.	8·13 N	77·28 W
142	Darjeeling (dŭr-jē'lĭng) India	27·05 N	88·16 E
110	Darlaston (där'lȧs-tŭn) Eng.	52·34 N	2·02 W
70	Darling (L.) (där'lĭng) N. D.	48·35 N	101·25 W
160	Darling (R.) Austl.	31·50 S	143·20 E
160	Darling Downs (Reg.) Austl.	27·22 S	150·50 E
158	Darling Ra. Austl.	30·30 S	115·45 E
116	Darlington (där'lĭng-tŭn) Eng.	54·32 N	1·35 W
79	Darlington S. C.	34·15 N	79·52 W
71	Darlington Wis.	42·41 N	90·06 W
120	Darlowo (där-lô'vô) Pol.	24·25 N	16·21 E
120	Darmstadt (därm'shtät) Ger.	49·53 N	8·40 E
165	Darnah Libya	32·44 N	22·41 E
64	Darnley B. (därn'lē) Alaska	70·00 N	124·00 W
165	Dar Nuba (Reg.) Sud.	12·22 N	30·39 E
124	Daroca (dä-rō-kä) Sp.	41·08 N	1·24 W
75	Darrowville (dăr'rō-vĭl) Ohio (Cleveland In.)	41·12 N	81·27 W
116	Dartmoor (därt'mōōr) Eng.	50·35 N	4·05 W
82	Dartmouth (därt'mŭth) Can.	44·41 N	63·36 W
116	Dartmouth Eng.	50·33 N	3·28 W
155	Daru (I.) (dä'rōō) Pap. Ter.	9·17 S	143·13 E
126	Daruvar (där'rōō-vär) Yugo.	45·37 N	17·16 E
154	Darvel B. (där'vĕl) N. Bor.	4·50 N	118·40 E
110	Darwen (där'wĕn) Eng.	53·42 N	2·28 W
158	Darwin (där'wĭn) Austl.	12·25 S	131·00 E
100	Darwin, Cordillera (Mts.) (kôr-dēl-yĕ'rä-där'wēn) Chile-Arg.	54·40 S	69·30 W
144	Daryācheh-ye Rezācheh (L.). Iran	38·07 N	45·17 E
124	Das Alturas, Serra (Mts.) (sĕ'r-rä-däs-äl-tōō'räs). Port.	40·43 N	7·48 W
165	Dasē Eth.	11·00 N	39·51 E
65	Dash Point (dăsh) Wash. (Seattle In.)	47·19 N	122·25 W
144	Dasht (R.) (dŭsht) W. Pak.	25·47 N	63·01 E
144	Dasht-E Kavir Des. (dŭsht-ê-ka-vēr'). Iran	34·43 N	53·30 E
155	Dasol B. (dä-sōl') Phil. (Manila In.)	15·53 N	119·40 E
123	Datteln (dät'tĕln). Ger. (Ruhr In.)	51·39 N	7·20 E
154	Datu, Tandjung (C.) Indon.	2·08 N	110·15 E
165	Daua R. (dä'wä) Eth.	4·34 N	41·34 E
128	Daugavpils (dä'ōō-gäv-pėls) Sov. Un.	55·52 N	25·32 E
86	Dauphin (dô'fĭn) Can.	51·09 N	100·01 W
84	Davant (dă'vănt) La. (New Orleans In.)	29·36 N	89·51 W
155	Davao (dä'vä-ô) Phil.	7·05 N	125·30 E
71	Davenport (dăv'ĕn-pōrt) Iowa	41 34 N	90·38 W
159	Davenport N. Z. (In.)	37·29 S	174·47 E
66	Davenport Wash.	47·39 N	118·07 W
93	David (dȧ-vēdh') Pan.	8·27 N	82·27 W
70	David City (dā'vĭd) Nebr.	41·15 N	97·10 W
121	David-Gorodok (dȧ-vēt' gō-rō'dôk) Sov. Un.	52·02 N	27·14 E
73	Davis (dā'vĭs) Okla.	34·34 N	97·08 W
81	Davis W. Va.	39·15 N	79·25 W
66	Davis L. Ore.	43·38 N	121·43 W
76	Davis Mts. Tex.	30·45 N	104·17 W
47	Davis Sea Ant.	66·00 S	92·00 E
49	Davis Str. Can.	66·00 N	60·00 W
155	Davo G. (dä'-vô) Phil.	6·30 N	125·45 E
120	Davos (dä'vōs) Switz.	46·47 N	9·50 E
144	Dawāsir, Wādī ad (R.). Sau. Ar.	20·48 N	44·07 E
110	Dawley (dô'lĭ) Eng.	52·38 N	2·28 W
154	Dawna Ra. (dô'nȧ) Bur.	17·02 N	98·01 E
86	Dawson (dô'sŭn) Can.	64·04 N	139·22 W
78	Dawson Ga.	31·45 N	84·29 W
70	Dawson Minn.	44·54 N	96·03 W
160	Dawson (R.) Austl.	24·20 S	149·45 E
86	Dawson Creek Can.	55·49 N	120·21 W
78	Dawson Springs Ky.	37·10 N	87·40 W
122	Dax (däks) Fr.	43·42 N	1·06 W
144	Dayr az Zawr (dȧ-ĕr'ez-zôr'). Syr.	35·15 N	40·01 E
168	Dayrūṭ U. A. R. (Nile In.)	27·33 N	30·48 E
75	Dayton (dā'tŭn) Ky. (Cincinnati In.)	39·07 N	84·28 W
72	Dayton N. Mex.	32·44 N	104·23 W
80	Dayton Ohio	39·45 N	84·15 W
78	Dayton Tenn.	35·30 N	85·00 W
77	Dayton Tex.	30·03 N	94·53 W
66	Dayton Wash.	46·18 N	117·59 W
79	Daytona Beach (dā-tō'nȧ) Fla.	29·11 N	81·02 W
81	Dayville (dā'vĭl) Conn.	41·50 N	71·55 W
166	De Aar (dē-är') S. Afr.	30·45 S	24·05 E
70	Dead (L.) (dĕd) Minn.	46·28 N	96·00 W
70	Deadwood (dĕd'wōōd) S. D.	44·23 N	103·43 W
81	Deal Island (dēl-ī'lȧnd) Md.	38·10 N	75·55 W
100	Deán Funes (dĕ-ä'n-fōō-nĕs). Arg.	30·26 S	64·12 W
75	Dearborn (dēr'bŭrn) Mich. (Detroit In.)	42·18 N	83·15 W
116	Dearg, Ben (Mtn.) (bĕn dŭrg) Scot.	57·48 N	4·59 W
86	Dease Str. (dēz) Can.	68·50 N	108·20 W
155	De Atauro (I.) (dĕ-ä-tä'ōō-rô) Port. Timor	8·20 S	126·15 E
68	Death Val. Calif.-Nev.	36·55 N	117·12 W
68	Death Valley Junction Calif.	36·18 N	116·26 W
68	Death Valley Natl. Mon. Calif.	36·34 N	117·00 W
129	Debal'tsevo (dyĕb'äl-tsyĕ'vô) Sov. Un.	48·23 N	38·29 E
127	Debar (Dibra) (dĕ'bär) (dā'brä) Yugo.	41·31 N	20·32 E
114	Debdou (dĕb-dōō') Mor.	34·01 N	2·50 W
121	Deblin (dăN'blĭn) Pol.	51·34 N	21·49 E
121	Debno (dĕb-nô') Sov. Un.	50·24 N	25·44 E
164	Debo Swp. (dā'bō) Mali	15·33 N	3·28 W
121	Debrecen (dĕ'brĕ-tsĕn) Hung.	47·32 N	21·40 E
78	Decatur (dė-kā'tŭr) Ala.	34·35 N	87·00 W
78	Decatur Ga. (Atlanta In.)	33·47 N	84·18 W
73	Decatur Ill.	39·50 N	88·59 W
80	Decatur Ind.	40·50 N	84·55 W
80	Decatur Mich.	42·10 N	86·00 W
72	Decatur Tex.	33·14 N	97·33 W
122	Decazeville (dē-käz'vēl') Fr.	44·33 N	2·16 E
143	Decean Plat. (dĕk'ăn) India	26·36 N	76·35 E
65	Deception P. (dė-sĕp'shŭn) Wash. (Seattle In.)	48·24 N	122·44 W
120	Decin (dyĕ'chĕn) Czech.	50·47 N	14·14 E
71	Decorah (dė-kō'rȧ) Iowa	43·18 N	91·48 W
65	Decoto (dē-cō'tō) Calif. (San Francisco In.)	37·36 N	122·01 W
139	Dedap Indon. (Singapore In.)	1·19 N	102·22 E
	Dedeagats, see Alexandroupolis		
136	Dedenevo (dyĕ-dyĕ'nyĕ-vô) Sov. Un. (Moskva In.)	56·14 N	37·31 E
83	Dedham (dĕd'ăm) Mass. (Boston In.)	42·15 N	71·11 W
100	Dedo do Deus (Mt.) (dĕ-dô-dô-dĕ'ōōs). Braz. (In.)	22·30 S	43·02 W
164	Dédougou (dā-dōō-gōō') Upper Volta	12·28 N	3·21 W
116	Dee (R.) Wales	53·00 N	3·10 W
116	Dee (R.) Scot.	57·05 N	2·25 W
79	Deep (R.) (dēp) N. C.	35·36 N	79·32 W
84	Deep Creek Va. (Norfolk In.)	36·44 N	76·22 W
73	Deep Fk. (R.) Okla.	35·35 N	96·42 W
73	Deepwater (dep-wô-tẽr) Mo.	38·15 N	93·46 W
83	Deer (dēr) Can.	49·06 N	57·45 W
82	Deer Maine	44·07 N	68·38 W
75	Deerfield (dēr'fēld) Ill. (Chicago In.)	42·10 N	87·51 W
65	Deer Island Ore. (Portland In.)	45·56 N	122·51 W
83	Deer Lake Can.	49·09 N	57·26 W
67	Deer Lodge (dēr lŏj) Mont.	46·23 N	112·42 W
75	Deer Park Ohio (Cincinnati In.)	39·12 N	84·24 W
66	Deer Park Wash.	47·58 N	117·28 W
71	Deer River Minn.	47·20 N	93·49 W
80	Defiance (dē-fī'ăns) Ohio	41·15 N	84·20 W
78	DeFuniak Springs (dē fū'nĭ-ăk) Fla.	30·42 N	86·06 W
120	Deggendorf (dĕ'ghĕn-dôrf) Ger.	48·50 N	12·59 E
90	Degollado (dā-gô-lyä'dō) Mex.	20·27 N	102·11 W
158	DeGrey (R.) (dē grā') Austl.	20·20 S	119·25 E
136	Degtyarsk (dĕg-ty'arsk) Sov. Un. (Urals In.)	56·42 N	60·05 E
142	Dehra Dun (dā'rŭ) India	30·09 N	78·07 E
121	Dej (dāzh) Rom.	47·09 N	23·53 E
71	De Kalb (dė kălb') Ill.	41·54 N	88·46 W
85	Delacour (dĕ-lä-kōōr') Can. (Calgary In.)	51·09 N	113·45 W
84	Delacroix (dĕl ȧ-krō') La. (New Orleans In.)	29·46 N	89·47 W
166	Delagoa B. (dĕl-ȧ-gō'ȧ) Moz.	26·14 S	33·30 E
72	Delagua (dĕl-ä'gwä) Colo.	37·19 N	104·42 W
79	De Land (dē lănd') Fla.	29·00 N	81·19 W
68	Delano (dĕl'ȧ-nō) Calif.	35·47 N	119·15 W
69	Delano, Mt. Utah	38·25 N	112·25 W
71	Delavan (dĕl'ȧ-văn) Wis.	42·39 N	88·38 W
80	Delaware (dĕl'ȧ-wâr) Ohio	40·15 N	83·05 W
63	Delaware (State) U. S.	38·40 N	75·30 W
73	Delaware (R.) Kans.	39·45 N	95·47 W
81	Delaware (R.) N. J.-Pa.	41·50 N	75·20 W
81	Delaware B. Del.-N. J.	39·05 N	75·10 W
80	Delaware Res. Ohio	40·30 N	83·05 W
124	Del Eje, Sierra (Mts.) (sē-ĕ'r-rä-dĕl-ĕ'кĕ). Sp.	42·15 N	6·45 W
120	Delemont (dē-lā-môN') Switz.	47·21 N	7·18 E
76	De Leon (dē lē-ŏn') Tex.	32·06 N	98·33 W
85	De Léry (dā lā-rī') Can. (Montreal In.)	45·21 N	73·49 W
101	Delfínópolis (dĕl-fē'nô'pō-lēs) Braz. (Rio de Janeiro In.)	20·20 S	46·50 W
111	Delft (dĕlft) Neth. (Amsterdam In.)	52·01 N	4·20 E
117	Delfzijl Neth.	53·20 N	6·50 E
100	Delgada Pta. (Pt.) (pōō'n-tä-dĕl-gä'dä). Arg.	43·46 S	63·46 W
167	Delgado, Cabo (C.) (kä'bô-dĕl-gä'dō). Moz.	10·30 S	41·00 E
165	Delgo (dĕl'gō) Sud.	20·07 N	30·41 E
74	Delhi (dĕl'hī). Ill. (St. Louis In.)	39·03 N	90·16 W
142	Delhi India	28·54 N	77·13 E
77	Delhi La.	32·26 N	91·29 W
125	Del Hoyo, Sierra (Mtn.) (sē-ĕ'r-rä-dĕl-ô'yô) Sp. (Madrid In.)	40·39 N	3·56 W
120	Delitzsch (dā'lĭch) Ger.	51·32 N	12·18 E
127	Dell Alice, Pt. (dĕl-ä-lē'chĕ) It.	39·23 N	17·10 E
70	Dell Rapids (dĕl) S. D.	43·50 N	96·43 W
74	Dellwood (dĕl'wōōd) Minn. (Minneapolis, St. Paul In.)	45·05 N	92·58 W
164	Dellys (dĕ'lēs') Alg.	36·59 N	3·40 E
68	Del Mar (dĕl mär') Calif. (San Diego In.)	32·57 N	117·16 W
168	Delmas (dĕl'mȧs) S. Afr. (Johannesburg & Pretoria In.)	26·08 S	28·43 E
120	Delmenhorst (dĕl'mĕn-hôrst). Ger.	53·03 N	8·38 E
69	Del Norte (dĕl nôrt') Colo.	37·40 N	106·25 W
135	De-Longa (I.) Sov. Un.	176·58 N	157·39 E
64	Delong Mts. (dē'lŏng) Alaska	68·30 N	163·25 W
80	Delphi (dĕl'fī) Ind.	40·35 N	86·40 W
80	Delphos (dĕl'fŏs) Ohio	40·50 N	84·20 W
79	Delray Beach (dĕl-rā'). Fla. (In.)	26·27 N	80·05 W
76	Del Rio (dĕl rē'ō) Tex.	29·21 N	100·52 W
85	Delson Village (dĕl'sŭn) Can. (Montreal In.)	45·24 N	73·32 W
69	Delta Colo.	38·45 N	108·05 W
69	Delta Utah	39·20 N	112·35 W
68	Delta Mendota can. Calif.	37·10 N	121·02 W
85	Delta Station. Can. (Winnipeg In.)	50·10 N	98·20 W
127	Delvine (dĕl'vē-nä) Alb.	39·58 N	20·10 E
132	Dëma (R.) (dyĕm'ä) Sov. Un.	53·40 N	54·30 E
128	Demidov (dzyĕ'mē-dô'f). Sov. Un.	55·16 N	31·32 E
69	Deming (dĕm'ĭng) N. Mex.	32·15 N	107·45 W
120	Demmin (dĕm'mēn) Ger.	53·54 N	13·04 E
164	Demnat (dĕm-nät) Mor.	31·58 N	7·03 W
78	Demopolis (dē-mŏp'ō-lĭs) Ala.	32·30 N	87·50 W
75	Demotte (dē'mŏt) Ind. (Chicago In.)	41·12 N	87·13 W
154	Dempo, Gunung (Vol.) (dĕm'pō) Indon.	4·04 S	103·11 E

ng-sing; ŋ-baŋk; N-nasalized n; nŏd; cŏmmit; ōld; ôbey; ôrder; fōōd; fŏŏt; ou-out; s-soft; sh-dish; th-thin; pūre; ûnite; ûrn; stŭd; circŭs; ü-as "y" in study; '-indeterminate vowel.

Page	Name Pronunciation	Region	Lat. °'	Long. °'
134	Dem'yanka (R.) (dyĕm-yän'kä)	Sov. Un.	59·07 N	72·58 E
128	Demyansk (dyĕm-yänsk')	Sov. Un.	57·39 N	32·26 E
122	Denain (dĕ-năN')	Fr.	50·23 N	3·21 E
116	Denbigh (dĕn'bĭ)	Wales	53·15 N	3·25 W
110	Denbigh (Co.)	Wales	53·01 N	2·59 W
111	Dendermonde. Bel. (Bruxelles In.)		51·02 N	4·04 E
79	Dendron (dĕn'drŭn)	Va.	37·02 N	76·53 W
136	Denezhkin Kamen, Gora (Mtn.) (dzyĕ-nĕʹzhkĕn kämʹĕn)	Sov. Un. (Urals In.)	60·26 N	59·35 E
93	D'Enfer, Pointe (Pt.)	Mart. (Le. & Wind. Is. In.)	14·21 N	60·48 W
94	Denham, Mt.	Jam.	18·20 N	77·30 W
117	Den Helder (dĕn hĕl'dĕr)	Neth.	52·55 N	5·45 E
125	Denia (dā'nyä)	Sp.	38·48 N	0·06 E
160	Deniliquin (dĕ-nĭl'ĭ-kwĭn)	Austl.	35·20 S	144·52 E
70	Denison (dĕn'ĭ-sŭn)	Iowa	42·01 N	95·22 W
73	Denison	Tex.	33·45 N	97·02 W
136	Denisovka (dĕ-nĕ'sof-kä)	Sov. Un. (Urals In.)	52·26 N	61·45 E
133	Denizli (dĕn-ĭz-lē')	Tur.	37·40 N	29·10 E
123	Denklingen (dĕn'klĕn-gĕn)	Ger. (Ruhr In.)	50·54 N	7·40 E
79	Denmark (dĕn'märk)	S. C.	33·18 N	81·09 W
102	Denmark	Eur.	56·14 N	8·30 E
49	Denmark Str.	Grnld.	66·30 N	27·00 W
168	Dennilton (dĕn-ĭl-tŭn)	S. Afr. (Johannesburg & Pretoria In.)	25·18 S	29·13 E
80	Dennison (dĕn'ĭ-sŭn)	Ohio	40·25 N	81·20 W
81	Denton (dĕn'tŭn)	Md.	38·55 N	75·50 W
73	Denton	Tex.	33·12 N	97·06 W
158	D'entrecasteaux (däN-tr'käs-tō')	Austl.	34·50 S	114·45 E
155	D'entrecasteaux Is. (däN-tr'käs-tō')	Pap. Ter.	9·45 S	152·00 E
72	Denver (dĕn'vĕr)	Colo.	39·44 N	104·59 W
142	Deoli	India	25·52 N	75·23 E
71	De Pere (dĕ pēr')	Wis.	44·25 N	88·04 W
75	Depew (dĕ pū') . N. Y. (Buffalo In.)		42·55 N	78·43 W
80	Depue (dē pū)	Ill.	41·15 N	89·55 W
73	De Queen (dĕ kwēn')	Ark.	34·02 N	94·21 W
77	De Quincy (dĕ kwĭn'sĭ)	La.	30·27 N	93·27 W
142	Dera Ghāzi Khān (dā'rū gä-zē' ʞän')	W. Pak.	30·09 N	70·39 E
142	Dera Ismail Khan (dā'rū ĭs-mä-ēl' ʞän')	W. Pak.	31·55 N	70·51 E
133	Derbent (dĕr-bĕnt')	Sov. Un.	42·00 N	48·10 E
158	Derby (där'bĕ)	Austl.	17·20 S	123·40 E
81	Derby (dûr'bĕ)	Conn.	41·20 N	73·05 W
110	Derby (där'bĕ)	Eng.	52·55 N	1·29 W
168	Derby (där'bĭ)	S. Afr. (Johannesburg & Pretoria In.)	25·55 S	27·02 E
110	Derby (Co.) (där'bĕ)	Eng.	53·11 N	1·30 W
168	Derdepoort	S. Afr. (Johannesburg & Pretoria In.)	24·39 S	26·21 E
116	Derg, Lough (B.) (lŏk dĕrg)	Ire.	53·00 N	8·09 W
77	De Ridder (dĕ rĭd'ĕr)	La.	30·50 N	93·18 W
73	Dermott (dûr'mŏt)	Ark.	33·32 N	91·24 W
83	Derry (dĕr'ĭ) . N. H. (Boston In.)		42·52 N	71·22 W
127	Derventa (dĕr'ven-tä)	Yugo.	45·58 N	17·58 E
160	Derwent (R.) (dûr'wĕnt)	Austl.	42·21 S	146·30 E
110	Derwent (R.) (dĕr'wĕnt)	Eng.	52·54 N	1·24 W
73	Des Arc (dāz ärk')	Ark.	34·59 N	91·31 W
101	Descalvado (dĕs-käl-vä-dô')	Braz. (Rio de Janeiro In.)	21·55 S	47·37 W
85	Deschenes . . . . . Can. (Ottawa In.)		45·23 N	75·47 W
85	Deschenes, L. . Can. (Ottawa In.)		54·25 N	75·53 W
66	Deschutes R. (dĕ-shōōt')	Ore.	44·25 N	121·21 W
76	Desdemona (dĕz-dĕ-mō'ná)	Tex.	32·16 N	98·33 W
100	Deseado, Rio (R.) (rĕ'-ō-dä-sā-ä'dhō)	Arg.	46·50 S	67·45 W
93	Desirade I. (dā-zē-räs')	Guad. (Le. & Wind. Is. In.)	16·21 N	60·51 W
70	De Smet (dĕ smĕt')	S. D.	44·23 N	97·33 W
71	Des Moines (dĕ moin')	Iowa	41·35 N	93·37 W
72	Des Moines . . . . N. Mex.		36·42 N	103·48 W
65	Des Moines . . . Wash. (Seattle In.)		46·24 N	122·20 W
63	Des Moines (R.)	U. S.	43·45 N	94·20 W
129	Desna (R.) (dĕs-nä') . . Sov. Un.		51·05 N	31·03 E
100	Desolación (dĕ-sô-lä-syô'n) (I.)	Chile	53·05 S	74·00 W
73	De Soto (dĕ sō'tō)	Mo.	38·07 N	90·32 W
74	Des Peres (dĕs pĕr'ēs) Mo. (St. Louis In.)		38·36 N	90·26 W
75	Des Plaines (dĕs plänz') Ill. (Chicago In.)		42·02 N	87·54 W
75	Des Plines R. Ill. (Chicago In.)		41·39 N	88·05 W
120	Dessau (dĕs'ou)	Ger.	51·50 N	12·15 E
120	Detmold (dĕt'môld)	Ger.	51·57 N	8·55 E
75	Detroit (dĕ-troit')	Mich. (Detroit In.)	42·22 N	83·10 W
73	Detroit	Tex.	33·41 N	95·16 W
70	Detroit Lakes (dĕ-troit' lākz)	Minn.	46·48 N	95·51 W
75	Detroit R. U. S.-Can. (Detroit In.)		42·08 N	83·07 W
121	Detva (dyĕt'vä)	Czech.	48·32 N	19·21 E
111	Deutsch Wagrum . Aus. (Wien In.)		48·19 N	16·34 E
85	Deux Montagnes, Lac des (dû mōn-tänˊ)	Can. (Montreal In.)	45·28 N	74·00 W
127	Deva (dā'vä)	Rom.	45·52 N	22·52 E
121	Dévaványa (dā'vô-vän-yô) . Hung.		47·01 N	20·58 E
133	Develi (dĕ'vä-lē)	Tur.	38·20 N	35·10 E
117	Deventer (dĕv'ĕn-tĕr)	Neth.	52·14 N	6·07 E
70	Devils (R.) (dĕv'ĭlz)	N. D.	47·57 N	99·04 W
76	Devils (R.)	Tex.	29·55 N	101·10 W
	Devils I., see Diable, Ile du			
62	Devils Lake	N. D.	48·10 N	98·55 W
70	Devils Lake Ind. Res.	N. D.	48·08 N	99·40 W
68	Devils Postpile Natl. Mon.	Calif.	37·42 N	119·12 W
67	Devils Tower Natl. Mon. . . . Wyo.		44·38 N	105·07 W

Page	Name Pronunciation	Region	Lat. °'	Long. °'
127	Devoll (R.)	Alb.	40·55 N	20·10 E
168	Devon (dĕv'ŭn)	S. Afr. (Johannesburg & Pretoria In.)	26·23 S	28·47 E
160	Devonport (dĕv'ŭn-pôrt) . . . Austl.		41·20 S	146·30 E
74	Devore (dĕ-vôr')	Calif. (Los Angeles In.)	34·13 N	117·24 W
77	Dewalt (dū'ált) . . . . . . Tex. (In.)		29·33 N	95·33 W
65	Dewatto (dĕ-wät'ô)	Wash. (Seattle In.)	47·27 N	123·04 W
73	Dewey (dū'ĭ)	Okla.	36·48 N	95·55 W
73	De Witt (dĕ wĭt')	Ark.	34·17 N	91·22 W
71	De Witt	Iowa	41·46 N	90·34 W
110	Dewsbury (dūz'bĕr-ĭ)	Eng.	53·42 N	1·39 W
82	Dexter (dĕks'tĕr)	Maine	45·01 N	69·19 W
73	Dexter	Mo.	36·46 N	89·56 W
79	Dexter (L.)	Fla.	29·07 N	81·24 W
144	Dezfūl	Iran	32·14 N	48·37 E
139	Dezhneva, Mys (East Cape) (dyĕzh'nyĭf) . Sov. Un.		68·00 N	172·00 W
	Dhahran, see AzZahrān			
143	Dharamtar Cr . India (Bombay In.)		18·49 N	72·54 E
143	Dharmavaram	India	14·32 N	77·43 E
142	Dhaulagiri, Mt. (dou-lá-gē'rē)	Nep.	33·50 N	83·32 E
127	Dhenoúsa (I.)	Grc.	37·09 N	25·53 E
139	Dhibān . . . . Jordan (Palestine In.)		31·30 N	35·46 E
127	Dhidhimótikhon	Grc.	41·20 N	26·27 E
127	Dhodhekánisos (Dodecanese) (Is.)	Grc.	38·00 N	26·10 E
142	Dhūlia (dōōl'yä)	India	20·58 N	74·43 E
142	Dhupgarth (Mt.)	India	27·30 N	78·27 E
126	Dia (I.) (dē'ä) . . . . Grc. (Inset)		35·27 N	25·17 E
99	Diable, Île du (Devils I.) . Fr. Gu.		5·15 N	57·10 W
65	Diablo, Mt. (dyä'blô)	Calif. (San Francisco In.)	37·52 N	121·55 W
88	Diablo Heights (dyä'blô)	C. Z. (Panama Canal In.)	8·58 N	79·34 W
65	Diablo Range (Mts.)	Calif. (San Francisco In.)	37·47 N	121·50 W
99	Diamantina (dē-á-män-tē'ná)	Braz.	14·22 S	56·23 W
99	Diamantina	Braz.	18·14 S	43·32 W
158	Diamantina (R.) (dĭ'man-tē'ná)	Austl.	25·38 S	139·53 E
84	Diamond (dī'á-mŭnd)	La. (New Orleans In.)	29·34 N	89·48 W
66	Diamond Pk.	Ore.	43·32 N	122·08 W
154	Diamond Pt. (dī'mŭnd) . . . Indon.		5·30 N	96·45 E
95	Diana Bk. (dī'än'ă)	Ba. Is.	20·30 N	74·45 W
155	Diapitan B. (dyä-pē-tä'n)	Phil. (Manila In.)	16·28 N	122·25 E
	Dibra, see Debar			
70	Dickinson (dĭk'ĭn-sŭn)	N. D.	46·52 N	102·49 W
77	Dickinson (dĭk'ĭn-sŭn) . Tex. (In.)		29·28 N	95·02 W
77	Dickinson Bay . . . . Tex. (In.)		29·26 N	95·08 W
78	Dickson (dĭk'sŭn)	Tenn.	36·03 N	87·24 W
81	Dickson City	Pa.	41·25 N	75·40 W
133	Dicle (R.) (dĭj'lä)	Tur.	37·50 N	40·40 E
110	Didcot (dĭd'cŏt)	Eng. (London In.)	51·35 N	1·15 W
123	Die (dē)	Fr.	44·45 N	5·22 E
95	Diego de Ocampo, Pico (Pk.) (pē'-kô-dyĕ'gô-dĕ-ô-kä'm-pô)	Dom. Rep.	19·40 N	70·45 W
100	Diego Ramirez, Islas (Is.) (dē ä'gō rä-mē'räz) . Chile		56·15 S	70·15 W
167	Diégo-Suarez (Antsirane) (dē-ä'gô-swä'räz) (änt-sē-rän') . Malagasy		12·18 S	49·16 E
146	Dien Bien Phan	Viet.	21·38 N	102·49 E
82	Dieppe (dĭ-ĕp')	Can.	46·08 N	64·45 W
122	Dieppe	Fr.	49·54 N	1·05 E
73	Dierks (dērks)	Ark.	34·06 N	94·02 W
111	Diessen (dēs'sĕn)	Ger. (München In.)	47·57 N	11·06 E
111	Diest	Bel. (Bruxelles In.)	50·59 N	5·05 E
82	Digby (dĭg'bĭ)	Can.	44·37 N	65·48 W
84	Dighton (dī-tŭn)	Mass. (Providence In.)	41·49 N	71·05 W
123	Digne (dēn'y')	Fr.	44·07 N	6·16 E
155	Digoel (R.) . . . . . Neth. N. Gui.		7·00 S	140·25 E
122	Digoin (dē-gwän')	Fr.	46·28 N	4·06 E
155	Dijohan Pt. (dē-kô-än')	Phil. (Manila In.)	16·24 N	122·25 E
122	Dijon (dē-zhōn')	Fr.	47·21 N	5·02 E
134	Dikson (dĭk'sŏn)	Sov. Un.	72·47 N	79·20 E
165	Dikwa (dē'kwä)	Nig.	12·06 N	13·53 E
155	Dili (dĭl'ē)	Port. Timor	8·35 S	125·35 E
114	Di Linosa I. (dē-lē-nō'sä)	Medit. Sea	36·01 N	12·43 E
133	Dilizhan	Sov. Un.	40·45 N	45·00 E
64	Dillingham (dĭl'ĕng-hăm) . Alaska		59·10 N	158·38 W
67	Dillon (dĭl'ŭn)	Mont.	45·12 N	112·40 W
79	Dillon	S. C.	34·24 N	79·28 W
166	Dilolo (dē-lō'lō)	Con. L.	10·19 S	22·23 E
139	Dimashq (Damascus) (dĭ-mäs'kŭs) . Syria (Palestine In.)		33·31 N	36·18 E
127	Dimbovita (R.)	Rom.	44·43 N	25·41 E
127	Dimitrovo (Pernik) (pĕr-nēk')	Bul.	42·36 N	23·04 E
155	Dinagate I. (dē-nä'gät) . . . . Phil.		10·15 N	126·15 E
142	Dinājpur	India	25·38 N	87·39 E
122	Dinan (dē-näN')	Fr.	48·27 N	2·03 W
117	Dinant (dē-näN')	Bel.	50·17 N	4·50 E
126	Dinara Planina (Mts.) (dē'nä-rä plä'nē-nä) . Yugo.		43·50 N	16·15 E
143	Dindigul	India	10·25 N	78·03 E
155	Dingalan B. (dĭn-gä'län)	Phil. (Manila In.)	15·19 N	121·33 E
116	Dingle (dĭng'l)	Ire.	52·10 N	10·13 W
116	Dingle B.	Ire.	52·02 N	10·17 W
159	Dingo (dĭn'gō)	Austl.	23·45 S	149·26 E
116	Dingwall (dĭng'wôl)	Scot.	57·37 N	4·23 W
67	Dinosaur Natl. Mon. (dī'nô-sôr)	Utah-Colo.	40·45 N	109·17 W

Page	Name Pronunciation	Region	Lat. °'	Long. °'
123	Dinslaken (dēns'lä-kĕn)	Ger. (Ruhr In.)	51·33 N	6·44 E
111	Dinterloord	Neth. (Amsterdam In.)	51·38 N	4·21 E
68	Dinuba (dĭ-nū'bá)	Calif.	36·33 N	119·29 W
164	Diorbivol (dē-ôr-bē-vôl') . Senegal		16·07 N	13·52 W
94	Dios, Cayo de (I.) (kä'yō-dĕ-dē-ōs') . Cuba		22·05 N	83·05 W
164	Diourbel (dē-ōōr-bĕl') . Senegal		14·37 N	16·28 W
93	Diquis R. (dē-kēs')	C. R.	8·59 N	83·24 W
168	Dirēdawā . Eth. (Horn of Afr. In.)		9·40 N	41·47 E
92	Diriamba (dēr-yäm'bä)	Nic.	11·52 N	86·15 W
158	Dirk Hartog (I.)	Austl.	26·25 S	113·15 E
111	Dirksland . Neth. (Amsterdam In.)		51·45 N	4·04 E
160	Dirranbandi (dĭ-rä-băn'dē) . Austl.		28·24 S	148·29 E
69	Dirty Devil (R.) (dûr'tĭ dĕv'l)	Utah	38·20 N	110·30 W
158	Disappointment (L.)	Austl.	23·20 S	120·20 E
65	Disappointment (C.) (dĭs'á-point' ment) . Wash. (Portland In.)		46·16 N	124·11 W
125	D'Ischia, I. (dē'sh-kyä)	It. (Napoli In.)	40·26 N	13·55 E
167	Discovery (dĭs-cŭv'ĕr-ĭ) . . . S. Afr. (Johannesburg & Pretoria In.)		26·10 S	27·53 E
65	Discovery Is. (dĭs-kŭv'ĕr-ĕ)	Can. (Seattle In.)	48·25 N	123·13 W
168	Dishnā (dĕsh'nä)	U. A. R. (Nile In.)	26·08 N	32·27 E
49	Disko (dĭs'kō) (I.)	Grnld.	70·00 N	54·00 W
79	Dismal Swp. (dĭz'mál) . N. C.-Va.		36·35 N	76·34 W
128	Disna (dēs'nä)	Sov. Un.	55·34 N	28·15 E
82	Disraeli (dĭs-rā'lĭ)	Can.	45·53 N	71·23 W
81	District of Columbia	U. S.	38·50 N	77·00 W
91	Districto Federal (Dist.) (dēs-trē'tô-fĕ-dĕ-rä'l) . Mex.		19·14 N	99·08 W
168	Disūq (dĕ-sōōk')	U. A. R. (Nile In.)	31·07 N	30·41 E
142	Diu (Port) (dē'ōō)	Asia	20·48 N	70·58 E
122	Dives (dēv)	Fr.	49·18 N	0·05 W
155	Divilacan B. (dē-vē-lä'kän) . Phil.		17·26 N	122·25 E
101	Divinópolis (dē-vē-nô'pō-lēs)	Braz. (Rio de Janeiro In.)	20·10 S	44·53 W
85	Dixie (dĭk'sĭ) . Can. (Toronto In.)		43·36 N	79·35 W
71	Dixon (dĭks'ŭn)	Ill.	41·50 N	89·30 W
86	Dixon Ent.	Alaska-Can.	54·25 N	132·32 W
133	Diyarbakir (dē-yär-bĕk'ĭr)	Tur.	38·00 N	40·10 E
165	Dja R.	Cam.	2·40 N	14·11 E
155	Djailolo Pass	Indon.	0·05 S	129·08 E
154	Djakarta (yä-kär'tä)	Indon.	6·17 S	106·45 E
154	Djambi (yäm'bē)	Indon.	1·45 S	103·28 E
164	Djanet (Fort Charlet)	Alg.	24·29 N	9·26 E
114	Djedi R.	Alg.	34·18 N	4·39 E
164	Djelfa (jĕl'fä)	Alg.	34·40 N	3·17 E
164	Djenné (jĕnnä')	Mali	13·55 N	4·26 W
114	Djerba, Île de (I.)	Tun.	33·53 N	11·26 E
164	Djerid, Chott (L.) (jĕr'ĭd) . . Tun.		33·15 N	8·29 E
168	Djibouti (jē-bōō-tē')	Fr. Som. (Horn of Afr. In.)	11·34 N	43·00 E
113	Djidjelli (jē-jē-lē')	Alg.	36·49 N	5·47 E
139	Djumrah . Indon. (Singapore In.)		1·48 N	101·04 E
126	Djurdevac (dûr'dyĕ-väts') . Yugo.		46·03 N	17·03 E
118	Djursholm (djōōrs'hôlm) . Swe.		59·26 N	18·01 E
129	Dmitriyevka (d'mē-trĕ-yĕf'kä)	Sov. Un.	47·57 N	38·56 E
129	Dmitriyev L'govskiy (d'mē'trĭ-yĕf l'gôf'skĭ) . Sov. Un.		52·07 N	35·05 E
136	Dmitrov (d'mē'trôf)	Sov. Un. (Moskva In.)	56·21 N	37·32 E
128	Dmitrovsk (d'mē'trôfsk) . Sov. Un.		52·30 N	35·10 E
129	Dnepr (Dnieper) (R.) (nē'pĕr)	Sov. Un.	46·47 N	32·57 E
129	Dneprodzerzhinsk (d'nyĕp'rô-zĕr-shĭnsk) . Sov. Un.		48·32 N	34·38 E
129	Dnepropetrovsk (d'nyĕp'rô-pä-trôfsk) . Sov. Un.		48·23 N	34·10 E
129	Dnepropetrovsk (Oblast) . Sov. Un.		48·15 N	34·08 E
129	Dnepr Zaliv (B.) (dnyĕp'r zä'lĭf) . Sov. Un.		46·33 N	31·45 E
129	Dnestr (Dniester) (R.) (nēst'rôôl)	Sov. Un.	48·21 N	28·10 E
129	Dnestrovskiy Líman (B.)	Sov. Un.	46·13 N	29·50 E
	Dnieper (R.), see Dnepr			
	Dniester (R.), see Dnestr			
128	Dno (d'nô')	Sov. Un.	57·49 N	29·59 E
84	Dobbs Ferry (dŏbz' fĕ'rĕ)	N. Y. (New York In.)	41·01 N	73·53 W
158	Dobbyn (dŏb'ĭn)	Austl.	19·45 S	140·02 E
119	Dobele (dô'bĕ-lĕ)	Sov. Un.	56·37 N	23·18 E
120	Döbeln (dû'bĕln)	Ger.	51·08 N	13·07 E
155	Dobo	Indon.	6·00 S	134·18 E
127	Doboj (dō'boi)	Yugo.	44·42 N	18·04 E
136	Dobryanka (dôb-ryän'kä)	Sov. Un. (Urals In.)	58·27 N	56·26 E
121	Dobšina (dôp'shĕ-nä) . . . Czech.		48·48 N	20·25 E
99	Doce (R.) (dô'sĕ)	Braz.	19·01 S	42·14 W
94	Doce Leguas, Cayos de las (Is.) (kä'yōs-dĕ-läs-dô-sĕ-lĕ'gwäs)	Cuba	20·55 N	79·05 W
90	Doctor Arroyo (dōk-tōr' är-rō'yô)	Mex.	23·41 N	100·10 W
110	Doddington (dŏd'dĭng-tŏn)	Eng. (London In.)	51·17 N	0·47 E
	Dodecanese (Is.), see Dhodhekánisos			
72	Dodge City (dŏj')	Kans.	37·44 N	100·01 W
81	Dodgeville (dŏj'vĭl)	N. Y.	43·10 N	74·45 W
71	Dodgeville	Wis.	42·58 N	90·07 W
166	Dodoma (dô'dô-mä)	Tan.	6·13 S	35·36 E
74	Dodson (dŏd's'n)	Mo. (Kansas City In.)	38·48 N	94·33 W
71	Dog (L.) (dŏg)	Can.	48·42 N	89·24 W
117	Dogger Bk. (dŏg'ĕr)	Eur.	55·00 N	2·30 E
94	Dog Rocks (I.)	Ba. Is.	24·05 N	79·50 W
133	Dogubayazit	Tur.	39·35 N	44·00 E

Page	Name Pronunciation Region	Lat. °′	Long. °′
142	Dohad....................India	22·52 N	74·18 E
127	Doiran (L.)................Grc.	41·10 N	23·00 E
153	Dōjō (dō-jō).....Jap. (Osaka In.)	34·51 N	135·14 E
128	Dokshitsy (dôk-shētsē)..Sov. Un.	54·53 N	27·49 E
82	Dolbeau...................Can.	48·52 N	72·16 W
123	Dôle (dōl)..................Fr.	47·07 N	5·28 E
129	Dolgaya, Kosa (C.) (kô'sà dôl-gä'yà).Sov. Un.	46·42 N	37·42 E
132	Dolgiy (I.).............Sov. Un.	69·20 N	59·20 E
121	Dolina (dô-lyē'nä).......Sov. Un.	48·57 N	24·01 E
152	Dolinsk (dà-lēnsk')......Sov. Un.	47·29 N	142·31 E
94	Dollar Hbr...............Ba. Is.	25·30 N	79·15 W
165	Dolo.....................Som.	4·01 N	42·14 E
84	Dolomite (dŏl'ô-mīt) Ala. (Birmingham In.)	33·28 N	86·57 W
126	Dolomitiche, Alpi (Mts.) (äl-pē-dô-lô'mē-tē'chĕ).It.	46·16 N	11·43 E
101	Dolores (dô-lō'rĕs) Arg. (Buenos Aires In.)	36·20 S	57·42 W
98	Dolores..............Col. (In.)	3·33 N	74·54 W
155	Dolores (dô-lô-rĕs) Phil. (Manila In.)	17·40 N	120·43 E
76	Dolores (dô-lō'rĕs)..........Tex.	27·42 N	99·47 W
101	Dolores....Ur. (Buenos Aires In.)	33·32 S	58·15 W
69	Dolores (R.).........Colo.-Utah	38·35 N	108·50 W
90	Dolores Hidalgo (dô-lô'rĕs-ē-däl'gō).Mex.	21·09 N	100·56 W
86	Dolphin and Union Str. (dŏl'fĭn ūn'yŭn).Can.	69·22 N	117·10 W
120	Domažlice (dō'mäzh-lê-tsĕ) Czech.	49·27 N	12·55 E
123	Dombasle (dôɴ-bäl')..........Fr.	48·38 N	6·18 E
121	Dombóvár (dŏm'bō-vär)...Hung.	46·22 N	18·08 E
122	Dôme, Puy de (Pk.) (pwē'dĕ-dôm').Fr.	45·47 N	2·54 E
98	Domeyko, Cordillera (Mts.) (kôr-dēl-yĕ'rä-dô-mā'kō).Chile	20·50 S	69·02 W
93	Dominica Chan. (dŏ-mĭ-nē'kà) N. A. (Le. & Wind. Is. In.)	15·00 N	61·30 W
93	Dominica I. W. I. F. (Le. & Wind. Is. In.)	15·24 N	61·05 W
88	Dominican Republic (dô-mĭn'ĭ-kăn).N. A.	18·59 N	70·40 W
83	Dominion (dô-mĭn'yŭn).....Can.	46·13 N	60·01 W
136	Domodedovo (dô-mô-dyĕ'do-vô) Sov. Un. (Moskva In.)	55·27 N	37·45 E
101	Dom Silvério (doɴ-sêl-vĕ'ryō) Braz. (Rio de Janeiro In.)	20·09 S	42·57 W
110	Don (R.) (dŏn)............Eng.	53·27 N	1·34 W
110	Don (R.).................Eng.	53·39 N	0·58 W
116	Don (R.).................Scot.	57·19 N	2·39 W
74	Donaldson (dŏn'ăl-sŭn) Mich. (Sault Ste. Marie In.)	46·19 N	84·22 W
77	Donaldsonville (dŏn'ăld-sŭn-vĭl) La.	30·05 N	90·58 W
78	Donalsonville..............Ga.	31·02 N	84·50 W
120	Donawitz (dō'nà-vĭts).......Aus.	47·23 N	15·05 E
142	Donazari...............E. Pak.	22·18 N	91·52 E
124	Don Benito Mérida (dōn' bā-nē'tō-mĕ'rē-dä).Sp.	38·55 N	6·08 W
161	Doncaster (doŋ'kăs-tēr) Austl. (Melbourne In.)	37·47 S	145·08 E
110	Doncaster (doŋ'kăs-tēr).....Eng.	53·32 N	1·07 W
166	Dondo (dōn'dō)............Ang.	9·35 S	14·25 E
166	Dondo.....................Moz.	19·33 S	34·47 E
116	Donegal (dŏn-ê-gôl').........Ire.	54·44 N	8·05 W
116	Donegal, Mts. of (dŏn-ê-gôl').Ire.	54·44 N	8·10 W
116	Donegal Bay (dŏn-ĕ-gôl')..N. Ire.	54·35 N	8·36 W
129	Donets (R.) (dō-nyĕts')..Sov. Un.	48·48 N	38·42 E
129	Donets Coal Basin (Reg.) (dō-nyĕts').Sov. Un.	48·15 N	38·50 E
133	Donetsk (Stalino) (dō-nyĕts'k) (stä'lĭ-nō).Sov. Un.	48·00 N	37·35 E
158	Dongara (dôŋ-gă'rà).......Austl.	29·15 S	115·00 E
154	Donggala (dôŋ-gä'lä)......Indon.	0·45 S	119·32 E
151	Dong Hoi (dông-hô-ĕ')......Viet.	17·25 N	106·42 E
166	Dongo (dôŋ'gō)............Ang.	14·45 S	15·30 E
165	Dongola (dŏŋ'gō-là)..........Sud.	19·21 N	30·19 E
155	Dongon Pt. (dŏng-ŏn') Phil. (Manila In.)	12·43 N	120·35 E
165	Dongou (dôŋ-gōō')........Con. B.	2·12 N	18·08 E
73	Doniphan (dŏn'ĭ-făn)........Mo.	36·37 N	90·50 W
126	Donji Vakuf (dōn'yĭ väk'ōōf) Yugo.	44·08 N	17·25 E
76	Don Martin, Presa de (Res.) (prĕ'sä-dĕ-dôn-mär-tē'n).Mex.	27·35 N	100·38 W
82	Donnacona.................Can.	46·40 N	71·46 W
123	Donnemarie-en-Montois (dôn-mä-rē'ĕɴ-môɴ-twä') Fr. (Paris In.)	48·29 N	3·09 E
66	Donner und Blitzen R. (dŏn'ēr ōōnt blĭ'tsĕn).Ore.	42·45 N	118·57 W
167	Donnybrook (dŏ-nĭ-brŏŏk) S. Afr. (Natal In.)	29·56 S	29·54 E
75	Donora (dŏ-nō'rā) Pa. (Pittsburgh In.)	40·10 N	79·51 W
64	Doonerak (dōō'nĕ-răk)....Alaska	68·00 N	150·34 W
111	Doorn....Neth. (Amsterdam In.)	52·02 N	5·21 E
71	Door Pen. (dōr)............Wis.	44·40 N	87·36 W
126	Dora Baltea (dō'rä bäl'tä-ä)...It.	45·40 N	7·34 E
84	Doraville (dō'rà-vĭ.) Ga. (Atlanta In.)	33·54 N	84·17 W
116	Dorchester (dôr'chĕs-tēr)....Eng.	50·45 N	2·34 W
122	Dordogne (R.) (dôr-dōn'yĕ)...Fr.	44·53 N	0·16 E
111	Dordrecht (dôr'drĕκt) Neth. (Amsterdam In.)	51·48 N	4·39 E
167	Dordrecht (dô'drĕκt) S. Afr. (Natal In.)	31·24 S	27·06 E
126	Dorgali (dôr'gä-lē)..........Sard.	40·18 N	9·37 E
164	Dori (dô-rē')..........Upper Volta	13·56 N	0·01 W
85	Dorion (dôr-yō) Can. (Montreal In.)	45·23 N	74·01 W
110	Dorking (dôr'kĭng) Eng. (London In.)	51·12 N	0·20 W
85	D'Orleans, Ile (I.) (dōr-lĕ-äɴ', yl) Can. (Quebec In.)	46·56 N	70·27 W
75	Dormont (dôr'mŏnt) Pa. (Pittsburgh In.)	40·24 N	80·02 W
120	Dornbirn (dôrn'bērn)........Aus.	47·24 N	9·45 E
116	Dornoch (dôr'nŏκ).........Scot.	57·55 N	4·01 W
116	Dornoch Firth (dôr'nŏκ fûrth) Scot.	57·55 N	3·55 W
128	Dorogobuzh (dôrôgô'-bōō'zh) Sov. Un.	54·57 N	33·18 E
121	Dorohoi (dō-rô-hoi')........Rom.	47·57 N	26·28 E
	Dorpat, see Tartu		
158	Dorre (I.) (dôr)...........Austl.	25·19 S	113·10 E
74	Dorsey (dôrsĭ)..Ill. (St. Louis In.)	38·59 N	90·00 W
84	Dorsey......Md. (Baltimore In.)	39·11 N	76·45 W
123	Dorsten (dōr'stĕn) Ger. (Ruhr In.)	51·40 N	6·58 E
123	Dortmund (dôrt'mōōnt) Ger. (Ruhr In.)	51·31 N	7·28 E
123	Dortmund-Ems Kanal (can.) (dōrt'mōōnd-ĕms' kä-näl') Ger. (Ruhr In.)	51·50 N	7·25 E
133	Dörtyal (dûrt'yôl)..........Tur.	36·50 N	36·20 E
85	Dorval (dôr-vål') Can. (Montreal In.)	45·26 N	73·44 W
99	Dos Caminos (dôs-kä-mē'nôs) Ven. (In.)	9·38 N	67·17 W
65	Dosewallips (R.) (dō'sê-wäl'lĭps) Wash. (Seattle In.)	47·45 N	123·04 W
124	Dos Hermanas (dōsĕr-mä'näs).Sp.	37·17 N	5·56 W
164	Dosso (dôs-ō')............Niger	13·03 N	3·09 E
78	Dothan (dō'thăn)............Ala.	31·13 N	85·23 W
122	Douai (dōō-ā')..............Fr.	50·23 N	3·04 E
164	Douala (dōō-ä'lä)..........Cam.	4·00 N	9·37 E
122	Douarnenez (dōō-är'nē-nĕs')...Fr.	48·06 N	4·18 W
77	Double Bay. (dŭb'"l bī'yōō) Tex. (In.)	29·40 N	94·38 W
125	Douéra (dōō-ā'rà)...........Alg.	36·40 N	2·55 E
64	Douglas (dŭg'lăs).........Alaska	58·18 N	134·35 W
69	Douglas...................Ariz.	31·20 N	109·30 W
78	Douglas.....................Ga.	31·30 N	82·53 W
116	Douglas (dŭg'lăs).....Isle of Man	54·10 N	4·24 W
83	Douglas (dŭg'lăs) Mass. (Boston In.)	42·04 N	71·45 W
67	Douglas (dŭg'lăs)..........Wyo.	42·45 N	105·21 W
110	Douglas (R.) (dŭg'lăs)......Eng.	53·38 N	2·48 W
78	Douglas (R.) (dŭg'lăs)......Tenn.	36·00 N	83·35 W
78	Douglasville (dŭg'lăs-vĭl).....Ga.	33·45 N	84·47 W
165	Doumé (dōō-mā')...........Cam.	4·14 N	13·26 E
99	Dourada, Serra (Mts.) (sĕ'r-rä-dōōō-rà'dä).Braz.	15·11 S	49·57 W
123	Dourdan (dōōr-däɴ') Fr. (Paris In.)	48·32 N	2·01 E
124	Douro, Rio (R.) (rē'ō-dô'ōō-rō) Port.	41·03 N	8·12 W
110	Dove (R.) (dŭv)...........Eng.	52·53 N	1·47 W
81	Dover (dō vēr)...............Del.	39·10 N	75·30 W
117	Dover.....................Eng.	51·08 N	1·19 E
81	Dover....................N. H.	43·15 N	71·00 W
84	Dover......N. J. (New York In.)	40·53 N	74·33 W
80	Dover.....................Ohio	40·35 N	81·30 W
168	Dover...S. Afr. (Johannesburg & Pretoria In.)	27·05 S	27·44 E
117	Dover, Str. of.............Eur.	50·50 N	1·15 W
82	Dover-Foxcroft (dō'vēr fôks'krôft) Maine	45·10 N	69·15 W
132	Dovlekanovo (dŏv'lyĕk-à-nô-vô) Sov. Un.	54·15 N	55·05 E
118	Dovre Fjeld (Plat.) (dôv'rĕ fyĕl') Nor.	62·03 N	8·36 E
74	Dow (dou).....Ill. (St. Louis In.)	39·01 N	90·20 W
80	Dowagiac (dô-wô'jăk)......Mich.	42·00 N	86·05 W
75	Downers Grove (dou'nērz grōv) Ill. (Chicago In.)	41·48 N	88·00 W
74	Downey (dou'nĭ) Calif. (Los Angeles In.)	33·56 N	118·08 W
62	Downieville (dou'nĭ-vĭl).....Calif.	39·35 N	120·48 W
72	Downs (dounz)............Kans.	39·29 N	98·32 W
75	Doylestown (doilz'toun) Ohio (Cleveland In.)	40·58 N	81·43 W
164	Draa, C. (drà)..............Mor.	28·39 N	12·15 W
164	Draa, Wadi R. (wä-dĭ drä')..Mor.	28·00 N	9·31 W
129	Drabov (drä'bôf)........Sov. Un.	49·57 N	32·14 E
123	Drac (R.) (dräκ)..............Fr.	44·50 N	5·47 E
83	Dracut (drā'kŭt) Mass. (Boston In.)	42·40 N	71·19 W
127	Draganovo (drä-gä-nō'vô)....Bul.	43·13 N	25·45 E
127	Drăgăsani (drä-gä-shän'ĭ)....Rom.	44·39 N	24·18 E
123	Draguignan (drä-gên-yäɴ')....Fr.	43·35 N	6·28 E
166	Drakensberg (Mts.) (drä'kĕnz-bĕrgh).S. Afr.	29·15 S	29·07 E
96	Drake Passage (drāk păs'ĭj) S. A.-Ant.	57·00 S	65·00 W
127	Dráma (drä'mä)............Grc.	41·09 N	24·10 E
118	Drammen (dräm'ĕn)........Nor.	59·45 N	10·15 E
120	Drau R. (drou)............Aus.	46·44 N	13·45 E
126	Drava (R.) (Drä'vä)........Yugo.	46·37 N	15·17 E
126	Dravograd (Drä'vô-gräd')..Yugo.	46·37 N	15·01 E
120	Drawsko Pomorskie (dräv'skō pō-mōr'skyĕ).Pol.	53·31 N	15·50 E
65	Drayton Hbr. (drā'tŭn) Wash. (Vancouver In.)	48·58 N	122·40 W
75	Drayton Plains Mich. (Detroit In.)	42·41 N	83·23 W
146	Dre Chu (R.)..............China	34·11 N	96·08 E
123	Drensteinfurt (drĕn'shtīn-fōōrt) Ger. (Ruhr In.)	51·47 N	7·44 E
120	Dresden (drās'dĕn)..........Ger.	51·05 N	13·45 E
123	Dreux (drû).......Fr. (Paris In.)	48·44 N	1·24 E
168	Driefontein S. Afr. (Johannesburg & Pretoria In.)	25·53 S	29·10 E
127	Drin (R.) (drēn)...........Alb.	42·13 N	20·13 E
127	Drina (R.) (drē'nä)........Yugo.	44·09 N	19·30 E
127	Drinit, Pellg I (Bght.).......Alb.	41·42 N	19·17 E
128	Drissa (drĭs'sä)........Sov. Un.	55·48 N	27·59 E
128	Drissa (R.)............Sov. Un.	55·44 N	28·58 E
84	Driver..........Va. (Norfolk In.)	36·50 N	76·30 W
118	Dröbak (drû'bäk)...........Nor.	59·40 N	10·35 E
116	Drogheda (drŏ'hē-dà).........Ire.	53·43 N	6·15 W
121	Drogichin (drō-gē'chĭn)..Sov. Un.	52·10 N	25·11 E
121	Drohobych (drô-hô'bĭch) Sov. Un.	49·21 N	23·31 E
122	Drôme (R.) (drōm)...........Fr.	44·42 N	4·53 E
110	Dronfield (drŏn'fēld)........Eng.	53·18 N	1·28 W
86	Drumheller (drŭm-hĕl-ēr)...Can.	51·30 N	112·42 W
80	Drummond (I.) (drŭm'ŭnd) Mich.	46·00 N	83·50 W
82	Drummondville (drŭm'ŭnd-vĭl) Can.	45·53 N	72·33 W
73	Drumright (drŭm'rīt).......Okla.	35·59 N	96·37 W
111	Drunen...Neth. (Amsterdam In.)	51·41 N	5·10 E
128	Drut' (R.) (drōōt)......Sov. Un.	53·40 N	29·45 E
128	Druya (drōō'yà)........Sov. Un.	55·45 N	27·26 E
115	Druze, Jebel (Mts.)........Syria	32·40 N	36·58 E
121	Drweca R. (d'r-văn'tsä)......Pol.	53·06 N	19·13 E
87	Dryden (drī-dĕn)............Can.	49·50 N	92·47 W
161	Drysdale..Austl. (Melbourne In.)	38·11 S	144·34 E
79	Dry Tortugas (I.) (tôr-tōō'gäz) Fla. (In.)	24·37 N	82·45 W
164	Dschang (dshäng)..........Cam.	5·34 N	10·09 E
85	Duagh......Can. (Edmonton In.)	53·43 N	113·24 W
101	Duas Barras (dōō'äs-bà'r-räs) Braz. (Rio de Janeiro In.)	22·03 S	42·30 W
86	Dubawnt (L.) (dōō-bônt')....Can.	63·27 N	103·30 W
86	Dubawnt (R.)..............Can.	61·30 N	103·49 W
144	Dubayy.................Sau. Ar.	25·18 N	55·26 E
160	Dubbo (dŭb'ō)............Austl.	32·20 S	148·42 E
65	Dublin (dŭb'lĭn) Calif. (San Francisco In.)	37·42 N	121·56 W
78	Dublin......................Ga.	32·33 N	82·55 W
76	Dublin....................Tex.	32·05 N	98·20 W
	Dublin, see Baile Atha Cliath		
121	Dubno (dōō'b-nô)......Sov. Un.	50·24 N	25·44 E
81	Du Bois (dōō-bois')...........Pa.	41·10 N	78·45 W
129	Dubossary (dōō-bō-sä'rĭ).Sov. Un.	47·16 N	29·11 E
133	Dubovka (dōō-bôf'kà)...Sov. Un.	49·00 N	44·50 E
136	Dubrovka (dōō-brôf'kà) Sov. Un. (Leningrad In.)	59·51 N	30·56 E
127	Dubrovnik (Ragusa) (dōō'brôv-nêk) (rä-gōō'sä) Yugo.	42·40 N	18·10 E
128	Dubrovno (dōō-brôf'nō)..Sov. Un.	54·39 N	30·54 E
71	Dubuque (dōō-būk')..........Iowa	42·30 N	90·43 W
69	Duchesne (dōō-shān').......Utah	40·12 N	110·23 W
69	Duchesne (R.).............Utah	40·20 N	110·50 W
158	Duchess (dŭch'ĕs).........Austl.	21·30 S	139·55 E
157	Ducie I. (dü-sē')........Oceania	25·30 S	126·20 W
80	Duck (I.) (dŭk)............Can.	45·35 N	83·00 W
78	Duck (R.)................Tenn.	35·55 N	87·40 W
65	Duckabush (R.) (dŭk'à-bōōsh) Wash. (Seattle In.)	47·41 N	123·09 W
86	Duck Mtn..................Can.	51·43 N	101·07 W
78	Ducktown (dŭk'toun)......Tenn.	35·03 N	84·20 W
68	Duckwater Pk. (dŭk-wô-tēr).Nev.	39·00 N	115·31 W
98	Duda (dōō'dä) (R.).....Col. (In.)	3·25 N	74·23 W
134	Dudinka (dōō-dĭn'kà)....Sov. Un.	69·15 N	85·42 E
110	Dudley (dŭd'lĭ)..............Eng.	52·31 N	2·04 W
111	Duerne.......Bel. (Bruxelles In.)	51·13 N	4·27 E
124	Duero (R.) (dwĕ'rô)..........Sp.	41·30 N	5·10 W
80	Dugger (dŭg'ēr)...............Ind.	39·00 N	87·10 W
126	Dugi Otok (I.) (dōō'gê O'tôk) Yugo.	44·03 N	14·40 E
123	Duisburg (dōō'ĭs-bōōrgh) Ger. (Ruhr In.)	51·26 N	6·46 E
98	Duitama (dōōê-tä'mä).......Col.	5·48 N	73·09 W
128	Dukhovshchina (dōō-κôfsh'chēnà) Sov. Un.	55·13 N	32·26 E
110	Dukinfield (dŭk'ĭn-fēld).....Eng.	53·28 N	2·05 W
121	Dukla P. (dōō'klä)...........Pol.	49·25 N	21·44 E
93	Dulce, Golfo (G.) (gōl'fô dōōl'sä) C. R.	8·25 N	83·13 W
	Dulcigno, see Ulčinj		
123	Dülken (dül'kĕn)..Ger. (Ruhr In.)	51·15 N	6·21 E
123	Dülmen (dül'mĕn) Ger. (Ruhr In.)	51·50 N	7·17 E
74	Duluth (dōō-lōōth') Minn. (Duluth In.)	46·50 N	92·07 W
139	Dūmā.......Syria (Palestine In.)	33·34 N	36·17 E
155	Dumaguete City (dōō-mä-gā'tā) Phil.	9·14 N	123·15 E
168	Dumaît, Masabb (R. Mth.) U. A. R. (Nile In.)	31·36 N	31·45 E
155	Dumali Pt. (dōō-mä'lē) Phil. (Manila Pt.)	13·07 N	121·42 E
116	Dumbarton (dŭm'bār-tŭn)..Scot.	56·00 N	4·35 W
142	Dum Dum...India (Calcutta In.)	22·37 N	88·25 E
116	Dumfries (dŭm-frēs').......Scot.	54·05 N	3·40 W
84	Dumont (dōō'mŏnt) N. J. (New York In.)	40·56 N	74·00 W
77	Dumont............Tex. (In.)	29·40 N	95·14 W
168	Dumyāţ (Damietta) (dōōm-yät') (dăm-ĭ-ĕt'à).U. A. R. (Nile In.)	31·22 N	31·50 E
121	Dunaföldvar (dōō'nô-fûld'vär) Hung.	46·48 N	18·55 E
121	Dunajec R. (dōō-nä'yĕts).....Pol.	49·52 N	20·53 E
121	Dunapataj (doo'nô-pô-toi).Hung.	46·42 N	19·03 E
121	Duna R. (dōō'nä)..........Hung.	46·07 N	18·45 E
136	Dunay (dōō'nĭ) Sov. Un. (Leningrad In.)	59·59 N	30·57 E
129	Dunayevtsy (dōō-nä'yĕf-tsĭ) Sov. Un.	48·52 N	26·51 E
116	Dunbar (dŭn'bär)...........Scot.	56·00 N	2·25 W
80	Dunbar...................W. Va.	38·20 N	81·45 W
66	Duncan (dŭŋ'kăn)...........Can.	48·46 N	123·42 W
72	Duncan.....................Okla.	34·29 N	97·56 W
116	Duncansby Hd. (dŭn'kănz-bĭ).. Scot.	58·40 N	3·01 W
74	Duncanville (dŭn'kăn-vĭl) Tex. (Dallas, Fort Worth In.)	32·39 N	96·55 W
116	Dundalk (dŭn'dôk)............Ire.	54·00 N	6·18 W
84	Dundalk.....Md. (Baltimore In.)	39·16 N	76·31 W
116	Dundalk B. (dŭn'dôk).........Ire.	53·55 N	6·15 W

ng-sing; ŋ-baŋk; ɴ-nasalized n; nŏd; cŏmmit; ōld; ôbey; ôrder; fōōd; fŏŏt; ou-out; s-soft; sh-dish; th-thin; pūre; ůnite; ûrn; stŭd; circŭs; ü-as "y" in study; '-indeterminate vowel

Page	Name Pronunciation Region	Lat. °′	Long. °′
85	Dundas (dŭn-dăs') Can. (Toronto In.)	43·16 N	79·58 W
75	Dundee (dŭn-dē') Ill. (Chicago In.)	42·06 N	88·17 W
116	Dundee Scot.	56·30 N	2·55 W
167	Dundee S. Afr. (Natal In.)	28·14 S	30·16 E
158	Dundras (L.) (dŭn-drȧs) Austl.	32·15 S	132·00 E
158	Dundras Str. (dŭn'drȧs) Austl.	10·35 S	131·15 E
116	Dundrum B. (dŭn-drŭm') Ire.	54·13 N	5·47 W
79	Dunedin (dŭn-ē'dĭn) Fla. (In.)	28·00 N	82·43 W
159	Dunedin N. Z. (In.)	45·48 S	170·32 E
84	Dunellen (dŭn-ĕl'l'n) N. J. (New York In.)	40·36 N	74·28 W
116	Dunfermline (dŭn-fẽrm'lĭn) Scot.	56·05 N	3·30 W
116	Dungarvin (dŭn-gȧr'vĭn) Ire.	52·06 N	7·50 W
65	Dungeness (dŭnj-nĕs') Wash. (Seattle In.)	48·09 N	123·07 W
65	Dungeness (R.) Wash. (Seattle In.)	48·03 N	123·10 W
65	Dungeness Spit Wash. (Seattle In.)	48·11 N	123·03 W
165	Dungu (dōōŋ-gōō') Con. L.	3·48 N	28·32 E
122	Dunkerque (dŭn-kĕrk') Fr.	51·02 N	2·37 E
80	Dunkirk (dŭn'kûrk) Ind.	40·20 N	85·25 W
81	Dunkirk N. Y.	42·30 N	79·20 W
116	Dun Laoghaire (dŭn-lā'rĕ) Ire.	53·16 N	6·09 W
70	Dunlap (dŭn'lăp) Iowa	41·53 N	95·33 W
78	Dunlap Tenn.	35·23 N	85·23 W
81	Dunmore (dŭn'mōr) Pa.	41·25 N	75·30 W
79	Dunn (dŭn) N. C.	35·18 N	78·37 W
79	Dunnellon (dŭn-ĕl'ŏn) Fla.	29·02 N	82·28 W
81	Dunnville (dŭn'vĭl) Can.	42·55 N	79·40 W
66	Dunsmuir (dŭnz'mūr) Calif.	41·08 N	122·17 W
84	Dunwoody (dŭn-wŏŏd'ĭ) Ga. (Atlanta In.)	33·57 N	84·20 W
75	Du Page R. (dōō pāj) Ill. (Chicago In.)	41·41 N	88·11 W
75	Du Page R., E. Br. Ill. (Chicago In.)	41·49 N	88·05 W
75	Du Page R., W. Br. Ill. (Chicago In.)	41·48 N	88·10 W
155	Dupax (dōō'päks) Phil. (Manila In.)	16·16 N	121·06 E
127	Dupnitsa (dōōp'nē-tsȧ) Bul.	42·15 N	23·07 E
74	Dupo (dū'pō) Ill. (St. Louis In.)	38·31 N	90·12 W
166	Duque de Bragança (dōō'kā dā brä-gäN'sä) Ang.	8·55 S	16·10 E
100	Duque de Caxias (dōō'kĕ-dĕ-kä'shyäs) Braz. (In.)	22·46 S	43·18 W
75	Duquesne (dŏŏ-kān') Pa. (Pittsburgh In.)	40·22 N	79·51 W
73	Du Quoin (dŏŏ-kwoin') Ill.	38·01 N	89·14 W
123	Durance (R.) (dü-räNs') Fr.	43·46 N	5·52 E
80	Durand (dŭ-rănd') Mich.	42·50 N	84·00 W
71	Durand Wis.	44·37 N	91·58 W
69	Durango (dŏŏ-räŋ'gō) Colo.	37·15 N	107·55 W
88	Durango (State) Mex.	25·00 N	106·00 W
78	Durant (dŭ-rănt') Miss.	33·05 N	89·50 W
73	Durant Okla.	33·59 N	96·23 W
124	Duratón (R.) (dōō-rä-tōn') Sp.	41·55 N	3·55 W
101	Durazno (dōō-räz'nō) Ur. (Buenos Aires In.)	33·21 S	56·31 W
101	Durazno (Dept.) Ur. (Buenos Aires In.)	33·00 S	56·35 W
167	Durban (dûr'băn) S. Afr. (Natal In.)	29·48 S	31·00 E
166	Durbanville (dûr-băn'vĭl) S. Afr. (Cape Town In.)	33·50 S	18·39 E
119	Durbe (dōōr'bĕ) Sov. Un.	56·36 N	21·24 E
123	Düren (dü'rĕn) Ger. (Ruhr In.)	50·48 N	6·30 E
116	Durham (dûr'ăm) Eng.	54·47 N	1·46 W
79	Durham N. C.	36·00 N	78·55 W
75	Durham Wis. (Milwaukee In.)	42·52 N	88·04 W
160	Durham Downs Austl.	27·30 S	141·55 E
127	Durrës (dōōr'ĕs) Alb.	41·19 N	19·27 E
155	D'urville, Kap (C.) (dûr'vĭl) Neth. N. Gui.	1·20 S	138·45 E
81	Duryea (dōōr-yā') Pa.	41·20 N	75·50 W
123	Düsseldorf (düs'ĕl-dôrf) Ger. (Ruhr In.)	51·14 N	6·47 E
111	Dussen Neth. (Amsterdam In.)	51·43 N	4·58 E
150	Dutalan Ula (Mtn.) Mong.	49·25 N	112·40 E
64	Dutch Harbor (dŭch här'bẽr) Alaska	53·58 N	166·30 W
65	Duvall (dōō'vâl) Wash. (Seattle In.)	47·44 N	121·59 W
95	Duvergé (dōō-vĕr-hĕ') Dom. Rep.	18·20 N	71·20 W
65	Duwamish (dōō-wăm'ĭsh) Wash. (Seattle In.)	47·24 N	122·18 W
	Dvina, Western, R., see Zapadnaya Dvina		
132	Dvinskaya Guba (G.) Sov. Un.	65·10 N	38·40 E
120	Dvur Kralove nad Labem (dvōōr' krä'lô-vā) Czech.	50·28 N	15·43 E
142	Dwārka India	22·18 N	68·59 E
80	Dwight (dwīt) Ill.	41·00 N	88·20 W
128	Dyat'kovo (dyät'kô-vô) Sov. Un.	53·36 N	34·19 E
75	Dyer (dī'ẽr) Ind. (Chicago In.)	41·30 N	87·31 W
78	Dyersburg (dī'ẽrz-bûrg) Tenn.	36·02 N	89·23 W
71	Dyersville (dī'ẽrz-vĭl) Iowa	42·28 N	91·09 W
65	Dyes Inlet (dīz) Wash. (Seattle In.)	47·37 N	122·45 W
144	Dyushanbe (Stalinabad) (dê-ōō'shä'n-bĕ) (stälyĭn-ŭ-bät') Sov. Un.	38·41 N	68·43 E
146	Dzabhan Gol (R.) Mong.	48·19 N	94·08 E
150	Dzamiin Üüde Mong.	44·38 N	111·32 E
167	Dzaoudzi (dzou'dzĭ) Comores, Arch. des	12·44 S	45·15 E
103	Dzaudzhikau (dzou-jĭ-kou') Sov. Un.	48·00 N	44·52 E
129	Dzerzhinsk (dzhĕr-zhĭnsk') Sov. Un.	48·24 N	37·58 E
128	Dzerzhinsk Sov. Un.	53·41 N	27·14 E
132	Dzerzhinsk Sov. Un.	56·20 N	43·50 E
134	Dzhalal-Abad (jȧ-läl'ȧ-bät') Sov. Un.	41·13 N	73·35 E
134	Dzhambul (dzhäm-bōōl') Sov. Un.	42·51 N	71·29 E
129	Dzhankoy (dzhän'koi) Sov. Un.	45·43 N	34·22 E
136	Dzhetygara (dzhĕt'-gä'rȧ) Sov. Un. (Urals In.)	52·12 N	61·18 E
134	Dzhizak (dzhĭ'zäk) Sov. Un.	40·13 N	67·58 E
135	Dzhugdzhur Khrebet (Mts.) (jŏŏg-jōōr') Sov. Un.	56·15 N	137·00 E
121	Działoszyce (jyä-wō-shē'tsĕ) Pol.	50·21 N	20·22 E
92	Dzibalchén (zē-bäl-chĕ'n) Mex. (Yucatan In.)	19·25 N	89·39 W
92	Dzidzantún (zēd-zän-tōō'n) Mex. (Yucatan In.)	21·18 N	89·00 W
120	Dzierzoniów (dzyĕr-zhôn'yŭf) Pol.	50·44 N	16·38 E
92	Dzilam Gonzalez (zē-lä'm-gôn-zä'lĕz) Mex. (Yucatan In.)	21·21 N	88·53 W
92	Dzitás (zē-tá's) Mex. (Yucatan In.)	20·47 N	88·32 W
92	Dzitbalché (dzēt-bäl-chā') Mex. (Yucatan In.)	20·18 N	90·03 W
146	Dzungaria (Reg.) (dzōōŋ-gä'rĭ-ȧ) China	44·39 N	86·13 E
64	Eagle (ē'g'l) Alaska	64·42 N	141·20 W
77	Eagle Tex. (In.)	29·40 N	94·40 W
80	Eagle W. Va.	38·10 N	81·20 W
69	Eagle (R.) Colo.	39·32 N	106·28 W
65	Eaglecliff (ē'g'l-klĭf) Wash. (Portland In.)	46·10 N	123·13 W
75	Eagle Cr. Ind. (Indianapolis In.)	39·54 N	86·17 W
74	Eagle Ford (ē'g'l fērd) Tex. (Dallas, Fort Worth In.)	32·47 N	96·52 W
71	Eagle Grove Iowa	42·39 N	93·55 W
82	Eagle Lake Maine	47·03 N	68·38 W
77	Eagle Lake Tex.	29·37 N	96·20 W
66	Eagle L. Calif.	40·45 N	120·52 W
74	Eagle Mountain L. Tex. (Dallas, Fort Worth In.)	32·56 N	97·27 W
76	Eagle Pass Tex.	28·49 N	100·30 W
66	Eagle Pk. Calif.	41·18 N	120·11 W
110	Ealing (ē'lĭng) Eng. (London In.)	51·29 N	0·19 W
73	Earle (ûrl) Ark.	35·14 N	90·28 W
78	Earlington (ûr'lĭng-tŭn) S. C.	37·15 N	87·31 W
79	Easley (ēz'lĭ) S. C.	34·48 N	82·37 W
88	East, Mt. C. Z. (Panama Canal In.)	9·09 N	79·16 W
74	East Alton (ôl'tŭn) Ill. (St. Louis In.)	38·53 N	90·08 W
81	East Angus (ăŋ'gŭs) Can.	45·35 N	71·40 W
75	East Aurora (ô-rō'rȧ) N. Y. (Buffalo In.)	42·46 N	78·38 W
84	East B. La. (New Orleans In.)	29·03 N	89·16 W
77	East B. Tex. (In.)	29·30 N	94·41 W
111	East Berlin (bĕr-lēn') Ger. (Berlin In.)	52·31 N	13·28 E
78	East Bernstadt (bûrn'stȧt) Ky.	37·09 N	84·08 W
65	Eastbound (ēst-bound) Wash. (Vancouver In.)	48·42 N	122·42 W
117	Eastbourne (ēst'bôrn) Eng.	50·48 N	0·16 E
95	East Caicos (I.) (kī'kōs) Ba. Is.	21·40 N	71·35 W
159	East C. N. Z. (In.)	37·37 S	178·33 E
	East Cape, see Dezhneva, Mys		
74	East Carondelet (kȧ-rŏn'dĕ-lĕt) Ill. (St. Louis In.)	38·33 N	90·14 W
75	East Chicago (shĭ-kô'gō) Ind. (Chicago In.)	41·39 N	87·29 W
147	East China Sea Asia	30·28 N	125·52 E
75	East Cleveland (klēv'lănd) Ohio (Cleveland In.)	41·33 N	81·35 W
77	East Cote Blanche B. (kōt bläNsh') La.	29·30 N	92·07 W
71	East Des Moines (R.) (dē moin') Iowa	42·57 N	94·17 W
75	East Detroit (dē-troit') Mich. (Detroit In.)	42·28 N	82·57 W
	Easter (I.), see Rapa Nui		
120	Eastern Alps (Mts.) Aus.-Switz.	47·03 N	10·55 E
143	Eastern Ghats (Mts.) India	19·35 N	78·08 E
146	Eastern Turkestan (Reg.) (tōōr-kĕ-stän') (tûr-kĕ-stăn') China	38·23 N	80·41 E
75	East Gary (gā'rĭ) Ind. (Chicago In.)	41·34 N	87·15 W
70	East Grand Forks (grănd fôrks) Minn.	47·56 N	97·02 W
84	East Greenwich (grĭn'ĭj) R. I. (Providence In.)	41·40 N	71·27 W
81	Easthampton (ēst-hămp'tŭn) Mass.	42·15 N	72·45 W
81	East Hartford (härt'fērd) Conn.	41·45 N	72·35 W
67	East Helena (hĕ-lē'nȧ) Mont.	46·31 N	111·50 W
110	East Ilsley (ĭl'slē) Eng. (London In.)	51·30 N	1·18 W
80	East Jordan (jôr'dăn) Mich.	45·05 N	85·05 W
74	East Kansas City (kăn'zȧs) Mo. (Kansas City In.)	39·09 N	94·30 W
76	Eastland (ēst'lănd) Tex.	32·24 N	98·47 W
80	East Lansing (lăn'sĭng) Mich.	42·45 N	84·30 W
74	East Leavenworth (lĕv'ĕn-wûrth) Mo. (Kansas City In.)	39·18 N	94·50 W
80	East Liverpool (lĭv'ẽr-pōōl) Ohio	40·40 N	80·35 W
167	East London (lŭn'dŭn) S. Afr. (Natal In.)	33·02 S	27·54 E
74	East Los Angeles (lōs ăŋ'hȧ-lās) Calif. (Los Angeles In.)	34·01 N	118·09 W
87	Eastmain (R.) (ēst'mān) Can.	52·12 N	73·19 W
78	Eastman (ēst-măn) Ga.	32·10 N	83·11 W
84	East Millstone (mĭl'stōn) N. J. (New York In.)	40·30 N	74·35 W
71	East Moline (mō-lēn') Ill.	41·31 N	90·28 W
73	East Nishnabotna (R.) (nĭsh-nȧ-bŏt'nȧ) Iowa	40·53 N	95·23 W
81	Easton (ēs'tŭn) Md.	72·45 N	76·05 W
75	Easton (ēst'ŭn) Ohio (Cleveland In.)	40·57 N	81·45 W
81	Easton Pa.	40·45 N	75·15 W
84	Easton L. Conn. (New York In.)	41·18 N	73·17 W
84	East Orange (ŏr'ĕnj) N. J. (New York In.)	40·46 N	74·12 W
80	East Peoria (pē-ō'rĭ-ȧ) Ill.	40·40 N	89·30 W
75	East Pittsburgh (pĭts'bûrg) Pa. (Pittsburgh In.)	40·24 N	79·50 W
84	East Point Ga. (Atlanta In.)	33·41 N	84·27 W
82	Eastport (ēst-pōrt) Can.	44·53 N	67·01 W
84	East Providence (prŏv'ĭ-dĕns) R. I. (Providence In.)	41·49 N	71·22 W
110	East Retford (rĕt'fērd) Eng.	53·19 N	0·56 W
110	East Riding (Co.) (rīd'ĭng) Eng.	53·47 N	0·36 W
81	East Rochester (rŏch'ĕs-tẽr) N. Y.	43·10 N	77·30 W
74	East St. Louis (sānt lōō'ĭs) (lōō-ĭ) Ill. (St. Louis In.)	38·38 N	90·10 W
130	East Siberian Sea (sī-bĭr'y'n) Sov. Un.	73·00 N	153·28 E
65	East Stanwood (stăn'wŏŏd) Wash. (Seattle In.)	48·14 N	122·21 W
81	East Stroudsburg (stroudz'bûrg) Pa.	41·00 N	75·10 W
81	East Syracuse (sĭr'ȧ-kūs) N. Y.	43·05 N	76·00 W
69	East Tavaputs Plat. (tă-vă'-pŭts) Utah	39·25 N	109·45 W
80	East Tawas (tô'wȧs) Mich.	44·15 N	83·30 W
85	Eastview (ēst'vyōō) Can. (Ottawa In.)	45·27 N	75·39 W
68	East Walker (R.) (wôk'ẽr) Nev.	38·36 N	119·02 W
75	Eaton (ē'tŭn) Colo.	40·31 N	104·42 W
80	Eaton Ohio	39·45 N	84·40 W
75	Eaton Ohio (Cleveland In.)	41·19 N	82·01 W
80	Eaton Rapids (răp'ĭdz) Mich.	42·30 N	84·40 W
78	Eatonton (ē'tŭn-tŭn) Ga.	33·20 N	83·24 W
84	Eatontown (ē'tŭn-toun) N. J. (New York In.)	40·18 N	74·04 W
71	Eau Claire (ō klâr') Wis.	44·47 N	91·32 W
118	Ebeltoft (ĕ'bĕl-tŭft) Den.	56·11 N	10·39 E
111	Ebersberg (ĕ'bĕrs-bĕrgh) Ger. (München In.)	48·05 N	11·58 E
120	Ebingen (ā'bĭng-ĕn) Ger.	48·13 N	9·04 E
146	Ebi Nuur (L.) (ā'bē) China	45·09 N	83·15 E
126	Eboli (ĕb'ō-lē) It.	40·38 N	15·04 E
164	Ebolowa Cam.	2·54 N	11·09 E
111	Ebreichsdorf Aus. (Wien In.)	47·58 N	16·24 E
125	Ebro, Río (R.) (rē'-ô-ā'brō) Sp.	41·22 N	0·17 W
110	Eccles (ĕk''lz) Eng.	53·29 N	2·20 W
80	Eccles W. Va.	37·45 N	81·10 W
110	Eccleshall (ĕk''lz-hôl) Eng.	52·51 N	2·15 W
127	Eceabat (Maidos) Tur.	40·10 N	26·21 E
155	Echague (ā-chä'gwä) Phil. (Manila In.)	16·43 N	121·40 E
93	Echandi, Cerro (Mt.) (sĕ'r-rô-ĕ-chä'nd) Pan.	9·05 N	82·51 W
74	Echo Bay (ĕk'ō) Can. (Sault Ste. Marie In.)	46·29 N	84·04 W
123	Echternach (ĕk'tẽr-näk) Lux.	49·48 N	6·25 E
160	Echuca (ê-chŏŏ'kȧ) Austl.	36·10 S	144·47 E
124	Écija (ā'thē-hä) Sp.	37·20 N	5·07 W
120	Eckernförde Ger.	54·27 N	9·51 E
84	Eclipse (ê-klĭps') Va. (Norfolk In.)	36·55 N	76·29 W
75	Ecorse (ê-kôrs') Mich. (Detroit In.)	42·15 N	83·09 W
96	Ecuador (ĕk'wȧ-dôr) S. A.	0·00 N	78·30 W
165	Edd Eth.	13·57 N	41·37 E
165	Ed Dāmer (ĕd dä'mẽr) Sud.	17·38 N	33·57 E
165	Ed Debba (dĕb'ȧ) Sud.	18·04 N	30·58 E
165	Ed Dueim (dōō-ām') Sud.	13·56 N	32·22 E
78	Eddyville (ĕd'ĭ-vĭl) Ky.	37·03 N	88·03 W
164	Edéa (ĕ-dā'ȧ) Cam.	3·45 N	10·08 E
74	Eden (ē'd'n) Calif. (Los Angeles In.)	33·54 N	117·05 W
74	Eden Utah (Salt Lake City In.)	41·18 N	111·49 W
116	Eden (R.) (ē'dĕn) Eng.	54·40 N	2·35 W
110	Edenbridge (ē'dĕn-brĭj) Eng. (London In.)	51·11 N	0·05 E
110	Edenham (ē'd'n-ăm) Eng.	52·46 N	0·25 W
74	Eden Prairie (prâr'ĭ) Minn. (Minneapolis, St. Paul In.)	44·51 N	93·29 W
79	Edenton (ē'dĕn-tŭn) N. C.	36·02 N	76·37 W
75	Edenton Ohio (Cincinnati In.)	39·14 N	84·02 W
167	Edenvale (ĕd'ĕn-vāl) S. Afr. (Johannesburg & Pretoria In.)	29·06 S	28·10 E
168	Edenville (ē'd'n-vĭl) S. Afr. (Johannesburg & Pretoria In.)	27·33 S	27·42 E
120	Eder R. (ā'dẽr) Ger.	51·05 N	8·52 E
164	Edeyen, Erg (Dunes) (ĕ-dā'yĕn) Alg.	27·30 N	7·30 E
79	Edgefield (ĕj'fēld) S. C.	33·52 N	81·55 W
70	Edgeley (ĕj'lĭ) N. D.	46·24 N	98·43 W
70	Edgemont (ĕj'mŏnt) S. D.	43·19 N	103·50 W
71	Edgerton (ĕj'ẽr-tŭn) Wis.	42·49 N	89·06 W
84	Edgewater (ĕj-wô-tẽr) Ala. (Birmingham In.)	33·31 N	86·52 W
127	Édhessa Grc.	40·48 N	22·04 E
74	Edina (ê-dī'nȧ) Minn. (Minneapolis, St. Paul In.)	44·55 N	93·20 W
73	Edina Mo.	40·10 N	92·11 W
80	Edinburg (ĕd''n-bûrg) Ind.	39·20 N	85·55 W
76	Edinburg Tex.	26·18 N	98·08 W
116	Edinburgh (ĕd''n-bŭr-ô) Scot.	55·57 N	3·10 W
127	Edirne (Adrianople) (ĕ-dĭr'nĕ) (ā-drĭ-ăn-ō'p'l) Tur.	41·41 N	26·35 E
79	Edisto, (R.) (ĕd'ĭs-tō) S. C.	33·10 N	80·50 W
79	Edisto (R.), North Fk. S. C.	33·42 N	81·24 W
79	Edisto (R.), South Fk. S. C.	33·43 N	81·35 W
79	Edisto Island S. C.	32·32 N	80·20 W
73	Edmond (ĕd'mŭnd) Okla.	35·39 N	97·29 W
65	Edmonds (ĕd'mŭndz) Wash. (Seattle In.)	47·49 N	122·23 W
85	Edmonton Can. (Edmonton In.)	53·30 N	113·45 W
82	Edmundston (ĕd'mŭn-stŭn) Can.	47·23 N	68·20 W
77	Edna (ĕd'nȧ) Tex.	28·59 N	96·39 W
127	Edremit (ĕd-rĕ-mĕt') Tur.	39·35 N	27·00 E

ăt; finăl; rāte; senâte; ärm; ȧsk; sofȧ; fâre; ch-choose; dh-as th in other; bē; êvent; bĕt; recĕnt; cratẽr; g-go; gh-guttural g; bĭt; ĭ-short neutral; rīde; K-guttural k as ch in German ich;

PRONOUNCING INDEX Edremit–Ems-Weser 203

Page	Name Pronunciation Region	Lat. °′	Long. °′
127	Edremit Körfezi (G.) Tur.	39·28 N	26·35 E
86	Edson (ĕd'sŭn) Can.	53·40 N	116·40 W
71	Edward (I.) (ĕd'wērd) Can.	48·21 N	88·29 W
166	Edward (L.) Con. L.	0·15 S	28·32 E
74	Edwardsville (ĕd'wērdz-vĭl) Ill. (St. Louis In.)	38·49 N	89·58 W
75	Edwardsville Ind. (Louisville In.)	38·17 N	85·53 W
74	Edwardsville Kans. (Kansas City In.)	39·04 N	94·49 W
66	Eel R. (ēl) Calif.	40·39 N	124·15 W
80	Eel (R.) Ind.	40·50 N	85·55 W
159	Efate (I.) (ā-fä'tä) New Hebr.	18·02 S	168·29 E
71	Effigy Mounds Natl. Mon. (ĕf'ĭ-jŭ mounds) Iowa	43·04 N	91·15 W
80	Effingham (ĕf'ĭng-hăm) Ill.	39·05 N	88·30 W
124	Ega (R.) (ā'gä) Sp.	42·40 N	2·20 W
126	Egadi, Isole (Is.) (ĕ'sō-lĕ-ĕ'gä-dē) It.	38·01 N	12·00 E
124	Egea de los Caballeros (â-kā'ä dā lōs kä-bäl-yā'rōs) Sp.	42·07 N	1·05 W
64	Egegik (ĕg'ĕ-jĭt) Alaska	58·10 N	157·22 W
121	Eger (ĕ gĕr) Hung.	47·53 N	20·24 E
	Eger, see Ohre R.		
118	Egersund (ĕ'ghĕr-sōōn') Nor.	58·29 N	6·01 E
81	Egg Harbor (ĕg här'bĕr) N. J.	39·30 N	74·35 W
110	Egham (ĕg'ŭm) Eng. (London In.)	51·24 N	0·33 W
146	Egiin Gol (R.) (â-gēn') Mong.	49·41 N	100·40 E
159	Egmont, C. (ĕg'mŏnt) N. Z. (In.)	39·18 S	173·49 E
133	Egridir Gölü (L.) (ā-rĭ-dĭr') Tur.	38·10 N	30·00 E
122	Eguilles (ĕ-gwē') Fr. (Marseille In.)	43·34 N	5·21 E
	Egypt, see United Arab Republic		
124	Eibar (ā'ē-bär) Sp.	43·12 N	2·20 W
120	Eichstätt (īk'shtät) Ger.	48·54 N	11·14 E
111	Eichwalde (īĸ'väl-dĕ) Ger. (Berlin In.)	52·22 N	13·37 E
118	Eid (īdh) Nor.	61·54 N	6·01 E
118	Eidsberg (īdhs'bĕrgh) Nor.	59·32 N	11·16 E
118	Eidsvoll (īdhs'vôl) Nor.	60·19 N	11·15 E
120	Eifel (Plat.) (ī'fĕl) Ger.	50·08 N	6·30 E
168	Eil Som. (Horn of Afr. In.)	7·53 N	49·45 E
139	Eilat Jordan (Palestine In.)	29·34 N	34·57 E
120	Eilenburg (ī'lĕn-bōōrgh) Ger.	51·27 N	12·38 E
167	Eilliot S. Afr. (Natal In.)	31·19 S	27·52 E
120	Einbeck (īn'bĕk) Ger.	51·49 N	9·52 E
117	Eindhoven (īnd'hō-vĕn) Neth.	51·29 N	5·20 E
98	Eirunepé (ā-rōō-nĕ-pĕ') Braz.	6·37 S	69·58 W
120	Eisenach (ī'zĕn-äĸ) Ger.	50·58 N	10·18 E
120	Eisenhuttenstadt Ger.	52·08 N	14·40 E
120	Eisleben (īs'lā'bĕn) Ger.	51·31 N	11·33 E
118	Ejdfjord (ĕīd'fyōr) Nor.	60·28 N	7·04 E
91	Ejutla de Crespo (ā-hōōt'lä dā krās'pō) Mex.	16·34 N	96·44 W
119	Ekenäs (Tammisaari) (ĕ'kĕ-nâs) (tàm'ĭ-sä'rĭ) Fin.	59·59 N	23·25 E
111	Ekeren Bel. (Bruxelles In.)	51·17 N	4·27 E
85	Ekhart (ĕk'ārt) Can. (Winnipeg In.)	50·08 N	97·26 W
118	Eksjö (ĕk'shû) Swe.	57·41 N	14·55 E
165	El Abyad, Bahr (R.) (White Nile) (bär ĕl ä-byäd') Sud.	14·09 N	32·27 E
125	El Affroun (ĕl ăf-froun') Alg	36·28 N	2·38 E
167	Elands (R.) S. Afr. (Natal In.)	31·48 S	26·09 E
168	Elands R. (ē'lănds) S. Afr. (Johannesburg & Pretoria In.)	25·11 S	28·52 E
165	El Arab, Buhr (R.) Sud.	9·46 N	26·52 E
124	El Arahal (ĕl ä-rä-äl') Sp.	37·17 N	5·32 W
139	El 'Auja (ăl oujä) Isr.-U. A. R. (Palestine In.)	30·53 N	34·28 E
133	Elâzig (ĕl-ä'zĕz) Tur.	38·30 N	39·10 E
165	El Azrag, Bahr (R.) (Blue Nile) (bär ĕlăz-räk') Sud.	13·59 N	33·45 E
78	Elba (ĕl'bȧ) Ala.	31·25 N	86·01 W
126	Elba, Isola di (I.) (ê-sō-lä-dē-ĕl'bȧ) It.	42·42 N	10·25 E
124	El Barco (ĕl bär'kō) Sp.	42·26 N	6·58 W
127	Elbasan (ĕl-bä-sän'') Alb.	41·08 N	20·05 E
	Elbe, see Labe R.		
120	Elbe R. (ĕl'bĕ) Ger.	53·47 N	9·20 E
69	Elbert, Mt. (ĕl'bērt) Colo.	39·05 N	106·25 W
78	Elberton (ĕl'bēr-tŭn) Ga.	34·05 N	82·53 W
122	Elbeuf (ĕl-bûf') Fr.	49·16 N	0·59 E
133	Elbistan (ĕl-bē-stän') Tur.	38·20 N	37·10 E
121	Elblag (ĕl'blăŋg) Pol.	54·11 N	19·25 E
124	El Bonillo (ĕl bō-nēl'yō) Sp.	38·56 N	2·31 W
94	Elbow Cay (I.) Ba. Is.	26·25 N	77·55 W
70	Elbow Lake Minn.	46·00 N	95·59 W
85	Elbow R. (ĕl'bō) Can. (Calgary In.)	51·03 N	114·24 W
133	El'brus, Gora (Mt.) (ĕl'brōōs') Sov. Un.	43·20 N	42·25 E
168	El Buheirat el Murrat el Kubra (Great Bitter) U. A. R. (Suez In.)	30·24 N	32·27 E
168	El Buheirat el Murrat el Sughra (Little Bitter) U. A. R. (Suez In.)	30·10 N	32·36 E
168	El Bur Som. (Horn of Afr. In.)	4·35 N	46·40 E
133	Elburz Mts. (ĕl'bōōrz') Iran	36·30 N	51·00 E
68	El Cajon Calif. (San Diego In.)	32·48 N	116·58 W
98	El Cajon (ĕl-kä-kō'n) Col. (In.)	4·50 N	76.35 W
99	El Cambur (käm-bōōr') Ven. (In.)	10·24 N	68·06 W
77	El Campo (kăm'pō) Tex.	29·13 N	96·17 W
101	El Carmen (kà'r-mĕn) Chile (Santiago In.)	34·14 S	71·23 W
98	El Carmen (kà'r-mĕn) Col.	9·54 N	75·12 W
74	El Casco (kăs'kō) Calif. (Los Angeles In.)	33·59 N	117·08 W
68	El Centro (sĕn'trō) Calif.	32·47 N	115·33 W
65	El Cerrito (sĕr-rē'tō) Calif. (San Francisco In.)	37·55 N	122·19 W
100	El Chaco (Prov.) (chä'kō) Arg.	26·00 S	60·45 W
125	Elche (ĕl'chā) Sp.	38·15 N	0·42 W
92	El Cuyo Mex. (Yucatan In.)	21·30 N	87·42 W
125	Elda (ĕl'dä) Sp.	38·28 N	0·44 W
120	Elde R. (ĕl'dĕ) Ger.	53·11 N	11·30 E
168	El Dilingat U. A. R. (Nile In.)	30·48 N	30·32 E
164	El Djouf (Des.) (ĕl djōōf) Mauritania	21·38 N	7·44 W
71	Eldon (ĕl-dŭn) Iowa	40·55 N	92·15 W
73	Eldon Mo.	38·21 N	92·36 W
65	Eldon Wash. (Seattle In.)	47·33 N	123·02 W
71	Eldora (ĕl-dō'rȧ) Iowa	42·21 N	93·08 W
73	El Dorado (ĕl dō-rä'dō) Ark.	33·13 N	92·39 W
80	Eldorado Ill.	37·50 N	88·30 W
73	El Dorado Kans.	37·49 N	96·51 W
73	Eldorado Springs (sprĭngz) Mo.	37·51 N	94·02 W
165	Eldoret (ĕl-dō-rĕt') Ken.	00·31 N	35·18 E
90	El Ebano (ā-bä'nō) Mex.	22·13 N	98·26 W
72	Electra (ē-lĕk'trȧ) Tex.	34·02 N	98·54 W
67	Electric Pk. (ē-lĕk'trĭk) Mont.	45·03 N	110·52 W
136	Elektrogorsk (ĕl-yĕk'trô-gôrsk) Sov. Un. (Moskva In.)	55·53 N	38·48 E
136	Elektrostal (ĕl-yĕk'trô-stál) Sov. Un. (Moskva In.)	55·47 N	38·27 E
69	Elephant Butte Res. (ĕl'ē-fănt būt) N. Mex.	33·25 N	107·10 W
125	El Escorial (ĕl-ĕs-kō-ryä'l) Sp. (Madrid In.)	40·38 N	4·08 W
92	El Espino (ĕl-ĕs-pē'nŏ) Nic.	13·26 N	86·48 W
95	Eleuthera (I.) (ē-lū'thēr-ȧ) Ba. Is.	25·05 N	76·10 W
95	Eleuthera Pt. Ba. Is.	24·35 N	76·05 W
73	Eleven Point (R.) (ē-lĕv'ĕn) Mo.	36·53 N	91·39 W
165	El Fāsher (fä'shēr) Sud.	13·38 N	25·21 E
124	El Ferrol (fă-rōl') Sp.	43·30 N	8·12 W
75	Elgin (ĕl'jĭn) Ill. (Chicago In.)	42·03 N	88·16 W
70	Elgin Nebr.	41·58 N	98·04 W
66	Elgin Ore.	45·34 N	117·58 W
116	Elgin Scot.	57·40 N	3·30 W
77	Elgin Tex.	30·21 N	97·22 W
65	Elgin Wash. (Seattle In.)	47·23 N	122·42 W
85	Elgin Mills (mĭls) Can. (Toronto In.)	43·54 N	79·26 W
164	El Goléa (gō-lā-ä') Alg.	30·39 N	2·52 E
165	Elgon, Mt. (ĕl'gŏn) Ken.	1·07 N	34·37 E
90	El Grullo (grōōl-yō) Mex.	19·46 N	104·10 W
99	El Guapo (gwä'pō) Ven. (In.)	10·07 N	66·00 W
114	El Hamada (Plat.) (häm'ä-dä) Alg.	30·53 N	1·52 W
164	El Hank (Bluffs) Mauritania-Mali	23·44 N	6·45 W
99	El Hatillo (ä-tē'l-yō) Ven. (In.)	10·08 N	65·13 W
85	Elie (ē'lē) Can. (Winnipeg In.)	49·55 N	97·45 W
166	Elila (R.) (ĕ-lē'lä) Con. L.	3·38 S	27·48 E
65	Elisa (I.) (ē-lī'sä) Wash. (Vancouver In.)	48·43 N	122·37 W
166	Élisabethville Con. L.	11·41 S	27·32 E
119	Elisenvaara (ā-lē'sĕn-vä'rä) Sov. Un.	61·25 N	29·46 E
77	Elizabeth (ē-lĭz'ȧ-bĕth) La.	30·50 N	92·47 W
84	Elizabeth N. J. (New York In.)	40·40 N	74·13 W
75	Elizabeth Pa. (Pittsburgh In.)	40·16 N	79·53 W
79	Elizabeth City N. C.	36·15 N	76·15 W
79	Elizabethton (ē-lĭz'ȧ-bĕth-tŭn) Tenn.	36·19 N	82·12 W
80	Elizabethtown (ē-lĭz'ȧ-bĕth-toun) Ky.	37·40 N	85·55 W
121	Ełk (ĕlk) Pol.	53·53 N	22·23 E
78	Elk (R.) Tenn.	35·05 N	86·36 W
80	Elk (R.) W. Va.	38·30 N	81·05 W
165	El Kāmlin (käm-lēn') Sud.	15·09 N	33·06 E
72	Elk City (ĕlk) Okla.	35·23 N	99·23 W
165	El Khandaq (kän-däk') Sud.	18·38 N	30·29 E
80	Elkhart (ĕlk'härt) Ind.	41·40 N	86·00 W
72	Elkhart Kans.	37·00 N	101·54 W
77	Elkhart Tex.	31·38 N	95·35 W
71	Elkhorn (ĕlk'hôrn) Wis.	42·39 N	88·32 W
70	Elkhorn (R.) Nebr.	42·06 N	97·46 W
79	Elkin (ĕl'kĭn) N. C.	36·15 N	80·50 W
81	Elkins (ĕl'kĭnz) W. Va.	38·55 N	79·50 W
86	Elk Island Natl. Park (ĕlk ī'lănd) Can.	53·21 N	115·46 W
66	Elko (ĕl'kō) Nev.	40·51 N	115·46 W
70	Elk Point S. D.	42·41 N	96·41 W
80	Elk Rapids (răp'ĭdz) Mich.	44·55 N	85·25 W
66	Elk River (rĭv'ēr) Idaho	46·47 N	116·11 W
71	Elk River Minn.	45·17 N	93·33 W
78	Elkton (ĕlk'tŭn) Ky.	36·47 N	87·08 W
81	Elkton Md.	39·35 N	75·50 W
70	Elkton S. D.	44·15 N	96·28 W
115	El Ladhiqiya (Latakia) Syria	35·32 N	35·51 E
168	El Lagodei Som. (Horn of Afr. In.)	9·20 N	49·09 E
110	Elland (el'ănd) Eng.	53·41 N	1·50 W
69	Ellen, Mt. (ĕl'ĕn) Utah	38·05 N	110·50 W
70	Ellendale (ĕl'ĕn-dāl) N. D.	46·01 N	98·33 W
66	Ellensburg (ĕl'ĕnz-bûrg) Wash.	47·00 N	120·31 W
81	Ellenville (ĕl'ĕn-vĭl) N. Y.	41·40 N	74·25 W
85	Ellerslie (ĕl'ērz-lê) Can. (Edmonton In.)	53·25 N	113·30 W
110	Ellesmere (ĕlz'mēr) Eng.	52·55 N	2·54 W
49	Ellesmere I. Can.	81·00 N	80·00 W
110	Ellesmere Port Eng.	53·17 N	2·54 W
155	Ellice Is. (ĕl'ĭs) Oceania	5·20 S	174·00 E
84	Ellicott City (ĕl'ĭ-kŏt sĭ'tê) Md. (Baltimore In.)	39·16 N	76·48 W
75	Ellicott Cr. N. Y. (Buffalo In.)	43·00 N	78·46 W
167	Elliotdale (ĕl-ĭ-ŏt'dāl) S. Afr. (Natal In.)	31·58 S	28·42 E
65	Elliott (el'ĭ-ŭt) Wash. (Seattle In.)	47·28 N	122·08 W
72	Ellis (ĕl'ĭs) Kans.	38·56 N	99·34 W
78	Ellisville (ĕl'ĭs-vĭl) Miss.	31·37 N	89·10 W
74	Ellisville Mo. (St. Louis In.)	38·35 N	90·35 W
143	Ellore (ĕl-lōr') India	16·44 N	80·09 E
72	Ellsworth (ĕlz'wûrth) Kans.	38·43 N	98·14 W
82	Ellsworth Maine	44·33 N	68·26 W
47	Ellsworth Highland Ant.	77·00 S	90·00 W
120	Ellwangen (ĕl'väŋ-gĕn) Ger.	48·57 N	10·08 E
111	Elm (ĕlm) Ger. (Hamburg In.)	53·31 N	9·13 E
70	Elm (R.) S. D.	45·47 N	98·28 W
80	Elm (R.) W. Va.	38·30 N	81·05 W
66	Elma (ĕl'mȧ) Wash.	47·02 N	123·20 W
114	El Maadid Mor.	31·32 N	4·30 W
73	Elm Cr. Tex.	33·34 N	97·03 W
164	E M mrhar Mauritania	19·30 N	16·18 W
74	Elmendorf (ĕl'mĕn-dôrf) Tex. (San Antonio In.)	29·16 N	98·20 W
164	El Meréié (Des.) Mauritania	19·45 N	8·00 W
74	Elm Fork (ĕlm fôrk) Tex. (Dallas, Fort Worth In.)	32·55 N	96·56 W
75	Elmhurst (ĕlm'hûrst) Ill. (Chicago In.)	41·54 N	87·56 W
81	Elmira (ĕl-mī'rȧ) N. Y.	42·05 N	76·50 W
81	Elmira Heights N. Y.	42·10 N	76·50 W
98	El Misti (Vol.) (mē's-tē) Peru	16·04 S	71·20 W
74	El Modena (mō-dē'nō) Calif. (Los Angeles In.)	33·47 N	117·48 W
74	El Monte (mōn'tā) Calif. (Los Angeles In.)	34·04 N	118·02 W
69	El Morro Natl. Mon. N. Mex.	35·05 N	108·20 W
111	Elmshorn (ĕlms'hôrn) Ger. (Hamburg In.)	53·45 N	9·39 E
75	Elmwood Pl. (ĕlm'wōōd plās) Ohio (Cincinnati In.)	39·11 N	84·30 W
165	El Obeid (ō-bād') Sud.	13·15 N	30·15 E
165	El Odaiya (ō-dī'yȧ) Sud.	12·06 N	28·16 E
65	Elokomin (R.) (ē-lō'kō-mĭn) Wash. (Portland In.)	46·16 N	123·16 W
90	El Oro (ô-rô) Mex.	19·49 N	100·04 W
164	El Oued (wĕd') Alg.	33·23 N	6·49 E
92	El Paraíso (pä-rä-ē'sō) Hond.	13·55 N	86·35 W
125	El Pardo (pä'r-dō) Sp. (Madrid In.)	40·31 N	3·47 W
76	El Paso (pas'ō) Tex.	31·47 N	106·27 W
99	El Pilar (pē-lä'r) Ven. (In.)	9·56 N	64·48 W
93	El Porvenir (pôr-vå-nēr') Pan.	9·34 N	78·55 W
124	El Puerto de Sta. María (pwĕr tō dā sän tä mä-rē'ä) Sp.	36·36 N	6·18 W
93	El Real (rā-äl) Pan.	8·07 N	77·43 W
72	El Reno (rē'nō) Okla.	35·31 N	97·57 W
99	El Roboré (rô-bō-rĕ') Bol.	18·23 S	59·43 W
71	Elroy (ĕl'roi) Wis.	43·44 N	90·17 W
74	Elsah (ĕl'zȧ) Ill. (St. Louis In.)	38·57 N	90·22 W
90	El Salto (säl'tō) Mex.	22·48 N	105·22 E
88	El Salvador N. A.	14·00 N	89·30 W
92	El Sauce (ĕl-sä'ōō-sĕ) Nic.	13·00 N	86·40 W
73	Elsberry (ĕlz'bĕr-ĭ) Mo.	39·09 N	90·44 W
123	Elsdorf (ĕls'dōrf) Ger. (Ruhr In.)	50·56 N	6·35 E
74	El Segundo (sĕgŭn'dō) Calif. (Los Angeles In.)	33·55 N	118·24 W
74	Elsinore (ĕl'sĭ-nôr) Calif. (Los Angeles In.)	33·40 N	117·19 W
74	Elsinore L. Calif. (Los Angeles In.)	33·38 N	117·21 W
111	Elstorf (ĕls'tōrf) Ger. (Hamburg In.)	53·25 N	9·48 E
165	El Sudd (Swp.) Sud.	8·45 N	30·45 E
161	Eltham (ĕl'thŭm) Austl. (Melbourne In.)	37·43 S	145·08 E
98	El Tigre (tē'grĕ) Ven.	8·49 N	64·15 W
133	El'ton (L.) Sov. Un.	49·10 N	47·00 E
74	El Toro (tō'rō) Calif. (Los Angeles In.)	33·37 N	117·42 W
92	El Triunfo (ĕl-trē-ōō'n-fô) Hond.	13·06 N	87·00 W
92	El Triunfo Sal.	13·17 N	88·32 W
69	El Vado Res. N. Mex.	36·37 N	106·30 W
124	Elvas (ĕl'väzh) Port.	38·53 N	7·11 W
118	Elverum (ĕl'vĕ-rōōm) Nor.	60·53 N	11·33 E
92	El Viego (ĕl-vyĕ'kŏ) Nic.	12·44 N	87·03 W
92	El Viejo (Vol.) Nic.	12·44 N	87·03 W
73	Elvins (ĕl'vĭnz) Mo.	37·49 N	90·31 W
165	El Wak (wäk') Ken.	3·00 N	41·00 E
75	Elwood (ĕl'wōōd) Ill. (Chicago In.)	41·24 N	88·07 W
80	Elwood Ind.	40·15 N	85·50 W
117	Ely (ē'lĭ) Eng.	52·25 N	0·17 E
71	Ely Minn.	47·54 N	91·53 W
68	Ely Nev.	39·16 N	114·53 W
75	Elyria (ē-lĭr'ĭ-ȧ) Ohio (Cleveland In.)	41·22 N	82·07 W
119	Ema (R.) (å'má) Sov. Un.	58·25 N	27·00 E
118	Emån (R.) Swe.	57·15 N	15·46 E
133	Emba (R.) (yĕm'bȧ) Sov. Un.	46·50 N	54·10 E
80	Embarrass (R.) (ĕm-băr'ăs) Ill.	39·15 N	88·05 W
85	Embrun (ĕm'brŭn) Can. (Ottawa In.)	45·16 N	75·17 W
123	Embrun (äN-brûN') Fr.	44·35 N	6·32 E
120	Emden (ĕm'dĕn) Ger.	53·21 N	7·15 E
159	Emerald (ĕm'ēr-ăld) Austl.	28·34 S	148·00 E
86	Emerson (ĕm'ēr-sŭn) Can.	49·00 N	97·18 W
65	Emeryville (ĕm'ēr-ĭ-vĭl) Calif. (San Francisco In.)	37·50 N	122·17 W
165	Emi Koussi (Mtn.) (ā'mê kōō-sē') Chad	19·50 N	18·30 E
126	Emilia (Reg.) (ā-mēl'yä) It.	44·35 N	10·48 E
91	Emiliano Zapata (ĕ-mē-lyä'nō-zä-pá'tà) Mex.	17·45 N	91·46 W
80	Eminence (ĕm'ĭ-nĕns) Ky.	38·25 N	85·15 W
155	Emirau (I.) (ā-mē-rä'ōō) N. Gui. Ter.	1·40 S	150·28 E
117	Emmen (ĕm'ĕn) Neth.	52·48 N	6·55 E
123	Emmerich (ĕm'ēr-ĭk) Ger. (Ruhr In.)	51·51 N	6·16 E
71	Emmetsburg (ĕm'ĕts-bûrg) Ia.	43·07 N	94·41 W
66	Emmett (ĕm'ĕt) Idaho	43·53 N	116·30 W
67	Emmons Mt. (ĕm'ŭnz) Utah	40·43 N	110·20 W
76	Emory Pk. (ĕ'mō-rē pēk) Tex.	29·13 N	103·20 W
84	Empire (ĕm'pīr) La. (New Orleans In.)	29·24 N	89·37 W
126	Empoli (ām'pō-lē) It.	43·43 N	10·55 E
73	Emporia (ĕm-pō'rĭ-ȧ) Kans.	38·24 N	96·11 W
79	Emporia Va.	37·40 N	77·34 W
81	Emporium (ĕm-pō'rĭ-ŭm) Pa.	41·30 N	78·15 W
	Empty Quarter, see Ar Al Khālī		
120	Ems R. (ĕms) Ger.	52·52 N	7·16 E
120	Ems-Weser (can.) (vä'zĕr) Ger.	52·23 N	8·11 E

ng-sing; ŋ-baŋk; N-nasalized n; nŏd; cŏmmit; ōld; ôbey; ôrder; fōōd; fŏŏt; ou-out; s-soft; sh-dish; th-thin; pūre; ûnite; ûrn; stŭd; circŭs; ü-as "y" in study; '-indeterminate vowel.

Page	Name Pronunciation Region	Lat. °′	Long. °′
118	Enånger (ĕn-ôn'gĕr) Swe.	61·36 N	16·55 E
88	Encantada, Cerro de la (Mtn.) (sĕ'r-rô-dĕ-lä-ĕn-kän-tä'dä) Mex.	31·58 N	115·15 W
155	Encanto Pt. (ĕn-kän'tō) Phil. (Manila In.)	15·44 N	121·46 E
100	Encarnación (ĕn-kär-nä-syōn') Par.	27·26 S	55·52 W
90	Encarnación de Diaz (ĕn-kär-nä-syōn dä dē'äz). Mex.	21·34 N	102·15 W
76	Encinal (ĕn'sĭ-nôl) Tex.	28·02 N	99·22 W
98	Encontrados (ĕn-kōn-trä'dōs) Ven.	9·01 N	72·10 W
160	Encounter B. (ĕn-koun'tēr). Austl.	35·50 S	138·45 E
139	Endau Mala. (Singapore In.)	2·39 N	103·38 E
139	Endau (R.). Mala. (Singapore In.)	2·29 N	103·40 E
47	Enderby Land (Reg.) (ĕn'dĕr bĭ) Ant.	72·00 S	52·00 E
70	Enderlin (ĕn'dĕr-lĭn) N. D.	46·38 N	97·37 W
81	Endicott (ĕn'dĭ-kŏt) N. Y.	42·05 N	76·00 W
64	Endicott Mts. Alaska	67·30 N	153·45 W
127	Enez Tur.	40·42 N	26·05 E
81	Enfield (ĕn'fēld) Conn.	41·55 N	72·35 W
110	Enfield Eng. (London In.)	51·38 N	0·06 W
79	Enfield N. C.	36·10 N	77·41 W
95	Engano, Cabo (C.) (kä'-bô-ĕn-gä-nô). Dom. Rep.	18·40 N	68·30 W
154	Engaño, C. (ĕn-gän'yō) Phil.	18·40 N	122·45 E
165	Engare Vaso Nyiro R. (ĕn-gä'rä wä'sô nyē'rô). Ken.	0·59 N	37·47 E
167	Engcobo (ĕng-cô-bô) S. Afr. (Natal In.)	31·41 S	27·59 E
133	Engel's (ĕn'gĕls) Sov. Un.	51·20 N	45·40 E
123	Engelskirchen (ĕn'gĕls-kēr'kĕn) Ger. (Ruhr In.)	50·59 N	7·25 E
72	Engelwood (ĕn'g'l-wŏŏd) Colo.	39·39 N	105·00 W
154	Enggano (ĕng-gä'nō) Indon.	5·22 S	102·18 E
73	England (ĭŋ'glănd) Ark.	34·33 N	91·58 W
116	England (ĭŋ'glănd) U. K.	51·35 N	1·40 W
83	Englee (ĕn-glē) Can.	50·46 N	56·07 W
80	English (ĭn'glĭsh) Ind.	38·15 N	86·25 W
87	English (R.) Can.	50·31 N	94·12 W
113	English Chan. Eng.	49·45 N	3·06 W
125	Enguera (ān'gārä) Sp.	38·58 N	0·42 W
72	Enid (ē'nĭd) Okla.	36·25 N	97.52 W
78	Enid Res. Miss.	34·13 N	89·47 W
166	Enkeldoorn (ĕŋ'k'l-dōōrn) Fed. of Rh. & Nya.	19·59 S	30·58 E
168	Enkeldoring (ĕŋ'k'l-dôr-ĭng) S. Afr. (Johannesburg & Pretoria In.)	25·24 S	28·43 E
118	Enköping (ên'kû-pĭng) Swe.	59·39 N	17·05 E
165	En Nahud (ĕn nä'hōōd) Sud.	12·39 N	28·18 E
165	Ennedi Plat. (ĕn-nĕd'ē) Chad.	16·36 N	22·58 E
116	Ennis (ĕn'ĭs) Ire.	52·54 N	9.05 W
77	Ennis Tex.	32·20 N	96·38 W
116	Enniscorthy (ĕn-ĭs-kôr'thĭ) Ire.	52·33 N	6·27 W
116	Enniskillen (ĕn-ĭs-kĭl'ĕn) N. Ire.	54·20 N	7·25 W
120	Enns R. (ĕns) Aus.	47·37 N	14·35 E
79	Enoree (ê-nō'rē) S. C.	34·43 N	81·58 W
79	Enoree, (R.) S. C.	34·35 N	81·55 W
95	Enriquillo (ĕn-rê-kē'l-yô) Dom. Rep.	17·55 N	71·15 W
95	Enriquillo, Lago (L.) (lä'gô-ĕn-rê-kē'l-yô). Dom. Rep.	18·35 N	71·35 W
117	Enschede (ĕns'kā-dĕ) Neth.	52·10 N	6·50 E
88	Ensenada (ĕn-sĕ-nä'dä) Mex.	32·00 N	116·30 W
101	Ensenada..Ur. (Buenos Aires In.)	34·50 S	57·55 W
151	Enshih China	30·18 N	109·25 E
153	Enshū-Nada (Sea) (ĕn'shōō nä-dä). Jap.	34·25 N	137·14 E
165	Entebbe (ĕn-tĕb'ĕ) Ug.	0·01 N	32·29 E
78	Enterprise (ĕn'tēr-prīz) Ala.	31·20 N	85·50 W
66	Enterprise Ore.	45·25 N	117·16 W
122	Entraygues (ĕn-trĕg') Fr.	44·39 N	2·33 E
100	Entre Ríos (Prov.) (ĕn-trā rē'ōs) Arg.	31·30 S	59·00 W
164	Enugu (ĕ-nōō'gōō) Nig.	6·13 N	7·18 E
65	Enumclaw (ĕn'ŭm-klô) Wash. (Seattle In.)	47·12 N	121·59 W
98	Envigado (ĕn-vē-gá'dô)..Col. (In.)	6·10 N	75·34 W
126	Eolie, Isole (Is.) (ê'sō-lĕ-ĕ-ô'lyĕ). It.	38·43 N	14·43 E
127	Epeirus (Reg.) Grc.	39·35 N	20·45 E
122	Epernay (ā-pĕr-nĕ') Fr.	49·02 N	3·54 E
123	Épernon (ā-pĕr-nôn') Fr. (Paris In.)	48·36 N	1·41 E
69	Ephraim (ē'frå-ĭm) Utah	39·20 N	111·40 W
66	Ephrata (ê frā'tá) Wash.	47·18 N	119·35 W
159	Epi (ā'pê) New Hebr.	16·59 S	168·29 E
124	Épila (ā'pê-lä) Sp.	41·38 N	1·15 W
123	Épinal (ā-pē-nál') Fr.	48·11 N	6·27 E
139	Episkopi B. Cyprus (Palestine In.)	34·34 N	32·41 E
110	Epping (ĕp'ĭng).Eng. (London In.)	51·41 N	0·06 E
166	Epping..S. Afr. (Cape Town In.)	33·56 S	18·35 E
110	Epworth (ĕp'wûrth) Eng.	53·31 N	0·50 W
122	Equeurdreville (ā-kûr-dr'vēl')..Fr.	49·38 N	1·42 W
85	Eramosa R. (ĕr-á-mō'sá) Can. (Toronto In.)	43·39 N	80·08 W
165	Erba (Mt.) (ĕr'bá) Sud.	20·53 N	36·45 E
115	Erciyas (Mtn.) Tur.	38·30 N	35·36 E
74	Erda (ĕr'dä) Utah (Salt Lake City In.)	40·41 N	112·17 W
111	Erding (ĕr'dēng) Ger. (München In.)	48·19 N	11·54 E
100	Erechim (ĕ-rĕ-shē'n) Braz.	27·43 S	52·11 W
133	Ereğli (ĕ-rā'ĭ-le) Tur.	37·40 N	34·00 E
133	Ereğli Tur.	41·15 N	31·25 E
120	Erfurt (ĕr'fōōrt) Ger.	50·59 N	11·04 E
127	Ergene (R.) (ĕr'gĕ-nĕ) Tur.	41·17 N	26·50 E
124	Erges (R.) (ĕr'-zhĕs) Port. Sp.	39·45 N	7·01 W
148	Erhlangtien (ē'läng'diän) China	31·33 N	114·07 E
124	Eria (R.) (ā-rē'ä) Sp.	42·10 N	6·08 W
72	Erick (âr'ĭk) Okla.	35·14 N	99·51 W
73	Erie (ē'rĭ) Kans.	37·35 N	95·17 W
81	Erie Pa.	42·05 N	80·05 W
63	Erie, L. U. S.-Can.	42·15 N	81·25 W
152	Erimo Saki (C.) (ā'rē-mō sä-kē) Jap.	41·53 N	143·20 E
85	Erin (ĕ'rĭn) Can. (Toronto In.)	43·46 N	80·04 W
165	Eritrea (Reg.) (ā-rê-trā'á) Eth.	16·15 N	38·30 E
120	Erlangen (ĕr'läng-ĕn) Ger.	49·36 N	11·03 E
75	Erlanger (ĕr'lăng-ĕr) Ky. (Cincinnati In.)	39·01 N	84·36 W
	Ermoúpolis, see Síros		
116	Erne, Upper, Lough (B.) (lŏk ûrn). N. Ire.	54·20 N	7·24 W
116	Erne, Lough (B.) N. Ire.	54·30 N	7·40 W
159	Eromanga (I.) New Hebr.	18·58 S	169·18 E
77	Eros (ē'rōs) La.	32·23 N	92·22 W
165	Er Renk (ĕr rĕnk') Sud.	11·45 N	32·53 E
114	Er Ricani Mor.	31·09 N	4·20 W
116	Errigal, Mt. (ĕr-ĭ-gôl') Ire.	54·60 N	8·13 W
165	Er Roseires (rô-sā'rĕs) Sud.	11·38 N	34·42 E
123	Erstein (ĕr'shtīn) Fr.	48·27 N	7·40 E
79	Erwin (ûr'wĭn) N. C.	35·16 N	78·40 W
79	Erwin Tenn.	36·07 N	82·25 W
120	Erzgebirge (Ore Mts.) (ĕrts'gĕ-bē'gĕ). Ger.	50·29 N	12·40 E
133	Erzincan (ĕr-zĭn-jän') Tur.	39·50 N	39·30 E
133	Erzurum (ĕrz'rōōm') Tur.	39·55 N	41·10 E
152	Esashi (ĕs'ä-shê) Jap.	41·50 N	140·10 E
118	Esbjerg (ĕs'byĕrgh) Den.	55·29 N	8·25 E
119	Esbo (ĕs'bô) Fin.	60·13 N	24·41 E
124	Escairón (ĕs-kī-rô'n) Sp.	42·34 N	7.40 W
69	Escalante (ĕs-kà-lăn'tē) Utah	37·50 N	111·40 W
69	Escalante (R.) Utah	37·40 N	111·20 W
78	Escambia (R.) (ĕs-kăm'bĭ-á)..Fla	30·38 N	87·20 W
71	Escanaba (ĕs-kȧ-nô'bȧ) Mich.	45·44 N	87·05 W
71	Escanaba (R.) Mich.	46·10 N	87·22 W
123	Esch-sur-Alzette Lux.	49·32 N	6·21 E
120	Eschwege (ĕsh'vä-gē) Ger.	51·11 N	10·02 E
123	Eschweiler (ĕsh'vī-lĕr) Ger. (Ruhr In.)	50·49 N	6·15 E
95	Escocesá, Bahia (B.) (bä-ē'ä-ĕs-kō-sĕ'sä). Dom. Rep.	19·25 N	69·40 W
68	Escondido (ĕs-kŏn-dē'dō) Calif.	33·07 N	117·07 W
76	Escondido, Rio (R.) (rê'ō-ĕs-kōn-dê'dô). Mex.	28·30 N	100·45 W
93	Escondido R Nic.	12·04 N	84·09 W
93	Escudo de Veraguas I. (ĕs-kōō'dä dā vä-rä'gwäs).Pan.	9·07 N	81·25 W
90	Escuinapa (ĕs-kwē-nä'pä) Mex.	22·49 N	105·44 W
92	Escuintla (ĕs-kwēn'tlä) Guat.	14·16 N	90·47 W
91	Escuintla Mex.	15·20 N	92·45 W
93	Ese, Cayos de (I.) Col.	12·24 N	81·07 W
164	Eséka (ĕ-sā'kä) Cam.	3·40 N	11·08 E
144	Esfahān Iran	32·38 N	51·30 E
124	Esgueva (R.) (ĕs-gĕ'vä) Sp.	41·48 N	4·10 W
167	Eshowe (ĕsh'ô-wê) S. Afr. (Natal In.)	28·54 S	31·28 E
80	Eskdale (ĕsk'dāl) W. Va.	38·05 N	81·25 W
112	Eskifjördhur (ĕs'kē-fyŭr'dōōr).Ice.	65·04 N	14·01 W
118	Eskilstuna (å'shĕl-stü-na) Swe.	59·23 N	16·28 E
86	Eskimo L. (ĕs'kĭ-mō) Can.	69·29 N	129·57 W
133	Eskişehir (ĕs-kê-shĕ'h'r) Tur.	39·40 N	30·20 E
74	Esko (ĕs'kô)..Minn. (Duluth In.)	46·27 N	92·22 W
124	Esla (R.) (ĕs-lä) Sp.	41·50 N	5·48 W
118	Eslöv (ĕs'lûv) Swe.	55·50 N	13·17 E
98	Esmeraldas (ĕs-mā-räl'däs) Ec.	0·58 N	79·45 W
95	Espada, Punta (Pt.) (pōō'n-tä-ĕs-pä'dä).Dom. Rep.	18·30 N	68·30 W
87	Espanola (ĕs-pȧ-nō'lȧ) Can.	46·11 N	81·59 W
93	Esparta (ĕs-pär'tä) C. R.	9·59 N	84·40 W
158	Esperance (ĕs'pê-răns) Austl.	33·45 S	122·07 E
94	Esperenza (ĕs-pĕ-rä'n-zä) Cuba	22·30 N	80·10 W
125	Espichel, Cabo (C.) (kå'bō-ĕs-pē-shĕl').Port. (Lisboa In.)	38·25 N	9·13 W
98	Espinal (ĕs-pê-näl') Col. (In.)	4·10 N	74·53 W
99	Espinhaço, Serra do (Mts.) (sĕ'r-rä-dô-ĕs-pê-nä-sô).Braz.	16·06 S	44·56 W
101	Espinillo, Punta (Pt.) (pōō'n-tä-ĕs-pê-nē'l-yô) Ur. (Buenos Aires In.)	34·49 S	56·27 W
99	Espirito Santo (ĕs-pē'rē-tô-sän'tô).Braz.	20·27 S	40·18 W
99	Espírito Santo (State) Braz.	19·57 S	40·58 W
92	Espíritu Santo, Bahia del (B.) (bä-ē'ä-dĕl-ĕs-pē'rē-tōō-sän'tô) Mex. (Yucatan In.)	19·25 N	87·28 W
159	Espiritu Santo (I.) (ĕs-pē'rê-tōō sän'tō).New Hebr.	15·45 S	166·50 E
92	Espita (ĕs-pē'tä) Mex. (Yucatan In.)	20·57 N	88·22 W
124	Esposende (ĕs-pō-zĕn'dä) Port.	41·33 N	8·45 W
100	Esquel (ĕs-kĕ'l) Arg.	42·47 S	71·22 W
65	Esquimalt (ĕs-kwī'mŏlt) Can. (Seattle In.)	48·26 N	123·25 W
111	Essen Bel. (Bruxelles In.)	51·28 N	4·27 E
123	Essen (ĕs'sĕn)...Ger. (Ruhr In.)	51·26 N	6·59 E
99	Essequibo (R.) (ĕs-ä-kē'bō) Br. Gu.	4·26 N	58·17 W
75	Essex (ĕs'ĕks)..Can. (Detroit In.)	42·10 N	82·50 W
75	Essex Ill. (Chicago In.)	41·11 N	88·11 W
84	Essex Md. (Baltimore In.)	39·19 N	76·29 W
83	Essex Mass. (Boston In.)	42·38 N	70·47 W
81	Essex Vt.	44·30 N	73·05 W
84	Essex Fells (ĕs'ĕks fĕlz) N. J. (New York In.)	40·50 N	74·16 W
80	Essexville (ĕs'ĕks-vĭl) Mich.	43·35 N	83·50 W
120	Esslingen (ĕs'slēn-gĕn) Ger.	48·45 N	9·19 E
62	Estacado, Llano (Plain) (yá-nō ĕs-tȧ-cȧ-dō').U. S.	33·50 N	103·20 W
100	Estados, Isla de los S. A.	55·05 S	63·00 W
99	Estância (ĕs-tän'sĭ-ä) Braz.	11·17 S	37·18 W
124	Estarreja (ĕs-tär-rä'zhä) Port.	40·44 N	8·39 W
167	Estcourt (ĕst-coort) S. Afr. (Natal In.)	29·04 S	29·53 E
126	Este (ĕs'tä) It.	45·13 N	11·40 E
92	Estelí (ĕs-tä-lē') Nic.	13·10 N	86·23 W
124	Estella (ĕs-tāl'yä) Sp.	42·40 N	2·01 W
124	Estepa (ĕs-tā'pä) Sp.	37·18 N	4·54 W
124	Estepona (ĕs-tā-pō'nä) Sp.	36·26 N	5·08 W
68	Esteros, B. (ĕs-tā'rōs) Calif.	35·22 N	121·04 W
86	Estevan (ĕ-stē'vȧn) Can.	49·11 N	102·57 W
71	Estherville (ĕs'tēr-vĭl) Iowa	43·24 N	94·49 W
79	Estill (ĕs'tĭl) S. C.	32·46 N	81 15 W
130	Estonian S. S. R. (ĕs-tō'nĭ-ä) Sov. Un.	59·10 N	25·00 E
100	Estrêla (R.) (ĕs-trĕ'là). Braz. (In.)	22·39 S	43·16 W
124	Estrêla, Serra da (Mts.) (sĕr'rá dä ĕs-trā'lȧ). Port.	40·25 N	7·45 W
124	Estremadura (Reg.) (ĕs-trā-mä-dōō'rȧ). Port.	41·35 N	8·36 W
124	Estremoz (ĕs-trā-mōzh') Port.	38·50 N	7·35 W
99	Estrondo, Serra do (Mts.) (sĕr'rȧ dōō ĕs-trôn'dōō). Braz.	9·52 S	48·56 W
121	Esztergom (ĕs'tĕr-gōm) Hung.	47·46 N	18·45 E
49	Etah (ē'tȧ) Grnld.	78·20 N	72·42 W
123	Étampes (ā-tänp').Fr. (Paris In.)	48·26 N	2·09 E
122	Étaples (ā-täp'l') Fr.	50·32 N	1·38 E
85	Etchemin, R. (ĕch'ĕ-mĭn) Can. (Quebec In.)	46·39 N	71·03 W
163	Ethiopia (ê-thê-ō'pê-ä) Afr.	7·53 N	37·55 E
74	Etiwanda (ĕ-tĭ-wän'dȧ) Calif. (Los Angeles In.)	34·07 N	117·31 W
	Etlatongo, see San Mateo		
75	Etna (ĕt'nȧ)..Pa. (Pittsburgh In.)	40·30 N	79·55 W
126	Etna, Mt. (Vol.) It.	37·48 N	15·00 E
85	Etobicoke Cr..Can. (Toronto In.)	43·44 N	79·48 W
64	Etolin Str. (ĕt ō lĭn) Alaska	60·35 S	165·40 W
166	Etosha Pan (ĕtō'shä)...S. W. Afr.	19·07 S	15·30 E
78	Etowah (ĕt'ô-wä) Tenn.	35·18 N	84·31 W
78	Etowah (R.) Ga.	34·23 N	84·19 W
123	E'trechy (ā-trā-shē') Fr. (Paris In.)	48·29 N	2·12 E
111	Etten Neth. (Amsterdam In.)	51·34 N	4·38 E
111	Etterbeek (ĕt'ĕr-bāk) Bel. (Bruxelles In.)	50·51 N	4·24 E
90	Etzatlán (ĕt-zä-tlän') Mex.	20·44 N	104·04 W
158	Eucla (ū'klȧ) Austl.	31·45 S	128·50 E
75	Euclid (ū'klĭd) Ohio (Cleveland In.)	41·34 N	81·32 W
73	Eudora (u-dō'rȧ) Ark.	33·07 N	91·16 W
78	Eufaula (û-fô'lȧ) Ala.	31·53 N	85·09 W
73	Eufaula Okla.	35·16 N	95·35 W
66	Eugene (û-jēn') Ore.	44·02 N	123·06 W
74	Euless (ū'lĕs) Tex. (Dallas, Fort Worth In.)	32·50 N	97·05 W
77	Eunice (ū'nĭs) La.	30·30 N	92·25 W
117	Eupen (oi'pĕn) Bel.	50·39 N	6·05 E
144	Euphrates, R. (û-frā'tēz) Asia	35·52 N	39·53 E
122	Eure (R.) (ûr) Fr.	49·03 N	1·22 E
66	Eureka (û-rē'kȧ) Calif.	40·45 N	124·10 W
73	Eureka Kans.	37·48 N	96·17 W
66	Eureka Mont.	48·53 N	115·07 W
68	Eureka Nev.	39·33 N	115·58 W
70	Eureka S. D.	45·46 N	99·38 W
69	Eureka Utah	39·55 N	112·10 W
73	Eureka Springs Ark.	36·24 N	93·43 W
144	Eurgun (Mtn.) Iran	28·47 N	57·00 E
7	Europe (ū'rŭp)		
79	Eustis (ūs'tĭs) Fla.	28·50 N	81·41 W
78	Eutaw (ū-tȧ) Ala.	32·48 N	87·50 W
118	Evanger (ĕ-vaŋ'gĕr) Nor.	60·40 N	6·06 E
75	Evanston (ĕv'ănz-tŭn) Ill. (Chicago In.)	42·03 N	87·41 W
67	Evanston Wyo.	41·17 N	111·02 W
80	Evansville (ĕv'ănz-vĭl) Ind.	38·00 N	87·30 W
71	Evansville Wis.	42·46 N	89·19 W
80	Evart (ĕv'ērt) Mich.	43·55 N	85·10 W
168	Evaton (ĕv'ȧ-tŏn) S. Afr. (Johannesburg & Pretoria In.)	26·32 S	27·53 E
71	Eveleth (ĕv'ĕ-lĕth) Minn.	47·27 N	92·35 W
158	Everard (L.) (ĕv'ēr-ărd) Austl.	36·20 S	134·10 E
158	Everard Ra. Austl.	27·15 S	132·00 E
142	Everest, Mt. (ĕv'ēr-ĕst) Nep.	32·58 N	86·57 E
83	Everett (ĕv'ēr-ĕt) Mass. (Boston In.)	42·24 N	71·03 W
65	Everett (ĕv'ēr-ĕt) Wash. (Seattle In.)	47·59 N	122·11 W
87	Everett Mts. Can.	62·34 N	68·00 W
79	Everglades (ĕv'ēr-glādz).Fla. (In.)	25·50 N	81·25 W
94	Everglades, The (Swp.) Fla.	25·35 N	80·55 W
79	Everglades Natl. Park..Fla. (In.)	25·39 N	80·57 W
78	Evergreen (ĕv'ēr-grēn) Ala.	31·25 N	87·56 W
75	Evergreen Park..Ill. (Chicago In.)	41·44 N	87·42 W
74	Everman (ĕv'ēr-măn) Tex. (Dallas, Fort Worth In.)	32·38 N	97·17 W
65	Everson (ĕv'ēr-sŭn) Wash. (Vancouver In.)	48·55 N	122·21 W
124	Évora (ĕv'ô-rä) Port.	38·35 N	7·54 W
122	Évreux (ā-vrû') Fr.	49·02 N	1·11 E
127	Evrotas (R.) (ĕv-rō'täs) Grc.	37·15 N	22·17 E
127	Evvoia (Pen.) Grc.	38·38 N	23·45 E
157	Ewa (ē'wä) Hawaii (In.)	21·17 N	158·03 E
155	Ewab, Palau-Palan Is. Indon.	5·55 S	131·30 E
74	Excelsior (ĕk-sel'sĭ-ŏr) Minn. (Minneapolis, St. Paul In.)	44·54 N	93·35 W
73	Excelsior Springs Mo.	39·20 N	94·13 W
116	Exe (R.) (ĕks) Eng.	50·57 N	3·37 W
68	Exeter (ĕk'sê-tēr) Calif.	36·18 N	119·09 W
116	Exeter Eng.	50·45 N	3·33 W
81	Exeter N. H.	43·00 N	71·00 W
116	Exmoor (ĕks'mōōr) Eng.	51·10 N	3·55 W
116	Exmouth (ĕks'mŭth) Eng.	50·40 N	3·20 W
158	Exmouth, G. Austl.	21·45 S	114·30 E
83	Exploits (R.) (ĕks-ploits') Can.	48·50 N	56·15 W
90	Extórrax (R.) (ĕx-tó'ràx) Mex.	21·04 N	99·39 W
101	Extrema (ĕs-trĕ'mä) Braz. (Rio de Janeiro In.)	22·52 S	46·19 W
124	Extremadura (Reg.) (ĕks-trā-mä-doo'rä).Sp.	38·43 N	6·30 W
95	Exuma Sd. (ĕk-sōō'mä) Ba. Is.	24·20 N	76·20 W

ăt; finăl; rāte; senåte; ärm; ȧsk; sofȧ; fâre; ch-choose; dh-as th in other; bē; ēvent; bĕt; recĕnt; cratēr; g-go; gh-guttural g; bĭt; ĭ-short neutral; rīde; ĸ-guttural k as ch in German ich;

Page	Name Pronunciation Region	Lat. °'	Long. °'
166	Eyasi (L.) (å-yä'sê) Tan.	3·41 S	34·14 E
112	Eyja Fd. Ice.	66·21 N	18·20 W
112	Eyrarbakki Ice.	63·51 N	20·52 W
158	Eyre (âr) Austl.	32·15 S	126·20 E
160	Eyre (L.) Austl.	28·43 S	37·50 E
158	Eyre Pen. Austl.	33·30 S	136·00 E
100	Ezeiza (ĕ-zä'zä) Arg. (In.)	34·36 S	58·31 W
127	Ezine (å'zĭ-nå) Tur.	39·47 N	26·18 E
118	Faaborg (fô'bôrg) Den.	55·06 N	10·19 E
76	Fabens (fā'bĕnz) Tex.	31·30 N	106·07 W
126	Fabriano (fä-brē-ä'nô) It.	43·20 N	12·55 E
98	Facatativá (fä-kä-tä-tê-vä') Col (In.)	4·49 N	74·09 W
165	Fada (fä'dä) Chad	17·06 N	21·18 E
164	Fada N'Gourma (fä'dä''n gōōr'mä) Upper Volta	12·11 N	00·21 E
135	Faddeya (I.) (fàd-yä') Sov. Un.	76·12 N	145·00 E
118	Faemund (L.) (fâ'mōōn') Nor.	62·17 N	11·40 E
126	Faenza (fä-ĕnd'zä) It.	44·16 N	11·53 E
112	Faeroe Is. (fâ'rō) Eur.	61·53 N	5·58 W
168	Fafan R. Eth. (Horn of Afr. (In.)	8·15 N	42·40 E
124	Fafe (fä'fā) Port.	41·30 N	8·10 W
127	Făgăras (fâ-gä'rāsh) Rom.	45·50 N	24·55 E
118	Fagerness (fä'ghĕr-nĕs) Nor.	61·00 N	9·10 E
100	Fagnano (fäk-nä'nô) (L.) Arg.-Chile	54·35 S	68·20 W
164	Faial I. (fä-yä'l) Azores (In.)	38·40 N	29·19 W
168	Fā'id (fä-yēd') U. A. R. (Suez In.)	30·19 N	32·18 E
151	Faifo (fä'ê-fō') Viet.	15·48 N	108·30 E
116	Fair (I.) (fâr) Scot.	59·34 N	1·41 W
64	Fairbanks (fâr'bănks) Alaska	64·50 N	147·48 W
80	Fairbury (fâr'bĕr-ĭ) Ill.	40·45 N	88·25 W
73	Fairbury Nebr.	40·09 N	97·11 W
85	Fairchild Cr. (fâr'chīld) Can. (Toronto In.)	43·18 N	80·10 W
71	Fairfax (fâr'făks) Minn.	44·29 N	94·44 W
79	Fairfax S. C.	32·29 N	81·13 W
84	Fairfield (fâr'fēld) Ala. (Birmingham In.)	33·30 N	86·50 W
161	Fairfield Austl. (Sydney In.)	33·52 S	150·57 E
84	Fairfield Conn. (New York In.)	41·08 N	73·22 W
80	Fairfield Ill.	38·25 N	88·20 W
71	Fairfield Iowa	41·00 N	91·59 W
82	Fairfield Maine	44·35 N	69·38 W
81	Fairhaven (fâr-hā'vĕn) Mass.	41·35 N	70·55 W
81	Fair Haven Vt.	43·35 N	73·15 W
80	Fairmont (fâr'mŏnt) Ind.	40·25 N	85·45 W
71	Fairmont Minn.	43·39 N	94·26 W
81	Fairmont W. Va.	39·30 N	80·10 W
74	Fairmont City Ill. (St. Louis In.)	38·39 N	90·05 W
74	Fairmount Kans. (Kansas City In.)	39·12 N	95·55 W
74	Fairmount Mo. (Kansas City In.)	39·06 N	94·28 W
84	Fair Oaks (fâr ōks) Ga. (Atlanta In.)	33·56 N	84·33 W
81	Fairport (fâr'pōrt) N. Y.	43·05 N	77·30 W
80	Fairport Harbor Ohio	41·45 N	81·15 W
75	Fairview (fâr'vū) Ohio (Cleveland In.)	41·27 N	81·52 W
72	Fairview Okla.	36·16 N	98·28 W
65	Fairview Ore. (Portland In.)	45·32 N	122·26 W
69	Fairview Utah	39·35 N	111·30 W
64	Fairweather, Mt. (fâr-wĕdh'ĕr) Can.	59·12 N	137·22 W
70	Faith (fāth) S. D.	45·02 N	120·02 W
142	Faizābād India	26·50 N	82·17 E
165	Fajao (fä-jä'ō) Ug.	2·13 N	31·44 E
89	Fajardo P. R. (Puerto Rico In.)	18·20 N	65·40 W
142	Fakiragram India	26·28 N	90·16 E
150	Fak'u China	42·28 N	123·20 E
151	Falalise, C. Viet.	19·20 N	106·18 E
99	Falcón (fäl-kô'n) (State) Ven. (In.)	11·00 N	68·28 W
81	Falconer (fô'k'n-ĕr) N. Y.	42·10 N	79·10 W
74	Falcon Heights (fô'k'n) Minn. (Minneapolis, St. Paul In.)	44·59 N	93·10 W
76	Falcon Res. (fôk'n) Tex.	26·47 N	99·03 W
164	Faleme R. (fä-lā-mā') Mali-Senegal	13·15 N	11·27 W
129	Faleshty (fä-lâsh'tĭ) Sov. Un.	47·33 N	27·46 E
76	Falfurrias (făl'fōō-rē'ás) Tex.	27·15 N	98·08 W
118	Falkenberg (fäl'kĕn-bĕrgh) Swe.	56·54 N	12·25 E
111	Falkensee (fäl'kĕn-zā) Ger. (Berlin In.)	52·34 N	13·05 E
111	Falkenthal (fäl'kĕn-täl) Ger. (Berlin In.)	52·54 N	13·18 E
116	Falkirk (fôl'kûrk) Scot.	55·59 N	3·55 W
100	Falkland Is. (fôk'lănd) S. A.	50·45 S	61·00 W
118	Falköping (fäl'chûp-ĭng) Swe.	58·09 N	13·30 E
65	Fall City Wash. (Seattle In.)	47·34 N	121·53 W
75	Fall Cr. (fôl) Ind. (Indianapolis In.)	39·52 N	86·04 W
68	Fallon (făl'ŭn) Nev.	39·30 N	118·48 W
84	Fall River Mass. (Providence In.)	41·42 N	71·07 W
73	Falls City Nebr.	40·04 N	95·37 W
116	Falmouth (făl'mŭth) Eng.	50·08 N	3·04 W
94	Falmouth Jam.	18·30 N	77·40 W
80	Falmouth Ky.	38·40 N	84·20 W
166	False B. (Valsbaai) S. Afr. (Cape Town In.)	34·14 S	18·35 E
143	False Divi Pt. India	20·43 N	81·06 E
95	Falso, Cabo (C.) (kä'bô-fäl-sô) Dom. Rep.	17·45 N	71·55 W
118	Falster (I.) (fäls'tĕr) Den.	54·43 N	12·16 E
121	Fălticeni (fŭl-tê-chān'y') Rom.	47·27 N	26·17 E
118	Falun (fä-lōōn') Swe.	60·38 N	15·35 E
115	Famagusta (fä-mä-gōōs'tä) Cyprus	35·08 N	33·59 E
100	Famatina, Sierra de (Mts.) (sē-ĕ'r-rä-dĕ-fä-mä-tē'-nä) Arg.	29·00 S	67·50 W
151	Fan Ching Shan (Mtns.) China	26·46 N	107·42 E
151	Fanghsien China	32·05 N	110·45 E
157	Fanning (I.) (făn'ĭng) Gilbert & Ellice Is.	4·20 N	159·00 W
85	Fannystelle (făn'ĭ-stĕl) Can. (Winnipeg In.)	49·45 N	97·46 W
126	Fano (fä'nō) It.	43·49 N	13·01 E
118	Fanö (I.) (fän'û) Den.	55·24 N	8·10 E
167	Farafangana (fä-rä-fäŋ-gä'nä) Malagasy	21·18 S	47·59 E
165	Farâfra (Oasis) (fä-rä'frä) U. A. R.	27·04 N	28·13 E
144	Farah (fä-rä') Afg.	32·15 N	62·13 E
90	Farallón, Punta (Pt.) (pōō'n-tä-fä-rä-lōn) Mex.	19·21 N	105·03 W
164	Faranah (fä-rä'nä) Gui.	10·02 N	10·52 W
165	Farasan Dahlak Arch. Eth.	16·45 N	41·08 E
115	Faras R. Libya	30·18 N	17·19 E
115	Faregh, Wadi al R. (wädê ĕl fä-rĕg') Libya	30·10 N	19·34 E
159	Farewell, C. (fâr-wĕl') N. Z. (In.)	40·37 S	171·46 E
155	Farfak Neth. N. Gui.	2.56 S	132·25 E
70	Fargo (fär'gō) N. D.	46·53 N	96·48 W
84	Far Hills (fär hĭlz) N. J. (New York In.)	40·41 N	74·38 W
71	Faribault (fâ'rĭ-bō) Minn.	44·19 N	93·16 W
124	Farilhoes (Is.) (fä-rê-lyôɴzh') Port.	39·28 N	9·32 W
160	Farina (fà-rē'nȧ) Austl.	30·03 S	138·20 E
110	Faringdon (fă'rĭng-dŏn) Eng. (London In.)	51·38 N	1·35 W
168	Fāriskūr (fä-rês-kōōr') U. A. R. (Nile In.)	31·19 N	31·46 E
165	Farit, Amba (Mt.) Eth.	10·51 N	37·52 E
121	Farkašd (fär'kāsht) Czech.	48·00 N	17·43 E
74	Farley (fär'lē) Mo. (Kansas City In.)	39·16 N	94·49 W
74	Farmers Branch (fär'mērz brânch) Tex. (Dallas, Fort Worth In.)	32·56 N	96·53 W
80	Farmersburg (fär'mērz-bûrg) Ind.	39·15 N	87·25 W
73	Farmersville (fär'mērz-vĭl) Tex.	33·11 N	96·22 W
84	Farmingdale (färm'ĕng-dāl) N. J. (New York In.)	40·11 N	74·10 W
84	Farmingdale N. Y. (New York In.)	40·44 N	73·26 W
83	Farmingham (färm-ĭng-hăm) Mass. (Boston In.)	42·17 N	71·25 W
73	Farmington (färm-ĭng-tŭn) Ill.	40·42 N	90·01 W
82	Farmington Maine	44·40 N	70·10 W
75	Farmington Mich. (Detroit In.)	42·28 N	83·23 W
73	Farmington Mo.	37·46 N	90 26 W
69	Farmington N. Mex.	36·40 N	108·10 W
74	Farmington Utah (Salt Lake City In.)	40·59 N	111·53 W
79	Farmville (färm-vĭl) N. C.	35·35 N	77·35 W
79	Farmville Va.	37·15 N	78·23 W
110	Farnborough (färn'bŭr-ô) Eng. (London In.)	51·15 N	0·45 W
116	Farne (I.) (färn) Eng.	55·40 N	1·32 W
81	Farnham (fär'năm) Can.	45·15 N	72·55 W
110	Farningham (fär'nĭng-ŭm) Eng.	51·22 N	0·14 E
110	Farnworth (färn'wŭrth) Eng.	53·34 N	2·24 W
99	Faro (fä'rōō) Braz.	2·05 S	56·32 W
124	Faro Port.	37·01 N	7·57 W
119	Fåron (I.) Swe.	57·57 N	19·10 E
158	Farquhar, C. (fär'kwȧr) Austl.	23·50 S	112·55 E
80	Farrell (făr'ĕl) Pa.	41·10 N	80·30 W
142	Farrukhābād (fŭ-rōōk-hä-bäd') India	27·29 N	79·35 E
127	Fársala (Pharsalus) Grc.	39·18 N	22·25 E
118	Farsund (fär'sōōn) Nor.	58·05 N	6·47 E
100	Fartura, Serra da (Mts.) (sĕ'r-rä-dä-fär-tōō'rä) Braz.	26·40 S	53·15 W
49	Farvel, Kap (C.) Grnld.	60·00 N	44·00 W
72	Farwell (fär'wĕl) Tex.	34·24 N	103·03 W
144	Fasā (fŭ-sä') Iran	28·59 N	53·44 E
127	Fasano (fä-zä'nō) It.	40·50 N	17·22 E
129	Fastov (fäs'tôf) Sov. Un.	50·04 N	29·57 E
129	Fatëzh Sov. Un.	52·06 N	35·51 E
133	Fatsa (fät'sä) Tur.	40·50 N	37·30 E
	Fatshan, see Nanhai		
123	Faucilles, Monts (Mts.) (môɴ' fō-sēl') Fr.	48·07 N	6·13 E
126	Favara (fä-vä'rä) It.	37·19 N	13·50 E
123	Faverolles (fä-vrôl') Fr. (Paris In.)	48·42 N	1·34 E
110	Faversham (fă'vĕr-sh'm) Eng. (London In.)	51·19 N	0·54 E
112	Faxaflói (B.) Ice.	64·33 N	22·40 W
165	Faya (fȧ-yä') Chad	17·45 N	19·26 E
78	Fayette (fâ-yĕt') Ala.	33·40 N	87·54 W
71	Fayette Iowa	42·49 N	91·49 W
78	Fayette Miss.	31·43 N	91·00 W
73	Fayette Mo.	39·09 N	92·41 W
73	Fayetteville (fâ-yĕt'vĭl) Ark.	36·03 N	94·08 W
79	Fayetteville N. C.	35·02 N	78·54 W
78	Fayetteville Tenn.	35·10 N	86·33 W
142	Fazilka India	30·30 N	74·02 E
165	Fazzān (Fezzan) Prov. Libya	26·45 N	13·01 E
165	Fazzān (Oasis) Libya	26·06 N	15·00 E
79	Fear, C. (fēr) N. C.	33·52 N	77·48 W
68	Feather (R.) (fĕth'ēr) Calif.	38·56 N	121·41 W
68	Feather, Middle Fk. of (R.) Calif.	39·49 N	121·10 W
68	Feather, North Fk. of (R.) Calif.	40·00 N	121·20 W
110	Featherstone (fĕdh'ĕr stŭn) Eng.	53·39 N	1·21 W
122	Fécamp (fā-käɴ') Fr.	49·45 N	0·20 E
85	Federal (fĕd'ĕr-ăl) Can. (Ottawa In.)	45·20 N	75·42 W
99	Federal, Distrito (Dist.) (dês-trê'tô-fĕ-dĕ-rä'l) Ven. (In.)	10·34 N	66·55 W
142	Federal Capital Dist. W. Pak.	29·55 N	67·01 E
163	Federation of Rhodesia and Nyasaland (rō-dē'zhĭ-ȧ) (nyä'sä-lănd) Afr.	14·00 S	25·00 E
136	Fëdorovka (fyô'dō-rôf-kȧ) Sov. Un. (Moskva In.)	56·15 N	37·14 E
120	Fehmarn I. (fā'märn) Ger.	54·28 N	11·15 E
111	Fehrbellin (fĕr'bĕl-lēn) Ger. (Berlin In.)	52·49 N	12·46 E
101	Feia, Logoa (L.) (lô-gôā-fĕ'yä) Braz. (Rio de Janeiro In.)	21·54 S	41·45 W
148	Feich'eng (fā'chĕng) China	36·18 N	116·45 E
148	Feihsien (fā'ê-hsyĕn') China	35·17 N	117·59 E
99	Feira de Santana (fĕ'ê-rä dä sänt-än'ä) Braz.	12·16 S	38·46 W
125	Felanitx (fā-lä-nēch') Sp.	39·29 N	3·09 E
120	Feldkirch (fĕlt'kĭrk) Aus.	47·15 N	9·36 E
111	Feldkirchen (fĕld'kĕr-ĸĕn) Ger. (München In.)	48·09 N	11·44 E
92	Felipe Carrillo Puerto (fĕ-lē'pĕ-kär-rē'l-yô-pwĕ'r-tô) Mex. (Yucatan In.)	19·36 N	88·04 W
126	Feltre (fĕl'trā) It.	46·02 N	11·56 E
167	Fénérive (fĕ-nâ-rēv') Malagasy	17·30 S	49·31 E
150	Fengchen (fûng'chĕn') China	40·28 N	113·20 E
150	Fengch'eng (fûng'chŭng') China	40·28 N	124·03 E
151	Fengchieh China	31·02 N	109·30 E
150	Fenghsiang China	34·25 N	107·20 E
149	Fenghsien (fûng'hsyĕn') China (Shanghai In.)	30·55 N	121·26 E
148	Fenghsien China	34·41 N	116·36 E
148	Fengjun (fĕng'yĕn) China	39·51 N	118·06 E
148	Fengming Tao (I.) (fĕng'mĭng dou) China	39·19 N	121·15 E
150	Fengt'ai (fûng'tī') China (Peking In.)	39·51 N	116·19 E
151	Fengtu (fûng'tōō') China	29·58 N	107·50 E
148	Fengyang (fûng'yäng') China	32·55 N	117·32 E
64	Fenimore P. (fĕn ĭ mōr) Alaska	51·40 N	175·38 W
80	Fenton (fĕn-tŭn) Mich.	42·50 N	83·40 W
74	Fenton Mo. (St. Louis In.)	38·31 N	90·27 W
150	Fenyang China	37·20 N	111·48 E
129	Feodosiya (Kefe) (fĕ-ô-dō'sē'yȧ) (kyĕ'fĕ) Sov. Un.	45·02 N	35·21 E
144	Ferdows Iran	34·00 N	58·13 E
126	Ferentino (fā-rĕn-tē'nō) It.	41·42 N	13·18 E
134	Fergana Sov. Un.	40·16 N	72·07 E
70	Fergus Falls (fûr'gŭs) Minn.	46·17 N	96·03 W
74	Ferguson (fûr-gŭ-sŭn) Mo. (St. Louis In.)	38·45 N	90·18 W
126	Fermo (fĕr'mō) It.	43·10 N	13·43 E
124	Fermoselle (fĕr-mō-sāl'yâ) Sp.	41·20 N	6·23 W
116	Fermoy (fûr-moi') Ire.	52·05 N	8·06 W
79	Fernandina (fûr-năn-dē'nȧ) Fla.	30·38 N	81·29 W
99	Fernando de Noronha, Arquipélago (Arch.) (är-kê-pĕ'lä-gô-fĕr-năn-dō-dĕ-nô-rō'n-yä) Braz.	3·50 S	33·15 W
164	Fernando Póo, Isla de (I.) (ê's-lä-dĕ-fĕr-năn'dōpō') (fĕr-năn'dō-pō'ō) Afr.	3·22 N	7·37 E
124	Fernān-Núñez (fĕr-nän'nōōn'yâth) Sp.	37·42 N	4·43 W
66	Ferndale (fûrn'dāl) Calif.	40·34 N	124·18 W
84	Ferndale Md. (Baltimore In.)	39·11 N	76·39 W
75	Ferndale Mich. (Detroit In.)	42·27 N	83·08 W
65	Ferndale Wash. (Vancouver In.)	48·51 N	122·36 W
86	Fernie (fûr'nĭ) Can.	49·29 N	114·56 W
65	Fern Prairie (fûrn prâr'ĭ) Wash. (Portland In.)	45·38 N	122·25 W
161	Ferntree Gully Austl. (Melbourne In.)	37·53 S	145·18 E
83	Ferolle, Pt. (fĕ-rōl') Can.	51·01 N	57·04 W
142	Ferozepore (fê-rōz-pōr') India	30·58 N	74·39 E
126	Ferrara (fĕr-rä'rä) It.	44·50 N	11·37 E
125	Ferrat, Cap (C.) (kăp fĕr-rät) Alg.	35·49 N	0·29 W
124	Ferreira do Alentejo (fĕr-rĕ'ê-rä dōō ä-lĕɴ-tā'zhōō) Port.	38·03 N	8·06 W
124	Ferreira do Zezere (fĕr-rĕ'ê-rä dōō zā-zā'rĕ) Port.	39·49 N	8·17 W
74	Ferrelview (fĕr'rĕl-vū) Mo. (Kansas City In.)	39 18 N	94·40 W
98	Ferreñafe (fĕr-rĕn-yä'fĕ) Peru	6·38 S	79·48 W
77	Ferriday (fĕr'ĭ-dā) La.	31·38 N	91·33 W
83	Ferryland (fĕr'ê-lănd) Can.	46·50 N	47·06 W
113	Ferryville (fĕr-ê-vēl') Tun.	37·12 N	9·51 E
136	Fershampenuaz (fĕr-shăm'pĕn-wäz) Sov. Un. (Urals In.)	53·32 N	59·50 E
70	Fertile (fûr'tĭl) Minn.	47·33 N	96·18 W
164	Fès (fĕs) Mor.	34·08 N	5·00 W
70	Fessenden (fĕs'ĕn-dĕn) N. D.	47·39 N	99·40 W
116	Festiniog (fĕs-tĭn-ĭ-ŏg) Wales	52·59 N	3·58 W
73	Festus (fĕst'ŭs) Mo.	38·12 N	90·22 W
133	Fethiye (fĕt-hē'yĕ) Tur.	36·40 N	29·05 E
	Fezzan, see Fazzān		
167	Fianarantsoa (fyȧ-nä'rȧn-tsō'ȧ) Malagasy	21·21 S	47·15 E
168	Ficksburg (fĭks'bûrg) S. Afr. (Johannesburg & Pretoria In.)	28·53 S	27·53 E
65	Fidalgo I. (fĭ-dăl'gō) Wash. (Seattle In.)	48·28 N	122·39 W
66	Fieldbrook (fēld'brōōk) Calif.	40·59 N	124·02 W
127	Fier (fyĕr) Alb.	40·43 N	19·34 E
116	Fife Ness (fīf'nes') Scot.	56·15 N	2·19 W
165	Fifth Cataract Sud.	18·27 N	33·38 E
124	Figalo, Cap (C.) (kăp fê-gä-lô) Alg.	35·35 N	1·12 W
122	Figeac (fē-zhäk') Fr.	44·37 N	2·02 E
118	Figeholm (fē-ghĕ-hōlm) Swe.	57·24 N	16·33 E
124	Figueira da Foz (fê-gwĕy-rä-dä-fô'z) Port.	40·10 N	8·50 W
164	Figuig Alg.	32·06 N	1·17 W
156	Fiji Is. (fē'jē) Oceania	18·50 S	175·00 E
92	Filadelfia (fĭl-ä-dĕl'fĭ-ȧ) C. R.	10·26 N	85·37 W
136	Filatovskoye (fĭ-lä'tôf-skô-yĕ) Sov. Un. (Urals In.)	56·49 N	62·20 E
79	Filbert (fĭl'bērt) W. Va.	37·18 N	81·29 W
47	Filchner Shelf Ice (fĭlk'nĕr) Ant.	77·30 S	38·00 W
127	Filiatrá Grc.	37·10 N	21·35 E
126	Filicudi (I.) (fē'le-kōō'dē) It.	38·34 N	14·39 E
115	Filigas (R.) Tur.	41·10 N	32·53 E
136	Filippovskoye (fĭ-lĭ-pôf'skô-yĕ) Sov. Un. (Moskva In.)	56·06 N	38·38 E
118	Filipstad (fĭl'ĭps-städh) Swe.	59·44 N	14·09 E
69	Fillmore (fĭl'mōr) Utah	39·00 N	112·20 W
166	Fimi (R) Con. L.	2·46 S	17·30 E

ng-sing; ŋ-baŋk; ɴ-nasalized n; nŏd; cŏmmit; ōld; ôbey; ôrder; fōōd; fŏŏt; ou-out; s-soft; sh-dish; th-thin; pūre; ûnite; ûrn; stŭd; circŭs; ü-as "y" in study; '-indeterminate vowel.

206 Finch–Fort Portal PRONOUNCING INDEX

Page	Name Pronunciation Region	Lat. °′	Long. °′
85	Finch (fĭnch)...Can. (Ottawa In.)	45·09 N	75·06 W
80	Findlay (fĭnd′lȧ)...Ohio	41·05 N	83·40 W
124	Finisterre, Cabo de (C.) (kȧ′bô-dĕ-fĭn-ĭs-târ′).Sp.	42·52 N	9·48 W
158	Finke (R.) (fĭŋ′kê)...Austl.	25·25 S	134·30 E
102	Finland, (fĭn′lănd)...Eur.	62·45 N	26·13 E
119	Finland, G. of (fĭn′lănd)...Eur.	59·35 N	23·35 E
98	Finlandia (fēn-lä′n-dêä).Col. (In.)	4·38 N	75·39 W
86	Finlay (R.) (fĭn′lâ)...Can.	56·57 N	124·40 W
111	Finofurt (fē′nō-fōōrt) Ger. (Berlin In.)	52·50 N	13·41 E
111	Finow (fē′nōv)..Ger. (Berlin In.)	52·50 N	13·44 E
120	Finsterwalde (fĭn′stĕr-väl-dĕ).Ger.	51·38 N	13·42 E
133	Firat (R.) (fē-rät′)...Tur.	39·40 N	38·30 E
65	Fircrest (fûr′krĕst) Wash. (Seattle In.)	47·14 N	122·31 W
126	Firenze (Florence) (fê-rĕnt′sä)..It.	43·47 N	11·15 E
126	Firenzuola (fē-rĕnt-swô′lä)....It.	44·08 N	11·21 E
165	First Cataract...U. A. R.	24·00 N	32·52 E
111	Fischa (R.)...Aus. (Wien In.)	48·04 N	16·33 E
111	Fischamend Markt Aus. (Wien In.)	48·07 N	16·37 E
95	Fish Cay (I.)...Ba. Is.	22·30 N	74·20 W
85	Fish Cr. (fĭsh)..Can. (Calgary In.)	50·52 N	114·21 W
77	Fisher (fĭsh′ẽr)...La.	31·28 N	93·30 W
87	Fisher Str...Can.	62·43 N	84·28 W
82	Fish River (L.) (fĭsh)...Maine	46·48 N	68·50 W
83	Fitchburg (fĭch′bûrg) Mass. (Boston In.)	42·35 N	71·48 W
78	Fitzgerald (fĭts-jĕr′ăld)...Ga.	31·42 N	83·17 W
158	Fitzroy (R.) (fĭts-roi′)...Austl.	18·00 S	124·05 E
159	Fitzroy (R.)...Austl.	23·45 S	150·02 E
158	Fitzroy Crossing...Austl.	18·08 S	126·00 E
80	Fitzwilliam (I.) (fĭts-wĭl′yŭm) Can.	45·30 N	81·45 W
	Fiume, see Rijeka		
125	Fiumicino (fyōō-mē-chê′nô) It. (Roma In.)	41·47 N	12·19 E
118	Fjällbacka (fyĕl′bäk-å)...Swe.	58·37 N	11·17 E
118	Flaam (flôm)...Nor.	60·51 N	7·01 E
69	Flagstaff (flăg-stȧf)...Ariz.	35·15 N	111·40 W
167	Flagstaff (flăg′stȧf) S. Afr. (Natal In.)	31·06 S	29·31 E
81	Flagstaff (L.) (flăg-stȧf)...Maine	45·05 N	70·30 W
111	Flalow (flä′lōv)..Ger. (Berlin In.)	52·44 N	12·58 E
71	Flambeau (R.) (flăm-bō′)...Wis.	45·32 N	91·05 W
79	Flamingo (flȧ-mĭŋ′gō)...Fla.	25·10 N	80·55 W
95	Flamingo Cay (I.) (flȧ-mĭŋ′gō) Ba. Is.	22·50 N	75·50 W
89	Flamingo Pt. Vir. Is. (U. S. A.) (St. Thomas In.)	18·19 N	65·00 W
117	Flanders (Reg.)...Fr.	50·53 N	2·29 E
70	Flandreau (flăn′drō)...S. D.	44·02 N	96·35 W
116	Flannan (Is.) (flăn′ăn)...Scot.	58·13 N	8·14 W
67	Flathead L. (flăt′hĕd)...Mont.	47·57 N	114·20 W
67	Flathead Ra...Mont.	47·50 N	113·40 W
67	Flathead R...Mont.	48·45 N	114·20 W
67	Flathead R., Middle Fork...Mont.	48·30 N	113·47 W
67	Flathead R., South Fork...Mont.	48·05 N	113·45 W
75	Flat Rock (flăt rŏk) Mich. (Detroit In.)	42·06 N	83·17 W
66	Flattery C. (flăt′ẽr-ĭ)...Wash.	48·22 N	125·10 W
67	Flat Willow Cr. (flat wĭl′ô).Mont.	46·45 N	108·47 W
118	Flekkefjord (flĕk′kĕ-fyôr)...Nor.	58·19 N	6·38 E
80	Flemingsburg (flĕm′ĭngz-bûrg) Ky.	38·25 N	83·45 W
120	Flensburg (flĕns′bŏŏrgh)...Ger.	54·48 N	9·27 E
122	Flers-del-l'Orne (flĕr-dĕ-lôrn′)..Fr.	48·43 N	0·37 W
158	Flinders (Reg.) (flĭn′dẽrz)...Austl.	32·15 S	138·45 E
160	Flinders (I.)...Austl.	39·35 S	148·10 E
159	Flinders (R.)...Austl.	18·48 S	141·07 E
160	Flinders Ra...Austl.	34·09 S	138·56 E
159	Flinders Rfs...Austl.	17·30 S	149·02 E
86	Flin Flon...Can.	54·50 N	101·52 W
110	Flint...Wales	53·15 N	3·07 W
80	Flint...Mich.	43·00 N	83·45 W
110	Flint (Co.)...Wales	53·13 N	3·06 W
78	Flint (R.) (flĭnt)...Ga.	31·25 N	84·15 W
118	Flisen (flē′sĕn)...Swe.	60·35 N	12·03 E
80	Flora (flō′rȧ)...Ill.	38·40 N	88·25 W
80	Flora...Ind.	40·25 N	86·30 W
78	Florala (flŏr-ăl′ȧ)...Ala.	31·01 N	86·19 W
84	Floral Park (flôr′ăl pärk) N. Y. (New York In.)	40·42 N	73·42 W
78	Florence (flŏr′ĕns)...Ala.	34·46 N	87·40 W
69	Florence...Ariz.	33·00 N	111·25 W
72	Florence...Colo.	38·23 N	105·08 W
73	Florence...Kans.	38·14 N	96·56 W
79	Florence...S. C.	34·10 N	79·45 W
65	Florence...Wash. (Seattle In.)	48·13 N	122·21 W
	Florence, see Firenze		
98	Florencia (flō-rĕn′sê-ȧ)...Col.	1·31 N	75·13 W
101	Florencio Sánchez (flō-rĕn-sêō-sä′n-chĕz).Ur. (Buenos Aires In.)	33.52 S	57·24 W
100	Florencio Varela (flō-rĕn′sê-o vä-rā′lä).Arg. (In.)	34·34 S	58·16 W
99	Flores (flō′rĕzh)...Braz.	7·57 S	37·48 W
92	Flores...Guat. (Yucatan In.)	16·53 N	89·54 W
101	Flores (Dept.) Ur. (Buenos Aires In.)	33·33 S	57·00 W
154	Flores (I.)...Indon.	8·14 S	121·08 E
101	Flores (R.) Arg. (Buenos Aires In.)	36·13 S	60·28 W
154	Flores Sea...Indon.	7·09 N	120·30 E
76	Floresville (flō′rĕs-vĭl)...Tex.	29·10 N	98·08 W
99	Floriano (flō-rē-ä′nōō)...Braz.	6·17 S	42·58 W
100	Florianópolis (flō-rê-ä-nō′pō-lēs) Braz.	27·30 S	48·30 W
98	Florida (flō-rē′-dä)...Col. (In.)	3·20 N	76·12 W
94	Florida...Cuba	22·10 N	79·50 W
84	Florida (flŏr′ĭ-dȧ) N. Y. (New York In.)	41·20 N	74·21 W
167	Florida...S. Afr. (Johannesburg & Pretoria In.)	26·11 S	27·56 E
101	Florida (flô-rê-dhä) Ur. (Buenos Aires In.)	34·06 S	56·14 W
63	Florida (State) (flŏr′ĭ-dȧ)...U. S.	30·30 N	84·40 W
101	Florida (Dept.) (flô-rē′dhä) Ur. (Buenos Aires In.)	33·48 S	56·15 W
159	Florida (I.)...Sol. Is.	8·56 S	159·45 E
94	Florida, Strs. of...N. A.	24·10 N	81·00 W
79	Florida B. (flŏr′ĭ-dȧ)...Fla. (In.)	24·55 N	80·55 W
79	Florida Keys (Is.)...Fla. (In.)	24·33 N	81·20 W
69	Florida Mts...N. Mex.	32·10 N	107·35 W
76	Florido, R. (flô-rē′dō)...Mex.	27·21 N	104·48 W
111	Floridsdorf (flô′rĭds-dôrf) Aus. (Wien In.)	48·16 N	16·25 E
127	Florina (flô-rē′nä)...Grc.	40·48 N	21·24 E
74	Florissant (flŏr′ĭ-sănt) Mo. (St. Louis In.)	38·47 N	90·20 W
118	Florö (flôr′ü)...Nor.	61·36 N	5·01 E
70	Floyd (R.) (floid)...Iowa	42·38 N	96·15 W
72	Floydada (floi-dā′dȧ)...Tex.	33·59 N	101·19 W
75	Floyds Fk. (R.) (floi-dz) Ky. (Louisville In.)	38·08 N	85·30 W
126	Flumendosa, R. (flōō-mĕn-dô′sä) It.	39·45 N	9·18 E
80	Flushing (flŭsh′ĭng)...Mich.	43·05 N	83·50 W
155	Fly (R.) (flī)...Austl.	8·00 S	141·45 E
127	Foča (fō′chä)...Yugo.	43·29 N	18·48 E
168	Fochville (fōk′vĭl)...S. Afr. (Johannesburg & Pretoria In.)	26·29 S	27·29 E
121	Focsani (fōk-shä′nê)...Rom.	45·41 N	27·17 E
126	Foggia (fôd′jä)...It.	41·30 N	15·34 E
83	Fogo (fō′gō)...Can.	49·43 N	54·14 W
83	Fogo (I.)...Can.	49·44 N	53·53 W
164	Fogo I...C. V. Is. (In.)	14·46 N	24·51 W
120	Fohnsdorf (fōns′dôrf)...Aus.	47·13 N	14·40 E
120	Föhr I. (fûr)...Ger.	54·47 N	8·30 E
122	Foix (fwä)...Fr.	42·58 N	1·34 E
151	Fokang...China	23·50 N	113·35 E
126	Foligno (fô-lēn′yō)...It.	42·58 N	12·41 E
110	Folkingham (fō′kĭng-ăm)...Eng.	52·53 N	0·24 W
117	Folkstone (fōk′stŭn)...Eng.	51·05 N	3·04 W
72	Folsom (fŏl′sŭm)...N. Mex.	36·47 N	103·56 W
68	Folsom City...Calif.	38·40 N	121·10 W
94	Fomento (fô-mĕ′n-tō)...Cuba	21·35 N	78·20 W
98	Fómeque (fô′mĕ-kĕ)...Col. (In.)	4·29 N	73·52 W
71	Fonda (fŏn′dȧ)...Iowa	42·33 N	94·51 W
71	Fond du Lac (fŏn dū lăk′)...Wis.	43·47 N	88·29 W
71	Fond du Lac Ind. Res...Minn.	46·44 N	93·04 W
126	Fondi (fōn′dē)...It.	41·23 N	13·25 E
124	Fonsagrada (fôn-sä-grä′dhä)...Sp.	43·08 N	7·07 W
92	Fonseca, Golfo de (G.) (gôl-fô-dĕ-fôn-sä′kä).Hond.	13·09 N	87·55 W
123	Fontainebleau (fôɴ-tĕn-blō′) Fr. (Paris In.)	48·24 N	2·42 E
74	Fontana (fŏn-tă′nȧ) Calif. (Los Angeles In.)	34·06 N	117·27 W
98	Fonte Boa (fōn′tå bō′ȧ)...Braz.	2·32 S	66·05 W
122	Fontenay-le-Comte (fôɴt-nĕ′lē-kôɴt′).Fr.	46·28 N	0·53 W
123	Fontenay-Trésigny (fôɴ-tē-hā′ tra-sēn-yē′).Fr. (Paris In.)	48·43 N	2·53 E
91	Fontera, Punta (Pt.) (pōō′n-tä-fôn-tĕ′rä).Mex.	18·36 N	92·43 W
98	Fontibón (fōn-tē-bôn′)..Col. (In.)	4·42 N	74·09 W
	Foochow, see Fuchou		
167	Foothills (fŏŏt-hĭls)...S. Afr. (Johannesburg & Pretoria In.)	25·55 S	27·36 E
64	Foraker, Mt. (fôr′ȧ-kẽr)...Alaska	62·40 N	152·40 W
123	Forbach (fôr′bäĸ)...Fr.	49·12 N	6·54 E
160	Forbes (fôrbz)...Austl.	33·24 S	148·05 E
164	Forcados (fôr-kä′dōs)...Nig.	5·19 N	5·26 E
120	Forchheim (fôrĸ′hīm)...Ger.	49·43 N	11·05 E
	Fordlândia, see Brasília Legal		
73	Fordyce (fôr′dīs)...Ark.	33·48 N	92·24 W
164	Forecariah (fōr-kȧ-rē′ȧ′)...Gui.	9·31 N	13·14 W
49	Forel, Mt...Grnld.	65·50 N	37·41 W
78	Forest (fŏr′ĕst)...Miss.	32·22 N	89·29 W
70	Forest (R.)...N. D.	48·08 N	97·45 W
71	Forest City...Iowa	43·14 N	93·40 W
79	Forest City...N. C.	35·20 N	81·52 W
81	Forest City...Pa.	41·35 N	75·30 W
65	Forest Grove (grōv) Ore. (Portland In.)	45·31 N	123·07 W
85	Forest Hill (hĭl) Can. (Toronto In.)	43·42 N	79·25 W
74	Forest Hill Tex. (Dallas, Fort Worth In.)	32·40 N	97·16 W
85	Forest Lawn (lôn) Can. (Calgary In.)	51·02 N	113·59 W
82	Forestville (fŏr′ĕst-vĭl)...Can.	48·46 N	69·05 W
122	Forez, Mts. du (môn dü fô-rā′).Fr.	44·55 N	3·43 E
116	Forfar (fôr′fȧr)...Scot.	57·10 N	2·55 W
125	Forio (Mtn.) (fô′ryō) It. (Napoli In.)	40·29 N	13·55 E
75	Forked Cr. (fôrk′d) Ill. (Chicago In.)	41·16 N	88·01 W
78	Forked Deer (R.)...Tenn.	35·53 N	89·29 W
126	Forli (fôr-lē′)...It.	44·13 N	12·03 E
110	Formby (fôrm′bê)...Eng.	53·34 N	3·04 W
110	Formby Pt...Eng.	53·33 N	3·06 W
125	Formello (fôr-mĕ′lō) It. (Roma In.)	42·04 N	12·25 E
125	Formentera, Isla de (I.) (ê′s-lä-dĕ-fôr-mĕn-tā′rä).Sp.	38·43 N	1·25 E
101	Formiga (fôr-mē′gȧ) Braz. (Rio de Janeiro In.)	20·27 S	45·25 W
95	Formigas Bk. (fōr-mē′gäs)..N. A.	18·30 N	75·40 W
100	Formosa (fôr-mō′sä)...Arg.	27·25 S	58·12 W
99	Formosa...Braz.	15·32 S	47·10 W
100	Formosa (Prov.)...Arg.	24·30 S	60·45 W
	Formosa, see Taiwan (I.)		
99	Formosa, Serra (Mts.) (sĕ′r-rä) Braz.	12·59 S	55·11 W
139	Formosa Str. (fŏr-mō′sȧ)...Asia	24·30 N	120·00 E
136	Fornosovo (fôr-nô′sô vô) Sov. Un. (Leningrad In.)	59·35 N	30·34 E
73	Forrest City (for′ĕst sĭ′tĭ)...Ark.	35·00 N	90·46 W
159	Forsayth (fôr-sīth′)...Austl.	18·33 S	143·42 E
118	Forshaga (fôrs′hä′gä)...Swe.	59·34 N	13·25 E
201	Forst (fôrst)...Ger.	51·45 N	14·38 E
78	Forsyth (fôr-sīth′)...Ga.	33·02 N	83·56 W
67	Forsyth...Mont.	46·15 N	106·41 W
87	Fort Albany (fôrt ôl′bȧ nĭ)...Can.	52·10 N	81·40 W
99	Fortaleza (Ceará) (fôr′tä-lā′zä) (sä-ä-rä′).Braz.	3·35 S	38·31 W
69	Fort Apache Ind. Res. (ȧ-păch′ê) Ariz.	34·02 N	110·27 W
165	Fort Archambault (är-chaɴ-bō′) Chad	9·04 N	18·17 E
71	Fort Atkinson (ăt′kĭn-sŭn)...Wis.	42·55 N	88·46 W
	Fort Bayard, see Chanchiang		
167	Fort Beaufort (bō′fôrt) S. Afr. (Natal In.)	32·47 S	26·39 E
74	Fort Bellefontaine (bĕl-fŏn-tān′) Mo. (St. Louis In.)	38·50 N	90·15 W
67	Fort Benton (bĕn′tŭn)...Mont.	47·51 N	110·40 W
70	Fort Berthould Ind. Res. (bĕrth′ôld).N. D.	47·47 N	103·28 W
80	Fort Branch (brănch)...Ind.	38·15 N	87·35 W
	Fort Charlet, see Djanet		
87	Fort Chimo...Can.	58·18 N	68·08 W
86	Fort Chipewyan...Can.	58·46 N	111·15 W
72	Fort Collins (kŏl′ĭns)...Colo.	40·36 N	105·04 W
165	Fort Crampel (kräm-pĕl′) Cen. Afr. Rep.	7·10 N	19·07 E
167	Fort-Dauphin (dō-făɴ′).Malagasy	24·59 S	46·58 E
93	Fort-de-France (dĕ fräɴs) Mart. (Le. & Wind. Is. In.)	14·37 N	61·06 W
78	Fort Deposit (dê-pŏz′ĭt)...Ala.	31·58 N	86·35 W
165	Fort de Possel (dĕ pô-sĕl′) Cen. Afr. Rep.	5·03 N	19·11 E
71	Fort Dodge (dŏj)...Iowa	42·31 N	94·10 W
81	Fort Edward (wẽrd)...N. Y.	43·15 N	73·30 W
75	Fort Erie (ē′rĭ) Can. (Buffalo In.)	42·55 N	78·56 W
158	Fortescue (R.) (fôr′tĕs-kū)..Austl.	21·25 S	116·50 E
82	Fort Fairfield (fâr′fēld)...Maine	46·46 N	67·53 W
86	Fort Fitzgerald (fĭts-jĕr′ăld).Can.	59·48 N	111·50 W
164	Fort Flatters (flȧ-târ′)...Alg.	28·06 N	6·34 E
87	Fort Frances (frăn′sĕs)...Can.	48·41 N	94·29 W
79	Fort Frederica Natl. Mon. (frĕd′ē-rĭ-kȧ).Ga.	31·12 N	85·25 W
78	Fort Gaines (gānz)...Ga.	31·35 N	85·03 W
85	Fort Garry (găr′ê) Can. (Winnipeg In.)	49·50 N	97·09 W
87	Fort George (jôrj)...Can.	53·40 N	78·58 W
87	Fort George (R.)...Can.	53·50 N	78·34 W
73	Fort Gibson (gĭb′sŭn)...Okla.	35·50 N	95·13 W
86	Fort Good Hope (gŏŏd hōp).Can.	66·19 N	128·52 W
164	Fort Gouraud...Mauritania	22·45 N	12·38 W
116	Forth, Firth of (fûrth ôv fôrth) Scot.	56·04 N	3·03 W
167	Fort Hall (hôl)...Ken.	0·47 S	37·13 E
67	Fort Hall Ind. Res...Idaho	43·02 N	112·21 W
84	Fort Howard (hou′ȧrd) Md. (Baltimore In.)	39·12 N	76·27 W
69	Fort Huachuca (wä-chōō′kä).Ariz.	31·30 N	110·25 W
85	Fortier (fôr-tyā′) Can. (Winnipeg In.)	49·56 N	97·55 W
166	Fort Jameson (jām′sŭn) Fed. of Rh. & Nya.	13·35 S	32·43 E
79	Fort Jefferson Natl. Mon. (jĕf′ẽr-sŭn).Fla. (In.)	24·42 N	83·02 W
166	Fort Johnston Fed. of Rh. & Nya.	14·16 S	35·14 E
82	Fort Kent (kĕnt)...Maine	47·14 N	68·37 W
164	Fort Lallemand (lȧ-lē-mäɴ′)..Alg.	31·17 N	6·13 E
165	Fort-Lamy (lȧ-mē′)...Chad	12·15 N	15·04 E
65	Fort Langley (lăng′lĭ) Can. (Vancouver In.)	49·10 N	122·35 W
164	Fort Laperrine (Tamanrasset) (fôr lȧ-pē-rēn′).Alg.	22·34 N	5·34 E
70	Fort Laramie Natl. Mon. (fôrt lăr′ȧ-mĭ).Wyo.	42·10 N	104·34 W
79	Fort Lauderdale (lô′dẽr-dāl) Fla. (In.)	26·07 N	80·09 W
86	Fort Liard...Can.	60·16 N	123·34 W
95	Fort Liberté (lê-bĕr-tā′)...Hai.	19·40 N	71·50 W
78	Fort Louden (R.) (fôrt lou′dĕn) Tenn.	35·52 N	84·10 W
72	Fort Lupton (lŭp′tŭn)...Colo.	40·04 N	104·45 W
66	Fort McDermitt Ind. Res. (măk Dẽr′mĭt).Ore.	42·04 N	118·07 W
86	Fort Macleod (mȧ-kloud′)...Can.	49·40 N	113·22 W
164	Fort MacMahon (mȧk mȧ-ôɴ′) Alg.	29·55 N	1·49 E
86	Fort McPherson (mȧk-fŭr′s′n) Can.	67·37 N	134·59 W
71	Fort Madison (măd′ĭ-sŭn)...Iowa	40·40 N	91·17 W
166	Fort Manning (măn′ĭng) Fed. of Rh. & Nya.	13·42 S	33·00 E
79	Fort Matanzas (mä-tän′zäs)..Fla.	29·39 N	81·17 W
79	Fort Meade (mēd)...Fla. (In.)	27·45 N	81·48 W
84	Fort Meade..Md. (Baltimore In.)	39·06 N	76·44 W
79	Fort Mill (mĭl)...N. C.	34·58 N	80·34 W
114	Fort Miribel (mē-rê-bĕl′)...Alg.	28·50 N	2·51 E
68	Fort Mojave Ind. Res. (mō-hä′vâ) Calif.	34·59 N	115·02 W
84	Fort Monroe (mŏn-rō′) Va. (Norfolk In.)	37·00 N	76·19 W
72	Fort Morgan (môr′gȧn)...Colo.	40·14 N	103·49 W
79	Fort Myers (mī′ẽrz)...Fla. (In.)	26·36 N	81·45 W
114	Fort National (fô nȧ-syō-nål′) Alg.	36·45 N	4·15 E
86	Fort Nelson (nĕl′sŭn)...Can.	58·57 N	122·30 W
86	Fort Nelson (R.) (nĕl′sŭn)...Can.	58·44 N	122·20 W
78	Fort Payne (pān)...Ala.	34·26 N	85·41 W
67	Fort Peck (pĕk)...Mont.	47·58 N	106·30 W
67	Fort Peck Res...Mont.	47·52 N	106·59 W
79	Fort Pierce (pērs)...Fla. (In.)	27·25 N	80·20 W
164	Fort Polignac (pô-lê-nyäk′)...Alg.	26·35 N	8·24 E
165	Fort Portal (pōr′tål)...Ug.	00·40 N	30·16 E

PRONOUNCING INDEX
Fort Providence – Fulda 207

Page	Name Pronunciation Region	Lat. °'	Long. °'
86	Fort Providence (prŏv'ĭ-dĕns) Can.	61·27 N	117·59 W
79	Fort Pulaski Natl. Mon. (pu-lăs'kĭ). Ga.	31·59 N	80·56 W
64	Fort Randall (răn'd'l)... Alaska	55·12 N	162·38 W
62	Fort Randall Dam... U. S.	43·05 N	100·15 W
70	Fort Randall Res... S. D.	43·35 N	99·12 W
86	Fort Resolution (rĕz'ō-lū'shŭn) Can.	61·08 N	113·42 W
73	Fort Riley (rī'lĭ)... Kans.	39·05 N	96·46 W
166	Fort Rosebery (rōz'bĕr-ĭ) Fed. of Rh. & Nya.	11·14 S	28·58 E
166	Fort Rousset (fôr rōō-sĕ').. Con. B.	0·23 S	15·42 E
86	Fort St. James (fôrt sānt jāmz) Can.	54·28 N	124·19 W
86	Fort St. John (sānt jŏn)... Can.	56·28 N	120·57 W
142	Fort Sandeman (săn'da-măn) W. Pak.	31·28 N	69·29 E
85	Fort Saskatchewan (săs-kăt'chōō-ân) Can. (Edmonton In.)	53·42 N	113·14 W
73	Fort Scott (skŏt)... Kans.	37·50 N	94·43 W
86	Fort Selkirk (sĕl-kûrk')... Can.	62·43 N	137·40 W
87	Fort Severn (sĕv'ērn)... Can.	56·58 N	87·50 W
133	Fort Shevchenko (shĕv-chĕn'kô) Sov. Un.	44·30 N	50·18 E
165	Fort Sibut (fôr sē-bü') Cen. Afr. Rep.	5·52 N	19·01 E
72	Fort Sill (fôrt sĭl)... Okla.	34·41 N	98·25 W
86	Fort Simpson (sĭmp'sŭn)... Can.	61·52 N	121·48 W
73	Fort Smith (smĭth)... Ark.	35.23 N	94·24 W
86	Fort Smith... Can.	60·09 N	112·08 W
76	Fort Stockton (stŏk'tŭn)... Tex.	30·54 N	102·51 W
72	Fort Sumner (sŭm'nēr)... N. Mex.	34·30 N	104·17 W
79	Fort Sumter Natl. Mon. (sŭm'tēr). S. C.	32·43 N	79·54 W
75	Fort Thomas (tŏm'ăs) Ky. (Cincinnati In.)	39·05 N	84·27 W
66	Fortuna (fŏr-tū'nå)... Calif.	40·36 N	124·10 W
83	Fortune (fôr'tŭn)... Can.	47·04 N	55·51 W
95	Fortune (I.)... Ba. Is.	22·35 N	74·20 W
83	Fortune B... Can.	47·25 N	55·30 W
72	Fort Union Natl. Mon. (ŭn'yŭn) N. Mex.	35·51 N	104·57 W
78	Fort Valley (văl'ĭ)... Ga.	32·33 N	83·53 W
66	Fort Vancouver Natl. Mon. (văn-kōō'vēr). Wash.	45·50 N	122·36 W
86	Fort Vermilion (vēr-mĭl'yŭn). Can.	58·23 N	115·50 W
166	Fort Victoria. Fed. of Rh. & Nya.	20·07 S	30·47 E
80	Fortville (fôrt-vĭl)... Ind.	40·00 N	85·50 W
80	Fort Wayne (wān)... Ind.	41·00 N	85·10 W
85	Fort Whyte (whĭt) Can. (Winnipeg In.)	49·49 N	97·13 W
87	Fort William (wĭl'yăm)... Can.	48·20 N	89·20 W
116	Fort William (wĭl'yăm)... Scot.	56·50 N	3·00 W
160	Fort William, Mt. (wĭ 'ĭ-ăm) Austl.	24·45 S	151·15 E
74	Fort Worth (wûrth) Tex. (Dallas, Fort Worth In.)	32·45 N	97·20 W
64	Fort Yukon (yōō'kŏn)... Alaska	66·30 N	145·00 W
68	Fort Yuma Ind. Res. (yōō'mä) Calif.	32·54 N	114·47 W
122	Fos, Golfe de (G.) (gôlf'dĕ-fôs') Fr. (Marseille In.)	43·22 N	4·55 E
	Foshan, see Ch'aoyang		
126	Fossano (fôs-sä'nō)... It.	44·34 N	7·42 E
74	Fossil Cr. (fŏs-ĭl) Tex. (Dallas, Fort Worth In.)	32·53 N	97·19 W
126	Fossombrone (fôs-sôm-brō'nā).. It.	43·41 N	12·48 E
70	Fosston (fôs'tŭn)... Minn.	47·34 N	95·44 W
74	Fosterburg (fŏs'tēr-bûrg) Ill. (St. Louis In.)	38·58 N	90·04 W
80	Fostoria (fŏs-tō'rĭ-å)... Ohio	41·10 N	83·20 W
148	Fouch'eng (fōō'chĕng)... China	37·53 N	116·08 E
122	Fougères (fōō-zhâr')... Fr.	48·23 N	1·14 W
150	Fouhsin... China	42·05 N	121·40 E
116	Foula (I.) (fou'lå)... Scot.	60·08 N	2·04 W
151	Fouliang... China	29·18 N	117·18 E
151	Fouling... China	29·40 N	107·30 E
159	Foulwind, C. (foul'wĭnd) N. Z. (In.)	41·45 S	171·37 E
164	Foumban (fōōm-bän')... Cam.	5·49 N	10·52 E
148	Founing (fōō'nĭng)... China	33·55 N	119·54 E
72	Fountain Cr. (foun'tĭn)... Colo.	38·36 N	104·37 W
73	Fourche la Fave (R.) (fōōrsh lä fåv'). Ark.	34·46 N	93·45 W
168	Fouriesburg (fōō'rēz-bûrg) S. Afr. (Johannesburg & Pretoria In.)	28·38 S	28·13 E
122	Fourmies (fōōr-mē')... Fr.	50·01 N	4·01 E
64	Four Mts., Is. of the (fōr).. Alaska	52·58 N	170·40 W
165	Fourth Cataract... Sud.	18·52 N	32·07 E
164	Fouta Djalon (Mts.) (fōō'tå jä-lôN). Gui.	11·37 N	12·29 W
148	Fouts'un (fōō'tsōōn)... China	36·38 N	117·26 E
148	Foutzuchi (fōō'tzĕ'jē)... China	33·48 N	118·13 E
148	Fouyang (fōō'yäng)... China	32·53 N	115·48 E
159	Foveaux Str. (fō-vō').. N. Z. (In.)	46·30 S	167·43 E
72	Fowler (foul'ēr)... Colo.	38·04 N	104·02 W
80	Fowler... Ind.	40·35 N	87·20 W
158	Fowler, Pt... Austl.	32·05 S	132·30 E
76	Fowlerton (foul'ēr-tŭn)... Tex.	28·26 N	98·48 W
65	Fox (I.) (fŏks). Wash. (Seattle In.)	47·15 N	122·08 W
71	Fox (R.)... Ill.	41·35 N	88·43 W
71	Fox (R.)... Wis.	44·18 N	88·23 W
83	Foxboro (fŏks'bŭrô) Mass. (Boston In.)	42·04 N	71·15 W
86	Foxe Basin (fŏks)... Can.	67·35 N	79·21 W
87	Foxe Chan... Can.	64·30 N	79·23 W
87	Foxe Pen... Can.	64·57 N	77·26 W
64	Fox Is. (fŏks)... Alaska	53·04 N	167·30 W
75	Fox Lake (lăk).. Ill. (Chicago In.)	42·24 N	88·11 W
75	Fox L... Ill. (Chicago In.)	42·24 N	88·07 W
75	Fox Point... Wis. (Milwaukee In.)	43·10 N	87·54 W
116	Folye, Lough (B.) (lŏk foil').. Ire.	54·69 N	6·75 W
125	Fraga (frä'gä)... Sp.	41·31 N	0·20 E
94	Fragoso, Cayo (I.) (kä'yō-frä-gō'sô). Cuba	22·45 N	79·30 W
127	Francavilla (frän-kä-vēl'lä)... It.	40·32 N	17·37 E
99	France (frä'n-kä)... Braz.	20·28 S	47·20 W
102	France (fråns)... Eur.	46·39 N	0·47 E
86	Frances (L.) (frăn'sĭs)... Can.	61·27 N	128·28 W
94	Frances, Cabo (C.) (kä'bô-frän-sĕ's). Cuba	21·55 N	84·05 W
94	Frances, Punta (Pt.) (pōō'n-tä-frän-sĕ's). Cuba	21·45 N	83·10 W
95	Frances Viejo, Cabo (C.) (kä'bô-frän'sås vyä'hô) Dom. Rep.	19·40 N	69·35 W
166	Franceville (fräNs-vēl')... Gabon.	1·37 S	13·37 E
101	Francisco Sales (frän-sē's-kô-sä'lĕs). Braz. (Rio de Janeiro In.)	21·42 S	44·26 W
166	Francistown (från'sis-toun).. Bech.	21·17 S	27·28 E
75	Frankfort (frăŋk'fŭrt) Ill. (Chicago In.)	41·30 N	87·51 W
80	Frankfort... Ind.	40·15 N	86·30 W
73	Frankfort... Kans.	39·42 N	96·27 W
80	Frankfort... Ky.	38·10 N	84·55 W
80	Frankfort... Mich.	44·40 N	86·15 W
81	Frankfort... N. Y.	43·05 N	75·05 W
168	Frankfort. S. Afr. (Johannesburg & Pretoria In.)	27·17 S	28·30 E
167	Frankfort (frănk'fōrt) S. Afr. (Natal In.)	32·43 S	27·28 E
120	Frankfurt (fräŋk'fōōrt)... Ger.	52·20 N	14·31 E
111	Frankfurt (Dist.). Ger. (Berlin In.)	52·42 N	13·37 E
120	Frankfurt am Main... Ger.	50·07 N	8·40 E
80	Franklin (frănk'lĭn)... Ind.	39·25 N	86·00 W
78	Franklin... Ky.	36·42 N	86·34 W
77	Franklin... La.	29·47 N	91·31 W
83	Franklin... Mass. (Boston In.)	42·05 N	71·24 W
72	Franklin... Nebr.	40·06 N	99·01 W
81	Franklin... N. H.	43·25 N	71·40 W
84	Franklin... N. J. (New York In.)	41·08 N	74·35 W
80	Franklin... Ohio	39·30 N	84·20 W
81	Franklin... Pa.	41·25 N	79·50 W
78	Franklin... Tenn.	35·54 N	86·54 W
167	Franklin... S. Afr. (Natal In.)	30·19 S	29·28 E
79	Franklin... Va.	36·41 N	76·57 W
86	Franklin, Dist. of... Can.	70·46 N	105·22 W
68	Franklin (L.)... Nev.	40·23 N	115·10 W
66	Franklin D. Roosevelt L... Wash.	48·12 N	118·43 W
86	Franklin Mts... Can.	65·36 N	125·55 W
75	Franklin Park... Ill. (Chicago In.)	41·56 N	87·53 W
77	Franklinton (frăŋk'lĭn-tŭn)... La.	30·49 N	90·09 W
161	Frankston. Austl. (Melbourne In.)	38·09 S	145·08 E
75	Franksville (frănkz'vĭl) Wis. (Milwaukee In.)	42·46 N	87·55 W
87	Franz (frånz)... Can.	48·27 N	84·28 W
	Franz Josef Land (Is.), see Zemlya Frantsa Iosifa		
125	Frascati (fräs-kä'tē) It. (Roma In.)	41·49 N	12·45 E
75	Fraser (frā'zēr) Mich. (Detroit In.)	42·32 N	82·57 W
160	Fraser (Great Sandy) (I.) (frā'zēr) Austl.	25·12 S	153·00 E
86	Fraser (R.)... Can.	51·41 N	122·19 W
116	Fraserburgh (frā'zēr-bûrg)... Scot.	57·40 N	2·01 W
87	Fraserdale (frā'zēr-dāl)... Can.	49·51 N	81·40 W
125	Frattamaggiore (frät-tä-mäg-zhyô'rĕ). It. (Napoli In.)	40·41 N	14·16 E
101	Fray Bentos (frī bĕn'tōs) Ur. (Buenos Aires In.)	33·10 S	58·19 W
70	Frazee (frā-zē')... Minn.	46·42 N	95·43 W
94	Fraziers Hog Cay (I.)... Ba. Is.	25·25 N	77·55 W
123	Frechen (frĕ'kĕn).. Ger. (Ruhr In.)	50·54 N	6·49 E
118	Fredericia (frĕdh-ĕ-rē'tsē-å).. Den.	55·35 N	9·45 E
81	Frederick (frĕd'ēr-ĭk)... Md.	39·25 N	77·25 W
72	Frederick... Okla.	34·23 N	99·01 W
76	Fredericksburg (frĕd'ēr-ĭkz-bûrg). Tex.	30·16 N	98·52 W
81	Fredericksburg... Va.	38·20 N	77·30 W
73	Fredericktown (frĕd'ēr-ĭk-toun). Mo.	37·32 N	90·16 W
82	Fredericton (frĕd'ēr-ĭk-tŭn).. Can.	45·58 N	66·40 W
155	Frederik Hendrik (I.) (frĕd'ēr-ĭk hĕn'drēk). Neth. N. Gui.	7·45 S	137·30 E
118	Frederikshavn (frĕdh'ĕ-rêks-houn). Den.	57·27 N	10·31 E
118	Frederikssund (frĕdh'ĕ-rêks-sōōn) Den.	55·51 N	12·04 E
98	Fredonia (frĕ-dō'nyå)... Col. (In.)	5·55 N	75·40 W
73	Fredonia (frê-dō'nĭ-å)... Kans.	36·31 N	95·50 W
81	Fredonia... N. Y.	42·25 N	79·20 W
118	Fredrikstad (frĕdh'rêks-städ). Nor.	59·14 N	10·58 E
74	Freeburg (frē'bûrg) Ill. (St. Louis In.)	38·26 N	89·59 W
84	Freehold (frē'hōld) N. J. (New York In.)	40·15 N	74·16 W
81	Freeland (frē'lănd)... Pa.	41·00 N	75·50 W
65	Freeland... Wash. (Seattle In.)	48·01 N	122·32 W
83	Freels, C. (frēlz)... Can.	49·18 N	53·10 W
85	Freelton (frēl'tŭn) Can. (Toronto In.)	43·24 N	80·02 W
71	Freeport (frē'pōrt)... Ill.	42·19 N	89·30 W
84	Freeport... N. Y. (New York In.)	40·39 N	73·35 W
77	Freeport... Tex.	28·56 N	95·21 W
164	Freetown (frē'toun)... S. L.	8·29 N	13·16 W
124	Fregenal de la Sierra (frā-hå-näl' dā lä syĕr'rä). Sp.	38·09 N	6·40 W
125	Fregene (frĕ-zhĕ'-nĕ) It. (Roma In.)	41·52 N	12·12 E
120	Freiberg (frī'bĕrgh)... Ger.	50·54 N	13·18 E
111	Freienried (frī'ĕn-rēd) Ger. (München In.)	48·20 N	11·08 E
100	Freirina (frå-ĭ-rē'nä)... Chile	28·35 S	71·26 W
111	Freising (frī'zĭng) Ger. (München In.)	48·25 N	11·45 E
123	Fréjus (frā-zhüs')... Fr.	43·28 N	6·46 E
158	Fremantle (frē'măn-t'l)... Austl.	32·03 S	116·05 E
65	Fremont (frê-mŏnt') Calif. (San Francisco In.)	37·33 N	122·00 W
80	Fremont... Mich.	43·25 N	85·55 W
70	Fremont... Nebr.	41·26 N	96·30 W
80	Fremont... Ohio	41·20 N	83·05 W
69	Fremont (R.)... Utah	38·20 N	111·30 W
67	Fremont Pk... Wyo.	43·05 N	109·35 W
78	French Broad (R.) (frĕnch brôd) Tenn.-N. C.	35·59 N	83·01 W
99	French Guiana (gē-ä'nä)... S. A.	4·20 N	53·00 W
80	French Lick (frĕnch lĭk)... Ind.	38·35 N	86·35 W
67	Frenchman Cr. (frĕnch-măn) Mont.	48·51 N	107·20 W
72	Frenchman Cr... Nebr.	40·24 N	101·50 W
68	Frenchman F... Nev.	36·55 N	116·11 W
74	French River. Minn. (Duluth In.)	46·54 N	91·54 W
	French, see Loyaute, Iles		
163	French Somaliland... Afr.	11·35 N	45·08 E
90	Fresnillo (frås-nēl'yô)... Mex.	23·10 N	102·52 W
68	Fresno (frĕz'nō)... Calif.	36·43 N	119·47 W
98	Fresno (frĕs'-nô)... Col. (In.)	5·10 N	75·01 W
68	Fresno (R.) (frĕz'nō)... Calif.	37·00 N	120·24 W
68	Fresno Slough... Calif.	36·39 N	120·12 W
120	Freudenstadt (froi'den-shtät). Ger.	48·28 N	8·26 E
160	Freycinet Pen. (frā-sē-nĕ').. Austl.	42·13 S	148·56 E
69	Fria (R.) (frê-ä)... Ariz.	34·03 N	112·12 W
166	Fria, C. (frĭå)... S. W. Afr.	18·15 S	12·10 E
100	Frias (frē-äs)... Arg.	28·43 S	65·03 W
120	Fribourg (frē-bōōr')... Switz.	46·48 N	7·07 E
74	Fridley (frĭd'lĭ) Minn. (Minneapolis, St. Paul In.)	45·05 N	93·16 W
120	Frieburg (frī'bōōrgh)... Ger.	47·59 N	7·50 E
111	Friedberg (frēd'bĕrgh) Ger. (München In.)	48·22 N	11·00 E
120	Friedland (frēt'länt)... Ger.	53·39 N	13·34 E
120	Friedrichshafen (frē-drēks-häf'ĕn) Ger.	47·39 N	9·28 E
73	Friend (frĕnd)... Nebr.	40·40 N	97·16 W
77	Friendswood (frĕnds'-wŏŏd) Tex. (In.)	29·31 N	95·11 W
79	Fries (frēz)... Va.	36·42 N	80·59 W
111	Friesack (frē'säk) Ger. (Berlin In.)	52·44 N	12·35 E
99	Frio, Cabo (C.) (kä'bō-frē'ō) Braz.	22·58 S	42·08 W
76	Frio R... Tex.	29·00 N	99·15 W
124	Friol (frē-ōl')... Sp.	43·02 N	7·48 W
121	Frisches Haff B. (frĭsh'ĕs häf). Pol.	54·22 N	19·38 E
117	Frisian (Is.) (frē'zhăn)... Neth.	53·30 N	5·20 E
86	Frobisher (L.) (frŏb'ĭsh-ēr)... Can.	56·33 N	107·57 W
87	Frobisher Bay... Can.	63·48 N	68·31 W
87	Frobisher B... Can.	62·49 N	66·41 W
110	Frodingham (frŏd'ĭng ăm)... Eng.	53·36 N	0·38 W
110	Frodsham (frŏdz'ăm)... Eng.	53·18 N	2·48 W
160	Frome, L. (frōōm)... Austl.	30·40 S	140·13 E
73	Frontenac (frŏn'tē-năk)... Kans.	37·27 N	94·41 W
91	Frontera (frôn-tā'rä)... Mex.	18·34 N	92·38 W
122	Frontignan (frôN-tē-nyäN')... Fr.	43·26 N	3·45 E
67	Front Ra. (frŭnt)... Wyo.	42·17 N	105·53 W
81	Front Royal (frŭnt)... Va.	38·55 N	78·10 W
112	Fro Sea (frô)... Nor.	63·49 N	9·12 E
126	Frosinone (frō-zē-nō'nå)... It.	41·38 N	13·22 E
81	Frostburg (frôst'bûrg)... Md.	39·40 N	78·55 W
74	Fruit (frōōt)... Ill. (St. Louis In.)	38·50 N	89·51 W
69	Fruita (frōōt-å)... Colo.	39·10 N	108·45 W
74	Fruitdale (frōōt'dāl) Tex. (Dallas, Fort Worth In.)	32·43 N	96·46 W
134	Frunze (frōōn'zĕ)... Sov. Un.	42·49 N	74·42 E
136	Fryanovo (f'ryä'nô-vô) Sov. Un. (Moskva In.)	56·08 N	38·28 E
136	Fryazino (f'ryä'zĭ-nô) Sov. Un. (Moskva In.)	55·58 N	38·05 E
121	Frydek (frē'dĕk)... Czech.	49·43 N	18·22 E
120	Frydlant (frēd'länt)... Czech.	50·56 N	15·05 E
147	Fuchien (Fukien) (Prov.)... China	25·39 N	117·21 E
147	Fuchin (fōō'chĭn')... China	47·13 N	132·11 E
151	Fuchou (Foochow) (fōō'chó) China	26·02 N	119·18 E
148	Fuchow (fōō'chō')... China	39·46 N	121·44 E
153	Fuchu (fōō'chōō). Jap. (Tōkyō In.)	35·41 N	139·29 E
151	Fuch'un (R.)... China	29·50 N	120·00 E
92	Fuego (Vol.) (fwā'gō)... Guat.	14·29 N	90·52 W
125	Fuencarral (fuān-kär-räl') Sp. (Madrid In.)	40·29 N	3·42 W
124	Fuensalida (fwān-sä-lē'dä)... Sp.	40·04 N	4·15 W
76	Fuente (fwĕn'-tĕ)... Mex.	28·39 N	100·34 W
124	Fuente de Cantos (fwĕn'tå dā kän'tōs). Sp.	38·15 N	6·18 W
125	Fuente el Saz (fwĕn'tå ĕl säth') Sp. (Madrid In.)	40·39 N	3·30 W
124	Fuente-Ovejuna (fwĕn'tå-ōvå-hōō'nä). Sp.	38·15 N	5·30 W
124	Fuentesaúco (fwĕn-tå-sä-ōō'kō) Sp.	41·18 N	5·25 W
88	Fuerte, Rio del (R.) (rê'ō-dĕl-fōō-ĕ'r-tĕ). Mex.	26·15 N	108·50 W
99	Fuerte Olimpo (fwĕr'tå ō-lēm-pō) Par.	21·10 S	57·49 W
164	Fuerteventura I. (fwĕr'tå-vĕn-tōō'rä). Can. Is.	28·24 N	13·21 W
146	Fuhai... China	47·01 N	87·07 E
148	Fuhsien (fōō'sĭän)... China	39·36 N	121·59 E
153	Fuji (R.)... Jap.	35·20 N	138·23 E
153	Fuji-san (Mtn.) (fōō'jē sän).. Jap.	35·23 N	138·44 E
153	Fujisawa (fōō'jē-sä'wa) Jap. (Tōkyō In.)	35·20 N	139·29 E
	Fukien (Prov.), see Fuchien		
153	Fukuchiyama (fōō'kōō-chê-yä'mä). Jap.	35·18 N	135·07 E
153	Fukue (I.) (fōō-kōō'ā)... Jap.	32·40 N	129·02 E
153	Fukui (fōō'kōō-ē)... Jap.	36·05 N	136·14 E
153	Fukuoka (fōō'kōō-ō'kå)... Jap.	33·35 N	130·23 E
152	Fukushima (fōō'kōō-shē'mä).. Jap.	37·45 N	140·29 E
153	Fukuyama (fōō'kōō-yä'mä).. Jap.	34·31 N	133·21 E
120	Fulda R. (fōōl'dä)... Ger.	51·05 N	9·40 E

ng-sing; ŋ-baŋk: N-nasalized n; nŏd; cŏmmit; ōld; ōbey; ôrder; fōōd; fŏŏt; ou-out; s-soft; sh-dish; th-thin; pūre; ûnite; ûrn; stŭd; circŭs; ü-as "y" in study; '-indeterminate vowel.

208 Fullerton–Gemlik PRONOUNCING INDEX

Page	Name Pronunciation Region	Lat. °′	Long. °′
74	Fullerton (fo͝ol'ẽr-tŭn) Calif. (Los Angeles In.)	33·53 N	117·56 W
77	Fullerton . . . . . La.	31·00 N	93·00 W
84	Fullerton . . . . Md. (Baltimore In.)	39·22 N	76·31 W
70	Fullerton . . . . . Nebr.	41·21 N	97·59 W
78	Fulton (fo͝ol'tŭn) . . . . . Ky.	36·30 N	88·53 W
73	Fulton . . . . . Mo.	38·51 N	91·56 W
81	Fulton . . . . . N. Y.	43·20 N	76·25 W
85	Fulton Cr. . . Can. (Edmonton In.)	53·30 N	113·24 W
84	Fultondale (fo͝ol'tŭn-dāl) Ala. (Birmingham In.)	33·37 N	86·48 W
153	Funabashi (fo͞o'nȧ-bä'shē) Jap. (Tōkyō In.)	35·43 N	139·59 E
153	Funaya (fo͞o-nä'yȧ) Jap. (Ōsaka In.)	34·45 N	135·52 E
164	Funchal (fo͝on-shäl') . . . . . Mad. Is.	32·41 N	16·15 W
98	Fundacion (fo͞on-dä-syō'n) . . . . Col.	10·43 N	74·13 W
124	Fundão (fo͞on-douN') . . . . . Port.	40·08 N	7·32 W
82	Fundy, B. of (fŭn'dĭ) . . . . . Can.	44·50 N	66·05 W
82	Fundy Natl. Park . . . . . Can.	45·38 N	65·25 W
148	Funing (fo͞o'nĭng') . . . . . China	39·55 N	119·16 E
151	Funing Wan (B.) (fo͞o'nĭng') . China	26·48 N	120·35 E
148	Funiu Shan (Mts.) (fo͞o'nēo shän) China	34·25 N	113·28 E
91	Furbero (fo͞or-bĕ'rô) . . . . . Mex.	20·21 N	97·32 W
128	Furmanov (fûr-mä'nôf) . . Sov. Un.	57·14 N	41·11 E
159	Furneaux Group (Is.) (fûr'nō) Austl.	40·15 S	146·27 E
120	Fürstenfeld (für'stĕn-fĕlt) . . . . Aus.	47·02 N	16·03 E
111	Fürstenfeldbruck (fur'stĕn-fĕld' bro͞ok) . Ger. (München In.)	48·11 N	11·16 E
120	Fürstenwalde (für'stĕn-väl-dĕ) Ger.	52·21 N	14·04 E
120	Fürth (fürt) . . . . . Ger.	49·28 N	11·03 E
153	Furuichi (fo͞o'ro͞o-ē'chē) Jap. (Ōsaka In.)	34·33 N	135·37 E
153	Fusa (fo͞o'sä) . . . . Jap. (Tōkyō In.)	35·52 N	140·08 E
98	Fusagasugá (fo͞o-sä-gä-so͞o-gä') Col. (In.)	4·22 N	74·22 W
153	Fuse (fo͞o'sȧ) . . . . Jap. (Ōsaka In.)	34·39 N	135·35 E
146	Fushih . . . . . China	36·46 N	109·15 E
153	Fushimi (fo͞o'shē-mē) Jap. (Osaka In.)	34·57 N	135·47 E
150	Fushun (fo͞o'sho͞on') . . . . . China	41·50 N	124·00 E
150	Fusung . . . . . China	42·12 N	127·12 E
153	Futtsu (fo͞ot'tso͞o') Jap. (Tōkyō In.)	35·19 N	139·49 E
153	Futtsu Misaki (C.) (fo͞ot'tso͞o' mē-sä'kē) . Jap. (Tōkyō In.)	35·19 N	139·46 E
168	Fuwah (fo͞o'wȧ) U. A. R. (Nile In.)	31·13 N	30·35 E
151	Fuyang . . . . . China	30·10 N	119·58 E
150	Fuyü (fo͞o'yo͞o') . . . . . China	45·20 N	125·00 E
118	Fyn (fü'n) . . . . . Den.	55·24 N	10·33 E
116	Fyne (L.) (fīn) . . . . . Scot.	56·14 N	5·10 W
118	Fyresdal Vand (L.) (fü'rĕs-däl vän) . Nor.	59·04 N	7·55 E
166	Gaberones (gȧ-bē-rō'nēz) . . . Bech.	24·28 S	25·59 E
164	Gabès (gä'bĕs) . . . . . Tun.	33·51 N	10·04 E
164	Gabès, Golfe de (G.) . . . . . Tun.	32·22 N	10·59 E
121	Gabin (gŏN'bēn) . . . . . Pol.	52·23 N	19·47 E
163	Gabon (gȧ-bôN') . . . . . Afr.	0·30 S	10·45 E
77	Gabriel R. (gā'brĭ-ĕl) . . . . . Tex.	30·38 N	97·15 W
127	Gabrovo (gäb'rô-vō) . . . . . Bul.	42·52 N	25·19 E
98	Gachetá (gä-chā'tä) . . . . . Col (In.)	4·50 N	73·36 W
127	Gacko (gäts'kô) . . . . . Yugo.	43·10 N	18·34 E
139	Gader . . . . . Jordan (Palestine In.)	32·39 N	35·41 E
78	Gadsden (gădz'dĕn) . . . . . Ala.	34·00 N	86·00 W
129	Gadyach (gäd-yäch') . . . . Sov. Un.	50·22 N	33·59 E
127	Gaesti (gä-yĕsh'tē) . . . . . Rom.	44·43 N	25·21 E
126	Gaeta (gä-ā'tä) . . . . . It.	41·18 N	13·34 E
79	Gaffney (găf'nĭ) . . . . . S. C.	35·04 N	81·47 W
164	Gafsa (gäf'sä) . . . . . Tun.	34·16 N	8·37 E
82	Gagetown (gāj'toun) . . . . . Can.	45·47 N	66·09 W
155	Gagrary (I.) (gä-grä-rē) Phil. (Manila In.)	13·23 N	123·58 E
126	Gaidhouronísi (I.) . . . . Grc. (Inset)	34·53 N	25·45 E
122	Gaillac-sur-Tarn (gȧ-yäk'sür-tärn') . Fr.	43·54 N	1·52 E
88	Gaillard Cut (gä-êl-yä'rd) C. Z. (Panama Canal In.)	9·03 N	79·42 W
79	Gainesville (gānz'vĭl) . . . . . Fla.	29·38 N	82·19 W
78	Gainesville . . . . . Ga.	34·16 N	83·48 W
73	Gainesville . . . . . Tex.	33·38 N	97·08 W
110	Gainsborough (gānz'bŭr-ô) . . . Eng.	53·23 N	0·46 W
160	Gairdner, L. (gârd'nẽr) . . . . . Austl.	32·20 S	136·30 E
142	Gajan . . . . . W. Pak.	28·45 N	67·30 E
139	Galala, Gebel el (Mts.) U. A. R. (Palestine In.)	28·51 N	32·14 E
125	Galapagar (gä-lä-pä-gär') Sp. (Madrid In.)	40·36 N	4·00 W
	Galápagos Is., see Colon, Archip. de		
116	Galashiels (găl-ȧ-shēlz) . . . . . Scot.	55·40 N	2·57 W
129	Galati (gȧ-lätz'ĭ) . . . . . Rom.	45·25 N	28·05 E
127	Galatina (gä-lä-tē'nä) . . . . . It.	40·10 N	18·12 E
127	Galaxidhion . . . . . Grc.	38·26 N	22·22 E
118	Galdhöpiggen (Mtn.) (gäld-hû-pĭggĕn) . Nor.	61·39 N	8·12 E
76	Galeana (gä-lå-ä'nä) . . . . . Mex.	24·50 N	100·04 W
71	Galena (gȧ-lē'nȧ) . . . . . Ill.	42·26 N	90·27 W
75	Galena . . . . . Ind. (Louisville In.)	38·21 N	85·55 W
73	Galena . . . . . Kans.	37·06 N	94·39 W
77	Galena Pk. . . . . . Tex. (In.)	29·44 N	95·14 W
88	Galera, Cerro (Mtn.) (sĕ'r-rô-gä-lĕ'rä) C. Z. (Panama Canal In.)	8·55 N	79·38 W
125	Galera (R.) (gä-lĕ'-rä) It. (Roma In.)	41·58 N	12·21 E
98	Galeras (Vol.) (gä-lĕ'rȧs) . . . . . Col.	0·57 N	77·27 W
65	Gales (R.) (gālz) Ore. (Portland In.)	45·33 N	123·11 W
73	Galesburg (gālz'bûrg) . . . . . Ill.	40·56 N	90·21 W
71	Galesville (gālz'vĭl) . . . . . Wis.	44·04 N	91·22 W
81	Galeton (gāl'tŭn) . . . . . Pa.	41·45 N	77·40 W
127	Galibolu (Gallipoli) (gĕ-lĭb'ō-lo͞o) (gȧ-lĭp'ō-lē) . Tur.	40·25 N	26·40 E
132	Galich (gäl'ĭch) . . . . . Sov. Un.	58·20 N	42·38 E
121	Galicia (Reg.) (gȧ-lĭsh'ĭ-ȧ) Pol.-Sov. Un.	49·48 N	21·05 E
124	Galicia (Reg.) (gä-lē'thyä) . . . . Sp.	43·35 N	8·03 W
159	Galilee (L.) (găl'ĭ-lē) . . . . . Austl.	22·23 S	145·09 E
139	Galilee, Sea of U. A. R. (Palestine In.)	32·53 N	35·45 E
94	Galina Pt. (gä-lē'nä) . . . . . Jam.	18·25 N	76·50 W
80	Galion (găl'ĭ-ŭn) . . . . . Ohio	40·45 N	82·50 W
69	Galisteo (gä-lĭs-tā'ō) . . . . N. Mex.	35·20 N	106·00 W
113	Galite, I. La (gä-lēt) . . . . . Alg.	37·36 N	8·03 E
165	Galla (Prov.) (gäl'lä) . . . . . Eth.	7·22 N	35·28 E
165	Gallabat (găl'ȧ-băt) . . . . . Sud.	12·55 N	36·12 E
126	Gallarate (gäl-lä-rä'tä) . . . . . It.	45·37 N	8·48 E
123	Gallardon (gä-lär-dôN') Fr. (Paris In.)	48·31 N	1·40 E
73	Gallatin (găl'ȧ-tĭn) . . . . . Mo.	39·55 N	93·58 W
78	Gallatin . . . . . Tenn.	36·23 N	86·28 W
67	Gallatin R . . . . . Mont.	45·12 N	111·10 W
143	Galle (gäl) . . . . . Ceylon	6·13 N	80·10 E
125	Gállego (R.) (gäl-yä'gō) . . . . . Sp.	42·27 N	0·37 W
98	Gallinas, Pta. de (Pt.) (gä-lyē'näs) Col.	12·10 N	72·10 W
127	Gallipoli (gäl-lē'pô-lē) . . . . . It.	40·03 N	17·58 E
	Gallipoli, see Galibolu		
80	Gallipolis (găl-ĭ-pô-lēs) . . . . . Ohio	38·50 N	82·10 W
112	Gällivare (yĕl-ĭ-vär'ĕ) . . . . . Swe.	68·06 N	20·29 E
124	Gallo (R.) (gäl'yō) . . . . . Sp.	40·43 N	1·42 W
69	Gallup (găl'ŭp) . . . . . N. Mex.	35·30 N	108·45 W
165	Galnale Doria R . . . . . Eth.	5·35 N	40·26 E
116	Galty Mts . . . . . Ire.	52·19 N	8·20 W
73	Galva (găl'vȧ) . . . . . Ill.	41·11 N	90·02 W
77	Galveston (găl'vĕs-tŭn) . Tex. (In.)	29·18 N	94·48 W
77	Galveston B . . . . . Tex.	29·39 N	94·45 W
77	Galveston I . . . . . Tex. (In.)	29·12 N	94·53 W
116	Galway . . . . . Ire.	53·16 N	9·05 W
116	Galway B. (gôl'wā) . . . . . Ire.	53·10 N	9·47 W
164	Gambaga (gäm-bä'gä) . . . . . Ghana	10·37 N	0·20 W
165	Gambēlā (gäm-bā'lȧ) . . . . . Eth.	8·15 N	34·33 E
163	Gambia (găm'bē-ȧ) . . . . . Afr.	13·38 N	19·38 W
164	Gambia R . . . . . Gam.-Senegal	12·58 N	12·58 W
166	Gamboma (gäm-bō'mä) . . . Con. B.	2·30 S	16·00 E
84	Gambrills (găm-brĭls) Md. (Baltimore In.)	39·04 N	76·38 W
118	Gamleby (gäm'lĕ-bü) . . . . . Swe.	57·54 N	16·20 E
155	Gamu (gä-mo͞o') . Phil. (Manila In.)	17·05 N	121·50 E
142	Gandak (R.) . . . . . India	26·37 N	84·22 E
83	Gander (găn'dẽr) . . . . . Can.	48·59 N	54·32 W
83	Gander (R.) . . . . . Can.	48·45 N	55·13 W
83	Gander L . . . . . Can.	48·57 N	55·10 W
125	Gandia (gän-dē'ä) . . . . . Sp.	38·56 N	0·10 W
142	Ganges, Mouths of (găn'jēz) . India	21·18 N	88·40 E
142	Ganges (R.) (găn'jēz) . . . . . India	24·32 N	87·58 E
126	Gangi (gän'jē) . . . . . It.	37·48 N	14·15 E
146	Gangtok . . . . . Sikkim	27·15 N	88·30 E
67	Gannett Pk. (găn'ĕt) . . . . . Wyo.	43·10 N	109·38 W
75	Gano (g'nô) . Ohio (Cincinnati In.)	39·18 N	84·24 W
111	Gänserndorf . . . . . Aus. (Wien In.)	48·21 N	16·43 E
164	Gao (gä'ō) . . . . . Mali	16·17 N	0·00
164	Gaoua (gȧ-o͞o-ȧ') . . . . . Upper Volta	10·21 N	3·11 W
123	Gap (gȧp) . . . . . Fr.	44·34 N	6·08 E
155	Gapan (gä-pän) . Phil. (Manila In.)	15·18 N	120·56 E
93	Garachiné (gä-rä-chē'nā) . . . . . Pan.	8·02 N	78·22 W
93	Garachiné, Punta (Pt.) (po͞o'n-tä-gä-rä-chē'nȧ) . Pan.	8·08 N	78·35 W
99	Garanhuns (gä-rän-yo͞oNsh') . Braz.	8·49 S	36·28 W
73	Garber (gär'bẽr) . . . . . Okla.	36·28 N	97·35 W
111	Garching (gär'kĕng) Ger. (München In.)	48·15 N	11·39 E
76	Garcia (gär-sē'ä) . . . . . Mex.	25·90 N	100·37 W
90	Garcia de la Cadena (dĕ-lä-kä-dĕ-nä) . Mex.	21·14 N	103·26 W
126	Garda, Lago di (L.) (lä'gō-dē-gär'dä) . It.	45·43 N	10·26 E
122	Gardanne (gȧr-dȧn') Fr. (Marseille In.)	43·28 N	5·29 E
120	Gardelegen (gär-dē-lā'ghĕn) . Ger.	52·32 N	11·22 E
80	Garden (I.) (gär'd'n) . . . . . Mich.	45·50 N	85·50 W
74	Gardena (gär-dē'nȧ) Calif. (Los Angeles In.)	33·53 N	118·19 W
75	Garden City . . Mich. (Detroit In.)	42·20 N	83·21 W
72	Garden City . . . . . Kan.	37·58 N	100·52 W
74	Garden Grove (gär'd'n grōv) Calif. (Los Angeles In.)	33·47 N	117·56 W
84	Garden Island B. La. (New Orleans In.)	29·03 N	89·07 W
74	Garden River Can. (Sault Ste. Marie In.)	46·33 N	84·10 W
82	Gardiner (gärd'nẽr) . . . . . Maine	44·12 N	69·46 W
67	Gardiner . . . . . Mont.	45·03 N	110·43 W
65	Gardiner . . . . . Wash. (Seattle In.)	48·03 N	122·55 W
142	Gardiz . . . . . Afg.	33·43 N	69·09 E
81	Gardner . . . . . Mass.	42·35 N	72·00 W
165	Gardulā . . . . . Eth.	5·43 N	37·40 E
142	Gar Dzong . . . . . China	32·28 N	79·50 E
64	Gareloi (I.) (gär-lo͞o-ä') . . . . . Alaska	51·40 N	178·48 W
84	Garfield (gär'fēld) N. J. (New York In.)	40·53 N	74·06 W
74	Garfield Utah (Salt Lake City In.)	40·45 N	112·10 W
75	Garfield Heights Ohio (Cleveland In.)	41·25 N	81·36 W
127	Gargaliánoi (gär-gȧ-lyä'nē) . . . Grc.	37·07 N	21·50 E
119	Gargždai (gärgzh'dī) . . . . Sov. Un.	55·43 N	20·09 E
100	Garin (gä-rē'n) . . . . . Arg. (In.)	34·10 S	58·44 W
74	Garland (gär'lănd) Tex. (Dallas, Fort Worth In.)	32·55 N	96·39 W
67	Garland . . . . . Utah	41·45 N	112·10 W
134	Garm . . . . . Sov. Un.	39·12 N	70·28 E
120	Garmisch-Partenkirchen (gär' mēsh pär'tĕn-kēr'kĕn) . Ger.	47·38 N	11·10 E
73	Garnett (gär'nĕt) . . . . . Kans.	38·16 N	95·15 W
122	Garonne Rivière (R.) (gȧ-rôn) Fr.	44·43 N	0·25 W
165	Garoua (gär'wä) . . . . . Cam.	9·16 N	13·24 E
80	Garrett (găr'ĕt) . . . . . Ind.	41·20 N	85·10 W
84	Garrison (găr'ĭ-sŭn) N. Y. (New York In.)	41·23 N	73·57 W
70	Garrison . . . . . N. D.	47·38 N	101·24 W
70	Garrison Dam Res . . . . . N. D.	47·49 N	101·58 W
124	Garrovillas (gä-rô-vēl'yäs) . . . . . Sp.	39·42 N	6·30 W
86	Garry (L.) (găr'ĭ) . . . . . Can.	66·16 N	99·23 W
111	Garstedt (gär'shtĕt) Ger. (Hamburg In.)	53·40 N	9·58 E
142	Gartok (gär-tŏk') . . . . . China	31·11 N	80·35 E
121	Garwolin (gär-vō'lēn) . . . . . Pol.	51·54 N	21·40 E
75	Gary (gā'rĭ) . . . . Ind. (Chicago In.)	41·35 N	87·21 W
98	Garzón (gär-thōn') . . . . . Col.	2·13 N	75·44 W
155	Gasan (gä-sän') . Phil. (Manila In.)	13·19 N	121·52 E
133	Gasan-Kuli . . . . . Sov. Un.	37·25 N	53·55 E
80	Gas City (găs) . . . . . Ind.	40·30 N	85·40 W
122	Gascogne (Reg.) (gȧs-kôN'yĕ) . Fr.	43·45 N	1·49 W
73	Gasconade (R.) (găs-kô-nād') . Mo.	37·46 N	92·15 W
158	Gascoyne (R.) (găs-koin') . . Austl.	25·15 S	117·00 E
74	Gashland (găsh'-lănd) Mo. (Kansas City In.)	39·15 N	94·35 W
123	Gasny (gȧs-nē') . . . . Fr. (Paris In.)	49·05 N	1·36 E
82	Gaspé, C . . . . . Can.	48·44 N	64·00 W
82	Gaspe (I.) . . . . . Can.	48·52 N	65·45 W
82	Gaspé B. (gas'pā) (gȧs-pā') . . Can.	48·40 N	64·07 W
82	Gaspé Passage . . . . . Can.	49·21 N	64·16 W
82	Gaspé Pen . . . . . Can.	48·51 N	64·32 W
95	Gasper Hernandez (gäs-pär' ĕr-nän'däth) . . . . . Dom. Rep.	19·40 N	70·15 W
80	Gassaway (găs'ȧ-wā) . . . . . W. Va.	38·40 N	80·45 W
65	Gaston (găs'tŭn) Ore. (Portland In.)	45·26 N	123·08 W
79	Gastonia (găs-tô'nĭ-ȧ) . . . . . N. C.	35·15 N	81·14 W
100	Gastre (gäs-trĕ) . . . . . Arg.	42·12 S	68·50 W
139	Gata, C. . . . Cyprus (Palestine In.)	34·31 N	33·08 E
124	Gata, Cabo de (C.) (kä'bô-dĕ-gä'tä) . Sp.	36·42 N	2·00 W
124	Gata, Sierra de (Mts.) (syĕr'rȧ dā gȧ'tä) . Sp.	40·12 N	6·39 W
136	Gatchina (gä-chē'nȧ) Sov. Un. (Leningrad In.)	59·33 N	30·08 E
116	Gateshead (gāts'hĕd) . . . . . Eng.	54·56 N	1·38 W
77	Gatesville (gāts'vĭl) . . . . . Mex.	31·26 N	97·43 W
85	Gatineau (gȧ'tē-nō) Can. (Ottawa In.)	45·29 N	75·38 W
81	Gatineau (R.) . . . . . Can.	45·45 N	75·50 W
166	Gatooma (gä-to͞o'mä) Fed. of Rh. & Nya.	18·14 S	29·46 E
111	Gattendorf . . . . . Aus. (Wien In.)	48·01 N	17·00 E
88	Gatun (gä-to͞on') C. Z. (Panama Canal In.)	9·16 N	79·25 W
88	Gatun, L. Pan.-C. Z. (Panama Canal In.)	9·13 N	79·24 W
88	Gatun (R.) Pan. (Panama Canal In.)	9·21 N	79·10 W
88	Gatun Locks C. Z. (Panama Canal In.)	9·16 N	79·27 W
142	Gauhati . . . . . India	26·09 N	91·51 E
119	Gauja (R.) (gä'o͞o-yȧ) . . . Sov. Un.	57·10 N	24·30 E
155	Gauttier-Gebergte (Mts.) (gō-tyā') Neth. N. Gui.	2·30 S	138·45 E
126	Gávdhos (I.) (gäv'dôs) . . Grc. (In.)	34·48 N	24·08 E
70	Gavins Point Dam (gă'-vĭns) Nebr.	42·47 N	97·47 W
118	Gävle (yĕv'lĕ) . . . . . Swe.	60·40 N	17·07 E
118	Gavle-bukten (B.) . . . . . Swe.	60·45 N	17·30 E
128	Gavrilov Posad (gä'vrē-lôf'ka po-sȧt) . Sov. Un.	56·34 N	40·09 E
128	Gavrilov-Yam (gä'vrē-lôf yäm') Sov. Un.	57·17 N	39·49 E
160	Gawler (gô'lẽr) . . . . . Austl.	34·35 S	138·47 E
160	Gawler Ra . . . . . Austl.	32·35 S	136·30 E
142	Gaya (gŭ'yȧ) (gī'ȧ) . . . . . India	24·53 N	85·04 E
164	Gaya (gä'yä) . . . . . Nig.	11·58 N	9·05 E
80	Gaylord (gā'lôrd) . . . . . Mich.	45·00 N	84·35 W
160	Gayndah (gān'dȧh) . . . . . Austl.	25·43 S	151·33 E
129	Gaysin . . . . . Sov. Un.	48·46 N	29·22 E
	Gaza, see Ghazzah		
133	Gaziantep (gä-zē-än'tĕp) . . . . . Tur.	37·10 N	37·30 E
121	Gdańsk (Danzig) (g'dänsk) (dän'tsĕg) . Pol.	54·20 N	18·40 E
128	Gdov (g'dôf') . . . . . Sov. Un.	58·44 N	27·51 E
121	Gdynia (g'dĕn'yä) . . . . . Pol.	54·29 N	18·30 E
72	Geary (gē'rĭ) . . . . . Okla.	35·36 N	98·19 W
168	Gebel el Galala el Bahariya (Plat.) U. A. R. (Nile In.)	29·23 N	31·50 E
67	Gebo (gĕb'ō) . . . . . Wyo.	43·49 N	108·13 W
77	Ged (gĕd) . . . . . La.	30·07 N	93·36 W
165	Gedaref . . . . . Sud.	14·03 N	35·11 E
115	Gediz (R.) . . . . . Tur.	38·44 N	28·45 E
65	Gedney (I.) (gĕd-nē) Wash. (Seattle In.)	48·01 N	122·18 W
120	Gedser . . . . . Den.	54·35 N	12·08 E
111	Geel . . . . . Bel. (Bruxelles In.)	51·09 N	5·01 E
161	Geelong City (jē-lông') Austl. (Melbourne In.)	38·06 S	144·13 E
155	Geelvink-baai (B.) (gäl'vĭnk) Neth. N. Gui.	2·20 S	135·30 E
164	Geidam . . . . . Nig.	12·49 N	11·49 E
158	Geikie Ra. (gē'kē) . . . . . Austl.	17·35 S	125·32 E
120	Geislingen (gis'lĭng-ĕn) . . . . . Ger.	48·37 N	9·52 E
75	Geist Res. (gēst) Ind. (Indianapolis In.)	39·57 N	85·59 W
111	Geldermalsen Neth. (Amsterdam In.)	51·53 N	5·18 E
123	Geldern (gĕl'dĕrn) Ger. (Ruhr In.)	51·31 N	6·20 E
127	Gelibolu, Yarimada (Pen.) (gĕ-lĭb'ō-lo͞o) . Tur.	40·23 N	25·10 E
129	Gel'myazov . . . . . Sov. Un.	49·49 N	31·54 E
123	Gelsenkirchen (gĕl-zĕn-kĭrk-ĕn) Ger. (Ruhr In.)	51·31 N	7·05 E
139	Gemas (jĕm'ȧs) Mala. (Singapore In.)	2·35 N	102·37 E
133	Gemlik (gĕm'lĭk) . . . . . Tur.	40·30 N	29·10 E

ăt; finăl; rāte; senâte; ärm; ȧsk; sofȧ; fâre; ch-choose; dh-as th in other; bē; ēvent; bĕt; recĕnt; craẽer; g-go; gh-guttural g; bĭt; ĭ-short neutral; rīde; K-guttural k as ch in Germa ich

PRONOUNCING INDEX

General Alvear–Goggingen 209

Page	Name Pronunciation Region	Lat. °'	Long. °'
101	General Alvear (gĕ-nĕ-räl'äl-vĕ-ä'r). Arg. (Buenos Aires In.)	36·04 s	60·02 w
101	General Arenales (ä-rĕ-nä'lĕs) Arg. (Buenos Aires In.)	34·19 s	61·16 w
101	General Belgrano (bĕl-grä'nō) Arg. (Buenos Aires In.)	35·45 s	58·32 w
76	General Cepeda (sĕ-pĕ'dä) Mex.	25·24 N	101·29 w
101	General Conesa (kō-nĕ'sä) Arg. (Buenos Aires In.)	36·30 s	57·19 w
101	General Guido (gē'dō) Arg. (Buenos Aires In.)	36·41 s	57·48 w
101	General Lavalle (lä-vä'l-yĕ) Arg. (Buenos Aires In.)	36·25 s	56·55 w
100	General Madariaga (män-dä-rēä'gä). Arg.	36·59 s	57·14 w
101	General Paz (pä'z) Arg. (Buenos Aires In.)	35·30 s	58·20 w
90	General Pedro Antonio Santios (pĕ'drō-än-tō'nyō-sän-tyōs). Mex.	21·37 N	98·58 w
100	General Pico (pē'kō) Arg.	36·46 s	63·44 w
100	General Roca (rō-kä) Arg.	39·01 s	67·31 w
100	General San Martín (sän-mär-tē'n) Arg. (In.)	34·19 s	58·32 w
101	General Viamonte (vēä'mōn-tĕ) Arg. (Buenos Aires In.)	35·01 s	60·59 w
76	General Zuazua (zwä'zwä). Mex.	25·54 N	100·07 w
71	Genesco (jĕ-nĕs'cō) Ill.	41·28 N	90·11 w
81	Genesee (R.) (jĕn-ē-sē') N. Y.	42·25 N	78·10 w
78	Geneva (jĕ-nē'vȧ) Ala.	31·03 N	85·50 w
75	Geneva Ill. (Chicago In.)	41·53 N	88·18 w
73	Geneva Nebr.	40·32 N	97·37 w
81	Geneva N. Y.	42·50 N	77·00 w
80	Geneva Ohio	41·45 N	80·55 w
	Geneva, see Génève		
120	Geneva, L. Switz.	46·28 N	6·30 E
120	Genève (Geneva) (zhē-nĕv'). Switz.	46·14 N	6·04 E
129	Genichesk (gĕ'nē-chyĕsk') Sov. Un.	46·11 N	34·47 E
124	Genil (R.) (hā-nēl') Sp.	37·12 N	4·30 w
73	Genoa (jen'ō-ȧ) Nebr.	41·26 N	97·43 w
77	Genoa Tex. (In.)	29·37 N	95·11 w
	Genoa, see Genova		
75	Genoa City. Wis. (Milwaukee In.)	42·31 N	88·19 w
126	Genova (Genoa) (jĕn'ō-vä) It.	44·23 N	9·52 E
126	Genova, Golfo di (G.) (gôl-fō-dē-jĕn'ō-vä). It.	44·10 N	8·45 E
98	Genovesa (I.) (ĕ's-lä-gĕ-nō-vĕ-sä) Ec.	0·08 N	90·15 w
117	Gent Bel.	51·05 N	3·40 E
120	Genthin (gĕn-tēn') Ger.	52·24 N	12·10 E
125	Genzano di Roma (gzhĕnt-zä'-nō-dē-rō'-mä) It. (Roma In.)	41·43 N	12·49 E
158	Geographe B. (jē-ō-grăf') Austl.	33·00 s	114·00 E
158	Geographic Chan. (jēō'gră-fĭk) Austl.	24·15 s	112·50 E
133	Geokchay (gĕ-ôk'chī) Sov. Un.	40·40 N	47·40 E
79	George (L.) (jôr-ĭj) Fla.	29·10 N	81·50 w
81	George (L.) (jôrj) N. Y.	43·40 N	73·30 w
83	George B. (jôr-ĭj) Can.	45·46 N	61·45 w
74	George L. (jôrg) Can.-U. S. (Sault Ste. Marie In.)	46·26 N	84·09 w
75	George, L. Ind. (Chicago In.)	41·31 N	87·17 w
161	Georges (R.). Austl. (Sydney In.)	33·57 s	151·00 E
95	George Town Ba. Is.	23·30 N	75·50 w
99	Georgetown (jôrj'toun) Br. Gu.	7·45 N	58·04 w
83	Georgetown (jôr-ĭj-toun) Can.	46·09 N	62·32 w
85	Georgetown (jôrg-toun) Can. (Toronto In.)	43·39 N	79·56 w
84	Georgetown. Conn. (New York In.)	41·15 N	73·25 w
81	Georgetown Del.	38·40 N	75·20 w
94	Georgetown Grand Cayman I.	19·20 N	81·20 w
80	Georgetown Ill.	40·00 N	87·40 w
80	Georgetown Ky.	38·10 N	84·35 w
81	Georgetown Md.	39·25 N	75·55 w
83	Georgetown (jôrg-toun) Mass. (Boston In.)	42·43 N	71·00 w
79	Georgetown (jôr-ĭj-toun) S. C.	33·22 N	79·17 w
77	Georgetown (jôrg-toun) Tex.	30·37 N	97·40 w
81	George Washington Birthplace Natl. Mon. (jôrj wŏsh'ĭng-tŭn) Va.	38·10 N	77·00 w
73	George Washington Carver Natl. Mon. (jôrg wăsh-ĭng-tŭn kär'-vēr). Mo.	36·58 N	94·21 w
63	Georgia (State) (jôr'ji-ȧ) U. S.	32·40 N	83·50 w
65	Georgia, Str. of Wash. (Vancouver In.)	48·56 N	123·06 w
130	Georgian (S. S. R.) Sov. Un.	42·17 N	43·00 E
78	Georgiana (jôr-jē-ăn'ȧ) Ala.	31·39 N	86·44 w
87	Georgian Is. Natl. Park (jôr'ji-ăn). Can.	45·15 N	81·10 w
158	Georgina (R.) (jôr-jē'nȧ). Austl.	22·00 s	138·15 E
133	Georgiyevsk (gyôr-gyĕfsk') Sov. Un.	44·05 N	43·30 E
120	Gera (gā'rä) Ger.	50·52 N	12·06 E
100	Geral, Serra (Mts.) (sĕr'rȧ zhä-räl'). Braz.	28·30 s	51·00 w
99	Geral de Goiás, Serra (Mts.) (zhä-räl'-dĕ-gô-yá's). Braz.	14·22 s	45·40 w
158	Geraldton (jĕr'ăld-tŭn) Austl.	28·40 s	114·35 E
87	Geraldton Can.	49·43 N	87·00 w
124	Gérgal (gĕr'gäl) Sp.	37·08 N	2·29 w
70	Gering (gē'rĭng) Nebr.	41·49 N	103·41 w
121	Gerlachovka Pk. Czech.	49·12 N	20·05 E
80	Germantown (jûr'mȧn-toun). Ohio	39·35 N	84·25 w
102	Germany (jûr'mȧ-nĭ) Eur.	51·44 N	8·46 E
167	Germiston (jûr'mĭs-tŭn) S. Afr. (Johannesburg & Pretoria In.)	26·19 s	28·11 E
155	Gerona (hä-rō'nä) Phil. (Manila In.)	15·36 N	120·36 E
124	Gerona (hĕ-rō'-nä) Sp.	41·55 N	2·48 E
110	Gerrards Cross (jĕr'ărds krŏs) Eng. (London In.)	51·34 N	0·33 w
125	Gers (R.) (zhĕr) Fr.	43·25 N	0·30 E
111	Gersthofen (gĕrst-hō'fĕn) Ger. (München In.)	48·26 N	10·54 E
114	Géryville (zhā-rē-vēl') Alg.	33·42 N	1·06 E
168	Gestro R. Eth. (Horn of Afr. In.)	5·18 N	41·50 E
125	Getafe (hā-tä'fā) Sp. (Madrid In.)	40·19 N	3·44 w
81	Gettysburg (gĕt'ĭs-bûrg) Pa.	39·50 N	77 15 w
70	Gettysburg S. D.	45·01 N	99·59 w
123	Gevelsberg (gĕ-fĕls'bĕrgh) Ger. (Ruhr In.)	51·18 N	7·20 E
142	Ghāghra (R.) India	27·19 N	81·22 E
163	Ghana (gän'ä) Afr.	8·00 N	2·00 w
142	Ghard W. Pak.	24·50 N	68·35 E
164	Ghardaïa (gär-dä'ē-ä) Alg.	32·29 N	3·38 E
164	Ghāt Libya	24·52 N	10·16 E
165	Ghazal, Bahr el (R.) (bär ĕl ghä-zäl'). Sud.	9·11 N	29·37 E
142	Ghazni (gŭz'nē) Afg.	33·43 N	68·18 E
139	Ghazzah (Gaza) Isr. (Palestine In.)	31·30 N	34·29 E
121	Gheorghieni Rom.	46·48 N	25·30 E
121	Gherla (gĕr'lä) Rom.	47·01 N	23·55 E
164	Ghugāmis Alg.	30·07 N	9·26 E
126	Giannutri, I. di (jän-nōō'trē) It.	42·15 N	11·06 E
95	Gibara (hē-bä'rä) Cuba	21·05 N	76·10 w
166	Gibeon (gĭb'ē-ŭn) S. W. Afr.	24·45 s	16·40 E
124	Gibraleón (hē-brä-lā-ōn') Sp.	37·24 N	7·00 w
124	Gibraltar (hê-bräl-tä'r) Eur.	36·08 N	5·22 w
124	Gibraltar, Bay of Sp.	35·04 N	5·10 w
124	Gibraltar, Strait of Afr.-Eur.	35·55 N	5·45 w
75	Gibson (gĭb'sŭn) Ind. (Louisville In.)	38·24 N	85·40 w
80	Gibson City Ill.	40·25 N	88·20 w
158	Gibson Des. Austl.	24·45 s	123·15 E
73	Gibson Res. Okla.	36·07 N	95·08 w
77	Giddings (gĭd'ĭngz) Tex.	30·11 N	96·55 w
73	Gideon (gĭd'ē-ŭn) Mo.	36·27 N	89·56 w
122	Gien (zhē-ăN') Fr.	47·43 N	2·37 E
120	Giessen (gēs'sĕn) Ger.	50·35 N	8·40 E
85	Giffard (zhē-fárd') Can. (Quebec In.)	46·51 N	71·12 w
153	Gifu (gē'fōō) Jap.	35·25 N	136·45 E
65	Gig Harbor (gĭg) Wash. (Seattle In.)	47·20 N	122·36 w
126	Giglio, I. di (jēl'yō) It.	42·23 N	10·55 E
124	Gigüela (R.) (hē-gā'lä) Sp.	39·53 N	2·54 w
124	Gijón (hê-hōn') Sp.	43·33 N	5·37 w
69	Gila (R.) (hē'lȧ) Ariz.	32·41 N	113·50 w
69	Gila Bend Ariz.	32·59 N	112·41 w
69	Gila Bend Ind. Res. Ariz.	33·02 N	112·48 w
69	Gila Cliff Dwellings Natl. Mon. N. Mex.	33·15 N	108·20 w
69	Gila River Ind. Res. Ariz.	33·11 N	112·38 w
71	Gilbert (gĭl'bērt) Minn.	47·27 N	92·29 w
159	Gilbert (R.) (gĭl'bērt) Austl.	17·15 s	142·09 E
156	Gilbert Is. Oceania	1·30 s	173·00 E
167	Gilboa, Mt. (gĭl-bōȧ) S. Afr. (Natal In.)	29·13 s	30·17 E
165	Gilf Kebir Plat. U. A. R.	24·09 N	25·29 E
142	Gilgit (gĭl'gĭt) India	35·58 N	73·48 E
158	Gillen (I.) (jĭl'ĕn) Austl.	26·15 s	125·15 E
73	Gillett (jĭ-lĕt') Ark.	34·07 N	91·22 w
67	Gillette Wyo.	44·17 N	105·30 w
110	Gillingham (gĭl'ĭng ăm) Eng. (London In.)	51·23 N	0·33 E
80	Gilman (gĭl'mȧn) Ill.	40·45 N	87·55 w
74	Gilman Hot Springs Calif. (Los Angeles In.)	33·49 N	116·57 w
77	Gilmer (gĭl'mēr) Tex.	32·43 N	94·57 w
84	Gilmore (gĭl'môr) Ga. (Atlanta In.)	33·51 N	84·29 w
68	Gilroy (gĭl-roi') Calif.	37·00 N	121·34 w
155	Giluwe, Mt. N. Gui. Ter.	6·04 s	144·00 E
122	Gimone (R.) (zhē-mōn') Fr.	43·26 N	0·36 E
168	Gineifa (jē-nā'fä) U. A. R. (Suez In.)	30·11 N	32·26 E
139	Gineina, Ras el (Mt.) U. A. R. (Palestine In.)	29·02 N	33·58 E
165	Ginir Eth.	7·13 N	40·44 E
126	Ginosa (jē-nō'zä) It.	40·35 N	16·48 E
124	Ginzo (hēn-thō') Sp.	42·03 N	7·43 w
126	Gioja del Colle (jō'yä dĕl kôl'lā) It.	40·48 N	16·55 E
99	Gi-Paraná (R.) (zhē-pä-rä-nä') Braz.	9·33 s	61·35 w
139	Girâfi (R.). U. A. R. (Palestine In.)	29·48 N	34·43 E
73	Girard (jĭ-rärd') Kans.	37·30 N	94·50 w
98	Girardot (hē-rär-dōt') Col. (In.)	4·19 N	75·47 w
133	Giresun (ghĕr'ĕ-sōōn') Tur.	40·55 N	38·20 E
142	Giridih (gē'rē-dē) India	24·12 N	81·18 E
122	Gironde (Est.) (zhē-rôNd') Fr.	45·31 N	1·00 w
116	Girvan (gûr'văn) Scot.	55·15 N	5·01 w
159	Gisborne (gĭz'bŭrn) N. Z. (In.)	38·40 s	178·08 E
122	Gisors (zhē-zōr') Fr.	49·19 N	1·47 E
127	Giurgiu (jōōr'jōō) Rom.	43·53 N	25·58 E
122	Givet (zhē-vĕ') Fr.	50·80 N	4·47 E
122	Givors (zhē-vōr') Fr.	45·35 N	4·46 E
135	Gizhiga (gē'zhi-gȧ) Sov. Un.	61·59 N	160·46 E
121	Gizycko (gĭ'zhĭ-ko) Pol.	54·03 N	21·48 E
127	Gjinokaster Alb.	40·04 N	20·10 E
118	Gjövik (gyû'vĕk) Nor.	60·47 N	10·36 E
111	Glabeek-Zuurbemde Bel. (Bruxelles In.)	50·52 N	4·59 E
64	Glacier Bay Natl. Mon. (glā'shēr) Alaska	58·40 N	136·50 w
86	Glacier Natl. Park Can.	51·35 N	120·00 w
66	Glacier Pk. Wash.	48·07 N	121·10 w
65	Glacier Pt. Can. (Seattle In.)	48·24 N	123·59 w
123	Gladbeck (glăd'bĕk) Ger. (Ruhr In.)	51·35 N	6·59 E
168	Gladdeklipkop S. Afr. (Johannesburg & Pretoria In.)	24·17 s	29·36 E
160	Gladstone (glăd'stōn) Austl.	23·45 s	150·00 E
160	Gladstone Austl.	33·15 s	138·20 E
62	Gladstone Can.	50·20 N	99·00 w
71	Gladstone Mich.	45·50 N	87·04 w
84	Gladstone. N. J. (New York In.)	40·43 N	74·39 w
65	Gladstone Ore. (Portland In.)	45·23 N	122·36 w
80	Gladwin (glăd'wĭn) Mich.	44·00 N	84·25 w
126	Glamoč (gläm'ôch) Yugo.	44·03 N	16·51 E
120	Glarus (glä'rōōs) Switz.	47·02 N	9·03 E
116	Glasgow (glȧs'gō) Scot.	55·54 N	4·25 w
78	Glasgow Ky.	37·00 N	85·55 w
73	Glasgow Mo.	39·14 N	92·48 w
67	Glasgow Mont.	48·14 N	106·39 w
83	Glass B. (glȧs) Can.	46·12 N	59·57 w
75	Glassport (glȧs'pōrt) Pa. (Pittsburgh In.)	40·19 N	79·53 w
120	Glauchau (glou'κou) Ger.	50·51 N	12·28 E
132	Glazov (glä'zôf) Sov. Un.	58·05 N	52·52 E
120	Glda R. (g'l'dȧ) Pol.	53·27 N	16·52 E
110	Glen (R.) (glĕn) Eng.	52·44 N	0·18 w
122	Glénans, Iles de (Is.) (ēl-dĕ-glā-näN'). Fr.	47·43 N	4·42 w
84	Glen Burnie (bûr'nē) Md. (Baltimore In.)	39·10 N	76·38 w
69	Glen Canyon Utah	37·05 N	111·20 w
69	Glen Canyon Dam (glĕn kăn'yŭn) Ariz.	36·57 N	111·25 w
74	Glen Carbon (kär'bŏn) Ill. (St. Louis In.)	38·45 N	89·59 w
75	Glencoe Ill. (Chicago In.)	42·08 N	87·45 w
71	Glencoe (glĕn'kō) Minn.	44·44 N	94·07 w
167	Glencoe (glĕn-cō) S. Afr. (Natal In.)	28·14 s	30·09 E
84	Glen Cove (kōv) N. Y. (New York In.)	40·51 N	73·38 w
69	Glendale (glĕn'dāl) Ariz.	33·30 N	112·15 w
74	Glendale. Calif. (Los Angeles In.)	34·09 N	118·15 w
75	Glendale Ohio (Cincinnati In.)	31·16 N	84·22 w
67	Glendive (glĕn'dīv) Mont.	47·08 N	104·41 w
74	Glendora (glĕn-dō'rȧ) Calif. (Los Angeles In.)	34·08 N	117·52 w
160	Glenelic (R.) (glĕn-ĕl-ĭk') Austl.	37·20 s	141·30 E
75	Glen Ellyn (glĕn ĕl'-lĕn) Ill. (Chicago In.)	41·53 N	88·04 w
160	Glen Innes (ĭn'ĕs) Austl.	29·45 s	152·02 E
77	Glenmora (glĕn-mō'rȧ) La.	30·58 N	92·36 w
66	Glenns Ferry (fĕr'ĭ) Idaho	42·58 N	115·21 w
79	Glennville (glĕn'vĭl) Ga.	31·55 N	81·56 w
84	Glen Olden (ōl'd'n) Pa. (Philadelphia In.)	39·54 N	75·17 w
84	Glen Rock (rŏk). Va. (Norfolk In.)	36·50 N	76·13 w
67	Glenrock (glĕn'rŏk) Wyo.	42·50 N	105·53 w
81	Glens Falls (glĕnz fôlz) N. Y.	43·20 N	73·40 w
75	Glenshaw (glĕn'shô) Pa. (Pittsburgh In.)	40·33 N	79·57 w
70	Glen Ullin (glĕn'ŭl'ĭn) N. D.	46·47 N	101·49 w
65	Glen Valley. Can. (Vancouver In.)	49·09 N	122·30 w
75	Glenview (glĕn'vū) Ill. (Chicago In.)	42·04 N	87·48 w
83	Glenwood (glĕn-wŏŏd) Can.	48·59 N	54·51 w
70	Glenwood Iowa	41·03 N	95·44 w
70	Glenwood Minn.	45·39 N	95·23 w
69	Glenwood Springs Colo.	39·35 N	107·20 w
111	Glienicke (glē'nē-kĕ) Ger. (Berlin In.)	52·38 N	13·19 E
111	Glinde (glĕn'dĕ) Ger. (Hamburg In.)	53·32 N	10·13 E
121	Gliwice (gwĭ-wĭt'sĕ) Pol.	50·18 N	18·40 E
69	Globe (glōb) Ariz.	33·20 N	110·50 w
129	Globino (glô-b'ē-nō) Sov. Un.	49·22 N	33·17 E
120	Głogów Szprotawa (gwō'gōōv shprō-tä'vä). Pol.	51·40 N	16·04 E
118	Glomma (R.) (glômmä) Nor.	61·22 N	11·02 E
118	Glommen (R.) (glôm'ĕn) Nor.	60·03 N	11·15 E
111	Glonn (glônn). Ger. (München In.)	47·59 N	11·52 E
167	Glorieuses, Îles (Is.) Malagasy	11·28 s	47·50 E
110	Glossop (glŏs'ŭp) Eng.	53·26 N	1·57 w
78	Gloster (glŏs'tēr) Miss.	31·10 N	91·00 w
116	Gloucester (glŏs'tēr) Eng.	51·54 N	2·11 w
83	Gloucester. Mass. (Boston In.)	42·37 N	70·40 w
84	Gloucester City N. J. (Philadelphia In.)	39·53 N	75·08 w
80	Glouster (glŏs'tēr) Ohio	39·35 N	82·05 w
83	Glover I. (glŭv'ēr) Can.	48·41 N	57·30 w
81	Gloversville (glŭv'ērz-vĭl) N. Y.	43·05 N	74·20 w
83	Glovertown (glŭv'ēr-toun) Can.	48·42 N	54·01 w
128	Glubokoye (glōō-bô-kō'yĕ) Sov. Un.	55·08 N	27·44 E
111	Glückstadt (glük-shtät) Ger. (Hamburg In.)	53·47 N	9·25 E
129	Glukhov (glōō'κôf') Sov. Un.	51·42 N	33·52 E
129	Glushkovo (glōōsh'kô-vō). Sov. Un.	51·21 N	34·43 E
120	Gmünden (g'mōōn'dĕn) Aus.	47·57 N	13·47 E
121	Gniezno (g'nyĕz'nō) Pol.	52·32 N	17·34 E
127	Gnjilane (gnyĕ'lä-nĕ) Yugo.	42·28 N	21·27 E
143	Gôa (Port.) (gō'ȧ) Asia	20·40 N	74·13 E
92	Goascorán (gō-äs'kō-rän') Hond.	13·37 N	87·43 w
165	Goba (gō'bä) Eth.	7·17 N	39·58 E
166	Gobabis (gō-bä'bĭs) S. W. Afr.	22·25 s	18·50 E
146	Gobi or Shamo (Des.) (gō'be) Mong.	43·29 N	103·15 E
65	Goble (gō'b'l). Ore. (Portland In.)	46·01 N	122·53 w
123	Goch (gôκ) Ger. (Ruhr In.)	51·35 N	6·10 E
142	Godāvari (R.) (gō-dä'vŭ-rē). India	17·42 N	81·15 E
158	Goddards Soak (Swp.) (gŏd'ärdz) Austl.	31·20 s	123·30 E
80	Goderich (gōd'rĭch) Can.	43·45 N	81·45 w
74	Godfrey (gŏd'frē) Ill. (St. Louis In.)	38·57 N	90·12 w
49	Godhavn (gōdh'hävn) Grnld.	69·15 N	53·30 w
86	Gods (L.) (gŏdz) Can.	54·38 N	95·23 w
49	Godthaab (gŏt'hŏŏb) Grnld.	64·10 N	51·32 w
146	Godwin Austen, Mt. (gŏd wĭn ôs'tĕn). China	36·06 N	76·38 E
68	Goffs (gôfs) Calif.	34·57 N	115·06 w
71	Gogebic (L.) (gō-gē'bĭk) Mich.	46·24 N	89·25 w
71	Gogebic Ra. Mich.	46·37 N	89·48 w
111	Goggingen (gûg'gĕn-gĕn) Ger. (München In.)	48·21 N	10·53 E

ng-sing; ŋ-baŋk; N-nasalized n; nŏd; cŏmmit; ōld; ôbey; ôrder; fōōd; fŏŏt; ou-out; s-soft; sh-dish; th-thin; pūre; ûnite; ûrn; stŭd; circŭs; ü-as "y" in study; '-indeterminate vowel.

210 Gogorron–Grangeville PRONOUNCING INDEX

Page	Name Pronunciation Region	Lat. °′	Long. °′
90	Gogorrón (gō-gô-rōn′) . . . . Mex.	21·51 N	100·54 W
153	Goi (gō′ê) . . . . Jap. (Tōkyō In.)	35·31 N	140·05 E
99	Goiânia (gô-vȧ′nyä) . . . . Braz.	16·41 S	48·57 W
99	Goiás (gô-yȧ′s) . . . . Braz.	15·57 S	50·10 W
99	Goiás (State) . . . . Braz.	12·35 S	48·38 W
111	Goirle . . . . Neth. (Amsterdam In.)	51·31 N	5·06 E
133	Göksu (R.) (gûk′sōō′) . . . . Tur.	36·40 N	33·30 E
118	Göl (gûl) . . . . Nor.	60·58 N	8·54 E
118	Göla älv (R.) . . . . Swe.	58·11 N	12·03 E
79	Golax (gō′lăks) . . . . Va.	36·41 N	80·56 W
110	Golcar (gŏl′kȧr) . . . . Eng.	53·38 N	1·52 W
73	Golconda (gŏl-kŏn′dȧ) . . . . Ill.	37·21 N	88·32 W
121	Gołdap (gôl′dăp) . . . . Pol.	54·17 N	22·17 E
72	Golden . . . . Colo.	39·44 N	105·15 W
84	Goldenbridge (gōl′dĕn-brĭj) N. Y. (New York In.)	41·17 N	73·41 W
66	Goldendale (gōl′dĕn-dāl) . . . Wash.	45·49 N	120·48 W
65	Golden Gate (Str.) (gōl′dĕn gāt) Calif. (San Francisco In.)	37·48 N	122·32 W
68	Goldfield (gōld-fēld) . . . . Nev.	37·42 N	117·15 W
88	Gold Hill (Mtn.) C. Z. (Panama Canal In.)	9·03 N	79·08 W
65	Gold Mtn. (gōld) Wash. (Seattle In.)	47·33 N	122·48 W
79	Goldsboro (gōldz-bûr′ô) . . . . . N. C.	35·23 N	77·59 W
76	Goldthwaite (gōld′thwāt) . . . . Tex.	31·27 N	98·34 W
120	Goleniów (gô-lĕ-nyŭf′) . . . . Pol.	53·33 N	14·51 E
135	Golets-Purpula, Gol′tsy (Mtn.) Sov. Un.	59·08 N	115·22 E
93	Golfito (gôl-fē′tō) . . . . C. R.	8·40 N	83·12 W
	Golfo Dulce, see Izabal, L.		
77	Goliad (gō-lĭ-ăd′) . . . . Tex.	28·40 N	97·21 W
155	Golo (gō′lō) . . . . Phil. (Manila In.)	13·38 N	120·17 E
126	Golo (R.) . . . . Cor.	42·28 N	9·18 E
129	Golovchino (gō-lôf′chê-nō) Sov. Un.	50·34 N	35·52 E
166	Golungo Alto (gô-lōōŋ′gô ȧl′tō) Ang.	9·10 S	14·40 E
127	Golyamo Konare (gō′lå-mō-kō′nä-rĕ) . Bul.	42·16 N	24·33 E
111	Golzow (gōl′tsōv) Ger. (Berlin In.)	52·17 N	12·36 E
164	Gombe . . . . Nig.	10·23 N	11·08 E
128	Gomel′ (gô′mĕl′) . . . . Sov. Un.	52·20 N	31·03 E
128	Gomel′ (Oblast) . . . . Sov. Un.	52·18 N	29·00 E
164	Gomera I. (gô-mā′rä) . . . . Can. Is.	28·00 N	18·01 W
76	Gomez Farias (gō′māz fä-rē′ȧs) Mex.	24·59 N	101·02 W
76	Gómez Palacio (pä-lä′syō) . . . Mex.	25·35 N	103·30 W
95	Gonaïves (gō-nȧ-ēv′) . . . . Hai.	19·25 N	72·45 W
95	Gonaïves, Golfe des (G.) (gō-nȧ-ēv′) . Hai.	19·20 N	73·20 W
95	Gonâve, Ile De La (I.) (gô-nȧv′) Hai.	18·50 N	73·30 W
142	Gonda . . . . India	27·13 N	82·00 E
142	Gondal . . . . India	22·02 N	70·47 E
165	Gondar (gŏn′dȧr) . . . . Eth.	12·39 N	37·30 E
123	Gonesse (gô-nĕs′) . . Fr. (Paris In.)	48·59 N	2·28 E
153	Gonō (R.) (gô′nō) . . . . Jap.	35·00 N	132·25 E
85	Gonor (gō′nŏr) Can. (Winnipeg In.)	50·04 N	96·57 W
167	Gonubie Mouth (gŏn′ōō-bē mouth) . S. Afr. (Natal In.)	32·56 S	28·02 E
90	Gonzales (gôn-zȧ′lĕs) . . . . Mex.	22·47 N	98·26 W
77	Gonzales (gŏn-zä′lĕz) . . . . Tex.	29·31 N	97·25 W
100	González Catán (gōn-zȧ′lĕz-kä-tȧ′n) . Arg. (In.)	34·31 S	58·39 W
166	Good Hope, C. of (kāp ov gōōd hôp) . S. Afr. (Cape Town In.)	34·21 S	18·29 E
66	Gooding (gōōd′ĭng) . . . . Idaho	42·55 N	114·43 W
80	Goodland (gōōd′lănd) . . . . Ind.	40·50 N	87·15 W
72	Goodland . . . . Kans.	39·19 N	101·43 W
166	Goodwood (gōōd′wōōd) S. Afr. (Cape Town In.)	33·54 S	18·33 E
110	Goole (gōōl) . . . . Eng.	53·42 N	0·52 W
70	Goose (R.) . . . . N. D.	47·40 N	97·41 W
87	Goose Bay . . . . Can.	53·19 N	60·33 W
67	Gooseberry Cr. (gōōs-bĕr′ĭ) . . Wyo.	44·04 N	108·35 W
67	Goose Cr. (gōōs) . . . . Idaho	42·07 N	113·53 W
75	Goose Lake (gōōs lāk) Ill. (Chicago In.)	41·21 N	88·18 W
66	Goose L . . . . Calif.	41·56 N	120·35 W
142	Gorakhpur (gō′rŭk-pōōr) . . . . India	26·45 N	82·39 E
94	Gorda, Punta (Pt.) (pōō′n-tä-gôr-dä) . Cuba	22·25 N	82·10 W
94	Gorda Cay (gôr′dä) . . . . Ba. Is.	26·05 N	77·30 W
85	Gordon (gôr′dŭn) Can. (Winnipeg In.)	50·00 N	97·20 W
70	Gordon . . . . Nebr.	42·47 N	102·14 W
165	Gorē (gō′rĕ) . . . . Eth.	8·12 N	35·34 E
144	Gorgān . . . . Iran	36·44 N	54·30 E
126	Gorgona (I.) (gôr-gō′nä) . . . . It.	43·27 N	9·55 E
133	Gori (gō′rê) . . . . Sov. Un.	42·00 N	44·08 E
111	Gorinchem (gō′rĭn-κĕm) Neth. (Amsterdam In.)	51·50 N	4·59 E
110	Goring (gôr′ĭng) Eng. (London In.)	51·30 N	1·08 W
126	Gorizia (gô-rê′tsê-yä) . . . . . . Yugo.	44·56 N	13·40 E
132	Gor′kiy (gôr′kē) . . . . Sov. Un.	56·15 N	44·05 E
132	Gor′kovskoye . . . . Sov. Un.	56·38 N	43·40 E
128	Gor′kovskoye (Gorkov) (L.) (gôr′kôf-skô-yĕ) . Sov. Un.	57·38 N	41·18 E
121	Gorlice (gôr-lē′tsĕ) . . . . Pol.	49·38 N	21·11 E
120	Gorlitz (gŭr′lĭts) . . . . Ger.	51·10 N	15·01 E
129	Gorlovka (gôr′lôf-kȧ) . . . . Sov. Un.	48·17 N	38·03 E
76	Gorman (gôr′măn) . . . . Tex.	32·13 N	98·40 W
127	Gorna-Oryakhovitsa (gôr′nä-ôr-yĕk′ô-vē-tsȧ) . Bul.	43·08 N	25·40 E
127	Gornji Milanovac (gôrn′yē-mē′la-nô-väts) . Yugo.	44·02 N	20·29 E
134	Gorno-Altay Aut. Oblast . Sov. Un.	51·00 N	86·00 E
134	Gorno-Altaysk (gôr′nŭ-ŭl-tīsk′) Sov. Un.	52·28 N	82·45 E
121	Gorodënka (gō-rô-deŋ′kä) Sov. Un.	48·40 N	25·30 E
132	Gorodets (Res.) . . . . Sov. Un.	57·00 N	43·55 E
136	Gorodishche (gô-rô′dĭsh-chĕ) Sov. Un. (Urals In.)	57·57 N	57·03 E
129	Gorodnya (gô-rôd′′nyä) Sov. Un.	51·54 N	31·31 E
121	Gorodok (gô-rô-dôk′) . . . . Sov. Un.	49·37 N	23·40 E
134	Gorodok . . . . Sov. Un.	50·30 N	103·58 E
128	Gorodok . . . . Sov. Un.	55·27 N	29·58 E
154	Gorontalo (gō-rōn-tä′lo) . . . Indon.	0·40 N	123·04 E
121	Goryn′ R. (gō′rĕn′) . . . . . . Sov. Un.	50·55 N	26·07 E
120	Gorzow Wielkopolski (gō-zhōōv′vyĕl-ko-pōl′skē) . Pol.	53·44 N	15·15 E
80	Goshen (gō′shĕn) . . . . Ind.	41·35 N	85·50 W
75	Goshen . . . . Ky. (Louisville In.)	38·24 N	85·34 W
84	Goshen . . . . N. Y. (New York In.)	41·24 N	74·19 W
75	Goshen . . . . . Ohio (Cincinnati In.)	39·14 N	84·09 W
65	Goshen . . . . Wash. (Vancouver In.)	48·52 N	122·20 W
69	Goshute Ind. Res. (gō-shōōt′) Utah	39·50 N	114·00 W
120	Goslar (gôs′lär) . . . . Ger.	51·55 N	10·25 E
99	Gospa (R.) (gôs-pä) . . . . Ven. (In.)	9·43 N	64·23 W
126	Gospić (gôs′pĭch) . . . . Yugo.	44·31 N	15·03 E
127	Gostivar (gos′tê-vär) . . . . Yugo.	41·46 N	20·58 E
121	Gostynin (gôs-tē′nĭn) . . . . Pol.	52·24 N	19·30 E
118	Göta Can. (yû′tȧ) . . . . Swe.	58·35 N	15·24 E
118	Göteborg (yû′tĕ-bôrgh) . . . . . . Swe.	57·39 N	11·56 E
164	Gotel Mts . . . . Nig.-Cam.	7·04 N	11·28 E
92	Gotera (gō-tā′rä) . . . . Sal.	13·41 N	88·06 W
120	Gotha (gō′tȧ) . . . . Ger.	50·57 N	10·43 E
72	Gothenburg (gŏth′ĕn-bûrg) . Nebr.	40·57 N	100·08 W
118	Gotland (I.) . . . . Swe.	57·35 N	17·35 E
153	Gotō-Rettō (Is.) (gō′tō rĕt′tō) Jap.	33·06 N	128·54 E
119	Gotska Sandön (I.) . . . . Swe.	58·24 N	19·15 E
120	Göttingen (gût′ĭng-ĕn) . . . . Ger.	51·32 N	9·57 E
111	Gouda (gou′dä) Neth. (Amsterdam In.)	52·00 N	4·42 E
87	Gouin Res. . . . . Can.	77·12 N	75·34 W
160	Goulburn (gōl′bŭrn) . . . . Austl.	34·47 S	149·40 E
164	Goumbou (gōōm-bōō′) . . . . Mali	15·02 N	7·35 W
164	Goundam (gōōn-däɴ′) . . . . Mali	16·29 N	3·37 W
164	Gouré (gōō-rā′) . . . . Niger	13·53 N	10·44 E
81	Gouverneur (gŭv-ēr-nōōr′) . . N. Y.	44·20 N	75·25 W
86	Govenlock (gŭvĕn-lŏk) . . . . . . Can.	49·09 N	109·42 W
100	Governador Ilhado (I.) (gô-vĕr-nä-dō′r-ē-lȧ′dô) . Braz. (In.)	22·48 S	43·13 W
100	Governador Portela (pōr-tĕ′lȧ) Braz. (In.)	22·28 S	43·30 W
99	Governador Valadares (vä-lä-dä′rĕs) . Braz.	18·47 S	41·45 W
95	Governor's Harbour . . . . Ba. Is.	25·15 N	76·15 W
81	Gowanda (gô-wŏn′dȧ) . . . . . . N. Y.	42·30 N	78·55 W
100	Goya (gō′yä) . . . . Arg.	29·06 S	59·12 W
110	Goyt (R.) (goit) . . . . Eng.	53·19 N	2·03 W
166	Graaff-Reinet (gräf′rī′nĕt) . . S. Afr.	32·10 S	24·40 E
126	Gračac (grä′chäts) . . . . Yugo.	44·16 N	15·50 E
127	Gračanica (grȧ-chän′′i-tsä) . Yugo.	44·42 N	18·19 E
78	Graceville (grās′vĭl) . . . . Fla.	30·57 N	85·30 W
70	Graceville . . . . Minn.	45·33 N	96·25 W
92	Gracias (grä′sê-äs) . . . . Hond.	14·35 N	88·37 W
93	Gracias a Dios, Cabo (C.) (kȧ′bô-grä-syäs-ä-dyô′s) . . Hond.	15·00 N	83·13 W
164	Graciosa I. (grä-syô′sä) Azores (In.)	39·07 N	27·30 W
127	Gradačac (gra-dä′chats) . . . . Yugo.	44·50 N	18·28 E
124	Gradelos (grä-dĕ-lôs) . . . . Sp.	42·38 N	5·15 W
129	Gradizhsk (grä-dēzhsk′) . Sov. Un.	49·12 N	33·06 E
124	Grado (grä′dō) . . . . Sp.	43·24 N	6·04 W
111	Grafelfing (grä′fĕl-fēng) Ger. (München In.)	48·07 N	11·27 E
111	Grafing (grä′fēng) Ger. (München In.)	48·03 N	11·58 E
160	Grafton (graf′tŭn) . . . . Austl.	29·38 S	153·05 E
74	Grafton . . . . Ill. (St. Louis In.)	38·58 N	90·26 W
83	Grafton . . . . Mass. (Boston In.)	42·13 N	71·41 W
70	Grafton . . . . N. D.	48·24 N	97·25 W
75	Grafton . . . . . Ohio (Cleveland In.)	41·16 N	82·04 W
81	Grafton . . . . W. Va.	39·20 N	80·00 W
125	Gragnano (grän-yä′nô) It. (Napoli In.)	40·27 N	14·32 E
79	Graham (grā′ăm) . . . . N. C.	36·03 N	79·23 W
72	Graham . . . . Tex.	33·07 N	98·34 W
65	Graham . . . . . . Wash. (Seattle In.)	47·03 N	122·18 W
86	Graham (I.) . . . . Can.	53·37 N	131·47 W
167	Grahamstown (grā′ăms′toun) S. Afr. (Natal In.)	33·19 S	26·33 E
123	Graian Alps (Mts.) (grā′yăn) Fr.-It.	45·17 N	6·52 E
99	Grajaú (grȧ-zhȧ-ōō′) . . . . Braz.	5·59 S	46·03 W
99	Grajaú (R.) . . . . Braz.	4·24 S	46·04 W
121	Grajewo (grä-yā′vo) . . . . Pol.	53·38 N	22·28 E
101	Grama, Serra de (Mtn.) (sĕ′r-rä-dĕ-grȧ′mȧ) Braz. (Rio de Janeiro In.)	23·42 S	42·28 W
127	Gramada (grä′mä-dä) . . . . Bul.	43·46 N	22·41 E
111	Gramatneusiedl . . . Aus. (Wien In.)	48·02 N	16·29 E
126	Grammichele (gräm-mê-kĕ′lā) . . It.	37·15 N	14·40 E
116	Grampian Mts. (grăm′pĭ-ăn) Scot.	56·30 N	4·55 W
92	Granada (grä-nä′dhä) . . . . Nic.	11·55 N	85·58 W
124	Granada (grä-nä′dä) . . . . Sp.	37·13 N	3·37 W
100	Gran Bajo (Dep.) (grȧn′bä′kō) Arg.	47·35 S	68·45 W
77	Granbury (grăn′bēr-ĭ) . . . . Tex.	32·26 N	97·45 W
81	Granby (grăn′bĭ) . . . . Can.	45·30 N	72:40 W
73	Granby . . . . Mo.	36·54 N	94·15 W
72	Granby (L.) . . . . Colo.	40·07 N	105·40 W
164	Gran Canaria I. (grän′kä-nä′rê-ä) . Can. Is.	27·39 N	15·39 W
100	Gran Chaco (Reg.) (grȧn′chȧ′kŏ) Arg.-Par.	25·30 S	62·15 W
71	Grand (I.) . . . . Mich.	46·37 N	86·38 W
82	Grand (L.) . . . . Can.	45·17 N	67·42 W
82	Grand (L.) . . . . Can.	66·15 N	45·59 W
80	Grand (R.) . . . . Can.	43·45 N	80·20 W
80	Grand (R.) . . . . Mich.	42·58 N	85·13 W
73	Grand (R.) . . . . Mo.	39·50 N	93·52 W
70	Grand (R.) . . . . S. D.	45·40 N	101·55 W
70	Grand (R.), North Fork . . . . S. D.	45·52 N	102·49 W
70	Grand (R.), South Fork . . . . . S. D.	45·38 N	102·56 W
94	Grand Bahama (I.) . . . . Ba. Is.	26·35 N	78·30 W
83	Grand Bank (grănd băngk) . . Can.	47·05 N	55·44 W
164	Grand Bassam (gräɴ bȧ-säɴ′) Ivory Coast	5·14 N	3·51 W
93	Grand Bourg (gräɴ bōōr′) Guad. (Le. & Wind. Is. In.)	15·54 N	61·20 W
95	Grand Caicos (I.) (grănd kä-ē′kōs) . Ba. Is.	21·45 N	71·50 W
116	Grand Canal . . . . Ire.	53·21 N	7·15 W
	Grand Canal, see Yün Ho		
69	Grand Canyon (grănd kăn′yŭn) Ariz.	36·05 N	112·10 W
69	Grand Canyon . . . . Ariz.	35·50 N	113·16 W
69	Grand Canyon Natl. Mon . . . Ariz.	36·18 N	113·26 W
69	Grand Canyon Natl. Park . . . Ariz.	36·15 N	112·20 W
94	Grand Cayman (I.) (kā′măn) W. I. F.	19·15 N	81·15 W
66	Grand Coulee Dam (kōō′lē) . Wash.	47·58 N	119·28 W
100	Grande, Bahia (B.) (bä-ē′ä-grȧn′dĕ) . Arg.	50·45 S	68·00 W
100	Grande, Salinas (F.) (sä-lê′näs) Arg.	29·45 S	65·00 W
98	Grande, Rio (R.) . . . . Bol.	16·49 S	63·19 W
99	Grande, Rio (R.) . . . . Braz.	19·48 S	49·54 W
101	Grande, Ilha (I.) (grän′dĕ) Braz. (Rio de Janeiro In.)	23·11 S	44·14 W
99	Grande, Salto (Falls) (säl-tô) Braz.	16·18 S	39·38 W
101	Grande (R.) . . Chile (Santiago In.)	35·25 S	70·14 W
91	Grande (R.) . . . . Mex.	17·37 N	96·41 W
88	Grande, Ciri (R.) (sē′rē-grän′dĕ) Pan. (Panama Canal In.)	8·55 N	80·04 W
62	Grande, Rio (Bravo del Norte, Rio) (R.) (grän′dā) . . U. S.-Mex.	26·50 N	99·10 W
101	Grande (R.) . Ur. (Buenos Aires In.)	33·19 S	57·15 W
100	Grande, Cuchilla (Mts.) (kōō-chē′l-yä) . Ur.	33·00 S	55·15 W
99	Grande, Boca (Est.) (bŏ′kä-grä′n-dĕ) . Ven.	8·46 N	60·17 W
82	Grande Baie (gräɴd bā′) . . . . . Can.	48·17 N	70·53 W
95	Grande Cayemite, Ile (I.) . . . . Hai.	18·45 N	73·55 W
167	Grande Comore (grä′n-dĕ-kô-mô-rĕ) . Comores, Arch. des	11·44 S	42·38 E
92	Grande de Otoro (grän′då dā ô-tō′rô) . Hond.	14·42 N	88·21 W
164	Grande Erg Occidental (Dunes) Alg.	29·37 N	6·04 E
85	Grande-Ligne (lēn′y′) Can. (Montreal In.)	45·13 N	73·17 W
83	Grande Miquelon (I.) (mĭk-ē-lôn′) Can.	47·03 N	56·20 W
85	Grande Pointe (grănd point′) Can. (Winnipeg In.)	49·47 N	97·03 W
86	Grande Prairie (prâr′ĭ) . . . . . . Can.	55·09 N	118·48 W
93	Grande R. (grän′dĕ) . . . . Nic.	13·01 N	84·21 W
95	Grande Rivière du Nord (rē-vyâr′ dü nôr′) . Hai.	19·35 N	72·10 W
66	Grande Ronde R. (rônd′) . . . . Ore.	45·32 N	117·52 W
68	Gran Desierto (Des.) (grän-dĕ-syĕ′r-tô) . Mex.	32·14 N	114·28 W
93	Grande Terre I. (târ′) Guad. (Le. & Wind. Is. In.)	16·28 N	61·13 W
93	Grande Vigie, Pointe de la (Pt.) (gräɴd vē-gē′) Guad. (Le. & Wind. Is. In.)	16·32 N	61·25 W
82	Grand Falls (fôlz) . . . . Can.	47·02 N	67·46 W
87	Grand Falls . . . . Can.	53·34 N	64·23 W
79	Grandfather, Mt. (grănd-fä-thēr) N. C.	36·07 N	81·48 W
72	Grandfield (grănd′fēld) . . . . . Okla.	34·13 N	98·39 W
86	Grand Forks (fôrks) . . . . Can.	49·00 N	118·27 W
70	Grand Forks . . . . N. D.	47·55 N	97·05 W
80	Grand Haven (hā′v′n) . . . . . Mich.	43·05 N	86·15 W
72	Grand Island (ī′lȧnd) . . . . . . Nebr.	40·56 N	98·20 W
75	Grand I . . . . . . N. Y. (Buffalo In.)	43·03 N	78·58 W
69	Grand Junction (jŭngk′shŭn) Colo.	39·05 N	108·35 W
164	Grand Lahou (lȧ-ōō′) . Ivory Coast	5·08 N	5·06 W
83	Grand Lake (lāk) . . . . Can.	49·00 N	57·10 W
77	Grand L . . . . La.	29·57 N	91·25 W
74	Grand L . . . . . . Minn. (Duluth In.)	46·54 N	92·26 W
80	Grand Ledge (lĕj) . . . . Mich.	42·45 N	84·50 W
122	Grand-Lieu, L. de (gräɴ′-lyû) . Fr.	46·00 N	1·45 W
82	Grand Manan (I.) (mă-năn) . Can.	44·42 N	66·50 W
82	Grand′Mere (gräɴ mâr′) . . . . . Can.	46·36 N	72·43 W
123	Grand Morin (R.) (mô-răɴ′) Fr. (Paris In.)	48·23 N	2·19 E
124	Grândola (grăɴ′dô-lȧ) . . . . . . Port.	38·10 N	8·36 W
164	Grand-Popo (pô-pô′) . . . . Dahomey	6·27 N	1·52 E
71	Grand Portage Ind. Res. (pōr′tĭj) Minn.	47·54 N	89·34 W
71	Grand Portage Nat′l Mon . . . Mich.	47·59 N	89·47 W
74	Grand Prairie (prĕ′rê) Tex. (Dallas, Fort Worth In.)	32·45 N	97·00 W
69	Grand Quivira Natl. Mon. (kē-vĕ′rȧ) . N. Mex.	34·10 N	106·05 W
80	Grand Rapids (răp′ĭdz) . . . . . Mich.	43·00 N	85·45 W
71	Grand Rapids . . . . Minn.	47·16 N	93·33 W
82	Grand-Riviere . . . . Can.	48·26 N	64·30 W
93	Grand Soufriere Vol. (sōō-frê-âr′) Guad. (Le. & Wind. Is. In.)	16·06 N	61·42 W
67	Grand Teton Mt. . . . . Wyo.	43·46 N	110·50 W
67	Grand Teton Natl. Park (tē′tŏn) Wyo.	43·54 N	110·15 W
80	Grand Traverse B. (trăv′ērs) Mich.	45·00 N	85·30 W
95	Grand Turk (I.) (tûrk) . . . . Ba. Is.	21·30 N	71·10 W
74	Grandview (grănd′vyōō) Mo. (Kansas City In.)	38·53 N	94·32 W
69	Grand Wash (R.) (wŏsh) . . . . Ariz.	36·20 N	113·52 W
67	Granger (grān′jēr) . . . . Wyo.	41·37 N	109·58 W
66	Grangeville (grānj′vĭl) . . . . . . Idaho	45·56 N	116·08 W

ăt; finăl; rāte; senâte; ärm; ȧsk; sofȧ; fâre; ch-choose; dh-as th in other; bē; êvent; bĕt; recĕnt; cratēr; g-go; gh-guttural g; bĭt; ĭ-short neutral; rīde; κ-guttural k as ch in German ich;

Page	Name Pronunciation Region	Lat. °′	Long. °′
84	Granite (grăn'ĭt) Md. (Baltimore In.)	39·21 N	76·51 W
74	Granite City Ill. (St. Louis In.)	38·42 N	90·09 W
70	Granite Falls (fôlz) Minn.	44·46 N	95·34 W
79	Granite Falls N. C.	35·49 N	81·25 W
65	Granite Falls..Wash. (Seattle In.)	48·05 N	121·59 W
67	Granite Pk Mont.	45·13 N	109·48 W
79	Graniteville (grăn'ĭt-vĭl) S. C.	33·35 N	81·50 W
99	Granito (grä-nē'tō) Braz.	7·39 S	39·34 W
124	Granja de Torrehermosa (grän'hä dā tôr'rā-ĕr-mō'sä) Sp.	38·21 N	5·38 W
118	Gränna (grĕn'å) Swe.	58·02 N	14·28 E
125	Granollérs (grä-nôl-yĕrs') Sp.	41·36 N	2·19 E
98	Gran Pajonal (Marsh) (grä'n-pä-kô-näl') Peru	11·14 S	71·45 W
95	Gran Piedra (Mtn.) (grän-pyĕ'drä) Cuba	20·00 N	75·40 W
110	Grantham (grăn'tăm) Eng.	52·54 N	0·38 W
75	Grant Park (grănt pärk) Ill. (Chicago In.)	41·14 N	87·39 W
66	Grants Pass (grȧnts pȧs) Ore.	42·26 N	123·20 W
122	Granville (gräN-vēl') Fr.	48·52 N	1·35 W
81	Granville (grăn'vĭl) N. Y.	43·25 N	73·15 W
86	Granville (L.) Can.	56·18 N	99·39 W
99	Grão Mogol (grouN' mōō-gôl') Braz.	16·34 S	42·35 W
74	Grapevine (grāp'vīn) Tex. (Dallas, Fort Worth In.)	32·56 N	97·05 W
118	Gräsö (I.) Swe.	60·30 N	18·35 E
81	Grass (R.) N. Y.	44·45 N	75·10 W
89	Grass Cay (I.) Vir. Is. (U.S.A.) (St. Thomas In.)	18·22 N	64·50 W
123	Grasse (gräs) Fr.	43·39 N	6·57 E
65	Grass Mtn. (grȧs) Wash. (Seattle In.)	47·13 N	121·48 W
68	Grass Valley Calif.	39·12 N	121·04 W
83	Grates Pt. (grāts) Can.	48·14 N	52·45 W
122	Graulhet (grō-lĕ') Fr.	43·46 N	1·58 E
86	Gravelbourg (grăv'ĕl-bôrg) Can.	49·55 N	106·53 W
110	Gravesend (grāvz'ĕnd') Eng. (London In.)	51·26 N	0·22 E
126	Gravina (grä-vē'nä) It.	40·48 N	16·27 E
74	Gravois (grav'ois) Mo. (St. Louis In.)	38·33 N	90·20 W
95	Gravois, Pte. (grȧ-vwä') Hai.	18·00 N	74·20 W
123	Gray (grā) Fr.	47·26 N	5·35 E
80	Grayling (grā'lĭng) Mich.	44·40 N	84·40 W
75	Grayslake (grāz'lāk) Ill. (Chicago In.)	42·20 N	88·20 W
72	Grays Pk. (grāz) Colo.	39·29 N	105·52 W
129	Grayvoron (grȧ-ē'vô-rôn) Sov. Un.	50·28 N	35·41 E
120	Graz (gräts) Aus.	47·05 N	15·26 E
160	Great (L.) Austl.	41·55 S	146·50 E
94	Great Abaco (I.) (ă'bä-kō) Ba. Is.	26·30 N	77·05 W
159	Great Artesian Basin (Reg.) (är-tēzh-ȧn bā-sĭn) Austl.	23·16 S	143·37 E
158	Great Australian Bight (ôs-trā'-lĭ-ăn bĭt) Austl.	33·30 S	127·00 E
94	Great Bahama Bk. (bȧ-hā'mȧ) Ba. Is.	25·00 N	78·50 W
159	Great Barrier (I.) (băr'ĭ-ĕr) N. Z. (In.)	37·00 S	175·31 E
159	Great Barrier Rf. (bȧ-rĭ-ĕr rēf) Austl.	16·43 S	146·34 E
62	Great Basin (grāt bā's'n) U. S.	40·08 N	117·10 W
86	Great Bear L. (bâr) Can.	66·10 N	119·53 W
72	Great Bend (bĕnd) Kans.	38·41 N	98·46 W
	Great Bitter, see El Buheirat el Murrat el Kubra		
116	Great Blasket (Is.) (blăs'kĕt) Ire.	52·05 N	10·55 W
102	Great Britain (brĭt''n) Eur.	56·53 N	0·02 W
166	Great Cataract (Falls) (căt'ȧ-răkt) Ang.-S. W. Afr.	17·25 S	14·20 E
93	Great Corn I. Nic.	12·10 N	82·54 W
67	Great Divide Basin (dĭ-vīd' bā's'n) Wyo.	42·10 N	108·10 W
159	Great Dividing Ra. (dĭ-vī-dĭng rānj) Austl.	35·16 S	146·38 E
	Greater Khingan Mts., see Tahsinganling Shanmo		
71	Greater Leech Ind. Res. (grāt'ĕr lēch) Minn.	47·39 N	94·27 W
95	Great Exuma (I.) (ĕk-sōō'mä) Ba. Is.	23·35 N	76·00 W
83	Great Falls Can.	48·58 N	55·37 W
67	Great Falls (fôlz) Mont.	47·30 N	111·15 W
79	Great Falls S. C.	34·32 N	80·53 W
166	Great Fish (R.) (fĭsh) S. W. Afr.	28·00 S	17·45 E
167	Great Fish (R.) S. Afr. (Natal In.)	33·04 S	26·08 E
95	Great Guana Cay (I.) (gwä'nä) Ba. Is.	24·00 N	76·20 W
94	Great Harbor Cay (I.) (kē) Ba. Is.	25·45 N	77·50 W
95	Great Inagua (I.) (ē-nä'gwä) Ba. Is.	21·00 N	73·15 W
142	Great Indian (Thar) Des. (tŭr) India	32·04 N	70·25 E
94	Great Isaac (I.) (ī'zăk) Ba. Is.	26·05 N	79·05 W
139	Great Karimun (Is.) Indon. (Singapore In.)	1·11 N	103·12 E
166	Great Karroo (Mts.) (grāt kȧ'rōō) S. Afr.	32·45 S	22·00 E
167	Great Kei (R.) (kē) S. Afr. (Natal In.)	32·17 S	27·30 E
84	Great Neck (nĕk) N. Y. (New York In.)	40·48 N	73·44 W
154	Great Nicobar I. (nĭk-ō-bär') India	7·00 N	94·18 E
154	Great Paternoster Is. (pā'tēr-nŏs-tēr) Indon.	7·35 S	118·00 E
94	Great Pedro Bluff (Hd.) Jam.	17·50 N	78·05 W
49	Great Plains, The (Reg.) (plāns) N. A.	45·00 N	104·00 W
95	Great Ragged (I.) Ba. Is.	22·10 N	75·45 W
126	Great St. Bernard Pass (sănt bēr-närd') Switz.-It.	45·53 N	7·15 E
94	Great Sale Cay (I.) (sāl kē) Ba. Is.	27·00 N	78·15 W
67	Great Salt L. (sôlt lāk) Utah	41·19 N	112·48 W
62	Great Salt Lake Des. U. S.	41·00 N	113·30 W
72	Great Salt Plains Res. Okla.	36·56 N	98·14 W
72	Great Sand Dunes Natl. Mon. Colo.	37·56 N	105·25 W
158	Great Sandy Des. (săn'dē) Austl.	21·50 S	123·10 E
66	Great Sandy Des. (săn'dĭ) Ore.	43·43 N	120·44 W
64	Great Sitkin (I.) (sĭt-kĭn) Alaska	52·18 N	176·22 W
86	Great Slave (L.) (slāv) Can.	61·37 N	114·58 W
78	Great Smoky Mts. Natl. Park (smōk-ē) N. C.	35·43 N	83·20 W
94	Great Stirrup Cay (I.) (stĭr-ŭp) Ba. Is.	25·50 N	77·55 W
158	Great Victoria Des. (vĭk-tō'rĭ-ȧ) Austl.	29·45 S	124·30 E
110	Great Waltham (wôl'thŭm) Eng.	51·47 N	0·27 E
87	Great Whale (R.) (hwāl) Can.	54·57 N	75·51 W
117	Great Yarmouth (yär-mŭth) Eng.	52·35 N	1·45 E
118	Grebbestad (grĕb-bĕ-städh) Swe.	58·42 N	11·15 E
139	Greco, C. Cyprus (Palestine In.)	34·57 N	34·11 E
124	Gredos, Sierra de (Mts.) (syĕr'rä dā grā'dōs) Sp.	40·13 N	5·30 W
102	Greece (grēs) Eur.	39·00 N	21·30 E
72	Greeley (grē'lĭ) Colo.	40·25 N	104·41 W
78	Green (R.) Ky.	37·13 N	86.30 W
70	Green (R.) N. D.	47·05 N	103·05 W
62	Green (R.) (grēn) U. S.	38·30 N	110·10 W
65	Green (R.) Wash. (Seattle In.)	47·17 N	121·57 W
65	Greenbank (grēn'bănk) Wash. (Seattle In.)	48·06 N	122·35 W
77	Green Bay Tex. (In.)	29·53 N	95·13 W
71	Green Bay Wis.	44·30 N	88·04 W
63	Green B. U. S.	44·55 N	87·40 W
80	Greencastle (grēn-kȧs''l) Ind.	39·40 N	86·50 W
94	Green Cay (I.) Ba. Is.	24·05 N	77·10 W
79	Green Cove Springs (kōv) Fla.	29·56 N	81·42 W
75	Greendale (grēn'dāl) Wis. (Milwaukee In.)	42·56 N	87·59 W
80	Greenfield (grēn'fēld) Ind.	39·45 N	85·40 W
71	Greenfield Iowa	41·16 N	94·30 W
81	Greenfield Mass.	42·35 N	72·35 W
73	Greenfield Mo.	37·23 N	93·48 W
80	Greenfield Ohio	39·15 N	83·25 W
78	Greenfield Tenn.	36·08 N	88·45 W
85	Greenfield Park Can. (Montreal In.)	45·29 N	73·29 W
75	Greenhills (grēn-hĭls) Ohio (Cincinnati In.)	39·16 N	84·31 W
49	Greenland (grēn'lănd) N. A.	74·00 N	40·00 W
83	Greenly (I.) (grēn'lē) Can.	51·23 N	57·15 W
65	Green Mtn. Ore. (Portland In.)	45·52 N	123·24 W
69	Green Mountain Res. Colo.	39·50 N	106·20 W
81	Green Mts. Vt.	43·10 N	73·05 W
116	Greenock (grēn'ŭk) Scot.	55·55 N	4·45 W
84	Green Pond Mtn. (pŏnd) N. J. (New York In.)	41·00 N	74·32 W
69	Greenriver (grēn-rĭv'ēr) Utah	39·00 N	110·05 W
67	Green River Wyo.	41·32 N	109·26 W
67	Green R., Blacks Fk. Wyo.	41·08 N	110·27 W
67	Green R., Hams Fk. Wyo.	41·55 N	110·40 W
78	Greensboro (grēnz'bŭro) Ala.	32·42 N	87·36 W
78	Greensboro (grēns-bûr'ô) Ga.	33·34 N	83·11 W
79	Greensboro N. C.	36·04 N	79·45 W
80	Greensburg (grēnz'bûrg) Ind.	39·20 N	85·30 W
72	Greensburg (grēns-bûrg) Kans.	37·36 N	99·17 W
81	Greensburg Pa.	40·20 N	79·30 W
78	Greenville (grēn'vĭl) Ala.	31·49 N	86·39 W
73	Greenville Ill.	38·52 N	89·22 W
78	Greenville Ky.	37·11 N	87·11 W
164	Greenville Lib.	5·06 N	8·44 W
82	Greenville Maine	45·26 N	69·35 W
80	Greenville Mich.	43·10 N	85·25 W
78	Greenville Miss.	33·25 N	91·00 W
79	Greenville N. C.	35·35 N	77·22 W
80	Greenville Ohio	40·05 N	84·35 W
80	Greenville Pa.	41·20 N	80·25 W
79	Greenville S. C.	34·50 N	82·25 W
78	Greenville Tenn.	36·08 N	82·50 W
73	Greenville Tex.	33·09 N	96·07 W
84	Greenwich Conn. (New York In.)	41·01 N	73·37 W
110	Greenwich (grĭn'ĭj) Eng. (London In.)	51·28 N	0·00
73	Greenwood (grēn-wŏŏd) Ark.	35·13 N	94·15 W
75	Greenwood Ind. (Indianapolis In.)	39·37 N	86·07 W
78	Greenwood Miss.	33·30 N	90·09 W
79	Greenwood S. C.	34·10 N	82·10 W
79	Greenwood (R.) S. C.	34·17 N	81·55 W
84	Greenwood L. N. Y. (New York In.)	41·13 N	74·20 W
79	Greer (grēr) S. C.	34·55 N	81·56 W
123	Grefrath (grĕf'rät) Ger. (Ruhr In.)	51·20 N	6·21 E
70	Gregory (grĕg'ō-rĭ) S. D.	43·12 N	99·27 W
160	Gregory (L.) (grĕg'ō-rē) Aust.	29·47 S	139·15 E
159	Gregory Ra. Austl.	19·23 S	143·45 E
111	Greifenberg (grī'fĕn-bĕrgh) Ger. (München In.)	48·04 N	11·06 E
120	Greifswald (grīfs'vält) Ger.	54·05 N	13·24 E
120	Greiz (grīts) Ger.	50·39 N	12·14 E
136	Gremyachinsk (grâ'myȧ-chĭnsk) Sov. Un. (Urals In.)	58·35 N	57·53 E
118	Grenaa (grēn'ô) Den.	56·25 N	10·51 E
78	Grenada (grē-nā'dȧ) Miss.	33·45 N	89·47 W
93	Grenada I. W. I. F. (Le. & Wind. Is. In.)	12·02 N	61·27 W
78	Grenada Res. Miss.	33·52 N	89·30 W
122	Grenade (grē-näd') Fr.	43·46 N	1·15 E
93	Grenadines, The (Is.) (grĕn'ȧ-dēnz) W. I. F. (Le. & Wind. Is. In.)	12·37 N	61·35 W
84	Grenloch (grĕn-lŏk) N. J. (Philadelphia In.)	39·48 N	75·04 W
123	Grenoble (grē-nô'bl') Fr.	45·14 N	5·45 E
70	Grenora (grē-nō'rȧ) N. D.	48·38 N	103·55 W
81	Grenville (grĕn'vĭl) Can.	45·40 N	74·35 W
93	Grenville W. I. F. (Le. & Wind. Is. In.)	12·07 N	61·38 W
65	Gresham (grĕsh'ăm) Ore. (Portland In.)	45·30 N	122·25 W
84	Gretna (grĕt'nȧ) La. (New Orleans In.)	29·56 N	90·03 W
111	Grevelingen Krammer, R. Neth. (Amsterdam In.)	51·42 N	4·03 E
127	Grevená (grĕ'vä-nä) Grc.	40·02 N	21·30 E
123	Grevenbroich (grĕ'fĕn-broik) Ger. (Ruhr In.)	51·05 N	6·36 E
123	Grevenbrück (grĕ'fĕn-brük) Ger. (Ruhr In.)	51·08 N	8·01 E
65	Grey, Pt. (grā) Can. (Vancouver In.)	49·22 N	123·16 W
67	Greybull (grā'bŏŏl) Wyo.	44·28 N	108·05 W
67	Greybull R. Wyo.	44·13 N	108·43 W
84	Greycourt (grā-kōrt) N. Y. (New York In.)	41·22 N	74·16 W
168	Greylingstad (grā-lĭng'shtȧt) S. Afr. (Johannesburg & Pretoria In.)	26·40 S	29·13 E
159	Greymouth (grā'mouth) N. Z. (In.)	42·27 S	171·17 E
160	Grey Ra. Austl.	28·40 S	142·05 E
66	Greys Hbr. (grās) Wash.	46·55 N	124·23 W
167	Greytown (grā'toun) S. Afr. (Natal In.)	29·07 S	30·38 E
	Greytown, see San Juan del Norte		
65	Grey Wolf Pk. (grā wŏŏlf) Wash. (Seattle In.)	48·53 N	123·12 W
68	Gridley (grĭd'lĭ) Calif.	39·22 N	121·43 W
78	Griffin (grĭf'ĭn) Ga.	33·15 N	84·16 W
64	Griffin Pt. Alaska	70·05 N	143·21 W
160	Griffith (grĭf-ĭth) Austl.	34·16 S	146·10 E
75	Griffith Ind. (Chicago In.)	41·31 N	87·26 W
129	Grigoriopol' (grĭ'gor-i-ô'pôl) Sov. Un.	47·09 N	29·18 E
91	Grijalva (R.) (grē-häl'vä) Mex.	18·15 N	92·45 W
160	Grim, C. (grĭm) Austl.	40·43 S	144·30 E
120	Grimma (grĭm'ȧ) Ger.	51·14 N	12·43 E
85	Grimsby (grĭmz'bĭ) Can. (Toronto In.)	43·11 N	79·33 W
112	Grimsey (I.) (grĭms'ȧ) Ice.	66·30 N	17·50 W
118	Grimstad (grĭm-städh) Nor.	58·21 N	8·30 E
71	Grinnel (grĭ-nĕl') Iowa	41·44 N	92·44 W
71	Griswold (grĭz'wŭld) Iowa	41·11 N	95·05 W
128	Griva (grē'vȧ) Sov. Un.	55·51 N	26·31 E
83	Groais (I.) Can.	50·56 N	55·35 W
119	Grobiņa (grō'bĭnĭa) Sov. Un.	56·35 N	21·10 E
168	Groblersdal S. Afr. (Johannesburg & Pretoria In.)	25·11 S	29·25 E
121	Grodno (grôd'nŏ) Sov. Un.	53·40 N	23·49 E
121	Grodzisk Masowieki (grō'jēsk mä-zō-vyĕts'ke) Pol.	52·06 N	20·40 E
120	Grodzisk Wielkopolski (grō'jēsk vyĕl-ko-pōl'skē) Pol.	52·14 N	16·22 E
77	Groesbeck (grōs'bĕk) Tex.	31·32 N	96·31 W
122	Groix, I. de (ēl dē grwä') Fr.	47·39 N	3·28 W
121	Grójec (grōō'yĕts) Pol.	51·53 N	20·52 E
120	Gronau (grō'nou) Ger.	52·12 N	7·05 E
117	Groningen (grō'nĭng-ĕn) Neth.	53·13 N	6·30 E
158	Groote Eyelandt (I.) (grō'tē ī'lănt) Austl.	13·50 S	137·30 E
166	Grootfontein (grōt'fŏn-tān') S. W. Afr.	18·15 S	19·30 E
166	Grootkop (Mtn.) S. Afr. (Cape Town In.)	34·11 S	18·23 E
168	Groot Marico S. Afr. (Johannesburg & Pretoria In.)	25·36 S	26·23 E
168	Groot R. S. Afr. (Johannesburg & Pretoria In.)	25·13 S	26·20 E
166	Groot Vloer (L.) (grōt' vlōōr') S. Afr.	30·00 S	20·16 E
83	Gros Morne (Mtn.) (grō môrn') Can.	49·37 N	57·45 W
83	Gros Pate (Mtn.) Can.	50·16 N	57·25 W
111	Gross Behnitz (grōss bĕ'nētz) Ger. (Berlin In.)	52·35 N	12·45 E
75	Grosse I. (grōs) Mich. (Detroit In.)	42·08 N	83·09 W
85	Grosse Isle (īl') Can. (Winnipeg In.)	50·04 N	97·27 W
166	Grosse Karras (Mts.) S. W. Afr.	27·10 S	18·30 E
120	Grossenhain (grōs'ĕn-hīn) Ger.	51·17 N	13·33 E
111	Grossenzerdorf Aus. (Wien In.)	48·13 N	16·33 E
75	Grosse Pointe (point') Mich. (Detroit In.)	42·23 N	82·54 W
75	Grosse Pointe Farms (färm) Mich. (Detroit In.)	42·25 N	82·53 W
75	Grosse Pointe Park (pärk) Mich. (Detroit In.)	42·23 N	82·55 W
126	Grosseto (grôs-sā'tō) It.	42·46 N	11·09 E
120	Gross Glockner Pk. (glôk'nĕr) Aus.	47·06 N	12·45 E
111	Gross Höbach (hû'bäk) Ger. (München In.)	48·21 N	11·36 E
111	Gross Kreutz (kroitz) Ger. (Berlin In.)	52·24 N	12·47 E
123	Gross Reken (rĕ'kĕn) Ger. (Ruhr In.)	51·50 N	7·20 E
111	Gross Schonebeck (shō'nĕ-bĕk) Ger. (Berlin In.)	52·54 N	13·32 E
67	Gros Ventre R. (grōvĕn't'r) Wyo.	43·38 N	110·34 W
81	Groton (grôt'ŭn) Conn.	41·20 N	72·00 W
83	Groton Mass. (Boston In.)	42·37 N	71·34 W
70	Groton Nebr.	42·44 N	97·32 W
127	Grottaglie (grôt-täl'yä) It.	40·32 N	17·26 E

ng-sing; ŋ-baŋk; N-nasalized n; nŏd; cŏmmit; ōld; ôbey; ôrder; fōōd; fŏŏt; ou-out; s-soft; sh-dish; th-thin; pūre; ůnite; ûrn; stŭd; circŭs; ü-as "y" in study; '-indeterminate vowel.

212 Grouard–Haifeng PRONOUNCING INDEX

Page	Name Pronunciation Region	Lat. °′	Long. °′
86	Grouard . . . Can.	55·35 N	116·11 W
83	Groveland (grōv'lănd) Mass. (Boston In.)	42·45 N	71·02 W
81	Groveton (grōv'tŭn) . . . N. H.	44·35 N	71·30 W
77	Groveton . . . Tex.	31·04 N	95·07 W
133	Groznyy (grôz'nĭ) . . . Sov. Un.	43·20 N	45·40 E
121	Grudziadz (grōō'jyônts) . . . Pol.	53·30 N	18·48 E
111	Grumpholds-Kirchen Aus. (Wien In.)	48·03 N	16·17 E
71	Grundy Center (grŭn'dĭ sĕn'tēr) Iowa	42·22 N	92·45 W
90	Gruñidora (grōō-nyē-dô'rō) . . Mex.	24·10 N	101·49 W
111	Grunwald (grōōn'väld) Ger. (Munchen In.)	48·04 N	11·34 E
128	Gryazi (gryä'zĭ) . . . Sov. Un.	52·31 N	39·59 E
128	Gryazovets (gryä'zô-vĕts) Sov. Un.	58·52 N	40·14 E
120	Gryfice (grĭ'fĭ-tsĕ) . . . Pol.	53·55 N	15·11 E
120	Gryfino (grĭ'fē-nô) . . . Pol.	53·16 N	14·30 E
93	Guabito (gwä-bē'tô) . . . Pan.	9·30 N	82·33 W
94	Guacanayabo, Golfo de (G.) (gôl-fô-dĕ-gwä-kä-nä-yä'bō) . . . Cuba	20·30 N	77·40 W
99	Guacara (gwä'-kä-rä) . . . Ven. (In.)	10·16 N	67·48 W
98	Guacarí (gwä-kä-rē') . . . Col. (In.)	3·45 N	76·20 W
101	Guaçuí (gwä'-sōō-ē') Braz. (Rio de Janeiro In.)	20·47 S	41·40 W
90	Guadalajara (gwä-dhä-lä-hä'rä) Mex.	20·41 N	103·21 W
124	Guadalajara (gwä-dä-lä-kä'-rä) Sp.	40·37 N	3·10 W
124	Guadalcanal (gwä-dhäl-kä-näl') Sp.	38·05 N	5·48 W
159	Guadalcanal (I.) . . . Sol. Is.	9·48 S	158·43 E
90	Guadalcázar (gwä-dhäl-kä'zär) Mex.	22·38 N	100·24 W
124	Guadalete (R.) (gwä-dhä-lā'tā) Sp.	38·53 N	5·38 W
124	Guadalhorce (R.) (gwä-dhäl-ôr'thā) . Sp.	37·05 N	4·50 W
124	Guadalimar (R.) (gwä-dhä-lē-mär') . Sp.	38·29 N	2·53 W
125	Guadalope (R.) (gwä-dä-lô-pĕ) Sp.	40·48 N	0·10 W
124	Guadalquivir, Río (R.) (rē'-ō-gwä-dhäl-kê-vēr') . Sp.	5·57 N	6·00 W
76	Guadalupe . . . Mex.	31·23 N	106·06 W
124	Guadalupe, Sierra de (Mts.) (Syĕr'rä dä gwä-dhä-lōō'pä) . Sp.	39·30 N	5·25 W
88	Guadalupe I. . . . Mex.	29·00 N	118·45 W
76	Guadalupe Mts. . . . N. Mex.-Tex.	32·00 N	104·55 W
76	Guadalupe Pk . . . Tex.	31·55 N	104·55 W
76	Guadalupe R. (gwä-dhä-lōō'pä) Tex.	29·54 N	99·03 W
124	Guadarrama, Sierra de (Mts.) (gwä-dhär-rä'mä) . Sp.	41·00 N	3·40 W
125	Guadarrama (R.) (gwä-dhär-rä'mä) Sp. (Madrid In.)	40·34 N	3·58 W
93	Guadeloupe (Is.) (gwä-dē-lōōp') N. A. (Le. & Wind. Is. In.)	16·07 N	61·19 W
93	Guadeloupe Pass Guad. (Le. & Wind. Is. In.)	16·26 N	62·00 W
94	Guadiana, Bahia de (B.) (bä-ē'ä-dĕ-gwä-dhē-ä'nä) . Cuba	22·10 N	84·35 W
124	Guadiana, Rio (R.) (rē'ō-gwä-dvä'nä) . Port.	37·43 N	7·43 W
124	Guadiana Alto (R.) (äl'tō) . . . Sp.	39·02 N	2·52 W
124	Guadiana Menor (R.) (mä'nôr) Sp.	37·43 N	2·45 W
124	Guadiaro (R.) (gwä-dhē-ä'rō) . Sp.	37·38 N	5·25 W
125	Guadiato (R.) (gwä-dhē-ä'tō) . Sp.	38·10 N	5·05 W
124	Guadiela (R.) (gwä-dhē-ā'lä) . Sp.	40·23 N	2·23 W
124	Guadix (gwä-dhēsh') . . . Sp.	37·18 N	3·09 W
99	Guaire (R.) (gwī'-rĕ) . . . Ven. (In.)	10·25 N	66·43 W
94	Guajaba, Cayo (I.) (kä'yō-gwä-hä'bä) . Cuba	21·50 N	77·35 W
98	Guajará Mirim (gwä-zhä-rä'mē-rēN' . Braz.	10·58 S	65·12 W
98	Guajira, Pen. de (Pen.) (pĕ-nē'ng-sōō-lä-dĕ-gwä-kē'rä) Col.-Ven.	12·35 N	73·00 W
92	Gualán (gwä-län') . . . Guat.	15·08 N	89·21 W
101	Gualeguay (gwä-lĕ-gwä'y) Arg. (Buenos Aires In.)	33·10 S	59·20 W
101	Gualeguay (R.) Arg. (Buenos Aires In.)	32·49 S	59·05 W
101	Gualeguaychú (gwä-lä-gwī-chōō') Arg. (Buenos Aires In.)	33·01 S	58·32 W
101	Gualeguaychú (R.) Arg. (Buenos Aires In.)	32·58 S	58·27 W
100	Gualicho, Salina (F.) (sä-lē'nä-gwä-lē'chō) . Arg.	40·20 S	65·15 W
156	Guam (I.) (gwäm) . . . Oceania	14·00 N	143·20 E
100	Guaminí (gwä-mē-nē') . . . Arg.	37·02 S	62·21 W
98	Guamo (gwä'mō) . . . Col. (In.)	4·02 N	74·58 W
95	Guanabacoa (gwä-nä-bä-kō'ä) Cuba (La Habana In.)	23·08 N	82·19 W
100	Guanabara (gwä-nä-bä'rä) . . Braz.	23·03 N	43·32 W
100	Guanabara, Baia de (B.) Braz. (In.)	22·44 S	43·09 W
92	Guanacaste Cord. (Mts.) (kôr-dēl-yĕ'rä-gwä-nä-käs'tä) C. R.	10·54 N	85·27 W
88	Guanacevi (gwä-nä-sĕ-vē') . . Mex.	25·30 N	105·45 W
94	Guanahacabibes, Pen. de (pĕ-nēn-sōō-lä-dĕ-gwä-nä hä-kä-bē'bäs) Cuba	21·55 N	84·35 W
94	Guanajay (gwä-nä-hī') . . . Cuba	22·55 N	82·40 W
90	Guanajuato (gwä-nä-hwä'tō) Mex.	21·01 N	101·16 W
88	Guanajuato (State) . . . Mex.	21·00 N	101·00 W
99	Guanape (gwä-nä'pĕ) . . . Ven. (In.)	9·55 N	65·32 W
99	Guanape (R.) . . . Ven. (In.)	9·52 N	65·20 W
98	Guanare (gwä-nä'rä) . . . Ven.	8·57 N	69·47 W
100	Guanduçu (R.) (gwä'n-dōō'sōō) Braz. (In.)	22·50 S	43·40 W
94	Guane (gwä'nä) . . . Cuba	22·10 N	84·05 W
99	Guanta (gwän'tä) . . . Ven. (In.)	10·15 N	64·35 W
95	Guantánamo (gwän-tä'nä-mō) Cuba	20·10 N	75·10 W
95	Guantanamo, Bahía de (B.) (bä-ē'ä-dĕ) . Cuba	19·35 N	75·35 W
101	Guapé (gwä-pĕ') Braz. (Rio de Janeiro In.)	20·45 S	45·55 W
93	Guapiles (gwä-pē-lĕs) . . . C. R.	10·05 N	83·54 W
100	Guapimirim (gwä-pē-mē-rē'N) Braz. (In.)	22·31 S	42·59 W
98	Guaporé (R.) (gwä-pô-rā') Bol.-Braz.	12·11 S	63·47 W
98	Guaqui (guä'kē) . . . Bol.	16·42 S	68·47 W
125	Guara, Sierra de (Mts.) (sē-ĕ'r-rä-dĕ-gwä'rä) . Sp.	42·24 N	0·15 W
99	Guarabira (gwä-rä-bē'rä) . . . Braz.	6·49 S	35·27 W
98	Guaranda (gwä-rän'dä) . . . Ec.	1·39 S	78·57 W
99	Guarapari (gwä-rä-pä'rē) . . . Braz.	20·34 S	40·31 W
101	Guarapiranga, Represa do (Res.) (r'ĕ-prĕ-sä-dô-gwä'rä-pē-rä'n-gä) Braz. (Rio de Janeiro In.)	23·45 S	46·44 W
100	Guarapuava (gwä-rä-pwä'vä) Braz.	25·29 S	51·26 W
101	Guaratinguetá (guä-rä-tĭN-gä-tä') Braz. (Rio de Janeiro In.)	22·49 S	45·10 W
124	Guarda (gwär'dä) . . . Port.	40·32 N	7·17 W
124	Guareña (gwä-rā'nyä) . . . Sp.	38·52 N	6·08 W
99	Guaribe (R.) (gwä-rē'bĕ) Ven. (In.)	9·48 N	65·17 W
99	Guarico (State) . . . Ven. (In.)	9·42 N	67·25 W
99	Guárico (R.) . . . Ven. (In.)	9·50 N	67·07 W
101	Guarulhos (gwä-rōō'l-yôs) Braz. (Rio de Janeiro In.)	32·28 S	46·30 W
101	Guarus (gwà'rōōs) Braz. (Rio de Janeiro In.)	21·44 S	41·19 W
98	Guasca (gwäs'kä) . . . Col. (In.)	4·52 N	73·52 W
99	Guasipati (gwä-sē-pä'tē) . . . Ven.	7·26 N	61·57 W
126	Guastalla (gwäs-täl'lä) . . . It.	44·53 N	10·39 E
74	Guasti (gwäs'tĭ) Calif. (Los Angeles In.)	34·04 N	117·35 W
92	Guatemala (guä-tä-mä'lä) . . Guat.	14·37 N	90·32 W
88	Guatemala . . . N. A.	15·45 N	91·45 W
99	Guatire (gwä-tē'rĕ) . . . Ven. (In.)	10·28 N	66·34 W
101	Guaxupé (gwä-shōō-pĕ') Braz. (Rio de Janeiro In.)	21·18 S	46·42 W
94	Guayabal (gwä-yä-bä'l) . . . Cuba	20·40 N	77·40 W
90	Guayalejo (R.) (gwä-yä-lĕ'hô) Mex.	23·24 N	99·09 W
89	Guayama (gwä-yä'mä) P. R. (Puerto Rico In.)	18·00 N	66·08 W
95	Guayamouc (R.) . . . Hai.	19·05 N	72·00 W
92	Guayape R. . . . Hond.	14·39 N	86·37 W
98	Guayaquil (gwī-ä-kēl') . . . Ec.	2·16 S	79·53 W
98	Guayaquil, Golfo de (G.) (gôl-fô-dĕ) . Ec.	3·03 S	82·12 W
98	Guayiare (R.) (gwä-yà'rĕ) . . . Col.	3·35 N	69·28 W
88	Guaymas (gwä'y-mäs) . . . Mex.	27·49 N	110·58 W
95	Guayubin (gwä-yōō-bē'n) Dom. Rep.	19·40 N	71·25 W
92	Guazacapán (gwä-zä-kä-pän') Guat.	14·04 N	90·26 W
136	Gubakha (gōō-bä'kä) Sov. Un. (Urals In.)	58·53 N	57·35 E
126	Gubbio (gōōb'byô) . . . It.	43·23 N	12·36 E
125	Gudar, Sierra de (Mts.) (syĕr'rä dä gōō'dhär) . Sp.	40·28 N	0·47 W
118	Gudenaa (R.) . . . Den.	56·20 N	9·47 E
118	Gudinge Fjärden (Fd.) . . . Swe.	57·43 N	16·55 E
118	Gudvangen (gōōdh'văŋ-gĕn) . Nor.	60·52 N	6·45 E
123	Guebwiller (gĕb-vē-lâr') . . . Fr.	47·53 N	7·10 E
164	Guelma (gwĕl'mä) . . . Alg.	36·32 N	7·17 E
85	Guelph (gwĕlf) . Can. (Toronto In.)	43·33 N	80·15 W
114	Guemar (gē-mär') . . . Alg.	33·32 N	6·42 E
99	Güere (gwĕ'rĕ) (R.) . . . Ven. (In.)	9·39 N	65·00 W
122	Guéret (gā-rĕ') . . . Fr.	46·09 N	1·52 E
122	Guernsey (I.) (gûrn'zĭ) . . Chan. Is.	49·27 N	2·36 W
114	Guerrara (gĕr-rä'rä) . . . Alg.	32·50 N	4·26 E
76	Guerrero (gĕr-rā'rō) . . . Mex.	26·47 N	99·20 W
76	Guerrero . . . Mex.	28·20 N	100·24 W
122	Gueugnon (gû-nyôN') . . . Fr.	46·35 N	4·01 E
77	Gueydan (gā'dăn) . . . La.	30·01 N	92·31 W
100	Guia de Pacobaíba (gwē'ä-dĕ-pä'kō-bī'bä) . Braz. (In.)	22·42 S	43·10 W
96	Guiana Highlands (Mts.) . . . Braz.	3·20 N	60·00 W
91	Guichicovi (San Juan) (gwē-chē-kō'vē) . Mex.	16·58 N	95·10 W
125	Guidonia (gwē-dō'nyä) It. (Roma In.)	42·00 N	12·45 E
123	Guignes (gēN'yĕ) . . . Fr. (Paris In.)	48·38 N	2·48 E
99	Güigüe (gwē'gwĕ) . . . Ven. (In.)	10·05 N	67·48 W
92	Guija, L. (gē'hä) . . . Sal.	14·16 N	89·21 W
110	Guildford (gĭl'fērd) Eng. (London In.)	51·13 N	0·34 W
75	Guilford (gĭl'fērd) Ind. (Cincinnati In.)	39·10 N	84·55 W
124	Guimarães (gē-mä-rănsh') . . . Port.	41·27 N	8·22 W
163	Guinea (gĭn'ē) . . . Afr.	10·48 N	12·28 W
163	Guinea, G. of . . . Afr.	2·00 N	1·00 E
94	Güines (gwē'näs) . . . Cuba	22·50 N	82·05 W
122	Guingamp (găN-gäN') . . . Fr.	48·35 N	3·10 W
94	Güira de Melena (gwē'rä dä mä-lā'nä) . Cuba	22·45 N	82·30 W
98	Güiria (gwē-rē'ä) . . . Ven.	10·43 N	62·16 W
114	Guir R. . . . Mor.-Alg.	31·55 N	2·48 W
123	Guise (guēz) . . . Fr.	49·54 N	3·37 E
92	Guisisil (Vol.) (gē-sē-sēl') . . . Nic.	12·40 N	86·11 W
142	Gujarat (State) . . . India	22·54 N	79·00 E
142	Gujranwala (gōōj-rän'va-lä) W. Pak.	32·08 N	74·14 E
118	Gula (R.) (gōō'lä) . . . Nor.	62·55 N	10·45 E
143	Gulbarga (gōōl-bûr'gä) . . . India	17·25 N	76·52 E
128	Gulbene (gōōl-bā'nĕ) . . . Sov. Un.	57·09 N	26·49 E
78	Gulfport (gŭlf'pōrt) . . . Miss.	30·24 N	89·05 W
129	Gulyay Pole . . . Sov. Un.	47·39 N	36·12 E
155	Gumaca (gōō-mä-kä') Phil. (Manila In.)	13·55 N	122·06 E
165	Gumbari (gōōm-bä-rē) . . . Con. L.	2·45 N	29·00 E
136	Gumbeyka R. (gōōm-bĕy'kä) Sov. Un. (Urals In.)	53·20 N	59·42 E
164	Gumel . . . Nig.	12·43 N	9·19 E
120	Gummersbach (gōōm'ĕrs-bäk) . Ger.	51·02 N	7·34 E
111	Gumpoldskirchen . . . Aus.	48·04 N	16·15 E
142	Guna . . . India	24·44 N	77·17 E
69	Gunnison (gŭn'ĭ-sŭn) . . . Colo.	38·30 N	107·00 W
69	Gunnison . . . Utah	39·10 N	111·50 W
69	Gunnison (R.) . . . Colo.	38·50 N	107·55 W
78	Guntersville (gŭn'tērz-vĭl) . . . Ala.	34·20 N	86·19 W
78	Guntersville L. . . . Ala.	34·30 N	86·20 W
111	Guntramsdorf . . . Aus. (Wien In.)	48·04 N	16·19 E
155	Gunungapi (I.) (gōō'nōōng-ä'pē) Indon.	6·52 S	127·15 E
139	Gunungkidjang Indon. (Singapore In.)	0·55 N	104·39 E
143	Guntūr (gōōn'tōōr) . . . India	16·22 N	80·29 E
73	Gurdon (gûr'dŭn) . . . Ark.	33·56 N	93·10 W
99	Gurgucia (R.) (gōōr-gōō'syä) Braz.	8·12 S	43·49 W
75	Gurnee (gûr'nē) . Ill. (Chicago In.)	42·22 N	87·55 W
118	Gurskōy (I.) (gōōrskûē) . . . Nor.	62·18 N	5·20 E
99	Gurupá (gōō-rōō-pä') . . . Braz.	1·28 S	51·32 W
99	Gurupi, Serra do (Mts.) (sĕ'r-rä-dô-gōō-rōō-pē') . Braz.	5·32 S	47·02 W
99	Gurupí (R.) (gōō-rōō-pē') . . . Braz.	2·37 S	46·45 W
142	Guru Sikhar Mt. . . . India	29·42 N	72·50 E
133	Gur'yev (gōōr'yĕf) . . . Sov. Un.	47·10 N	51·50 E
134	Gur'yevsk (gōōr-yĭfsk') . Sov. Un.	54·14 N	86·07 E
164	Gusau (gōō-zä'ōō) . . . Nig.	12·11 N	6·40 E
119	Gusev (gōō'sĕf) . . . Sov. Un.	54·35 N	22·15 E
127	Gusinje (gōō-sēn'yĕ) . . . Yugo.	42·34 N	19·54 E
128	Gus'-Khrustal'nyy (gōōs-kröō-stäl'ny') . Sov. Un.	55·39 N	40·41 E
91	Gustavo A. Madero (gōōs-tä'vô-ä-mä-dĕ'rô) . Mex. (Mexico In.)	19·29 N	99·07 W
120	Gustrow (güs'trō) . . . Ger.	53·48 N	12·12 E
121	Gúta (gōō'tä) . . . Czech.	47·54 N	17·59 E
120	Gütersloh (gü'tērs-lō) . . . Ger.	51·54 N	8·22 E
73	Guthrie (gŭth'rĭ) . . . Okla.	35·52 N	97·26 W
71	Guthrie Center . . . Iowa	41·41 N	94·33 W
91	Gutiérrez Zamora (gōō-tĭ-âr'räz zä-mō'rä) . Mex.	20·27 N	97·17 W
71	Guttenberg (gŭt'ĕn-bûrg) . . . Iowa	42·48 N	91·09 W
72	Guymon (gī'mŏn) . . . Okla.	36·41 N	101·29 W
83	Guysborough (gīz'bŭr-ô) . . . Can.	45·25 N	61·30 W
119	Gvardeysk (gvår-dĕysk') . Sov. Un.	54·39 N	21·11 E
144	Gwadar (gwä'dŭr) . . . W. Pak.	25·15 N	62·29 E
165	Gwane (gwän) . . . Con. L.	4·49 N	26·46 E
166	Gwelo (gwā'lō) . Fed. of Rh. & Nya.	19·15 S	29·48 E
71	Gwinn (gwĭn) . . . Mich.	46·15 N	87·30 W
146	Gyangtse (gyäng'tsĕ') . . . China	29·00 N	89·28 E
142	Gyantse . . . China	28·53 N	89·39 E
135	Gydan, Khrebet (Kolymskiy) (Mts.) . Sov. Un.	61·45 N	155·00 E
134	Gydanskiy, P-Ov (Pen.) . Sov. Un.	70·42 N	76·03 E
160	Gympie (gĭm'pē) . . . Austl.	26·20 S	152·50 E
121	Gyöngyös (dyûn'dyûsh) . . . Hung.	47·47 N	19·55 E
121	Györ (dyûr) . . . Hung.	47·40 N	17·37 E
153	Gyōtoku (gyō'tô-kōō') Jap. (Tōkyō In.)	35·42 N	139·56 E
86	Gypsumville (jĭp'sŭm-vĭl) . . . Can.	51·49 N	98·42 W
121	Gyula (dyōō'lä) . . . Hung.	46·38 N	21·18 E
128	Gzhatsk (g'zhätsk) . . . Sov. Un.	55·32 N	34·58 E
123	Haan (hän) . . . Ger. (Ruhr In.)	51·12 N	7·00 E
119	Haapamaki (häp'ä-mĕ-kē) . . . Fin.	62·16 N	24·20 E
119	Haapsalu (häp'sä-lōō) . . . Sov. Un.	58·56 N	23·33 E
111	Haar (här) . . . Ger. (München In.)	48·06 N	11·44 E
139	Ha'arava (R.) (Araba) Isr. (Palestine In.)	30·32 N	35·16 E
111	Haarlem (här'lĕm) Neth. (Amsterdam In.)	52·22 N	4·37 E
94	Habana (State) (hä-vä'nä) . . Cuba	22·55 N	82·15 W
125	Habibas (C.) (hä-bē'bäs) . . . Alg.	35·50 N	0·45 W
152	Hachinohe (hä'chē-nō'hå) . . . Jap.	40·29 N	141·40 E
153	Hachiōji (hä'chē-ō'jē) . . . Jap.	35·39 N	139·18 E
84	Hackensack (hăk'ĕn-săk) N. J. (New York In.)	40·54 N	74·03 W
84	Haddonfield (hăd'ŭn-fēld) N. J. (Philadelphia In.)	39·53 N	75·02 W
84	Haddon Heights (hăd'ŭn hīts) N. J. (Philadelphia In.)	39·53 N	75·03 W
164	Hadejia (hä-dā'jä) . . . Nig.	12·32 N	10·04 E
139	Hadera (kä-dĕ'rä) Isr. (Palestine In.)	32·26 N	34·55 E
118	Haderslev (hä'dhĕrs-lĕv) . . . Den.	55·17 N	9·28 E
168	Hadibu . . . Som. (Horn of Afr. In.)	12·40 N	53·50 E
65	Hadlock (hăd'lŏk) Wash. (Seattle In.)	48·02 N	122·46 W
144	Hadramawt (Reg.) . Sau. Ar.-Aden	15·15 N	48·32 E
152	Haeju (hä'ĕ-jü) . . . Kor.	38·03 N	125·42 E
150	Haerhpin (Harbin) (hàr-bēn') China	45·40 N	126·30 E
112	Hafnarfjördhur . . . Ice.	64·02 N	21·32 W
168	Hafun, Ras (C.) (hä-fōōn') Som. (Horn of Afr. In.)	10·15 N	51·35 E
67	Hageland (hăge'lănd) . . . Mont.	48·53 N	108·43 W
123	Hagen (hä'gĕn) . . . Ger. (Ruhr In.)	51·21 N	7·29 E
85	Hagermans Corners (hăg'ēr-măns kôr'nērz) . Can. (Toronto In.)	43·51 N	79·19 W
80	Hagerstown (hā'gērz-toun) . . . Ind.	39·55 N	85·10 W
81	Hagerstown . . . Md.	39·40 N	77·45 W
153	Hagi (hä'gĭ) . . . Jap.	34·25 N	131·25 E
122	Hague, C. de la (dē lä äg') . . . Fr.	49·44 N	1·55 W
	Hague, The, see 's Gravenhagen		
123	Haguenau (äg'nō') . . . Fr.	48·47 N	7·48 E
148	Haian (hăi'äN) . . . China	32·35 N	120·25 E
153	Haibara (hä'ē-bä'rä) . . . Jap.	34·29 N	135·57 E
150	Haich'eng . . . China	40·58 N	122·45 E
148	Haichou Wan (B.) (hăi'jō wän) China	34·58 N	119·27 E
139	Haifa (hä'ē-fà) Isr. (Palestine In.)	32·48 N	35·00 E
151	Haifeng (hä'ē-fĕng') . . . China	23·00 N	115·20 E

ăt; finăl; rāte; senâte; ärm; åsk; sofà; fâre; ch-choose; dh-as th in other; bē; êvent; bĕt; recĕnt; cratēr; g-go; gh-guttural g; bĭt; ĭ-short neutral; rīde; K-guttural k as ch in German ich;

Page	Name Pronunciation Region	Lat. °′	Long. °′
148	Haifuchen (hăī'fōō'jĕn)......China	31·57 N	121·48 E
144	Hā'il (hāl)..............Sau. Ar.	27·30 N	41·57 E
150	Hailaerh (Hailar) (hä-ē-lär') China	49·10 N	118·40 E
	Hailar, see Hailaerh		
67	Hailey (hā'lĭ).............Idaho	43·31 N	114·19 W
73	Haileyville (hā'lĭ-vĭl).......Okla.	34·51 N	95·34 W
152	Hailin (hä'ē-lēn')..........China	44·31 N	129·11 E
151	Hailing Tao (I.)...........China	21·30 N	112·15 E
150	Hailun (hä'ē-lōōn')........China	47·18 N	126·50 E
150	Hailung (hä'ē-lŏŏng').......China	42·32 N	125·52 E
151	Hainan Tao (I.) (hä'e-nän'dou) China	19·00 N	111·10 E
111	Hainburg an der Donau Aus. (Wien In.)	48·09 N	16·57 E
64	Haines (hānz)............Alaska	59·10 N	135·38 W
79	Haines City............Fla. (In.)	28·05 N	81·38 W
151	Haiphong (hī'fông') (hä'ēp-hŏng) Viet.	20·52 N	106·40 E
150	Haiten........China (Peking In.)	39·59 N	116·17 E
89	Haiti (hā'tĭ)...............N. A.	19·00 N	72·15 W
121	Hajduböszörmeny (hôl'dŏŏ-bû'sûr-mān'). Hung.	47·41 N	21·30 E
121	Hajduhadház (hô'ĭ-dŏŏ-hôd'häz) Hung.	47·32 N	21·32 E
121	Hajdunánás (hô'ĭ-dŏŏ-nä'näsh) Hung.	47·52 N	21·27 E
121	Hajduszoboszló (hô'ĭ-dŏŏ-sô'bôs-lō). Hung.	47·24 N	21·25 E
152	Hakodate (hä-kō-dä'tå)......Jap.	41·46 N	140·42 E
153	Haku-San (Mtn.) (hä'kōō-sän') Jap.	36·11 N	136·45 E
91	Halachó (ä-lä-chō')..........Mex.	20·28 N	90·06 W
165	Halaib (hä-lä'ēb)........U. A. R.	22·10 N	36·40 E
157	Halawa (hä-lä'wä)...Hawaii (In.)	21·12 N	156·55 E
139	Halbā........Leb. (Palestine In.)	34·33 N	36·03 E
111	Halbe (häl'bĕ)...Ger. (Berlin In.)	52·07 N	13·43 E
120	Halberstadt (häl'bĕr-shtät)...Ger.	51·54 N	11·07 E
155	Halcon, Mt. (häl-kōn') Phil. (Manila In.)	13·19 N	120·55 E
118	Halden (häl'dĕn)............Nor.	59·10 N	11·21 E
110	Hale (hāl)..................Eng.	53·22 N	2·20 W
157	Haleakala Crater (hä'lå-ä'kä-lä) Hawaii (In.)	20·44 N	156·15 W
157	Haleakala Natl. Park Hawaii (In.)	20·46 N	156·00 W
75	Hales Corners (hālz kŏr'nẽrz) Wis. (Milwaukee In.)	42·56 N	88·03 W
110	Halesowen (hālz'ô-wĕn).....Eng.	52·26 N	2·03 W
81	Halethorpe (hāl-thôrp).......Md.	39·15 N	76·40 W
78	Haleyville (hā'lĭ-vĭl).........Ala.	34·11 N	87·36 W
65	Half Moon Bay (hăf'mōōn). Calif. (San Francisco In.)	37·28 N	122·26 W
167	Halfway House (häf-wā hous) S. Afr. (Johannesburg & Pretoria In.)	26·00 S	28·08 E
111	Halfweg Neth. (Amsterdam In.)	52·23 N	4·45 E
82	Halifax (hăl'ĭ-făks)..........Can.	44·40 N	63·36 W
110	Halifax....................Eng.	53·44 N	1·52 W
159	Halifax B. (hăl'ĭ-făx).......Austl.	18·56 S	147·07 E
82	Halifax Hbr................Can.	44·35 N	63·25 W
139	Halīlah (R.) Jordan (Palestine In.)	30·28 N	35·57 E
152	Halla San (Mt.) (häl'lå-sän). Kor.	33·20 N	126·37 E
139	Hallat 'Ammar Sau. Ar. (Palestine In.)	29·09 N	36·05 E
111	Halle (häl'lĕ) Bel. (Bruxelles In.)	50·45 N	4·13 E
120	Halle......................Ger.	51·30 N	11·59 E
77	Hallettsville (hăl'ĕts-vĭl).....Tex.	29·26 N	96·55 W
70	Hallock (hăl'ŭk)............Minn.	48·46 N	96·57 W
87	Hall Pen (hôl)..............Can.	63·14 N	65·40 W
77	Halls Bay............Tex. (In.)	29·55 N	95·23 W
118	Hallsberg (häls'bĕrgh).......Swe.	59·04 N	15·04 E
158	Halls Creek (hôlz).........Austl.	18·15 S	127·45 E
82	Halls Strm. (hôls)....Can.-Maine	45·07 N	71·34 W
155	Halmahera (I.) (häl-mä-hā'rä) Indon.	0·45 N	128·45 E
118	Halmstad (hälm'städ)........Swe.	56·40 N	12·46 E
118	Halse Fd. (häl'sĕ fyôrd).....Nor.	63·03 N	8·23 E
84	Halsey (hôl'zē) N. J. (New York In.)	41·06 N	74·45 W
118	Hälsingborg (hĕl'sĭng-bôrgh). Swe.	56·04 N	12·40 E
73	Halstead (hôl'stĕd).........Kans.	38·02 N	97·36 W
151	Halt'an Tao (I.)...........China	25·40 N	119·45 E
123	Haltern (häl'tĕrn) Ger. (Ruhr In.)	51·45 N	7·10 E
74	Haltom City (hôl'tŏm) Tex. (Dallas, Fort Worth In.)	32·48 N	97·17 W
	Halunrshan, see Wenchüan		
111	Halvarenbeek Neth. (Amsterdam In.)	51·29 N	5·10 E
115	Hama (hä'mä)..............Syr.	35·08 N	36·53 E
144	Hamadān (hŭ-mŭ-dān')......Iran	34·45 N	48·07 E
153	Hamamatsu (hä'mä-mät'sŏŏ). Jap.	34·41 N	137·43 E
118	Hamar (hä'mär).............Nor.	60·49 N	11·05 E
153	Hamasaka (hă'må-sä'kå).....Jap.	35·37 N	134·27 E
123	Hamborn (häm'bōrn) Ger. (Ruhr In.)	51·30 N	6·43 E
73	Hamburg (hăm'bûrg)........Ark.	33·15 N	91·49 W
111	Hamburg (häm'bōōrgh) Ger. (Hamburg In.)	53·34 N	10·02 E
70	Hamburg..................Iowa	40·39 N	95·40 W
84	Hamburg...N. J. (New York In.)	41·09 N	74·35 W
75	Hamburg.....N. Y. (Buffalo In.)	42·44 N	78·51 W
167	Hamburg (hăm'bürg) S. Afr. (Natal In.)	33·18 S	27·28 E
81	Hamden (hăm'dĕn)........Conn.	41·20 N	72·55 W
119	Hämeenlinna (hĕ'mån-lĭn-nå). Fin.	61·00 N	24·29 E
74	Hamel (hăm'ĕl). Ill. (St. Louis In.)	38·53 N	89·51 W
120	Hameln (hä'mĕln)...........Ger.	52·06 N	9·23 E
111	Hamelwörden (hä'mĕl-vûr-dĕn) Ger. (Hamburg In.)	53·47 N	9·19 E
158	Hamersley Ra. (hăm'ẽrz-lē) Austl.	22·15 S	117·50 E
152	Hamhung (häm'hŏŏng').....Kor.	39·57 N	127·35 E
146	Hami (Qomul) (hä'mē) (kô-mōōl') China	42·58 N	93·14 E
160	Hamilton (hăm'ĭl-tŭn)......Austl.	37·50 S	142·10 E
85	Hamilton.....Can. (Toronto In.)	43·15 N	79·52 W
83	Hamilton.....Mass. (Boston In.)	42·37 N	70·52 W
73	Hamilton...................Mo.	39·43 N	93·59 W
67	Hamilton.................Mont.	46·15 N	114·09 W
159	Hamilton............N. Z. (In.)	37·45 S	175·28 E
75	Hamilton...Ohio (Cincinnati In.)	39·22 N	84·33 W
76	Hamilton..................Tex.	31·42 N	98·07 W
73	Hamilton, L................Ark.	34·25 N	93·32 W
85	Hamilton Hbr. Can. (Toronto In.)	43·17 N	79·50 W
87	Hamilton Inlet.............Can.	54·20 N	56·57 W
119	Hamina (hå'mē-nå)..........Fin.	60·34 N	27·15 E
79	Hamlet (hăm'lĕt)..........N. C.	35·52 N	79·46 W
72	Hamlin (hăm'lĭn)...........Tex.	32·54 N	100·08 W
123	Hamm (häm)....Ger. (Ruhr In.)	51·40 N	7·48 E
168	Hammanskraal (hä-måns-kräl') S. Afr. (Johannesburg & Pretoria In.)	25·24 S	28·17 E
111	Hamme.......Bel. (Bruxelles In.)	51·06 N	4·07 E
111	Hamme-Oste Kanal (Can.) (hä'mĕ-ōs'tĕ kă-näl) Ger. (Hamburg In.)	53·20 N	8·59 E
112	Hammerfest (häm'mĕr-fĕst)..Nor.	70·38 N	23·59 E
75	Hammond (hăm'ŭnd) Ind. (Chicago In.)	41·37 N	87·31 W
77	Hammond...................La.	30·30 N	90·28 W
65	Hammond....Ore. (Portland In.)	46·12 N	123·57 W
81	Hammonton (hăm'ŭn-tŭn)..N. J.	39·40 N	74·45 W
82	Hampden (hăm'dĕn).......Maine	44·44 N	68·51 W
116	Hampshire Downs (hămp'shĭr dounz). Eng.	51·01 N	1·05 W
110	Hampstead Norris (hămp-stĕd nŏ'rĭs). Eng. (London In.)	51·27 N	1·14 W
82	Hampton (hămp'tŭn).......Can.	45·34 N	65·50 W
71	Hampton...................Iowa	42·43 N	93·15 W
84	Hampton.......Va. (Norfolk In.)	37·02 N	76·21 W
84	Hampton Roads (Inlet) (Va. (Norfolk In.)	36·56 N	76·23 W
164	Ḫamrā, Ḫammādah al (Plat.) Libya	29·39 N	10·53 E
118	Hamrånge (häm'rông'ĕ).....Swe.	60·56 N	17·00 E
75	Hamtramck (hăm-trăm'ĭk) Mich. (Detroit In.)	42·24 N	83·03 W
144	Hāmūn-l Māshkel (L.) (hā-mōōn'ē māsh-kĕl'). W. Pak.	28·28 N	64·13 E
152	Han (R.)...................Kor.	37·10 N	127·40 E
157	Hana (hä'nä)........Hawaii (In.)	20·43 N	155·59 W
94	Hanábana (R.) (hä-nä-bä'nä) Cuba	22·30 N	80·55 W
157	Hanalei B. (hä-nä-lā'ē) Hawaii (In.)	22·15 N	159·40 W
120	Hanau (hä'nou)............Ger.	50·08 N	8·56 E
151	Han Chiang (R.)..........China	25·00 N	116·35 E
71	Hancock (hăn'kŏk)........Mich.	47·08 N	88·37 W
65	Haney (hā-nē) Can. (Vancouver In.)	49·13 N	122·36 W
68	Hanford (hăn'fẽrd).........Calif.	36·20 N	119·38 W
146	Hangayn Nuruu (Khangai Mts.) Mong.	48·03 N	99·45 E
151	Hangchou (hăng'chō')......China	30·17 N	120·12 E
151	Hangchou Wan (B.) (hăng'chō') China	30·20 N	121·25 E
119	Hangö (häŋ'gû).............Fin.	59·49 N	22·56 E
77	Hankamer (hăŋ'kå-mẽr). Tex.(In.)	29·52 N	94·42 W
151	Han Kiang (R.) (hän'kyäng') China	31·40 N	112·04 E
70	Hankinson (häŋ'kĭn-sŭn)...N. D.	46·04 N	96·54 W
151	Hank'ou (hăn'kō').........China	30·42 N	114·22 E
158	Hann, Mt. (hän)..........Austl.	16·05 S	126·07 E
86	Hanna (hăn' å).............Can.	51·36 N	111·58 W
67	Hanna.....................Wyo.	41·51 N	106·34 W
70	Hannah...................N. D.	48·58 N	98·42 W
73	Hannibal (hăn'ĭ băl)........Mo.	39·42 N	91·22 W
120	Hannover (hän-ō'vĕr)........Ger.	52·22 N	9·45 E
118	Hanö-bukten (B.)...........Swe.	55·54 N	14·55 E
151	Hanoi (hä-noi')............Viet.	21·04 N	105·50 E
80	Hanover (hăn'ô-vẽr)........Can.	44·10 N	81·05 W
83	Hanover......Mass. (Boston In.)	42·07 N	70·49 W
81	Hanover...................N. H.	43·45 N	72·15 W
81	Hanover.....................Pa.	39·50 N	77·00 W
100	Hanover (I.)...............Chile	51·00 S	74·45 W
148	Hanshan (hän'shän').......China	31·43 N	118·06 E
89	Hans Lollick (I.) (häns'lôl'ĭk) Vir. Is. (U. S. A.) (St. Thomas In.)	18·24 N	64·55 W
83	Hanson (hăn'sŭn) Mass. (Boston In.)	42·04 N	70·53 W
65	Hansville (hăns'-vĭl) Wash. (Seattle In.)	47·55 N	122·33 W
148	Hantan (hän'tän').........China	36·37 N	114·30 E
82	Hantsport (hănts'pōrt)......Can.	45·05 N	64·12 W
151	Hanyang (han'yäng')......China	30·30 N	114·10 E
148	Haoch'engchi (hou'chĕng'jē). China	33·19 N	117·33 E
112	Haparanda (hä-pä-rän'dä)...Swe.	65·54 N	23·57 E
84	Hapeville (hāp'vĭl) Ga. (Atlanta In.)	33·39 N	84·25 W
84	Happy Jack (hăp'ĭ jăk) La. (New Orleans In.)	29·31 N	89·44 W
153	Hara-machida (hă-ră mă-chē'dă) Jap. (Tōkyō In.)	35·32 N	139·28 E
124	Harana, Sierra (Mts.) (sē-ĕ'r-ră-ră'nă). Sp.	37·17 N	3·28 W
146	Hara Nuur (L.)...........Mong.	47·47 N	94·01 E
168	Hārar (hå-rär') Eth. (Horn of Afr. In.)	9·43 N	42·10 E
165	Harar (Prov.)..............Eth.	8·15 N	41·00 E
146	Hara Usa (L.)............Mong.	48·00 N	92·32 E
	Harbin, see Haerhpin		
80	Harbor Beach (här'bẽr bēch) Mich.	43·50 N	82·40 W
80	Harbor Springs............Mich.	45·25 N	85·05 W
83	Harbour Breton (brĕt'ŭn) (brē-tôN'). Can.	47·28 N	55·50 W
83	Harbour Grace (grās).......Can.	47·39 N	53·15 W
111	Harburg (här-bŏŏrgh) Ger. (Hamburg In.)	53·28 N	9·58 E
82	Harcourt (här'côrt) (år-kōōr') Can.	46·28 N	65·14 W
118	Hardanger Fd. (hăr-dăng'ĕr fyôrd). Nor.	59·58 N	6·30 E
118	Hardanger Fjeld (Mts.) (fyĕl') Nor.	60·15 N	6·56 E
118	Hardanger Jöklen (Mtn.) (yû'kŏŏl-ĕn). Nor.	60·33 N	7·23 E
67	Hardin (här'dĭn)..........Mont.	45·44 N	107·36 W
167	Harding (här'dĭng) S. Afr. (Natal In.)	30·34 S	29·54 E
78	Harding (L.)............Ala.-Ga.	32·43 N	85·00 W
142	Hardwar (hŭr'dvär)........India	29·56 N	78·06 E
68	Hardy (R.) (här'dĭ).........Mex.	32·04 N	115·10 W
83	Hare B. (hâr)..............Can.	51·21 N	55·45 W
168	Hargeisa (här-gā'ē-så) Som. (Horn of Afr. In.)	9·20 N	43·57 E
121	Harghita, Muntii (Mts.)....Rom.	46·25 N	25·40 E
153	Harima-Nada (Sea) (hä'rē-mä nä-dä). Jap.	34·34 N	134·37 E
111	Haring Vliet (R.) Neth. (Amsterdam In.)	51·49 N	4·03 E
73	Harlan (här'lăn)............Iowa	41·40 N	95·10 W
78	Harlan......................Ky.	36·50 N	83·19 W
72	Harlan Co. Res............Nebr.	40·03 N	99·51 W
67	Harlem (hår'lĕm)..........Mont.	48·33 N	108·50 W
143	Harlhar...................India	14·32 N	75·41 E
117	Harlingen (här'lĭng-ĕn).....Neth.	53·10 N	5·24 E
77	Harlingen..................Tex.	26·12 N	97·42 W
110	Harlow (här'lō) Eng. (London In.)	51·46 N	0·08 E
67	Harlowton (hår'lô-tun).....Mont.	46·26 N	109·50 W
80	Harmony (här'mô-nĭ)........Ind.	39·35 N	87·00 W
66	Harney Basin (här'nĭ).......Ore.	43·26 N	120·19 W
66	Harney L..................Ore.	43·11 N	119·23 W
70	Harney Pk.................S. D.	43·52 N	103·32 W
118	Härnösand (hĕr-nû-sänd)....Swe.	62·37 N	17·54 E
124	Haro (ä'rō)..................Sp.	42·35 N	2·49 W
65	Haro Str. (hă'rō)......Can.-U. S.	48·27 N	123·11 W
110	Harpenden (här'pĕn-d'n) Eng. (London In.)	51·48 N	0·22 W
72	Harper (här'pẽr)...........Kans.	37·17 N	98·02 W
164	Harper.....................Lib.	4·28 N	7·52 W
65	Harper.......Wash. (Seattle In.)	47·31 N	122·32 W
81	Harpers Ferry (här'pẽrz)..W. Va.	39·20 N	77·45 W
133	Harput (kär-pōōt')..........Tur.	38·45 N	39·10 E
78	Harriman (hăr'ĭ-măn)......Tenn.	35·55 N	84·34 W
81	Harrington (hăr'ĭng-tŭn).....Del.	38·55 N	75·35 W
87	Harrington Harbour (här'bẽr) Can.	50·30 N	59·19 W
144	Harri Rud (R.).............Afg.	34·29 N	61·16 E
116	Harris (I.) (hăr'ĭs).........Scot.	57·55 N	6·40 W
79	Harris (L.)............Fla. (In.)	28·43 N	81·40 W
80	Harrisburg (hăr'ĭs-bûrg).......Ill.	37·45 N	88·35 W
81	Harrisburg..................Pa.	40·15 N	76·50 W
168	Harrismith (hă-rĭs'mĭth) S. Afr. (Johannesburg & Pretoria In.)	28·17 S	29·08 E
73	Harrison (hăr'ĭ-sŭn)........Ark.	36·13 N	93·06 W
75	Harrison....Ohio (Cincinnati In.)	39·16 N	84·45 W
81	Harrisonburg (hăr'-ĭ-sŭn-bûrg) Va.	38·30 N	78·50 W
73	Harrisonville (hăr-ĭ-sŭn-vĭl)...Mo.	38·39 N	94·21 W
74	Harrisville (hăr'ĭs-vĭl) Utah (Salt Lake City In.)	41·17 N	112·00 W
80	Harrisville..............W. Va.	39·10 N	81·05 W
80	Harrodsburg (hăr'ŭdz-bûrg)..Ky.	37·45 N	84·50 W
75	Harrods Cr. (hăr'ŭdz) Ky. (Louisville In.)	38·24 N	35·33 W
110	Harrow (hăr'ō). Eng. (London In.)	51·34 N	0·21 W
111	Harsefeld (här'zĕ-fĕld') Ger. (Hamburg In.)	53·27 N	9·30 E
112	Harstad (här'städh).........Nor.	68·49 N	16·10 E
80	Hart (härt)................Mich.	43·40 N	86·25 W
167	Hartbeespoort............S. Afr. (Johannesburg & Pretoria In.)	25·44 S	27·51 E
167	Hartbeespoortdam (L.)....S. Afr. (Johannesburg & Pretoria In.)	25·47 S	27·43 E
168	Hartbeestfontein S. Afr. (Johannesburg & Pretoria In.)	26·46 S	26·25 E
78	Hartford (härt'fẽrd).........Ala.	31·05 N	85·42 W
73	Hartford...................Ark.	35·01 N	94·21 W
81	Hartford..................Conn.	41·45 N	72·40 W
74	Hartford.......Ill. (St. Louis In.)	38·50 N	90·06 W
78	Hartford....................Ky.	37·25 N	86·50 W
80	Hartford..................Mich.	42·15 N	86·15 W
71	Hartford...................Wis.	43·19 N	88·25 W
80	Hartford City..............Ind.	40·35 N	85·25 W
110	Hartington (härt'ĭng-tŭn)....Eng.	53·08 N	1·48 W
70	Hartington................Nebr.	42·37 N	97·18 W
82	Hartland (härt'lănd).........Can.	46·19 N	67·32 W
116	Hartland Pt................Eng.	51·03 N	4·40 W
166	Hartley......Fed. of Rh. & Nya.	18·11 S	30·08 E
70	Hartley (härt'lĭ)............Iowa	43·12 N	95·29 W
78	Hartselle (härt'sĕl)..........Ala.	34·24 N	86·55 W
73	Hartshorne (härts'hôrn).....Okla.	34·49 N	95·34 W
79	Hartsville (härts'vĭl)........S. C.	34·20 N	80·04 W
78	Hartwell (härt'wĕl)..........Ga.	34·21 N	82·56 W
142	Hārua.......India (Calcutta In.)	22·36 N	88·40 E
71	Harvard (här'vård)...........Ill.	42·25 N	88·39 W
83	Harvard......Mass. (Boston In.)	42·30 N	71·35 W
72	Harvard...................Nebr.	40·36 N	98·08 W
69	Harvard, Mt...............Colo.	38·55 N	106·20 W
67	Harve (här'vĭ)............Mont.	48·34 N	109·42 W
75	Harvey.........Ill. (Chicago In.)	41·37 N	87·39 W
84	Harvey....La. (New Orleans In.)	29·54 N	90·05 W
70	Harvey...................N. D.	47·46 N	99·55 W
117	Harwich (här'wĭch).........Eng.	51·53 N	1·13 E
120	Harz Mts. (härts)...........Ger.	51·42 N	10·50 E
139	Hasa (R.)..Jordan (Palestine In.)	30·57 N	35·51 E
153	Hashimoto (hä'shē-mō'tō)....Jap.	34·19 N	135·37 E
119	Häsijärvi (L.) (hĕ'sē-yĕr'vē)..Fin.	61·42 N	24·05 E

ng-sing; ŋ-baŋk; N-nasalized n; nŏd; cŏmmit; ōld; ôbey; ôrder; fōōd; fŏŏt; ou-out; s-soft; sh-dish; th-thin; pūre; ûnite; ûrn; stŭd; circŭs; ü-as "y" in study; '-indeterminate vowel.

214 Haskell–Highland Park PRONOUNCING INDEX

Page	Name Pronunciation	Region	Lat. °′	Long. °′
73	Haskell (hăs'kĕl)	Okla.	35·49 N	95·41 W
72	Haskell	Tex.	33·09 N	99·43 W
74	Haslet (hăs'lĕt)	Tex. (Dallas, Fort Worth In.)	32·58 N	97·21 W
110	Haslingden (hăz'lĭng dĕn)	Eng.	53·43 N	2·19 W
118	Hassela (häs'ĕl-ô)	Swe.	62·05 N	16·46 E
111	Hasselt (häs'ĕlt)	Bel. (Bruxelles In.)	50·56 N	5·23 E
164	Hassi Inifel	Alg.	29·54 N	3·47 E
118	Hässjö (hĕs'shû)	Swe.	62·36 N	17·33 E
118	Hassleholm (häs'lĕ-hōlm)	Swe.	56·10 N	13·44 E
117	Hastings (hās'tĭngz)	Eng.	50·52 N	0·28 E
80	Hastings	Mich.	42·40 N	85·20 W
74	Hastings	Minn. (Minneapolis, St. Paul In.)	44·44 N	92·51 W
72	Hastings	Nebr.	40·34 N	98·42 W
159	Hastings	N. Z. (In.)	39·33 S	176·53 E
84	Hastings-on-Hudson (ŏn-hŭd'sŭn)	N. Y. (New York In.)	40·59 N	73·53 W
78	Hatchie (R.) (hăch'ē)	Tenn.	35·28 N	89·14 W
127	Hateg (kät-säg')	Rom.	45·35 N	22·57 E
110	Hatfield Broad Oak (hăt-fēld brôd ōk)	Eng.	51·50 N	0·14 E
153	Hatogaya (hä'tō-gä-yä)	Jap. (Tōkyō In.)	35·50 N	139·45 E
153	Hatsukaichi (hät'sōō-kä'ē-chē)	Jap.	34·22 N	132·19 E
79	Hatteras, C. (hăt'ēr-ăs)	N. C.	35·15 N	75·24 W
78	Hattiesburg (hăt'ĭz-bûrg)	Miss.	31·20 N	89·18 W
123	Hattingen (hä'tĕn-gĕn)	Ger. (Ruhr In.)	51·24 N	7·11 E
121	Hatvan (hôt'vôn)	Hung.	47·39 N	19·44 E
118	Haugesund (hou'gē-soon')	Nor.	59·26 N	5·20 E
119	Haukivesi (L.) (hou'kē-vĕ'sē)	Fin.	62·02 N	29·02 E
168	Hauptsrus	S. Afr. (Johannesburg & Pretoria In.)	26·35 S	26·16 E
159	Hauraki, G. (hä-ōō-rä'kē)	N. Z. (In.)	36·44 S	175·15 E
119	Hausjärvi (hä'ōōs-yĕr'vē)	Fin.	60·44 N	24·44 E
82	Haut, Isle au (hō)	Maine	44·03 N	68·13 W
144	Hauta (hou'tä)	Sau. Ar.	23·12 N	45·38 E
114	Haut Atlas (Mts.)	Mor.	32·10 N	5·49 W
82	Hauterive	Can.	49·12 N	68·15 W
122	Hautmont (ō-môɴ')	Fr.	50·14 N	3·50 E
73	Havana (hȧ-vă'nȧ)	Ill.	40·17 N	90·02 W
	Havana, see La Habana			
69	Havasu (L.) (hăv'ȧ-sōō)	Ariz.	34·26 N	114·09 W
82	Havelock (hăv'lŏk)	Can.	56·58 N	65·20 W
120	Havel R. (hä'fĕl)	Ger.	53·09 N	13·10 E
81	Haven (hā-vĕn)	Pa.	40·31 N	76·14 W
83	Haverhill (hā'vēr-hĭl)	Mass. (Boston In.)	42·46 N	71·05 W
81	Haverhill	N. H.	44·00 N	72·05 W
84	Haverstraw (hā'vēr-strô)	N. Y. (New York In.)	41·11 N	73·58 W
83	Havre (hăv'rȧ)	Can.	45·42 N	61·30 W
81	Havre de Grace (hăv'ēr dē grăs')	Md.	39·35 N	76·05 W
79	Haw (R.) (hô)	N. C.	36·17 N	79·46 W
62	Hawaii (State)	U. S.	20·00 N	157·40 W
157	Hawaii (I.)	Hawaii (In.)	19·35 N	155·30 W
62	Hawaiian Is. (hȧ-wī'ăn)	Oceania	22·00 N	158·00 W
157	Hawaii Vol. Natl. Park (hȧ-wī'ē)	Hawaii (In.)	19·15 N	155·20 W
70	Hawarden (hā'wȧr-dĕn)	Iowa	43·00 N	96·28 W
157	Hawi (hä'wē)	Hawaii (In.)	20·16 N	155·48 W
116	Hawick (hô'ĭk)	Scot.	55·25 N	2·55 W
159	Hawke B. (hôk)	N. Z. (In.)	39·17 S	177·58 E
160	Hawker (hô'kēr)	Austl.	31·58 S	138·12 E
81	Hawkesbury (hôks'bĕr-ĭ)	Can.	45·35 N	74·35 W
83	Hawkesbury, Port	Can.	45·39 N	60·48 W
78	Hawkinsville (hô'kĭnz-vĭl)	Ga.	32·15 N	83·30 W
95	Hawks Nest Pt.	Ba. Is.	24·05 N	75·30 W
70	Hawley (hô'lĭ)	Minn.	46·52 N	96·18 W
110	Haworth (hā'wûrth)	Eng.	53·50 N	1·57 W
144	Hawtah	Sau. Ar.	15·58 N	48·26 E
74	Hawthorne (hô'thôrn)	Calif. (Los Angeles In.)	33·55 N	118·22 W
68	Hawthorne	Nev.	38·33 N	118·39 W
72	Haxtun (hăks'tŭn)	Colo.	40·39 N	102·38 W
158	Hay (R.) (hā)	Austl.	123·00 S	136·45 E
86	Hay (R.)	Can.	60·21 N	117·14 W
153	Hayama (hä-yä'mä)	Jap. (Tōkyō In.)	35·16 N	139·35 E
153	Hayashi (hä-yä'shē)	Jap. (Tōkyō In.)	35·13 N	139·38 E
69	Hayden (hā'dĕn)	Ariz.	33·00 N	110·50 W
64	Hayes, Mt. (hāz)	Alaska	63·32 N	146·40 W
86	Hayes (R.)	Can.	55·30 N	94·00 W
77	Haynesville (hānz'vĭl)	La.	32·55 N	93·08 W
127	Hayrabolu	Tur.	41·14 N	27·05 E
86	Hay River	Can.	60·50 N	115·53 W
72	Hays (hāz)	Kans.	38·51 N	99·20 W
65	Haystack Mtn. (hā-stăk')	Wash. (Seattle In.)	48·26 N	122·07 W
65	Hayward (hā'wērd)	Calif. (San Francisco In.)	37·40 N	122·06 W
71	Hayward	Wis.	46·01 N	91·31 W
78	Hazard (hăz'ȧrd)	Ky.	37·13 N	83·10 W
79	Hazelhurst (hā'z'l-hûrst)	Ga.	31·50 N	82·36 W
78	Hazelhurst	Miss.	31·52 N	90·23 W
75	Hazel Park	Mich. (Detroit In.)	42·28 N	83·06 W
86	Hazelton (hā'z'l-tŭn)	Can.	55·18 N	127·11 W
81	Hazleton	Pa.	41·00 N	76·00 W
85	Headingley (hĕd'ĭng-lĭ)	Can. (Winnipeg In.)	49·53 N	97·25 W
78	Headland (hĕd'lănd)	Ala.	31·22 N	85·20 W
68	Healdsburg (hēldz'bûrg)	Calif.	38·37 N	122·52 W
73	Healdton (hēld'tŭn)	Okla.	34·13 N	97·28 W
110	Heanor (hēn'ŏr)	Eng.	53·01 N	1·22 W
47	Heard I. (hûrd)	Ind. O.	53·10 S	74·35 E
77	Hearne (hûrn)	Tex.	30·53 N	96·35 W
87	Hearst (hûrst)	Can.	49·36 N	83·40 W
70	Heart (R.) (härt)	N. D.	46·46 N	102·34 W
83	Hearts Content (härts kŏn'tĕnt)	Can.	47·55 N	53·20 W
83	Heath Pt. (hēth)	Can.	49·06 N	61·45 W
73	Heavener (hēv'nēr)	Okla.	34·52 N	94·36 W
76	Hebbronville (hē'brŭn-vĭl)	Tex.	27·18 N	98·40 W
69	Heber (hē'bēr)	Utah	40·30 N	111·25 W
73	Heber Springs	Ark.	35·28 N	91·59 W
67	Hebgen Res. (hĕb'gĕn)	Mont.	44·47 N	111·38 W
116	Hebrides, Sea of	Scot.	56·63 N	6·41 W
87	Hebron (hē'brŭn)	Can.	58·11 N	62·56 W
75	Hebron	Ind. (Chicago In.)	41·19 N	87·13 W
75	Hebron	Ky. (Cincinnati In.)	39·04 N	84·43 W
73	Hebron	Nebr.	40·11 N	97·36 W
70	Hebron	N. D.	46·54 N	102·04 W
	Hebron, see Al Khalil			
118	Heby (hĭ'bü)	Swe.	59·56 N	16·48 E
86	Hecate Str. (hĕk'ȧ-tē)	Can.	53·34 N	130·53 W
91	Hecelchakán (ā-sĕl-chä-kän')	Mex.	20·10 N	90·09 W
118	Hedemora (hĭ-dĕ-mō'rä)	Swe.	60·16 N	15·55 E
118	Hedesunda Fd. (hi-de-sŏŏn'dä)	Swe.	60·22 N	16·50 E
110	Hedon (hĕd'ŭn)	Eng.	53·44 N	0·12 W
152	Hedo Saki (C.) (hā'dō sä'kē)	Jap.	26·48 N	128·40 E
111	Heemstede	Neth. (Amsterdam In.)	52·20 N	4·36 E
117	Heerlen	Bel.	50·55 N	5·58 E
78	Heflin (hĕf'lĭn)	Ala.	33·40 N	85·33 W
120	Heide (hī'dē)	Ger.	54·13 N	9·06 E
161	Heidelberg (hī'dĕl-bûrg)	Austl. (Melbourne In.)	37·45 S	145·04 E
120	Heidelberg (hīdĕl-bĕrgh)	Ger.	49·24 N	8·43 E
120	Heidenheim (hī'dĕn-hīm)	Ger.	48·41 N	10·09 E
168	Heilbron (hĭl'brōn)	S. Afr. (Johannesburg & Pretoria In.)	27·17 S	27·58 E
120	Heilbronn (hīl'brōn)	Ger.	49·09 N	9·16 E
123	Heiligenhaus (hī'lē-gĕn-houz)	Ger. (Ruhr In.)	51·19 N	6·58 E
120	Heiligenstadt (hī'lē-gĕn-shtät)	Ger.	51·21 N	10·10 E
147	Heilungkiang (Prov.) (hā-lōōng' kyăng')	China	46·36 N	128·07 E
119	Heinola (hā-nō'lā)	Fin.	61·13 N	26·03 E
123	Heinsberg (hīnz'bĕrgh)	Ger. (Ruhr In.)	51·04 N	6·07 E
139	Heisi (R.)	U. A. R. (Palestine In.)	29·21 N	34·30 E
111	Heist-op-den-Berg	Bel. (Bruxelles In.)	51·05 N	4·14 E
112	Hekla (Vol.) (hĕk'lȧ)	Ice.	63·53 N	19·37 W
121	Hel (hāl)	Pol.	54·37 N	18·53 E
118	Helagsfjället	Swe.	62·54 N	12·24 E
73	Helena (hē-lē'nȧ)	Ark.	34·33 N	90·35 W
67	Helena (hĕ-lĕ'nȧ)	Mont.	46·35 N	112·01 W
161	Helensburgh (hĕl'ĕnz-bŭr-ō)	Austl. (Sydney In.)	34·11 S	150·59 E
116	Helensburgh	Scot.	56·01 N	4·53 W
118	Helge (R.) (hĕl'gĕ)	Swe.	56·31 N	13·47 E
120	Helgoland I. (hĕl'gō-länd)	Ger.	54·13 N	7·30 E
79	Hellier (hĕl'yēr)	Ky.	37·16 N	82·27 W
124	Hellín (ĕl-yĕn')	Sp.	38·30 N	1·40 W
144	Helmand (R.) (hĕl'mŭnd)	Afg.	31·00 N	63·48 E
117	Helmond (hĕl'mŏnt) (ĕl'môɴ')	Neth.	51·35 N	5·04 E
120	Helmstedt (hĕlm'shtĕt)	Ger.	52·14 N	11·03 E
74	Helotes (hē'-lōts)	Tex. (San Antonio In.)	29·35 N	98·41 W
69	Helper (hĕlp'ēr)	Utah	39·40 N	110·55 W
	Helsingfors, see Helsinki			
118	Helsingör (hĕl-sĭng-ûr')	Den.	56·03 N	12·33 E
119	Helsinki (Helsingfors) (hĕl'sĕn-kē) (hĕl'sĭng-fôrs')	Fin.	60·10 N	24·53 E
167	Helvellyn (Mts.) (hĕl-vĕl-lĭn)	S. Afr. (Natal In.)	30·32 S	27·18 E
110	Hemel Hempstead (hĕm'ĕl hĕmp'stĕd)	Eng. (London In.)	51·43 N	0·29 W
74	Hemet (hĕm'ĕt)	Calif. (Los Angeles In.)	33·45 N	116·57 W
70	Hemingford (hĕm'ĭng-fērd)	Nebr.	42·21 N	103·30 W
77	Hemphill (hĕmp'hĭl)	Tex.	31·20 N	93·48 W
84	Hempstead (hĕmp'stĕd)	N. Y. (New York In.)	40·42 N	73·37 W
77	Hempstead	Tex.	30·07 N	96·05 W
118	Hemse (hĕm'sē)	Swe.	57·15 N	18·25 E
118	Hemsö (I.)	Swe.	62·43 N	18·22 E
118	Hen (hĭn)	Nor.	60·14 N	10·10 E
124	Henares (R.) (å-nä'rås)	Sp.	40·50 N	2·55 W
122	Hendaye (äɴ-dā')	Fr.	43·20 N	1·46 W
80	Henderson (hĕn'dēr-sŭn)	Ky.	37·50 N	87·30 W
68	Henderson	Nev.	36·09 N	115·04 W
79	Henderson	N. C.	36·18 N	78·24 W
78	Henderson	Tenn.	35·25 N	88·40 W
77	Henderson	Tex.	32·09 N	94·48 W
79	Hendersonville (hĕn'dēr-sŭn-vĭl)	N. C.	35·17 N	82·28 W
110	Hendon (hĕn'dŭn)	Eng. (London In.)	51·34 N	0·13 W
168	Hendrina (hĕn-drē'nȧ)	S. Afr. (Johannesburg & Pretoria In.)	26·10 S	29·44 E
151	Hengch'un (hĕng'chŭn')	China	22·00 N	120·42 E
117	Hengelo (hĕng'ĕ-lō)	Neth.	52·20 N	6·45 E
151	Henghsien	China	22·40 N	104·20 E
151	Hengshan (hĕng'shän')	China	27·20 N	112·40 E
148	Hengshui (hĕng'shōō-ē')	China	37·43 N	115·42 E
151	Hengyang	China	26·58 N	112·30 E
110	Henley on Thames (hĕn'lē ŏn tĕmz)	Eng. (London In.)	51·31 N	0·54 W
81	Henlopen, C. (hĕn-lō'pĕn)	Del.	38·45 N	75·05 W
122	Hennebont (ĕn-bôɴ')	Fr.	47·47 N	3·16 W
168	Hennenman	S. Afr. (Johannesburg & Pretoria In.)	27·59 S	27·03 E
72	Hennessey (hĕn'ĕ-sĭ)	Okla.	36·04 N	97·53 W
111	Hennigsdorf (hĕ'nĕngz-dōrf)	Ger. (Berlin In.)	52·39 N	13·12 E
167	Hennops (R.) (hĕn'ŏps)	S. Afr. (Johannesburg & Pretoria In.)	25·51 S	27·57 E
167	Hennopsrivier	S. Afr. (Johannesburg & Pretoria In.)	25·50 S	27·59 E
73	Henrietta (hĕn-rĭ-ĕt'ȧ)	Okla.	35·25 N	95·58 W
72	Henrietta (hen-rĭ-ĕ'tȧ)	Tex.	33·47 N	98·11 W
87	Henrietta Maria, C. (hĕn-rĭ-ĕt'ȧ)	Can.	55·10 N	82·20 W
69	Henry Mts. (hĕn'rĭ)	Utah	38·55 N	110·45 W
150	Henteyn Nuruu (Mts.)	Sov. Un.	49·40 N	111·00 E
66	Heppner (hĕp'nēr)	Ore.	45·21 N	119·33 W
144	Herāt (hĕ-rät')	Afg.	34·28 N	62·13 E
127	Hercegovina (Reg.) (hĕr-tsĕ-gô'vē-nȧ)	Yugo.	43·23 N	17·52 E
167	Hercules (hĕr'ku-lēs)	S. Afr. (Johannesburg & Pretoria In.)	25·43 S	28·10 E
123	Herdecke (hĕr'dĕ-kĕ)	Ger. (Ruhr In.)	51·24 N	7·26 E
93	Heredia (ā-rā'dhē-ä)	C. R.	10·04 N	84·06 W
116	Hereford (hĕrĕ'fērd)	Eng.	52·05 N	2·44 W
110	Hereford (Co.)	Eng.	52·22 N	2·52 W
72	Hereford (hĕr'ē-fērd)	Tex.	34·47 N	102·25 W
139	Hereidin (R.)	U. A. R. (Palestine In.)	31·02 N	34·03 E
124	Herencia (å-rān'thē-ä)	Sp.	39·23 N	3·22 W
111	Herentals	Bel. (Bruxelles In.)	51·10 N	4·51 E
120	Herford (hĕr'fôrt)	Ger.	52·06 N	8·42 E
73	Herington (hĕr'ĭng-tŭn)	Kans.	38·41 N	96·57 W
120	Herisau (hā'rē-zou)	Switz.	47·23 N	9·18 E
111	Herk-de-Stad	Bel. (Bruxelles In.)	50·56 N	5·13 E
81	Herkimer (hûr'kĭ-mēr)	N. Y.	43·05 N	75·00 W
116	Herma Ness (Prom.) (hûr'mȧ nĕs)	Scot.	60·50 N	1·10 W
73	Hermann (hûr'măn)	Mo.	38·41 N	91·27 W
80	Hermansville (hûr'măns-vĭl)	Mich.	45·40 N	87·35 W
74	Hermantown (hēr'măn-toun)	Minn. (Duluth In.)	46·46 N	92·12 W
168	Hermanusdorings	S. Afr. (Johannesburg & Pretoria In.)	24·08 S	27·46 E
75	Herminie (hûr-mī'nē)	Pa. (Pittsburgh In.)	40·16 N	79·45 W
83	Hermitage B. (hûr'mĭ-tĕj)	Can.	47·31 N	56·30 W
155	Hermit Is. (hûr'mĭt)	N. Gui. Ter.	1·48 S	144·55 E
74	Hermosa Beach (hēr-mō'sȧ)	Calif. (Los Angeles In.)	33·51 N	118·24 W
88	Hermosill	Mex.	29·00 N	110·57 W
123	Herne (hĕr'nē)	Ger. (Ruhr In.)	51·32 N	7·13 E
118	Herning (hĕr'nĭng)	Den.	56·08 N	8·55 E
70	Heron (L.) (hĕr'ŭn)	Minn.	43·42 N	95·23 W
87	Heron Bay	Can.	48·32 N	86·20 W
70	Heron Lake	Minn.	43·48 N	95·20 W
92	Herrero, Punta (pt.) (pōō'n-tä-ĕr-rĕ'rô)	Mex. (Yucatan In.)	19·18 N	87·24 W
80	Herrin (hĕr'ĭn)	Ill.	37·50 N	89·00 W
167	Herschel (hēr'-shĕl)	S. Afr. (Natal In.)	30·37 S	27·12 E
75	Herscher (hēr'shēr)	Ill. (Chicago In.)	41·03 N	88·06 W
117	Herstal (hĕr'stäl)	Bel.	50·42 N	5·32 E
110	Hertford (hûrt'fērd)	Eng.	51·46 N	0·05 W
79	Hertford	N. C.	36·10 N	76·30 W
111	Hertzberg (hĕrtz'bĕrgh)	Ger. (Berlin In.)	52·54 N	12·58 E
167	Hertzog (hērt'zŏg)	S. Afr. (Natal In.)	32·36 S	26·46 E
139	Herzlia	Isr. (Palestine In.)	32·10 N	34·49 E
122	Hesdin (ē-dăɴ')	Fr.	50·24 N	1·59 E
120	Hessen (State) (hĕs'ĕn)	Ger.	50·16 N	8·48 E
68	Hetch Hetchy Aqueduct (hĕtch hĕt'-chĭ ăk'wē-dŭkt)	Calif.	37·27 N	120·54 W
70	Hettinger (hĕt'ĭn-jēr)	N. D.	45·58 N	102·36 W
168	Heuningspruit	S. Afr. (Johannesburg & Pretoria In.)	27·28 S	27·26 E
168	Heystekrand	S. Afr. (Johannesburg & Pretoria In.)	25·16 S	27·14 E
110	Heywood (hā'wŏŏd)	Eng.	53·36 N	2·12 W
79	Hialeah (hī-ȧ-lē'-ăh)	Fla. (In.)	25·49 N	80·18 W
73	Hiawatha (hī-ȧ-wô'thȧ)	Kans.	39·50 N	95·33 W
69	Hiawatha	Utah	39·25 N	111·05 W
71	Hibbing (hĭb'ĭng)	Minn.	47·26 N	92·58 W
78	Hickman (hĭk'măn)	Ky.	34·33 N	89·10 W
74	Hickman Mills	Mo. (Kansas City In.)	38·56 N	94·32 W
79	Hickory (hĭk'ō-rĭ)	N. C.	35·43 N	81·21 W
84	Hicksville (hĭks'vĭl)	N. Y. (New York In.)	40·47 N	73·25 W
80	Hicksville	Ohio	41·15 N	84·45 W
76	Hico (hī'kō)	Tex.	32·00 N	98·02 W
90	Hidalgo (ē-dhäl'gō)	Mex.	24·14 N	99·25 W
76	Hidalgo	Mex.	27·49 N	99·53 W
88	Hidalgo (State)	Mex.	20·45 N	99·30 W
76	Hidalgo del Parral (ē-dä'l-gō-dĕl-păr-rä'l)	Mex.	26·55 N	105·40 W
91	Hidalgo Yalalag (ē-dhäl'gō-yä-lä-läg)	Mex.	17·12 N	96·11 W
168	Hiedelberg	S. Afr. (Johannesburg & Pretoria In.)	26·32 S	28·22 E
164	Hierro I. (yĕ'r-rō)	Can. Is.	27·37 N	18·29 W
80	Higgins (L.) (hĭg'ĭnz)	Mich.	44·20 N	84·45 W
73	Higginsville (hĭg'ĭnz-vĭl)	Mo.	39·05 N	93·44 W
80	High (I.)	Mich.	45·45 N	85·45 W
85	High Bluff	Can. (Winnipeg In.)	50·01 N	98·08 W
94	Highborne Cay (hibôrn kē)	Ba. Is.	24·45 N	76·50 W
74	Highgrove (hī'grōv)	Calif. (Los Angeles In.)	34·01 N	117·20 W
77	High Island	Tex. (In.)	29·34 N	94·24 W
74	Highland (hī'lănd)	Calif. (Los Angeles In.)	34·08 N	117·13 W
73	Highland	Ill.	38·44 N	89·41 W
75	Highland	Ind. (Chicago In.)	41·33 N	87·28 W
75	Highland	Mich. (Detroit In.)	42·38 N	83·37 W
65	Highland	Wash. (Portland In.)	45·55 N	122·37 W
75	Highland Park	Ill. (Chicago In.)	42·11 N	87·47 W
75	Highland Park	Mich. (Detroit In.)	42·24 N	83·06 W
84	Highland Park	N. J. (New York In.)	40·30 N	74·25 W

ăt; finăl; rāte; senâte; ärm; ȧsk; sofȧ; fâre; ch-choose; dh-as th in other; bē; ēvent; bĕt; recĕnt; cratēr; g-go; gh-guttural g; bĭt; ĭ-short neutral; rīde; ĸ-guttural k as ch in German ich;

PRONOUNCING INDEX Highland Park–Horten 215

Page	Name Pronunciation Region	Lat. °′	Long. °′
74	Highland Park Tex. (Dallas, Fort Worth In.)	32·49 N	96·48 W
84	Highlands (hī-lǎndz) N. J. (New York In.)	40·24 N	73·59 W
77	Highlands Tex. (In.)	29·49 N	95·01 W
70	Highmore (hī′-mōr) S. D.	44·30 N	99·26 W
110	High Ongar (on′gẽr) Eng. (London In.)	51·43 N	0·15 E
155	High Pk. Phil. (Manila In.)	15·38 N	120·05 E
79	High Point N. C.	35·55 N	80·00 W
86	High Prairie Can.	55·30 N	116·47 W
74	High Ridge Mo. (St. Louis In.)	38·27 N	90·32 W
86	High River Can.	50·40 N	113·47 W
79	Highrock (R.) (hī′-rŏk) N. C.	35·40 N	80·15 W
79	High Springs Fla.	29·48 N	82·38 W
121	High Tatra Mts. (tä′trȧ) Czech.-Pol.	49·15 N	19·40 E
84	Hightstown (hīts-toun) N. J. (New York In.)	40·16 N	74·32 W
110	High Wycombe (wĭ-kŭm) Eng. (London In.)	51·36 N	0·45 W
89	Higuero, Pta. (Pt.) P. R. (Puerto Rico In.)	18·21 N	67·11 W
99	Higuerote (ē-gĕ-rō′-tĕ) Ven. (In.)	10·29 N	66·06 W
95	Higüey (ê-gwĕ′y) Dom. Rep.	18·40 N	68·45 W
119	Hiiumaa (D′Ago) (hē′ŏŏm-ô) Sov. Un.	58·47 N	22·05 E
153	Hikone (hē′kô-nĕ) Jap.	35·15 N	136·15 E
120	Hildburghausen (hĭld′bŏŏrg hou-zĕn) Ger.	50·26 N	10·45 E
123	Hilden (hēl′dĕn) Ger. (Ruhr In.)	51·10 N	6·56 E
120	Hildesheim (hĭl′dĕs-hīm) Ger.	52·08 N	9·56 E
93	Hillaby, Mt. (hĭl′ȧ-bĭ) W. I. F. (Le. & Wind. Is. In.)	13·15 N	59·35 W
72	Hill City (hĭl) Kans.	39·22 N	99·54 W
71	Hill City Minn.	46·58 N	93·38 W
111	Hillegersberg Neth. (Amsterdam In.)	51·57 N	4·29 E
118	Hilleröd (hê′lĕ-rûdh) Den.	55·56 N	12·17 E
73	Hillsboro (hĭlz′bŭr-ō) Ill.	39·09 N	89·28 W
73	Hillsboro Kans.	38·22 N	97·11 W
81	Hillsboro N. H.	43·05 N	71·55 W
70	Hillsboro N. D.	47·23 N	97·05 W
80	Hillsboro Ohio	39·10 N	83·40 W
65	Hillsboro Ore. (Portland In.)	45·31 N	122·59 W
77	Hillsboro Tex.	32·01 N	97·06 W
71	Hillsboro Wis.	43·39 N	90·20 W
85	Hillsburgh (hĭlz′bûrg) Can. (Toronto In.)	43·48 N	80·09 W
80	Hillsdale (hĭls-dāl) Mich.	41·55 N	84·35 W
157	Hilo (hē′lō) Hawaii (In.)	19·44 N	155·01 W
111	Hilversum (hĭl′vẽr-sŭm) Neth. (Amsterdam In.)	52·13 N	5·10 E
142	Himachal Pradesh (Ter.) India	36·03 N	77·41 E
145	Himalaya Mts. (hĭ-mä′lȧ-yȧ) Asia	29·30 N	85·02 E
153	Himeji (hē′mȧ-jĕ) Jap.	34·50 N	134·42 E
111	Himmelpforten (hē′mĕl-pfōr-tĕn) Ger. (Hamburg In.)	53·37 N	9·19 E
95	Hinche (hēn′chȧ) (ănsh) Hai.	19·10 N	72·05 W
159	Hinchinbrook (I.) (hĭn-chĭn-brŏŏk) Austl.	18·23 S	146·57 W
110	Hinckley (hĭnk′lĭ) Eng.	52·32 N	1·21 W
110	Hindley (hĭnd′lĭ) Eng.	53·32 N	2·35 W
145	Hindu Kush Mts. (hĭn′dōō kōōsh′) Asia	35·15 N	68·44 E
143	Hindupur (hĭn′dōō-pōōr) India	13·52 N	77·34 E
86	Hines Creek (hīnz) Can.	56·15 N	118·33 W
83	Hingham (hĭng′ăm) Mass. (Boston In.)	42·14 N	70·53 W
75	Hinkley (hĭnk′-lĭ) Ohio (Cleveland In.)	41·14 N	81·45 W
124	Hinojosa (ē-nô-kô′sȧ) Sp.	38·30 N	5·09 W
75	Hinsdale (hĭnz′dāl) Ill. (Chicago In.)	41·48 N	87·56 W
80	Hinton (hĭn′tŭn) W. Va.	37·40 N	80·55 W
153	Hirado (I.) (hē′rä-dō) Jap.	33·19 N	129·18 E
153	Hirakata (hē′rä-kä′tä) Jap. (Ōsaka In.)	34·49 N	135·40 E
153	Hiraoka (hē′rä-ō′kȧ) Jap. (Ōsaka In.)	34·40 N	135·39 E
153	Hiratsuka (hē-rät-sōō′kȧ) Jap.	35·20 N	139·19 E
146	Hirgis Nuur (L.) Mong.	49·18 N	94·21 E
152	Hirosaki (hē′rô-sä′kê) Jap.	40·31 N	140·38 E
153	Hirose (hē′rô-sä) Jap.	35·20 N	133·11 E
153	Hiroshima (hē-rô-shē′mȧ) Jap.	34·22 N	132·25 E
122	Hirson (ēr-sôɴ′) Fr.	49·54 N	4·00 E
89	Hispaniola (I.) (hĭ′spăn-ĭ-ō-lȧ) N. A.	17·30 N	73·15 W
142	Hissar India	29·15 N	75·47 E
144	Hit (hĭt) Iraq	33·32 N	42·35 E
152	Hitachi (hē-tä′chē) Jap.	36·42 N	140·47 E
77	Hitchcock (hĭch′kŏk) Tex. (In.)	29·21 N	95·01 W
123	Hitdorf (hēt′dōrf) Ger. (Ruhr In.)	51·04 N	6·56 E
153	Hitoyoshi (hē′tô-yō′shê) Jap.	32·13 N	130·45 E
112	Hitra (I.) (hĭträ) Nor.	63·34 N	7·37 E
111	Hittefeld (hē′tĕ-fĕld) Ger. (Hamburg In.)	53·23 N	9·59 E
153	Hiwasa (hē′wȧ-sä) Jap.	33·44 N	134·31 E
78	Hiwassee (R.) (hī-wôs′sē) Tenn.	35·10 N	84·35 W
118	Hjälmaren (L.) Swe.	59·07 N	16·05 E
118	Hjo (yō) Swe.	58·19 N	14·11 E
118	Hjöring (jûr′ĭng) Den.	57·27 N	9·59 E
121	Hlohovec (hlō′hô-vĕts) Czech.	48·24 N	17·49 E
160	Hobart (hō′bȧrt) Austl.	43·00 S	147·30 E
75	Hobart Ind. (Chicago In.)	41·31 N	87·15 W
72	Hobart Okla.	35·02 N	99·06 W
65	Hobart Wash. (Seattle In.)	47·25 N	121·58 W
72	Hobbs (hŏbs) N. Mex.	32·41 N	104·04 W
146	Hobdo Gol (R.) Mong.	49·06 N	91·16 E
111	Hoboken (hō′bō-kĕn) Bel. (Bruxelles In.)	51·11 N	4·20 E
84	Hoboken N. J. (New York In.)	40·43 N	74·03 W
118	Hobro (hô-brô′) Den.	56·38 N	9·47 E
84	Hobson (hŏb′-sŭn) Va. (Norfolk In.)	36·54 N	76·31 W
161	Hobson's B. (hŏb′sŭnz) Austl. (Melbourne In.)	37·54 S	144·45 E
148	Hochien (hŭ′jĭän) China	38·28 N	116·05 E
148	Hochiu China	32·19 N	116·17 E
120	Höchst (hûĸst) Ger.	50·06 N	8·37 E
151	Hoch'uan China	30·00 N	106·20 E
65	Hockinson (hŏk′-ĭn-sŭn) Wash. (Portland In.)	45·44 N	122·29 W
92	Hoctún (ôk-tōō′n) Mex. (Yucatan In.)	20·52 N	89·10 W
80	Hodgenville (hŏj′ĕn-vĭl) Ky.	37·35 N	85·45 W
83	Hodges Hill (hŏj′ĕz) Can.	49·03 N	55·54 W
86	Hodgson (hŏj-sŭn) Can.	51·16 N	97·40 W
121	Hódmezövásárhely (hōd′mĕ-zû-vô′shôr-hĕl-y′) Hung.	46·24 N	20·21 E
121	Hodonin (hē′dô-nén) Czech.	48·50 N	17·06 E
111	Hoegaarden Bel. (Bruxelles In.)	50·46 N	4·55 E
111	Hoek van Holland Neth. (Amsterdam In.)	51·59 N	4·05 E
152	Hoeryŏng (hwĕr′yŭng) Kor.	42·28 N	129·39 E
123	Hoetmar (hût′mär) Ger. (Ruhr In.)	51·52 N	7·54 E
120	Hof (hōf) Ger.	50·19 N	11·55 E
148	Hofei (hô′fā) China	31·51 N	117·15 E
112	Hofsjökull (Gl.) (hôfs′yü′kŏŏl) Ice.	64·55 N	18·40 W
	Hofuf, see Al Hufūf		
94	Hog (I.) (hŏg) Ba. Is.	25·05 N	77·20 W
80	Hog (I.) Mich.	45·50 N	85·20 W
78	Hogansville (hō′gănz-vĭl) Ga.	33·10 N	84·54 W
95	Hog Cay (I.) Ba. Is.	23·35 N	75·30 W
95	Hogsty Rf. Ba. Is.	21·45 N	73·50 W
111	Hohenbrunn (hō′hĕn-brōōn) Ger. (München In.)	48·03 N	11·42 E
123	Hohenlimburg (hō′hĕn lĕm′bŏŏrg) Ger. (Ruhr In.)	51·20 N	7·35 E
111	Hohen Neuendorf (hō′hĕn noi′ĕn-dōrf) Ger. (Berlin In.)	52·40 N	13·22 E
120	Hohe Tauern (Mts.) (hō′ĕ tou′ĕrn) Aus.	47·11 N	12·12 E
84	Hohokus (hō-hō-kŭs) N. J. (New York In.)	41·01 N	74·08 W
151	Hohsien China	24·20 N	24·20 E
148	Hohsien (hō′syĕn′) China	31·44 N	118·20 E
148	Ho Hu (L.) (hŭ′hoo) China	31·37 N	119·57 E
72	Hoisington (hoi′zĭng-tŭn) Kans.	38·30 N	98·46 W
153	Hojo (hō′jô) Jap.	33·58 N	132·50 E
159	Hokitika (hō-kĭ-tē′kä) N. Z. (In.)	42·43 S	171·12 E
152	Hokkaido (I.) (hôk′kĭ-dō) Jap.	43·30 N	142·45 E
151	Hokou (hō′kō′) China	29·58 N	116·20 E
118	Holbaek (hôl′bĕk) Den.	55·42 N	11·40 E
92	Holbox (ôl-bŏ′x) Mex. (Yucatan In.)	21·33 N	87·19 W
92	Holbox, Isla (I.) (ē′s-lä-ôl-bŏ′x) Mex. (Yucatan In.)	21·40 N	87 21 W
69	Holbrook (hōl′brŏŏk) Ariz.	34·55 N	110·15 W
83	Holbrook Mass. (Boston In.)	42·10 N	71·01 W
83	Holden (hōl′dĕn) Mass. (Boston In.)	42·21 N	71·51 W
73	Holden Mo.	38·42 N	94·00 W
80	Holden W. Va.	37·45 N	82·05 W
73	Holdenville (hōl′dĕn-vĭl) Okla.	35·05 N	96·25 W
72	Holdrege (hōl′drĕj) Nebr.	40·25 N	99·28 W
118	Hölen (hûl′ĕn) Nor.	59·34 N	10·40 E
95	Holguín (ôl-gēn′) Cuba	20·55 N	76·15 W
81	Holidaysburg (hŏl′ĭ-dāz-bûrg) Pa.	40·30 N	78·30 W
120	Hollabrunn Aus.	48·33 N	16·04 E
80	Holland (hŏl′ănd) Mich.	42·45 N	86·10 W
155	Hollandia (hō-län′dĭ-ä) Neth. N. Gui.	2·30 S	140·45 E
111	Hollandsch Diep (Chan.) Neth. (Amsterdam In.)	51·43 N	4·25 E
111	Hollenstedt (hō′lĕn-shtĕt) Ger. (Hamburg In.)	53·22 N	9·43 E
74	Holliday (hŏl′ĭ-dā) Mo. (Kansas City In.)	39·02 N	94·48 W
83	Hollis (hŏl′ĭs) N. H. (Boston In.)	42·30 N	71·29 W
72	Hollis Okla.	34·39 N	99·56 W
68	Hollister (hŏl′ĭs-tẽr) Calif.	36·50 N	121·25 W
83	Holliston (hŏl′ĭs-tŭn) Mass. (Boston In.)	42·12 N	71·25 W
80	Holly (hŏl′ĭ) Mich.	42·45 N	83·30 W
65	Holly Wash. (Seattle In.)	47·34 N	122·58 W
78	Holly Springs (hŏl′ĭ sprĭngz) Miss.	34·45 N	89·28 W
74	Hollywood (hŏl′ê-wŏŏd) Calif. (Los Angeles In.)	34·06 N	118·20 W
79	Hollywood Fla. (In.)	26·00 N	80·11 W
74	Holmes Park Mo. (Kansas City In.)	38·57 N	94·33 W
159	Holmes Rfs. (hōmz) Austl.	16·33 S	148·43 E
118	Holmestrand (hôl′mĕ-strän) Nor.	59·29 N	10·17 E
118	Holmsbu (hôlms′bōō) Nor.	59·36 N	10·26 E
118	Holmsjön (L.) Swe.	62·23 N	15·43 E
118	Holstebro (hôl′stĕ-brō′) Den.	56·22 N	8·39 E
78	Holston (R.) (hōl′stŭn) Tenn.	36·02 N	83·42 W
110	Holt (hōlt) Eng.	53·05 N	2·53 W
73	Holton (hōl′tŭn) Kans.	39·27 N	95·43 W
116	Holy (I.) (hō′lĭ) Wales	53·45 N	4·45 W
116	Holy (I.) Eng.	55·43 N	1·48 W
64	Holy Cross (hō′lĭ krôs) Alaska	62·10 N	159·40 W
116	Holyhead (hŏl′ê-hĕd) Wales	53·48 N	4·45 W
72	Holyoke (hōl′yōk) Colo.	40·36 N	102·18 W
81	Holyoke Mass.	42·10 N	72·40 W
153	Homano (hō-mä′nō) Jap. (Tōkyō In.)	35·33 N	140·08 E
123	Homberg (hōm′bĕrgh) Ger. (Ruhr In.)	51·27 N	6·42 E
74	Home Gardens (hōm gär′d′nz) Calif. (Los Angeles In.)	33·53 N	117·32 W
74	Homeland (hōm′lănd) Calif. (Los Angeles In.)	33·44 N	117·07 W
84	Homeplace (hōm-plās) La. (New Orleans In.)	29·27 N	89·40 W
64	Homer (hō′mẽr) Alaska	59·42 N	151·30 W
77	Homer La.	32·46 N	93·05 W
79	Homestead (hōm′stĕd) Fla. (In.)	25·27 N	80·28 W
74	Homestead Mich. (Sault Ste. Marie In.)	46·20 N	84·07 W
75	Homestead Pa. (Pittsburgh In.)	40·29 N	79·55 W
73	Homestead Natl. Mon. of America Nebr.	40·16 N	96·51 W
84	Homewood (hōm′wŏŏd) Ala. (Birmingham In.)	33·28 N	86·48 W
75	Homewood Ill. (Chicago In.)	41·34 N	87·40 W
73	Hominy (hŏm′ĭ-nĭ) Okla.	36·25 N	96·24 W
78	Homochiho (R.) (hō-mō-chĭt′ō) Miss.	31·23 N	91·15 W
115	Homs (hōms) Syr.	34·42 N	36·52 E
147	Honan (Prov.) (hō′nän′) China	33·58 N	112·33 E
98	Honda (hōn′dȧ) Col. (In.)	5·13 N	74·45 W
94	Honda, Bahía (B.) (bä-ē′ä-ô′n-dä) Cuba	23·10 N	83·20 W
76	Hondo Tex.	29·20 N	99·08 W
92	Hondo, Rio (R.) (hon-dō′) Br. Hond. (Yucatan In.)	18·16 N	88·32 W
72	Hondo (R.) N. Mex.	33·22 N	105·06 W
88	Honduras (hŏn-dōō′rȧs) N. A.	14·30 N	88·00 W
88	Honduras, Gulf of N. A.	16·30 N	87·30 W
79	Honea Path (hŭn′ĭ păth) S. C.	34·25 N	82·16 W
118	Hønefoss (hē′nē-fôs) Nor.	60·10 N	10·15 E
81	Honesdale (hōnz′dāl) Pa.	41·30 N	75·15 W
68	Honey (R.) (hŭn′ĭ) Calif.	40·11 N	120·34 W
73	Honey Grove (hŭn′ĭ grōv) Tex.	33·35 N	95·54 W
85	Honfleur (ôɴ-flûr′) Can. (Quebec In.)	46·39 N	70·53 W
122	Honfleur (ôɴ-flûr′) Fr.	49·26 N	0·13 E
151	Hon Gay Viet.	20·58 N	107·10 E
116	Honiton (hŏn′ĭ-tŏn) Eng.	50·49 N	3·10 W
151	Hong Kong (I.) (hŏng′ kŏng′) Asia	22·15 N	114·40 E
157	Honolulu (hŏn-ô-lōō′lōō) Hawaii (In.)	21·18 N	157·50 W
157	Honomu (hŏn′ô-mōō) Hawaii (In.)	19·50 N	155·04 W
152	Honshū (I.) (hŏn′shōō) Jap.	36·50 N	135·20 E
66	Hood, Mt. Ore.	45·20 N	121·43 W
65	Hood Can. (hŏŏd) Wash. (Seattle In.)	47·45 N	122·45 W
66	Hood River Ore.	45·42 N	121·30 W
65	Hoodsport (hŏŏdz′pōrt) Wash. (Seattle In.)	47·25 N	123·09 W
142	Hoogly (R.) (hōōg′lĭ) India	21·30 N	87·28 E
111	Hoogstraten Bel. (Bruxelles In.)	51·24 N	4·46 E
157	Hookena (hŏŏk-ĕ-nȧ) Hawaii (In.)	19·23 N	155·51 W
72	Hooker (hŏŏk′ẽr) Okla.	36·49 N	101·13 W
92	Hool (ōō′l) Mex. (Yucatan In.)	19·32 N	90·22 W
64	Hoonah (hōō′nä) Alaska	58·05 N	135·25 W
66	Hoopa Valley Ind. Res. (hōō′pȧ) Calif.	41·18 N	123·35 W
73	Hooper (hŏŏp′ẽr) Nebr.	41·37 N	96·31 W
74	Hooper Utah (Salt Lake City In.)	41·10 N	112·08 W
64	Hooper Bay Alaska	61·32 N	166·02 W
80	Hoopeston (hōōps′tŭn) Ill.	40·35 N	87·40 W
81	Hoosick Falls (hōō′sĭk) N. Y.	42·55 N	73·15 W
68	Hoover Dam (hōō′vẽr) Nev.	36·00 N	115·06 W
84	Hopatcong, L. (hō-păt′kong) N. J. (New York In.)	40·57 N	74·38 W
64	Hope (hōp) Alaska	60·54 N	149·48 W
73	Hope Ark.	33·41 N	93·35 W
86	Hope Can.	49·25 N	121·10 W
70	Hope N. D.	47·17 N	97·45 W
87	Hopedale (hōp′dāl) Can.	55·26 N	60·11 W
83	Hopedale (hōp′dāl) Mass. (Boston In.)	42·08 N	71·33 W
147	Hopeh (Prov.) China	39·09 N	115·22 E
92	Hopelchén (o-pĕl-chĕ′n) Mex. (Yucatan In.)	19·47 N	89·51 W
87	Hope Mts. Can.	53·58 N	62·29 W
87	Hopes Advance, C. (hōps ăd-våns′) Can.	61·00 N	69·12 W
158	Hopetoun (hōp′toun) Austl.	33·50 S	120·15 E
84	Hopewell (hōp′wĕl) N. J. (New York In.)	40·23 N	74·45 W
79	Hopewell Va.	37·14 N	77·15 W
166	Hopetown (hōp′toun) S. Afr.	29·35 S	24·10 E
69	Hopi Ind. Res. (hō′pê) Ariz.	36·20 N	110·30 W
74	Hopkins (hŏp′-kĭns) Minn. (Minneapolis, St. Paul In.)	44·55 N	93·24 W
78	Hopkinsville (hŏp′-kĭns-vĭl) Ky.	36·50 N	87·28 W
83	Hopkinton (hŏp′-kĭn-tŭn) Mass. (Boston In.)	42·14 N	71·31 W
151	Hop'u China	21·28 N	109·10 E
66	Hoquiam (hō′kwĭ-ăm) Wash.	47·00 N	123·53 W
118	Horby (hûr′bü) Swe.	55·50 N	13·41 E
93	Horconcitos (ŏr-kôn-sê′-tôs) Pan.	8·18 N	82·11 W
168	Hordio Som. (Horn of Afr. In.)	10·43 N	51·05 E
120	Horgen (hôr′gĕn) Switz.	47·16 N	8·35 E
71	Horicon (hŏr′ĭ-kŏn) Wis.	43·26 N	88·40 W
144	Hormuz, Str. of (hôr′mŭz′) Asia	26·37 N	15·27 E
	Horn, C., see Hornos, Cabo de		
159	Horn (Is.) (hôrn) Austl.	10·30 S	143·30 E
112	Hornavan (L.) Swe.	65·54 N	16·17 E
111	Horneburg (hôr′nĕ-bŏŏrgh) Ger. (Hamburg In.)	53·30 N	9·35 E
81	Hornell (hôr-nĕl′) N. Y.	42·10 N	77·40 W
86	Horn Mts. Can.	62·12 N	120·29 W
100	Hornos, C. de (Horn, C.) (kȧ′-bô-dĕ-ô′r-nôs) (kȧ′p-hôr′n) Chile	56·00 S	67·00 W
161	Hornsby (hôrnz′ bĭ) Austl. (Sydney In.)	33·43 S	151·06 E
118	Hornslandet (I.) Swe.	61·40 N	17·58 E
100	Horqueta (ŏr-kĕ′tä) Par.	23·20 S	57·00 W
72	Horse Cr. (hôrs) Colo.	38·49 N	103·48 W
70	Horse Cr. Wyo.	41·33 N	104·39 W
118	Horsens (hôrs′ĕns) Den.	55·50 N	9·49 E
65	Horseshoe B. (hôrs-shōō) Can. (Vancouver In.)	49·23 N	123·16 W
110	Horsforth (hôrs′fŭrth) Eng.	53·50 N	1·38 W
160	Horsham (hô shăm) (hôrs′ăm) Austl.	36·42 S	142·17 E
111	Horst (hôrst) Ger. (Hamburg In.)	53·49 N	9·37 E
118	Horten (hôr′tĕn) Nor.	59·26 N	10·27 E

216 Horton–Huntingdon PRONOUNCING INDEX

Page	Name Pronunciation Region	Lat. °′	Long. °′
73	Horton (hôr'tŭn) Kans.	39·38 N	95·32 W
64	Horton (R.) (hôr'tŭn) Alaska	68·38 N	122·00 W
110	Horwich (hŏr'ĭch) Eng.	53·36 N	2·33 W
151	Hoshan China	31·30 N	116·25 E
153	Hososhima (hō'sô-shē'mä) Jap.	32·25 N	131·40 E
100	Hoste (ôs'tā) (I.) Chile	55·20 S	70·45 W
90	Hostotipaquillo (ôs-tō'tĭ-pä-kēl'yō) Mex.	21·09 N	104·05 W
153	Hota (hō'tä) Jap. (Tōkyō In.)	35·08 N	139·50 E
146	Hotien (Khotan) (hō'tyĕn') (kō-tän') China	37·11 N	79·50 E
95	Hoto Mayor (ô-tô-mä-yô'r) Dom. Rep.	18·45 N	69·10 W
64	Hot Springs (hŏt sprĭngs) Alaska	65·00 N	150·20 W
73	Hot Springs Ark.	34·29 N	93·02 W
70	Hot Springs S. D.	43·28 N	103·32 W
81	Hot Springs Va.	38·00 N	79·55 W
73	Hot Springs Natl. Park Ark.	34·30 N	93·00 W
95	Hotte, Massif de la (Mts.) Hai.	18·25 N	74·00 W
68	Hotville (hŏt'-vĭl) Calif.	32·50 N	115·24 W
148	Houchen (hō'jĕn) China	36·59 N	118·59 E
123	Houdan (ōō-däN') Fr. (Paris In.)	48·47 N	1·36 E
71	Houghton (hŏ'tŭn) Mich.	47·06 N	88·36 W
80	Houghton (L.) Mich.	44·20 N	84·45 W
123	Houilles (ōō-yēs') Fr. (Paris In.)	48·55 N	2·11 E
82	Houlton (hōl'tŭn) Maine	46·07 N	67·50 W
77	Houma (hōō'mȧ) La.	29·36 N	90·43 W
81	Housatonic (R.) (hōō-sȧ-tŏn'ĭk) Conn.-Mass.	41·50 N	73·25 W
74	House Springs (hous sprĭngs) Mo. (St. Louis In.)	38·24 N	90·34 W
78	Houston (hūs'tŭn) Miss.	33·53 N	89·00 W
77	Houston Tex. (In.)	29·46 N	95·21 W
77	Houston Ship Chan. Tex. (In.)	29·38 N	94·57 W
166	Houtbaai S. Afr. (Cape Town In.)	34·03 S	18·22 E
158	Houtman Rocks (Is.) (hout'män) Austl.	28·15 S	112·45 E
116	Hove (hōv) Eng.	50·50 N	0·09 W
69	Hovenweep Natl. Mon. (hō'v'n-wēp) Colo.-Utah	37·27 N	108·50 W
73	Howard (hou'ȧrd) Kans.	37·27 N	96·10 W
70	Howard S. D.	44·01 N	97·31 W
110	Howden (hou'dĕn) Eng.	53·44 N	0·52 W
160	Howe, C. (hou) Austl.	37·30 S	150·40 E
80	Howell (hou'ĕl) Mich.	42·40 N	84·00 W
85	Howick (hou'ĭk) Can. (Montreal In.)	45·11 N	73·51 W
167	Howick S. Afr. (Natal In.)	29·29 S	30·16 E
156	Howland (I.) (hou'lănd) Oceania	1·00 N	176·00 W
142	Howrah (hou'rä) India (Calcutta In.)	22·33 N	88·20 E
73	Hoxie (hŏk'sĭ) Ark.	36·03 N	91·00 W
116	Hoy (I.) (hoi) Scot.	58·53 N	3·10 W
150	Hoyang China	35·18 N	110·18 E
110	Hoylake (hoi-lāk') Eng.	53·23 N	3·11 W
151	Hoyüan China	23·48 N	114·45 E
120	Hradec Králové (hrä'dĕts krä'lô-vä) Czech.	50·14 N	15·50 E
121	Hranice (hrän'yĕ-tsĕ) Czech.	49·33 N	17·45 E
121	Hrinová (hrĕn'yô-vä) Czech.	48·36 N	19·32 E
121	Hron R. Czech.	48·22 N	18·42 E
121	Hrubieszów (hrōō-byä'shōōf) Pol.	50·48 N	23·54 E
126	Hrvatska (Croatia) (Reg.) (hr-väts'kä) Yugo.	45·24 N	15·18 E
149	Hsaiolung China (Canton In.)	22·27 N	113·26 E
146	Hsawnhsup Bur.	24·29 N	94·45 E
148	Hsiaching (sĭä'jĭn) China	36·58 N	115·59 E
148	Hsiai (sĭä'yē) China	34·15 N	116·07 E
151	Hsiamen China	24·28 N	118·20 E
	Hsiamen, see Amoy		
	Hsian, see Sian		
148	Hsiang (hsē'äng') China	39·43 N	116·08 E
148	Hsiangch'eng (sĭäng'chĕng) China	33·11 N	114·52 E
148	Hsiangch'eng China	33·52 N	113·31 E
150	Hsiangho (hsē'äng'-hō') China (Peking In.)	39·46 N	116·59 E
147	Hsiaohsinganling Shanmo (Lesser Khingan Mts.) China	49·50 N	127·26 E
148	Hsiaoku Ho (R.) (sĭou'gōō hŭ) China	36·29 N	120·06 E
151	Hsiap'u China	27·00 N	120·00 E
148	Hsiats'un (sĭä'ts'ün) China	36·54 N	121·31 E
151	Hsich'ang China	26·50 N	102·25 E
151	Hsi Chiang (R.) China	22·00 N	109·18 E
149	Hsi Chiang (R.) China (Canton In.)	22·47 N	113·01 E
148	Hsichung Tao (I.) (sē'joong'dou) China	39·27 N	121·06 E
149	Hsients'unhsü China (Canton In.)	23·10 N	113·41 E
150	Hsienyang China	34·20 N	108·40 E
150	Hsifeng (hsē'fĕng') China	42·40 N	124·40 E
148	Hsihoying (sē'hŭ'yĭng) China	39·58 N	114·50 E
148	Hsihsienchen (sē'sĭän'jĕn) China	37·21 N	119·59 E
148	Hsi Hu (L.) (sē'hōō) China	32·31 N	116·04 E
150	Hsiliao (R.) China	43·23 N	121·40 E
149	Hsinch'ang China (Shanghai In.)	31·02 N	121·38 E
148	Hsincheng (sĭn'jeng) China	34·24 N	113·43 E
148	Hsinchiachai (sĭn'jĭä'jäĭ) China	36·59 N	117·33 E
142	Hsinchiang (Mts.) China	41·52 N	81·20 E
151	Hsinchu (hsĭn'chōō') China	24·48 N	121·00 E
151	Hsingan China	25·44 N	110·32 E
148	Hsingcheng (sĭng'chĕng) China	40·38 N	120·41 E
148	Hsingchiawan (sĭng'jĭä'wäN) China	37·16 N	114·54 E
148	Hsinghua (sĭng'hōōȧ) China	32·58 N	119·48 E
148	Hsingt'ai (sĭng'täĭ) China	37·04 N	114·33 E
148	Hsinhsiang (sĭn'sĭäng) China	35·17 N	113·49 E
148	Hsinhsien (sĭn'sĭäN) China	36·14 N	115·38 E
150	Hsinhsien China	38·20 N	112·45 E
151	Hsinhua China	27·45 N	111·20 E
151	Hsinhui China	22·40 N	113·08 E
146	Hsining China	36·32 N	101·36 E
151	Hsinkao Shan (Mtn.) China	23·38 N	121·05 E

Page	Name Pronunciation Region	Lat. °′	Long. °′
	Hsinking, see Ch'angch'un		
150	Hsinmin China	42·00 N	122·42 E
148	Hsinp'u (sĭn'pōō) China	34·35 N	119·09 E
148	Hsint'ai (sĭn'täĭ) China	35·55 N	117·44 E
149	Hsint'ang China (Canton In.)	23·06 N	113·06 E
149	Hsinti China (Canton In.)	22·43 N	113·20 E
148	Hsintien (sĭn'dĭäN) China	31·33 N	115·17 E
148	Hsinyang (sĭn'yäng) China	32·08 N	114·04 E
150	Hsinyeh China	32·40 N	112·20 E
148	Hsip'ing (sē'pĭng) China	33·21 N	114·01 E
151	Hsisha Ch'üntao (Parcel Is.) China	16·40 N	113·00 E
151	Hsishui China	30·30 N	115·10 E
148	Hsiungyüen China	40·10 N	122·08 E
148	Hsiyang (sē'yäng) China	37·37 N	113·42 E
151	Hsüancheng China	30·52 N	118·48 E
150	Hsuanhua China	40·35 N	115·05 E
148	Hsuanhuatien (sōōäN'hōōä'dĭäN) China	31·42 N	114·29 E
148	Hsüch'ang (sü'chäng) China	34·02 N	113·49 E
148	Hsüchou (Süchow) China	34·17 N	117·10 E
148	Hsüi (sü'yē) China	31·02 N	113·49 E
151	Hsün Chiang (R.) China	23·28 N	110·30 E
98	Huacho (wä'chō) Peru	11·13 S	77·29 W
148	Huaian (hōōäĭ'äN) China	33·31 N	119·11 E
147	Huai Ho (R.) (hōōäĭ'hŭ) China	32·07 N	114·38 E
148	Huai Ho (R.) China	33·05 N	117·50 E
150	Huailai China	40·20 N	115·45 E
148	Huailinchen (hōōäĭlĭn'jĕn) China	31·27 N	117·36 E
	Huaining, see Anking		
148	Huaiyang (hōōäĭ'yang) China	33·45 N	114·54 E
148	Huaiyin (hōōäĭ'yĭn) China	33·34 N	118·58 E
148	Huaiyüan (hōōäĭ'yōōäN) China	32·53 N	117·13 E
90	Huajicori (wä-jē-kō'rē) Mex.	22·41 N	105·24 W
91	Huajuapan de León (wäj-wä'päm dā lā-ōn') Mex.	17·46 N	97·45 W
151	Hualien (hwä'lyĕn') China	23·58 N	121·58 E
98	Huallaga (R.) (wäl-yä'gä) Peru	8·12 S	76·34 W
69	Hualpai Ind. Res. (wäl'pī) Ariz.	35·41 N	113·38 W
69	Hualpai Mts. Ariz.	34·53 N	113·54 W
98	Huamachuco (wä-mä-chōō'kō) Peru	7·52 S	78·11 W
91	Huamantla (wä-män'tlȧ) Mex.	19·18 N	97·54 W
90	Huamuxtitlán (wä-mōōs-tē-tlän') Mex.	17·49 N	98·38 W
98	Huancavelica (wän'kä-vä-lē'kä) Peru	12·47 S	75·02 W
98	Huancayo (wän-kä'yō) Peru	12·09 S	75·04 W
98	Huanchaca (wän-chä'kä) Bol.	20·90 S	66·40 W
146	Huan Chiang (R.) China	36·45 N	106·30 E
148	Huangch'iao (hōōäNg'chĭou) China	32·15 N	120·13 E
148	Huangch'uan (hōōäNg'chōōäN) China	32·07 N	115·01 E
148	Huang Ho, Old Course of the (R.) (hōōäng' hu) China	34·28 N	116·59 E
150	Huanghoutien China (Peking In.)	39·22 N	116·53 E
148	Huanghsien (hōōäNg'sĭäN) China	37·39 N	120·32 E
148	Huangli (hōōäNg'lē) China	31·39 N	119·42 E
149	Huanglien China (Canton In.)	22·53 N	113·09 E
149	Huangp'u Chiang (R.) China (Shanghai In.)	30·56 N	121·16 E
146	Huangyüan China	37·00 N	101·01 E
150	Huanjen China	41·10 N	125·30 E
98	Huánuco (wä-nōō'kō) Peru	9·50 S	76·17 W
98	Huanuni (wä-nōō'-nē) Bol.	18·11 S	66·43 W
93	Huapí, Montañas de (Mts.) (môn-tä'n-yäs-dĕ-wä'-pē') Nic.	12·35 N	84·43 W
90	Huaquechula (wä-kĕ-chōō'-lä) Mex.	18·44 N	98·37 W
98	Huaral (wä-rä'l) Peru	11·28 S	77·11 W
98	Huarás (ōōä'rä's) Peru	9·32 S	77·29 W
98	Huascarán, Nevs. (Pk.) (wäs-kä-rän') Peru	9·05 S	77·50 W
100	Huasco (wäs'kō) Chile	28·32 S	71·16 W
150	Huatien China	42·38 N	126·45 E
91	Huatla de Jiménez (wä'-tlä-dĕ-kē-mĕ'-nĕz) Mex.	18·08 N	96·49 W
90	Huatlatlauch (wä'tlä-tlä-ōō'ch) Mex.	18·40 N	98·04 W
91	Huatusco (wä-tōōs'kô) Mex.	19·09 N	96·57 W
90	Huauchinango (wä-ōō-chē-näŋ'gô) Mex.	20·09 N	98·03 W
93	Huaunta (wä-ōō'n-tä) Nic.	13·30 N	83·32 W
93	Huaunta, Laguna (L.) (lä-gōō'-nä-wä-ōō'n-tä) Nic.	13·35 N	83·46 W
90	Huautla (wä-ōō'tlä) Mex.	21·04 N	98·13 W
148	Huayhe Hu (L.) (hōōäĭ'hŭ'hōō) China	32·49 N	117·00 E
90	Huaynamota, Rió de (R.) (rē'ō-dĕ-wäy-nä-mō'tä) Mex.	22·10 N	104·36 W
148	Huayüan Hu (L.) (hōōä'yüan'hoo) China	33·03 N	117·33 E
91	Huazolotitlán (Sta. María) (wäzô-lô-tlē-tlän') Mex.	16·18 N	97·55 W
85	Hubalta (hu-bôl'tȧ) Can. (Calgary In.)	51·02 N	113·58 W
83	Hubbard (hŭb'ērd) N. H. (Boston In.)	42·53 N	71·12 W
77	Hubbard Tex.	31·53 N	96·46 W
80	Hubbard (L.) Mich.	44·45 N	83·30 W
64	Hubbard, Mt. Can.	60·24 N	139·00 W
143	Hubli (hŏŏ'blē) India	15·25 N	75·09 E
123	Hückeswagen (hü'kĕs-vä'gĕn) Ger. (Ruhr In.)	51·09 N	7·20 E
110	Hucknall (hŭk'nȧl) Eng.	53·02 N	1·12 W
110	Huddersfield (hŭd'ērz-fēld) Eng.	53·39 N	1·47 W
118	Hudiksvall (hōō'dĭks-väl) Swe.	61·44 N	17·05 E
85	Hudson (hŭd'sŭn) Can. (Montreal In.)	45·26 N	74·08 W
83	Hudson Mass. (Boston In.)	42·24 N	71·34 W
80	Hudson Mich.	41·50 N	84·15 W
81	Hudson N.Y.	42·15 N	73·45 W
75	Hudson Ohio (Cleveland In.)	41·15 N	81·27 W
74	Hudson Wis. (Minneapolis, St. Paul In.)	44·59 N	92·45 W
87	Hudson B. Can.	60·15 N	85·30 W

Page	Name Pronunciation Region	Lat. °′	Long. °′
81	Hudson Falls N. Y.	43·20 N	73·30 W
85	Hudson Heights Can. (Montreal In.)	45·28 N	74·09 W
81	Hudson R. N. Y.	41·55 N	73·55 W
87	Hudson Str. Can.	62·34 N	72·13 W
151	Hué (ü-ā') Viet.	16·28 N	107·42 E
124	Huebra (R.) (wĕ'brä) Sp.	40·44 N	6·17 W
92	Huehuetenango (wā-wâ-tâ-näŋ'gō) Guat.	15·19 N	91·26 W
90	Huejotzingo (wā-hô-tzĭŋ'gō) Mex.	19·09 N	98·24 W
90	Huejúcar (wā-hōō'kär) Mex.	22·26 N	103·12 W
90	Huejuquilla el Alto (wā-hōō-kēl'yä ĕl äl'tō) Mex.	22·42 N	102·54 W
90	Huejutla (wā-hōō'tlä) Mex.	21·08 N	98·26 W
124	Huelma (wĕl'mä) Sp.	37·39 N	3·36 W
124	Huelva (wĕl'vä) Sp.	37·16 N	6·58 W
124	Huercal-Overa (wĕr-käl' ō-vä'rä) Sp.	37·12 N	1·58 W
72	Huerfano (R.) (wâr'fȧ-nō) Colo.	37·41 N	105·13 W
125	Huésca (wĕs'kä) Sp.	42·07 N	0·25 W
124	Huéscar (wās'kär) Sp.	37·50 N	2·34 W
90	Huetamo de Múñez (wâ-tä'mō dā-mōōn'yĕz) Mex.	18·34 N	100·53 W
124	Huete (wā'tâ) Sp.	40·09 N	2·42 W
90	Hueycatenango (wĕy-kä-tĕ-nä'n-gô) Mex.	17·31 N	99·10 W
91	Hueytlalpan (wā'ĭ-tläl'pän) Mex.	20·03 N	97·41 W
84	Huffman (hŭf'mȧn) Ala. (Birmingham In.)	33·36 N	86 42 W
159	Hughenden (hū'ĕn-dĕn) Austl.	20·58 S	144·13 E
158	Hughes (hūz) Austl.	30·45 S	129·30 E
74	Hugo (hū'gō) Minn. (Minneapolis, St. Paul In.)	45·10 N	93·00 W
73	Hugo Okla.	34·01 N	95·32 W
72	Hugoton (hū'gō-tŭn) Kans.	37·10 N	101·28 W
90	Huichapan (wē-chä-pän') Mex.	20·22 N	99·39 W
98	Huila (wē'lä) (Dept.) Col. (In.)	3·10 N	75·20 W
98	Huila, Nevado de (Pk.) (nĕ-vä-dô-de-wē'lä) Col. (In.)	2·59 N	76·01 W
151	Huilai China	23·02 N	116·18 E
151	Huili China	26·48 N	102·20 E
91	Huimanguillo (wē-män-gēl'yō) Mex.	17·50 N	93·16 W
148	Huimin (hōōĭ mĭn) China	37·29 N	117·32 E
91	Huitzilac (ōōē't-zē-lä'k) Mex. (Mexico In.)	19·01 N	99·16 W
90	Huitzitzilingo (wē-tzē-tzē-lē'n-go) Mex.	21·11 N	98·42 W
90	Huitzuco (wê-tzōō'kō) Mex.	18·16 N	99·20 W
91	Huixquilucan (ōōē'x-kē-lōō-kä'n) Mex. (Mexico In.)	19·21 N	99·22 W
91	Huixtla (wēs'tlä) Mex.	15·12 N	92·28 W
151	Huiyang China	23·05 N	114·25 E
148	Hukouchi (hōōgō jē) China	33·22 N	117·07 E
150	Hulan (hōō'län') China	45·58 N	126·32 E
150	Hulan (R.) China	42·20 N	126·30 E
152	Hulin (hōō'lĭn') China	45·45 N	133·25 E
85	Hull (hŭl) Can. (Ottawa In.)	45·26 N	75·43 W
110	Hull Eng.	53·45 N	0·25 W
83	Hull Mass. (Boston In.)	42·18 N	70·54 W
110	Hull (R.) Eng.	53·47 N	0·20 W
111	Hulst (hŏŏlst) Neth. (Amsterdam In.)	51·17 N	4·01 E
149	Huluk'eng China (Canton In.)	22·41 N	113·25 E
150	Hulutao (hōō'lōō-tä'ō) China	40·40 N	122·55 E
168	Ḩulwān (hĕl'wän) U. A. R. (Nile In.)	29·50 N	31·22 E
89	Humacao (ōō-mä-kä'ō) P. R. (Puerto Rico In.)	18·09 N	65·49 W
98	Humaitá (ōō-mä-ē-tä') Braz.	7·37 S	62·58 W
100	Humaitá Par.	27·08 S	58·18 W
166	Humansdorp (hōō'mäns-dôrp) S. Afr.	33·57 S	24·45 E
166	Humbe (hŏŏm'bā) Ang.	16·50 S	14·55 E
116	Humber (L.) (hŭm'bēr)		
116	Humber (L.) (hŭm'bēr) Eng.	53·38 N	0·40 W
83	Humbermouth (hŭm'bēr-mŭth) Can.	48·54 N	57·35 W
85	Humber R. Can. (Toronto In.)	43·53 N	79·40 W
77	Humble (hŭm'b'l) Tex.	29·58 N	95·15 W
86	Humboldt (hŭm'bōlt) Can.	52·15 N	105·01 W
71	Humboldt Iowa	42·43 N	94·11 W
73	Humboldt Kans.	37·48 N	95·26 W
73	Humboldt Nebr.	40·10 N	95·57 W
62	Humboldt (R.) U. S.	40·30 N	116·50 W
155	Humboldt-Baai (B.) (hŭm'bōlt) Neth. N. Gui.	2·30 S	141·30 E
66	Humboldt B. Calif.	40·48 N	124·25 W
66	Humboldt R., East Fork Nev.	40·59 N	115·21 W
66	Humboldt R., North Fork Nev.	41·25 N	115·45 W
78	Humboldt Tenn.	35·47 N	88·55 W
68	Humbolt Ra. Nev.	40·12 N	118·16 W
68	Humbolt Salt Marsh Nev.	39·49 N	117·41 W
68	Humbolt Sink Nev.	39·58 N	118·54 W
149	Humenchai China (Canton In.)	22·49 N	113·39 E
69	Humphreys Pk. (hŭm'frĭs) Ariz.	35·20 N	111·40 W
120	Humpolec (hŏŏm'pō-lĕts) Czech.	49·33 N	15·21 E
92	Humuya R. (ōō-mōō'yä) Hond.	14·38 N	87·36 W
112	Hunaflói (B.) (hōō'nä-flō'ĭ) Ice.	65·41 N	20·44 W
147	Hunan (Prov.) (hōō'nän') China	28·08 N	111·25 E
147	Hunch'un (hōōn'chōōn') China	42·53 N	130·34 E
127	Hunedoara (kōō'nĕd-wä'rȧ) Rom.	45·45 N	22·54 E
127	Hungary (hŭŋ'gȧ-rĭ) Eur.	46·44 N	17·55 E
160	Hungerford (hŭn'gĕr-fērd) Austl.	28·50 S	144·32 E
67	Hungry Horse Res. (hŭŋ'gȧ-rĭ hôrs) Mont.	48·11 N	113·30 W
151	Hung Shui Ho (R.) (hŏŏng) China	25·00 N	107·22 E
148	Hungtse Hu (L.) (hōōngzhŭ hōō) China	33·17 N	118·37 E
120	Hunsrück (Mts.) (hōōns'rûk) Ger.	49·43 N	7·12 E
120	Hunte R. (hōōn'tē) Ger.	52·45 N	8·26 E
159	Hunters Is. (hŭn-tērs) Austl.	40·33 S	143·36 E
80	Huntingburg (hŭnt'ĭng-bûrg) Ind.	38·15 N	86·55 W
81	Huntingdon (hŭnt'ĭng-dŭn) Can.	45·10 N	74·05 W
65	Huntingdon Can. (Vancouver In.)	49·00 N	122·16 W

ăr; finȧl; rāte; senāte; ärm; ȧsk; sofȧ; fâre; ch-choose; dh-as th in other; bē; ēvent; bĕt; recĕnt; cratēr; g-go; gh-guttural g; bĭt; ĭ-short neutral; rīde; K-guttural k as ch in German ich;

PRONOUNCING INDEX Huntingdon–Inner Brass 217

Page	Name Pronunciation Region	Lat. °′	Long. °′
78	Huntingdon...............Tenn.	36·00 N	88·23 W
110	Huntingdon (Co.)..........Eng.	52·26 N	0·19 W
80	Huntington...............Ind.	40·55 N	85·30 W
84	Huntington.N. Y. (New York In.)	40·51 N	73·25 W
81	Huntington...............Pa.	40·30 N	78·00 W
80	Huntington.............W. Va.	38·25 N	82·25 W
74	Huntington Beach Calif. (Los Angeles In.)	33·39 N	118·00 W
74	Huntington Park Calif. (Los Angeles In.)	33·59 N	118·14 W
78	Huntsville (hŭnts′-vĭl).......Ala.	35·43 N	86·36 W
81	Huntsville................Can.	45·20 N	79·15 W
73	Huntsville................Mo.	39·24 N	92·32 W
77	Huntsville................Tex.	30·44 N	95·34 W
74	Huntsville Utah (Salt Lake City In.)	41·16 N	111·46 W
91	Hunucmá (hōō-nōōk-mä′)...Mex.	21·01 N	89·54 W
148	Huolu (hōō̆ lōō).........China	38·05 N	114·20 E
155	Huon G.............N. Gui. Ter.	7·15 S	147·45 E
147	Hupeh (Prov.)...........China	31·20 N	111·58 E
80	Hurd, C. (hûrd)...........Can.	45·15 N	81·45 W
71	Hurley (hûr′lĭ)............Wis.	46·26 N	90·11 W
100	Hurlingham (ōō′r-lēn-gäm) Arg. (In.)	34·20 S	58·38 W
80	Huron (hū′rŏn)............Ohio	41·20 N	82·35 W
70	Huron...................S. D.	44·22 N	98·15 W
63	Huron, L. (hū′rŏn)....U. S.-Can.	45·15 N	82·40 W
71	Huron Mts.(hū′rŏn)........Mich.	46·47 N	87·52 W
75	Huron R......Mich. (Detroit In.)	42·12 N	83·26 W
64	Hurricane (hŭr′ĭ-kān).....Alaska	63·00 N	149·30 W
69	Hurricane................Utah	37·10 N	113·20 W
94	Hurricane Flats (Shoal) (hŭ-rĭ-kăn flăts).Ba. Is.	23·35 N	78·30 W
112	Húsavik..................Ice.	66·00 N	17·10 W
129	Huşi (kōōsh′)...........Sov. Un.	46·52 N	28·04 E
118	Huskvarna (hōōsk-vär′nå)...Swe.	57·48 N	14·16 E
120	Husum (hōō′zōōm)..........Ger.	54·29 N	9·04 E
74	Hutchins (hŭch′ĭnz) Tex. (Dallas, Fort Worth In.)	32·38 N	96·43 W
72	Hutchinson (hŭch′ĭn-sŭn)...Kans.	38·02 N	97·56 W
71	Hutchinson...............Minn.	44·53 N	94·23 W
150	Hut′o Ho (R.) (hōō′tō′hō′).China	38·10 N	114·00 E
148	Huwu (hōō wōō)..........China	31·17 N	119·48 E
117	Huy (û-ē′) (hû′ē)...........Bel.	50·33 N	5·14 E
112	Hvannadalshnukur (Mtn.)....Ice.	64·09 N	16·46 W
147	Hwang Ho (Yellow R.) (hwäng′hō′).China	35·06 N	113·39 E
146	Hwang Ho, Old beds of the.China	40 28 N	106·34 E
126	Hvar (I.) (кhvär)..........Yugo.	43·08 N	16·28 E
152	Hwangju (hwäng′jōō′).......Kor.	38·39 N	125·49 E
64	Hydaburg (hī-dă′bûrg)....Alaska	55·18 N	132·40 W
110	Hyde (hīd)................Eng.	53·27 N	2·05 W
143	Hyderābād (hī-dēr-å-băd′)..India	17·29 N	79·28 E
142	Hyderabad (hī-dēr-å-băd′) W. Pak.	25·29 N	68·28 E
143	Hyderabad (State).........India	23·29 N	76·50 E
123	Hyères (ē-âr′)..............Fr.	43·09 N	6·08 E
123	Hyères, Iles d′ (Is.) (ēl′dyâr′)..Fr.	42·57 N	6·17 E
152	Hyesanjin (hyĕ′sän-jĭn′).....Kor.	41·11 N	128·12 E
80	Hymera (hī-mē′rá)..........Ind.	39·10 N	87·20 W
67	Hyndman Pk. (hīnd′măn)..Idaho	43·38 N	114·04 W
153	Hyōgo (Pref.) (hĭyō′gō) Jap. (Ōsaka In.)	34·54 N	135·15 E
86	Hythe....................Can.	55·18 N	119·34 W
153	Ia (R.) (ē′ä)....Jap. (Ōsaka In.)	34·54 N	135·34 E
121	Iaşi (yä′shē)..............Rom.	47·10 N	27·40 E
155	Iba (ē′bä)......Phil. (Manila In.)	15·20 N	119·59 E
164	Ibadan (ē-bä′dän)...........Nig.	7·26 N	3·48 E
98	Ibagué (ē-bä-gā′).......Col. (In.)	4·27 N	75·13 W
127	Ibar (R.) (ē′bär)..........Yugo.	43·22 N	20·35 E
153	Ibaragi (ē-bä′rä-gē) Jap. (Ōsaka In.)	34·49 N	135·35 E
98	Ibarra (ē-bär′rä)............Ec.	0·19 N	78·08 W
163	Iberian Pen..............Port.-Sp.	41·00 N	0·07 W
82	Iberville (ē-bàr-vēl′) (ī′bēr-vĭl) Can.	45·14 N	73·01 W
164	Ibi (ē′bē)..................Nig.	8·08 N	9·45 E
99	Ibiapaba, Serra da (Mts.) (sĕ′r-rä-dä-ē-byä-på′bä).Braz.	3·30 S	40·55 W
125	Ibiza (ē-bē′thä)..............Sp.	38·55 N	1·24 E
125	Ibiza, Isla de (Iviza I.) (ē′s-lä-dĕ-ē-bē′zä).Sp.	39·07 N	1·05 E
167	Ibo (ē′bō)..................Moz.	12·17 S	40·45 E
144	Ibrahim, Jabal (Mtn.)...Sau. Ar.	20·31 N	41·17 E
168	Ibrahim, Port.U. A. R. (Suez In.)	29·57 N	32·33 E
98	Ica (ē′kä)..................Peru	14·09 S	75·42 W
98	Icá (R.) (ē-kä′)...........Braz.	2·56 S	69·12 W
98	Içana (ē-sä′nä)............Braz.	0·15 N	67·19 W
66	Ice Harbor Dam...........Wash.	46·15 N	118·54 W
102	Iceland (īs′lănd)............Eur.	65·12 N	19·45 W
151	Ich′ang (ē′chäng′).........China	30·38 N	111·22 E
142	Ichāpur......India (Calcutta In.)	22·47 N	88·21 E
153	Ichibusayama (Mt.) (ē′chē-bōō′sä-yä′mä).Jap.	32·19 N	131·08 E
153	Ichikawa (ē′chē-kä′wä) Jap. (Tōkyō In.)	35·44 N	139·54 E
153	Ichinomiya (ē′chē-nō-mē′yä) Jap.	35·19 N	136·49 E
152	Ichinomiya.................Jap.	35·23 N	140·33 E
153	Ichinomoto (ē-chē′nō-mō-tō) Jap. (Ōsaka In.)	34·37 N	135·50 E
129	Ichnya (ĭch′nyä)........Sov. Un.	50·47 N	32·23 E
99	Icó (ē-kō′)................Braz.	6·25 S	38·43 W
98	Icutú, Cerro (Mtn.) (sĕ′r-rô-ē-kōō-tōō′) Ven.	7·07 N	65·30 W
64	Icy C. (ī′sĭ)..............Alaska	70·20 N	161·40 W
73	Idabel (ī′dá-bĕl)..........Okla.	33·52 N	94·47 W
70	Idagrove (ī′dá-grōv)........Iowa	42·22 N	95·29 W
164	Idah (ē′dä).................Nig.	7·08 N	6·45 E
62	Idaho (State) (ī′dá-hō)......U. S.	44·00 N	115·10 W
67	Idaho Falls...............Idaho	43·30 N	112·01 W
72	Idaho Springs..............Colo.	39·43 N	105·32 W
124	Idanha-a-Nova (ē-dän′yä-ä-nō′vá).Port.	39·58 N	7·13 W
146	Ideriin Gol (R.)...........Mong.	48·58 N	98·38 E
168	Idfū (ĕd′fōō)..U. A. R. (Nile In.)	24·57 N	32·53 E
127	Idhra (I.).....................Grc.	37·20 N	23·30 E
154	Idi (ē′dē)..................Indon.	4·58 N	97·47 E
168	Idkū (ĕd′kōō).U. A. R. (Nile In.)	31·18 N	30·20 E
168	Idkū L.........U. A. R. (Nile In.)	31·13 N	30·22 E
110	Idle (R.) (īd″l)............Eng.	53·22 N	0·56 W
126	Idrija (ē′drē-å)............Yugo.	46·01 N	14·01 E
167	Idutywa (ē-dōō-tī′wá) S. Afr. (Natal In.)	32·06 S	28·18 E
117	Ieper......................Bel.	50·50 N	2·53 E
126	Ierápetra...........Grc. (Inset)	35·01 N	25·48 E
126	Iesi (yā′sē)..................It.	43·37 N	13·20 E
164	Ife........................Nig.	7·36 N	4·38 E
164	Iferouane (ēf′rōō-än′).......Niger	19·23 N	8·24 E
163	Ifni (ēf′nē)................Afr.	29·45 N	11·00 W
134	Igarka (ē-gär′kå)........Sov. Un.	67·22 N	86·16 E
126	Iglesias (ē-lĕ′syôs)...........It.	39·20 N	8·34 E
164	Igli (ē-glē′)................Alg.	30·32 N	2·15 W
87	Igloolik...................Can.	69·33 N	81·18 W
139	′Igma, Gebel el (Mts.) U. A. R. (Palistine In.)	29·12 N	33·42 E
65	Ignacio (ĭg-nā′cĭ-ō) Calif. (San Francisco In.)	38·05 N	122·32 W
100	Iguaçu (R.) (ē-gwä-sōō′).Braz.(In.)	22·42 S	43·19 W
90	Iguala (ē-gwä′lä)...........Mex.	18·18 N	99·34 W
125	Igualada (ē-gwä-lä′dä)........Sp.	41·35 N	1·38 E
100	Iguassu (R.) (ē-gwä-sōō′)....Braz.	25·45 S	52·30 W
100	Iguassu Falls (Falls).......Braz.	25·40 S	54·16 W
101	Iguatama (ē-gwä-tá′mä) Braz (Rio de Janeiro In.)	20·13 S	45·40 W
99	Iguatu (ē-gwä-tōō′).........Braz.	6·22 S	39·17 W
164	Iguidi, Erg (Dune)..........Alg.	26·22 N	6·53 W
155	Iguig (ē-gēg′).Phil. (Manila In.)	17·46 N	121·44 E
150	Ihsien.....................China	41·30 N	121·15 E
148	I Ho (R.) (yē′hŭ)..........China	34·38 N	118·07 E
150	Iian.......................China	46·10 N	129·40 E
153	Iida (ē′ē-dä)................Jap.	35·39 N	137·53 E
132	Iijoki (R.) (ē′yō′kĭ)..........Fin.	65·28 N	27·00 E
153	Iizuka (ē′ē-zōō-kå)...........Jap.	33·39 N	130·39 E
164	Ijebu Ode (ē-jĕ′bōō ōdå).....Nig.	6·46 N	3·59 E
117	Ijselmeer (L.).............Neth.	52·46 N	5·14 E
119	Ikaalinen (ē′kä-lĭ-nĕn).......Fin.	61·47 N	22·55 E
127	Ikaría (I.) (ē-kä′ryä).........Grc.	37·43 N	26·07 E
153	Ikeda-Kawanishi (ē′kä-dä kä-wä′nē-shē).Jap. (Osaka In.)	34·49 N	135·26 E
127	Ikhtiman (ēk′tē-män)........Bul.	42·26 N	23·49 E
153	Iki (I.) (ē′kē)...............Jap.	33·46 N	129·44 E
166	Ikoma (ē-kō′mä).............Tan.	2·08 S	34·47 E
136	Iksha (ĭk′shå) Sov. Un. (Moskva In.)	56·10 N	37·30 E
155	Ilagen (ē-lä′gän).Phil. (Manila In.)	17·09 N	121·52 E
151	Ilan (ē′län′)...............China	24·50 N	121·42 E
121	Ilawa (ē-lä′vå)..............Pol.	53·35 N	19·36 E
85	Ile-Bizard Valois (yl-bē-zär vä-lōō-ä′).Can. (Montreal In.)	45·29 N	73·53 W
133	Ilek (ē′lyĕk)............Sov. Un.	51·30 N	53·10 E
133	Ilek (R.)................Sov. Un.	51·20 N	53·10 E
85	Ile-Perrot (yl-pĕ-rōt′) Can. (Montreal In.)	45·21 N	73·54 W
164	Ilesha......................Nig.	7·45 N	4·50 E
110	Ilford (ĭl′fērd)..Eng. (London In.)	51·33 N	0·06 E
116	Ilfracombe (ĭl-frá-kōōm′)....Eng.	51·13 N	4·08 W
101	Ilhabela (ē′lä-bĕ′lä) Braz. (Rio de Janeiro In.)	23·47 S	45·21 W
101	Ilha Grande, Baia de (B.) (ēl′yä grän′dĕ) Braz. (Rio de Janeiro In.)	23·17 S	44·25 W
124	Ilhavo (ēl′yä-vô)...........Port.	40·36 N	8·41 W
99	Ilhéus (ē-lĕ′ōōs)...........Braz.	14·52 S	39·00 W
64	Iliamna (ē-lē-ăm′nä)......Alaska	59·45 N	155·05 W
64	Iliamna (L.)..............Alaska	59·25 N	155·30 W
64	Iliamna Vol.)..............Alaska	60·18 N	153·25 W
134	Ilim (R.) (ē-lyêm′).......Sov. Un.	57·28 N	103·00 E
134	Ilimsk (ē-lyêmsk′)......Sov. Un.	56·47 N	103·43 E
155	Ilin (I.) (ē-lyēn′) Phil. (Manila In.)	12·16 N	120·57 E
129	Il′intsiy.................Sov. Un.	49·07 N	29·13 E
127	Iliodhrómia (I.)..............Grc.	39·18 N	23·35 E
81	Ilion (ĭl′ĭ-ŭn)..............N. Y.	43·00 N	75·05 W
146	Ili R. (ē′lē′).............Sov. Un.	43·46 N	77·41 E
110	Ilkeston (ĭl′kĕs-tŭn)..........Eng.	52·58 N	1·19 W
98	Illampu, Nevado (Pk.) (nĕ-vá′dô-ēl-yäm-pōō′).Bol.	15·50 S	68·15 W
155	Illano B. (ēl-yä-nô)..........Phil.	7·38 N	123·41 E
101	Illapel (ē-zhä-pĕ′l) Chile (Santiago In.)	31·37 S	71·10 W
120	Iller R. (ĭl′er)..............Ger.	47·52 N	10·06 E
98	Illimani, Nevado (Pk.) (nĕ-vá′dô-ēl-yē-mä′nē).Bol.	16·50 S	67·38 W
63	Illinois (State) (ĭl-ĭ-noi′) (ĭl-ĭ-noiz′) U. S.	40·25 N	90·40 W
73	Illinois (R.)..................Ill.	40·52 N	89·31 W
128	Il′men′, Ozero (L.) (ô′zĕ-rô el″men″) (ĭl′mĕn).Sov. Un.	58·18 N	32·00 E
117	Ilmenau (ēl′mē-nou).........Ger.	50·37 N	13·02 E
117	Ilmenau (R.).................Ger.	53·20 N	10·20 E
164	Ilo (ē′lō)....................Nig.	11·30 N	3·41 E
98	Ilo..........................Peru	17·46 S	71·13 W
92	Ilobasco (ē-lô-bäs′kô)........Sal.	13·57 N	88·46 W
154	Iloilo (ē-lô-ē′lō)............Phil.	10·49 N	122·33 E
92	Ilopango, L. (ē-lô-päŋ′gō).....Sal.	13·48 N	88·50 W
164	Ilorin (ē-lô-rēn′)............Nig.	8·32 N	4·30 E
128	Ilūkste...................Sov. Un.	55·59 N	26·20 E
65	Ilwaco (ĭl-wä′kô) Wash. (Portland In.)	46·19 N	124·02 W
132	Ilych (R.) (ē′l′ĭch).......Sov. Un.	62·30 N	57·30 E
153	Imabari (ē′mä-bä′rē)..........Jap.	34·05 N	132·58 E
153	Imai (ê-mī′).....Jap. (Ōsaka In.)	34·30 N	135·47 E
152	Iman (R.) (ē-män′).......Sov. Un.	45·40 N	134·31 E
135	Iman.....................Sov. Un.	46·07 N	133·21 E
132	Imandra (L.) (ē-män′drä).Sov. Un.	67·40 N	32·30 E
168	Imbābah (ēm-bä′bå) U. A. R. (Nile In.)	30·06 N	31·09 E
100	Imbarié (ēm-bä-ryĕ′)..Braz. (In.)	22·38 S	43·13 W
136	Imeni Morozova (ĭm-yĕ′nyĭ mô rô′zô vá) Sov. Un. (Leningrad In.)	59·58 N	31·02 E
128	Imeni Moskvy, Kanal (Moscow Can.) (kå-näl′ ĭm-yä′nĭ mŏs-kvĭ).Sov. Un.	56·33 N	37·15 E
152	Imienpo (yēmĭänpŭ).......China	44·59 N	127·56 E
80	Imlay City (ĭm′lā).........Mich.	43·00 N	83·15 W
120	Immenstadt (ĭm′ĕn-shtät)....Ger.	47·34 N	10·12 E
168	Immerpan (ĭmĕr-pän).....S. Afr. (Johannesburg & Pretoria In.)	24·29 S	29·14 E
126	Imola (ē′mô-lä)...............It.	44·19 N	11·43 E
126	Imotski (ê-môts′kē)........Yugo.	43·25 N	17·15 E
167	Impendle (ĭm-pĕnd′lå) S. Afr. (Natal In.)	29·38 S	29·54 E
126	Imperia (êm-pā′rē-ä)..........It.	43·52 N	8·00 E
75	Imperial (ĭm-pē′rĭ-ăl) Pa. (Pittsburgh In.)	40·27 N	80·15 W
68	Imperial Beach Calif. (San Diego In.)	32·34 N	117·08 W
69	Imperial Res...............Ariz.	32·57 N	114·19 W
68	Imperial Valley............Calif.	33·00 N	115·22 W
165	Impfondo (ĭmp-fōn′dô)...Con. B.	1·46 N	17·53 E
145	Imphal (ĭmp′hŭl)..........India	24·42 N	94·00 E
127	Imroz (I.) (ĭm′rŏz)..........Tur.	40·10 N	25·27 E
153	Ina (R.) (ê-nä′).Jap. (Ōsaka In.)	34·56 N	135·21 E
68	Inaja Ind. Res. (ê-nä′hä)....Calif.	32·56 N	116·37 W
112	Inari (L.)...................Fin.	69·02 N	26·22 E
164	In Azaoua (Oasis) (ēn-ä-zou′å).Alg.	20·57 N	7·24 E
125	Inca (ēŋ′kä)..................Sp.	39·43 N	2·53 E
133	Ince Burun (C.) (ĭn′jå)......Tur.	42·00 N	35·00 E
152	Inch′ŏn (ĭn′chŭn)...........Kor.	37·26 N	126·46 E
126	Incudine, Mt. (Mtn.) (ēn-kōō-dē′nå) (ăɴ-kü-dēn′).Cor.	41·53 N	9·17 E
118	Indals-älven (R.)...........Swe.	62·50 N	16·50 E
155	Indang (ēn′däng′) Phil. (Manila In.)	14·11 N	120·53 E
76	Indé (ēn′dā)................Mex.	25·53 N	105·15 W
73	Independence (ĭn-dē-pĕn′dĕns) Kans.	37·14 N	95·42 W
74	Independence Mo. (Kansas City In.)	39·06 N	94·26 W
75	Independence Ohio (Cleveland In.)	41·23 N	81·39 W
66	Independence...............Ore.	44·49 N	123·13 W
66	Independence Mts...........Nev.	41·15 N	116·02 W
133	Inder (L.)...............Sov. Un.	48·20 N	52·10 E
138	India (ĭn′dĭ-á)..............Asia	23·00 N	77·30 E
71	Indian (L.) (ĭn′dĭ-ăn)......Mich.	46·04 N	86·34 W
81	Indian (R.).................N. Y.	44·05 N	75·45 W
81	Indiana (ĭn-dĭ-ăn′á)..........Pa.	40·40 N	79·10 W
63	Indiana (State)..............U. S.	39·50 N	86·45 W
75	Indianapolis (ĭn-dĭ-ăn-ăp′ô-lĭs) Ind. (Indianapolis In.)	39·45 N	86·08 W
65	Indian Arm (R.) (ĭn′dĭ-ăn ärm) Can. (Vancouver In.)	49·21 N	122·55 W
86	Indian Head (ĭn′dĭ-ăn hĕd)..Can.	50·36 N	103·42 W
7	Indian Ocean		
71	Indianola (ĭn-dĭ-ăn-ō′lá).....Iowa	41·22 N	93·33 W
78	Indianola..................Miss.	33·29 N	90·35 W
135	Indigirka (R.) (ên-dē-gēr′kå) Sov. Un.	67·45 N	145·45 E
88	Indio (R.) (ē′n-dyô) Pan. (Panama Canal In.)	9·13 N	78·28 W
154	Indochina (Reg.) (ĭn-dô-chī′nå) Asia	17·22 N	105·18 E
154	Indonesia (ĭn′dô-nē-zhá).....Asia	4·38 S	118·45 E
142	Indore (ĭn-dōr′)............India	22·48 N	76·51 E
154	Indragiri (R.) (ĭn-drå-jē′rē).Indon.	0·27 S	102·05 E
142	Indrāvati (R.) (ĭn-drŭ-vä′tē) India	19·15 N	80·54 E
122	Indre (R.) (ăɴ′dr′)...........Fr.	47·13 N	0·29 E
118	Indre Solund (I.) (ĭndrĕ-sô-lûnd) Nor.	61·09 N	4·37 E
85	Indus (ĭn′dŭs).Can. (Calgary In.)	50·55 N	113·45 W
142	Indus (R.).............W. Pak.	26·43 N	67·41 E
167	Indwe (ĭnd′wå).S. Afr. (Natal In.)	31·30 S	27·21 E
133	Inebolu (ē-nå-bō′lōō)...... Tur.	41·50 N	33·40 E
133	Inego (ē′nå-gŭ).............Tur.	40·05 N	29·20 E
155	Infanta (ēn-fän′tä) Phil. (Manila In.)	14·44 N	121·39 E
155	Infanta........Phil. (Manila In.)	15·50 N	119·53 E
124	Infantes (ēn-fän′tås)..........Sp.	38·44 N	3·00 W
91	Inferror, Laguna (L.) (lä-gōō′nä-ēn-fĕr-rôr).Mex.	16·18 N	94·40 W
124	Infiesto (ēn-fyĕ′s-tô)..........Sp.	43·21 N	5·24 W
80	Ingersoll (ĭn′gēr-sŏl).........Can.	43·05 N	81·00 W
159	Ingham (ĭng′ăm)...........Austl.	18·45 S	146·14 E
94	Ingles, Cayos (Is.) (kä′yōs-ē′n-glĕ′s).Cuba	21·55 N	82·35 W
74	Inglewood (ĭn′g′l-wŏŏd) Calif. (Los Angeles In.)	33·57 N	118·22 W
85	Inglewood..Can. (Toronto In.)...	43·48 N	79·56 W
135	Ingoda (R.) (ēn-gō′dá)...Sov. Un.	51·29 N	112·32 E
120	Ingolstadt (ĭŋ′gôl-shtät)......Ger.	48·46 N	11·27 E
129	Ingul (R.) (ēn-gōōl′).....Sov. Un.	47·22 N	32.52 E
129	Ingulets (R.) (ēn-gōōl′yĕts′) Sov. Un.	47·12 N	33·12 E
133	Ingur (R.) (ēn-gōōr′)....Sov. Un.	42·30 N	42·00 E
166	Inhambane (ēn-năm-bä′n)....Moz.	23·47 S	35·28 E
99	Inhambupe (ēn-yăm-bōō′pä) Braz.	11·47 S	38·13 W
166	Inharrime (ēn-yär-rē′mä)....Moz.	24·17 S	35·07 E
100	Inhomirim (ē-nô-mē-rē′ɴ) Braz. (In.)	22·34 S	43·11 W
167	Inhiuzan (Mtn.) S. Afr. (Natal In.)	29·34 S	30·03 E
146	Ining (ē′nĭng′).............China	43·58 N	80·49 E
98	Inirida (R.) (ē-nē-rē′dä)......Col.	2·25 N	70·38 W
160	Injune (ĭn′jōōn)............Austl.	25·52 S	148·30 E
165	Inkermann (ĭŋ-kĕr-män).......Alg.	35·55 N	0·57 E
119	Inkeroinem (ĭn′kĕr-oi-nĕn)....Fin.	60·42 N	26·50 E
75	Inkster (ĭngk′stēr) Mich. (Detroit In.)	42·18 N	83·19 W
160	Innamincka (ĭnn-á′mĭn-ká).Austl.	27·50 S	140·48 E
89	Inner Brass (I.) (bräs) Vir. Is. (U. S. A.) (St. Thomas In.)	18·23 N	64·58 W

ng-sing; ŋ-baŋk; ɴ-nasalized n; nŏd; cŏmmit; ōld; ôbey; ôrder; fōōd; fŏŏt; ou-out; s-soft; sh-dish; th-thin; pūre; ûnite; ûrn; stŭd; circŭs; ü as "y" in study; ′-indeterminate vowel.

218 Inner Hebrides–Izhma PRONOUNCING INDEX

Page	Name Pronunciation Region	Lat. °′	Long. °′
116	Inner Hebrides (Is.) . . . . Scot.	57·20 N	6·20 W
146	Inner Mongolian Aut. Reg. (mŏŋ-gō'lĭ-ăn) . China	40·39 N	104·13 E
86	Innisfail . . . . Can.	52·01 N	113·57 W
114	Inn R. (ĭn) . . . . Ger.-Aus.	48·19 N	13·16 E
120	Innsbruck (ĭns'brŏŏk) . . . . Aus.	47·15 N	11·25 E
153	Ino (ē'nō) . . . . Jap.	33·34 N	133·23 E
166	Inongo (ē-nôŋ'gō) . . . . Con. L.	1·58 S	18·27 E
121	Inowroctaw (ē-nō-vrŏts'läf) . . . Pol.	52·48 N	18·16 E
164	In Salah (ēn-sà-lä') . . . . Alg.	27·13 N	2·22 E
69	Inscription House Ruin (ĭn'skrĭp-shŭn hous rōō'ĭn) . Ariz.	36·45 N	110·47 W
90	Inter-American Hy. (ĭn'tēr ȧ-mĕr'ĭ-kăn) . Mex.	22·30 N	99·08 W
71	International Falls (ĭn'tēr-năsh'ŭn-ăl fôlz) . Minn.	48·34 N	93·26 W
153	Inuyama (ē'nōō-yä'mä) . . . . . . Jap.	35·24 N	137·01 E
159	Invercargil (ĭn-vēr-kär'gĭl) N. Z. (In.)	47·18 S	167·27 E
160	Inverel (ĭn-vēr-el') . . . . Austl.	29·50 S	151·32 E
74	Invergrove (ĭn'vēr-grōv) Minn. (Minneapolis, St. Paul In.)	44·51 N	93·01 W
83	Inverness (ĭn-vēr-nĕs') . . . . Can.	46·14 N	61·20 W
79	Inverness . . . . Fla.	28·48 N	82·22 W
116	Inverness . . . . Scot.	57·30 N	4·07 W
160	Investigator Str. (ĭn-vĕst'ĭ'gā-tôr) Austl.	35·33 S	137·00 E
166	Inyangani, Mt. (ēn-yän-gä'nê) Fed. of Rh. & Nya.	18·06 S	32·37 E
68	Inyo Mts. (ĭn'yō) . . . . Calif.	36·55 N	118·04 W
136	Inzer R. (ĭn'zĕr) Sov. Un. (Urals In.)	54·24 N	57·17 E
164	In Zize (Oasis) (ēn-zē'zē) . . . . . Alg.	23·25 N	2·36 E
153	Iō (I.) (ē'wō) . . . . Jap.	30·46 N	130·15 E
127	Ioánnina (Yannina) (yô-ä'nê-nà) (yä'nê-nà) . Grc.	39·39 N	20·52 E
65	Ioco . . . . Can. (Vancouver In.)	49·18 N	122·53 W
73	Iola (ī-ō'lȧ) . . . . Kans.	37·55 N	95·23 W
80	Ionia (ī-ō'nĭ-ȧ) . . . . Mich.	43·00 N	85·10 W
127	Ionian Is. (ī-ō'nĭ-ăn) . . . . Grc.	39·10 N	20·05 E
115	Ionian Sea . . . . Eur.	38·59 N	18·48 E
127	Ios (I.) (ī'ŏs) . . . . Grc.	36·48 N	25·25 E
63	Iowa (State) (ī'ō-wȧ) . . . . U. S.	42·05 N	94·20 W
71	Iowa (R.) . . . . Iowa	41·44 N	91·50 W
71	Iowa City . . . . Iowa	41·39 N	91·31 W
71	Iowa Falls . . . . Iowa	42·32 N	93·16 W
72	Iowa Park . . . . Tex.	33·57 N	98·39 W
99	Ipamerí (ē-pä-mà-rē') . . . . Braz.	17·44 S	48·03 W
121	Ipel R. (ē'pĕl) . . . . . . Czech.-Hung.	48·08 N	19·00 E
98	Ipiales (ē-pê-ä'lâs) . . . . Col.	0·48 N	77·45 W
151	Ipin (Süchow) . . . . China	28·50 N	104·40 E
160	Ipswich (ĭps'wĭch) . . . . Austl.	27·45 S	152·58 E
117	Ipswich . . . . Eng.	52·05 N	1·05 W
83	Ipswich . . . . Mass. (Boston In.)	42·41 N	70·50 W
70	Ipswich . . . . S. D.	45·26 N	99·01 W
99	Ipu (ē-pōō) . . . . Braz.	4·11 S	40·45 W
128	Iput' (R.) (ē-pōōt') . . . . Sov. Un.	52·53 N	31·57 E
98	Iquique (ē-kē'kĕ) . . . . Chile	20·16 S	70·07 W
98	Iquitos (ê-kē'tōs) . . . . Peru	3·39 S	73·18 W
75	Ira (ī'rā) . . . . Ohio (Cleveland In.)	41·11 N	81·35 W
126	Iráklion (Candia) . . . . Gr. (In.)	35·20 N	25·10 E
138	Iran (Persia) (ē-rän') . . . . Asia	31·15 N	53·30 E
144	Iran, Plat. of . . . . Iran	32·28 N	58·00 E
154	Iran Mts . . . . Sar.	2·30 N	114·30 E
90	Irapuato (ē-rä-pwä'tō) . . . . . . Mex.	20·41 N	101·24 W
138	Iraq (ē-räk') . . . . Asia	32·00 N	42·30 E
93	Irazu Vol. (ē-rä-zōō') . . . . C. R.	9·58 N	83·54 W
139	Irbid (ēr-bēd') Jordan (Palestine In.)	32·33 N	35·51 E
133	Irbil . . . . Iraq	36.10 N	44·00 E
132	Irbit (ēr-bēt') . . . . Sov. Un.	57·40 N	63·10 E
166	Irebu (ē-rā'bōō) . . . . Con. L.	0·40 S	17·48 E
102	Ireland (īr-lănd) . . . . Eur.	53·33 N	13·00 W
136	Iremel', Gora (Mt.) (gà-rä' ĭ-rĕ'mĕl) . Sov. Un. (Urals In.)	54·32 N	58·52 E
167	Irene (ĭ-rē-nē) . . . . S. Afr. (Johannesburg & Pretoria In.)	25·53 S	28·13 E
134	Irgiz (ĭr-gēz') . . . . Sov. Un.	48·30 N	61·17 E
134	Irgiz (R.) . . . . Sov. Un.	49·30 N	60·32 E
166	Iringa (ē-rĭŋ'gä) . . . . Tan.	7·44 S	35·43 E
92	Iriona (ē-rê-ō'nä) . . . . Hond.	15·53 N	85·12 W
116	Irish Sea (ī'rĭsh) . . . . Eur.	53·55 N	5·25 W
134	Irkutsk (ĭr-kŏŏtsk') . . . . . . Sov. Un.	52·16 N	104·00 E
110	Irlam (ûr'lăm) . . . . Eng.	53·26 N	2·26 W
95	Irois, Cap des (C.) . . . . Hai.	18·25 N	74·50 W
151	Iromote Jima (I.) . . . . China	24·20 N	123·30 E
84	Irondale (ī'ērn-dāl) Ala. (Birmingham In.)	33·32 N	86·43 W
127	Iron Gate (Gorge) . . . . Yugo.-Rom.	44·43 N	22·32 E
160	Iron Knob (ī-ăn nŏb) . . . . . . Austl.	32·47 S	137·10 E
71	Iron Mountain (ī'ērn) . . . . . . Mich.	45·49 N	88·04 W
71	Iron River . . . . Mich.	46·09 N	88·39 W
80	Ironton (ī'ērn-tŭn) . . . . Ohio	38·30 N	82·45 W
71	Ironwood (ī'ērn-wŏŏd) . . . . . . Mich.	46·28 N	90·10 W
80	Iroquois (R.) (ĭr'ō-kwoi) . . Ill.-Ind.	40·55 N	87·20 W
87	Iroquois Falls . . . . Can.	48·41 N	80·39 W
153	Irō-Saki (C.) (ē'rō sä'kē) . . . . Jap.	34·35 N	138·54 E
129	Irpen' (R.) (ĭr-pĕn') . . . . . Sov. Un.	50·13 N	29·55 E
145	Irrawaddy (R.) . . . . Bur.	23·27 N	96·25 E
154	Irrawaddy, Mouths of the (ĭr-ȧ-wäd'ē) . Bur.	15·40 N	94·32 E
146	Irrawaddy R. . . . . Bur.	20·39 N	94·38 E
134	Irtysh (R.) (ĭr-tĭsh') . . . . . Sov. Un.	58·32 N	68·31 E
165	Irumu (ē-rōō'mōō) . . . . Con. L.	1·30 N	29·52 E
124	Irun (ē-rōōn') . . . . Sp.	43·20 N	1·47 W
74	Irvine (ûr'vĭn) Calif. (Los Angeles In.)	33·40 N	117·45 W
116	Irvine . . . . Scot.	55·39 N	4·40 W
80	Irvine . . . . Ky.	37·40 N	84·00 W
85	Irvine Cr. . . Can. (Edmonton In.)	53·23 N	113·27 W
74	Irving (ûr'vēng) Tex. (Dallas, Fort Worth In.)	32·49 N	96·57 W
84	Irvington (ûr'vēng-tŭn) N. J. (New York In.)	40·43 N	74·15 W
75	Irwin (ûr'-wĭn) Pa. (Pittsburgh In.)	40·19 N	79·42 W
136	Is (ēs) . . . . Sov. Un. (Urals In.)	58·48 N	59·44 E
88	Isaacs, Mt. (ē-sä-ä'ks) Pan. (Panama Canal In.)	9·22 N	79·01 W
90	Isabela (I.) (ê-sä-bē'-lä) . . . . . Mex.	21·56 N	105·53 W
98	Isabela (I.) (ē-sä-bā'lä) . . . . Ec.	0·47 S	91·35 W
95	Isabela, Cabo (C.) (kà'bô-ê-sä-bĕ'lä) . Dom. Rep.	20·00 N	71·00 W
92	Isabella, Cord. (Mts.) (kôr-dēl-yĕ'rä-ē-sä-bĕlä) . Nic.	13·20 N	85·37 W
80	Isabella Ind. Res. (ĭs-ȧ-bĕl'-lȧ) Mich.	43·35 N	84·55 W
129	Isaccea (ê-säk'chä) . . . . Rom.	45·16 N	28·26 E
112	Isafjördhur (ēs'à-fyûr-dŏŏr) . . . Ice.	66·09 N	22·39 W
165	Isangi (ē-säŋ'gē) . . . . Con. L.	0·48 N	24·13 E
120	Isar R. (ē'zär) . . . . Ger.	48·27 N	12·02 E
126	Isarco (R.) (ê-sär'kō) . . . . It.	46·37 N	11·25 E
155	Isaroga, Vol. (ê-sä-rô-gä) Phil. (Manila In.)	13·40 N	123·23 E
125	Ischia (ēs'kyä) . . . . It. (Napoli In.)	40·29 N	13·58 E
168	Iscia Baidoa Som. (Horn of Afr. In.)	3·19 N	44·20 E
126	Iseo, Lago di (L.) (lä'-gō-dē-ê-zĕ'ō) . It.	45·50 N	9·55 E
123	Isère (R.) (ē-zâr') . . . . Fr.	45·24 N	6·04 E
123	Iserlohn (ē'zĕr-lōn) Ger. (Ruhr In.)	51·22 N	7·42 E
126	Isernia (ê-zĕr'nyä) . . . . It.	41·35 N	14·14 E
153	Ise-Wan (B.) (ē'sĕ wän) . . . . . . Jap.	34·49 N	136·44 E
164	Iseyin . . . . Nig.	8·13 N	3·21 E
151	Ishan . . . . China	24·32 N	108·42 E
152	Ishikari Wan (B.) (ē'shē-kä-rē wän) . Jap.	43·30 N	141·05 E
134	Ishim (ĭsh-ĕm') . . . . Sov. Un.	56·07 N	69·13 E
134	Ishim (R.) . . . . Sov. Un.	53·17 N	67·45 E
136	Ishimbay (ē-shĕm-bī') Sov. Un. (Urals In.)	53·28 N	56·02 E
148	Ishing (yēsĭng) . . . . China	31·26 N	119·57 E
152	Ishinomaki (ĭsh-nō-mä'kē) . . . . Jap.	38·22 N	141·22 E
152	Ishinomaki Wan (B.) (ē-shē-nō-mä'kē wän) . Jap.	38·10 N	141·40 E
136	Ishly (ĭsh'lĭ) . Sov. Un. (Urals In.)	54·13 N	55·55 E
136	Ishlya (ĭsh'lyȧ) Sov. Un. (Urals In.)	53·54 N	57·48 E
127	Ishm . . . . Alb.	41·32 N	19·35 E
168	Ishmant . . . . . . U. A. R. (Nile In.)	29·17 N	31·15 E
71	Ishpeming (ĭsh'pê-mĭng) . . . . Mich.	46·28 N	87·42 W
148	Ishui (yē suī) . . . . China	35·49 N	118·40 E
167	Isipingo (ĭs-ĭ-pĭŋg-gō) S. Afr. (Natal In.)	29·59 S	30·58 E
133	Iskenderun (ĭs-kĕn'dĕr-ōōn) . . Tur.	36·45 N	36·15 E
115	İskenderun Körfezi (G.) . . . . . Tur.	36·22 N	35·25 E
133	Iskilip (ēs'kĭ-lĕp') . . . . Tur.	40·40 N	34·30 E
127	Iskŭr (R.) (ĭs'k'r) . . . . Bul.	43·05 N	23·37 E
124	Isla-Cristina (ĭs'lä-krê-stē'nä) . . Sp.	37·13 N	7·20 W
145	Islamabad . . . . W. Pak.	33·55 N	73·05 E
92	Isla Mujeres (ê's-lä-mōō-kĕ'rĕs) Mex. (Yucatan In.)	21·25 N	86·53 W
86	Island (I.) (ī'lănd) . . . . Can.	53·35 N	89·58 W
83	Islands, B. of (ī'lăndz) . . . . . . Can.	49·11 N	58·45 W
116	Islay (I.) (ī'lā) . . . . Scot.	55·55 N	6·35 W
122	Isle (R.) (ēl) . . . . Fr.	45·02 N	0·29 E
110	Isle of Axholme (Reg.) (ăks'-hôm) Eng.	53·33 N	0·48 W
116	Isle of Man (măn) . . . . Eur.	54·26 N	4·21 W
71	Isle Royale Nat'l Park (īl'roi-ăl') U. S.	47·57 N	88·37 W
69	Isleta (ês-lā'tä) (ī-lē'tȧ) . . N. Mex.	34·55 N	106·45 W
82	Isle Verte (ēl vĕrt') . . . . Can.	48·01 N	69·20 W
85	Islington (ĭs'lĭng-tŏn) Can. (Toronto In.)	43·39 N	79·31 W
	Ismailia, see Al Ismā'īlīyah		
168	Ismā'īlīyah Can. U. A. R. (Suez In.)	30·25 N	31·45 E
111	Ismaning (ēz'mä-nēng) Ger. (München In.)	48·14 N	11·41 E
168	Isnā (ēs'nȧ) . . . U. A. R. (Nile In.)	25·17 N	32·33 E
119	Isojärvi (L.) . . . . Fin.	61·47 N	22·00 E
133	Isparta (ē-spär'tȧ) . . . . Tur.	37·50 N	30·40 E
138	Israel . . . . Asia	31·00 N	35·00 E
65	Issaquah (ĭz'sä-kwăh) Wash. (Seattle In.)	47·32 N	122·02 W
123	Isselburg (ē'sĕl-bŏŏrg) Ger. (Ruhr In.)	51·50 N	6·28 E
122	Issoire (ē-swȧr') . . . . Fr.	45·32 N	3·13 E
122	Issoudun (ē-sōō-dăN') . . . . Fr.	46·56 N	2·00 E
123	Issum (ē'sōōm) . . . Ger. (Ruhr In.)	51·32 N	6·24 E
134	Issyk-Kul, Ozero (L.) . . . Sov. Un.	42·13 N	76·12 E
142	Istāda, Ab-i (L.) . . . . Afg.	32·29 N	69·25 E
133	Istanbul (ê-stän-bōōl') . . . . . Tur.	41·02 N	29·00 E
127	Istiaía (ĭs-tyī'yä) . . . . Grc.	38·58 N	23·11 E
98	Istmina (ēst-mē'nä) . . . . . . Col. (In.)	5·10 N	76·40 W
79	Istokpoga (L.) (ĭs-tŏk-pō'gȧ) Fla. (In.)	27·20 N	81·33 W
126	Istra (pen.) (ê-strä) . . . . Yugo.	45·18 N	13·48 E
127	Istranca Dağ (Mts.) (ĭ-strän'jȧ) Bul.-Turk.	41·50 N	27·25 E
122	Istres (ēs'tr') . . . Fr. (Marseille In.)	43·30 N	5·00 E
100	Itá (ē-tà') . . . . Par.	25·39 S	57·14 W
99	Itabaiana (ē-tä-bä-yà-nä) . . Braz.	10·42 S	37·17 W
101	Itabapoana (ē-tä'-bä-pôä'nä) Braz. (Rio de Janeiro In.)	21·19 S	40·58 W
101	Itabapoana (R.) Braz. (Rio de Janeiro In.)	21·11 S	41·18 W
101	Itabirito (ē-tä-bê-rē'tô) Braz. Rio de Janeiro (In.)	20·15 S	43·46 W
101	Itaboraí (ē-tä-bō-räē') Braz. (Rio de Janeiro In.)	22·46 S	42·50 W
99	Itabuna . . . . Braz.	14·47 S	39·17 W
101	Itacoara (ē-tä-kô'ä-rä) Braz. (Rio de Janeiro In.)	21·41 S	42·04 W
99	Itacoatiara (ē-tà-kwä-tyä'rä) Braz.	3·03 S	58·18 W
101	Itaguaí (ē-tä-gwä-ē') Braz. (Rio de Janeiro In.)	22·52 S	43·46 W
98	Itagüí (ē-tä'gwê) . . . . Col. (In.)	6·11 N	75·36 W
100	Itagui (R.) . . . . Braz. (In.)	22·53 S	43·43 W
100	Itaipava (ē-tī-pà'-vä) . . Braz. (In.)	22·23 S	43·09 W
100	Itaipu (ē-tī'pōō) . . . . Braz. (In.)	22·58 S	43·02 W
99	Itaituba (ê-tä'ĭ-tōō'bȧ) . . . . . . Braz.	4·12 S	56·00 W
100	Itajái (ē-tä-zhī') . . . . Braz.	26·52 S	48·39 W
101	Itajubá (ē-tä-zhōō-bä') Braz. (Rio de Janeiro In.)	22·26 S	45·27 W
168	Itala . . . . . . Som. (Horn of Afr. In.)	2·45 N	46·15 E
102	Italy (ĭt'ȧ-lê) . . . . Eur.	43·58 N	11·14 E
77	Italy . . . . Tex.	32·11 N	96·51 W
100	Itambi (ē-tà'm-bê) . . . . Braz. (In.)	22·44 S	42·57 W
153	Itami (ē'tä'mē') . . Jap. (Osaka In.)	34·47 N	135·25 E
101	Itapecerica (ē-tä-pĕ-sĕ-rē'kȧ) Braz. (Rio de Janeiro In.)	21·29 S	45·08 W
99	Itapecurú (R.) (ē-tä-pĕ-kōō-rōō') Braz.	4·05 S	43·49 W
99	Itapēcuru-Mirim (ê-tä-pĕ'kōō-rōō-mê-rēN') . . Braz.	3·17 S	44·15 W
101	Itaperuna (ē-tà-pâ-rōō'nä) Braz. (Rio de Janeiro In.)	21·12 S	41·53 W
101	Itapetininga (ē-tä-pĕ-tē-nē'N-gä) Braz. (Rio de Janeiro In.)	23·37 S	48·03 W
99	Itapira (ē-tȧ-pē'rȧ) . . . . Braz.	20·42 S	51·19 W
101	Itapira . Braz. (Rio de Janeiro In.)	21·27 S	46·47 W
142	Itarsi . . . . India	22·43 N	77·45 E
77	Itasca (ī-tăs'kȧ) . . . . Tex.	32·09 N	97·08 W
71	Itasca (L.) . . . . Minn.	47·13 N	95·14 W
101	Itatiaia, Pico da (Pk.) (pē'-kô-dȧ-ē-tä-tyȧ'ēä) Braz. (Rio de Janeiro In.)	22·18 S	44·41 W
101	Itatiba (ē-tä-tē'bȧ) Braz. (Rio de Janeiro In.)	23·01 S	46·48 W
101	Itaúna (ē-tä-ōō'nä) Braz. (Rio de Janeiro In.)	20·05 S	44·35 W
101	Itaverá (ē-tä-vĕ-rȧ') Braz. (Rio de Janeiro In.)	22·44 S	44·07 W
80	Ithaca (ĭth'ȧ-kȧ) . . . . Mich.	43·20 N	84·35 W
81	Ithaca . . . . N. Y.	42·25 N	76·30 W
127	Itháki (I.) (ē'thä-kē) . . . . Grc.	38·27 N	20·48 E
166	Itoko (ē-tō'kō) . . . . Con. L.	1·13 S	22·07 E
168	Iṭsā (ĕt'sȧ) . . . . U. A. R. (Nile In.)	29·13 N	30·47 E
101	Itu (ê-tōō') Braz. (Rio de Janeiro In.)	23·16 S	47·16 W
148	Itu . . . . China	36·42 N	118·30 E
98	Ituango (ē-twäŋ'gō) . . . . Col. (In.)	7·07 N	75·44 W
99	Ituiutaba (ē-tōō-ēōō-tä'bȧ) . . Braz.	18·56 S	49·17 W
101	Itumirim (ē-tōō-mê-rē'N) Braz. (Rio de Janeiro In.)	21·20 S	44·51 W
91	Itundujia Santa Cruz (ē-tōōn-dōō-hē'ä sä'n-tä krōō'z) . Mex.	16·50 N	97·43 W
152	It'ung . . . . China	43·15 N	125·10 E
92	Iturbide (ē'tōōr-bē'dhȧ) Mex. (Yucatan In.)	19·38 N	89·31 W
135	Iturup (I.) (ē-tōō-rōōp') . Sov. Un.	45·35 N	147·15 E
100	Ituzaingo (ē-tōō-zä-ē'n-gō) Arg. (In.)	34·24 S	58·40 W
111	Itzehoe (ē'tzĕ-hō) Ger. (Hamburg In.)	53·55 N	9·31 E
78	Iuka (ī-ū'kȧ) . . . . Miss.	34·47 N	88·10 W
101	Iúna (ē-ōō'-nä) Braz. (Rio de Janeiro In.)	20·22 S	41·32 W
134	Iva (R.) . . . . Sov. Un.	53·45 N	99·30 E
160	Ivanhoe (ĭv'ăn-hō) . . . . Austl.	32·53 S	144·10 E
128	Ivanovo (ê-vä'nô-vō) . . . . Sov. Un.	57·02 N	41·54 E
128	Ivanovo (Oblast) . . . . Sov. Un.	56·55 N	40·30 E
129	Ivanpol' (ē-vän'pôl) . . . . . Sov. Un.	49·51 N	28·11 E
136	Ivanteyevka (ê-vàn-tyĕ'yĕf-kȧ) Sov. Un. (Moskva In.)	55·58 N	37·56 E
136	Ivdel' (ĭv'dyĕl) Sov. Un. (Urals In.)	60·42 N	60·27 E
75	Ives (ī'vĕs) . Wis. (Milwaukee In.)	43·48 N	87·49 W
	Iviza I., see Ibiza, Isla de		
167	Ivohibé (ē-vô-hê-bā') . . . Malagasy	22·28 S	46·59 E
163	Ivory Coast . . . . Afr.	7·43 N	6·30 W
126	Ivrea (ê-vrĕ'ä) . . . . It.	45·25 N	7·54 E
87	Ivugivik . . . . Can.	62·17 N	77·52 W
152	Iwate Yama (Mt.) (ē-wä-tĕ-yä'mä) . Jap.	39·50 N	140·56 E
153	Iwaya (ē'wȧ-yȧ) . . Jap. (Osaka In.)	34·35 N	135·01 E
164	Iwo . . . . Nig.	7·52 N	4·04 E
90	Ixcateopán (ēs-kä-tā-ō-pän') . Mex.	18·29 N	99·49 W
111	Ixelles . . . . . . Bel. (Bruxelles In.)	50·49 N	4·23 E
91	Ixhuatán (San Francisco) (ēs-hwä-tän') . Mex.	16·19 N	94·30 W
90	Ixhuatlán (ēs-wàt-län') . . . . . . Mex.	20·41 N	98·01 W
90	Ixmiquilpan (ēs-mê-kēl'pän) . Mex.	20·30 N	99·12 W
167	Ixopo . . . . S. Afr. (Natal In.)	30·10 S	30·04 E
91	Ixtacalco (ēs-tà-käl'kō) Mex. (Mexico In.)	19·23 N	99·07 W
91	Ixtacihuatl (Mtn.) (ē'ks-tä-sē-wä'tl) . Mex. (Mexico In.)	19·10 N	98·38 W
91	Ixtaltepec (Asunción) (ēs-täl-tĕ-pĕk') . Mex.	16·33 N	95·04 W
91	Ixtapalapa (ēs'tä-pä-lä'pä) Mex. (Mexico In.)	19·21 N	99·06 W
91	Ixtapaluca (ēs'tä-pä-lōō'kä) Mex. (Mexico In.)	19·18 N	98·53 W
91	Ixtepec (êks-tĕ'pĕk) . . . . Mex.	16·37 N	95·09 W
91	Ixtlahuaca (ēs-tlä-wä'kä) Mex. (Mexico In.)	19·34 N	99·46 W
91	Ixtlán de Juárez (ēs-tlän' dā hwä'râz) . Mex.	17·20 N	96·29 W
90	Ixtlán del Río (ēs-tlän'dĕl rē'ō) Mex.	21·05 N	104·22 W
151	Iyang (ē'yäng') . . . . China	28·52 N	112·12 E
153	Iyo-Nada (Sea) (ē'yō nä-dä) . . Jap.	33·33 N	132·07 E
92	Izabal (ē'zä-bäl') . . . . Guat.	15·23 N	89·10 W
92	Izabal, L. (Golfo Dulce) (gôl'fō dōōl'sä) . Guat.	15·30 N	89·04 W
92	Izalco (ē-zäl'kō) . . . . Sal.	13·50 N	89·40 W
92	Izamal (ē-zä-mä'l) . Mex. (Yucatan)	20·55 N	89·00 W
132	Izhevsk (ē-zhyĕfsk') . . . . . Sov. Un.	56·50 N	53·15 E
132	Izhma (ĭzh'mȧ) . . . . Sov. Un.	65·00 N	54·05 E

ăt; finăl; rāte; senâte; ärm; ȧsk; sofȧ; fâre; ch-choose; dh-as th in other; bē; êvent; bĕt; recĕnt; cratēr; g-go; gh-guttural g; bĭt; ĭ-short neutral; rīde; K-guttural k as ch in German ich;

Page	Name	Pronunciation	Region	Lat. °'	Long. °'
132	Izhma (R.)		Sov. Un.	64·00 N	53·00 E
136	Izhora R. (ēz′hô-rà)				
			Sov. Un. (Leningrad In.)	59·36 N	30·20 E
129	Izmail (ēz-mà-ēl′)		Sov. Un.	27·21 N	28·49 E
127	Izmir (Smyrna)				
		(ĭz-mēr′) (smûr′nà)	Tur.	38·25 N	27·05 E
127	Izmir Körfezi (G.)		Tur.	38·43 N	26·37 E
133	Izmit (ĭz-mēt′)		Tur.	40·45 N	29·45 E
153	Izu (I.) (ē′zōō)		Jap.	34·32 N	139·25 E
153	Izuhara (ē′zōō-hä′rä)		Jap.	34·11 N	129·18 E
153	Izumo (ē′zōō-mō)		Jap.	35·22 N	132·45 E
153	Izumu-Ōtsu (ē′zōō-mōō ō′tsōō)		Jap. (Ōsaka In.)	34·30 N	135·24 E
111	Jaachimsthal (yä′kēm-stäl)		Ger. (Berlin In.)	52·58 N	13·45 E
144	Jabal Rema (Mtn.)		Yemen	14·13 N	44·38 E
120	Jablonec (Nad Nisou)				
		(yäb′lô-nyěts)	Czech.	50·43 N	15·12 E
121	Jablunkov P. (yäb′lōōn-kôf)	Czech.	49·31 N	18·35 E
99	Jaboatão (zhä-bô-à-toun′)	Braz.	8·14 S	35·08 W
144	Jabul Hadur Shuayb (Mtn.)		Yemen	15·45 N	43·45 E
125	Jaca (hä′kä)		Sp.	42·35 N	0·30 W
90	Jacala (hä-kä′lä)		Mex.	21·01 N	99·11 W
92	Jacaltenango (hä-käl-tě-näŋ′gō)	Guat.	15·39 N	91·41 W
101	Jacareí (zhä-kà-rě-ē′)		Braz. (Rio de Janeiro In.)	23·19 S	45·57 W
100	Jacarepagua (zhä-kä-rä′pä-gwä′)	Braz. (In.)	22·55 S	43·22 W
99	Jacarézinho (zhä-kä-rě′zě-nyô)	Braz.	23·13 S	49·58 W
120	Jachymov (yä′chĭ-môf)	Czech.	50·22 N	12·51 E
77	Jacinto City (hä-sěn′tō) (jà-sĭn′tō)	Tex. (In.)	29·45 N	95·14 W
72	Jacksboro (jäks′bŭr-ô)	Tex.	33·13 N	98·11 W
78	Jackson (jăk′sŭn)	Ala.	31·31 N	87·52 W
68	Jackson	Calif.	38·22 N	120·47 W
78	Jackson	Ga.	33·19 N	83·55 W
78	Jackson	Ky.	37·32 N	83·17 W
77	Jackson	La.	30·50 N	91·13 W
80	Jackson	Mich.	42·15 N	84·25 W
71	Jackson	Minn.	43·37 N	95·00 W
78	Jackson	Miss.	32·17 N	90·10 W
73	Jackson	Mo.	37·23 N	89·40 W
80	Jackson	Ohio	39·00 N	82·40 W
78	Jackson	Tenn.	35·37 N	88·49 W
161	Jackson, Port. Austl. (Sydney In.)	33·50 S	151·18 E
67	Jackson L.	Wyo.	43·57 N	110·28 W
167	Jacksontuin	S. Afr. (Johannesburg & Pretoria In.)	25·44 S	27·45 E
78	Jacksonville (jäk′sŭn-vĭl)	Ala.	33·52 N	85·45 W
79	Jacksonville	Fla.	30·20 N	81·40 W
73	Jacksonville	Ill.	39·43 N	90·12 W
77	Jacksonville	Tex.	31·58 N	95·18 W
79	Jacksonville Beach	Fla.	31·18 N	81·25 W
92	Jacmel (zhäk-měl′)	Hai.	18·15 N	72·30 W
76	Jaco, L. (hä′kō)	Mex.	27·51 N	103·50 W
142	Jacobābād	W. Pak.	28·22 N	28·27 E
99	Jacobina (zhä-kô-bē′nà)	Braz.	11·13 S	40·30 W
82	Jacques Cartier, Mt. (Tabletop) (zhäk′kär-tyā′)	Can.	48·59 N	65·59 W
85	Jacques-Cartier, R.	Can. (Quebec In.)	47·04 N	71·28 W
83	Jacques Cartier Pass	Can.	50·04 N	63·43 W
82	Jacquet River (zhä-kě′) (jäk′ět)	Can.	47·54 N	66·01 W
101	Jacuí (zhä-kōō-ē′)	Braz. (Rio de Janeiro In.)	21·03 S	46·43 W
101	Jacutinga (zhä-kōō-tēn′gä)	Braz. (Rio de Janeiro In.)	21·17 S	46·36 W
139	Jad′ah	Jordan (Palestine In.)	31·23 N	35·45 E
120	Jade B. (yä′dě)	Ger.	53·28 N	8·17 E
166	Jadotville	Con. L.	11·01 N	26·52 E
165	Jādū	Libya	31·57 N	12·04 E
98	Jaén (kä-ě′n)	Peru	5·38 S	78·49 W
124	Jaén	Sp.	37·45 N	3·48 W
160	Jaffa, C. (jăf′à)	Austl.	36·58 S	139·29 E
143	Jaffna (jäf′nà)	Ceylon	9·44 N	80·09 E
94	Jagüey Grande (hä′gwä grän′dä)	Cuba	22·35 N	81·05 W
139	Jahore Str.. Mala. (Singapore In.)	1·22 N	103·37 E
95	Jaibo (R.) (hä-ē′bō)	Cuba	20·10 N	75·20 W
142	Jaipur	India	26·45 N	77·00 E
142	Jaisaimer	India	27·00 N	70·54 E
126	Jajce (yī′tsě)	Yugo.	44·20 N	17·19 E
112	Jakobstad (yä′kôb-städh)	Fin.	63·33 N	22·31 E
91	Jalacingo (hä-lä-sĭŋ′gō)	Mex.	19·47 N	97·16 N
145	Jalalabād (jŭ-lä-lä-bäd′)	Afg. (Khyber Pass In.)	34·25 N	70·27 E
92	Jalapa (hä-lä′pä)	Guat.	14·38 N	89·58 W
91	Jalapa de Diaz (San Felipe) (dä dē-äz′) (sän fä-lē′pā)	Mex.	18·06 N	96·33 W
91	Jalapa del Marqués (děl mär-kās′)	Mex.	16·30 N	95·29 W
91	Jalapa Enriquez (ěn-rē′kāz)	Mex.	19·32 N	96·53 W
142	Jalgaon	India	21·08 N	75·33 E
90	Jalisco (hä-lēs′kō)	Mex.	21·27 N	104·54 W
88	Jalisco (State)	Mex.	20·00 N	104·45 W
127	Jalomita (R.)	Rom.	44·37 N	26·42 E
124	Jalón (R.) (hä-lōn′)	Sp.	41·22 N	1·46 W
91	Jalostotitlán (hä-lōs-tē-tlän′)	Mex.	21·09 N	102·30 W
91	Jalpa (häl′pä)	Mex.	18·12 N	93·06 W
90	Jalpa	Mex.	21·40 N	103·04 W
90	Jalpan (häl′pän)	Mex.	21·13 N	99·31 W
142	Jalpur	India	20·49 N	86·37 E
91	Jaltepec (häl-tä-pěk′)	Mex.	17·20 N	95·15 W
91	Jaltipan (häl′tē-pän)	Mex.	17·59 N	94·42 W
90	Jaltocan (häl-tô-kän′)	Mex.	21·08 N	98·32 W
165	Jālū (Oasis)	Libya	28·58 N	21·45 E
94	Jamaica (I.)	N. A.	18·21 N	77·31 W
95	Jamaica Cay (I.)	Ba. Is.	22·45 N	75·55 W
142	Jamalpur	E. Pak.	24·56 N	89·58 E
90	Jamay (hä-mī′)	Mex.	20·16 N	103·43 W
127	Jambol (yäm′bôl)	Bul.	42·28 N	26·31 E

Page	Name	Pronunciation	Region	Lat. °'	Long. °'
155	Jamdena (I.)	Indon.	7·23 S	130·30 E
73	James (R.)	Mo.	36·51 N	93·22 W
79	James (R.)	N. C.	36·07 N	81·48 W
62	James (R.)	U. S.	46·25 N	98·55 W
81	James (R.)	Va.	37·35 N	77·50 W
87	James B. (jāmz)	Can.	53·53 N	80·40 W
84	Jamesburg (jāmz′bûrg)	N. J. (New York In.)	40·21 N	74·26 W
95	James Pt.	Ba. Is.	25·20 N	76·30 W
158	James Ra.	Austl.	24·15 S	133·30 E
96	James Ross (I.)	Ant.	64·20 S	58·20 W
81	Jamestown (jāmz′toun)	N. Y.	42·05 N	79·15 W
70	Jamestown	N. D.	46·54 N	98·42 W
84	Jamestown.R. I.	(Providence In.)	41·30 N	71·21 W
167	Jamestown	S. Afr. (Natal In.)	31·07 S	26·49 E
70	Jamestown Res.	N. D.	47·16 N	98·40 W
91	Jamiltepec (hä-mēl-tä-pěk′)	Mex.	16·16 N	97·54 W
118	Jammerburgt (B.)	Den.	57·20 N	9·28 E
142	Jammu	India	32·50 N	32·51 E
142	Jammu and Kashmir (State) (kăsh-mēr′)	India	39·10 N	75·05 E
142	Jamnagar (jäm-nû′gŭr)	India	22·33 N	70·03 E
145	Jamrud (jäm′rōōd)	W. Pak. (Khyber Pass In.)	34·00 N	71·22 E
142	Jamshedpur (jäm′shěd-pōōr)	India	22·52 N	86·11 E
98	Jamundí (hä-mōō′n-dē′).Col. (In.)	3·15 N	76·32 W
124	Jándula (R.) (hän′dōō-lä)	Sp.	38·28 N	3·52 W
71	Janesville (jānz′vĭl)	Wis.	42·41 N	89·03 W
139	Janin	Jordan (Palestine In.)	32·27 N	35·19 E
112	Jan Mayen (I.) (yän mī′ěn)	Nor.	70·59 N	8·05 W
118	Jannelund (yän′ě-lōōnd)	Swe.	59·14 N	14·24 E
121	Jánoshalma (yä′nôsh-hôl-mô)	Hung.	46·17 N	19·18 E
121	Janów Lubelski (yä′nōōf lŭ-běl′skĭ)	Pol.	50·40 N	22·25 E
99	Januária (zhä-nwä′rě-à)	Braz.	15·31 S	44·17 W
145	Janvo Pk.	India	25·32 N	94·33 E
148	Jaoyang (jä′ō-yäng′)	China	38·16 N	115·45 E
139	Japan (jà-păn′)	Asia	36·30 N	133·30 E
152	Japan, Sea of (jà-păn′)	Asia	40·08 N	132·55 E
155	Japen (I.) (yä′pěn) . Neth. N. Gui.	1·30 S	136·15 E
100	Japeri (zhä-pě′rě)	Braz. (In.)	22·38 S	43·40 W
98	Japurá (R.) (zhä-pōō-rä′)	Braz.	1·30 S	67·54 W
95	Jarabacoa (kä-rä-bä-kô′à)	Dom. Rep.	19·05 N	70·40 W
90	Jaral del Progreso (hä-räl děl prô-grä′sō)	Mex.	20·21 N	101·05 W
124	Jarama (R.) (hä-rä′mä)	Sp.	40·33 N	3·30 W
139	Jarash	Jordan (Palestine In.)	32·17 N	35·53 E
94	Jardines, Banco (Bk.) (bä′n-kō-här-dē′nâs)	Cuba	21·45 N	81·40 W
99	Jari (R.) (zhä-rē′)	Braz.	0·28 S	53·00 W
122	Jarnac (zhär-näk′)	Fr.	45·42 N	0·09 W
121	Jarocin (yä-rō′tsyěn)	Pol.	51·58 N	17·31 E
146	Jaro Pk. (hä′rō)	China	30·45 N	101·49 E
121	Jaroslaw (yä-rôs-wäf)	Pol.	50·01 N	22·41 E
139	Jasin	Mala. (Singapore In.)	2·19 N	102·26 E
119	Jašiūnai (dzä-shōō-nà′yě)	Sov. Un.	54·27 N	25·25 E
144	Jāsk (jäsk)	Iran	25·46 N	57·48 E
121	Jaslo (yäs′wō)	Pol.	49·44 N	21·28 E
139	Jason B.	Mala. (Singapore In.)	1·53 N	104·14 E
80	Jasonville (jä′sŭn-vĭl)	Ind.	39·10 N	87·15 W
78	Jasper (jăs′pěr)	Ala.	33·50 N	87·17 W
86	Jasper	Can.	52·54 N	118·18 W
78	Jasper	Fla.	30·30 N	82·56 W
80	Jasper	Ind.	38·20 N	86·55 W
70	Jasper	Minn.	43·51 N	96·22 W
77	Jasper	Tex.	30·55 N	93·59 W
86	Jasper Natl. Park	Can.	53·09 N	117·45 W
85	Jasper Place..Can. (Edmonton In.)	53·32 N	113·36 W
121	Jászapáti (yäs′ō-pä-tě)	Hung.	47·29 N	20·10 E
91	Jataté (R.) (hä-tä-tä′)	Mex.	16·30 N	91·29 W
94	Jatibonico (hä-tē-bô-nē′kô)	Cuba	22·00 N	79·15 W
125	Játiva (hä′tē-vä)	Sp.	38·58 N	0·31 W
100	Jaú (zhä-ōō′)	Braz.	22·16 S	48·31 W
98	Jauja (zhä-ōō′zhä)	Peru	11·43 S	75·32 W
90	Jaumave (hou-mä′vä)	Mex.	23·23 N	99·24 W
119	Jaunjelgava (youn′yěl′gä-vä)	Sov. Un.	56·37 N	25·06 E
128	Jaunlatgale (youn′lat′gä-lě)	Sov. Un.	57·04 N	27·54 E
154	Java (I.) (jä′vá) (jä′và)	Indon.	8·35 S	111·11 E
98	Javari (R.) (kä-vä-rē)	Col.-Peru	4·25 S	72·07 W
154	Java Sea (jä′vá)	Indon.	5·10 S	110·30 E
125	Jávea (hä-vä′ä)	Sp.	38·45 N	0·07 E
120	Jawor (yä′vôr)	Pol.	51·04 N	16·12 E
121	Jaworzno (yä-vôzh′nô)	Pol.	50·11 N	19·18 E
136	Jayva R. (yäy′vä)	Sov. Un. (Urals In.)	59·13 N	57·17 E
121	Jázberény (yäs′bě-rän′)	Hung.	47·30 N	19·56 E
139	Jazzin	Leb. (Palestine In.)	33·34 N	35·37 E
77	Jeanerette (jěn-ēr-et′) (zhän-rět′)	La.	29·54 N	91·41 W
114	Jebal Aures (Mts.)	Alg.	35·16 N	5·53 E
164	Jebba (jěb′à)	Nig.	9·07 N	4·46 E
165	Jebel, Bahr el (R.)	Sud.	28·22 N	30·31 E
121	Jedrzejów (yän-dzhä′yōōf)	Pol.	50·38 N	20·18 E
85	Jefferson (jěf′ēr-sŭn)	Can. (Toronto In.)	43·55 N	79·26 W
78	Jefferson	Ga.	34·05 N	83·35 W
71	Jefferson	Iowa	42·10 N	94·22 W
77	Jefferson	Tex.	32·47 N	94·21 W
71	Jefferson	Wis.	42·59 N	88·45 W
66	Jefferson, Mt.	Ore.	44·41 N	121·50 W
73	Jefferson City	Mo.	38·34 N	92·10 W
67	Jefferson R.	Mont.	45·37 N	112·22 W
75	Jeffersontown (jěf′ēr-sŭn-toun)	Ky. (Louisville In.)	38·11 N	85·34 W
75	Jeffersonville (jěf′ēr-sŭn-vĭl)	Ind. (Louisville In.)	38·17 N	85·44 W
	Jehol, see Ch'engte			
115	Jeib, Wadi el (R.)	Jordan-Isr.	30·30 N	35·20 E
119	Jēkabpils (yěk′äb-pĭls)	Sov. Un.	56·29 N	25·50 E
120	Jelenia Góra (yě-lěn′yà gŏō′rà)	Pol.	50·53 N	15·43 E

Page	Name	Pronunciation	Region	Lat. °'	Long. °'
119	Jelgava (yěl′gä-và)	Sov. Un.	56·39 N	23·40 E
78	Jellico (jěl′ĭ-kō)	Tenn.	36·34 N	84·06 W
113	Jemmapes (zhě-map′)	Alg.	36·43 N	7·21 E
120	Jena (yā′nà)	Ger.	50·55 N	11·37 E
148	Jench'iu (rěnchēō)	China	38·44 N	116·05 E
79	Jenkins (jěn′kĭnz)	Ky.	37·09 N	82·38 W
84	Jenkintown (jěn′kĭn-toun)	Pa. (Philadelphia In.)	40·06 N	75·08 W
77	Jennings (jěn′ĭngz)	La.	30·14 N	92·40 W
80	Jennings	Mich.	44·20 N	85·20 W
74	Jennings.. Mo. (St. Louis In.)	38·43 N	90·16 W
99	Jequié (zhě-kyě′)	Braz.	13·53 S	40·06 W
99	Jequitinhonha (R.) (zhě-kē-tēn-ŏ′n-yä)	Braz.	16·47 S	41·19 W
95	Jérémie (zhä-rà-mē′)	Hai.	18·40 N	74·10 W
99	Jeremoabo (zhě-rä-mō-ä′bô)	Braz.	10·03 S	38·13 W
91	Jerez, Punta (Pt.) (pōō′n-tä-kě-rāz′)	Mex.	23·04 N	97·44 W
124	Jerez de la Frontera (kě-rāth′ dä lä frôn-tä′rä)	Sp.	36·42 N	6·09 W
124	Jerez de los Caballeros (kě-rath′ dä lōs kä-väl-yä′rôs)	Sp.	38·20 N	6·45 W
159	Jericho (jěr′ĭ-kō)	Austl.	28·38 S	146·24 E
168	Jericho (jěr-ĭkŏ)	S. Afr. (Johannesburg & Pretoria In.)	25·16 S	27·47 E
	Jericho, see Arīhā			
69	Jerome (jě-rōm′)	Ariz.	34·45 N	112·10 W
67	Jerome	Idaho	42·44 N	114·31 W
122	Jersey (I.) (jûr′zĭ)	Chan. Is.	49·13 N	2·07 W
84	Jersey City. N. J. (New York In.)	40·43 N	74·05 W
81	Jersey Shore	Pa.	41·10 N	77·15 W
85	Jerseyville (jěr′zě-vĭl)	Can. (Toronto In.)	43·12 N	80·08 W
73	Jerseyville	Ill.	39·07 N	90·18 W
139	Jerusalem (jě-rōō′sà-lěm)	Isr.-Jordan (Palestine In.)	31·46 N	35·14 E
154	Jesselton	N. Bor.	3·55 N	116·05 E
84	Jesuit Bend (jěz′ū-ĭt)	La. (New Orleans In.)	29·45 N	90·02 W
79	Jesup (jěs′ŭp)	Ga.	31·36 N	81·53 W
91	Jesús Carranza (hě-sōō′s-kär-rà′n-zä)	Mex.	17·26 N	95·01 W
70	Jewel Cave Natl. Mon.	S. D.	43·44 N	103·52 W
65	Jewell (jū′ěl) .. Ore. (Portland In.)	45·56 N	123·30 W
142	Jhālawār	India	24·29 N	79·09 E
142	Jhang Maghian	W. Pak.	31·21 N	72·19 E
142	Jhansi (jän′sě)	India	25·29 N	78·32 E
142	Jharsuguda	India	22·51 N	86·13 E
142	Jhelum (R.) (jā′lŭm)	W. Pak.	31·40 N	71·51 E
146	Jibhalanta	Mong.	47·49 N	97·00 E
69	Jicarilla Ind. Res. (kě-kä-rēl′yà)	N. Mex.	36·45 N	107·00 W
93	Jicaron, Isla (I.) (kě-kä-rōn′)	Pan.	7·14 N	81·41 W
121	Jiffa R.	Rom.	47·35 N	27·02 E
158	Jiggalong (jĭg′à-lông)	Austl.	23·20 S	120·45 E
95	Jiguani (kě-gwä-nē′)	Cuba	20·20 N	76·30 W
94	Jigüey, Bahía (B.) (bä-ě′à-kě′gwä)	Cuba	22·15 N	78·10 W
148	Jihchao (rě′jou)	China	35·27 N	119·28 E
120	Jihlava (yě′hlä-vä)	Czech.	49·23 N	15·33 E
168	Jijiga	Eth. (Horn of Afr. In.)	9·15 N	42·48 E
125	Jijona (kě-hō′nä)	Sp.	38·31 N	0·29 W
142	Jikyop	China	28·41 N	91·42 E
124	Jiloca (R.) (kě-lō′kä)	Sp.	41·13 N	1·30 W
92	Jilotepeque (kě-lō-tě-pě′kě)	Guat.	14·39 N	89·36 W
165	Jima	Eth.	7·41 N	36·52 E
127	Jimbolia (zhǐm-bô′lyä)	Rom.	45·45 N	20·44 E
90	Jiménez (kě-mä′nāz)	Mex.	24·12 N	98·29 W
76	Jimenez	Mex.	27·09 N	104·55 W
76	Jimenez	Mex.	29·03 N	100·42 W
90	Jiménez del Téul (tě-ōō′l)	Mex.	21·28 N	103·51 W
81	Jim Thorpe (jĭm′ thôrp′)	Pa.	40·50 N	75·45 W
78	Jim Woodruff Res.	Fla.-Ga.	30·57 N	84·46 W
120	Jindřichov Hradec (yěn′d′r-zhǐ-kōōf hrä′děts)	Czech.	49·09 N	15·02 E
165	Jinja (jĭn′jä)	Ug.	0·29 N	33·11 E
92	Jinotega (kě-nô-tā′gä)	Nic.	13·07 N	86·00 W
92	Jinotepe (kě-nô-tā′pě)	Nic.	11·52 N	86·12 W
153	Jinzū-Gawa (Strm.) (jěn′zōō gä′wä)	Jap.	36·26 N	137·18 E
98	Jipijapa (kě-pě-hä′pä)	Ec.	1·36 S	80·52 W
92	Jiquilisco (kě-kě-lē′s-kô)	Sal.	13·18 N	88·32 W
90	Jiquilpan de Juarez (kě-kēl′pän dä hwä′rāz)	Mex.	20·00 N	102·43 W
91	Jiquipilco (hě-kě-pē′l-kô)	Mex. (Mexico In.)	19·32 N	99·37 W
168	Jirga (jēr′gá) . U. A. R. (Nile In.)	26·20 N	31·51 E
146	Jirgalanta	Mong.	48·08 N	91·40 E
124	Jistredo, Sierra de (Mts.) (sě-ě′r-rä-dě-kěs-trě′dô)	Sp.	42·50 N	6·15 W
91	Jitotol (kě-tô-tōl′)	Mex.	17·03 N	92·54 W
99	João Pessoa (Paraíba) (shô-oun′ pě-sôá′) (pä-rä-ē′bä)	Braz.	7·09 S	34·45 W
101	João Ribeiro (zhô-oun-rē-bā′rōō)	Braz. (Rio de Janeiro In.)	20·42 S	44·03 W
94	Jobabo (R.) (hô-bä′bä)	Cuba	20·50 N	77·15 W
85	Jock R. (jök) . Can. (Ottawa In.)	45·08 N	75·51 W
90	Jocotepec (hô-kô-tä-pěk′)	Mex.	20·17 N	103·26 W
124	Jodar (hō′där)	Sp.	37·54 N	3·20 W
142	Jodhpur (jŏd′pōōr)	India	26·23 N	83·00 E
167	Joels	Bas. (Natal In.)	28·45 S	28·22 E
119	Joensuu (yŏ-ěn′sōō)	Fin.	62·35 N	29·46 E
153	Jōga-Shima (I.) (jō′gä shě′mä)	Jap. (Tōkyō In.)	35·07 N	139·37 E
128	Jõgeva (yû′gě-và)	Sov. Un.	58·45 N	26·23 E
82	Jogins	Can.	45·41 N	64·27 W
154	Jogjakarta (yŏg-yä-kär′tä)	Indon.	7·50 S	110·20 E
167	Johannesburg	S. Afr. (Johannesburg & Pretoria In.)	26·08 S	27·54 E
66	John Day R. (jŏn dä)	Ore.	44·46 N	120·15 W
66	John Day R., Middle Fork	Ore.	44·53 N	119·04 W
66	John Day R., North Fork	Ore.	45·03 N	118·50 W

220 John Martin–Kamen'-na-Obi PRONOUNCING INDEX

Page	Name Pronunciation Region	Lat. °′	Long. °′
72	John Martin Res. (jŏn mär'tĭn) Colo.	37·57 N	103·04 W
65	Johnson (R.) (jŏn'sŭn) Ore. (Portland In.)	45·27 N	122·20 W
81	Johnsonburg (jŏn'sŭn-bûrg) Pa.	41·30 N	78·40 W
80	Johnson City (jŏn'sŭn) Ill.	37·50 N	88·55 W
81	Johnson City N. Y.	42·10 N	76·00 W
79	Johnson City Tenn.	36·17 N	82·23 W
156	Johnston (I.) (jŏn'stŭn) Oceania	17·00 N	168·00 W
81	Johnstown (jonz'toun) N. Y.	43·00 N	74·20 W
81	Johnstown Pa.	40·20 N	78·50 W
147	Joho (Prov.) China	42·31 N	118·12 E
154	Johore (State) (jŭ-hōr') Mala.	2·15 N	103·00 E
139	Johore (R.) (jŭ-hōr') Mala. (Singapore In.)	1·39 N	103·52 E
139	Johore Bahru (bȧ-hŭ-rōō') Mala. (Singapore In.)	1·28 N	103·46 E
128	Jōhvi (yû'vĭ) Sov. Un.	59·21 N	27·21 E
122	Joigny (zhwȧn-yē') Fr.	47·58 N	3·26 E
100	Joinville (zhwăN-vēl') Braz.	26·18 S	48·47 W
122	Joinville Fr.	48·28 N	5·05 E
96	Joinville (I.) Ant.	63·80 S	53·80 W
90	Jojutla (hō-hōō'tlȧ) Mex.	18·39 N	99·11 W
112	Jökullsá (R.) (yû'kŏŏls-ô) Ice.	65·38 N	16·08 W
90	Jola (kō'lä) Mex.	21·08 N	104·26 W
75	Joliet (jō-lĭ-ĕt') Ill. (Chicago In.)	41·37 N	88·05 W
82	Joliette (zhô-lyĕt') Can.	46·01 N	73·30 W
154	Jolo (hō-lō) Phil.	5·59 N	121·05 E
154	Jolo (I.) Phil.	5·55 N	121·15 E
155	Jomalig (I.) (hô-mä'lēg) Phil. (Manila In.)	14·44 N	122·34 E
90	Jomulco (hô-mōōl'kô) Mex.	21·08 N	104·24 W
90	Jonacatepec (hō-nä-kä-tȧ-pĕk') Mex.	18·39 N	98·46 W
119	Jonava (yō-nä'vȧ) Sov. Un.	55·05 N	24·15 E
118	Jondal (yōn'dāl) Nor.	60.16 N	6·16 E
155	Jones (jōnz) Phil. (Manila In.)	13·56 N	122·05 E
155	Jones Phil. (Manila In.)	16·35 N	121·39 E
87	Jones, C. Can.	54·35 N	79·51 W
73	Jonesboro (jōnz'bûro) Ark.	35·49 N	90·42 W
77	Jonesboro La.	32·14 N	92·43 W
77	Jonesville (jōnz'vĭl) La.	31·35 N	91·50 W
80	Jonesville Mich.	42·00 N	84·45 W
119	Joniškis (yô'nĭsh-kĭs) Sov. Un.	56·14 N	23·36 E
118	Jönköping (yûn'chû-pĭng) Swe.	57·47 N	14·10 E
82	Jonquière (zhôN-kyâr') Can.	48·24 N	71·16 W
91	Jonuta (hô-nōō'tä) Mex.	18·07 N	92·09 W
122	Jonzac (zhôN-zȧk') Fr.	45·27 N	0·27 W
73	Joplin (jŏp'lĭn) Mo.	37·05 N	94·31 W
138	Jordan (jôr'dăn) Asia	30·15 N	38·00 E
139	Jordan (R.) Jordan (Palestine In.)	31·58 N	35·36 E
74	Jordan R. Utah (Salt Lake City In.)	40·42 N	111·56 W
145	Jorhat (jôr-hät') India	26·43 N	94·16 E
90	Jorullo, Vol. de (vôl-kȧ'n-dĕ-hô-rōōl'yō) Mex.	18·54 N	101·38 W
164	Jos (jôs) Nig.	9·53 N	8·56 E
158	Joseph Bonaparte, G. (jô'sĕf bô'nȧ-pȧrt) Austl.	13·30 S	128·40 E
85	Joseph L. (jô'sĕf lāk) Can. (Edmonton In.)	53·18 N	113·06 W
68	Joshua Tree Natl. Mon. (jô'shū-ȧ trē) Calif.	34·02 N	115·53 W
118	Jostedalsbroeen (Gl.) (yôstĕ-däls-brĕĕn) Nor.	61·40 N	6·55 E
118	Jotun Fjeld (Mts.) (yō'tōōn fyel') Nor.	61·44 N	8·11 E
94	Joulter's Cays (Is.) (jōl'tērz) Ba. Is.	25·20 N	78·10 W
123	Jouy-le-Chatel (zhwē-lĕ-shä-tĕl') Fr. (Paris In.)	48·40 N	3·07 E
94	Jovellanos (hō-vĕl-yä'nōs) Cuba	22·50 N	81·10 W
148	Ju (R.) (rōō) China	33·07 N	114·18 E
90	Juan Aldama (kōōȧ'n-äl-dä'mä) Mex.	24·16 N	103·21 W
66	Juan de Fuca, Str. of (hwän' dā fōō'kȧ) Wash.-Can.	48·25 N	124·37 W
167	Juan de Nova (I.) Malagasy	17·18 S	43·07 E
88	Juan Diaz, (R.) (kōōȧ'n-dē'-äz) Pan. (Panama Canal In.)	9·05 N	79·30 W
96	Juan Fernández, Islasde (Is.) (ē's-läs-dĕ-hwän' fĕr-nän'dāth) Chile	33·30 S	79·00 W
101	Juan L. Lacaze (hōōȧ'n-ĕ'lĕ-lä-kä'zĕ) Ur. (Buenos Aires In.)	34·25 S	57·28 W
94	Juan Luis, Cayos de (Is.) (kä-yōs-dĕ-hwän lōō-ēs') Cuba	22·15 N	82·00 W
99	Juázeiro (zhōōȧ'zā'rô) Braz.	9·27 S	40·28 W
99	Juazeiro do Norte (zhōōȧ'zā'rô-dô-nôr-tĕ) Braz.	7·16 S	38·57 W
100	Juárez (hōōȧ'rĕz) Arg.	37·42 S	59·46 W
165	Juba Sud.	4·58 N	31·37 E
168	Juba R. (jōō'bȧ) Som. (Horn of Afr. In.)	1·30 N	42·25 E
139	Jubayl (Byblos) (jōō-bĭl') Leb. (Palestine In.)	34·07 N	35·38 E
142	Jubbulpore (jŭb-ŭl-pōr') India	23·18 N	79·59 E
124	Júcar (R.) (hōō'kär) Sp.	39·10 N	1·22 W
94	Júcaro (hōō'kȧ-rô) Cuba	21·40 N	78·50 W
90	Juchipila (hōō-chē-pē'lä) Mex.	21·26 N	103.09 W
88	Juchitan (hōō-chē-tän') Mex.	16·15 N	95·00 W
91	Juchitán de Zaragoza (hōō-chē-tän' dā thä-rä-gō'thä) Mex.	16·27 N	95·03 W
90	Juchitlán (hōō-chē-tlän) Mex.	20·05 N	104·07 W
92	Jucuapa (kōō-kwä'pä) Sal.	13·30 N	88·24 W
144	Juddah Sau. Ar.	21·30 N	39·15 E
120	Judenburg (jōō'dĕn-bûrg) Aus.	47·10 N	14·40 E
67	Judith R. (jōō'dĭth) Mont.	47·20 N	109·36 W
127	Jui Rom.	44·45 N	23·17 E
151	Juian (jwĭ'än') China	27·48 N	120·40 E
92	Juigalpa (hwē-gäl'pä) Nic.	12·02 N	85·24 W
123	Juilly (zhwē-yē') Fr. (Paris In.)	49·01 N	2·41 E
117	Juist (I.) (yōō'ēst) Ger.	53·41 N	6.50 E
101	Juiz de Fora (zhōō-ēzh' dā fō'rä) Braz. (Rio de Janeiro In.)	21·47 S	43·20 W
100	Jujuy (hōō-hwē') Arg.	24·14 S	65·15 W
100	Jujuy (Prov.) (hōō-hwē') Arg.	23·00 S	65·45 W
148	Jukao (rōōgou) China	32·24 N	120·33 E
167	Jukskei (R.) S. Afr. (Johannesburg & Pretoria In.)	25·58 S	27·58 E
72	Julesburg (jōōlz'bûrg) Colo.	40·59 N	102·16 W
98	Juliaca (hōō-lē-ä'kä) Peru	15·26 S	70·12 W
49	Julianehaab Grnld.	60·70 N	46·20 W
123	Jülich (yü'lēk) Ger. (Ruhr In.)	50·55 N	6·22 E
126	Julijske Alpe (Mts.) (ū'lēy-skĕ' äl'pĕ) Yugo.	46·05 N	14·05 E
95	Jullia Molina (kōō'l-yä-mô-lē'nä) Dom. Rep.	19·20 N	69·40 W
142	Jullundur India	31·29 N	75·39 E
142	Julpaiguri India	26·35 N	88·48 E
167	Jumbla (Mtn.) (jum'blȧ) S. Afr. (Natal In.)	30·29 S	28·52 E
95	Jumento Cays (Is.) (hōō-mĕn'tō) Ba. Is.	23·05 N	75·40 W
117	Jumet (zhü-mĕ') Bel.	50·28 N	4·30 E
124	Jumilla (hōō-mēl'yä) Sp.	38·28 N	1·20 W
71	Jump (R.) (jŭmp) Wis.	45·18 N	90·53 W
85	Jumpingpound Cr. (jŭmp-ĭng-pound) Can. (Calgary In.)	51·01 N	114·34 W
99	Jumundá (R.) (zhōō-mōō'n-dä') Braz.	1·33 S	57·42 W
142	Junagādh (jōō-nä'gŭd) India	21·33 N	70·25 E
148	Junan (rōō nän) China	32·59 N	114·22 E
76	Junction (jŭŋk'shŭn) Tex.	30·29 N	99·48 W
73	Junction City Kans.	39·01 N	96·49 W
101	Jundiaí (zhōō'n-dyä-ē') Braz. (Rio de Janeiro In.)	23·12 S	46·52 W
64	Juneau (jōō'nō) Alaska	58·25 N	134·30 W
148	Jungch'eng (jōōng'chĕng') China	37·23 N	122·31 E
151	Jungchiang China	25·52 N	108·45 E
120	Jungfrau Pk. (yōōng'frou) Switz.	46·30 N	7·59 E
151	Junghsien China	22·48 N	110·38 E
101	Junín (hōō-nē'n) Arg. (Buenos Aires In.)	34·35 S	60·56 W
98	Junín Col. (In.)	4·47 N	73·39 W
139	Juniyah (jōō-nē'ē) Leb. (Palestine In.)	33·59 N	35·38 E
112	Junkeren (Mtn.) (yōōn'kĕ-rĕn) Nor.	66·29 N	14·58 E
83	Jupiter (jōō'pĭ-tēr) Can.	49·30 N	63·25 W
65	Jupiter, Mt. Wash. (Seattle In.)	47·42 N	123·04 W
116	Jura (I.) (jōō'rȧ) Scot.	56·09 N	6·45 W
123	Jura (Mts.) (zhü-rä') Switz.	46·55 N	6·49 E
116	Jura, Sd. of (jōō'rȧ) Scot.	55·45 N	5·55 W
119	Jurbarkas (yōōr-bär'käs) Sov. Un.	55·06 N	22·50 E
139	Jurf ad Darāwīsh Jordan (Palestine In.)	30·41 N	35·51 E
165	Jur R. (jōōr) Sud.	6·38 N	27·52 E
98	Juruá (R.) (zhōō-rōō-ä') Braz.	5·27 S	67·39 W
99	Juruena (R.) (zhōō-rōōĕ'nä) Braz.	12·22 S	58·34 W
98	Jutai (zhōō-tȧy) Braz.	4·26 S	68·16 W
92	Jutiapa (hōō-tē-ä'pä) Guat.	14·16 N	89·55 W
92	Juticalpa (hōō-tē-käl'pä) Hond.	14·35 N	86·17 W
90	Juventino Rosas (kōō-vĕn-tē'-nô-rō-säs) Mex.	20·38 N	101·02 W
123	Juvisy-sur-Orge (zhü-vē-sē'sür ôrzh') Fr. (Paris In.)	48·41 N	2·22 E
90	Juxtahuaca (hōōs-tlȧ-hwä'kä) Mex.	17·20 N	98·02 W
127	Južna Morava (R.) (ū'zhnȧ mô'rȧ-vȧ) Yugo.	42·30 N	22·00 E
118	Jylland (Reg.) Den.	56·04 N	9·00 E
119	Jyväskylä (yû'vĕs-kū-lĕ) Fin.	62·14 N	25·46 E
167	Kaalfontein (kärl-fōn-tān) S. Afr. (Johannesburg & Pretoria In.)	26·02 S	28·16 E
166	Kaappunt S. Afr. (Cape Town In.)	34·21 S	18·29 E
154	Kabaena (I.) (kȧ-bȧ-ā'nȧ) Indon.	5·35 S	121·07 E
164	Kabala (kȧ-bä'lȧ) S. L.	9·43 N	11·39 W
166	Kabalo (kȧ-bä'lō) Con. L.	6·09 S	26·52 E
166	Kabambare (kä-bäm-bä'rȧ) Con. L.	4·47 S	27·45 E
153	Kabe (kä'bā) Jap.	34·32 N	132·30 E
166	Kabinda (kȧ-bĕN'dä) Con. L.	6·13 S	24·16 E
139	Kabir (R.) Leb. (Palestine In.)	34·40 N	36·06 E
166	Kabompo (R.) (kȧ-bôm'pō) Fed. of Rh. & Nya.	13·52 S	23·45 E
166	Kabongo (kȧ-bông'ō) Con. L.	7·47 S	25·13 E
114	Kaboudia, Ras (C.) Tun.	35·17 N	11·28 E
142	Kābul (kä'bōōl) Afg.	34·39 N	69·14 E
145	Kabul (R.) (kä'bōōl) Asia	34·44 N	69·43 E
135	Kachuga (kȧ-chōō-gȧ) Sov. Un.	54·09 N	105·43 E
129	Kadiyevka (kȧ-dĭ-yĕf'kȧ) Sov. Un.	48·34 N	38·37 E
132	Kadnikov (käd'nē-kôf) Sov. Un.	59·30 N	40·10 E
164	Kaduna (kä-dōō'nä) Nig.	10·29 N	7·32 E
164	Kaédi (kä-ā-dē') Mauritania	16·20 N	13·32 W
157	Kaena Pt. (kä'ā-nä) Hawaii (In.)	21·33 N	158·19 W
152	Kaesong (Kaijo) (kä'ĕ-sŭng) (kī'jō) Kor.	38·00 N	126·35 E
165	Kafia Kingi (kä'fē-ȧ kĭŋ'gē) Sud.	9·17 N	24·28 E
166	Kafue (kä'fōō-ȧ) Fed. of Rh. & Nya.	15·45 S	28·17 E
166	Kafue (R.) Fed. of Rh. & Nya.	15·31 S	26·33 E
129	Kagal'nik (R.) (kä-gäl''nēk) Sov. Un.	46·58 N	39·25 E
166	Kagera (R.) (kȧ-gä'rȧ) Tan.	1·17 S	31·04 E
153	Kagoshima (kä'gō-shē'mä) Jap.	31·35 N	130·31 E
153	Kagoshima-Wan (B.) (kä'gō-shē'mä wän) Jap.	31·24 N	130·39 E
129	Kagul (ka-gōōl') Sov. Un.	45·49 N	28·17 E
154	Kahajan (R.) Indon.	1·45 S	113·40 E
73	Kahoka (kȧ-hō'kȧ) Mo.	40·26 N	91·42 W
157	Kahoolawe (I.) (kä-hōō-lä'wē) Hawaii (In.)	20·28 N	156·48 W
71	Kahshahpiwi (R.) Can.	48·24 N	90·56 W
157	Kahuku Pt. (kä-hōō'kōō) Hawaii (In.)	21·50 N	157·50 W
139	Kaiang Mala. (Singapore In.)	3·00 N	101·47 E
69	Kaibab Ind. Res. (kä'ē-bȧb) Ariz.	36·55 N	112·45 W
69	Kaibab Plat Ariz.	36·30 N	112·10 W
99	Kaieteur Fall (kī-ĕ-tōōr') Br. Gu.	4·48 N	59·24 W
148	K'aifeng (käi'fĕng) China	34·48 N	114·22 E
	Kaijo, see Kaesong		
152	Kaikyo, Sōya (Str.) (sô'yȧ kȧ-ē'kĭ-ō) Sov. Un.	45·45 N	141·20 E
157	Kailua (kä'ē-lōō'ä) Hawaii (In.)	19·49 N	155·59 W
155	Kaimana Neth. N. Gui.	3·32 S	133·47 E
159	Kaimanawa Ra. (kä'ē-mȧ-nä'wȧ) N. Z. (In.)	39·13 S	176·02 E
153	Kainan (kä'ē-nän') Jap.	34·09 N	135·14 E
148	Kaip'ing (kī-pĭng') China	40·25 N	122·20 E
164	Kairouan (kĕr-ōō-äN') Tun.	35·46 N	10·04 E
120	Kaiserslautern (kī-zĕrs-lou'tĕrn) Ger.	49·26 N	7·46 E
159	Kaitaia (kä-ē-tä'ē-ȧ) N. Z. (In.)	35·30 S	173·28 E
157	Kaiwi Chan (kä'ē-wē) Hawaii (In.)	21·10 N	157·38 W
151	Kaiyüan (kĭ'yōō-än') China	23·42 N	103·20 E
150	Kaiyuan (kĭ'yōō-än') China	42·30 N	124·00 E
64	Kaiyuh Mts. (kī-yōō') Alaska	64·25 N	157·38 W
112	Kajaani (kä'yȧ-nē) Fin.	64·15 N	27·16 E
154	Kajan, Sungai (Strm.) Indon.	1·45 N	115·38 E
139	Kajang, Gunong (Mt.) Mala. (Singapore In.)	2·47 N	104·05 E
153	Kajiki (kä'jē-kē) Jap.	31·44 N	130·41 E
129	Kakhovka (kä-kôf'kȧ) Sov. Un.	46·46 N	33·32 E
129	Kakhovskoye (L.) (kȧ-kôf'skô-yĕ) Sov. Un.	47·21 N	33·33 E
165	Kakindu (kȧ-kĭn'dōō) Ug.	1·06 N	32·59 E
64	Kaktovik (kăk-tō'vĭk) Alaska	70·08 N	143·51 W
168	Kalābishah U. A. R. (Nile In.)	23·26 N	32·55 E
133	Kalach (kȧ-lȧch') Sov. Un.	50·15 N	40·55 E
146	Kaladan (R.) Bur.	21·07 N	93·04 E
166	Kalahari Des. (kä-lä-hä'rē) Bech.	23·00 S	22·03 E
65	Kalama (kȧ-lăm'ȧ) Wash. (Portland In.)	46·01 N	122·50 W
65	Kalama (R.) Wash. (Portland In.)	46·03 N	122·47 W
127	Kalámai (kä-lä-mī') Grc.	37·04 N	22·08 E
80	Kalamazoo (kăl-ȧ-mȧ-zōō') Mich.	42·20 N	85·40 W
80	Kalamazoo (R.) Mich.	42·35 N	86·00 W
129	Kalanchak (kä-län-chäk') Sov. Un.	46·17 N	33·14 E
157	Kalapana (kä-lä-pȧ'nä) Hawaii (In.)	19·25 N	155·00 W
144	Kalar (Mtn.) Iran	31·43 N	51·41 E
142	Kalat (kŭ-lät') W. Pak.	29·05 N	66·36 E
154	Kalatoa (I.) Indon.	7·22 S	122·30 E
123	Kaldenkirchen (käl'dĕn-kēr-kĕn) Ger. (Ruhr In.)	51·19 N	6·13 E
150	Kalgan (käl-gän') China	40·45 N	114·58 E
158	Kalgoorlie (kăl-gōōr'lē) Austl.	30·45 S	121·35 E
115	Kaliakra, Nos (Pt.) Rom.	43·25 N	28·42 E
154	Kalimantan (Prov.) Indon.	1·00 S	113·48 E
128	Kalinin (Tver) (kä'lē-nēn) (tvĕr) Sov. Un.	56·52 N	35·57 E
128	Kalinin (Oblast) Sov. Un.	56·50 N	33·08 E
119	Kaliningrad (Königsberg) (kä-lē-nēn'grät) (kû'nĕks-bĕrgh) Sov. Un.	54·42 N	20·32 E
136	Kaliningrad (kä-lē-nēn'grät) Sov. Un. (Moskva In.)	55·55 N	37·49 E
129	Kalinkovichi (kä-lēn-ko-vē'chē) Sov. Un.	52·07 N	29·19 E
66	Kalispel Ind. Res. (kăl-ĭ-spĕl') Wash.	48·25 N	117·30 W
67	Kalispell (kăl'ĭ-spĕl) Mont.	48·12 N	114·18 W
121	Kalisz (kä'lēsh) Pol.	51·45 N	18·05 E
112	Kalix (R.) (kä'lēks) Swe.	67·12 N	21·41 E
166	Kalkfeld (kälk'fĕlt) S. W. Afr.	21·05 S	16·05 E
166	Kalkfontein (kälk'fōn-tān) S. W. Afr.	27·50 S	18·40 E
118	Kalmar (käl'mär) Swe.	56·40 N	16·19 E
118	Kalmar Sund (Sd.) (käl'mär) Swe.	56·30 N	16·17 E
129	Kal'mius (R.) (käl''myōōs) Sov. Un.	47·15 N	37·38 E
111	Kalmthout Bel. (Bruxelles In.)	51 23 N	4·28 E
143	Kalmunai Ceylon	7·22 N	81·49 E
133	Kalmyk A. S. S. R. (kăl'mĭk) Sov. Un.	46·56 N	46·00 E
121	Kalocsa (kä'lō-chä) Hung.	46·32 N	19·00 E
157	Kalohi Chan. (kä-lō'hĭ) Hawaii (In.)	20·55 N	157·15 W
166	Kalomo (kä-lō'mō) Fed. of Rh. & Nya.	17·06 S	26·22 E
142	Kalsubai Mt India	24·43 N	73·47 E
111	Kaltenkirchen (käl'tĕn-kēr-kĕn) Ger. (Hamburg In.)	53·50 N	9·57 E
143	Kālu (R.) India (Bombay In.)	19·18 N	73·14 E
128	Kaluga (kȧ-lōō'gä) Sov. Un.	54·29 N	36·12 E
128	Kaluga (Oblast) Sov. Un.	54·10 N	34·30 E
118	Kalundborg (kä-lōōn''bôr') Den.	55·42 N	11·07 E
121	Kalush (kä'lōōsh) Sov. Un.	49·02 N	24·24 E
119	Kalvarija (käl-vä-rē'yȧ) Sov. Un.	54·24 N	23·17 E
136	Kal'ya (käl'yȧ) Sov. Un. (Urals In.)	60·17 N	59·58 E
143	Kalyān India (Bombay In.)	19·16 N	73·07 E
128	Kalyazin (käl-yȧ'zĕn) Sov. Un.	57·13 N	37·55 E
135	Kalyma (R.) Sov. Un.	66·32 N	152·46 E
132	Kama (L.) Sov. Un.	55·28 N	51·00 E
132	Kama (R.) (kä'mä) Sov. Un.	56·52 N	54·35 E
164	Kamabai (kä-mä-bä'ē) S. L.	9·13 N	11·56 W
152	Kamaishi (kä'mä-ē'shē) Jap.	39·16 N	142·03 E
153	Kamakura (kä'mä-kōō'rä) Jap. (Tōkyō In.)	35·19 N	139·33 E
144	Kamarān (I.) (Br.) Aden	15·19 N	41·47 E
166	Kambove (käm-bō'vĕ) Con. L.	10·58 S	26·43 E
135	Kamchatka, P-Ov (Pen.) Sov. Un.	55·19 N	157·45 E
135	Kamchatka (R.) Sov. Un.	54·15 N	158·38 E
123	Kamen (kä'mĕn) Ger. (Ruhr In.)	51·35 N	7·40 E
129	Kamenets Podol'skiy (kȧ-mä'nĕts pô-dôl'skĭ) Sov. Un.	48·41 N	26·34 E
126	Kamenjak, Rt (C.) (kä'mĕ-nyäk) Yugo.	44·45 N	13·57 E
129	Kamenka (kä-mĕŋ'kȧ) Sov. Un.	48·02 N	28·43 E
121	Kamenka Sov. Un.	50·06 N	24·20 E
134	Kamen'-na-Obi (kä-mĭny'nŭ ô'bē) Sov. Un.	53·43 N	81·28 E

ăt; finăl; rāte; senȧte; ärm; ȧsk; sofȧ; fâre; ch-choose; dh-as th in other; bē; ēvent; bĕt; recĕnt; cratēr; g-go; gh-guttural g; bĭt; ĭ-short neutral; rīde· K-guttural k as ch in German ich;

PRONOUNCING INDEX Kamensk-Shakhtinskiy–Kawagoe 221

Page	Name Pronunciation Region	Lat. °′	Long. °′
129	Kamensk-Shakhtinskiy (kä'mĕnsk shäk'tĭn-skĭ) . Sov. Un.	48·17 N	40·16 E
136	Kamensk-Ural'skiy (kä'mĕn-skĭ o͞o-räl'skĭ) Sov. Un. (Urals In.)	56·27 N	61·55 E
120	Kamenz (kä'mĕnts) ... Ger.	51·16 N	14·05 E
153	Kameoka (kä'mä-ōkä) Jap. (Ōsaka In.)	35·01 N	135·35 E
142	Kāmet (Mt.) ... India	35·50 N	79·42 E
120	Kamień Pomorski ... Pol.	53·57 N	14·48 E
153	Kamikoma (kä'mê-kō'mä) Jap. (Ōsaka In.)	34·45 N	135·50 E
166	Kamina ... Con. L.	8·41 S	25·01 E
71	Kaministikwia (R.) (kȧ-mĭ-nĭ-stĭk'wĭ-ȧ) . Can.	48·40 N	89·41 W
86	Kamloops (kăm'lo͞ops) ... Can.	50·41 N	120·19 W
	Kammer, see Atter See		
142	Kampa Dzong ... China	28·23 N	89·42 E
165	Kampala (käm-pä'lä) ... Ug.	0·14 N	32·34 E
154	Kampar (Strm.) (käm'pär) Indon.	0·30 N	101·30 E
111	Kampenhout Bel. (Bruxelles In.)	50·56 N	4·33 E
123	Kamp-Lintfort (kämp-lĕnt'fŏrt) Ger. (Ruhr In.)	51·30 N	6·34 E
154	Kampot (käm'pōt) ... Camb.	10·41 N	104·07 E
120	Kamp R. (kämp) ... Aus.	48·30 N	15·45 E
86	Kamsack (kăm'săk) ... Can.	51·32 N	102·00 W
136	Kamskoye Vodokranilishche (L.) Sov. Un. (Urals In.)	59·03 N	56·48 E
93	Kamuk, Cerro (Mt.) (sĕ'r-rô-kä-mo͞o'k) . C. R.	9·18 N	83·02 W
152	Kamu Misaki (C.) (kä'mo͞o mê-sä'kē) . Jap.	43·25 N	139·35 E
129	Kamyshevatskaya (kȧ-mwēsh'ĕ-vät'skä-yȧ) . Sov. Un.	46·24 N	37·58 E
133	Kamyshin (kä-mwēsh'ĭn) Sov. Un.	50·08 N	45·20 E
132	Kamyshlov (kä-mēsh'lôf) Sov. Un.	56·50 N	62·32 E
151	Kan (R.) (kän) ... China	26·50 N	115·00 E
134	Kan (R.) ... Sov. Un.	56·30 N	94·17 E
69	Kanab (kăn'ăb) ... Utah	37·00 N	112·30 W
69	Kanab Plat. ... Ariz.	36·31 N	112·55 W
136	Kanabeki (kȧ-nä'byĕ-kĭ) Sov. Un. (Urals In.)	57·48 N	57·16 E
64	Kanaga (I.) (kă-nä'gä) ... Alaska	52·02 N	177·38 W
153	Kanagawa (Pref.) (kä'nä-gä'wä) Jap. (Tōkyō In.)	35·29 N	139·32 E
153	Kanamachi (kä-nä-mä'chē) Jap. (Tōkyō In.)	35·46 N	139·52 E
136	Kananikol'skoye (kȧ-nȧ-nĭ-kôl' skô-yĕ) . Sov. Un. (Urals In.)	52·48 N	57·29 E
92	Kanasín (kä-nä-sē'n) Mex. (Yucatan In.)	20·54 N	89·31 W
64	Kanatak (kă-nă'tŏk) ... Alaska	57·35 N	155·48 W
63	Kanawha (R.) (kȧ-nô'wȧ) ... U. S.	37·55 N	81·50 W
153	Kanaya (kä-nä'yä) Jap. (Tōkyō In.)	35·10 N	139·49 E
115	Kanayis, Rasel (C.) ... U. A. R.	31·14 N	28·08 E
153	Kanazawa (kä'nȧ-zä'wȧ) ... Jap.	36·34 N	136·38 E
142	Kanchenjunga, Mt. (kĭn-chĭn-jo͝oŋ'gȧ) . Nep.	32·40 N	88·18 E
145	Kandahār (kŭn-dŭ-här') ... Afg.	31·43 N	65·58 E
166	Kanda Kanda (kän'dȧ kän'dȧ) Con. L.	6·51 S	23·27 E
132	Kandalaksha (kȧn-dȧ-lȧk'shȧ) Sov. Un.	67·10 N	33·05 E
132	Kandalakshskiy Zaliv (B.) Sov. Un.	66·20 N	35·00 E
119	Kandava (kän'dȧ-vȧ) ... Sov. Un.	57·03 N	22·45 E
164	Kandi (käN-dē') ... Dahomey	11·09 N	3·02 E
142	Kandiaro ... W. Pak.	27·09 N	68·12 E
143	Kandy (kän'dê) ... Ceylon	7·18 N	80·42 E
81	Kane (kān) ... Pa.	41·40 N	78·50 W
157	Kaneohe B. (kä-nä-ō'hā) Hawaii (In.)	21·32 N	157·40 W
129	Kanëv (kä-nyôf') ... Sov. Un.	49·46 N	31·27 E
129	Kanevskaya (kȧ-nyĕf'skȧ-yȧ) Sov. Un.	46·07 N	38·58 E
160	Kangaroo (I.) (kăŋ-gȧ-ro͞o') Austl.	36·05 S	137·05 E
144	Kangāvar (kŭŋ'gä-vär) ... Iran	34·37 N	46·45 E
154	Kangean (I.) (käŋ'gê-än) .. Indon.	6·50 S	116·22 E
152	Kanggye (käng'gyĕ) ... Kor.	40·55 N	126·40 E
152	Kanghwa (I.) (käng'hwä) ... Kor.	37·28 N	126·00 E
152	Kangnŭng (käng'no͝ong) ... Kor.	37·42 N	128·50 E
166	Kango (käN-gō') ... Gabon	0·14 N	10·07 E
146	K'angting ... China	30·15 N	101·58 E
151	Kanhsien ... China	25·50 N	115·00 E
87	Kaniapiskau (L.) (kă-nĭ-ăp'ĭs-kô) Can.	54·04 N	71·20 W
87	Kaniapiskau (R.) ... Can.	56·52 N	68·53 W
132	Kanin, P-Ov. (Pen.) (kȧ-nēn') Sov. Un.	68·00 N	45·00 E
132	Kanin Nos, Mys (C.) ... Sov. Un.	68·40 N	44·00 E
127	Kanjiža (kä'nyê-zhä) ... Yugo.	46·05 N	20·02 E
75	Kankakee (kăŋ-kȧ-kē') Ill. (Chicago In.)	41·07 N	87·53 W
80	Kankakee (R.) ... Ill.	41·15 N	88·15 W
164	Kankan (käN-käN) (kän-kän') . Gui	10·20 N	9·16 W
150	Kannan ... China	47·50 N	123·30 E
79	Kannapolis (kăn-ăp'ô-lĭs) ... N. C.	35·30 N	80·38 W
153	Kannoura (kä'nō-o͞o'rä) ... Jap.	33·34 N	134·18 E
164	Kano (kä'nō) ... Nig.	12·03 N	8·32 E
166	Kanonberg (Mtn.) S. Afr. (Cape Town In.)	33·49 S	18·37 E
72	Kanopolis Res. (kăn-ŏp'ô-lĭs) Kans.	38·44 N	98·01 W
142	Kānpur (kän'pûr) ... India	26·33 N	80·19 E
62	Kansas (State) (kăn'zȧs) ... U. S.	38·30 N	99·40 W
73	Kansas (R.) ... Kans.	39·08 N	95·52 W
74	Kansas City Kans. (Kansas City In.)	39·06 N	94·39 W
74	Kansas City . Mo. (Kansas City In.)	39·05 N	94·35 W
134	Kansk ... Sov. Un.	56·14 N	95·43 E
152	Kansōng ... Kor.	38·09 N	128·29 E
146	Kansu (Prov.) (kän'so͞o') ... China	38·00 N	102·06 E
154	Kan Tang (kän'täng') ... Thai.	7·26 N	99·28 E
92	Kantunilkin (kän-to͞o-nēl-kē'n) Mex. (Yucatan In.)	21·07 N	87·30 W
136	Kanzhakovskiy Kamen Gora (kȧn-zhä'kôvs-kēê kämĭen) Sov. Un. (Urals In.)	59·38 N	59·12 E
151	Kaoan ... China	28·30 N	115·02 E
148	Kaoch'eng (kä'ō-chĕng') ... China	34·56 N	114·57 E
149	Kaoch'iao ... China (Shanghai In.)	31·21 N	121·35 E
151	Kaohsiung (kä'ō-syo͝ong') ... China	22·35 N	120·25 E
148	Kaoi (gou'yē) ... China	37·37 N	114·39 E
164	Kaolack ... Senegal	14·02 N	16·16 W
148	Kaomi (gou'mē) ... China	36·23 N	119·46 E
148	Kaoshun (gou'sho͞on) ... China	31·22 N	118·50 E
148	Kaot'ang (kä'ō-täng') ... China	36·52 N	116·12 E
151	Kaoteng Shan (Mtns.) ... China	26·30 N	110·00 E
165	Kaovar (Oasis) ... Niger	19·16 N	13·09 E
151	Kaoyao ... China	23·08 N	112·25 E
148	Kaoyu (gou'yü) ... China	32·46 N	119·26 E
151	Kaoyu Hu (L.) (kä'ō-yo͞o'ho͞o) China	32·42 N	118·40 E
134	Kapal (kȧ-päl') ... Sov. Un.	45·13 N	79·08 E
120	Kapfenberg (kȧp'fĕn-bĕrgh) .. Aus.	47·27 N	15·16 E
121	Kaposvár (kô'pôsh-vär) ... Hung.	46·21 N	17·45 E
152	Kapsan (käp'sän') ... Kor.	40·59 N	128·22 E
154	Kapuas, Sungai (Strm.) (kä'po͞o-äs) . Indon.	2·05 S	114·15 E
87	Kapuskasing ... Can.	49·28 N	82·22 W
133	Kapustin Yar (kä'po͞os-tĕn yär') Sov. Un.	48·30 N	45·40 E
160	Kaputar, Mt. (kă-pû-tăr) ... Austl.	30·11 S	150·11 E
120	Kapuvár (kô'po͞o-vär) ... Hung.	47·35 N	17·02 E
134	Kara (kärȧ) ... Sov. Un.	68·42 N	65·30 E
132	Kara (R.) ... Sov. Un.	68·30 N	65·20 E
136	Karabanovo (kä'rȧ-bȧ-nō-vô) Sov. Un. (Moskva In.)	56·19 N	38·43 E
136	Karabash (kô-rȧ-bäsh') Sov. Un. (Urals In.)	55·27 N	60·14 E
133	Kara-Bogaz-Gol, Zaliv (B.) (kȧrä' bŭ-gäs') . Sov. Un.	41·30 N	53·40 E
128	Karachev (kȧ-rä-chôf') ... Sov. Un.	53·08 N	34·54 E
142	Karachi ... Pak.	24·59 N	68·56 E
103	Karacumy (Des.) ... Sov. Un.	39·08 N	59·53 E
133	Karadeniz Boğazi (Bosporous) (Str.) . Tur.	41·10 N	29·10 E
133	Karaganda (kȧ-rȧ-gän'dä) Sov. Un.	49·42 N	73·18 E
136	Karaidel (kä'rĭ-dĕl) Sov. Un. (Urals In.)	55·52 N	56·54 E
133	Kara-Khobda (R.) (kä-rä ĸôb'dȧ) . Sov. Un.	50·40 N	55·00 E
145	Karakoram Pass ... India	35·35 N	77·45 E
146	Karakoram Ra. (kä'rä kō'ro͝om) India	35·24 N	76·38 E
146	Karakorum (Ruins) ... Mong.	47·25 N	102·22 E
133	Karaköse (kä-rä-kŭ'sĕ) ... Tur.	39·50 N	43·10 E
130	Karakumy (kara-kum) (Des.) Sov. Un.	40·00 N	57·00 E
133	Karaman (kä-rä-män') ... Tur.	37·10 N	33·00 E
159	Karamea Bght. (kȧ-rȧ-mē'ȧ bĭt) N. Z. (In.)	41·10 S	170·42 E
144	Karand ... Iran	34·08 N	46·19 E
	Kara Sea, see Karskoye More		
153	Karatsu (kä'rȧ-tso͞o) ... Jap.	33·28 N	129·59 E
134	Karaul (kä-rä-o͞ol') ... Sov. Un.	70·13 N	83·46 E
120	Karawanken Mts. ... Aus.	46·32 N	14·07 E
144	Karbala (kŭr'bȧ-lä) ... Iraq	32·31 N	43·58 E
121	Karcag (kär'tsäg) ... Hung.	47·18 N	20·58 E
127	Kardhítsa ... Grc.	39·23 N	21·57 E
119	Kärdla (kĕrd'lȧ) ... Sov. Un.	58·59 N	22·44 E
165	Kareima (kä-rā'mȧ) ... Sud.	18·34 N	31·49 E
130	Karelian (A. S. S. R.) ... Sov. Un.	62·30 N	32·35 E
166	Karema ... Tan.	6·47 S	30·29 E
134	Kargat (kär-gät') ... Sov. Un.	55·17 N	80·07 E
	Karghalik, see Yehch'eng		
132	Kargopol (kär-gō-pōl'') ... Sov. Un.	61·30 N	38·50 E
127	Kariaí ... Grc.	40·14 N	24·15 E
166	Kariba Res. ... Fed. of Rh. & Nya.	17·30 S	28·06 E
166	Karibib (kȧr'ȧ-bĭb) ... S. W. Afr.	21·55 S	15·50 E
143	Kārikāl (kä-rê-käl') ... India	10·58 N	79·49 E
164	Karimama (kä-rê-mä'mȧ) Dahomey	12·04 N	3·09 E
154	Karimata, Pulau-Pulau (Is.) (kä-rê-mä'tȧ) . Indon.	1·08 S	108·10 E
154	Karimata, Selat (Str.) ... Indon.	1·15 S	107·10 E
154	Karimundjawa (I.) (kä'rê-mo͞on-yä'vä) . Indon.	5·36 S	110·15 E
168	Karin (kȧr'ĭn) Som. (Horn of Afr. In.)	10·43 N	45·50 E
155	Karkar (I.) (kär'kär) . N. Gui. Ter.	4·50 S	146·45 E
134	Karkaralinsk (kär-kär-ä-lēnsk') Sov. Un.	49·18 N	75·28 E
129	Karkinitskiy Zailv (B.) (kär-kê-net'skĭ-ê zä'lĭf) . Sov. Un.	45·50 N	32·45 E
120	Karl-Marx-Stadt (Chemnitz) . Ger.	50·48 N	12·53 E
126	Karlobag (kär-lō-bäg') ... Yugo.	44·30 N	15·03 E
126	Karlovac (kär'lô-väts) ... Yugo.	45·29 N	15·16 E
129	Karlovka (kär'lôv-kȧ) ... Sov. Un.	49·26 N	35·08 E
127	Karlovo (kär'lô-vô) ... Bul.	42·39 N	24·48 E
120	Karlovy Vary (kär'lô-vê vä'rê) Czech.	50·13 N	12·53 E
118	Karlshamn (kärls'häm) ... Swe.	56·11 N	14·50 E
118	Karlskrona (kärls'krô-nä) ... Swe.	56·10 N	15·33 E
120	Karlsruhe (kärls'ro͞o-ĕ) ... Ger.	49·00 N	8·23 E
118	Karlstad (kärl'städ) ... Swe.	59·25 N	13·28 E
64	Karluk (kär'lŭk) ... Alaska	57·30 N	154·22 W
118	Karmöy (I.) (kärm-ûe) ... Nor.	59·14 N	5·00 E
127	Karnobat (kär-nō'bät) ... Bul.	42·39 N	26·59 E
120	Kärnten (Carinthia) (State) (kĕrn'tĕn) . Aus.	46·55 N	13·42 E
166	Karonga (kȧ-rōŋ'gȧ) Fed. of Rh. & Nya.	9·52 S	33·57 E
115	Kárpathos (I.) ... Grc.	35·34 N	27·26 E
136	Karpinsk (kär'pĭnsk) Sov. Un. (Urals In.)	59·46 N	60·00 E
133	Kars (kärs) ... Tur.	40·35 N	43·00 E
134	Karsakpay (kär-säk-pī') .. Sov. Un.	47·47 N	67·07 E
128	Kārsava (kär'sä-vä) ... Sov. Un.	56·46 N	27·39 E
145	Karshi (kär'shē) ... Sov. Un.	38·30 N	66·08 E
134	Karskiye Vorota, Proliv (Str.) Sov. Un.	70·30 N	58·07 E
134	Karskoye More (Kara Sea) Sov. Un.	74·08 N	65·45 E
136	Kartaly (kȧr'tá lê) Sov. Un. (Urals In.)	53·05 N	60·40 E
143	Karunagapalli ... India	9·09 N	76·34 E
121	Karvina ... Czech.	49·50 N	18·30 E
166	Kasaī (R.) ... Con. L.	3·45 S	19·07 E
166	Kasama (kȧ-sä'mȧ) Fed. of Rh. & Nya.	10·15 S	31·13 E
166	Kasanga (kȧ-säŋ'gȧ) ... Tan.	8·27 S	31·13 E
153	Kasaoka (kä'sȧ-ō'kȧ) ... Jap.	34·33 N	133·29 E
152	Kasari Saki (C.) (kä'sä-rē sä-kē) Jap.	28·25 N	130·10 E
164	Kasba-Tadla (käs'bȧ-täd'lȧ) . Mor.	32·37 N	5·57 W
166	Kasempa (kȧ-sĕm'pȧ) Fed. of Rh. & Nya.	13·15 S	25·41 E
166	Kasenga (kȧ-seŋ'gȧ) ... Con. L.	10·27 S	28·42 E
144	Kash (R.) (kŭsh) ... Afg.	32·27 N	64·15 E
144	Kāshān (kä-shän') ... Iran	33·52 N	51·15 E
	Kashqar, see Sufu		
153	Kashihara (kä'shê-hä'rä) Jap. (Ōsaka In.)	34·35 N	135·38 E
128	Kashin (kä-shēn') ... Sov. Un.	57·20 N	37·38 E
128	Kashira (kä-shē'rȧ) ... Sov. Un.	54·49 N	38·11 E
153	Kashiwa (kä'shê-wä) Jap. (Tōkyō In.)	35·51 N	139·58 E
152	Kashiwazaki (kä'shē-wä-zä'kê) Jap.	37·06 N	138·17 E
	Kashmir, see Jammu and Kashmir		
142	Kashmor ... W. Pak.	28·33 N	69·34 E
136	Kashtak (kăsh'tȧk) Sov. Un. (Urals In.)	55·18 N	61·25 E
128	Kasimov (kȧ-sē'môf) ... Sov. Un.	54·56 N	41·23 E
64	Kaskanak (kăs-kă'năk) ... Alaska	60·00 N	158·00 W
80	Kaskaskia (R.) (kăs-kăs'kĭ-ȧ) .. Ill.	38·45 N	89·15 W
	Kaskinem, see Kaskö		
119	Kaskö (Kaskinen) (käs'kû) (käs'kē-nĕn) . Fin.	62·24 N	21·18 E
136	Kasli (käs'lĭ) . Sov. Un. (Urals In.)	55·54 N	60·46 E
166	Kasongo (kä-sôŋ'gō) ... Con. L.	4·31 S	26·42 E
115	Kásos (I.) ... Grc.	35·20 N	26·55 E
165	Kassala (kä-sä'lä) ... Sud.	15·26 N	36·28 E
120	Kassel (käs'ĕl) ... Ger.	51·19 N	9·30 E
71	Kasson (kăs'ŭn) ... Minn.	44·01 N	92·45 W
133	Kastamonu (kä-stä-mō'no͞o) .. Tur.	41·20 N	33·50 E
126	Kastélli ... Grc. (Inset)	35·13 N	24·11 E
115	Kastellórizon (C.) ... Tur.	36·01 N	30·00 E
127	Kastoría (kȧs-tō'rĭ-ȧ) ... Grc.	40·28 N	21·17 E
127	Kastron (käs'trôn) ... Grc.	39·52 N	25·01 E
142	Kasur ... W. Pak.	31·10 N	74·29 E
167	Kat (R.) (kăt) . S. Afr. (Natal In.)	32·57 S	26·50 E
82	Katahdin, Mt. (kȧ-tä'dĭn) .. Maine	45·56 N	68·57 W
166	Katanga (Reg.) (kȧ-täŋ'gȧ) Con. L.	8·35 S	23·59 E
158	Katanning (kȧ-tăn'ĭng) ... Austl.	33·45 S	117·45 E
136	Katav-Ivanovsk (kä'tăf ĭ-vä'nôfsk) . Sov. Un. (Urals In.)	54·46 N	58·13 E
136	Kateninskiy (kȧtyĕ'nĭs-kĭ) Sov. Un. (Urals In.)	53·12 N	61·05 E
127	Kateríni ... Grc.	40·18 N	22·36 E
165	Katherina, G. (Pk.) ... U. A. R.	28·43 N	34·00 E
158	Katherine (kăth'ĕr-ĭn) ... Austl.	14·15 S	132·20 E
142	Kathiawar Pen. (kä'tyȧ-wär') India	27·18 N	70·32 E
85	Kathryn (kăth'rĭn) Can. (Calgary In.)	51·13 N	113·42 W
74	Kathryn .. Calif. (Los Angeles In.)	33·42 N	117·45 W
142	Katiha ... India	25·39 N	87·39 E
64	Katmai Natl. Mon. (kăt'mī) Alaska	58·38 N	155·00 W
142	Kātmāndu (kät-män-do͞o') ... Nep.	27·49 N	85·21 E
142	Katni (kăt'nê) ... India	23·38 N	80·10 E
121	Katowice ... Pol.	50·15 N	19·00 E
118	Katrineholm (kȧ-trē'nĕ-hōlm) Swe.	59·01 N	16·10 E
136	Katsbakhskiy (kȧts-băk'skĭ) Sov. Un. (Urals In.)	52·57 N	59·37 E
164	Katsina (kät'sê-nȧ) ... Nig.	13·03 N	7·39 E
164	Katsina Ala (ä'lȧ) ... Nig.	7·15 N	9·12 E
153	Katsura (R.) (kä'tso͞o-rä) Jap. (Ōsaka In.)	34·55 N	135·43 E
134	Katta-Kurgan (kȧ-tȧ-ko͞or-gän') Sov. Un.	39·45 N	66·42 E
118	Kattegat (Str.) (kăt'ĕ-găt) ... Eur.	56·57 N	11·25 E
134	Katun' (R.) (kȧ-to͞on') ... Sov. Un.	51·30 N	86·18 E
111	Katwijkaan Zee Neth. (Amsterdam In.)	52·12 N	4·23 E
157	Kauai (I.) ... Hawaii (In.)	22·09 N	159·15 W
157	Kauai Chan. (kä-o͞o-ä'ē) Hawaii (In.)	21·35 N	158·52 W
120	Kaufbeuren (kouf'boi-rĕn) ... Ger.	47·52 N	10·38 E
77	Kaufman (kôf'măn) ... Tex.	32·36 N	96·18 W
71	Kaukauna (kô-kô'nȧ) ... Wis.	44·17 N	88·15 W
157	Kaulakahi Chan. (kä'o͞o-lȧ-kä'hê) Hawaii (In.)	22·00 N	159·55 W
157	Kaunakakai (kä'o͞o-nȧ-kä'kĭ) Hawaii (In.)	21·06 N	156·59 E
119	Kaunas (Kovno) (kou'nȧs) (kôv'nō) . Sov. Un.	54·52 N	23·54 E
164	Kaure Namoda ... Nig.	12·41 N	7·32 E
127	Kavajë (kä-vä'yŭ) ... Alb.	41·11 N	19·36 E
127	Kavála (kä-vä'lä) ... Grc.	40·55 N	24·24 E
127	Kavallas, Kólpos (G.) ... Grc.	40·45 N	24·20 E
155	Kavieng (kä-vê-ĕng') . N. Gui. Ter.	2·44 S	151·02 E
144	Kavir-E Lut (Des.) ... Iran	31·47 N	58·38 E
153	Kawagoe (kä-wä-gō'ā) Jap. (Tōkyō In.)	35·55 N	139·29 E

PRONOUNCING INDEX Kilmarnock–Kolyma 223

Page	Name Pronunciation Region	Lat. °′	Long. °′
116	Kilmarnock (kĭl mär'nŭk)...Scot.	55·38 N	4·25 W
116	Kilrush (kĭl'rŭsh)...Ire.	52·40 N	9·16 W
167	Kilwa Kivinje...Tan.	8·43 S	39·18 E
160	Kimba (kĭm'bȧ)...Austl.	33·08 S	136·25 E
70	Kimball (kĭm-bȧl)...Nebr.	41·14 N	103·41 W
70	Kimball...S. D.	43·44 N	98·58 W
86	Kimberley (kĭm'bēr-lĭ)...Can.	49·48 N	115·55 W
166	Kimberley...S. Afr.	28·40 S	24·50 E
127	Kími...Grc.	38·38 N	24·05 E
127	Kímolos (I.) (kē'mô-lôs)...Grc.	36·52 N	24·20 E
128	Kimry (kĭm'rė)...Sov. Un.	56·53 N	37·24 E
154	Kinabalu, Mt...N. Bor.	5·45 N	115·26 E
80	Kincardine (kĭn-kär'dĭn)...Can.	44·10 N	81·15 W
77	Kinder (kĭn'dēr)...La.	30·30 N	92·50 W
86	Kindersley (kĭn'dērz-lė)...Can.	51·30 N	109·10 W
164	Kindia (kĭn'dė-ȧ)...Gui.	10·02 N	12·49 W
166	Kindu-Port-Empain...Con. L.	2·59 S	25·59 E
132	Kinel'-Cherkassy...Sov. Un.	53·32 N	51·32 E
128	Kineshma (kė-nĕsh'mȧ)..Sov. Un.	57·27 N	41·02 E
85	King (kĭng)...Can. (Toronto In.)	43·56 N	79·32 W
160	King (I.)...Austl.	39·35 S	143·40 E
160	Kingaroy (kĭŋ'gȧ-roi)...Austl.	26·37 S	151·50 E
68	King City (kĭng sĭ'tĭ)...Calif.	36·12 N	121·08 W
72	Kingfisher (kĭng'fĭsh-ēr)...Okla.	35·51 N	97·55 W
158	King George Sd. (jôrj)...Austl.	35·17 S	118·30 E
128	Kingisepp (kĭŋ-gė-sep')..Sov. Un.	59·22 N	28·38 E
158	King Leopold Ranges (lē'ô-pōld) Austl.	16·35 S	125·00 E
69	Kingman (kĭng'mȧn)...Ariz.	35·10 N	114·05 W
72	Kingman (kĭng'mȧn)...Kans.	37·38 N	98·07 W
68	Kings (R.)...Calif.	36·28 N	119·43 W
68	Kings Canyon Natl. Park (kăn'yŭn) Calif.	36·52 N	118·53 W
110	Kingsclere (kĭngs-clēr) Eng. (London In.)	51·18 N	1·15 W
160	Kingscote (kĭngz'kŭt)...Austl.	35·45 S	137·32 E
117	Kings Lynn (kĭngz lĭn')...Eng.	52·45 N	0·20 E
79	Kings Mt...N. C.	35·13 N	81·30 W
110	Kings Norton (nôr'tŭn)...Eng.	52·25 N	1·54 W
158	King Sd...Austl.	16·50 S	123·35 E
84	Kings Park (kĭngz pärk) N. Y. (New York In.)	40·53 N	73·16 W
67	Kings Pk...Utah	40·46 N	110·20 W
79	Kingsport (kĭngz'pōrt)...Tenn.	36·33 N	82·36 W
160	Kingston (kĭngz'tŭn)...Austl.	37·52 S	139·52 E
81	Kingston...Can.	44·15 N	76·30 W
94	Kingston...Jam.	18·00 N	76·45 W
81	Kingston...N. Y.	42·00 N	74·00 W
81	Kingston...Pa.	41·15 N	75·50 W
65	Kingston...Wash. (Seattle In.)	47·04 N	122·29 W
93	Kingstown (kĭngz'toun)... W. I. F. (Le. & Wind. Is. In.)	13·10 N	61·14 W
79	Kingstree (kĭngz'trē)...S. C.	33·30 N	79·50 W
76	Kingsville (kĭngz'vĭl)...Tex.	27·32 N	97·52 W
86	King William I. (kĭng wĭl'yăm) Can.	69·25 N	97·00 W
167	King William's Town (kĭng-wĭl'-yŭmz-toun). S. Afr. (Natal In.)	32·53 S	27·24 E
74	Kinloch (kĭn-lŏk) Mo. (St. Louis In.)	38·44 N	90·19 W
116	Kinnairds Hd. (kĭn-ârdś hĕd) Scot.	57·42 N	3·55 W
153	Kinomoto (kē'nō-mōtō)...Jap.	33·53 N	136·07 E
153	Kinosaki (kē'nō-sä'kė)...Jap.	35·38 N	134·47 E
116	Kinsale Hbr. (kĭn-sāl')...Ire.	51·35 N	8·17 W
72	Kinsley (kĭnz'lĭ)...Kans.	37·55 N	99·24 W
79	Kinston (kĭnz'tŭn)...N. C.	35·15 N	77·35 W
164	Kintampo (kēn-tăm'pō)...Ghana	8·05 N	1·44 W
116	Kintyre Pen...Scot.	55·50 N	5·40 W
	Kiorashi, see Ōmori		
72	Kiowa (kī'ō-wȧ)...Kans.	37·01 N	98·30 W
73	Kiowa...Okla.	34·42 N	95·53 W
127	Kiparissía...Grc.	37·17 N	21·43 E
127	Kiparissiakós Kólpos (G.)...Grc.	37·28 N	21·15 E
166	Kipembawe (kė-pĕm-bä'wȧ).Tan.	7·43 S	33·22 E
74	Kirby (kŭr'bĭ) Tex. (San Antonio In.)	29·29 N	98·23 W
77	Kirbyville (kŭr'bĭ-vĭl)...Tex.	30·39 N	93·54 W
135	Kirenga (R.) (kė-rĕŋ'gȧ).Sov. Un.	56·30 N	103·18 E
135	Kirensk (kē-rĕnsk')...Sov. Un.	57·47 N	108·22 E
145	Kirgizskiy Khrebet (Kirgiz) (Mts.).Sov. Un.	37·58 N	72·23 E
130	Kirgiz S. S. R. (kĭr-gēz').Sov. Un.	41·45 N	74·38 E
130	Kirgiz Steppe (Plain)...Sov. Un.	49·28 N	57·07 E
	Kirin, see Chilin		
	Kirin, see Chilung		
110	Kirkby-in-Ashfield (kûrk'bē-ĭn-ăsh'fēld)..Eng.	53·06 N	1·16 W
116	Kirkcaldy (kēr-kô'dĭ)...Scot.	56·06 N	3·15 W
85	Kirkfield Park (kûrk-fēld) Can. (Winnipeg In.)	49·53 N	97·16 W
110	Kirkham (kûrk'ăm)...Eng.	53·47 N	2·53 W
65	Kirkland (kûrk'lănd) Wash. (Seattle In.)	47·41 N	122·12 W
87	Kirkland Lake...Can.	48·14 N	80·06 W
127	Kirklareli (kêrk'lár-ĕ'lė)...Tur.	41·44 N	41·43 E
73	Kirksville (kûrks'vĭl)...Mo.	40·12 N	92·35 W
144	Kirkūk (kĭr-ko͞ok')...Iraq	35·28 N	44·22 E
116	Kirkwall (kûrk'wôl)...Scot.	58·58 N	2·59 W
74	Kirkwood (kûrk'wo͝od) Mo. (St. Louis In.)	38·35 N	90·24 W
167	Kirkwood...S. Afr. (Natal In.)	33·26 S	25·24 E
120	Kirn (kêrn)...Ger.	49·47 N	7·23 E
128	Kirov...Sov. Un.	54·04 N	34·19 E
132	Kirov...Sov. Un.	58·35 N	49·35 E
133	Kirovabad (kē-rŭ-vŭ-bät') Sov. Un.	40·40 N	46·20 E
136	Kirovgrad (kē'rŭ-vŭ-grad) Sov. Un. (Urals In.)	57·26 N	60·03 E
129	Kirovograd (kē-rŭ-vŭ-grät') Sov. Un.	48·33 N	32·17 E
129	Kirovograd (Oblast)...Sov. Un.	48·23 N	31·10 E
132	Kirovsk...Sov. Un.	67·40 N	33·58 E
136	Kirovsk (kė-rôfsk') Sov. Un. (Leningrad In.)	59·52 N	30·59 E
133	Kirsanov (kêr-sȧ'nôf)...Sov. Un.	52·40 N	42·40 E
133	Kirşehir (kêr-shĕ'hēr)...Tur.	39·10 N	34·00 E
142	Kirthar Ra. (kĭr-tŭr)...W. Pak.	30·40 N	67·20 E
110	Kirton (kûr'tŭn)...Eng.	53·29 N	0·35 W
112	Kiruna (kē-ro͞o'nä)...Swe.	67·49 N	20·08 E
72	Kirwin Res. (kûr'wĭn)...Kans.	39·34 N	99·04 W
153	Kiryū (kē'rĭ-o͞o)...Jap.	36·26 N	139·18 E
128	Kirzhach (kêr-zhäk')...Sov. Un.	56·08 N	38·53 E
167	Kisaki (kē-sä'kē)...Tan.	7·37 S	37·43 E
126	Kisámou, Kólpos (G.) Grc. (Inset)	35·40 N	23·37 E
153	Kisarazu (kē'sȧ-rȧ'zo͞o) Jap. (Tōkyō In.)	35·23 N	139·55 E
134	Kiselëvsk (kē-sĭ-lyôfsk') Sov. Un.	54·05 N	86·19 E
166	Kisenyi (kē'sĕn'yē)...Con. L.	1·43 S	29·15 E
129	Kishinëv (ke-shė-nyôf')..Sov. Un.	47·02 N	28·52 E
153	Kishiwada (kē'shė-wä'dä)...Jap.	34·25 N	135·18 E
136	Kishkino (kēsh'kĭ-nô) Sov. Un. (Moskva In.)	55·15 N	38·04 E
64	Kiska (I.) (kĭs'kä)...Alaska	52·08 N	177·10 E
121	Kiskunfélegyháza (kĭsh'ko͝on-fā'lĕd-y'hä'zô).Hung.	46·42 N	19·52 E
121	Kiskunhalas (kĭsh'ko͝on-hô'lôsh) Hung.	46·24 N	19·26 E
121	Kiskunmajsa (kĭsh'ko͝on-mī'shô) Hung.	46·29 N	19·42 E
167	Kismayu...Som.	0·18 S	42·30 E
153	Kiso-Gawa (Strm.) (kē'sō-gä'wä) Jap.	35·29 N	137·12 E
153	Kiso-Sammyaku (Mts.) (kē'sō säm'myȧ-ko͞o).Jap.	35·47 N	137·39 E
164	Kissidougou (kē'sė-do͞o'go͞o)..Gui.	9·19 N	10·26 W
79	Kissimmee (kĭ-sĭm'ė)...Fla. (In.)	28·17 N	81·25 W
79	Kissimmee (L.)...Fla. (In.)	27·58 N	81·17 W
79	Kissimmee (R.)...Fla. (In.)	27·45 N	81·07 W
112	Kistrand (kē'stränd)...Nor.	70·29 N	25·01 E
121	Kisujszallás (kĭsh'o͞o'y'sä'lāsh) Hung.	47·12 N	20·47 E
166	Kisumu (kē'so͞o-mo͞o)...Ken.	0·05 S	34·49 E
139	Kiswah...Syria (Palestine In.)	33·31 N	36·13 E
164	Kita (kē'tȧ)...Mali	13·05 N	9·33 W
152	Kitakami Gawa (R.) (kė'tȧ-kä'mē gä-wä).Jap.	39·20 N	141·10 E
80	Kitchener (kĭch'ĕ-nēr)...Can.	43·25 N	80·35 W
166	Kitega (kē-tä'gä).Ruanda Urundi	3·39 S	30·05 E
165	Kitgum (kĭt'go͞om)...Ug.	3·29 N	33·04 E
115	Kíthira (I.)...Grc.	36·15 N	22·56 E
127	Kíthnos (I.)...Grc.	37·24 N	24·10 E
86	Kitimat...Can.	54·01 N	128·11 W
65	Kitsap (kĭt-săp) Wash. (Seattle In.)	47·45 N	122·32 W
153	Kitsuki (kēt'so͞o-kē)...Jap.	33·24 N	131·35 E
81	Kittaning (kĭ-tăn'ĭng)...Pa.	40·50 N	79·30 W
84	Kittatinny Mts. (kĭ-tȧ-tĭ'nė) N. J. (New York In.)	41·16 N	74·44 W
82	Kittery (kĭt'ēr-ĭ)...Maine	43·07 N	70·45 W
111	Kittsee...Aus. (Wien In.)	48·05 N	17·05 E
79	Kitty Hawk (kĭt'tė hôk)...N. C.	36·04 N	75·42 W
120	Kitzingen (kĭt'zĭng-ĕn)...Ger.	49·44 N	10·08 E
166	Kivu (L.)...Con. L.	2·00 S	28·30 E
136	Kizel (kē'zĕl).Sov. Un. (Urals In.)	59·05 N	57·42 E
133	Kizil Irmak (R.) (kĭz'ĭl ĭr-mäk') Tur.	40·15 N	34·00 E
136	Kizil'skoye (kĭz'ĭl-skô-yĕ) Sov. Un. (Urals In.)	52·43 N	58·53 E
133	Kizlyar (kĭz-lyär')...Sov. Un.	44·00 N	46·50 E
153	Kizu (kē'zo͞o)...Jap. (Ōsaka In.)	34·43 N	135·49 E
103	Kizyl-Arvat (kē'zĭl-ŭr-vät') Sov. Un.	38·55 N	56·33 E
111	Klaaswaal.Neth. (Amsterdam In.)	51·46 N	4·25 E
120	Kladno (kläd'nō)...Czech.	50·10 N	14·05 E
120	Klagenfurt (klä'gĕn-fo͝ort)...Aus.	46·38 N	14·19 E
119	Klaipéda (Memel) (klī'pȧ-dȧ) (mā'mĕl).Sov. Un.	55·43 N	21·10 E
66	Klamath Falls...Ore.	42·13 N	121·49 W
66	Klamath Ind. Res. (klăm'ăth).Ore.	42·48 N	121·40 E
66	Klamath Mts...Calif.	42·00 N	123·25 W
66	Klamath R...Calif.	41·27 N	123·35 W
139	Klang...Mala. (Singapore In.)	3·02 N	101·27 E
139	Klang (R.).Mala. (Singapore In.)	3·00 N	101·38 E
118	Klar-älven (R.)...Swe.	60·40 N	13·00 E
65	Klaskanine (R.) (klăs'kȧ-nīn) Ore. (Portland In.)	46·02 N	123·43 W
120	Klatovy (klȧ'tô-vė)...Czech.	49·23 N	13·18 E
64	Klawak (klā'wăk)...Alaska	55·32 N	133·10 W
85	Kleinburg (klīn-bûrg) Can. (Toronto In.)	43·51 N	79·38 W
111	Klein Machnow (klīn-mäĸ'nō) Ger. (Berlin In.)	52·22 N	13·12 E
167	Kleinmond...S. Afr. (Natal In.)	33·33 S	27·04 E
168	Klerksdorp (klĕrks'dôrp)..S. Afr. (Johannesburg & Pretoria In.)	26·52 S	26·40 E
168	Klerkskraal (klĕrks'kräl)..S. Afr. (Johannesburg & Pretoria In.)	26·15 S	27·10 E
128	Kletnya (klyĕt'nyȧ)...Sov. Un.	52·19 N	33·14 E
128	Kletsk (klĕtsk)...Sov. Un.	53·04 N	26·43 E
123	Kleve (klĕ'fĕ)...Ger. (Ruhr In.)	51·47 N	6·09 E
66	Klickitat R...Wash.	46·01 N	121·07 W
128	Klimovichi (klē-mô-vē'chė) Sov. Un.	53·37 N	31·21 E
136	Klimovsk (klĭ'môfsk) Sov. Un. (Moskva In.)	55·21 N	37·32 E
128	Klin (klēn)...Sov. Un.	56·18 N	36·43 E
118	Klintehamn (klēn'tē-häm)...Swe.	57·24 N	18·14 E
128	Klintsy (klĭn'tsĭ)...Sov. Un.	52·46 N	32·14 E
168	Klipgat...S. Afr. (Johannesburg & Pretoria In.)	25·26 S	27·57 E
168	Klip R. (klĭp)...S. Afr. (Johannesburg & Pretoria In.)	27·18 S	29·25 E
126	Ključ (klyo͞och)...Yugo.	44·32 N	16·48 E
120	Kłodzko (klôd'skô)...Pol.	50·26 N	16·38 E
64	Klondike Reg. (klŏn'dīk) Alaska-Can.	64·12 N	142·38 W
111	Klosterfelde (klōs'tĕr-fĕl-dĕ) Ger. (Berlin In.)	52·47 N	13·29 E
111	Klosterneuburg (klōs-tĕr-noi'bo͞orgh).Aus. (Wien In.)	48·19 N	16·20 E
139	Kluang...Mala. (Singapore In.)	2·01 N	103·19 E
121	Kluczbork (klo͞och'bŏrk)...Pol.	50·59 N	18·15 E
128	Klyaz'ma (R.) (klyäz'mȧ) Sov. Un.	55·49 N	39·19 E
135	Klyuchevskaya (Vol.) (klyo͞o-chĕfskä'yä).Sov. Un.	56·13 N	160·00 E
136	Klyuchi (klyo͞o'chĭ) Sov. Un. (Urals In.)	57·03 N	57·20 E
127	Knežha (knyā'zhȧ)...Bul.	43·27 N	24·03 E
70	Knife (R.) (nīf)...N. D.	47·06 N	102·33 W
80	Knightstown (nīts'toun)...Ind.	39·45 N	85·30 W
126	Knin (knēn)...Yugo.	44·02 N	16·14 E
120	Knittelfeld...Aus.	47·13 N	14·50 E
155	Knob Pk. (nŏb).Phil. (Manila In.)	12·30 N	121·20 E
116	Knockmealdowa Mts. (nŏk-mēl'doun).Ire.	52·13 N	8·09 W
110	Knottingley (nŏt'ĭng-lĭ)...Eng.	53·42 N	1·14 W
80	Knox (nŏks)...Ind.	41·15 N	86·40 W
71	Knoxville (nŏks'vĭl)...Iowa	41·19 N	93·05 W
78	Knoxville...Tenn.	35·58 N	83·55 W
110	Knutsford (nŭts'fērd)...Eng.	53·18 N	2·22 W
121	Knyszyn (knĭ'shĭn)...Pol.	53·16 N	22·59 E
148	Ko (R.) (go͞oŭ)...China	33·04 N	117·16 E
153	Kobayashi (kō'bȧ-yä'shė)...Jap.	31·58 N	130·59 E
153	Kōbe (kō'bĕ)...Jap. (Ōsaka In.)	34·30 N	135·10 E
129	Kobelyaki (kō-bĕl-yä'kė).Sov. Un.	49·11 N	34·12 E
118	København (Copenhagen) (kû-b'n-houn').Den.	55·43 N	12·27 E
120	Koblenz (kō'blĕntz)...Ger.	50·18 N	7·36 E
128	Kobozha (R.) (kô-bō'zhȧ).Sov. Un.	58·55 N	35·18 E
121	Kobrin (kō'brēn')...Sov. Un.	52·13 N	24·23 E
136	Kobrinskoye (kô-brĭn'skô-yĕ) Sov. Un. (Leningrad In.)	59·25 N	30·07 E
64	Kobuk (R.) (kō'bŭk)...Alaska	66·58 N	158·48 W
133	Kobuleti (kô-bo͞o-lyā'tē).Sov. Un.	41·50 N	41·40 E
127	Kocani (kô'chä-nĕ)...Yugo.	41·54 N	22·25 E
126	Kočevje (kô'chāv-ye)...Yugo.	45·38 N	14·51 E
74	Koch (kōk)...Mo. (St. Louis In.)	38·28 N	90·17 W
120	Kocher R. (kôĸ'ēr)...Ger.	49·00 N	9·52 E
153	Kōchi (kō'chė)...Jap.	33·35 N	133·32 E
64	Kodiak (kō'dyăk)...Alaska	57·50 N	152·30 W
64	Kodiak (I.)...Alaska	57·24 N	153·32 W
165	Kodok (ko'dŏk)...Sud.	9·57 N	32·08 E
166	Koekenaap...S. Afr.	31·25 S	18·20 E
164	Koforidua (kō fō-rĭ-do͞o'ȧ)..Ghana	6·07 N	0·16 W
153	Kōfu (kō'fo͞o')...Jap.	35·41 N	138·34 E
153	Koga (kō'gȧ)...Jap.	36·13 N	139·40 E
153	Kogane (kō'gä-nä) Jap. (Tōkyō In.)	35·50 N	139·56 E
153	Koganei (kō'gä-nā) Jap. (Tōkyō In.)	35·42 N	139·31 E
118	Köge (kû'gĕ)...Den.	55·27 N	12·09 E
129	Kogil'nik (R.) (kô-gēl-nēk') Sov. Un.	46·08 N	29·10 E
142	Koh-i Baba Mt...Afg.	39·39 N	67·09 E
145	Kohima (kô-ē'mȧ)...India	25·45 N	94·41 E
153	Koito (R.) (kô'ē-tō) Jap. (Tōkyō In.)	35·19 N	139·58 E
152	Kŏje (I.) (kû'jĕ)...Kor.	34·53 N	129·00 E
134	Kokand (kô-känt')...Sov. Un.	40·27 N	71·07 E
134	Kokchetav (kôk'chĕ-tăf).Sov. Un.	53·15 N	69·13 E
119	Kokemäen (R.) (kô'kē-mȧ'ĕn).Fin.	61·23 N	22·03 E
128	Kokhma (kôĸ'mȧ)...Sov. Un.	56·57 N	41·08 E
143	Kokkanisseri...India	12·08 N	74·14 E
112	Kokkola (kô'kô-lȧ)...Fin.	63·47 N	22·58 E
80	Kokomo (kō'kô-mō)...Ind.	40·30 N	86·20 W
	Koko Nor, see Ch'ing Hai		
155	Kokopo (kô-kō'pō)...N. Gui. Ter.	4·25 S	152·27 E
87	Koksoak (R.) (kôk'sō-ăk)...Can.	57·42 N	69·50 W
167	Kokstad (kôk'shtät) S. Afr. (Natal In.)	30·33 S	29·27 E
148	Koku (gŏ'gō)...China	39·00 N	117·30 E
153	Kokubu (kō'ko͞o-bo͞o)...Jap.	31·42 N	130·46 E
153	Kokubunji (kō'ko͞o-bo͞on'jė) Jap. (Tōkyō In.)	35·43 N	139·29 E
153	Kokuou (kô'ko͞o-ō'o͞o) Jap. (Ōsaka In.)	34·34 N	135·39 E
153	Kokura (kō'ko͞o-rä)...Jap.	33·53 N	130·54 E
164	Kolahun (kô-lä'ho͞on)...Lib.	8·24 N	10·11 W
	Kola Pen., see Kol'skiy P-Ov.		
143	Kolār (kôl-är')...India	13·39 N	78·33 E
143	Kolār Gold Fields (kôl-är')..India	13·15 N	79·55 E
127	Kolarovgrad...Bul.	43·15 N	26·54 E
128	Kol'chugino (kôl-cho͞o'gē-nô) Sov. Un.	56·19 N	39·29 E
118	Kolding (kŭl'dĭng)...Den.	55·29 N	9·24 E
166	Kole (kō'lȧ)...Con. L.	3·19 S	22·46 E
132	Kolguyev (I.) (kôl-go͞o'yĕf) Sov. Un.	69·00 N	49·00 E
120	Kolin (kō'lēn)...Czech.	50·01 N	15·11 E
119	Kolkasrags (Pt.) (kôl-käs'rägz) Sov. Un.	57·46 N	22·39 E
123	Köln (Cologne)...Ger. (Ruhr In.)	50·56 N	6·57 E
121	Kolno (kôw'nô)...Pol.	53·23 N	21·56 E
121	Koło (kô'wô)...Pol.	52·11 N	18·37 E
120	Kołobrzeg (kô-lôb'zhĕk)...Pol.	54·10 N	15·35 E
136	Kolomna (kål-ôm'nȧ) Sov. Un. (Moskva In.)	55·06 N	38·47 E
121	Kolomyya (kō'lô-mē'yȧ).Sov. Un.	48·32 N	25·04 E
128	Kolp' (R.) (kôlp)...Sov. Un.	59·29 N	35·32 E
134	Kolpashevo (kŭl pȧ shô'vȧ) Sov. Un.	58·16 N	82·43 E
136	Kolpino (kôl'pē-nô) Sov. Un. (Leningrad In.)	59·45 N	30·37 E
128	Kolpny (kôlp'nyĕ)...Sov. Un.	52·14 N	36·54 E
132	Kol'skiy P-Ov. (Kola Pen.) Sov. Un.	67·15 N	37·40 E
132	Kolva (R.)...Sov. Un.	61·00 N	57·00 E
136	Kolyberovo (kô-lĭ-byâ'rô-vô) Sov. Un. (Moksva In.)	55·16 N	38·45 E
135	Kolyma (R.)...Sov. Un.	66·30 N	151·45 E

ng-sing; ŋ-baŋk; ɴ-nasalized n; nŏd; cŏmmit; ōld; ōbey; ôrder; fo͞od; fo͝ot; ou-out; s-soft; sh-dish; th-thin; pūre; ůnite: ûrn: stŭd; circŭs; ü-as "y" in study; '-indeterminate vowel.

224 Kolymskiy–Krymskiye PRONOUNCING INDEX

Page	Name Pronunciation Region	Lat. °′	Long. °′
	Kolymskiy (Mts.), see Gydan, Khrebet		
134	Kolyvan' (kôl-ê-vän')...Sov. Un.	55·28 N	82·59 E
130	Komadorskie Ostrova (Is.) Sov. Un.	55·40 N	167·13 E
164	Komadugu-Yobe R..........Nig.	12·14 N	10·00 E
121	Komárno (kô'mär-nô).....Czech.	47·46 N	18·08 E
121	Komarno..............Sov. Un.	49·38 N	23·43 E
121	Komaron (kô'mä-rôm).....Hung.	47·45 N	18·06 E
166	Komatipoort (kō-mä'tê-pōrt) S. Afr.	25·21 S	32·00 E
153	Komatsu (kō-mät'sōō).......Jap.	36·23 N	136·26 E
153	Komatsushima (kō-mät'sōō-shê'mä).Jap.	34·04 N	134 32 E
167	Komga (kōm'gà) S. Afr. (Natal In.)	32·36 S	27·54 E
130	Komi (A. S. S. R.) (kômê) Sov. Un.	61·31 N	53·15 E
166	Kommetjie S. Afr. (Cape Town In.)	34·09 S	18·19 E
127	Komotiní.................Grc.	41·07 N	25·22 E
154	Kompong Thom (kŏm'pŏng-tŏm) Camb.	12·41 N	104·39 E
129	Komrat (kôm-rät')......Sov. Un.	46·17 N	28·38 E
136	Komsomolets (kôm-sô-mô'lĕts) Sov. Un. (Urals In.)	53·45 N	63·04 E
133	Komsomolets Zaliv (B.)..Sov. Un.	45·40 N	52·00 E
135	Komsomol'sk-na-Amure (kŭm-sŭ-môlsk'nŭ-ŭ-mōōr'yĭ).Sov. Un.	50·46 N	137·14 E
129	Komsomol'skoye (kôm-sô-môl'skô-yĕ).Sov. Un.	48·42 N	28·44 E
132	Konda (R.) (kôn'dà)....Sov. Un.	60·50 N	64·00 E
136	Kondas R. (kôn'dàs) Sov. Un. (Urals In.)	59·30 N	56·28 E
166	Kondoa (kôn-dō'à)..........Tan.	4·52 S	36·00 E
164	Kong (kông).........Ivory Coast	9·05 N	4·41 W
164	Kong (Reg.).........Ivory Coast	9·19 N	4·03 W
166	Kongolo (kôŋ'gō'lō)......Con. L.	5·20 S	26·58 E
118	Kongsberg (kŭngs'bĕrg).....Nor.	59·40 N	9·36 E
118	Kongsvinger (kŭngs'vĭŋ-gẽr).Nor.	60·12 N	12·00 E
166	Koni (kō'nē)..............Con. L.	10·32 S	27·27 E
	Königsberg, see Kaliningrad		
111	Königsbrunn (kû'nēgs-brōōn) Ger. (München In.)	48·16 N	10·53 E
111	Königs Wusterhausen (kû'nēgs vōōs'tẽr-hou-zĕn) Ger. (Berlin In.)	52·18 N	13·38 E
121	Konin (kô'nyên)............Pol.	52·11 N	18·17 E
127	Kónitsa (kô'nyĕ'tsà)........Grc.	40·03 N	20·46 E
127	Konjic (kôn'yēts)..........Yugo.	43·38 N	17·59 E
152	Konju....................Kor.	36·21 N	127·05 E
129	Konotop (kô-nô-tôp')....Sov. Un.	51·13 N	33·14 E
121	Końskie (koin''skyĕ).........Pol.	51·12 N	20·26 E
129	Konstantinovka (kôn-stàn-tē'nôf-kà).Sov. Un.	48·33 N	37·42 E
120	Konstanz (kôn'-shtänts).....Ger.	47·39 N	9·10 E
164	Kontagora (kōn-tà-gō'rä)....Nig.	10·27 N	5 30 E
164	Kontcha (kōn'chà).........Cam.	8·03 N	12·21 E
133	Konya (kōn'yà)............Tur.	36·55 N	32·25 E
160	Kooringa (kō-ŭ-rĭŋ'gà).....Austl.	33·32 S	138·55 E
86	Kootenay Natl. Park (kōō'tê-nâ) Can.	51·06 N	117·02 W
86	Kootenay (R.) (kōō'tê-nâ)...Can.	50·28 N	115·50 W
153	Kōō-zan (Mtn.) (kōō'zän) Jap. (Ōsaka In.)	34·53 N	135·32 E
118	Kopervik (kô'pĕr-vêk).......Nor.	59·18 N	5·20 E
144	Kopet, Mts..................Iran	37·28 N	58·29 E
136	Kopeysk (kô-pāsk') Sov. Un. (Urals In.)	55·07 N	61·36 E
118	Köping (chû'pĭng)..........Swe.	59·32 N	15·58 E
118	Kopparberg (kŏp'pàr-bĕrgh)..Swe.	59·53 N	15·00 E
168	Koppies..S. Afr. (Johannesburg & Pretoria In.)	27·15 S	27·35 E
126	Koprivnica (kô'prēv-nē'tsà).Yugo.	46·10 N	16·48 E
121	Kopychintsy (kô-pê-chēn'tsĕ) Sov. Un.	49·06 N	25·55 E
127	Korcë (kôr'chĕ)............Alb.	40·37 N	20·48 E
126	Korčula (I.) (kôr'chōō-là)...Yugo.	42·50 N	17·05 E
165	Kordofan (Prov.) (kôr-dô-fän') Sud.	14·08 N	28·39 E
152	Korea B.............China-Kor.	39·18 N	123·50 E
139	Korea Chosen (kô-rē'ā)......Asia	38·45 N	130·00 E
152	Korean Arch................Kor.	39·05 N	125·35 E
152	Korea Str.............Kor.-Jap.	33·30 N	128·30 E
121	Korets (kô-rĕts')...........Sov. Un.	50·35 N	27·13 E
164	Korhogo (kôr-hō'gō)..Ivory Coast	9·22 N	5·21 W
127	Korinthiakós Kólpos (G.)....Grc.	38·15 N	22·33 E
127	Korinthos (Corinth) (kô-rên'thôs) (kŏr'ĭnth).Grc.	37·56 N	22·54 E
153	Kōriyama (kō'rê-yä'mä)......Jap.	37·18 N	140·25 E
153	Kōriyama.......Jap. (Ōsaka In.)	34·39 N	135·48 E
136	Korkino (kôr'kē-nŭ) Sov. Un. (Urals In.)	54·53 N	61·25 E
120	Körmend (kûr'mĕnt).......Hung.	47·02 N	16·36 E
126	Kornat (I.) (kôr-nät').......Yugo.	43·46 N	15·10 E
111	Korneuburg (kôr'noi-bŏŏrgh) Aus. (Wien In.)	48·22 N	16·21 E
129	Korocha (kô-rō'chà).....Sov. Un.	50·50 N	37·13 E
129	Korop (kō'rôp).........Sov. Un.	51·33 N	33·54 E
129	Korosten' (kô'rôs-tĕn)...Sov. Un.	50·51 N	28·39 E
129	Korostyshev (kô-rôs'tê-shôf) Sov. Un.	50·19 N	29·05 E
129	Korotoyak (kô'rô-tô-yàk') Sov. Un.	51·00 N	39·06 E
135	Korsakov (kôr'sà-kôf')...Sov. Un.	46·42 N	143·16 E
119	Korsnas (kôrs'nĕs)..........Fin.	62·51 N	21·17 E
118	Korsör (kôrs'ûr')...........Den.	55·19 N	11·08 E
165	Kōrti (kôr'tê)..............Sud.	18·08 N	31·39 E
117	Kortrijk...................Bel.	50·49 N	3·10 E
135	Koryakskiy Khrebet (Mts.) Sov. Un.	62·00 N	168·45 E
129	Koryukovka (kôr-yōō-kôf'kà) Sov. Un.	51·44 N	32·24 E
142	Kosa.....................India	23·37 N	68·35 E
120	Kóscian (kŭsh'tsyàn).......Pol.	52·05 N	16·38 E
121	Kóścierzyna (kŭsh-tsyĕ-zhē'nà) Pol.	54·08 N	17·59 E
78	Kosciusko (kŏs-ĭ-ŭs'kō).....Miss.	33·04 N	89·35 W
160	Kosciusko, Mt...........Austl.	36·26 S	148·20 E
128	Kosel'sk (kô-zĕlsk')......Sov. Un.	54·01 N	35·49 E
165	Kosha (kō'shä)............Sud.	20·49 N	30·27 E
150	K'oshan (kō'shän')........China	48·00 N	126·30 E
153	Koshigaya (kô'shê-gä'yä) Jap. (Tōkyō In.)	35·53 N	139·48 E
153	Koshiki-Rettō (Is.) (kō-shē'kê rât'tō).Jap.	31·51 N	129·40 E
142	Kosi (R.) (kō'sē)..........India	26·00 N	86·20 E
121	Košice (kō'shê-tsĕ').......Czech.	48·43 N	21·17 E
167	Kosmos (kŏz'mŏs) S. Afr. (Johannesburg & Pretoria In.)	25·45 S	27·51 E
136	Kosobrodskiy (kä-sô'brôd-skĭ) Sov. Un. (Urals In.)	54·14 N	60·53 E
	Koso Lake, see Khōbsögol Dalai		
127	Kosovska Mitrovica (kô'sôv-skä' mē'trô-vê-tsä').Yugo.	42·51 N	20·50 E
126	Kostajnica (kôs'tä-ê-nē'tsà).Yugo.	45·14 N	16·32 E
168	Koster...S. Afr. (Johannesburg & Pretoria In.)	25·52 S	26·52 E
165	Kosti (kôs'tê)..............Sud.	13·09 N	32·39 E
136	Kostino (kôs'tĭ-nô) Sov. Un. (Moskva In.)	55·54 N	37·51 E
128	Kostroma (kôs-trô-mà')..Sov. Un.	57·46 N	40·55 E
128	Kostroma (Oblast)......Sov. Un.	57·50 N	41·10 E
120	Kostrzyn' (kôst'chĕn)........Pol.	52·35 N	14·38 E
136	Kos'va R. (kôs'vå) Sov. Un. (Urals In.)	58·44 N	57·08 E
120	Koszalin (kô-shä'lĭn).........Pol.	54·12 N	16·10 E
120	Köszeg (kû'sĕg)...........Hung.	47·21 N	16·32 E
142	Kota.....................India	25·17 N	75·49 E
154	Kotabaru.................Indon.	3·22 S	116·15 E
166	Kota Kota (kō-tà kō-tà) Fed. of Rh. & Nya.	12·52 S	34·16 E
139	Kota Tinggi Mala. (Singapore In.)	1·43 N	103·54 E
127	Kotel (kō-tĕl')..............Bul.	42·54 N	26 28 E
132	Kotel'nich (kô-tyĕl'nēch).Sov. Un.	58·15 N	48·20 E
135	Kotel'nyy (I.) (kô-tyĕl'nê) Sov. Un.	74·51 N	134·09 E
143	Kothapur.................India	16·48 N	74·15 E
119	Kotka (kŏt'kà).............Fin.	60·28 N	26·56 E
132	Kotlas (kôt'làs).........Sov. Un.	61·10 N	46·50 E
136	Kotlin, Ostrov (I.) (ôs-trôf' kôt'lĭn) Sov. Un. (Leningrad In.)	60·02 N	29·49 E
127	Kotor (kō'tôr)............Yugo.	42·26 N	18·48 E
128	Kotorosl' (R.) (kô-tô'rôsl) Sov. Un.	57·18 N	39·08 E
126	Kotor Varoš (kō'tôr vä'rôsh).Yugo.	44·37 N	17·23 E
129	Kotovsk (kô-tôfsk').....Sov. Un.	47·49 N	29·31 E
148	Kotse (hŏ'zhē)............China	35·13 N	115·28 E
165	Kotto R..........Cen. Afr. Rep.	5·17 N	22·04 E
135	Kotuy (R.) (kô-tōō')....Sov. Un.	71·00 N	103·15 E
64	Kotzebue (kŏt'sē-bōō).....Alaska	66·48 N	162·42 W
64	Kotzebue Sd..............Alaska	67·00 N	164·28 W
165	Kouandé (kwän-dā') Cen. Afr. Rep.	6·08 N	14·32 E
164	Koudougou (kōō-dōō'gōō) Upper Volta	12·02 N	2·15 W
164	Koulikoro (kōō-lê-kō'rō).....Mali	13·00 N	7·29 W
166	Kouilou (R.)...............Con. B.	4·10 S	11·45 E
164	Koumbia (kōōm'bĭ-ä)........Gui.	11·35 N	13·01 W
164	Koundé (kōōn-dā').....Dahomey	10·19 N	1·42 E
134	Kounradskiy (kŭ-ōōn-rät'skē) Sov. Un.	47·25 N	75·10 E
164	Kouroussa (kōō-rōō'sà).......Gui.	10·43 N	9·59 W
165	Koussi, Emi (Mt.) (ā'mê kōō-sē') Chad	19·56 N	18·34 E
164	Koutiala (kōō-tê-ä'lä).......Mali	12·29 N	5·29 W
119	Kouvola (kō'ŏŏ-vô-lä)........Fin.	60·51 N	26·40 E
132	Kovda (L.) (kôv'dà).....Sov. Un.	66·45 N	32·00 E
121	Kovel' (kō'vĕl)..........Sov. Un.	51·13 N	24·45 E
	Kovno, see Kaunas		
128	Kovrov (kôv-rôf')........Sov. Un.	56·23 N	41·21 E
	Kowie, see Port Alfred		
151	Kowloon (kō'lōōn')....Hong Kong	22·28 N	114·20 E
148	Koyang (gōōŭ'yäNG).........China	33·32 N	116·10 E
127	Koynare....................Bul.	43·23 N	24·07 E
64	Koyuk (kô-yōōk')..........Alaska	65·00 N	161·18 W
64	Koyukuk (R.) (kô-yōō'kŏŏk) Alaska	66·25 N	153·50 W
127	Kozáni....................Grc.	40·16 N	21·51 E
129	Kozelets (kôzĕ-lyĕts)....Sov. Un.	50·53 N	31·07 E
121	Kozience (kō-zyĕ-nē'tsĕ).......Pol.	51·34 N	21·35 E
121	Koźle (kôzh'lĕ)..............Pol.	50·19 N	18·10 E
127	Kozlodui (kŭz'lô-dwĕ).......Bul.	43·45 N	23·42 E
153	Kōzu (I.) (kō'zōō)..........Jap.	34·16 N	139·03 E
154	Kra, Isth. of..............Thai.	9·30 S	99·45 E
167	Kraai (R.) (krä'ê) S. Afr. (Natal In.)	30·50 S	27·03 E
111	Krabbendijke Neth. (Amsterdam In.)	51·26 N	4·05 E
118	Kragerō (krä'gẽr-û).........Nor.	58·53 N	9·21 E
127	Kragujevac (krä'gōō'yĕ-vàts) Yugo.	44·01 N	20·55 E
121	Kraków (krä'kŏŏf)..........Pol.	50·05 N	20·00 E
127	Kraljevo (kräl'ye-vô).......Yugo.	43·39 N	20·48 E
129	Kramatorsk (krá-mä'tôrsk) Sov. Un.	48·43 N	37·32 E
118	Kramfors (kräm'fôrs).......Swe.	62·54 N	17·49 E
126	Kranj (krän').............Yugo.	46·16 N	14·23 E
167	Kranskop (kränz'kŏp) S. Afr. (Natal In.)	28·57 S	30·54 E
128	Krāslava (kräs'lä-vä)....Sov. Un.	55·53 N	27·12 E
120	Kraslice (kräs'lê-tsĕ)........Czech.	50·19 N	12·30 E
136	Krasnaya Gorka (kräs'nà-yà gôr'kà).Sov. Un. (Urals In.)	55·13 N	56·43 E
133	Krasnaya Sloboda.......Sov. Un.	43·20 N	44·30 E
121	Kraśnik (kräsh'nĭk)...........Pol.	50·53 N	22·15 E
136	Krasnoarmeysk (kräs'nô-àr-maśk') Sov. Un. (Moskva In.)	56·06 N	38·09 E
129	Krasnoarmeyskoye........Sov. Un.	48·19 N	37·04 E
129	Krasnodar (kräs'nô-där).Sov. Un.	45·03 N	38·55 E
129	Krasnodarskiy (Oblast) Province (kràs-nô-där'skĭ ôb'làst) Sov. Un.	47·28 N	38·13 E
136	Krasnogorskiy (kräs-nô-gôr'skĭ) Sov. Un. (Urals In.)	54·36 N	61·25 E
129	Krasnograd (kräs'nô-grät) Sov. Un.	49·23 N	35·26 E
136	Krasnogvardeyskiy (krå'sno-gvär-dzyē ês-kēê) Sov. Un. (Urals In.)	57·17 N	62·05 E
132	Krasnokamsk (kräs-nô-kämsk') Sov. Un.	58·00 N	55·45 E
129	Krasnokutsk (kràs-nô-kōōtsk') Sov. Un.	50·03 N	35·05 E
129	Krasnosel'ye (kräs'nô-sĕl'yĕ) Sov. Un.	48·44 N	32·24 E
132	Krasnoslobodsk (kräs'nô-slôbôtsk') Sov. Un.	54·20 N	43·50 E
136	Krasnotur'insk (krŭs-nŭ-tōō-rensk') Sov. Un. (Urals In.)	59·47 N	60·15 E
136	Krasnoufimsk (krŭs-nŭ-ōō-fēmsk') Sov. Un. (Urals In.)	56·38 N	57·46 E
136	Krasnoural'sk (kräs'nô-ōō-rälsk') Sov. Un. (Urals In.)	58·21 N	60·05 E
136	Krasnousol'skiy (kräs-nô-ōō-sôl'skĭ) Sov. Un. (Urals In.)	53·53 N	56·30 E
132	Krasnovishersk (kräs-nô-vêshersk').Sov. Un.	60·22 N	57·20 E
133	Krasnovodsk (kràs-nô-vôtsk') Sov. Un.	40·00 N	52.50 E
134	Krasnoyarsk (kräs-nô-yàrsk') Sov. Un.	56·13 N	93·12 E
136	Krasnoye Selo (kräs'nŭ-yŭ sâ'lō) Sov. Un. (Leningrad In.)	59·44 N	30·06 E
128	Krasny Kholm (kräs'nê kōlm) Sov. Un.	58·03 N	37·11 E
121	Krasnystaw (kräs-nê-stàf')...Pol.	50·59 N	23·11 E
136	Krasnyy Bor (kräs'nê bôr) Sov. Un. (Leningrad In.)	59·41 N	30·40 E
136	Krasnyy Klyuch (kräs'nê klyûch') Sov. Un. (Urals In.)	55·24 N	56·43 E
133	Krasnyy Kut (kràs-nê kōōt') Sov. Un.	50·50 N	47·00 E
154	Kratie (krà-tyā').........Camb.	12·28 N	106·06 E
136	Kratovo (krä'tô-vô) Sov. Un. (Moskva In.)	55·35 N	38·10 E
127	Kratovo (krä'tô-vô)........Yugo.	42·04 N	22·12 E
123	Krefeld (krā'fĕlt).Ger. (Ruhr In.)	51·20 N	6·34 E
129	Kremenchug (krĕm'ĕn-chōōgh') Sov. Un.	49·04 N	33·26 E
121	Kremenets (krĕ-mĕn-yĕts') Sov. Un.	50·06 N	25·43 E
111	Kremmen (krĕ'mĕn) Ger. (Berlin In.)	52·45 N	13·02 E
111	Krempe (krĕm'pĕ) Ger. (Hamburg In.)	53·50 N	9·29 E
120	Krems (krĕms).............Aus.	48·25 N	15·36 E
128	Kresttsy (krâst'sê).......Sov. Un.	58·16 N	32·25 E
119	Kretinga (krĕ-tĭŋ'gà)....Sov. Un.	55·55 N	21·17 E
164	Kribi (krē'bê)..............Cam.	3·03 N	9·58 E
128	Krichëv (krē'chôf)......Sov. Un.	53·44 N	31·39 E
152	Krillon, Mys (Pt.) (mĭs krĭl' ôn) Sov. Un.	45·58 N	142·00 E
111	Krimpenald Ijssel Neth. (Amsterdam In.)	51·55 N	4·34 E
142	Krishnagar................India	23·29 N	88·33 E
118	Kristiansand (krĭs-tyàn-sän'') Nor.	58·09 N	7·59 E
118	Kristianstad(krĭs-tyàn-städ').Swe.	56·02 N	14·09 E
118	Kristiansund (krĭs-tyàn-sōōn'') Nor.	63·07 N	7·49 E
118	Kristinehamn (krês-tē'nĕ-häm') Swe.	59·20 N	14·05 E
119	Kristinestad (krĭs-tē'nĕ-städh).Fin.	62·16 N	21·28 E
127	Kriva-Palanka (krē-và-pà-läŋ'kà) Yugo.	42·12 N	22·21 E
129	Krivoy Rog (krê-voi' rôgh') Sov. Un.	47·54 N	33·22 E
129	Krivoye Ozero..........Sov. Un.	47·57 N	30·21 E
126	Križevci (krē'zhĕv-tsĭ).....Yugo.	46·02 N	16·30 E
126	Krk (I.) (k'rk)...........Yugo.	45·06 N	14·33 E
121	Krnov (k'r'nôf)...........Czech.	50·05 N	17·41 E
118	Kröderen (krû'dĕ-rĕn).......Nor.	60·07 N	9·49 E
129	Krolevets (krô-lĕ'vyĕts).Sov. Un.	51·33 N	33·21 E
121	Kroměříž (krô'myĕr-zhĕzh).Czech.	49·18 N	17·23 E
128	Kromy (krô'mê)........Sov. Un.	52·44 N	35·41 E
135	Kronotskiy, Mys (C.) (krô'nôt'skĭ-ê).Sov. Un.	54·58 N	163·15 E
136	Kronshtadt (krōn'shtät) Sov. Un. (Leningrad In.)	59·59 N	29·47 E
168	Kroonstad (krōn'shtät)....S. Afr. (Johannesburg & Pretoria In.)	27·40 S	27·15 E
133	Kropotkin (krà-pôt'kĭn).Sov. Un.	45·25 N	40·30 E
121	Krosno (krôs'nô)............Pol.	49·41 N	21·46 E
121	Krotoszyn (krô-tō'shĭn)......Pol.	51·41 N	17·25 E
126	Krško (k'rsh'kô)..........Yugo.	45·58 N	15·30 E
166	Kruger Natl. Park (krōō'gẽr) (krü'gẽr).S. Afr.	23·22 S	30·18 E
167	Krugersdorp (krōō'gẽrz-dôrp) S. Afr. (Johannesburg & Pretoria In.)	26·06 S	27·46 E
127	Kruje.....................Alb.	41·32 N	19·49 E
154	Krung Thep (Bangkok).....Thai.	13·50 N	100·29 E
127	Kruševac (krōō'shĕ-vàts)...Yugo.	43·34 N	21·21 E
127	Krušovo (krōō'shô-vô)......Yugo.	41·20 N	21·15 E
119	Krustpils (krōōst'pêls)...Sov. Un.	56·31 N	25·51 E
118	Krylbo (krŭl'bô)............Swe.	60·07 N	16·14 E
129	Krymskaya (krĭm'skà-yà).Sov. Un.	44·58 N	38·01 E
129	Krymskaya (Oblast).....Sov. Un.	45·08 N	34·05 E
129	Krymskiye Gory (Mts.) (krēm'skĭ-yĕ gô'rĭ).Sov. Un.	65·21 N	117·13 E

ăt; finăl; rāte; senâte; ärm; åsk; sofà; fâre; ch-choose; dh-as th in other; bē; êvent; bĕt; recĕnt; cratẽr; g-go; gh-guttural g; bĭt; ĭ-short neutral; rīde; K-guttural k as ch in German ich;

Page	Name Pronunciation Region	Lat. °′	Long. °′
129	Krymskiy (Crimea) Poluostrov (Pen.) (krēm'skĭ pô-lo͞o-ôs'trôf) Sov. Un.	45·18 N	33·30 E
121	Krynki (krĭn'kê)............Pol.	53·15 N	23·47 E
129	Kryukov (k'r'yo͞o-kôf')..Sov. Un.	49·02 N	33·26 E
139	Ktima.....Cyprus (Palestine In.)	34·46 N	32·27 E
139	Kuala Klawang Mala. (Singapore In.)	2·57 N	102·04 E
139	Kuala Lumpur (kwä'lä lo͝om-po͞or') Mala. (Singapore In.)	3·08 N	101·42 E
150	Kuan (ko͞o'än').China (Peking In.)	39·25 N	116·18 E
148	Kuan (R.) (go͞oäN)........China	31·56 N	115·19 E
151	Kuangchang..............China	25·50 N	116·18 E
	Kuangchou, see Canton		
151	Kuangchou Wan (B.)......China	20·40 N	111·00 E
	Kuanghsi, see Kwangsi Chuang		
148	Kuangjao (go͞oäNg'rou).....China	37·04 N	118·24 E
148	Kuanglu Tao (I.) (go͞oäng'lo͞o dou) China	39·13 N	122·21 E
148	Kuangp'ing (go͞oäNg'pĭng).China	36.30 N	114·57 E
148	Kuangshan (go͞oäNg'shan)..China	32·02 N	114·53 E
151	Kuangte.................China	30·40 N	119·20 E
147	Kuangtung (Kwangtung) (Prov.) China	23·49 N	113·02 E
148	Kuanhsien (go͞oäN'sĭäN)....China	36·30 N	115·28 E
148	Kuanhu (go͞oäN'hoo).......China	34·26 N	117·59 E
148	Kuankü Shan (Mts.) (go͞oäN'go͞o shäN).China	35·20 N	117·27 E
148	Kuant'ao (go͞oäN'tou)......China	36·39 N	115·25 E
15(	Kuantien................China	40·40 N	24·50 E
148	Kuanyün (go͞oän'yün).....China	34·28 N	119·16 E
133	Kuba (ko͞o'bȧ)..........Sov. Un.	41·05 N	48·30 E
129	Kuban' (R.) (ko͝o-bȧn'').Sov. Un.	45·10 N	37·55 E
133	Kuban (R.)............Sov. Un.	45·20 N	40·05 E
115	Kuban R..............Sov. Un	45·14 N	38·20 E
132	Kubenskoye (L.)........Sov. Un.	59·40 N	39·40 E
	Kucha, see Kuch'e		
146	Kuch'e (Kucha) (ko͞o'chĕ') (kō'chä').China	41·34 N	82·44 E
148	Kuchen (ko͞o'jĕn)..........China	33·20 N	117·18 E
148	Kuch'eng (ko͞o'chĕng').....China	39·09 N	115·43 E
154	Kuching (ko͞o'chĭng).........Sar.	1·30 N	110·26 E
153	Kuchinoerabo (I.) (ko͞o'chê nō ĕr'ȧ-bō).Jap.	30·31 N	129·53 E
153	Kudamatsu (ko͞o'dȧ-mä'tso͞o).Jap.	34·00 N	131·51 E
154	Kudat (ko͞o-dät')........N. Bor.	6·56 N	116·48 E
119	Kudirkos Naumiestis (ko͞odĭr-kôs nȧ'o͝o-mĕ'stĭs).Sov. Un.	54·51 N	23·00 E
134	Kudymakar (ko͞o-dĭm-kär') Sov. Un.	58·43 N	54·52 E
127	Kŭdzhati.................Bul.	41·39 N	25·21 E
148	Kuei (R.) (ko͞oä).........China	33·30 N	116·56 E
151	Kueichih................China	30·35 N	117·28 E
149	Kueichou.....China (Canton In.)	22·46 N	113·15 E
146	Kueichou (Kweichow) (Prov.) China	27·03 N	106·31 E
151	Kueilin.................China	25·18 N	110·22 E
150	Kueisui.................China	41·05 N	111·50 E
151	Kueiyang................China	26·45 N	107·00 E
146	K'uerhlo................China	41·37 N	86·03 E
120	Kufstein (ko͞of'shtīn)........Aus.	47·34 N	12·11 E
111	Kuhstedt (ko͞o'shtĕt) Ger. (Hamburg In.)	53·23 N	8·58 E
	Kuibyshev, see Kuybyshev		
166	Kuilsrivier S. Afr. (Cape Town In.)	33·56 S	18·41 E
153	Kujū-san (Mt.) (ko͞o'jo͝o-sän').Jap.	33·07 N	131·14 E
165	Kukawa (ko͞o-kä'wä)........Nig.	12·55 N	13·35 E
127	Kukës (ko͞o'kĕs)............Alb.	42·03 N	20·25 E
127	Kula (ko͞o'lȧ)...............Bul.	43·52 N	23·13 E
133	Kula.....................Tur.	38·32 N	28·30 E
142	Kula Kangri Mt..........China	33·11 N	90·36 E
135	Kul r, Khrebet (Mts.) (ko͝o-lär') Sov. Un.	69·00 N	131·45 E
119	Kuldīga (ko͝ol'dê-gȧ).....Sov. Un.	56·59 N	21·59 E
132	Kulebaki (ko͞o-lĕ-bäk'ĭ)..Sov. Un.	55·22 N	42·30 E
120	Kulmbach (klo͝olm'bäK).....Ger.	50·07 N	11·28 E
126	Kulpa (R.) (ko͝ol'pȧ).......Yugo.	45·32 N	14·50 E
134	Kulunda (ko͝o-lo͝on'dȧ)...Sov. Un.	52·38 N	74·00 E
134	Kulundinskoye (L.).....Sov. Un.	52·45 N	77·18 E
152	Kum (R.) (ko͝om)..........Kor.	36·50 N	127·30 E
133	Kuma (R.) (ko͞o'mä)....Sov. Un.	44·50 N	45·10 E
153	Kumamoto (ko͞o'mä-mō'tô)..Jap.	32·49 N	130·40 E
153	Kumano-Nada (Sea) (ko͞o-mä'nō nä-dä).Jap.	34·03 N	136·36 E
127	Kumanovo (ko͝o-mä'nô-vô).Yugo.	42·10 N	21·41 E
164	Kumasi (ko͞o-mä'sê).......Ghana	6·45 N	1·39 W
164	Kumba (ko͝om'bȧ)..........Nig.	4·41 N	9·26 E
143	Kumbakonam (ko͝om'bŭ-kō'nŭm) India	10·59 N	79·25 E
127	Kumkale..................Tur.	39·59 N	26·10 E
143	Kumta...................India	14·19 N	75·28 E
136	Kunashak (kû-nä'shȧk) Sov. Un. (Urals In.)	55·43 N	61·35 E
152	Kunashir (I.) (ko͞o-nŭ-shēr') Sov. Un.	44·40 N	145·45 E
148	Kunch'eng Hu (L.) (ko͞oN'chĕng hoo).China	31·36 N	120·57 E
128	Kunda (ko͝o'dȧ).........Sov. Un.	59·30 N	26·28 E
163	Kundelungu, Plateau des (Plat). Bel. Congo	9·00 S	25·30 E
136	Kundravy (ko͞on'drȧ-vĭ) Sov. Un. (Urals In.)	54·50 N	60·14 E
139	Kundur (I.) Indon. (Singapore In.)	0·49 N	103·20 E
	Kunene (R.), see Cunene		
118	Kungälv (kŭng'ĕlf).........Swe.	57·53 N	12·01 E
136	Kungur (ko͝on-go͞or') Sov. Un. (Urals In.)	57·27 N	56·53 E
103	Kungrad (ko͝on-grät')...Sov. Un.	42·59 N	59·00 E
118	Kungsbacka (kŭngs'bä-kȧ)...Swe.	57·31 N	12·04 E
142	Kungsherya..............China	31·33 N	84·38 E
146	K'un Lun Shan (Mts.) (ko͝on'lo͞on' shän').China	35·26 N	83·09 E
151	K'unming (Yünnanfu) (ko͝on' mĭng') (yûn'nän'fo͞o').China	25·10 N	102·50 E
152	Kunsan (ko͝on'sän')........Kor.	35·54 N	126·46 E
149	K'unshan (ko͞on'shän') China (Shanghai In.)	31·23 N	120·57 E
136	Kuntsëvo (ko͝on-tsyô'vô) Sov. Un. (Moskva In.)	55·43 N	37·27 E
136	Kun'ya Sov. Un. (Urals In.)	58·42 N	56·47 E
128	Kun'ya (R.) (ko͝on'yȧ)...Sov. Un.	56·45 N	30·53 E
112	Kuopio (ko͝o-ô'pê-ŏ).........Fin.	62·48 N	28·30 E
155	Kupang..................Indon.	10·14 S	123·37 E
134	Kupino (ko͞o-pĭ'nô)......Sov. Un.	54·00 N	77·47 E
119	Kupiškis (ko͝o-pĭsh'kĭs)..Sov. Un.	55·50 N	24·55 E
129	Kupyansk (ko͝op-yănsk') Sov. Un.	49·44 N	37·38 E
133	Kura (R.) (ko͞o'rȧ)......Sov. Un.	41·10 N	45·40 E
146	Kurak Darya (R.).........China	41·09 N	87·46 E
153	Kurashiki (ko͞o'rä-shē'kê)....Jap.	34·37 N	133·44 E
153	Kurayoshi (ko͞o'rȧ-yō'shê)....Jap.	35·25 N	133·49 E
133	Kurdistan (Reg.) (kûrd'ĭ-stăn) Tur.-Iran	37·40 N	43·30 E
153	Kure (ko͞o'rĕ)..............Jap.	34·17 N	132·35 E
119	Kuressaare (ko͝o'rĕ-sä'rĕ).Sov. Un.	58·15 N	22·26 E
134	Kurgan (ko͝or-găn')......Sov. Un.	55·28 N	65·14 E
134	Kurgan Tyube (ko͝or-gän' tyo͝o'bĕ) Sov. Un.	38·00 N	68·49 E
144	Kuria Muria Is. (Br.) (ko͞o-rê-ȧ mo͝o'rê-ȧ).Aden	17·27 N	56·02 E
153	Kurihama (ko͞o-rē-hä'mä) Jap. (Tōkyō In.)	35·14 N	139·42 E
135	Kuril Is. (ko͞o'rĭl).......Sov. Un.	46·20 N	149·30 E
119	Kurisches Haff (Bay)....Sov. Un.	55·10 N	21·08 E
165	Kurmuk (ko͝or'mo͞ok)........Sud.	10·40 N	34·13 E
143	Kurnool (ko͝or-no͞ol').......India	16·00 N	78·04 E
153	Kuro (I.) (ko͞o'rô)..........Jap.	30·49 N	129·56 E
161	Kurrajong Austl. (Sydney In.)	33·33 S	150·40 E
119	Kuršenai (ko͝or'shȧ-nī)...Sov. Un.	56·01 N	22·56 E
129	Kursk (ko͝orsk).........Sov. Un.	51·44 N	36·08 E
129	Kursk (Oblast) (ko͝orsk).Sov. Un.	51·30 N	35·13 E
127	Kuršumlija (ko͝or'sho͝om'lĭ-yȧ) Yugo.	43·08 N	21·18 E
166	Kuruman (ko͞o-ro͞o-män')..S. Afr.	27·25 S	23·30 E
153	Kurume (ko͞o'ro͝o-mĕ)........Jap.	33·20 N	130·26 E
153	Kururi (ko͞o'ro͝o-rê) Jap. (Tōkyō In.)	35·17 N	140·05 E
165	Kuruskū (ko͞o-ro͞os-ko͞o').U. A. R.	22·33 N	32·24 E
136	Kusa (ko͞o'sȧ) Sov. Un. (Urals In.)	55·19 N	59·27 E
129	Kushchëvskaya........Sov. Un.	46·34 N	39·40 E
134	Kushevat.............Sov. Un.	65·05 N	65·28 E
148	Kushih (go͞o'sēĭ)..........China	32·11 N	115·39 E
153	Kushikino (ko͞o'shĭ-kē'nō)....Jap.	31·44 N	130·19 E
153	Kushimoto (ko͞o'shĭ-mō'tō)...Jap.	33·29 N	135·47 E
152	Kushiro (ko͞o'shē-rō).........Jap.	43·00 N	144·22 E
134	Kush-Murun (L.) (ko͞osh-mo͝o-ro͞on').Sov. Un.	52·30 N	64·15 E
133	Kushum (R.) (ko͝o-sho͝om') Sov. Un.	50·30 N	50·40 E
136	Kushva (ko͞osh'vȧ) Sov. Un. (Urals In.)	58·18 N	59·51 E
64	Kuskokwim (R.)..........Alaska	61·32 N	160·36 W
64	Kuskokwim B. (kŭs'kô-kwĭm) Alaska	59·25 N	163·14 W
64	Kuskokwim Mts..........Alaska	62·08 N	158·00 W
64	Kuskovak (kŭs-kō'văk)...Alaska	60·10 N	162·50 W
134	Kustanay (ko͞os-tȧ-nī')...Sov. Un.	53·10 N	63·39 E
133	Kutahya (kû-tä'hyȧ)........Tur.	39·20 N	29·50 E
133	Kutaisi (ko͞o-tŭ-ē'sē).....Sov. Un.	42·15 N	42·40 E
154	Kutaradja................Indon.	5·30 N	95·20 E
142	Kutch, Gulf of............India	22·45 N	68·33 E
142	Kutch, Rann of (Swp.).....India	23·59 N	69·13 E
111	Kutenholz (ko͞o'tĕn-hōlts) Ger. (Hamburg In.)	53·29 N	9·20 E
136	Kutim (ko͞o'tĭm) Sov. Un. (Urals In.)	60·22 N	58·51 E
126	Kutina (ko͞o'tê-nȧ).........Yugo.	45·29 N	16·48 E
121	Kutno (ko͝ot'nô)............Pol.	52·14 N	19·22 E
132	Kutno (L.)..............Sov. Un.	65·15 N	31·30 E
134	Kutulik (ko͝o to͞o'lyĭk)...Sov. Un.	53·12 N	102·51 E
121	Kuty (ko͞o'tê)...........Sov. Un.	48·16 N	25·12 E
112	Kuusamo (ko͞o'sȧ-mô).......Fin.	65·59 N	29·10 E
128	Kuvshinovo (ko͝ov-shē'nô-vô) Sov. Un.	57·01 N	34·09 E
	Kuwait, see Al Kuwayt		
138	Kuwait....................Asia	29·00 N	48·45 E
153	Kuwana (ko͞o'wȧ-nȧ).........Jap.	35·02 N	136·40 E
132	Kuybyshev (Kuibyshev) (ko͞o'ē-bĭ-shĭf).Sov. Un.	53·10 N	50·05 E
134	Kuybyshev.............Sov. Un.	55·45 N	76·45 E
132	Kuybyshevskoye (Res.)..Sov. Un.	53·40 N	49·00 E
148	Kuyeh (go͞o'yĕ)...........China	39·46 N	118·23 E
133	Kuzey Anadolu Dağ'ari (Mts.) Tur.	41·20 N	34·30 E
133	Kuznetsk (ko͞oz-nyĕtsk') Sov. Un.	53·10 N	48·10 E
134	Kuznetsk Basin.........Sov. Un.	57·15 N	86·15 E
136	Kuznetsovka (ko͝oz-nyĕt'sôf-kȧ) Sov. Un. (Urals In.)	54·41 N	56·40 E
128	Kuznetsovo (ko͝oz-nyĕt-sô'vô) Sov. Un.	56·39 N	36·55 E
126	Kvarnerski Zaliv (B.) (kvär'nĕr-skê' zä'lêv).Yugo.	44·41 N	14·05 E
64	Kvichak (vĭc'-hăk)........Alaska	59·00 N	156·48 W
166	Kwango (R.) (kwäng'ō').....Ang.	8·30 S	18·00 E
146	Kwangsi Chuang (Aut. Reg.) China	23·52 N	108·30 E
	Kwangtung, see Kuangtung		
	Kweichow, see Kueichou		
	Kweitun, see Wusu		
166	Kwenge (R.) (kwĕŋ'gĕ)...Con. L.	6·45 S	18·34 E
121	Kwidzyń (kvē'dzĭn')........Pol.	53·45 N	18·56 E
166	Kwilu (R.) (kwē'lo͞o).....Con. L.	7·00 S	19·20 E
164	Kwitta (kwĭt'ȧ)..........Ghana	6·00 N	1·00 E
135	Kyakhta (kyäK'ta)......Sov. Un.	51·00 N	107·30 E
142	Kyang Tsho (L.)..........China	30·37 N	88·33 E
142	Kyayisu (R.)..............India	38·05 N	74·36 E
146	Kyaukpyu (chouk'pyoo')....Bur.	19·19 N	93·33 E
119	Kybartai (kē'bär-tī')....Sov. Un.	54·40 N	22·46 E
136	Kyn (kĭn')...Sov. Un. (Urals In.)	51·52 N	58·42 E
159	Kynuna (kī-no͞o'nȧ)........Austl.	21·30 S	142·12 E
165	Kyoga L....................Ug.	1·27 N	33·51 E
153	Kyōga-Saki (C.) (kyǫ'gä sa'kê) Jap.	35·46 N	135·14 E
152	Kyōngju (kyŭng'yo͞o).......Kor.	35·48 N	129·12 E
153	Kyōtō (kyō'tō')..Jap. (Ōsaka In.)	35·00 N	135·46 E
153	Kyōto (Pref.)....Jap. (Ōsaka In.)	34·56 N	135·42 E
134	Kyren (kĭ-rĕn').........Sov. Un.	51·46 N	102·13 E
119	Kyrön (R.) (kû'rô)..........Fin.	63·03 N	22·20 E
136	Kyrya (kēr'yȧ) Sov. Un. (Urals In.)	59·18 N	59·03 E
136	Kyshtym (kĭsh-tĭm') Sov. Un. (Urals In.)	55·43 N	60·33 E
136	Kytlym (kĭt'lĭm) Sov. Un. (Urals In.)	59·30 N	59·15 E
153	Kyūshū (I.) (kyo͞o'sho͞o').....Jap.	32·27 N	131·03 E
127	Kyustendil (kyo͝os-tĕn-dĭl')...Bul.	42·16 N	22·39 E
134	Kyzyl (kĭ zĭl)..........Sov. Un.	51·37 N	93·38 E
103	Kyzylkum (Des.) (kĭ zĭl ko͞om) Sov. Un.	42·47 N	64·45 E
146	Kyzylsu (R.)..............China	39·26 N	74·30 E
134	Kzyl-Orda (kzêl-ôr'dȧ)...Sov. Un.	44·58 N	65·45 E
120	Laa.......................Aus.	48·42 N	16·23 E
124	La Almunia de Doña Godina (lä'äl-mo͞on'yä dā dō nyä gô-dē'nä).Sp.	41·29 N	1·22 W
98	La Asunción (lä ä-so͞on-syōn') Ven.	11·02 N	63·57 W
100	La Banda (lä bän'dä).......Arg.	27·48 S	64·12 W
90	La Barca (lä bär'kȧ)........Mex.	20·17 N	102·33 W
164	Labé (lȧ-bā')..............Gui.	11·15 N	12·16 W
120	Labe (Elbe) R. (lä'bĕ) (ĕl'bĕ) Czech.	50·05 N	15·20 E
86	Laberge (R.) (lȧ-bĕrzh').....Can.	61·08 N	136·42 W
94	Laberinto de las Doce Leguas (Is.) (lä-bȧ-rēn tô dā läs dō'sȧ lā'gwäs).Cuba	20·40 N	78·35 W
133	Labinsk...............Sov. Un.	44·30 N	40·40 E
139	Labis (läb'ĭs) Mala. (Singapore In.)	2·23 N	103·01 E
125	La Bisbal (lä bēs-bäl')........Sp.	41·55 N	3·00 E
155	Labo (lä'bô)....Phil. (Manila In.)	13·39 N	121·14 E
155	Labo..........Phil. (Manila In.)	14·11 N	122·49 E
155	Labo, Mt......Phil. (Manila In.)	14·00 N	122·47 E
85	L'Abord-a-Plouffe (lä-bōr'dä-plo͞of).Can. (Montreal In.)	45·32 N	73·45 W
122	Labouheyre (lȧ-bo͞o-âr').......Fr.	44·14 N	0·58 W
100	Laboulaye (lä-bô'o͞o-lä-yĕ)...Arg.	34·01 S	63·10 W
87	Labrador (Reg.) (lăb'rȧ-dôr) Can.	53·05 N	63·30 W
98	Lábrea (lä-brā'ä)...........Braz.	7·28 S	64·39 W
155	Labuan (lä-bwä'n) Phil. (Manila In.)	13·43 N	120·07 E
154	Labuan (I.) (lä-bo͝o-än')..N. Bor.	5·28 N	115·11 E
155	Labuha..................Indon.	0·43 S	127·35 E
85	L'Acadie (lȧ-kȧ-dē') Can. (Montreal In.)	45·18 N	73·22 W
85	L'Acadie, Riviére (rê-vyâr') Can. (Montreal In.)	45·24 N	73·21 W
101	La Calera (lä-kä-lĕ-rä) Chile (Santiago In.)	32·47 S	71·11 W
98	La Calera............Col. (In.)	4·43 N	73·58 W
113	La Calle (lȧ kȧl')............Alg.	36·52 N	8·23 E
74	La Canada (lä kän-yä'dä) Calif. (Los Angeles In.)	34·13 N	118·12 W
91	Lacantum (R.) (lä-kän-to͞o'm) Mex.	16·13 N	90·52 W
124	La Carolina (lä kä-rô-lē'nä)...Sp.	38·16 N	3·48 W
91	La Catedral, Cerro (Mtn.) (sĕ'r-rô-lä-kä-tĕ-drȧ'l) Mex. (Mexico In.)	19·32 N	99·31 W
82	Lac-au-Saumon.............Can.	48·24 N	67·23 W
85	Lac-Beauport (läk-bō-pōr') Can. (Quebec In.)	46·58 N	71·17 W
143	Laccadive Is. (lăk'ȧ-dīv)....India	16·16 N	73·02 E
142	Laccadive Sea.............Asia	9·10 N	75·17 E
71	Lac Court Oreille Ind. Res. (lāk kôrt-ô-rēl) (lȧk ko͞or tô-rā'y').Wis.	46·04 N	91·18 W
71	Lac du Flambeau Ind. Res...Wis.	46·12 N	89·50 W
92	La Ceiba (lȧ sēbä).........Hond.	15·45 N	86·52 W
98	La Ceja (lä-sĕ-Kä)......Col. (In.)	6·02 N	75·25 W
87	Lac Frontiere..............Can.	46·41 N	70·04 W
132	Lacha (L.) (lȧ'chä)......Sov. Un.	61·15 N	39·05 E
120	La Chaux de Fonds (lȧ shō-dē-fôN').Switz.	47·07 N	6·47 E
85	L'Achigan, R. (lä-shē-gäN) Can. (Montreal In.)	45·49 N	73·48 W
85	Lachine (lȧ-shēn') Can. (Montreal In.)	45·26 N	73·40 W
160	Lachlan (R.) (läk'lăn)......Austl.	33·54 S	145·15 E
85	Lachute (lȧ-sho͞ot') Can. (Montreal In.)	45·39 N	74·20 W
123	La Ciotat (lȧ syô-tȧ').........Fr.	43·13 N	5·35 E
75	Lackawanna (lak-ȧ-wŏn'á) N. Y. (Buffalo In.)	42·49 N	78·50 W
86	Lac la Biche...............Can.	54·46 N	112·04 W
82	Lac Megantic..............Can.	45·34 N	70·53 W
	La Columna, see Bolivar		
86	Lacombe..................Can.	52·29 N	113·41 W
91	La Concordia (lä-kōn-kô'r-dyä) Mex.	16·07 N	92·40 W
81	Laconia (lȧ-kō'nĭ-ȧ)........N. H.	43·30 N	71·30 W
65	La Conner (lȧ kŏn'ēr) Wash. (Seattle In.)	48·23 N	122·30 W
124	La Coruña (lȧ kô-ro͞on'yä)....Sp.	43·20 N	8·20 W
70	Lacreek (L.) (lȃ'krēk).......S. D.	43·04 N	101·46 W
74	La Cresenta (lȧ krĕs'ĕnt-ȧ) Calif. (Los Angeles In.)	34·14 N	118·13 W
72	La Cross (lȧ-krôs').........Kans.	38·30 N	99·20 W
71	La Crosse..................Wis.	43·48 N	91·14 W
92	La Cruz (lä-kro͞o'z).........C. R.	11·05 N	85·37 W

ng-sing; ŋ-baŋk; N-nasalized n; nŏd; cŏmmit; ōld; ôbey; ôrder; fo͞od; fo͝ot; ou-out; s-soft; sh-dish; th-thin; pūre; ûnite; ûrn; stŭd; circŭs; ü-as "y" in study; '-indeterminate vowel.

Page	Name Pronunciation Region	Lat. °′	Long. °′
98	La Cruz (lȧ krōōz′)..........Col.	1·37 N	77·00 W
70	Lacs, Riviere des (R.) (rē-vyĕr′ de läk). N. D.	48·30 N	101·45 W
85	Lac-St-Charles (läk-sĕN-shärl) Can. (Quebec In.)	46·55 N	71·23 W
93	La Cuesta (lä-kwĕ′s-tä).....C. R.	8·32 N	82·51 W
124	La Culebra, Sierra de (Mts.) (sē-ĕ′r-rä-dĕ-lä-kōō-lĕ-brä) .Sp.	41·52 N	6·21 W
73	La Cygne (lȧ-sēn′y′) (lȧ-sēn′) Kans.	38·20 N	94·45 W
80	Ladd (lăd)..................Ill.	41·25 N	89·25 W
124	La Demanda, Sierra de (Mts.) (sē-ĕ′r-rä-dĕ-lä-dĕ-mä′n-dä) .Sp.	42·10 N	2·35 W
125	Ladíspoli (lä-dê′s-pô-lē) It. (Roma In.)	41·57 N	12·05 E
65	Ladner (lăd′nēr) Can. (Vancouver In.)	49·05 N	123·06 W
	Ladoga, Lake, see Ladozhskoye Ozero		
98	La Dorado (lä dô-rä′dȧ) . Col. (In.)	5·28 N	74·42 W
119	Ladozhskoye Ozero (Lake Ladoga) (lȧ-dôsh′skô-yē ô′zĕ-rô) .Sov. Un.	60·59 N	31·30 E
85	La Durantaye (lä dü-räN-tā′) Can. (Quebec In.)	46·51 N	70·51 W
167	Lady Frere (lā-dē frâ′r′) S. Afr. (Natal In.)	31·48 S	27·16 E
167	Lady Grey.....S. Afr. (Natal In.)	30·44 S	27·17 E
66	Ladysmith (lā′dĭ-smĭth).....Can.	48·59 N	123·50 W
167	Ladysmith.....S. Afr. (Natal In.)	28·38 S	29·48 E
71	Ladysmith.................Wis.	45·27 N	91·07 W
155	Lae (lä′å)...........N. Gui. Ter.	6·15 S	146·57 E
118	Laerdal (lâr′däl)............Nor.	61·03 N	7·24 E
118	Laerdalsören (lâr′dȧls-û′rĕn) . Nor.	61·08 N	7·26 E
118	Laesö (I.) (lâs′û)..........Den.	57·17 N	10·57 E
92	La Esperanza (lä ĕs-på-rän′zä) Hond.	14·20 N	88·21 W
124	La Estrada (lä ĕs-trä′dä)......Sp.	42·42 N	8·29 W
152	Lafa (lä′fä)..............China	43·49 N	127·19 E
122	La-Fare-les-Oliviers (lä-fär′lā-ô-lē-vyā) Fr. (Marseille In.)	43·33 N	5·12 E
78	Lafayette.................Ala.	32·52 N	85·25 W
65	Lafayette Calif. (San Francisco In.)	37·53 N	122·07 W
78	Lafayette (lă-fȧ-yĕt′).........Ga.	34·41 N	85·19 W
80	La Fayette................Ind.	40·25 N	86·55 W
77	Lafayette..................La.	30·15 N	92·02 W
84	La Fayette . R. I. (Providence In.)	41·34 N	71·29 W
123	La Ferté-Alais (lä-fĕr-tā′-ä-lā′) Fr. (Paris In.)	48·29 N	2·19 E
123	La Ferté-sous-Jouarre (lȧ fĕr-tā′sōō-zhōō-är′) Fr. (Paris In.)	48·56 N	3·07 E
84	Lafitte (lă-fēt′) La. (New Orleans In.)	29·45 N	90·08 W
122	La Flèche (lȧ flăsh′)..........Fr.	47·43 N	0·03 W
122	La Flotte (lȧ flôt′)...........Fr.	46·09 N	1·20 W
78	La Follette (lä-fŏl′ĕt).......Tenn.	36·23 N	84·07 W
77	Lafourche, Bay. (bä-yōō′lȧ-fōōrsh′) . La.	29·25 N	90·15 W
99	La Gaiba (lä-gī′bä).........Braz.	17·54 S	57·32 W
116	Lagan (lā′gȧn)...........N. Ire.	54·30 N	6·00 W
118	Lagan (R.)................Swe.	56·34 N	13·25 E
112	Laganes (Pt.)...............Ice.	66·21 N	14·02 W
88	Lagarto, R. (lä-gä′r-tô) Pan. (Panama Canal In.)	9·08 N	80·05 W
92	Lagartos L. (lä-gä′r-tôs) Mex. (Yucatan In.)	21·32 N	88·15 W
118	Lågen (R.) (lô′ghĕn)........Nor.	59·15 N	9·47 E
164	Laghouat (lä-gwät′).........Alg.	33·45 N	2·49 E
123	Lagny (län-yē′)....Fr. (Paris In.)	48·53 N	2·41 E
101	Lagoa da Prata (lȧ-gô′ä-dȧ-prä′tȧ) Braz. (Rio de Janeiro In.)	20·04 S	45·33 W
101	Lagoa Dourada (lȧ-gô′ä-dōō-rä′dä) Braz. (Rio de Janeiro In.)	20·55 S	44·03 W
155	Lagonoy (lä-gô-noi′) Phil. (Manila In.)	13·44 N	123·31 E
155	Lagonoy G.....Phil. (Manila In.)	13·34 N	123·46 E
164	Lagos (lä′gōs).............Nig.	6·31 N	3·15 E
124	Lagos (lä′gôzh)............Port.	37·08 N	8·43 W
90	Lagos de Moreno (lä′gōs dā mô-rā′nō) . Mex.	21·21 N	101·55 W
122	La Grand' Combe (lȧ gräN kaNb′) Fr.	44·12 N	4·03 E
66	La Grande (lȧ grănd′).......Ore.	45·20 N	118·06 W
158	La Grange (lä grānj).......Austl.	18·40 S	122·00 E
78	La Grange (lȧ-grānj′)........Ga.	33·01 N	85·00 W
75	La Grange......Ill. (Chicago In.)	41·49 N	87·53 W
80	Lagrange..................Ind.	41·40 N	85·25 W
80	La Grange..................Ky.	38·20 N	85·25 W
73	La Grange..................Mo.	40·04 N	91·30 W
75	Lagrange....Ohio (Cleveland In.)	41·14 N	82·07 W
77	Lagrange..................Tex.	29·55 N	96·50 W
98	La Grita (lä grē′tȧ).........Ven.	8.02 N	71·59 W
99	La Guaira (lä gwä′ê-rä) . Ven. (In.)	10·36 N	66·54 W
124	La Guardia (lä gwär′dê-ȧ)....Sp.	41·55 N	8·48 W
100	Laguna (lä-gōō′nä).........Braz.	28·19 S	48·42 W
94	Laguna, Cayos (Is.) (kä′yōs-lä-gōō′nä) . Cuba	22·15 N	82·45 W
155	Laguna de Bay (L.) (lä-gōō′nä dȧ bä′ê) . Phil. (Manila In.)	14·24 N	121·13 E
69	Laguna Ind. Res.........N. Mex.	35·00 N	107·30 W
98	Lagunillas (lä-gōō-nēl′yäs)....Bol.	19·42 S	63·38 W
90	Lagunillas (lä-gōō-nê′l-yäs) . . Mex.	21·34 N	99·41 W
95	La Habana (Havana) (lä-ä-bȧ′nä) Cuba (La Habana In.)	23·08 N	82·23 W
74	La Habra (lȧ hȧb′rȧ) Calif. (Los Angeles In.)	34·56 N	117·57 W
157	Lahaina (lä-hä′ē-nä) . Hawaii (In.)	20·52 N	156·39 W
122	La Haye-Descartes (lȧ å-dȧ-kärt′) Fr.	46·58 N	0·42 E
120	Lahn R. (län)..............Ger.	50·21 N	7·54 E
118	Laholm (lä′hôlm)...........Swe.	56·30 N	13·00 E
65	La Honda (lā hôn′dă) Calif. (San Francisco In.)	37·20 N	122·16 W
142	Lahore (lä-hōr′).........W. Pak.	31·39 N	74·22 E
120	Lahr (lär)..................Ger.	48·19 N	7·52 E
119	Lahti (lä′tê)................Fin.	60·59 N	27·39 E
151	Lai, C....................Viet.	17·08 N	107·30 E
148	Laian (lāī′äN).............China	32·27 N	118·25 E
148	Laichou Wan (B.) (lāī′jō wäN) China	37·22 N	119·19 E
122	Laigle (lĕ′gl′)................Fr.	48·45 N	0·37 E
151	Laipin (lī′pĭn′)............China	23·42 N	109·20 E
148	Laiyang (lāī′yäNg).........China	36·59 N	120·42 E
90	Laja, Río de la (R.) (rê′ō-dĕ-lä-lȧ′Kä) . Mex.	20·17 N	100·57 W
94	Lajas (lä′häs)..............Cuba	22·25 N	80·20 W
100	Lajeado (lä-zhĕȧ′dô)........Braz.	29·24 S	51·46 W
100	Lajes (lȧ′-zhĕs)............Braz.	27·47 S	50·17 W
101	Lajinha (lä-zhē′nyä) Braz. (Rio de Janeiro In.)	20·08 S	41·36 W
68	La Jolla (lȧ hōl′yȧ) Calif. (San Diego In.)	32·51 N	117·16 W
68	La Jolla Ind. Res..........Calif.	33·19 N	116·21 W
72	La Junta (lȧ hōōn′tȧ).......Colo.	37 59 N	103·35 W
168	Lak Dera (R.) (läk dā′rä) Som. (Horn of Afr. In.)	0·45 N	41·26 E
77	Lake Arthur (är′thŭr)........La.	30·06 N	92·40 W
70	Lake Benton (bĕn′tŭn).....Minn.	44·15 N	96·17 W
75	Lake Bluff (blŭf) . Ill. (Chicago In.)	42·17 N	87·50 W
158	Lake Brown (broun).......Austl.	31·03 S	118·30 E
77	Lake Charles (chärlz′)........La.	30·15 N	93·14 W
79	Lake City..................Fla.	30·09 N	82·40 W
71	Lake City.................Iowa	42·14 N	94·43 W
71	Lake City................Minn.	44·28 N	92·19 W
79	Lake City..................S. C.	33·57 N	79·45 W
71	Lake Crystal (krĭs′tȧl).....Minn.	44·05 N	94·12 W
116	Lake Dist. (lāk).............Eng.	54·25 N	3·20 W
74	Lake Elmo (ĕlmō) Minn. (Minneapolis, St. Paul In.)	45·00 N	92·53 W
75	Lake Forest (fŏr′ĕst) Ill. (Chicago In.)	42·16 N	87·50 W
69	Lake Fork (R.).............Utah	40·30 N	110·25 W
71	Lake Geneva (jĕ-nē′vȧ)......Wis.	42·36 N	88·28 W
87	Lake Harbour (här′bēr).....Can.	62·43 N	69·40 W
74	Lake June (jōōn) Tex. (Dallas, Fort Worth In.)	32·43 N	96·45 W
79	Lakeland (lāk′lănd).....Fla. (In.)	28·02 N	81·58 W
78	Lakeland...................Ga.	31·02 N	83·02 W
74	Lakeland Minn. (Minneapolis, St. Paul In.)	44·57 N	92·47 W
71	Lake Linden (lĭn′dĕn)......Mich.	47·11 N	88·26 W
71	Lake Mills (mĭlz′)..........Iowa	43·25 N	93·32 W
75	Lakemore (lāk-mōr) Ohio (Cleveland In.)	41·01 N	81·24 W
80	Lake Odessa.............Mich.	42·50 N	85·15 W
74	Lake Point Utah (Salt Lake City In.)	40·41 N	112·16 W
68	Lakeport (lāk′pōrt)........Calif.	39·03 N	122·54 W
70	Lake Preston (prēs′tŭn).....S. D.	44·21 N	97·23 W
77	Lake Providence (prŏv′ĭ-dĕns) . La.	32·48 N	91·12 W
68	Lakeside (lāk′sīd) Calif. (San Diego In.)	32·52 N	116·55 W
166	Lakeside . S. Afr. (Cape Town In.)	34·05 S	18·28 E
65	Lake Stevens Wash. (Seattle In.)	48·01 N	122·04 W
84	Lake Success (sŭk-sĕs′) N. Y. (New York In.)	40·46 N	73·43 W
74	Lakeview (lāk-vū′) Calif. (Los Angeles In.)	33·50 N	117·07 W
66	Lakeview..................Ore.	42·11 N	120·21 W
84	Lakeville (lāk′vĭl) N. Y. (New York In.	41·12 N	74·16 W
67	Lake Walcott Res..........Idaho	42·35 N	113·15 W
79	Lake Wales (wālz′).....Fla. (In.)	27·54 N	81·35 W
72	Lakewood (lāk′wŏŏd).......Colo.	39·44 N	105·06 W
75	Lakewood...Ohio (Cleveland In.)	41·29 N	81·48 W
81	Lakewood..................Pa.	40·05 N	74·10 W
65	Lakewood.....Wash. (Seattle In.)	47·10 N	122·31 W
65	Lakewood.....Wash. (Seattle In.)	48·09 N	122·13 W
74	Lakewood Village Calif. (Los Angeles In.)	33·50 N	118·09 W
79	Lake Worth (wûrth′)...Fla. (In.)	26·37 N	80·04 W
74	Lake Worth Village Tex. (Dallas, Fort Worth In.)	32·49 N	97·26 W
75	Lake Zürich (tsü′rĭk) Ill. (Chicago In.)	42·11 N	88·05 W
119	Lakhdenpokh'ya (l′ăK-dĭe′npōKyȧ).....Sov. Un.	61·33 N	30·10 E
136	Lakhtinskiy (lȧk-tĭn′skĭ) Sov. Un. (Leningrad In.)	59·59 N	30·10 E
127	Lakonikós Kólpos (G.)......Grc.	36·38 N	22·40 E
70	Lakota (lȧ-kō′tȧ)..........N. D.	48·04 N	98·21 W
92	La Libertad (lä lē-bĕr-tădh′) . Guat.	15·31 N	91·44 W
92	La Libertad..Guat. (Yucatan In.)	16·46 N	90·12 W
92	La Libertad................Sal.	13·29 N	89·20 W
101	La Ligua (lä lē′gwä) Chile (Santiago In.)	32·21 S	71·13 W
124	Lalín (lä-lê′n)...............Sp.	42·40 N	8·05 W
124	La Línea (lä lē′nå-ä).........Sp.	36·11 N	5·22 W
114	Lalla-Maghnia (lä′lä-mäg′nêȧ) Alg.	34·52 N	1·40 W
117	La Louviere (lȧ lōō-vyâr′)....Bel.	50·30 N	4·10 E
90	La Luz (lä lōōz′)...........Mex.	21·04 N	101·19 W
122	La Machine (lȧ mȧ-shēn′).....Fr.	46·53 N	3·26 E
82	La Malbaie (lȧ mäl-bå′).....Can.	47·39 N	70·11 W
124	La Mancha (Mts.) (lä män′chä) Sp.	38·55 N	4·20 W
72	Lamar (lȧ-mär′)............Colo.	38·04 N	102·44 W
73	Lamar.....................Mo.	37·28 N	94·15 W
126	La Marmora, Pta. (Mtn.) (lä-mä′r-mô-rä) . It.	40·00 N	9·28 E
77	La Marque (lå-märk)...Tex. (In.)	29·23 N	94·58 W
98	Lamas (lä′mȧs).............Peru	6·24 S	76·41 W
122	Lamballe (läN-bäl′)...........Fr.	48·29 N	2·36 W
166	Lambaréné (läN-bȧ-rå-nā′) . Gabon	0·48 S	10·07 E
101	Lambari (läm-bȧ′rē) Braz. (Rio de Janeiro In.)	21·58 S	45·22 W
98	Lambayeque (läm-bä-yā′kå) . Peru	6·41 S	79·58 W
78	Lambert (lăm′bērt).........Miss.	34·10 N	90·16 W
81	Lambertville (lăm′bērt-vĭl) . . N. J.	40·20 N	75·00 W
67	Lame Deer (lām dēr′)......Mont.	45·36 N	106·40 W
124	Lamego (lä-mā′gō).........Port.	41·07 N	7·47 W
68	La Mesa (lä mā′sä) Calif. (San Diego In.)	32·46 N	117·01 W
98	La Mesa..............Col. (In.)	4·38 N	74·27 W
72	Lamesa...................Tex.	32·44 N	101·54 W
127	Lamía (lȧ-mē′ȧ).............Grc.	38·54 N	22·25 E
155	Lamon B. (lä-mōn′) Phil. (Manila In.)	14·35 N	121·52 E
101	La Mora (lä-mō′rä) Chile (Santiago In.)	32·28 S	70·56 W
70	La Moure (lȧ mōōr′).......N. D.	46·23 N	98·17 W
101	Lampa (R.) (lȧ′m-pä) Chile (Santiago In.)	33·15 S	70·55 W
76	Lampasas (lăm-păs′ȧs)......Tex.	31·06 N	98·10 W
76	Lampasas R...............Tex.	31·18 N	98·08 W
76	Lampazos (läm-pä′zōs)......Mex.	27·03 N	100·30 W
113	Lampedusa (I.) (läm-på-dōō′sä) It.	35·29 N	12·58 E
111	Lamstedt (läm′shtĕt) Ger. (Hamburg In.)	53·38 N	9·06 E
167	Lamu (lä′mōō).............Ken.	2·17 S	41·07 E
123	La Mure (lȧ mür′)...........Fr.	44·55 N	5·50 E
128	Lan' (R.) (lȧn′).........Sov. Un.	52·38 N	27·05 E
157	Lanai (I.) (lä-nä′ê) . . Hawaii (In.)	20·48 N	157·06 W
125	La Nao, Cabo de (C.) (kȧ′bô-dĕ-lä-nă′ō) . Sp.	38·43 N	0·14 E
116	Lanark (lăn′ȧrk)...........Scot.	55·40 N	3·50 W
110	Lancashire (Co.) (lăŋ′kȧ-shĭr) Scot.	53·38 N	2·30 W
82	Lancaster (lăŋ′kăs-tēr)......Can.	45·16 N	66·06 W
116	Lancaster.................Eng.	54·04 N	2·55 W
80	Lancaster..................Ky.	37·35 N	84·30 W
83	Lancaster.....Mass. (Boston In.)	42·28 N	71·40 W
81	Lancaster................N. H.	44·25 N	71·30 W
75	Lancaster.....N. Y. (Buffalo In.)	42·54 N	78·42 W
80	Lancaster.................Ohio	39·40 N	82·35 W
81	Lancaster..................Pa.	40·05 N	76·20 W
79	Lancaster.................S. C.	34·42 N	80·45 W
74	Lancaster Tex. (Dallas, Fort Worth In.)	32·36 N	96·45 W
71	Lancaster.................Wis.	42·51 N	90·44 W
150	Lanchou (län′chōō)........China	35·55 N	103·55 E
122	Lançon-Provence (läN-sôN′prô-vĕNs′) Fr. (Marseille In.)	43·35 N	5·08 E
166	Lândana (län-dä′nä)........Ang.	5·15 S	12·07 E
120	Landau (län′dou)...........Ger.	49·13 N	8·07 E
67	Lander (lăn′dēr)...........Wyo.	42·49 N	108·24 W
122	Landerneau (läN-dĕr-nō′)......Fr.	48·28 N	4·14 W
122	Landes (Moorland) (Plain) (läNd) Fr.	44·22 N	0·52 W
111	Landsberg (länds′bōōrgh) Ger. (München In.)	48·03 N	10·53 E
116	Lands End Pt.............Eng.	50·03 N	5·45 W
120	Landshut (länts′hōōt).......Ger.	48·32 N	12·09 E
118	Landskrona (lȧns-krōō′nȧ)...Swe.	55·51 N	12·47 E
78	Lanett (lȧ-nĕt′).............Ala.	32·52 N	85·13 W
150	Lanfang......China (Peking In.)	39·31 N	116·42 E
127	Langadhás.................Grc.	40·44 N	24·10 E
139	Langat (R.) . Mala. (Singapore In.)	2·46 N	101·33 E
148	Langch'i (läNg′che)........China	31·10 N	119·09 E
151	Langchung................China	31·40 N	106·05 E
85	Langdon (lăng′dŭn) Can. (Calgary In.)	50·58 N	113·40 W
74	Langdon Minn. (Minneapolis, St. Paul In.)	44·49 N	92·56 W
85	L'Ange-Gardien (läNzh gȧr-dyăN′) Can. (Quebec In.)	46·55 N	71·06 W
118	Lange Land...............Den.	54·52 N	10·46 E
65	Langeley Prairie (lăng′lĭ prâr′ĭ) Can. (Vancouver In.)	49·06 N	122·40 W
123	Langenthal..............Switz.	47·11 N	7·50 E
111	Langenzerdorf....Aus. (Wien In.)	48·30 N	16·22 E
118	Langesund (läng′ĕ-sōōn′)....Nor.	58·59 N	9·38 E
118	Lang Fd. (läng′fyôr′)........Nor.	62·40 N	7·45 E
84	Langhorne (lăng′hôrn) Pa. (Philadelphia In.)	40·10 N	74·55 W
112	Langjökoll (Gl.) (läng-yû′kōōl) Ice.	64·40 N	20·31 W
79	Langley (lăng′lĭ)...........S. C.	33·32 N	81·52 W
65	Langley......Wash. (Seattle In.)	48·02 N	122·25 W
65	Langley Ind. Res. Can. (Vancouver In.)	49·12 N	122·31 W
120	Langnau (läng′nou)........Switz.	46·56 N	7·46 E
122	Langogne (laN-gōn′y′)........Fr.	44·43 N	3·50 E
122	Langon (läN-gôN′)...........Fr.	44·34 N	0·16 W
122	Langres (läN′gr′)............Fr.	47·53 N	5·20 E
122	Langres, Plateaux de (Plat.) (plä-tō′dĕ-läN′grĕ) . Fr.	47·39 N	5·00 E
154	Langsa (läng′sȧ)..........Indon.	4·33 N	97·52 E
85	Langstaff (lăng′stăf) Can. (Toronto In.)	43·51 N	79·25 W
73	L'Anguille (R.) (läN-gē′y′)...Ark.	35·23 N	90·52 W
86	Lanigan (lăn′ĭ-gȧn).........Can.	51·53 N	105·04 W
146	Lanisung Chiang (Mekong) . China	24·45 N	100·31 E
81	Lansdale (lănz′dāl)...........Pa.	40·20 N	75·15 W
84	Lansdowne (lănz′doun) Md. (Baltimore In.)	39·14 N	76·39 W
84	Lansdowne Pa. (Philadelphia In.)	39·57 N	75·17 W
71	L'Anse (lȧns).............Mich.	46·43 N	88·28 W
85	L'Anse-a-Giles (läNz-ä-zhēl) Can. (Quebec In.)	47·05 N	70·26 W
71	L'Anse and Vieux Desert Ind. Res. Mich.	46·41 N	88·12 W
81	Lansford (lănz′fērd).........Pa.	40·50 N	75·50 W
85	Lansing (lăn′sĭng) Can. (Toronto In.)	43·46 N	79·24 W
75	Lansing........Ill. (Chicago In.)	41·34 N	87·33 W
71	Lansing...................Iowa	43·22 N	91·16 W
74	Lansing..Kans. (Kansas City In.)	39·15 N	94·53 W
80	Lansing..................Mich.	42·45 N	84·35 W
100	Lanús (lä-nōōs′).......Arg. (In.)	34·27 S	58·24 W

ăt; finăl; rāte; senåte; ärm; ȧsk; sofȧ; fâre; ch-choose; dh-as th in other; bē; êvent; bĕt; recĕnt; cratēr; g-go; gh-guttural g; bĭt; ĭ-short neutral; rīde; K-guttural k as ch in German ich;

PRONOUNCING INDEX Lanusei–Legnano 227

Page	Name Pronunciation Region	Lat. °′	Long. °′
126	Lanusei (lä-nōō-sĕ'y) It.	39·51 N	9·34 E
125	Lanúvio (lä-nōō'vyô) It. (Roma In.)	41·41 N	12·42 E
164	Lanzarote I. (län-zȧ-rō'tä) Can. Is.	29·04 N	13·03 W
154	Laoag (lä-wäg') Phil.	18·13 N	120·38 E
147	Lao Ho (R.) (lä'ō hō') China	43·37 N	120·05 E
154	Lao Kay (lä'ōkä'ē) Viet.	22·30 N	102·32 E
122	Laon (läN) Fr.	49·36 N	3·35 E
98	La Orova (lä-ô-rō'yä) Peru	11·44 S	76·12 W
138	Laos (lä'ōs) (là-ōs') Asia	19·30 N	102·45 E
93	La Palma (lä-päl'mä) Pan.	8·25 N	78·07 W
124	La Palma Sp.	37·24 N	6·36 W
164	La Palma I. Can. Is.	28·42 N	19·03 W
100	La Pampa (Prov.) Arg.	37·25 S	67·00 W
100	Lapa Rio Negro (lä-pä-rē'ō-nĕ'grô) Braz.	26·12 S	49·56 W
100	La Paz (lä päz') Arg.	30·48 S	59·47 W
98	La Paz Bol.	16·31 S	68·03 W
92	La Paz Hond.	14·15 N	87·40 W
90	La Paz (lä-pà'z) Mex.	23·39 N	100·44 W
88	La Paz Mex.	24·00 N	110·15 W
155	La Paz Phil. (Manila In.)	17·41 N	120·41 E
80	Lapeer (lȧ-pēr') Mich.	43·05 N	83·15 W
122	La-Penne-sur-Huveaune (la-pĕn'sür-ü-vōn') Fr. (Marseille In.)	43·18 N	5·33 E
90	La Piedad Cabadas (lä pyä-dhädh' kä-bä'dhäs) Mex.	20·20 N	102·04 W
112	Lapland (Reg.) (lăp'lȧnd) Eur.	68·20 N	22·00 E
101	La Plata (lä plä'tä) Arg. (Buenos Aires In.)	34·54 S	57·57 W
73	La Plata (lȧ plā'tȧ) Mo.	40·03 N	92·28 W
69	La Plata Pk. Colo.	39·00 N	106·25 W
125	La Pobla de Lillet (lä-pô'blä-dĕ-lēl-yĕ't) Sp.	42·14 N	1·58 E
155	Lapog (lä-pôg') Phil. (Manila In.)	17·44 N	120·28 E
83	La Poile B. (lȧ pwäl') Can.	47·28 N	58·35 W
80	La Porte (lȧ pōrt') Ind.	41·35 N	86·45 W
75	Laporte Ohio (Cleveland In.)	41·19 N	82·05 W
77	La Porte Tex. (In.)	29·40 N	95·01 W
71	La Porte City Iowa	42·20 N	92·10 W
119	Lappeenranta (lä'pēn-rän'tä) Fin.	61·04 N	28·08 E
85	Laprairie (lȧ-prâ-rē') Can. (Montreal In.)	45·24 N	73·30 W
127	Lapseki (läp'sȧ-kē) Tur.	40·20 N	26·41 E
130	Laptev Sea (läp'tyĭf) Sov. Un.	75·39 N	120·00 E
125	La Puebla (lä pwä'blä) Sp.	39·46 N	3·02 E
124	La Puebla de Montalbán (lä pwä'blä dā mōnt-äl-bän') Sp.	39·54 N	4·21 W
121	Lapusul R. (lä'pōō-shōōl) Rom.	47·29 N	23·46 E
100	La Quiaca (lä kē-ä'kä) Arg.	22·15 S	65·44 W
126	L'Aquila (là'kē-lä) It.	42·22 N	13·24 E
144	Lar (lär) Iran	27·31 N	54·12 E
161	Lara Austl. (Melbourne In.)	38·02 S	144·24 E
164	Larache (lä-räsh') Mor.	35·15 N	6·09 W
62	Laramie (lăr'ȧ-mĭ) Wyo.	41·20 N	105·40 W
72	Laramie (R.) Colo.	40·56 N	105·55 W
125	L'Arba (l'är'bȧ) Alg.	36·35 N	3·10 E
84	Larchmont (lärch'mŏnt) N. Y. (New York In.)	40·56 N	73·46 W
65	Larch Mtn. (lärch) Ore. (Portland In.)	45·32 N	122·06 W
124	Laredo (lä-rā'dhō) Sp.	43·24 N	3·24 W
76	Laredo Tex.	27·31 N	99·29 W
122	La Réole (lȧ rȧ-ōl') Fr.	44·37 N	0·03 W
94	Largo, Cayo (kä'yō-lär'gō) Cuba	21·40 N	81·30 W
70	Larimore (lăr'ĭ-môr) N. D.	47·53 N	97·38 W
126	Larino (lä-rē'nô) It.	41·48 N	14·54 E
100	La Rioja (lä rê-ōhä) Arg.	29·18 S	67·42 W
100	La Rioja (Prov.) (lä-rê-ô'-kä) Arg.	28·45 S	68·00 W
127	Lárisa (lä'rê-sȧ) Grc.	39·38 N	22·25 E
142	Lārkāna W. Pak.	27·40 N	68·12 E
139	Larnaca (lär'nȧ-kä) Cyprus (Palestine In.)	34·55 N	33·37 E
139	Larnaca (B.) Cyprus (Palestine In.)	34·55 N	33·51 E
72	Larned (lär'nĕd) Kans.	38·09 N	99·07 W
124	La Robla (lä rōb'lä) Sp.	42·48 N	5·36 W
122	La Rochelle (lä rô-shĕl') Fr.	46·10 N	1·09 W
122	La Roche-sur-Yon (lȧ rōsh'sûr-yôN') Fr.	46·39 N	1·27 W
124	La Roda (lä rō'dä) Sp.	39·13 N	2·08 W
95	La Romona (lä-rä-mô'nä) Dom. Rep.	18·25 N	69·00 W
158	Larrey Pt. (lăr'ē) Austl.	19·15 S	118·15 E
122	Laruns (lȧ-răNs') Fr.	42·58 N	0·28 W
118	Larvik (lär'vēk) Nor.	59·06 N	10·03 E
99	La Sabana (lä-sä-bȧ'nä) Ven. (In.)	10·38 N	66·24 W
95	La Sabina (lä-sä-bē'nä) Cuba (La Habana In.)	22·10 N	82·07 W
124	La Sagra (Mtn.) (lä sä'grä) Sp.	37·56 N	2·35 E
69	La Sal (lȧ sȧl') Utah	38·10 N	109·20 W
75	La Salle (lȧ săl') Can. (Detroit In.)	42·14 N	83·06 W
85	La Salle Can. (Winnipeg In.)	49·41 N	97·16 W
80	La Salle Ill.	41·20 N	89·05 W
72	Las Animas (läs ȧ'nĭ-mȧs) Colo.	38·03 N	103·16 W
168	Las Anod (läs ăn'ŏd) Som. (Horn of Afr. In.)	8·24 N	47·20 E
87	La Sarre Can.	48·43 N	79·12 W
95	Lascahobas (läs-kä-ō'bȧs) Hai.	19·00 N	71·55 W
91	Las Cruces (läs-krōō'-sĕs) Mex.	16·37 N	93·54 W
69	Las Cruces N. Mex.	32·20 N	106·50 W
95	La Selle, Massif De (Mts.) (lȧ sĕl') Hai.	18·25 N	72·05 W
100	La Serena (lä-sĕ-rĕ'nä) Chile	29·55 S	71·24 W
123	La Seyne-sur-Mer (lȧ-sân'sür-mĕr') Fr.	43·07 N	5·52 E
101	Las Flores (läs flo'rĕs) Arg. (Buenos Aires In.)	36·01 S	59·07 W
146	Lashio (lăsh'ē-ō) Bur.	22·58 N	98·03 E
74	La Sierra (lȧ sĭ-ĕr'ȧ) Calif. (Los Angeles In.)	33·54 N	117·29 W
92	Las Juntas (läs-Kōō'n-täs) C. R.	10·15 N	85·00 W
168	Las Khoreh (läs Kō'rȧ) Som. (Horn of Afr. In.)	11·13 N	48·19 E
124	Las Maismas (Reg.) (läs-mī's-mäs) Sp.	37·05 N	6·25 W
124	La Solano (lä-sô-lä-nō) Sp.	38·56 N	3·13 W
164	Las Palmas (läs päl'mäs) Can. Is.	28·07 N	15·28 W
93	Las Palmas Pan.	8·08 N	81·30 W
126	La Spezia (lä-spĕ'zyä) It.	44·07 N	9·48 E
101	Las Piedras (läs-pyĕ'drȧs) Ur. (Buenos Aires In.)	34·42 S	56·08 W
92	Las Pilas (Vol.) (läs-pē'läs) Nic.	12·32 N	86·43 W
91	Las Rosas (läs rō thȧs) Mex.	16·24 N	92·23 W
125	Las Rozas de Madrid (läs rō'thas dā mä-dhrēdh') Sp. (Madrid In.)	40·29 N	3·53 W
111	Lassee Aus. (Wien In.)	48·14 N	16·50 E
66	Lassen Pk. (lăs'ĕn) Calif.	40·30 N	121·32 W
66	Lassen Volcanic Natl. Park Calif.	40·43 N	121·35 W
85	L'Assomption (lás-sôm-syôN) Can. (Montreal In.)	45·50 N	73·25 W
93	Las Tablas (läs tä'bläs) Pan.	7·48 N	80·16 W
86	Last Mountain (L.) (làst moun'tĭn) Can.	51·07 N	105·50 W
166	Lastoursville (lȧs-tōōr-vēl') Gabon	1·00 S	12·49 E
88	Las Tres Marías (I.) (läs-trĕ's mä-rē'äs) Mex.	21·30 N	106·40 W
88	Las Tres Virgenes, Vol. (vē'r-hĕ-nĕs) Mex.	26·00 N	111·45 W
91	Las Vacas (läs-vȧ'kȧs) Mex.	16·24 N	95·48 W
101	Las Vegas (läs-vĕ'gäs) Chile (Santiago In.)	30·50 S	70·59 W
68	Las Vegas (läs vā'gäs) Nev.	36·12 N	115·10 W
72	Las Vegas N. Mex.	35·36 N	105·13 W
99	Las Vegas (läs-vĕ'gäs) Ven. (In.)	10·26 N	64·08 W
90	Las Vigas Mex.	19·38 N	97·03 W
94	Las Villas (State) (läs-vē'l-läs) Cuba	22·15 N	80·50 W
100	Las Vizcachas, Meseta de (Plat.) (mĕ-sĕ'tä-dĕ-läs-vêz-kä'-chȧs) Arg.	49·35 S	71·00 W
98	Latacunga (lä-tä-kōōŋ'gä) Ec.	1·02 S	78·33 W
	Latakia, see El Ladhiqiya		
115	Latakia (Reg.) (lä-tä-kē'ä) U. A. R.	35·10 N	35·49 E
122	La Teste-de-Buch (lȧ-tĕst-dĕ-büsh) Fr.	44·38 N	1·11 W
73	Lathrop (lā'thrŭp) Mo.	39·32 N	94·21 W
	Latium (Reg.), see Lazio		
121	Latoritsa R. (lȧ-tô'rĭ-tsȧ) Sov. Un.	48·27 N	22·30 E
85	La Tortue, R. (lä tōr-tü') Can. (Montreal In.)	45·12 N	73·32 W
65	Latourell (lȧ-tou'rĕl) Ore. (Portland In.)	45·32 N	122·13 W
122	La Tremblade (lä-trĕN-bläd') Fr.	45·45 N	1·12 W
81	Latrobe (lȧ-trōb') Pa.	40·25 N	79·15 W
82	La Tuque (lȧ tük') Can.	47·27 N	72·49 W
130	Latvian (S. S. R.) Sov. Un.	57·28 N	24·29 E
160	Launceston (lôn'sĕs-tŭn) Austl.	41·35 S	147·22 E
116	Launceston (lôrn'stŏn) Eng.	50·38 N	4·26 W
100	La Unión (lä-ōō-nyô'n) Chile	40·15 S	73·04 W
90	La Unión (lä ōōn-nyōn') Mex.	17·59 N	101·48 W
92	La Unión Sal.	13·18 N	87·51 W
125	La Unión Sp.	37·38 N	0·50 W
157	Laupahoehoe (lä'ōō-pä-hō'ē-hō-ē) Hawaii (In.)	19·58 N	155·13 W
159	Laura (lôrȧ) Austl.	15·40 S	144·45 E
128	Laura (lou'rȧ) Sov. Un.	57·36 N	27·29 E
81	Laurel (lô'rĕl) Del.	38·30 N	75·40 W
84	Laurel Md. (Baltimore In.)	39·06 N	76·51 W
78	Laurel Miss.	31·42 N	89·07 W
67	Laurel Mont.	45·41 N	108·45 W
65	Laurel Wash. (Vancouver In.)	48·52 N	122·29 W
65	Laurelwood (lô'rĕl-wŏŏd) Ore. (Portland In.)	45·25 N	123·05 W
79	Laurens (lô'rĕnz) S. C.	34·29 N	82·03 W
49	Laurentian Highlands (Reg.) (lô'rĕn-tĭ-ȧn) Can.	49·00 N	74·50 W
82	Laurentides Park (lô'rĕn-tīdz) Can.	47·53 N	71·26 W
126	Lauria (lou'rê-ä) It.	40·03 N	15·02 E
79	Laurinburg (lô'rĭn-bûrg) N. C.	34·45 N	79·27 W
71	Laurium (lô'rĭ-ŭm) Mich.	47·13 N	88·28 W
154	Laurot Pulau-Pulau Is. Indon.	4·44 S	115·43 E
120	Lausanne (lō-zȧn') Switz.	46·32 N	6·35 E
154	Laut (I.) Indon.	3·39 S	116·07 E
100	Lautaro (lou-tä'rō) Chile	38·40 S	72·24 W
85	Lauzon (lō-zōN') Can. (Quebec In.)	46·50 N	71·10 W
66	Lava Beds Natl. Mon. (lä'vȧ bĕds) Calif.	41·38 N	121·44 W
77	Lavaca R. (lȧ-vȧk'ȧ) Tex.	29·05 N	96·50 W
67	Lava Hot Springs Idaho	42·37 N	111·58 W
85	Laval (lȧ-vȧl') Can. (Montreal In.)	45·33 N	73·42 W
122	Laval (lä-väl') Fr.	48·05 N	0·47 W
122	Lavaur (lȧ-vōr') Fr.	43·41 N	1·48 E
122	Lavaveix-les-Mines (lȧ-vȧ-vĕ'lā-mēn') Fr.	46·05 N	2·05 E
95	La Vega (lä-vĕ'-gä) Dom. Rep.	19·15 N	70·35 W
159	Lavella (I.) Sol. Is.	7·50 S	155·45 E
126	Lavello (lä-vĕl'lō) It.	41·05 N	15·50 E
74	La Verne (lȧ vûrn') Calif. (Los Angeles In.)	34·06 N	117·46 W
158	Laverton (lā'vēr-tŭn) Austl.	28·45 S	122·30 E
99	La Victoria (lä vêk-tō'rê-ä) Ven. (In.)	10·14 N	67·20 W
78	Lavonia (lȧ-vō'nĭ-ȧ) Ga.	34·26 N	83·05 W
101	Lavras (lä'vräzh) Braz. (Rio de Janeiro In.)	21·15 S	44·59 W
127	Lávrion (läv'rĭ-ôn) Grc.	37·44 N	24·05 E
74	Lawndale (lôn'dāl) Calif. (Los Angeles In.)	33·54 N	118·22 W
75	Lawrence (lô'rĕns) Ind. (Indianapolis In.)	39·59 N	86·01 W
73	Lawrence Kans.	38·57 N	95·13 W
83	Lawrence Mass. (Boston In.)	42·42 N	71·09 W
75	Lawrence Pa. (Pittsburgh In.)	40·18 N	80·07 W
65	Lawrence Wash. (Vancouver In.)	48·52 N	122·18 W
75	Lawrenceburg (lô'rĕns-bûrg) Ind. (Cincinnati In.)	39·06 N	84·47 W
80	Lawrenceburg Ky.	38·00 N	85·00 W
78	Lawrenceburg Tenn.	35·13 N	87·20 W
78	Lawrenceville (lô-rĕns-vĭl) Ga.	33·56 N	83·57 W
80	Lawrenceville Ill.	38·45 N	87·45 W
84	Lawrenceville N. J. (New York In.)	40·17 N	74·44 W
79	Lawrenceville Va.	36·43 N	77·52 W
81	Lawsonia (lô-sō'nĭ-ȧ) Md.	38·00 N	75·50 W
72	Lawton (lô'tŭn) Okla.	34·36 N	98·25 W
139	Layang Layang (lä-yäng' lä-yäng') Mala. (Singapore In.)	1·49 N	103·28 E
74	Layton (lā'tŭn) Utah (Salt Lake City In.)	41·04 N	111·58 W
119	Laždijai (läzh'dē-yī') Sov. Un.	54·12 N	23·35 E
126	Lazio (Latium) (Reg.) (lä'zyô) (lā't-zēōōm) It.	42·05 N	12·25 E
70	Lead (lēd) S. D.	44·22 N	103·47 W
72	Leadville (lĕd'vĭl) Colo.	39·14 N	106·18 W
87	Leaf (R.) (lēf) Can.	59·12 N	72·50 W
78	Leaf (R.) Miss.	31·43 N	89·20 W
77	League City (lēg) Tex. (In.)	29·31 N	95·05 W
80	Leamington (lĕm'ĭng-tŭn) Can.	42·05 N	82·35 W
116	Leamington (lĕ'mĭng-tŭn) Eng.	52·17 N	1·25 W
85	Leaside (lē'sīd) Can. (Toronto In.)	43·42 N	79·22 W
110	Leatherhead (lĕdh'ĕr-hĕd') Eng. (London In.)	51·17 N	0·20 W
74	Leavenworth (lĕv'ĕn-wûrth) Kans. (Kansas City In.)	39·19 N	94·54 W
66	Leavenworth Wash.	47·35 N	120·39 W
74	Leawood (lē'wŏŏd) Mo. (Kansas City In.)	38·58 N	94·37 W
121	Leba (lā'bȧ) Pol.	54·45 N	17·34 E
139	Lebam R. Mala. (Singapore In.)	1·35 N	104·09 E
74	Lebanon (lĕb'ȧ-nŭn) Ill. (St. Louis In.)	38·36 N	89·49 W
80	Lebanon Ind.	40·00 N	86·30 W
78	Lebanon Ky.	37·32 N	85·15 W
73	Lebanon Mo.	37·40 N	92·43 W
81	Lebanon N. H.	43·40 N	72·15 W
80	Lebanon Ohio	39·25 N	84·10 W
66	Lebanon Ore.	44·31 N	122·53 W
81	Lebanon Pa.	40·20 N	76·20 W
78	Lebanon Tenn.	36·10 N	86·16 W
138	Lebanon Asia	34·00 N	35·00 E
115	Lebanon Mts. Leb.	33·30 N	35·32 E
129	Lebedin (lyĕ'bĕ-dēn) Sov. Un.	48·56 N	31·35 E
129	Lebedin Sov. Un.	50·34 N	34·27 E
128	Lebedyan' (lyĕ'bĕ-dyän') Sov. Un.	53·03 N	39·08 E
122	Le Blanc (lĕ-bläN') Fr.	46·38 N	0·59 E
95	Le Borgne (lē bōrn'y') Hai.	19·50 N	72·30 W
121	Lebork (lăN-bōōrk') Pol.	54·33 N	17·46 E
122	Le Boucau (lĕ-bōō-Kō') Fr.	43·33 N	1·28 W
122	Le Bouscat (lē bōōs-kȧ) Fr.	44·53 N	0·38 W
124	Lebrija (lā-brē'hä) Sp.	36·55 N	6·06 W
100	Lebú (lā-bōō') Chile	37·35 S	73·37 W
127	Lecce (lĕt'chā) It.	40·22 N	18·11 E
126	Lecco (lĕk'kō) It.	45·52 N	9·28 E
123	Le Châtelet-en-Brie (lĕ-shä-tĕ-lā' ĕN-brē') Fr. (Paris In.)	48·29 N	2·50 E
94	Leche, Laguna de (L.) (lä-gōō'nä-dĕ-lĕ'chĕ) Cuba	22·10 N	78·30 W
76	Leche, Laguna de la (L.) Mex.	27·16 N	102·45 W
123	Lechenich (lĕ'Kĕ-nēK) Ger. (Ruhr In.)	50·47 N	6·46 E
120	Lech R. (lĕk) Ger.	47·41 N	10·52 E
77	Lecompte La.	31·06 N	92·25 W
122	Le Coteau (lē kō-tō') Fr.	46·01 N	4·06 E
122	Le Creusot (lĕkrû-zō') Fr.	46·48 N	4·23 E
122	Lectoure (lĕK-tōōr) Fr.	43·56 N	0·38 E
124	Ledesma (lā-dĕs'mä) Sp.	41·05 N	5·59 W
85	Leduc (lĕ-dōōk') Can. (Edmonton In.)	53·16 N	113·34 W
71	Leech (L.) (lēch) Minn.	47·06 N	94·16 W
84	Leeds (lēdz) Ala. (Birmingham In.)	33·33 N	86·33 W
110	Leeds Eng.	53·48 N	1·33 W
70	Leeds N. D.	48·18 N	99·24 W
110	Leeds and Liverpool Can. (lĭv'ēr-pōōl) Eng.	53·36 N	2·38 W
111	Leegebruch (lĕh'gĕn-brōōK) Ger. (Berlin In.)	52·43 N	13·12 E
110	Leek (lēk) Eng.	53·06 N	2·01 W
120	Leer (lār) Ger.	53·14 N	7·27 E
116	Lee R. (lē) Ire.	51·52 N	8·30 W
79	Leesburg (lēz'bûrg) Fla.	28·49 N	81·53 W
81	Leesburg Va.	39·10 N	77·30 W
69	Lees Ferry Ariz.	36·55 N	111·45 W
74	Lees Summit Mo. (Kansas City In.)	38·55 N	94·23 W
95	Lee Stocking (I.) Ba. Is.	23·45 N	76·05 W
77	Leesville (lēz'vĭl) La.	31·09 N	93·17 W
80	Leetonia (lē-tō-nĭ-ȧ) Ohio	40·50 N	80·45 W
117	Leeuwarden (lā'wär-dĕn) Neth.	52·12 N	5·50 E
158	Leeuwin, C. (lōō'wĭn) Austl.	34·15 S	114·30 E
89	Leeward Is. (lē'wērd) N. A.	12·25 N	62·15 W
93	Le Francois Mart. (Le. & Wind. Is. In.)	14·37 N	60·55 W
158	Lefroy (L.) (lē-froi') Austl.	31·30 S	122·00 E
125	Leganés (lā-gä'nās) Sp. (Madrid In.)	40·20 N	3·46 W
155	Legaspi (lā-gäs'pē) Phil. (Manila In.)	13·09 N	123·44 E
160	Legge Pk. (lĕg) Austl.	41·33 S	148·10 E
	Leghorn, see Livorno		
126	Legnano (lå-nyä'nō) It.	45·35 N	8·53 E

ng-sing; ŋ-baŋk; N-nasalized n; nŏd; cŏmmit; ōld; ôbey; ôrder; fōōd; fŏŏt; ou-out; s-soft; sh-dish; th-thin; pūre; ûnite; ûrn; stŭd; circŭs; ü-as "y" in study; '-indeterminate vowel.

228 Legnica—Limbe PRONOUNCING INDEX

Page	Name Pronunciation Region	Lat. °′	Long. °′
120	Legnica (lĕk-nĭt′sȧ) . . . . Pol.	51·13 N	16·10 E
142	Leh (lā) . . . . India	34·10 N	77·40 E
122	Le Havre (lē ȧv′r′) . . . . Fr.	49·31 N	0·07 E
69	Lehi (lē′hī) . . . . Utah	40·25 N	111·55 W
69	Lehman Caves Natl. Mon. (lē′măn) . Nev.	38·54 N	114·08 W
111	Lehnin (lĕh′nēn) . Ger. (Berlin In.)	52·19 N	12·45 E
110	Leicester (lĕs′tẽr) . . . . Eng.	52·37 N	1·08 W
110	Leicester (Co.) . . . . Eng.	52·40 N	1·12 W
158	Leichhardt, (R.) (līk′härt) . . Austl.	18·30 S	139·45 E
111	Leiden (lī′dĕn) Neth. (Amsterdam In.)	52·09 N	4·29 E
118	Leikanger (lī′käŋ′gẽr) . . . . Nor.	61·11 N	6·51 E
111	Leimuiden . Neth. (Amsterdam In.)	52·13 N	4·40 E
120	Leine R. (lī′nĕ) . . . . Ger.	51·58 N	9·56 E
116	Leinster (lĕn-stẽr) . . . . Ire.	52·45 N	7·19 W
80	Leipsic (līp′sĭk) . . . . Ohio	41·05 N	84·00 W
120	Leipzig (līp′tsĭk) . . . . Ger.	51·20 N	12·24 E
124	Leiria (lā-rē′ȧ) . . . . Port.	39·45 N	8·50 W
78	Leitchfield (lēch′fēld) . . . . Ky.	37·28 N	86·20 W
111	Leitha (R.) . . . . . . Aus. (Wien In.)	48·04 N	16·57 E
85	Leitrim . . . . Can. (Ottawa In.)	45·20 N	75·36 W
	Leixoes, see Matozinhos		
117	Lek (R.) (lĕk) . . . . Neth.	51·59 N	5·30 E
113	Lekef (lĕkĕf′) . . . . Tun.	36·14 N	8·42 E
118	Leksand (lĕk′sänd) . . . . Swe.	60·45 N	14·56 E
65	Leland (lē′lănd) Wash. (Seattle In.)	47·54 N	122·53 W
120	Le Locle (lē lô′kl′) . . . . Switz.	47·03 N	6·43 E
100	Le Maire, Estrecho de (Str.) (ĕs-trĕ′chô-dĕ-lĕ-mī′rĕ) . Arg.	55·15 S	65·30 W
122	Le Mans (lē mäN′) . . . . Fr.	48·01 N	0·12 E
93	Le Marin Mart. (Le. & Wind. Is. In.)	14·28 N	60·55 W
70	Le Mars (lē märz′) . . . . Iowa	42·46 N	96·09 W
155	Lemery (lā-mā-rē′) Phil. (Manila In.)	13·51 N	120·55 E
67	Lemhi Ra. (Mts.) (lĕm′hī) . . Idaho	44·35 N	113·33 W
67	Lemhi R. . . . . Idaho	44·40 N	113·27 W
70	Lemmon (lĕm′ŭn) . . . . S. D.	45·55 N	102·10 W
95	Le Môle (lē mōl′) . . . . Hai.	19·50 N	73·20 W
68	Lemon Grove (lĕm′ŭn-grōv) Calif. (San Diego In.)	32·44 N	117·02 W
75	Lemont (lē′-mŏnt) Ill. (Chicago In.)	41·40 N	87·59 W
93	Le Moule (lē mōōl′) Guad. (Le. & Wind. Is. In.)	16·19 N	61·22 W
92	Lempa R. (lĕm′pä) . . . . Sal.	13·20 N	88·46 W
118	Lemvig (lĕm′vēgh) . . . . Den.	56·33 N	8·16 E
118	Lena (lī′nä) . . . . Swe.	60·01 N	17·40 E
135	Lena (R.) . . . . Sov. Un.	68·39 N	124·15 E
100	Lençóes Paulista (lĕN-sôNs′ pou-lēs′tȧ) . Braz.	22·30 S	48·45 W
99	Lençóis (lĕn-sóis) . . . . Braz.	12·38 S	41·28 W
74	Lenexa (lē-nĕx′ȧ) Mo. (Kansas City In.)	38·58 N	94·44 W
103	Lenger (lyĭn′gyĕr) . . . . Sov. Un.	41·38 N	70·00 E
139	Lenik (R.) . . Mala. (Singapore In.)	1·59 N	102·51 E
134	Leninabad (lĕ-nyē-nȧ bȧt′) Sov. Un.	40·15 N	69·49 E
133	Leninakan (lĕ-nyē-nȧ-kän′) Sov. Un.	40·40 N	43·50 E
136	Leningrad (lyĕ-nēn-grȧt′) Sov. Un. (Leningrad In.)	59·57 N	30 20 E
128	Leningrad (Oblast) . . . . . Sov. Un.	59·15 N	30·30 E
129	Leningradskaya (lyĕ-nĭn-gräd′skȧ-yȧ) . Sov. Un.	46·19 N	39·23 E
136	Lenino (lyĕ′nĭ-nô) Sov. Un. (Moskva In.)	55·37 N	37·41 E
134	Leninogorsk (lyĕ-nĭn ŭ gôrsk′) Sov. Un.	50·29 N	83·25 E
133	Leninsk (lyĕ-nēnsk′) . . . . . Sov. Un.	48·40 N	45·10 E
134	Leninsk-Kuznetskiy (lyĕ-nênsk′ kōōz-nyĕt′skĭ-ê) . Sov. Un.	54·28 N	86·48 E
133	Lenkoran′ (lĕn-kô-rän′) . . Sov. Un.	38·52 N	48·58 E
70	Lennox (lĕn′ŭks) . . . . S. D.	43·22 N	96·53 W
79	Lenoir (lê-nōr′) . . . . N. C.	35·54 N	81·35 W
78	Lenoir City . . . . Tenn.	35·47 N	84·16 W
71	Lenox . . . . Iowa	40·51 N	94·29 W
120	Leoben (lā-ō′bĕn) . . . . Aus.	47·22 N	15·09 E
95	Léogane (lā-ô-gan′) . . . . Hai.	18·30 N	72·35 W
70	Leola (lē-ō′lȧ) . . . . S. D.	45·43 N	99·55 W
83	Leominster (lĕm′ĭn-stẽr) Mass. (Boston In.)	42·32 N	71·45 W
71	Leon (lē′ŏn) . . . . Iowa	40·43 N	93·44 W
90	León (lā-ōn′) . . . . Mex.	21·08 N	101·41 W
92	León (lĕ-ô′n) . . . . Nic.	12·28 N	86·53 W
124	León (lĕ-ô′n) . . . . Sp.	42·38 N	5·33 W
124	Leon (Reg.) (lĕ-ô′n) . . . . Sp.	41·18 N	5·50 W
126	Leonforte (lā-ôn-fôr′tā) . . . . It.	37·40 N	14·27 E
76	Leon R. (lē′ōn) . . . . Tex.	31·54 N	98·20 W
101	Leopoldina (lā-ô-pôl-dē′nä) Braz. (Rio de Janeiro In.)	21·32 S	42·38 W
111	Leopoldsburg . Bel. (Bruxelles In.)	51·07 N	5·18 E
111	Leopoldsdorf im Marchfelde (lā′ô-pôlts-dôrf′) Aus. (Wien In.)	48·14 N	16·42 E
166	Leopold II (L.) (lā′ô-pōld) Con. L.	2·16 S	19·00 E
166	Léopoldville (lā-ô-pôld-vēl′) Con. L.	4·28 S	15·16 E
129	Leovo (lȧ-ō′vô) . . . . Sov. Un.	46·30 N	28·16 E
124	Lepe (lā′pā) . . . . Sp.	37·15 N	7·12 W
128	Lepel′ (lyĕ-pĕl′) . . . . Sov. Un.	54·52 N	28·41 E
85	L'Epiphanie (lā-pē-fā-nē′) Can. (Montreal In.)	45·51 N	73·29 W
123	Le Plessis-Belleville (lĕ-plĕ-sē′ bĕl-vēl′) . Fr. (Paris In.)	49·05 N	2·46 E
120	Lepontine Alpi (Mts.) (lē-pŏn′tĭn) Switz.	46·28 N	8·38 E
82	Lepreau (lē-prō′) . . . . Can.	45·10 N	66·28 W
134	Lepsinsk . . . . Sov. Un.	45·32 N	80·47 E
122	Le Puy-en-Velay (lē pwē′) . . . . . Fr.	45·02 N	3·54 E
126	Lercara (lĕr-kä′rä) . . . . It.	36·47 N	13·36 E
76	Lerdo (lĕr′dō) . . . . Mex.	25·31 N	103·30 W
165	Léré (lā-rā′) . . . . Chad	9·42 N	14·14 E
167	Leribe . . . . Bas. (Natal In.)	28·53 S	28·02 E
125	Lérida (lā′rē-dhä) . . . . Sp.	41·38 N	0·37 E
91	Lerma (lĕr′mä) . . . . Mex.	19·49 N	90·34 W
91	Lerma . . . . Mex. (Mexico In.)	19·17 N	99·30 W
124	Lerma (lĕ′r-mä) . . . . Sp.	42·03 N	3·45 W
90	Lerma (R.) . . . . Mex.	20·14 N	101·50 W
81	Le Roy (lê roi′) . . . . N. Y.	43·00 N	78·00 W
116	Lerwick (lĕr′ĭk) (lûr′wĭk) . . . . Scot.	60·08 N	1·27 W
84	Lery, L. (lĕ′rē) La. (New Orleans In.)	29·48 N	89·45 W
123	Les Andelys (lā-zäN-dē-lē′) Fr. (Paris In.)	49·15 N	1·25 E
95	Les Cayes . . . . Hai.	18·15 N	73·45 W
85	Les Cèdres (lā-sĕdr′) Can. (Montreal In.)	45·18 N	74·03 W
127	Lesh (Alessio) (lĕshĕ) (ä-lā′sē-ō) Alb.	41·47 N	19·40 E
126	Lésina, Lago di (L.) (lä′gō dē lā′zē-nä) . It.	41·48 N	15·12 E
127	Leskovac (lĕs′kô-vȧts) . . . . . . Yugo.	43·00 N	21·58 E
73	Leslie (lĕz′lī) . . . . Ark.	35·49 N	92·32 W
168	Leslie S. Afr. (Johannesburg & Pretoria In.)	26·23 S	28·57 E
132	Lesnoy (lĕs′noi) . . . . Sov. Un.	66·45 N	34·45 E
152	Lesogorsk (lyĕs′ô-gôrsk) . Sov. Un.	49·28 N	141·59 E
152	Lesozavodsk (lyĕ-sô-zȧ-vôdsk′) Sov. Un.	45·21 N	133·19 E
122	Lesparre (lē-spär) . . . . Fr.	45·18 N	0·57 W
122	Les-Pennes-Mirabeau (lā-pĕn′ mĭ-rä-bō′) . Fr. (Marseille In.)	43·25 N	5·19 E
122	Les Sables-d'Olonne (lā sä′bl′dô-lŭn′) . Fr.	46·30 N	1·47 W
93	Les Saintes Is. (lā-säNt′) Guad. (Le. & Wind. Is. In.)	15·50 N	61·40 W
	Lesser Khingan Mts. see Hsiaohsinganling Shanmo		
86	Lesser Slave L. (lĕs′ẽr slāv) . . Can.	55·10 N	116·18 W
122	L'Estague (lĕs-täl) Fr. (Marseille In.)	43·22 N	5·20 E
123	Les Thilliers-en-Vexin (lā-tē-yā′ ĕN-vĕ-säN′) . Fr. (Paris In.)	49·19 N	1·36 E
71	Le Sueur (lē sōōr′) . . . . Minn.	44·27 N	93·53 W
127	Lésvos (I.) . . . . Grc.	39·15 N	25·40 E
120	Leszno (lĕsh′nô) . . . . Pol.	51·51 N	16·35 E
122	Le Teil (lē tā′y′) . . . . Fr.	44·34 N	4·39 E
86	Lethbridge (lĕth′brĭj) . . . . Can.	49·40 N	112·39 W
166	Letiahau (R.) . . . . Bech.	21·16 S	22·17 E
129	Letichev (lyĕ-tê-chĕf′) . . . Sov. Un.	49·22 N	27·29 E
98	Leticia (lĕ-tē′syä) . . . . Col.	4·04 S	69·57 W
123	Letmathe (lĕt′mät-hĕ) Ger. (Ruhr In.)	51·22 N	7·37 E
122	Le Tréport (lē-trā-pôr′) . . . . Fr.	50·03 N	1·21 E
154	Leuser, Gulung (Mtn.) . . . . . Indon.	3·36 N	97·17 E
111	Leuven . . . . . . Bel. (Bruxelles In.)	50·53 N	4·42 E
127	Levádhia . . . . Grc.	38·25 N	22·51 E
123	Levallois-Perret (lē-vál-wá′pĕ-rĕ′) Fr. (Paris In.)	48·53 N	2·17 E
112	Levanger (lĕ-vàng′ẽr) . . . . Nor.	63·42 N	11·01 E
126	Levanna (Mtn.) (lā-vä′nä) . Fr.-It.	45·25 N	7·14 E
158	Leveque, C. (lê-vĕk′) . . . . Austl.	16·25 S	123·08 E
123	Leverkusen (lĕ′fẽr-kōō-zĕn) Ger. (Ruhr In.)	51·01 N	6·59 E
166	Leverville (lē-vä-vēl′) . . . . . Con. L.	5·13 S	18·43 E
121	Levice (lā′vēt-sĕ) . . . . Czech.	48·13 N	18·37 E
126	Levico (lā′vē-kō) . . . . It.	46·02 N	11·20 E
122	Le Vigan (lē vē-gäN′) . . . . Fr.	43·59 N	3·36 E
85	Levis (lā-vē′) (lē′vĭs) Can. (Quebec In.)	46·48 N	71·11 W
84	Levittown (lĕ′vĭt-toun) Pa. (Philadelphia In.)	40·08 N	74·50 W
127	Levkás (lyĕfkäs′) . . . . Grc.	38·49 N	20·43 E
127	Levkás (I.) . . . . Grc.	38·42 N	20·22 E
121	Levoča (lā′vô-chȧ) . . . . Czech.	49·03 N	20·38 E
79	Levy (L.) (lē′vĭ) . . . . Fla.	29·31 N	82·23 W
81	Lewes (lōō′ĭs) . . . . Del.	38·45 N	75·10 W
116	Lewes . . . . Eng.	50·51 N	0·01 E
116	Lewis (I.) (lōō′ĭs) . . . . Scot.	58·05 N	6·07 W
65	Lewis (R.) East Fk. Wash. (Portland In.)	45·52 N	122·40 E
78	Lewisburg (lū′ĭs-bûrg) . . . . . . Tenn.	35·27 N	86·47 W
80	Lewisburg (lū′ĭs-bûrg) . . . . . W. Va.	37·50 N	80·20 W
83	Lewis Hills . . . . Can.	48·49 N	58·28 W
83	Lewisporte (lū′ĭs-pōrt) . . . . . . Can.	49·15 N	55·06 W
67	Lewis Ra. (lū′ĭs) . . . . Mont.	48·05 N	113·06 W
66	Lewis R. . . . . Wash.	46·05 N	122·09 W
66	Lewiston (lū′ĭs-tŭn) . . . . Idaho	46·24 N	116·59 W
82	Lewiston . . . . Maine	44·05 N	70·14 W
75	Lewiston . . . . . . N. Y. (Buffalo In.)	43·11 N	79·02 W
67	Lewiston . . . . Utah	41·58 N	111·51 W
73	Lewistown (lū′ĭs-toun) . . . . Ill.	40·23 N	90·06 W
67	Lewistown . . . . Mont.	47·05 N	109·25 W
81	Lewistown . . . . Pa.	40·35 N	77·30 W
80	Lexington (lĕk′sĭng-tŭn) . . . . . . Ky.	38·05 N	84·30 W
83	Lexington . . . . . Mass. (Boston In.)	42·27 N	71·14 W
78	Lexington . . . . Miss.	33·08 N	90·02 W
73	Lexington . . . . Mo.	39·11 N	93·52 W
72	Lexington . . . . Nebr.	40·46 N	99·44 W
79	Lexington . . . . N. C.	35·47 N	80·15 W
78	Lexington . . . . Tenn.	35·37 N	88·24 W
81	Lexington . . . . Va.	37·45 N	79·20 W
155	Leyte (I.) (lā′tā) . . . . Phil.	10·35 N	125·35 E
121	Lezajsk (lĕ′zhä-ĭsk) . . . . Pol.	50·14 N	22·25 E
128	Lezha (R.) (lĕ-zhä′) . . . . . Sov. Un.	58·59 N	40·27 E
122	Lézignan (lā-zē-nyäN′) . . . . Fr.	43·13 N	2·48 E
129	L'gov (lgôf) . . . . Sov. Un.	51·42 N	35·15 E
142	Lhasa (läs′ä) . . . . China	29·41 N	91·12 E
148	Lhsien (lē′sĭăN) . . . . China	37·09 N	119·57 E
150	Lianghsiang (lyäng′syän′) China (Peking In.)	39·43 N	116·08 E
136	Lianozovo (lĭ-á-nô′zô-vô) Sov. Un. (Moskva In.)	55·54 N	37·36 E
148	Liaoch'eng (lĭou′chĕng) . . . . China	36·27 N	115·56 E
150	Liao Ho (R.) (lyä′ō hō′) . . . . China	41·40 N	122·40 E
147	Liaoning (Prov.) . . . . China	41·31 N	122·11 E
148	Liaotung Pantao (Pen.) (lĭou′dōōng băN′dou) . China	39·45 N	122·22 E
150	Liaotung Wan (B.) . . . . China	40·25 N	121·15 E
150	Liaoyang (lyä′ō-yäng′) . . . . . China	41·18 N	123·10 E
147	Liaoyüan (lyä′ō-yü-än′) . . . . China	43·37 N	123·30 E
86	Liard (R.) (lē-är′) . . . . Can.	59·43 N	126·42 W
98	Libano (lē′-bȧ-nô) . . . . . . Col. (In.)	4·55 N	75·05 W
124	Libar, Sierra de (Mts.) (sē-ĕ′r-rä-dĕ-lē-bär) . Sp.	39·42 N	5·28 W
66	Libby (lĭb′ê) . . . . Mont.	48·27 N	115·35 W
165	Libenge (lê-bĕŋ′gā) . . . . Con. L.	3·39 N	18·40 E
72	Liberal (lĭb′ẽr-ăl) . . . . Kans.	37·01 N	100·56 W
120	Liberec (lē′bĕr-ĕts) . . . . Czech.	15·47 N	15·06 E
163	Liberia (lī-bē′rĭ-ȧ) . . . . Afr.	6·30 N	9·55 W
92	Liberia . . . . C. R.	10·38 N	85·28 W
99	Libertad de Orituco (lē-bĕr-tä′d-dĕ-ō-rê-tōō′kô) . Ven. (In.)	9·32 N	66·24 W
80	Liberty (lĭb′ẽr-tĭ) . . . . Ind.	39·35 N	84·55 W
74	Liberty . . . . Mo. (Kansas City In.)	39·15 N	94·25 W
79	Liberty . . . . S. C.	34·47 N	82·41 W
77	Liberty . . . . Tex.	30·03 N	94·46 W
74	Liberty . Utah (Salt Lake City In.)	41·20 N	111·52 W
65	Liberty B. . . . . Wash. (Seattle In.)	47·43 N	122·41 W
75	Libertyville (lĭb′ẽr-tĭ-vĭl) Ill. (Chicago In.)	42·17 N	87·57 W
155	Libmanan (lĭb-mä′nän) Phil. (Manila In.)	13·42 N	123·04 E
167	Libode (lĭ-bō′dĕ) S. Afr. (Natal In.)	31·33 S	29·03 E
95	Libón, R. . . . . Hai.	19·30 N	71·45 W
122	Libourne (lē-bōōrn′) . . . . Fr.	44·55 N	0·12 W
91	Libres (lē′brās) . . . . Mex.	19·26 N	97·41 W
164	Libreville (lē-br′vēl′) . . . . . . Gabon	0·29 N	9·26 E
84	Liburn (lĭb′ûrn) Ga. (Atlanta In.)	33·53 N	84·09 W
163	Libya (lĭb′ê-ä) . . . . Afr.	27·38 N	15·00 E
165	Libyan Des. (lĭb′ê-ăn) . . . . . . Libya	28·23 N	23·34 E
115	Libyan Plat . . . . U. A. R.	30·58 N	26·20 E
100	Licancábur, Cerro (Mtn.) (sĕ′r-rô-lē-kȧn-kȧ′bōōr) . Chile	22·45 S	67·45 W
101	Licanten (lē-kän-tĕ′n) Chile (Santiago In.)	34·58 S	72·00 W
110	Lichfield (lĭch′fēld) . . . . Eng.	52·41 N	1·49 W
146	Lichiang . . . . China	27·06 N	100·08 E
148	Liching (lē′jĭn) . . . . China	37·24 N	118·12 E
168	Lichtenburg (lĭk′tĕn-bĕrgh) S. Afr. (Johannesburg & Pretoria In.)	26·09 S	26·10 E
75	Lick Cr. (lĭk) Ind. (Indianapolis In.)	39·43 N	86·06 W
80	Licking (R.) (lĭk′ĭng) . . . . Ky.	38·30 N	84·10 W
126	Licosa, Pt. (lê-kō′sä) . . . . It.	40·17 N	14·40 E
121	Lida (lē′dȧ) . . . . Sov. Un.	53·53 N	25·19 E
70	Lidgerwood (lĭj′ẽr-wood) . . . . N. D.	46·04 N	97·10 W
118	Lidköping (lēt′chû-pĭng) . . . . . Swe.	58·31 N	13·06 E
125	Lido di Roma (Ostia Lido) (lē′dô-dē-rô′mä) (ô′s-tyä-lê-dô) It. (Roma In.)	41·19 N	12·17 E
121	Lidzbark (lĭts′bärk) . . . . Pol.	54·07 N	20·36 E
168	Liebenbergs R. . . . . S. Afr. (Johannesburg & Pretoria In.)	27·35 S	28·25 E
111	Liebenwalde (lē′bĕn-väl-dĕ) Ger. (Berlin In.)	52·52 N	13·24 E
151	Liechou Pan-Tao (Pen.) . . . . China	20·40 N	109·25 E
120	Liechtenstein (lēk′tĕn-shtīn) . Eur.	47·14 N	9·15 E
117	Liége (lē-ăzh′) . . . . Bel.	50·40 N	5·30 E
151	Lienchiang . . . . China	21·38 N	110·15 E
148	Lienshui (lĭăN′sōōā) . . . . China	33·46 N	119·15 E
147	Lienyün . . . . China	33·10 N	120·01 E
148	Lienyun (lĭăN′yüN) . . . . China	34·43 N	119·27 E
120	Lienz (lē-ĕnts′) . . . . Aus.	46·49 N	12·45 E
119	Liepāja (le′pä-yä′) . . . . . . Sov. Un.	56·31 N	20·59 E
111	Lier . . . . Bel. (Bruxelles In.)	5·08 N	4·34 E
111	Liesing (lē′sĭng) . . . Aus. (Wien In.)	48·09 N	16·17 E
120	Liestal (lēs′täl) . . . . Switz.	47·28 N	7·44 E
81	Lievre, Rivière du (R.) . . . . . . Can.	45·00 N	75·25 W
116	Liffey R. (lĭf′ĭ) . . . . Ire.	53·21 N	6·35 W
159	Lifou, (I.) . . . . N. Cal. Is.	21·15 S	167·32 E
155	Ligao (lē-gä′ô) . . Phil. (Manila In.)	13·14 N	123·33 E
160	Lightning Ridge . . . . Austl.	29·23 S	147·50 E
167	Ligonha (R.) (lê-gō′nyȧ) . . . . . Moz.	16·14 S	39·00 E
80	Ligonier (lĭg-ô-nēr′) . . . . Ind.	41·30 N	85·35 W
136	Ligovo (lē′gô-vô) Sov. Un. (Leningrad In.)	59·51 N	30·13 E
126	Liguria (Reg.) (lê-gōō-rē-ä) . . . . It.	44·24 N	8·27 E
126	Ligurian Sea (lĭ-gū′rĭ-ăn) . . . . Eur.	43·42 N	8·32 E
159	Lihou Rfs. (lē-hōō′) . . . . Austl.	17·23 S	152·43 E
151	Lihsien (lē′hsyĕn′) . . . . China	29·42 N	111·40 E
148	Lihsien . . . . China	38·30 N	115·38 E
148	Lihuang (lē′hōōäNg) . . . . China	31·32 N	115·46 E
157	Lihue (lê-hōō′ā) . . . . . Hawaii (In.)	21·59 N	159·23 W
119	Lihula (lē′hōō-lȧ) . . . . Sov. Un.	58·41 N	23·50 E
128	Likhoslavl′ (lyê-kôslav′′l) Sov. Un.	57·07 N	35·27 E
129	Likhovka (lyê-kôf′kȧ) . . . Sov. Un.	48·52 N	33 57 E
122	Lille (lēl) . . . . Fr.	50·38 N	3·01 E
118	Lille Baelt (str.) . . . . Den.	55·09 N	9·53 E
118	Lillehammer (lēl′ĕ-häm′mĕr) . Nor.	61·07 N	10·25 E
118	Lillesand (lēl′ĕ-sän′) . . . . Nor.	58·16 N	8·19 E
118	Lilleström (lēl′ĕ-strûm) . . . . . . Nor.	59·56 N	11·04 E
65	Lilliwaup (lĭl′ĭ-wŏp) Wash. (Seattle In.)	47·28 N	123·07 W
86	Lillooet . . . . Can.	50·49 N	122·02 W
166	Lilongwe (lê-lô-ăn) Fed. of Rh. & Nya.	13·51 S	33·47 E
80	Lima (lī′mȧ) . . . . Ohio	40·40 N	84·05 W
98	Lima (lē′mä) . . . . Peru	12·06 S	76·55 W
124	Lima (R.) . . . . Port.	41·45 N	8·22 W
101	Lima Duarte (dwä′r-tĕ) Braz. (Rio de Janeiro In.)	21·52 S	43·47 W
67	Lima Res. . . . . Mont.	44·45 N	112·15 W
139	Limassol (lē-mä-sōl′) Cyprus (Palestine In.)	34·39 N	33·02 E
100	Limay (lē-mä′ê) (R.) . . . . Arg.	39·50 S	69·15 W
119	Limbaži (lēm′bä-zĭ) . . . . Sov. Un.	57·32 N	24·44 E
95	Limbé . . . . Hai.	19·45 N	72·30 W

ăt; finăl; rāte; senāte; ärm; ȧsk; sofȧ; fâre; ch-choose; dh-as th in other; bē; êvent; bĕt; recĕnt; cratẽr; g-go; gh-guttural g; bĭt; ĭ-short neutral; rīde; K-guttural k as ch in German ich;

PRONOUNCING INDEX Limboli–Lodgepole 229

Page	Name Pronunciation Region	Lat. °′	Long. °′
142	Limboli, India	22·39 N	71·49 E
120	Limburg (lem-bōōrg′), Ger.	50·22 N	8·03 E
118	Limedsforsen (lē′mĕs-fôrs′ĕn), Swe.	60·54 N	13·24 E
101	Limeira (lē-mā′rä) Braz. (Rio de Janeiro In.)	22·34 S	47·24 W
118	Limfjorden (Fd.), Den.	56·14 N	7·55 E
118	Limfjorden (Fd.), Den.	56·56 N	10·35 E
158	Limmen Bght. (lĭm′ĕn), Austl.	14·45 S	136·00 E
127	Limni (lēm′nē), Grc.	38·47 N	23·22 E
127	Limnos (I.), Grc.	39·58 N	24·48 E
85	Limoges (lē-môzh′) Can. (Ottawa In.)	45·20 N	75·15 W
122	Limoges, Fr.	45·50 N	1·15 E
72	Limon (lī′mŏn), Colo.	39 15 N	103·41 W
93	Limón (lē-mōn′), C. R.	10·01 N	83·02 W
92	Limón (lē-mô′n), Hond.	15·53 N	85·34 W
95	Limon (R.), Dom. Rep.	18·20 N	71·40 W
88	Limón B. C. Z. (Panama Canal In.)	9·21 N	79·58 W
123	Limours (lē-mōōr′), Fr. (Paris In.)	48·39 N	2·05 E
122	Limousin, Plateaux du (Plat.) (plä-tō′ dü lē-mōō-zăɴ′), Fr.	45·44 N	1·09 E
122	Limoux (lē-mōō′), Fr.	43·03 N	2·14 E
166	Limpopo R. (lĭm-pō′pō), Afr.	23·15 S	27·46 E
101	Linares (lē-nä′räs) Chile (Santiago In.)	35·51 S	71·35 W
76	Linares, Mex.	24·53 N	99·34 W
124	Linares (lē-nä′rĕs), Sp.	38·07 N	3·38 W
101	Linares (Prov.) Chile (Santiago In.)	35·53 S	71·30 W
126	Linaro, C. (lē-nä′rä), It.	42·02 N	11·53 E
148	Linchang (lĭn′chäng′), China	36·19 N	114·40 E
150	Linchiang (lĭn′chäng′), China	41·45 N	127·00 E
148	Linch′ing (lĭn′chĭng), China	36·49 N	115·42 E
151	Linch′uan, China	27·58 N	116·18 E
101	Lincoln (lĭŋ′kŭn) Arg. (Buenos Aires In.)	34·51 S	61·29 W
68	Lincoln, Calif.	38·51 N	121·19 W
110	Lincoln, Eng.	53·14 N	0·33 W
73	Lincoln, Ill.	40·09 N	89·21 W
72	Lincoln, Kans.	39·02 N	98·08 W
82	Lincoln, Maine	45·23 N	68·31 W
83	Lincoln, Mass. (Boston In.)	42·25 N	71·19 W
73	Lincoln, Nebr.	40·49 N	96·43 W
110	Lincoln (Co.), Eng.	53·12 N	0·29 W
72	Lincoln, Mt., Colo.	39·20 N	106·19 W
110	Lincoln Heights (Reg.), Eng.	53·23 N	0·39 W
75	Lincoln Park Mich. (Detroit In.)	42·14 N	83·11 W
84	Lincoln Park N. J. (New York In.)	40·56 N	74·18 W
79	Lincolnton –lĭŋ′kŭn-tŭn), N. C.	35·27 N	81·15 W
116	Lincoln Wolds (woldz′), Eng.	53·25 N	0·23 W
78	Lindale (lĭn′dāl), Ga.	34·10 N	85·10 W
120	Lindau (lĭn′dou), Ger.	47·33 N	9·40 E
78	Linden (lĭn′dĕn), Ala.	32·16 N	87·47 W
74	Linden, Mo. (Kansas City In.)	39·13 N	94·35 W
84	Linden, N. J. (New York In.)	40·38 N	74·16 W
84	Lindenhurst (lĭn′dĕn-hûrst) N. Y. (New York In.)	40·41 N	73·23 W
84	Lindenwold (lĭn′dĕn-wôld) N. J. (Philadelphia In.)	39·50 N	75·00 W
118	Lindesberg (lĭn′dĕs-bĕrgh), Swe.	59·37 N	15·14 E
117	Lindesnes (C.) (lĭn′ĕs-nĕs), Nor.	58·00 N	7·05 E
150	Lindho, China	40·45 N	107·30 E
167	Lindi (lĭn′dē), Tan.	9·59 S	39·43 E
165	Lindi R., Con. L.	1·00 N	27·13 E
168	Lindley (lĭnd′lē) .S. Afr. (Johannesburg & Pretoria In.)	27·52 S	27·55 E
111	Lindow (lĕn′dōv) Ger. (Berlin In.)	54·58 N	12·59 E
81	Lindsay (lĭn′zē), Can.	44·20 N	78·45 W
72	Lindsay, Okla.	34·50 N	97·38 W
72	Lindsborg (lĭnz′bôrg), Kans.	38·34 N	97·42 W
110	Lindsey (Co.) (lĭn′zĭ), Eng.	53·25 N	0·32 W
148	Lineh′ü (lĭn′chü), China	36·31 N	118·33 E
78	Lineville (līn′vĭl), Ala.	33·18 N	85·45 W
150	Linfen, China	36·00 N	111·38 E
155	Lingayen (lĭŋ′gä-yän′) Phil. (Manila In.)	16·01 N	120·13 E
155	Lingayen G., Phil. (Manila In.)	16·18 N	120·11 E
120	Lingen (lĭŋ′gĕn), Ger.	52·32 N	7·20 E
154	Lingga, Pulau-Pulau (Is.) (lĭng-gä′). Indon.	0·35 S	105·05 E
151	Lingling, China	26·10 N	111·40 E
148	Lingpi (lĭng′pĭ′), China	33·33 N	117·33 E
148	Lingtienchen (lĭng′diăɴ′jĕn) China	31·52 N	121·28 E
151	Lingting Yang (Can.), China	22·00 N	114·00 E
164	Linguere (lĭŋ-gĕr′), Senegal	15·22 N	14·55 W
150	Lingwu, China	38·05 N	106·18 E
150	Lingyüan, China	41·12 N	119·20 E
151	Linhai, China	28·52 N	121·08 E
150	Linhsi, China	43·30 N	118·02 E
148	Linhuaikuan (lĭnhōōäĭ′gōōăɴ) China	32·55 N	117·38 E
148	Linhuanchi (lĭn′hōōaɴ′jē), China	33·42 N	116·33 E
148	Lini (lĭn′yē), China	35·04 N	118·21 E
151	Linkao, China	19·58 N	109·40 E
118	Linköping (lĭn′chû-pĭng), Swe.	58·25 N	15·35 E
148	Linmingkuan (lĭɴ′mĭng′gōōän) China	36·47 N	114·32 E
116	Linnhe (L.) (lĭn′ē), Scot.	56·35 N	4·30 W
99	Lins (lē′ɴs), Braz.	21·42 S	49·41 W
84	Linthicum Heights (lĭn′thĭ-kŭm) Md. (Baltimore In.)	39·12 N	76·39 W
150	Lintien, China	42·08 N	124·59 E
80	Linton (lĭn′tŭn), Ind.	39·05 N	87·15 W
70	Linton, N. D.	46·16 N	100·15 W
151	Linwu (lĭn′wōō′), China	25·20 N	112·30 E
148	Linying (lĭn′yĭng′), China	33·48 N	113·56 E
148	Linyü (lĭn′yü), China	40·01 N	119·45 E
120	Linz (lĭnts), Aus.	48·18 N	14·18 E
155	Lipa (lē-pä′), Phil. (Manila In.)	13·55 N	121·10 E
126	Lipari (lē′pä-rē), It.	38·29 N	15·00 E
126	Lipari (I.), It.	38·32 N	15·04 E
128	Lipetsk (lyĕ′pĕtsk), Sov. Un.	52·26 N	39·34 E
128	Lipetsk (Oblast), Sov. Un.	52·18 N	38·30 E
151	Lip′ing (lē′pĭng′), China	26·18 N	109·00 E
121	Lipno (lēp′nō), Pol.	52·50 N	19·12 E
117	Lippe (R.) (lĭp′ĕ), Ger.	51·36 N	6·45 E
120	Lippstadt (lĭp′shtät), Ger.	51·39 N	8·20 E
84	Lipscomb (lĭp′skŭm) Ala. (Birmingham In.)	33·26 N	86·56 W
129	Liptsy (lyēp′tsē), Sov. Un.	50·11 N	36·25 E
151	Lip′u, China	24·38 N	110·35 E
126	Liri (R.) (lē′rē), It.	41·49 N	13·30 E
125	Liria (lē′ryä), Sp.	39·35 N	0·34 W
165	Lisala (lē-sä′lä), Con. L.	2·14 N	21·38 E
125	Lisboa (Lisbon) (lēzh-bō′ä) (lĭz′bŭn). Port. (Lisboa In.)	38·42 N	9.05 W
82	Lisbon, Maine	43·59 N	70·03 W
70	Lisbon, N. D.	46·21 N	97·43 W
80	Lisbon, Ohio	40·45 N	80·50 W
	Lisbon, see Lisboa		
116	Lisburn (lĭs′bŭrn), N. Ire.	54·35 N	6·05 W
64	Lisburne, C., Alaska	68·20 N	165·40 W
150	Lishih, China	37·32 N	111·12 E
150	Lishu, China	43·12 N	124·18 E
150	Lishuchen, China	45·01 N	130·50 E
151	Lishui, China	28·28 N	120·00 E
148	Lishui (lĭ′shwĭ′), China	31·41 N	119·01 E
149	Lishui, China (Canton In.)	23·12 N	113·09 E
122	Lisieux (lē-zyû′), Fr.	49·10 N	0·13 E
136	Lisiy Nos (lĭ′sĭy nôs) Sov. Un. (Leningrad In.)	60·01 N	30·00 E
129	Liski (lyēs′kē), Sov. Un.	50·56 N	39·28 E
75	Lisle (lĭl), Ill. (Chicago In.)	41·48 N	88·04 W
123	L′Isle-Adam (lēl-ädäɴ′) Fr. (Paris In.)	49·05 N	2·13 E
160	Lismore (lĭz′môr), Austl.	28·48 S	153·18 E
47	Lister, Mt. (lĭs′tēr), Ant.	78·05 S	163·00 E
139	Litani (R.), Leb. (Palestine In.)	33·28 N	35·42 E
73	Litchfield (lĭch′fēld), Ill.	39·10 N	89·38 W
71	Litchfield, Minn.	45·08 N	94·34 W
75	Litchfield, Ohio (Cleveland In.)	41·10 N	82·01 W
160	Lithgow (lĭth′gō), Austl.	33·23 S	149·31 E
126	Lithinon, Ark. (C.), Grc. (In.)	34·59 N	24·35 E
84	Lithonia (lĭ-thō′nĭ-ȧ) Ga. (Atlanta In.)	33·43 N	84·07 W
130	Lithuanian S. S. R. (lĭth-ū-ā′-nĭ-ȧ) Sov. Un.	55·42 N	23·30 E
129	Litin (lē-tēn), Sov. Un.	49·16 N	28·11 E
127	Litókhoron (lē′tô-κō′rôn), Grc.	40·05 N	22·29 E
120	Litomerice (lē′tô-myĕr′zhĭ-tsĕ) Czech.	50·33 N	14·10 E
120	Litomyšl (lē′tô-mêsh′l), Czech.	49·52 N	16·14 E
161	Little (R.), Austl. (Melbourne In.)	37·54 S	144·27 E
78	Little (R.), Tenn.-Mo.	36·28 N	89·39 W
77	Little R., Tex.	30·48 N	96·50 W
94	Little Abaco (I.) (ä′bä-kō). Ba. Is.	26·55 N	77·45 W
47	Little America, Ant.	78·30 S	161·30 W
154	Little Andaman I. (ăn-dȧ-măn′) Andaman Is.	10·39 N	93·08 E
94	Little Bahama Bk. (bȧ-hā′mȧ) Ba. Is.	26·55 N	78·40 W
67	Little Belt Mts. (bĕlt), Mont.	47·00 N	110·50 W
67	Little Bighorn R. (bĭg-hôrn). Mont.	45·08 N	107·30 W
	Little Bitter, see el Buheirat el Murrat el Sughra		
66	Little Bitterroot R. (bĭt′ēr-ōōt) Mont.	47·45 N	114·45 W
72	Little Blue (R.), Nebr.	40·15 N	98·01 W
74	Little Blue R. (blōō) Mo. (Kansas City In.)	38·52 N	94·25 W
110	Littleborough (lĭt′l-bŭr-ō), Eng.	53·39 N	2·06 W
75	Little Calumet R. (kăl-ū-mĕt′) Ill. (Chicago In.)	41·38 N	87·38 W
94	Little Cayman (I.) (kā′mȧn) W. I. F.	19·40 N	80·05 W
69	Little Colorado (R.) (kŏl-ô-rä′dō) Ariz.	36·05 N	111·35 W
84	Little Compton (kŏmp′tŏn) R. I. (Providence In.)	41·31 N	71·07 W
93	Little Corn I., Nic.	12·19 N	82·50 W
95	Little Exuma (I.) (ĕk-sōō′mä) Ba. Is.	23·25 N	75·40 W
71	Little Falls (fôlz), Minn.	45·58 N	94·23 W
81	Little Falls, N. Y.	43·05 N	74·55 W
72	Littlefield (lĭt′′l-fēld), Tex.	33·55 N	102·17 W
71	Little Fork (R.) (fôrk), Minn.	48·24 N	93·30 W
89	Little Hans Lollick (I.) (häns lôl′lĭk). Vir. Is. (U. S. A.) (St. Thomas In.)	18·25 N	64·54 W
66	Little Humboldt R. (hŭm′bōlt) Nev.	41·10 N	117·40 W
95	Little Inagua (I.) (ē-nä′gwä) Ba. Is.	21·30 N	73·00 W
94	Little Isaac (I.) (ī′zȧk), Ba. Is.	25·55 N	79·00 W
80	Little Kanawha (R.) (kȧ-nô′wȧ) W. Va.	39·05 N	81·30 W
166	Little Karroo (Mts.) (kä-rōō) S. Afr.	33·50 S	21·02 E
87	Little Mecatina (R.) (mĕ cȧ tĭ nä) Can.	52·40 N	62·21 W
75	Little Miami R. (mī-ăm′ĭ) Ohio (Cincinnati In.)	39·19 N	84·15 W
75	Little Miami R., E. Fk. Ohio (Cincinnati In.)	39·01 N	84·03 W
73	Little Missouri (R.) (mĭ-sōō′rĭ) Ark.	34·15 N	93·54 W
70	Little Missouri (R.), S. D.	45·46 N	103·48 W
83	Little or Gray (R.) (lĭt′l) (grā). Can.	47·50 N	57·05 W
79	Little Pee Dee (R.) (pē-dē′). S. C.	34·35 N	79·21 W
67	Little Powder R. (pou′dēr), Wyo.	44·51 N	105·20 W
73	Little Red (R.) (rĕd), Ark.	35·42 N	92·14 W
73	Little Red R., Okla.	33·53 N	94·38 W
73	Little Rock (rŏk), Ark.	34·42 N	92·16 W
123	Little St. Bernard P. (sȧntbĕr-närd′) (săɴ bĕr-när′). Fr.-It.	45·49 N	6·50 E
95	Little San Salvador (I.) (săn săl′vȧ-dôr). Ba. Is.	24·35 N	75·55 W
79	Little Satilla (R.) (sȧ-tĭl′ȧ), Ga.	31·43 N	82·47 W
70	Little Sioux (R.) (sōō), Iowa	42·22 N	95·47 W
67	Little Snake R.(snāk), Colo.	40·40 N	108·21 W
78	Little Tallapoosa (R.) (tăl-ȧ-pōō′sȧ). Ala.	32·25 N	85·28 W
78	Little Tennessee (R.) (tĕn-ĕ-sē′) Tenn.	35·36 N	84·05 W
72	Littleton (lĭt′′l-tŭn), Colo.	39·34 N	105·01 W
83	Littleton, Mass. (Boston In.)	42·32 N	71·29 W
81	Littleton, N. H.	44·15 N	71·45 W
80	Little Wabash (R.) (wô′băsh), Ill.	38·50 N	88·30 W
67	Little Wood R. (wŏŏd), Idaho	43·00 N	114·08 W
148	Liuan (lyōō′än′), China	31·45 N	116·29 E
151	Liuchou (lōō′chōō), China	24·25 N	109·30 E
148	Liuho (lyōō′hō′), China	32·22 N	118·50 E
150	Liuho, China	42·10 N	125·38 E
150	Liup′an Shan (Mts.), China	36·20 N	105·30 E
151	Liuyang (lyōō′yäng′), China	28·10 N	113·35 E
148	Liuyüan (lü′yüän), China	36·09 N	114·37 E
128	Līvāni (lē′vȧ-nē), Sov. Un.	56·24 N	26·12 E
64	Livengood (liv′ĕn-gŏŏd), Alaska	65·30 N	148·35 W
78	Live Oak (lĭv′ōk), Fla.	30·15 N	83·00 W
65	Livermore (lĭv′ēr-mōr) Calif. (San Francisco In.)	37·41 N	121·46 W
80	Livermore, Ky.	37·30 N	87·05 W
161	Liverpool (lĭv′ēr-pōōl) Austl. (Sydney In.)	33·55 S	150·56 E
82	Liverpool, Can.	44·02 N	64·44 W
110	Liverpool, Eng.	53·25 N	2·52 W
77	Liverpool, Tex. (In.)	29·18 N	95·17 W
64	Liverpool B., Alaska	70·25 N	129·35 W
159	Liverpool Ra., Austl.	31·47 S	31·00 E
165	Livindo R., Gabon	1·09 N	13·30 E
78	Livingston (lĭv′ĭng-stŭn), Ala.	32·35 N	88·09 W
92	Livingston, Guat.	15·50 N	88·45 W
74	Livingston, Ill. (St. Louis In.)	38·58 N	89·51 W
67	Livingston, Mont.	45·40 N	110·35 W
78	Livingston, Tenn.	36·23 N	85·20 W
166	Livingstone (lĭv-ĭng-stôn) Fed. of Rh. & Nya.	17·51 S	25·48 E
166	Livingstonia (lĭv-ĭng-stō′nĭ-ȧ) Fed. of Rh. & Nya.	10·35 S	34·07 E
126	Livno (lēv′nō), Yugo.	43·50 N	17·03 E
128	Livny (lēv′nē), Sov. Un.	52·28 N	37·36 E
75	Livonia (lĭ-vō-nĭ-ȧ) Mich. (Detroit In.)	42·25 N	83·23 W
126	Livorno (Leghorn) (lē-vôr′nō) (lĕg′hôrn). It.	43·32 N	11·18 E
100	Livramento (lē-vrä-mĕ′n-tō). Braz.	30·46 S	55·21 W
123	Lixy-sur-Ourcq (lēk-sē′sür-ōōrk′) Fr. (Paris In.)	49·01 N	3·02 E
148	Liyang (lē′yäng′), China	31·30 N	119·29 E
116	Lizard Pt. (lĭz′ȧrd), Eng.	49·55 N	5·09 W
111	Ljmuiden. Neth. (Amsterdam In.)	52·27 N	4·35 E
126	Ljubljana (lyōō′blyȧ′na), Yugo.	46·04 N	14·29 E
126	Ljubuški (lyōō′bōōsh-kē), Yugo.	43·11 N	17·29 E
118	Ljungan (R.), Swe.	62·50 N	13·45 E
118	Ljungby (lyōōng′bü), Swe.	56·49 N	13·56 E
118	Ljusdal (lyōōs′dāl), Swe.	61·50 N	16·11 E
118	Ljusnan (R.), Swe.	61·55 N	15·33 E
116	Llandudno (lăn-düd′nō), Wales	53·20 N	3·46 W
116	Llanelly (lȧ-nĕl′ĭ), Wales	51·44 N	4·09 W
124	Llanes (lyä′nås), Sp.	43·25 N	4·41 W
76	Llano (lä′nō) (lyä′nō), Tex.	30·45 N	98·41 W
76	Llano R., Tex.	30·38 N	99·04 W
98	Llanos (lyä′nŏs) (Reg.), Col.-Ven.	4·00 N	71·15 W
90	Llera (lyā′rä), Mex.	23·16 N	99·03 W
124	Llerena (lyā-rā′nä), Sp.	38·14 N	6·02 W
116	Lleyn Prom. (lĭn), Wales	52·55 N	3·10 W
125	Llobregat (R.) (lyô-brĕ-gät′), Sp.	41·55 N	1·55 E
85	Lloyd L. (loid). Can. (Calgary In.)	50·52 N	114·13 W
86	Lloydminster, Can.	53·18 N	109·50 W
125	Lluchmayor (lyōōch-mä-yôr′), Sp.	39·28 N	2·53 E
100	Llullaillaco (Vol.) (lyōō-lyī-lyä′kō). Arg.	24·50 S	68·30 W
166	Loange (R.) (lō-äŋ′gā), Con. L.	4·46 S	20·18 E
100	Lobería (lô-bĕ-rē′ä), Arg.	38·13 S	58·48 W
166	Lobito (lô-bē′tō), Ang.	12·15 S	13·35 E
136	Lobnya (lôb′nyȧ) Sov. Un.(Moskva In.)	56·01 N	37·29 E
101	Lobos (lō′bôs) Arg. (Buenos Aires In.)	35·10 S	59·08 W
94	Lobos, Cayo (I.) (lō′bôs), Ba. Is.	22·25 N	77·40 W
91	Lobos, Isla de (I.) (ē′s-lä-dĕ-lô-bōs). Mex.	21·24 N	97·11 W
98	Lobos de Tierra (I.) (lô′bō-dĕ-tyĕ′r-rä), Peru	6·29 S	80·55 W
136	Lobva (lôb′vȧ) Sov. Un. (Urals In.)	59·12 N	60·28 E
136	Lobva R., Sov. Un. (Urals In.)	59·14 N	60·17 E
120	Locarno (lô-kär′nō), Switz.	46·10 N	8·43 E
122	Loches (lôsh), Fr.	47·08 N	0·56 E
151	Loching, China	28·02 N	120·40 E
79	Lochloosa (L.) (lŏk-lō′sȧ), Fla.	29·33 N	82·07 W
116	Lochy (L.) (lŏk′ĭ), Scot.	56·57 N	4·45 W
79	Lockhart (lŏk′hȧrt), S. C.	34·47 N	81·30 W
77	Lockhart, Tex.	29·54 N	97·40 W
81	Lock Haven (lŏk′hā-vĕn), Pa.	41·05 N	77·30 W
75	Lockland (lŏk′lănd) Ohio (Cincinnati In.)	39·14 N	84·27 W
85	Lockport (lŏk′pōrt) Can. (Winnipeg In.)	50·05 N	96·58 W
75	Lockport, Ill. (Chicago In.)	41·35 N	88·04 W
75	Lockport, N. Y. (Buffalo In.)	43·11 N	78·43 W
84	Lock Raven Res. (lŏk ra′vĕn) Md. (Baltimore In.)	39·28 N	76·38 W
85	Locust Hill (lō′kŭst hĭl) Can. (Toronto In.)	43·54 N	79·11 W
139	Lod (lôd), Isr. (Palestine In.)	31·57 N	34·55 E
122	Lodève (lô-dĕv′), Fr.	43·43 N	3·18 E
119	Lodeynoye Pole (lô-dĕy-nô′yĕ) Sov. Un.	60·43 N	33·24 E
67	Lodge Cr., Mont.	48·51 N	109·30 W
70	Lodgepole Cr. (lŏj′pōl), Wyo.	41·22 N	104·48 W

ng-sing; ŋ-baŋk; ɴ-nasalized n; nŏd; cŏmmit; ōld; ôbey; ôrder; fōōd; fŏŏt; ou-out; s-soft; sh-dish; th-thin; pūre; ûnite; ûrn; stŭd; circŭs; ü-as "y" in study; ′-indeterminate vowel.

230 Lodhran–Lucea PRONOUNCING INDEX

Page	Name Pronunciation	Region	Lat. °′	Long. °′
142	Lodhran	W. Pak.	29·40 N	71·39 E
68	Lodi (lō'dī)	Calif.	38·07 N	121·17 W
126	Lodi (lô'dē)	It.	45·18 N	9·30 E
75	Lodi (lō'dī)	Ohio (Cleveland In.)	41·02 N	82·01 W
124	Lodosa (lô-dô'-sä)	Sp.	42·27 N	2·04 W
121	Łódź (wōōdzh)	Pol.	51·46 N	19·13 E
125	Loeches (lô-āch'ěs)	Sp. (Madrid In.)	40·22 N	3·25 W
112	Lofoten (Is.) (lô'fō-tĕn)	Nor.	68·26 N	13·42 E
80	Logan (lō'găn)	Ohio	39·35 N	82·25 W
67	Logan	Utah	41·46 N	111·51 W
80	Logan	W. Va.	37·50 N	82·00 W
86	Logan, Mt.	Can.	60·54 N	140·33 W
80	Logansport (lō'gănz-pōrt)	Ind.	40·45 N	86·25 W
165	Logone R. (lō-gō'nä) (lô-gôn')	Chad-Cam.	10·28 N	15·22 E
164	Logoualé (lô-gwä-lā')	Ivory Coast	7·19 N	7·38 W
124	Logroño (lô-grō'nyō)	Sp.	42·28 N	2·25 W
124	Logrosán (lô-grô-sän')	Sp.	39·22 N	5·29 W
118	Løgstør (lûgh-stûr')	Den.	56·56 N	9·15 E
148	Lohochai (lou'wŭ'jäi)	China	33·35 N	114·02 E
122	Loir (R.) (lwår)	Fr.	47·40 N	0·07 E
122	Loire (R.)	Fr.	47·19 N	1·11 W
98	Loja (lō'hä)	Ec.	3·49 S	79·13 W
124	Loja (lô'-kä)	Sp.	37·10 N	4·11 W
168	Lokala Drift (lô'kä-lȧ drĭft)	S. Afr. (Johannesburg & Pretoria In.)	24·00 S	26·38 E
129	Lokhvitsa (lôk-vêt'sà)	Sov. Un.	50·21 N	33·16 E
164	Lokoja (lô-kō'yä)	Nig.	7·50 N	6·39 E
165	Lol R. (lōl)	Sud.	9·06 N	28·09 E
118	Lolland (lôl'än')	Den.	54·41 N	11·00 E
164	Lolo (lō'lō)	Cam.	3·14 N	10·38 E
127	Lom (lōm)	Bul.	43·48 N	23·15 E
74	Loma Linda (lō'mȧ lĭn'dȧ)	Calif. (Los Angeles In.)	34·04 N	117·16 W
110	Lomas de Zamora (lō'mäs dā zä-mō'rä)	Arg. (In.)	34·31 S	58·24 W
75	Lombard (lŏm-bärd)	Ill. (Chicago In.)	41·53 N	88·01 W
126	Lombardia (Reg.) (lôm-bär-dē'ä)	It.	45·20 N	9·30 E
155	Lomblen (I.) (lŏm-blĕn')	Indon.	8·08 S	123·45 E
154	Lombok (I.) (lŏm-bŏk')	Indon.	9·15 S	116·15 E
154	Lombok Selat (Str.)	Indon.	9·00 S	115·28 E
164	Lomé (lō-mā') (lô'mā)	Togo.	6·13 N	1·14 E
166	Lomela (lō-mā'lȧ)	Con. L.	2·19 S	23·33 E
166	Lomela (R.)	Con. L.	0·21 S	21·11 E
76	Lometa (lô-mē'tȧ)	Tex.	31·10 N	98·25 W
165	Lomié (lô-mē-ā')	Cam.	3·14 N	13·34 E
74	Lomita (lō-mē'tȧ)	Calif. (Los Angeles In.)	33·48 N	118·20 W
111	Lommel	Bel. (Bruxelles In.)	51·14 N	5·21 E
116	Lomond, Loch (L.) (lŏk lō'mŭnd)	Scot.	56·15 N	4·40 W
136	Lomonosov (lô-mô'nô-sof)	Sov. Un. (Leningrad In.)	59·54 N	29·47 E
68	Lompoc (lŏm-pōk')	Calif.	34·39 N	120·30 W
121	Lomza (lôm'zhȧ)	Pol.	53·11 N	22·04 E
81	Lonaconing (lō-nȧ-kō'nĭng)	Md.	39·35 N	78·55 W
80	London (lŭn'dŭn)	Can.	43·00 N	81·20 W
110	London	Eng. (London In.)	51·30 N	0·07 W
78	London	Ky.	37·07 N	84·06 W
80	London	Ohio	39·50 N	83·30 W
82	Londonderry (lŭn'dŭn-dĕr-ĭ)	Can.	45·29 N	63·40 W
116	Londonderry	N. Ire.	54·60 N	6·80 W
158	Londonderry, C.	Austl.	13·30 S	127·00 E
99	Londrina (lôn-drē'nä)	Braz.	21·53 S	51·17 W
80	Lonely (I.) (lōn'lĭ)	Can.	45·35 N	81·30 W
93	Lone Star	Nic.	13·58 N	84·25 W
95	Long (I.)	Ba. Is.	23·25 N	75·10 W
82	Long (I.)	Can.	44·21 N	66·25 W
155	Long (I.)	N. Gui. Ter.	5·10 S	147·30 E
70	Long (L.)	N. D.	46·47 N	100·14 W
65	Long (L.)	Wash. (Seattle In.)	47·29 N	122·36 W
166	Longa (R.) (lôŋ'gä)	Ang.	10·20 S	15·10 E
79	Long B.	S. C.	33·30 N	78·54 W
74	Long Beach (lông bēch)	Calif. (Los Angeles In.)	33·46 N	118·12 W
84	Long Beach	N. Y. (New York In.)	40·35 N	73·38 W
85	Long Branch (lông brånch)	Can. (Toronto In.)	43·36 N	79·32 W
84	Long Branch	N. J. (New York In.)	40·18 N	73·59 W
70	Longdon (lông'-dŭn)	N. D.	48·45 N	98·23 W
110	Long Eaton (ē'tŭn)	Eng.	52·54 N	1·16 W
116	Longford (lŏng'fērd)	Ire.	53·43 N	7·40 W
74	Longhorn (lông-hôrn)	Tex. (San Antonio In.)	29·33 N	98·23 W
81	Long I. (lông)	N. Y.	40·50 N	72·50 W
81	Long Island Sd. (lông ī'lănd)	Conn.-N. Y.	41·05 N	72·45 W
123	Longjumeau (lôn-zhü-mō')	Fr. (Paris In.)	48·42 N	2·17 E
148	Longk'ou (lōōng'kō)	China	37·39 N	120·21 E
87	Longlac (lông'lăk)	Can.	49·41 N	86·28 W
70	Longlake (lông-lāk)	S. D.	45·52 N	99·06 W
72	Longmont (lông'mŏnt)	Colo.	40·11 N	105·07 W
123	Longnes (lôn'y')	Fr. (Paris In.)	48·56 N	1·37 W
110	Longnor (lông'nôr)	Eng.	53·11 N	1·52 W
70	Long Pine (lông pīn)	Nebr.	42·31 N	99·42 W
81	Lont Pt.	Can.	42·35 N	80·05 W
83	Long Pt.	Can.	48·46 N	58·47 W
80	Long Point B.	Can.	42·40 N	80·10 W
71	Long Prairie (lông prâr'ĭ)	Minn.	45·58 N	94·49 W
83	Long Range Mts.	Can.	47·45 N	58·52 W
159	Longreach (lông'rēch)	Austl.	23·32 S	144·17 E
82	Long Reach (R.)	Can.	45·26 N	66·05 W
161	Long Rf.	Austl. (Sydney In.)	33·45 S	151·22 E
110	Longridge (lông'rĭj)	Eng.	53·51 N	2·37 W
72	Longs Pk. (lôngz)	Colo.	40·17 N	105·37 W
110	Longton (lông'tŭn)	Eng.	52·59 N	2·08 W
85	Longueuil (lôn-gû'y')	Can. (Montreal In.)	45·32 N	73·30 W
65	Longview (lông-vū)	Ore. (Portland In.)	46·06 N	123·02 W
77	Longview	Tex.	32·29 N	94·44 W
77	Longville (lông'vĭl)	La.	30·36 N	93·14 W
123	Longwy (lôn-wē')	Fr.	49·32 N	6·14 E
73	Lonoke (lō'nōk)	Ark.	34·48 N	91·52 W
123	Lons-le-Saunier (lôn-lē-sō-nyā')	Fr.	46·40 N	5·33 E
101	Lontué (lôn-tōōě') (R.)	Chile (Santiago In.)	35.20 S	70·45 W
155	Looc (lô-ōk')	Phil. (Manila In.)	12·16 N	121·59 E
80	Loogootee	Ind.	38·40 N	86·55 W
79	Lookout, C. (lŏŏk'out)	N. C.	34·34 N	76·38 W
85	Looma (lōō'mă)	Can. (Edmonton In.)	53·22 N	113·15 W
116	Loop Head (lōōp)	Ire.	52·32 N	9·59 W
78	Loosahatchie (R.) (lōz-à-hă'chē)	Tenn.	35·20 N	89·45 W
111	Loosdrechtsche Plassen (L.)	Neth. (Amsterdam In.)	52·11 N	5·09 E
135	Lopatka, Mys (C.) (lô-pät'kȧ)	Sov. Un.	51·00 N	156·52 E
163	Lopez, Cap (C.)	Gabon	0·41 S	9·00 E
155	Lopez B. (lō'pāz)	Phil. (Manila In.)	14·04 N	122·00 E
65	Lopez I.	Wash. (Seattle In.)	48·25 N	122·53 W
151	Lop'ing (lō'pĭng')	China	29·02 N	117·12 E
165	Lopori R. (lō-pō'rê)	Con. L.	1·23 N	21·18 E
124	Lora (lō'rä)	Sp.	37·40 N	5·31 W
142	Lora (R.)	Afg.	31·43 N	67·08 E
75	Lorain (lô-rān')	Ohio (Cleveland In.)	41·28 N	82·10 W
142	Loralai (lō-rŭ-lī')	W. Pak.	30·31 N	68·35 E
124	Lorca (lôr'kä)	Sp.	37·39 N	1·40 W
159	Lord Howe (I.) (lôrd hou)	Austl.	31·44 S	157·56 E
69	Lordsburg (lôrdz'bûrg)	N. Mex.	32·20 N	108·45 W
101	Lorena (lō-rā'nȧ)	Braz. (Rio de Janeiro In.)	22·45 S	45·07 W
99	Loreto (lô-rā'tō)	Braz.	7·09 S	45·10 W
85	Loretteville (lô-rĕt-vēl')	Can. (Quebec In.)	46·51 N	71·21 W
163	Loriami (R.)	Con. L.	4·30 S	24·28 E
98	Lorica (lô-rē'kä)	Col.	9·14 N	75·54 W
122	Lorient (lô-rē'äN')	Fr.	47·45 N	3·22 W
116	Lorne, Firth of (fûrth ŏv lôrn')	Scot.	56·10 N	6·09 W
85	Lorne Park (lôrn)	Can. (Toronto In.)	43·31 N	79·36 W
120	Lörrach (lûr'äĸ)	Ger.	47·36 N	7·38 E
74	Los Alamitos (lōs ăl-à-mē'tôs)	Calif. (Los Angeles In.)	33·48 N	118·04 W
69	Los Alamos (ăl-ȧ-mōs')	N. Mex.	35·53 N	106·20 W
65	Los Altos (ăl-tôs')	Calif. (San Francisco In.)	37·23 N	122·06 W
101	Los Andes (än'dĕs)	Chile (Santiago In.)	32·44 S	70·36 W
74	Los Angeles (ăŋ'gĕl-ĕs) (ăn'jĕl-ĕs) (äŋ'hä-lâs)	Calif. (Los Angeles In.)	34·00 N	118·15 W
100	Los Angeles (äŋ'hä-lās)	Chile	37·27 S	72·15 W
68	Los Angeles Aqueduct	Calif.	35·12 N	118·02 W
74	Los Angeles R.	Calif. (Los Angeles In.)	33·50 N	118·13 W
101	Los Bronces (lôs brōn'-sĕs)	Chile (Santiago In.)	33·09 S	70·18 W
66	Loscha R. (lŏs'chă)	Idaho	46·20 N	115·11 W
100	Los Chonos, Archipielago de (är-chē-pyĕ'lä-gô dĕ lôs chô'nôs)	Chile	44·35 S	76·15 W
100	Los Estados, Isla de (I.) (ē's-lä dĕ lôs ĕs-tá'dôs)	Arg.	54·45 S	64·25 W
124	Los Filabres, Sierra de (Mts.) (sē-ĕ'r-rä dĕ lôs fē-lä'brĕs)	Sp.	37·19 N	2·48 W
68	Los Gatos (gă'tôs)	Calif.	37·13 N	121·59 W
151	Loshan (lō'shän')	China	29·40 N	103·40 E
76	Los Herreras (ĕr-rä-räs)	Mex.	25·55 N	99·23 W
95	Los Ilanos (lôs ē-lä'nōs)	Dom. Rep.	18·35 N	69·30 W
94	Los Indios, Cayos de (Is.) (kä'yōs dĕ lôs ē'n-dyô's)	Cuba	21·50 N	83·10 W
126	Lošinj (lō'shēn')	Yugo.	44·30 N	14·29 E
126	Lošinj (I.)	Yugo.	44·35 N	14·34 E
168	Loskopdam (L.)	S. Afr. (Johannesburg & Pretoria In.)	25·30 S	29·26 E
125	Los Monegros (Mts.) (mô-nĕ'grōs)	Sp.	41·31 N	0·18 W
74	Los Nietos (nyā'tôs)	Calif. (Los Angeles In.)	33·57 N	118·05 W
94	Los Patacios (pä-tä'sē-ōs)	Cuba	22·35 N	83·15 W
69	Los Pinos (R.) (pē'nôs)	Colo.-N. Mex.	36·58 N	107·35 W
90	Los Reyes (rā'yĕs)	Mex.	19·35 N	102·29 W
91	Los Reyes	Mex. (Mexico In.)	19·21 N	98·58 W
93	Los Santos (săn'tôs)	Pan.	7·57 N	80·24 W
124	Los Santos (sän'tôs)	Sp.	38·38 N	6·30 W
99	Los Teques (tĕ'kĕs)	Ven. (In.)	10·22 N	67·04 W
67	Lost R. (lôst)	Idaho	43·56 N	113·38 W
66	Lost R.	Ore.	42·07 N	121·30 W
67	Lost River Mts. (rĭ'vĕr)	Idaho	44·23 N	113·48 W
101	Los Vilos (vē'lôs)	Chile (Santiago In.)	31·56 S	71·29 W
122	Lot (R.) (lôt)	Fr.	44·32 N	1·08 E
100	Lota (lō'tä)	Chile	37·11 S	73·14 W
149	Lotien (lō'tyĕn')	China (Shanghai In.)	31·25 N	121·20 E
151	Loting (lō'tĭng')	China	23·42 N	111·35 E
148	Lot'ing (lō'tĭng)	China	39·26 N	118·53 E
120	Lötschen Tun. (lŭt'shĕn)	Switz.	46·26 N	7·54 E
78	Loudon (lou'dŭn)	Tenn.	35·43 N	84·20 W
80	Loudonville (lou'dŭn-vĭl)	Ohio	40·40 N	82·15 W
122	Loudun (lōō-dûN')	Fr.	47·03 N	0·00
164	Louga (lōō'gä)	Senegal	15·36 N	16·24 W
110	Loughborough (lŭf'bŭr-ô)	Eng.	56·46 N	1·12 W
80	Louisa (lōō'ĕz-ȧ)	Ky.	38·05 N	82·40 W
159	Louisade Arch. (lōō-ĭs-ād är-kĭ-pĕl-ĭ-gō)	Austl.	10·44 S	153·58 E
79	Louisberg (lōō'ĭs-bûrg)	N. C.	36·05 N	79·19 W
83	Louisbourg (lōō'ĭs-bourg)	Can.	45·56 N	59·59 W
73	Louisiana (lōō-ē-zê-ăn'ȧ)	Mo.	39·24 N	91·03 W
63	Louisiana (State)	U. S.	30·50 N	92·50 W
166	Louis Trichardt (lōō'ĭs trĭch'ārt)	S. Afr.	22·52 S	29·53 E
72	Louisville (lōō'ĭs-vĭl) (lōō'ê-vĭl)	Colo.	39·58 N	105·08 W
79	Louisville	Ga.	33·00 N	82·25 W
75	Louisville	Ky. (Louisville In.)	38·15 N	85·45 W
78	Louisville	Miss.	33·07 N	89·02 W
166	Loukoléla	Con. B.	1·00 S	17·13 E
124	Loule (lô-lā')	Port.	37·08 N	8·03 W
120	Louny (lō'nê)	Czech.	50·20 N	13·47 E
70	Loup (R.) (lōōp)	Nebr.	41·17 N	97·58 W
70	Loup City	Nebr.	41·15 N	98·59 W
122	Lourdes (lōōrd)	Fr.	43·06 N	0·03 W
166	Lourenço Marques (lô-rĕn'sô măr'kĕs)	Moz.	25·52 S	32·41 E
125	Loures (lō'rĕzh)	Port. (Lisboa In.)	38·49 N	9·10 W
124	Lousa (lō'zȧ)	Port.	40·05 N	8·12 W
116	Louth (louth)	Eng.	53·27 N	0·02 W
122	Louviers (lōō-vyā')	Fr.	49·13 N	1·11 E
123	Louvres (lōōv'r')	Fr. (Paris In.)	49·02 N	2·28 E
128	Lovat' (lô-vàt'y')	Sov. Un.	57·23 N	31·18 E
127	Lovech (lō'vĕts)	Bul.	43·10 N	24·40 E
72	Loveland (lŭv'lănd)	Colo.	40·24 N	105·04 W
75	Loveland	Ohio (Cincinnati In.)	39·16 N	84·15 W
67	Lovell (lŭv'ĕl)	Wyo.	44·50 N	108·23 W
68	Lovelock (lŭv'lŏk)	Nev.	40·10 N	118·37 W
84	Lovick (lŭ'vĭk)	Ala. (Birmingham In.)	33·34 N	86·38 W
119	Loviisa (lô'vē-sȧ)	Fin.	60·28 N	26·10 E
87	Low, C. (lō)	Can.	62·58 N	86·50 W
166	Lowa (lō'wȧ)	Con. L.	1·30 S	27·18 E
69	Lowell (lō'ĕl)	Ariz.	31·25 N	109·55 W
75	Lowell	Ind. (Chicago In.)	41·17 N	87·26 W
83	Lowell	Mass. (Boston In.)	42·38 N	71·18 W
80	Lowell	Mich.	42·55 N	85·20 W
65	Lowell	Wash. (Seattle In.)	47·57 N	122·12 W
111	Löwenberg (lû' vĕn-bĕrgh)	Ger. (Berlin In.)	52·53 N	13·09 E
86	Lower Arrow (L.) (ăr'ō)	Can.	49·41 N	118·40 W
	Lower Austria (State), see Niederösterreich			
70	Lower Brule Ind. Res. (brü'lā)	S. D.	44·15 N	100·21 W
159	Lower Hutt (hŭt)	N. Z. (In.)	41·08 S	175·00 E
66	Lower Klamath L. (klăm'ȧth)	Calif.	41·55 N	121·50 W
66	Lower L.	Calif.-Nev.	41·21 N	119·53 W
71	Lower Red (L.) (rĕd)	Minn.	47·58 N	94·31 W
68	Lower Otay Res. (ō'tā)	Calif. (San Diego In.)	32·37 N	116·46 W
	Lower Saxony (State), see Niedersachsen			
117	Lowestoft (lō'stŏft)	Eng.	52·31 N	1·45 E
121	Łowicz (lô'vĭch)	Pol.	52·06 N	19·57 E
121	Low Tatra Mts.	Czech.	48·57 N	19·18 E
81	Lowville (lou'vĭl)	N. Y.	43·45 N	75·30 W
91	Loxicha (Santa Caterina) (lô-zē'chä) (sän-tä kä-tä-rē'nä)	Mex.	16·03 N	96·46 W
75	Loyal Oak (loi'ăl ōk)	Ohio (Cleveland In.)	41·03 N	81·38 W
150	Loyang	China	34·45 N	112·32 E
159	Loyauté, Iles	N. Cal.	21·17 S	168·16 E
144	Loz, Jabal Al (Mtn.)	Sau. Ar.	28·46 N	35·37 E
127	Ložnica (lôz'nê-tsä)	Yugo.	44·31 N	19·16 E
111	Lozorno	Czech. (Wien In.)	48·21 N	17·03 E
129	Lozova (lô-zô'vá)	Sov. Un.	48·54 N	36·17 E
129	Lozovatka (lô-zô-vät'kȧ)	Sov. Un.	48·03 N	33·19 E
129	Lozovaya Pavlovka (lô-zo-vä'yä päv-lôf'kȧ)	Sov. Un.	48·27 N	38·37 E
125	Lozoya, Canal de (kä-nä'l dĕ lô-thō'yä)	Sp. (Madrid In.)	40·36 N	3·41 W
166	Lualaba (lōō-ȧ-lä'bȧ)	Con. L.	10·02 S	25·16 E
166	Luama (lōō-ä'mȧ)	Con. L.	4·47 S	27·32 E
150	Luan (R.)	China	41·25 N	117·15 E
166	Luanda (lōō-än'dä)	Ang.	8·50 S	13·15 E
154	Luang Prabang (lōō-ang'-prä-bäng')	Laos	19·47 N	102·15 E
166	Luanguinga (R.) (lōō-än-gĭŋ'gȧ)	Ang.	14·00 S	20·45 E
166	Luangwa (R.) (lōō-äŋ'gwȧ)	Fed. of Rh. & Nya.	12·38 S	32·41 E
148	Luanhsien (lōōän'sĭän')	China	39·47 N	118·40 E
124	Luarca (lwär'kä)	Sp.	43·33 N	6·30 W
113	Luarsens, Monts de (Mts.) (lwȧ-sŏŋ)	Alg.	35·44 N	0·50 E
121	Lubaczów (lōō-bä'chōōf)	Pol.	50·08 N	23·10 E
120	Lubán (lōō'bän')	Pol.	51·08 N	15·17 E
119	Lubānas Ezers (L.) (lōō-bä'nás ā'zērs)	Sov. Un.	56·48 N	26·30 E
155	Lubang (lōō-bäng')	Phil. (Manila In.)	13·49 N	120·07 E
155	Lubang (Is.)	Phil. (Manila In.)	13·47 N	119·56 E
155	Lubao (lōō-bä'ō)	Phil. (Manila In.)	14·55 N	120·36 E
121	Lubartow (lōō-bär'tōōf)	Pol.	51·27 N	22·37 E
121	Lubawa (lōō-bä'vä)	Pol.	53·31 N	19·47 E
120	Lübben (lüb'ĕn)	Ger.	51·56 N	13·53 E
72	Lubbock (lŭb'ŭk)	Tex.	33·35 N	101·50 W
82	Lubec (lū'bĕk)	Maine	44·49 N	67·01 W
120	Lübeck (lü'bĕk)	Ger.	53·53 N	10·42 E
120	Lübecker Bucht (B.) (lü'bĕ-kĕr bŏŏĸt)	Ger.	54·10 N	11·20 E
166	Lubilash (R.) (lōō-bē-lāsh')	Con. L.	7·45 S	24·09 E
120	Lubin (lyōō'bĭn)	Pol.	51·24 N	16·14 E
121	Lublin (lyōō'blĕn')	Pol.	51·14 N	22·33 E
129	Lubny (lōōb'nē)	Sov. Un.	50·01 N	33·02 E
155	Lubuagan (lōō-bwä-gä'n)	Phil. (Manila In.)	17·24 N	121·11 E
166	Lubudi (R.) (lōō-bōō'dē)	Con. L.	10·03 S	24·28 E
126	Lucca (lōōk'kä)	It.	43·51 N	10·29 E
116	Luce B. (lūs)	Scot.	54·45 N	4·45 W
94	Lucea	Jam.	18·25 N	78·10 W

ăt; finăl; rāte; senåte; ärm; åsk; sofȧ; fâre; ch-choose; dh-as th in other; bē; êvent; bĕt; recĕnt; cratēr; g-go; gh-guttural g; bĭt; ĭ-short neutral; rīde; ĸ-guttural k as ch in German ich;

PRONOUNCING INDEX Lucena–Mackinaw 231

Page	Name Pronunciation Region	Lat. °′	Long. °′
155	Lucena (lo͞o-sä'nä) Phil. (Manila In.)	13·55 N	121·36 E
124	Lucena (loo-thā'nä) . . . Sp.	37·25 N	4·28 W
125	Lucena del Cid (lo͞o-thā'nä dā thēdh') . Sp.	40·08 N	0·18 W
121	Lučenec (lo͞o'chå-nyĕts) . . . Czech.	48·19 N	19·41 E
126	Lucera (lo͞o-châ'rä) . . . It.	41·31 N	15·22 E
151	Luchi . . . China	28·18 N	110·10 E
148	Luchia (lo͞o'jiä) . . . China	32·12 N	115·53 E
148	Luchih (lo͞o'jĕī) . . . China	31·17 N	120·54 E
67	Lucin (lů-sēn') . . . Utah	41·23 N	113·59 W
155	Lucipara (I.) (lo͞o-sē-pä'rä) . Indon.	5·45 S	128·15 E
111	Luckenwalde (lo͝ok-ĕn-väl'dĕ) Ger. (Berlin In.)	52·05 N	13·10 E
142	Lucknow (lŭk'nou) . . . India	26·54 N	80·58 E
122	Luçon (lü-sôɴ') . . . Fr.	46·27 N	1·12 W
95	Lucrecia, Cabo (C.) (kä'bô-lo͞o-krā'sē-ä) . Cuba	21·05 N	75·30 W
127	Luda Kamchiya (R.) . . . Bul.	42·46 N	27·13 E
123	Lüdenscheid (lü'dĕn-shīt) Ger. (Ruhr In.)	51·13 N	7·38 E
166	Lüderitz (lü'dēr-ĭts) (lü'dĕ-rĭts) S. W. Afr.	26·35 S	15·15 E
166	Lüderitz B. . . . S. W. Afr.	26·35 S	14·30 E
142	Ludhiana . . . India	31·00 N	75·52 E
123	Lüdinghausen (lü'dĕng-hou-zĕn) Ger. (Ruhr In.)	51·46 N	7·27 E
80	Ludington (lŭd'ĭng-tŭn) . . . Mich.	44·00 N	86·25 W
110	Ludlow (lŭd'lō) . . . Eng.	52·22 N	2·43 W
75	Ludlow . . . Ky. (Cincinnati In.)	39·05 N	84·33 W
118	Ludvika (loodh-vē'kå) . . . Swe.	60·10 N	15·09 E
120	Ludwigsburg (lo͞ot'vēks-bo͝orgh) Ger.	48·53 N	9·14 E
111	Ludwigsfelde (lo͞od'vēgs-fĕl-dĕ) Ger. (Berlin In.)	52·18 N	13·16 E
120	Ludwigshafen (lo͞ot'vēks-hä'fĕn) Ger.	49·29 N	8·26 E
120	Ludwigslust (lo͞ot'vēks-lo͞ost) . Ger.	53·18 N	11·31 E
128	Ludza (lo͞od'zå) . . . Sov. Un.	56·33 N	27·45 E
166	Luebo (lo͞o-ā'bô) . . . Con. L.	5·15 S	21·22 E
166	Lufira (R.) (lo͞o-fē'rå) . . . Con. L.	9·32 S	27·15 E
77	Lufkin (lŭf'kĭn) . . . Tex.	31·21 N	94·43 W
128	Luga (lo͞o'gå) . . . Sov. Un.	58·43 N	29·52 E
128	Luga (R.) . . . Sov. Un.	59·00 N	29·25 E
120	Lugano (lo͞o-gä'nō) . . . Switz.	46·01 N	8·52 E
129	Lugansk (lo͞o-gänsk') . . . Sov. Un.	48·34 N	39·18 E
129	Lugansk (Oblast) (ôb'låst) . Sov. Un.	49·08 N	38·37 E
168	Lugh Ferrandi Som. (Horn of Afr. In.)	3·38 N	42·35 E
116	Lugnaquilla, Mt. (lo͝ok-nå-kwĭ-lå) . Ire.	52·56 N	6·30 W
126	Lugo (lo͞o'gô) . . . It.	44·28 N	11·57 E
124	Lugo (lo͞o'gō) . . . Sp.	43·01 N	7·32 W
115	Lugoj . . . Rom.	45·42 N	22·00 E
127	Lugoj . . . Rom.	45·51 N	21·56 E
	Luhe, see Winsen		
151	Luhsien . . . China	28·58 N	105·25 E
148	Lui (lo͞o'yĭ) . . . China	33·52 N	115·32 E
166	Luilaka (R.) (lo͞o-ē-lä'kå) . . Con. L.	2·18 S	21·15 E
116	Luimneach (lĭm'nåk) . . . Ire.	52·39 N	8·35 W
90	Luis Moya (lo͞oē's-mô-yä) . . . Mex.	22·26 N	102·14 W
101	Luján (lo͞o-hän') Arg. (Buenos Aires In.)	34·36 S	59·07 W
101	Luján (R.) Arg. (Buenos Aires In.)	34·33 S	58·59 W
147	Lujchow Pen . . . China	20·40 N	110·30 E
166	Lukanga Swp. (lo͞o-käŋ'gå) Fed. of Rh. & Nya.	14·08 S	28·32 E
166	Lukenie (R.) (lo͞o-kā'nyå) . Con. L.	2·48 S	18·45 E
127	Lukovit (lo͞o'kō-vēt') . . . Bul.	43·13 N	24·07 E
121	Łuków (wo͞o'ko͞of) . . . Pol.	51·57 N	22·25 E
166	Lukuga (R.) (lo͞o-ko͞o'gå) . . Con. L.	5·47 S	27.48 E
132	Lule (R.) . . . Swe.	66·20 N	20·25 E
112	Luleå (lo͞o'lĕ-ô) . . . Swe.	65·39 N	21·52 E
127	Lüleburgaz (lü'lĕ-bo͝or-gäs') . . Tur.	41·25 N	27·23 E
148	Luling (lü'lĭng) . . . China	39·54 N	118·53 E
77	Luling . . . Tex.	29·41 N	97·38 W
65	Lulu (I.) (lū'lo͞o) Can. (Vancouver In.)	49·10 N	123·04 W
166	Lulua (R.) (lo͞o'lo͞o-å) . . . Con. L.	6·30 S	22·15 E
166	Luluabourg (lo͞o'lo͞o-a-bo͝org') Con. L.	6·14 S	22·17 E
79	Lumber (R.) (lŭm'bēr) . . . N. C.	35·12 N	79·35 W
78	Lumberton (lŭm'bēr-tŭn) . . . Miss.	31·00 N	89·25 W
79	Lumberton . . . N. C.	34·37 N	79·00 W
101	Luminárias (lo͞o-mē-nä'ryäs) Braz. (Rio de Janeiro In.)	21·32 S	44·53 W
65	Lummi (I.) Wash. (Vancouver In.)	48·42 N	122·43 W
65	Lummi B. (lŭm'ĭ) Wash. (Vancouver In.)	48·47 N	122·44 W
65	Lummi Island Wash. (Vancouver In.)	48·44 N	122·42 W
155	Luna (lo͞o'nå) . . Phil. (Manila In.)	16·51 N	120·22 E
118	Lund (lŭnd) . . . Swe.	55·42 N	13·10 E
163	Lunda (Reg.) (lo͞on'dä) . . . Ang.	8·53 S	20·00 E
166	Lundi (R.) (lo͞on'dē) Fed. of Rh. & Nya.	21·09 S	30·10 E
116	Lundy (I.) (lŭn'dē) . . . Eng.	51·12 N	4·50 W
120	Lüneberger Heide (Reg.) (lü'nĕ-bo͝or-gĕr hī'dĕ) . Ger.	53·08 N	10·00 E
120	Lüneburg (lü'nē-bo͝orgh) . . . Ger.	53·16 N	10·25 E
122	Lunel (lü-nĕl') . . . Fr.	43·41 N	4·07 E
123	Lünen (lü'nĕn) . . . Ger. (Ruhr In.)	51·36 N	7·30 E
82	Lunenburg (lo͞o'nĕn-bûrg) . . . Can.	44·24 N	64·16 W
83	Lunenburg . . . Mass. (Boston In.)	42·36 N	71·44 W
123	Lunéville (lü-nå-vel') . . . Fr.	48·37 N	6·29 E
166	Lunga (R.) (lo͞oŋ'gå) Fed. of Rh. & Nya.	12·58 S	26·18 E
152	Lungchen (lo͝ong'chĕn) . . . China	48·38 N	122·12 E
135	Lungchen (lo͝ong'chĕn) . . . China	48·47 N	126·43 E
151	Lungch'i . . . China	24·35 N	117·45 E
151	Lungching . . . China	22·20 N	107·02 E
150	Lungchingts'un (lo͝ong'chĭng'tso͞on') . China	42·45 N	129·30 E
166	Lungé-Bungo (R.) (lŭn'gā bŭn'gô) Ang.	13·00 S	20·15 E
150	Lunghsi . . . China	35·00 N	104·40 E
148	Lungku (lo͝ong'kō) . . . China	34·52 N	116·48 E
149	Lungyentung . . China (Canton In.)	23·12 N	113·21 E
167	Lunhenda (R.) (lo͞o'n-yĕ'n-dä) Moz.	12·16 S	37·29 E
142	Lūni (R.) . . . India	24·64 N	71·10 E
128	Luninets (R.) (lo͞o-nēn'yets) Sov. Un.	52·14 N	26·54 E
150	Lupei (lo͞o'pī) . . . China	44·35 N	120·40 E
150	Lupin (Manchouli) (lo͞o'pĭn') (män-cho͞o'lē) . China	49·25 N	117·15 E
100	Luque (loo'kā) . . . Par.	25·18 S	57·17 W
81	Luray (lū-rā') . . . Va.	38·40 N	78·25 W
116	Lurgan (lûr'gǎn) . . . N. Ire.	54·27 N	6·28 W
167	Lúrio (lo͞o'rē-ô) . . . Moz.	13·17 S	40·29 E
167	Lúrio (R.) . . . Moz.	13·58 S	37·52 E
166	Lusaka (lo͞o-sä'kå) Fed. of Rh. & Nya.	15·19 S	28·15 E
166	Lusambo (lo͞o-säm'bō) . . . Con. L.	4·57 S	23·28 E
142	Lushai Hills . . . Bur.	28·28 N	92·50 E
150	Lushan . . . China	33·45 N	113·00 E
167	Lushoto (lo͞o-shō'tō) . . . Tan.	4·47 S	38·17 E
148	Lüshun (Port Arthur) (lü'shŭn) China	38·49 N	121·15 E
167	Lusikisiki (lo͞o-sē-kē-sē'kē) S. Afr. (Natal In.)	31·22 S	29·37 E
70	Lusk (lŭsk) . . . Wyo.	42·46 N	104·27 W
148	Lüta (lüdå) . . . China	38·55 N	121·19 E
148	Lut'ai (lo͞o'tăī) . . . China	39·20 N	117·50 E
77	Lutcher (lŭch'ēr) . . . La.	30·03 N	90·43 W
84	Lutherville (lo͞o'thŭr-vĭl) Md. (Baltimore In.)	39·26 N	76·38 W
116	Luton (lū'tŭn) . . . Eng.	51·55 N	0·28 W
121	Lutsk (lo͞otsk) . . . Sov. Un.	50·45 N	25·20 E
78	Luverne (lū-vûrn') . . . Ala.	31·42 N	86·15 W
70	Luverne (lū-vûrn') . . . Minn.	43·40 N	96·13 W
166	Luvua (R.) (lo͞o'vo͞o-ä) . . . Con. L.	6·49 S	27·17 E
166	Luvungi (lo͞o-vo͞oŋ'gē) . . . Con. L.	2·54 S	29·00 E
78	Luxapalila Cr. (lŭk-så-pŏl'ĭ-lå) Ala.	33·36 N	88·08 W
123	Luxembourg (lŭk-sĕm-bûrg) (lük sän-bo͞or') (look-sĕm-bo͝orgh) . Lux.	49·38 N	6·30 E
102	Luxembourg . . . Eur.	49·30 N	6·22 E
74	Luxemburg . . . Mo. (St. Louis In.)	38·32 N	90·17 W
123	Luxeuil (lŭk-sû'y') . . . Fr.	47·49 N	6·19 E
84	Luxomni (lŭx'ŏm-nī) Ga. (Atlanta In.)	33·54 N	84·07 W
	Luxor, see Al Uqṣur		
150	Luya Shan (Mtn.) . . . China	38·50 N	111·40 E
132	Luza (R.) (lo͞o'zä) . . . Sov. Un.	60·30 N	47·10 E
120	Luzern (lo͞o-tsĕrn) . . . Switz.	47·03 N	8·18 E
99	Luziânia (lo͞o-zyä'nēä) . . . Braz	16·17 S	47·44 W
154	Luzon (I.) (lo͞o-zŏn') . . . Phil.	17·10 N	119·45 E
151	Luzon Str. (lo͞o-zŏn') . . . Phil.	20·40 N	121·00 E
121	L'vov (l'vo͞of) . . . Sov. Un.	49·51 N	24·01 E
135	Lyakhovskiye (Is.) (lya'ᴋo͞o'v-skyê) . Sov. Un.	73·45 N	145·15 E
142	Lyallpur (lī'ǎl-pûr) . . . W. Pak.	31·29 N	73·06 E
85	Lyalta . . . Can. (Calgary In.)	51·07 N	113·36 W
136	Lyalya R. (lyå'lyå) Sov. Un. (Urals In.)	58·58 N	60·17 E
127	Lyaskovets . . . Bul.	43·07 N	25·41 E
166	Lydenburg (lī'dĕn-bûrg) . . . S. Afr.	25·06 S	30·21 E
68	Lyell, Mt. (lī'ĕl) . . . Calif.	37·44 N	119·22 W
81	Lykens (lī'kĕnz) . . . Pa.	40·35 N	76·45 W
121	Lyna R. (lĭn'å) . . . Pol.	53·56 N	20·30 E
78	Lynch (lĭnch) . . . Ky.	36·56 N	82·55 W
79	Lynchburg (lĭnch'bûrg) . . . Va.	37·23 N	79·08 W
65	Lynch Cove (lĭnch) Wash. (Seattle In.)	47·26 N	122·54 W
85	Lynden (lĭn'dĕn) Can. (Toronto In.)	43·14 N	80·08 W
65	Lynden . . . Wash. (Vancouver In.)	48·56 N	122·27 W
161	Lyndhurst . Austl. (Melbourne In.)	38·03 S	145·14 E
75	Lyndon (lĭn'dŭn) Ky. (Louisville In.)	38·15 N	85·36 W
81	Lyndonville (lĭn'dŭn-vĭl) . . . Vt.	44·35 N	72·00 W
83	Lynn (lĭn) . . . Mass. (Boston In.)	42·28 N	70·57 W
84	Lynnhaven (lĭn'hā-vĕn) Va. (Norfolk In.)	36·50 N	76·04 W
86	Lynn Lake (lāk) . . . Can.	56·48 N	101·10 W
74	Lynwood (lĭn'wo͝od) Calif. (Los Angeles In.)	33·56 N	118·13 W
122	Lyon (lē-ôɴ') . . . Fr.	45·44 N	4·52 E
79	Lyons (lī'ŭnz) . . . Ga.	32·08 N	82·19 W
72	Lyons . . . Kans.	38·20 N	98·11 W
70	Lyons . . . Nebr.	41·57 N	96·28 W
84	Lyons . . . N. J. (New York In.)	40·41 N	74·33 W
81	Lyons . . . N. Y.	43·05 N	77·00 W
118	Lyse Fd. (lü'sĕ fyôr') . . . Nor.	58·59 N	6·35 E
118	Lysekil (lü'sĕ-kĕl) . . . Swe.	58·17 N	11·22 E
136	Lys'va (lĭs'vå) Sov. Un. (Urals In.)	58·07 N	57·47 E
110	Lytham (lĭth'ǎm) . . . Eng.	53·44 N	2·58 W
167	Lyttelton (lĭt'l'ton) . . . S. Afr. (Johannesburg & Pretoria In.)	25·51 S	28·13 E
86	Lytton (lĭt'ŭn) . . . Can.	50·16 N	121·29 W
136	Lyuban' (lyo͞o' bän) Sov. Un. (Leningrad In.)	59·21 N	31·15 E
129	Lyubar (lyo͞o'bär) . . . Sov. Un.	49·56 N	27·44 E
136	Lyubertsy (lyo͞o'bĕr-tsê) Sov. Un. (Moskva In.)	55·40 N	37·55 E
128	Lyubim (lyo͞o-bêm') . . . Sov. Un.	58·24 N	40·39 E
136	Lyublino (lyo͞ob'lĭ-nô) Sov. Un. (Moskva In.)	55·41 N	37·45 E
128	Lyudinovo (lü-dē'novō) . . Sov. Un.	53·52 N	34·28 E
146	Lyung . . . Mong.	47·58 N	104·52 E
139	Ma'an (mä-än') Jordan (Palestine In.)	30·12 N	35·45 E
118	Maarianhamina (Mariehamn) (mä'rē-ån-hä'mē-nä) (må-rē'ĕ-häm''n) . Fin.	60·07 N	19·57 E
111	Maartensdijk Neth. (Amsterdam In.)	52·09 N	5·10 E
123	Maas (R.) . . . Neth. (Ruhr In.)	51·32 N	6·07 E
117	Maastricht (mäs'trĭᴋt) . . . Bel.	50·51 N	5·35 E
165	Maaten Bishidra (Oasis) . . . Libya	23·11 N	22·34 E
65	Mabana (mä-bä-nä) Wash. (Seattle In.)	48·06 N	122·25 W
77	Mabank (mā'bǎnk) . . . Tex.	32·21 N	96·05 W
168	Mabeskraal . . . S. Afr. (Johannesburg & Pretoria In.)	25·12 S	26·47 E
84	Mableton (mā'b'l-tŭn) Ga. (Atlanta In.)	33·49 N	84·34 W
114	Mabrouk (må-bro͞ok') . . . Alg.	29·30 N	0·20 E
164	Mabrouk . . . Mali	19·27 N	1·16 W
139	Mabruk (R.) Sau. Ar. (Palestine In.)	29·16 N	35·22 E
168	Mabula (mă'bo͞o-la) . . . S. Afr. (Johannesburg & Pretoria In.)	24·49 S	27·59 E
82	McAdam (măk-ăd'ăm) . . . Can.	45·37 N	67·21 W
101	Macaé (mä-kä-ā') Braz. (Rio de Janeiro In.)	22·22 S	41·47 W
84	McAfee (mǎk-ǎ'fē) N. J. (New York In.)	41·10 N	74·32 W
99	Macaira (R.) (mä-kī'rä) Ven. (In.)	9·37 N	66·16 W
155	Macalelon (mä-kä-lä-lōn') Phil. (Manila In.)	13·46 N	122·09 E
73	McAlester (mǎk ăl'ĕs-tēr) . . . Okla.	34·55 N	95·45 W
76	McAllen (mǎk-ăl'ĕn) . . . Tex.	26·12 N	98·14 W
99	Macapá (mä-kä-pä') . . . Braz.	0·08 N	50·02 W
151	Macau (mä-kä'o͞o) . . . Asia	22·10 N	113·35 E
99	Macau (mä-kä'o͞o) . . . Braz.	5·12 S	36·34 W
95	Macaya, Pico de (Pk.) . . . Hai.	18·25 N	74·00 W
86	McBride (mǎk-brīd) . . . Can.	53·25 N	120·15 W
84	McCalla (mǎk-kăl'lå) Ala. (Birmingham In.)	33·20 N	87·00 W
76	McCamey (mǎ-kā'mĭ) . . . Tex.	31·08 N	102·13 W
125	Maccarese (mäk-kä-rĕ'zĕ) It. (Roma In.)	41·53 N	12·13 E
74	McCarron (măk kăr'ŭn) Mich. (Sault Ste. Marie In.)	46·20 N	84·17 W
78	McCaysville (mǎ-kāz'vĭl) . . . Ga.	34·57 N	84·21 W
110	Macclesfield (mǎk''lz-fēld) . . . Eng.	53·15 N	2·07 W
110	Macclesfield Can. (mǎk''lz-fēld) Eng.	53·14 N	2·07 W
79	McColl (mǎ-kól') . . . S. C.	34·40 N	79·34 W
78	McComb (mǎ-kōm') . . . Miss.	31·14 N	90·27 W
70	McConaughy, L. (mǎk kō'nō ĭ') Nebr.	41·24 N	101·40 W
72	McCook (mǎ-ko͝ok') . . . Nebr.	40·13 N	100·37 W
79	McCormick (mǎ-kôr'mĭk) . . . S. C.	33·56 N	82·20 W
116	Macdhui, Ben (Mtn.) (bĕn mǎk-do͞o'ē) . Scot.	57·06 N	3·45 W
74	Macdona (mǎk-dō'nä) Tex. (San Antonio In.)	29·20 N	98·42 W
75	McDonald (mǎk-dŏn'ăld) Pa. (Pittsburgh In.)	40·22 N	80·13 W
158	Macdonald (I.) (mǎk-dŏn'ăld) Austl.	23·40 S	127·40 E
47	McDonald I. . . . Austl.	53·00 S	72·45 E
85	McDonald L. (mǎk-dŏn-ăld) Can. (Calgary In.)	51·12 N	113·53 W
158	Macdonnell Ra. (mǎk-dŏn'ĕl) Austl.	23·40 S	131·30 E
75	Macedonia (măs-ē-dō'nĭ-å) Ohio (Cleveland In.)	41·19 N	81·30 W
127	Macedonia (Reg.) (măs-ē-dō'nĭ-å) Eur.	41·05 N	22·15 E
99	Maceió (mä-sā-yō') . . . Braz.	9·33 S	35·35 W
166	Macequece (mä-så-kä'så) . . . Moz.	18·48 S	32·49 E
126	Macerata (mä-chå-rä'tä) . . . It.	43·18 N	13·28 E
160	Mcfarlane (L.) (mǎc'fär-lān) . Austl.	32·10 S	137·00 E
73	McGehee (mǎ-gē') . . . Ark.	33·39 N	91·22 W
68	McGill (mǎ-gĭl') . . . Nev.	39·25 N	114·47 W
65	McGowan (mǎk-gou'ǎn) Wash. (Portland In.)	46·15 N	123·55 W
64	McGrath (mǎk gräth) . . . Alaska	62·58 N	155·20 W
75	McGregor (mǎk-grĕg'ēr) Can. (Detroit In.)	42·08 N	82·58 W
71	McGregor . . . Iowa	42·58 N	91·12 W
77	McGregor . . . Tex.	31·26 N	97·23 W
85	McGregor L. (mǎk-grĕg'ēr) Can. (Ottawa In.)	45·38 N	75·44 W
167	Machache (Mtn.) . Bas. (Natal In.)	29·22 S	27·53 E
101	Machado (mä-shä-dô) Braz. (Rio de Janeiro In.)	21·42 S	45·55 W
98	Machala (mä-chä'lä) . . . Ec.	3·18 S	78·54 W
75	McHenry (mǎk-hĕn'rĭ) Ill. (Chicago In.)	42·21 N	88·16 W
74	Machens (mǎk'ĕns) Mo. (St. Louis In.)	38·54 N	90·20 W
82	Machias (må-chī'ǎs) . . . Maine	44·22 N	67·29 W
98	Machu Picchu (mä'cho͞o-pē'k-cho͞o) . Peru	8·01 S	72·24 W
129	Măcin (mǎ-chēn') . . . Rom.	45·15 N	28·09 E
70	McIntosh (mǎk'ĭn-tŏsh) . . . S. D.	45·54 N	101·22 W
159	Mackay (mǎ-kī') . . . Austl.	21·15 S	149·08 E
67	Mackay (mǎk-kā') . . . Idaho	43·55 N	113·38 W
158	Mackay (I.) (mǎ-kī') . . . Austl.	22·30 S	127·45 E
86	MacKay (L.) (mǎk-kā') . . . Can.	64·00 N	113·13 W
65	McKay (R.) . . . Ore.	45·43 N	123·00 W
85	MacKayville (mǎk-kā-vĭl) Can. (Montreal In.)	45·28 N	73·28 W
75	McKeesport (mǎ-kez'pôrt) Pa. (Pittsburgh In.)	40·21 N	79·51 W
75	McKees Rocks (mǎ-kēz' rŏks) Pa. (Pittsburgh In.)	40·29 N	80·05 W
78	McKenzie (må-kĕn'zĭ) . . . Tenn.	36·07 N	88·30 W
86	Mackenzie, Dist. of . . . Can.	63·48 N	125·25 W
86	Mackenzie (R.) . . . Can.	63·28 N	124·23 W
64	Mackenzie B. . . . Alaska	69·20 N	137·10 W
86	Mackenzie Mts. (mǎ-kĕn'zĭ) . Can.	63·41 N	129·27 W
66	McKenzie R. . . . Ore.	44·07 N	122·20 W
80	Mackinac, Str. of (mǎk'ĭ-nô) (mǎk'ĭ-nǎk) . Mich.	45·50 N	84·40 W
80	Mackinaw (R.) . . . Ill.	40·35 N	89·25 W

ng-sing; ŋ-baŋk; ɴ-nasalized n; nŏd; cŏmmit; ōld; ôbey; ôrder; fo͞od; fo͝ot; ou-out; s-soft; sh-dish; th-thin; pūre; ûnite; ûrn; stŭd; circŭs; ü-as "y" in study; '-indeterminate vowel.

Page	Name Pronunciation Region	Lat. °′	Long. °′
80	Mackinaw City (măk′ĭ-nô) . . Mich.	45·45 N	84·45 W
64	McKinley, Mt. (mȧ-kĭn′lĭ) . Alaska	63·00 N	151·02 W
73	McKinney (mȧ-kĭn′ĭ) . . . . Tex.	33·12 N	96·35 W
86	Macklin (măk′lĭn) . . . . Can.	52·22 N	109·51 W
70	McLaughlin (mȧk-lŏf′lĭn) . . S. D.	45·48 N	100·45 W
80	McLeansboro (mȧ-klānz′bŭr-ŏ) Ill.	38·10 N	88·35 W
167	Macleantown (măk-lān′toun)		
	S. Afr. (Natal In.)	32·48 s	27·48 E
167	Maclear (mȧ-klēr′)		
	S. Afr. (Natal In.)	31·06 s	28·23 E
86	McLennan (măk-lĕn′nȧn) . . . . Can.	55·51 N	117·10 W
66	McLoughlin, Mt. (măk-lŏk′lĭn)		
	Ore.	42·27 N	122·20 W
76	McMillan L. (mȧk-mĭl′ȧn) . . . Tex.	32·40 N	104·09 W
65	McMillin (mȧk-mĭl′ĭn)		
	Wash. (Seattle In.)	47·08 N	122·14 W
66	McMinnville (măk-mĭn′vĭl) . . Ore.	45·13 N	123·13 W
78	McMinnville . . . . Tenn.	35·41 N	85·47 W
86	McMurray (măk-mŭr′ĭ) . . . . . Can.	56·45 N	111·15 W
65	McMurray . . . . Wash. (Seattle In.)	48·19 N	122·15 W
69	McNary (mȧk-nâr′ĕ) . . . . Ariz.	34·10 N	109·55 W
77	McNary . . . . La.	30·58 N	92·32 W
66	McNary Dam . . . . . . Ore.-Wash.	45·57 N	119·15 W
73	Macomb (mȧ-kōōm′) . . . . Ill.	40·27 N	90·40 W
122	Mâcon (mä-kôn′) . . . . Fr.	46·19 N	4·51 E
78	Macon (mā′kŏn) . . . . Ga.	32·49 N	83·39 W
78	Macon . . . . Miss.	32·07 N	88·31 W
69	Macon . . . . N. Mex.	34·10 N	107·45 W
73	Macon . . . . Mo.	39·42 N	92·29 W
73	McPherson (mȧk-fŭr′s′n) . . Kans.	38·21 N	97·41 W
160	Macquarie (R.) . . . . Austl.	31·43 s	148·04 E
47	Macquarie Is. (mȧ-kwŏr′ĕ) Austl.	54·36 s	158·45 E
78	McRae (măk-rā′) . . . . Ga.	32·02 N	82·55 W
78	McRoberts (măk-rŏb′ẽrts) . . . Ky.	37·12 N	82·40 W
92	Macuelizo (mä-kwĕ-lē′zŏ) . . Hond.	15·22 N	88·32 W
139	Ma'dabā) . . Jordan (Palestine In.)	31·43 N	35·47 E
163	Madagascar (I.) (măd-ȧ-găs′kȧr)		
	Malagasy	21·30 s	46·00 E
83	Madame (I.) (mȧ-dăm′) . . . . . Can.	45·31 N	60·45 W
143	Madanapalle . . . . India	13·06 N	78·09 E
155	Madang (mä-däng′) . N. Gui. Ter.	5·15 s	145·45 E
164	Madaoua (mä-dou′ä) . . . . Niger	14·04 N	6·03 E
74	Madart (mä′dȧrt)		
	Minn. (Minneapolis, St. Paul In.)	44·48 N	93·02 W
81	Madawaska (R.) (măd-ȧ-wŏs′kȧ)		
	Can.	45·20 N	77·25 W
88	Madden, L.		
	C. Z. (Panama Canal In.)	9·15 N	79·34 W
164	Madeira, Ilha da (I.) (mä-dā′rȧ)		
	Mad. Is.	32·41 N	16·15 W
164	Madeira, Arquipelago da (Is.)		
	(är-kē-pĕ′lä-gō-dä-mä-dĕ́y-rä)		
	Port.	33·26 N	16·44 W
98	Madeira (R.) . . . . Braz.	6·48 s	62·43 W
82	Madeleine, C. (măd′lĕn′) . . . . Can.	49·15 N	65·20 W
71	Madelia (mä-dē′lĭ-ȧ) . . . . . . Minn.	44·03 N	94·23 W
71	Madeline (I.) (măd′ĕ-lĭn) . . . . Wis.	46·47 N	91·30 W
68	Madera (mȧ-dā′rȧ) . . . . Calif.	36·57 N	120·04 W
92	Madera (Vol.) . . . . Nic.	11·27 N	85·30 W
142	Madhya Pradesh (State)		
	((mŭd′vū prŭ-dāsh′) . India	27·04 N	77·48 E
73	Madill (mȧ-dĭl′) . . . . Okla.	34·04 N	96·45 W
78	Madison (măd′ĭ-săn) . . . . Fla.	30·25 N	85·25 W
78	Madison . . . . Ga.	33·34 N	83·29 W
74	Madison . . Ill. (St. Louis In.)	38·40 N	90·09 W
80	Madison . . . . Ind.	38·45 N	85·25 W
73	Madison . . . . Kans.	38·08 N	96·07 W
82	Madison . . . . Maine	44·47 N	69·52 W
70	Madison . . . . Minn.	44·59 N	96·13 W
70	Madison . . . . Nebr.	41·49 N	97·27 W
84	Madison . . N. J. (New York In.)	40·46 N	74·25 W
79	Madison . . . . N. C.	36·22 N	79·59 W
70	Madison . . . . S. D.	44·01 N	97·08 W
71	Madison . . . . Wis.	43·05 N	89·23 W
67	Madison Res. . . . . Mont.	45·25 N	111·28 W
67	Madison R. . . . . Mont.	45·15 N	111·30 W
80	Madisonville (măd′ĭ-săn-vĭl) . . Ky.	37·20 N	87·30 W
77	Madisonville . . . . La.	30·22 N	90·10 W
77	Madisonville . . . . Tex.	30·57 N	95·55 W
154	Madjene . . . . Indon.	3·34 s	119·00 E
128	Madona (mä′dŏ′nä) . . . . . Sov. Un.	56·50 N	26·14 E
143	Madras (mȧ-drȧs′) (mŭ-drŭs′)		
	India	13·08 N	80·15 E
143	Madras (State) (mŭ-drŭs′)		
	(mȧ-drȧs′) . India	15·20 N	78·20 E
77	Madre, Laguna L.		
	(lä-gōō′nȧ mä′drȧ) . Mex.	25·08 N	97·41 W
90	Madre, Sierra (Mts.)		
	(sē-ĕ́r-rä-mä′drĕ) . Mex.	15·55 N	92·40 W
155	Madre, Sierra (Mts.)		
	Phil. (Manila In.)	16·40 N	122·10 E
100	Madre de Dios, Arch.		
	(mä′drȧ dä dē-ōs′) . Chile	50·40 s	76·30 W
98	Madre de Dios, Rio (R.)		
	(rē′ō-mä′drä dä dē-ōs′) . Bol.	12·07 s	68·20 W
90	Madre del Sur, Sierra (Mts.)		
	(sē-ĕ́r-rä-mä′drä dĕlsōōr′) . Mex.	17·35 N	100·35 W
71	Madrid (măd′rĭd) . . . . Iowa	41·51 N	93·48 W
125	Madrid (mä-drē′d) Sp. (Madrid In.)	40·26 N	3·42 W
124	Madridejos (mä-dhrĕ-dhā′hōs).Sp.	39·29 N	3·32 W
66	Mad R. (măd) . . . . Calif.	40·38 N	123·37 W
143	Madura (mä-dōō′rä) . . . . India	9·57 N	78·04 E
154	Madura (I.) (mä-dōō′rä) . . . Indon.	6·45 s	113·30 E
100	Madureira, Serra do (Mtn.) (sĕ́r-rä-		
	dŏ-mä-dōō-ra′rä) Braz. (In.)	22·49 s	43·30 W
153	Maebashi (mä-ĕ-bä′shĕ) . . . . Jap.	36·26 N	139·04 E
125	Maella (mä-āl′yä) . . . . Sp.	41·10 N	0·07 E
155	Maeor (I.) . . . . Neth. N. Gui.	0·45 s	135·00 E
94	Maestra, Sierra (Mts.)		
	(sē-ĕ́r-rä-mä-äs′trä) . Cuba	20·05 N	77·05 W
159	Maewo (I.) . . . . New Hebr.	15·17 s	168·16 E
166	Mafeking (măf′ĕ-kĭng) . . . . S. Afr.	25·46 s	24·45 E
167	Mafia (I.) (mä-fē′ä) . . . . Tan.	7·45 s	39·45 E
100	Mafra (mä′frä) . . . . Braz.	26·21 s	49·59 W
125	Mafra (mäf′rä) Port. (Lisboa In.)	38·56 N	9·20 W
135	Magadan (mȧ-gȧ-dän′) . Sov. Un.	59·39 N	150·43 E

Page	Name Pronunciation Region	Lat. °′	Long. °′
135	Magadan Oblast . . . . Sov. Un.	63·00 N	170·30 E
167	Magadi (L.) (mȧ-gä′dĕ) . . . . . Ken.	2·12 s	37·32 E
167	Magalies (R.) (mȧ-gä′lyĕs)		
	S. Afr. (Johannesburg &		
	Pretoria In.)	25·51 s•	27·42 E
167	Magaliesberg (Mts.)		
	S. Afr. (Johannesburg &		
	Pretoria In.)	25·45 s	27·43 E
168	Magaliesburg . . . . S. Afr.		
	(Johannesburg & Pretoria In.)	26·01 s	27·32 E
155	Magallanes (mä-gȧl-yä′näs)		
	Phil. (Manila In.)	12·48 N	123·52 E
100	Magallanes, Estrecho de (Str.)		
	(ĕs-trĕ′chŏ-dĕ-mä-gäl-yä′nĕs)		
	Arg.-Chile	52·30 s	68·45 W
98	Magangué (mä-gän′gä) . . . . . . Col.	9·08 N	74·56 W
155	Magat (R.) (mä-gät′)		
	Phil. (Manila In.)	16·45 N	121·16 E
101	Magdalena (mäg-dä-lā′nä)		
	Arg. (Buenos Aires In.)	35·05 s	57·32 W
98	Magdalena . . . . Bol.	13·17 s	63·57 W
62	Magdalena . . . . Mex.	30·34 N	110·50 W
69	Magdalena . . . . N. Mex.	34·10 N	107·45 W
100	Magdalena (I.) . . . . Chile	44·45 s	73·15 W
88	Magdalena, Bahía (B.)		
	(bä-ē′ä-mäg-dä-lā′nä) . Mex.	24·30 N	114·00 W
98	Magdalena, Rio (R.) . . . . Col.	7·45 N	74·04 W
83	Magdalen Is. (măg′dȧ-lĕn) . . Can.	47·27 N	61·25 W
120	Magdeburg (mäg′dĕ-bōōrgh) . Ger.	52·07 N	11·39 E
100	Magé (mä-zhä′) . . . . . . Braz. (In.)	22·39 s	43·02 W
126	Magenta (mȧ-jĕn′tä) . . . . It.	45·26 N	8·53 E
112	Magerøy (I.) (mä′ghĕr-ûĕ) . . Nor.	71·10 N	24·11 E
126	Maggiore, Lago di (L.) . . . . . . It.	46·03 N	8·25 E
168	Maghāghah . . U. A. R. (Nile In.)	28·38 N	30·50 E
90	Magiscatzin (mä-kĕs-kät-zēn′)		
	Mex.	22·48 N	98·42 W
127	Maglaj (mȧ′glä-ĕ) . . . . Yugo.	44·34 N	18·12 E
127	Maglić (mäg′lĕch) . . . . Yugo.	43·36 N	20·36 E
127	Maglie (mäl′yä) . . . . It.	40·06 N	18·20 E
74	Magna (măg′nä)		
	Utah (Salt Lake City In.)	40·43 N	112·06 W
136	Magnitogorsk (mäg-nyē′tŏ-		
	gŏrsk) . Sov. Un. (Urals In.)	53·26 N	59·05 E
73	Magnolia (măg-nō′lĭ-ȧ) . . . . . Ark.	33·16 N	93·13 W
84	Magnolia . . . . Md. (Baltimore In.)	39·24 N	76·19 W
78	Magnolia . . . . Miss.	31·08 N	90·27 W
123	Magny-en-Vexin (mä-nyē′		
	ĕⁿ-vĕ-săⁿ′).Fr. (Paris In.)	49·09 N	1·45 E
81	Magog (mȧ-gŏg′) . . . . Can.	45·15 N	72·10 W
82	Magpie (L.) (măg′pī) . . . . Can.	50·56 N	64·30 W
71	Magpie (R.) . . . . Can.	48·13 N	84·50 W
86	Magrath . . . . Can.	49·22 N	112·52 W
166	Magude (mä-gōō′dä) . . . . Moz.	24·58 s	32·39 E
146	Magwe (mŭg-wä′) . . . . Bur.	20·19 N	94·57 E
133	Mahabād . . . . Iran	36·55 N	45·50 E
165	Mahagi, Sungai (Strm.) . . . Indon.	0·30 s	116·15 E
167	Mahaly (mȧ-hȧl-ē′) . . . . Malagasy	24·09 s	46·20 E
154	Mahakam, Sungai (Strm.) . . Indon.	0·30 s	116·15 E
167	Mahaly (mȧ-hȧl-ē′) . . . . Malagasy	24·09 s	46·20 E
154	Mahameru, Gunung (Mtn.) . Java	8·00 s	112·50 E
142	Mahānadi (R.) (mȧ-hä-nŭd′ĕ)		
	India	20·50 N	84·27 E
167	Mahanoro (mä-hä-nô′rō).Malagasy	19·57 s	48·47 E
81	Mahanoy City (mä-hȧ-noi′) . . Pa.	40·50 N	76·10 W
142	Maharashtra (State) . . . . . . India	20·25 N	75·00 E
139	Mahasham (R.)		
	U. A. R. (Palestine In.)	30·08 N	34·09 E
167	Mahavavy (R.) (mä-hä-vä′vĕ)		
	Malagasy	17·42 s	46·06 E
142	Mahaweli (R.) . . . . Ceylon	7·47 N	80·43 E
113	Mahdia (mä-dē′ä) (mä′dĕ-ȧ).Tun.	35·30 N	11·09 E
143	Mahe (mä-ā′) . . . . India	11·42 N	75·39 E
167	Mahenge (mä-hĕn′gä) . . . . . . Tan.	8·41 s	36·43 E
142	Mahi (R.) . . . . India	23·16 N	73·20 E
143	Māhīm Bay . India (Bombay In.)	19·03 N	72·45 E
167	Mahlabatini (mä′lä-bä-tē′nĕ)		
	S. Afr. (Natal In.)	28·15 s	31·29 E
111	Mahlow (mä′lōv) Ger. (Berlin In.)	52·23 N	13·24 E
70	Mahnomen (mô-nō′mĕn) . . . Minn.	47·18 N	95·58 W
125	Mahón (mä-ōn′) . . . . Sp.	39·52 N	4·15 E
82	Mahone Bay (mȧ-hōn′) . . . . . Can.	44·27 N	64·24 W
82	Mahone B. . . . . Can.	44·27 N	64·05 W
84	Mahopac, L. (mä-hō′păk)		
	N. Y. (New York In.)	41·24 N	73·45 W
84	Mahwah (mȧ-wä′)		
	N. J. (New York In.)	41·05 N	74·09 W
110	Maidenhead (mād′ĕn-hĕd)		
	Eng. (London In.)	51·30 N	0·44 W
	Maidos, see Eceabat		
110	Maidstone (mād′stăn)		
	Eng. (London In.)	51·17 N	0·32 E
165	Maiduguri (mä′ē-dä-gōō′rĕ) . . Nig.	11·53 N	13·12 E
98	Maigualide Sierra (Mts.)		
	(sē-ĕ́r-rä-mī-gwä′lē-dĕ) . Ven.	6·30 N	65·50 W
142	Maijdi . . . . E. Pak.	22·59 N	91·08 E
	Maikop, see Maykop		
144	Maimana (mī-mä-nä′) . . . . . . Afg.	35·53 N	64·38 E
160	Main Barrier Ra. (băr′ĩer).Austl.	31·25 s	141·40 E
63	Maine (State) (mān) . . . . . . U. S.	45·25 N	69·50 W
116	Mainland (I.) (mān′lănd)		
	Scot. (In.)	60·19 N	2·40 W
120	Main R. (mīn) . . . . Ger.	49·49 N	9·20 E
123	Maintenon (măⁿ-t′nôⁿ′)		
	Fr. (Paris In.)	48·35 N	1·35 E
167	Maintirano (mä′ĕn-tĕ-rä′nō)		
	Malagasy	18·05 s	44·08 E
120	Mainz (mīnts) . . . . Ger.	49·59 N	8·16 E
164	Maio I. (mä′yō) . . C. V. Is. (In.)	15·15 N	22·50 W
101	Maipo (mī′pŏ) (R.)		
	Chile (Santiago In.)	33·45 s	71·08 W
100	Maipo (Vol.) . . . . Arg.	34·08 s	69·51 W
101	Maipú (mī′pōō′)		
	Arg. (Buenos Aires In.)	36·51 s	57·54 W
99	Maiquetía (mī-kĕ-tē′ä).Ven. (In.)	10·37 N	66·56 W
95	Maisí, Punta (Pt.)		
	(pōōn′n-tä-mī-sē′).Cuba	20·10 N	74·00 W

Page	Name Pronunciation Region	Lat. °′	Long. °′
123	Maison-Rouge (mä-zŏⁿ-rōōzh′)		
	Fr. (Paris In.)	48·34 N	3·09 E
168	Mait I. (mät)		
	Som. (Horn of Afr. In.)	11·24 N	46·38 E
160	Maitland (mät′lănd) . . . . Austl.	32·45 s	151·40 E
80	Maitland (R.) . . . . Can.	45·50 N	81·10 W
153	Maizuru (mä-i′zōō-rōō) . . . . . Jap.	35·26 N	135·15 E
	Majorca I., see Mallorca, Isle de		
167	Majunga (mȧ-jŭn′gä) . Malagasy	15·12 s	46·26 E
66	Makah Ind. Res. (mä ki′) . . Wash.	48·17 N	124·52 W
165	Mak'alē . . . . Eth.	13·31 N	39·19 E
167	Makanya (mä-kän′yä) . . . . . . Tan.	4·15 s	37·49 E
166	Makarikari Salt Pan (L.) . . Bech.	20·38 s	21·31 E
126	Makarska (mȧ′kär-skȧ) . . . . . Yugo.	43·17 N	17·05 E
132	Makar'yev . . . . Sov. Un.	57·50 N	43·48 E
154	Makasar . . . . Indon.	5·08 s	119·28 E
154	Makasar, Selat (Str.) (mȧ-käs′ẽr)		
	Indon.	2·00 s	118·07 E
153	Make (I.) (mä′kȧ) . . . . Jap.	30·43 N	130·49 E
129	Makeyevka (mŭk-yä′ŭf-kŭ)		
	Sov. Un.	48·03 N	38·00 E
133	Makhachkala (mäk′äch-kä′lä)		
	Sov. Un.	43·00 N	47·40 E
167	Makhaleng (R.) . . Bas. (Natal In.)	29·53 s	27·33 E
127	Makhlata (mäk′lä-tä) . . . . Bul.	43·27 N	24·16 E
144	Makkah (Mecca) (mĕk′ȧ).Sau. Ar.	21·27 N	39·45 E
87	Makkovik . . . . Can.	55·01 N	59·10 W
121	Makó (mŏ′kō) . . . . Hung.	46·13 N	20·30 E
164	Makokou (mä-kô-kōō′) . . . . Gabon	0·39 N	12·46 E
121	Maków Mazowiecki (mä′kŏov		
	mä-zō-vyĕts′kē) . Pol.	52·51 N	21·07 E
153	Makuhari (mä-kōō-hä′rē)		
	Jap. (Tōkyō In.)	35·39 N	140·04 E
153	Makurazaki (mä′kōō-rä-zä′kĕ) Jap.	31·16 N	130·18 E
164	Makurdi . . . . Nig.	7·44 N	8·34 E
64	Makushin (mä-kōō′shĭn) . . Alaska	53·57 N	166·28 W
134	Makushino (mä-kōō-shēn′ŏ)		
	Sov. Un.	55·03 N	67·43 E
143	Malabar Coast (măl′ȧ-bär) . . India	16·30 N	75·33 E
139	Malacca (mä-lăk′ȧ)		
	Mala. (Singapore In.)	2·11 N	102·15 E
139	Malacca (State)		
	Mala. (Singapore In.)	2·19 N	102·09 E
154	Malacca, Str. of (mȧ-lăk′ȧ) . . Asia	4·15 N	99·44 E
67	Malad (mȧ-lăd′) . . . . Idaho	42·11 N	112·15 W
125	Maladetta (Mts.) (mä-lä-dĕt′tä)		
	Sp.	42·30 N	0·38 E
125	Malafede (R.) (mä-lä-fĕ′dĕ)		
	It. (Roma In.)	41·43 N	12·28 E
98	Málaga (mä′lä-gȧ) . . . . Col.	6·41 N	72·46 W
124	Málaga . . . . Sp.	36·45 N	4·25 W
124	Málaga, Bahía de (B.)		
	(bä-ē′ä-dĕ-mä′lä-gä) . Col.	36·35 N	4·10 W
163	Malagasy . . . . Afr.	18·05 s	43·12 E
124	Malagón (mä-lä-gōn′) . . . . Sp.	39·12 N	3·52 W
159	Malaita (I.) (mȧ-lä′ē-tȧ) . . . Sol. Is.	8·38 s	161·15 E
165	Malakal (mä-lä-käl′) . . . . Sud.	9·46 N	31·54 E
136	Malakhovka (mä-läk′ŏf-kä)		
	Sov. Un. (Moskva In.)	55·38 N	38·01 E
166	Malange (mä-läng′gä) . . . . . . Ang.	9·30 s	16·15 E
82	Malapedia (R.) . . . . Can.	48·11 N	67·08 W
93	Mala Punta (Pt.) (pōō′n-tä-mä′lä)		
	Pan.	7·32 N	79·44 W
118	Mälaren (L.) . . . . Swe.	59·38 N	16·55 E
87	Malartic . . . . Can.	48·07 N	78·11 W
133	Malatya (mä-lä′tyä) . . . . Tur.	38·30 N	38·15 E
154	Malaya Vishera (vĕ-shä′rä)		
	Sov. Un.	58·51 N	32·13 E
128	Malaya Vishera (vĕ-shä′rä)		
	Sov. Un.	58·51 N	32·13 E
154	Malay Pen. (mȧ-lā′) (mä′lā).Asia	7·46 N	101·06 E
116	Mal B. (măl) . . . . Ire.	52·51 N	9·45 E
158	Malbon (măl′bŭn) . . . . Austl.	21·15 s	140·30 E
121	Malbork (mäl′bŏrk) . . . . Pol.	54·02 N	19·04 E
125	Malcabran (R.) (mäl-kä-brän′)		
	Port. (Lisboa In.)	38·47 N	8·46 W
83	Malden (môl′dĕn)		
	Mass. (Boston In.)	42·26 N	71·04 W
73	Malden . . . . Mo.	36·32 N	89·56 W
157	Malden (I.) . . . . Oceania	4·20 s	154·34 W
138	Maldive Is. (măl′dĭv) . . . . . . Asia	4·30 N	71·30 E
110	Maldon (môrl′dŏn)		
	Eng. (London In.)	51·44 N	0·39 E
100	Maldonado (mäl-dŏ-nä′dŏ) . . . Ur.	34·54 s	54·57 W
90	Maldonado, Punta (Pt.)		
	(pōō′n-tä) . Mex.	16·18 N	98·34 W
127	Maléa, Akr. (C.) . . . . Grc.	37·31 N	23·13 E
121	Male Karpaty (Mts.) . . . . . Czech.	48·31 N	17·15 E
159	Malekula (I.) (mä-lä-kōō′lä)		
	New Hebr.	16·44 s	167·45 E
124	Malhão da Estrêla (Mtn.)		
	(mäl-you′ɴ-dä-ĕs-trĕ′lä).Sp.	40·20 N	7·38 W
66	Malheur L. (mȧ-lōōr′) . . . . . . Ore.	43·16 N	118·37 W
66	Malheur R. (mȧ-lōōr′) . . . . . . Ore.	43·45 N	117·41 W
164	Mali . . . . Afr.	15·45 N	0·15 W
74	Malibu (mä′lĭ-bōō)		
	Calif. (Los Angeles In.)	34·03 N	118·38 W
129	Malin (mä-lēn′) . . . . Sov. Un.	50·44 N	29·15 E
90	Malinalco (mä-lē-näl′kō) . . . Mex.	18·54 N	99·31 W
90	Malinaltepec (mä-lē-näl-tä-pĕk′)		
	Mex.	17·01 N	98·41 W
167	Malindi (mä-lēn′dĕ) . . . . Ken.	3·14 s	40·04 E
121	Malineč (mä′lē-nyets′) . . . . Czech.	48·31 N	19·40 E
116	Malin Hd. . . . . N. Ire.	54·84 N	6·70 W
116	Malinmore Hd, (mä′lĭn-mōr).Ire.	54·45 N	8·30 W
136	Malino (mä′lĭ-nŏ)		
	Sov. Un. (Moskva In.)	55·07 N	38·12 E
129	Malinovka (mä-lē-nŏf′kä).Sov. Un.	49·50 N	36·43 E
127	Malkara (măl′kȧ-rä) . . . . Tur.	40·51 N	26·52 E
127	Malko Tŭrnovo		
	(mäl′kŏ-t′r′nŏ-vä).Bul.	41·59 N	27·28 E
116	Mallaig (măl′ăg) . . . . Scot.	56·59 N	5·55 W
168	Mallawī (mȧ-lä′wĕ)		
	U. A. R. (Nile In.)	27·43 N	30·49 E
75	Mallet Creek (măl′ĕt)		
	Ohio (Cleveland In.)	41·10 N	81·55 W

Page	Name Pronunciation Region	Lat. °′	Long. °′
125	Mallorca, Isla de (Majorca I.) (ē's-lä-dĕ-mäl-yô'r-kä). Sp.	39·18 N	2·22 E
116	Mallow (măl'ō) Ire.	52·07 N	9·04 W
117	Malmédy (màl-mā-dē') Bel.	50·25 N	6·01 E
166	Malmesbury (mämz'bēr-ĭ) S. Afr.	33·30 S	18·35 E
118	Malmköping (mälm'chû'pĭng) Swe.	59·09 N	16·39 E
118	Malmö (mälm'û) Swe.	55·36 N	12·58 E
135	Malmyzh (màl-mêzh') Sov. Un.	49·58 N	137·07 E
132	Malmyzh Sov. Un.	56·30 N	50·48 E
128	Maloarkhangelsk (mä'lô-är-kän'gĕlsk). Sov. Un.	52·26 N	36·29 E
155	Malolos (mä-lô'lôs) Phil. (Manila In.)	14·58 N	120·53 E
136	Malomal'sk (mà-lô-mälsk') Sov. Un. (Urals In.)	58·47 N	59·55 E
81	Malone (mà-lōn') N. Y.	44·50 N	74·20 W
128	Maloyaroslavets (mä'lô-yä-rô-slä-vyĕts). Sov. Un.	55·01 N	36·25 E
132	Malozemel'skaya Tundra (Plains) Sov. Un.	67·30 N	50·00 E
110	Malpas (măl'pàz) Eng.	53·01 N	2·46 W
98	Malpelo, Isla de (I.) (mäl-pä'lō) Col.	3·55 N	81·30 W
82	Malpeque B. (môl-pĕk') Can.	46·41 N	63·40 W
67	Malta (môl'tà) Mont.	48·20 N	107·50 W
113	Malta (I.) Eur.	35·52 N	14·26 E
166	Maltahöhe (mäl'tä-hō'ĕ) S. W. Afr.	24·45 S	16·45 E
85	Malton (môl'tŭn) Can. (Toronto In.)	43·42 N	79·39 W
91	Maltrata (mäl-trä'tä) Mex.	18·48 N	97·16 W
167	Maluti Mts. (mà-lōō-tĭ) Bas. (Natal In.)	29·00 S	28·29 E
143	Malvan India	16·08 N	73·32 E
73	Malvern (măl'vērn) Ark.	34·21 N	92·47 W
135	Malyy Anyuy (R.) Sov. Un.	67·52 N	164·30 E
135	Malyy Lyakhovskiye (I.) Sov. Un.	74·15 N	142·30 E
135	Malyy Tamir (I.) Sov. Un.	78·10 N	107·30 E
91	Mamantel (mä-màn-tĕl') Mex.	18·36 N	91·06 W
84	Mamaroneck (măm'à-rō-nĕk) N. Y. (New York In.)	40·57 N	73·44 W
164	Mamau Gui.	10·26 N	12·07 W
155	Mamberamo (R.) (mäm-bà-rä'mō). Neth. N. Gui.	2·30 S	138·00 E
155	Mamburao (mäm-bōō'rä-ō) Phil. (Manila In.)	13·14 N	120·35 E
124	Mamede, Serra de (Mts.) (sĕ'r-rä-dĕ-mä-mĕ'dĕ). Port.	39·29 N	7·11 W
164	Mamfe (mäm'fĕ) Nig.	9·06 E	5·52 N
153	Mamihara (mä'mê-hä-rä) Jap.	32·41 E	131·12 N
78	Mammoth Cave (măm'ŏth) Ky.	37·10 N	86·04 W
78	Mammoth Cave Natl. Park Ky.	37·20 N	86·21 W
67	Mammoth Hot Springs (măm'ŭth hôt sprĭngz). Wyo.	44·55 N	110·50 W
143	Mamnoli India (Bombay In.)	19·17 N	73·15 E
98	Mamoré (R.) (mä-mô-rā') Bol.	13·19 S	65·27 W
121	Mamry L. (mäm'rĭ) Pol.	54·10 N	21·28 E
139	Mamshit Isr. (Palestine In.)	31·02 N	35·04 E
125	Manacor (mä-nä-kôr') Sp.	39·35 N	3·15 E
95	Managua (mä-nä'gwä) Cuba (La Habana In.)	22·14 N	82·17 W
92	Managua Nic.	12·10 N	86·16 W
92	Managua, Lago de (L.) (lä'gô-dĕ) Nic.	12·28 N	86·10 W
167	Mananare (R.) (mä-nà-nä'rà) Malagasy	23·15 S	48·15 E
167	Mananjary (mä-nän-zhä'rē) Malagasy	20·16 S	48·13 E
	Manáos, see Manaus		
142	Manasaroar (L.) China	30·40 N	81·58 E
81	Manassas (mà-năs'às) Va.	38·45 N	77·30 W
99	Manaus (Manáos) (mä-nä'ōōzh) Braz.	3·01 S	60·00 W
80	Mancelona (măn-sê-lō'nà) Mich.	44·50 N	85·05 W
124	Mancha Real (män'chä rā-äl'). Sp.	37·48 N	3·37 W
136	Manchazh (män'chàsh) Sov. Un. (Urals In.)	56·30 N	58·10 E
81	Manchester (măn'chĕs-tēr) Conn.	41·45 N	72·30 W
110	Manchester Eng.	53·28 N	2·14 W
78	Manchester Ga.	32·50 N	84·37 W
71	Manchester Iowa	42·30 N	91·30 W
83	Manchester Mass. (Boston In.)	42·35 N	70·47 W
74	Manchester Mo. (St. Louis In.)	38·36 N	90·31 W
81	Manchester N. H.	43·00 N	71·30 W
80	Manchester Ohio	38·40 N	83·35 W
110	Manchester Ship Canal Eng.	53·20 N	2·40 W
	Manchouli, see Lupin		
147	Manchuria (Reg.) (măn-chōō'rē-à) China	48·00 N	124·58 E
144	Mand, Rud-e (R.) Iran	28·30 N	51·43 E
118	Mandal (män'däl) Nor.	58·03 N	7·28 E
146	Mandalay (măn'dà-lā) Bur.	22·00 N	96·08 E
118	Mandalselv (R.) (män'dälsĕlv) Nor.	58·25 N	7·30 E
70	Mandan (măn'dăn) N. D.	46·49 N	100·54 W
165	Mandara Mts. (män-dä'rä). Cam.	10·55 N	14·10 E
139	Mandau Siak (R.) Indon. (Singapore In.)	1·03 N	101·25 E
93	Mandinga (män-dĭŋ'gä) Pan.	9·32 N	79·04 W
142	Mandla India	22·43 N	80·23 E
127	Mándra (män'drä) Grc.	38·06 N	23·32 E
167	Mandritsara (màn-drēt-sä'rà) Malagasy	15·49 S	48·47 E
127	Manduria (män-dōō'rē-ä) It.	40·23 N	17·41 E
143	Mandve India (Bombay In.)	18·47 N	72·52 E
143	Māndvi (mŭnd'vē) India (Bombay In.)	19·29 N	72·53 E
142	Māndvi (mŭnd'vē) India	22·54 N	69·23 E
168	Manfalūţ (män-fà-loot') U. A. R. (Nile In.)	27·18 N	30·59 E
126	Manfredonia (män-frâ-dô'nyä). It.	41·39 N	15·55 E
126	Manfredónia, Golfo di (G.) (gôl-fô-dē). It.	41·34 N	16·05 E
99	Mangabeiras, Chap. das (Plains) (shä-pä'däs-däs-mäŋ-gä-bā'ē-räzh). Braz.	8·05 S	47·32 W
143	Mangalore (mŭŋ-gŭ-lōr') India	12·53 N	74·52 E
101	Mangaratiba (män-gä-rä-tē'bà) Braz. (Rio de Janeiro In.)	22·56 S	44·03 W
155	Mangatarem (män'gà-tä'rĕm) Phil. (Manila In.)	15·48 N	120·18 E
155	Mangguli (I.) (män-gōō-lē'). Indon.	1·35 S	126·22 E
154	Mangkalihat, Tandjoeng (C.) (mäng'kà-lē-hät'). Indon.	1·25 N	119·55 E
94	Mangles, Islas de (ē's-läs-dĕ-mäŋ'gläs) (măn'g'lz) Cuba	22·05 N	83·50 W
167	Mangoky (R.) (män-gō'kē) Malagasy	22·02 S	44·11 E
124	Mangualde (män-gwäl'dĕ) Port.	40·38 N	7·44 W
100	Mangueira, L. da (L.) (män-gā'ē-rà). Braz.	33·15 S	52·45 W
72	Mangum (măŋ'gŭm) Okla.	34·52 N	99·31 W
133	Mangyshlak, P.-ov. (Pen.) Sov. Un.	44·30 N	50·40 E
75	Manhattan Ill. (Chicago In.)	41·25 N	87·29 W
73	Manhattan (măn-hăt'ăn) Kans.	39·11 N	96·34 W
74	Manhattan Beach Calif. (Los Angeles In.)	33·53 N	118·24 W
101	Manhuaçu (män-ōōà'sōō) Braz. (Rio de Janeiro In.)	20·17 S	42·01 W
101	Manhumirim (män-ōō-mê-rē'ɴ) Braz. (Rio de Janeiro In.)	20·22 S	41·57 W
167	Mania (R.) (män'yä) Malagasy	19·52 S	46·02 E
99	Manicoré (mä-nê-kō-rā') Braz.	5·53 S	61·13 W
87	Manicouagan (R.) Can.	50·24 N	68·29 W
99	Manicuare (mä-nē-kwä'rĕ) Ven. (In.)	10·35 N	64·10 W
157	Manihiki Is. (mä'nē-hē'kê) Oceania	9·40 S	158·00 W
155	Manila (mà-nĭl'à) Phil. (Manila In.)	14·37 N	121·00 E
155	Manila B. Phil. (Manila In.)	14·38 N	120·46 E
133	Manisa (mä'nê-sà) Tur.	38·40 N	27·30 E
80	Manistee (măn-ĭs-tē') Mich.	44·15 N	86·20 W
80	Manistee (R.) Mich.	44·25 N	85·45 W
71	Manistique (măn-ĭs-tēk') Mich.	45·58 N	86·16 W
71	Manistique (L.) Mich.	46·14 N	85·30 W
71	Manistique (R.) Mich.	46·05 N	86·09 W
86	Manitoba (Prov.) (măn-ĭ-tō'bà) Can.	55·12 N	97·29 W
86	Manitoba (L.) Can.	50·38 N	98·40 W
72	Manitou (măn'ĭ-tōō) Colo.	38·51 N	104·58 W
71	Manitou (I.) Mich.	47·21 N	87·33 W
71	Manitou (L.) Can.	49·21 N	93·01 W
80	Manitou Is. Mich.	45·05 N	86·00 W
80	Manitoulin I. (măn-ĭ-tōō'lĭn). Can.	45·45 N	81·30 W
71	Manitowoc (măn-ĭ-tô-wŏk'). Wis.	44·05 N	87·42 W
98	Manizales (mä-nê-zä'läs). Col. (In.)	5·05 N	75·31 W
166	Manjacaze (man'yä-kä'zĕ) Moz.	24·37 S	33·49 E
144	Manjil (mŭn-jēl') Iran	36·45 N	49·15 E
142	Mānjra (R.) India	18·18 N	77·00 E
72	Mankato (măn-kā'tō) Kans.	39·45 N	98·12 W
71	Mankato Minn.	44·10 N	93·59 W
125	Manlleu (män-lyā'ōō) Sp.	42·00 N	2·16 E
161	Manly (măn'lĭ) Austl. (Sydney In.)	33·48 S	151·16 E
143	Mannar (mà-när') Ceylon	9·48 N	80·03 E
142	Mannar, G. of India	8·47 N	78·33 E
111	Mannersdorf am Leithagebirge Aus. (Wien In.)	47·58 N	16·36 E
120	Mannheim (män'hīm) Ger.	49·30 N	8·31 E
71	Manning (măn'ĭng) Iowa	41·53 N	95·04 W
79	Manning S. C.	33·41 N	80·12 W
80	Mannington (măn'ĭng-tŭn). W. Va.	39·30 N	80·55 W
126	Mannu (R.) (mä'n-nōō) It.	39·32 N	9·03 E
95	Man of War B. Ba. Is.	21·05 N	74·05 W
95	Man of War Chan. Ba. Is.	22·45 N	76·10 W
155	Manokwari (mà-nŏk-wä'rē) Neth. N. Gui.	0·56 S	134·10 E
65	Manor (măn'ēr) Wash. (Portland In.)	45·45 N	122·36 W
143	Manori India (Bombay In.)	19·13 N	72·43 E
123	Manosque (mà-nôsh') Fr.	43·51 N	5·48 E
85	Manotick Can. (Ottawa In.)	45·13 N	75·41 W
125	Manresa (män-rā'sä) Sp.	41·44 N	1·52 E
87	Mansel (I.) (măn'sĕl) Can.	61·56 N	81·10 W
98	Manseriche, Pongo de (Water Gap) (pŏ'n-gô-dĕ-män-sĕ-rē'chĕ). Peru	4·15 S	77·45 W
110	Mansfield (mănz'fēld) Eng.	53·08 N	1·12 W
77	Mansfield La.	32·02 N	93·43 W
80	Mansfield Ohio	40·45 N	82·30 W
66	Mansfield Wash.	47·48 N	119·39 W
81	Mansfield, Mt. Vt.	44·30 N	72·45 W
110	Mansfield Woodhouse (wŏŏd-hous). Eng.	53·08 N	1·12 W
98	Manta (män'tä) Ec.	1·03 S	80·16 W
75	Manteno (măn-tē-nō) Ill. (Chicago In.)	41·15 N	87·50 W
123	Mantes-la-Jolie (mäɴt-ĕ-là-zhō-lē') Fr. (Paris In.)	48·59 N	1·42 E
69	Manti (măn'tī) Utah	39·15 N	111·40 W
101	Mantiqueira, Serra da (Mts.) (sĕr'rà dä män-tê-kā'ē-rà) Braz. (Rio de Janeiro In.)	22·40 S	45·12 W
126	Mantova (Mantua) (män'tô-vä) (măn'tû-à). It.	45·09 N	10·47 E
94	Mantua (män-tōō'á) Cuba	22·20 N	84·15 W
74	Mantua (măn'tû-à) Utah (Salt Lake City In.)	41·30 N	111·57 W
	Mantua, see Mantova		
82	Manuan (L.) (mà-nōō'àn) Can.	50·36 N	70·50 W
82	Manuan, Riviere (R.) Can.	49·50 N	70·55 W
155	Manui (Is.) (mà-nōō'ē) Indon.	3·35 S	123·38 E
155	Manus (I.) (mä'nōōs). N. Gui. Ter.	2·22 S	146·22 E
77	Manvel (măn'vĕl) Tex. (In.)	29·28 N	95·22 W
84	Manville (măn'vĭl) N. J. (New York In.)	40·33 N	74·36 W
84	Manville R. I. (Providence In.)	41·57 N	71·27 W
133	Manych (R.) (mä-nĭch'). Sov. Un.	47·00 N	41·10 E
103	Manych Dep. Sov. Un.	46·32 N	42·44 E
133	Manych-Gudilo (Lake) Sov. Un.	46·40 N	42·50 E
168	Manzala L. U. A. R. (Nile In.)	31·14 N	32·04 E
98	Manzanares (män-sä-nä'rĕs) Col. (In.)	5·15 N	75·09 W
125	Manzanares (R.) (mänz-nä'rĕs) Sp. (Madrid In.)	40·36 N	3·48 W
125	Manzanares, Canal de (kä-nä'l-dĕ-män-thä-nä'rĕs) Sp. (Madrid In.)	40·20 N	3·38 W
94	Manzanillo (män'zä-nēl'yō). Cuba	20·20 N	77·05 W
90	Manzanillo Mex.	19·02 N	104·21 W
95	Manzanillo, Bahía de (B.) Hai.	19·55 N	71·50 W
90	Manzanillo, Bahía de (B.) (bä-ē'ä-dĕ-män-zä-nē'l-yō). Mex.	19·00 N	104·38 W
165	Mao (mä'ō) Chad	14·07 N	15·15 E
151	Maoming China	21·55 N	110·40 E
91	Mapastepec (mä-päs-tà-pĕk'). Mex.	15·24 N	92·52 W
155	Mapia (I.) (mä'pē-ä) Neth. N. Gui.	0·57 N	134·22 E
76	Mapimi (mä-pê-mē') Mex.	25·50 N	103·50 W
85	Maple (mā'p'l). Can. (Toronto In.)	43·51 N	79·30 W
86	Maple Creek (crēk) Can.	49·52 N	109·32 W
85	Maple Grove (grōv) Can. (Montreal In.)	45·19 N	73·51 W
75	Maple Heights Ohio (Cleveland In.)	41·25 N	81·34 W
84	Maple Shade (shād) N. J. (Philadelphia In.)	39·57 N	75·01 W
65	Maple Valley (văl'ē) Wash. (Seattle In.)	47·24 N	122·02 W
74	Maplewood (wŏŏd) Mo. (St. Louis In.)	38·37 N	90·20 W
74	Maplewood Park (wŏŏd pärk) Ill. (St. Louis In.)	38·34 N	90·11 W
167	Mapumulo (mä-pä-mōō'lō) S. Afr. (Natal In.)	29·12 S	31·05 E
155	Maqueda Chan. (mä-kā'dä) Phil. (Manila In.)	13·40 N	123·52 E
166	Maquela do Zombo (mà-kā'là dŏŏ zôm'bŏŏ). Ang.	6·08 S	15·15 E
71	Maquoketa (mà-kō-kê-tà) Iowa	42·04 N	90·42 W
71	Maquoketa (R.) Iowa	42·08 N	90·40 W
100	Mar, Serra do (Mts.) (sĕr'rà dōō mär'). Braz.	26·30 S	49·15 W
98	Maracaibo (mä-rä-kī'bō) Ven.	10·38 N	71·45 W
98	Maracaibo, Lago de (L.) (lä'gô-dĕ-mä-rä-kī'bō). Ven.	9·55 N	72·13 W
99	Maracay (mä-rä-kāy'). Ven. (In.)	10·15 N	67·35 W
165	Marādah Libya	29·10 N	19·07 E
164	Maradi (mà-rà-dē') Niger	13·30 N	7·11 E
133	Marāgheh Iran	37·20 N	46·10 E
167	Maraisburg S. Afr. (Johannesburg & Pretoria In.)	26·12 S	27·57 E
99	Marajó, Ilha de (I.) (mä-rä-zhō') Braz.	0·30 S	50·00 W
166	Marandelles (mä-ràn-dĕl'ās) Fed. of Rh. & Nya.	18·08 S	31·36 E
99	Maranguape (mä-ràŋ-gwä'pĕ) Braz.	3·48 S	38·38 W
	Maranhão, see São Luis		
99	Maranhão (State) (mä-rän-youɴ) Braz.	5·15 S	45·52 W
160	Maranoa (R.) (mä-rä-nō'ä). Austl.	27·01 S	148·03 E
125	Marano di Napoli (mä-rä'nô-dē-nä'pô-lē) It. (Napoli In.)	40·39 N	14·12 E
98	Marañón, Rio (R.) (rē'ō-mä-rä-nyōn'). Peru	4·26 S	75·08 W
99	Marapanim (mä-rä-pä-nē'ɴ) Braz.	0·45 S	47·42 W
133	Maras (mä-räsh') Tur.	37·40 N	36·50 E
79	Marathon (măr'à-thŏn). Fla. (In.)	24·41 N	81·06 W
75	Marathon Ohio (Cincinnati In.)	39·09 N	83·59 W
154	Maratua (I.) Indon.	2·14 N	118·30 E
90	Maravatio (mä-rä-vä'tê-ō) Mex.	19·54 N	100·25 W
158	Marble Bar (märb''l bär) Austl.	21·15 S	119·15 E
69	Marble Can. (mär'b'l) Ariz.	36·21 N	111·48 W
168	Marble Hall (hâll) S. Afr. (Johannesburg & Pretoria In.)	24·59 S	29·19 E
83	Marblehead (mär'b'l-hĕd) Mass. (Boston In.)	42·30 N	70·51 W
120	Marburg (mär'bŏŏrgh) Ger.	50·49 N	8·46 E
92	Marcala (mär-kä-lä) Hond.	14·08 N	88·01 W
126	Marche (Reg.) (mär'kā) It.	43·35 N	12·33 E
111	Marchegg Aus. (Wien In.)	48·18 N	16·55 E
124	Marchena (mär-chā'nä) Sp.	37·20 N	5·25 W
98	Marchena (I.) (ē's-lä-mär-chĕ'nä) Ec.	0·29 N	90·31 W
74	March Field (märch) Calif. (Los Angeles In.)	33·54 N	117·17 W
73	Marceline (mär-sê-lēn') Mo.	39·42 N	92·56 W
101	Marcos Paz (mär-kōs' päz) Arg. (Buenos Aires In.)	34·49 S	58·51 W
156	Marcus (I.) (mär'kŭs) Asia	24·00 N	155·00 E
84	Marcus Hook (mär'kŭs hŏŏk) Pa. (Philadelphia In.)	39·49 N	75·25 W
81	Marcy, Mt. (mär'sê) N. Y.	44·10 N	73·55 W
101	Mar de Espanha (mär-dĕ-ĕs-pä'nyà) Braz. (Rio de Janeiro In.)	21·53 S	43·00 W
100	Mar del Plata (mär dĕl plä'tä) Arg.	37·59 S	57·35 W
133	Mardin (mär-dēn') Tur.	37·25 N	40·40 E
159	Mare (I.) (mà-rā') N. Cal.	21·53 S	168·30 E
116	Maree (L.) (mà-rē') Scot.	57·40 N	5·44 W
71	Marengo (mà-rĕŋ'gō) Iowa	41·47 N	92·04 W
122	Marennes (mà-rĕn') Fr.	45·49 N	1·08 W
123	Mareuil-sur-Ourcq (mä-rû'yĕ-sür-ōōrk'). Fr. (Paris In.)	49·08 N	2·04 E
76	Marfa (mär'fà) Tex.	30·19 N	104·01 W
129	Marganets Sov. Un.	47·41 N	34·33 E

ng-sing; ŋ-baŋk; ɴ-nasalized n; nŏd; cŏmmit; ōld; ôbey; ôrder; fōōd; fŏŏt; ou-out; s-soft; sh-dish; th-thin; pūre; ûnite; ûrn; stŭd; circŭs; ü-as "y" in study; '-indeterminate vowel.

234 Margarita—Mataro PRONOUNCING INDEX

Page	Name Pronunciation Region	Lat. °′	Long. °′
88	Margarita (mär-gōō-rē'tä) C.Z. (Panama Canal In.)	9·20 N	79·55 W
99	Margarita, Isla de (I.) (mär-gȧ-rē'tä) . Ven. (In.)	11·00 N	64·15 W
116	Margate (mär'gāt) Eng.	51·21 N	1·17 E
.167	Margate (mär-gāt') S. Afr. (Natal In.)	30·52 S	30·21 E
82	Marguerite, Riviere (R.) Can.	50·36 N	66·40 W
132	Mari (A. S. S. R.) (mä'rê) . Sov. Un.	56·20 N	48·00 E
82	Maria (mȧ-rē'ȧ) Can.	48·10 N	66·04 W
124	Maria, Sierra de (Mts.) (sē-ĕ'r-rä-dĕ-mä-ryä) . Sp.	37·42 N	2·25 W
90	María Cleofas (I.) (mä-rē'ä klā'ô-fäs) . Mex.	21·17 N	106·14 W
118	Mariager (mä-rê-ägh'ĕr) Den.	56·38 N	10·00 E
118	Mariager Fd Den.	56·44 N	10·32 E
90	Maria Madre Mex.	21·43 N	106·17 W
90	María Magdalena (I.) (mä rē'ä mäg-dä-lā'nä) . Mex.	21·25 N	106·23 W
101	Mariana (mä-ryà'nä) Braz. (Rio de Janeiro In.)	20·23 S	43·24 W
156	Mariana Is. (mä-rê-ä'nà) Pac. Is. Trust. Ter.	17·20 N	145·00 E
156	Mariana Trench Oceania	12·00 N	144·00 E
95	Marianao (mä-rê-ä-nä'ō) Cuba (La Habana In.)	23·05 N	82·26 W
73	Marianna (mā-rĭ-ăn'ȧ) Ark.	34·45 N	90·45 W
78	Marianna Fla.	30·46 N	85·14 W
75	Marianna .... Pa. (Pittsburgh In.)	40·01 N	80·05 W
100	Mariano Acosta (mä-rêä'nô-ä-kôs'tä) . Arg. (In.)	34·28 S	58·48 W
120	Mariánské Lázně (mär'yán-skĕ'läz'nyĕ) . Czech.	49·58 N	12·42 E
67	Marias R. (mȧ-rī'ăz) Mont.	48·17 N	111·47 W
118	Maribo (mä'rê-bô Den.	54·46 N	11·29 E
126	Maribor (mä're-bôr) Yugo.	46·33 N	15·37 E
101	Maricá (mä-rē-kä') Braz. (Rio de Janeiro In.)	22·55 S	42·49 W
155	Maricaban (I.) (mä-rê-kä-bän') Phil. (Manila In.)	13·40 N	120·44 E
168	Marico R. (mä'rĭ-cô) S. Afr. (Johannesburg & Pretoria In.)	24·53 S	26·22 E
47	Marie Byrd Land (mà rē' bûrd') Ant.	78·00 S	130·00 W
118	Mariefred (mä-rē'ĕ-frĭd) Swe.	59·17 N	17·09 E
93	Marie Galante I. (mà-rē' gà-länt') Guad. (Le. & Wind. Is. In.)	15·58 N	61·05 W
	Mariehamn, see Maarianhamina		
118	Mariestad (mä-rē'ĕ-ståd') Swe.	58·43 N	13·45 E
84	Marietta (mā-rĭ-ĕt'ȧ) Ga. (Atlanta In.)	33·57 N	84·33 W
80	Marietta Ohio	39·25 N	81·30 W
73	Marietta Okla.	33·53 N	97·07 W
65	Marietta .. Wash. (Vancouver In.)	48·48 N	122·35 W
134	Mariinsk (mà-re'ĭnsk) Sov. Un.	56·15 N	87·28 E
119	Marijampole (mä-rê-yäm-pô'lĕ) Sov. Un.	54·33 N	23·26 E
168	Marikana (mă'-rĭ-kä-nȧ) S. Afr. (Johannesburg & Pretoria In.)	25·40 S	27·28 E
99	Marília (mä-rē'lyä) Braz.	22·02 S	49·48 W
155	Marinduque (I.) (mä-rên-dōō'kä) Phil. (Manila In.)	13·14 N	121·45 E
74	Marine (mà-rēn') Ill. (St. Louis In.)	38·48 N	89·47 W
74	Marine Minn. (Minneapolis, St. Paul In.)	45·11 N	92·51 W
80	Marine City Mich.	42·45 N	82·30 W
74	Marine L. Minn. (Minneapolis, St. Paul In.)	45·13 N	92·55 W
74	Marine on St. Croix (ăn sĕn krōō-ä) Minn. (Minneapolis, St. Paul In.)	45·11 N	92·47 W
71	Marinette (măr-ĭ-nĕt') Wis.	45·05 N	87·40 W
165	Maringa R. (mä-riŋ'gä) ... Con. L.	0·30 N	21·08 E
124	Marinha Grande (mä-rēn'yȧ grän'dĕ) . Port.	39·49 N	8·53 W
78	Marion (măr'ĭ-ŭn) Ala.	32·36 N	87·19 W
80	Marion Ill.	37·40 N	88·55 W
80	Marion Ind.	40·35 N	85·45 W
71	Marion Iowa	42·01 N	91·39 W
73	Marion Kans.	38·21 N	97·02 W
78	Marion Ky.	37·19 N	88·05 W
79	Marion N. C.	35·40 N	82·00 W
70	Marion N. D.	46·37 N	98·20 W
80	Marion Ohio	40·35 N	83·10 W
79	Marion S. C.	34·08 N	79·23 W
79	Marion Va.	36·48 N	81·33 W
79	Marion (R.) S. C.	33·25 N	80·35 W
159	Marion Rf Austl.	18·57 S	151·31 E
101	Mariposa (mä-rê-pō'sä) Chile (Santiago In.)	35·33 S	71·21 W
68	Mariposa Cr Calif.	37·14 N	120·30 W
98	Mariquita (mä-rē-kē'tä).Col. (In.)	5·13 N	74·52 W
99	Mariscal Estigarribia (mä-rēs-käl'ĕs-tē-gär-rē'byä) Par.	22·03 S	60·28 W
100	Marisco, Ponta do (Pt.) (pô'n-tä-dô-mä-rē's-kō) Braz. (In.)	23·01 S	43·17 W
123	Maritime Alps (Mts.) (mà'rĭ-tīm ălps) . Fr.-It.	44·20 N	7·02 E
127	Maritsa (R.) (mä'rê-tsȧ) . Gr.-Tur.	40·43 N	26·19 E
155	Mariveles ...... Phil. (Manila In.)	14·27 N	120·29 E
139	Marj Uyan ... Leb. (Palestine In.)	33·21 N	35·36 E
146	Marka Kul' (L.) Sov. Un.	49·15 N	85·48 E
118	Markaryd (mär'kä-rüd) Swe.	56·30 N	13·34 E
73	Marked Tree (märkt trē) ... Ark.	35·31 N	90·26 W
111	Marken, I. Neth. (Amsterdam In.)	52·26 N	5·08 E
110	Market Bosworth (bŏz'wûrth) Eng.	52·37 N	1·23 W
110	Market Deeping (dēp'ĭng) ... Eng.	52·40 N	0·19 W
110	Market Drayton (drā'tŭn) ... Eng.	52·54 N	2·29 W
110	Market Harborough (här'bŭr-ô) Eng.	52·28 N	0·55 W
110	Market Rasen (rā'zĕn) Eng.	53·23 N	0·21 W
85	Markham (märk'ȧm) Can. (Toronto In.)	43·53 N	79·15 W
47	Markham, Mt Ant.	82·59 S	159·30 E
129	Markovka (mär-kôf'kä) .. Sov. Un.	49·32 N	39·34 E
135	Markovo (mär'kô-vô) ... Sov. Un.	64·46 N	170·48 E
142	Markrāna India	27·08 N	74·43 E
133	Marks Sov. Un.	51·40 N	46·40 E
77	Marksville (märks'vĭl) La.	31·09 N	92·05 W
111	Markt Indersdorf (märkt ĕn'dĕrs-dōrf) Ger. (München In.)	48·22 N	11·23 E
120	Marktredwitz (märk-rĕd'vēts).Ger.	50·02 N	12·05 E
111	Markt Schwaben (märkt shvä'bĕn) Ger. (München In.)	48·12 N	11·52 E
123	Marl (märl) ...... Ger. (Ruhr In.)	51·40 N	7·05 E
83	Marlboro (märl'bŭr-ô) Mass. (Boston In.)	42·21 N	71·33 W
84	Marlboro ... N. J. (New York In.)	40·18 N	74·15 W
80	Marlette (mär-lĕt') Mich.	43·25 N	83·05 W
77	Marlin (mär'lĭn) Tex.	31·18 N	96·52 W
81	Marlinton (mär'lĭn-tŭn) ... W. Va.	38·15 N	80·10 W
110	Marlow (mär'lō) Eng. (London In.)	51·33 N	0·46 W
72	Marlow Okla.	34·38 N	97·56 W
94	Marls, The (Shoals) (märls) . Ba. Is.	26·30 N	77·15 W
143	Marmagoā India	15·09 N	73·58 E
122	Marmande (mår-mänd') Fr.	44·30 N	0·10 E
127	Marmara (I.) (mär'mà-rȧ) ... Tur.	40·38 N	27·35 E
133	Marmara Denizi (Sea) Tur.	40·40 N	28·00 E
70	Marmarth (mär'mårth) N. D.	46·19 N	103·57 W
91	Mar Muerto (L.) (mär-mōōĕ'r-tô) Mex.	16·13 N	94·22 W
111	Marne (mär'nĕ) Ger. (Hamburg In.)	53·57 N	9·01 E
122	Marne (R.) (märn) Fr.	49·08 N	3·39 E
124	Marnia (mår-nyä) Alg.	35·07 N	2·10 W
98	Maroa (mä-rō'ä) Ven.	2·43 N	67·37 W
167	Maroantsetra (mà-rō-äŋ-tsä'trà) Malagasy	15·18 S	49·48 E
98	Maro Jarapeto (Mtn.) (mä-rô-hä-rä-pĕ'tô) . Col. (In.)	6·29 N	76·39 W
167	Maromokotro (Mtn.) ... Malagasy	14·00 S	49·11 E
99	Maroni (R.) (mà-rō'nê) Fr. Gu.-Sur.	3·02 N	53·54 W
165	Maroua (mär'wä) Cam.	10·41 N	14·14 E
110	Marple (mär'p'l) Eng.	53·24 N	2·04 W
168	Marquard S. Afr. (Johannesburg & Pretoria In.)	28·41 S	27·26 E
157	Marquesas Is. (mär-kĕ'säs) Fr. Polynesia	8·50 S	141·00 W
79	Marquesas Keys (Is.) (mår-kē'zȧs) Fla. (In.)	24·37 N	82·15 W
101	Marquês de Valença (mår-kĕ's-dĕ-vä-lĕ'n-sä) Braz. (Rio de Janeiro In.)	22·16 S	43·42 W
85	Marquette (mår-kĕt') Can. (Winnipeg In.)	50·04 N	97·43 W
71	Marquette Mich.	46·32 N	87·25 W
77	Marquez (mär-käz') Tex.	31·14 N	96·15 W
165	Marra, Jebel (Mt.) (jĕb'ĕl mär'ä) Sud.	13·00 N	23·47 E
164	Marrakech (mår-rä'kĕsh) .... Mor.	31·38 N	8·00 W
160	Marree (măr'rē) Austl.	29·38 S	137·55 E
124	Marroqui, Pta. (mä-rō-kē') ... Sp.	36·03 N	5·36 W
75	Mars (märz) .. Pa. (Pittsburgh In.)	40·42 N	80·01 W
165	Marsá al Buraygah Libya	30·25 N	19·20 E
165	Marsa Fatma Eth.	14·54 N	40·14 E
126	Marsala (mär-sä'lä) It.	37·48 N	12·28 E
111	Marschfeld (Reg.) Aus. (Wien In.)	48·14 N	16·37 E
110	Marsden (märz'dĕn) Eng.	53·36 N	1·55 W
122	Marseille (mår-sâ'y') Fr. (Marseille In.)	43·18 N	5·25 E
122	Marseille, Canal de (mår-sâ-yaN') Fr. (Marseille In.)	43·34 N	5·16 E
80	Marseilles (mär-sĕlz') Ill.	41·20 N	88·40 W
80	Marshall (mär'shȧl) Ill.	39·20 N	87·40 W
80	Marshall Mich.	42·20 N	84·55 W
70	Marshall Minn.	44·28 N	95·49 W
73	Marshall Mo.	39·07 N	93·12 W
77	Marshall Tex.	32·33 N	94·22 W
156	Marshall Is. ... Pac. Is. Trust Ter.	10·00 N	165·00 E
71	Marshalltown (mär'shȧl-toun) Iowa	42·02 N	92·55 W
78	Marshallville (mär'shȧl-vĭl) ... Ga.	32·29 N	83·55 W
83	Marshfield (märsh'fēld) Mass. (Boston In.)	42·06 N	70·43 W
73	Marshfield Mo.	37·20 N	92·53 W
71	Marshfield Wis.	44·40 N	90·10 W
94	Marsh Harbour Ba. Is.	26·30 N	77·00 W
75	Mars Hill (märz' hĭl') Ind. (Indianapolis In.)	39·43 N	86·15 W
82	Mars Hill Maine	46·34 N	67·54 W
82	Marsqui Can.	49·13 N	66·08 W
118	Marstrand (mär'stränd) Swe.	57·54 N	11·33 E
136	Marsyaty (märs'yà-tĭ) Sov. Un. (Urals In.)	60·03 N	60·28 E
77	Mart (märt) Tex.	31·32 N	96·49 W
154	Martaban, G. of (mär-tŭ-bän') Bur.	16·34 N	96·58 E
154	Martapura Indon.	3·19 S	114·45 E
86	Marten Hills Can.	55·40 N	114·09 W
81	Marthas Vineyard (I.) (mär'thȧz vĭn'yȧrd) . Mass.	41·25 N	70·35 W
94	Martí (mär-tē') Cuba	23·00 N	80·55 W
120	Martigny-Bourg (mår-tē-nyē') Switz.	46·06 N	7·00 E
122	Martigues (mår-tēg') Fr. (Marseille In.)	43·24 N	5·05 E
78	Martin (mär'tĭn) Tenn.	36·20 N	88·45 W
78	Martin (R.) Ala.	32·40 N	86·05 W
127	Martina Franca (mär-tē'nä frăŋ'kä) . It.	40·43 N	17·21 E
74	Martin City (mär-tĭn sĭ'tĭ) Mo. (Kansas City In.)	38·53 N	94·35 W
65	Martinez (mär-tē'nĕz) Calif. (San Francisco In.)	38·01 N	122·08 W
74	Martinez .. Tex. (San Antonio In.)	29·25 N	98·20 W
87	Martin Falls (mär'tĭn) Can.	51·35 N	86·40 W
93	Martinique I. (mår-tê-nēk') N. A. (Le. & Wind. Is. In.)	14·30 N	60·37 W
81	Martinsburg (mär'tĭnz-bûrg) W. Va.	39·30 N	78·00 W
80	Martins Ferry (mär'tĭnz) .... Ohio	40·05 N	80·45 W
80	Martinsville (mär'tĭnz-vĭl) .... Ind.	39·25 N	86·25 W
79	Martinsville Va.	36·40 N	79·53 W
124	Martos (mär'tōs) Sp.	37·43 N	3·58 W
86	Martre, Lac la (L.) (läk la märtr) . Can.	63·24 N	119·58 W
153	Marugame (mä'rōō-gä'mā) ... Jap.	34·19 N	133·48 E
118	Mårvatn (L.) (môr-vät'n) ... Nor.	60·10 N	8·28 E
124	Marvín (mär-vē'n) Sp.	42·24 N	8·40 W
103	Mary (mä'rê) Sov. Un.	37·45 N	61·47 E
129	Mar'yanskaya (mår-yän'skà-yà) Sov. Un.	45·04 N	38·39 E
160	Maryborough (mā'rĭ-bŭr-ô) . Austl.	25·35 S	152·40 E
160	Maryborough Austl.	37·00 S	143·50 E
63	Maryland (State) (mĕr'ĭ-lȧnd) U. S.	39·10 N	76·25 W
66	Mary's R. (mā'rĭz) Nev.	41·25 N	115·10 W
83	Marystown (mā'rĭz-toun) .... Can.	47·11 N	55·11 W
82	Marysville Can.	45·59 N	66·40 W
68	Marysville (mā'rĭz-vĭl) Calif.	39·09 N	121·37 W
73	Marysville Kans.	39·49 N	96·38 W
80	Marysville Ohio	40·15 N	83·25 W
65	Marysville Wash. (Seattle In.)	48·03 N	122·11 W
168	Maryūţ (L.) ... U. A. R. (Nile In.)	31·09 N	30·10 E
74	Maryville (mā'rĭ-vĭl) Ill. (St. Louis In.)	38·44 N	89·57 W
73	Maryville Mo.	40·21 N	94·51 W
78	Maryville Tenn.	35·44 N	83·59 W
165	Mārzuq Libya	26·00 N	14·09 E
163	Masai Steppe Tan.	5·05 S	36·16 E
154	Masalembo (I.) Indon.	5·40 S	114·28 E
152	Masan (mä-sän') Kor.	35·10 N	128·31 E
167	Masasi (mä-sä'sê) Tan.	10·41 S	38·05 E
92	Masatepe (mä-sä-tĕ'pĕ) Nic.	11·57 N	86·10 W
92	Masaya (mä-sä'yä) Nic.	11·58 N	86·05 W
155	Masbate (mäs-bä'tä) Phil. (Manila In.)	12·21 N	123·38 E
155	Masbate (I.) .. Phil. (Manila In.)	12·19 N	123·03 E
164	Mascara (mäs'kä-rä) (mäs-kà-rà') Alg.	35·25 N	0·08 E
47	Mascarene Is. Afr.	20·20 S	56·40 E
78	Mascot (măs'kŏt) Tenn.	36·04 N	83·45 W
90	Mascota (mäs-kō'tä) Mex.	20·33 N	104·45 W
90	Mascota (R.) Mex.	20·33 N	104·52 W
85	Mascouche (mås-kōōsh') Can. (Montreal In.)	45·45 N	73·36 W
85	Mascouche (R.) Can. (Montreal In.)	45·44 N	73·45 W
74	Mascoutah (măs-kū'tā) Ill. (St. Louis In.)	38·29 N	89·48 W
166	Maseru (măz'ĕr-ōō) Bas.	29·09 S	27·11 E
144	Mashhad Iran	36·17 N	59·30 E
165	Masindi (mä-sēn'dê) Ug.	1·44 N	31·43 E
144	Masīra (I.) Oman	20·43 N	58·58 E
116	Mask, Lough (B.) (lŏk måsk) . Ire.	53·35 N	9·23 W
136	Maslovo (mäs'lô-vô) Sov. Un. (Urals In.)	60·08 N	60·28 E
80	Mason (mā'sŭn) Mich.	42·35 N	84·25 W
75	Mason ...... Ohio (Cincinnati In.)	39·22 N	84·18 W
76	Mason Tex.	30·46 N	99·14 W
71	Mason City Iowa	43·08 N	93·14 W
83	Masquaro (L.) Can.	50·34 N	60·40 W
126	Massa (mäs'sä) It.	44·02 N	10·08 E
63	Massachusetts (State) (măs-ȧ-chōō'sĕts) . U. S.	42·20 N	72·30 W
82	Massachusetts B. Mass.	42·26 N	70·20 W
126	Massafra (mäs-sä'frä) It.	40·35 N	17·05 E
126	Massa Marittima (mäs'sä mä-rē'tê-mä) . It.	43·03 N	10·55 E
165	Massaua (mäs-sä'wä) Eth.	15·40 N	39·19 E
81	Massena (mă-sē'nȧ) N. Y.	44·55 N	74·55 W
165	Massénia (mä-sĕn'yä) Chad	11·28 N	16·13 E
86	Massett (măs'ĕt) Can.	54·03 N	132·11 W
122	Massif Central (Plat.) (mà-sēf' säN-tràl') . Fr.	45·12 N	3·02 E
80	Massillon (măs'ĭ-lŏn) Ohio	40·50 N	81·35 W
166	Massinga (mä-sĭn'gä) Moz.	23·18 S	35·18 E
69	Massive, Mt. (màs'ĭv) Colo.	39·05 N	106·30 W
85	Masson (măs-sŭn) Can. (Ottawa In.)	45·33 N	75·25 W
153	Masuda (mä-sōō'dà) Jap.	34·42 N	131·53 E
121	Masuria (Reg. Pol.	53·40 N	21·10 E
166	Matadi (mà-tä'dê) Con. L.	5·48 S	13·35 E
92	Matagalpa (mä-tä-gäl'pä) Nic.	12·52 N	85·57 W
77	Matagorda B. (măt-ȧ-gôr'dȧ) . Tex.	28·32 N	96·13 W
77	Matagorda I. Tex.	28·13 N	96·27 W
164	Matam (mä-täm') Senegal	15·41 N	13·20 W
76	Matamoros (mä-tä-mō'rôs) .. Mex.	25·32 N	103·13 W
77	Matamoros Mex.	25·52 N	97·30 W
82	Matane (mà-tàn') Can.	48·49 N	67·35 W
166	Matanga (mä-täŋ'gä) Ang.	7·35 S	17·25 E
64	Matanuska (mä-tä-nōōs'kà) Alaska	61·32 N	149·38 W
94	Matanzas (mä-tän'zäs) Cuba	23·00 N	81·40 W
94	Matanzas (State) Cuba	22·45 N	81·20 W
94	Matanzas, Bahía (B.) (bä-ē'-ä) Cuba	23·10 N	81·30 W
93	Matapalo, Cabo (C.) (kä'bô-mä-tä-pä'lō) . C. R.	8·22 N	83·25 W
82	Matapedia (mă-tȧ-pē'dĭ-ȧ) ... Can.	48·00 N	66·55 W
82	Matapedia (L.) Can.	48·36 N	67·20 W
101	Mataquito (R.) (mä-tä-kē'tô) Chile (Santiago In.)	35·08 S	71·35 W
143	Matara (mä-tä'rä) Ceylon	5·59 N	80·35 E
154	Mataram Indon.	8·45 S	116·15 E
125	Mataró (mä-tä-rō') Sp.	41·33 N	2·27 E

ăt; finȧl; rāte; senâte; ärm; åsk; sofȧ; fâre; ch-choose; dh-as th in other; bē; ēvent; bĕt; recĕnt; cratēr; g-go; gh-guttural g; bĭt; ĭ-short neutral; rīde; K-guttural k as ch in German ich;

PRONOUNCING INDEX Matatiele–Mendes 235

Page	Name Pronunciation Region	Lat. °′	Long. °′
167	Matatiele (mä-tä-tyā'lä) S. Afr. (Natal In.)	30·21 s	28·49 E
84	Matawana (mȧ-tȧ-wŏn'ȧ) N. J. (New York In.)	40·24 N	74·13 W
90	Matehuala (mä-tå-wä'lä)....Mex.	23·38 N	100·39 W
126	Matera (mä-tå'rä)...........It.	40·42 N	16·37 E
113	Mateur (mȧ-tûr')...........Tun.	37·09 N	9·43 E
143	Mātherān....India (Bombay In.)	18·58 N	73·16 E
74	Mathews, L. (măth'ūz) Calif. (Los Angeles In.)	33·50 N	117·24 W
142	Mathura (mu-tōō'rŭ).......India	27·39 N	77·39 E
101	Matias Barbosa (mä-tē'äs-bär-bô-sä) Braz. (Rio de Janeiro In.)	21·53 s	43·19 W
91	Matillas, Laguna (L.) (lä-gōō'nä-mä-tē'l-yäs).Mex.	18·02 N	92·36 W
93	Matina (mä-tē'nä)........C. R.	10·06 N	83·20 W
119	Matiši (mä'tē-sē)........Sov. Un.	57·43 N	25·09 E
154	Matjan (I.)..............Indon.	6·52 s	121·45 E
90	Matlalcueyetl, Cerra (sĕ'r-rä-mä-tläl-kwĕ'yĕtl).Mex.	19·13 N	98·02 W
110	Matlock (măt'lŏk).........Eng.	53·08 N	1·33 W
110	Matlock Bath (măt'lŏk bàth) Eng.	53·06 N	1·34 W
134	Matochkin Shar (mä'tŏch-kĭn) Sov. Un.	73·57 N	56·16 E
99	Mato Grosso (mät'ōō grōs'ōō) Braz.	15·04 s	59·58 W
99	Mato Grosso (State)........Braz.	14·38 s	55·36 W
99	Mato Grosso, Chapada de (Plain) (shä-pä'dä-dĕ).Braz.	13·39 s	55·42 W
124	Matozinhos (Leixoes) (mä-tô-zēn'yōzh) (lĕ'y-shô'-ĕs) Port.	41·10 N	8·48 W
144	Matrah (mȧ-trä')....Mus. & Om.	23·36 N	58·27 E
165	Maṭrūḥ...............U .A. R.	31·19 N	27·14 E
153	Matsudo (mät'sōō-dô) Jap. (Tōkyō In.)	35·48 N	139·55 E
153	Matsue (mät'sōō-ĕ)..........Jap.	35·29 N	133·04 E
153	Matsumoto (mät'sōō-mō'tô)..Jap.	36·15 N	137·59 E
153	Matsuyama (mät'sōō-yä'mä).Jap.	33·48 N	132·45 E
153	Matsuzaka (mät'sōō-zä'kä)...Jap.	34·35 N	136·34 E
87	Mattagami (L.) (mȧ-tä-gä'mê) Can.	50·10 N	78·49 W
79	Mattamuskeet (R.) (măt-tȧ-mŭs'kēt).N. C.	35·34 N	76·03 W
81	Mattaponi (R.) (măt'ȧ-poni').Va.	37·45 N	77·00 W
87	Mattawa (măt'ȧ-wȧ)........Can.	46·15 N	78·49 W
82	Mattawin (R.) (măt'ȧ-wĭn)..Can.	46·55 N	73·20 W
120	Matterhorn Mt. (mät'ĕr-hôrn) Switz.	45·57 N	7·36 E
75	Matteson (mătt'ê-sŭn) Ill. (Chicago In.)	41·30 N	87·42 W
95	Matthew Town (măth'ū toun) Ba. Is.	21·00 N	73·40 W
80	Mattoon (mă-tōōn')..........Ill.	39·30 N	88·20 W
98	Maturín (mä-tōō-rēn').......Ven.	9·48 N	63·16 W
155	Mauban (mä'ōō-bän') Phil. (Manila In.)	14·11 N	121·44 E
122	Maubeuge (mô-bûzh')........Fr.	50·18 N	3·57 E
75	Maud (môd) Ohio (Cincinnati In.)	39·21 N	84·23 W
111	Mauer (mou'ĕr)..Aus. (Wien In.)	48·09 N	16·16 E
99	Maués (mà-wĕ's)...........Braz.	3·34 s	57·30 W
157	Maui (I.) (mä'ōō-ē) Hawaii (In.)	20·52 N	156·02 W
101	Maule (R.) (mà'ōō-lĕ) Chile (Santiago In.)	35·45 s	70·50 W
80	Maumee (mô-mē').........Ohio	41·30 N	83·40 W
80	Maumee (R.)..........Ind.-Ohio	41·10 N	84·50 W
80	Maumee B...............Ohio	41·50 N	83·20 W
157	Mauna Kea (Vol.) (mä'ōō-näkä'ä) Hawaii (In.)	19·52 N	155·30 W
157	Mauna Loa (Vol.) (mä'ōō-nälō'ä) Hawaii (In.)	19·28 N	155·38 W
154	Maung Nakhon Sawan.....Thai.	16·00 N	99·52 E
77	Maurepas L. (mō-rē-pä').......La.	30·18 N	90·40 W
163	Mauritania (mô-rê-tā'nĭ-ȧ)...Afr.	19·38 N	13·30 W
47	Mauritius I. (mô-rĭsh'ĭ-ŭs)...Afr.	20·18 s	57·36 E
65	Maury (mô'rĭ) Wash. (Seattle In.)	47·22 N	122·23 W
71	Mauston (môs'tŭn).........Wis.	43·46 N	90·05 W
69	Maverick, (R.) (mă-vûr'ĭk)..Ariz.	33·40 N	109·30 W
91	Maxcanú (mäs-kä-nōō')....Mex.	20·35 N	89·59 W
85	Maxville (măks'vĭl) Can. (Ottawa In.)	45·17 N	74·52 W
74	Maxville......Mo. (St. Louis In.)	38·26 N	90·24 W
135	Maya (R.) (mä'yä)......Sov. Un.	58·00 N	135·45 E
95	Mayaguana (I.)..........Ba. Is.	22·25 N	73·00 W
95	Mayaguana Passage (Str.).Ba. Is.	22·20 N	73·25 W
89	Mayagüez (mä-yä-gwāz') P. R. (Puerto Rico In.)	18·12 N	67·10 W
95	Mayarí (mä-yä-rē').........Cuba	20·45 N	75·40 W
95	Mayari (R.)...............Cuba	20·25 N	75·35 W
92	Mayas, Montañas (Mts.) (mŏntăn̤'äs mä'äs) Br. Hond. (Yucatan In.)	16·43 N	89·00 W
120	Mayen (mī'ĕn).............Ger.	50·19 N	7·14 E
122	Mayenne (mȧ-yĕn')..........Fr.	48·19 N	0·35 W
122	Mayenne (R.)...............Fr.	48·14 N	0·45 W
78	Mayfield (mā'fēld)...........Ky.	36·44 N	88·19 W
79	Mayfield Cr. ....Ky.	36·54 N	88·47 W
75	Mayfield Heights Ohio (Cleveland In.)	41·31 N	81·26 W
133	Maykop (Maikop) (mī-kôp') Sov. Un.	44·35 N	40·10 E
136	Maykor (mī-kôr') Sov. Un. (Urals In.)	59·01 N	55·52 E
146	Maymyo (mī'myō').........Bur.	22·14 N	96·32 E
83	Maynard (mā'nȧrd) Mass. (Boston In.)	42·25 N	71·27 W
65	Maynard.....Wash. (Seattle In.)	47·59 N	122·54 W
65	Mayne (mān) Can. (Vancouver In.)	48·51 N	123·18 W
65	Mayne (I.)..Can. (Vancouver In.)	48·52 N	123·14 W
78	Mayo (mā-yō')............Fla.	30·02 N	83·08 W
64	Mayo (L.)...............Alaska	63·50 N	135·30 W
116	Mayo, Mts. of..............Ire.	54·01 N	9·01 W
79	Mayodan (mā-yō'dăn)......N. C.	36·25 N	79·59 W
86	Mayo Landing............Can.	63·40 N	135·51 W
155	Mayon (Vol.) (mä-yōn') Phil. (Manila In.)	13·21 N	123·43 E
167	Mayotte (I.) (mȧ-yôt') Comores, Arch. des	13·07 s	45·32 E
94	May Pen..................Jam.	18·00 N	77·25 W
151	Mayraira Pt...............Phil.	18·40 N	120·45 E
76	Mayran, Laguna de (L.) (lä-ōō'nä-dĕ-mī-rän')......Mex.	25·40 N	102·35 W
80	Maysville (māz'vĭl)..........Ky.	38·35 N	83·45 W
166	Mayumba...............Gabon	3·15 s	10·10 E
81	Mayville (mā'vĭl)..........N. Y.	42·15 N	79·30 W
70	Mayville..................N. D.	47·30 N	97·20 W
71	Mayville...................Wis.	43·30 N	88·45 W
74	Maywood (mā'wŏŏd) Calif. (Los Angeles In.)	33·59 N	118·11 W
75	Maywood.......Ill. (Chicago In.)	41·53 N	87·51 W
166	Mazabuka (mä-zä-bōō'kä) Fed. of Rh. & Nya.	16·00 s	27·43 E
164	Mazagan (mȧ-zȧ-gän).......Mor.	33·14 N	8·34 W
99	Mazagão (mä-zȧ-gou'ɴ).....Braz.	0·05 s	51·27 W
76	Mazapil (mä-zä-pēl').......Mex.	24·40 N	101·30 W
142	Mazar-i-Sharif (mȧ-zär'-ē-shȧ-rēf').Afg.	36·48 N	67·12 E
124	Mazarrón (mä-zär-rô'n).......Sp.	36·37 N	1·29 W
99	Mazaruni (R.) (mä-zä-rōō'nē) Br. Gu.	5·58 N	59·37 W
92	Mazatenango (mä-zä-tå-näŋ'gō) Guat.	14·30 N	91·30 W
91	Mazatla.......Mex. (Mexico In.)	19·30 N	99·24 W
91	Mazatlán (San Juan) (mä-zä-tlän') (sän hwän').Mex.	17·05 N	95·26 W
90	Mazatlán...................Mex.	23·14 N	106·27 W
119	Mažeikiai (mȧ-zhā'kē-ī)..Sov. Un.	56·19 N	22·24 E
139	Mazhafah, Jabal (Mts.) Sau. Ar. (Palestine In.)	28·56 N	35·05 E
126	Mazzara del Vallo (mät-sä'rä dĕl väl'lō).It.	37·40 N	12·37 E
126	Mazzarino (mät-sä-rē'nō)......It.	37·16 N	14·15 E
166	Mbabane (m'bä-bä'nĕ).....Swaz.	26·18 s	31·14 E
165	Mbaiki (m'bä-ē'kē).Cen. Afr. Rep.	3·54 N	17·57 E
166	Mbigou (m-bê-gōō')......Con. B.	2·07 s	12·07 E
165	M'Bomu R. (m'bō'mōō)..Con. L.	4·38 N	23·48 E
164	M'Bout (m'bōō').....Mauritania	16·03 N	12·31 W
72	Meade (mēd)............Kans.	37·17 N	100·21 W
69	Meade, L.............Nev.-Ariz.	36·20 N	114·14 W
67	Meade Pk.................Idaho	42·19 N	111·16 W
65	Meadowdale (mĕd'ō-dāl) Wash. (Seattle In.)	47·51 N	122·20 W
86	Meadow Lake (mĕd'ō lāk)...Can.	54·10 N	108·30 W
85	Meadows (mĕd'ōz) Can. (Winnipeg In.)	50·02 N	97·35 W
81	Meadville (mēd'vĭl).........Pa.	41·40 N	80·10 W
80	Meaford (mē'fērd)..........Can.	44·35 N	80·40 W
87	Mealy Mts. (mē'lē)..........Can.	53·32 N	57·58 W
160	Meandarra (mē-ăn-dă'rȧ)...Austl.	27·47 s	149·40 E
123	Meaux (mō).......Fr. (Paris In.)	48·58 N	2·53 E
91	Mecapalapa (mā-kä-pä-lä'pä) Mex.	20·32 N	97·52 W
83	Mecatina (I.) (mā-kȧ-tē'nȧ).Can.	50·50 N	58·33 W
83	Mecatina (R.) (mā-kȧ-tē'nȧ).Can.	50·50 N	59·45 W
	Mecca, see Makkah		
82	Mechanic Falls (mê-kăn'ĭk).Maine	44·05 N	70·23 W
81	Mechanicsburg (mê-kăn'ĭks-bûrg).Pa.	40·15 N	77·00 W
81	Mechanicsville (mê-kăn'ĭks-vĭl) N. Y.	42·55 N	73·45 W
111	Mechelen.....Bel. (Bruxelles In.)	51·01 N	4·28 E
114	Mecheria..................Mor.	33·30 N	0·13 W
120	Mecklenburg (Reg.) (mĕk'lĕn-bōōrgh). Ger.	53·34 N	12·18 E
154	Medan (mā-dän').........Indon.	3·35 N	98·35 E
100	Medanosa, Punta (Pt.) (pōō'n-tä-mĕ-dä-nô'sä).Arg.	47·50 s	65·53 W
110	Medden (R.) (mĕd'ĕn)......Eng.	53·14 N	1·05 W
125	Médéa (mā-dā'ä)...........Alg.	36·18 N	2·40 E
98	Medellín (mā-dhĕl-yēn').Col. (In.)	6·15 N	75·34 W
91	Medellín (mĕ-dĕl-yĕ'n).....Mex.	19·03 N	96·08 W
114	Medenine (mā-dĕ-nēn')......Tun.	33·22 N	10·33 E
83	Medfield (mĕd'fēld) Mass. (Boston In.)	42·11 N	71·19 W
83	Medford (mĕd'fērd) Mass. (Boston In.)	42·25 N	71·07 W
84	Medford..N. J. (Philadelphia In.)	39·54 N	74·50 W
72	Medford..................Okla.	36·47 N	97·44 W
66	Medford...................Ore.	42·19 N	122·52 W
71	Medford...................Wis.	45·09 N	90·22 W
84	Media (mē'dĭ-ȧ) Pa. (Philadelphia In.)	39·55 N	75·24 W
121	Medias (mĕd-yäsh')........Rom.	46·09 N	24·21 E
66	Medical Lake (mĕd'ĭ-kăl)..Wash.	47·34 N	117·40 W
72	Medicine Bow Ra. (mĕd'ĭ-sĭn bō).Colo.-Wyo.	40·55 N	106·02 W
67	Medicine Bow R............Wyo.	41·58 N	106·30 W
86	Medicine Hat (mĕd'ĭ-sĭn hăt).Can.	50·09 N	110·50 W
67	Medicine L. (mĕd'ĭ-sĭn)....Mont.	48·24 N	104·15 W
72	Medicine Lodge..........Kans.	37·17 N	98·37 W
72	Medicine Lodge (R.).......Kans.	37·20 N	98·57 W
81	Medina (mê-dī'nȧ)..........N. Y.	43·15 N	78·20 W
75	Medina.....Ohio (Cleveland In.)	41·08 N	81·52 W
124	Medina del Campo (mä-dē'nä dĕl käm'pō).Sp.	41·18 N	4·54 W
124	Medina de Rioseco (mȧ-dē'nä dā rê-ô-sā'kō).Sp.	41·53 N	5·05 W
76	Medina L..................Tex.	29·36 N	98·47 W
76	Medina R..................Tex.	29·45 N	99·13 W
124	Medina Sidonia (sê-dō'nyä)...Sp.	36·28 N	5·58 W
101	Medio (mĕ'dyô) (R.) Arg. (Buenos Aires In.)	33·40 s	60·30 W
114	Mediterranean Sea (mĕd-ĭ-tēr-ā'nē-ăn).Afr.-Asia-Eur.	36·22 N	13·25 E
113	Medjerda, Oued (R.) (wĕd mĕ-jĕr'dȧ).Tun.	36·43 N	9·54 E
134	Mednogersk...........Sov. Un.	51·27 N	57·22 E
133	Medveditsa (R.) (mĕd-vyĕ'dê tsȧ).Sov. Un.	50·10 N	43·40 E
132	Medvezhegorsk (mĕd-vyĕzh'yĕ-gôrsk').Sov. Un.	63·00 N	34·20 E
135	Medvezh'y (Is.)........Sov. Un.	71·00 N	161·25 E
83	Medway (mĕd'wā) Mass. (Boston In.)	42·08 N	71·23 W
128	Medyn' (mĕ-dēn').......Sov. Un.	54·58 N	35·53 E
129	Medzhibozh (mĕd-zhê-bōzh') Sov. Un.	49·23 N	27·29 E
158	Meekatharra (mē-kȧ-thăr'ȧ).Austl.	26·30 s	118·38 E
69	Meeker (mēk'ēr)...........Colo.	40·00 N	107·55 W
120	Meerane (mā-rä'nē).........Ger.	50·51 N	12·27 E
142	Meerut (mē'rŏŏt)..........India	28·59 N	77·43 E
165	Mēgā......................Eth.	6·14 N	35·34 E
127	Megalópolis (mĕg-ȧ lŏ'pō-lĭs).Grc.	37·22 N	22·08 E
129	Meganom, M. (C.) (mĭs mĕ-gȧ-nôm').Sov. Un.	44·48 N	35·17 E
127	Mégara (mĕg'ȧ-rȧ)..........Grc.	37·59 N	23·21 E
79	Megget (mĕg'ĕt)...........S. C.	32·44 N	80·15 W
65	Megler (mĕg'lēr) Wash. (Portland In.)	46·15 N	123·52 W
128	Meglino (L.) (mȧ-glē'nô).Sov. Un.	58·32 N	35·27 E
79	Meherrin (R.) (mê-hĕr'ĭn)....Va.	36·40 N	77·49 W
142	Mehsāna..................India	23·42 N	72·23 E
122	Mehun-sur-Yèvre (mē-ŭɴ-sür-yĕvr').Fr.	47·11 N	2·14 E
148	Meichu (mā'jĕōō)..........China	31·17 N	119·12 E
151	Meihsien..................China	24·20 N	116·10 E
151	Meiling Pass (mā'lĭng')....China	25·22 N	115·00 E
123	Meinerzhagen (mī'nĕrts-hä-gĕn) Ger. (Ruhr In.)	51·06 N	7·39 E
120	Meiningen (mī'nĭng-ĕn)......Ger.	50·35 N	10·25 E
100	Mejillones (mȧ-ᴋē-lyō'nås)..Chile	23·07 s	70·31 W
164	Meknés (mĕk'nĕs) (mĕk-nĕs').Mor.	33·56 N	5·44 W
	Mekong, see Lanisung Chiang		
154	Mekong, Mouths of the (mē'kông')...Viet.	10·09 N	107·15 E
154	Mekong R............Thai.-Laos	17·53 N	103·57 E
161	Melbourne (mĕl'bŭrn) Austl. (Melbourne In.)	37·52 s	145·08 E
79	Melbourne.............Fla. (In.)	28·02 N	28·37 W
110	Melbourne..................Eng.	52·49 N	1·26 W
75	Melbourne...Ky. (Cincinnati In.)	39·02 N	84·22 W
71	Melcher (mĕl'chēr)..........Iowa	41·13 N	93·11 W
132	Melekess (mĕl-yĕk ĕs)....Sov. Un.	54·20 N	49·30 E
128	Melenki (mĕ-lyĕŋ'kē)....Sov. Un.	55·25 N	41·34 E
86	Melfort (mĕl'fôrt)..........Can.	52·55 N	104·31 W
165	Melik, Wadi el (R.).........Sud.	16·48 N	29·30 E
164	Melilla (Sp.) (mā-lēl'yä)......Afr.	35·24 N	3·03 W
101	Melipilla (mȧ-lê-pē'lyä) Chile (Santiago In.)	33·40 s	71·12 W
129	Melitopol' (mā-lê-tô'pôl-y') Sov. Un.	46·49 N	35·19 E
168	Melkrivier...............S. Afr. (Johannesburg & Pretoria In.)	24·01 s	28·23 E
71	Mellen (mĕl'ĕn)..............Wis.	46·20 N	90·40 W
118	Mellerud (mål'ĕ-rōōdh)......Swe.	58·43 N	12·25 E
167	Melmoth......S. Afr. (Natal In.)	28·38 s	31·26 E
100	Melo (mā'lō).................Ur.	32·18 s	54·07 W
85	Melocheville (mĕ-lôsh-vēl') Can. (Montreal In.)	45·24 N	73·56 W
136	Melozha R. (myĕ'lô-zhȧ) Sov. Un. (Moskva In.)	56·06 N	38·34 E
164	Melrhir Chott (L.) (mĕl'rēr)..Alg.	33·52 N	5·22 E
83	Melrose (mĕl'rōz) Mass. (Boston In.)	42·29 N	71·06 W
71	Melrose..................Minn.	45·39 N	94·49 W
75	Melrose Park....Ill. (Chicago In.)	41·54 N	87·52 W
166	Melsetter (mĕl-sĕt'ēr) Fed. of Rh. & Nya.	19·44 s	32·51 E
110	Meltham (mĕl'thăm)........Eng.	53·35 N	1·51 W
161	Melton (mĕl'tŭn) Austl. (Melbourne In.)	37·41 s	144·35 E
110	Melton Mowbray (mō'brȧ)..Eng.	52·45 N	0·52 W
123	Melun (mĕ-lŭɴ')...Fr. (Paris In.)	48·32 N	2·40 E
165	Melut (mȧ-lōōt').............Sud.	10·30 N	32·17 E
86	Melville (mĕl'vĭl)...........Can.	51·00 N	102·52 W
77	Melville......................La.	30·39 N	91·45 W
159	Melville, C..................Austl.	14·15 s	145·50 E
158	Melville (I.)................Austl.	11·30 s	131·12 E
87	Melville (R.)................Can.	53·46 N	59·31 W
86	Melville Hills...............Can.	69·18 N	124·57 W
87	Melville Pen.................Can.	67·44 N	84·09 W
75	Melvindale (mĕl'vĭn-dāl) Mich. (Detroit In.)	42·17 N	83·11 W
121	Mélykút (mā'l'kōōt).......Hung.	46·14 N	19·21 E
168	Memal (mĕ'măl) S. Afr. (Johannesburg & Pretoria In.)	27·42 s	29·35 E
167	Memba (mĕm'bȧ)..........Moz.	14·12 s	40·35 E
	Memel, see Klaipéda		
120	Memmingen (mĕm'ĭng-ĕn)...Ger.	47·59 N	10·10 E
99	Memo (R.) (mĕ'mō)....Ven. (In.)	9·32 N	66·30 W
73	Memphis (mĕm'fĭs)..........Mo.	40·27 N	92·11 W
78	Memphis (mĕm'fĭs)........Tenn.	35·07 N	90·03 W
72	Memphis....................Tex.	34·42 N	100·33 W
168	Memphis (Ruins) U. A. R. (Nile In.)	29·50 N	31·12 E
81	Memphremagog (L.) (mĕm'frê-mā'gŏg).Can.	45·05 N	72·10 W
73	Mena (mē'nȧ)...............Ark.	34·35 N	94·09 W
129	Mena (mā-nȧ')...........Sov. Un.	51·31 N	32·14 E
155	Menado...................Indon.	1·29 N	124·50 E
161	Menangle.....Austl. (Sydney In.)	34·08 s	150·48 E
76	Menard (mê-närd')..........Tex.	30·56 N	99·48 W
71	Menasha (mê-năsh'ȧ).......Wis.	44·12 N	88·29 W
122	Mende (mäɴd)...............Fr.	44·31 N	3·30 E
123	Menden (mĕn'dĕn) Ger. (Ruhr In.)	51·26 N	7·47 E
133	Menderes (R.) (mĕn'dĕr-ĕs)..Tur.	37·50 N	28·20 E
100	Mendes (mĕ'n-dĕs).....Braz. (In.)	22·32 s	43·44 W

ng-sing; ŋ-baŋk; ɴ-nasalized n; nŏd; cŏmmit; ōld; ôbey; ôrder; fōōd; fŏŏt; ou-out; s-soft; sh-dish; th-thin; pūre; ûnite; ûrn; stŭd; circŭs; ü-as "y" in study; '-indetermin te vowel.

236 Mendocino–Mikura PRONOUNCING INDEX

Page	Name Pronunciation Region	Lat. °′	Long. °′
66	Mendocino, C. (mĕn′dô-sē′nō) Calif.	40·25 N	124·22 W
71	Mendota (mĕn-dō′tȧ) Ill.	41·34 N	89·06 W
71	Mendota (L.) Wis.	43·09 N	89·41 W
100	Mendoza (mĕn-dō′sä) Arg.	32·48 S	68·45 W
100	Mendoza (Prov.) Arg.	35·10 S	69·00 W
151	Mengtzu China	23·22 N	103·20 E
160	Menindee (mĕ-nĭn-dē) Austl.	32·23 S	142·30 E
65	Menlo Park (mĕn′lō pärk) Calif. (San Francisco In.)	37·27 N	122·11 W
70	Menno (mĕn′ô) S. D.	43·14 N	97·34 W
71	Menominee (mē-nŏm′ĭ-nē) Mich.	45·08 N	87·40 W
71	Menominee (R.) Mich.-Wis.	45·37 N	87·54 W
75	Menomonee Falls (fôls) Wis. (Milwaukee In.)	43·11 N	88·06 W
71	Menominee Ra. Mich.	46·07 N	88·53 W
75	Menomonee R. Wis. (Milwaukee In.)	43·09 N	88·06 W
71	Menomonie Wis.	44·53 N	91·55 W
125	Menorca, Isla de (Minorca) (I.) (ē′s-lä-dĕ-mĕ-nō′r-kä) Sp.	40·05 N	3·58 E
125	Mentana (mĕn-tá′nä) It. (Roma In.)	42·02 N	12·40 E
154	Mentawai, Pulau-Pulau (Is.) (mĕn-tä-vī′) Indon.	1·08 S	98·10 E
123	Menton (mäɴ-tôɴ′) Fr.	43·46 N	7·37 E
74	Mentone (mĕn′tōne) Calif. (Los Angeles In.)	34·05 N	117·08 W
167	Mentz (R.) (mĕnts) S. Afr. (Natal In.)	33·13 S	25·15 E
132	Menzelinsk (mĕn′zyĕ-lênsk′) Sov. Un.	55·40 N	53·15 E
158	Menzies (mĕn′zēz) Austl.	29·45 S	122·15 E
76	Meoqui (mâ-ō′gē) Mex.	28·17 N	105·28 W
117	Meppel (mĕp′ĕl) Neth.	52·41 N	6·08 E
120	Meppen (mĕp′ĕn) Ger.	52·40 N	7·18 E
126	Merabéllou, Kólpos (G.) Grc. (Inset)	35·16 N	25·55 E
73	Meramec (R.) (mĕr′ȧ-mĕk) Mo.	38·06 N	91·06 W
126	Merano (mâ-rä′nō) It.	46·39 N	11·10 E
83	Merasheen (I.) (mē′rá-shēn) Can.	47·23 N	54·15 W
155	Merauke (mâ-rou′kä) Neth. N. Gui.	8·32 S	140·17 E
84	Meraux (mē-rō′) La. (New Orleans In.)	29·56 N	89·56 W
168	Merca (mĕr′kä) Som. (Horn of Afr. In.)	1·45 N	44·47 E
125	Mercato San Severino (mĕr-kä′tō sän sĕ-vĕ-rē′nō) It. (Nápoli In.)	40·34 N	14·38 E
68	Merced (mēr-sĕd′) Calif.	37·17 N	120·30 W
68	Merced (R.) Calif.	37·25 N	120·31 W
101	Mercedario, Cerro (Mtn.) (mĕr-sâ-dhä′rê-ō) Chile (Santiago In.)	31·58 S	70·07 W
100	Mercedes (mĕr-sā′dhās) Arg.	29·04 S	58·01 W
101	Mercedes Arg. (Buenos Aires In.)	34·41 S	59·26 W
76	Mercedes Tex.	26·09 N	97·55 W
101	Mercedes Ur. (Buenos Aires In.)	33·17 S	58·04 W
101	Mercedita (mĕr-sĕ-dē′tä) Chile (Santiago In.)	33·51 S	71·10 W
65	Mercer Island (mûr′sēr) Wash. (Seattle In.)	47·35 N	122·15 W
101	Mercês (mĕr-sĕ′s) Braz. (Rio de Janeiro In.)	21·13 S	43·20 N
139	Merchong (R.) Mala. (Singapore In.)	3·08 N	103·13 E
111	Merchtem Bel. (Bruxelles In.)	50·57 N	4·13 E
125	Mercier-Lacombe (mĕr-syā′ lȧ-kônb) Alg.	35·18 N	0·11 W
87	Mercy, C. Can.	64·48 N	63·22 W
81	Meredith (mĕr′ē-dĭth) N. H.	43·35 N	71·35 W
129	Merefa (mâ-rĕf′á) Sov. Un.	49·49 N	36·04 E
92	Merendón, Serrania de (Mts.) (sĕr-rä-nē′ä-dä mâ-rĕn-dōn′) Hond.	15·01 N	89·05 W
110	Mereworth (mĕ-rĕ′wûrth) Eng. (London In.)	51·15 N	0·23 E
	Mergen, see Nench′eng		
154	Mergui (mĕr-gē′) Bur.	12·29 N	98·39 E
154	Mergui Archip. Asia	12·04 N	97·02 E
91	Mérida (mā′rē-dhä) Mex. (Yucatan In.)	20·57 N	89·38 W
98	Mérida Ven.	8·30 N	71·15 W
98	Mérida, Sierra Nevada de (Mts.) (sē-ĕ′r-rä-nĕ-vä′dä-dĕ-mĕ′rē-dhä) Ven.	8·30 N	70·45 W
81	Meriden (mĕr′ĭ-dĕn) Conn.	41·30 N	72·50 W
78	Meridian (mê-rĭd-ĭ-ăn) Miss.	32·21 N	88·41 W
77	Meridian Tex.	31·56 N	97·37 W
119	Merikarvia (mā′rē-kär′vē-ȧ) Fin.	61·51 N	21·30 E
111	Mering (mĕ′rĕng) Ger. (München In.)	48·16 N	11·00 E
78	Meriwether Lewis Natl. Mon. (mĕr′ĭ-wĕth-ēr lōō′ĭs) Tenn.	35·25 N	87·25 W
76	Merkel (mûr′kĕl) Tex.	32·26 N	100·02 W
119	Merkine (mĕr′kĭ-nê) Sov. Un.	54·09 N	24·10 E
111	Merksem Bel. (Bruxelles In.)	51·15 N	4·27 E
121	Merkys R. (măr′kĭs) Sov. Un.	54·23 N	25·00 E
100	Merlo (mĕr-lô) Arg. (In.)	34·25 S	58·44 W
165	Merowe Sud.	18·07 N	31·57 E
74	Merriam (mĕr-rĭ-yăm) Minn. (Minneapolis, St. Paul In.)	44·44 N	93·36 W
74	Merriam Mo. (Kansas City In.)	39·01 N	94·42 W
84	Merrick (mĕr′ĭk) N. Y. (New York In.)	40·40 N	73·33 W
71	Merrill (mĕr′ĭl) Wis.	45·11 N	89·42 W
83	Merrimac (mĕr′ĭ-măk) Mass. (Boston In.)	42·50 N	71·00 W
83	Merrimack N. H. (Boston In.)	42·51 N	71·25 W
81	Merrimack (R.) (mĕr′ĭ-măk) Mass.-N. H.	43·10 N	71·30 W
83	Merrimack R. Mass. (Boston In.)	42·49 N	70·44 W
86	Merritt (mĕr′ĭt) Can.	50·10 N	120·48 W
85	Merritton (mĕr′ĭt-tŭn) Can. (Toronto In.)	43·14 N	79·13 W

Page	Name Pronunciation Region	Lat. °′	Long. °′
77	Merryville (mĕr′ĭ-vĭl) La.	30·46 N	93.34 W
120	Merseburg (mĕr′zĕ-bōōrgh) Ger.	51·21 N	11·59 E
110	Mersey (R.) (mûr′zē) Eng.	52·52 N	2·04 W
116	Mersey (R.) Eng.	53·15 N	2·51 W
133	Mersin (mĕr-sēn′) Tur.	37·00 N	34·40 E
139	Mersing Mala. (Singapore In.)	2·25 N	103·51 E
116	Merthyr Tydfil (mûr′thēr tĭd′vĭl) Wales	51·46 N	3·30 W
124	Mértola Almodóvar (mĕr-tô-lȧ-äl-mô-dô′vär) Port.	37·39 N	8·04 W
123	Méru (mā-rü′) Fr. (Paris In.)	49·14 N	2·08 E
165	Meru (mā′rōō) Ken.	00·01 N	37·45 E
99	Merume Mts. (mĕr-ü′mĕ) Br. Gu.	5·45 N	60·15 W
111	Merwerde, Kanal (can.) Neth. (Amsterdam In.)	52·15 N	5·01 E
65	Merwin (R.) (mĕr′wĭn) Wash. (Portland In.)	45·58 N	122·27 W
133	Merzifon (mĕr′ze-fōn) Tur.	40·50 N	35·30 E
123	Merzig (mĕr′tsēg) Ger.	49·27 N	6·54 E
69	Mesa (mā′sȧ) Ariz.	33·25 N	111·50 W
71	Mesabi Ra. (mā-sŏb′bē) Minn.	47·17 N	93·04 W
127	Mesagne (mā-sän′yâ) It.	40·34 N	17·51 E
69	Mesa Verde Natl. Park. (vĕr′dē) Colo.	37·22 N	108·27 W
69	Mescalero Ind. Res. (mĕs-kä-lā′rō) N. Mex.	33·10 N	105·45 W
128	Meshchovsk (myĕsh′chĕfsk) Sov. Un.	54·17 N	35·19 E
165	Meshra er Req Sud.	8·28 N	29·15 E
69	Mesilla (mâ-sē′yä) N. Mex.	32·15 N	106·45 W
127	Mesolóngion (mĕ-sô-lôŋ′gē-ôn) Grc.	38·23 N	21·28 E
126	Messina (mĕ-sē′nȧ) It.	38·11 N	15·34 E
166	Messina S. Afr.	22·17 S	30·13 E
126	Messina, Stretto di (Str.) (strĕ′t-tô dē) It.	38·10 N	15·34 E
127	Messíni Grc.	37·05 N	22·00 E
127	Méssiniakós Kólpos (G.) Grc.	36·59 N	22·00 E
127	Mesta (R.) (mĕ-stä′) Bul.	41·42 N	23·40 E
126	Mestre (mĕs′trā) It.	45·29 N	12·15 E
98	Meta (Dept.) (mĕ′tä) Col. (In.)	3·28 N	74·07 W
98	Meta (R.) Col.	4·33 N	72·09 W
83	Metabetchouan (R.) (mĕ-tȧ-bĕt-chōō-än′) Can.	47·45 N	72·00 W
77	Metairie (mĕ-trâr′ĭ) La.	30·00 N	90·11 W
100	Metán (mĕ-tà′n) Arg.	25·32 S	64·51 W
92	Metapán (mâ-tä-pän′) Sal.	14·21 N	89·26 W
85	Metcalfe (mĕt-käf) Can. (Ottawa In.)	45·14 N	75·27 W
65	Metchosin Can. (Seattle In.)	48·22 N	123·33 W
90	Metepec (mâ-tĕ-pĕk′) Mex.	18·56 N	98·31 W
91	Metepec Mex. (Mexico In.)	19·15 N	99·36 W
66	Methow R. (mĕt′hou) (mĕt hou′) Wash.	48·26 N	120·15 W
83	Methuen (mê-thū′ĕn) Mass. (Boston In.)	42·44 N	71·11 W
82	Metis Beach (mâ-tē′) (mā-tĭs′) Can.	48·40 N	68·04 W
127	Metkovic′ (mĕt′kô-vĭch) Yugo.	43·02 N	17·40 E
64	Metlakatla (mĕt-lȧ-kăt′lȧ) Alaska	55·10 N	131·30 W
73	Metropolis (mê-trŏp′ô-lĭs) Ill.	37·09 N	88·46 W
79	Metter (mĕt′ēr) Ga.	32·21 N	82·05 W
123	Mettmann (mĕt′män) Ger. (Ruhr In.)	51·15 N	6·58 E
84	Metuchen (mĕ-tŭ′chĕn) N. J. (New York In.)	40·32 N	74·21 W
123	Metz (mĕtz) Fr.	49·08 N	6·10 E
90	Metztitlán (mĕtz-tēt-län′) Mex.	20·36 N	98·45 W
122	Meuse (R.) (mûz) (müz) Eur.	50·32 N	5·22 E
110	Mexborough (mĕks′bŭr-ô) Eng.	53·30 N	1·17 W
77	Mexia (mā-hē′ä) Tex.	31·32 N	96·29 W
91	Mexicalcingo (mĕ-kē-käl-sĕn′go) Mex. (Mexico In.)	19·13 N	99·34 W
68	Mexicali (măk-sê-kä′lē) Mex.	32·28 N	115·29 W
69	Mexican Hat (mĕk′sĭ-kăn hăt) Utah	37·10 N	109·55 W
82	Mexico (mĕk′sĭ-kō) Maine	44·34 N	70·33 W
91	México Mex. (Mexico In.)	19.26 N	99·09 W
73	Mexico Mo.	39·09 N	91·51 W
88	Mexico (State) (măk′sĕ-kō) Mex.	19·50 N	99·50 W
49	Mexico N. A.	23·45 N	104·00 W
88	Mexico, G. of N. A.	25·15 N	93·45 W
90	Mexticacán (mĕs′tē-kä-kän′) Mex.	21·12 N	102·43 W
144	Meydān-e Naftūn Iran	31·45 N	49·17 E
81	Meyersdale (mī′ērz-dāl) Pa.	39·55 N	79·00 W
132	Mezen′ Sov. Un.	65·50 N	44·05 E
132	Mezen′ (R.) Sov. Un.	65·20 N	44·45 E
122	Mézenc, Mt. (mŏɴ-mā-zĕɴ′) Fr.	44·55 N	4·12 E
128	Mezha (R.) (myā′zhà) Sov. Un.	55·53 N	31·44 E
122	Mézières (mā-zyâr′) Fr.	49·45 N	4·40 E
123	Mézières-sur-Seine (mā-zyâr′sür-sân′) Fr. (Paris In.)	48·58 N	1·49 E
121	Mezökövesd (mĕ′zû-kû′vĕsht) Hung.	47·49 N	20·36 E
121	Mezötur (mĕ′zû-tōōr) Hung.	47·00 N	20·36 E
90	Mezquital (mâz-kê-täl′) Mex.	23·30 N	104·20 W
90	Mezquital (R.) Mex.	23·07 N	104·52 W
90	Mezquitic (mâz-kê-tēk′) Mex.	22·25 N	103·43 W
90	Mezquitic (R.) Mex.	22·25 N	103·45 W
136	Mga (m′gà) Sov. Un. (Leningrad In.)	59·45 N	31·04 E
128	Mglin (m′glēn′) Sov. Un.	53·03 N	32·52 E
90	Miacatlán (mē′ä-kä-tlän′) Mex.	18·42 N	99·17 W
91	Miahuatlán (mē′ä-wä-tlän′) Mex.	16·20 N	96·38 W
124	Miajadas (mê-ä-hä′däs) Sp.	39·10 N	5·53 W
69	Miami (mī-ăm′ĭ) Ariz.	33·20 N	110·55 W
79	Miami Fla. (In.)	25·45 N	80·11 W
73	Miami Okla.	36·51 N	94·51 W
72	Miami Tex.	35·41 N	100·39 W
80	Miami (R.) Ohio	39·20 N	84·45 W
79	Miami Beach Fla. (In.)	25·47 N	80·07 W
94	Miami Drainage Can. Fla.	26·25 N	80·50 W
80	Miamisburg (mī-ăm′ĭz-bûrg) Ohio	39·40 N	84·20 W
75	Miamitown (mī-ăm′ĭ-toun) Ohio (Cincinnati In.)	39·13 N	84·43 W

Page	Name Pronunciation Region	Lat. °′	Long. °′
144	Mīāneh Iran	37·15 N	47·13 E
155	Miangas (I.) (myä′n-gäs) Phil.	5·30 N	127·00 E
148	Miaochen (mĭou′zhen) China	31·44 N	121·28 E
151	Miaoli (mê-ou′lĭ) China	24·30 N	120·48 E
148	Miao Liehtao (Is.) (miou′ lĭĕdou) China	38·06 N	120·35 E
136	Miass (mī-äs′) Sov. Un. (Urals In.)	55·00 N	60·03 E
120	Miastko (myäst′kô) Pol.	54·01 N	17·00 E
121	Michalovce (mē′Kä-lôf′tsĕ) Czech.	48·44 N	21·56 E
83	Michel (L.) (mê-shĕl′) (mĭch′ĕl) Can.	50·21 N	56·45 W
64	Michelson, Mt. (mĭch′ĕl-sŭn) Alaska	69·11 N	144·12 W
111	Michendorf (mē′kĕn-dōrf) Ger. (Berlin In.)	52·19 N	13·02 E
95	Miches (mē′-chĕs) Dom. Rep.	19·00 N	69·05 W
63	Michigan (State) (mĭsh′ĭ-găn) U. S.	45·55 N	87·00 W
63	Michigan, L. U. S.	43·20 N	87·10 W
80	Michigan City Ind.	41·40 N	86·55 W
87	Michikamau (L.) Can.	54·11 N	63·21 W
71	Michipicoten (I.) (mĕ-shĭ-pĭ-kō′tĕn) Can.	47·49 N	85·50 W
71	Michipicoten (R.) Can.	47·56 N	84·42 W
71	Michipicoten Harbour Can.	47·58 N	84·58 W
128	Michurinsk (mĭ-chōō-rĭnsk′) Sov. Un.	52·53 N	40·32 E
93	Mico, Punta (Pt.) (pōō′n-tä-mē′kô) Nic.	11·38 N	83·24 W
66	Midas (mī′dȧs) Nev.	41·15 N	116·50 W
166	Middelburg (mĭd′ĕl-bûrg) S. Afr.	31·30 S	25·00 E
168	Middelburg S. Afr. (Johannesburg & Pretoria In.)	25·47 S	29·30 E
168	Middelwit (mĭd′l′wĭt) S. Afr. (Johannesburg & Pretoria In.)	24·50 S	27·00 E
154	Middle Andaman I. (ăn-dȧ-măn′) India	12·44 N	93·21 E
77	Middle Bay (mĭd″l bā) Tex. (In.)	29·38 N	95·06 W
94	Middle Bight (B.) (bīt) Ba. Is.	24·20 N	77·35 W
81	Middlebury (mĭd″l-bĕr-ĭ) Vt.	44·00 N	73·10 W
76	Middle Concho (kŏn′chō) Tex.	31·21 N	100·50 W
118	Middlefart (mêd″l-fårt) Den.	55·30 N	9·45 E
70	Middle Loup (R.) (lōōp) Nebr.	41·49 N	100·20 W
80	Middleport (mĭd″l-pōrt) Ohio	39·00 N	82·05 W
84	Middle River. Md. (Baltimore In.)	39·20 N	76·27 W
78	Middlesboro (mĭd″lz-bŭr-ô) Ky.	36·36 N	83·42 W
116	Middlesbrough (mĭd″lz-brŭ) Eng.	54·35 N	1·18 W
84	Middlesex (mĭd″l-sĕks) N. J. (New York In.)	40·34 N	74·30 W
110	Middleton (mĭd″l-tŭn) Eng.	53·04 N	2·12 W
64	Middleton (I.) Alaska	59·35 N	146·35 W
82	Middletown (mĭd″l-toun) Can.	44·56 N	65·03 W
81	Middletown Conn.	41·35 N	72·40 W
81	Middletown Del.	39·30 N	75·40 W
83	Middletown Mass. (Boston In.)	42·35 N	71·01 W
84	Middletown N. Y. (New York In.)	41·26 N	74·25 W
80	Middletown Ohio	39·30 N	84·25 W
110	Middlewich (mĭd″l-wĭch) Eng.	53·11 N	2·27 W
125	Midi, Canal du (kä-näl-dü-mē-dē′) Fr.	43·22 N	1·35 E
167	Mid Illovo (mĭd ĭl′ô-vō) S. Afr. (Natal In.)	29·59 S	30·32 E
81	Midland (mĭd′lănd) Can.	44·45 N	79·50 W
80	Midland Mich.	43·40 N	84·20 W
76	Midland Tex.	32·00 N	102·04 W
85	Midnapore (mĭd′-nȧ-pōr) Can. (Calgary In.)	50·56 N	114·04 W
74	Midvale (mĭd′vāl) Utah (Salt Lake City In.)	40·37 N	111·54 W
78	Midway (mĭd′wā) Ala.	32·03 N	85·30 W
67	Midwest (mĭd-wĕst′) Wyo.	43·25 N	106·15 W
133	Midye (mēd′yĕ) Tur.	41·35 N	28·10 E
120	Miedzyrzecz (myăn-dzû′zhĕch) Pol.	52·26 N	15·35 E
121	Mielec (myĕ′lĕts) Pol.	50·17 N	21·27 E
76	Mier (myâr) Mex.	26·26 N	99·08 W
124	Mieres (myā′rās) Sp.	43·14 N	5·45 W
120	Mieringen Switz.	46·45 N	8·11 E
90	Mier y Noriega (myâr′ê nô-rê-ā′gä) Mex.	22·28 N	100·08 W
120	Miessen (mē′sĕn) Ger.	51·11 N	13·28 E
139	Migdal Ashkelon (mĭg′däl äsh′kĕ-lōn) Isr. (Palestine In.)	31·40 N	34·36 E
129	Migorod Sov. Un.	49·56 N	33·36 E
90	Miguel Auza (mē-gĕ′l-ä-ōō′zä) Mex.	24·17 N	103·27 W
100	Miguel Pereira (pĕ-rā′-rä) Braz. (In.)	22·27 S	43·28 W
95	Mija, Monte (Mtn.) (mô′n-tĕ-mē′kä) Dom. Rep.	19·10 N	71·15 W
125	Mijares (R.) (mē-hä′râs) Sp.	40·05 N	0·42 W
153	Mikage (mē′kȧ-gȧ) Jap. (Ōsaka In.)	34·42 N	135·15 E
153	Mikawa-Wan (B.) (mē′kä-wä wän) Jap.	34·43 N	137·09 E
128	Mikhaylov (mē-kāy′lôf) Sov. Un.	54·14 N	39·03 E
129	Mikhaylovka Sov. Un.	47·16 N	35·12 E
133	Mikhaylovka Sov. Un.	50·05 N	43·10 E
136	Mikhaylovka (mê-kä′ē-lôf-kä) Sov. Un. (Urals In.)	55·35 N	57·57 E
136	Mikhaylovka Sov. Un. (Leningrad In.)	59·20 N	30·21 E
136	Mikhnëvo (mĭk-nyô′vô) Sov. Un. (Moskva In.)	55·08 N	37·57 E
153	Miki (mē′kē) Jap. (Ōsaka In.)	34·47 N	134·59 E
167	Mikindani (mê-kēn-dä′nê) Tan.	10·17 S	40·06 E
119	Mikkeli (mēk′ĕ-lĭ) Fin.	61·42 N	27·14 E
127	Míkonos (I.) Grc.	37·26 N	25·30 E
120	Mikulov (mĭ′kōō-lôf) Czech.	48·47 N	16·39 E
153	Mikuni (mē′kōō-nê) Jap.	36·09 N	136·14 E
153	Mikuni-Sammyaku (Mts.) (sâm′myä-kōō) Jap.	36·51 N	138·38 E
153	Mikura (I.) (mē′kōō-rä) Jap.	33·53 N	139·26 E

ăt; finăl; rāte; senâte; ärm; åsk; sofȧ; fâre; ch-choose; dh-as th in other; bē; ēvent; bĕt; recĕnt; cratēr; g-go; gh-guttural g; bĭt; ĭ-short neutral; rīde; ĸ-guttural k as ch in German ich;

Page	Name Pronunciation	Region	Lat. °′	Long. °′
164	Mila (mē'lä)	Alg.	36·30 N	6.16 E
71	Milaca (mê-lăk'ȧ)	Minn.	45·45 N	93·41 W
80	Milan (mī'lăn)	Mich.	42·05 N	83·40 W
73	Milan	Mo.	40·13 N	93·07 W
78	Milan	Tenn.	35·54 N	88·47 W
	Milan, see Milano			
126	Milano (Milan) (mê-lä'nō)	It.	45·29 N	9·12 E
133	Milas (mê'läs)	Tur.	37·10 N	27·25 E
126	Milazzo (mê-lät'sô)	It.	38·13 N	15·17 E
70	Milbank (mĭl'băŋk)	S. D.	45·13 N	96·38 W
160	Mildura (mĭl-dū'rȧ)	Austl.	34·10 S	142·18 E
67	Miles City (mīlz)	Mont.	46·24 N	105·50 W
81	Milford (mĭl'fērd)	Conn.	41·15 N	73·05 W
81	Milford	Del.	38·55 N	75·25 W
83	Milford	Mass. (Boston In.)	42·09 N	71·31 W
75	Milford	Mich. (Detroit In.)	42·35 N	83·36 W
81	Milford	N. H.	42·50 N	71·40 W
75	Milford	Ohio (Cincinnati In.)	39·11 N	84·18 W
69	Milford	Utah	38·20 N	113·05 W
116	Milford Haven (hāv'n)	Wales	51·40 N	5·10 W
113	Miliana (mêl-yä'nä)	Alg.	36·19 N	1·56 E
158	Miling (mĭl'ĭng)	Austl.	30·30 S	116·25 E
65	Milipitas (mĭl-ĭ-pĭ'tȧs)	Calif. (San Francisco In.)	37·26 N	121·54 W
67	Milk R. (mĭlk)	Mont.	48·25 N	108·45 W
68	Mill Cr.	Calif.	40·07 N	121·55 W
85	Mill Cr. (mĭl)	Can. (Edmonton In.)	53·13 N	113·25 W
122	Millau (mē-yō')	Fr.	44·06 N	3·04 E
65	Millbrae (mĭl'brā)	Calif. (San Francisco In.)	37·36 N	122·23 W
83	Millbury (mĭl'bĕr-ĭ)	Mass. (Boston In.)	42·12 N	71·46 W
78	Milledgeville (mĭl'ĕj-vĭl)	Ga.	33·05 N	83·15 W
85	Mille Iles, R. des (rê-vyâr' dā mīl'īl')	Can. (Montreal In.)	45·41 N	73·40 W
71	Mille Lac Ind. Res. (mĭl lăk')	Minn.	46·14 N	94·13 W
71	Mille Lacs (L.)	Minn.	46·25 N	93·22 W
71	Mille Lacs, Lac des (L.) (läk dĕ mēl läks)	Can.	48·52 N	90·53 W
79	Millen (mĭl'ĕn)	Ga.	32·47 N	81·55 W
70	Miller (mĭl'ēr)	S. D.	44·31 N	99·00 W
129	Millerovo (mĭl'ĕ-rô-vô)	Sov. Un.	48·58 N	40·27 E
80	Millersburg (mĭl'ērz-bûrg)	Ky.	38·15 N	84·10 W
80	Millersburg	Ohio	40·35 N	81·55 W
81	Millersburg	Pa.	40·35 N	76·55 W
82	Millerton (mĭl'ēr-tŭn)	Can.	46·56 N	65·40 W
83	Millertown (mĭl'ēr-toun)	Can.	48·48 N	56·33 W
160	Millicent (mĭl-ĭ'sĕnt)	Austl.	37·30 S	140·20 E
82	Millinocket (mĭl-ĭ-nŏk'ĕt)	Maine	45·40 N	68·44 W
83	Millis (mĭl'ĭs)	Mass. (Boston In.)	42·10 N	71·22 W
74	Millstadt (mĭl'stăt)	Ill. (St. Louis In.)	38·27 N	90·06 W
84	Millstone R. (mĭl'stōn)	N. J. (New York In.)	40·27 N	74·38 W
158	Millstream (mĭl'strēm)	Austl.	21·45 S	117·10 E
82	Milltown (mĭl'toun)	Can.	45·13 N	67·19 W
75	Millvale (mĭl'vāl)	Pa. (Pittsburgh In.)	40·29 N	79·58 W
65	Mill Valley (mĭl)	Calif. (San Francisco In.)	37·54 N	122·32 W
81	Millville (mĭl'vĭl)	N. J.	39·25 N	75·00 W
123	Milly-la-Forêt (mē-yē'-la-fō-rĕ')	Fr. (Paris In.)	48·24 N	2·28 E
166	Milnerton (mĭl'nēr-tŭn)	S. Afr. (Cape Town In.)	33·52 S	18·30 E
70	Milnor (mĭl'nēr)	N. D.	46·17 N	97·29 W
82	Milo (mī'lō)	Maine	44·16 N	69·01 W
	Milo (I.), see Mílos			
127	Mílos (Milo) (I.) (mē'lŏs)	Grc.	36·45 N	24·35 E
91	Milpa Alta (mē'l-pä-ȧ'l-tä)	Mex. (Mexico In.)	19·11 N	99·01 W
78	Milton (mĭl'tŭn)	Fla.	30·37 N	87·02 W
74	Milton	Ill. (St. Louis In.)	38·54 N	90·08 W
83	Milton	Mass. (Boston In.)	42·16 N	71·03 W
81	Milton	Pa.	41·00 N	76·50 W
74	Milton	Utah (Salt Lake City In.)	41·04 N	111·44 W
65	Milton	Wash. (Seattle In.)	47·15 N	122·20 W
71	Milton	Wis.	42·45 N	89·00 W
66	Milton-Freewater	Ore.	45·57 N	118·25 W
85	Milton West	Can. (Toronto In.)	43·31 N	79·53 W
75	Milwaukee	Wis. (Milwaukee In.)	43·03 N	87·55 W
89	Milwaukee Depth	Atl. O.	19·45 N	68·00 W
75	Milwaukee R.	Wis. (Milwaukee In.)	43·10 N	87·56 W
65	Milwaukie (mĭl-wô'kē)	Ore. (Portland In.)	45·27 N	122·38 W
91	Mimiapan (mē-myä-pàn')	Mex. (Mexico In.)	19·26 N	99·28 W
85	Mimico (mĭ'mĭ-kō)	Can. (Toronto In.)	43·37 N	79·30 W
101	Mimoso do Sul (mē-mô'sō-dô-sōō'l)	Braz. (Rio de Janeiro In.)	21·03 S	41·21 W
125	Mina (R.) (mē'nȧ)	Alg.	35·24 N	0·51 E
153	Minakuchi (mē'nȧ-kōō'chē)	Jap.	34·59 N	136·06 E
94	Minas (mē'näs)	Cuba	21·30 N	77·35 W
139	Minas	Indon. (Singapore In.)	0·52 N	101·29 E
100	Minas (mē'näs)	Ur.	34·18 S	55·12 W
92	Minas, Sierra de las (Mts.) (syĕr'rä dā läs mē'näs)	Guat.	15·08 N	90·25 W
82	Minas Basin (mī'nȧs)	Can.	45·19 N	64·10 W
82	Minas Chan.	Can.	45·13 N	64·55 W
92	Minas de Oro (mē'-näs-dĕ-ô-rô)	Hond.	14·52 N	87·19 W
124	Minas de Ríontinto (mē'näs dā rē-ô-tēn'tō)	Sp.	37·43 N	6·35 W
99	Minas Gerais (State) (mē'näzh-zhĕ-rä'ēs)	Braz.	17·45 S	43·50 W
99	Minas Novas (mē'näzh nō'vàzh)	Braz.	17·20 S	42·19 W
70	Minatare (L.) (mĭn'ȧ-târ)	Nebr.	41·56 N	103·07 W
91	Minatitlán (mê-nä-tē-tlän')	Mex.	17·59 N	94·33 W
90	Minatitlán	Mex.	19·21 N	104·02 W
153	Minato (mē'nȧ-tô)	Jap. (Tōkyō In.)	35·13 N	139·52 E
116	Minch, The (Chan.)	Scot.	58·04 N	6·04 W
116	Minch, The Little (Chan.) (mĭnch)	Scot.	56·85 N	6·42 W
151	Min Chiang (R.)	China	26·30 N	118·30 E
151	Min Chiang (R.)	China	29·30 N	104·00 E
155	Mindanao (I.) (mĭn-dä-nou')	Phil.	7·30 N	125·10 E
155	Mindanao Sea	Phil.	8·55 N	124·00 E
120	Minden (mĭn'dĕn)	Ger.	52·17 N	8·58 E
77	Minden	La.	32·36 N	93·19 W
72	Minden	Nebr.	40·30 N	98·54 W
155	Mindoro (I.) (mĭn-dō'rō)	Phil. (Manila In.)	13·04 N	121·06 E
155	Mindoro Str.	Phil. (Manila In.)	12·28 N	120·33 E
136	Mindyak (mēn'dyăk)	Sov. Un. (Urals In.)	54·01 N	58·48 E
84	Mineola (mĭn-ê-ō'lȧ)	N. Y. (New York In.)	40·43 N	73·38 W
77	Mineola	Tex.	32·39 N	95·31 W
90	Mineral del Chico (mê-nå-räl'dĕl chē'kô)	Mex.	20·13 N	98·46 W
90	Mineral del Monte (mê-nȧ-räl dĕl mōn'tâ)	Mex.	20·18 N	98·39 W
133	Mineral'nyye Vody	Sov. Un.	44·10 N	43·15 E
71	Mineral Point (mĭn'ēr-ăl)	Wis.	42·50 N	90·10 W
76	Minerál Wells (mĭn'ēr-ăl wĕlz)	Tex.	32·48 N	98·06 W
80	Minerva (mĭ-nûr'vȧ)	Ohio	40·45 N	81·10 W
126	Minervino (mē-nĕr-vē'nô)	It.	41·07 N	16·05 E
153	Mineyama (mē-nĕ-yä'mä)	Jap.	35·38 N	135·05 E
82	Mingan (mĭŋ'gȧn)	Can.	50·19 N	64·02 W
133	Mingechaur (R.)	Sov. Un.	41·00 N	47·20 E
158	Mingenew (mĭn'gĕ-nū)	Austl.	29·15 S	115·45 E
148	Mingkuang (mĭng'gōōäng)	China	32·41 N	118·00 E
80	Mingo Junction (mĭŋ'gō)	Ohio	40·15 N	80·40 W
124	Minho (Reg.) (mēn yōō)	Port.	41·32 N	8·13 W
94	Minho (R.)	Jam.	17·55 N	77·20 W
124	Minho, Rio (R.) (rê'ō-mē'n-yô)	Port.	41·48 N	9·05 W
85	Ministik L. (mĭ-nĭs'tĭk)	Can. (Edmonton In.)	53·23 N	113·05 W
164	Minna (mĭn'ȧ)	Nig.	9·40 N	6·34 E
73	Minneapoli (mĭn-ê-ăp'ô-lĭ)	Kans.	39·07 N	97·41 W
74	Minneapolis (mĭn-ê-ăp'ô-lĭs)	Minn. (Minneapolis, St. Paul In.)	44·58 N	93·15 W
86	Minnedosa (mĭn-ê-dō'sȧ)	Can.	50·16 N	99·50 W
70	Minneota (mĭn-ê-ō'tȧ)	Minn.	44·34 N	95·59 W
63	Minnesota (State) (mĭn-ê-sō'tȧ)	U. S.	46·10 N	90·20 W
70	Minnesota (R.)	Minn.	45·04 N	96·03 W
71	Minnetonka (L.) (mĭn-ê-tôŋ'kȧ)	Minn.	44·52 N	93·34 W
69	Minnie Maud Cr. (mĭn'ĭmôd')	Utah	39·50 N	110·30 W
153	Mino (R.) (mē'nō)	Jap. (Ōsaka In.)	34·56 N	135·06 E
124	Miño (R.) (mē'nyō)	Sp.	42·28 N	7·48 W
80	Minonk (mī'nŏnk)	Ill.	40·55 N	89·00 W
75	Minooka (mĭ-nōō'kȧ)	Ill. (Chicago In.)	41·27 N	88·15 W
	Minorca (I.), see Menorca, Isla de			
70	Minot (mī'nŏt)	N. D.	48·13 N	101·16 W
128	Minsk (mênsk)	Sov. Un.	53·54 N	27·35 E
128	Minsk (Oblast)	Sov. Un.	53·50 N	27·43 E
121	Mińsk Mazowiecki (mên'sk mä-zô-vyĕt'skĭ)	Pol.	52·10 N	21·35 E
110	Minsterley (mĭnstēr-lē)	Eng.	52·38 N	2·55 W
82	Minto (mĭn'tô)	Can.	46·05 N	66·05 W
87	Minto (L.)	Can.	57·18 N	75·50 W
126	Minturno (mēn-tōōr'nō)	It.	41·17 N	13·44 E
168	Minūf (mē-nōōf')	U. A. R. (Nile In.)	30·26 N	30·55 E
134	Minusinsk (mē-nōō-sênsk')	Sov. Un.	53·47 N	86·43 E
146	Minya Konka (Mt.) (mēn'yȧ kôŋ'kȧ)	China	29·16 N	101·46 E
136	Min'yar (mēn'yȧr)	Sov. Un. (Urals In.)	55·06 N	57·33 E
85	Miquelon L. (mĭ'kē-lôn)	Can. (Edmonton In.)	53·16 N	112·55 W
90	Miquihuana (mê-kê-wä'nä)	Mex.	23·36 N	99·45 W
121	Mir (mēr)	Sov. Un.	53·27 N	26·25 E
124	Mira (R.) (mē'rä)	Port.	37·29 N	8·15 W
101	Miracema (mē-rä-sĕ'mä)	Braz. (Rio de Janeiro In.)	21·24 S	42·10 W
99	Mirador (mē-rä-dōr')	Braz.	6·19 S	44·12 W
98	Miraflores (mē-rä-flō'räs)	Col.	5·10 N	73·13 W
98	Miraflores	Peru	16·19 S	71·20 W
88	Miraflores Locks	C. Z. (Panama Canal In.)	9·00 N	79·35 W
95	Miragoâne (mē-rä-gwän')	Hai.	18·25 N	73·05 W
101	Miraí (mē-rä-ē')	Braz. (Rio de Janeiro In.)	21·13 S	42·36 W
143	Miraj (mê-rŭj')	India	16·55 N	74·40 E
74	Mira Loma (mĭ'rȧ lō'mȧ)	Calif. (Los Angeles In.)	34·01 N	117·32 W
68	Miramar (mĭr'ȧ-mär)	Calif. (San Diego In.)	32·53 N	117·08 W
122	Miramas	Fr. (Marseille In.)	43·35 N	5·00 E
82	Miramichi (R.)	Can.	46·36 N	66·08 W
82	Miramichi B. (mĭr'ȧ-mê'shē)	Can.	47·14 N	64·45 W
98	Miranda (mē-rä'n-dä)	Col. (In.)	3·14 N	76·11 W
99	Miranda	Ven. (In.)	10·09 N	68·24 W
99	Miranda (State)	Ven. (In.)	10·17 N	66·41 W
124	Miranda de Elbro (mē-rä'n-dä-dĕ-ĕ'l-brô)	Sp.	42·42 N	2·59 W
124	Miranda do Duero (mê-rän'dä dōō-dwĕ'rô)	Port.	41·30 N	6·17 W
124	Mirandela (mê-rän-dä'lȧ)	Port.	41·28 N	7·10 W
76	Mirando City (mĭr-ăn'dō)	Tex.	27·25 N	99·03 W
95	Mira Por Vos Islets (Is.) (mē'rä pôr vōs')	Ba. Is.	22·05 N	74·30 W
95	Mira Por Vos Pass (Str.)	Ba. Is.	22·10 N	74·35 W
144	Mirbāt	Mus. & Om.	16·58 N	54·42 E
95	Mirebalais (mēr-bȧ-lĕ')	Hai.	18·50 N	72·05 W
123	Mirecourt (mēr-kōōr')	Fr.	48·20 N	6·08 E
122	Mirepoix (mēr-pwä')	Fr.	43·06 N	1·52 E
110	Mirfield (mûr'fēld)	Eng.	53·41 N	1·42 W
154	Miri (mē'rē)	Sar.	4·13 N	113·56 E
100	Mirim, L. (mê-rêN')	Braz.-Ur.	33·00 S	53·15 W
129	Miropol'ye (mē-rô-pôl'yĕ)	Sov. Un.	51·02 N	35·13 E
142	Mirzapur (mēr'zä-pōōr)	India	25·12 N	82·38 E
164	Misa	Togo	7·00 N	00·34 E
153	Misaki (mē'sȧ-kê)	Jap. (Tōkyō In.)	35·08 N	139·37 E
91	Misantla (mê-sän'tlä)	Mex.	19·55 N	96·49 W
82	Miscou (I.) (mĭs'kō)	Can.	47·58 N	64·35 W
82	Miscou Pt.	Can.	48·04 N	64·25 W
125	Miseno, C. (mê-zĕ'nō)	It. (Nápoli In.)	40·33 N	14·12 E
93	Misery, Mt. (mĭz'rē-ĭ)	Neth. Antilles (Le. & Wind. Is. In.)	17·28 N	62·47 W
152	Mishan (mĭ'shäN)	China	45·32 N	132·19 E
80	Mishawaka (mĭsh-ȧ-wôk'ȧ)	Ind.	41·45 N	86·15 W
153	Mishima (mē'shê-mä)	Jap.	35·09 N	138·56 E
100	Misiones (Prov.) (mê-syō'näs)	Arg.	27·00 S	54·30 W
93	Miskito, Cayos (Is.)	Nic.	14·34 N	82·30 W
121	Miskolc (mĭsh'kôlts)	Hung.	48·07 N	20·50 E
155	Misol (I.) (mê-sōl')	Neth. N. Gui.	2·00 S	130·05 E
71	Misquah Hills (mĭs-kwä' hĭlz)	Minn.	47·50 N	90·30 W
168	Miṣr al Jadīdah (Ruins)	U. A. R. (Nile In.)	30·06 N	31·35 E
165	Misratāh	Libya	32·23 N	14·58 E
87	Missinaibi (R.) (mĭs'ĭn-ä'ê-bê)	Can.	50·27 N	83·01 W
74	Mission (mĭsh'ŭn)	Mo. (Kansas City In.)	39·02 N	94·39 W
76	Mission	Tex.	26·14 N	98·19 W
65	Mission City (sĭ'tĭ)	Can. (Vancouver In.)	49·08 N	122·19 W
80	Mississinewa (R.) (mĭs-ĭ-sĭn'ê-wä)	Ind.	40·30 N	85·45 W
63	Mississippi (State) (mĭs-ĭ-sĭp'ê)	U. S.	32·30 N	89·45 W
81	Mississippi (L.)	Can.	45·05 N	76·15 W
63	Mississippi (R.)	U. S.	31·50 N	91·30 W
84	Mississippi Delta, The	La. (New Orleans In.)	28·59 N	89·14 W
78	Mississippi Sd.	Miss.	34·16 N	89·10 W
67	Missoula (mĭ-zōō'lȧ)	Mont.	46·52 N	114·00 W
63	Missouri (State) (mĭ-sōō'rê)	U. S.	38·00 N	93·40 W
63	Missouri (R.)	U. S.	40·40 N	96·00 W
77	Missouri City	Tex. (In.)	29·37 N	95·32 W
62	Missouri Coteau, (Plat.)	U. S.	47·30 N	101·00 W
70	Missouri Valley	Iowa	41·35 N	95·53 W
65	Mist (mĭst)	Ore. (Portland In.)	46·00 N	123·15 W
82	Mistassibi (R.) (mĭs-tȧ-sĭ'bê)	Can.	49·45 N	71·58 W
82	Mistassini (mĭs-tȧ-sĭ'nê)	Can.	48·56 N	71·55 W
87	Mistassini (L.) (mĭs-tȧ-sĭ'nê)	Can.	50·48 N	75·00 W
120	Mistelbach (mĭs'tĕl-bäk)	Aus.	48·34 N	16·33 E
92	Misteriosa, L. (mēs-tĕ-ryô'sä)	Mex. (Yucatan In.)	18·05 N	90·15 W
126	Mistretta (mê-strĕt'tä)	It.	37·54 N	14·22 E
90	Mita, Punta de (Pt.) (pōō'n-tä-dĕ-mē'tä)	Mex.	20·44 N	105·34 W
153	Mitaka (mê'tä-kä)	Jap. (Tōkyō In.)	35·42 N	139·34 E
74	Mitchell (mĭch'ĕl)	Ill. (St. Louis In.)	38·46 N	90·05 W
80	Mitchell	Ind.	38·45 N	86·25 W
70	Mitchell	Nebr.	41·56 N	103·49 W
70	Mitchell	S. D.	43·42 N	98·01 W
159	Mitchell (R.)	Austl.	15·30 S	142·15 E
79	Mitchell, Mt	N. C.	35·47 N	82·15 W
168	Mīt Ghamr	U. A. R. (Nile In.)	30·43 N	31·20 E
127	Mitilíni	Grc.	39·09 N	26·35 E
153	Mito (mē'tō)	Jap.	36·20 N	140·23 E
153	Mitsu (mēt'sōō)	Jap.	34·21 N	132·49 E
120	Mittelland (can.) (mĭt'ĕl-lănd)	Ger.	52·18 N	10·42 E
111	Mittenwalde (mē'tĕn-väl-dĕ)	Ger. (Berlin In.)	52·16 N	13·33 E
120	Mittweida (mĭt-vī'dä)	Ger.	50·59 N	12·58 E
136	Mityayevo (mĭt-yä'yĕ-vô)	Sov. Un. (Urals In.)	60·17 N	61·02 E
129	Mius (R.) (mê-ōōs')	Sov. Un.	47·30 N	38·48 E
153	Miwa (mē'wä)	Jap. (Ōsaka In.)	34·32 N	135·51 E
92	Mixico (mēs'kô)	Guat.	14·37 N	90·37 W
91	Mixquiahuala (mēs-kē-wä'lä)	Mex.	20·12 N	99·13 W
90	Mixteco (R.) (mês-tä'kō)	Mex.	17·45 N	98·10 W
153	Miyake (mē'yä-kȧ)	Jap. (Ōsaka In.)	34·35 N	135·34 E
153	Miyake (I.) (mē'yä-kȧ)	Jap.	34·06 N	139·21 E
153	Miyakonojō (mē'yȧ-kō'nō-jō)	Jap.	31·42 N	131·03 E
153	Miyazaki (mē'yä-zä'kē)	Jap.	31·55 N	131·27 E
153	Miyoshi (mē-yō'shē')	Jap.	34·48 N	132·49 E
114	Mizdah (mēz'dä)	Libya	31·29 N	13·09 E
127	Mizil (mē'zēl)	Rom.	45·01 N	26·30 E
	Mizonokuchi, see Takatsu			
118	Mjölby (myûl'bü)	Swe.	58·20 N	15·09 E
118	Mjörn (L.)	Swe.	57·55 N	12·22 E
118	Mjösa (myûsȧ)	Nor.	60·41 N	11·25 E
118	Mjösvatn (myûs-vät'n)	Nor.	59·55 N	7·50 E
166	Mkalamo (m'kä-lä'mō)	Tan.	4·07 S	34·38 E
120	Mladá Boleslav (mlä'dä bô'lĕ-släf)	Czech.	50·26 N	14·52 E
121	Mława (mwä'vȧ)	Pol.	53·07 N	20·25 E
127	Mljet (I.) (mlyĕt)	Yugo.	42·40 N	17·45 E
155	Moa (I.)	Indon.	8·30 S	128·30 E
69	Moab (mō'ăb)	Utah	38·35 N	109·35 W
68	Moapa River Ind. Res. (mō-ăp'ȧ)	Nev.	36·44 N	115·01 W
165	Mobaye (mô-bä'y')	Cen. Afr. Rep.	4·30 N	21·10 E
73	Moberly (mō'bēr-lĭ)	Mo.	39·24 N	92·25 W
78	Mobile (mô-bēl')	Ala.	30·42 N	88·03 W
78	Mobile (R.)	Ala.	31·15 N	88·00 W

ng-sing; ŋ-baŋk; N-nasalized n; nŏd; cŏmmit; ōld; ôbey; ôrder; fōōd; fŏŏt; ou-out; s-soft; sh-dish; th-thin; pūre; ûnite; ûrn; stŭd; circŭs; ü-as "y" in study; '-indeterminate vowel.

238 Mobile–Montoro PRONOUNCING INDEX

Page	Name Pronunciation Region	Lat. °′	Long. °′
78	Mobile B. . . . . . Ala.	30·26 N	87·56 W
70	Mobridge (mō′brĭj) . . . . S. D.	45·32 N	100·26 W
95	Moca (mô′kä) . . . . Dom. Rep.	19·25 N	70·35 W
167	Moçambique (mō-sän-bē′kĕ) . Moz.	15·07 S	40·48 E
166	Moçâmedes . . . . . Ang.	15·10 S	12·15 E
166	Moçâmedes (Reg.) (mô-zà-mĕ-dĕs) Ang.	16·00 S	12·15 E
144	Mocha (mō′kä) . . . . Yemen	13·11 N	43·20 E
90	Mochitlán (mō-chē-tlän′) . . . Mex.	17·10 N	99·19 W
166	Mochudi (mō-choo′dē) . . . Bech.	24·13 S	26·07 E
101	Mococa (mô-kô′kà) Braz. (Rio de Janeiro In.)	21·29 S	46·58 W
90	Moctezuma (môk′tà-zoo′mä) Mex.	22·44 N	101·06 W
167	Modderfontein . . . . S. Afr. (Johannesburg & Pretoria In.)	26·06 S	28·10 E
168	Modderpoort . . . . S. Afr. (Johannesburg & Pretoria In.)	29·08 S	27·27 E
126	Modena (mô′dĕ-nä) . . . . It.	44·38 N	10·54 E
68	Modesto (mô-dĕs′tō) . . . . Calif.	37·39 N	121·00 W
113	Modica (mô-dē-kä) . . . . It.	36·50 N	14·43 E
111	Mödling (mûd′lĭng) Aus. (Wien In.)	48·06 N	16·17 E
118	Möen (I.) (mû′ĕn) . . . . Den.	54·54 N	12·30 E
99	Moengo . . . . Fr. Gu.	5·43 N	54·19 W
123	Moers (mûrs) . . . . Ger. (Ruhr In.)	51·27 N	6·38 E
72	Moffat Tun. (môf′ăt) . . . . Colo.	39·52 N	106·20 W
168	Mogadiscio (mô-gä-dē′shō) Som. (Horn of Afr. In.)	2·08 N	45·22 E
164	Mogador (mŏg-à-dōr′) . . . . Mor.	31·34 N	9·44 W
75	Mogadore (mŏg-à-dōr′) Ohio (Cleveland In.)	41·04 N	81·23 W
146	Mogaung (mô-gä′ŏŏng) . . . . Bur.	25·30 N	96.52 E
101	Mogi das Cruzes (mô-gê-däs-kroo′sĕs) Braz. (Rio de Janeiro In.)	23·33 S	46·10 W
101	Mogi-Guaçu (R.) (mô-gê-gwä′soo) Braz. (Rio de Janeiro In.)	22·06 S	47·12 W
128	Mogilëv (mô-gê-lyôf′) . . . Sov. Un.	53·53 N	30·22 E
128	Mogilëv (Oblast) (mô-gê-lyôf′) Sov. Un.	53·28 N	30·15 E
129	Mogilëv-Podol′skiy (mô-gê-lyôf) (pô-dôl′skĭ) Sov. Un.	48·27 N	27·51 E
121	Mogilno (mô-gēl′nô) . . . . Pol.	52·38 N	17·58 E
101	Mogi-Mirim (mô-gê-mē-rē′n) Braz. (Rio de Janeiro In.)	22·26 S	46·57 W
146	Mogok (mô-gōk′) . . . . Bur.	23·14 N	96.38 E
69	Mogollon (mō-gô-yōn′) . . . N. Mex.	33·25 N	108·45 W
69	Mogollon, Plat. (mō-gô-yōn′) Ariz.	34·26 N	111·17 W
168	Mogol R. (mô-gŏl) . . . . S. Afr. (Johannesburg & Pretoria In.)	24·12 S	27·55 E
124	Moguer (mô-gĕr′) . . . . Sp.	37·15 N	6.50 W
121	Mohács (mô′häch) . . . . Hung.	45·59 N	18·38 E
167	Mohales Hoek . . . . Bas. (Natal In.)	30·09 S	27·28 E
70	Mohall (mō′hôl) . . . . N. D.	48·46 N	101·29 W
68	Mohave (L.) (mô-hä′vä) . . . . Nev.	35·23 N	114·40 W
81	Mohawk (R.) (mō′hôk) . . . N. Y.	43·15 N	75·20 W
167	Mohéli (I.) (mô-ā-lē′) (mô-hā′lē) Comores, Arch. des	12·23 S	43·38 E
147	Moho (mō′hō′) . . . . China	53·33 N	122·30 E
119	Mõisaküla (mẽē′sà-kü′là) . Sov. Un.	58·07 N	25·12 E
87	Moisie (R.) (mwä-zē′) . . . . Can.	51·24 N	66·11 W
122	Moissac (mwä-sàk′) . . . . Fr.	44·07 N	1·05 E
125	Moita (mô-ē′tà) . Port. (Lisboa In.)	38·39 N	9·00 W
68	Mojave . . . . Calif.	35·06 N	118·09 W
68	Mojave (R.) (mô-hä′vä) . . . . Calif.	34·46 N	117·24 W
68	Mojave Desert . . . . Calif.	35·05 N	117·30 W
153	Moji (mō′jē) . . . . Jap.	33·56 N	130·59 E
68	Mokelumne (R.) (mō-kē-lŭm′nē) Calif.	38·12 N	121·09 W
167	Mokhotlong . . . . Bas. (Natal In.)	29·18 S	29·06 E
152	Mokpo (môk′pō′) . . . . Kor.	34·50 N	126·30 E
132	Moksha (R.) (môk-shä′) . Sov. Un.	54·50 N	43·20 E
111	Mol . . . . Bel. (Bruxelles In.)	51·21 N	5·09 E
126	Molat (I.) (mō′lät) . . . . Yugo.	44·15 N	14·40 E
121	Moldavia (Reg.) . . . . Rom.	47·20 N	27·12 E
118	Molde (môl′dĕ) . . . . Nor.	62·44 N	7·15 E
118	Molde Fd. (môl′dĕ fyôrd) . . . . Nor.	62·40 N	7·05 E
121	Moldova R. . . . . Rom.	47·17 N	26·27 E
166	Molepolole (mō-lā-pô-lō′là) . Bech.	24·15 S	25·33 E
126	Molfetta (môl-fĕt′tä) . . . . It.	41·11 N	16·38 E
101	Molina (mŏ-lē′nä) Chile (Santiago In.)	35·07 S	71·17 W
124	Molina de Aragón (mô-lē′nä dĕ ä-rä-gô′n) . . Sp.	41·40 N	1·54 W
124	Molína de Segura (mô-lē′nä dĕ sĕ-goo′rä) . . . Sp.	38·03 N	1·07 W
71	Moline (mŏ-lēn′) . . . . Ill.	41·31 N	90·34 W
166	Moliro . . . . Con. L.	8·08 S	30·30 E
126	Moliterno (mōl-ē-tĕr′nō) . . . . It.	40·13 N	15·54 E
98	Mollendo (mō-lyĕn′dō) . . . . Peru	17·02 S	71·59 W
64	Moller, Port (pōrt mōl′ĕr) . . Alaska	56·18 N	161·30 W
118	Mölndal (mûln′däl) . . . . Swe.	57·39 N	12·01 E
129	Molochnaya (R.) (mô-lôch′nà-yà) (rĕ-kä′) Sov. Un.	47·05 N	35·22 E
129	Molochnoye, Ozero (L.) (ô′zĕ-rô mô-lôch′nô-yĕ) Sov. Un.	46·35 N	35·32 E
128	Molodechno (mô-lô-dĕch′nō) Sov. Un.	54·18 N	26·57 E
128	Molodechno (Oblast) . . . . Sov. Un.	54·27 N	27·38 E
136	Molody Tud (mō-lō-dô′ē too′d) Sov. Un. (Moskva In.)	55·17 N	37·31 E
128	Mologa (R.) (mô-lô′gà) . Sov. Un.	58·05 N	35·43 E
157	Molokai (I.) (mō-lô-kä′ē) Hawaii (In.)	21·15 N	157·05 E
136	Molokcha R. (mô′lôk-chä) Sov. Un. (Moskva In.)	56·15 N	38·29 E
166	Molopo (R.) (mō-lō-pô) . . . S. Afr.	27·45 S	20·45 E
167	Molteno (môl-tä′nô) S. Afr. (Natal In.)	31·24 S	26·23 E
155	Molucca Pass. (mô-lŭk′à) . . Indon.	1·55 N	126·30 E
155	Moluccas (Is.) (mô-lŭk′àz) . Indon.	2·40 S	127·15 E
155	Molucca Sea . . . . Indon.	0·15 N	125·41 E
167	Mombasa (mōm-bä′sä) . . . . Ken.	4·01 S	39·43 E
152	Mombetsu (môm′bĕt-soo′) . . . Jap.	44·21 N	142·48 E
75	Momence (mô-mĕns′) Ill. (Chicago In.)	41·09 N	87·40 W
92	Momostenango (mô-môs-tä-näŋ′gô) . Guat.	15·02 N	91·25 W
92	Momotombo . . . . Nig.	12·25 N	86·43 W
155	Mompog Pass (mŏm-pōg′) Phil. (Manila In.)	13·35 N	122·09 E
98	Mompos (mōm-pōs′) . . . . Col.	8·05 N	74·30 W
75	Monaca (mŏ-nă′kō) Pa. (Pittsburgh In.)	40·41 N	80·17 W
123	Monaco (mŏn′à-kō) . . . . Eur.	43·43 N	7·47 E
116	Monaghan (mŏn′à-găn) . . . . Ire.	54·16 N	7·20 W
89	Mona Pass. (mō′nä) . . . . N. A.	18·00 N	68·10 W
113	Monastir (mōn-às-tēr′) . . . . Tun.	35·49 N	10·56 E
	Monastir, see Bitola		
129	Monastyrishche (mô-nàs-tē-rēsh′chà) . Sov. Un.	48·57 N	29·53 E
128	Monastyrshchina (mô-nàs-tērsh′chĭ-nà) . Sov. Un.	54·19 N	31·49 E
99	Monção (moŋ-souɴ′) . . . . Braz.	3·39 S	45·23 W
124	Moncayo (Mtn.) (môn-kä′yō) . Sp.	41·44 N	1·48 W
132	Monchegorsk (mōn′chĕ-gôrsk) Sov. Un.	69·00 N	33·35 E
123	Mönchen Gladbach (mûn′kĕn gläd′bäk) Ger. (Ruhr In.)	51·12 N	6·28 E
124	Moncique, Serra de (Mts.) (sĕr′rä dä mōn-chē′kĕ) . Port.	37·22 N	8.37 W
76	Monclova (môn-klō′vä) . . . . Mex.	26·53 N	101·25 W
82	Moncton (mŭŋk′tŭn) . . . . Can.	46·06 N	64·49 W
124	Mondego, Cabo (C.) (kà′bō môn-dā′gŏŏ) . Port.	40·12 N	8·55 W
124	Mondêgo (R.) (môn-dĕ′gō) . Port.	40·10 N	8·36 W
166	Mondombe (môn-dôm′bā) Con. L.	0·45 S	23·06 E
124	Mondoñedo (môn-dô-nyā′dō) . . Sp.	43·35 N	7·18 W
126	Mondoví (môn-dô′vē′) . . . . It.	44·23 N	7·53 E
71	Mondovi (mŏn-dō′vĭ) . . . . Wis.	44·35 N	91·42 W
75	Monee (mŏ-nĭ) . Ill. (Chicago In.)	41·25 N	87·45 W
75	Monessen (mô-nĕs′sĕn) Pa. (Pittsburgh In.)	40·09 N	79·53 W
73	Monett (mô-nĕt′) . . . . Mo.	36·55 N	93·55 W
124	Monforte de Lemos (môn-fôr′tä dĕ lĕ′môs) . . Sp.	42·30 N	7·30 W
165	Mongala R. (mŏn-gäl′à) . . Con. L.	3·20 N	21·30 E
165	Mongalla . . . . Sud.	5·11 N	31·46 E
142	Monghyr (mōn-gēr′) . . . . India	25·23 N	86·34 E
138	Mongolia (mŏŋ-gō′lĭ-à) . . . . Asia	46·00 N	100·00 E
165	Mongoumba (mŏŋ-gŏŏm′bà) Con. B.	3·41 N	18·21 E
166	Mongu (mŏŋ-goo′) Fed. of Rh. & Nya.	15·14 S	23·07 E
92	Monkey River (mŭŋ′kĭ) Br. Hond. (Yucatan In.)	16·22 N	88·33 W
85	Monkland Sta. (mŭngk-lănd) Can. (Ottawa In.)	45·12 N	74·52 W
166	Monkoto (môn-kō′tô) . . . . Con. L.	1·45 S	20·51 E
73	Monmouth (mŏn′mŭth) (mŏn′mouth) . Ill.	40·54 N	90·38 W
84	Monmouth Junction (mŏn′mouth jŭngk′shŭn) N. J. (New York In.)	40·23 N	74·33 W
68	Mono (L.) (mō′nō) . . . . Calif.	38·04 N	119·00 W
80	Monon (mō′nŏn) . . . . Ind.	40·55 N	86·55 W
81	Monongah (mô-nŏŋ′gà) . . . W. Va.	39·25 N	80·10 W
75	Monongahela (mô-nōn-gà-hē′là) Pa. (Pittsburgh In.)	40·11 N	79·55 W
81	Monongahela (R.) . . . . W. Va.	39·30 N	80·10 W
127	Monopoli (mô-nô′pô-lē) . . . . It.	40·55 N	17·17 E
125	Monovar (mô-nō′vär) . . . . Sp.	38·26 N	0·50 W
126	Monreale (mōn-rā-ä′lā) . . . . It.	38·04 N	13·15 E
78	Monroe (mŭn-rō′) . . . . Ga.	33·47 N	83·43 W
77	Monroe . . . . La.	32·30 N	92·06 W
80	Monroe . . . . Mich.	41·55 N	83·25 W
84	Monroe . . . . N. Y. (New York In.)	41·19 N	74·11 W
79	Monroe . . . . S. C.	35·03 N	80·57 W
69	Monroe . . . . Utah	38·35 N	112·10 W
65	Monroe . . . . Wash. (Seattle In.)	47·52 N	121·58 W
71	Monroe . . . . Wis.	42·35 N	89·40 W
79	Monroe (L.) . . . . Fla.	28·50 N	81·15 W
73	Monroe City . . . . Mo.	39·38 N	91·41 W
78	Monroeville (mŭn-rō′vĭl) . . . . Ala.	31·33 N	87·19 W
74	Monrovia (mŏn-rō′vĭ-à) Calif. (Los Angeles In.)	34·09 N	118·00 W
164	Monrovia . . . . Lib.	6·21 N	10·59 W
117	Mons (môɴ′) . . . . Bel.	50·29 N	3·55 E
82	Monson (mŏn′sŭn) . . . . Maine	45·17 N	69·28 W
118	Mönsterås (mŭn′stĕr-ôs) . . . . Swe.	57·04 N	16·24 E
146	Montagh Ata (Mt.) . . . . China	38·26 N	75·23 E
87	Montagne Tremblant Park . . Can.	46·30 N	75·51 W
83	Montague (mŏn′tà-gū) . . . . Can.	46·11 N	62·35 W
80	Montague . . . . Mich.	43·30 N	86·25 W
64	Montague (I.) . . . . Alaska	60·10 N	147·00 W
155	Montalban (mŏnt-äl-băn) Phil. (Manila In.)	14·47 N	121·11 E
99	Montalbán . . . . Ven. (In.)	10·14 N	68·19 W
126	Montalcone (mōn-täl-kō′nĕ) . . . It.	45·49 N	13·30 E
124	Montalegre (mōn-tä-lā′grĕ) . . Port.	41·49 N	7·48 W
62	Montana (State) (mŏn-tăn′à) U. S.	47·10 N	111·50 W
124	Montánchez (môn-tän′châth) . . Sp.	39·18 N	6·09 W
122	Montargis (môɴ-tàr-zhē′) . . . . Fr.	47·59 N	2·42 E
123	Montataire (môɴ-tà-târ) Fr. (Paris In.)	49·15 N	2·26 E
122	Montauban (môɴ-tō-bäɴ′) . . . . Fr.	44·01 N	1·22 E
81	Montauk Pt. (mŏn-tôk′) . . . N. Y.	41·05 N	71·55 W
125	Montbanch (mōnt-bän′ch) . . . Sp.	41·20 N	1·08 E
122	Montbard (môɴ-bàr′) . . . . Fr.	47·40 N	4·19 E
123	Montbéliard (môɴ-bā-lyàr′) . . . Fr.	47·32 N	6·45 E
77	Mont Belview (mŏnt bĕl′vū) Tex. (In.)	29·51 N	94·53 W
122	Montbrison (môɴ-brē-zôɴ′) . . . . Fr.	45·38 N	4·06 E
122	Montcalm, Pic de (Pk.) (pĕk dē môɴ-kàm′) . Fr.	42·43 N	1·13 E
122	Montceau-les-Mines (môɴ-sō′lā-mēn′) . Fr.	46·39 N	4·22 E
84	Montclair (mŏnt-klâr′) N. J. (New York In.)	40·49 N	74·13 W
122	Mont-de-Marsan (môɴ-dē-màr-säɴ′) . Fr.	43·54 N	0·32 W
122	Montdidier (môɴ-dē-dyā′) . . . . Fr.	49·42 N	2·33 E
101	Monte (mŏ′n-tĕ) Arg. (Buenos Aires In.)	35·25 S	58·49 W
98	Monteagudo (mōn′tà-ä-goo′dhō) Bol.	19·49 S	63·48 W
74	Montebello (mŏn-tê-bĕl′ō) Calif. (Los Angeles In.)	34·01 N	118·06 W
85	Montebello . . . . Can. (Ottawa In.)	45·40 N	74·56 W
158	Monte Bello (Is.) . . . . Austl.	20·30 S	114·10 E
100	Monte Caseros (mŏ′n-tĕ-kä-sĕ′rôs) . Arg.	30·16 S	57·39 W
92	Mont Ecillos, Cord. de (Mts.) (kôr-dēl-yĕ′rä dĕ mō′nt ĕ-sē′l-yōs) . Hond.	14·19 N	87·52 W
95	Monte Cristi (mō′n-tĕ-krē′s-tē) Dom. Rep.	19·50 N	71·40 W
126	Montecristo, I. di (mōn′tà-krēs′tō) . It.	42·20 N	10·19 E
90	Monte Escobedo (mōn′tà ĕs-kô-bā′dhō) . Mex.	22·18 N	103·34 W
125	Monteforte Irpino (môn-tĕ-fô′r-tĕ ē′r-pē′nō) It. (Napoli In.)	40·39 N	14·42 E
124	Montefrío (mōn-tà-frē′ō) . . . . Sp.	37·20 N	4·02 W
94	Montego Bay (mŏn-tē′gō) . . . Jam.	18·30 N	77·55 W
100	Monte Grande (mŏ′n-tĕ grän′dĕ) Arg. (In.)	34·34 S	58·28 W
125	Montelavar (mōn-tĕ-là-vär′) Port. (Lisboa In.)	38·51 N	9·20 W
122	Montélimar (môɴ-tā-lē-mär′) . . Fr.	44·33 N	4·47 E
124	Montellano (mōn-tä-lyä′nō) . . . Sp.	37·00 N	5·34 W
71	Montello (mŏn-tĕl′ō) . . . . Wis.	43·47 N	89·20 W
76	Montemorelos (mōn′tà-mō-rā′lōs) Mex.	25·14 N	99·50 W
124	Montemor-o-Novo (mōɴ-tĕ-môr′ŏŏ-nô′vŏŏ) . . . Port.	38·39 N	8·11 W
	Montenegro (Reg.), see Črna Gora		
126	Montepulciano (mōn′tà-pōōl-chä′nō) . It.	43·05 N	11·48 E
122	Montereau-faut-Yonne (môɴ-t′rō′fō-yôn′) . Fr.	48·24 N	2·57 E
68	Monterey (mŏn-tĕ-rā′) . . . . Calif.	36·36 N	121·53 W
78	Monterey . . . . Tenn.	36·06 N	85·15 W
68	Monterey B. . . . . Calif.	36·48 N	122·01 W
74	Monterey Park Calif. (Los Angeles In.)	34·04 N	118·08 W
98	Montería (mōn-tà-rā′ä) . . . . Col.	8·47 N	75·57 W
100	Monteros (môn-tĕ′rôs) . . . . Arg.	27·14 S	65·29 W
125	Monterotondo (môn-tĕ-rô-tô′n-dō) It. (Roma In.)	42·03 N	12·39 E
76	Monterrey (mōn-tĕr-rā′) . . . . Mex.	25·43 N	100·19 W
126	Monte Sant′ Angelo (mô′n-tĕ săn ä′n-gzhĕ-lô) . It.	41·43 N	15·59 E
66	Montesano (mŏn-tē-sä′nō) . . Wash.	46·59 N	123·35 W
99	Montes Claros (môn-tĕs-klà′rôs) Braz.	16·44 S	43·41 W
78	Montevallo (môn-tê-văl′ō) . . . . Ala.	33·05 N	86·49 W
126	Montevarchi (mōn-tà-vär′kē) . . It.	43·30 N	11·45 E
101	Montevideo (mōn′tà-vê-dhā′ō) Ur. (Buenos Aires In.)	34·50 S	56·10 W
69	Monte Vista (mŏn′tē vĭs′tà) . Colo.	37·35 N	106·10 W
78	Montezuma (mŏn-tē-zoo′mà) . . Ga.	32·17 N	84·00 W
69	Montezuma Castle Natl. Mon. Ariz.	34·38 N	111·50 W
111	Montfoort . Neth. (Amsterdam In.)	52·02 N	4·56 E
123	Montfort l′Amaury (mŏɴ-fōr′lä-mō-rē′) Fr. (Paris In.)	48·47 N	1·49 E
122	Montfort-sur-Meu (mŏɴ-fōr-sür-mû′) . Fr.	48·09 N	1·58 W
78	Montgomery (mŏnt-gŭm′ēr-ĭ) . Ala.	32·23 N	86·17 W
142	Montgomery . . . . W. Pak.	30·43 N	73·04 E
80	Montgomery . . . . W. Va.	38·10 N	81·25 W
73	Montgomery City . . . . Mo.	38·58 N	91·29 W
73	Monticello (mŏn-tĭ-sĕl′ō) . . . . Ark.	33·38 N	91·47 W
78	Monticello . . . . Fla.	30·32 N	83·53 W
78	Monticello . . . . Ga.	33·00 N	83·11 W
80	Monticello . . . . Ill.	40·05 N	88·35 W
80	Monticello . . . . Ind.	40·40 N	86·50 W
71	Monticello . . . . Iowa	42·14 N	91·13 W
78	Monticello . . . . Ky.	36·47 N	84·50 W
82	Monticello . . . . Maine	46·19 N	67·53 W
71	Monticello . . . . Minn.	45·18 N	93·48 W
81	Monticello . . . . N. Y.	41·35 N	74·40 W
69	Monticello . . . . Utah	37·55 N	109·25 W
123	Montigny-lès-Metz (môɴ-tēn-yē′lā-mĕts′) . Fr.	49·06 N	6·07 E
125	Montijo (môn-tē′zhō) Port. (Lisboa In.)	38·42 N	8·58 W
124	Montijo (môn-tē′hō) . . . . Sp.	38·55 N	6·35 W
93	Montijo, Bahia (B.) (bä-ē′ä môn-tē′hō) . Pan.	7·36 N	81·11 W
82	Mont Joli (môɴ zhō-lē′) . . . . Can.	48·37 N	68·09 W
122	Montluçon (môɴ-lü-sôɴ′) . . . . Fr.	46·20 N	2·35 E
85	Montmagny (môɴ-màn-yē′) Can. (Quebec In.)	46·59 N	70·33 W
85	Montmorency (mŏnt-mō-rĕn′sĭ) Can. (Quebec In.)	46·53 N	71·09 W
123	Montmorency (môɴ′mô-räɴ-sē′) Fr. (Paris In.)	48·59 N	2·19 E
85	Montmorency, Rivière (R.) (rē-vyâr′ mŏnt-mō-rĕn′sĭ) Can (Quebec In.)	47·04 N	71·12 W
122	Montmorillon (môɴ′mô-rē-yôɴ′) Fr.	46·26 N	0·50 E
126	Montone (R.) (môn-tô′nĕ) . . . . It.	44·03 N	11·45 E
124	Montoro (môn-tō′rô) . . . . Sp.	38·01 N	4·22 W

ăt; finăl; rāte; senâte; ärm; àsk; sofà; fâre; ch-choose; dh-as th in other; bē; êvent; bĕt; recĕnt; cratĕr; g-go; gh-guttural g; bĭt; ĭ-short neutral; rīde; ĸ-guttural k as ch in German ich;

PRONOUNCING INDEX Montpelier–Mount Union 239

Page	Name Pronunciation Region	Lat. °'	Long. °'
80	Montpelier (mŏnt-pēl'yẽr) Ind.	40·35 N	85·20 W
67	Montpelier Idaho	42·19 N	111·19 W
80	Montpelier Ohio	41·35 N	84·35 W
81	Montpelier Vt.	44·20 N	72·35 W
122	Montpellier (môN-pĕ-lyā') Fr.	43·38 N	3·53 E
85	Montreal (mŏn-trē-ôl') Can. (Montreal In.)	45·30 N	73·35 W
85	Montreal North Can. (Montreal In.)	45·36 N	73·38 W
85	Montreal South Can. (Montreal In.)	45·31 N	73·30 W
120	Montreux (môn-trû') Switz.	46·26 N	6·52 E
74	Montrose (mŏnt-rōz) Calif. (Los Angeles In.)	34·13 N	118·13 W
69	Montrose (mŏn-trōz') Colo.	38·30 N	107·55 W
116	Montrose Scot.	56·45 N	2·25 W
75	Montrose Ohio (Cleveland In.)	41·08 N	81·38 W
81	Montrose (mŏnt-rōz') Pa.	41·50 N	75·50 W
82	Monts, Pointe des (Pt.) (pwăNt' dā môN') Can.	49·19 N	67·22 W
123	Mont St. Martin (mŏN săN mär-tăN') Fr.	49·34 N	6·13 E
93	Montserrat I. (mŏnt-sĕ-răt') W. I. F. (Le. & Wind. Is. In.)	16·48 N	62·00 W
84	Montvale (mŏnt-vāl') N. J. (New York In.)	41·02 N	74·01 W
154	Monywa (mŏn'yōō-wȧ) Bur.	22·02 N	95·16 E
126	Monza (mōn'tsä) It.	45·34 N	9·17 E
125	Monzón (mōn-thōn') Sp.	41·54 N	1·09 E
77	Moody (mōō'dĭ) Tex.	31·18 N	97·20 W
168	Mooi (R.) (mōō'ĭ) S. Afr. (Johannesburg & Pretoria In.)	26·34 S	27·03 E
167	Mooi (R.) S. Afr. (Natal In.)	29·00 S	30·15 E
167	Mooirivier S. Afr. (Natal In.)	29·14 S	29·59 E
161	Moolap Austl. (Melbourne In.)	38·11 S	144·26 E
161	Moonta (mōōn'tȧ) Austl.	34·05 S	137·42 E
158	Moora (mŏŏr'ȧ) Austl.	30·35 S	116·12 E
67	Moorcroft (mōr'krŏft) Wyo.	44·17 N	104·59 W
158	Moore (L.) (mōr) Austl.	29·50 S	128·12 E
111	Moorenweis (mō'rĕn-vīz) Ger. (München In.)	48·10 N	11·05 E
84	Moorestown (mōrz'toun) N. J. (Philadelphia In.)	39·58 N	74·56 W
75	Mooresville (mōrz'vĭl) Ind. (Indianapolis In.)	39·37 N	86·22 W
79	Mooresville (mōrz'vĭl) N. C.	35·34 N	80·48 W
70	Moorhead (mōr'hĕd) Minn.	46·52 N	96·44 W
78	Moorhead Miss.	33·25 N	90·30 W
	Moorland, see Landes		
86	Moose (L.) (mōōs) Can.	54·14 N	99·28 W
87	Moose (R.) Can.	51·01 N	80·42 W
85	Moose Creek Can. (Ottawa In.)	45·16 N	74·58 W
82	Moosehead (mōōs'hĕd) Maine	45·37 N	69·15 W
86	Moose Jaw (mōōs jô) Can.	50·26 N	105·40 W
82	Mooselookmeguntic (L.) (mōō-sĕ-lŏŏk-mê-gŭn'tĭk) Maine	44·54 N	70·20 W
86	Moose Mtn. Can.	50·10 N	102·54 W
80	Moosilauke (Mtn.) (mōō-sĭ-lȧ'kē) N. H.	44·00 N	71·50 W
111	Moosinning (mō'zē-nēng) Ger. (München In.)	48·17 N	11·51 E
87	Moosonee (mōō'sô-nē) Can.	51·20 N	80·44 W
164	Mopti (mŏp'tê) Mali	14·27 N	3·56 W
98	Moquegua (mô-kā'gwä) Peru	17·15 S	70·54 W
121	Mór (mōr) Hung.	47·51 N	18·14 E
71	Mora (mō'rȧ) Minn.	45·52 N	93·18 W
72	Mora N. Mex.	35·58 N	105·17 W
124	Mora (mô-rä) Sp.	39·42 N	3·45 W
125	Mora Sp.	41·06 N	0·25 E
142	Morādābād (mô-rä-dä-bäd') India	28·57 N	78·48 E
92	Morales (mô-rä'lĕs) Guat.	15·29 N	88·46 W
167	Moramanga (mō-rä-mäŋ'gä) Malagasy	18·48 S	48·09 E
123	Morant (mŏr-äN') Fr. (Paris In.)	48·35 N	2·54 E
95	Morant Pt. (mô-rănt') Jam.	17·55 N	76·10 W
118	Morastrand (mō'rä-strănd) Swe.	61·00 N	14·29 E
125	Morata de Tajuña (mô-rä'tä dā tä-hōō'nyä) Sp. (Madrid In.)	40·14 N	3·27 W
121	Morava (Moravia) (Prov.) (mô'rä-vä) (mô-rā'vĭ-ȧ) Czech.	49·21 N	16·57 E
120	Morava R. Czech.	49·53 N	16·53 E
	Moravia, see Morava		
99	Morawhanna (mô-rȧ-hwä'nȧ) Br. Gu.	8·12 N	59·33 W
116	Moray Firth (mŭr'ā) Scot.	57·41 N	3·55 W
118	Mörbylånga (mûr'bü-lôŋ'gȧ) Swe.	56·32 N	16·23 E
86	Morden (môr'dĕn) Can.	49·08 N	98·19 W
161	Mordialloc (môr-dĭ-ăl'ŏk) Austl. (Melbourne In.)	38·00 S	145·05 E
116	More, Ben (Mtn.) (bĕn môr) Scot.	58·09 N	5·01 W
70	Moreau (R.) (mô-rō') S. D.	45·13 N	102·22 W
116	Morecambe B. (mōr'kăm) Eng.	53·55 N	3·25 W
160	Moree (mō'rē) Austl.	29·20 S	149·50 E
80	Morehead Ky.	38·10 N	83·25 W
79	Morehead City (mōr'hĕd) N. C.	34·43 N	76·43 W
73	Morehouse (mōr'hous) Mo.	36·49 N	89·41 W
90	Morelia (mô-rā'lyä) Mex.	19·43 N	101·12 W
125	Morella (mô-räl'yä) Sp.	40·38 N	0·07 W
90	Morelos (mô-rā'lōs) Mex.	22·46 N	102·36 W
76	Morelos Mex.	28·24 N	100·51 W
91	Morelos Mex. (Mexico In.)	19·41 N	99·29 W
76	Morelos, R. Mex.	25·27 N	99·35 W
65	Morena, Sierra (Mt.) (syĕr'rä mô-rā'nä) Calif. (San Francisco In.)	37·24 N	122·19 W
124	Morena, Sierra (Mts.) (syĕr'rä mô-rā'nä) Sp.	38·15 N	5·45 W
69	Morenci (mô-rĕn'sĭ) Ariz.	33·05 N	109·25 W
80	Morenci Mich.	41·50 N	84·05 W
100	Moreno (mô-rĕ'nō) Arg. (In.)	34·25 S	58·47 W
74	Moreno Calif. (Los Angeles In.)	33·55 N	117·09 W
94	Mores (I.) (mōrz) Ba. Is.	26·20 N	77·35 W
65	Moresby (I.) (mōrz'bĭ) Can. (Vancouver In.)	48·43 N	123·15 W
86	Moresby I. Can	52·54 N	131·00 W
160	Moreton (I.) (môr'tŭn) Austl.	26·53 S	152·42 E
160	Moreton B. (môr'tŭn) Austl.	27·12 S	153·10 E
85	Morewood (mōr'wŏŏd) Can. (Ottawa In.)	45·11 N	75·17 W
67	Morgan (môr'gȧn) Utah	41·04 N	111·42 W
77	Morgan City La.	29·41 N	91·11 W
80	Morganfield (môr'gȧn-fēld) Ky.	37·40 N	87·55 W
167	Morgansbaai S. Afr. (Natal In.)	32·42 S	28·19 E
79	Morganton (môr'gȧn-tŭn) N. C.	35·44 N	81·42 W
81	Morgantown (môr'gȧn-toun) W. Va.	39·40 N	79·55 W
168	Morganzon (môr'gănt-sŏn) S. Afr. (Johannesburg & Pretoria In.)	26·44 S	29·39 E
145	Morga Ra. Afg. (Khyber Pass In.)	34·02 N	70·38 E
161	Moriac Austl. (Melbourne In.)	38·15 S	144·12 E
153	Moriguchi (mō'rê-gōō'chê) Jap. (Ōsaka In.)	34·44 N	135·34 E
85	Morinville (mō'-rĭn-vĭl) Can. (Edmonton In.)	53·47 N	113·40 W
152	Morioka (mō'rê-ō'kȧ) Jap.	39·40 N	141·21 E
135	Morkoka (R.) (mōr-kō'kȧ) Sov. Un.	65·35 N	111·00 E
122	Morlaix (mŏr-lĕ') Fr.	48·36 N	3·48 W
85	Morley (môr'lē) Can. (Calgary In.)	51·10 N	114·51 W
93	Morne Diablotin, Mt. (môrn dē-ȧ-blō-tăN') W. I. F. (Le. & Wind. Is. In.)	15·31 N	61·24 W
93	Morne Gimie, Mt. (môrn' zhē-mē') W. I. F. (Le. & Wind. Is. In.)	13·53 N	61·03 W
161	Mornington Austl. (Melbourne In.)	38·13 S	145·02 E
74	Moro (mō'rō) Ill. (St. Louis In.)	38·56 N	90·01 W
155	Morobe N. Gui. Ter.	8·03 S	147·45 E
165	Morocco (mô-rŏk'ō) Afr.	32·00 N	7·00 W
167	Morogoro (mō-rō-gō'rō) Tan.	6·49 S	37·46 E
90	Moroleón (mô-rō-lā-ōn') Mex.	20·07 N	101·15 W
100	Morón (mō-rŏ'n) Arg. (In.)	34·24 S	58·37 W
94	Morón (mô-rōn') Cuba	22·05 N	78·35 W
99	Morón (mô-rŏ'n) Ven. (In.)	10·29 N	68·11 W
167	Morondava (mō-rōn-dä'vä) Malagasy	20·17 S	44·18 E
124	Morón de la Frontera (mô-rōn'dā läf rôn-tā'rä) Sp.	37·08 N	5·20 W
68	Morongo Ind. Res. (mō-rôŋ'gō) Calif.	33·54 N	116·47 W
69	Moroni (mô-rō'nĭ) Utah	39·30 N	111·40 W
155	Morotai (I.) (mō-rō-tä'ê) Indon.	2·12 N	128·30 E
133	Morozovsk Sov. Un.	48·20 N	41·50 E
70	Morrill (mŏr'ĭl) Nebr.	41·59 N	103·54 W
73	Morrilton (mŏr'ĭl-tŭn) Ark.	35·09 N	92·42 W
99	Morrinhos (mō-rēn'yōzh) Braz.	17·45 S	48·56 W
86	Morris (mŏr'ĭs) Can.	49·19 N	97·32 W
80	Morris Ill.	41·20 N	88·25 W
70	Morris Minn.	45·35 N	95·53 W
71	Morrison (mŏr'ĭ-sŭn) Ill.	41·48 N	89·58 W
84	Morris Plains (mŏr'ĭs pláns) N. J. (New York In.)	40·49 N	74·29 W
74	Morris Res. Calif. (Los Angeles In.)	34·11 N	117·49 W
84	Morristown (mŏr'rĭs-toun) N. J. (New York In.)	40·48 N	74·29 W
78	Morristown Tenn.	36·10 N	83·18 W
84	Morrisville (mŏr'ĭs vĭl) Pa. (Philadelphia In.)	40·12 N	74·46 W
82	Morrisville Vt.	44·33 N	72·39 W
99	Morro do Chapéu (môr-ōō dōō-shä-pĕ'ōō) Braz.	11·34 S	41·03 W
75	Morrow (mŏr'ō) Ohio (Cincinnati In.)	39·21 N	84·07 W
133	Morshansk (môr-shȧnsk') Sov. Un.	53·25 N	41·35 E
118	Mors (I.) Den.	56·46 N	8·38 E
126	Mortara (môr-tä'rä) It.	45·13 N	8·47 E
100	Morteros (môr-tĕ'rôs) Arg.	30·47 S	62·00 W
101	Mortes, Rio das (R.) (rē'-o-dăs-mô'r-tĕs) Braz. (Rio de Janeiro In.)	21·04 S	44·29 W
71	Morton Ind. Res. (mŏr'tŭn) Minn.	44·35 N	94·48 W
111	Mortsel (môr-sĕl') Bel. (Bruxelles In.)	51·10 N	4·28 E
122	Morvan, Mts. du (môr-väN') Fr.	46·45 N	4·00 E
132	Morzhovets (I.) (môr'zhô-vyĕts') Sov. Un.	66·40 N	42·30 E
128	Mosal'sk (mō-zȧlsk') Sov. Un.	54·27 N	34·57 E
66	Moscow (mŏs'kō) Idaho	46·44 N	116·57 W
	Moscow, see Moskva		
	Moscow Canal, see Imeni Moskvy, Kanal		
120	Mosel R. (mō'sĕl) (mô-zĕl) Ger.	49·49 N	7·00 E
66	Moses Lake Wash.	47·08 N	119·15 W
66	Moses L. (mō'zĕz) Wash.	47·09 N	119·30 W
168	Moses R. S. Afr. (Johannesburg & Pretoria In.)	25·17 S	29·04 E
119	Moshchnyy (Is.) (môsh'chnĭ) Sov. Un.	59·56 N	28·07 E
167	Moshi (mō'shê) Tan.	3·17 S	37·18 E
136	Moskva (Moscow) (mŏs-kvä') Sov. Un. (Moskva In.)	55·45 N	37·37 E
128	Moskva (Oblast) Sov. Un.	55·38 N	36·48 E
128	Moskva (R.) Sov. Un.	55·50 N	37·05 E
121	Mosonmagyaróvár Hung.	47·51 N	17·16 E
93	Mosquitos, Costa de (kôs-tä-dĕ-mŏs-kē'tō) Nic.	12·05 N	83·49 W
93	Mosquitos, Gulfo de los (G.) (gōō'l-fō-dĕ-lôs-mŏs-kē'tōs) Pan.	9·17 N	80·59 W
118	Moss (môs) Nor.	59·29 N	10·39 E
65	Moss Beach (môs bēch) Calif. (San Francisco In.)	37·32 N	122·31 W
166	Mosselbaai S. Afr.	34·06 S	21·01 E
110	Mossley (mŏs'lĭ) Eng.	53·31 N	2·02 W
99	Mossoró (mō-sō-rōō') Braz.	5·13 S	37·14 W
78	Moss Point (môs) Miss.	30·25 N	88·32 W
120	Most (mōst) Czech.	50·32 N	13·37 E
164	Mostaganem (mŏs'tä-gȧ-nĕm') Alg.	36·04 N	00·11 E
127	Mostar (môs'tär) Yugo.	43·20 N	17·51 E
125	Móstoles (môs-tō'lās) Sp. (Madrid In.)	40·19 N	3·52 W
92	Motagua R. (mô-tä'gwä) Guat.	15·29 N	88·39 W
118	Motala (mô-tô'lä) Swe.	58·34 N	15·00 E
116	Motherwell (mŭdh'ẽr-wĕl) Scot.	55·45 N	4·05 W
124	Motril (mô-trēl') Sp.	36·44 N	3·32 W
92	Motul (mō-tōō'l) Mex. (Yucatan In.)	21·07 N	89·14 W
95	Mouchoir Bk. (mōō-shwär') Ba. Is.	21·35 N	70·40 W
95	Mouchoir Passage (Str.) Ba. Is.	21·05 N	71·05 W
123	Moudon Switz.	46·40 N	6·47 E
166	Mouille Pt. S. Afr. (Cape Town In.)	33·54 S	18·19 E
122	Moulins (mōō-lăN') Fr.	46·34 N	3·19 E
85	Moulin Vallie're (mōō-lĕN' vä-lē-ĕr') Can. (Quebec In.)	46·58 N	71·12 W
154	Moulmein (mōl-mān') Bur.	16·30 N	97·39 E
114	Moulouya Oued (R.) (mōō-lōō'yȧ) Mor.	34·07 N	3·27 W
78	Moultrie (mōl'trĭ) Ga.	31·10 N	83·48 W
79	Moultrie (Dam) S. C.	33·12 N	80·00 W
73	Mound City (mound) Ill.	37·06 N	89·13 W
73	Mound City Mo.	40·08 N	95·13 W
80	Mound City Group Natl. Mon. Ohio	39·25 N	83·00 W
80	Moundsville (moundz'vĭl) W. Va.	39·50 N	80·50 W
123	Mounier, Mt. (mōō-nyā') Fr.	44·10 N	6·59 E
84	Mountain Brook (moun'tĭn brŏŏk) Ala. (Birmingham In.)	33·30 N	86·45 W
74	Mountain Creek L. Tex. (Dallas, Fort Worth In.)	32·43 N	97·03 W
65	Mountaindale (dāl) Ore. (Portland In.)	45·37 N	123·02 W
73	Mountain Grove (grōv) Mo.	37·07 N	92·16 W
66	Mountain Home (hōm) Idaho	43·08 N	115·43 W
86	Mountain Park (pärk) Can.	52·57 N	117·22 W
65	Mountain View (moun'tĭn vū) Calif. (San Francisco In.)	37·25 N	122·07 W
73	Mountain View Mo.	36·59 N	91·46 W
84	Mountain View N. J. (New York In.)	40·55 N	74·17 W
79	Mount Airy (âr'ĭ) N. C.	36·28 N	80·37 W
	Mount Athos (Reg.), see Áyion Óros		
167	Mount Ayliff (ā'lĭf) S. Afr. (Natal In.)	30·48 S	29·24 E
71	Mount Ayr (âr) Iowa	40·43 N	94·06 W
80	Mount Carmel (kär'mĕl) Ill.	38·25 N	87·45 W
81	Mount Carmel Pa.	40·50 N	76·25 W
71	Mount Carroll Ill.	42·05 N	89·55 W
75	Mount Clemens (klĕm'ĕnz) Mich. (Detroit In.)	42·36 N	82·52 W
166	Mount Darwin Fed. of Rh. & Nya.	15·44 S	31·40 E
82	Mount Desert (I.) (dē-zûrt') Can.	44·15 N	68·08 W
79	Mount Dora (dō'rȧ) Fla. (In.)	28·45 N	81·38 W
161	Mount Duneed Austl. (Melbourne In.)	38·15 S	144·20 E
161	Mount Eliza Austl. (Melbourne In.)	38·11 S	145·05 E
70	Mountevideo (mŏn'tȧ-vê-dhā'ō) Minn.	44·56 N	95·42 W
167	Mount Fletcher (flĕ'chẽr) S. Afr. (Natal In.)	30·42 S	28·32 E
80	Mount Forest (fŏr'ĕst) Can.	44·00 N	80·45 W
167	Mount Frere (frâr') S. Afr. (Natal In.)	30·54 S	29·02 E
160	Mount Gambier (găm'bēr) Austl.	37·30 S	140·53 E
80	Mount Gilead (gĭl'ēăd) Ohio	40·30 N	82·50 W
75	Mount Healthy (hĕlth'ê) Ohio (Cincinnati In.)	39·14 N	84·32 W
84	Mount Holly (hŏl'ĭ) N. J. (Philadelphia In.)	39·59 N	74·47 W
85	Mount Hope Can. (Toronto In.)	43·09 N	79·55 W
84	Mount Hope (hōp) N. J. (New York In.)	40·55 N	74·32 W
80	Mount Hope W. Va.	37·55 N	81·10 W
158	Mount Isa (ī'zȧ) Austl.	21·00 S	139·45 E
84	Mount Kisco (kĭs'ko) N. Y. (New York In.)	41·12 N	73·44 W
65	Mountlake Terrace (mount lāk tĕr'ĭs) Wash. (Seattle In.)	47·48 N	122·19 W
75	Mount Lebanon (lĕb'ȧ-nŭn) Pa. (Pittsburgh In.)	40·22 N	80·03 W
64	Mount McKinley Natl. Park (mȧ-kĭn'lĭ) Alaska	63·48 N	153·02 W
158	Mount Magnet (măg-nĕt) Austl.	28·00 S	118·00 E
161	Mount Martha Austl. (Melbourne In.)	38·17 S	145·01 E
159	Mount Morgan (môr-gȧn) Austl.	23·42 S	150·45 E
161	Mount Moriac Austl. (Melbourne In.)	38·13 S	144·12 E
80	Mount Morris (mŏr'ĭs) Mich.	43·10 N	83·45 W
81	Mount Morris N. Y.	42·45 N	77·50 W
79	Mount Olive (ŏl'ĭv) N. C.	35·11 N	78·05 W
69	Mount Peale Utah	38·26 N	109·16 W
71	Mount Pleasant (plĕz'ănt) Iowa	40·59 N	91·34 W
80	Mount Pleasant Mich.	43·35 N	84·45 W
79	Mount Pleasant S. C.	32·46 N	79·51 W
78	Mount Pleasant Tenn.	35·31 N	87·12 W
73	Mount Pleasant Tex.	33·10 N	94·56 W
69	Mount Pleasant Utah	39·35 N	111·20 W
75	Mount Prospect (prŏs'pĕkt) Ill. (Chicago In.)	42·03 N	87·56 W
66	Mount Rainier Natl. Park (rȧ-nēr') Wash.	46·47 N	121·17 W
86	Mount Revelstoke Natl. Park (rĕv'ĕl-stōk) Can.	51·22 N	120·15 W
81	Mount Savage (săv'āj) Md.	39·45 N	78·55 W
66	Mount Shasta (shăs'tȧ) Calif.	41·18 N	122·17 W
73	Mount Sterling (stûr'lĭng) Ill.	39·59 N	90·44 W
80	Mount Sterling Ky.	38·05 N	84·00 W
83	Mount Stewart (stū'ărt) Can.	46·21 N	62·54 W
81	Mount Union (ūn'yŭn) Pa.	40·25 N	77·50 W

ng-sing; ŋ-baŋk: N-nasalized n; nŏd; cŏmmit; ōld; ôbey; ôrder; fōōd; fŏŏt; ou-out; s-soft; sh-dish; th-thin; pūre; ûnite; ûrn; stŭd; circŭs; ü-as "y" in study; '-indeterminate vowel.

240 Mount Vernon–Naha PRONOUNCING INDEX

Page	Name Pronunciation Region	Lat. °′	Long. °′
80	Mount Vernon (vûr'nŭn)......Ill.	38·20 N	88·50 W
80	Mount Vernon..............Ind.	37·55 N	87·50 W
73	Mount Vernon..............Mo.	37·09 N	93·48 W
84	Mount Vernon N. Y. (New York In.)	40·55 N	73·51 W
80	Mount Vernon.............Ohio	40·25 N	82·30 W
65	Mount Vernon.Wash. (Seattle In.)	48·25 N	122·20 W
155	Mount Wilhelm.....New Guinea	5·45 S	144·30 E
148	Moup'ing (mō'pĭng)........China	37·23 N	121·36 E
99	Moura (mō'rȧ)............Braz.	1·33 S	61·38 W
124	Moura....................Port.	38·08 N	7·28 W
116	Mourne, Mts. (môrn).....N. Ire.	54·10 N	6·09 W
123	Moûtiers (mōō-tyâr').........Fr.	45·31 N	6·34 E
160	Mowbullan, Mt. (mō'bōō-lȧn) Austl.	26·50 S	151·34 E
90	Moyahua (mō-yä'wä).......Mex.	21·16 N	103·10 W
165	Moyale (mō-yä'lä)..........Ken.	3·28 N	39·04 E
164	Moyamba (mō-yäm'bä).....S. L.	8·11 N	12·27 W
114	Moyen Atlas (Mts.)........Mor.	32·49 N	5·28 W
123	Moyeuvre Grande............Fr.	49·15 N	6·26 E
66	Moyie R. (moi'yē)..........Idaho	48·50 N	116·10 W
98	Moyobamba (mō-yō-bäm'bä).Peru	6·12 S	76·56 W
92	Moyuta (mō-ē-ōō'tä).......Guat.	14·01 N	90·05 W
135	Moyyero (R.)..........Sov. Un.	67·15 N	104·10 E
163	Mozambique (Portuguese East Africa) (mō-zȧm-bēk').Afr.	20·15 S	33·53 E
84	Mozambique, Pt. La. (New Orleans In.)	29·38 N	89·26 W
167	Mozambique Chan. (mō-zȧm-bek') Ind. O.	52·18 S	4·28 E
133	Mozdok (mōz-dōk').....Sov. Un.	43·45 N	44·35 E
128	Mozhaysh (mō-zhäysh').Sov. Un.	55·31 N	36·02 E
136	Mozhayskiy (mō-zhäy'skĭ) Sov. Un. (Leningrad In.)	59·42 N	30·08 E
129	Mozyr' (mō-zür').......Sov. Un.	52·03 N	29·14 E
166	Mporokoso ('m-pō-rō-kō'sō) Fed. of Rh. & Nya.	9·28 S	30·06 E
167	Mpwapwa ('m-pwä'pwä).....Tan.	6·20 S	36·39 E
167	Mqanduli ('m-kän'dōō-lē) S. Afr. (Natal In.)	31·50 S	28·42 E
121	Mragowo (mrăṅ'gō-vō).......Pol.	53·52 N	21·18 E
164	M'sila (m'sē'lȧ)............Alg.	35·47 N	4·34 E
128	Msta (R.) (m'stä').........Sov. Un.	58·33 N	32·08 E
128	Mstislavl' (m'stē-släv'l')..Sov. Un.	54·01 S	31·42 E
166	Mtengula ('m-tĕṅ-gōō'lȧ)....Moz.	12·42 S	34·48 E
166	Mtetwe Pan (Basin) ('m-tĕt'wĕ) Bech.	20·00 S	24·18 E
128	Mtsensk (m'tsĕnsk)....Sov. Un.	53·17 N	36·33 E
154	Muang Khon Kaen.........Thai.	16·37 N	102·41 E
154	Muang Lamphum...........Thai.	18·40 N	98·59 E
154	Muang Phitsanulok........Thai.	16·51 N	100·15 E
154	Muang Ubon..............Thai.	15·15 N	104·52 E
139	Muar (R.)..Mala. (Singapore In.)	2·18 N	102·43 E
123	Much (mōōκ).Ger. (Ruhr In.)	50·54 N	7·24 E
110	Much Wenlock (mŭch wĕn'lŏk) Eng.	52·35 N	2·33 W
78	Muckalee Cr. (mŭk'ă lē)......Ga.	31·55 N	84·10 W
65	Muckleshoot Ind. Res. (mŭck''l-shōōt) Wash. (Seattle In.)	47·21 N	122·04 W
99	Mucugê (mōō-kōō-zhĕ').....Braz.	13·02 S	41·19 W
71	Mud (L.) (mŭd)..........Mich.	46·12 N	84·32 W
68	Mud (L.)..................Nev.	40·28 N	119·11 W
68	Muddy (R.) (mŭd'ĭ)........Nev.	36·56 N	114·42 W
73	Muddy Boggy Cr. (mud'ĭ bôg'ĭ) Okla.	34·42 N	96·11 W
69	Muddy Cr. (mŭd'ĭ).........Utah	38·45 N	111·10 W
160	Mudgee (mŭ-jē)...........Austl.	32·47 S	149·10 E
124	Mugia (mōō-kē'ä)...........Sp.	43·05 N	9·14 W
133	Muğla (mōōg'lä)............Tur.	37·10 N	28·20 E
120	Mühldorf (mül-dôrf).........Ger.	48·15 N	12·33 E
120	Mühlhausen (mül'hou-zĕn)...Ger.	51·13 N	10·25 E
119	Muhu (I.) (mōō'hōō)....Sov. Un.	58·41 N	22·55 E
151	Mui Ron, C...............Viet.	18·05 N	106·45 E
68	Muir Woods Natl. Mon. (mūr) Calif.	37·54 N	123·22 W
166	Muizenberg (mwĭz-ĕn-bûrg') S. Afr. (Cape Town In.)	34·07 S	18·28 E
121	Mukachëvo (mōō-kȧ-chyô'vō) Sov. Un.	48·25 N	22·43 E
	Mukden, see Shenyang		
135	Mukhtuya (mōōk-tōō'yȧ).Sov. Un.	61·00 N	113·00 E
65	Mukilteo (mū-kĭl-tā'ō) Wash. (Seattle In.)	47·57 N	122·18 W
153	Muko (R.) (mōō'kō) Jap. (Ōsaka In.)	34·52 N	135·17 E
75	Mukwonago (mū-kwō-nȧ'gō) Wis. (Milwaukee In.)	42·52 N	88·19 W
124	Mula (mōō'lä)...............Sp.	38·05 N	1·12 W
120	Mulde R. (mōōl'dĕ).........Ger.	50·30 N	12·30 E
150	Muleng..................China	44·32 N	130·18 E
150	Muleng (R.)..............China	44·40 N	130·30 E
90	Muleros (mōō-lā'rōs).......Mex.	23·44 N	104·00 W
84	Mulga (mŭl'gȧ) Ala. (Birmingham In.)	33·33 N	86·59 W
83	Mulgrave (mŭl'grāv)........Can.	45·37 N	61·22 W
159	Mulgrave (I.).............Austl.	10·08 S	142·14 E
124	Mulhacén (Mtn.)............Sp.	37·04 N	3·18 W
123	Mülheim (mül'hīm) Ger. (Ruhr In.)	51·25 N	6·53 E
123	Mulhouse (mü-lōōz').........Fr.	47·46 N	7·20 E
116	Mull (mŭl).................Scot.	56·40 N	6·19 W
66	Mullan (mŭl'ăn)...........Idaho	47·26 N	115·50 W
154	Müller Mts. (mül'ēr)......Indon.	0·22 N	113·05 E
116	Mullet Pen..................Ire.	54·15 N	10·12 W
116	Mullinger (mŭl-ĭn-gär).......Ire.	53·31 N	7·26 W
79	Mullins (mŭl'ĭnz)...........S. C.	34·11 N	79·13 W
92	Mullins River Br. Hond. (Yucatan In.)	17·08 N	88·18 W
142	Multan (mōōl-tän')......W. Pak.	30·17 N	71·13 E
65	Multnomah Chan. (mŭl nō mȧ) Ore. (Portland In.)	45·41 N	122·53 W
154	Mulu, Gunung (Mtn.).......Sar.	3·56 N	115·11 E
73	Mulvane (mŭl-vān').........Kans.	37·30 N	97·13 W
166	Mumbwa (mōōm'bwä) Fed. of Rh. & Nya.	14·58 S	27·06 E
92	Muna (mōō'nä) Mex. (Yucatan In.)	20·28 N	89·42 W
111	München (Munich) (mün'kĕn) Ger. (München In.)	48·08 N	11·35 E
80	Muncie (mŭn'sĭ).............Ind.	40·10 N	85·30 W
75	Mundelein (mŭn-dē-lĭn') Ill. (Chicago In.)	42·16 N	88·00 W
98	Mundonueva, Pico de (Pk.) (pē'kō-dĕ-mōō'n-dō-nwĕ'vä) Col. (In.)	4·18 N	74·12 W
91	Muneco, Cerro (Mtn.) (sĕ'r-rō-mōō-nĕ'kō) Mex. (Mexico In.)	19·13 N	99·20 W
159	Mungana (mŭn-găn'ȧ).....Austl.	17·15 S	144·18 E
74	Munger (mŭn'gẽr) Minn. (Duluth In.)	46·48 N	92·20 W
160	Mungindi (mŭn-gĭn'dē)......Austl.	32·00 S	148·45 E
75	Munhall (mŭn'hôl) Pa. (Pittsburgh In.)	40·24 N	79·53 W
166	Munhanga (mōōn-häṅ'gȧ)...Ang.	12·15 S	18·55 E
	Munich, see München		
71	Munising (mū'nĭ-sĭng)......Mich.	46·24 N	86·41 W
134	Munku Sardyk (Mtn.) (mōōn'kōō sär-dĭk') Sov. Un.-Mong.	51·45 N	100·30 E
155	Muños (mōōn-nyōth') Phil. (Manila In.)	15·44 N	120·53 E
123	Münster (mün'stĕr) Ger. (Ruhr In.)	51·57 N	7·38 E
75	Munster (mŭn'stẽr) Ind. (Chicago In.)	41·34 N	87·31 W
116	Munster (mŭn-stẽr)..........Ire.	52·30 N	9·24 W
154	Muntok (mōōn-tŏk')........Indon.	2·05 S	105·11 E
101	Munzi Freire (mōō-nĕ'z-frâ'rĕ) Braz. (Rio de Janeiro In.)	20·29 S	41·25 W
154	Muong Sing (mōō'ông-sĭng').Laos	21·06 N	101·17 E
112	Muonio (R.)...........Fin.-Swe.	68·15 N	23·00 E
101	Muqui (mōō-kōōē) Braz. (Rio de Janeiro In.)	20·56 S	41·20 W
133	Muradiye (mōō-rä'dē-yĕ)....Tur.	39·00 N	43·40 E
122	Murat (mü-rä')..............Fr.	45·05 N	2·56 E
133	Murat (R.) (mōō-rät')......Tur.	38·50 N	40·40 E
158	Murchison (R.) (mûr'chĭ-sŭn) Austl.	26·45 S	116·15 E
165	Murchison Falls (mûr'chĭ-sŭn).Ug.	2·19 N	31·50 E
124	Murcia (mōōr'thyä)..........Sp.	38·00 N	1·10 W
124	Murcia (Reg.)...............Sp.	38·35 N	1·51 W
70	Murdo (mûr'dō)............S. D.	43·53 N	100·42 W
82	Murdochville (mŭr-dŏk'vĭl)..Can.	48·56 N	65·37 W
121	Muresul R. (mōō'rĕsh-ōōl)..Rom.	46·02 N	21·50 E
122	Muret (mü-rĕ')..............Fr.	43·28 N	1·17 E
78	Murfreesboro (mûr'frēz-bŭr-ō) Tenn.	35·50 N	86·19 W
103	Murgab (R.) (mōōr-gäb').Sov. Un.	37·07 N	62·32 E
101	Muriaé (mōō-ryȧ-ĕ') Braz. (Rio de Janeiro In.)	21·10 S	42·21 W
101	Muriaé (R.) Braz. (Rio de Janeiro In.)	21·20 S	41·40 W
136	Murino (mōō'rĭ-nō) Sov. Un. (Leningrad In.)	60·03 N	30·28 E
120	Müritz See (L.) (mür'ĭts)....Ger.	53·20 N	12·33 E
146	Murku Sardyk (Pk.) Sov. Un.-Mong.	51·56 N	100·21 E
132	Murmansk(mōōr-mänsk').Sov. Un.	69·00 N	33·20 E
132	Murom (mōō'rôm)......Sov. Un.	55·30 N	42·00 E
152	Muroran (mōō'rō-rän).......Jap.	42·21 N	141·05 E
124	Muros (mōō'rōs).............Sp.	42·48 N	9·00 W
153	Muroto-Zaki (Pt.) (mōō'rō-tō zä'kē).Jap.	33·14 N	134·12 E
74	Murphy (mŭr'fĭ) Mo. (St. Louis In.)	38·29 N	90·29 W
78	Murphy..................N. C.	35·05 N	84·00 W
73	Murphysboro (mŭr'fĭz-bŭr-ō).Ill.	37·46 N	89·21 W
78	Murray (mŭr'ĭ)..............Ky.	36·39 N	88·17 W
74	Murray.Utah (Salt Lake City In.)	40·40 N	111·53 W
79	Murray (R.) (mŭr'ĭ).......S. C.	34·07 N	81·18 W
159	Murray Reg. (mŭ'rē).......Austl.	33·20 S	142·30 E
160	Murray R.................Austl.	34·12 S	141·20 E
120	Mur R. (mōōr).............Aus.	47·10 N	14·08 E
160	Murrumbidgee (R.) (mŭr-ŭm-bĭd'jē).Austl.	34·30 S	145·20 E
142	Murshidabad (mōōr'shē-dä-bäd') India	24·08 N	87·11 E
126	Murska Sobota (mōōr'skä sō'bō-tä).Yugo.	46·40 N	16·14 E
142	Murwāra..................India	23·54 N	80·23 E
120	Mürz R. (mürts)............Aus.	47·30 N	15·21 E
165	Murzūg..................Libya	26·00 N	14·09 E
120	Murzzuschlag (mürts'tsōō-shlägh) Aus.	47·37 N	15·41 E
133	Mus (mōōsh)...............Tur.	38·55 N	41·30 E
	Musala, Pk., see Stalin		
152	Musan (mōō'sän)...........Kor.	41·11 N	129·10 E
153	Musashino (mōō-sä'shē-nō) Jap. (Tōkyō In.)	35·43 N	139·35 E
144	Muscat (mŭs-kăt')...Mus. & Om.	23·23 N	58·30 E
144	Muscat & Oman...........Asia	18·50 N	56·45 E
71	Muscatine (mŭs-kȧ-tēn')....Iowa	41·26 N	91·00 W
78	Muscle Shoals (mŭs''l shōlz)..Ala.	34·44 N	87·38 W
158	Musgrave Ra. (mŭs'grāv)..Austl.	26·15 S	131·15 E
166	Mushie (mŭsh'ē).........Con. L.	3·04 S	16·50 E
154	Musi, Air (Strm.) (mōō'sē).Indon.	2·40 S	103·42 E
98	Musinga, Alto (Ht.) (ȧ'l-tō-mōō-sĕ'n-gä).Col. (In.)	6·40 N	76·13 W
75	Muskego L. (mŭs-kē'gō) Wis. (Milwaukee In.)	42·53 N	88·10 W
80	Muskegon (mŭs-kē'gŭn)....Mich.	43·15 N	86·20 W
80	Muskegon (R.)............Mich.	43·20 N	85·55 W
80	Muskegon Heights.........Mich.	43·10 N	86·20 W
80	Muskingum (R.) (mŭs-kĭṅ'gŭm) Ohio	39·45 N	81·55 W
73	Muskogee (mŭs-kō'gē).......Okla.	35·44 N	95·21 W
81	Muskoka (L.) (mŭs-kō'kȧ)...Can.	45·00 N	79·30 W
155	Mussau (I.) (mōō-sä'ōō) N. Gui. Ter.	1·30 S	149·32 E
116	Musselburgh (mŭs''l-bŭr-ō)..Scot.	55·55 N	3·08 W
67	Musselshell R. (mŭs''l-shĕl).Mont.	46·25 N	108·20 W
133	Mustafakemalpasa..........Tur.	40·05 N	28·30 E
77	Mustang Bay..........Tex. (In.)	29·22 N	95·12 W
72	Mustang Cr. (mŭs'tăng).....Tex.	36·22 N	102·46 W
77	Mustang I.................Tex.	27·43 N	97·00 W
93	Mustique I. (müs-tēk') W. I. F. (Le. & Wind. Is. In.)	12·53 N	61·03 W
128	Mustvee (mōōst'vĕ-ĕ)....Sov. Un.	58·50 N	26·54 E
147	Musu Dan (C.) (mōō'sōō dän) Kor.	40·51 N	130·00 E
152	Musu Dan (Pt.) (mōō'sōō dän) Sov. Un.	40·48 N	129·50 E
150	Mutan (R.)..............China	45·30 N	129·40 E
150	Mutanchiang.............China	44·28 N	129·38 E
166	Mutombo Mukulu (mōō-tôm'bō mōō-kōō'lōō) Con. L.	8·12 S	23·56 E
152	Mutsu Wan (B.) (mōōt'sōō wän) Jap.	41·20 N	140·55 E
83	Mutton B. (mŭt''n).........Can.	50·47 N	58·58 W
101	Mutum (mōō-tōō'm) Braz. (Rio de Janeiro In.)	19·48 S	41·24 W
134	Muyun-Kum, Peski (Des.) (mōō-yōōn' kōōm').Sov. Un.	44·30 N	70·00 E
142	Muzaffargarh...........W. Pak.	30·09 N	71·15 E
76	Muzquiz (mōōz'kēz)........Mex.	27·53 N	101·31 W
166	Mwanza (mwän'zä)..........Tan.	2·31 S	32·52 E
167	Mwatate (mwä-tä'tä).......Ken.	3·28 S	38·19 E
166	Mwaya (mwä'yä)...........Tan.	9·19 S	33·51 E
166	Mweru, L. (mwā'rōō).....Con. L.	8·45 S	27·45 E
114	Mya R. (myä')..............Alg.	29·26 N	3·15 E
168	Myerton (mī'ēr-tŏn).......S. Afr. (Johannesburg & Pretoria In.)	26·35 S	28·01 E
168	Myerville (mī'ēr-vĭl)......S. Afr. (Johannesburg & Pretoria In.)	27·01 S	29·17 E
146	Myingyan (myĭng-yŭn')......Bur.	21·37 N	95·26 E
154	Myinmoletkat (Pk.).........Bur.	13·58 N	98·34 E
146	Myitkyina (myĭ'chē-nȧ).....Bur.	25·33 N	97·25 E
121	Myjava (mûē'yȧ-vä)......Czech.	48·45 N	17·33 E
142	Mymensingh (mī-mŭn-sĭng') E. Pak.	24·48 N	90·28 E
152	Myohyang San (Mtn.) (myō'hyang).Kor.	40·00 N	126·12 E
112	Mýrdalsjökull (Gl.) (mür'däls-yû'kōōl).Ice.	63·34 N	18·04 W
79	Myrtle Beach (mûr't'l)......S. C.	33·42 N	78·53 W
84	Myrtle Grove (grōv) La. (New Orleans In.)	29·38 N	89·57 W
66	Myrtle Point...............Ore.	43·04 N	124·08 W
128	Myshkino (mēsh'kē-nō)..Sov. Un.	57·48 N	38·21 E
143	Mysore (mī-sōr')...........India	12·31 N	76·42 E
143	Mysore (State)............India	20·15 N	75·32 E
71	Mystic (mĭs'tĭk)............Iowa	40·47 N	92·54 W
136	Mytishchi (mê-tēsh'chi) Sov. Un. (Moskva In.)	55·55 N	37·46 E
166	Mzimba ('m-zĭm'bä) Fed. of Rh. & Nya.	11·41 S	33·39 E
120	Naab R. (näp)..............Ger.	49·38 N	12·15 E
111	Naaldwijk.Neth. (Amsterdam In.)	52·00 N	4·11 E
164	Naama (nä'ȧ-mä)...........Lib.	7·18 N	9·31 W
119	Naantali (nän'tȧ-lē).........Fin.	60·29 N	22·03 E
158	Nabberu (L.) (năb'ēr-ōō)...Austl.	26·05 S	120·35 E
164	Nabeul (nā-bûl')...........Tun.	36·34 N	10·45 E
168	Naboomspruit............S. Afr. (Johannesburg & Pretoria In.)	24·32 S	28·43 E
139	Nābulus....Jordan (Palestine In.)	32·13 N	35·16 E
92	Nacaome (nä-kä-ō'mȧ).....Hond.	13·32 N	87·28 W
114	Naceur, Bou Mt...........Mor.	33·50 N	3·55 W
151	Na Cham (nä chäm')........Viet.	22·02 N	106·30 E
66	Naches R. (năch'ĕz)........Wash.	46·51 N	121·03 W
120	Nachod (näk'ōt)...........Czech.	50·25 N	16·08 E
87	Nachvak..................Can.	59·08 N	63·57 W
68	Nacimiento (R.) (nȧ-sĭ-myĕn'tō) Calif.	35·50 N	121·00 W
77	Nacogdoches (năk'ō-dō'chĕz).Tex.	31·36 N	94·40 W
76	Nadadores (nä-dä-dō'räs).....Mex.	27·04 N	101·36 W
142	Nadaid...................India	22·45 N	72·51 E
89	Nadir.........Vir. Is. (U. S. A.) (St. Thomas In.)	18·19 N	64·53 W
127	Nădlac..................Rom.	46·09 N	20·52 E
	Nad Nisou, see Jablonec		
	Nad Vahom, see Nové Mesto		
121	Nadvornaya (nȧd-vōōr'nȧ-yȧ) Sov. Un.	48·37 N	24·35 E
134	Nadym (R.) (nä'dĭm).....Sov. Un.	64·30 N	72·48 E
118	Naestved (nĕst'vĭdh)........Den.	55·14 N	11·46 E
168	Nafishah..............U. A. R.	30·34 N	32·15 E
155	Naga (nä'gä)...Phil. (Manila In.)	13·37 N	123·12 E
153	Naga (I.).................Jap.	32·09 N	130·16 E
153	Nagahama (nä'gä-hä'mä).....Jap.	33·32 N	132·29 E
153	Nagahama.................Jap.	35·23 N	136·16 E
146	Naga Hills (nä'gä)........China	28·49 N	93·30 E
145	Naga Hills (nä'gä)........India	25·47 N	94·15 E
153	Nagano (nä'gä-nō).........Jap.	36·42 N	138·12 E
153	Nagaoka (nä'gȧ-ō'kȧ).......Jap.	37·22 N	138·49 E
143	Nagapatam................India	10·48 N	79·51 E
92	Nagarote (nä-gä-rō'tĕ)......Nic.	12·17 N	86·35 W
153	Nagasaki (nä'gȧ-sä'kē).....Jap.	32·48 N	129·53 E
153	Nagasu (nä'gäs-ōō).........Jap.	33·31 N	131·22 E
142	Nāgaur...................India	27·19 N	73·41 E
136	Nagaybakskiy (nȧ-gäy-bäk'skĭ) Sov. Un. (Urals In.)	53·33 N	59·33 E
155	Nagcarlan (näg-kär-län') Phil. (Manila In.)	14·07 N	121·24 E
143	Nagercoil.................India	8·15 N	77·29 E
133	Nagornokarabakh (Reg.) (nu-gôr'nŭ-kŭ-rŭ-bäk') Sov. Un.	40·10 N	46·50 E
153	Nagoya (nä'gō'yȧ)..........Jap.	35·09 N	136·53 E
142	Nagpur (näg'pōōr)..........India	21·12 N	79·09 E
155	Naguilian (nä-gwē-lē'än) Phil. (Manila In.)	16·33 N	120·23 E
120	Nagykanizsa (nôd'y'kô'nē-shô) Hung.	46·27 N	17·00 E
121	Nagykőrös (nôd'y'kŭ'rŭsh) Hung.	47·02 N	19·46 E
152	Naha (nä'hä)...............Jap.	26·02 N	127·43 E

ăt; finăl; rāte; senāte; ärm; åsk; sofȧ; fâre; ch-choose; dh-as th in other; bē; ēvent; bĕt; recĕnt; cratẽr; g-go; gh-guttural g; bĭt; ĭ-short neutral; rīde; κ-guttural k as ch in German ich;

PRONOUNCING INDEX Nahant–Negri 241

Page	Name Pronunciation Region	Lat. °′	Long. °′
83	Nahant (nȧ-hănt) Mass. (Boston In.)	42·26 N	70·55 W
139	Nahariya ... Isr. (Palestine In.)	33·01 N	35·06 E
133	Nahr al Khābūr (R.) ... U. A. R.	35·50 N	41·00 E
125	Nahr-Ouassel (R.) (när-wä-sĕl') Alg.	35·30 N	1·55 E
100	Nahuel Huapi (L.) (nä'wâl wä'pē) Arg.	41·00 S	71·30 W
92	Nahuizalco (nä-wē-zäl'kō) ... Sal.	13·50 N	89·43 W
155	Naic (nä'ēk) ... Phil. (Manila In.)	14·20 N	120·46 E
76	Naica (nä-ē'kä) ... Mex.	27·53 N	105·30 W
99	Naiguatá (nī-gwä-tà') .. Ven. (In.)	10·37 N	66·44 W
99	Naiguata, Pico (Mtn.) (pē'kō) Ven. (In.)	10·32 N	66·44 W
142	Naihāti ... India (Calcutta In.)	22·54 N	88·25 E
87	Nain (nīn) ... Can.	56·29 N	61·52 W
84	Nairn (nărn) La. (New Orleans In.)	29·27 N	89·37 W
116	Nairn (nârn) ... Scot.	57·35 N	3·54 W
167	Nairobi (nī-rō'bē) ... Ken.	1·18 S	36·47 E
167	Naivasha (nī-vä'shȧ) ... Ken.	0·47 S	36·29 E
144	Najd (Des.) ... Sau. Ar.	25·18 N	42·38 E
168	Naj 'Ḥammādi (näg'hä-mä'dē) U. A. R. (Nile In.)	26·02 N	32·12 E
152	Najin (nä'jĭn) ... Kor.	42·04 N	136·06 E
144	Najran (Des.) (nŭj-rän') . Sau. Ar.	17·29 N	45·30 E
152	Naju (nä'jōō') ... Kor.	35·02 N	126·42 E
94	Najusa (R.) (nä-hōō'sä) ... Cuba	21·55 N	77·55 W
150	Nakadorishima (I.) (nä'kä'dô'rē-shē'mä) . Jap.	33·00 N	128·20 E
165	Nak'amet ... Eth.	9·09 N	36·29 E
153	Nakatsu (nä'käts-ōō) ... Jap.	33·34 N	131·10 E
133	Nakhichevan' (nȧ-kĕ-chĕ-vän') Sov. Un.	49·10 N	45·30 E
135	Nakhodka (nŭ-kôt'kŭ) ... Sov. Un.	43·03 N	133·08 E
154	Nakhon Ratchasima ... Thai.	14·56 N	102·14 E
154	Nakhon Si Thammarat ... Thai.	8·27 N	99·58 E
87	Nakina ... Can.	50·10 N	86·40 W
118	Nakskov (näk'skou) ... Den.	54·51 N	11·06 E
121	Nakto nad Notecia (näk'wō näd nō-tĕ'chōn) . Pol.	53·10 N	17·35 E
152	Naktong (R.) (näk'tŭng) ... Kor.	36·10 N	128·30 E
133	Nal'chik (nål-chĕk') ... Sov. Un.	43·30 N	43·35 E
124	Nalón (R.) (nä-lōn') ... Sp.	43·15 N	5·38 W
166	Nālūt (nä-lōōt') ... Libya	31·51 N	10·49 E
144	Namak, Daryacheh-ye (L.) .. Iran	34·58 N	51·33 E
71	Namakan (L.) (nă'mȧ-kȧn) . Minn.	48·20 N	92·43 W
144	Namakzār E Shahdād (L.) (nŭ-mŭk-zär') . Iran	31·20 N	57·59 E
134	Namangan (nȧ-mȧn-gän') Sov. Un.	41·08 N	71·59 E
85	Namao ... Can. (Edmonton In.)	53·43 N	113·30 W
166	Namaqualand (Reg.) (nă-mä'kwă'lănd) . S. W. Afr.	25·30 S	16·30 E
155	Namatanai (nä'mä-tȧ-nä'ē) N. Gui. Ter.	3·43 S	152·26 E
69	Nambe Pueblo Ind. Res. (näm'bā pwĕb'lō) . N. Mex.	35·52 N	105·39 W
154	Nam Dinh (näm dēnk') ... Viet.	20·30 N	106·10 E
74	Nameoki (nă'mē-ō-kē) Ill. (St. Louis In.)	38·44 N	90·07 W
152	Namhae (I.) (näm'hī') ... Kor.	34·23 N	128·05 E
166	Namib Des. (nä-mēb') .. S. W. Afr.	24·00 S	15·00 E
160	Namoi (R.) (năm'oi) ... Austl.	30·10 S	148·43 E
114	Namous, Oued en (R.) (nȧ-mōōs') Alg.	31·48 N	00·19 W
66	Nampa (năm'pȧ) ... Idaho	43·35 N	116·35 W
112	Namsos (näm'sôs) ... Nor.	64·28 N	11·14 E
142	Nam Tsho (L.) ... China	30·30 N	91·10 E
117	Namur (nȧ-mür') ... Bel.	50·29 N	4·55 E
166	Namutoni (nä-mōō-tō'nē) S. W. Afr.	18·45 S	17·00 E
154	Nan, Mae Nam (R.) ... Thai.	18·11 N	100·29 E
91	Nanacamilpa (nä-nä-kä-mē'l-pä) Mex. (Mexico In.)	19·30 N	98·33 W
66	Nanaimo (nȧ-nī'mō) ... Can.	49·09 N	123·57 W
152	Nanam (nä'nän') ... Kor.	41·38 N	129·37 E
153	Nanao (nä'nä-ō) ... Jap.	37·03 N	136·59 E
151	Nanao Tao (I.) (nä'nä-ō dou) China	23·30 N	117·30 E
151	Nanch'ang (nän'chäng') ... China	28·38 N	115·48 E
151	Nancheng ... China	26·50 N	116·40 E
150	Nancheng ... China	33·02 N	107·00 E
148	Nanch'enghuang Tai (I.) (nan'chĕng'hōōäng'dou) . China	38·22 N	120·54 E
	Nanching, see Nanking		
151	Nanch'ung ... China	30·45 N	106·05 E
123	Nancy (nän-sē') ... Fr.	48·42 N	6·11 E
84	Nancy Cr. (năn'cē) Ga. (Atlanta In.)	33·51 N	84·25 W
142	Nanda Devi (Mt.) (năn'dȧ dā'vē) India	35·20 N	80·25 E
142	Nander ... India	19·13 N	77·21 E
142	Nandurbār ... India	21·29 N	74·13 E
143	Nandyal ... India	15·54 N	78·09 E
142	Nanga Parbat (Pk.) ... India	40·05 N	74·35 E
123	Nangis (nän-zhē') .. Fr. (Paris In.)	48·33 N	3·01 E
149	Nanhai (Fatshan) China (Canton In.)	23·02 N	113·07 E
149	Nanhsiang .. China (Shanghai In.)	31·17 N	121·17 E
151	Nanhsiung ... China	25·10 N	114.20 E
149	Nanhui ... China (Shanghai In.)	31·03 N	121·45 E
148	Naniana ... China	35·14 N	116·24 E
151	Nani Dinh ... Viet.	20·25 N	106·08 E
148	Nani Hu (L.) (nän'yē' hōō) . China	31·12 N	119·05 E
148	Nanking (Nanching) (nän'kĭng) (nän'jĭng) . China	32·04 N	118·46 E
148	Nankung (nän'kōōng') ... China	37·22 N	115·22 E
151	Nan Ling (Mtns.) ... China	25·15 N	111·40 E
148	Nanlo (nän'lō') ... China	36·03 N	115·13 E
158	Nannine (nă-nēn') ... Austl.	26·50 S	118·30 E
151	Nanning (nän'nĭng') ... China	22·56 N	108·10 E
151	Nanp'an (R.) ... China	24·50 N	105·30 E
151	Nanpling ... China	26·40 N	118·05 E
84	Nansemond (năn'sē-mŭnd) Va. (Norfolk In.)	36·46 N	76·32 W
84	Nansemond R. . Va. (Norfolk In.)	36·50 N	76·34 W
146	Nan Shan (Mts.) (nän'shän') China	38·43 N	98·00 E
153	Nantai-zan (Mtn.) (nän-täê zän) Jap.	36·47 N	139·28 E
122	Nantes (nänt') ... Fr.	47·13 N	1·37 W
123	Nanteuil-le-Haudouin (nän-tû-lĕ-ō-dwăn') . Fr. Paris In.)	49·08 N	2·49 E
81	Nanticoke (năn'tĭ-kōk) ... Pa.	41·10 N	76·00 W
81	Nantucket (I.) (năn-tŭk'ĕt) . Mass.	41·15 N	70·05 W
148	Nantung (nän'tōōng') ... China	32·02 N	120·51 E
110	Nantwich (nănt'wĭch) ... Eng.	53·04 N	2·31 W
150	Nanyang ... China	33·00 N	112·42 E
150	Nanyüan ... China (Peking In.)	39·48 N	116·24 E
148	Nanyün (nän'yün') ... China	38·11 N	116·37 E
151	Nao Chou (I.) ... China	20·58 N	110·58 E
91	Naolinco (nä-ō-lēn'kō) ... Mex.	19·39 N	96·50 W
84	Naomi (nā-ō'mĭ) La. (New Orleans In.)	29·42 N	89·59 W
127	Náousa (nä'ōō-sȧ) ... Grc.	40·38 N	22·05 E
68	Napa (năp'ȧ) ... Calif.	38·20 N	122·17 W
81	Napanee (năp'ȧ-nē) ... Can.	44·15 N	77·00 W
75	Naperville (nā'pēr-vĭl) Ill. (Chicago In.)	41·46 N	88·09 W
159	Napier (nā'pĭ-ēr) ... N. Z. (In.)	39·30 S	177·00 E
85	Napierville (nā'pĭ-ēr-vĭl) Can. (Montreal In.)	45·11 N	73·24 W
79	Naples (nā'p'lz) ... Fla. (In.)	26·07 N	81·46 W
	Naples, see Nápoli		
98	Napo (R.) (nä'pō) ... Peru	1·49 S	74·20 W
80	Napoleon (nȧ-pō'lē-ŭn) ... Ohio	41·20 N	84·10 W
77	Napoleonville (nȧ-pō'lē-ŭn-vĭl) . La.	29·56 N	91·03 W
125	Napoli (Naples) (nä'pô-lē) It. (Napoli In.)	40·37 N	14·12 E
125	Napoli, Golfo di (G.) (gôl-fô-dē) . It. (Napoli In.)	40·29 N	14·08 E
80	Nappanee (năp'ȧ-nē) ... Ind.	41·30 N	86·00 W
153	Nara (nä'rä) ... Jap. (Osaka In.)	34·41 N	135·50 E
164	Nara ... Mali	15·09 N	7·27 W
153	Nara (Pref.) ... Jap. (Osaka In.)	34·36 N	135·49 E
128	Nara (R.) ... Sov. Un.	55·05 N	37·16 E
160	Naracoorte (nȧ-rȧ-kōōn'tē) . Austl.	36·50 S	140·50 E
93	Naranjas, Punta (Pt.) (pōō'n-tä-nä-rä'n-käs) . Pan.	7·17 N	81·09 W
143	Naraspur ... India	16·32 N	81·43 E
84	Narberth (när'bûrth) Pa. (Philadelphia In.)	40·01 N	75·17 W
122	Narbonne (når-bôn') ... Fr.	43·12 N	3·00 E
127	Nardò (när-dô') ... It.	40·11 N	18·02 E
98	Nare (nä'rē) ... Col. (In.)	6·12 N	74·37 W
121	Narew R. (nä'rĕf) ... Pol.	52·43 N	21·19 E
142	Narmada (R.) ... India	22·17 N	74·45 E
128	Naroch' (L.) (nä'rôch) ... Sov. Un.	54·51 N	27·00 E
132	Narodnaya, Gora (Mtn.) (nȧ-rôd'nȧ-yȧ) . Sov. Un.	65·10 N	60·10 E
128	Naro Fominsk (nä'rô-fô-mēnsk') Sov. Un.	55·23 N	36·43 E
119	Närpesȧ (R.) ... Fin.	62·35 N	21·24 E
161	Narrabeen (năr-ȧ-bĭn) Austl. (Sydney In.)	33·44 S	151·18 E
160	Narrabri (nȧ-rä'brē) ... Austl.	30·17 S	149·46 E
84	Narragansett (năr-ȧ-găn'sĕt) R. I. (Providence In.)	41·26 N	71·27 W
81	Narragansett B. ... R. I.	41·20 N	71·15 W
160	Narrandera (nȧ-rȧn-dē'rȧ) .. Austl.	34·40 S	146·40 E
158	Narrogin (năr'ō-gĭn) ... Austl.	33·00 S	117·15 E
128	Narva (nȧr'vȧ) ... Sov. Un.	59·24 N	28·12 E
155	Narvacan (när-vä-kän') Phil. (Manila In.)	17·27 N	120·29 E
128	Narva Jõesuu (nȧr'vȧ ōō-ô-ă'sōō-ōō) . Sov. Un.	59·26 N	28·02 E
112	Narvik (när'vēk) ... Nor.	68·21 N	17·18 E
119	Narvskiy Zaliv (B.) (nȧr'vskĭ zä'lĭf) . Sov. Un.	59·35 N	27·25 E
132	Nar'yan-Mar (när'yȧn mär') Sov. Un.	67·42 N	53·30 E
160	Naryilco (năr-ĭl'kō) ... Austl.	28·40 S	141·50 E
134	Narym (nä-rēm') ... Sov. Un.	58·47 N	82·05 E
145	Naryn (R.) (nŭ-rĭn') ... Sov. Un.	41·46 N	73·00 E
110	Naseby (nāz'bĭ) ... Eng.	52·23 N	0·59 W
74	Nashua (năsh'ŭ-ȧ) Mo. (Kansas City In.)	39·18 N	94·34 W
83	Nashua ... N. H. (Boston In.)	42·47 N	71·23 W
73	Nashville (năsh'vĭl) ... Ark.	33·56 N	93·50 W
78	Nashville ... Ga.	31·12 N	83·15 W
73	Nashville ... Ill.	38·21 N	89·42 W
80	Nashville ... Mich.	42·35 N	85·05 W
78	Nashville ... Tenn.	36·10 N	86·48 W
71	Nashwauk (năsh'wôk) ... Minn.	47·21 N	93·12 W
127	Našice (nä'shē-tsĕ) ... Yugo.	45·29 N	18·06 E
121	Nasielsk (nä'syĕlsk) ... Pol.	52·35 N	20·50 E
142	Nāsik (nä'sĭk) ... India	20·02 N	73·49 E
165	Nasir (nä-zēr') ... Sud.	8·30 N	33·06 E
142	Nasirabād ... India	26·13 N	74·48 E
87	Naskaupi (R.) (năs'kō-pĭ) ... Can.	53·59 N	61·10 W
94	Nassau (năs'ô) ... Ba. Is.	25·05 N	77·20 W
155	Nassau-Gebergte (Mts.) Neth. N. Gui.	3·48 S	136·45 E
111	Nassenheide (nä'sĕn-hī-dĕ) Ger. (Berlin In.)	52·49 N	13·13 E
118	Nässjö (nĕs'shû) ... Swe.	57·39 N	14·39 E
155	Nasugbu (nȧ-sōōg-bōō') Phil. (Manila In.)	14·05 N	120·37 E
76	Nasworthy L. (năz'wûr-thē) .. Tex.	31·17 N	100·30 W
151	Nata ... China	19·30 N	109·38 E
93	Natá (nȧ-tȧ') ... Pan.	8·20 N	8·30 W
98	Natagaima (nä-tä-gī'mä) Col. (In.)	3·38 N	75·07 W
99	Natal (nä-täl') ... Braz.	6·00 S	35·13 W
166	Natal (Prov.) (nȧ-täl') ... S. Afr.	28·50 S	30·07 E
83	Natashguan (nä-täsh'kwän) .. Can.	50·09 N	61·46 W
87	Natashguan (R.) ... Can.	51·34 N	61·46 W
78	Natchez (năch'ĕz) ... Miss.	31·35 N	91·20 W
77	Natchitoches (năk'ĭ-tŏsh) (nȧch-ĭ-tŏsh') . La.	31·46 N	93·06 W
139	Nathanya ... Isr. (Palestine In.)	32·19 N	34·52 E
83	Natick (nā'tĭk) . Mass. (Boston In.)	42·17 N	71·21 W
135	National Area (Reg.) ... Sov. Un.	66·30 N	170·30 E
67	National Bison Ra. (Mts.) (năsh'ŭn-ăl bī's'n) . Mont.	47·18 N	113·58 W
68	National City Calif. (San Diego In.)	32·38 N	117·01 W
85	Nation R. (nā'shŭn) Can. (Ottawa In.)	45·21 N	75·07 W
99	Natividade (nä-tē-vē-dä'dĕ) . Braz.	11·43 S	47·34 W
75	Natrona (nā'trŏ nȧ) Pa. (Pittsburgh In.)	40·38 N	79·43 W
166	Natron L. (nā'trŏn) ... Tan.	2·29 S	35·17 E
168	Natrum, Wadi el (Val.) U. A. R. (Nile In.)	30·33 N	30·12 E
154	Natuna, Pulau-Pulau (Is.) . Indon.	3·22 N	108·00 E
69	Natural Bridges Natl. Mon. (năt'ū-răl brĭj'ĕs) . Utah	37·20 N	110·20 W
158	Naturaliste, C. (năt-ū-rȧ-lĭst') Austl.	33·30 S	115·10 E
91	Naucalpan (nä'ōō-käl-pä'n) Mex. (Mexico In.)	19·28 N	99·14 W
91	Nauchampatepetl (Mtn.) (näōō-chäm-pä-tĕ'pĕtl) . Mex.	19·32 N	97·09 W
82	Naudville ... Can.	48·36 N	71·40 W
111	Nauen (nou'ĕn) .. Ger. (Berlin In.)	52·36 N	12·53 E
81	Naugatuck (nô'gȧ-tŭk) ... Conn.	41·25 N	73·05 W
155	Naujan (nä-ōō-hän') Phil. (Manila In.)	13·19 N	121·17 E
120	Naumburg (noum'bōōrgh) ... Ger.	51·10 N	11·50 E
156	Nauru I. ... Oceania	0·30 S	167·00 E
91	Nautla (nä-ōōt'lä) ... Mex.	20·14 N	96·44 W
76	Nava (nä'vä) ... Mex.	28·25 N	100·44 W
124	Nava, L. de la ... Sp.	42·05 N	4·42 W
124	Nava del Rey (nä-vä dĕl rā'ē) . Sp.	41·22 N	5·04 W
124	Navahermosa (nä-vä-ĕr-mō'sä) . Sp.	39·39 N	4·28 W
94	Navajas (nä-vä-häs') ... Cuba	22·40 N	81·20 W
69	Navajo Ind. Res. (năv'ȧ-hō) Ariz.-N. Mex.	36·31 N	109·24 W
69	Navajo Natl. Mon. ... Ariz.	36·43 N	110·39 W
125	Navalcarnero (nä-väl'kär-nä'rō) Sp. (Madrid In.)	40·17 N	4·05 W
124	Navalmoral de la Mata (nä-väl'mōräl' dā lä mä'tä) . Sp.	39·53 N	5·32 W
85	Navan (nă'vȧn) . Can. (Ottawa In.)	45·25 N	75·26 W
100	Navarino (nȧ-vä-rē'nō) (I.) .. Chile	55·30 S	68·15 W
124	Navarra (Reg.) (nä-vär'rä) ... Sp.	42·40 N	1·35 W
101	Navarro (nä-vä'r-rō) Arg. (Buenos Aires In.)	35·00 S	59·16 W
77	Navasota (năv-ȧ-sō'tȧ) ... Tex.	30·24 N	96·05 W
77	Navasota R. ... Tex.	31·03 N	96·11 W
95	Navassa (I.) (nȧ-văs'ȧ) ... N. A.	18·25 N	75·15 W
124	Navia (R.) (nä-vē'ä) ... Sp.	43·10 N	6·45 W
101	Navidad (nä-vē-dä'd) Chile (Santiago In.)	34·57 S	71·51 W
95	Navidad Bk. (nä-vē-dädh') . Ba. Is.	20·05 N	69·00 W
101	Navidade do Carangola (nȧ-vē-dä'dĕ-dô-kȧ-rän-gô'la) Braz. (Rio de Janeiro In.)	21·04 S	41·58 W
88	Navojoa (nạ-vô-kô'ä) ... Mex.	27·00 N	109·40 W
127	Návplion ... Grc.	37·33 N	22·46 E
145	Nawagai (nŭ-wŭ-gī') W. Pak. (Khyber Pass In.)	34·40 N	71·18 E
127	Náxos (I.) (nák'sôs) ... Grc.	37·15 N	25·20 E
88	Nayarit (State) (nä-yä-rēt') . Mex.	22·00 N	105·15 W
90	Nayarit, Sierra de (Mts.) (sē-ĕ'r-rä-dĕ) . Mex.	23·20 N	105·07 W
99	Nazaré (nä-zä-rĕ') ... Braz.	13·04 S	38·49 W
124	Nazaré (nä-zä-rā') ... Port.	39·38 N	9·04 W
99	Nazaré da Mata (dä-mä-tä) . Braz.	7·46 S	35·13 W
139	Nazareth (năz'ȧ-rĕth) Isr. (Palestine In.)	32·43 N	35·19 E
76	Nazas (nä'zäs) ... Mex.	25·14 N	104·08 W
76	Nazas, R. ... Mex.	25·08 N	104·20 W
133	Nazilli (nȧ-zĭ-lē') ... Tur.	37·40 N	28·10 E
136	Naziya R. (nä-zē'yȧ) Sov. Un. (Leningrad In.)	59·48 N	31·18 E
165	Ndélé (n'dā-lā') ... Cen. Afr. Rep.	8·21 N	20·43 E
166	Ndjolé (n'dzhô-lā') ... Gabon	0·15 S	10·45 E
166	Ndola (n'dō'lä) Fed. of Rh. & Nya.	12·52 S	28·44 E
116	Neagh Lough (B.) (lŏk nā) N. Ire.	54·40 N	6·47 W
161	Neapean (R.) . Austl. (Sydney In.)	33·40 S	150·39 E
127	Neápolis (nā-ŏp' ô-lĭs) ... Grc.	36·35 N	23·08 E
126	Neápolis ... Grc. (In.)	35·17 N	25·37 E
64	Near Is. (nēr) ... Alaska	52·20 N	172·40 E
116	Neath (nēth) ... Wales	51·41 N	3·50 W
160	Nebine Cr. (nĕ-bēne') ... Austl.	27·50 S	147·00 E
133	Nebit-Dag (nyĕ-bēt'däg') . Sov. Un.	39·30 N	54·20 E
62	Nebraska (State) (nē-brăs'kȧ) U. S.	41·45 N	101·30 W
73	Nebraska City ... Nebr.	40·40 N	95·50 W
77	Neches R. (nĕch'ĕz) ... Tex.	31·03 N	94·40 W
120	Neckar R. (nĕk'är) ... Ger.	49·16 N	9·06 E
100	Necochea (nā-kô-chā'ä) ... Arg.	38·30 S	58·45 W
129	Nedrigaylov (nĕ-drĭ-gī'lôf) Sov. Un.	50·49 N	33·52 E
83	Needham (nēd'ăm) Mass. (Boston In.)	42·17 N	71·14 W
68	Needles (nē'd'lz) ... Calif.	34·51 N	114·39 W
71	Neenah (nē'nȧ) ... Wis.	44·10 N	88·30 W
86	Neepawa ... Can.	50·17 N	99·31 W
72	Nee Res. (nē) ... Colo.	38·26 N	102·56 W
117	Neetze (R.) (nĕ'tzē) ... Ger.	53·04 N	11·00 E
153	Negareyama (nā'gȧ-rȧ-yä'mä) Jap. (Tōkyō In.)	35·52 N	139·54 E
71	Negaunee (nē-gô'nē) ... Mich.	46·30 N	87·37 W
139	Negev (Des.) (nĕ'gĕv) Isr. (Palestine In.)	30·34 N	34·43 E
127	Negoi (Mtn.) (nā-goi') ... Rom.	45·33 N	24·38 E
143	Negombo ... Ceylon	7·39 N	79·49 E
127	Negotin (nĕ'gô-tēn) ... Yugo.	44·13 N	22·33 E
154	Negrais, C. (nĕ'grīs) ... Bur.	16·08 N	93·34 E
139	Negri Sembilan (State) (nā'grē sĕm-bē-län') Mala. (Singapore In.)	2·46 N	101·54 E

ng-sing; ŋ-baŋk; ɴ-nasalized n; nŏd; cŏmmit; ōld; ôbey; ôrder; fōōd; fŏŏt; ou-out; s-soft; sh-dish; th-thin; pūre; ûnite; ûrn; stŭd; circŭs; ü-as "y" in study; '-indeterminate vowel.

Page	Name Pronunciation Region	Lat. °′	Long. °′
100	Negro (R.) . . . Arg.	39·50 s	65·00 w
98	Negro, Rio (R.) (rĕ'ō nä'grōō) Braz.	0·18 s	63·21 w
124	Negro, C. (na'grô) . . . Mor.	35·25 n	4·51 w
93	Negro, Cerro (Mt.) (sĕ'r-rô-nā'grô) . Pan.	8·44 n	80·37 w
101	Negro (R.) . Ur. (Buenos Aires In.)	33·17 s	58·18 w
92	Negro R. . . . Nic.	13·01 n	87·10 w
154	Negros (I.) (nā'grōs) . . . Phil.	9·50 n	121·45 e
98	Neguá (nā-gwá') . . . Col. (In.)	5·51 n	76·36 w
66	Nehalem R. (nê-hăl'ĕm) . . . Ore.	45·52 n	123·37 w
123	Neheim (nĕ'hīm) . . Ger. (Ruhr In.)	51·28 n	7·58 e
95	Neiba (nå-ē'bä) . . . Dom. Rep.	18·30 n	71·20 w
95	Neiba, Bahai de (B.) (bä-ä'ē-dĕ) Dom. Rep.	18·10 n	71·00 w
95	Neiba, Sierra de (Mts.) (sē-ĕr'rä-dĕ) . . Dom. Rep.	18·40 n	71·40 w
151	Neichiang . . . China	29·38 n	105·01 e
148	Neich'iu (nā'chĭō) . . . China	37·17 n	114·32 e
67	Neihart (nī'hart) . . . Mont.	46·54 n	110·39 w
150	Neihsiang . . . China	33·00 n	111·54 e
71	Neillsville (nēlz'vĭl) . . . Wis.	44·35 n	90·37 w
98	Neira (nā'rä) . . . Col. (In.)	5·10 n	75·32 w
98	Neiva (nå-ē'vä) (nā'vä) . Col. (In.)	2·55 n	75·16 w
71	Nekoosa (nê-kōō'sȧ) . . . Wis.	44·19 n	89·54 w
118	Neksö (nĕk'sû) . . . Den.	55·05 n	15·05 e
70	Neligh (nē'lĭg) . . . Nebr.	42·06 n	98·02 w
135	Nel'kan (nĕl-kän') . . . Sov. Un.	57·45 n	136·36 e
143	Nellore (nĕl-lōr') . . . India	14·28 n	79·59 e
152	Nel'ma (nĕl-mä') . . . Sov. Un.	47·34 n	139·05 e
86	Nelson (nĕl'sŭn) . . . Can.	49·27 n	117·24 w
110	Nelson . . . Eng.	53·50 n	2·13 w
159	Nelson . . . N. Z. (In.)	41·15 s	173·22 e
64	Nelson (I.) . . . Alaska	60·38 n	164·42 w
160	Nelson, C. . . . Austl.	38·29 s	141·20 e
86	Nelson (R.) . . . Can.	56·20 n	93·59 w
68	Nelson Cr. . . . Nev.	40·22 n	114·43 w
80	Nelsonville (nĕl'sŭn-vĭl) . . . Ohio	39·30 n	82·15 w
160	Néma (nā'mä) . . . Mauritania	16·46 n	7·03 w
74	Nemadji R. (nĕ-măd'jê) Wis. (Duluth In.)	46·33 n	92·16 w
119	Neman (nĕ'-mán) . . . Sov. Un.	55·02 n	22·01 e
121	Neman R. . . . Sov. Un.	53·28 n	24·45 e
120	Německý Brod (nyĕ'myĕt-skyĭ brōd') . Czech.	49·38 n	15·34 e
129	Nemirov (nyå-mê'rôf) . . . Sov. Un.	48·56 n	28·51 e
113	Nemours (nē-mōōr') . . . Alg.	35·19 n	1·09 w
122	Nemours . . . Fr.	48·16 n	2·41 e
152	Nemuro (nā'mōō-rō) . . . Jap.	43·13 n	145·10 e
152	Nemuro Str. . . . Jap.	43·07 n	145·10 e
110	Nen (nĕn) . . . Eng.	52·32 n	0·19 w
116	Nenagh (nē'nȧ) . . . Ire.	52·50 n	8·05 w
64	Nenana (nå-nä'nȧ) . . . Alaska	64·28 n	149·18 w
150	Nench'eng (Mergen) . . . China	49·02 n	125·15 e
147	Nen Chiang (R.) . . . China	47·07 n	123·28 e
148	Nengcheng . . . China	33·15 n	116·34 e
136	Nenikyul' (nĕ-nyē'kyûl) Sov. Un. (Leningrad In.)	59·26 n	30·40 e
73	Neodesha (nē-ô-dĕ-shô') . . . Kans.	37·24 n	95·41 w
73	Neosho . . . Mo.	36·51 n	94·22 w
73	Neosho (R.) (nê-ō'shō) . . . Kans.	38·21 n	95·53 w
138	Nepal (nĕ-pôl') . . . Asia	28·45 n	83·00 e
69	Nephi (nē'fī) . . . Utah	39·40 n	111·50 w
101	Nepomuceno (nĕ-pô-mōō-sĕ'nō) Braz. (Rio de Janeiro In.)	21·15 s	45·13 w
126	Nera (R.) (nā'rä) . . . It.	42·45 n	12·54 e
122	Nérac (nā-räk') . . . Fr.	44·08 n	0·19 e
135	Nerchinsk (nyĕr' chĕnsk) . Sov. Un.	51·47 n	116·17 e
135	Nerchinskiy Khrebet (Mts.) Sov. Un.	50·30 n	118·30 e
135	Nerchinskiy Zavod (nyĕr'chĕn-skĭzȧ-vôt') . Sov. Un.	51·35 n	119·46 e
128	Nerekhta (nyĕ-rĕĸ'tȧ) . . . Sov. Un.	57·29 n	40·34 e
127	Neretva (R.) (nĕ'rĕt-vȧ) . . . Yugo.	43·08 n	17·50 e
124	Nerja (nĕr'hä) . . . Sp.	36·45 n	3·53 w
128	Nerl' (R.) (nyĕrl) . . . Sov. Un.	56·59 n	37·57 e
84	Nero (nĕr'ō) La. (New Orleans In.)	29·37 n	89·52 w
136	Nerskaya R. (nyĕr'skȧ-yȧ) Sov. Un. (Moskva In.)	55·31 n	38·46 e
128	Nerussa (R.) (nyå-rōō'sȧ) . Sov. Un.	52·24 n	34·20 e
116	Ness, Loch (L.) (lŏĸ nĕs) . . . Scot.	57·23 n	4·20 w
72	Ness City (nĕs) . . . Kans.	38·27 n	99·55 w
121	Nesterov (nĕs'-tzhyĕ-rôf) . Sov. Un.	50·03 n	23·58 e
119	Nesterov (nyĕs-tā'rôf) . . . Sov. Un.	54·39 n	22·38 e
127	Néstos (R.) (nās'tōs) . . . Grc.	41·25 n	24·12 e
128	Nesvizh (nyĕs'vēsh) . . . Sov. Un.	53·13 n	26·44 e
84	Netcong (nĕt'cŏnj) N. J. (New York In.)	40·54 n	74·42 w
102	Netherlands (nĕdh'ĕr-lăndz) . . Eur.	53·01 n	3·57 e
	Netherlands Guiana, see Surinam		
155	Netherlands New Guinea (nū gĭn'ê) . Asia	3·05 s	135·00 e
71	Nett Lake Ind. Res. (nĕt lāk) . Minn.	48·23 n	93·19 w
125	Nettuno (nĕt-tōō'nô) It. (Roma In.)	41·28 n	12·40 e
123	Neubeckum (noi'bĕ-kōōm) Ger. (Ruhr In.)	51·48 n	8·01 e
120	Neubrandenburg (noi-brän'dĕn-bōōrgh) . Ger.	53·33 n	13·16 e
120	Neuburg (noi'bōōrgh) . . . Ger.	48·43 n	11·12 e
120	Neuchâtel (nû-shȧ-tĕl') . . . Switz.	47·00 n	6·52 e
120	Neuchatel, Lac de (L.) . . . Switz.	46·48 n	6·53 e
111	Neuenhagen (noi'ĕn-hä-gĕn) Ger. (Berlin In.)	52·31 n	13·41 e
123	Neuenrade (noi'ĕn-rä-dĕ) Ger. (Ruhr In.)	51·17 n	7·47 e
122	Neufchâtel-en-Bray (nû-shä-tĕl'ĕɴ-brā') . Fr.	49·43 n	1·25 e
120	Neuhaldensleben (noi-häl'dĕns-lā'bĕn) . Ger.	52·18 n	11·23 e
111	Neuhaus (Oste) (noi' houz) (ōz'tĕ) Ger. (Hamburg In.)	53·48 n	9·02 e
111	Neulengbach . . . Aus. (Wien In.)	48·13 n	15·55 e
120	Neumarkt (noi'märkt) . . . Ger.	49·17 n	11·30 e
120	Neumünster (noi'münstĕr) . . . Ger.	54·04 n	10·00 e
120	Neunkirchen (noin'kĭrĸ-ĕn) . . . Aus.	47·43 n	16·05 e
123	Neunkirchen . . . Ger.	49·21 n	7·20 e
100	Neuquén (nĕ-ōō-kān') . . . Arg.	38·52 s	68·12 w
100	Neuquen (Prov.) . . . Arg.	39·40 s	70·45 w
100	Neuquén (R.) . . . Arg.	38·45 s	69·00 w
111	Neuruppin (noi'rōō-pēn) Ger. (Berlin In.)	52·55 n	12·48 e
79	Neuse (R.) (nūz) . . . N. C.	36·12 n	78·50 w
120	Neusiedler See (L.) (noi-zēd'lĕr) Aus.	47·54 n	16·31 e
123	Neuss (nois) . . . Ger. (Ruhr In.)	51·12 n	6·41 e
120	Neustadt (noi'shtät) . . . Ger.	49·21 n	8·08 e
120	Neustadt . . . Ger.	54·06 n	10·50 e
120	Neustadt bei Coburg (bī kō'bōōrgh) . Ger.	50·20 n	11·09 e
120	Neustrelitz (noi-strā'lĭts) . . . Ger.	53·21 n	13·05 e
120	Neu Ulm (noi ōō lm') . . . Ger.	48·23 n	10·01 e
85	Neuville (nū'vĭl) . Can. (Quebec In.)	46·39 n	71·35 w
120	Neuwied (noi'vēdt) . . . Ger.	50·26 n	7·28 e
71	Nevada (nê-vä'dȧ) . . . Iowa	42·01 n	93·27 w
73	Nevada . . . Mo.	37·49 n	94·21 w
62	Nevada (State) . . . U. S.	39·30 n	123·20 w
124	Nevada, Sierra (Mts.) (syĕr'rä nā-vä'dhä) . Sp.	37·01 n	3·28 w
62	Nevada, Sierra (Mts.) (sē-ĕ'r-rä nê-vä'dȧ) . U. S.	39·20 n	120·25 w
68	Nevada City . . . Calif.	39·16 n	120·01 w
98	Nevado, Cerro el (Mtn.) (sĕ'r-rô-ĕl-nĕ-vä'dô) . Col. (In.)	4·02 n	74·08 w
90	Nevado de Colima (Mtn.) (nå-vä'dhô dā kô-lē'mä) . Mex.	19·34 n	103·39 w
136	Neva R. (nyĕ-vä') Sov. Un. (Leningrad In.)	59·49 n	30·54 e
136	Neva Stantsiya (nyĕ-vä' stän'tsĭ-yȧ) Sov. Un. (Leningrad In.)	59·53 n	30·30 e
128	Nevel' (nyĕ'vĕl) . . . Sov. Un.	56·03 n	29·57 e
99	Neveri (nĕ-vĕ-rē) (R.) . . Ven. (In.)	10·13 n	64·18 w
122	Nevers (nē-vår') . . . Fr.	46·59 n	3·10 e
127	Nevesinje (nĕ-vĕ'sēn-yĕ) . . . Yugo.	43·15 n	18·08 e
116	Nevis, Ben (Mtn.) (bĕn) . . . Scot.	56·47 n	5·00 w
93	Nevis I. (nē'vĭs) W. I. F. (Le. & Wind. Is. In.)	17·05 n	62·38 w
93	Nevis Pk. W. I. F. (Le. & Wind. Is. In.)	17·11 n	62·33 w
127	Nevrokop (nĕv'rō-kôp') . . . Bul.	41·35 n	23·46 e
133	Nevşehir (nĕv-shĕ'hĕr) . . . Tur.	38·40 n	34·35 e
136	Nev'yansk (nĕv-yänsk') Sov. Un. (Urals In.)	57·29 n	60·14 e
79	New (R.) (nū) . . . Va.	37·20 n	80·35 w
79	New (R.), South Fork . . Va.-N. C.	36·37 n	81·15 w
75	New Albany (nú ôl'bȧ-nĭ) Ind. (Louisville In.)	38·17 n	85·49 w
78	New Albany . . . Miss.	34·28 n	89·00 w
99	New Amsterdam (ăm'stĕr-dăm) Br. Gu.	6·14 n	57·30 w
47	New Amsterdam I. . . . Ind. O.	37·52 s	77·32 e
65	Newark (nū'ĕrk) Calif. (San Francisco In.)	37·32 n	122·02 w
81	Newark . . . Del.	39·40 n	75·45 w
110	Newark . . . Eng.	53·04 n	0·49 w
84	Newark . . . N. J. (New York In.)	40·44 n	74·10 w
81	Newark . . . N. Y.	43·05 n	77·10 w
80	Newark . . . Ohio	40·05 n	82·25 w
75	New Augusta (ô-gŭs'tȧ) Ind. (Indianapolis In.)	39·53 n	86·14 w
80	Newaygo (nū'wā-go) . . . Mich.	43·25 n	85·50 w
81	New Bedford (bĕd'fērd) . . . Mass.	41·35 n	70·55 w
66	Newberg (nū'bûrg) . . . Ore.	45·17 n	122·58 w
79	New Bern (bûrn) . . . N. C.	35·05 n	77·05 w
78	Newbern . . . Tenn.	36·05 n	89·12 w
71	Newberry (nū'bĕr-ĭ) . . . Mich.	46·22 n	85·31 w
79	Newberry . . . S. C.	34·15 n	81·40 w
75	New Bethel (bĕth'ĕl) Ind. (Indianapolis In.)	39·30 n	86·00 w
75	New Boston (bôs'tŭn) Mich. (Detroit In.)	42·10 n	83·24 w
80	New Boston . . . Ohio	38·45 n	82·55 w
76	New Braunfels (nū broun'fĕls) Tex.	29·43 n	98·07 w
74	New Brighton (brī'tŭn) . . . Minn. (Minneapolis, St. Paul In.)	45·04 n	93·12 w
75	New Brighton . Pa. (Pittsburgh In.)	40·34 n	80·18 w
81	New Britain (brĭt''n) . . . Conn.	41·40 n	72·45 w
155	New Britain (I.) . . . N. Gui. Ter.	6·45 s	149·38 e
84	New Brunswick (brŭnz'wĭk) N. J. (New York In.)	40·29 n	74·27 w
87	New Brunswick (Prov.) . . . Can.	47·14 n	66·30 w
80	Newburg . . . Ind.	38·00 n	87·25 w
73	Newburg . . . Mo.	37·54 n	91·53 w
81	Newburgh . . . N. Y.	41·30 n	74·00 w
75	Newburgh Heights Ohio (Cleveland In.)	41·27 n	81·40 w
116	Newbury (nū'bĕr-ĭ) . . . Eng.	51·24 n	1·26 w
83	Newbury . . . Mass. (Boston In.)	42·48 n	70·52 w
83	Newburyport (nū'bĕr-ĭ-pōrt) Mass. (Boston In.)	42·48 n	70·53 w
84	New Canaan (kā-nȧn) Conn. (New York In.)	41·06 n	73·30 w
82	New Carlisle (kär-līl') . . . Can.	48·01 n	65·22 w
160	Newcastle (nū-kås''l) . . . Austl.	33·00 s	151·55 e
82	Newcastle . . . Can.	47·00 n	65·36 w
81	New Castle . . . Del.	39·40 n	75·35 w
110	Newcastle (nû-kås''l) (nû-käs''l) Eng.	53·01 n	2·14 w
80	Newcastle . . . Ind.	39·55 n	85·25 w
80	New Castle . . . Ohio	40·20 n	82·10 w
80	New Castle . . . Pa.	41·00 n	80·25 w
72	Newcastle . . . Tex.	33·13 n	98·44 w
70	Newcastle . . . Wyo.	43·51 n	104·11 w
116	Newcastle-on-Tyne . . . Eng.	55·00 n	1·45 w
158	Newcastle Waters (wô'tērz) . Austl.	17·10 s	133·25 e
80	Newcomerstown (nū'kŭm-ērz-toun) . Ohio	40·15 n	81·40 w
84	New Croton Res. (krō'tôn) N. Y. (New York In.)	41·15 n	73·47 w
142	New Delhi (dĕl'hī) . . . India	28·43 n	77·18 e
70	Newell (nū'ĕl) . . . S. D.	44·43 n	103·26 w
159	New England Ra. (nû ĭŋ'glȧnd) Austl.	29·32 s	152·30 e
64	Newenham, C. (nū-ĕn-hăm) Alaska	58·40 n	162·32 w
75	Newfane (nū-fān) N. Y. (Buffalo In.)	43·17 n	78·44 w
87	Newfoundland (Prov.) (nû-fŭn'lănd') (nū'fŭnd-lănd) (nû'found-lănd') Can. (Newfoundland In.)	48·15 n	56·53 w
159	New Georgia (I.) (jôr'jĭ-ȧ) Sol. Is.	8·08 s	158·00 e
83	New Glasgow (glȧs'gō) . . . Can.	45·36 n	62·40 w
155	New Guinea, Territory of . Oceania	3·45 s	145·45 e
155	New Guinea (I.) (gĭne) N. Gui. Ter.	5·45 s	140·00 e
66	Newhalem (nū hā'lŭm) . . . Wash.	48·44 n	121·11 w
63	New Hampshire (State) (hămp'shĭr) . U. S.	43·55 n	71·40 w
71	New Hampton (hămp'tŭn) . . Iowa	43·03 n	92·20 w
167	New Hanover (hăn'ôvĕr) S. Afr. (Natal In.)	29·23 s	30·32 e
155	New Hanover (I.) . . . N. Gui. Ter.	2·37 s	150·15 e
80	New Harmony (nū här'mô-nĭ) Ind.	38·10 n	87·55 w
81	New Haven (hā'vĕn) . . . Conn.	41·20 n	72·55 w
117	Newhaven . . . Eng.	50·45 n	0·15 e
80	New Haven (nū hāv''n) . . . Ind.	41·05 n	85·00 w
159	New Hebrides (Is.) (hĕb'rĭ-dēz) Oceania	16·02 s	169·15 e
110	New Holland (hŏl'ănd) . . . Eng.	53·42 n	0·21 w
79	New Holland . . . N. C.	35·27 n	76·14 w
84	New Hope Mtn. (hōp) Ala. (Birmingham In.)	33·23 n	86·45 w
75	New Hudson (hŭd'sŭn) Mich. (Detroit In.)	42·30 n	83·36 w
77	New Iberia (ī-bē'rĭ-ȧ) . . . La.	30·00 n	91·50 w
85	Newington (nū'ĕng-tŏn) Can. (Ottawa In.)	45·07 n	75·00 w
155	New Ireland (I.) (ĭr'lănd) N. Gui. Ter.	3·15 s	152·30 e
63	New Jersey (State) (jûr'zĭ) . . U. S.	40·30 n	74·50 w
75	New Kensington (kĕn'zĭng-tŭn) Pa. (Pittsburgh In.)	40·34 n	79·35 w
73	Newkirk (nū'kûrk) . . . Okla.	36·52 n	97·03 w
166	Newlands (nû'lănds) S. Afr. (Cape Town In.)	33·58 s	18·28 e
75	New Lenox (lĕn'ŭk) Ill. (Chicago In.)	41·31 n	87·58 w
80	New Lexington (lĕk'sĭng-tŭn) . Ohio	39·40 n	82·10 w
71	New Lisbon (lĭz'bŭn) . . . Wis.	43·52 n	90·11 w
81	New London (lŭn'dŭn) . . . Conn.	41·20 n	72·05 w
71	New London . . . Wis.	44·24 n	88·45 w
73	New Madrid (măd'rĭd) . . . Mo.	36·34 n	89·31 w
78	Newman (nū'mȧn) . . . Ga.	33·22 n	84·47 w
79	Newman (L.) . . . Fla.	29·41 n	82·13 w
70	Newman's Grove (nū'mȧn grōv) Nebr.	41·46 n	97·44 w
81	Newmarket (nū'mär-kĕt) . . . Can.	44·00 n	79·30 w
80	New Martinsville (mär'tĭnz-vĭl) . W. Va.	39·35 n	80·50 w
62	New Mexico (State) (mĕk'sĭ-kō) U. S.	34·30 n	107·10 w
110	New Mills (mĭlz) . . . Eng.	53·22 n	2·00 w
75	New Munster (mŭn'stĕr) Wis. (Milwaukee In.)	42·35 n	88·13 w
160	New Norfolk (nôr'fŏk) . . . Austl.	42·50 s	147·17 e
84	New Orleans (ôr'lê-ănz) La. (New Orleans In.)	30·00 n	90·05 w
80	New Philadelphia (fĭl-ȧ-dĕl'fĭ-ȧ) . Ohio	40·30 n	81·30 w
159	New Plymouth (plĭm'ūth) N. Z. (In.)	39·04 s	174·13 e
73	Newport (nū'pōrt) . . . Ark.	35·35 n	91·16 w
161	Newport . . . Austl. (Sydney In.)	33·39 s	151·19 e
116	Newport (nū-pôrt) . . . Eng.	50·41 n	1·25 w
116	Newport . . . Wales	51·36 n	3·05 w
110	Newport . . . Eng.	52·46 n	2·22 w
75	Newport . . . Ky. (Cincinnati In.)	39·05 n	84·30 w
82	Newport . . . Maine	44·49 n	69·20 w
74	Newport . . . Minn. (Minneapolis, St. Paul In.)	44·52 n	92·59 w
81	Newport . . . N. H.	43·20 n	72·10 w
66	Newport . . . Ore.	44·39 n	124·02 w
84	Newport . . R. I. (Providence In.)	41·29 n	71·16 w
78	Newport . . . Tenn.	35·55 n	83·12 w
81	Newport . . . Vt.	44·55 n	72·15 w
66	Newport . . . Wash.	48·12 n	117·01 w
74	Newport Beach (bēch) Calif. (Los Angeles In.)	33·36 n	117·55 w
84	Newport News . Va. (Norfolk In.)	36·59 n	76·24 w
71	New Prague (nū prāg) . . . Minn.	44·33 n	93·35 w
94	New Providence (I.) (prŏv'ĭ-dĕns) . Ba. Is.	25·00 n	77·25 w
80	New Richmond (rĭch'mŭnd) . Ohio	38·55 n	84·15 w
71	New Richmond . . . Wis.	45·07 n	92·34 w
77	New Roads (rōds) . . . La.	30·42 n	91·26 w
84	New Rochelle (rû-shĕl') N. Y. (New York In.)	40·55 n	73·47 w
70	New Rockford (rŏk'fōrd) . . . N. D.	47·40 n	99·08 w
116	New Ross (rôs) . . . Ire.	52·25 n	6·55 w
85	New Sarepta . Can. (Edmonton In.)	53·17 n	113·09 w
149	New Shanghai China (Shanghai In.)	31·18 n	121·31 e
	New Siberian Is., see Novosibirskiye O-va		
79	New Smyra (smûr'nȧ) . . . Fla.	29·00 n	80·57 w
159	New South Wales (State) (wālz) Austl.	32·45 s	146·14 e
110	Newton (nû'tŭn) . . . Eng.	53·27 n	2·37 w
80	Newton . . . Ill.	39·00 n	88·10 w
71	Newton . . . Iowa	41·42 n	93·04 w
73	Newton . . . Kans.	38·03 n	97·22 w
83	Newton . . . Mass. (Boston In.)	42·21 n	71·13 w

ăt; finăl; rāte; senâte; ärm; åsk: sofȧ; fâre; ch-choose; dh-as th in other; bē; ēvent; bĕt; recĕnt; cratĕr; g-go; gh-guttural g; bĭt; ĭ-short neutral; rīde; ĸ-guttural k as ch in German ich;

Page	Name Pronunciation Region	Lat. °′	Long. °′
78	Newton Miss.	32·18 N	89·10 W
84	Newton N. J. (New York In.)	41·03 N	74·45 W
79	Newton N. C.	35·40 N	81·19 W
77	Newton Tex.	30·47 N	93·45 W
85	Newton Brook (brŏŏk) Can. (Toronto In.)	43·48 N	79·25 W
85	Newton Siding (sīd'ĭng) Can. (Winnipeg In.)	49·56 N	98·04 W
75	Newtonsville (nū'tŭnz-vĭl) Ohio (Cincinnati In.)	39·11 N	84·04 W
85	New Toronto (tô-rŏn'tō) Can. (Toronto In.)	43·37 N	79·30 W
70	Newtown (nū'toun) N. D.	47·57 N	102·25 W
75	Newtown Ohio (Cincinnati In.)	39·08 N	84·22 W
84	Newtown Pa. (Philadelphia In.)	40·13 N	74·56 W
116	Newtownards (nu-t'n-ardz') Ire.	54·35 N	5·39 W
71	New Ulm (ŭlm) Minn.	44·18 N	94·27 W
83	New Waterford (wô'tēr-fērd) Can.	46·14 N	60·04 W
65	New Westminster (wĕst'mĭn-stēr) Can. (Vancouver In.)	49·12 N	122·55 W
84	New York (yôrk) N. Y. (New York In.)	40·40 N	73·58 W
63	New York (State) U. S.	42·45 N	78·05 W
159	New Zealand (zē'lănd) Oceania	39·14 S	169·30 E
90	Nexapa (R.) (nĕks-ä'pä) Mex.	18·32 N	98·29 W
153	Neya-gawa (nå'yä gä'wä) Jap. (Ōsaka In.)	34·47 N	135·38 E
144	Neyshābūr Iran	36·06 N	58·45 E
136	Neyva R. (nĕy'vå) Sov. Un. (Urals In.)	57·39 N	60·37 E
129	Nezhin (nyĕzh'ēn) Sov. Un.	50·03 N	31·52 E
66	Nez Perce (nĕz' pûrs') Idaho	46·16 N	116·15 W
166	Ngami (R.) (n'gä'mē) Bech.	20·56 S	22·31 E
142	Nganglaring Tsho (L.) China	31·42 N	82·53 E
165	Ngaoundéré (n'gōn-dā-rā') Cam.	7·19 N	13·30 E
167	Ngong ('n-gông) Ken.	1·27 S	36·39 E
167	Ngqeleni ('ng-kĕ-lā'nē) S. Afr. (Natal In.)	31·41 S	29·04 E
165	Nguigmi ('n-gēg'mē) Niger	14·14 N	13·04 E
164	Nguru ('n-gōō'rōō) Nig.	12·53 N	10·26 E
154	Nha Trang (nyä-träng') Viet.	12·08 N	108·56 E
164	Naifounke Mali	16·03 N	4·17 W
71	Niagara (nī-ăg'á-rá) Wis.	45·45 N	88·05 W
75	Niagara Falls Can. (Buffalo In.)	43·05 N	79·05 W
75	Niagara Falls N. Y. (Buffalo In.)	43·06 N	79·02 W
85	Niagara-on-the-Lake Can. (Toronto In.)	43·16 N	79·05 W
75	Niagara R. U. S.-Can. (Buffalo In.)	43·12 N	79·03 W
164	Niamey (nē-ä-mā') Niger	13·33 N	2·08 E
165	Niangara (nē-äŋ-gä'rå) Con. L.	3·36 N	28·00 E
73	Niangua (R.) (nī-ăŋ'gwå) Mo.	37·45 N	92·56 W
154	Nias (I.) (nē'äs') Indon.	0·58 N	97·43 E
118	Nibe (nē'bĕ) Den.	56·57 N	9·36 E
88	Nicaragua (nĭk-á-rä'gwå) N. A.	12·45 N	86·15 W
92	Nicaragua, Lago de (L.) (lä'gô dĕ) Nic.	11·45 N	85·28 W
126	Nicastro (nê-käs'trō) It.	38·39 N	16·15 E
92	Nicchehabin, Punta (Pt.) (pōō'n-tä-nĕk-chĕ-ä-bē'n) Mex. (Yucatan In.)	19·50 N	87·20 W
123	Nice (nēs) Fr.	43·42 N	7·21 E
149	Nich'engchen China (Shanghai In.)	30·54 N	121·48 E
87	Nichicun (L.) (nĭch'ĭ-kŭn) Can.	53·07 N	72·10 W
94	Nicholas Chan. (nĭk'ô-lás) Ba. Is.	23·30 N	80·20 W
80	Nicholasville (nĭk'ô-lás-vĭl) Ky.	37·55 N	84·35 W
154	Nicobar Is. (nĭk-ô-bär') India	8·28 N	94·04 E
65	Nicolai Mtn. (nē-cō lī') Ore. (Portland In.)	46·05 N	123·27 W
91	Nicolás Romero (nē-kō-lä's-rô-mĕ'rô) Mex. (Mexico In.)	19·38 N	99·20 W
74	Nicolet, L. (nĭ'kô-lĕt) Mich. (Sault Ste. Marie In.)	46·22 N	84·14 W
94	Nicolls Town Ba. Is.	25·10 N	78·00 W
74	Nicols (nĭk'ĕls) Minn. (Minneapolis, St. Paul In.)	44·50 N	93·12 W
65	Nicomeki (R.) Can. (Vancouver In.)	49·04 N	122·47 W
115	Nicosia (nē-kô-sē'á) Cyprus	35·10 N	33·22 E
92	Nicoya (nē-kō'yä) C. R.	10·08 N	85·27 W
92	Nicoya, Golfo de (G.) (gôl-fô-dĕ) C. R.	10·03 N	85·04 W
92	Nicoya, Pen. de C. R.	10·05 N	86·00 W
	Nidaros, see Trondheim		
121	Nidzica (nê-jĕt'sá) Pol.	53·21 N	20·30 E
120	Niedere Tauern (Mts.) Aus.	47·15 N	13·41 E
123	Niederkrüchten (nē'dĕr-krük-tĕn) Ger. (Ruhr In.)	51·12 N	6·14 E
111	Niederösterreich (Lower Austria) (State) Aus. (Wien In.)	48·24 N	16·20 E
120	Niedersachsen (Lower Saxony) (State) (nē'dĕr-zäk-sĕn) Ger.	52·52 N	8·27 E
120	Nienburg (nē'ĕn-bŏŏrgh) Ger.	52·40 N	9·15 E
120	Niesse (R.) (nēs) Pol.	51·30 N	15·00 E
168	Nietverdiend S. Afr. (Johannesburg & Pretoria In.)	25·02 S	26·10 E
99	Nieuw Nickerie (nē-nē'kĕ-rē') Sur.	5·51 N	57·00 W
90	Nieves (nyā'vås) Mex.	24·00 N	102·57 W
133	Niğde (nĭg'dĕ) Tur.	37·55 N	34·40 E
168	Nigel (nī'jĕl) S. Afr. (Johannesburg & Pretoria In.)	26·26 S	28·27 E
163	Niger (nī'jēr) Afr.	18·02 N	8·30 E
164	Niger R. Afr.	8·22 N	6·11 E
163	Nigeria (nī-jē'rĭ-á) Afr.	8·57 N	6·30 E
153	Nii (I.) (nē) Jap.	34·26 N	139·23 E
152	Niigata (nē'ē-gä'tå) Jap.	37·47 N	139·04 E
157	Niihau (nē'ē-hä'ōō) Hawaii (In.)	21·50 N	160·05 W
157	Niihau (I.) Hawaii (In.)	21·50 N	160·05 W
153	Niimi (nē'mē) Jap.	34·59 N	133·28 E
117	Nijmegen (nī'mä-gĕn) Neth.	51·50 S	5·52 E
153	Nikaidō (nē'kī-dō) Jap. (Ōsaka In.)	34·36 N	135·48 E
128	Nikitinka (nê-kĭ'tĭn-kå) Sov. Un.	55·33 N	33·19 E
153	Nikkō (nēk'kō) Jap.	36·44 N	139·35 E
129	Nikolayev (nē-kô-lä'yĕf) Sov. Un.	46·58 N	32·02 E
129	Nikolayev (Oblast) (ôb'låst) Sov. Un.	47·27 N	31·25 E
152	Nikolayevka Sov. Un.	48·37 N	134·49 E
136	Nikolayevka (nē-kô-lä'yĕf-kå) Sov. Un. (Leningrad In.)	59·29 N	29·48 E
133	Nikolayevskiy Sov. Un.	50·00 N	45·30 E
135	Nikolayevsk-na-Amure Sov. Un.	53·18 N	140·49 E
132	Nikol'sk (nê-kôlsk') Sov. Un.	59 30 N	45·40 E
136	Nikol'skoye (nê-kôl'skô-yĕ) Sov. Un. (Leningrad In.)	59·27 N	30·00 E
127	Nikopol (nē'kô-pŏl') Bul.	43·41 N	24·52 E
129	Nikopol' Sov. Un.	47·36 N	34·24 E
127	Nikšić (nēk'shēch) Yugo.	42·45 N	18·57 E
101	Nilahue (R.) (nē-lä'wĕ) Chile (Santiago In.)	36·36 S	71·50 W
163	Nile (R.) (nīl) Afr.	23·00 N	33·00 E
80	Niles (nīlz) Mich.	41·50 N	86·15 W
80	Niles Ohio	41·15 N	80·45 W
143	Nilgiri Hills India	17·05 N	76·22 E
100	Nilópolis (nē-lô'pō-lēs) Braz. (In.)	22·48 S	43·25 W
142	Nimach India	24·32 N	74·51 E
164	Nimba, Mt. (nĭm'bå) Ivory Coast	7·40 N	8·33 W
122	Nîmes (nēm) Fr.	43·49 N	4·22 E
73	Nimrod Res. (nĭm'rŏd) Ark.	34·58 N	93·46 W
165	Nimule (nê-mōō'lå) Sud.	3·38 N	32·12 E
160	Ninety Mile Bch. Austl.	38·20 S	147·30 E
133	Nineveh (Ruins) (nĭn'ē-vå) Iraq	36·30 N	43·10 E
150	Ningan (nĭŋ'gän') China	44·20 N	129·20 E
148	Ningchin (nĭng'jĭn) China	37·39 N	116·47 E
148	Ningching (nĭng'jĭn) China	37·37 N	114·55 E
146	Ningerh China	23·14 N	101·14 E
151	Ninghai (nĭng'hī') China	29·20 N	121·20 E
148	Ningho (nĭng'hō') China	39·27 N	117·44 E
	Ninghsia, see Yinch'uan		
146	Ninghsia Hui Aut. Reg. China	37·45 N	106·30 E
151	Ningming China	22·22 N	107·06 E
155	Ningo Is. N. Gui. Ter.	1·15 S	143·30 E
151	Ningpo (nĭng'pō') China	29·56 N	121·30 E
151	Ningte China	26·38 N	119·33 E
150	Ningwu (nĭng'wōō') China	39·00 N	112·12 E
148	Ningyang (nĭng'yäng') China	35·46 N	116·48 E
151	Ninh Binh (nēn bēnk') Viet.	20·22 N	106·00 E
72	Ninnescah (R.) (nĭn'ĕs-kä) Kans.	37·37 N	98·31 W
99	Nioaque (nēō-ä'-kĕ) Braz.	21·14 S	55·41 W
70	Niobrara (R.) (nī-ô-brâr'á) Nebr.	42·46 N	98·46 W
164	Nioro (nē-ō'rō) Mali	15·16 N	9·22 W
122	Niort (nê-ôr') Fr.	46·17 N	0·28 W
86	Nipawin Can.	53·24 N	103·52 W
95	Nipe, Bahía de (B.) (bä-ē'ä-dĕ-nē'pä) Cuba	20·50 N	75·30 W
95	Nipe, Sierra de (Mts.) (sē-ĕ'r-rå-dĕ) Cuba	20·20 N	75·50 W
87	Nipigon (nĭp'ĭ-gŏn) Can.	48·58 N	88·17 W
87	Nipigon (L.) Can.	49·37 N	89·55 W
71	Nipigon B. Can.	48·56 N	88·00 W
82	Nipisiguit (R.) (nĭ-pĭ'sĭ-kwĭt) Can.	47·26 N	66·15 W
87	Nipissing (L.) (nĭp'ĭ-sĭng) Can.	45·59 N	80·19 W
94	Niquero (nē-kä'rō) Cuba	20·00 N	77·35 W
127	Niš (nêsh) Yugo.	43·18 N	21·55 E
124	Nisa (nē'sá) Port.	39·32 N	7·41 W
127	Nišava (R.) (nē'shå-vå) Yugo.	43·17 N	22·17 E
153	Nishino (I.) (nēsh'ē-nô) Jap.	36·06 N	132·49 E
153	Nishinomiya (nēsh'ē-nô-mē'yå) Jap. (Ōsaka In.)	34·44 N	135·21 E
153	Nishinoomote (nēsh'ē-nô-ô-mō'tō) Jap.	30·44 N	130·59 E
153	Nishio (nēsh'ē-ô) Jap.	34·50 N	137·01 E
121	Nisko (nēs'kô) Pol.	50·30 N	22·07 E
85	Nisku (nĭs-kū') Can. (Edmonton In.)	53·21 N	113·33 W
66	Nisqually R. (nĭs-kwôl'ĭ) Wash.	46·51 N	122·33 W
118	Nissan (R.) Swe.	57·06 N	13·22 E
118	Nisser Vand (L.) (nĭs'ĕr vän) Nor.	59·14 N	8·35 E
118	Nissum Fd. Den.	56·24 N	7·35 E
100	Niterói (nē-tĕ-rô'ĭ) Braz. (In.)	22·53 S	43·07 W
116	Nith (R.) (nĭth) Scot.	55·13 N	3·55 W
121	Nitra (nē'trå) Czech.	48·18 N	18·04 E
121	Nitra R. Czech.	48·13 N	18·14 E
80	Nitro (nī'trô) W. Va.	38·25 N	81·50 W
117	Nivelles (nē'vĕl') Bel.	50·33 N	4·17 E
122	Nivernais, Côtes de (hills) (nē-vĕr-nĕ') Fr.	47·40 N	3·09 E
77	Nixon (nĭk'sŭn) Tex.	29·16 N	97·48 W
135	Nizhne-Angarsk (nyēzh'nyĭ-ŭngärsk') Sov. Un.	55·49 N	108·46 E
133	Nizhne-Chirskaya (nyĭ-ŭn-gärsk') Sov. Un.	48·20 N	42·50 E
135	Nizhne-Kolymsk (kô-lêmsk') Sov. Un.	68·32 N	160·56 E
134	Nizhneudinsk (nêzh'nyĭ-ōōdênsk') Sov. Un.	54·58 N	99·15 E
136	Nizhniye Sergi (nyēzh'[nyē] sĕr'gĕ) Sov. Un. (Urals In.)	56·41 N	59·19 E
129	Nizhniye Serogozy (nyēzh'nyĭ sĕ-rō-gô'zĭ) Sov. Un.	46·51 N	34·25 E
136	Nizhniy Tagil (tŭgĕl') Sov. Un. (Urals In.)	57·54 N	59·59 E
136	Nizhnyaya Kur'ya (nyē'zhnyå-yå koor'yå) Sov. Un. (Urals In.)	58·01 N	56·00 E
136	Nizhnyaya Salda (nyē'zh[nya'ya] säl'da') Sov. Un. (Urals In.)	58·05 N	60·43 E
134	Nizhnyaya Taymyra (R.) Sov. Un.	72·30 N	95·18 E
134	Nizhnyaya (Lower) Tunguska (R.) (tōōn-gōōs'kå) Sov. Un.	64·13 N	91·30 E
136	Nishnyaya Tura (tōō'rå) Sov. Un. (Urals In.)	58·38 N	59·50 E
136	Nizhnyaya Us'va (ōōs'vå) Sov. Un. (Urals In.)	59·05 N	58·53 E
118	Njurunda (nyōō-rōōn'då) Swe.	62·15 N	17·24 E
167	Nkandla ('n-känd'lä) S. Afr. (Natal In.)	28·40 S	31·06 E
142	Noākhāli E. Pak.	22·52 N	91·08 E
64	Noatak (nô-á'tăk) Alaska	67·22 N	163·28 W
64	Noatak (R.) Alaska	67·58 N	162·15 W
153	Nobeoka (nō-bå-ō'kå) Jap.	32·36 N	131·41 E
80	Noblesville (nō'bl'z-vĭl) Ind.	40·00 N	86·00 W
85	Nobleton (nō'bl'tŭn) Can. (Toronto In.)	43·54 N	79·39 W
125	Nocero Inferiore (nô-chĕ'rô-ēn-fĕ-ryô'rĕ) It. (Napoli In.)	40·30 N	14·38 E
90	Nochistlán (nô-chēs-tlän') Mex.	21·23 N	102·52 W
91	Nochixtlan (Asunción) (ä-sōōn-syōn') Mex.	17·28 N	97·12 W
155	Noemfoor (I.) (nōōm'fōr) Neth. N. Gui.	1·20 S	134·48 E
69	Nogales (nô-gä'lĕs) Ariz.	31·20 N	110·55 W
91	Nogales (nô-gä'lĕs) Mex.	18·49 N	97·09 W
88	Nogales Mex.	31·15 N	111·00 W
168	Nogal Val. (nô'gäl) Som. (Horn of Afr. In.)	8·30 N	47·50 E
129	Nogaysk (nô-gīsk') Sov. Un.	46·43 N	36·21 E
123	Nogent-le-Roi (nŏ-zhōn-lĕ-rwä') Fr. (Paris In.)	48·39 N	1·32 E
122	Nogent-le-Rotrou (rŏ-trōō') Fr.	48·22 N	0·47 E
136	Noginsk (nô-gēnsk') Sov. Un. (Moskva In.)	55·52 N	38·28 E
124	Nogueira (nô-gă'rä) Sp.	42·25 N	7.43 W
125	Nogueira Pallaresa (R.) (nô-gĕ'y-rä-päl-yä-rĕ-sä) Sp.	42·18 N	1·03 E
150	Noho (nô'hô') China	48·23 N	124·58 E
122	Noires, Mts. (nwár) Fr.	48·07 N	3·42 W
122	Noirmoutier, Île de (I.) (nwår-mōō-tyā') Fr.	47·03 N	3·08 W
153	Nojimā-Zaki (Pt.) (nō'jê-mä zä-kê) Jap.	34·54 N	139·48 E
86	Nokomis (nô-kō'mĭs) Can.	51·30 N	104·58 W
80	Nokomis Ill.	39·15 N	89·10 W
125	Nola (nô'lä) It. (Napoli In.)	40·41 N	14·32 E
79	Nolichucky (nŏl-ĭ-chŭck'ĭ) N. C.	35·59 N	82·20 W
132	Nolinsk (nô-lênsk') Sov. Un.	57·32 N	49·50 E
153	Noma Misaki (C.) (nô'mä mē'sä-kē) Jap.	31·25 N	130·09 E
90	Nombre de Dios (nôm-brĕ-dĕ-dyô's) Mex.	23·50 N	104·14 W
93	Nombre de Dios (nô'm-brĕ) Pan.	9·34 N	79·28 W
64	Nome (nōm) Alaska	64·30 N	165·20 W
86	Nonacho (L.) Can.	61·48 N	111·20 W
166	Nongoma (nŏn-gō'má) S. Afr.	27·48 S	31·45 E
65	Nooksack (nŏŏk'săk) Wash. (Vancouver In.)	48·55 N	122·19 W
65	Nooksack (R.) Wash. (Vancouver In.)	48·54 N	122·31 W
111	Noorden Neth. (Amsterdam In.)	52·09 N	4·49 E
111	Noordwijkaan Zee Neth. (Amsterdam In.)	52·14 N	4·25 E
111	Noordzee, Kanal, (Can.) Neth. (Amsterdam In.)	52·27 N	4·42 E
86	Nootka (I.) (nōōt'ká) Can.	49·38 N	127·38 W
166	Noqui (nô-kē') Ang.	5·50 S	13·35 E
152	Nor (R.) (nou') China	46·55 N	132·45 E
75	Nora (nō'rä) Ind. (Indianapolis In.)	39·54 N	86.08 W
118	Nora Swe.	59·32 N	14·56 E
73	Norborne (nôr'bôrn) Mo.	39·17 N	93·39 W
74	Norco (nôr'kô) Calif. (Los Angeles In.)	33·57 N	117·33 W
84	Norcross (nôr'krôs) Ga. (Atlanta In.)	33·56 N	84·13 W
85	Nord, Riviere du (rēv-yĕr' dü nôr) Can. (Montreal In.)	45·45 N	74·02 W
120	Norden (nôr'dĕn) Ger.	53·35 N	7·14 E
120	Norderney I. (nôr'dĕr-nĕy) Ger.	53·45 N	6·58 E
118	Nord Fd. (nôr'fyôr) Nor.	61·50 N	5·35 E
120	Nordhausen (nôrt'hau-zĕn) Ger.	51·30 N	10·48 E
120	Nordhorn (nôrt'hôrn) Ger.	52·26 N	7·05 E
112	Nord Kapp (C.) (nôr-kapp) Nor.	71·07 N	25·57 E
65	Nordland (nôrd'lănd) Wash. (Seattle In.)	48·03 N	122·41 W
120	Nördlingen (nûrt'lĭng-ĕn) Ger.	48·51 N	10·30 E
120	Nord-Ostsee (Kiel) Can. (nōrd-ōzt-zā) (kēl) Ger.	54·03 N	9·23 E
120	Nordrhein-Westfalen (North Rhine-Westphalia) (State) (nōrd'hīn-vĕst-fä-lĕn) Ger.	50·50 N	6.53 E
135	Nordvik (nôrd'vĕk) Sov. Un.	73·57 N	111·15 E
116	Nore R. (nōr) Ire.	52·34 N	7·15 W
78	Norfield (nôr'fēld) Miss.	31·24 N	90·25 W
83	Norfolk (nôr'fŏk) Mass. (Boston In.)	42·07 N	71·19 W
70	Norfolk Nebr.	42·10 N	97·25 W
84	Norfolk Va. (Norfolk In.)	36·55 N	76·15 W
73	Norfolk, L. Ark.	36·25 N	92·09 W
90	Noria (nō'rē-å) Mex.	23·04 N	106·20 W
134	Noril'sk (nô rēlsk') Sov. Un.	69·00 N	87·11 E
80	Normal (nôr'măl) Ill.	40·35 N	89·00 W
73	Norman (nôr'măn) Okla.	35·13 N	97·25 W
159	Norman (R.) Austl.	18·27 S	141·29 E
122	Normandie (Reg.) (nôr-mäN-dē') Fr.	49·02 N	0·17 E
122	Normandie, Collines de (Hills) (kŏ-lēn'dĕ-nŏr-män-dē') Fr.	48·35 N	0·30 W
159	Normanton (nôr'măn-tŭn) Austl.	17·45 S	141·10 E
110	Normanton Eng.	53·40 N	1·21 W
75	Normantown (nôr'măn toun) Ill. (Chicago In.)	41·39 N	88·14 W
86	Norman Wells Can.	65·26 N	127·00 W
158	Nornalup (nôr-năl'ŭp) Austl.	35·00 S	117·00 E
118	Norra Dellen (L.) Swe.	61·57 N	16·25 E
118	Norre Sundby (nû-rĕ-sōōn'bü) Den.	57·04 N	9·55 E
78	Norris (nŏr'ĭs) Tenn.	36·09 N	84·05 W
78	Norris (R.) Tenn.	36·17 N	83·55 W
84	Norristown (nŏr'ĭs-town) Pa. (Philadelphia In.)	40·07 N	75·21 W
118	Norrköping (nôr'chûp'ĭng) Swe.	58·37 N	16·10 E
118	Norrtälje (nôr-tĕl'yĕ) Swe.	59·47 N	18·39 E

ng-sing; ŋ-baŋk; N-nasalized n; nŏd; cŏmmit; ōld; ôbey; ôrder; fōōd; fŏŏt; ou-out; s-soft; sh-dish; th-thin; pūre; ûnite; ûrn; stŭd; circŭs; ü-as "y" in study; '-indeterminate vowel.

Page	Name Pronunciation Region	Lat. °′	Long. °′
158	Norseman (nôrs'măn) Austl.	32·15 S	122·00 E
101	Norte, Punta (Pt.) (pōō'n-tä-nôr'tě) Arg. (Buenos Aires In.)	36·17 S	56·46 W
99	Norte, Serra do (Mts.) (sě'r-rä-dô-nôr'te). Braz.	12·04 S	59·08 W
83	North, C. Can.	47·05 N	60·15 W
159	North, C. N. Z. (In.)	34·31 S	173·02 E
68	North, I. Calif. (San Diego In.)	32·39 N	117·14 W
159	North, I. N. Z. (In.)	37·34 S	171·12 E
81	North Adams (ăd'ămz) Mass.	42·40 N	73·05 W
158	Northam (nôr-dhăm) Austl.	31·50 S	116·45 E
168	Northam (nôr'thăm) S. Afr. (Johannesburg & Pretoria In.)	24·52 S	27·16 E
6	North America (à-měr'ĭ-kà)		
89	North American Basin (à-měr'ĭ-kăn). Atl. O.	23·45 N	62·45 W
158	Northampton (nôr-thămp'tŭn) Austl.	28·22 S	114·45 E
116	Northampton (nôrth-ămp'tŭn) Eng.	52·14 N	0·56 W
81	Northampton (nôr-thămp'tŭn) Mass.	42·20 N	72·45 W
81	Northampton Pa.	40·45 N	75·30 W
110	Northampton (Co.) Eng.	52·25 N	0·47 W
154	North Andaman I. (ăn-dà-măn') India	13·15 N	93·30 E
83	North Andover (ăn'dô-vēr) Mass. (Boston In.)	42·42 N	71·07 W
65	North Arm (ärm) Can. (Vancouver In.)	49·13 N	123·01 W
84	North Atlanta (ăt-lăn'tà) Ga. (Atlanta In.)	33·52 N	84·20 W
84	North Attleboro (ăt''l-bŭr-ô) Mass. (Providence In.)	41·59 N	71·18 W
80	North Baltimore (bôl'tĭ-môr). Ohio	41·10 N	83·40 W
76	North Basque (băsk) Tex.	31·56 N	98·01 W
86	North Battleford (băt''l-fērd). Can.	52·52 N	108·22 W
87	North Bay Can.	46·13 N	79·26 W
66	North Bend (bĕnd) Ore.	43·23 N	124·13 W
82	North Berwick (bûr'wĭk) Maine	43·18 N	70·46 W
94	North Bght. (bĭt) Ba. Is.	24·30 N	77·40 W
94	North Bimini (I.) (bĭ'mĭ-nê) Ba. Is.	25·45 N	79·20 W
154	North Borneo (bôr'nê-ō) Asia	5·10 N	116·25 E
83	Northboro (nôrth'bûr-ô) Mass. (Boston In.)	42·19 N	71·39 W
83	Northbridge (nôrth'brĭj) Mass. (Boston In.)	42·09 N	71·39 W
95	North Caicos (I.) (kī'kōs). Ba. Is.	21·55 N	72·00 W
72	North Canadian R. (cà nā'dĭ-ăn) Okla.	36·22 N	99·17 W
63	North Carolina (State) (kăr-ô-lī'nà). U. S.	35·40 N	81·30 W
94	North Cat Cay (I.) Ba. Is.	25·35 N	79·20 W
80	North Channel (B.) (chăn'ĕl). Can.	46·10 N	83·20 W
116	North Chan. N. Ire.-Scot.	55·15 N	7·56 W
79	North Charleston (chärlz'tŭn) S. C.	32·49 N	79·57 W
75	North Chicago (shĭ-kô'gō) Ill. (Chicago In.)	42·19 N	87·51 W
75	North College Hill (kŏl'ĕj hĭl) Ohio (Cincinnati In.)	39·13 N	84·33 W
76	North Concho (kŏn'chō) Tex.	31·40 N	100·48 W
85	North Cooking Lake (ko͝ok'ĭng lāk) Can. (Edmonton In.)	53·28 N	112·57 W
62	North Dakota (State) (dà-kō'tà) U. S.	47·20 N	101·55 W
116	North Downs (dounz) Eng.	51·11 N	0·01 W
64	Northeast C. (nôrth-ēst) Alaska	63·15 N	169·04 W
95	Northeast Pt. Ba. Is.	21·25 N	73·00 W
95	Northeast Pt. Ba. Is.	22·45 N	73·50 W
94	Northeast Providence Chan. (prŏv'ĭ-dĕns). Ba. Is.	25·45 N	77·00 W
120	Northeim (nôrt'hīm) Ger.	51·42 N	9·59 E
94	North Elbow Cays (Is.) Ba. Is.	23·55 N	80·30 W
	Northern Dvina, see Severnaya Dvina		
102	Northern Ireland (ĭr'lănd) U. K.	54·56 N	8·58 W
	Northern Land (Is.), see Severnaya Zemlya		
71	Northern Light (L.) (nôr'thērn līt). Can.	46·16 N	90·25 W
164	Northern Region (Div.) Nig.	10·54 N	6·37 E
166	Northern Rhodesia (Prot.) (rô-dē'zhĭ-à). Fed. of Rh. & Nya.	14·45 S	26·15 E
158	Northern Territory (State). Austl.	18·15 S	133·00 E
71	Northfield (nôrth'fēld) Minn.	44·28 N	93·11 W
82	Northfield Vt.	44·10 N	72·39 W
160	North Flinders, Ra. (flĭn'dērz) Austl.	31·55 S	138·45 E
117	North Foreland (fōr'lànd) Eng.	51·20 N	1·30 E
76	North Franklin Mt. (frăŋ'klĭn) Tex.	31·55 N	106·30 W
118	North Frisian Is. Den.	55·16 N	8·15 E
88	North Gamboa (gäm-bô'ä) C. Z. (Panama Canal In.)	9·07 N	79·40 W
85	North Gower (gŏw'ēr) Can. (Ottawa In.)	45·08 N	75·43 W
74	North Hollywood (hŏl'ê-wo͝od) Calif. (Los Angeles In.)	34·10 N	118·23 W
80	North Judson (jŭd'sŭn) Ind.	41·15 N	86·50 W
74	North Kansas City (kăn'zàs) Mo. (Kansas City In.)	39·08 N	94·34 W
73	North Little Rock (lĭt''l rŏk). Ark.	34·46 N	92·13 W
70	North Loup (R.) (lo͞op) Nebr.	42·05 N	100·10 W
80	North Manchester (măn'chĕs-tēr) Ind.	41·00 N	85·45 W
74	Northmoor (nôrth'mo͞or) Mo. (Kansas City In.)	39·10 N	94·37 W
74	North Ogden (ŏg'dĕn) Utah (Salt Lake City In.)	41·18 N	111·58 W
74	North Ogden Pk. Utah (Salt Lake City In.)	41·23 N	111·59 W
75	North Olmsted (ōlm-stĕd) Ohio (Cleveland In.)	41·25 N	81·55 W
72	North Pease (R.) (pēz) Tex.	34·19 N	100·58 W
65	North Pender (I.) (pĕn'dēr) Can. (Vancouver In.)	48·48 N	123·16 W
65	North Plains (plānz) Ore. (Portland In.)	45·36 N	123·00 W
70	North Platte (plăt) Nebr.	41·08 N	100·45 W
62	North Platte, (R.) U. S.	41·20 N	102·40 W
80	North Pt. Mich.	45·00 N	83·20 W
93	North Pt. W. I. F. (Le. & Wind. Is. In.)	13·22 N	59·36 W
78	Northport (nôrth'pōrt) Ala.	33·12 N	87·35 W
84	Northport. N. Y. (New York In.)	40·53 N	73·20 W
66	Northport Wash.	48·53 N	117·47 W
83	North Reading (rĕd'ĭng) Mass. (Boston In.)	42·34 N	71·04 W
	North Rhine-Westphalia, see Nordrhein-Westfalen		
74	Northridge (nôrth'ridj) Calif. (Los Angeles In.)	34·14 N	118·32 W
75	North Ridgeville (rĭj-vĭl) Ohio (Cleveland In.)	41·23 N	82·01 W
75	North Royalton (roi'ăl-tŭn) Ohio (Cleveland In.)	41·19 N	81·44 W
74	North St. Paul (sånt pôl'). Minn. (Minneapolis, St. Paul In.)	45·01 N	92·59 W
74	North Salt Lake (sôlt lāk) Utah (Salt Lake City In.)	40·50 N	111·55 W
86	North Saskatchewan (R.) (săs-kăch'ê-wän). Can.	53·54 N	112·37 W
112	North Sea Eur.	56·09 N	3·16 E
71	North Skunk (R.) (skŭnk) Iowa	41·39 N	92·46 W
83	North Sydney (sĭd'nê) Can.	46·14 N	60·28 W
159	North Taranaki Bght. (tà-rà-nä'kĭ bĭt). N. Z. (In.)	38·23 S	172·03 E
84	North Tarrytown (tăr'ĭ-toun) N. Y. (New York In.)	41·05 N	73·52 W
84	North Tiverton (tĭv'ēr-tŭn) R. I. (Providence In.)	41·40 N	71·08 W
75	North Tonawanda (tŏn-à-wŏn'dà) N. Y. (Buffalo In.)	43·02 N	78·53 W
69	North Truchas Pks. (Mts.) (tro͞o'chäs). N. Mex.	35·58 N	105·37 W
116	North Uist (I.) (ū'ĭst) Scot.	56·99 N	6·56 W
82	Northumberland Str. (nôr thŭm'bēr-lànd). Can.	46·25 N	64·20 W
81	Northumberland N. H.	44·30 N	71·30 W
159	Northumberland, Is. Austl.	21·42 S	151·30 E
66	North Umpqua R. (ŭmp'kwà) Ore.	43·20 N	122·50 W
65	North Vancouver (văn-ko͞o'vēr) Can. (Vancouver In.)	49·19 N	123·05 W
80	North Vernon (vûr'nŭn) Ind.	39·05 N	85·45 W
154	North Vietnam (vyĕt'näm'). Asia	18·40 N	106·22 E
75	Northville (nôrth-vĭl) Mich. (Detroit In.)	42·26 N	83·28 W
84	North Wales (wālz) Pa. (Philadelphia In.)	40·12 N	75·16 W
158	North West, C. (nôrth'wĕst) Austl.	21·50 S	112·25 E
79	Northwest Cape Fear, (R.) (cāp fēr). N. C.	34·34 N	79·46 W
116	Northwest Highlands Scot.	56·50 N	5·20 W
94	Northwest Providence Chan. (prŏv'ĭ-dĕns). Ba. Is.	26·15 N	78·45 W
86	Northwest Territories (tĕr'ĭ-tō'rĭs). Can.	64·42 N	119·09 W
110	Northwich (nôrth'wĭch) Eng.	53·15 N	2·31 W
79	North Wilkesboro (wĭlks'bûrô) N. C.	36·08 N	81·10 W
71	Northwood (nôrth'wo͝od) Iowa	43·26 N	93·13 W
70	Northwood N. D.	47·44 N	97·36 W
67	North Wood Cr. Wyo.	44·02 N	107·37 W
65	North Yamhill (R.) (yăm' hĭl) Ore. (Portland In.)	45·22 N	123·21 W
116	North York Moors (yôrk mo͞orz') Eng.	54·20 N	0·40 W
72	Norton (nôr'tŭn) Kans.	39·40 N	99·54 W
84	Norton. Mass. (Providence In.)	41·58 N	71·08 W
79	Norton Va.	36·54 N	82·36 W
64	Norton B. Alaska	64·22 N	162·18 W
84	Norton Res. Mass. (Providence In.)	42·01 N	71·07 W
64	Norton Sd. Alaska	63·48 N	164·50 W
85	Norval (nôr'vàl) Can. (Toronto In.)	43·39 N	79·52 W
74	Norwalk (nôr'wôk) Calif. (Los Angeles In.)	33·54 N	118·05 W
84	Norwalk. Conn. (New York In.)	41·06 N	73·25 W
80	Norwalk Ohio	41·15 N	82·35 W
102	Norway (nôr'wā) Eur.	63·48 N	11·17 E
82	Norway Maine	44·11 N	70·35 W
71	Norway Mich.	45·47 N	87·55 W
86	Norway House Can.	54·00 N	97·54 W
112	Norwegian Sea (nôr-wē'jăn) Eur.	66·54 N	1·43 E
83	Norwell (nôr'wĕl) Mass. (Boston In.)	42·10 N	70·47 W
81	Norwich (nôr'wĭch) Conn.	41·20 N	72·00 W
117	Norwich Eng.	52·40 N	1·15 E
81	Norwich N. Y.	42·35 N	75·30 W
83	Norwood (nôr'wo͝od) Mass. (Boston In.)	42·11 N	71·13 W
79	Norwood N. C.	35·15 N	80·08 W
75	Norwood. Ohio (Cincinnati In.)	39·10 N	84·27 W
85	Nose Cr. (nōz). Can. (Calgary In.)	51·09 N	114·02 W
152	Noshiro (nō'shê-rô) Jap.	40·09 N	140·02 E
166	Nosob (R.) (nō'sŏb) S. W. Afr.	24·15 S	19·10 E
129	Nosovka (nō'sôf-kà) Sov. Un.	50·54 N	31·35 E
167	Nosy Bé (B.) Malagasy	13·14 S	47·28 E
120	Noteć R. (nō'tĕch) Pol.	52·50 N	16·19 E
113	Noto (nō'tō) It.	36·49 N	15·08 E
118	Notodden (nôt'ôd'n) Nor.	59·35 N	9·15 E
153	Noto-Hantō (Pen.) (nō'tō hän'tō) Jap.	37·18 N	137·03 E
83	Notre Dame B. (nō't'r dàm'). Can.	49·48 N	55·27 W
85	Notre-Dame-des-Laurentides (dě-lō-räN-tēd'). Can. (Quebec In.)	46·55 N	71·20 W
82	Notre-Dame-du-Lac Can.	47·37 N	68·51 W
82	Notre Dame Mts. Can.	48·10 N	67·40 W
80	Nottawasaga B. (nŏt'à-wà-sā'gà) Can.	44·45 N	80·35 W
87	Nottaway (R.) (nôt'à-wā) Can.	50·58 N	78·02 W
110	Nottingham (nŏt'ĭng-ăm) Eng.	52·58 N	1·09 W
110	Nottingham (Co.) Eng.	53·03 N	1·05 W
87	Nottingham I. Can.	62·58 N	78·53 W
167	Nottinghamweg (nŏt-ĭng-hăm-vĕg) S. Afr. (Natal In.)	29·21 S	30·00 E
79	Nottoway, (R.) (nôt'ŏ-wā) Va.	36·53 N	77·47 W
164	Nouakchott Mauritania	18·15 N	15·56 W
159	Noumea (no͞o-mā'ä) N. Cal.	22·18 S	166·48 E
82	Nouvelle (no͞o-vĕl') Can.	48·08 N	66·19 W
165	Nouvelle Anvers (äN-vår'). Con. L.	1·42 N	19·08 E
159	Nouvelle Caledonie, (Is.). Oceania	21·28 S	164·15 E
122	Nouzonville (no͞o-zôN-vēl') Fr.	49·51 N	4·43 E
99	Nova Cruz (nō'và-kro͞o'z) Braz.	6·22 S	35·20 W
101	Nova Friburgo (frê-bo͞or'go͞o) Braz. (Rio de Janeiro In.)	22·18 S	42·31 W
100	Nova Iguaçu (nō'vä-ē-gwä-so͞o') Braz. (In.)	22·45 S	43·27 W
101	Nova Lima (lē'mä) Braz. (Rio de Janeiro In.)	19·59 S	43·51 W
166	Nova Lisboa (lèzh-bō'à) Ang.	12·45 S	15·45 E
126	Novara (nô-vä'rä) It.	45·24 N	8·38 E
101	Nova Resende Braz. (Rio de Janeiro In.)	21·12 S	46·25 W
87	Nova Scotia (Prov.) (skō'shà) Can.	44·28 N	65·00 W
127	Nova Varoš (nō'và vä'rôsh). Yugo.	43·24 N	19·53 E
119	Novaya Ladogo (nô'và-yà là-dô-gô). Sov. Un.	60·06 N	32·16 E
136	Novaya Lyalya (lyà'lyà) Sov. Un. (Urals In.)	59·03 N	60·36 E
129	Novaya Odessa (ô-dĕs'ă) Sov. Un.	47·18 N	31·48 E
129	Novaya Praga (prä'gà). Sov. Un.	48·34 N	32·54 E
135	Novaya Sibir (I.) (sê-bēr') Sov. Un.	75·42 N	150·00 E
129	Novaya Vodolaga (vô-dôl'á-gà) Sov. Un.	49·43 N	35·51 E
134	Novaya Zemlya (I.) (zĕm-lyà') Sov. Un.	72·00 N	54·46 E
127	Nova Zagora (zä'gô-rà) Bul.	42·30 N	26·01 E
125	Novelda (nō-vĕl'dä) Sp.	38·22 N	0·46 W
121	Nové Mesto (Nad Váhom) (nô'vĕ myĕs'tô). Czech.	48·44 N	17·47 E
121	Nové Zámky (zäm'kê) Czech.	47·58 N	18·10 E
128	Novgorod (nôv'gô-rŏt) Sov. Un.	58·32 N	31·16 E
128	Novgorod (Oblast) Sov. Un.	58·27 N	31·55 E
126	Novi (nō'vè) It.	44·43 N	8·48 W
75	Novi (nō'vĭ). Mich. (Detroit In.)	42·29 N	83·28 W
126	Novi Grad (gräd) Yugo.	44·09 N	15·34 E
73	Novinger (nŏv'ĭn-jēr) Mo.	40·14 N	92·43 W
127	Novi Pazar (pà-zär') Yugo.	43·08 N	20·30 E
127	Novi-Pozar Bul.	43·22 N	27·26 E
127	Novi Sad (säd') Yugo.	45·15 N	19·53 E
136	Novoasbest (nô-vô-ä-bĕst') Sov. Un. (Urals In.)	57·43 N	60.14 E
129	Novoaydar (nô'vô-ī-där') Sov. Un.	48·57 N	39·01 E
129	Novocherkassk (nô'vô-chĕr-kàsk') Sov. Un.	47·25 N	40·04 E
129	Novogorod-Severskiy Sov. Un.	52·01 N	33·14 E
121	Novogrudok (nô-vô-gro͞o'dôk) Sov. Un.	53·35 N	25·51 E
103	Novo-Kazalinsk (nô-vŭ-kŭ-zà-lyēnsk'). Sov. Un.	45·47 N	62·00 E
134	Novokuznetsk (Stalinsk) (nŏ'vô-ko͞o'z-nyĕ'tsk) (stà'lĕnsk). Sov. Un.	53·43 N	86·59 E
136	Novoladozhskiy Kanal (Can.) (nô-vô-lä'dôzh-skĭ kà-näl') Sov. Un. (Leningrad In.)	59·54 N	31·19 E
126	Novo Mesto (nôvô mās'tô). Yugo.	45·48 N	15·13 E
129	Novomirgorod (nô'vô-mēr'gô-rôt) Sov. Un.	48·46 N	31·44 E
129	Novomoskovsk (nô'vô-môs-kôfsk') Sov. Un.	48·37 N	35·12 E
136	Novonikol'skiy (nô'vô-nyĭ-kôl'skĭ) Sov. Un. (Urals In.)	52·28 N	57·12 E
166	Novo Redondo (nô'vo͞o rà-dôn'do͞o). Ang.	11·15 S	13·50 E
129	Novorossiysk (nô'vô-rô-sēsk') Sov. Un.	44·43 N	37·48 E
128	Novorzhev (nô'vô-rzhêv') Sov. Un.	57·01 N	29·17 E
127	Novo-Selo (nô'vô-sĕ'lô) Bul.	44·09 N	22·46 E
134	Novosibirsk (nô'vô-sê-bērsk') Sov. Un.	55·09 N	82·58 E
135	Novosibirskiye O-va (New Siberian Is.) (no'vŭ-sĭ-bĭr'skē-ĕ). Sov. Un.	76·45 N	140·30 E
128	Novosil' (nô'vô-sĭl) Sov. Un.	52·58 N	37·03 E
128	Novosokol'niki (nô'vô-sô-kôl'nê-kê). Sov. Un.	56·18 N	30·07 E
136	Novotatishchevskiy (nô'vô-tà-tyĭsh'chĕv-skĭ) Sov. Un. (Urals In.)	53·22 N	60·24 E
129	Novoukrainka (nōvō-o͞o'krà) Sov. Un.	48·18 N	31·33 E
133	Novouzensk (nô-vô-o͞o-zĕnsk') Sov. Un.	50·40 N	48·08 E
128	Novozybkov (nô'vô-zêp'kôf) Sov. Un.	52·31 N	31·54 E
121	Novy Jičin (nô'vê yĕ'chēn). Czech.	49·36 N	18·02 E
129	Novyy Bug (bo͝oK) Sov. Un.	47·43 N	32·33 E
129	Novyy Oskol (ôs-kôl') Sov. Un.	50·46 N	37·53 E
134	Novyy Port (nô'vē) Sov. Un.	67·19 N	72·28 E
121	Nowa Huta (nô'vä ho͞o'tä) Pol.	50·04 N	20·20 E
120	Nowa Sól (nô'vä sŭl') Pol.	51·49 N	15·41 E
73	Nowata (nô-wä'tà) Okla.	36·42 N	95·38 W
160	Nowra (nou'rà) Austl.	34·55 S	150·45 E

ăt; finăl; rāte; senâte; ärm; åsk; sofà; fâre; ch-choose; dh-as th in other; bē; êvent; bĕt; recĕnt; cratēr; g-go; gh-guttural g; bĭt; ĭ-short neutral; rīde; K-guttural k as ch in German ich;

Page	Name Pronunciation Region	Lat. °′	Long. °′
121	Nowy Dwór Mazowiecki (nō′vĭ dvōōr mä-zō-vyĕts′ke) Pol.	52·26 N	20·46 E
121	Nowy Sacz (nô′vê sônch′) . . . . Pol.	49·36 N	20·42 E
121	Nowy Targ (tärk′) . . . . Pol.	49·29 N	20·02 E
78	Noxubee (R.) (nŏks′ū-bē) . . . Miss.	33·20 N	88·55 W
124	Noya (nō′yä) . . . . Sp.	42·46 N	8·50 W
153	Nozaki (nō′zä-kê) Jap. (Ōsaka In.)	34·43 N	135·39 E
167	Nqamakwe (′n-gä-mä′kwå) S. Afr. (Natal In.)	32·13 S	27·57 E
167	Nqutu (′n-kōō′tōō) S. Afr. (Natal In.)	28·17 S	30·41 E
165	Nubian Des. (nōō′bĭ-ăn) . . . . . Sud.	21·13 N	33·09 E
98	Nudo Coropuna (Mt.) (nōō′dô kō-rō-pōō′nä) . Peru	15·53 S	72·04 W
98	Nudo de Pasco (Mt.) (dĕ päs′kô) Peru	10·34 S	76·12 W
76	Nueces R. (nû-ā′sås) . . . . Tex.	28·20 N	98·08 W
86	Nueltin (L.) (nwĕl′tin) . . . . . . Can.	60·14 N	101·00 W
92	Nueva Armenia (nwā′vä är-mā′nê-ȧ) . Hond.	15·47 N	86·32 W
99	Nueva Esparta (State) (nwĕ′vä ĕs-pä′r-tä) . Ven. In.	10·50 N	64·35 W
94	Nueva Gerona (kĕ-rô′nä) . . . . Cuba	21·55 N	82·45 W
101	Nueva Palmira (päl-mē′rä) Ur. (Buenos Aires In.)	33·53 S	58·23 W
62	Nueva Rosita (nōōĕ′vä rô-sē′tä) Mex.	27·55 N	101·10 W
92	Nueva San Salvador (Santa Tecla) (sän′ säl-vá-dōr) (sän′tä tĕ′klä) Sal.	13·41 N	89·16 W
101	Nueve de Julio (nwā′vā dā hōō′lyō) Arg. (Buenos Aires In.)	35·26 S	60·51 W
94	Nuevitas (nwā-vē′täs) . . . . . . Cuba	21·35 N	77·15 W
94	Nuevitas, Bahía de (bä-ē′ä dĕ nwā-vē′täs) . Cuba	21·30 N	77·05 W
74	Nuevo (nwā′vō) Calif. (Los Angeles In.)	33·48 N	117·09 W
76	Nuevo Laredo (lä-rā′dhō) . . . Mex.	27·29 N	99·30 W
88	Nuevo Leon (State) (lå-ōn′) . Mex.	26·00 N	100·00 W
88	Nuevo San Juan (nwĕ′vô sän kōō-ä′n) C. Z. (Panama Canal In.)	9·14 N	79·43 W
136	Nugumanovo (nû-gû-mä′nô-vô) Sov. Un. (Urals In.)	55·28 N	61·50 E
133	Nukha (nōō′kä) . . . . Sov. Un.	41·10 N	47·10 E
64	Nulato (nōō-lä′tō) . . . . Alaska	64·40 N	158·18 W
158	Nullagine (nŭ-lă′jēn) . . . . Austl.	22·00 S	120·07 E
158	Nullarbor Plain, (Reg.) (nŭ-lăr′bōr) . Austl.	31·45 S	126·30 E
111	Numansdorp Neth. (Amsterdam In.)	51·43 N	4·25 E
153	Numazu (nōō′mä-zōō) . . . . Jap.	35·06 N	138·55 E
101	No. 1, Canal Arg. (Buenos Aires In.)	36·43 S	58·14 W
101	No. 9, Canal Arg. (Buenos Aires In.)	36·22 S	58·19 W
101	No. 12, Canal Arg. (Buenos Aires In.)	36·47 S	57·20 W
167	Numolani . . . . . . Bas. (Natal In.)	29·06 S	28·59 E
110	Nuneaton (nŭn′ē-tŭn) . . . . Eng.	52·31 N	1·28 W
150	Nungan . . . . China	44·25 N	125·10 E
64	Nunivak (I.) (nōō′nĭ-văk) . Alaska	60·25 N	167·42 W
92	Nunkiní (nōōn-kē-nē′) Mex. (Yucatan In.)	20·19 N	90·14 W
64	Nunyama (nûn-yä′må) . . Sov. Un.	65·49 N	170·32 W
126	Nuoro (nwô′rō) . . . . It.	40·29 N	9·20 E
134	Nura (R.) (nōō′rä) . . . . . . Sov. Un.	49·48 N	73·54 E
134	Nurata (nōōr′ät′ȧ) . . . . . . Sov. Un.	40·33 N	65·28 E
120	Nürnberg (nürn′bĕrgh) . . . . . . Ger.	49·28 N	11·07 E
95	Nurse Cay (I.) . . . . Ba. Is.	22·30 N	75·50 W
133	Nusabyin (nōō′sĭ-bēn) . . . . Tur.	37·05 N	41·10 E
64	Nushagak (R.) (nū-shä-găk′) Alaska	59·28 N	157·40 W
148	Nushan Hu (L.) (nü′shän hōō) China	32·50 N	117·59 E
145	Nushki (nŭsh′kê) . . . . W. Pak.	29·30 N	66·02 E
111	Nuthe R. (nōō′tê) Ger. (Berlin In.)	52·15 N	13·11 E
84	Nutley (nŭt′lê) N. J. (New York In.)	40·49 N	74·09 W
81	Nutter Fort (nŭt′ẽr fôrt) . . W. Va.	39·15 N	80·15 W
74	Nutwood (nŭt′wŏŏd) Ill. (St. Louis In.)	39·05 N	90·34 W
139	Nuwaybi ′al Muzayyinah U. A. R. (Palestine In.)	28·59 N	34·40 E
84	Nyack (nī′ăk) N. Y. (New York In.)	41·05 N	73·55 W
166	Nyangwe (nyäng′wā) . . . . . Con. L.	4·09 S	26·16 E
166	Nyasa, L. (nyä′sä) . . . . . Tan.-Moz.	11·32 S	35·15 E
167	Nyasaland (Prot.) (nyä′sä-lănd) Tan.	11·15 S	33·45 E
136	Nyazepetrovsk (nyä′zĕ-pĕ-trôvsk′) Sov. Un. (Urals In.)	56·04 N	59·38 E
118	Nyborg (nü′bôr″) . . . . Den.	55·20 N	10·45 E
118	Nybro (nü′brô) . . . . Swe.	56·44 N	15·56 E
146	Nyenchhen Thanglha (Mts.) China	29·55 N	88·08 E
118	Nyhem (nü′hĕm) . . . . Swe.	56·39 N	12·50 E
121	Nyiregyháza (nyē′rĕd-y′hä′zä) Hung.	47·58 N	21·45 E
118	Nykøbing (nü′kû-bĭng) . . . . . . Den.	56·46 N	8·47 E
118	Nykøbing Fl . . . . Den.	54·45 N	11·54 E
118	Nykøbing S . . . . Den.	55·55 N	11·37 E
118	Nyköping (nü′chû-pĭng) . . . . . . Swe.	58·46 N	16·58 E
168	Nyl R. (nĭl) . . . . S. Afr. (Johannesburg & Pretoria In.)	24·30 S	28·55 E
168	Nylstroom (nĭl′strōm) S. Afr. (Johannesburg & Pretoria In.)	24·42 S	28·25 E
160	Nymagee (nī-mȧ-gē′) . . . . Austl.	32·17 S	146·18 E
120	Nymburk (nêm′bŏŏrk) . . . . . . Czech.	50·12 N	15·03 E
116	Nymphe Bk. (nĭmpf) . . . . Ire.	51·36 N	7·35 W
118	Nynashamn (nü-nĕs-häm′n) . . Swe.	58·53 N	17·55 E
160	Nyngan (nĭŋ′gȧn) . . . . Austl.	31·31 S	147·25 E
164	Nyong R. (nyông) . . . . Cam.	3·41 N	12·21 E
120	Nýrány (nêr-zhä′nê) . . . . Czech.	49·43 N	13·13 E
121	Nysa (nē′sä) . . . . Pol.	50·29 N	17·20 E
	Nystad, see Uusikaupunki		
132	Nytva . . . . Sov. Un.	58·00 N	55·10 E
135	Nyuya (R.) (nyōō′yȧ) . . . Sov. Un.	60·30 N	111·45 E
70	Oahe Dam (ō-ȧ-hē) . . . . S. D.	44·28 N	100·34 W
70	Oahe Res. . . . . S. Dak.	45·20 N	100·00 W
157	Oahu (I.) (ō-ä′hōō) (ō-ä′hū) Hawaii (In.)	21·38 N	157·48 W
85	Oak Bluff (ōk blŭf) Can. (Winnipeg In.)	49·47 N	97·21 W
67	Oak Creek (ōk krēk′) . . . . Colo.	40·20 N	106·50 W
68	Oakdale (ōk′dāl) . . . . Calif.	37·45 N	120·52 W
80	Oakdale . . . . Ky.	38·15 N	85·50 W
77	Oakdale . . . . La.	30·49 N	92·40 W
75	Oakdale . . . . . . Pa. (Pittsburgh In.)	40·24 N	80·11 W
110	Oakengates (ōk′ĕn-gāts) . . . . . Eng.	52·41 N	2·27 W
70	Oakes (ōks) . . . . N. D.	46·10 N	98·50 W
82	Oakfield (ōk′fēld) . . . . Maine	46·08 N	68·10 W
84	Oakford (ōk′fōrd) Pa. (Philadelphia In.)	40·08 N	74·58 W
65	Oak Grove (grōv) Ore. (Portland In.)	45·25 N	122·38 W
110	Oakham (ōk′ăm) . . . . Eng.	52·40 N	0·38 W
80	Oakharbor (ōk′här′bẽr) . . . . . . Ohio	41·30 N	83·05 W
65	Oak Harbor . . . Wash. (Seattle In.)	48·18 N	122·39 W
74	Oak Knoll (nōl) Tex. (Dallas, Fort Worth In.)	32·47 N	97·17 W
65	Oakland (ōk′lănd) Calif. (San Francisco In.)	37·48 N	122·16 W
70	Oakland . . . . Nebr.	41·50 N	96·28 W
80	Oakland City . . . . Ind.	38·20 N	87·20 W
75	Oaklawn (ōk′lôn) Ill. (Chicago In.)	41·43 N	87·45 W
161	Oakleigh (ōk′lȧ) Austl. (Melbourne In.)	37·54 S	145·05 E
67	Oakley (ōk′lĭ) . . . . Idaho	42·15 N	113·53 W
72	Oakley . . . . Kans.	39·08 N	100·49 W
78	Oakman (ōk′măn) . . . . Ala.	33·42 N	87·20 W
75	Oakmont (ōk′mōnt) Pa. (Pittsburgh In.)	40·31 N	79·50 W
84	Oak Mtn. . Ala. (Birmingham In.)	33·22 N	86·42 W
75	Oak Park (pärk) Ill. (Chicago In.)	41·53 N	87·48 W
65	Oak Point . . . Wash. (Portland In.)	46·11 N	123·11 W
78	Oak Ridge (rĭj) . . . . Tenn.	36·01 N	84·15 W
74	Oak Ridge Park Mich. (Sault Ste. Marie In.)	46·18 N	84·12 W
85	Oakville (ōk′vĭl) Can. (Toronto In.)	43·27 N	79·40 W
85	Oakville . . . . . Can. (Winnipeg In.)	49·56 N	98·00 W
84	Oakville . . . . La. (New Orleans In.)	29·47 N	90·02 W
74	Oakville . . . . . . Mo. (St. Louis In.)	38·27 N	90·18 W
85	Oakville Cr. . . . Can. (Toronto In.)	43·34 N	79·54 W
77	Oakwood (ōk′wŏŏd) . . . . Tex.	31·36 N	95·48 W
75	Oakwood . . . Wis. (Milwaukee In.)	42·51 N	88·30 W
69	Oatman (ōt′măn) . . . . Ariz.	34·00 N	114·25 W
88	Oaxaca (State) (wä-hä′kä) . . . Mex.	16·45 N	97·00 W
91	Oaxaca, Sierra de (Mts.) (sē-ĕ′r-rä dĕ) . Mex.	16·15 N	97·25 W
91	Oaxaca de Juárez (kōōȧ′rĕz) . Mex.	17·03 N	96·42 W
134	Ob′ (R.) . . . . Sov. Un.	62·15 N	67·00 E
87	Oba (ō′bȧ) . . . . Can.	48·58 N	84·09 W
153	Obama (ō′bȧ-mä) . . . . Jap.	35·29 N	135·44 E
116	Oban (ō′băn) . . . . Scot.	56·25 N	5·35 W
75	O′Bannon (ō-băn′nŏn) Ky. (Louisville In.)	38·17 N	85·30 W
82	Obatogamau (L.) (ō-bȧ-tō′găm-ō) . Can.	49·38 N	74·10 W
168	Obbia (ōb′byä) Som. (Horn of Afr. In.)	5·24 N	48·28 E
123	Oberhausen (ō′bĕr-hou′zĕn) Ger. (Ruhr In.)	51·27 N	6·51 E
72	Oberlin (o′bẽr-lĭn) . . . . Kans.	39·49 N	100·30 W
80	Oberlin . . . . Ohio	41.15 N	82·15 W
120	Oberösterreich (Prov.) . . . . Aus.	48·05 N	13·15 E
111	Oberroth (ō′bĕr-rōt) Ger. (München In.)	48·19 N	11·20 E
111	Ober-Schleissheim (ō′bĕr-shlīs-hēm) Ger. (München In.)	48·15 N	11·34 E
155	Obi (I.) (ō′bê) . . . . Indon.	1·25 S	128·15 E
99	Óbidos (ō′bê-dŏŏzh) . . . . Braz.	1·57 S	55·32 W
152	Obihiro (ō′bē-hē′rō) . . . . Jap.	42·55 N	142·50 E
78	Obion (R.) . . . . Tenn.	36·10 N	89·25 W
78	Obion (R.), North Fk. (ō-bī′ŏn) Tenn.	35·49 N	89·06 W
129	Obitochnaya, Kosa (C.) (kô-sä′ ô-bē-tôch′nȧ-yȧ) Sov. Un.	46·32 N	36·07 E
153	Obitsu (R.) (ō′bēt′sōō) Jap. (Tōkyō In.)	35·19 N	140·03 E
168	Obock (ō-bŏk′) Fr. Som. (Horn of Afr. In.)	11·55 N	43·15 E
128	Obol′ (R.) (ô-bŏl′) . . . . . . Sov. Un.	55·24 N	29·24 E
129	Oboyan′ (ô-bô-yän′) . . . . . Sov. Un.	51·14 N	36·16 E
134	Obskaya Guba (R.) . . . . . . Sov. Un.	67·13 N	73·45 E
129	Obukhov (ō′bōō-kôf) . . . . Sov. Un.	50·07 N	30·36 E
79	Ocala (ō-kä′lȧ) . . . . Fla.	29·11 N	82·09 W
90	Ocampo (ō-käm′pō) . . . . Mex.	22·49 N	99·23 W
98	Ocaña (ô-kän′yä) . . . . Col.	8·15 N	73·37 W
124	Ocaña (ô-kä′n-yä) . . . . Sp.	39·58 N	3·31 W
164	Occidental, Grand Erg (Dunes) Alg.	29·30 N	00·45 W
98	Occidental, Cordillera (Mts.) (kôr-dēl-yĕ′rä ŏk-sē-dĕn-täl′) Col. (In.)	5·05 N	76·04 W
98	Occidental, Cordillera (Mts.) Peru	10·12 S	76·58 W
88	Occidental, Sierra Madre, (Mts.) (sē-ĕ′r-rä-mä′drĕ-ôk-sê-dĕn-tä′l) Mex.	29·30 N	107·30 W
84	Oceana (ō′shĕ′ăn-ȧ) Va. (Norfolk In.)	36·51 N	76·01 W
68	Ocean Beach (ō′shăn bēch) Calif. (San Diego In.)	32·44 N	117·14 W
95	Ocean Bight (B.) . . . . Ba. Is.	21·15 N	73·15 W
81	Ocean City . . . . Md.	38·20 N	75·10 W
81	Ocean City . . . . N. J.	39·15 N	74·35 W
86	Ocean Falls (Fôls) . . . . Can.	52·27 N	127·50 W
161	Ocean Grove Austl. (Melbourne In.)	38·16 S	144·32 E
81	Ocean Grove (grōv) . . . . N. J.	40·10 N	74·00 W
74	Ocean Park (pärk) Calif. (Los Angeles In.)	34·00 N	118·28 W
84	Oceanport (ō′-shăn-pōrt) N. J. (New York In.)	40·18 N	74·02 W
68	Oceanside (ō′shăn-sīd) . . . . . . Calif.	33·11 N	117·22 W
78	Ocean Springs (sprĭngs) . . . . . Miss.	30·25 N	88·49 W
127	Ocenele Mari . . . . Rom.	45·05 N	24·17 E
129	Ochakov (ô-chä′kôf) . . . . . Sov. Un.	46·38 N	31·33 E
146	Ochina Ho (R.) . . . . China	41·15 N	100·46 E
150	Ochir . . . . China	45·38 N	115·35 E
78	Ochlockonee R. (ŏk-lô-kō′nē) Fla.-Ga.	30·10 N	84·38 W
78	Ocilla (ô-sĭl′ȧ) . . . . Ga.	31·36 N	83·15 W
118	Ockelbo (ôk′ĕl-bô) . . . . Swe.	60·54 N	16·35 E
79	Ocmulgee, (R.) . . . . Ga.	32·35 N	83·30 W
78	Ocmulgee Natl. Mon. (ôk-mŭl′gē) Ga.	32·45 N	83·28 W
127	Ocna-Sibiului (ōk′nȧ-sê-byōō-lōō-ê) Rom.	45·52 N	24·04 E
95	Ocoa, Bahai de (B.) (bȧ-ä′ē-ô-kō′ä) Dom. Rep.	18·20 N	70·40 W
91	Ococingo (ô-kô-sē′n-gô) . . . . . Mex.	17·03 N	92·18 W
92	Ocom, L. (ô-kō′m) Mex. (Yucatan In.)	19·26 N	88·18 W
78	Oconee, (R.) (ô-kō′nē) . . . . Ga.	32·45 N	83·00 W
71	Oconomowoc (ô-kŏn′ô-mô-wŏk′) Wis.	43·06 N	88·24 W
71	Oconto (ô-kŏn′tō) . . . . Wis.	44·54 N	87·55 W
71	Oconto (R.) . . . . Wis.	45·08 N	88·24 W
71	Oconto Falls . . . . Wis.	44·53 N	88·11 W
92	Ocós (ô-kōs′) . . . . Guat.	14·31 N	92·12 W
92	Ocotal (ō-kō-täl′) . . . . Nic.	13·36 N	86·31 W
92	Ocotepeque (ô-kō-tȧ-pä′kå) . Hond.	14·25 N	89·13 W
90	Ocotlán (ō-kō-tlän′) . . . . Mex.	20·19 N	102·44 W
91	Ocotlán de Morelos (dā mō-rā′lōs) Mex.	16·46 N	96·41 W
91	Ocozocoautla (ô-kō′zō-kwä-ōō′tlä) Mex.	16·44 N	93·22 W
99	Ocumare del Tuy (ô-kōō-mä′rā del twē′) Ven. (In.)	10·07 N	66·47 W
155	Ocussi . . . . Port. Tim.	9·00 S	128·53 E
153	Odawara (ō′dȧ-wä′rä) . . . . Jap.	35·15 N	139·10 E
118	Odda (ôdh-ȧ) . . . . Nor.	60·04 N	6·30 E
168	Oddur . . . . Som. (Horn of Afr. In.)	3·55 N	43·45 E
70	Odebolt (ō′dê-bōlt) . . . . Iowa	42·20 N	95·14 W
124	Odemira (ō-dȧ-mē′rȧ) . . . . Port.	37·35 N	8·40 W
133	Ödemis (ū′dĕ-mēsh) . . . . Tur.	38·12 N	28·00 E
168	Odendaalsrus (ō′dĕn-däls-rûs′) S. Afr. (Johannesburg & Pretoria In.)	27·52 S	26·41 E
118	Odense (ō′dhĕn-sĕ) . . . . Den.	55·24 N	10·20 E
84	Odenton (ō′dĕn-tŭn) Md. (Baltimore In.)	39·05 N	76·43 W
120	Odenwald (For.) (ō′dĕn-väld) Ger.	49·39 N	8·55 E
120	Oder R. (ō′dẽr) . . . . Ger.	52·40 N	14·19 E
129	Odessa (ô-dĕs′sä) . . . . Sov. Un.	46·28 N	30·44 E
76	Odessa (ô-dĕs′ȧ) . . . . Tex.	31·52 N	102·21 W
66	Odessa . . . . Wash.	47·20 N	118·42 W
129	Odessa (Oblast) . . . . Sov. Un.	46·05 N	29·48 E
124	Odiel (R.) (ō-dê-ĕl′) . . . . Sp.	37·47 N	6·42 W
164	Odienné (ō-dê-ĕn-nā′) Ivory Coast	9·47 N	7·32 W
110	Odiham (ŏd′ē-ăm) Eng. (London In.)	51·14 N	0·56 W
138	Odintsovo (ô-dēn′tsô-vô) Sov. Un. (Moskva In.)	55·40 N	37·16 E
155	Odioñgan (ō-dê-ôŋ′gän) Phil. (Manila In.)	12·24 N	121·59 E
125	Odivelas (ō-dê-vā′lyäs) Port. (Lisboa In.)	38·47 N	9·11 W
121	Odobesti (ō-dô-bēsh′t′) . . . . . Rom.	45·46 N	27·08 E
72	O′Donnell (ō-dŏn′ĕl) . . . . Tex.	32·59 N	101·51 W
121	Odorhei (ō-dôr-hā′) . . . . Rom.	46·18 N	25·17 E
121	Odra R. (ô′drȧ) . . . . Pol.	50·28 N	17·55 E
99	Oeiras (wȧ-ē-räzh′) . . . . Braz.	7·05 S	42·01 W
125	Oeirás (ō-ĕ′y-rä′s) Port. (Lisboa In.)	38·42 N	9·18 W
71	Oelwein (ōl′wīn) . . . . Iowa	42·40 N	91·56 W
74	O′Fallon (ō-făl′ŭn) Ill. (St. Louis In.)	38·36 N	89·55 W
67	O′Fallon Cr. . . . . Mont.	46·25 N	104·47 W
126	Ofanto (R.) (ō-făn′tō) . . . . It.	41·08 N	15·33 E
120	Offenbach (ôf′ĕn-băk) . . . . Ger.	50·06 N	8·50 E
120	Offenburg (ôf′ĕn-bŏŏrgh) . . . . . Ger.	48·28 N	7·57 E
153	Ofuna (ō′fōō-nä) . Jap. (Tōkyō In.)	35·21 N	139·32 E
168	Ogaden Plat. Eth. (Horn of Afr. In.)	6·45 N	44·53 E
153	Ōgaki . . . . Jap.	35·21 N	136·36 E
70	Ogallala (ō-gä-lä′lȧ) . . . . Nebr.	41·80 N	101·44 W
156	Ogasawara (Bonin Is.) (ō-gä′sȧ-wä′rä) (bō′nĭn) . Asia	26·30 N	141·00 E
164	Ogbomosho (ŏg-bô-mō′shō) . . . Nig.	8·06 N	4·04 E
71	Ogden (ŏg′dĕn) . . . . Iowa	42·10 N	94·20 W
74	Ogden . . Utah (Salt Lake City In.)	41·14 N	111·58 W
74	Ogden Pk. Utah (Salt Lake City In.)	41·11 N	111·51 W
74	Ogden R. Utah (Salt Lake City In.)	41·16 N	111·54 W
84	Ogdensburg (ŏg′dĕnz-bûrg) N. J. (New York In.)	41·05 N	74·36 W
81	Ogdensburg . . . . N. Y.	44·40 N	75·30 W
79	Ogeechee, (R.) (ō-gē′chē) . . . . . Ga.	32·35 N	81·50 W
168	Ogies . . . . S. Afr. (Johannesburg & Pretoria In.)	26·03 S	29·04 E
86	Ogilvie Ra. (ō′g′l-vĭ) . . . . Can.	64·43 N	138·36 W
80	Oglesby (ō′g′lz-bĭ) . . . . Ill.	41·20 N	89·00 W
126	Oglio (R.) (ōl′yō) . . . . It.	45·15 N	10·19 E

ng-sing; ŋ-baŋk; N-nasalized n; nŏd; cŏmmit; ōld; ôbey; ôrder; fōōd; fŏŏt; ou-out; s-soft; sh-dish; th-thin; pūre; ûnite; ûrn; stŭd; circŭs; ü-as "y" in study; ′-indeterminate vowel.

Page	Name Pronunciation Region	Lat. °′	Long. °′
153	Ōgo (ō'gô).......Jap. (Ōsaka In.)	34·49 N	135·06 E
154	Ogoamas, Bulu (Mtn.).....Indon.	0·45 N	120·15 E
166	Ogooué (R.).............Gabon	0·20 S	11·07 E
136	Ogudnëvo (ôg-ōōg-nyô'vô) Sov. Un. (Moskva In.)	56·04 N	38·17 E
126	Ogulin (ō-gōō-lēn').........Yugo.	45·17 N	15·11 E
157	Ohia (ō-hī'ä)........Hawaii (In.)	19·35 N	155·01 W
101	O'Higgins (Prov.) (ô-kē'gēns) Chile (Santiago In.)	34·17 S	70·52 W
63	Ohio, (State) (ô'hī'ō)........U. S.	40·30 N	83·15 W
80	Ohio R....................U. S.	37·25 N	88·05 W
79	Ohoopee (R.) (ō-hōō'pē)......Ga.	32·32 N	82·38 W
120	Ohre (Eger) R. (ōr'zhě) (ā'gĕr) Czech.	50·08 N	12·45 E
127	Ohrid (ō'ĸrēd)............Yugo.	41·08 N	20·46 E
127	Ohrid (L.)............Alb. Yugo.	40·58 N	20·35 E
153	Ōi (oi')........Jap. (Tōkyō In.)	35·51 N	139·31 E
118	Oieren (L.) (ûĭĕrĕn)........Nor.	59·50 N	11·25 E
153	Oi-Gawa (Strm.) (ō'ê-gä'wà)..Jap.	35·09 N	138·05 E
83	Oil City (oil sĭ'tĭ)...........Pa.	41·25 N	79·40 W
111	Oirschot..Neth. (Amsterdam In.)	51·30 N	5·20 E
122	Oise (R.) (wäz).............Fr.	49·30 N	2·56 E
111	Oisterwijk.Neth. (Amsterdam In.)	51·34 N	5·13 E
153	Oita (ō'ê-tä)..............Jap.	33·14 N	131·38 E
153	Oji (ō'jê)........Jap. (Ōsaka In.)	34·36 N	135·43 E
76	Ojinaga (ō-Kê-nä'gä).......Mex.	29·34 N	104·26 W
91	Ojitlán (San Lucas) (ōkê-tlän') (sän-lōō'käs).Mex.	18·04 N	96·23 W
90	Ojo Caliente (ōĸō käl-yĕn'tå).Mex.	21·50 N	100·43 W
90	Ojocaliente (ô-ĸô-kä-lyĕ'n-tĕ) Mex.	22·39 N	102·15 W
94	Ojo del Toro, Pico (Pk.) (pē'kô-ô-kō-dĕl-tô'rô).Cuba	19·55 N	77·25 W
85	Oka (ō-kä)...Can. (Montreal In.)	45·28 N	74·05 W
133	Oka (R.) (ô-kä')........Sov. Un.	52·10 N	35·20 E
134	Oka (R.) (ō-kä')........Sov. Un.	53·28 N	101·09 E
132	Oka (R.) (ô-kä')........Sov. Un.	55·10 N	42·10 E
166	Okahandja............S. W. Afr.	21·50 S	16·45 E
86	Okanagan (ō'kȧ-näg'ȧn).....Can.	49·56 N	120·23 W
66	Okanogan................Wash.	48·20 N	119·34 W
66	Okanogan R..............Wash.	48·36 N	119·33 W
164	Okano R. (ô'kä'nō)........Gabon	0·15 N	11·08 E
78	Okatibbee (R.) (ō'kä-tĭb'ē)..Miss.	32·37 N	88·54 W
78	Okatoma Cr. (ô-kȧ-tō'mă)...Miss.	31·43 N	89·34 W
153	Okaya (ō'kȧ-yȧ)............Jap.	36·04 N	138·01 E
153	Okayama (ō'kȧ-yä'mȧ).......Jap.	34·39 N	133·54 E
153	Okazaki (ō'kȧ-zä'kê).......Jap.	34·58 N	137·09 E
79	Okeechobee (ō-kê-chō'bē) Fla. (In.)	27·15 N	26·48 W
79	Okeechobee, L.........Fla. (In.)	27·00 N	80·49 W
72	Okeene (ô-kēn')..............Okla.	36·06 N	98·19 W
79	Okefenokee Swp.(ō'kê-fê-nō'kê) Ga.	30·54 N	82·20 W
73	Okemah (ô-kē'mä).........Okla.	35·26 N	96·18 W
117	Oker (R.) (ō'kĕr)...........Ger.	52·23 N	10·00 E
135	Okha (ŭ-ĸä')...........Sov. Un.	53·44 N	143·12 E
136	Okhotino (ô-ĸô'tĭ-nô) Sov. Un. (Moskva In.)	56·14 N	38·24 E
135	Okhotsk (ô-kôtsk')......Sov. Un.	59·28 N	143·32 E
139	Okhotsk, Sea of (ô-kôtsk')...Asia	56·45 N	146·00 E
153	Oki-Guntō (Arch.) (ō'kê gōōn'tō) Jap.	36·17 N	133·05 E
152	Okinawa (I.) (ō'kê-nä'wȧ)....Jap.	26·30 N	128·30 E
152	Okinawa Guntō (Is.) (gōōn'tō') Jap.	26·50 N	127·25 E
153	Okino (I.) (ō'kê-nō)..........Jap.	36·22 N	133·27 E
152	Ōkino Erabu (I.) (ō-kē'nô-ä-rä'bōō).Jap.	27·18 N	129·00 E
62	Oklahoma (State) (ō-klȧ-hō'mȧ).U. S.	36·00 N	98·20 W
73	Oklahoma City............Okla.	35·27 N	97·32 W
79	Oklawaha (R.) (ŏk-lȧ-wô'hô)..Fla.	29·13 N	82·00 W
73	Okmulgee (ôk-mŭl'gē).......Okla.	35·37 N	95·58 W
75	Okolona (ō-kô-lō'nȧ) Ky. (Louisville In.)	38·08 N	85·41 W
78	Okolona..................Miss.	33·59 N	88·43 W
166	Okovanggo (R.)...Ang.-S. W. Afr.	17·50 S	19·30 E
166	Okovanggo Swp.............Bech.	19·30 S	23·02 E
152	Okushiri (I.) (ō'koo-shē'rê)...Jap.	42·12 N	139·30 E
65	Olalla (ō-lä'lä).Wash. (Seattle In.)	47·26 N	122·33 W
92	Olanchito (ō'län-chē'tō)....Hond.	15·28 N	86·35 W
118	Öland (û-länd')............Swe.	57·03 N	17·15 E
74	Olathe (ô-lā'thê) Mo. (Kansas City In.)	38·53 N	94·49 W
100	Olavarría (ō-lä-vär-rē'ä).....Arg.	36·49 S	60·15 W
121	Oława (ô-lä'vȧ)..............Pol.	50·57 N	17·18 E
101	Olazcoago (ô-läz-kôä'gô) Arg. (Buenos Aires In.)	35·14 S	60·37 W
126	Olbia (ô'l-byä)..............It.	40·55 N	9·28 E
111	Olching (ōl'kēng) Ger. (München In.)	48·13 N	11·21 E
94	Old Bahama Chan. (bȧ-hā'mȧ) N. A.	22·45 N	78·30 W
95	Old Bight.................Ba. Is.	24·15 N	75·20 W
84	Old Bridge (brĭj) N. J. (New York In.)	40·24 N	74·22 W
110	Oldbury (ōld'bĕr-ĭ).........Eng.	52·30 N	2·01 W
86	Old Crow (crō)............Can.	67·51 N	139·58 W
120	Oldenburg (ôl'dĕn-bōōrgh)...Ger.	53·09 N	8·13 E
81	Old Forge (fôrj)............Pa.	41·20 N	75·50 W
110	Oldham (ōld'ȧm)............Eng.	53·32 N	2·07 W
64	Old Harbor (här'bēr).......Alaska	57·18 N	153·20 W
116	Old Head of Kinsdale (ōld hĕd ŏv kĭn-sāl).Ire.	51·35 N	8·35 W
77	Old R...............Tex. (In.)	29·54 N	94·52 W
86	Olds (ōldz)...............Can.	51·50 N	114·00 W
82	Old Town (toun)...........Maine	44·55 N	68·42 W
81	Olean (ō-lê-ăn')............N. Y.	42·05 N	78·25 W
82	O'Leary (ō-lēr'ē)..........Can.	46·43 N	64·10 W
121	Olecko (ô-lĕt'skô)...........Pol.	54·02 N	22·29 E
135	Olekma (R.) (ô-lyĕk-mä').Sov. Un.	55·41 N	120·33 E
135	Olëkminsk (ô-lyĕk-mênsk') Sov. Un.	60·39 N	120·40 E
135	Olenëk (R.) (ô-lyĕ-nyôk').Sov. Un.	70·18 N	121·15 E
122	Oléron, Île d' (I.) (ēl' dō lā-rôɴ').Fr.	45·52 N	1·58 W
121	Olesnica (ô-lĕsh-nĭ'tsä).......Pol.	51·13 N	17·24 E
123	Olfen (ōl'fĕn).....Ger. (Ruhr In.)	51·43 N	7·22 E
135	Ol'ga (ôl'gȧ)...........Sov. Un.	43·48 N	135·44 E
84	Olga (ōl'gȧ).La. (New Orleans In.)	29·22 N	89·25 W
152	Ol'gi, Zaliv (B.) (zä'lĭf ôl'gĭ) Sov. Un.	43·43 N	135·25 E
129	Ol'gopol (ôl-gô-pôl'y')...Sov. Un.	48·11 N	29·28 E
124	Olhão (ôl-youɴ')..........Port.	37·02 N	7·54 W
167	Olievenhoutpoort..........S. Afr. (Johannesburg & Pretoria In.)	25·58 S	27·55 E
166	Olifants (R.) (ŏl'ĭ-fănts)....S. Afr.	23·58 S	31·00 E
167	Olifantsfontein............S. Afr. (Johannesburg & Pretoria In.)	25·58 S	28·19 E
127	Ólimbos...................Grc.	40·03 N	22·22 E
90	Olinalá (ô-lê-nä-lä')........Mex.	17·47 N	98·51 W
99	Olinda (ô-lē'n-dä).........Braz.	8·00 S	34·58 W
74	Olinda (ô-lĭn'dȧ) Calif. (Los Angeles In.)	33·55 N	117·51 W
125	Oliva (ô-lē'vä).............Sp.	38·54 N	0·07 W
124	Oliva de Jerez (ô-lē'vä dā hā'rĕth) Sp.	38·33 N	6·55 W
125	Olivais (ô-lê-vȧ'ys) Port. (Lisboa In.)	38·46 N	9·06 W
74	Olive (ŏl'ĭv).................. Calif. (Los Angeles In.)	33·50 N	117·51 W
80	Olive Hill..................Ky.	38·15 N	83·10 W
101	Oliveira (ô-lē-vä'rä) Braz. (Rio de Janeiro In.)	20·42 S	44·49 W
124	Olivenza (ō-lê-vĕn'thä).......Sp.	38·42 N	7·06 W
86	Oliver (ŏ'lĭ-vēr)............Can.	49·09 N	119·36 W
85	Oliver......Can. (Edmonton In.)	53·38 N	113·21 W
74	Oliver (ŏ'lĭvēr).Wis. (Duluth In.)	46·39 N	92·12 W
85	Oliver L....Can. (Edmonton In.)	53·19 N	113·00 W
71	Olivia (ō-lĭv'ē-ȧ)...........Minn.	44·46 N	95·00 W
100	Olivos (ōlē'vōs)........Arg. (In.)	34·15 S	58·29 W
121	Olkusz (ôl'kōōsh)............Pol.	50·16 N	19·41 E
98	Ollagüe (ō-lyä'gā).........Chile	21·17 S	68·17 W
110	Ollerton (ôl'ēr-tŭn)...........Eng.	53·12 N	1·02 W
74	Olmos Park (ōl'mŭs pärk') Tex. (San Antonio In.)	29·27 N	98·32 W
80	Olney (ŏl'nĭ)................Ill.	38·45 N	88·05 W
65	Olney (ŏl'nē).Ore. (Portland In.)	46·06 N	123·45 W
72	Olney.....................Tex.	33·24 N	98·43 W
83	Olomane (R.) (ō'lō mä'nē)...Can.	50·50 N	60·30 W
121	Olomouc (ô'lô-mōts).......Czech.	49·37 N	17·15 E
119	Olonets (ô-lô'nĕts).......Sov. Un.	60·58 N	32·54 E
122	Oloron, Gave d' (Strm.) (gäv-dĕ-lô-rôɴ').Fr.	43·21 N	0·44 W
122	Oloron-Ste. Marie (ō-lô-rôɴt'săɴt mȧ-rē').Fr.	43·11 N	1·37 W
125	Olot (ô-lōt')...............Sp.	42·09 N	2·30 E
123	Olpe (ōl'pĕ).....Ger. (Ruhr In.)	51·02 N	7·51 E
129	Ol'shanka (ôl'shäŋ-kȧ)...Sov. Un.	48·14 N	30·52 E
129	Ol'shany (ôl'shȧn-ê).....Sov. Un.	50·02 N	35·54 E
120	Olsnitz (ōlz'nētz)..........Ger.	50·25 N	12·11 E
121	Olsztyn (ôl'shtĕn)...........Pol.	53·47 N	20·28 E
120	Olten (ôl'tĕn)..............Switz.	47·20 N	7·53 E
127	Oltenita (ôl-tā'nĭ-tsä).......Rom.	44·05 N	26·39 E
115	Olt R......................Rom.	44·09 N	24·40 E
124	Olvera (ôl-vĕ'rä)............Sp.	36·55 N	7·16 W
66	Olympia (ô-lĭm'pĭ-ȧ).......Wash.	47·02 N	122·52 W
66	Olympic Mts..............Wash.	47·54 N	123·58 W
66	Olympic Natl. Park (ô-lĭm'pĭk) Wash.	47·54 N	123·00 W
66	Olympus Mt. (ô-lĭm'pŭs)..Wash.	47·43 N	123·30 W
139	Olympus Mts. Cyprus (Palestine In.)	34·50 N	32·44 E
81	Olyphant (ŏl'ĭ-fănt).........Pa.	41·30 N	75·40 W
135	Olyutorskiy, Mys (C.) (ŭl-yōō'tôr-skê).Sov. Un.	59·49 N	167·16 E
153	Omae-Zaki (Pt.) (ō'mä-ā zä'kê) Jap.	34·37 N	138·15 E
165	Om Ager..................Eth.	14·06 N	36·46 E
116	Omagh (ō'mä)...........N. Ire.	54·35 N	7·25 W
70	Omaha (ō'mȧ-hä)..........Nebr.	41·18 N	95·57 W
70	Omaha Ind. Res...........Nebr.	42·09 N	96·08 W
144	Oman, G. of................Asia	24·24 N	58·58 E
166	Omaruru (ō-mä-rōō'rōō).S. W. Afr.	21·25 S	16·50 E
126	Ombrone (R.) (ôm-brō'nä).....It.	42·48 N	11·18 E
165	Omdurman (ŏm-dōōr-män')..Sud.	15·45 N	32·30 E
91	Omealca (ōmā-äl'kō)..........Mex.	18·44 N	96·45 W
90	Ometepec (ô-mā-tȧ-pĕk')....Mex.	16·41 N	98·27 W
153	Ōmiya (ō'mê-yȧ).Jap. (Tōkyō In.)	35·54 N	139·38 E
92	Omoa (ô-mō'rä)............Hond.	15·43 N	88·03 W
135	Omolon (R.) (ō'mō).....Sov. Un.	67·43 N	159·15 E
153	Ōmori (Kioroshi) (ō'mô-rê) (kê'ō-rō'shē) Jap. (Tōkyō In.)	35·50 N	140·09 E
165	Omo R. (ō'mō)...............Eth.	5·54 N	36·09 E
92	Omotepe, Isla de (I.) (ē's-lä-dĕ-ō-mô-tā'pȧ).Nic.	11·32 N	85·30 W
71	Omro (ŏm'rō).............Wis.	44·01 N	89·46 W
134	Omsk (ômsk)..........Sov. Un.	55·12 N	73·19 E
153	Ōmura (ō'mōō-rȧ)..........Jap.	32·56 N	129·57 E
153	Ōmuta (ō-mōō-tȧ)..........Jap.	33·02 N	130·28 E
132	Omutninsk (ō'mōō-tēnsk).Sov. Un.	58·38 N	52·10 E
70	Onawa (ŏn-ȧ-wȧ)..............Iowa	42·02 N	96·05 W
80	Onaway....................Mich.	45·25 N	84·10 W
125	Onda (ōn'dä)................Sp.	39·58 N	0·13 W
121	Ondava R. (ōn'dȧ-vȧ).....Czech.	48·51 N	21·40 E
150	Öndör Haan..............Mong.	47·20 N	110·40 E
132	Onega (ô-nyĕ'gȧ)........Sov. Un.	63·50 N	38·08 E
132	Onega (R.)..............Sov. Un.	63·20 N	39·20 E
	Onega, L., see Onezhskoye Ozero		
81	Oneida (ō-nī'dȧ)............N. Y.	43·05 N	75·40 W
81	Oneida (L.)................N. Y.	43·10 N	76·00 W
70	O'Neill (ō-nēl')............Nebr.	42·28 N	98·38 W
135	Onekotan (ŭ-nyĕ-kŭ-tän').Sov. Un.	49·45 N	153·45 E
81	Oneonta (ō-nē-ŏn'tȧ)........N. Y.	42·25 N	75·05 W
132	Onezhskaja Guba (B.)...Sov. Un.	64·30 N	36·00 E
132	Onezhskiy, P-Ov. (Pen.).Sov. Un.	64·30 N	37·40 E
132	Onezhskoye Ozero (L. Onega) (ô-năsh'skô-yĕ ô'zĕ-rô).Sov. Un.	62·02 N	34·35 E
146	Ongin (ŏn'gĭn')............Mong.	46·00 N	102·46 E
143	Ongole.....................India	15·36 N	80·03 E
167	Onilahy (R.)..........Malagasy	23·41 S	45·00 E
164	Onitsha (ô-nĭt'shȧ)..........Nig.	6·13 N	5·47 E
153	Onomichi (ō'nô-mē'chê)......Jap.	34·27 N	133·12 E
135	Onon (R.) (ô'nôn)......Sov. Un.	50·33 N	114·18 E
135	Onon Gol (R.) (ô'nôn)...Sov. Un.	48·30 N	110·38 E
99	Onoto (ô-nô'tô)........Ven. (In.)	9·38 N	65·03 W
158	Onslow (ŏnz'lō)............Austl.	21·53 S	115·00 E
79	Onslow B. (ŏnz'lō).........N. C.	34·22 N	77·35 W
153	Ontake-san (Mtn.) (ŏn'tä-kȧ sän) Jap.	35·55 N	137·29 E
74	Ontario (ŏn-tā'rĭ-ō) Calif. (Los Angeles In.)	34·04 N	117·39 W
66	Ontario....................Ore.	44·02 N	116·57 W
87	Ontario (Prov.).............Can.	50·47 N	88·50 W
63	Ontario, L.............U. S.-Can.	43·35 N	79·05 W
125	Onteniente (ōn-tȧ-nyĕn'tā)....Sp.	38·48 N	0·35 W
71	Ontonagon (ŏn-tô-năg'ŏn)...Mich.	46·50 N	89·20 W
153	Ōnuki (ō'nōō-kê) Jap. (Tōkyō In.)	35·17 N	139·51 E
158	Oodnadatta (ōōd'nȧ-dȧ'tȧ)..Austl.	27·38 S	135·40 E
158	Ooldea Station (ōōl-dā'ä)...Austl.	30·35 S	132·08 E
111	Ooltgensplaat Neth. (Amsterdam In.)	51·41 N	4·19 E
78	Oostanaula (R.) (ōō-stȧ-nô'lȧ) Ga.	34·25 N	85·10 W
117	Oostende (ōst-ĕn'dē).......Bel.	51·14 N	2·55 E
111	Oosterhout Neth. (Amsterdam In.)	51·38 N	4·52 E
117	Ooster Schelde (R.).......Neth.	51·40 N	3·40 E
92	Opalaca, Sierra de (Mts.) (sē-ĕ'r-rä-dĕ-ô-pä-lä'kä).Hond.	14·30 N	88·29 W
121	Opatow (ô-pä'tōōf)..........Pol.	50·47 N	21·25 E
121	Opava (ō'pä-vä)..........Czech.	49·56 N	17·52 E
118	Opdal (ôp'däl)..............Nor.	62·37 N	9·41 E
78	Opelika (ŏp-ê-lī'kȧ)..........Ala.	32·39 N	85·23 W
77	Opelousas (ŏp-ē-lōō'sȧs)......La.	30·33 N	92·04 W
81	Opeongo (L.) (ŏp-ê-ŏŋ'gō)...Can.	45·40 N	78·20 W
67	Opheim (ō-fīm')...........Mont.	48·51 N	106·19 W
64	Ophir (ō'fēr)..............Alaska	63·10 N	156·28 W
139	Ophir, Mt...Mala. (Singapore In.)	2·22 N	102·37 E
92	Opico (ô-pē'kō)...............Sal.	13·50 N	89·23 W
87	Opinaca (R.) (ŏp-ĭ-nä'kȧ)....Can.	52·28 N	77·40 W
123	Opladen (ōp'lä-dĕn) Ger. (Ruhr In.)	51·04 N	7·00 E
128	Opochka (ō-pôch'kȧ)....Sov. Un.	56·43 N	28·39 E
121	Opoczno (ō-pôch'nô).........Pol.	51·22 N	20·18 E
121	Opole (ō-pôl'ä)..............Pol.	50·42 N	17·55 E
121	Opole Lubelskie (ō-pō'lä lōō-bĕl'skyĕ).Pol.	51·09 N	21·58 E
	Oporto, see Pôrto		
66	Oportunity (ŏp-ŏr tū'nĭ tĭ)..Wash.	47·37 N	117·20 W
129	Oposhnya (ō-pôsh'nyȧ)..Sov. Un.	49·57 N	34·34 E
78	Opp (ŏp)...................Ala.	31·18 N	86·15 W
74	Oquirrh Mts. (ō'kwēr)... Utah (Salt Lake City In.)	40·38 N	112·11 W
121	Oradea (ô-räd'yä)...........Rom.	47·02 N	21·55 E
164	Oran (ō-rän') (ō-räɴ')......Alg.	35·46 N	0·45 W
100	Orán (ô-rä'n)..............Arg.	23·13 S	64·17 W
73	Oran (ŏr'ȧn)...............Mo.	37·05 N	89·39 W
160	Orange (ŏr'ĕnj)............Austl.	33·15 S	149·08 E
74	Orange...Calif. (Los Angeles In.)	33·48 N	117·51 W
81	Orange.....................Conn.	41·15 N	73·00 W
122	Orange (ô-ranzh')............Fr.	44·08 N	4·48 E
84	Orange.....N. J. (New York In.)	40·46 N	74·14 W
77	Orange.....................Tex.	30·07 N	93·44 W
99	Orange, Cabo (C.) (kȧ-bô-rȧ'n-zhĕ).Braz.	4·25 N	51·30 W
79	Orange (L.)................Fla.	29·30 N	82·12 W
166	Orange (R.).......S. W. Afr.-S. Afr.	29·15 S	17·30 E
79	Orangeburg (ŏr'ĕnj-bûrg)....S. C.	33·30 N	80·50 W
94	Orange Cay (I.) (ŏr-ĕnj kē).Ba. Is.	24·55 N	79·05 W
70	Orange City...............Iowa	43·01 N	96·06 W
166	Orange Free State (Prov.) S. Afr.	28·15 S	26·00 E
85	Orangeville (ŏr'ĕnj-vĭl) Can. (Toronto In.)	43·55 N	80·06 W
168	Orangeville.............S. Afr. (Johannesburg & Pretoria In.)	27·05 S	28·13 E
92	Orange Walk (wôl''k) Br. Hond. (Yucatan In.)	18·09 N	88·32 W
155	Orani (ō-rä'nē).Phil. (Manila In.)	14·47 N	120·32 E
111	Oranienburg (ō-rä'nê-ĕn-bōōrgh) Ger. (Berlin In.)	52·45 N	13·14 E
155	Oranje-Gebergte (Mts.) Neth. N. Gui.	4·22 S	139·25 E
127	Orastie (ô-rûsh'tyȧ)........Rom.	45·50 N	23·14 E
	Orașul-Stalin, see Brașov		
126	Orbetello (ôr-bȧ-tĕl'lō).......It.	42·27 N	11·15 E
124	Orbigo (R.) (ôr-bē'gō).......Sp.	42·30 N	5·55 W
160	Orbost (ôr'bŭst)...........Austl.	37·43 S	148·20 E
65	Orcas (I.) (ôr'kȧs) Wash. (Vancouver In.)	48·43 N	122·52 W
74	Orchard Farm (ôr'chērd färm) Mo. (St. Louis In.)	38·53 N	90·27 W
75	Orchard Park.N. Y. Buffalo In.)	42·46 N	78·46 W
65	Orchards (ôr'chēdz) Wash. (Portland In.)	45·40 N	122·33 W
98	Orchilla (ôr-kĭl-ȧ)..........Ven.	11·47 N	66·34 W
70	Ord (ôrd)..................Nebr.	41·35 N	98·57 W
158	Ord (R.)..................Austl.	17·30 S	128·40 E
136	Orda (ôr'dȧ). Sov. Un. (Urals In.)	56·50 N	57·12 E
124	Órdenes (ōr'dā-nās)..........Sp.	43·46 N	8·24 W
150	Ordos Des.................China	39·12 N	108·10 E
69	Ord Pk....................Ariz.	33·55 N	109·40 W
133	Ordu (ôr'dōō)...............Tur.	41·00 N	37·50 E
124	Orduña (ôr-dōō'nyä).........Sp.	42·59 N	3·01 W
72	Ordway (ôrd'wā)............Colo.	38·11 N	103·46 W
133	Ordzhonikidze (yĕ-nȧ-kyĕ'vô) Sov. Un.	43·05 N	44·35 E
118	Örebro (û'rē-brō)...........Swe.	59·16 N	15·11 E
136	Oredezh R. (ô'rĕ-dĕzh) Sov. Un. (Leningrad In.)	59·23 N	30·21 E
71	Oregon.....................Ill.	42·01 N	89·21 W
62	Oregon (State)..............U. S.	43·40 N	121·50 W
66	Oregon Caves Natl. Mon. (cāvz) Ore.	42·05 N	123·13 W
65	Oregon City...Ore. (Portland In.)	45·21 N	122·36 W
118	Oregrund (û'rĕ-grōōnd).....Swe.	60·20 N	18·26 E
129	Orekhov (ôr-yĕ'ĸôf).....Sov. Un.	47·34 N	35·51 E

ăt; finăl; rāte; senâte; ärm; åsk; sofȧ; fâre; ch-choose; dh-as th in other; bē; ēvent; bĕt; recĕnt; cratēr; g-go; gh-guttural g; bĭt; ĭ-short neutral; rīde: ĸ-guttural k as ch in German ich;

Page	Name Pronunciation	Region	Lat. °′	Long. °′
128	Orekhovo-Zuyevo (ôr-yĕ'kô-vô zōō'yĕ-vô)	Sov. Un.	55·46 N	39·00 E
128	Orël (ôr-yôl')	Sov. Un.	52·54 N	36·03 E
128	Orël (Oblast)	Sov. Un.	52·35 N	36·08 E
129	Orel' (R.)	Sov. Un.	49·08 N	34·55 E
69	Orem (ŏ'rĕm)	Utah	40·15 N	111·50 W
	Ore Mts., see Erzgebirge			
133	Orenburg (ô'rĕn-bŏŏrg)	Sov. Un.	51·50 N	55·05 E
124	Orense (ô-rĕn'sā)	Sp.	42·20 N	7·52 W
118	Öresund (Sd.)	Den.	55·30 N	12·25 E
94	Organos, Sierra de los (Mts.) (sē-ĕ'r-rä-dĕ-lôs-ŏ'r-gä-nôs)	Cuba	22·20 N	84·10 W
69	Organ Pipe Cactus Natl. Mon. (ôr'găn pīp kăk'tŭs)	Ariz.	32·14 N	113·05 W
101	Orgãos, Serra das (Mtn.) (sĕ'r-rä-däs-ôr-gouɴ's)	Braz. (Rio de Janeiro In.)	22·30 S	43·01 W
129	Orgeyev (ôr-gyĕ'yĕf)	Sov. Un.	47·27 N	28·49 E
146	Orhon Gol (R.)	Mong.	48·33 N	103·07 E
98	Oriental, Cordillera (Mts.) (kôr-dēl-yĕ'rä ō-rē-ĕn-täl')	Bol.	14·00 S	68·33 W
98	Oriental, Cordillera (Mts.) (kôr-dēl-yĕ'rä)	Col. (In.)	3·30 N	74·27 W
95	Oriental, Cordillera (Mts.) (kôr-dēl-yĕ'rä-ô-ryĕ'n-täl)	Dom. Rep.	18·55 N	69·40 W
88	Oriental, Sierra Madre, (Mts.) (sē-ĕ'r-rä-mä'drĕ-ô-ryĕ'n-täl')	Mex.	25·30 N	100·45 W
95	Oriente (State) (ō-rê-ĕn'tā)	Cuba	20·25 N	76·15 W
125	Orihuela (ō'rê-wā'lä)	Sp.	38·04 N	0·55 W
119	Orihvesi (L.) (ô'rĭ-vĕ-sĭ)	Fin.	62·15 N	29·55 E
81	Orillia (ô-rĭl'ĭ-ȧ)	Can.	44·35 N	79·25 W
98	Orinoco, Rio (R.) (rê'ō-ō-rĭ-nō'kō)	Ven.	8·32 N	63·13 W
155	Orion (ō-rê-ōn')	Phil. (Manila In.)	14·37 N	120·34 E
142	Orissa (State) (ō-rĭs'ȧ)	India	25·09 N	83·50 E
126	Oristano (ô-rês-tä'nō)	It.	39·53 N	8·38 E
126	Oristano, Golfo di (G.) (gôl-fô-dē-ô-rês-tä'nō)	It.	39·53 N	8·12 E
99	Orituco (R.) (ô-rē-tōō'kō)	Ven. (In.)	9·37 N	66·25 W
99	Oriuco (ô-rêōō'kō) (R.)	Ven. (In.)	9·36 N	66·25 W
91	Orizaba (ô-rê-zä'bä)	Mex.	18·52 N	97·05 W
118	Örkan	Swe.	57·10 N	14·45 E
118	Orkdal (ôr'k-däl)	Nor.	63·19 N	9·54 E
112	Örkedalen (ûr'kĕ-dä-lĕn)	Nor.	63·13 N	9·53 E
118	Örken (L.) (ûr'kĕn)	Swe.	57·11 N	14·45 E
118	Orkla (R.) (ôr'klȧ)	Nor.	62·55 N	9·50 E
168	Orkney (ôrk'nĭ)	S. Afr. (Johannesburg & Pretoria In.)	26·58 S	26·39 E
116	Orkney (Is.)	Scot.	59·01 N	2·08 W
79	Orlando (ôr-lăn'dō)	Fla. (In.)	28·32 N	81·22 W
167	Orlando (ôr-lăn-dō)	S. Afr. (Johannesburg & Pretoria In.)	26·15 S	27·56 E
75	Orland Park (ôr-lăn')	Ill. (Chicago In.)	41·38 N	87·52 W
85	Orleans (ôr-lȧ-äɴ')	Can. (Ottawa In.)	45·28 N	75·31 W
122	Orléans (ôr-lā-äɴ')	Fr.	47·55 N	1·56 E
80	Orleans (ôr-lēnz')	Ind.	38·40 N	86·25 W
164	Orléansville (ôr-lȧ-äɴ-vēl')	Alg.	36·14 N	1·32 E
79	Ormond (ôr'mŏnd)	Fla.	29·15 N	81·05 W
110	Ormskirk (ôrms'kĕrk)	Eng.	53·34 N	2·53 W
85	Ormstown (ôrms'toun)	Can. (Montreal In.)	45·07 N	74·00 W
122	Orne (R.) (ôrn')	Fr.	49·05 N	0·32 W
121	Orneta (ôr-nyĕ'tä)	Pol.	54·07 N	20·10 E
118	Ornö (I.)	Swe.	59·02 N	18·35 E
112	Örnsköldsvik (ûrn'skôlts-vĕk)	Swe.	63·10 N	18·32 E
90	Oro, Rio del (R.) (rē'ō dĕl ō'rō)	Mex.	18·04 N	100·59 W
76	Oro, Rio del (R.)	Mex.	26·04 N	105·40 W
126	Orobie, Alpi (Mts.) (äl'pē-ô-rŏ'byĕ)	It.	46·05 N	9·47 E
98	Orocué (ô-rô-kwā')	Col.	4·48 N	71·26 W
116	Oronsay, Pass. of (ŏ'rŏn-sȧ)	Scot.	55·55 N	6·25 W
126	Orosei, Golfo di (G.) (gôl-fô-dē-ō-rô-sā'ē)	It.	40·12 N	9·45 E
121	Orosháza (ô-rôsh-hä'sô)	Hung.	46·33 N	20·31 E
92	Orosi Vol. (ō-rō'sē)	C. R.	11·00 N	85·30 W
68	Oroville (ōr'ô-vĭl)	Calif.	39·29 N	121·34 W
66	Oroville	Wash.	48·55 N	119·25 W
80	Orrville (ôr'vĭl)	Ohio	40·45 N	81·50 W
118	Orsa (ōr'sä)	Swe.	61·08 N	14·35 E
118	Örsdals Vand (L.) (ûrs-däls vän)	Nor.	58·39 N	6·06 E
128	Orsha (ôr'shȧ)	Sov. Un.	54·29 N	30·28 E
133	Orsk (ôrsk)	Sov. Un.	51·15 N	58·50 E
127	Orşova (ôr'shô-vȧ)	Rom.	44·43 N	22·26 E
98	Ortega (ôr-tĕ'gä)	Col. (In.)	3·56 N	75·12 W
124	Ortegal, Cabo (C.) (kȧ'bô-ôr-tȧ-gäl')	Sp.	43·46 N	8·15 W
111	Orth	Aus. (Wien In.)	48·09 N	16·42 E
125	Orthez (ôr-tĕz')	Fr.	43·29 N	0·43 W
124	Ortigueira (ôr-tē-gā'ē-rä)	Sp.	43·40 N	7·50 W
65	Orting (ôrt'ĭng)	Wash. (Seattle In.)	47·06 N	122·12 W
126	Ortona (ôr-tō'nä)	It.	42·22 N	14·22 E
70	Ortonville (ôr-tŭn-vĭl)	Minn.	45·18 N	96·26 W
98	Oruro (ô-rōō'rō)	Bol.	17·57 S	66·59 W
126	Orvieto (ôr-vyâ'tō)	It.	42·43 N	12·08 E
127	Oryakhovo	Bul.	43·43 N	23·59 E
118	Os (ôs)	Nor.	60·24 N	5·22 E
132	Osa (ô'sȧ)	Sov. Un.	57·18 N	55·25 E
93	Osa, Pen. de (ō'sä)	C. R.	8·30 N	83·25 W
71	Osage (ō'sāj)	Iowa	43·16 N	92·49 W
73	Osage (R.)	Mo.	38·10 N	93·12 W
73	Osage City (ō'sāj sĭ'tĭ)	Kans.	38·28 N	95·53 W
153	Ōsaka (ō'sä-kä)	Jap. (Ōsaka In.)	34·40 N	135·27 E
153	Ōsaka (Pref.)	Jap. (Ōsaka In.)	34·45 N	135·36 E
153	Ōsaka-Wan (B.) (wän)	Jap.	34·34 N	135·16 E
71	Osakis (ô-sā'kĭs)	Minn.	45·51 N	95·09 W
71	Osakis (L.)	Minn.	45·55 N	94·55 W
153	Ōsawa (ō'sä-wä)	Jap. (Tōkyō In.)	35·54 N	129·48 E
73	Osawatomie (ŏs-ȧ-wăt'ō-mê)	Kans.	38·29 N	94·57 W
72	Osborne (ŏz'bŭrn)	Kans.	39·25 N	98·42 W
71	Osceola (ŏs-ē-ō'lȧ)	Iowa	41·04 N	93·45 W
73	Osceola	Mo.	38·02 N	93·41 W
70	Osceola	Nebr.	41·11 N	97·34 W
73	Osceola	Tenn.	35·42 N	89·58 W
80	Oscoda (ŏs-kō'dȧ)	Mich.	44·25 N	83·20 W
128	Osëtr (R.) (ō'sĕt'r)	Sov. Un.	54·27 N	38·15 E
80	Osgood (ŏz'gŏŏd)	Ind.	39·10 N	85·20 W
85	Osgoode Sta.	Can. (Ottawa In.)	45·09 N	75·37 W
134	Osh (ôsh)	Sov. Un.	40·28 N	72·47 E
81	Oshawa (ŏsh'ȧ-wȧ)	Can.	43·50 N	78·50 W
153	Ōshima (I.) (ō'shē'mä)	Jap.	34·47 N	139·35 E
70	Oshkosh (ŏsh'kŏsh)	Nebr.	41·24 N	102·22 W
71	Oshkosh	Wis.	44·01 N	88·35 W
119	Oshmyany (ôsh-myä'nĭ)	Sov. Un.	54·27 N	25·55 E
164	Oshogbo	Nig.	7·53 N	4·23 E
127	Osijek (ôs'ĭ-yĕk)	Yugo.	45·33 N	18·48 E
134	Osinniki (ŭ-sē'nyĭ-kē)	Sov. Un.	53·29 N	85·19 E
129	Osipenko (ŭ-sē'pyĭn-kō)	Sov. Un.	46·45 N	36·47 E
71	Oskaloosa (ŏs-kȧ-lōō'sȧ)	Iowa	41·16 N	92·40 W
118	Oskarshamn (ôs'kärs-häm'n)	Swe.	57·16 N	16·24 E
118	Oskarsström (ôs'kärs-strûm)	Swe.	56·48 N	12·55 E
129	Oskol (R.) (ôs-kôl')	Sov. Un.	49·25 N	37·41 E
118	Oslo (ôs'lō)	Nor.	59·56 N	10·41 E
118	Oslo Fd (fyôrd)	Nor.	59·03 N	10·35 E
124	Osma (ōs'mä)	Sp.	41·35 N	3·02 W
133	Osmaniye	Tur.	37·10 N	36 30 E
120	Osnabrück (ôs-nä-brük')	Ger.	52·16 N	8·05 E
100	Osorno (ô-sō'r-nō)	Chile	40·42 S	73·13 W
159	Osprey Reef (I.) (ŏs'prȧ)	Austl.	14·00 S	146·45 E
160	Ossa, Mt. (ŏsȧ)	Austl.	41·45 S	146·05 E
74	Osseo (ŏs'sĕ-ō)	Minn. (Minneapolis, St. Paul In.)	45·07 N	93·24 W
84	Ossining (ŏs'ĭ-nĭng)	N. Y. (New York In.)	41·09 N	73·51 W
82	Ossipee (ŏs'ĭ-pē)	N. H.	43·42 N	71·08 W
118	Ossjöen (L.) (ôs-syûĕn)	Nor.	61·20 N	12·00 E
128	Ostashkov (ôs-täsh'kôf)	Sov. Un.	57·07 N	33·04 E
117	Oste (R.) (ōz'tĕ)	Ger.	53·20 N	9·19 E
129	Oster (ōs'tĕr)	Sov. Un.	50·55 N	30·52 E
118	Oster-daläven (R.)	Swe.	61·40 N	13·00 E
118	Oster Fd. (ûs'tĕr fyôr')	Nor.	60·40 N	5·25 E
118	Ostersund (ûs'tĕr-sōōnd)	Swe.	63·09 N	14·49 E
118	Östhammar (ûst'häm'är)	Swe.	60·16 N	18·21 E
125	Ostia Antica (ô's-tyä-än-tē'kä)	It. (Roma In.)	41·46 N	12·24 E
	Ostia Lido, see Lido di Roma			
121	Ostrava	Czech.	49·51 N	18·18 E
121	Ostróda (ôs'trōōt-ä)	Pol.	53·41 N	19·58 E
129	Ostróg (ôs-trôk')	Sov. Un.	50·21 N	26·40 E
129	Ostrogozhsk (ôs-trô-gôzhk')	Sov. Un.	50·53 N	39·03 E
121	Ostrołeka (ôs-trô-wôɴ'kȧ)	Pol.	53·04 N	21·35 E
129	Ostropol' (ôs-trô-pôl')	Sov. Un.	49·48 N	27·32 E
128	Ostrov (ôs-trôf')	Sov. Un.	57·21 N	28·22 E
121	Ostrowiec Świetokrzyski (ôs-trō'vyĕts shvyĕɴ-tō-kzhĭ'ske)	Pol.	50·55 N	21·24 E
121	Ostrów Lubelski (ôs'trōōf lōō'bĕl-skĭ)	Pol.	51·32 N	22·49 E
121	Ostrów Mazowiecka (mä-zô-vyĕt'skȧ)	Pol.	52·47 N	21·54 E
121	Ostrow Wielkopolski (ôs'trōōv vyĕl-kō-pōl'skē)	Pol.	51·38 N	17·49 E
121	Ostrzeszów (ôs-tzhä'shōōf)	Pol.	51·26 N	17·56 E
127	Ostuni (ôs-tōō'nē)	It.	40·44 N	17·35 E
127	Osum (R.) (ō'sōōm)	Alb.	40·37 N	20·00 E
153	Ōsumi-Guntō (Arch.) (ō'sōō-mē gōōn'tō)	Jap.	30·34 N	130·30 E
153	Ōsumi (Van Diemen) Kaikyō (Str.) (văn dē'mĕn) (kä'ē'kyō)	Jap.	31·02 N	130·10 E
124	Osuna (ô-sōō'nä)	Sp.	37·18 N	5·05 W
128	Osveya (ôs'vĕ-yȧ)	Sov. Un.	56·00 N	28·08 E
110	Oswaldtwistle (ŏz-wȧld-twĭs''l)	Eng.	53·44 N	2·23 W
81	Oswegatchie (R.) (ŏs-wê-găch'ĭ)	N. Y.	44·15 N	75·20 W
73	Oswego (ŏs-wē'gō)	Kans.	37·10 N	95·08 W
81	Oswego	N. Y.	43·25 N	76·30 W
65	Oswego	Ore. (Portland In.)	45·25 N	122·40 W
121	Oswiecim (ôsh-vyăɴ'tsyĭm)	Pol.	50·02 N	19·17 E
152	Otaru (ō'tȧ-rōō)	Jap.	43·07 N	141·00 E
98	Otavalo (ōtä-vä'lō)	Ec.	0·14 N	78·16 W
166	Otavi (ô-tä'vē)	S. W. Afr.	19·35 S	17·20 E
68	Otay (ō'tā)	Calif. (San Diego In.)	32·36 N	117·04 W
128	Otepää (ō'tĕ-pȧ)	Sov. Un.	58·03 N	26·31 E
127	Othonoí (I.)	Grc.	40·51 N	19·26 E
127	Óthris, Óros (Mts.)	Grc.	39·00 N	22·15 E
87	Otish Mts. (ô-tĭsh')	Can.	52·24 N	70·01 W
166	Otjiwarongo (ŏt-jē-wȧ-rōŋ'gō)	Ang.	20·20 S	16·25 E
126	Otočac (ō'tô-chȧts)	Yugo.	44·53 N	15·15 E
136	Otradnoye (ô-trâ'd-nôyĕ)	Sov. Un. (Leningrad In.)	59·46 N	30·50 E
127	Otranto (ō'trän-tô) (ô-trän'tō)	It.	40·07 N	18·30 E
127	Otranto, C. di	It.	40·06 N	18·32 E
127	Otranto, Strait of	It.-Alb.	40·30 N	18·45 E
136	Otra R. (ôt'rȧ)	Sov. Un. (Moskva In.)	55·22 N	38·20 E
80	Otsego (ŏt-sē'gō)	Mich.	42·25 N	85·45 W
153	Otsu (ō'tsōō)	Jap. (Ōsaka In.)	35·00 N	135·54 E
118	Ottavand (L.) (ôt'tȧ-vän)	Nor.	61·53 N	8·40 E
85	Ottawa (ŏt'ȧ-wȧ)	Can. (Ottawa In.)	45·25 N	75·43 W
80	Ottawa	Ill.	41·20 N	88·50 W
73	Ottawa	Kans.	38·37 N	95·16 W
80	Ottawa	Ohio	41·00 N	84·00 W
87	Ottawa (R.)	Can.	46·05 N	77·20 W
87	Ottawa Is.	Can.	59·50 N	81·00 W
168	Ottensville (ŏt'ĕns-vĭl)	S. Afr. (Johannesburg & Pretoria In.)	24·46 S	29·34 E
118	Otteråen (ôt'ĕr-ôĕn)	Nor.	59·13 N	7·20 E
69	Otter Cr. (ŏt'ĕr)	Utah	38·20 N	111·55 W
81	Otter Cr.	Vt.	44·05 N	73·15 W
65	Otter Pt.	Can. (Seattle In.)	48·21 N	123·50 W
70	Otter Tail (L.)	Minn.	46·21 N	95·52 W
74	Otterville (ŏt'ĕr-vĭl)	Ill. (St. Louis In.)	39·03 N	90·24 W
166	Ottery (ŏt'ĕr-ĭ)	S. Afr. (Cape Town In.)	34·02 S	18·31 E
71	Ottumwa (ô-tŭm'wȧ)	Iowa	41·00 N	92·26 W
91	Otumba (ô-tŭm'bä)	Mex. (Mexico In.)	19·41 N	98·46 W
160	Otway, C. (ŏt'wā)	Austl.	38·55 S	153·40 E
100	Otway, Seno (B.) (sĕ'nō-ô't-wä'y)	Chile	53·00 S	73·00 W
121	Otwock (ôt'vôtsk)	Pol.	52·05 N	21·18 E
63	Ouachita, (R.)	U. S.	33·25 N	92·30 W
73	Ouachita Mts. (wŏsh'ĭ-tô)	Okla.	34·29 N	95·01 W
164	Ouagadougou (wä'gȧ-dōō'gōō)	Upper Volta	12·20 N	1·43 W
164	Ouahigouya (wä-ê-gōō'yä)	Upper Volta	13·34 N	2·22 W
164	Oualata (wä-lä'tä)	Mauritania	17·11 N	6·50 W
164	Ouallene (wäl-lân')	Alg.	24·43 N	1·15 E
95	Ouanaminthe	Hai.	19·35 N	71·45 W
165	Ouanda-Djalé (wän'dȧ jȧ-lā')	Cen. Afr. Rep.	8·56 N	22·46 E
164	Ouarane (Dunes)	Mauritania	20·44 N	10·27 W
164	Ouargla (wär'glä)	Alg.	32·00 N	5·18 E
111	Oude Rijn (R.)	Neth. (Amsterdam In.)	52·09 N	4·33 E
111	Oudewater	Neth. (Amsterdam In.)	52·01 N	4·52 E
111	Oud Gastel	Neth. (Amsterdam In.)	51·35 N	4·27 E
114	Oudrhes, L. (Mt.)	Mor.	32·33 N	4·49 W
166	Oudtshoorn (outs'hōrn)	S. Afr.	33·33 S	23·36 E
114	Oued-Zem (wĕd-zĕm')	Mor.	33·05 N	5·49 W
122	Ouessant, I. d' (ēl-dwĕ-säɴ')	Fr.	48·28 N	5·00 W
165	Ouesso	Con. B.	1·38 N	16·04 E
95	Ouest, Pt	Hai.	19·00 N	73·25 W
164	Ouezzane (wĕ-zan')	Mor.	34·48 N	5·40 W
116	Oughter (L.) (lôk ok'tĕr)	Ire.	54·02 N	7·40 W
164	Ouidah (wē-dä')	Dahomey	6·25 N	2·05 E
114	Ouled Nail, Montes des (Mts.)	Alg.	34·43 N	2·44 E
123	Oulins (ōō-läɴ')	Fr. (Paris In.)	48·52 N	1·27 E
122	Oullins (ōō-lăɴ')	Fr.	45·44 N	4·46 E
112	Oulu (ō'lōō)	Fin.	64·58 N	25·43 E
112	Oulu-jarvi (L.)	Fin.	64·20 N	25·48 E
112	Ounas (R.) (ō'nȧs)	Fin.	67·46 N	24·40 E
110	Oundle (ōn'd'l)	Eng.	52·28 N	0·28 W
165	Ounianga Kerber (ōō-nē-äŋ'gȧ kē-bēr')	Chad	19·04 N	20·22 E
69	Ouray (ōō-rä')	Colo.	38·00 N	107·40 W
99	Ourinhos (ôōō-rê'nyôs)	Braz.	23·04 S	49·45 W
124	Ourique (ō-rē'kĕ)	Port.	37·39 N	8·10 W
101	Ouro Fino (ōŭ-rô-fē'nō)	Braz. (Rio de Janeiro In.)	22·18 S	46·21 W
101	Ouro Prêto (ō'rōō prä'tōō)	Braz. (Rio de Janeiro In.)	20·24 S	43·30 W
117	Ouse (ōōz)	Eng.	52·39 N	0·21 W
116	Ouse (R.)	Eng.	53·45 N	1·09 W
87	Outardes, R. aux (ōō-tärdz')	Can.	50·33 N	69·10 W
164	Outat el Hadj	Mor.	33·25 N	3·44 W
83	Outer (I.) (out'ĕr)	Can.	51·06 N	58·23 W
71	Outer (I.) (out'ĕr)	Wis.	47·03 N	90·20 W
89	Outer Brass (I.) (bräs)	Vir. Is. (U. S. A.) (St. Thomas In.)	18·24 N	64·58 W
116	Outer Hebrides (Is.)	Scot.	57·20 N	7·50 W
166	Outjo (ōt'yō)	S. W. Afr.	20·05 S	17·10 E
85	Outremont (ōō-trē-môɴ')	Can. (Montreal In.)	45·31 N	73·36 W
160	Ouyen (ōō-ĕn)	Austl.	35·05 S	142·10 E
100	Ovalle (ō-väl'yä)	Chile	30·43 S	71·16 W
166	Ovamboland (Reg.)	S. W. Afr.	18·10 S	15·00 E
95	Ovando, Bahía de (B.) (bä-ē'ä-dĕ-ô-vä'n-dō)	Cuba	20·10 N	74·05 W
124	Ovar (ô-vär')	Port.	40·52 N	8·38 W
111	Overijsche	Bel. (Bruxelles In.)	50 46 N	4·32 E
74	Overland (ō'vĕr-lănd)	Mo. (St. Louis In.)	38·42 N	90·22 W
74	Overland Park	Mo. (Kansas City In.)	38·59 N	94·40 W
84	Overlea (ō'vĕr-lā) (ō'vĕr-lē)	Md. (Baltimore In.)	39·21 N	76·31 W
112	Overtornea	Swe.	66·19 N	23·31 E
129	Ovidiopol' (ô-vê-dê-ô'pôl')	Sov. Un.	46·15 N	30·28 E
95	Oviedo (ô-vyĕ'dō)	Dom. Rep.	17·50 N	71·25 W
124	Oviedo (ô-vê-ā'dhō)	Sp.	43·22 N	5·50 W
129	Ovruch (ôv'rōōch)	Sov. Un.	51·19 N	28·51 E
153	Owada (ō'wä-dȧ)	Jap. (Tōkyō In.)	35·43 N	140·06 E
153	Owada	Jap. (Tōkyō In.)	35·49 N	139·33 E
81	Owasco (L.) (ō-wăs'kō)	N. Y.	42·50 N	76·30 W
153	Owashi (ō'wä-shê)	Jap.	34·03 N	136·12 E
81	Owego (ō-wē'gō)	N. Y.	42·05 N	76·15 W
71	Owen (ō'ĕn)	Wis.	44·56 N	90·35 W
68	Owens (L.) (ō'ĕnz)	Calif.	36·27 N	117·45 W
68	Owens (R.)	Calif.	37·13 N	118·20 W
80	Owensboro (ō'ĕnz-bŭr-ô)	Ky.	37·45 N	87·05 W
80	Owen Sound (ō'ĕn)	Can.	44·30 N	80·55 W
155	Owen Stanley Ra. (stăn'lê)	Pap. Ter.	9·00 S	147·30 E
80	Owensville (ō'ĕnz-vĭl)	Ind.	38·15 N	87·40 W
73	Owensville	Mo.	38·20 N	91·29 W
75	Owensville	Ohio (Cincinnati In.)	39·08 N	84·07 W
80	Owenton (ō'ĕn-tŭn)	Ky.	38·35 N	84·55 W
164	Owerri (ō-wĕr'ê)	Nig.	5·26 N	7·04 E
67	Owl Cr. (oul)	Wyo.	43·45 N	108·46 W
80	Owosso (ō-wŏs'ō)	Mich.	43·00 N	84·15 W
66	Owyhee Mts. (ō-wī'hê)	Idaho	43·15 N	116·48 W
66	Owyhee Res.	Ore.	43·27 N	117·30 W
66	Owyhee R.	Ore.	43·04 N	117·45 W
66	Owyhee R., South Fork	Idaho	42·07 N	116·43 W
91	Oxchuc (ôs-chōōk')	Mex.	16·47 N	92·24 W
78	Oxford (ŏks'fērd)	Ala.	33·38 N	8·46 W
82	Oxford (ŏks'fērd)	Can.	45·44 N	63·51 W
110	Oxford	Eng. (London In.)	51·43 N	1·16 W
83	Oxford	Mass. (Boston In.)	42·07 N	71·52 W

ng-sing; ŋ-baŋk; ɴ-nasalized n; nŏd; cŏmmit; ōld; ôbey; ôrder; fōōd; fŏŏt; ou-out: s-soft; sh-dish; th-thin; pūre; ûnite; ûrn; stŭd; circŭs; ü-as "y" in study; '-indeterminate vowel.

Page	Name Pronunciation Region	Lat. °'	Long. °'
80	Oxford . . . . Mich.	42·50 N	83·15 W
78	Oxford . . . . Miss.	34·22 N	89·30 W
79	Oxford . . . . N. C.	36·17 N	78·35 W
80	Oxford . . . . Ohio	39·30 N	84·45 W
92	Oxkutzcab (ôx-kōō'tz-kāb) Mex. (Yucatan In.)	20·18 N	89·22 W
84	Oxmoor (ŏks'mŏŏr) Ala. (Birmingham In.)	33·25 N	86·52 W
116	Ox Mts. (ŏks) . . . . Ire.	54·05 N	9·05 W
68	Oxnard (ŏks'närd) . . . . Calif.	34·08 N	119·12 W
91	Oxtotepec (ôx-tô-tĕ'pĕk) Mex. (Mexico In.)	19·10 N	99·04 W
168	Oxyrhyncus (Ruins) U. A. R. (Nile In.)	28·37 N	30·48 E
99	Oyapock (ō-yá-pŏk'). Braz.-Fr. Gu.	2·45 N	52·15 W
164	Oyem (ô-yĕm) (ô-yăN') . . . . Gabon	1·42 N	11·38 E
135	Oymyakon (oi-myŭ-kôn'). Sov. Un.	63·14 N	142·58 E
164	Oyo (ō'yō) . . . . Nig.	7·52 N	3·51 E
123	Oyonnax (ô-yô-näks') . . . . Fr.	46·16 N	5·40 E
84	Oyster Bay. N. Y. (New York In.)	40·52 N	73·32 W
77	Oyster Bay . . . . Tex. (In.)	29·41 N	94·33 W
77	Oyster Cr. (ois'tēr) . . . . Tex. (In.)	29·13 N	95·29 W
95	Ozama (R.) (ō-zä'mä) . Dom. Rep.	18·45 N	69·55 W
155	Ozamiz (ô-zä'mēz) . . . . Phil.	8·06 N	123·43 E
78	Ozark (ō'zärk) . . . . Ala.	31·28 N	85·28 W
73	Ozark . . . . Ark.	35·29 N	93·49 W
73	Ozarks, L. of the (ō'zärkz) . . . Mo.	38·06 N	93·26 W
73	Ozark Plat. . . . . Mo.	36·37 N	93·56 W
128	Ozëry (ô-zyô'rê) . . . . Sov. Un.	54·53 N	38·31 E
126	Ozieri . . . . Sard.	40·38 N	8·53 E
121	Ozorków (ô-zôr'kōōf) . . . . Pol.	51·58 N	19·20 E
91	Ozuluama (ō'zōō-lōō-ä'mä) . . Mex.	21·34 N	97·52 W
91	Ozumba (ô-zōō'm-bä) Mex. (Mexico In.)	19·02 N	98·48 W
146	Paan . . . . China	30·08 N	99·00 E
166	Paarl (pärl) . . . . S. Afr.	33·45 S	18·55 E
157	Paauilo (pä-ä-ōō'ē-lō) Hawaii (In.)	20·03 N	155·25 W
121	Pabianice (pä-byà-nē'tsĕ) . . . . Pol.	51·40 N	19·29 E
98	Pacaás Novos, Massiço de (Mts.) (mä-sē'sô-dĕ-pä-kà's-nô'vōs) Braz.	11·03 S	64·02 W
98	Pacaraima, Serra (Mts.) (sĕr'rá pä-kä-rä-ē'má) Braz.-Ven.	3·45 N	62·30 W
98	Pacasmayo (pä-käs-mä'yō) . . . Peru	7·24 S	79·30 W
146	Pach'u (pä'chōō') . . . . China	39·50 N	78·23 E
90	Pachuca (pä-chōō'kä) . . . . Mex.	20·07 N	98·43 W
65	Pacific (pá-sĭf'ĭk) Wash. (Seattle In.)	47·16 N	122·15 W
65	Pacifica (pá-sĭf'ĭ-kä) Calif. (San Francisco In.)	37·38 N	122·29 W
68	Pacific Beach Calif. (San Diego In.)	32·47 N	117·22 W
68	Pacific Grove . . . . Calif.	36·37 N	121·54 W
157	Pacific O.		
79	Pacolet (R.) (pă'cō-lĕt) . . . . S. C.	34·55 N	81·49 W
123	Pacy-sur-Eure (pä-sē-sür-ûr') Fr. (Paris In.)	49·01 N	1·24 E
154	Padang (pä-däng') . . . . Indon.	1·01 S	100·28 E
139	Padang, Palau (I.) Indon. (Singapore In.)	1·12 N	102·21 E
80	Paden City (pā'dĕn) . . . . W. Va.	39·30 N	80·55 W
120	Paderborn (pä-dĕr-bōrn') . . . . Ger.	51·43 N	8·46 E
110	Padiham (păd'ĭ-hăm) . . . . Eng.	53·48 N	2·19 W
90	Padilla (pä-dēl'yä) . . . . Mex.	24·00 N	98·45 W
65	Padilla B. (pä-dĕl'lä) Wash. (Seattle In.)	48·31 N	122·34 W
126	Padova (Padua) (pä'dô-vä) (păd'ū-á) . It.	45·24 N	11·53 E
77	Padre I. (pä'drā) . . . . Tex.	27·09 N	97·15 W
	Padua, see Padova		
78	Paducah (pá-dū'ká) . . . . Ky.	37·05 N	88·36 W
152	Paektu San (Mt.) (pâk'tōō-sän') China-Kor.	42·00 N	128·03 E
126	Pag (I.) (päg) . . . . Yugo.	44·30 N	14·48 E
154	Pagai Selatan (I.) . . . . Indon.	2·48 S	100·22 E
154	Pagai Utara (I.) . . . . Indon.	2·45 S	100·02 E
127	Pagasitikós Kólpos (G.) . . . . Grc.	39·15 N	23·00 E
69	Pagosa Springs (pá-gō'sá) . . . Colo.	37·15 N	107·05 W
157	Pahala (pä-hä'lä) . . . . Hawaii (In.)	19·11 N	155·28 W
139	Pahang (State) Mala. (Singapore In.)	3·02 N	102·57 E
154	Pahang R. . . . . Mala.	3·39 N	102·41 E
79	Pahokee (pá-hō'kē) . . . . Fla. (In.)	26·45 N	80·40 W
148	Paichü (bäī'gü) . . . . China	33·04 N	120·17 E
150	Paich'uan . . . . China	47·22 N	126·00 E
119	Paide (pī'dĕ) . . . . Sov. Un.	58·54 N	25·30 E
150	Paiho . . . . China	32·30 N	110·15 E
148	Pai Hu (L.) (bäī' hōō) . . . . China	31·22 N	117·38 E
119	Päijänna (L.) (pĕ'ē-yĕn-nĕ) . . . Fin.	61·38 N	25·05 E
148	Paikouchen (bäī'gō'jen) . . . . China	39·08 N	116·02 E
150	Pailingmiao . . . . China	41·42 N	110·55 E
157	Pailolo Chan. (pä-ē-lō'lō) Hawaii (In.)	21·05 N	156·41 W
101	Paine (pī'nĕ). Chile (Santiago In.)	33·49 S	70·44 W
80	Painesville (pānz'vĭl) . . . . Ohio	41·40 N	81·15 W
69	Painted Des. (pānt'ĕd) . . . . Ariz.	36·15 N	111·35 W
80	Paintsville (pānts'vĭl) . . . . Ky.	37·50 N	82·50 W
148	Paip'u (bäī'pōō) . . . . China	32·15 N	120·47 E
151	Paise . . . . China	24·00 N	106·38 E
116	Paisley (pāz'lĭ) . . . . Scot.	55·50 N	4·30 W
98	Paita (pä-ē'tä) . . . . Peru	5·11 S	81·12 W
150	Pai T'ou Shan (Mts.) . . . . Korea	40·30 N	127·20 E
69	Paiute Ind. Res. . . . . Utah	38·17 N	113·50 W
150	Paiyü Shan (Mtns.) . . . . China	37·02 N	108·30 E
91	Pajápan (pä-hä'pän) . . . . Mex.	18·16 N	94·41 W
154	Pakanburu . . . . Indon.	0·43 N	101·15 E
154	Pakhoi (päk'hoi') . . . . China	21·58 N	108·51 E
136	Pakhra R. (päK'rá) Sov. Un. (Moskva In.)	55·29 N	37·51 E
138	Pakistan . . . . Asia	28·00 N	67·30 E
142	Pakistan, East . . . . Asia	24·15 N	89·50 E
142	Pakistan, West . . . . Asia	32·20 N	71·30 E
154	Pakokku (pä-kŏk'kōō) . . . . Bur.	21·29 N	95·00 E
126	Pakrac (pä'kräts) . . . . Yugo.	45·25 N	17·13 E
121	Paks (pôksh) . . . . Hung.	46·38 N	18·53 E
77	Palacios (pá-lä'syōs) . . . . Tex.	28·42 N	96·12 W
125	Palafrogell (pä-lä-frô-gĕl) . . . . Sp.	41·55 N	3·09 E
126	Palagruža (Is.) (pä'lä-grōō'zhä) Yugo.	42·20 N	16·23 E
123	Palaiseau (pá-lĕ-zō') Fr. (Paris In.)	48·44 N	2·16 E
135	Palana . . . . Sov. Un.	59·07 N	159·58 E
155	Palanan B. (pä-lä'nän) Phil. (Manila In.)	17·14 N	122·35 E
155	Palanan Pt. . . . Phil. (Manila In.)	17·12 N	122·40 E
127	Palanka (pä'län-kä) . . . . Yugo.	45·14 N	19·24 E
142	Pālanpur (pä'lŭn-pōōr) . . . . India	24·08 N	73·29 E
166	Palapye (pá-lăp'yĕ) . . . . Bech.	22·34 S	27·28 E
75	Palatine (păl'á-tīn) Ill. (Chicago In.)	42·07 N	88·03 W
79	Palatka (pá-lăt'ká) . . . . Fla.	29·39 N	81·40 W
155	Palau (Pelew) Is. (pä-lä'ōō) Pac. Is. Trust. Ter.	7·15 N	134·30 E
155	Palauig (pá-lou'ēg) Phil. (Manila In.)	15·27 N	119·54 E
155	Palauig Pt. . . . . Phil. (Manila In.)	15·28 N	119·41 E
154	Palawan (I.) (pä-lä'wán) . . . . Phil.	9·50 N	117·38 E
119	Paldiski (päl'dĭ-skĭ) . . . . Sov. Un.	59·22 N	24·04 E
154	Palembang (pä-lĕm-bäng') . Indon.	2·57 S	104·40 E
92	Palencia (pä-lĕn'sē-ä) . . . . Guat.	14·40 N	90·22 W
124	Palencia (pä-lĕ'n-syä) . . . . Sp.	42·02 N	4·32 W
91	Palenque (pä-lĕŋ'kä) . . . . Mex.	17·34 N	91·58 W
95	Palenque, Punta (Pt.) (pōō'n-tä) Dom. Rep.	18·10 N	70·10 W
85	Palermo (pä-lĕr'mô) Can. (Toronto In.)	43·26 N	79·47 W
98	Palermo . . . . Col. (In.)	2·53 N	75·26 W
126	Palermo . . . . It.	38·08 N	13·24 E
77	Palestine . . . . Tex.	31·46 N	95·38 W
139	Palestine (Reg.) (păl'ĕs-tīn) Asia (Palestine In.)	31·33 N	35·00 E
146	Paletwa (pŭ-lĕt'wä) . . . . Bur.	21·19 N	92·52 E
143	Palghāt . . . . India	10·49 N	76·40 E
142	Pali . . . . India	25·53 N	73·18 E
92	Palín (pä-lēn') . . . . Guat.	14·42 N	90·42 W
66	Palisade (păl-ĭ-sād') . . . . Nev.	40·39 N	116·11 W
91	Palizada (pä-lē-zä'dä) . . . . Mex.	18·17 N	92·04 W
142	Palk Str. (pôk) . . . . India	10·00 N	79·23 E
101	Palma. . Braz. (Rio de Janeiro In.)	21·23 S	42·18 W
167	Palma (päl'mä) . . . . Moz.	10·46 S	40·38 E
125	Palma, Ba. de (B.) (bä-ē'ä-dĕ). Sp.	39·24 N	2·37 E
124	Palma del Río (dĕl rē'ō) . . . . Sp.	37·43 N	5·19 W
125	Palma de Mallorca (dĕ-mäl-yô'r-kä) . Sp.	39·35 N	2·38 E
99	Palmares (päl-mà'rĕs) . . . . Braz.	8·46 S	35·28 W
100	Palmas (päl'mäs) . . . . Braz.	26·20 S	51·56 W
164	Palmas, C. . . . . Lib.	4·30 N	9·20 W
95	Palma Soriano (sô-ré-ä'nō) . . Cuba	20·15 N	76·00 W
79	Palm Beach (päm bēch') . Fla. (In.)	26·43 N	80·03 W
99	Palmeira dos Índios (päl-mā'rä-dôs-ē'n-dyôs) . Braz.	9·26 S	36·33 W
125	Palmela (päl-mā'lä) Port. (Lisboa In.)	38·34 N	8·54 W
64	Palmer (päm'ēr) . . . . Alaska	61·38 N	149·15 W
65	Palmer . . . . Wash. (Seattle In.)	47·19 N	121·53 W
47	Palmer Pen. . . . . Ant.	70·00 S	65·00 W
159	Palmerston North (päm'ēr-stŭn) N. Z. (In.)	40·21 S	175·43 E
159	Palmerville (päm'ēr-vĭl) . . . Austl.	16·08 S	144·15 E
79	Palmetto (păl-mĕt'ō) . . . . Fla. (In.)	27·32 N	82·34 W
95	Palmetto Pt. . . . . Ba. Is.	21·15 N	73·25 W
126	Palmi (päl'mē) . . . . It.	38·21 N	15·54 E
98	Palmira (päl-mē'rä) . . . . Col. (In.)	3·33 N	76·17 W
94	Palmira . . . . Cuba	22·15 N	80·25 W
73	Palmyra (păl-mī'rá) . . . . Mo.	39·45 N	91·32 W
84	Palmyra. . N. J. (Philadelphia In.)	40·01 N	75·00 W
157	Palmyra (I.) . . . . Oceania	6·00 N	162·20 W
142	Palmyras Pt. . . . . India	25·42 N	87·45 E
103	Palmyre . . . . Syr.	30·35 N	37·58 E
65	Palo Alto (pä'lō ăl'tō) Calif. (San Francisco In.)	37·27 N	122·09 W
72	Paloduro Cr. (pä-lô-dōō'rô) . . Tex.	36·16 N	101·12 W
139	Paloh . . . . Mala. (Singapore In.)	2·11 N	103·12 E
76	Paloma, L. (pä-lō'mä) . . . . Mex.	26·53 N	104·02 W
101	Palomo, Cerro el (Mtn.) (sĕ'r-rō-ĕl-pä-lô'mō) Chile (Santiago In.)	34·36 S	70·20 W
125	Palos, Cabo de (C.) (kà'bō-dĕ-pä'lôs) . Sp.	39·38 N	0·43 W
74	Palos Verdes Estates (pă'lŭs vûr'dĭs) Calif. (Los Angeles In.)	33·48 N	118·24 W
66	Palouse (pá-lōōz') . . . . Wash.	46·54 N	117·04 W
66	Palouse Hills . . . . Wash.	46·48 N	117·47 W
66	Palouse R. . . . . Wash.	47·02 N	117·35 W
133	Palu (pä-lōō') . . . . Tur.	38·55 N	40·10 E
155	Paluan (pä-lōō'än) Phila. (Manila In.)	13·25 N	120·29 E
135	Pamamushir (I.) . . . . Sov. Un.	50·42 N	153·45 E
122	Pamiers (pà-myā') . . . . Fr.	43·07 N	1·34 E
145	Pamirs (Plat.) . . . . Sov. Un.	38·14 N	72·27 E
79	Pamlico R. (păm'lĭ-kō) . . . . N. C.	35·25 N	76·59 W
79	Pamlico Sd. . . . . N. C.	35·10 N	76·10 W
72	Pampa (păm'pá) . . . . Tex.	35·32 N	100·56 W
100	Pampa de Castillo (Plat.) (pä'm-pä-dĕ-käs-tē'l-yô) . Arg.	45·30 S	67·30 W
155	Pampanga (R.) (päm-päŋ'gä) Phil. (Manila In.)	15·20 N	120·48 E
100	Pampas (Reg.) (päm'päs) . . . Arg.	37·00 S	64·30 W
124	Pampilhosa do Botão (päm-pê-lyō'sá-dô-bō-to'uN) Port.	40·21 N	8·23 W
98	Pamplona (päm-plō'nä) . . . . Col.	7·19 N	72·41 W
124	Pamplona (päm-plô'nä) . . . . Sp.	42·49 N	1·39 W
81	Pamunkey (R.) (pá-mŭŋ'kĭ) . . . Va.	37·40 N	77·20 W
80	Pana (pā'ná) . . . . Ill.	39·25 N	89·05 W
92	Panabá (pä-nä-bà') Mex. (Yucatan In.)	21·18 N	88·15 W
127	Panagyurište (pá-ná-gyōō'rēsh-tĕ) Bul.	42·30 N	24·11 E
88	Panamá (păn-á-mä') N. A. (Panama Canal In.)	8·27 N	79·03 W
89	Panama, G. of . . . . Pan.	7·45 N	79·20 W
89	Panama, Isth. of . . . . Pan.	9·00 N	81·00 W
93	Panama, B. of . . . . Pan.	8·50 N	79·08 W
78	Panama City (păn-á mä' sĭ'tĭ) . Fla.	30·08 N	85·39 W
68	Panamint Ra. (păn-à-mĭnt') Calif.	36·40 N	117·30 W
126	Panaria (Is.) (pä-nä'rê-á) . . . . It.	38·37 N	15·05 E
126	Panaro (R.) (pä-nä'rô) . . . . It.	44·47 N	11·06 E
154	Panay (I.) (pä-nī') . . . . Phil.	11·15 N	121·38 E
127	Pančevo (pàn'chĕ-vô) . . . . Yugo.	44·52 N	20·42 E
139	Panchor . . . Mala. (Singapore In.)	2·10 N	102·43 E
166	Panda (pän'dä') . . . . Con. L.	10·59 S	27·24 E
94	Pan de Guajaibon (Mtn.) (pän dā gwä-jä-bōn') . Cuba	22·50 N	83·20 W
154	Pandjang, Selat (Str.) . . . . Indon.	1·00 N	102·00 E
119	Panevėžys (pä'nyĕ-väzh'ēs) Sov. Un.	55·44 N	24·21 E
134	Panfilov (pŭn-fē'lôf) . . . . Sov. Un.	44·12 N	79·58 E
165	Panga (päŋ'gä) . . . . Con. L.	1·58 N	26·45 E
167	Pangani (pän-gä'nē) . . . . Tan.	5·28 S	38·58 E
149	P'angchiang . . China (Canton In.)	22·57 N	113·15 E
148	Pangfou (bäng'fōō) . . . . China	32·54 N	117·22 E
154	Pangkalpinang (päng-käl'pê-näng') Indon.	2·11 S	106·04 E
142	Pangkong Tsho (L.) . . . . China	33·40 N	79·30 E
87	Pangnirtung . . . . Can.	66·08 N	65·26 W
69	Panguitch (päŋ'gwĭch) . . . . Utah	37·50 N	112·30 W
101	Panimávida (pä-nē-mà'vē-dä) Chile (Santiago In.)	36·44 S	71·26 W
143	Panjim . . . . Gôa	15·33 N	73·52 E
150	Panshih . . . . China	42·50 N	126·48 E
151	Pan Si Pan (Mtn.) . . . . Viet.	22·25 N	103·50 E
155	Pantar (I.) (pän'tär) . . . . Indon.	8·40 S	123·45 E
74	Pantego (păn'tĭ-gō) Tex. (Dallas, Fort Worth In.)	32·45 N	97·06 W
113	Pantelleria (I.) (pän-tĕl-lå-rē'ä) It.	36·43 N	11·59 E
91	Pantepec (pän-tå-pĕk') . . . . Mex.	17·11 N	93·04 W
90	Panuco (pä'nōō-kô) . . . . Mex.	22·04 N	98·11 W
90	Pánuco (pä'nōō-kô) . . . . Mex.	29·47 N	105·55 W
90	Panuco (R.) . . . . Mex.	21·59 N	98·20 W
76	Pánuco de Coronado (pä'nōō-kô dā kō-rô-nä'dhō) Mex.	24·33 N	104·20 W
143	Panvel . . . . India (Bombay In.)	18·59 N	73·06 E
92	Panzós (pän-zós') . . . . Guat.	15·26 N	89·40 W
99	Pao (pà'ō) (R.) . . . . Ven. (In.)	9·52 N	67·57 W
150	Paochang . . . . China	41·52 N	115·25 E
150	Paocheng . . . . China	33·15 N	106·58 E
150	Paochi . . . . China	34·10 N	106·58 E
73	Paola (pā-ō'lá) . . . . Kans.	38·34 N	94·51 W
80	Paoli (pā-ō'lī) . . . . Ind.	38·35 N	86·30 W
84	Paoli . . . . Pa. (Philadelphia In.)	40·03 N	75·29 W
69	Paonia (pā-ō'nyá) . . . . Colo.	38·50 N	107·40 W
146	Paoshan (pä'ō-shän') . . . . China	25·14 N	99·03 E
149	Paoshan . . . . China (Shanghai In.)	31·25 N	121·29 E
148	Paoti (pä'ō-tē') . . . . China	39·44 N	117·19 E
150	Paot'ou . . . . China	40·28 N	110·10 E
148	Paoying (pä'ô-yĭng) . . . . China	33·14 N	119·20 E
121	Pápa (pä'pô) . . . . Hung.	47·18 N	17·27 E
92	Papagayo, Golfo del (G.) (gôl-fô-dĕl-pä-pä-gá'yō) . C. R.	10·44 N	85·56 W
90	Papagayo, Laguna (L.) (lä-ōō-nä) . . . Mex.	16·44 N	99·44 W
90	Papagayo (R.) (pä-pä-gä'yō) Mex.	16·52 N	99·41 W
69	Papago Ind. Res. (pä'pä-gō) . Ariz.	32·33 N	112·12 W
88	Papantla de Olarte (pä-pän'tlä dā-ô-lä'r-tĕ) . Mex.	20·30 N	97·15 W
91	Papatoapan (R.) (pä-pä-tô-ä-pä'n) . Mex.	18·00 N	96·22 W
120	Papenburg (päp'ĕn-bŏŏrgh) . Ger.	53·05 N	7·23 E
101	Papinas (pä-pē'näs) Arg. (Buenos Aires In.)	35·30 S	57·19 W
85	Papineauville (pä-pē-nō'vēl) Can. (Ottawa In.)	45·38 N	75·01 W
155	Papua, Territory of (păp'ōō-á) Austl.	7·30 S	142·30 E
155	Papua, Gulf of (păp-ōō-á) Pap. Ter.	8·20 S	144·45 E
101	Papudo (pä-pōō'dô) Chile (Santiago In.)	32·30 S	71·25 W
100	Paquequer Pequeno (pä-kĕ-kĕ'r-pĕ-kĕ'nô) . Braz. (In.)	22·19 S	43·02 W
	Pará, see Belém		
99	Pará (State) (pä-rä') . . . . Braz.	4·45 S	53·30 W
101	Pará (pä-rä') (R.) Braz. (Rio de Janeiro In.)	20·21 S	44·38 W
99	Pará, Rio do (R.) (rē'ō-dô-pä-rä') Braz.	1·09 S	48·48 W
128	Para (R.) . . . . Sov. Un.	53·45 N	40·58 E
155	Paracale (pä-rä-kä'lä) Phil. (Manila In.)	14·17 N	122·47 E
100	Paracambi (pä-rä-kà'm-bē) Braz. (In.)	22·36 S	43·43 W
99	Paracatu (pä-rä-kä-tōō') . . . . Braz.	17·17 S	46·43 W
160	Parachilna (pä-rá-chĭl'nä) . . Austl.	31·09 S	138·20 E
127	Paraćin (pá'rä-chĕn) . . . . Yugo.	43·51 N	21·26 E
101	Para de Minas (pä-rä-dĕ-mē'näs) Braz. (Rio de Janeiro In.)	19·52 S	44·37 W
66	Paradise Valley (păr'á-dīs) . . . Nev.	41·28 N	117·32 W
98	Parados, Cerro de los (Mtn.) (sĕ'r-rō-dĕ-lôs-pä-rä'dōs) Col. (In.)	5·44 N	75·13 W
73	Paragould (păr'á-gōōld) . . . . Ark.	36·03 N	90·29 W
99	Paraguaçu (R.) (pä-rä-gwä-zōō') Braz.	12·25 S	39·46 W
98	Paraguaná, Pen. de (Pen.) (pĕ-nē'ng-sōō-lä-dĕ-pä-rä-gwä-nä') . Ven.	12·00 N	69·55 W
96	Paraguay (păr'á-gwā) . . . . S. A.	24·00 S	57·00 W
99	Paraguay, Rio (R.) (rē'ō-pä-rä-gwä'y) . S. A.	21·12 S	57·31 W
	Paraíba, see João Pessoa		
99	Paraíba (State) (pä-rä-ē'bä) . Braz.	7·11 S	37·05 W

ăt; finăl; rāte; senāte; ärm; åsk; sofá; fâre; ch-choose; dh-as th in other; bē; ēvent; bĕt; recĕnt; cratēr; g-go; gh-guttural g; bĭt; ĭ-short neutral; rīde; K-guttural k as ch in German ich;

PRONOUNCING INDEX Paraiba–Pegnitz 249

Page	Name Pronunciation Region	Lat. °′	Long. °′
101	Paraiba (R.) Braz. (Rio de Janeiro In.)	23·02 S	45·43 W
101	Paraíba do Sul (dô-sōō'l) Braz. (Rio de Janeiro In.)	22·10 S	43·18 W
101	Paraibuna (pä-rä-ē-bōō'nä) Braz. (Rio de Janeiro In.)	23·23 S	45·38 W
88	Paraiso (pä-rä-ē'sō) C. Z. (Panama Canal In.)	9·02 N	79·38 W
93	Paraíso C. R.	9·50 N	83·53 W
91	Paraíso Mex.	18·24 N	93·11 W
101	Paraisópolis (pä-rä-ē-sô'pō-lēs) Braz. (Rio de Janeiro In.)	22·35 S	45·45 W
101	Paraitinga (pä-rä-ē-tē'n-gä) (R.) Braz. (Rio de Janeiro In.)	23·15 S	45·24 W
164	Parakou (pȧ-rȧ-kōō') Dahomey	9·16 N	2·37 E
99	Paramaribo (pȧ-rȧ-mä'rē-bō) Sur.	5·50 N	55·15 W
161	Paramatta (păr-ȧ-măt'ȧ) Austl. (Sydney In.)	33·49 S	150·59 E
122	Paramé (pȧ-rȧ-mā') Fr.	48·40 N	1·58 W
98	Paramillo (Mtn.) (pä-rä-mē'l-yō) Col. (In.)	7·06 N	75·55 W
135	Paramushir (I.) Sov. Un.	50·45 N	154·00 E
139	Paran (R.) Isr. (Palestine In.)	30·05 N	34·50 E
100	Paraná (pä-rä-nä') Arg.	31·44 S	60·29 W
100	Paraná (State) Braz.	24·25 S	52·00 W
100	Paraná, Rio (R.) Arg.	32·15 S	60·55 W
99	Paraná (R.) Braz.	13·05 S	47·11 W
100	Paranaguá (pä-rä'nä-gwä') Braz.	25·39 S	48·42 W
99	Paranaíba (pä-rä-nȧ-ē'bȧ) Braz.	19·43 S	51·13 W
99	Paranaíba (R.) Braz.	18·58 S	50·44 W
101	Parana Ibicuy (R.) (ē-bē-kōō'ē) Arg. (Buenos Aires In.)	33·27 S	59·26 W
99	Paranam Sur.	5·39 N	55·13 W
100	Paránápanema (R.) (pä-rä'nä'pä-nĕ-mä) Braz.	22·28 S	52·15 W
101	Paraopeda (R.) (pä-rä-o-pĕ'dä) Braz. (Rio de Janeiro In.)	20·09 S	44·14 W
99	Parapara (pä-rä-pä-rä) Ven. (In.)	9·44 N	67·17 W
101	Parati (pä-rätē) Braz. (Rio de Janeiro In.)	23·14 S	44·43 W
122	Paray-le-Monial (pȧ-rĕ'lē-mô-nyäl') Fr.	46·27 N	4·14 E
142	Pārbati (R.) India	24·50 N	76·44 E
	Parcel Is., see Hsisha Ch'üntao		
120	Parchin (pär'кēn) Ger.	53·25 N	11·52 E
121	Parczew (pär'chĕf) Pol.	51·38 N	22·53 E
99	Pardo (R.) (pär'dō) Braz.	15·25 S	39·40 W
101	Pardo (R.) Braz. (Rio de Janeiro In.)	21·32 S	46·40 W
120	Pardubice (pär'dōō-bit-sĕ) Czech.	50·02 N	15·47 E
99	Parecis, Serra dos (Mts.) (sĕr'rȧ dōs pä-rȧ-sēzh') Braz.	13·45 S	59·28 W
124	Paredes de Nava (pä-rā'dås dä nä'vä) Sp.	42·10 N	4·41 W
87	Parent Can.	47·56 N	74·30 W
136	Pargolovo (pár-gô'lô vô) Sov. Un. (Leningrad In.)	60·04 N	30·18 E
98	Paria, Golfo de (G.) (gôl-fô-dĕ-pä'rē-ä) Ven.	10·33 N	62·14 W
69	Paria (R.) Utah-Ariz.	37·07 N	111·51 W
90	Paricutín, Vol. (pä-rē-kōō-tē'n) Mex.	19·27 N	102·14 W
76	Parida, Rio de la (R.) (rē'ō-dĕ-lä-pä-rē'dä) Mex.	26·23 N	104·40 W
98	Parima, Serra (Mts.) (sĕr'rȧ pä-rē'mȧ) Braz.-Ven.	3·45 N	64·00 W
98	Pariñas, Punta (Pt.) (pōō'n-tä-pä-rē'n-yäs) Peru	4·30 S	81·23 W
99	Parintins (pä-rĭn-tĭnzh') Braz.	2·34 S	56·30 W
74	Paris (păr'ĭs) Ark.	35·17 N	93·43 W
80	Paris Can.	43·15 N	82·20 W
123	Paris (pȧ-rē') Fr. (Paris In.)	48·51 N	2·20 E
80	Paris Ill.	39·35 N	87·40 W
80	Paris Ky.	38·15 N	84·15 W
73	Paris Mo.	39·27 N	91·59 W
78	Paris Tenn.	36·16 N	88·20 W
73	Paris Tex.	33·39 N	95·33 W
93	Parita, Golfo de (G.) (gôl-fô-dĕ-pä-rē'tä) Pan.	8·06 N	80·10 W
67	Park City Utah	40·39 N	111·33 W
70	Parker (pär'kēr) S. D.	43·24 N	97·10 W
69	Parker Dam Calif.-Ariz.	34·20 N	114·00 W
80	Parkersburg (pär'kērz-bûrg) W. Va.	39·15 N	81·35 W
160	Parkes (pärks) Austl.	33·10 S	148·10 E
71	Park Falls (pärk) Wis.	45·55 N	90·29 W
75	Park Forest Ill. (Chicago In.)	41·29 N	87·41 W
65	Parkland (pärk'lǎnd) Wash. (Seattle In.)	47·09 N	122·26 W
67	Park Ra. Colo.	40·54 N	106·40 W
71	Park Rapids Minn.	46·53 N	95·05 W
75	Park Ridge Ill. (Chicago In.)	42·00 N	87·50 W
70	Park River N. D.	48·22 N	97·43 W
65	Parkrose (pärk'rōz) Ore. (Portland In.)	45·33 N	122·33 W
167	Park Rynie S. Afr. (Natal In.)	30·22 S	30·43 E
70	Parkston (pärks'tŭn) S. D.	43·22 N	97·59 W
69	Park View (vū) N. Mex.	36·45 N	106·30 W
84	Parkville (pärk'vĭl) Md. (Baltimore In.)	39·23 N	76·33 W
74	Parkville Mo. (Kansas City In.)	39·12 N	94·41 W
125	Parla (pär'lä) Sp. (Madrid In.)	40·14 N	3·46 W
126	Parma (pär'mä) It.	44·48 N	10·20 E
75	Parma Ohio (Cleveland In.)	41·23 N	81·44 W
75	Parma Heights Ohio (Cleveland In.)	41·23 N	81·36 W
99	Parnaguá (pär-nä-gwä') Braz.	9·52 S	44·27 W
99	Parnaíba (pär-nä-ē'bä) Braz.	3·00 S	41·42 W
99	Parnaíba (R.) Braz.	3·57 S	42·30 W
127	Parnassós (Mtn.) Grc.	38·33 N	22·35 E
111	Parndorf Aus. (Wien In.)	48·00 N	16·52 E
119	Pärnu (pĕr'nōō) Sov. Un.	58·24 N	24·29 E
119	Pärnu (R.) Sov. Un.	58·40 N	25·05 E
119	Pärnu Laht (B.) (läкt) Sov. Un.	58·15 N	24·17 E
160	Paroo (R.) (pä'rōō) Austl.	29·40 S	144·24 E
144	Paropamisus (Mts.) Afg.	34·45 N	63·58 E
127	Páros (pä'rôs) (pā'rŏs) Grc.	37·05 N	25·14 E
127	Páros (I.) Grc.	37·11 N	25·00 E
166	Parow (pă'rô) S. Afr. (Cape Town In.)	33·54 S	18·36 E
69	Parowan (păr'ô-wăn) Utah	37·50 N	112·50 W
100	Parral (pär-rä'l) Chile	36·07 S	71·47 W
76	Parral, R. Mex.	27·25 N	105·08 W
161	Parramatta (R.) (păr-ȧ-măt'ȧ) Austl. (Sydney In.)	33·42 S	150·58 E
76	Parras (pär-räs') Mex.	25·28 N	102·08 W
93	Parrita (pär-rē'tä) C. R.	9·32 N	84·17 W
82	Parrsboro (pärz'bŭr-ô) Can.	45·25 N	64·20 W
80	Parry (I.) Can.	45·15 N	80·00 W
64	Parry, C. (păr'ĭ) Can.	70·20 N	124·31 W
49	Parry Is. Can.	75·30 N	110·00 W
81	Parry Sound Can.	45·20 N	80·00 W
73	Parsons (pär's'nz) Kans.	37·20 N	95·16 W
81	Parsons W. Va.	39·05 N	79·40 W
122	Parthenay (pȧr-t'nĕ') Fr.	46·39 N	0·16 W
126	Partinico (pär-tē'nē-kô) It.	38·02 N	13·11 E
168	Parys (pȧ-rīs') S. Afr. (Johannesburg & Pretoria In.)	26·53 S	27·28 E
74	Pasadena (păs-ȧ-dē'nȧ) Calif. (Los Angeles In.)	34·09 N	118·09 W
84	Pasadena Md. (Baltimore In.)	39·06 N	76·35 W
77	Pasadena Tex. (In.)	29·43 N	95·13 W
78	Pascagoula (păs-kȧ-gōō'lȧ) Miss.	30·22 N	88·33 W
78	Pascagoula (R.) Miss.	30·52 N	88·48 W
121	Pascani (päsh-kän'') Rom.	47·46 N	26·42 E
66	Pasco (păs'kō) Wash.	46·13 N	119·04 W
120	Pasewalk (pä'zē-välk) Ger.	53·31 N	14·01 E
136	Pashiya (pä'shĭ-yȧ) Sov. Un. (Urals In.)	58·27 N	58·17 E
152	Pashkovo (pȧsh-kô'vô) Sov. Un.	48·52 N	131·09 E
129	Pashkovskaya (pȧsh-kôf'skȧ-yȧ) Sov. Un.	45·29 N	39·04 E
92	Pasión, Rio de la (R.) (rē'ō-dĕ-lä-pä-syōn') Guat. (Yucatan In.)	16·31 N	90·11 W
100	Paso de los Libres (pä-sō-dĕ-lôs-lē'brĕs) Arg.	29·33 S	57·05 W
101	Paso de los Toros (tŏ'rôs) Ur. (Buenos Aires In.)	32·43 S	56·33 W
68	Paso Robles (pă'sō rō'blĕs) Calif.	35·38 N	120·44 W
84	Passaic (pă-sā'ĭk) N. J. (New York In.)	40·52 N	74·08 W
84	Passaic R. N. J. (New York In.)	40·42 N	74·26 W
82	Passamaquoddy B. (păs'ȧ-mȧ-kwŏd'ĭ) Can.	45·00 N	66·45 W
101	Passa Tempo (pä's-sä-tĕ'm-pô) Braz. (Rio de Janeiro In.)	21·40 S	44·29 W
120	Passau (pä'sou) Ger.	48·34 N	13·27 E
78	Pass Christian (pås krĭs'tyĕn) Miss.	30·20 N	89·15 W
113	Passero, C. (päs-sĕ'rô) It.	36·34 N	15·13 E
100	Passo Fundo (pä'sŏ fōō'n'dōō) Braz.	28·16 S	52·13 W
101	Passos (pä's-sōs) Braz. (Rio de Janeiro In.)	20·45 S	46·37 W
98	Pastaza (R.) (päs-tä'zä) Peru	3·05 S	76·18 W
98	Pasto (päs'tō) Col.	1·15 N	77·19 W
90	Pastora (päs-tô-rä) Mex.	22·08 N	100·04 W
154	Pasuruan Indon.	7·45 S	112·50 E
119	Pasvalys (päs-vä-lēs') Sov. Un.	56·04 N	24·23 E
100	Patagonia (Reg.) (păt-ȧ-gō'nĭ-ȧ) Arg.	46·45 S	69·30 W
143	Pātālganga (R.) India (Bombay In.)	18·52 N	73·08 E
142	Patan (pä'tŭn) Nep.	27·23 N	85·24 E
84	Patapsco R. (pȧ-tăps'kō) Md. (Baltimore In.)	39·12 N	76·30 W
126	Paternò (pä-tĕr-nô') It.	37·35 N	14·58 E
84	Paterson (păt'ēr-sŭn) N. J. (New York In.)	40·55 N	74·10 W
67	Pathfinder Res. (păth'fīn-dēr) Wyo.	42·22 N	107·10 W
142	Patiāla (pŭt-ē-ä'lŭ) India	30·25 N	76·28 E
100	Pati do Alferes (pä-tē-dô-äl-fĕ'rĕs) Braz. (In.)	22·25 S	43·25 W
142	Patna (pŭt'nŭ) India	25·33 N	85·18 E
155	Patnanongan (pät-nä-nôŋ'gän) Phil. (Manila In.)	14·50 N	122·25 E
80	Patoka (R.) (pȧ-tō'kȧ) Ind.	38·25 N	87·25 W
135	Patom Plat. Sov. Un.	59·30 N	115·00 E
99	Patos (pä'tōzh) Braz.	7·03 S	37·14 W
65	Patos (pă'tōs) Wash. (Vancouver In.)	48·47 N	122·57 W
100	Patos, Lago dos (L.) (lä'gō-ȧ dozh pä'tōzh) Braz.	31·15 S	51·30 W
99	Patos de Minas (dĕ-mē'näzh) Braz.	18·39 S	46·31 W
127	Pátrai (Patras) (pä-trī') (pä-träs') Grc.	38·15 N	21·48 E
127	Patraïkós Kólpos (G.) Grc.	38·16 N	21·19 E
	Patras, see Pátrai		
99	Patrocínio (pä-trō-sē'nē-ōō) Braz.	18·48 S	46·47 W
154	Pāttani (păt'ȧ-nê) Thai.	6·56 N	101·13 E
82	Patten (păt''n) Maine	45·59 N	68·27 W
77	Patterson (păt'ēr-sŭn) La.	29·41 N	91·20 W
81	Patton Pa.	40·40 N	78·45 W
93	Patuca, Punta (Pt.) (pōō'n-tä-pä-tōō'kä) Hond.	15·23 N	84·05 W
93	Patuca R. Hond.	15·22 N	84·31 W
81	Patuxent (R.) (pȧ-tŭk'sĕnt) Md.	39·10 N	77·10 W
90	Pátzcuaro (päts'kwä-rô) Mex.	19·30 N	101·36 W
90	Pátzcuaro, Lago de (L.) (lä'gô-dĕ) Mex.	19·36 N	101·38 W
92	Patzicia (pät-zē'syä) Guat.	14·36 N	90·57 W
92	Patzún (pät-zōōn') Guat.	14·40 N	91·00 W
122	Pau (pō) Fr.	43·18 N	0·23 W
122	Pau, Gave de (strm.) (gäv-dĕ) Fr.	43·33 N	0·51 W
122	Pauillac (pō-yäk') Fr.	45·12 N	0·46 W
80	Paulding (pôl'dĭng) Ohio	41·05 N	84·35 W
111	Paulinenaue (pou'lē-nĕ-nou-ĕ) Ger. (Berlin In.)	52·40 N	12·43 E
99	Paulistana (pȧ'ōō-lēs-tȧ-nä) Braz.	8·13 S	41·06 W
99	Paulo Afonso, Salto (falls) (säl-tô-pou'lōō äf-fôɴ'sōō) Braz.	9·33 S	38·32 W
168	Paul Roux (pôrl rōō) S. Afr. (Johannesburg & Pretoria In.)	28·18 S	27·57 E
84	Paulsboro (pôlz'bē-rô) N. J. (Philadelphia In.)	39·50 N	75·16 W
73	Pauls Valley (pôlz văl'ē) Okla.	34·43 N	97·13 W
157	Pauwela (pä-ōō-wā'lä) Hawaii (In.)	20·58 N	156·19 W
98	Pavarandocito (pä-vä-rän-dô-sē'tô) Col. (In.)	7·18 N	76·32 W
136	Pavda (päv'dá) Sov. Un. (Urals In.)	59·16 N	59·32 E
126	Pavia (pä-vē'ä) It.	45·12 N	9·11 E
134	Pavlodar (páv-lô-där') Sov. Un.	52·17 N	77·23 E
64	Pavlo'f B. (păv-lôf) Alaska	55·20 N	161·20 W
129	Pavlograd (pȧv-lô-grȧt') Sov. Un.	48·32 N	35·52 E
129	Pavlovsk (pȧv-lôfsk') Sov. Un.	50·28 N	40·05 E
136	Pavlovsk Sov. Un. (Leningrad In.)	59·41 N	30·27 E
136	Pavlovskiy Posad (pȧv-lôf'skĭ pô-sȧt') Sov. Un. (Moskva In.)	55·47 N	38·39 E
100	Pavuna (pä-vōō'nȧ) Braz. (In.)	22·48 S	43·21 W
111	Päwesin (pă'vĕ-zēn) Ger. (Berlin In.)	52·31 N	12·44 E
73	Pawhuska (pô-hŭs'kȧ) Okla.	36·41 N	96·20 W
73	Pawnee (pô-nē') Okla.	36·20 N	96·47 W
72	Pawnee (R.) Kans.	38·18 N	99·42 W
73	Pawnee City Nebr.	40·08 N	96·09 W
80	Paw Paw (pô'pô) Mich.	42·15 N	85·55 W
71	Paw Paw (R.) Mich.	42·14 N	86·21 W
84	Pawtucket (pô-tŭk'ĕt) R. I. (Providence In.)	41·53 N	71·23 W
127	Paxoi (I.) Grc.	39·14 N	20·15 E
80	Paxton (păks'tŭn) Ill.	40·35 N	88·00 W
150	Payen (pä'yĕn') China	46·00 N	127·20 E
66	Payette (pȧ-ĕt') Idaho	44·05 N	116·55 W
66	Payette R. Idaho	43·57 N	116·26 W
66	Payette R., North Fork Idaho	44·35 N	116 10 W
66	Payette R., South Fork Idaho	44·07 N	115·43 W
	Payintala, see Tungliao		
132	Pay-Khoy, Khrebet (Mts.) Sov. Un.	68·08 N	63·04 E
87	Payne (L.) (pān) Can.	59·22 N	73·16 W
71	Paynesville (pānz'vĭl) Minn.	45·23 N	94·43 W
139	Payong, Bukit (Mt.) Mala. (Singapore In.)	3·04 N	101·58 E
	Payo Obispo, see Ciudad Chetumal		
100	Paysandú (pī-sän-dōō') Ur.	32·16 S	57·55 W
69	Payson (pā's'n) Utah	40·05 N	111·45 W
127	Pazardzhik (pä-zär-dzhek') Bul.	42·10 N	24·22 E
126	Pazin (pä'zên) Yugo.	45·13 N	13·37 E
73	Peabody (pē'bŏd-ĭ) Kans.	38·09 N	97·09 W
83	Peabody Mass. (Boston In.)	42·32 N	70·56 W
86	Peace (R.) Can.	57·29 N	117·32 W
79	Peace Cr. (pēs) Fla. (In.)	27·16 N	81·53 W
84	Peace Dale (dāl) R. I. (Providence In.)	41·27 N	71·30 W
86	Peace River (rĭv'ēr) Can.	56·19 N	117·22 W
86	Peacock Hills (pē-kŏk' hĭlz) Can.	66·08 N	109·55 W
110	Peak, The (Mt.) (pēk) Eng.	53·23 N	1·52 W
158	Peak Hill Austl.	25·38 S	118·50 E
78	Pearl (R.) (pûrl) Miss.-La.	31·06 N	89·44 W
77	Pearland (pûrl'ǎnd) Tex. (In.)	29·34 N	95·17 W
	Pearl R., see Chu Chiang		
76	Pearsall (pēr'sôl) Tex.	28·53 N	99·06 W
167	Pearston (pē'ērstŏn) S. Afr. (Natal In.)	32·36 S	25·09 E
48	Peary Land (Reg.) (pēr'ĭ) Grnld.	82·00 N	40·00 W
72	Pease (R.) (pēz) Tex.	34·07 N	99·53 W
77	Peason (pēz'n) La.	31·25 N	93·19 W
127	Peć (pĕch) Yugo.	42·39 N	20·18 E
76	Pecan Bay (pê-kăn') Tex.	32·04 N	99·15 W
99	Peçanha (pā-kän'yä) Braz.	18·37 S	42·26 W
71	Pecatonica (R.) (pĕk-ȧ-tŏn-ĭ-kȧ) Ill.	42·21 N	89·28 W
132	Pechenga (pyĕ'chĕŋ-gȧ) Sov. Un.	69·30 N	31·10 E
132	Pechora (R.) Sov. Un.	66·00 N	52·30 E
134	Pechora Basin (pyĕ-chô'rȧ) Sov. Un.	67·55 N	58·37 E
132	Pechorskaya Guba (B.) Sov. Un.	68·40 N	55·00 E
76	Pecos (pā'kôs) Tex.	31·26 N	103·30 W
62	Pecos (R.) U. S.	31·10 N	103·10 W
121	Pécs (pāch) Hung.	46·04 N	18·15 E
167	Peddie S. Afr. (Natal In.)	33·13 S	27·09 E
128	Pededze (R.) (pă'dĕd-zĕ) Sov. Un.	57·18 N	27·13 E
74	Pedley (pĕd'lē) Calif. (Los Angeles In.)	33·59 N	117·29 W
99	Pedra Azul (pā'drä-zōō'l) Braz.	16·03 S	41·13 W
99	Pedreiras (pĕ-drā'räs) Braz.	4·30 S	44·31 W
143	Pedro, Pt. (pē'drô) Cey.	15·05 N	80·28 E
92	Pedro Antonio Santos (Sta. Cruz Chico) (pā'drô än-tō'nē-ô săn'tōs) (sän'tä krōōz' chē'kô) Mex. (Yucatan In.)	18·55 N	88·13 W
94	Pedro Betancourt (bā-tăŋ-kōrt') Cuba	22·40 N	81·15 W
100	Pedro de Valdivia (pĕ'drô-dĕ-väl-dē'vê-ä) Chile	22·32 S	69·55 W
100	Pedro do Rio (dô-rē'ô) Braz. (In.)	22·20 S	43·09 W
99	Pedro Juan Caballero (hŏōä'n-kä-bäl-yĕ'rō) Par.	22·40 S	55·42 W
88	Pedro Miguel (mê-gäl') C. Z. (Panama Canal In.)	9·01 N	79·36 W
88	Pedro Miguel Locks (mê-gäl') C. Z. (Panama Canal In.)	9·01 N	79·36 W
99	Pedro II (pā'drōō sâ-gōōn'dōō) Braz.	4·20 S	41·27 W
160	Peebinga (pê-bĭng'ȧ) Austl.	34·43 S	140·55 E
116	Peebles (pē'b'lz) Scot.	55·40 N	3·15 W
79	Pee Dee (R.) (pē-dē') S. C.-N. C.	34·01 N	79·26 W
84	Peekskill (pēks'kĭl) N. Y. (New York In.)	41·17 N	73·55 W
159	Pegasus B. (pĕg'ȧ-sŭs) N. Z.	43·18 S	173·37 E
120	Pegnitz R. (pĕgh-nēts) Ger.	49·38 N	11·40 E

ng-sing; ŋ-baŋk; ɴ-nasalized n; nŏd; cŏmmit; ōld; ôbey; ôrder; fōōd; fŏŏt; ou-out; s-soft; sh-dish; th-thin; pūre; ûnite; ûrn; stŭd; circŭs; ü-as "y" in study; '-indeterminate vowel.

Page	Name Pronunciation Region	Lat. °′	Long. °′
125	Pego (pā'gō) Sp.	38·50 N	0·09 W
154	Pegu (pĕ-gōō') Bur.	17·17 N	96·29 E
146	Pegu Yoma (Mts.) (pĕ-gōō'yō'mä) Bur.	19·16 N	95·59 E
127	Pehčevo (pĕĸ'chĕ-vô) Yugo.	41·42 N	22·57 E
150	Peian (pĕ'ē-än') China	48·05 N	126·26 E
149	Pei-Chiang (R.) China (Canton In.)	22·54 N	113·08 E
148	Peich'iao (bā'chiou) China	31·03 N	121·27 E
148	Peich'enghuang Tao (I.) (bā'chĕng'hōōäng' dou) China	38·23 N	120·55 E
150	Peiching (Peking) China (Peking In.)	39·55 N	116·23 E
148	Peiching Shih (Dist.) (bā'jĭng' shē) China	40·07 N	115·56 E
150	Peifeng China	43·00 N	124·59 E
151	Peihai China	21·30 N	109·10 E
151	Peili China	19·08 N	108·42 E
	Peilintzu, see Suihua		
	Peipus, L., see Chudskoye Oz.		
148	Pei Wan (B.) (bā'wän) China	36·21 N	120·48 E
150	Peiyün Ho (R.) China (Peking In.)	39·42 N	116·48 E
80	Pekin (pē'kĭn) Ill.	40·35 N	89·30 W
	Peking, see Peiching		
114	Pelagie, Isole I. Medit. Sea	35·46 N	12·32 E
127	Pélagos (I.) Grc.	39·17 N	24·05 E
78	Pelahatchee (pĕl-å-hăch'ē) Miss.	32·17 N	89·48 W
123	Pelat, Mt. (pē-lá') Fr.	44·16 N	6·43 E
135	Peleduy (pyĕl-yĭ-dōō'ē) Sov. Un.	59·50 N	112·47 E
93	Pelee, Mt. (Vol.) (pē-lā') Mart. (Le. & Wind. Is. In.)	14·49 N	61·10 W
80	Pelee, Pt. Can.	41·55 N	82·30 W
80	Pelee I. (pē'lē) Can.	41·45 N	82·30 W
101	Pelequén (pĕ-lĕ-kĕ'n) Chile (Santiago In.)	34·26 S	71·52 W
	Pelew, see Palau		
78	Pelham (pĕl'hăm) Ga.	31·07 N	84·10 W
83	Pelham N. H. (Boston In.)	42·43 N	71·22 W
71	Pelican (L.) Minn.	46·36 N	94·00 W
94	Pelican Hbr. (pĕl'ĭ-kăn) Ba. Is.	26·20 N	76·45 W
70	Pelican Rapids (pĕl'ĭ-kăn) Minn.	46·34 N	96·05 W
71	Pella (pĕl'å) Iowa	41·25 N	92·50 W
120	Pell-Worm I. (pĕl'vôrm) Ger.	54·33 N	8·25 E
86	Pelly (L.) Can.	66·08 N	102·57 W
86	Pelly (R.) Can.	62·20 N	133·26 W
86	Pelly B. (pĕl-ĭ) Can.	68·57 N	91·05 W
86	Pelly Ra. Can.	61·47 N	133·32 W
69	Peloncillo Mts. (pĕl-ôn-sĭl'lō) Ariz.	32·40 N	109·20 W
127	Peloponnisos (Reg.) Grc.	37·28 N	22·14 E
100	Pelotas (pā-lō'tăzh) Braz.	31·45 S	52·18 W
75	Pelton (pĕl-tŭn) Can. (Detroit In.)	42·15 N	82·57 W
123	Pelvoux, Mt. (pĕl-vōō') Fr.	44·56 N	6·24 E
132	Pelym (R.) Sov. Un.	60·20 N	63·05 E
79	Pelzer (pĕl'zẽr) S. C.	34·38 N	82·30 W
139	Pemanggil (I.) Mala. (Singapore In.)	2·37 N	104·41 E
166	Pemba (pĕm'bå) Fed. of Rh. & Nya.	15·29 S	27·22 E
167	Pemba (I.) Tan.	5·13 S	40·05 E
70	Pembina (pĕm'bĭ-nå) N. D.	48·58 N	97·15 W
70	Pembina (R.) Can.	49·16 N	98·38 W
81	Pembroke (pĕm' brōk) Can.	45·50 N	77·00 W
83	Pembroke (pĕm'brōk) Mass. (Boston In.)	42·05 N	70·49 W
116	Pembroke Wales	51·40 N	5·00 W
143	Pen India (Bombay In.)	18·44 N	73·06 E
124	Penafiél (pā-nà-fyĕl') Port.	41·12 N	8·19 W
124	Peñafiel (pā-nyå-fyĕl') Sp.	41·38 N	4·08 W
124	Peñalara (Mtn.) (pā-nyä-lä'rä) Sp.	40·52 N	3·57 W
90	Pena Nevada, Cerro Mex.	23·47 N	99·52 W
154	Penang (pē-năng') Mala.	5·21 N	100·09 E
155	Penaranda (pā-nyä-rän'dä) Phil. (Manila In.)	15·20 N	120·59 E
124	Peñaranda de Bracamonte (pā-nyä-rän'dä dā brä-kä-mōn'tå) Sp.	40·54 N	5·11 W
125	Peña Roya (Mtn.) (pā'nyä rō'yä) Sp.	40·18 N	0·42 W
124	Peñarroya-Pueblonuevo (pĕn-yär-rō'yä-pwĕ'blō-nwĕ'vô) Sp.	38·18 N	5·18 W
124	Peñas, Cabo de (C.) (kå'bô-dĕ-pā'nyäs) Sp.	43·42 N	6·12 W
100	Penas, Golfo de (gôl-fô-dĕ-pĕ'n-äs) Chile	47·15 S	77·30 W
76	Penasco R. (pā-näs'kō) Tex.	32·50 N	104·45 W
150	Pench'i China	41·25 N	123·50 E
164	Pendembu (pĕn-dĕm'bōō) S. L.	8·14 N	10·52 W
70	Pender (pĕn'dẽr) Nebr.	42·08 N	96·43 W
98	Penderisco (R.) (pĕn-dĕ-rē's-kô) Col. (In.)	6·30 N	76·21 W
66	Pendleton (pĕn'd'l-tŭn) Ore.	45·41 N	118·47 W
66	Pend Oreille L. (pŏn-dô-rā') (pĕn-dô-rĕl') Idaho	48·09 N	116·38 W
66	Pend Oreille R. Wash.	48·44 N	117·20 W
99	Penedo (pā-nā'dōō) Braz.	10·17 S	36·28 W
81	Penetanguishene (pĕn'ē-tăŋ-gĭ-shēn') Can.	44·45 N	79·55 W
148	P'engchengchen (pĕng'chĕng'jĕn) China	36·24 N	114·11 E
148	P'englai (pĕng'lāi) China	37·49 N	120·45 E
124	Peniche (pĕ-nē'chå) Port.	39·22 N	9·24 W
75	Peninsula (pĕn-ĭn'sū-lå) Ohio (Cleveland In.)	41·14 N	81·32 W
110	Penistone (pĕn'ĭ-stŭn) Eng.	53·31 N	1·38 W
90	Penjamillo (pĕn-hä-mēl'yō) Mex.	20·06 N	101·56 W
90	Penjamo (pān'hä-mō) Mex.	20·27 N	101·43 W
154	Penju, Pulau-Pulau (Is.) Indon.	0·18 S	120·43 E
110	Penk (R.) (pĕnk) Eng.	52·41 N	2·10 W
110	Penkridge (pĕnk'rĭj) Eng.	52·43 N	2·07 W
126	Penne (pĕn'nā) It.	42·28 N	13·57 E
142	Penner (R.) (pĕn'ẽr) India	14·43 N	79·09 E
120	Pennine Alpi (Mts.) Switz.	46·02 N	7·07 E
116	Pennine Chain (Mts.) (pĕn-īn') Eng.	53·44 N	1·59 W
80	Pennsboro (pĕnz'bŭr-ô) W. Va.	39·10 N	81 00 W
84	Penns Grove (pĕnz grōv) N. J. (Philadelphia In.)	39·44 N	75·28 W
63	Pennsylvania (State) (pĕn-sĭl-vā'nĭ-å) U. S.	41·00 N	78·10 W
81	Penn Yan (pĕn yăn') N. Y.	42·40 N	77·00 W
87	Penny Highland (pĕnz hī'lănd) Can.	66·55 N	65·30 W
128	Peno (L.) (pā'nô) Sov. Un.	56·55 N	32·28 E
82	Penobscot (R.) Maine	45·00 N	68·36 W
82	Penobscot B. (pē-nŏb'skŏt) Maine	44·20 N	69·00 W
158	Penong (pē-nông') Austl.	32·00 S	133·00 E
93	Penonomé (pā-nō-nô-mā') Pan.	8·32 N	80·21 W
161	Penrith Austl. (Sydney In.)	33·45 S	150·42 E
78	Pensacola (pĕn-så-kō'lå) Fla.	30·25 N	87·13 W
73	Pensacola Dam Okla.	36·27 N	95·02 W
98	Pensilvania (pĕn-sêl-vá'nyä) Col. (In.)	5·31 N	75·05 W
159	Pentecost (I.) (pĕn'tê-kŏst) New Hebr.	16·05 S	168·28 E
86	Penticton Can.	49·29 N	119·28 W
116	Pentland Firth (pĕnt'lănd) Scot.	58·44 N	3·25 W
133	Penza (pĕn'zå) Sov. Un.	53·10 N	45·00 E
116	Penzance (pĕn-zăns') Eng.	50·07 N	5·40 W
120	Penzberg (pĕnts'bĕrgh) Ger.	47·43 N	11·21 E
135	Penzhina (R.) (pyĭn-zē-nŭ) Sov. Un.	62·15 N	166·30 E
135	Penzhino Sov. Un.	63·42 N	168·00 E
135	Penzhinskay'a Guba (B.) Sov. Un.	60·30 N	161·30 E
80	Peoria (pē-ō'rĭ-å) Ill.	40·45 N	89·35 W
90	Peotillos (pā-ō-tel'yōs) Mex.	22·30 N	100·39 W
75	Peotone (pē'ō-tōn) Ill. (Chicago In.)	41·20 N	87·47 W
81	Pepacton Res. (pĕp-ăc'tŭn) N. Y.	42·05 N	74·40 W
94	Pepe, Cabo (kå'bô-pĕ'pĕ) (C.) Cuba	21·30 N	83·10 W
83	Pepperell (pĕp'ẽr-ĕl) Mass. (Boston In.)	42·40 N	71·36 W
127	Peqin (pĕ-kēn') Alb.	41·03 N	19·48 E
125	Perales (R.) (pā-rä'lās) Sp.	40·24 N	4·07 W
125	Perales de Tajuña (dā tä-hōō'nyä) Sp. (Madrid In.)	40·14 N	3·22 W
82	Percé (pĕr-sā') Can.	48·32 N	64·15 W
111	Perchtoldsdorf (pĕrk'tôlts-dôrf) Aus. (Wien In.)	48·07 N	16·17 E
168	Perdekop S. Afr. (Johannesburg & Pretoria In.)	27·11 S	29·38 E
125	Perdido, Mt. (pĕr-dē'dō) Sp.	42·40 N	0·00
78	Perdido (R.) (pĕr-dī'dō) Ala.-Fla.	30·45 N	87·38 W
101	Perdões (pĕr-dô'ĕs) Braz. (Rio de Janeiro In.)	21·05 S	45·05 W
98	Pereira (pā-rā'rä) Col. (In.)	4·49 N	75·42 W
129	Perekop (pĕr-ā-kôp') Sov. Un.	46·08 N	33·39 E
80	Pere Marquette Mich.	43·55 N	86·10 W
129	Pereshchepino (pā'râsh-chĕ'pē-nô) Sov. Un.	49·02 N	35·19 E
128	Pereslavl'-Zalesskiy (pâ-râ-slâv'l zâ-lyĕs'kĭ) Sov. Un.	56·43 N	38·52 E
129	Pereyaslav (pĕ-rä-yäs' lâv) Sov. Un.	50·05 N	31·25 E
101	Pergamino (pĕr-gä-mē'nō) Arg. (Buenos Aires In.)	33·53 S	60·36 W
70	Perham (pĕr'hăm) Minn.	46·37 N	95·35 W
87	Peribonca (R.) (pĕr-ĭ-bŏŋ'kå) Can.	50·57 N	71·19 W
122	Périgueux (pā-rē-gû') Fr.	45·12 N	0·43 E
98	Perija, Sierra de (Mts.) (sē-ĕ'r-rà-dĕ-pĕ-rē'ĸá) Col.	9·25 N	73·30 W
85	Perkins (pĕr'kĕns) Can. (Ottawa In.)	45·37 N	75·37 W
93	Perlas, Arch. de Las (är-chē-pyĕ'lä-gô-dĕ-läs-pĕr'läs) Pan.	8·29 N	79·15 W
93	Perlas, Laguna las (L.) (lä-gōō'nä-dĕ-läs) Nic.	12·34 N	83·19 W
120	Perleberg (pĕr'lĕ-bĕrg) Ger.	53·06 N	11·51 E
136	Perm' (pĕrm) Sov. Un. (Urals In.)	58·00 N	56·15 E
	Pernambuco, see Recife		
99	Pernambuco (State) (pĕr-näm-bōō'kō) Braz.	8·08 S	38·54 W
	Pernik, see Dimitrovo		
122	Peronne (pā-rôn') Fr.	49·57 N	2·49 E
91	Perote (pĕ-rô'tĕ) Mex.	19·33 N	97·13 W
136	Perovo (pĕ'rô-vô) Sov. Un. (Moskva In.)	55·43 N	37·47 E
122	Perpignan (pĕr-pē-nyäɴ') Fr.	42·42 N	2·48 E
125	Perregaux (pĕr-rē-gō') Alg.	35·35 N	0·05 E
74	Perris (pĕr'ĭs) Calif. (Los Angeles In.)	33·46 N	117·14 W
94	Perros, Bahía (B.) (bä-ē'ä-pā'rōs) Cuba	22·25 N	78·35 W
85	Perrot I. (pĕr'ŭt) Can. (Montreal In.)	45·23 N	73·57 W
78	Perry (pĕr'ĭ) Ga.	32·27 N	83·44 W
78	Perry Fla.	30·06 N	83·35 W
71	Perry Iowa	41·49 N	94·40 W
81	Perry N. Y.	42·45 N	78·00 W
73	Perry Okla.	36·17 N	97·18 W
74	Perry Utah (Salt Lake City In.)	41·27 N	112·02 W
84	Perry Hall Md. (Baltimore In.)	39·25 N	76·27 W
75	Perryopolis (pĕ-rē-ŏ'pō-lĭs) Pa. (Pittsburgh In.)	40·05 N	79·45 W
80	Perrysburg (pĕr ĭz-bûrg) Ohio	41·35 N	83·35 W
72	Perryton (pĕr'ĭ-tŭn) Tex.	36·23 N	100·48 W
64	Perryville (pĕr ĭ-vĭl) Alaska	55·58 N	159·28 W
73	Perryville Mo.	37·41 N	89·52 W
123	Persan (pĕr-säɴ') Fr. (Paris In.)	49·09 N	2·15 E
103	Persepolis (Ruins) (pēr-sĕp'o-lĭs) Iran	30·15 N	53·08 E
	Persia, see Iran		
144	Persian G. (pûr'zhån) Asia	27·38 N	50·30 E
158	Perth (pûrth) Austl.	31·50 S	116·10 E
81	Perth Can.	44·40 N	76·15 W
116	Perth Scot.	56·24 N	3·25 W
84	Perth Amboy (ăm'boi) N. J. (New York In.)	40·31 N	74·16 W
123	Pertuis (pĕr-tüē') Fr.	43·43 N	5·29 E
80	Peru (pē-rōō') Ill.	41·20 N	89·10 W
80	Peru Ind.	40·45 N	86·00 W
96	Peru S. A.	10·00 S	75·00 W
126	Perugia (pā-rōō'jä) It.	43·08 N	12·24 E
74	Peruque (pĕ rō'kĕ) Mo. (St. Louis In.)	38·52 N	90·36 W
129	Pervomaysk (pĕr-vô-mīsk') Sov. Un.	48·04 N	30·52 E
136	Pervoural'sk (pĕr-vô-ōō-rálsk') Sov. Un. (Urals In.)	56·54 N	59·58 E
135	Pervyy Kuril'skiy Proliv (Str.) Sov. Un.	51·43 N	154·32 E
126	Pesaro (pā'zä-rō) It.	43·54 N	12·55 E
99	Pescado (pĕs-kä'dō) (R.) Ven. (In.)	9·33 N	65·32 W
	Pescadores (Is.) (pĕs-ka-dō'rĕs) China	23·30 N	119·00 E
126	Pescara (pās-kä'rä) It.	42·26 N	14·15 E
126	Pescara (R.) It.	42·18 N	13·22 E
133	Peschanyy, Mys (C.) Sov. Un.	43·10 N	51·20 E
126	Pescia (pā'shä) It.	43·53 N	11·42 E
145	Peshāwar (pĕ-shä'wŭr) W. Pak. (Khyber Pass In.)	34·01 N	71·34 E
127	Peshtera Bul.	42·03 N	24·19 E
71	Peshtigo (pĕsh'tê-gō) Wis.	45·03 N	87·46 W
71	Peshtigo (R.) Wis.	45·15 N	88·14 W
103	Peski Sov. Un.	39·46 N	59·47 E
103	Peski Sov. Un.	44·07 N	63·17 E
136	Peski (pyås'kĭ) Sov. Un. (Moskva In.)	55·13 N	38·48 E
124	Pêso da Régua (pā-sōō-dä-rā'gwä) Port.	41·09 N	7·47 W
92	Pespire (pås-pē'râ) Hond.	13·35 N	87·20 W
76	Pesqueria, R. (pĕs-kå-rē'å) Mex.	25·55 N	100·25 W
90	Petacalco, Bahía de (B.) (bä-ē'ä-dĕ-pĕ-tä-käl'kô) Mex.	17·55 N	102·00 W
139	Petah Tiqva (pĕ'tak tĭk'vâ) Isr. (Palestine In.)	32·05 N	34·53 E
68	Petaluma (pét-å-lōō'må) Calif.	38·15 N	122·38 W
99	Petare (pĕ-tä'rĕ) Ven. (In.)	10·28 N	66·48 W
90	Petatlán (pā-tä-tlän') Mex.	17·31 N	101·17 W
92	Petén, Laguna de (L.) (lä-gōō'nä-dĕ-på-tān') Guat. (Yucatan In.)	17·05 N	89·54 W
71	Petenwell Res. Wis.	44·10 N	89·55 W
81	Peterborough (pē'tẽr-bŭr-ô) Can.	44·20 N	78·20 W
160	Peterborough Austl.	32·53 S	138·58 E
110	Peterborough Eng.	52·35 N	0·14 W
116	Peterhead (pē-tẽr-hĕd') Scot.	57·36 N	3·47 W
81	Peter Pt. Can.	43·50 N	77·00 W
86	Peter Pond L. (pŏnd) Can.	56·03 N	109·23 W
64	Petersburg (pē'tẽrz-bûrg) Alaska	56·52 N	133·10 W
73	Petersburg Ill.	40·01 N	89·51 W
80	Petersburg Ind.	38·30 N	87·15 W
75	Petersburg Ky. (Cincinnati In.)	39·04 N	84·52 W
79	Petersburg Va.	37·12 N	77·30 W
111	Petershagen (pĕ'tĕrs-hä-gĕn) Ger. (Berlin In.)	52·32 N	13·46 E
111	Petershausen (pĕ'tĕrs-hou-zĕn) Ger. (München In.)	48·25 N	11·29 E
95	Pétionville Hai.	18·30 N	72·20 W
82	Petitcodiac (pē-tē-kō-dyåk') Can.	45·55 N	65·11 W
83	Petite Miquelon (I.) (mē-k'lon') (mĭk-ē-lŏn') Can.	46·50 N	56·20 W
93	Petite Terre I. (pē-tēt'târ') Guad. (Le. & Wind. Is. In.)	16·12 N	61·00 W
95	Petit Goâve (pē-tē' gô-áv') Hai.	18·25 N	72·50 W
73	Petit Jean Cr. (pē-tē' zhäɴ') Ark.	35·05 N	93·55 W
91	Petlalcingo (pĕ-tläl-sĕŋ'gô) Mex.	18·05 N	97·53 W
92	Peto (pĕ'tô) Mex (Yucatan In.)	20·07 N	88·49 W
101	Petorca (pā-tōr'kä) Chile (Santiago In.)	32·14 S	70·55 W
80	Petoskey (pē-tŏs'kĭ) Mich.	45·25 N	84·55 W
139	Petra Jordan (Palestine In.)	30·21 N	35·25 E
152	Petra Velikogo, Zaliv (B.) (zä'lĭf pĕt-rä' vĕ-lĭ'kô-vô) Sov. Un.	42·40 N	131·50 E
127	Petrich (pā'trĭch) Bul.	41·24 N	23·13 E
69	Petrified Forest Natl. Mon. (pĕt'rĭ-fīd fôr'ĕst) Ariz.	34·58 N	109·35 W
129	Petrikovka (pyĕ'trê-kôf-kä) Sov. Un.	48·43 N	34·29 E
129	Petrikov (pyĕ'trê-kô-v) Sov. Un.	52·09 N	28·30 E
126	Petrinja (pā'trēn-yä) Yugo.	45·25 N	16·17 E
136	Petrodvorets (pyĕ-trô-dvô-ryĕts') Sov. Un. (Leningrad In.)	59·53 N	29·55 E
136	Petrokrepost' (pyĕ'trô-krĕ-pôst) Sov. Un. (Leningrad In.)	59·56 N	31·03 E
80	Petrolia (pē-trō'lĭ-å) Can.	42·50 N	82·10 W
99	Petrolina (pĕ-trō-lē'nå) Braz.	9·18 S	40·28 W
111	Petronell Aus. (Wien In.)	48·07 N	16·52 E
129	Petropavlovka (pyĕ'trô-päv'lôf-kå) Sov. Un.	48·24 N	36·23 E
136	Petropavlovka Sov. Un. (Urals In.)	54·10 N	59·50 E
134	Petropavlovsk (pyĕ-trô-päv'lôfsk) Sov. Un.	54·44 N	69·07 E
135	Petropavlovsk-Kamchatskiy (käm-chät'skĭ) Sov. Un.	53·13 N	158·56 E
100	Petrópolis (pâ-trô-pô-lēzh') Braz. (In.)	22·31 S	43·10 W
127	Petroseni Rom.	45·24 N	23·24 E
133	Petrovsk (pyĕ-trôfsk') Sov. Un.	52·20 N	45·15 E
129	Petrovskaya (pyĕ-trôf'skå-yå) Sov. Un.	45·25 N	37·50 E
133	Petrovskoye Sov. Un.	45·20 N	43·00 E
135	Petrovsk-Zabaykal'skiy (pyĕ-trôfskzä-bī-käl'skĭ) Sov. Un.	51·13 N	109·08 E
119	Petrozavodsk (pyā'trô-zå-vôtsk') Sov. Un.	61·46 N	34·25 E
168	Petrus Steyn (pä'trōōs stän') S. Afr. Johannesburg & Pretoria In.)	27·40 S	28·09 E

ăt; finăl; rāte; senâte; ärm; åsk; sofå; fâre; ch-choose; dh-as th in other; bē; ēvent; bĕt; recĕnt; cratẽr; g-go; gh-guttural g; bĭt; ĭ-short neutral; rīde; ĸ-guttural k as ch in German ich;

PRONOUNCING INDEX Petseri–Plain City 251

Page	Name Pronunciation	Region	Lat. °′	Long. °′
128	Petseri (pĕt'sĕ-rê)	Sov. Un.	57·48 N	27·33 E
75	Pewaukee (pĭ-wô'kē)	Wis. (Milwaukee In.)	43·05 N	88·15 W
75	Pewaukee L.	Wis. (Milwaukee In.)	43·03 N	88·18 W
75	Pewee Valley (pe wē)	Ky. (Louisville In.)	38·19 N	85·29 W
132	Peza (R.) (pyå'zå)	Sov. Un.	65·35 N	46·50 E
122	Pézenas (pā-zē-nä')	Fr.	43·26 N	3·24 E
120	Pforzheim (pfôrts'hīm)	Ger.	48·52 N	8·43 E
142	Phalodi	India	26·50 N	73·54 E
142	Phalodi	India	27·13 N	72·22 E
154	Phan Rang (p'hän'räng')	Viet.	11·30 N	108·43 E
	Pharsalus, see Fársala			
78	Phenix City (fē'nĭks)	Ala.	32·29 N	85·00 W
154	Phet Buri	Thai.	13·07 N	99·53 E
78	Philadelphia (fĭl-ȧ-dĕl'phĭ-ȧ)	Miss.	32·45 N	89·07 W
84	Philadelphia	Pa. (Philadelphia In.)	40·00 N	75·13 W
70	Philip (fĭl'ĭp)	S. D.	44·03 N	101·35 W
164	Philippeville (fē-lēp'vēl')	Alg.	36·58 N	6·51 E
155	Philippines (fĭl'ĭ-pēnz)	Asia	14·25 N	125·00 E
156	Philippine Sea (fĭl'ĭ-pēn)	Asia	16·00 N	133·00 E
155	Philippine Trench	Phil.	10·30 N	127·15 E
	Philippopolis, see Plovdiv			
81	Philipsburg (fĭl'lĭps-bērg)	Pa.	40·55 N	78·10 W
67	Philipsburg	Wyo.	46·19 N	113·19 W
160	Phillip (I.) (fĭl'ĭp)	Austl.	38·32 S	145·10 E
139	Phillip Chan.	Indon. (Singapore In.)	1·04 N	103·40 E
81	Phillipi (fĭ-lĭp'ĭ)	W. Va.	39·10 N	80·00 W
71	Phillips (fĭl'ĭps)	Wis.	45·41 N	90·24 W
72	Phillipsburg (fĭl'lĭps-bērg)	Kans.	39·44 N	99·19 W
81	Phillipsburg	Pa.	40·45 N	75·10 W
154	Phnom Penh (nŏm'pĕn')	Camb.	11·39 N	104·53 E
84	Phoebus (fē'bŭs)	Va. (Norfolk In.)	37·02 N	76·19 W
69	Phoenix (fē'nĭks)	Ariz.	33·30 N	112·00 W
84	Phoenix	La. (New Orleans In.)	29·39 N	89·56 W
156	Phoenix Is	Oceania	4·00 S	174·00 W
84	Phoenixville (fē'nĭks-vĭl)	Pa. (Philadelphia In.)	40·08 N	75·31 W
154	Phu Bia (Pk.)	Laos	19·36 N	103·00 E
154	Phuket	Thai.	7·57 N	98·19 E
148	P'i (R.) (pē')	China	32·06 N	116·31 E
126	Piacenza (pyä-chĕnt'sä)	It.	45·02 N	9·42 E
126	Pianosa (I.) (pyä-nō'sä)	It.	42·13 N	15·45 E
121	Piatra-Neamt (pyä'trà-nā-āmts')	Rom.	46·54 N	26·24 E
99	Piauí (State) (pyou'ē)	Braz.	7·40 S	42·25 W
99	Piauí, Serra do (Mts.) (sĕr'rä dŏŏ pyou'ē)	Braz.	10·45 S	44·36 W
126	Piave (R.) (pyä'vā)	It.	45·45 N	12·15 E
126	Piazza Armerina (pyät'sä är-mâ-rē'nä)	It.	37·23 N	14·26 E
165	Pibor R. (pē'bôr)	Sud.	7·21 N	32·54 E
71	Pic (R.) (pĕk)	Can.	48·48 N	86·28 W
89	Picara Pt. (pê-kä'rä)	Vir. Is. (U. S. A.) (St. Thomas In.)	18·23 N	64·57 W
78	Picayune (pĭk'à yōōn)	Miss.	30·32 N	89·41 W
126	Piccole Dolomitche Alpi (Mts.) (pē'k-kô-le-dô-lô'mē-tē'chĕ-äl'pē)	It.	46·05 N	12·17 E
125	Pic du Midi d'Ossau (Mtn.) (pēk dü mê-dē' dôs-sō')	Fr.	42·51 N	0·25 W
73	Picher (pĭch'ēr)	Okla.	36·58 N	94·49 W
151	Pichieh	China	27·20 N	105·18 E
101	Pichilemu (pē-chē-lĕ'mōō)	Chile (Santiago In.)	34·22 S	72·01 W
91	Pichucalco (pē-chōō-käl'kō)	Mex.	17·34 N	93.06 W
91	Pichucalco (R.)	Mex.	17·40 N	93·02 W
71	Pickerel (L.) (pĭk'ēr-ĕl)	Can.	48·35 N	91·10 W
78	Pickwick (R.) (pĭk'wĭck)	Tenn.	35·04 N	88·05 W
74	Pico (pē'kō)	Calif. (Los Angeles In.)	34·01 N	118·05 W
125	Pico de Aneto (Mtn.) (pē'kō-dĕ-ä-nĕ'tō)	Sp.	42·35 N	0·38 E
164	Pico I. (pē'kōō)	Azores (In.)	38·16 N	28·49 W
99	Picos (pē'kōzh)	Braz.	7·13 S	41·23 W
161	Picton (pĭk'tŭn)	Austl. (Sydney In.)	34·11 S	150·37 E
83	Pictou (pĭk-tōō')	Can.	45·43 N	62·44 W
143	Pidurutalagala Mt. (pē'dōō-rōō-tä'lä-gä'lä)	Cey.	12·27 N	80·45 E
71	Pie (I.) (pī)	Can.	48·10 N	89·07 W
101	Piedade (pyā-dä'dĕ)	Braz. (Rio de Janeiro In.)	23·42 S	47·25 W
78	Piedmont (pēd'mŏnt)	Ala.	33·54 N	85·36 W
65	Piedmont	Calif. (San Francisco In.)	37·50 N	122·14 W
73	Piedmont	Mo.	37·09 N	90·42 W
79	Piedmont	S. C.	34·40 N	82·27 W
81	Piedmont	W. Va.	39·30 N	79·05 W
124	Piedrabuena (pyā-drä-bwā'nä)	Sp.	39·01 N	4·10 W
101	Piedras, Punta (Pt.) (pōō'n-tä-pyĕ'dräs)	Arg. (Buenos Aires In.)	35·25 S	57·10 W
76	Piedras Negras (pyā'dräs nā'gräs)	Mex.	28·41 N	100·33 W
119	Pieksämäki (pyĕk'sĕ-mĕ-kē)	Fin.	62·18 N	27·14 E
124	Piélagos (pyā'lä-gōs)	Sp.	43·23 N	3·55 W
126	Piemonte (Reg.) (pyĕ-mô'n-tĕ)	It.	44·30 N	7·42 E
168	Pienaars R.	S. Afr. (Johannesburg & Pretoria In.)	25·13 S	28·05 E
168	Pienaarsrivier	S. Afr. (Johannesburg & Pretoria In.)	25·12 S	28·18 E
70	Pierce (pērs)	Nebr.	42·11 N	97·33 W
81	Pierce	W. Va.	39·15 N	79·30 W
84	Piermont (pēr'mŏnt)	N. Y. (New York In.)	41·03 N	73·55 W
70	Pierre (pēr)	S. D.	44·22 N	100·20 W
121	Pieštany (pyĕsh'tyá-nûĭ)	Czech.	48·36 N	17·48 E
167	Pietermaritzburg (pē-tēr-mä-rĭts-bûrg)	S. Afr. (Natal In.)	29·36 S	30·23 E
168	Pietersburg (pē'tērz-bûrg)	S. Afr. (Johannesburg & Pretoria In.)	23·56 S	29·30 E
81	Pieton	Can.	44·00 N	77·15 W
166	Piet Retief (pēt rĕ-tēf')	S. Afr.	27·00 S	30·58 E
121	Pietrosul Pk.	Rom.	47·35 N	24·49 E
126	Pieve di Cadore (pyā'vå dē kä-dō'rå)	It.	46·26 N	12·22 E
71	Pigeon (R.) (pĭj'ŭn)	Can.-Minn.	48·05 N	90·13 W
85	Pigeon Lake	Can. (Winnipeg In.)	49·57 N	97·36 W
73	Piggott (pĭg'ŭt)	Ark.	36·22 N	90·10 W
91	Pijijiapan (pēkē-kē-ä'pän)	Mex.	15·40 N	93·12 W
111	Pijnacker	Neth. (Amsterdam In.)	52·01 N	4·25 E
72	Pikes Pk. (pīks)	Colo.	38·49 N	105·03 W
79	Pikeville (pīk'vĭl)	Ky.	37·28 N	82·31 W
120	Piła (pē'là)	Pol.	53·09 N	16·44 E
168	Pilansberg (pē'ănsbûrg)	S. Afr. (Johannesburg & Pretoria In.)	25·08 S	26·55 E
101	Pilar (pē'lär)	Arg. (Buenos Aires In.)	34·27 S	58·55 W
100	Pilar	Par.	27·00 S	58·15 W
155	Pilar (pē'lär)	Phil. (Manila In.)	12·55 N	123·41 E
155	Pilar	Phil. (Manila In.)	17·24 N	120·36 E
99	Pilar de Goiás (dĕ-gô'yà's)	Braz.	14·47 S	49·33 W
65	Pilchuck (R.)	Wash. (Seattle In.)	48·03 N	121·58 W
65	Pilchuck Cr. (pĭl'chŭk)	Wash. (Seattle In.)	48·19 N	122·11 W
65	Pilchuck Mtn.	Wash. (Seattle In.)	48·03 N	121·48 W
100	Pilcomayo (pēl-kō-mä'yō)	Par.	24·45 S	69·15 W
155	Pili (pē'lē)	Phil. (Manila In.)	13·34 N	123·17 E
121	Pilica R. (pê-lēt'sä)	Pol.	51·00 N	19·48 E
65	Pillar Pt. (pĭl'ȧr)	Can. (Seattle In.)	48·14 N	124·06 W
65	Pillar Rock	Wash. (Portland In.)	46·16 N	123·35 W
90	Pilón (R.) (pê-lōn')	Mex.	24·13 N	99·03 W
73	Pilot Point (pī'lŭt)	Tex.	33·24 N	97·00 W
84	Pilottown (pī'lŭt-toun)	La. (New Orleans In.)	29·11 N	89·15 W
	Pilsen, see Plzeň			
119	Piltene (pĭl'tĕ-nĕ)	Sov. Un.	57·17 N	21·40 E
90	Pimal, Cerra (Mtn.) (sĕ'r-rä-pē-mäl')	Mex.	22·58 N	104·19 W
158	Pimba (pĭm'bȧ)	Austl.	31·15 S	146·50 E
167	Pimville (pĭm'vĭl)	S. Afr. (Johannesburg & Pretoria In.)	26·17 S	27·54 E
88	Pinacate, Cerro (Mtn.) (sĕ'r-rô-pē-nä-kä'tĕ)	Mex.	31·45 N	113·30 W
155	Pinamalayan (pē-nä-mä-lä'yän)	Phil. (Manila In.)	13·04 N	121·31 E
133	Pinarbasi (pē'när-bä'shĭ)	Tur.	38·50 N	36·10 E
94	Pinar del Rio (pē-när' dĕl rē'ō)	Cuba	22·25 N	83·35 W
94	Pinar del Rio (State)	Cuba	22·45 N	83·25 W
155	Pinatubo (Mtn.) (pē-nä-tōō'bō)	Phil. (Manila In.)	15·09 N	120·19 E
73	Pinckneyville (pĭnk'nĭ-vĭl)	Ill.	38·06 N	89·22 W
121	Pińczow (pēn''chōōf)	Pol.	50·32 N	20·33 E
101	Pindamonhangaba (pē'n-dä-mōnyä'n-gä-bä)	Braz. (Rio de Janeiro In.)	22·56 S	45·26 W
127	Píndhos Oros (Mts.)	Grc.	39·48 N	21·19 E
83	Pine, C (pīn)	Can.	46·36 N	53·35 W
71	Pine (R.)	Wis.	45·50 N	88·37 W
73	Pine Bluff (pīn blŭf)	Ark.	34·13 N	92·01 W
71	Pine City (pīn)	Minn.	45·50 N	93·01 W
158	Pine Creek	Austl.	13·45 S	132·00 E
68	Pine Cr.	Nev.	40·15 N	116·17 W
66	Pine Forest Ra.	Nev.	41·35 N	118·45 W
132	Pinega (pê-nyĕ'gȧ)	Sov. Un.	64·40 N	43·30 E
132	Pinega (R.)	Sov. Un.	64·10 N	42·30 E
84	Pine Hill (pīn hĭl)	N. J. (Philadelphia In.)	39·47 N	74·59 W
65	Pinehurst (pīn'hûrst)	Wash. (Seattle In.)	47·56 N	122·13 W
79	Pine Is.	Fla. (In.)	24·48 N	81·32 W
79	Pine Island Sd.	Fla. (In.)	26·32 N	82·30 W
84	Pine Lake Estates (läk ĕs-tāts')	Ga. (Atlanta In.)	33·47 N	84·13 W
166	Pinelands (pīn'lănds)	S. Afr. (Cape Town In.)	33·57 S	18·30 E
74	Pine Lawn (lôn)	Mo. (St. Louis In.)	38·42 N	90·17 W
84	Pine Mountain (moun'tĭn)	Ga. (Atlanta In.)	33·39 N	84·09 W
70	Pine Ridge Ind. Res. (rĭj)	S. D.	43·33 N	102·13 W
126	Pinerola (pē-nâ-rô'lō)	It.	44·47 N	7·18 E
167	Pinetown (pīn'toun)	S. Afr. (Natal In.)	29·47 S	30·52 E
74	Pine View Res. (vū)	Utah (Salt Lake City In.)	41·17 N	111·54 W
78	Pineville (pīn'vĭl)	Ky.	36·48 N	83·43 W
77	Pineville	La.	31·20 N	92·25 W
154	Ping, Mae Nam (R.)	Thai.	17·54 N	98·29 E
149	Pingchoupao	China (Canton In.)	23·01 N	113·11 E
150	Pingchüan	China	40·58 N	118·40 E
139	Pinggir	Indon. (Singapore In.)	1·05 N	101·12 E
151	P'ingho (pĭng'hō')	China	24·30 N	117·02 E
151	Pinghsiang	China	27·40 N	113·50 E
150	Pingliang (pĭng'lyäng')	China	35·12 N	106·50 E
151	P'inglo (pĭng'lō')	China	24·30 N	110·22 E
151	P'ingt'an	China	25·30 N	119·45 E
150	Pingting (pĭng'tĭng')	China	37·50 N	113·30 E
148	P'ingtu (pĭng'tōō')	China	36·46 N	119·57 E
151	P'ingtung	China	22·40 N	120·35 E
150	P'ingwu	China	32·20 N	104·40 E
148	P'ingyuan (pĭng'yü-än')	China	37·11 N	116·26 E
101	Pinhal (pē-nyä'l)	Braz. (Rio de Janeiro In.)	22·11 S	46·43 W
125	Pinhal Novo (nō vōō)	Port. (Lisboa In.)	38·38 N	8·54 W
124	Pinhel (pēn-yĕl')	Port.	40·45 N	7·03 W
148	Pinhsien (pĭn'siän)	China	38·29 N	117·58 E
150	Pinhsien	China	45·40 N	127·20 E
154	Pini (I.) (pē'nê)	Indon.	0·07 N	98·38 E
127	Piniós (R.)	Grc.	40·33 N	21·40 E
68	Pinnacles Natl. Mon. (pĭn'ȧ-k'lz)	Calif.	36·30 N	121·00 W
111	Pinneberg (pĭn'ĕ-bĕrg)	Ger. (Hamburg In.)	53·40 N	9·48 E
65	Pinole (pĭ-nō'lē)	Calif. (San Francisco In.)	38 01 N	122·17 W
94	Pinos, Isla de (I.) (ē's-lä-dĕ-pē'nōs)	Cuba	21·40 N	82·45 W
124	Pinos-Puente (pwān'tå)	Sp.	37·15 N	3·43 W
90	Pinotepa Nacional (pē-nô-tā'pä nä-syô-näl')	Mex.	16·21 N	98·04 W
159	Pins, Ile des	N. Cal.	22·44 S	167·44 E
121	Pinsk (pēn'sk)	Sov. Un.	52·07 N	26·05 E
98	Pinta (I.)	Ec.	0·41 N	90·47 W
85	Pintendre (pĕN-täNdr')	Can. (Quebec In.)	46·45 N	71·07 W
125	Pinto (pēn'tō)	Sp. (Madrid In.)	40·14 N	3·42 W
69	Pioche (pī-ō'chē)	Nev.	37·56 N	114·28 W
126	Piombino (pyôm-bē'nō)	It.	42·56 N	10·33 E
65	Pioneer (pī'ō-nēr')	Wash. (Portland In.)	45·49 N	122·40 W
67	Pioneer Mts	Mont.	45·23 N	112·51 W
121	Piotrkow Trybunalski (pyōtr'kōōv trĭ-bōō-nal'skē)	Pol.	51·23 N	19·44 E
78	Piper (pī'pēr)	Ala.	33·04 N	87·00 W
74	Piper	Kans. (Kansas City In.)	39·09 N	94·51 W
127	Pipéri (I.) (pē'per-ē)	Grc.	39·19 N	24·20 E
69	Pipe Spring Natl. Mon. (pīp sprĭng)	Ariz.	36·50 N	112·45 W
70	Pipestone (pīp'stōn)	Minn.	44·00 N	96·19 W
71	Pipestone (R.)	Can.	48·34 N	92·22 W
70	Pipestone Natl. Mon.	Minn.	44·03 N	96·24 W
82	Pipmaukin, L. (pĭp-mä-kän')	Can.	49·36 N	69·55 W
80	Piqua (pĭk'wȧ)	Ohio	40·10 N	84·15 W
101	Piracaia (pē-rä-kå'yä)	Braz. (Rio de Janeiro In.)	23·04 S	46·20 W
101	Piracicaba (pê-rä-sē-kä'bä)	Braz. (Rio de Janeiro In.)	22·43 S	47·39 W
101	Piraí (pē-rä-ē')	Braz. (Rio de Janeiro In.)	22·38 S	43·54 W
101	Piraíba (R.) (pä-rä-ē'bä)	Braz. (Rio de Janeiro In.)	21·38 S	41·29 W
134	Piramida, Gol'tsy (Mtn.)	Sov. Un.	54·00 N	96·00 E
126	Piran (pē-rå'n)	Yugo.	45·31 N	13·34 E
101	Piranga (pē-rä'n-gä)	Braz. (Rio de Janeiro In.)	20·41 S	43·17 W
101	Pirapetinga (pē-rä-pĕ-tē'n-gä)	Braz. (Rio de Janeiro In.)	21·40 S	42·20 W
99	Pirapóra (pê-rà-pō'rȧ)	Braz.	17·39 S	44·54 W
101	Pirassununga (pē-rä-sōō-nōō'n-gä)	Braz. (Rio de Janeiro In.)	22·00 S	47·24 W
99	Pirenópolis (pē-rĕ-nô'pō-lēs)	Braz.	15·56 S	48·49 W
127	Pírgos	Grc.	37·51 N	21·28 E
99	Piritu, Laguna de (L.) (lä-gōō'nä-dĕ-pē-rē'tōō)	Ven. (In.)	10·00 N	64·57 W
120	Pirmasens (pĭr-mä-zĕns')	Ger.	49·12 N	7·34 E
120	Pirna (pĭr'nä)	Ger.	50·57 N	13·56 E
155	Piroe (pē-rōō')	Indon.	3·15 S	128·25 E
127	Pirot (pē'rōt)	Yugo.	43·09 N	22·35 E
69	Pirtleville (pûr't'l-vĭl)	Ariz.	31·25 N	109·35 W
129	Piryatin (pēr-yä-tēn')	Sov. Un.	50·13 N	32·31 E
126	Pisa (pē'sä)	It.	43·52 N	10·24 E
98	Pisagua (pē-sä'gwä)	Chile	18·43 S	70·12 W
98	Pisco (pēs'kō)	Peru	13·43 S	76·07 W
98	Pisco, Bahia de (B.) (bä-ē'ä-dĕ)	Peru	13·43 S	77·48 W
81	Piseco (L.) (pĭ-sā'kō)	N. Y.	43·25 N	74·35 W
120	Pisek (pē'sĕk)	Czech.	49·18 N	14·08 E
100	Pissis, Monte (Vol.) (mō'n-tĕ-pē-sēs')	Arg.	27·50 S	68·35 W
139	Pissouri	Cyprus (Palestine In.)	34·39 N	32·42 E
126	Pisticci (pēs-tē'chē)	It.	40·24 N	16·34 E
126	Pistoia (pēs-tô'yä)	It.	43·57 N	11·54 E
83	Pistolet B. (pĭs-tô-lā')	Can.	51·40 N	55·43 W
124	Pisuerga (R.) (pē-swĕr'gä)	Sp.	41·48 N	4·28 W
98	Pitalito (pē-tä-lē'tō)	Col.	1·45 N	75·09 W
75	Pitcairn (pĭt'kârn)	Pa. (Pittsburgh In.)	40·29 N	79·47 W
157	Pitcairn (I.)	Oceania	24·30 S	133·00 W
112	Pite (R.) (pē'tĕ)	Swe.	66·08 N	18·51 E
112	Piteå (pē'tĕ-ô')	Swe.	65·21 N	21·10 E
127	Pitesti (pê-tĕsht'')	Rom.	44·51 N	24·51 E
158	Pithara (pĭt'ărȧ)	Austl.	30·27 S	116·45 E
122	Pithiviers (pē-tē-vyā')	Fr.	48·12 N	2·14 E
84	Pitman (pĭt'mȧn)	N. J. (Philadelphia In.)	39·44 N	75·08 W
93	Pitons du Carbet, Mt.	Mart. (Le. & Wind. Is. In.)	14·40 N	61·05 W
66	Pit R. (pĭt)	Calif.	40·58 N	121·42 W
167	Pitseng	Bas. (Natal In.)	29·03 S	28·13 E
65	Pitt (R.)	Can. (Vancouver In.)	49·19 N	122·39 W
64	Pitt Pt. (pĭt)	Alaska	70·48 N	152·00 W
65	Pittsburg (pĭts'bûrg)	Calif. (San Francisco In.)	38·01 N	121·52 W
73	Pittsburg	Kans.	37·25 N	94·43 W
65	Pittsburg	Ore. (Portland In.)	45·54 N	123·09 W
73	Pittsburg	Tex.	32·00 N	94·57 W
75	Pittsburgh	Pa. (Pittsburgh In.)	40·26 N	80·01 W
73	Pittsfield (pĭts'fēld)	Ill.	39·37 N	90·47 W
82	Pittsfield	Maine	44·45 N	69·44 W
81	Pittsfield	Mass.	42·25 N	73·15 W
81	Pittston (pĭts'tŭn)	Pa.	41·20 N	75·50 W
148	P'itzuwo (Hsinchin) (pē'zhē'wō) (sĭn'jĭn)	China	39·25 N	122·19 E
101	Piūi (pē-ōō'ē)	Braz. (Rio de Janeiro In.)	20·27 S	45·57 W
98	Piura (pê-ōō'rä)	Peru	5·13 S	80·46 W
136	Piya (pē'yȧ)	Sov. Un. (Urals In.)	58·34 N	61·12 E
74	Placentia (plă-sĕn'shĭ-ȧ)	Calif. (Los Angeles In.)	33·52 N	117·50 W
83	Placentia	Can.	47·16 N	53·59 W
83	Placentia B.	Can.	47·14 N	54·30 W
68	Placerville (plăs'ēr-vĭl)	Calif.	38·43 N	120·47 W
94	Placetas (plä-thā'täs)	Cuba	22·10 N	79·40 W
81	Placid (L.) (plăs'ĭd)	N. Y.	44·20 N	74·00 W
74	Plain City (plān)	Utah (Salt Lake City In.)	41·18 N	112·06 W

ng-sing; ŋ-baŋk; N-nasalized n; nŏd; cŏmmit; ōld; ôbey; ôrder; fōōd; fŏŏt; ou-out; s-soft; sh-dish; th-thin; pūre; ûnite; ûrn; stŭd; circŭs; ü-as "y" in study; '-indeterminate vowel.

252 Plainfield—Port Blair PRONOUNCING INDEX

Page	Name Pronunciation Region	Lat. °′	Long. °′
75	Plainfield (plān'fēld) Ill. (Chicago In.)	41·37 N	88·12 W
75	Plainfield..Ind. (Indianapolis In.)	39·42 N	86·23 W
84	Plainfield...N. J. (New York In.)	40·38 N	74·25 W
73	Plainview (plān'vū)........Ark.	34·59 N	93·15 W
71	Plainview...............Minn.	44·09 N	93·12 W
70	Plainview...............Nebr.	42·20 N	97·47 W
72	Plainview...............Tex.	34·11 N	101·42 W
80	Plainwell (plan'wĕl)........Mich.	42·25 N	85·40 W
85	Plaisance (plĕ-zäNs') Can. (Ottawa In.)	45·37 N	75·07 W
95	Plana or Flat Cays (Is.) (plä'nä) Ba. Is.	22·35 N	73·35 W
122	Plan-de-Cuques (plä-dĕ-kük') Fr. (Marseille In.)	43·22 N	5·29 E
111	Planegg (plä'nĕg) Ger. (München In.)	48·06 N	11·27 E
73	Plano (plā'nō).............Tex.	33·01 N	96·42 W
85	Plantagenet (plăN-täzh-nĕ') Can. (Ottawa In.)	45·33 N	75·00 W
79	Plant City (plănt sĭ'tĭ)..Fla. (In.)	28·00 N	82·07 W
77	Plaquemine (plăk'mēn')......La.	30·17 N	91·14 W
124	Plasencia (plä-sĕn'thē-ä)......Sp.	40·02 N	6·07 W
136	Plast (plást)..Sov. Un. (Urals In.)	54·22 N	60·48 E
82	Plaster Rock (plás'tēr rŏk)...Can.	46·54 N	67·22 W
152	Plastun (plás-tōōn').....Sov. Un.	44·41 N	136·08 E
100	Plata, R. de la (R.) (dālä plä'tä) Arg.-Ur.	34·35 S	58·15 W
126	Platani (R.) (plä-tä'nē).......It.	37·26 N	13·28 E
95	Plateforme, Pte............Hai.	19·35 N	73·50 W
64	Platinum (plăt'ĭ-nŭm).....Alaska	59·00 N	161·27 W
98	Plato (plä'tō)..............Col.	9·49 N	74·48 W
90	Platón Sánchéz (plä-tōn' sän'chĕz).Mex.	21·14 N	98·20 W
73	Platt Natl. Park (plăt)......Okla.	34·31 N	96·44 W
70	Platte (plăt)..............S. D.	43·22 N	98·51 W
73	Platte (R.)................Mo.	40·09 N	94·40 W
62	Platte (R.)...............U. S.	40·50 N	100·40 W
71	Platteville (plăt'vĭl).........Wis.	42·44 N	90·31 W
73	Plattsburg (plăts'bûrg).......Mo.	39·33 N	94·26 W
81	Plattsburgh................N. Y.	44·40 N	73·30 W
70	Plattsmouth (plăts'mŭth)...Nebr.	41·00 N	95·53 W
120	Plauen (plou'ĕn)...........Ger.	50·30 N	12·08 E
95	Playa de Guanabo (plä-yä-dĕ-gwä-nä'bō) Cuba (La Habana In.)	23·10 N	82·07 W
95	Playa de Santa Fe (sä'n-tä-fĕ') Cuba (La Habana In.)	23·05 N	82·31 W
69	Playas (L.) (plä'yás).....N. Mex.	31·50 N	108·30 W
91	Playa Vicente (vē-sĕn'tā)....Mex.	17·49 N	95·49 W
91	Playa Vicente (R.).........Mex.	17·36 N	96·13 W
81	Pleasant (L.) (plĕz'ănt).....N. Y.	43·25 N	74·25 W
65	Pleasant Hill Calif. (San Francisco In.)	37·57 N	122·04 W
73	Pleasant Hill...............Mo.	38·46 N	94·18 W
65	Pleasanton (plĕz'ăn-tŭn) Calif. (San Francisco In.)	37·40 N	121·53 W
73	Pleasanton................Kans.	38·10 N	94·41 W
76	Pleasanton.................Tex.	28·58 N	98·30 W
75	Pleasant Plain (plĕz'ănt) Ohio (Cincinnati In.)	39·17 N	84·06 W
75	Pleasant Ridge. Mich. (Detroit In.)	42·28 N	83·09 W
75	Pleasure Ridge Park (plĕzh'ēr rĭj) Ky. (Louisville In.)	38·09 N	85·49 W
74	Pleasant View (plĕz'ănt vū) Utah (Salt Lake City In.)	41·20 N	112·02 W
84	Pleasantville (plĕz'ănt-vĭl) N. Y. (New York In.)	41·08 N	73·47 W
159	Plenty, B. of (plĕn'tē).N. Z. (In.)	37·23 S	177·10 E
67	Plentywood (plĕn'tē-wŏŏd).Mont.	48·47 N	104·38 W
128	Ples (plyĕs)...........Sov. Un.	57·26 N	41·29 E
128	Pleshcheyevo (L.) (plĕsh-chä'yĕ-vô).Sov. Un.	56·50 N	38·22 E
82	Plessisville (plĕ-sē'vēl')......Can.	46·12 N	71·47 W
121	Pleszew (plĕ'zhĕf)...........Pol.	51·54 N	17·48 E
123	Plettenberg (plĕ'tĕn-bĕrgh) Ger. (Ruhr In.)	51·13 N	7·53 E
127	Pleven (plĕ'vĕn)............Bul.	43·24 N	24·26 E
127	Pljevlja (plĕv'lyä).........Yugo.	43·20 N	19·21 E
121	Płock (pwôtsk)..............Pol.	52·32 N	19·44 E
122	Ploërmel (plō-ĕr-mĕl')........Fr.	47·56 N	2·25 W
127	Ploeşti (plō-yĕsht'')........Rom.	44·56 N	26·01 E
127	Plomárion (plō-mä'rĭ-ŏn).....Grc.	38·51 N	26·24 E
122	Plomb du Cantal (Mt.) (plôN'dükän-tál'). Fr.	45·30 N	2·49 E
127	Plovdiv (Philippopolis) (plôv'dĭf) (fĭl-ĭp-ŏp'ō-lĭs).Bul.	42·09 N	24·43 E
91	Pluma Hidalgo (plōō'mä ē-dăl'gō) Mex.	15·54 N	96·23 W
119	Plunge (plōōn'gä).......Sov. Un.	55·56 N	21·45 E
116	Plymouth (plĭm'ŭth)........Eng.	50·25 N	4·14 W
80	Plymouth...................Ind.	41·20 N	86·20 W
81	Plymouth..................Mass.	42·00 N	70·45 W
75	Plymouth.....Mich. (Detroit In.)	42·23 N	83·27 W
81	Plymouth..................N. H.	43·50 N	71·40 W
79	Plymouth..................N. C.	35·50 N	76·44 W
81	Plymouth...................Pa.	41·15 N	75·55 W
93	Plymouth W. I. F. (Le. & Wind. Is. In.)	16·43 N	62·12 W
71	Plymouth..................Wis.	43·45 N	87·59 W
128	Plyussa (R.) (plyōō'sȧ)..Sov. Un.	58·33 N	28·30 E
120	Plzeň (Pilsen)............Czech.	49·46 N	13·25 E
126	Po, Bocche del (Mouth) (bô'chĕ-dĕl-pô').It.	44·57 N	12·38 E
126	Po, Fiume (R.) (fyōō'mĕ-pō)...It.	45·00 N	11·23 E
150	Poar.....................China	35·10 N	113·08 E
164	Pobé (pô-bā')...........Dahomey	6·56 N	2·32 E
73	Pocahontas (pō-kȧ-hŏn'tȧs)..Ark.	36·15 N	91·01 W
71	Pocahontas................Iowa	42·43 N	94·41 W
67	Pocatello (pō-kȧ-tĕl'ō)......Idaho	42·54 N	112·30 W
128	Pochëp (pô-chĕp').......Sov. Un.	52·56 N	32·27 E
128	Pochinok (pô-chē'nôk)...Sov. Un.	54·14 N	32·27 E
132	Pochinski..............Sov. Un.	54·40 N	44·50 E
90	Pochotitán (pô-chō-tē-tä'n)..Mex.	21·37 N	104·33 W
91	Pochutla (San Pedro) (pō-chōō'tlä) (sän pā'drō).Mex.	15·46 N	96·28 W
81	Pocomoke City (pō-kō-mōk').Md.	38·05 N	75·35 W
81	Pocono Mts. (pō-cō'nō).......Pa.	41·10 N	75·05 W
101	Poços de Caldas (pō-sôs-dĕ-käl'dás) Braz. (Rio de Janeiro In.)	21·48 S	46·34 W
164	Poder (pô-dôr')..........Senegal	16·35 N	15·04 W
134	Podkamennaya (Stony) Tunguska (R.).Sov. Un.	61·43 N	93·45 E
136	Podol'sk (pô-dôl''sk) Sov. Un. (Moskva In.)	55·26 N	37·33 E
129	Podvolochisk..........Sov. Un.	49·32 N	26·16 E
126	Poggibonsi (pôd-jē-bôn'sē).....It.	43·27 N	11·12 E
128	Pogodino (pô-gô'dē-nô)..Sov. Un.	54·17 N	31·00 E
152	Pohai Str. (pō'hī')..........China	38·05 N	121·40 E
152	P'ohangdong...............Kor.	35·57 N	129·23 E
148	Pohsien...................China	33·52 N	115·47 E
148	Pohsing (pō'hsĭng').........China	37·09 N	118·08 E
85	Pointe-a'-Gatineau (pōō-ăNt'á-gä-tē-nō') Can. (Ottawa In.)	45·28 N	75·42 W
84	Pointe a la Hache (point' á lá ăsh') La. (New Orleans In.)	29·35 N	89·47 W
93	Pointe-à-Pitre (pwăNt' à pē-tr') Guad. (Le. & Wind. Is. In.)	16·15 N	61·32 W
85	Pointe-aux-Pins (pōō-ăNt' ō-pĕN) Can. (Edmonton In.)	53·38 N	113·15 W
85	Pointe-aux-Trembles (pōō-ăNt' ō-trăNbl) Can. (Montreal In.)	45·39 N	73·30 W
85	Pointe Claire (pōō-ăNt' klĕr) Can. (Montreal In.)	45 26 N	73 50 W
85	Pointe Fortune (fôr'tün) Can. (Montreal In.)	45·34 N	74·23 W
166	Pointe Noire...........Con. B.	4·48 S	11·50 E
64	Point Hope (hōp).........Alaska	68·18 N	166·38 W
80	Point Pleasant (plĕz'ănt)..W. Va.	38·50 N	82·10 W
65	Point Roberts (rŏb'ērts) Wash. (Vancouver In.)	48·59 N	123·04 W
123	Poissy (pwá-sē')....Fr. (Paris In.)	48·55 N	2·02 E
122	Poitiers (pwá-tyā')...........Fr.	46·35 N	0·18 E
150	Pok'ot'u (pō'kô-tōō')........China	48·45 N	121·42 E
128	Pokrov (pô'krôf)........Sov. Un.	55·56 N	39·09 E
129	Pokrovskoye (pô-krôf'skô-yĕ) Sov. Un.	47·27 N	38·54 E
128	Pola (R.) (pō'lä)........Sov. Un.	54·44 N	31·53 E
124	Pola de Allade (dĕ-äl-yä'dĕ)...Sp.	43·18 N	6·35 W
124	Pola de Laviana (dĕ-lä-vyä'nä) Sp.	43·15 N	5·29 W
102	Poland (pō'lănd)............Eur.	52·37 N	17·01 E
155	Polangui (pô-län'gē) Phil. (Manila In.)	13·18 N	123·29 E
136	Polazna (pô'láz-ná) Sov. Un. (Urals In.)	58·18 N	56·25 E
119	Polessk (pô'lĕsk).........Sov. Un.	54·50 N	21·14 E
133	Poles'ye (Pripyat' Marshes) Sov. Un.	52·10 N	27·30 E
136	Polevskoy (pô-lĕ'vs-kô'ē) Sov. Un. (Urals In.)	56·28 N	60·14 E
121	Polgár (pôl'gär)...........Hung.	47·54 N	21·10 E
150	P'oli (pô'lĭ)...............China	45·40 N	130·38 E
126	Policastro, Golfo di (G.).......It.	41·00 N	13·23 E
123	Poligny (pō-lē-nyē')..........Fr.	46·48 N	5·42 E
127	Políkhnitos.................Grc.	39·05 N	26·11 E
155	Polillo (pô-lēl'yō) Phil. (Manila In.)	14·42 N	121·56 E
155	Polillo Is......Phil. (Manila In.)	15·05 N	122·15 E
155	Polillo Str......Phil. (Manila In.)	15·02 N	121·40 E
128	Polist' (R.) (pô'lĭst).....Sov. Un.	57·42 N	31·02 E
126	Polistena (pō-lēs-tā'nä)........It.	40·25 N	16·05 E
127	Políyiros...................Grc.	40·23 N	23·27 E
134	Polkan, Gol'tsy (Mtn.)..Sov. Un.	60·18 N	92·08 E
125	Pollensa (pōl-yĕn'sä)..........Sp.	39·50 N	3·00 E
92	Polochic R. (pō-lō-chēk')...Guat.	15·19 N	89·45 W
129	Polonnoye (pô'lô-nô-yĕ)..Sov. Un.	50·07 N	27·31 E
128	Polotsk (pô'lôtsk)........Sov. Un.	55·30 N	28·48 E
101	Polpaico (pôl-pá'y-kô) Chile (Santiago In.)	33·10 S	70·53 W
67	Polson (pōl'sŭn)...........Mont.	47·40 N	114·10 W
129	Poltava (pôl-tä'vä)......Sov. Un.	49·35 N	34·33 E
129	Poltava (Oblast).........Sov. Un.	49·53 N	32·58 E
128	Põltsamaa (pôlt'sá-mä)..Sov. Un.	58·39 N	26·00 E
128	Põltsamaa (R.)...........Sov. Un.	58·35 N	25·55 E
136	Polunochnoye (pô-lōō-nô'ch-nô'yĕ) Sov. Un. (Urals In.)	60·52 N	60·27 E
134	Poluy (R.) (pôl'wē).....Sov. Un.	65·45 N	68·15 E
136	Polyakovka (pŭl-yä'kôv-kȧ) Sov. Un. (Urals In.)	54·38 N	59·42 E
132	Polyarnyy (pŭl-yär'nē)..Sov. Un.	69·10 N	33·30 E
101	Pomba (pô'm-bá) (R.) Braz. (Rio de Janeiro In.)	21·28 S	42·28 W
120	Pomerania (Reg.) (pŏm-ē-rā'nĭ-ȧ) Pol.	53·50 N	15·20 E
118	Pomeranian B. (pō'mĕ-rä-ny-än) Ger.	54·10 N	14·20 E
80	Pomeroy...................Ohio	39·00 N	82·00 W
167	Pomeroy (pŏm'ēr-roi) S. Afr. (Natal In.)	28·36 S	30·26 E
66	Pomeroy (pŏm'ēr-oi).......Wash.	46·28 N	117·35 W
125	Pomezia (pô-mĕ't-zyä) It. (Roma In.)	41·41 N	12·31 E
125	Pomigliano d'Arco (pô-mē-lyá'nô-d-ä'r-kô) It. (Napoli In.)	40·39 N	14·23 E
70	Pomme de Terre (pôm dē tĕr') Minn.	45·22 N	95·52 W
74	Pomona (pô-mō'nȧ) Calif. (Los Angeles In.)	34·04 N	117·45 W
127	Pomorie....................Bul.	42·24 N	27·41 E
142	Pomo Tsho (L.)............China	23·38 N	89·58 E
79	Pompano (pŏm'pȧ-nō)..Fla. (In.)	26·12 N	80·07 W
84	Pompton Lakes (pŏmp'tŏn) N. J. (New York In.)	41·01 N	74·16 W
92	Pomuch (pô-mōō'ch) Mex. (Yucatan In.)	20·12 N	90·10 W
70	Ponca (pŏn'kȧ).............Nebr.	42·34 N	96·43 W
73	Ponca City.................Okla.	36·42 N	97·07 W
85	Ponce (pōn'sā) P. R. (Puerto Rico In.)	18·01 N	66·43 W
143	Pondicherry (pôn-dĭ-shĕr'ē') (pŏn-dĭ-shĕr'ē).India	11·58 N	79·48 E
124	Ponferrada (pōn-fĕr-rä'dhä)...Sp.	42·33 N	6·38 W
86	Ponoca (pō-nō'cȧ)...........Can.	52·43 N	113·32 W
132	Ponoy...................Sov. Un.	66·58 N	41·00 E
132	Ponoy (R.)...............Sov. Un.	65·50 N	38·40 E
164	Ponta Delgada (pôn'tȧ dĕl-gä'dȧ) Azores (In.)	37·40 N	25·45 W
100	Ponta Grossa (grō'sȧ).......Braz.	25·09 S	50·05 W
123	Pont-à-Mousson (pôN'tà-mōōsôN') Fr.	48·55 N	6·02 E
99	Ponta Porã.................Braz.	22·30 S	55·31 W
123	Pontarlier (pôN'tár-lyā').......Fr.	46·53 N	6·22 E
122	Pont-Audemer (pôN'tōd'mâr').Fr.	49·23 N	0·28 E
123	Pontcarré (pôN-ká-rā') Fr. (Paris In.)	48·48 N	2·42 E
77	Pontchartrain L. (pôN-shár-trăN') La.	30·10 N	90·10 W
126	Pontedera (pōn-tā-dā'rä)......It.	43·37 N	10·37 E
124	Ponte de Sor (pōŋ'tĕ dā sōr') Port.	39·14 N	8·03 W
110	Pontefract (pŏn'tē-frăkt)....Eng.	53·41 N	1·18 W
101	Ponte Nova (pô'n-tĕ-nô'vá) Braz. (Rio de Janeiro In.)	20·26 S	42·52 W
124	Pontevedra (pôn-tĕ-vĕ-drä)...Sp.	42·28 N	8·38 W
166	Ponthierville (pôN-tyā-vēl') Con. L.	0·28 S	25·19 E
80	Pontiac (pŏn'tĭ-ăk)...........Ill.	40·55 N	88·35 W
75	Pontiac.......Mich. (Detroit In.)	42·37 N	83·17 W
154	Pontianak (pôn-tē-ä'nák)..Indon.	0·04 S	109·20 E
139	Pontian Kechil Mala (Singapore In.)	1·29 N	103·24 E
122	Pontivy (pôN-tē-vē')..........Fr.	48·05 N	2·57 W
122	Pont-l'Abbe (pôN-lá-bā')......Fr.	47·53 N	4·12 W
123	Pontoise (pôN-twáz') Fr. (Paris In.)	49·03 N	2·05 E
136	Pontonnyy (pôn'tôn-nyĭ) Sov. Un. (Leningrad In.)	59·47 N	30·39 E
78	Pontotoc (pŏn-tô-tŏk')......Miss.	34·11 N	88·59 W
126	Pontremoli (pôn-trĕm'ô-lē).....It.	44·21 N	9·50 E
126	Ponza, Isole di (I.) (ē'sō-lĕ-dē-pōn'tsä)..........It.	40·55 N	12·58 E
116	Poole (pōōl)...............Eng.	50·43 N	2·00 W
142	Poona (pōō'nŭ)............India	18·38 N	73·53 E
98	Poopó, Lago de (L.) (lä'gô-dĕ-pō-ō-pô').Bol.	18·16 S	67·57 W
98	Popayán (pō-pä-yän').......Col.	2·21 N	76·43 W
67	Poplar (pŏp'lēr)...........Mont.	48·08 N	105·10 W
73	Poplar Bluff (blŭf)..........Mo.	36·43 N	90·22 W
80	Poplar Plains (plāns)........Ky.	38·20 N	83·40 W
85	Poplar Point. Can. (Winnipeg In.)	50·04 N	97·58 W
67	Poplar R..................Mont.	48·34 N	105·20 W
67	Poplar R., West Fork......Mont.	48·59 N	106·06 W
78	Poplarville (pŏp'lēr-vĭl).....Miss.	30·50 N	89·33 W
91	Popocatépetl (Mtn.) (pô-pô-kä-tā'pĕt'l) Mex. (Mexico In.)	19·01 N	98·38 W
166	Popokabaca (pō'pô-kȧ-bä'kȧ) Con. L.	5·38 S	16·47 E
129	Popovka (pô'pôf-kȧ).....Sov. Un.	50·03 N	33·41 E
129	Popovka..............Sov. Un.	51·13 N	33·08 E
127	Popovo (pô'pô-vō)..........Bul.	43·23 N	26·17 E
142	Porbandar (pōr-bŭn'dŭr).....India	21·44 N	69·49 E
98	Porce (pôr-sē) (R.).....Col. (In.)	7·11 N	74·55 W
124	Porcuna (pôr-kōō'nä)..........Sp.	37·54 N	4·10 W
64	Porcupine (R.)............Alaska	67·00 N	143·25 W
86	Porcupine (R.).............Can.	67·38 N	140·07 W
67	Porcupine Cr. (pôr'kū-pīn).Mont.	46·38 N	107·04 W
67	Porcupine Cr.............Mont.	48·27 N	106·24 W
126	Pordenone (pōr-dȧ-nō'nȧ).....It.	45·58 N	12·38 E
126	Poreč (pô'rĕch)............Yugo.	45·14 N	13·57 E
119	Pori (Björneborg) (pô'rē) (byûr'nĕ-bôrgh)....Fin.	61·29 N	21·45 E
101	Poriúncula (po-rēōō'n-kōō-lä) Braz. (Rio de Janeiro In.)	20·58 S	42·02 W
112	Porjus (pôr'yōōs)...........Swe.	66·54 N	19·40 E
128	Porkhov (pôr'kôf)........Sov. Un.	57·46 N	29·33 E
98	Porlamar (pôr-lä-mär').......Ven.	11·00 N	63·55 W
122	Pornic (pôr-nēk')..............Fr.	47·08 N	2·07 W
135	Poronaysk (pô'rô-nīsk)..Sov. Un.	49·21 N	143·23 E
120	Porrentruy (pō-răN-trüē')..Switz.	47·25 N	7·02 E
118	Porsgrunn (pōrs'grōōn')......Nor.	59·09 N	9·36 E
98	Portachuelo (pôrt-ä-chwä'lô).Bol.	17·20 S	63·12 W
81	Portage (pôr'tāj)..............Pa.	40·25 N	78·35 W
71	Portage.....................Wis.	43·33 N	89·29 W
74	Portage Des Sioux (dē sōō) Mo. (St. Louis In.)	38·56 N	90·21 W
85	Portage-la-Prairie (lä-prā'rĭ) Can. (Winnipeg In.)	49·58 N	98·18 W
86	Port Alberni (pōr ăl-bĕr-nē').Can.	49·20 N	124·51 W
124	Portalegre (pôr-tä-lā'grĕ).....Port.	39·18 N	7·26 W
72	Portales (pôr-tä'lĕs).......N. Mex.	34·10 N	103·11 W
82	Port-Alfred (ăl'frĕd)........Can.	48·19 N	70·55 W
167	Port Alfred (Kowie) (kou'ĭ) S. Afr. (Natal In.)	33·36 S	26·55 E
86	Port Alice..................Can.	50·29 N	127·29 W
81	Port Allegany (ăl-ē-gā'nĭ)....Pa.	41·50 N	78·10 W
166	Port Amboim...............Ang.	11·01 S	13·45 E
66	Port Angeles (ăn'jē-lĕs)....Wash.	48·07 N	123·26 W
95	Port Antonio...............Jam.	18·10 N	76·25 W
161	Portarlington Austl. (Melbourne In.)	38·07 S	144·39 E
87	Port Arthur (är'thŭr)........Can.	48·28 N	89·12 W
77	Port Arthur.................Tex.	29·52 N	93·59 W
	Port Arthur, see Lüshun		
83	Port aux Basques (pôr'tō básk') Can.	47·36 N	59·09 W
160	Port Augusta (ô-gŭs'tȧ)....Austl.	32·28 S	137·50 E
83	Port au Port B. (pôr'tō pōr') Can.	48·41 N	58·45 W
95	Port-au-Prince (prăNs')......Hai.	18·35 N	72·20 W
80	Port Austin (ôs'tĭn).........Mich.	44·00 N	83·00 W
166	Port Beaufort (bō'fērt).....S. Afr.	34·14 S	20·59 E
154	Port Blair (blâr)....Andaman Is.	12·07 N	92·45 E

ăt; finăl; rāte; senāte; ärm; àsk; sofȧ; fâre; ch-choose; dh-as th in other; bē; ēvent; bĕt; recĕnt; cratēr; g-go; gh-guttural g; bĭt; ĭ-short neutral; rīde; K-guttural k as ch in German ich;

PRONOUNCING INDEX
Port Bolivar–Prince Edward Pen. 253

Page	Name Pronunciation Region	Lat. °′	Long. °′
77	Port Bolivar (bŏl'ĭ-vȧr) . Tex. (In.)	29·22 N	94·46 W
84	Port Chester (chĕs'tẽr) N. Y. (New York In.)	40·59 N	73·40 W
65	Port Chicago (shĭ-kô'gō) Calif. (San Francisco In.)	38·03 N	122·01 W
80	Port Clinton (klĭn'tŭn) Ohio	41·30 N	83·00 W
75	Port Colborne (kōl'bôrn) Can. (Buffalo In.)	43·53 N	79·13 W
65	Port Coquitlam (kô-kwĭt'lăm) Can. (Vancouver In.)	49·16 N	122·47 W
85	Port Credit (krĕd'ĭt) Can. (Toronto In.)	43·33 N	79·35 W
85	Port Dalhousie (dăl-hōō'zĭ) Can. (Toronto In.)	43·12 N	79·17 W
122	Port-de-Bouc (pôr-dē-bōōk') Fr. (Marseille In.)	43·24 N	5·00 E
95	Port de Paix (pĕ') Hai.	19·55 N	72·50 W
139	Port Dickson (dĭk'sŭn) Mala. (Singapore In.)	2·33 N	101·49 E
65	Port Discovery (B.) (dĭs-kŭv'ẽr-ĭ) Wash. (Seattle In.)	48·05 N	122·55 W
167	Port Edward (ĕd'wẽrd) S. Afr. (Natal In.)	31·04 S	30·14 E
82	Port Elgin (ĕl'jĭn) Can.	46·03 N	64·06 W
167	Port Elizabeth (ē-lĭz'ȧ-bĕth) S. Afr. (Natal In.)	33·57 S	25·37 E
78	Porterdale (pōr'tẽr-dāl) Ga.	33·34 N	83·53 W
68	Porterville (pōr'tẽr-vĭl) Calif.	36·03 N	119·05 W
164	Port Étienne (pôr tā-tyĕn') Mauritania	21·02 N	17·09 W
100	Portezuelo de Tupungato (Vol.) (pôr-tĕ-zwĕ-lō-dĕ-tōō-pōō'n-gä-tô) Arg.-Chile	33·30 S	69·52 W
166	Port Francqui (frän-kē') . Con. L.	4·15 S	20·43 E
65	Port Gamble (găm'bŭl) Wash. (Seattle In.)	47·52 N	122·36 W
65	Port Gamble Ind. Res. Wash. (Seattle In.)	47·54 N	122·33 W
166	Port Gentil (zhän-tē') Gabon	1·30 S	8·45 E
78	Port Gibson (gĭb'sŭn) Miss.	31·56 N	90·57 W
164	Port Harcourt (här'kŭrt) Nig.	4·47 N	7·00 E
158	Port Headland (hĕd'lănd) Austl.	20·30 S	118·30 E
166	Port Herald (hĕr'ăld) Fed. of Rh. & Nya.	16·52 S	35·16 E
83	Port Hood (hŏŏd) Can.	46·03 N	61·30 W
81	Port Hope (hōp) Can.	43·55 N	78·10 W
80	Port Huron (hū rŏn) Mich.	43·00 N	82·30 W
125	Portici (pôr'tê-chê) It. (Napoli In.)	40·34 N	14·20 E
101	Portillo (pôr-tē'l-yô) Chile (Santiago In.)	32·51 N	70·09 W
124	Portimão (pôr-tē-mo'un) Port.	37·09 N	8·34 W
84	Port Jarvis (jûr'vĭs) N. Y. (New York In.)	41·22 N	74·41 W
160	Portland (pōrt'lănd) Austl.	38·20 S	142·40 E
80	Portland Ind.	40·25 N	85·00 W
82	Portland Maine	43·40 N	70·16 W
80	Portland Mich.	42·50 N	85·00 W
65	Portland Ore. (Portland In.)	45·31 N	123·41 W
94	Portland Bight (B.) Jam.	17·45 N	77·05 W
94	Portland Pt. Jam.	17·40 N	77·20 W
77	Port Lavaca (lȧ-vä'kȧ) Tex.	28·36 N	96·38 W
160	Port Lincoln (lĭŋ'kŭn) Austl.	34·39 S	135·50 E
65	Port Ludlow (lŭd'lō) Wash. (Seattle In.)	47·26 N	122·41 W
	Port Lyautey, see Kenitra		
160	Port Macquarie (mȧ-kwŏ'rĭ) . Austl.	31·22 S	152·50 E
65	Port Madison Ind. Res. (măd'ĭ-sŭn) . Wash. (Seattle In.)	47·46 N	122·38 W
94	Port Maria (mȧ-rī'ȧ) Jam.	18·20 N	76·55 W
82	Port Menier (mē-nyā') Can.	49·51 N	64·19 W
65	Port Moody (mōōd'ĭ) Can. (Vancouver In.)	49·17 N	122·51 W
155	Port Moresby (mōrz'bē) . Pap. Ter.	9·34 S	147·20 E
77	Port Neches (nĕch'ĕz) Tex.	29·59 N	93·57 W
49	Port Nelson (nĕl'sŭn) Can.	56·59 N	92·57 W
82	Portneuf-Sur-Mer (pôr-nûf'sür mẽr) . Can.	48·40 N	69·10 W
166	Port Nolloth (nŏl'ŏth) S. Afr.	29·10 S	17·00 E
124	Pôrto (Oporto) (pōr'tōō) Port.	41·10 N	8·38 W
98	Pôrto Acre (ä'krĕ) Braz.	9·38 S	67·34 W
100	Pôrto Alegre (ä-lā'grĕ) Braz.	29·58 S	51·11 W
166	Porto Alexandre (ä-lĕ-zhän'drĕ) Ang.	16·00 S	11·50 E
167	Pôrto Amelia (ȧ-mā'lyȧ) Moz.	12·59 S	40·32 E
93	Portobelo (pôr'tô-bä'lō) Pan.	9·32 N	79·40 W
99	Pôrto de Pedras (pā'dräzh) . Braz.	9·09 S	35·20 W
101	Pôrto Feliz (fĕ-lĕ's) Braz. (Rio de Janeiro In.)	23·12 S	47·30 W
126	Portoferraio (pōr'tô-fĕr-rä'yō) . It.	42·47 N	10·20 E
99	Port-of-Spain (spān) W. I. F.	10·44 N	61·24 W
126	Portogruaro (pōr'tô-grōō-ä'rō) . It.	45·48 N	12·49 E
99	Pôrto Guaira (gwä-ē-rä) Braz.	24·03 S	44·02 W
68	Portola (pôr'tō-lȧ) Calif.	39·47 N	120·29 W
99	Pôrto Mendes (mĕ'n-dĕs) Braz.	24·41 S	54·13 W
99	Pôrto Murtinho (mōōr-tēn'yōō) Braz.	21·43 S	57·43 W
99	Pôrto Nacional (nä-syô-näl') . Braz.	10·43 S	48·14 W
164	Porto Novo (pōr'tô-nō'vō) Dahomey	6·31 N	2·32 E
65	Port Orchard (ôr'chẽrd) Wash. (Seattle In.)	47·32 N	122·38 W
65	Port Orchard (B.) Wash. (Seattle In.)	47·40 N	122·39 W
164	Porto Santo, Ilha de (I.) (sän'tōō) . Mad. Is.	32·41 N	16·15 W
99	Pôrto Seguro (sā-gōō'rōō) Braz.	16·26 S	38·59 W
126	Porto Torres (tôr'rĕs) It.	40·49 N	8·25 E
126	Porto-Vecchio (vĕk'ē-ô) Fr.	41·36 N	9·17 E
98	Pôrto Velho (väl'yōō) Braz.	8·45 S	63·43 W
98	Portoviejo (pôr-tô-vyā'hō) Ec.	1·11 S	80·28 W
160	Port Phillip B. (fĭl'ĭp) Austl.	37·57 S	144·50 E
160	Port Pirie (pĭ'rē) Austl.	33·10 S	138·10 E
86	Port Radium (rā'dē-ŭm) Can.	66·06 N	118·03 W
94	Port Royal (B.) (roi'ăl) Jam.	17·50 N	76·45 W
	Port Said, see Būr Sa'īd		
167	Port St. Johns (sȧnt jŏnz) S. Afr. (Natal In.)	31·37 S	29·32 E
167	Port Shepstone (shĕps'tŭn) S. Afr. (Natal In.)	30·45 S	30·23 E
116	Portsmouth (pôrts'mŭth) Eng.	50·45 N	1·03 W
81	Portsmouth N. H.	43·05 N	70·50 W
80	Portsmouth Ohio	38·45 N	83·00 W
84	Portsmouth Va. (Norfolk In.)	36·50 N	76·19 W
93	Portsmouth W. I. F. (Le. & Wind. Is. In.)	15·33 N	61·28 W
100	Port Stanley Falk. Is.	51·46 S	57·59 W
165	Port Sudan (sōō-dän') Sud.	19·30 N	37·10 E
84	Port Sulphur (sŭl'fẽr) La. (New Orleans In.)	29·28 N	89·41 W
65	Port Susan (B.) (sū-zăn') Wash. (Seattle In.)	48·11 N	122·25 W
139	Port Swettenham (swĕt'ĕn-hăm) Mala. (Singapore In.)	3·00 N	101·25 E
79	Port Tampa (tăm'pȧ) . Fla. (In.)	27·50 N	82·30 W
65	Port Townsend (tounz'ĕnd) Wash. (Seattle In.)	48·07 N	122·46 W
65	Port Townsend (B.) Wash. (Seattle In.)	48·05 N	122·47 W
102	Portugal (pōr'tū-găl) Eur.	38·15 N	8·08 W
124	Portugalete (pōr-tōō-gä-lā'tā) . Sp.	43·18 N	3·05 W
	Portuguese East Africa, see Mozambique		
163	Portuguese Guinea (gĭn'ê) Afr.	12·00 N	20·00 W
	Portuguese India, see Damão, Diu & Gôa		
155	Portuguese Timor (tê-mōr') . Asia	4·22 S	126·15 E
	Portuguese West Africa, see Angola		
122	Port Vendres (pôr vän'dr') Fr.	42·32 N	3·07 E
160	Port Wakefield (wāk'fēld) . Austl.	34·12 S	138·10 E
84	Port Washington (wôsh'ĭng-tŭn) N. Y. (New York In.)	40·49 N	73·42 W
71	Port Washington Wis.	43·24 N	87·52 W
100	Posadas (pō-sä'dhäs) Arg.	27·32 S	55·56 W
124	Posadas (pô-sä-däs) Sp.	37·48 N	5·09 W
148	Poshan (pō'shän') China	36·32 N	117·51 E
128	Poshekhon'ye Volodarsk (pô-shyĕ'kôn-yĕ vôl'ô-dàrsk) Sov. Un.	58·31 N	39·07 E
154	Poso, Danau (L.) (pō'sō) . Indon.	2·00 S	119·40 E
136	Pospelkova (pôs-pyĕl'kô-vȧ) Sov. Un. (Urals In.)	59·25 N	60·50 E
65	Possession Sd. (pŏ-zĕsh'ŭn) Wash. (Seattle In.)	47·59 N	122·17 W
76	Possum Kingdom Res. (pŏs'ŭm kĭng'dŭm) . Tex.	32·58 N	98·12 W
72	Post (pōst) Tex.	33·12 N	101·21 W
126	Postojna (pôs-tōynȧ) Yugo.	45·45 N	14·13 E
152	Pos'yet (pos-yĕt') Sov. Un.	42·27 N	130·47 E
84	Potash (pŏ'tăsh) La. (New Orleans In.)	29·29 N	89·43 W
73	Potawatomi Ind. Res. (pŏt-ȧ-wä'tō mē) . Kans.	39·30 N	96·11 W
168	Potchefstroom (pŏch'ĕf-strōm) S. Afr. (Johannesburg & Pretoria In.)	26·42 S	27·06 E
73	Poteau (pô-tō') Okla.	35·03 N	94·37 W
76	Poteet (pô-tēt) Tex.	29·05 N	98·35 W
126	Potenza (pô-tĕnt'sä) It.	40·39 N	15·49 E
126	Potenza (R.) It.	43·09 N	13·00 E
168	Potgietersrust (pŏt'gē-tẽrz-rüst') S. Afr. (Johannesburg & Pretoria In.)	24·09 S	29·04 E
133	Poti (pô'tē) Sov. Un.	42·10 N	41·40 E
164	Potiskum Nig.	11·45 N	11·05 E
81	Potomac (R.) (pō-tō'măk) Va.	38·15 N	76·55 W
98	Potosí (pō-tô-sē') Bol.	19·42 S	65·42 W
73	Potosi (pŏ-tō'sĭ) Mo.	37·56 N	90·46 W
76	Potosi, R. (pō-tô-sē') Mex.	25·04 N	99·36 W
148	Pot'ou (bŭ'tō) China	38·05 N	116·35 E
92	Potrerillos (pō-trä-rēl'yōs) . Hond.	15·13 N	87·58 W
111	Potsdam (pŏts'dăm) Ger. (Berlin In.)	52·24 N	13·04 E
81	Potsdam (pŏts'dăm) N. Y.	44·40 N	75·00 W
111	Potsdam (Dist.) (pŏts'dăm) Ger. (Berlin In.)	52·31 N	12·45 E
111	Pottenstein Aus. (Wien In.)	47·58 N	16·06 E
110	Potters Bar (pŏt'ẽrz bär) Eng. (London In.)	51·41 N	0·12 W
81	Pottstown (pŏts'toun) Pa.	40·15 N	75·40 W
81	Pottsville (pôts'vĭl) Pa.	40·40 N	76·15 W
143	Pottuvil Ceylon	6·33 N	81·48 E
81	Poughkeepsie (pô-kĭp'sĭ) N. Y.	41·45 N	73·55 W
154	Poulo Condore, Iles de (Is.) . Viet.	8·30 N	106·28 E
65	Poulsbo (pōlz'bōō) Wash. (Seattle In.)	47·44 N	122·38 W
110	Poulton-le-Fylde (pōl'tŭn-lē-fīld') Eng.	53·52 N	2·59 W
101	Pouso Alegre (pō'zōō ä-lā'grĕ) Braz. (Rio de Janeiro In.)	22·13 S	45·56 W
124	Póvoa de Varzim (pō-vō'ȧ dä vär'zēn) . Port.	41·23 N	8·44 W
87	Povungnituk Can.	59·12 N	77·51 W
67	Powder River Wyo.	43·06 N	106·55 W
67	Powder R. (pou'dẽr) . Mont.-Wyo.	45·18 N	105·37 W
66	Powder R. Ore.	44·55 N	117·35 W
67	Powder R., South Fk. Wyo.	43·13 N	106·54 W
67	Powell (pou'ĕl) Wyo.	44·44 N	108·44 W
95	Powell Pt. Ba. Is.	24·50 N	76·20 W
78	Powell Res. Ky.-Tenn.	36·30 N	83·35 W
86	Powell River Can.	49·54 N	124·25 W
151	Poyang (pō'yăng') China	29·00 N	116·42 E
151	P'oyang Hu (L.) China	29·20 N	116·28 E
71	Poygan (R.) (poi'gȧn) Wis.	44·10 N	89·05 W
127	Požarevac (pō'zhä'rĕ-vȧts) . Yugo.	44·38 N	21·12 E
120	Poznań (pôz'nän'') Pol.	52·24 N	16·55 E
124	Pozoblanco (pô-thō-bläŋ'kō) . Sp.	38·23 N	4·50 W
91	Pozo Rica (pô-zô-rē'kä) Mex.	20·32 N	97·25 W
90	Pozos (pô'zōs) Mex.	22·05 N	100·50 W
125	Pozuelo de Alarcón (pô-thwā'lō dā ä-lär-kōn') Sp. (Madrid In.)	40·27 N	3·49 W
125	Pozzuoli (pôt-swô'lē) It. (Napoli In.)	40·34 N	14·08 E
128	Pra (R.) (prȧ) Sov. Un.	55·00 N	40·13 E
154	Prachin Buri (prä'chên) Thai.	13·59 N	101·15 E
98	Pradera (prä-dĕ'rä) Col. (In.)	3·24 N	76·13 W
122	Prades (pråd) Fr.	42·37 N	2·23 E
98	Prado (prä'dō) Col. (In.)	3·44 N	74·55 W
74	Prado Dam (prä'dō) Calif. (Los Angeles In.)	33·53 N	117·39 W
101	Prados (prå'dôs) Braz. (Rio de Janeiro In.)	21·05 S	44·04 W
	Prague, see Praha		
120	Praha (Prague) (prä'hȧ) (präg) Czech.	50·05 N	14·30 E
164	Praia (prä'yȧ) C. V. Is. (In.)	15·00 N	23·30 W
100	Praia Funda, Ponta da (Pt.) (pôn'tä-dȧ-prä'yȧ-fōō'n-dä) Braz. (In.)	23·04 S	43·34 W
66	Prairie City (prā'rĭ) Ore.	44·25 N	118·42 W
71	Prairie du Chien (prā'rĭ dōō shēn') Wis.	43·02 N	91·10 W
85	Prairie Grove (prā'rĭ grōv) Can. (Winnipeg In.)	49·48 N	96·57 W
71	Prairie Island Ind. Res. Minn.	44·42 N	92·32 W
85	Prairies, R. des (rē-vyâr' dā prȧ-rē') Can. (Montreal In.)	45·40 N	73·35 W
74	Prairietown (prā'rĭ-toun) Ill. (St. Louis In.)	38·58 N	89·55 W
151	Pratas (Is.) China	20·40 N	116·30 E
126	Prato (prä'tō) It.	43·53 N	11·03 E
122	Prats-de-Mollo (prȧ-dē-mô-lō') . Fr.	42·26 N	2·36 E
72	Pratt (prăt) Kans.	37·37 N	98·43 W
78	Prattville (prăt'vĭl) Ala.	32·28 N	86·27 W
119	Pravdinsk Sov. Un.	54·26 N	20·11 E
136	Pravdinskiy (pràv-dēn'skĭ) Sov. Un. (Moskva In.)	56·03 N	37·52 E
124	Pravia (prä'vê-ä) Sp.	43·30 N	6·08 W
119	Pregolya (R.) (prĕ-gô'lȧ) . Sov. Un.	54·37 N	20·50 E
76	Premont (prē-mŏnt') Tex.	27·20 N	98·07 W
120	Prenzlau (prĕnts'lou) Ger.	53·19 N	13·52 E
121	Přerov (przhĕ'rôf) Czech.	49·28 N	17·28 E
91	Presa Aleman (L.) (prä'sä-lĕ-mȧ'n) Mex.	18·20 N	96·35 W
110	Prescot (prĕs'kŭt) Eng.	53·25 N	2·48 W
69	Prescott (prĕs'kŏt) Ariz.	34·30 N	112·30 W
73	Prescott Ark.	33·47 N	93·23 W
81	Prescott (prĕs'kŭt) Can.	44·45 N	75·35 W
74	Prescott (prĕs'kŏt) Wis. (Minneapolis, St. Paul In.)	44·45 N	92·48 W
70	Presho (prĕsh'ō) S. D.	43·56 N	100·04 W
100	Presidencia Rogue Sáenz Peña (prĕ-sē-dĕ'n-sêä-rô'kĕ-sä'ĕnz-pĕ'n-yȧ) . Arg.	26·52 S	60·15 W
99	Presidente Epitácio (prā-sê-dĕn'tĕ ȧ-pê-tä'syōō) Braz.	21·56 S	52·01 W
76	Presidio (prĕ-sĭ'dĭ-ô) Tex.	29·33 N	104·23 W
90	Presidio, Rio del (R.) (rē'ō-dĕl-prĕ-sê'dyô) . Mex.	23·54 N	105·44 W
121	Prešov (prĕ'shôf) Czech.	49·00 N	21·18 E
127	Prespa (L.) (prĕs'pȧ) . Alb.-Yugo.	40·49 N	20·50 E
99	Prespuntal (R.) (prĕs-pōōn-täl') Ven. (In.)	9·55 N	64·32 W
82	Presque Isle (prĕsk'ēl') Maine	46·41 N	68·03 W
111	Pressbaum Aus. (Wien In.)	48·12 N	16·06 E
110	Preston (prĕs'tŭn) Eng.	53·46 N	2·42 W
67	Preston (prĕs'tŭn) Idaho	42·05 N	111·54 W
71	Preston (prĕs'tŭn) Minn.	43·42 N	92·06 W
65	Preston Wash. (Seattle In.)	47·31 N	121·56 W
80	Prestonburg (prĕs'tŭn-bûrg) . Ky.	37·35 N	82·50 W
110	Prestwich (prĕst'wĭch) Eng.	53·32 N	2·17 W
167	Pretoria (prē-tō'rĭ-ȧ) S. Afr. (Johannesburg & Pretoria In.)	25·43 S	28·16 E
167	Pretoria Noord (prĕ-tō'rĭ-ȧ nōōrd) S. Afr. (Johannesburg & Pretoria In.)	25·41 S	28·11 E
127	Préveza (prĕ'vȧ-zä) Grc.	38·58 N	20·44 E
64	Pribilof (Is.) (prĭ'bĭ-lof) Alaska	57·00 N	169·20 W
127	Priboj (prē'boi) Yugo.	43·33 N	19·33 E
69	Price (prīs) Utah	39·35 N	110·50 W
69	Price (R.) Utah	39·21 N	110·35 W
85	Priddis (prĭd'dĭs) Can. (Calgary In.)	50·53 N	114·20 W
85	Priddis Cr. Can. (Calgary In.)	50·56 N	114·32 W
124	Priego (prê-ä'gō) Sp.	37·27 N	4·13 W
119	Prienai (prê-ĕn'ī) Sov. Un.	54·38 N	23·56 E
166	Prieska (prē-ĕs'kȧ) S. Afr.	29·40 S	22·50 E
66	Priest L. (prēst) Idaho	48·30 N	116·43 W
66	Priest Rapids Dam Wash.	46·39 N	119·55 W
136	Priiskovaya (prĭ-ēs'kô-vȧ-yȧ) Sov. Un. (Urals In.)	60·50 N	58·55 E
126	Prijedor (prē'yĕ-dôr) Yugo.	44·58 N	16·43 E
127	Prijepolje (prē'yĕ-pō'lyĕ) . Yugo.	43·22 N	19·41 E
127	Prilep (prē'lĕp) Yugo.	41·20 N	21·35 E
129	Priluki (prê-lōō'kê) Sov. Un.	50·36 N	32·21 E
119	Primorsk (prē-môrsk') . Sov. Un.	60·24 N	28·35 E
129	Primorsko-Akhtarskaya (prē-môr'skô äk-tär'skĭ-ê) Sov. Un.	46·03 N	38·09 E
74	Primrose (prĭm'rōz) Tex. (Dallas, Fort Worth In.)	32·36 N	97·28 W
167	Primrose S. Afr. (Johannesburg & Pretoria In.)	26·11 S	28·11 E
86	Prince Albert (prĭns ăl'bẽrt) . Can.	53·17 N	105·33 W
86	Prince Albert Natl. Park Can.	54·10 N	105·25 W
86	Prince Albert Sd. Can.	70·23 N	116·57 W
87	Prince Charles I. (chärlz) Can.	67·41 N	74·10 W
82	Prince Edward Natl. Park (ĕd'wẽrd) . Can.	46·33 N	63·35 W
83	Prince Edward I. (Prov.) Can.	46·45 N	63·10 W
47	Prince Edward Is. S. Afr.	46·36 S	37·57 E
81	Prince Edward Pen. Can.	44·00 N	77·15 W

ng-sing; ŋ-baŋk; n-nasalized n; nŏd; cŏmmit; ōld; ôbey; ôrder; fōōd; fŏŏt; ou-out; s-soft; sh-dish; th-thin; pūre; ûnite; ûrn; stŭd; circŭs; ü-as "y" in study; '-indeterminate vowel.

254 Prince George–Qibliya PRONOUNCING INDEX

Page	Name Pronunciation Region	Lat. °′	Long. °′
86	Prince George (jôrj)........Can.	53·51 N	122·57 W
64	Prince of Wales (I.).......Alaska	55·48 N	133·46 W
159	Prince of Wales (I.)........Austl.	10·47 S	142·15 E
64	Prince of Wales, C. (wālz) .Alaska	65·48 N	169·08 W
86	Prince Rupert (roo'pẽrt).....Can.	54·20 N	130·11 W
110	Princes Risborough (prĭns'ĕz rĭz'brŭ) Eng. (London In.)	51·41 N	0·51 W
84	Princess Anne (prĭn'sĕs ăn) Va. (Norfolk In.)	36·44 N	76·03 W
159	Princess Charlotte B. (shär'lŏt) Austl.	13·45 S	144·15 E
47	Princess Martha Coast (mär'thȧ) Ant.	72·00 S	5·00 W
86	Princeton (prĭns'tŭn)........Can.	49·21 N	120·20 W
80	Princeton...................Ill.	41·20 N	89·25 W
80	Princeton..................Ind.	38·20 N	87·35 W
78	Princeton...................Ky.	37·07 N	87·52 W
71	Princeton.................Mich.	46·16 N	87·33 W
71	Princeton.................Minn.	45·34 N	93·36 W
73	Princeton..................Mo.	40·23 N	93·34 W
84	Princeton...N. J. (New York In.)	40·21 N	74·40 W
79	Princeton................W. Va.	37·21 N	81·05 W
71	Princeton..................Wis.	43·50 N	89·09 W
64	Prince William Sd. (wĭl'yăm) Alaska	60·40 N	147·10 W
164	Príncipe, Ilha do (I.) (ēl'yȧ dô prēn'sê-pě) .Afr.	1·42 N	5·38 E
66	Prineville (prĭn'vĭl)..........Ore.	44.17 N	120.48 W
93	Prinzapolca (prēn-zä-pōl'kä)..Nic.	13·18 N	83·35 W
93	Prinzapolca R..............Nic.	13·23 N	84·23 W
74	Prior Lake (prī'ẽr) Minn. (Minneapolis, St. Paul In.)	44·43 N	93·26 W
119	Priozërsk (prĭ-ô'zĕrsk)...Sov. Un.	61·03 N	30·08 E
133	Pripyat (Pripet) (R.) (prē'pyȧt) Sov. Un.	51·50 N	29·45 E
	Pripyat' Marshes, see Poles'ye		
127	Priština (prēsh'tĭ-nä).......Yugo.	42·39 N	21·12 E
78	Pritchard (prĭt'chârd).......Ala.	30·44 N	87·04 W
120	Pritzwalk (prēts'välk).......Ger.	53·09 N	12·12 E
122	Privas (prē-väs')............Fr.	44·44 N	4·37 E
129	Privol'noye (prē'vôl-nô-yĕ) Sov. Un.	47·30 N	32·21 E
127	Prizren (prē'zrĕn)..........Yugo.	42·11 N	20·45 E
125	Procida (prô'chē-dä) It. (Napoli In.)	40·31 N	14·02 E
125	Procida, I. di.......It. (Napoli In.)	40·32 N	13·57 E
74	Proctor (prŏk'tẽr) Minn. (Duluth In.)	46·45 N	92·14 W
81	Proctor......................Vt.	43·40 N	73·00 W
65	Proebstel (prōb'stĕl) Wash. (Portland In.)	45·40 N	122·29 W
124	Proenca-a-Nova (prô-ān'sȧ-ä-nō'vȧ).......Port.	39·44 N	7·55 W
92	Progreso (prô-grĕ'sô)......Hond.	15·28 N	87·49 W
91	Progreso (prô-grā'sō).......Mex.	21·14 N	89·39 W
76	Progreso....................Mex.	27·29 N	101·05 W
134	Prokop'yevsk...........Sov. Un.	53·52 N	86·38 E
127	Prokuplje (prô'ko͝op'l-yĕ)...Yugo.	43·16 N	21·40 E
154	Prome (prōm)...............Bur.	18·46 N	95·15 E
128	Pronya (R.) (prô'nyȧ)...Sov. Un.	54·08 N	30·58 E
128	Pronya (R.)............Sov. Un.	54·08 N	39·30 E
99	Propriá (prō-prē-ä')........Braz.	10·17 S	36·47 W
75	Prospect (prŏs'pĕkt) Ky. (Louisville In.)	38·21 N	85·36 W
84	Prospect Park (prŏs'pĕkt pärk) Pa. (Philadelphia In.)	39·53 N	75·18 W
66	Prosser (prŏs'ẽr)...........Wash.	46·10 N	119·46 W
121	Prostějov (prôs'tyě-yôf)....Czech.	49·28 N	17·08 E
65	Protection (I.) (prô-tĕk'shŭn) Wash. (Seattle In.)	48·07 N	122·56 W
128	Protoka (R.) (prôt'ô-kȧ) Sov. Un.	55·00 N	36·42 E
127	Provadiya (prō-väd'ê-yȧ)....Bul.	43·13 N	27·28 E
80	Providence (prŏv'ĭ-dĕns).....Ky.	37·25 N	87·45 W
84	Providence..R. I. (Providence In.)	41·50 N	71·23 W
67	Providence.................Utah	41·42 N	111·50 W
93	Providencia, Isla de (I.)......Col.	13·21 N	80·55 W
95	Providenciales (I.) (prō-vê-dĕn-sē-ä'lâs) (prŏ-vĭ-dĕn'shȧlz).Ba. Is.	21·50 N	72·15 W
64	Provideniya (prô-vĭ-dă'nĭ-yȧ) Sov. Un.	64·30 N	172·54 W
69	Provo (prō'vō).............Utah	40·15 N	111·40 W
126	Prozor (prô'zôr)...........Yugo.	43·48 N	17·59 E
84	Prudence I. (pro͞o'dĕns) R. I. (Providence In.)	41·38 N	71·20 W
121	Prudnik (pro͝od'nĭk).........Pol.	50·19 N	17·34 E
119	Prunkkala (pro͝oŋk'ȧ-lȧ)......Fin.	60·38 N	22·32 E
120	Prussia (Reg.) (prŭsh'ȧ).....Ger.	50·43 N	8·35 E
121	Pruszków (pro͞osh'ko͞of)......Pol.	52·09 N	20·50 E
129	Prut (R.) (pro͞ot).......Sov. Un.	48·05 N	27·07 E
73	Pryor (prī'ẽr)..............Okla.	36·16 N	95·19 W
133	Prypeć (R.).............Sov. Un.	51·50 N	25·35 E
121	Przedbórz (pzhĕd'bo͞ozh).....Pol.	51·05 N	19·53 E
121	Przedbórz...................Pol.	53·01 N	20·54 E
121	Przemyśl (pzhĕ'mĭsh'l)........Pol.	49·47 N	22·45 E
134	Przheval'sk (p'r-zhĭ-välsk') Sov. Un.	42·25 N	78·18 E
127	Psará (I.) (psä'rȧ)...........Grc.	38·39 N	25·26 E
129	Psël (R.) (psĕl).........Sov. Un.	49·45 N	33·42 E
127	Psevdhókavos (Pen.).........Grc.	39·58 N	24·05 E
128	Pskov (pskôf)...........Sov. Un.	57·48 N	28·19 E
128	Pskov (Oblast)..........Sov. Un.	57·33 N	29·05 E
128	Pskovskoye Ozero (L.) (p'skôv'skô'yĕ ôzê-rô) .Sov. Un.	58·05 N	28·15 E
128	Ptich' (R.) (p'têch).......Sov. Un.	53·17 N	28·16 E
126	Ptuj (pto͞o'ê)...............Yugo.	46·24 N	15·54 E
139	Puak (po͞o'ä) Indon. (Singapore In.)	1·39 N	101·31 E
151	Pucheng (po͞o'chĕng')......China	28·02 N	118·25 E
121	Puck (po͞otsk)...............Pol.	54·43 N	18·23 E
146	Pudog......................China	33·29 N	79·26 E
132	Pudozh (po͞o'dôzh)......Sov. Un.	61·50 N	36·50 E
90	Puebla (pwā'blä)............Mex.	19·02 N	98·11 W
124	Puebla de Don Fadrique (pwĕ'blä dā dōn fä-drē'kā)..Sp.	37·55 N	2·55 W
72	Pueblo (pwā'blō)............Colo.	38·15 N	104·36 W
90	Pueblo Nuevo (nwā'vô).....Mex.	23·23 N	105·21 W
91	Pueblo Viejo (vyā'hô).......Mex.	17·23 N	93·46 W
74	Puente (pwĕn'tê) Calif. (Los Angeles In.)	34·01 N	117·57 W
101	Puente Alto (pwĕ'n-tě äl'tô) Chile (Santiago In.)	33·36 S	70·34 W
124	Puenteareas (pwĕn-tä-ä-rä'äs) .Sp.	42·09 N	8·23 W
124	Puente Ceso (pwĕn'tȧ thā'sô)..Sp.	43·15 N	8·53 W
124	Puentedeume (pwĕn-tȧ-dhȧ-o͞o'mȧ).Sp.	43·28 N	8·09 W
124	Puente-Genil (pwĕn'tȧ-hȧ-nēl') Sp.	37·25 N	4·18 W
69	Puerco (R.) (pwĕr'kō)...N. Mex.	35·15 N	107·05 W
100	Puerto Aisén (pwĕ'r-tō ȧ'y-sĕ'n) Chile	45·28 S	72·44 W
91	Puerto Ángel (pwĕ'r-tō äŋ'hâl) Mex.	15·42 N	96·32 W
93	Puerto Armuelles (pwe'r-tô är-mo͞o-ā'lyās)..Pan.	8·18 N	82·52 W
92	Puerto Barrios (pwĕ'r-tô bär'rê-ôs) Guat.	15·43 N	88·36 W
98	Puerto Bermúdez (pwĕ'r-tō bĕr-mo͞o'däz).Peru	10·17 S	74·57 W
98	Puerto Berrío (pwĕ'r-tō bĕr-rē'ō) Col. (In.)	6·29 N	74·27 W
99	Puerto Cabello (pwĕ'r-tō kä-bĕl'yō).Ven. (In.)	10·28 N	68·01 W
93	Puerto Cabezas (pwĕ'r-tô kä-bā'zäs).Nic.	14·01 N	83·26 W
100	Puerto Casado (pwĕ'r-tō kä-sä'dō) Par.	22·16 S	57·57 W
92	Puerto Castilla (pwĕ'r-tō käs-tēl'yō) Hond.	16·01 N	86·01 W
98	Puerto Chicama (pwĕ'r-tō chē-kä'mä).Peru	7·46 S	79·18 W
98	Puerto Columbia (pwĕr'tô kô-lôm'bê-ä).Col.	11·08 N	75·09 W
93	Puerto Cortés (pwĕ'r-tô kôr-tās') C. R.	9·00 N	83·37 W
92	Puerto Cortés (pwĕ'r-tô kôr-tās') Hond.	15·48 N	87·57 W
98	Puerto Cumarebo (pwĕ'r-tō ko͞o-mä-rĕ'bô).Ven.	11·25 N	69·17 W
125	Puerto de Beceite (Mts.) (pwĕ'r-tō dĕ bĕ-sĕ'y-tĕ).Sp.	40·43 N	0·05 W
72	Puerto de Luna (pwĕr'tô dȧ lo͞o'nȧ).N. Mex.	34·49 N	104·36 W
98	Puerto de Nutrias (pwĕ'r-tō dĕ no͞o-trê-äs').Ven.	8·02 N	69·19 W
100	Puerto Deseado (pwĕ'r-tō dā-sȧ-ä'dhō).Arg.	47·38 S	66·00 W
98	Puerto Eten (pwĕ'r-tô ĕ-tĕ'n).Peru	6·59 S	79·51 W
93	Puerto Jimenez (pwĕ'r-tô ĸê-mĕ'nĕz).C. R.	8·35 N	83·23 W
99	Puerto La Cruz (pwĕ'r-tō lä kro͞o'z).Ven. (In.)	10·14 N	64·38 W
124	Puertollano (pwĕr-tôl-yä'nō)..Sp.	38·41 N	4·05 W
100	Puerto Madryn (pwĕ'r-tō mä-drĕn').Arg.	42·45 S	65·01 W
98	Puerto Maldonado (pwĕ'r-tō mäl-dō-nä'dô).Peru	12·43 S	69·01 W
	Puerto Mexico, see Coatzacoalcos		
90	Puerto Miniso (pwĕ'r-tō mē-nē'sô) Mex.	16·06 N	98·02 W
100	Puerto Montt (pwĕ'r-tō mô'nt) Chile	41·29 S	73·00 W
100	Puerto Natales (pwĕ'r-tō nä-tá'lĕs) Chile	51·48 S	72·01 W
98	Puerto Niño (pwĕ'r-tō nē'n-yō) Col. (In.)	5·57 N	74·36 W
94	Puerto Padre (pwĕ'r-tō pä'drā) Cuba	21·10 N	76·40 W
88	Puerto Peñasco (pwĕ'r-tô pĕn-yä's-kô).Mex.	31·39 N	113·15 W
100	Puerto Pinasco (pwĕ'r-tō pē-nä's-kô).Par.	22·31 S	57·50 W
99	Puerto Píritu (pwĕ'r-tō pē'rē-to͞o) Ven. (In.)	10·05 N	65·04 W
95	Puerto Plata (pwĕ'r-tô plä'tä) Dom. Rep.	19·50 N	70·40 W
154	Puerto Princesa (pwĕr-tō prēn-sā'sä).Phil.	9·45 N	118·41 E
89	Puerto Rico (pwĕr'tô rē'kō) N. A. (In.)	18·16 N	66·50 W
89	Puerto Rico Trough........N. A.	19·45 N	66·30 W
98	Puerto Salgar (pwĕ'r-tō säl-gär').Col (In.)	5·30 N	74·39 W
100	Puerto Santa Cruz (pwĕ'r-tō sän'tä kro͞oz').Arg.	50·04 S	68·32 W
99	Puerto Suárez (pwĕ'r-tō swä'râz).Bol.	18·55 S	57·39 W
98	Puerto Tejada (pwĕ'r-tō tĕ-ĸä'dä).Col. (In.)	3·13 N	76·23 W
90	Puerto Vallarta (pwĕ'r-tō väl-yär'tä).Mex.	20·36 N	105·13 W
100	Puerto Varas (pwĕ'r-tō vä'räs) Chile	41·16 S	73·03 W
98	Puerto Wilches (pwĕ'r-tō vēl'c-hĕs).Col.	7·19 N	73·54 W
133	Pugachëv (po͞o'gȧ-chyôf) Sov. Un.	52·00 N	48·40 E
65	Puget (pū'jĕt) Wash. (Portland In.)	46·10 N	123·23 W
66	Puget Sd...................Wash.	47·49 N	122·26 W
126	Puglia (Apulia) (Reg.) (po͞o'lyä) (ȧ-po͞o'lyȧ).It.	41·13 N	16·10 E
148	Puhsien (po͞o'siän)........China	35·43 N	115·22 E
139	Pukin (R.)..Mala. (Singapore In.)	2·53 N	102·54 E
126	Pula (po͞o'lä)...............Yugo.	44·52 N	13·55 E
98	Pulacayo (po͞o-lä-kä'yō)......Bol.	20·12 S	66·33 W
148	P'ulantien (po͞o'län'chĕn')..China	39·23 N	121·57 E
78	Pulaski (pů-lăs'kĭ)..........Tenn.	35·11 N	87·03 W
79	Pulaski.....................Va.	37·00 N	81·45 W
121	Puławy (po͞o-wä'vê).........Pol.	51·24 N	21·59 E
142	Pulizat (R.)...............India	13·58 N	79·52 E
66	Pullman (po͞ol'măn).........Wash.	46·44 N	117·10 W
155	Pulog (Mtn.) (po͞o'lôg) Phil. (Manila In.)	16·38 N	120·53 E
112	Pultusk (po͞ol'to͞osk)..........Pol.	52·40 N	21·09 E
67	Pumpkin Cr. (pŭmp'kĭn)...Mont.	45·47 N	105·35 W
142	Punakhapo͞o-nŭk'ŭ)..........Bhu.	27·45 N	89·59 E
98	Punata (po͞o-nä'tä)..........Bol.	17·43 S	65·43 W
142	Punjab (State) (pŭn'jäb')...India	35·50 N	75·20 E
98	Puno (po͞o'nô)..............Peru	15·58 S	7·02 W
100	Punta Arenas (po͞o'n-tä-rĕ'näs) Chile	53·09 S	70·48 W
99	Punta de Piedras (po͞o'n-tä dĕ pyĕ'dräs) Ven. (In.)	10.54 N	64·06 W
92	Punta Gorda (po͞on'tä gôr'dä) Br. Hond.	16·07 N	88·50 W
79	Punta Gorda (pŭn'tȧ gôr'dȧ) Fla. (In.)	26·55 N	82·02 W
93	Punta Gorda, Rio (R.) (po͞o'n-tä gô'r-dä).Nic.	11·34 N	84·13 W
101	Punta Indio, Can. (po͞o'n-tä ē'n-dyô) Arg. (Buenos Aires In.)	34·56 S	57·20 W
93	Puntarenas (po͞ont-ä-rä'näs).C. R.	9·59 N	84·49 W
98	Punto Fijo (po͞o'n-tô fē'ĸô)..Ven.	11·48 N	70·14 W
164	Punto Grande (grä'n-dĕ) C. V. Is. (In.)	16·53 N	25·00 W
81	Punxsutawney (pŭnk-sŭ-tô'nê) Pa.	40·55 N	79·00 W
98	Puquio (po͞o'kyô)...........Peru	14·43 S	74·02 W
134	Pur (R.)...............Sov. Un.	65·30 N	77·30 E
73	Purcell (pûr-sĕl')..........Okla.	35·01 N	97·22 W
65	Purdy (pûr'dē) Wash. (Seattle In.)	47·23 N	122·37 W
90	Purépero (po͞o-rā'pȧ-rō).....Mex.	19·56 N	102·02 W
72	Purgatoire (R.) (pûr-gȧ-twär') Colo.	37·25 N	103·53 W
142	Puri (po͞o'rê)...............India	19·52 N	85·51 E
95	Purial, Sierra de (Mts.) (sē-ĕ'r-rȧ-dĕ-po͞o-rê-äl').Cuba	20·15 N	74·40 W
98	Purificacion (po͞o-rê-fê-kä-syōn') Col. (In.)	3·52 N	74·54 W
90	Purificación (po͞o-rē-fē-kä-syô'n) Mex.	19·44 N	104·38 W
90	Purificación (R.)...........Mex.	19·30 N	104·54 W
111	Purkersdorf......Aus. (Wien In.)	48·13 N	16·11 E
154	Pursat (po͞or-sät')........Camb.	12·33 N	103·51 E
90	Puruandiro (po͞o-ro͞o-än'dê-rō) Mex.	20·04 N	101·33 W
98	Purús (R.) (po͞o-ro͞o's)......Braz.	6·45 S	64·34 W
152	Pusan.......................Kor.	35·08 N	129·05 E
136	Pushkin (po͞osh'kĭn) Sov. Un. (Leningrad In.)	59·43 N	30·25 E
136	Pushkino (po͞osh'kê-nô) Sov. Un. (Moskva In.)	56·01 N	37·51 E
128	Pustoshka (pûs-tôsh'kȧ) .Sov. Un.	56·20 N	29·33 E
91	Pustunich (po͞os-to͞o'nēch)...Mex.	19·10 N	90·29 W
101	Putaendo (po͞o-tä-ĕn-dô) Chile (Santiago In.)	32·37 S	70·42 W
123	Puteaux (pü-tō')..Fr. (Paris In.)	48·52 N	2·12 E
167	Putfontein (po͞ot'fŏn-tān)..S. Afr. (Johannesburg & Pretoria In.)	26·08 S	28·24 E
151	P'ut'ien....................China	25·40 N	119·02 E
129	Putivl' (po͞o-tēv'l')......Sov. Un.	51·22 N	33·24 E
91	Putla de Guerrero (po͞o'tlä-dĕ-gĕr-rĕ'rō).Mex.	17·03 N	97·55 W
81	Putnam (pŭt'nȧm)........Conn.	41·55 N	71·55 W
134	Putorana, Gory (Mts.)...Sov. Un.	68·45 N	93·15 E
143	Puttālām.....................Cey.	8·02 N	79·44 E
98	Putumayo (R.) (po͞o-to͞o-mä'yō) Col.-Peru	1·02 S	73·50 W
149	Putung (po͞o'to͝ong') China (Shanghai In.)	31·14 N	121·29 E
154	Putung, Tandjung (C.)....Indon.	3·35 S	111·50 E
119	Puulavesi (L.)...............Fin.	61·49 N	27·10 E
65	Puyallup (pū-ăl'ŭp) Wash. (Seattle In.)	47·12 N	122·18 W
148	P'uyang (po͞o'yäng)........China	35·42 N	114·58 E
166	Pweto (pwä'tō)..........Con. L.	8·29 S	28·58 E
134	Pyasina (R.) (pyä-sē'nȧ).Sov. Un.	72·45 N	87·37 E
133	Pyatigorsk (pyä-tê-gôrsk') Sov. Un.	44·00 N	43·00 E
119	Pyhäjärvi (L.)...............Fin.	60·57 N	21·50 E
146	Pyinmana (pyĕn-mä'nŭ).....Bur.	19·47 N	96·15 E
80	Pymatuning Res. (pī-mȧ-tûn'ĭng) Pa.	41·40 N	80·30 W
152	Pyŏnggang (pyŭng'gäng')....Kor.	38·21 N	127·18 E
152	P'yŏngyang.................Kor.	39·03 N	125·48 E
68	Pyramid (L.) (pĭ'rȧ-mĭd).....Nev.	40·02 N	119·50 W
68	Pyramid Lake Ind. Res.....Nev.	40·17 N	119·52 W
168	Pyramids.........U. A. R. (Nile In.)	29·53 N	31·10 E
125	Pyrenees (Mts.) (pĭr-ē-nēz') Fr.-Sp.	43·00 N	0·05 E
120	Pyrzyce (pĕzhĭ'tsĕ)..........Pol.	53·09 N	14·53 E
168	Qana el Suweis (Suez Can.) U. A. R. (Suez In.)	30·53 N	32·21 E
115	Qārah (Oasis)...........U. A. R.	29·28 N	26·29 E
133	Qareh Sū (R.)...............Iran	38·50 N	47·10 E
168	Qārūn, Birket (L.) U. A. R. (Nile In.)	29·34 N	30·34 E
144	Qaryat al Ulya...........Sau. Ar.	27·43 N	47·43 E
165	Qasr Banī Walīd............Libya	31·45 N	14·04 E
138	Qatar (kä'tär)...............Asia	25·00 N	52·45 E
115	Qattarah, Munkhafad al (Dep.) U. A. R.	30·07 N	27·30 E
144	Qāyen.......................Iran	33·45 N	59·08 E
168	Qena, Wadi (val.) U. A. R. (Nile In.)	26·38 N	32·53 E
144	Qeshm..............Qeshm (I.)	26·51 N	56·10 E
144	Qeshm (I.)...................Iran	26·52 N	56·15 E
144	Qezel Owzan.................Iran	37·00 N	48·23 E
133	Qezel Owzan (R.)............Iran	37·00 N	47·35 E
139	Qiblīya, el (cliff) U. A. R. (Palestine In.)	28·47 N	32·22 E

Page	Name Pronunciation Region	Lat. °′	Long. °′
168	Qift (kĕft) U. A. R. (Nile In.)	25·58 N	32·52 E
168	Qinā (kä'nȧ) U. A. R. (Nile In.)	26·10 N	32·48 E
139	Qiraiya (R.) U. A. R. (Palestine In.)	30·14 N	34·21 E
144	Qom Iran	34·28 N	50·53 E
	Qomul see Hami		
81	Quabbin Res. (kwā'bĭn) Mass.	42·20 N	72·10 W
73	Quachita, L. (kwä shĭ'tô) Ark.	34·47 N	93·37 W
165	Quada (Reg.) Chad	13·04 N	20·00 E
81	Quakertown (kwā'kẽr-toun) Pa.	40·30 N	75·20 W
72	Quanah (kwä'nȧ) Tex.	34·19 N	99·43 W
151	Quang Ngai (kwäng n'gä'ē) Viet.	15·05 N	108·58 E
151	Quang Ngai (Mtn.) Viet.	15·10 N	108·20 E
154	Quang Tri (kwäng'trē') Viet.	16·39 N	107·05 E
86	Qu'Appelle (R.) (kȧ-pĕl') Can.	50·55 N	104·12 W
126	Quartu Sant' Elena (kwär-tōō' sänt a'lâ-nä) It.	39·16 N	9·12 E
85	Quebec (kwē-bĕk') (kȧ-bĕk') Can. (Quebec In.)	46·49 N	71·14 W
87	Quebec (Prov.) Can.	51·07 N	70·25 W
120	Quedlinburg (kvĕd'lĕn-bŏŏrgh) Ger.	51·49 N	11·10 E
86	Queen Charlotte Is. (kwēn shär'lŏt) Can.	53·40 N	132·50 W
86	Queen Charlotte Str. (strāt) Can.	51·19 N	128·42 W
49	Queen Elizabeth Is. (ē-lĭz'á-bĕth) Can.	78·20 N	110·00 W
86	Queen Maud G. (mäd) Can.	68·27 N	102·55 W
47	Queen Maud Land Ant.	75·00 S	10·00 E
47	Queen Maud Ra Ant.	85·00 S	179·00 W
158	Queens Chan. (kwēnz) Austl.	14·25 S	129·10 E
161	Queenscliff Austl. (Melbourne In.)	38·16 S	144·39 E
159	Queensland (State) (kwēnz'lănd) Austl.	22·45 S	141·01 E
160	Queenstown (kwēnz'toun) Austl.	42·00 S	145·40 E
167	Queenstown S. Afr. (Natal In.)	31·54 S	26·53 E
124	Queija, Sierra de (Mts.) (sē-ĕ'r-rä-dĕ-kĕ'y-kä) Sp.	42·08 N	7·23 W
100	Queimados (kā-mȧ'dôs) Braz. (In.)	22·42 S	43·34 W
166	Quelimane (kā-lê-mä'nĕ) Moz.	17·48 S	37·05 E
	Quelpart, see Cheju		
94	Quemado de Güines (kā-mä'dhä-dĕ-gwē'nĕs) Cuba	22·45 N	80·20 W
151	Quemoy (Chinmen) China	24·30 N	118·20 E
93	Quepos (kā'pôs) C. R.	9·26 N	84·10 W
93	Quepos, Punta (pt.) (pōō'n-tä) C. R.	9·23 N	84·20 W
166	Queque (kwĕ'kwĕ) Fed. of Rh. & Nya.	18·49 S	29·45 E
90	Querétaro (kå-rā'tä-rō) Mex.	20·37 N	100·25 W
124	Quesada (kå-sä'dhä) Sp.	37·51 N	3·04 W
86	Quesnel (kā-nĕl') Can.	53·00 N	122·28 W
86	Quesnel (L.) Can.	52·28 N	121·40 W
98	Quetame (kĕ-tä'mĕ) Col. (In.)	4·20 N	73·50 W
87	Quetico Park (kwĕ'tĭ-kô) Can.	48·29 N	91·50 W
142	Quetta (kwĕt'ȧ) W. Pak.	30·19 N	67·01 E
92	Quezaltenango (kå-zäl'tå-näŋ'gō) Guat.	14·50 N	91·30 W
92	Quezaltepeque (kå-zäl'tå-pā'kå) Guat.	14·39 N	89·26 W
92	Quezaltepeque (kĕ-zäl'tĕ'pĕ-kĕ) Sal.	13·50 N	89·17 W
155	Quezon City (kā-zōn) Phil. (Manila In.)	14·40 N	121·02 E
98	Quibdo (kēb'dō) Col. (In.)	5·42 N	76·41 W
122	Quiberon (kē-bē-rôN') Fr.	47·29 N	3·08 W
92	Quiché (kē-shā') Guat.	15·05 N	91·08 W
111	Quicksborn (kvēks'bōrn) Ger. (Hamburg In.)	53·44 N	9·54 E
65	Quilcene (kwĭl-sēn') Wash. (Seattle In.)	47·50 N	122·53 W
101	Quilimari (kē-lē-mä'rē) Chile (Santiago In.)	32·06 S	71·28 W
86	Quill (L.) (kwĭl) Can.	52·10 N	103·34 W
122	Quillan (kē-yäN') Fr.	42·53 N	2·13 E
101	Quillota (kêl-yō'tä) Chile (Santiago In.)	32·52 S	71·14 W
100	Quilmes (kēl'mäs) Arg. (In.)	34·28 S	58·16 W
143	Quilon (kwê-lōn') India	8·58 N	76·16 E
160	Quilpie (kwĭl'pē) Austl.	26·34 S	149·20 E
101	Quilpué (kēl-pōō ĕ') Chile (Santiago In.)	33·03 S	71·22 W
98	Quimbaya (kēm-bä'yä) Col. (In.)	4·38 N	75·46 W
122	Quimper (käN-pĕr') Fr.	47·59 N	4·04 W
155	Quinabucasan Pt. (kē-nä-bōō-kä'sän) Phil. (Manila In.)	14·09 N	123·33 E
66	Quinalt R. Wash.	47·23 N	124·10 W
66	Quinault Ind. Res. Wash.	47·27 N	124·34 W
78	Quincy (kwĭn'sē) Fla.	30·35 N	84·35 W
73	Quincy Ill.	39·55 N	91·23 W
83	Quincy Mass. (Boston In.)	42·15 N	71·00 W
80	Quincy Mich.	42·00 N	84·50 W
65	Quincy Ore. (Portland In.)	46·08 N	123·10 W
154	Qui Nhon (kwĭnyôn) Viet.	13·51 N	109·03 E
66	Quinn R. (kwĭn) Nev.	41·42 N	117·45 W
124	Quintana de la Serena (kēn-tä'nä dā lä så-rā'nä) Sp.	38·45 N	5·39 W
124	Quintanar (kēn-tä-när') Sp.	39·36 N	3·02 W
88	Quintana Roo (Ter.) (rô'ô) Mex.	19·30 N	88·35 W
101	Quintero (kēn-tĕ'rô) Chile (Santiago In.)	32·48 S	71·30 W
90	Quiroga (kē-rō'gä) Mex.	19·39 N	101·30 W
124	Quiroga (kē-rō'gä) Sp.	42·28 N	7·18 W
78	Quitman (kwĭt'măn) Ga.	30·46 N	83·35 W
78	Quitman Miss.	33·02 N	88·43 W
98	Quito (kē'tō) Ec.	0·17 S	78·32 W
99	Quixadá (kē-shä-dä') Braz.	4·58 S	38·58 W
168	Qulūşanā (kōō-lōōs'nä) U. A. R. (Nile In.)	28·22 N	30·44 E
167	Qumbu (kōōm'bōō) S. Afr. (Natal In.)	29·12 S	28·53 E
165	Qum Chalouba (kōōm shä-lōō'bä) Chad	15·48 N	20·30 E
139	Qumran Jordan (Palestine In.)	31·45 N	35·28 E
84	Quonset Point (kwän'sĕt) R. I. (Providence In.)	41·36 N	71·25 W
160	Quorn (kwôrn) Austl.	32·20 S	138·00 E
168	Qūs (kōōs) U. A. R. (Nile In.)	25·53 N	32·48 E
167	Quthing Bas. (Natal In.)	30·35 S	27·42 E
159	Quvea (I.) N. Cal.	20·43 S	166·48 E
144	Quzvīn Iran	36·10 N	49·59 E
120	Raab R. (räp) Aus.	46·55 N	15·55 E
112	Raahe (rä'ĕ) Fin.	64·39 N	24·22 E
126	Rab (I.) (räb) Yugo.	44·45 N	14·40 E
154	Raba Indon.	8·32 S	118·49 E
121	Raba R. Hung.	47·28 N	17·12 E
164	Rabat (rȧ-bät') Mor.	33·59 N	6·47 W
155	Rabaul (rä'boul) N. Gui. Ter.	4·15 S	152·19 E
127	Rača (rä'chȧ) Yugo.	44·13 N	21·01 E
71	Raccoon (R.) (ră-kōōn') Iowa	42·07 N	94·45 W
95	Raccoon Cay (I.) Ba. Is.	22·25 N	75·50 W
83	Race, C. (rās) Can.	46·37 N	52·55 W
139	Rachado, C. Mala. (Singapore In.)	2·26 N	101·29 E
121	Racibórz (rä-chē'bōōzh) Pol.	50·06 N	18·14 E
75	Racine (rȧ-sēn') Wis. (Milwaukee In.)	42·43 N	87·49 W
74	Raco (rȧ cō) Mich. (Sault Ste. Marie In.)	46·22 N	84·43 W
121	Rădăuti (rû-dû-ōōts'') Rom.	47·53 N	25·55 E
110	Radcliffe (răd'klĭf) Eng.	53·34 N	2·20 W
123	Radevormwald (rä'dĕ-fōrm-väld) Ger. (Ruhr In.)	51·12 N	7·22 E
79	Radford (răd'fẽrd) Va.	37·06 N	81·33 W
142	Rādhanpur India	23·57 N	71·38 E
74	Radio Center (ra'dĭ-ō cĕn'tẽr) Minn. (Minneapolis, St. Paul In.)	44·50 N	93·06 W
168	Radium (rā'dĭ-ŭm) S. Afr. (Johannesburg & Pretoria In.)	25·06 S	28·18 E
116	Radnor Forest (răd'nôr) Wales	52·11 N	3·25 W
121	Radom (rä'dôm) Pol.	51·24 N	21·11 E
127	Radomir (rä'dô-mêr) Bul.	42·33 N	22·58 E
121	Radomsko (rä-dôm'skô) Pol.	51·04 N	19·27 E
129	Radomyshl (rä-dô-mēsh''l) Sov. Un.	50·30 N	29·13 E
127	Radoviš (rä'dô-vêsh) Yugo.	41·39 N	22·28 E
118	Radöy (I.) (räd-ûê) Nor.	60·43 N	4·40 E
129	Radul' (rä'dōōl) Sov. Un.	51·52 N	30·46 E
119	Radviliškis (råd'vê-lēsh'kēs) Sov. Un.	55·49 N	23·31 E
144	Radwah, Jabal (Mtn.) Sau. Ar.	24·44 N	38·14 E
121	Radzyń Podlaski (räd'zēn-y' pŭd-lä'skĭ) Pol.	51·49 N	22·40 E
79	Raeford (rā'fẽrd) N. C.	34·57 N	79·15 W
123	Raesfeld (răz'fĕld) Ger. (Ruhr In.)	51·46 N	6·50 E
158	Raeside (rā'sīd) Austl.	29·20 S	122·30 E
86	Rae Str. (rā) Can.	68·40 N	95·03 W
100	Rafaela (rä-fä-ā'lä) Arg.	31·15 S	61·21 W
115	Rafah (rä'fä) U. A. R.	31·14 N	34·12 E
165	Rafai (rȧ-fī') Cen. Afr. Rep.	4·59 N	23·58 E
144	Rafhā Sau. Ar.	29·43 N	43·13 E
67	Raft R. (răft) Idaho	42·20 N	113·17 W
142	Raga China	29·31 N	85·52 E
155	Ragay (rä-gī') Phil. (Manila In.)	13·49 N	122·45 E
155	Ragay G. Phil. (Manila In.)	13·44 N	122·38 E
133	Ragga U. A. R.	36·00 N	39·00 E
118	Ragunda (rä-gōōn'dä) Swe.	63·07 N	16·24 E
113	Ragusa (rä-gōō'sä) It.	36·58 N	14·41 E
	Ragusa, see Dubrovnik		
84	Rahway (rô'wā) N. J. (New York In.)	40·37 N	74·16 W
143	Raichur (rä'ê-chōōr') India	16·23 N	77·18 E
142	Raigarh (rī'gŭr) India	21·57 N	83·32 E
69	Rainbow Bridge Natl. Mon. (rān'bō) Utah	37·05 N	111·00 W
88	Rainbow City C. Z. (Panama Canal In.)	9·20 N	79·23 W
65	Rainier Oreg. (Portland In.)	46·05 N	122·56 W
65	Rainier, Mt. (rā-nēr') Wash.	46·52 N	121·46 W
71	Rainy (L.) (rān'ē) Can.-Minn.	48·50 N	93·06 W
71	Rainy (R.) Can.-Minn.	48·36 N	94·14 W
87	Rainy River Can.	48·42 N	94·29 W
142	Raipur (rä'jŭ-bōō-rē') India	21·25 N	81·37 E
80	Raisin (R.) (rā'zĭn) Mich.	42·00 N	83·35 W
84	Raitan (rā-tăn) (N. J. (New York In.)	40·34 N	74·40 W
154	Raja, Bukit (Mtn.) Indon.	0·45 S	112·11 E
143	Rajahmundry (räj-ŭ-mŭn'drê) India	17·03 N	81·51 E
154	Rajang, Balang (strm.) Sar.	2·10 N	113·30 E
142	Rājasthān (State) (rä'jŭs-tän) India	31·20 N	72·00 E
142	Rājkot (räj'kōt) India	22·20 N	70·48 E
142	Rakers Tal (L.) China	30·42 N	80·40 E
121	Rakhov (rä'kôf) Sov. Un.	48·02 N	24·13 E
136	Rakh'ya (räk'yȧ) Sov. Un. (Leningrad In.)	60·06 N	30·50 E
129	Rakitnoye (rȧ-kēt'nô-yĕ) Sov. Un.	50·51 N	35·53 E
120	Rakovnik (rä'kôv-nyĕk) Czech.	50·07 N	13·45 E
128	Rakvere (råk'vĕ-rĕ) Sov. Un.	59·22 N	26·14 E
79	Raleigh (rô'lȧ) N. C.	35·45 N	78·39 W
79	Raleigh, B. N. C.	34·50 N	76·15 W
93	Rama (rä'mä) Nic.	12·11 N	84·14 W
101	Ramallo (rä-mä'l-yô) Arg. (Buenos Aires In.)	33·28 S	60·02 W
123	Rambouillet (räN-bōō-yĕ') Fr. (Paris In.)	48·39 N	1·49 E
167	Rame Hd. S. Afr. (Natal In.)	31·48 S	29·22 E
136	Ramenskoye (rä'mĕn-skô-yĕ) Sov. Un. (Moskva In.)	55·34 N	38·15 E
144	Ramlat As Sab Atayn (Reg.) Sau. Ar.	16·02 N	45·30 E
139	Ramm, Jabal (Mts.) Jordan (Palestine In.)	29·37 N	35·32 E
143	Rāmnād India	9·13 N	78·52 E
90	Ramos (rä'mōs) Mex.	22·46 N	101·52 W
76	Ramos Arizpe (ä-rēz'pȧ) Mex.	25·33 N	100·57 W
64	Rampart (răm'pärt) Alaska	65·28 N	150·18 W
84	Rampo Mts. (răm'pō) N. J.-N. Y. (New York In.)	41·06 N	74·12 W
142	Rāmpur (räm'pōōr) India	28·53 N	79·03 E
142	Rāmpur-Boālia (bō-ä'lē-ä) E. Pak.	24·26 N	88·39 E
154	Ramree (I.) (răm'rē') Bur.	19·01 N	93 23 E
85	Ramsayville (răm'zê vĭl) Can. (Ottawa In.)	45·23 N	75·34 W
110	Ramsbottom (rămz'bŏt-ŭm) Eng.	53·39 N	2·20 W
116	Ramsey (răm'zē) Isle of Man	54·20 N	4·25 W
84	Ramsey N. J. (New York In.)	41·03 N	74·09 W
117	Ramsgate (rămz'gāt) Eng.	51·19 N	1·20 E
118	Ramsjö (räm'shû) Swe.	62·11 N	15·44 E
155	Ramu (R.) (rä'mōō) N. Gui. Ter.	5·35 S	145·16 E
154	Ranau, L. (rä-nä'ōō) Indon.	4·52 S	103·52 E
101	Rancagua (rän-kä'gwä) Chile (Santiago In.)	34·10 S	70·43 W
122	Rance (räNs) Fr.	48·17 N	2·30 W
142	Rānchi (rän'chē) India	23·24 N	85·18 E
95	Rancho Boyeros (rä'n-chô-bô-yĕ'rôs) Cuba (La Habana In.)	23·00 N	82·23 W
84	Randallstown (răn'dălz-toun) Md. (Baltimore In.)	39·22 N	76·48 W
118	Randers (rän'ĕrs) Den.	56·28 N	10·03 E
167	Randfontein (rănt'fŏn-tān) S. Afr. (Johannesburg & Pretoria In.)	26·10 S	27·42 E
79	Randleman (răn'd'l-măn) N. C.	35·49 N	79·50 W
83	Randolph (răn'dŏlf) Mass. (Boston In.)	42 10 N	71·03 W
70	Randolph Nebr.	42·22 N	97·22 W
81	Randolph Vt.	43·55 N	72·40 W
83	Random I. (răn'dŭm) Can.	48·12 N	53·25 W
118	Rands Fd. (räns' fyôr) Nor.	60·35 N	10·10 E
82	Rangeley (rānj'lē) Maine	44·56 N	70·38 W
81	Rangeley (L.) Maine	44·55 N	70·40 W
76	Ranger (rān'jẽr) Tex.	32·26 N	98·41 W
142	Rangia India	26·32 N	91·39 E
154	Rangoon (ràŋ-gōōn') Bur.	16·46 N	96·09 E
142	Rangpur (rŭng'pōōr) E. Pak.	25·48 N	89·19 E
139	Rangsang, Palau (I.) (räng'säng') Indon. (Singapore In.)	1·03 N	102·54 E
111	Rangsdorf (rängs'dōrf) Ger. (Berlin In.)	52·17 N	13·25 E
142	Raniganj (rä-nē-gŭnj') India	23·40 N	87·08 E
86	Rankin Inlet (răŋ'kĕn) Can.	62·45 N	94·27 W
128	Ranova (R.) (rä'nô-vȧ) Sov. Un.	53·55 N	40·03 E
75	Ransomville (răn'sum-vĭl) N. Y. (Buffalo In.)	43·15 N	78·54 W
139	Rantau Mala. (Singapore In.)	2·35 N	101·58 E
154	Rantemario, Bulu (Mtn.) Indon.	3·22 S	119·50 E
80	Rantoul (răn-tōōl') Ill.	40·25 N	88·05 W
126	Rapallo (rä-päl'lō) It.	44·21 N	9·14 E
157	Rapa Nui (Easter) (I.) (rä'pä nōō'ē) (ēs'tẽr) Chile	26·50 S	109·00 W
101	Rapel (rä-pål') (R.) Chile (Santiago In.)	34·05 S	71·30 W
71	Rapid (R.) (răp'ĭd) Minn.	48·21 N	94·50 W
70	Rapid City S. D.	44·06 N	103·14 W
119	Rapla (räp'lä) Sov. Un.	59·02 N	24·46 E
81	Rappahannock (R.) (răp'ȧ-hăn'ŭk) Va.	38·20 N	75·25 W
81	Raquette (L.) (răk'ĕt) N. Y.	43·50 N	74·35 W
81	Raquette (R.) N. Y.	44·20 N	74·50 W
121	Rara Mazowiecka (rä'rä mä-zō-vyĕts'kä) Pol.	51·46 N	20·17 E
84	Raritan R. (răr'ĭ-tăn) N. J. (New York In.)	40·32 N	74·27 W
157	Rarotonga (rä'rō-tôŋ'gȧ) Cook Is.	20·40 S	163·00 W
144	Ras Al Hadd (C.) Mus. & Om.	22·29 N	59·46 E
139	Ra's an Naqb Jordan (Palestine In.)	30·00 N	35·29 E
163	Ras Dashan (Mtn.) (räs dä-shän') Eth.	12·49 N	38·14 E
119	Raseiniai (rä-syä'nyĭ) Sov. Un.	55·23 N	23·04 E
144	Ras Fartak (C.) Aden	15·43 N	52·17 E
139	Rashayya Leb. (Palestine In.)	33·30 N	35·50 E
168	Rashīd (Rosetta) (rȧ-shēd') (rô-zĕt'ȧ) U. A. R. (Nile In.)	31·22 N	30·25 E
168	Rashīd, Masabb (R. Mth.) U. A. R. (Nile In.)	31·30 N	29·58 E
136	Rashkina (råsh'kĭ-nȧ) Sov. Un. (Urals In.)	59·57 N	61·30 E
129	Rashkov (räsh'kôf) Sov. Un.	47·55 N	28·51 E
144	Rasht Iran	37·13 N	49·45 E
127	Raška (räsh'kȧ) Yugo.	43·16 N	20·40 E
142	Ras Kuh Mt. W. Pak.	34·03 N	65·10 E
144	Ras Madrakah (C.) Mus. & Om.	18·53 N	57·48 E
133	Rasskazovo (räs-kä'sô-vô) Sov. Un.	52·40 N	41·40 E
144	Ra's Tannūrah Sau. Ar.	26·45 N	49·59 E
120	Rastatt (rä-shtät) Ger.	48·51 N	8·12 E
136	Rastes (rås'tĕs) Sov. Un. (Urals In.)	59·24 N	58·49 E
136	Rastunovo (räs-tōō'nô-vô) Sov. Un. (Moskva In.)	55·15 N	37·50 E
124	Ras Uarc (C.) Mor.	35·28 N	2·58 W
154	Rat Buri Thai.	13·30 N	99·46 E
77	Ratcliff (răt'klĭf) Tex.	31·22 N	95·09 W
120	Rathenow (rä'tĕ-nō) Ger.	52·36 N	12·20 E
116	Rathlin (I.) (răth-lĭn) Ire.	54·80 N	6·10 W
123	Ratingen (rä'tĕn-gĕn) Ger. (Ruhr In.)	51·18 N	6·51 E
64	Rat Is. (răt) Alaska	51·35 N	176·48 E
142	Ratlam India	23·19 N	75·05 E
143	Ratnāgir India	17·04 N	73·24 E
72	Raton (rȧ-tōn') N. Mex.	36·52 N	104·26 W
66	Rattlesnake Cr. (răt''l snāk) Ore.	42·38 N	117·39 W
118	Rättvik (rĕt'vēk) Swe.	60·54 N	15·07 E
120	Ratzeburger See (L.) (rä'tzĕ-bōōr-gĕr-zā) Ger.	53·48 N	11·02 E
101	Rauch (rà'ōōch) Arg. (Buenos Aires In.)	36·47 S	59·05 W
118	Raufoss (rou'fôs) Nor.	60·44 N	10·30 E
101	Raúl Soares (rä-ōō'l-sôä'rĕs) Braz. (Rio de Janeiro In.)	20·05 S	42·28 W
119	Rauma (rä'ōō-mà) Fin.	61·07 N	21·31 E

ng-sing; ŋ-baŋk; N-nasalized n; nŏd; cŏmmit; ōld; ôbey; ôrder; fōōd; fŏŏt; ou-out; s-soft; sh-dish; th-thin; pūre; ûnite; ûrn; stŭd; circŭs; ü-as "y" in study; '-indeterminate vowel.

Page	Name Pronunciation Region	Lat. °′	Long. °′
119	Rauna (rȧū'-nȧ) Sov. Un.	57·21 N	25·31 E
154	Raung, Gunung (Mtn.) Indon.	8·15 S	113·56 E
119	Rautalampi (rä'o͞o-tĕ-läm'pô) Fin.	62·39 N	26·25 E
121	Rava-Russkaya (rä'vȧ ro͞os'kä-yȧ) Sov. Un.	50·14 N	23·40 E
126	Ravenna (rä-vĕn'nä) It.	44·27 N	12·13 E
70	Ravenna (rȧ-vĕn'ȧ) Nebr.	41·20 N	98·50 W
80	Ravenna Ohio	41·10 N	81·20 W
120	Ravensburg (rä'vĕns-bo͞orgh) Ger.	47·48 N	9·35 E
65	Ravensdale (rā'vĕnz-dāl) Wash. (Seattle In.)	47·22 N	121·58 W
158	Ravensthorpe (rā'vĕns-thôrp) Austl.	33·30 S	120·20 E
80	Ravenswood (rā'vĕnz-wo͝od) W. Va.	38·55 N	81·50 W
142	Rawalpindi (rä-wŭl-pên'dê) W. Pak.	33·42 N	73·04 E
144	Rawanduz Iraq	36·37 N	44·30 E
120	Rawicz (rä'vêch) Pol.	51·36 N	16·51 E
158	Rawlina (rôr-lēnȧ) Austl.	31·13 S	125·45 E
67	Rawlins (rô'lĭnz) Wyo.	41·46 N	107·15 W
100	Rawson (rô'sŭn) Arg.	43·16 S	65·09 W
101	Rawson...Arg. (Buenos Aires In.)	34·36 S	60·03 W
110	Rawtenstall (rô'tĕn-stôl) Eng.	53·42 N	2·17 W
83	Ray, C. (rā) Can.	47·38 N	59·25 W
135	Raychikinsk (rī'chĭ-kēnsk) Sov. Un.	49·52 N	129·17 E
110	Rayleigh (rā'lê) Eng. (London In.)	51·35 N	0·36 E
86	Raymond (rā'mŭnd) Can.	49·32 N	112·38 W
66	Raymond Wash.	46·41 N	123·42 W
77	Raymondville (rā'mŭnd-vĭl) Tex.	26·30 N	97·46 W
64	Ray Mts. Alaska	65·40 N	151·45 W
77	Rayne (rān) La.	30·12 N	92·15 W
90	Rayón'(rä-yōn') Mex.	21·49 N	99·39 W
167	Rayton (rā'tŭn) S. Afr. (Johannesburg & Pretoria In.)	25·45 S	28·33 E
74	Raytown (rā'toun) Mo. (Kansas City In.)	39·01 N	94·48 W
77	Rayville (rā-vĭl) La.	32·28 N	91·46 W
122	Raz, Pte. du (Pt.) (pwănt dü rä) Fr.	48·02 N	4·43 W
129	Razdel'naya (räz-dĕl'nä-yȧ) Sov. Un.	46·47 N	30·08 E
152	Razdol'noye (räz-dôl'nô-yĕ) Sov. Un.	43·38 N	131·58 E
127	Razgrad Bulg.	43·32 N	26·32 E
127	Razlog (räz'lôk) Bul.	41·54 N	23·32 E
122	Ré, Île de (I.) (ēl dē rā') Fr.	46·10 N	1·53 W
110	Rea (R.) (rē) Eng.	52·25 N	2·31 W
85	Reaburn (rā'bûrn) Can. (Winnipeg In.)	50·06 N	97·53 W
110	Reading (rĕd'ĭng) Eng. (London In.)	51·25 N	0·58 W
83	Reading...Mass. (Boston In.)	42·32 N	71·07 W
80	Reading Mich.	41·45 N	84·45 W
75	Reading...Ohio (Cincinnati In.)	39·14 N	84·26 W
81	Reading Pa.	40·20 N	75·55 W
100	Realango (rĕ-ä-län-gô) Braz. (In.)	22·25 S	43·25 W
165	Rebiana (Oasis) Libya	24·10 N	22·03 E
152	Rebun (I.) (rē'bo͞on) Jap.	45·25 N	140·54 E
126	Recanati (rā-kä-nä'tē) It.	43·25 N	13·35 E
158	Recherche, Arch. of the (rē-shârsh') Austl.	34·17 S	122·30 E
128	Rechitsa (ryĕ'chēt-sȧ) Sov. Un.	52·22 N	30·24 E
99	Recife (Pernambuco) (rȧ-sē'fĕ) (pĕr-näm-bo͞o'kô) Braz.	8.09 S	34·59 W
167	Recife, C. (rȧ-sē'fĕ) S. Afr. (Natal In.)	34·03 S	25·43 E
100	Reconquista (rā-kôn-kēs'tä) Arg.	29·01 S	59·41 W
73	Rector (rĕk'tēr) Ark.	36·16 N	90·21 W
78	Red (R.) Tenn.	36·30 N	87·10 W
72	Red (R.), North Fk. Tex.	35·20 N	100·08 W
63	Red. (R.) U. S.	31·40 N	92·55 W
62	Red (R.) (rĕd) U. S.-Can.	48·10 N	97·00 W
84	Redan (rê-dăn') (rĕd'ăn) Ga. (Atlanta In.)	33·44 N	84·09 W
84	Red Bank (băngk) N. J. (New York In.)	40·21 N	74·06 W
68	Red Bluff (blŭf) Calif.	40·10 N	122·14 W
76	Red Bluff Res. Tex.	32·03 N	103·52 W
71	Redby (rĕd'bê) Minn.	47·52 N	94·55 W
71	Red Cedar (R.) (sē'dēr) Wis.	45·03 N	91·48 W
86	Redcliff (rĕd'clĭf) Can.	50·10 N	111·09 W
71	Red Cliff Ind. Res. Wis.	46·48 N	91·22 W
160	Redcliffe (rĕd'clĭf) Austl.	27·20 S	153·12 E
72	Red Cloud (kloud) Nebr.	40·06 N	98·32 W
86	Red Deer (dēr) Can.	52·12 N	113·52 W
86	Red Deer (R.) Can.	50·55 N	111·32 W
75	Reddick (rĕd'dĭk) Ill. (Chicago In.)	41·06 N	88·16 W
84	Redding (rĕd'ĭng) Ala. (Birmingham In.)	33·27 N	86·54 W
66	Redding Calif.	40·36 N	122·25 W
101	Redenção da Serra (rĕ-dĕn-souN-dä-sĕ'r-rä) Braz. (Rio de Janeiro In.)	23·17 S	45·31 W
70	Redfield (rĕd'fēld) S. D.	44·53 N	98·30 W
77	Red Fish Bar Tex. (In.)	29·29 N	94·53 W
83	Red Indian L. (ĭn'dĭ-ăn) Can.	48·42 N	56·40 W
123	Redklinghausen (rĕk'lĭng-hou-zĕn) Ger. (Ruhr In.)	51·36 N	7·13 E
87	Red Lake (lāk) Can.	51·01 N	93·55 W
70	Red Lake (R.) Minn.	48·02 N	96·04 W
70	Red Lake Falls (lāk fôls) Minn.	47·52 N	96·17 W
70	Red Lake Ind. Res. Minn.	48·09 N	95·55 W
74	Redlands (rĕd'lăndz) Calif. (Los Angeles In.)	34·04 N	117·11 W
81	Red Lion (lī'ŭn) Pa.	39·55 N	76·30 W
67	Red Lodge Mont.	45·13 N	107·16 W
65	Redmond (rĕd'mŭnd) Wash. (Seattle In.)	47·40 N	122·07 W
120	Rednitz R. (rĕd'nētz) Ger.	49·49 N	10·57 E
70	Red Oak (ōk) Iowa	41·00 N	95·12 W
122	Redon (rē-dôN') Fr.	47·42 N	2·03 W

Page	Name Pronunciation Region	Lat. °′	Long. °′
100	Redonda, Isla (ē's-lä-rĕ-dô'n-dä) Braz. (In.)	23·05 S	43·11 W
93	Redonda I. W. I. F. (Le. & Wind. Is. In.)	16·55 N	62·28 W
124	Redondela (rā-dhôn-dā'lä) Sp.	42·16 N	8·34 W
124	Redondo (rå-dôn'do͞o) Port.	38·40 N	7·32 W
65	Redondo (rê-dŏn'dō) Wash. (Seattle In.)	47·21 N	122·19 W
74	Redondo Beach Calif. (Los Angeles In.)	33·50 N	118·23 W
72	Red R., Prairie Dog Town Fk. (prā'rĭ) Tex.	34·54 N	101·31 W
72	Red R., Salt Fk. Tex.	35·04 N	100·31 W
146	Red R. Viet.	22·25 N	103·50 E
67	Red Rock Cr. Mont.	44·54 N	112·44 W
165	Red Sea Afr.-Asia	23·15 N	37·00 E
67	Redwater Cr. (rĕd-wô'tēr) Mont.	47·37 N	105·25 W
71	Red Wing Minn.	44·34 N	92·35 W
65	Redwood City (rĕd' wo͝od) Calif. (San Francisco In.)	37·29 N	122·13 W
71	Redwood Falls Minn.	44·32 N	95·06 W
116	Ree, Lough (B.) (lŏK'rē') Ire.	53·30 N	7·45 W
80	Reed City (rēd) Mich.	43·50 N	85·35 W
68	Reedley (rēd'lê) Calif.	36·37 N	119·27 W
71	Reedsburg (rēdz'bûrg) Wis.	43·32 N	90·01 W
66	Reedsport (rēdz'pōrt) Ore.	43·42 N	124·08 W
78	Reelfoot (R.) (rēl'fo͝ot) Tenn.	36·18 N	89·20 W
123	Rees (rĕz) Ger. (Ruhr In.)	51·46 N	6·25 E
74	Reese (rēs) Utah (Salt Lake City In.)	41·15 N	112·09 W
160	Reeves, Mt. (rēv's) Austl.	33·50 S	149·56 E
78	Reform (rê-fôrm') Ala.	33·23 N	88·00 W
77	Refugio (rå-fo͞o'hyô) (rĕ-fū'jō) Tex.	28·18 N	97·15 W
120	Rega (R.) (rĕ-gä) Pol.	53·48 N	15·30 E
120	Regen R. (rā'ghĕn) Ger.	49·09 N	12·21 E
120	Regensburg(rā'ghĕns-bo͞orgh) Ger.	49·02 N	12·06 E
126	Reggio (rĕ'jô) It.	44·43 N	10·34 E
84	Reggio (rĕg'jĭ-ō) La. (New Orleans In.)	29·50 N	89·46 W
126	Reggio di Calabria (rĕ'jô dē kä-lä'brē-ä) It.	38·07 N	15·42 E
121	Reghin (rå-gēn') Rom.	46·47 N	24·44 E
86	Regina (rê-jī'nȧ) Can.	50·31 N	104·30 W
144	Registan (Reg.) Afg.	30·53 N	64·42 E
95	Regla (rāg'lä) Cuba (La Habana In.)	23·08 N	82·20 W
124	Reguengos de Monsaraz (rå-gĕŋ'gōzh dā mōn-sä-räzh') Port.	38·26 N	7·30 W
84	Rehoboth (rê-hō'bŏth) Mass. (Providence In.)	41·50 N	71·13 W
166	Rehoboth S. W. Afr.	23·10 S	17·15 E
139	Rehovoth...Isr. (Palestine In.)	31·53 N	34·49 E
120	Reichenbach (rī'kĕn-bäK) Ger.	50·36 N	12·18 E
79	Reidsville (rēdz'vĭl) N. C.	36·20 N	79·37 W
110	Reigate (rī'gāt) Eng. (London In.)	51·12 N	0·12 W
122	Reims (răNs) Fr.	49·16 N	4·00 E
100	Reina Adelaida, Arch. (är-chê'-pyĕ'lä-gô-rā'nä-ä-dĕ-lī'dä) Chile	52·00 S	74·15 W
71	Reinbeck (rīn'bĕk) Iowa	42·22 N	92·34 W
86	Reindeer (L.) (rān'dēr) Can.	57·36 N	101·23 W
124	Reinosa (rå-ē-nō'sä) Sp.	43·01 N	4·08 W
84	Reistertown (rēs'tēr-toun) Md. (Baltimore In.)	39·28 N	76·50 W
168	Reitz S. Afr. (Johannesburg & Pretoria In.)	27·48 S	28·25 E
84	Relay (rē'lā)..Md. (Baltimore In.)	39·14 N	76·44 W
125	Relizane (rē-lē-zän') Alg.	35·43 N	0·34 E
139	Rembau...Mala. (Singapore In.)	2·36 N	102·06 E
98	Remedios (rĕ-mĕ'dyôs)..Col. (In.)	7·03 N	74·42 W
94	Remedios (rā-mā'dhē-ōs) Cuba	22·30 N	79·35 W
93	Remedios (rĕ-mĕ'dyōs) Pan.	8·14 N	81·46 W
123	Remiremont (rē-mēr-môN') Fr.	48·01 N	6·35 E
139	Rempang I. Indon. (Singapore In.)	0·51 N	104·04 E
123	Remscheid (rĕm'shīt) Ger. (Ruhr In.)	51·10 N	7·11 E
159	Rendova (I.) (rĕn'dô-vȧ) Sol. Is.	8·38 S	156·26 E
120	Rendsburg (rĕnts'bo͞orgh) Ger.	54·19 N	9·39 E
81	Renfrew (rĕn'fro͞o) Can.	45·30 N	76·30 W
139	Rengam (rĕn'gäm') Mala. (Singapore In.)	1·53 N	103·24 E
101	Rengo (rĕn'gō) Chile (Santiago In.)	34·22 S	70·50 W
129	Reni (ran') Sov. Un.	45·26 N	28·18 E
160	Renmark (rĕn'märk) Austl.	34·10 S	140·50 E
159	Rennel (I.) (rĕn-nĕl') Sol. Is.	11·50 S	160·38 E
122	Rennes (rĕn) Fr.	48·07 N	1·02 W
81	Rensselaer (rĕn'sē-lâr) N. Y.	42·40 N	73·45 W
68	Reno (rē'nō) Nev.	39·32 N	119·49 W
126	Reno (R.) (rā'nô) It.	44·10 N	10·55 E
81	Renovo (rê-nō'vō) Pa.	41·20 N	77·50 W
80	Rensselaer (rĕn'sē-lâr) Ind.	41·00 N	87·10 W
74	Rentchler (rĕnt'chlēr) Ill. (St. Louis In.)	38·30 N	89·52 W
65	Renton (rĕn'tŭn) Wash. (Seattle In.)	47·29 N	122·13 W
71	Renville (rĕn'vĭl) Minn.	44·44 N	95·13 W
84	Republic (rê-pŭb'lĭk) Ala. (Birmingham In.)	33·37 N	86·54 W
66	Republic Wash.	48·38 N	118·44 W
72	Republican (R.), South Fk. (rê-pŭb'lĭ-kăn) Colo.	39·35 N	102·28 W
73	Republican (R.) Kans.	39·22 N	97·14 W
159	Repulse B. (rê-pŭls') Austl.	20·56 S	149·22 E
124	Requena (rå-kā'nä) Sp.	39·29 N	1·03 W
101	Resende (rĕ-sĕ'n-dĕ) Braz. (Rio de Janeiro In.)	22·30 S	44·26 W
101	Resende Costa (kôs-tä) Braz. (Rio de Janeiro In.)	20·55 S	44·12 W
129	Reshetilovka (ryĕ' shĕ-tē-lôf-kȧ) Sov. Un.	49·34 N	34·04 E
100	Resistencia (rā-sēs-tĕn'syä) Arg.	27·24 S	58·54 W
127	Reşita (rā'shē-tä) Rom.	45·18 N	21·56 E

Page	Name Pronunciation Region	Lat. °′	Long. °′
87	Resolution (I.) (rĕz-ô-lū'shŭn) Can.	61·30 N	63·58 W
159	Resolution (I.) (rĕz-ŏl-ûshŭn) N. Z. (In.)	45·43 S	166·00 E
82	Restigouche (R.) (rĕs-tē-go͞osh') Can.	47·35 N	67·35 W
98	Restrepo (rĕs-trĕ'pô) Col. (In.)	3·49 N	76·31 W
98	Restrepo Col. (In.)	4·16 N	73·32 W
92	Retalhuleu (rā-täl-o͞o-lān') Guat.	14·31 N	91·41 W
122	Rethel (r-tl') Fr.	49·34 N	4·20 E
126	Réthimnon Grc. (In.)	35·21 N	24·30 E
111	Retie Bel. (Bruxelles In.)	51·16 N	5·08 E
65	Retsil (rĕt'sĭl) Wash. (Seattle In.)	47·33 N	122·37 W
47	Reunion I. (rā-ü-nyôn') Ind. O.	21·06 S	55·36 E
125	Reus (rā'o͞os) Sp.	41·08 N	1·05 E
120	Reutlingen (roit'lĭng-ĕn) Ger.	48·29 N	9·14 E
136	Reutov (rĕ-o͞ot'ôf) Sov. Un.(Moskva In.)	55·45 N	37·52 E
	Reval, see Tallinn		
136	Revda (ryâv'dá) Sov. Un. (Urals In.)	56·48 N	59·57 E
86	Revelstoke (rĕv'ĕl-stōk) Can.	51·02 N	118·19 W
93	Reventazon, R. (rå-vĕn-tä-zōn') C. R.	10·10 N	83·30 W
83	Revere (rê-vēr') Mass. (Boston In.)	42·24 N	71·01 W
88	Revillagigedo, Islas De (I.) (ê's-läs-dĕ-rĕ-vêl-yä-hĕ'gĕ-dô) Mex.	18·45 N	111·00 W
122	Revin (rē-văN') Fr.	49·56 N	4·34 E
142	Rewa (rā'wä) India	24·41 N	81·11 E
142	Rewāri India	28·19 N	76·39 E
67	Rexburg (rĕks'bûrg) Idaho	43·50 N	111·48 W
76	Rey, L. (rā) Mex.	27·00 N	103·33 W
93	Rey, Isla del (I.) (ê's-lä-dĕl-rā'ê) Pan.	8·20 N	78·40 W
98	Reyes (rā'yĕs) Bol.	14·19 S	67·16 W
68	Reyes, Pt. Calif.	38·00 N	123·00 W
102	Reykjanes (C.) (rā'kyȧ-nĕs) Ice.	63·37 N	24·33 W
112	Reykjavik (rā'kyȧ-vĕk) Ice.	64·09 N	21·39 W
76	Reynosa (rā-ê-nō'sä) Mex.	26·05 N	98·21 W
144	Rezā'īyeh (Urmia) (rĕ-zī'ā) (o͞or'mê-ä) Iran	37·30 N	45·15 E
128	Rēzekne (rå'zĕk-nĕ) Sov. Un.	56·31 N	27·19 E
136	Rezh (rĕzh')..Sov. Un. (Urals In.)	57·22 N	61·23 E
129	Rezina (ryĕzh'ĕ-nĭ) Sov. Un.	47·44 N	28·56 E
126	Rhaetien Alps (Mts.) It.	46·22 N	10·33 E
117	Rheden (rā'dĕn) Neth.	52·02 N	6·02 E
123	Rheinberg (rīn'bĕrgh) Ger. (Ruhr In.)	51·33 N	6·37 E
120	Rheine (rī'nĕ) Ger.	52·16 N	7·26 E
120	Rheinland-Pfalz (Rhineland-Palatinate) (State) Ger.	50·05 N	6·40 E
120	Rhein R. (rīn) Ger.	50·34 N	7·21 E
123	Rheydt (rĕ'yt)...Ger. (Ruhr In.)	51·10 N	6·28 E
71	Rhinelander (rīn'lăn-dēr) Wis.	45·39 N	89·25 W
111	Rhin Kanal (Can.) (rēn kä-näl') Ger. (Berlin In.)	52·47 N	12·40 E
111	Rhin R. (rēn)...Ger. (Berlin In.)	52·52 N	12·49 E
63	Rhode Island (State) (rōd ī'lȧnd) U. S.	41·35 N	71·40 W
167	Rhodes (rôdz)..S. Afr. (Natal In.)	30·48 S	27·56 E
127	Rhodope Mts. (rô'dô-pĕ) Bul.	42·00 N	24·08 E
116	Rhondda (rŏn'dhȧ) Wales	51·40 N	3·40 W
122	Rhône (R.) (rōn) Fr.	45·14 N	4·53 E
111	Rhoon...Neth. (Amsterdam In.)	51·52 N	4·24 E
116	Rhum (I.) (rŭm) Scot.	56·63 N	6·20 W
99	Riachão (rê-ä-chouN') Braz.	6·55 S	46·33 W
74	Rialto (rê-ăl'tō) Calif. (Los Angeles In.)	34·06 N	117·23 W
124	Riaza (R.) (rê-ä'thä) Sp.	41·25 N	3·25 W
124	Ribadavia (rē-bä-dhä'vē-ä) Sp.	42·18 N	8·06 W
124	Ribadeo (rē-bä-dhā'ō) Sp.	37·32 N	7·05 W
124	Ribadesella (rē'bä-dā-säl'yä) Sp.	43·30 N	5·02 W
116	Ribble, R. (rĭb''l) Eng.	53·10 N	3·15 W
118	Ribe (rē'bĕ) Den.	55·20 N	8·45 E
101	Ribeirão Prêto (rē-bā-rouN-prĕ'tô) Braz. (Rio de Janeiro In.)	21·11 S	47·47 W
72	Ribera (rē-bĕ'rä) N. Mex.	35·23 N	105·27 W
98	Riberalta (rē-bā-räl'tä) Bol.	11·06 S	66·02 W
71	Rib Lake (rĭb lāk) Wis.	45·20 N	90·11 W
68	Rice (rīs) Calif.	34·05 N	114·50 W
81	Rice (L.) Can.	44·05 N	78·10 W
74	Rice L...Minn. (Minneapolis, St. Paul In.)	45·10 N	93·09 W
71	Rice Lake Wis.	45·30 N	91·44 W
64	Richards I. (rĭch'ērds) Can.	69·45 N	135·30 W
74	Richards Landing (lănd'ĭng) Can. (Sault Ste. Marie In.)	46·18 N	84·02 W
74	Richardson (rĭch'ērd-sŭn) Tex. (Dallas, Fort Worth In.)	32·56 N	96·44 W
65	Richardson...Wash. (Seattle In.)	48·27 N	122·54 W
86	Richardson Mts. Can.	66·58 N	136·19 W
81	Richardson Park (pärk) Del.	39·45 N	75·35 W
81	Richelieu (R.) (rēsh'lyû') Can.	45·05 N	73·25 W
74	Richfield (rĭch'fēld) Minn. (Minneapolis, St. Paul In.)	44·53 N	93·17 W
75	Richfield...Ohio (Cleveland In.)	41·14 N	81·38 W
69	Richfield Utah	38·45 N	112·05 W
81	Richford (rĭch'fērd) Vt.	45·00 N	72·35 W
73	Rich Hill (rĭch hĭl) Mo.	38·05 N	94·21 W
82	Richibucto (rĭ-chĭ-bŭk'tō) Can.	46·42 N	64·55 W
78	Richland (rĭch'lănd) Ga.	32·05 N	84·40 W
66	Richland Wash.	46·17 N	119·19 W
71	Richland Center (sĕn'tēr) Wis.	43·20 N	90·25 W
159	Richmond (rĭch'mŭnd) Austl.	20·47 S	143·14 E
161	Richmond...Austl. (Sydney In.)	33·36 S	150·45 E
65	Richmond Calif. (San Francisco In.)	37·56 N	122·21 W
82	Richmond Can.	45·40 N	72·07 W
85	Richmond...Can. (Ottawa In.)	45·12 N	75·49 W
75	Richmond...Ill. (Chicago In.)	42·29 N	88·18 W
80	Richmond Ind.	39·50 N	85·00 W
80	Richmond Ky.	37·45 N	84·20 W
73	Richmond Mo.	39·16 N	93·58 W

ăt; finăl; rāte; senâte; ärm; åsk; sofȧ; fåre; ch-choose; dh-as th in other; bē; êvent; bĕt; recĕnt; cratēr; g-go; gh-guttural g; bĭt; ĭ-short neutral; rīde; K-guttural k as ch in German ich;

PRONOUNCING INDEX Richmond–Rogoaguado 257

Page	Name Pronunciation Region	Lat. °′	Long. °′
77	Richmond . . . Tex.	29·35 N	95·45 W
167	Richmond . . . S. Afr. (Natal In.)	29·52 S	30·17 E
167	Richmond . . . S. Afr. (Natal In.)	33·44 S	26·36 E
67	Richmond . . . Utah	41·55 N	111·50 W
81	Richmond . . . Va.	37·35 N	77·30 W
65	Richmond Beach Wash. (Seattle In.)	47·47 N	122·23 W
74	Richmond Heights Mo. (St. Louis In.)	38·38 N	90·20 W
85	Richmond Hill (hĭl) Can. (Toronto In.)	43·53 N	79·26 W
93	Richmond Pk. W. I. F. (Le. & Wind. Is. In.)	13·19 N	61·12 W
78	Richton (rĭch'tŭn) . . . Miss.	31·20 N	89·54 W
80	Richwood (rĭch'wo͝od) . . . W. Va.	38·10 N	80·30 W
111	Ridderkerk Neth. (Amsterdam In.)	51·52 N	4·35 E
81	Rideau L. (rê-dō') . . . Can.	44·40 N	76·20 W
85	Rideau R. . . . Can. (Ottawa In.)	45·17 N	75·41 W
84	Ridgefield (rij'fēld) Conn. (New York In.)	41·16 N	73·30 W
65	Ridgefield . . . Wash. (Portland In.)	45·49 N	122·40 W
81	Ridgeley (rĭj'lê) . . . W. Va.	39·40 N	78·45 W
75	Ridgeway (rĭj'wā) Can. (Buffalo In.)	42·53 N	79·02 W
81	Ridgeway . . . Pa.	41·25 N	78·40 W
84	Ridgewood (ridj'wo͝od) N. J. (New York In.)	40·59 N	74·08 W
86	Riding Mountain Natl. Park (rīd'ĭng) . Can.	50·59 N	99·19 W
94	Riding Rocks (Is.) . . . Ba. Is.	25·20 N	79·10 W
167	Riebeek-Oos . . . S. Afr. (Natal In.)	33·14 S	26·09 E
120	Ried (rēd) . . . Aus.	48·13 N	13·30 E
120	Riesa (rē'zȧ) . . . Ger.	51·17 N	13·17 E
167	Riet (R.) (rēt) . . . S. Afr. (Johannesburg & Pretoria In.)	25·54 S	27·54 E
126	Rieti (rê-ā'tē) . . . It.	42·25 N	12·51 E
167	Rievleidam (L.) . . . S. Afr. (Johannesburg & Pretoria In.)	25·52 S	28·18 E
69	Rifle (rī'f'l) . . . Colo.	39·35 N	107·50 W
119	Riga (rē'gȧ) . . . Sov. Un.	56·55 N	24·05 E
119	Riga, G. of . . . Sov. Un.	57·56 N	23·05 E
144	Rīgān . . . Iran	28·45 N	58·55 E
85	Rigaud (rê-gō') Can. (Montreal In.)	45·29 N	74·18 W
67	Rigby (rĭg'bê) . . . Idaho	43·40 N	111·55 W
87	Rigolet (rĭg-ō-lā') . . . Can.	54·10 N	58·40 W
126	Rijeka (Fiume) (rĭ-yě'kä) . . . Yugo.	45·22 N	14·24 E
111	Rijkevorsel . . . Bel. (Bruxelles In.)	51·21 N	4·46 E
111	Rijswijk . . Neth. (Amsterdam In.)	52·03 N	4·19 E
121	Rika R. (rê'kȧ) . . . Sov. Un.	48·21 N	23·37 E
122	Rille (R.) (rēl) . . . Fr.	49·12 N	0·43 E
144	Rimach, Wādi ar (R.) . . . Sau. Ar.	26·17 N	41·13 E
121	Rimavska Sobota (rĕ'mäf-skä sô'bô-tȧ) . Czech.	48·25 N	20·01 E
118	Rimbo (rēm'bo͞o) . . . Swe.	59·45 N	18·22 E
126	Rimini (rē'mê-nē) . . . It.	44·03 N	12·33 E
127	Rîmnicul Sărat . . . Rom.	45·24 N	27·06 E
127	Rîmnicu Valcea . . . Rom.	45·07 N	24·22 E
82	Rimouski (rê-mo͞os'kê) . . . Can.	48·27 N	68·32 W
90	Rincón de Romos (rēn-kōn dā rô-mōs') . Mex.	22·13 N	102·21 W
154	Rindjani, Gunung (Mtn.) . . Indon.	8·39 S	116·22 E
118	Ringköbing (rĭng'kûb-ĭng) . . . Den.	56·06 N	8·14 E
118	Ringköbing Fd . . . Den.	55·55 N	8·04 E
118	Ringsaker (rĭngs'äk-ēr) . . . Nor.	60·55 N	10·40 E
118	Ringsted (rĭng'stědh) . . . Den.	55·27 N	11·49 E
112	Ringvassöy (I.) (rĭng'väs-ûê) . Nor.	69·58 N	16·43 E
161	Ringwood . Austl. (Melbourne In.)	37·49 S	145·14 E
88	Rio Abajo (rē'ō-ä-bä'kô) Pan. (Panama Canal In.)	9·01 N	78·30 W
90	Rio Balsas (rê'ō-bäl-säs) . . . Mex.	17·59 N	99·45 W
98	Riobamba (rē'ō-bäm'bä) . . . Ec.	1·45 S	78·37 W
101	Rio Bonito (rē'o͞o bō-nē'to͞o) Braz. (Rio de Janeiro In.)	22·44 S	42·38 W
98	Rio Branco (rē'o͞o bräŋ'ko͞o) . Braz.	9·57 S	67·50 W
99	Rio Branco (Ter.) . . . Braz.	2·35 N	61·25 W
101	Rio Casca (rē'ō-kȧ's-kä) Braz. (Rio de Janeiro In.)	20·15 S	42·39 W
99	Rio Chico (rê'ō chē'kô) . Ven. (In.)	10·20 N	65·58 W
101	Rio Claro (rē'o͞o klä'ro͞o) Braz. (Rio de Janeiro In.)	21·25 S	47·33 W
100	Río Cuarto (rē'ō kwär'tō) . . . Arg.	33·05 S	64·15 W
101	Rio das Flores (rē'ō-däs-flô-rěs) Braz. (Rio de Janeiro In.)	22·10 S	43·35 W
100	Rio de Janeiro (rē'o͞o dā zhä-nâ'ê-ro͞o) Braz. (In.)	22·50 S	43·20 W
99	Rio de Janeiro (State) . . . Braz.	22·27 S	42·43 W
93	Río de Jesús (rē'ō-dě-ĸě-so͞o's) Pan.	7·54 N	80·59 W
164	Rio del Rey (rē'ō děl rā'ê) . . . Nig.	4·41 N	8·38 E
164	Rio de Oro (Ter.) (rē'ō dā ō'rō) Sp. Sah.	23·11 N	14·15 W
100	Río Dercero (rê'ō děr-sě'rō) . . Arg.	32·12 S	63·59 W
91	Río Frío (rê'ō-frē'ō) Mex. (Mexico In.)	19·21 N	98·40 W
100	Río Gallegos (rē'o͞o gä-lā'gōs) . . Arg.	51·43 S	69·15 W
100	Rio Grande (rē'o͞o grän'dě) . . Braz.	31·04 S	52·14 W
90	Rio Grande (rē'o͞o grän'dä) . . . Mex.	23·51 N	102·59 W
76	Riogrande (rē'ō grän'dä) . . . Tex.	26·23 N	98·48 W
69	Rio Grande (R.) (rē'o͞o grän'dě) Colo.	37·44 N	106·51 W
99	Rio Grande do Norte (State) (rē'o͞o grän'dě do͞o nôr'tě) . Braz.	5·26 S	37·20 W
100	Rio Grande do Sul (State) (rē'o͞o grän'dě-dô-so͞o'l) . Braz.	29·00 S	54·00 W
98	Ríohacha (rē'ō-ä'chä) . . . Col.	11·30 N	72·54 W
93	Río Hato (rē'ō-ä'tō) . . . Pan.	8·19 N	80·11 W
122	Riom (rê-ôɴ') . . . Fr.	45·54 N	3·08 E
163	Rio Muni (Col.) (rē'ō mo͞o'nē) . Afr.	1.47 N	8·33 E
98	Ríonegro (rē'ō-ně'grō) . . . Col. (In.)	6·09 N	75·22 W
100	Rio Negro (Prov.) (rē'ō nā'grō) Arg.	40·15 S	68·15 W
101	Río Negro (Dept.) (rê'ō-ně'grō) Ur. (Buenos Aires In.)	32·48 S	57·45 W
100	Rio Negro, Embalse del (Res.) (ěm-bä'l-sě-děl-rê'ō-ně'grō) . Ur.	32·45 S	55·50 W
126	Rionero (rē-ō-nā'rō) . . . It.	40·55 N	15·42 E
101	Rio Novo (rē'ō-nô'vô) Braz. (Rio de Janeiro In.)	21·30 S	43·08 W
99	Rio Pardo de Minas (rē'ō pär'dō-dě-mē'näs) . Braz.	15·43 S	42·24 W
101	Rio Pombo (rē'ō pôm'bä) Braz. (Rio de Janeiro In.)	21·17 S	43·09 W
101	Rio Sorocaba, Represado (Res.) (rě-prě-sä-dô-rē'ō-sô-rō-kä'bä) Braz. (Rio de Janeiro In.)	23·37 S	47·19 W
98	Ríosucio (rē'ō-so͞o'syô) . . Col. (In.)	5·25 N	75·41 W
125	Riou, Oued (R.) (o͞o-ěd rĭ-o͞o) Alg.	35·45 N	1·18 E
139	Riouw Arch. Indon. (Singapore In.)	0·49 N	103·45 E
154	Riouw, Pulau-Pulau (Is.) . . Indon.	0·30 N	104·55 E
139	Riouw, Selat (Str.) Indon. (Singapore In.)	0·49 N	104·24 E
99	Rio Verde (věr'dě) . . . Braz.	17·47 S	50·49 W
90	Ríoverde (rē'ō-věr'dâ) . . . Mex.	21·54 N	99·59 W
110	Ripley (rĭp'lê) . . . Eng.	53·03 N	1·24 W
78	Ripley . . . Miss.	34·44 N	88·55 W
78	Ripley . . . Tenn.	35·44 N	89·34 W
125	Ripoll (rê-pōl'') . . . Sp.	42·10 N	2·10 E
71	Ripon (rĭp'ŏn) . . . Wis.	43·49 N	88·50 W
158	Ripon (I.) . . . Austl.	20·05 S	118·10 E
165	Ripon Falls . . . Ug.	0·38 N	33·02 E
159	Risdon (rĭz'dŭn) . . . Austl.	42·37 S	147·32 E
152	Rishiri (I.) (rē-shē'rē) . . . Jap.	45·10 N	141·08 E
139	Rishon le Zion . Isr. (Palestine In.)	31·57 N	34·48 E
80	Rising Sun (rīz'ĭng sŭn) . . . Ind.	38·55 N	84·55 W
118	Risor (rēs'ûr) . . . Nor.	58·44 N	9·10 E
98	Ritacuva, Alto (Mtn.) (ä'l-tô-rē-tä-ko͞o'vä) . Col.	6·22 N	72·13 W
75	Rittman (rĭt'măn) Ohio (Cleveland In.)	40·58 N	81·47 W
66	Ritzville (rĭts'vĭl) . . . Wash.	47·08 N	118·23 W
118	Riuvenfjeld (Mts.) (rĭû-věn-fyěl') Nor.	59·20 N	6·55 E
95	Riva (rē'vä) . . . Dom. Rep.	19·10 N	69·55 W
126	Riva (rê'vä) . . . It.	45·54 N	10·49 E
92	Rivas (rē'väs) . . . Nic.	11·25 N	85·51 W
122	Rive-de-Gier (rēv-dē-zhê-ā') . . . Fr.	45·32 N	4·37 E
100	Rivera (rê-vā'rä) . . . Ur.	30·52 S	55·32 W
164	River Cess (rĭv'ēr sěs) . . . Lib.	5·46 N	9·52 W
75	Riverdale (rĭv'ēr dāl) Ill. (Chicago In.)	41·38 N	87·36 W
74	Riverdale Utah (Salt Lake City In.)	41·11 N	112·00 W
78	River Falls . . . Ala.	31·20 N	86·25 W
71	River Falls . . . Wis.	44·48 N	92·38 W
81	Riverhead (rĭv'ēr hěd) . . . N. Y.	40·55 N	72·40 W
160	Riverina (Reg.) (rĭv-ēr-ē'nȧ) . Austl.	34·55 S	144·30 E
65	River Jordan (jôr'dăn) Can. (Seattle In.)	48·26 N	124·02 W
74	River Oaks (ōkz) Tex. (Dallas, Fort Worth In.)	32·47 N	97·24 W
75	River Rouge (ro͞ozh) Mich. (Detroit In.)	42·16 N	83·09 W
74	Riverside (rĭv'ēr-sīd) Calif. (Los Angeles In.)	33·59 N	117·21 W
75	Riverside . . . Can. (Detroit In.)	42·20 N	82·57 W
84	Riverside . N. J. (Philadelphia In.)	40·02 N	74·58 W
161	Riverstone . . . Austl. (Sydney In.)	33·41 S	150·52 E
86	Riverton (rĭv'ēr-tŭn) . . . Can.	51·02 N	97·12 W
81	Riverton . . . Va.	39·00 N	78·15 W
67	Riverton . . . Wyo.	43·02 N	108·24 W
122	Rivesaltes (rēv'zält') . . . Fr.	42·48 N	2·48 E
79	Riviera Beach (rĭv-ĭ-ĕr'ȧ bēch) Fla. (In.)	26·46 N	80·04 W
82	Riviere (rê-vyâr') . . . Can.	46·43 N	72·00 W
82	Riviere (R.) . . . Can.	49·05 N	72·04 W
85	Rivie're Beaudette (bō-dět') Can. (Montreal In.)	45·14 N	74·20 W
82	Riviere du Loup (rê-vyâr' dü lo͞o') Can.	47·50 N	69·34 W
85	Rivie're-Qui-Barre (rēv-yěr' kē-bär) Can. (Edmonton In.)	53·47 N	113·51 W
133	Rize (rē'zě) . . . Tur.	41·00 N	40·30 E
127	Rizzuto, C. (rēt-so͞o'tô) . . . It.	38·53 N	17·05 E
118	Rjukan (ryo͞o'kän) . . . Nor.	59·53 N	8·30 E
122	Roanne (rō-än') . . . Fr.	46·02 N	4·04 E
78	Roanoke (rō'ȧ-nōk) . . . Ala.	33·08 N	85·21 W
79	Roanoke . . . Va.	37·16 N	79·55 W
79	Roanoke (R.) . . . N. C.-Va.	36·17 N	77·22 W
79	Roanoke Rapids . . . N. C.	36·25 N	77·40 W
69	Roan Plat. (rōn) . . . Colo.	39·25 N	108·50 W
92	Roatan (rō-ä-tän') . . . Hond.	16·18 N	86·33 W
92	Roatan I. . . . Hond.	16·19 N	86·46 W
166	Robbeneiland (I.) S. Afr. (Cape Town In.)	33·48 S	18·22 E
75	Robbins (rŏb'ĭnz) . Ill. (Chicago In.)	41·39 N	87·42 W
74	Robbinsdale (rŏb'ĭnz-dāl) Minn. (Minneapolis, St. Paul In.)	45·03 N	93·22 W
65	Robe (rōb) . . . Wash. (Seattle In.)	48·06 N	121·50 W
159	Roberts, Mt. (rŏb'ērts) . . . Austl.	32·05 S	152·30 E
65	Roberts, Pt. (rŏb'ērts) Wash. (Vancouver In.)	48·58 N	123·05 W
83	Robertson (rŏb'ērt-sŭn) . . . Can.	51·05 N	59·07 W
164	Robertsport (rŏb'ērts-pōrt) . . . Lib.	6·45 N	11·31 W
82	Roberval (rŏb'ēr-văl) (rô-běr-väl') Can.	48·32 N	72·15 W
80	Robinson (rŏb'ĭn-sŭn) . . . Ill.	39·00 N	87·45 W
83	Robinsons . . . Can.	48·16 N	58·50 W
160	Robinvale (rŏb-ĭn'văl) . . . Austl.	34·45 S	142·45 E
86	Robson, Mt. (rŏb'sŭn) . . . Can.	53·13 N	119·02 W
77	Robstown (rŏbz'toun) . . . Tex.	27·46 N	97·41 W
125	Roca, Cabo da (C.) (kȧ'bō-dä-rō'kä) Port. (Lisboa In.)	38·47 N	9·30 W
99	Rocas, Atol das (Atoll) (ä-tôl-däs-rō'kàs) . Braz.	3·50 S	33·46 W
168	Rocca Littotorio Som. (Horn of Afr. In.)	7·00 N	47·30 E
96	Rocedos São Pedro E São Paulo (I.) (rô-zě'dôs-souɴ-pě'drô-ě-souɴ-päo͞o-lô) . Braz.	1·50 N	30·00 W
100	Rocha (rō'chȧs) . . . Ur.	34·26 S	54·14 W
110	Rochdale (rŏch'dāl) . . . Eng.	53·37 N	2·09 W
95	Roche à Bateau (rôsh ȧ bȧ-tō') Hai.	18·10 N	74·00 W
122	Rochefort (rôsh-fŏr') . . . Fr.	45·55 N	0·57 W
71	Rochelle (rô-shěl') . . . Ill.	41·53 N	89·06 W
80	Rochester (rŏch'ěs-tēr) . . . Ind.	41·05 N	86·20 W
75	Rochester . . . Mich. (Detroit In.)	42·41 N	83·09 W
71	Rochester . . . Minn.	44·01 N	92·30 W
81	Rochester . . . N. H.	43·20 N	71·00 W
81	Rochester . . . N. Y.	43·15 N	77·35 W
75	Rochester . . . Pa. (Pittsburgh In.)	40·42 N	80·16 W
71	Rock (R.) . . . Ill.	41·40 N	89·52 W
70	Rock (R.) . . . Iowa	43·17 N	96·13 W
65	Rock (R.) . . . Ore. (Portland In.)	45·34 N	122·52 W
65	Rock (R.) . . . Ore. (Portland In.)	45·52 N	123·14 W
84	Rockaway (rŏck'ȧ-wā) N. J. (New York In.)	40·54 N	74·30 W
161	Rockbank . Austl. (Melbourne In.)	37·44 S	144·40 E
85	Rockcliffe Park (rok'klĭf pärk) Can. (Ottawa In.)	45·27 N	75·40 W
75	Rock Cr. (rŏk) . . . Ill. (Chicago In.)	41·16 N	87·54 W
67	Rock Cr. . . . Mont.	46·25 N	113·40 W
66	Rock Cr. . . . Ore.	45·30 N	120·06 W
66	Rock Cr. . . . Wash.	47·09 N	117·50 W
77	Rockdale (rŏck'dāl) . . . Tex.	30·39 N	97·00 W
71	Rock Falls (rŏck fôlz) . . . Ill.	41·45 N	89·42 W
71	Rockford (rŏck'fērd) . . . Ill.	42·16 N	89·07 W
159	Rockhampton (rŏk-hămp'tŭn) Austl.	23·26 S	150·29 E
79	Rockhill (rŏk'hĭl) . . . S. C.	34·55 N	81·01 W
79	Rockingham (rŏk'ĭng-hăm) . . N. C.	34·54 N	79·45 W
110	Rockingham For. (rok'ĭng-hăm) Eng.	52·29 N	0·43 W
71	Rock Island . . . Ill.	41·31 N	90·37 W
66	Rock Island Dam (ī lănd) . . Wash.	47·17 N	120·33 W
85	Rockland (rŏk'lănd) Can. (Ottawa In.)	45·33 N	75·17 W
82	Rockland . . . Maine	44·06 N	69·09 W
83	Rockland . . . Mass. (Boston In.)	42·07 N	70·55 W
160	Rockland Res. . . . Austl.	36·55 S	142·20 E
78	Rockmart (rŏk'märt) . . . Ga.	33·58 N	85·00 W
74	Rockmont (rŏk'mŏnt) Wis. (Duluth In.)	46·34 N	91·54 W
80	Rockport (rŏk'pōrt) . . . Ind.	38·20 N	87·00 W
83	Rockport . . . Mass. (Boston In.)	42·39 N	70·37 W
73	Rockport . . . Mo.	40·25 N	95·30 W
77	Rockport . . . Tex.	28·03 N	97·03 W
70	Rock Rapids (răp'ĭdz) . . . Iowa	43·26 N	96·10 W
95	Rock Sd. . . . Ba. Is.	24·50 N	76·05 W
76	Rocksprings (rŏk sprĭngs) . . . Tex.	30·02 N	100·12 W
67	Rock Springs . . . Wyo.	41·35 N	109·13 W
99	Rockstone (rŏk'stôn) . . . Br. Gu.	5·55 N	57·27 W
85	Rockton (rŏk'tŭn) Can. (Toronto In.)	43·18 N	80·08 W
70	Rock Valley (văl'ĭ) . . . Iowa	43·13 N	96·17 W
80	Rockville (rŏk'vĭl) . . . Ind.	39·45 N	87·15 W
84	Rockville Centre (sĕn'tēr) N. Y. (New York In.)	40·39 N	73·39 W
73	Rockwall (rŏk'wôl) . . . Tex.	32·55 N	96·23 W
71	Rockwell City (rŏk'wěl) . . . Iowa	42·22 N	94·37 W
85	Rockwood (rŏk-wo͝od) Can. (Toronto In.)	43·37 N	80·08 W
82	Rockwood . . . Maine	45·39 N	69·45 W
78	Rockwood . . . Tenn.	35·51 N	84·41 W
67	Rocky Boys Ind. Res. . . . Mont.	48·08 N	109·34 W
72	Rocky Ford . . . Colo.	38·02 N	103·43 W
84	Rocky Hill (hĭl) N. J. (New York In.)	40·24 N	74·38 W
79	Rocky Mount . . . N. C.	35·55 N	77·47 W
72	Rocky Mountain Natl. Park . Colo.	40·29 N	106·06 W
49	Rocky Mts. (rŏk'ē) . . . N. A.	50·00 N	114·00 W
75	Rocky River . Ohio (Cleveland In.)	41·29 N	81·51 W
75	Rocky R., E. Br. Ohio (Cleveland In.)	41·13 N	81·43 W
75	Rocky R., W. Br. Ohio (Cleveland In.)	41·17 N	81·54 W
95	Rodas (rō'dhàs) . . . Cuba	22·20 N	80·35 W
110	Roden (R.) (rō'děn) . . . Eng.	52·49 N	2·38 W
65	Rodeo (rō'dēō) Calif. (San Francisco In.)	38·02 N	122·16 W
76	Rodeo (rô-dā'ō) . . . Mex.	25·12 N	104·34 W
122	Rodez (rō-děz') . . . Fr.	44·22 N	2·34 E
115	Rōdhos . . . Grc.	36·24 N	28·15 E
115	Ródhos (I.) . . . Grc.	36·00 N	28·29 E
121	Rodnei, Muntii (Mts.) (rôd'ně-ê) Rom.	47·41 N	24·05 E
128	Rodniki (rôd'nê-kê) . . . Sov. Un.	57·08 N	41·48 E
127	Rodonit, Kep I (C.) . . . Alb.	41·38 N	19·01 E
	Rodosto, see Tekirdağ		
84	Roebling (rōb'lĭng) N. J. (Philadelphia In.)	40·07 N	74·48 W
158	Roebourne (rō'bŭrn) . . . Austl.	20·50 S	117·15 E
158	Roebuck, B. (rō'bŭck) . . . Austl.	18·15 S	121·10 E
168	Roedtan . . . S. Afr. (Johannesburg & Pretoria In.)	24·37 S	29·08 E
117	Roermond (ro͞or'mônt) . . . Neth.	41·11 N	5·59 E
117	Roeselare . . . Bel.	50·55 N	3·05 E
65	Roesiger (L.) (rŏz'ĭ-gēr) Wash. (Seattle In.)	47·59 N	121·56 W
87	Roes Welcome Sd. (rōz) . . . Can.	64·10 N	87·23 W
128	Rogachëv (rôg'ȧ-chyôf) . . Sov. Un.	53·07 N	30·04 E
127	Rogatica (rô-gä'tê-tsä) . . . Yugo.	43·46 N	19·00 E
121	Rogatin (rô-gä'tĭn) . . . Sov. Un.	49·22 N	24·37 E
73	Rogers (rŏj-ērz) . . . Ark.	36·19 N	94·07 W
80	Rogers City . . . Mich.	45·30 N	83·50 W
78	Rogersville (rŏj'ērz-vĭl) . . . Tenn.	36·21 N	83·00 W
122	Rognac (rŏn-yäk') Fr. (Marseille In.)	43·29 N	5·15 E
98	Rogoaguado (L.) (rō'gō-ä-gwä'dō) Bol.	12·42 S	66·46 W

ng-sing; ŋ-baŋk; ɴ-nasalized n; nŏd; cŏmmit; ōld; ôbey; ôrder; fo͞od; fo͝ot; ou-out; s-soft; sh-dish; th-thin; pūre; ûnite; ûrn; stŭd; circŭs; ü-as "y" in study; '-indeterminate vowel.

258 Rogovskaya–Rybatskoye PRONOUNCING INDEX

Page	Name Pronunciation Region	Lat. °′	Long. °′
129	Rogovskaya (rô-gôf'skȧ-yȧ) Sov. Un.	45·43 N	38·42 E
120	Rogózno (rô'gôzh-nô) . . . . Pol.	52·44 N	16·53 E
66	Rogue R. (rōg) . . . . Ore.	42·32 N	124·13 W
118	Röikenviken (rûē'kĕn-vêk-ĕn) Nor.	60·27 N	10·26 E
101	Rojas (rō'häs) Arg. (Buenos Aires In.)	34·11 S	60·42 W
91	Rojo, Cabo (C.) (rō'hō) . . . . . Mex.	21·35 N	97·16 W
89	Rojo, Cabo (C.) (rō'hō) P. R. (Puerto Rico In.)	17·55 N	67·14 W
153	Rokkō-Zan (Mtn.) (rôk'kō zän) Jap. (Ōsaka In.)	34·46 N	135·16 E
120	Rokycany (rô'kĭ'tsȧ-nĭ) . . . . Czech.	49·44 N	13·37 E
98	Roldanillo (rôl-dä-nē'l-yō) Col. (In.)	4·24 N	76·09 W
73	Rolla (rŏl'ȧ) . . . . Mo.	37·56 N	91·45 W
70	Rolla . . . . N. D.	48·52 N	99·32 W
118	Rollag (rōō'lägh) . . . . Nor.	59·55 N	8·48 E
95	Rolleville . . . . Ba. Is.	23·40 N	76·00 W
160	Roma (rō'mȧ) . . . . Austl.	26·30 S	148·48 E
167	Roma . . . . Bas. (Natal In.)	29·28 S	27·43 E
125	Roma (Rome) (rō'mä) (rōm) It. (Roma In.)	41·52 N	12·37 E
126	Romagna (Reg.) (rô-mä'n-yä) . It.	44·18 N	10·48 E
83	Romaine (rô-mĕn') . . . . Can.	50·12 N	60·38 W
87	Romaine (R.) . . . . Can.	51·22 N	63·23 W
121	Roman (rō'män) . . . . Rom.	46·56 N	26·57 E
102	Romania (rō-mā'nê-ȧ) . . . . Eur.	46·18 N	22·53 E
79	Romano, C. (rō-mä'nō) . Fla. (In.)	25·48 N	82·00 W
94	Romano, Cayo (I.) (kä'yō-rô-mä'nô) . Cuba	22·15 N	78·00 W
136	Romanovo (rô-mä'nô-vô) Sov. Un. (Urals In.)	59·09 N	61·24 E
122	Romans-sur-Isère (rô-mäN'-sür-ē-sĕr') . Fr.	45·04 N	4·49 E
64	Romanzof, C. (rō'män zôf) . Alaska	62·00 N	167·18 W
155	Romblon (rōm-blōn') Phil. (Manila In.)	12·34 N	122·16 E
155	Romblon (I.) . Phil. (Manila In.)	12·33 N	122·17 E
78	Rome (rōm) . . . . Ga.	34·14 N	85·10 W
81	Rome . . . . N. Y.	43·15 N	75·25 W
	Rome, see Roma		
80	Romeo (rō'mē-ō) . . . . Mich.	42·50 N	83·00 W
110	Romford (rŭm'fērd) Eng. (London In.)	51·35 N	0·11 E
122	Romilly-sur-Seine (rô-mê-yē'sür-sān') . Fr.	48·32 N	3·41 E
90	Romita (rō-mē'tä) . . . . Mex.	20·53 N	101·32 W
129	Romny (rôm'nĭ) . . . . Sov. Un.	50·46 N	33·31 E
118	Römö (rûm'û) . . . . Den.	55·08 N	8·17 E
74	Romoland (rō'mō'lănd) Calif. (Los Angeles In.)	33·44 N	117·11 W
122	Romorantin (rô-mô-räN-täN') . . Fr.	47·24 N	1·46 E
139	Rompin . . . . Mala. (Singapore In.)	2·42 N	102·30 E
139	Rompin (R.) Mala. (Singapore In.)	2·54 N	103·10 E
75	Romulus (rom'ū lŭs) Mich. (Detroit In.)	42·14 N	83·24 W
116	Ronaldsay, North (I.) . . . . . . Scot.	59·21 N	2·23 W
116	Ronaldsay, South (I.) (rŏn'ăld-sā) . Scot.	59·48 N	2·55 W
67	Ronan (rō'năn) . . . . Mont.	47·28 N	114·03 W
99	Roncador, Serra do (Mts.) (sĕr'rȧ dōō rôn-kä-dôr') . Braz.	12·44 S	52·19 W
124	Roncesvalles (rôn-sĕs-vä'l-yĕs) . Sp.	43·00 N	1·17 W
80	Ronceverte (rŏn'sē-vûrt) . . W. Va.	37·45 N	80·30 W
124	Ronda (rōn'dä) . . . . Sp.	37·45 N	5·10 W
98	Rondônia (Ter.) . . . . Braz.	10·15 S	63·07 W
86	Ronge, Lac la (L.) . . . . Can.	55·16 N	104·16 W
118	Ronne (rûn'ĕ) . . . . Den.	55·08 N	14·46 E
118	Ronneby (rōn'ĕ-bü) . . . . Swe.	56·13 N	15·17 E
72	Ront Ra. (Mts.) (rŏnt) . . . . . Colo.	40·59 N	105·29 W
167	Roodepoort (rō'dĕ-pōrt) . . . . S. Afr. (Johannesburg & Pretoria In.)	26·10 S	27·52 E
73	Roodhouse (rōōd'hous) . . . . Ill.	39·29 N	90·21 W
168	Rooiberg . . . . S. Afr. (Johannesburg & Pretoria In.)	24·46 S	27·42 E
111	Roosendaal (rō'zĕn-däl) Neth. (Amsterdam In.)	51·32 N	4·27 E
69	Roosevelt (rōz''vĕlt) . . . . Utah	40·20 N	110·00 W
69	Roosevelt (R.) . . . . Ariz.	33·45 N	111·00 W
99	Roosevelt (R.) (rō'sĕ-vĕlt) . . Braz.	9·22 S	60·28 W
47	Roosevelt I . . . . Ant.	79·30 S	168·00 W
75	Root R. (rōōt) Wis. (Milwaukee In.)	42·49 N	87·54 W
158	Roper (R.) (rōp'ēr) . . . . Austl.	14·50 S	134·00 E
136	Ropsha (rôp'shȧ) Sov. Un. (Leningrad In.)	59·44 N	29·53 E
122	Roquefort . . . . Fr.	43·59 N	3·00 E
98	Roques, Islas los (Is.) . . . . Ven.	21·25 N	67·40 W
101	Ruque Pérez (rô'kĕ-pĕ'rĕz) Arg. (Buenos Aires In.)	35·23 S	59·22 W
125	Roquetas (rô-kā'täs) . . . . Sp.	40·50 N	0·32 E
99	Roraima, Mtn. (rô-rä-ē'mä) Ven.-Br. Gu.	5·12 N	60·52 W
118	Röros (rûr'ôs) . . . . Nor.	62·36 N	11·25 E
120	Rorschach (rōr'shäk) . . . . Switz.	47·27 N	9·28 E
129	Ros' (R.) (rôs) . . . . Sov. Un.	49·40 N	30·22 E
120	Rosa, Monte (Mt.) (mōn'tä rō'zä) . It.	45·56 N	7·51 E
76	Rosales (rō-zä'läs) . . . . Mex.	28·15 N	100·43 W
155	Rosales (rô-sä'lĕs) Phil. (Manila In.)	15·54 N	120·38 E
90	Rosamorada (rō'zä-mō-rä'dhä) Mex.	22·06 N	105·16 W
91	Rosaria, Laguna (L.) (lä-gōō'nä-rô-sä'ryä) . Mex.	17·50 N	93·51 W
101	Rosario (rô-zä'rē-ō) Arg. (Buenos Aires In.)	32·58 S	60·42 W
99	Rosario (rô-zä'rē-ōō) . . . . Braz.	2·49 S	44·15 W
90	Rosario . . . . Mex.	22·58 N	105·54 W
155	Rosario . . . . Phil. (Manila In.)	13·49 N	121·13 E
101	Rosario . . . . Ur. (Buenos Aires In.)	34·19 S	57·24 W
94	Rosario, Cayo (I.) (kä'yō-rô-sä'ryō) . Cuba	21·40 N	81·55 W
100	Rosário do Sul (rô-zä'rê-ōō-dô-sōō'l) . Braz.	30·17 S	54·52 W
99	Rosário Oeste (ō'ĕst'ĕ) . . . . . . Braz.	14·47 S	56·20 W
65	Rosario Str. . . Wash. (Seattle In.)	48·27 N	122·45 W
125	Rosas, Golfo de (G.) (gôl-fô-dĕ-rō'zäs) . Sp.	42·10 N	3·20 E
123	Rosbach (rōz'bäK) . Ger. (Ruhr In.)	50·47 N	7·38 E
76	Roscoe (rôs'kō) . . . . Tex.	32·26 N	100·38 W
70	Roseau (rô-zō') . . . . Minn.	48·52 N	95·47 W
93	Roseau W. I. F. (Le. & Wind. Is. In.)	15·17 N	61·23 W
70	Roseau (R.) . . . . Minn.	48·52 N	96·11 W
66	Roseberg (rōz'bûrg) . . . . Ore.	43·13 N	123·20 W
67	Rosebud Cr. . . . . Mont.	45·48 N	106·34 W
70	Rosebud Ind. Res. (rōz'bud) . S. D.	43·13 N	100·42 W
78	Rosedale (rōz'dāl) . . . . Miss.	33·49 N	90·56 W
65	Rosedale . . . . . . Wash. (Seattle In.)	47·20 N	122·39 W
75	Roselle (rō-zĕl') . . Ill. (Chicago In.)	41·59 N	88·05 W
85	Rosemere (rōz'mēr) Can. (Montreal In.)	45·38 N	73·48 W
74	Rosemount (rōz'mount) Minn. (Minneapolis, St. Paul In.)	44·44 N	93·08 W
168	Rosendal (rô-sĕn'täl) . . . . . . S. Afr. (Johannesburg & Pretoria In.)	28·32 S	27·56 E
120	Rosenheim (rō'zĕn-hīm) . . . . . . Ger.	47·52 N	12·06 E
86	Rosetown (rōz'toun) . . . . Can.	51·37 N	108·10 W
	Rosetta, see Rashīd		
167	Rosettenville . . . . S. Afr. (Johannesburg & Pretoria In.)	26·15 S	28·04 E
68	Roseville (rōz'vĭl) . . . . Calif.	38·44 N	121·19 W
75	Roseville . . . . . Mich. (Detroit In.)	42·30 N	82·55 W
74	Roseville . . . . Minn. (Minneapolis, St. Paul In.)	45·01 N	93·10 W
80	Rosiclare (rōz'ĭ-klâr) . . . . Ill.	37·30 N	88·15 W
99	Rosignol (rŏs-ĭg-nŏl) . . . . . . Br. Gu.	6·16 N	57·37 W
127	Rosiorii de Vede (rô-shôr'ê dĕ vĕ-dĕ) . Rom.	44·06 N	25·00 E
118	Roskilde (rôs'kĕl-dĕ) . . . . Den.	55·39 N	12·04 E
128	Roslavl' (rôs'läv'l) . . . . . . Sov. Un.	53·56 N	32·52 E
66	Roslyn (rŏz'lĭn) . . . . Wash.	47·14 N	121·00 W
129	Rosovka . . . . Sov. Un.	47·14 N	36·35 E
123	Rösrath (rûz'rät) . Ger. (Ruhr In.)	50·53 N	7·11 E
75	Ross (rôs) . . . Ohio (Cincinnati In.)	39·19 N	84·39 W
126	Rossano (rô-sä'nō) . . . . It.	39·34 N	16·38 E
85	Ross Cr. . . . . Can. (Edmonton In.)	53·50 N	113·08 W
66	Ross Dam . . . . Wash.	48·40 N	121·07 W
81	Rosseau (L.) (rôs-sō') . . . . Can.	45·15 N	79·30 W
159	Rossel (I.) (rô-sĕl') . . . . Austl.	11·31 S	154·00 E
85	Rosser (rôs'sēr) Can. (Winnipeg In.)	49·59 N	97·27 W
82	Rossignol (rô-sê-nyôl') . . . . Can.	44·15 N	65·25 W
86	Rossland (rôs'lănd) . . . . Can.	49·00 N	118·08 W
129	Rossosh' (rôs'sŭsh) . . . . . . Sov. Un.	50·12 N	39·32 E
167	Rossouw . . . . . . S. Afr. (Natal In.)	31·12 S	27·18 E
47	Ross Sea . . . . Ant.	76·00 S	178·00 W
47	Ross Shelf Ice . . . . Ant.	81·30 S	175·00 W
78	Rossville (rôs'vĭl) . . . . Ga.	34·57 N	85·22 W
120	Rostock (rôs'tŭk) . . . . Ger.	54·04 N	12·06 E
128	Rostov . . . . Sov. Un.	57·13 N	39·23 E
129	Rostov (Oblast) . . . . Sov. Un.	47·38 N	39·15 E
133	Rostov-na-Donu (rôstôv-nä-dô-nōō) . Sov. Un.	47·16 N	39·47 E
112	Rösvatn (L.) (rûs-vät'n) . . . . . Nor.	65·36 N	13·08 E
78	Roswell (rŏz'wĕl) . . . . Ga.	34·02 N	84·21 W
72	Roswell . . . . N. Mex.	33·23 N	104·32 W
72	Rotan (rō-tăn') . . . . Tex.	32·51 N	100·27 W
120	Rothenburg . . . . Ger.	49·20 N	10·10 E
110	Rotherham (rŏdh'ēr-ăm) . . . . . Eng.	53·26 N	1·21 W
82	Rothesay . . . . Can.	45·25 N	65·59 W
116	Rothesay (rôth'sȧ) . . . . Scot.	55·50 N	3·14 W
110	Rothwell (rôth'wĕl) . . . . Eng.	53·44 N	1·30 W
154	Roti (I.) (rō'tê) . . . . Indon.	10·30 S	122·52 E
160	Roto (rō'tō) . . . . Austl.	33·07 S	145·30 E
111	Rotterdam (rôt'ĕr-däm') Neth. (Amsterdam In.)	51·55 N	4·27 E
120	Rottweil (rōt'vīl) . . . . Ger.	48·10 N	8·36 E
122	Roubaix (rōō-bĕ') . . . . Fr.	50·42 N	3·10 E
122	Rouen (rōō-äN') . . . . Fr.	49·25 N	1·05 E
75	Rouge, R. . . . Mich. (Detroit In.)	42·30 N	83·15 W
85	Rouge R. (rōōzh) Can. (Toronto In.)	43·53 N	79·21 W
75	Round Lake . . . . Ill. (Chicago In.)	42·21 N	88·05 W
83	Round Pd. (round) . . . . Can.	48·12 N	53·50 W
65	Round Top (Mtn.) (tŏp) Ore. (Portland In.)	45·41 N	123·22 W
67	Roundup (round'ŭp) . . . . Mont.	46·25 N	108·35 W
116	Rousay (I.) (rōō'zȧ) . . . . Scot.	59·10 N	3·04 W
87	Rouyn (rōōn) . . . . Can.	48·22 N	79·03 W
112	Rovaniemi (rô'vȧ-nyĕ'mĭ) . . . . Fin.	66·29 N	25·45 E
126	Rovato (rō-vä'tō) . . . . It.	45·33 N	10·00 E
129	Roven'ki (rô-vĕn'kĭ') . . . . Sov. Un.	48·06 N	39·44 E
129	Roven'ki . . . . Sov. Un.	49·54 N	38·54 E
126	Rovereto (rô-vâ-rā'tô) . . . . It.	45·53 N	11·05 E
126	Rovigo (rô-vē'gô) . . . . It.	45·05 N	11·48 E
126	Rovinj (rô'vēn') . . . . Yugo.	45·05 N	13·40 E
98	Rovira (rô-vē'rä) . . . . Col. (In.)	4·14 N	75·13 W
121	Rovno (rôv'nô) . . . . Sov. Un.	50·37 N	26·17 E
129	Rovno (Oblast) . . . . Sov. Un.	50·55 N	27·00 E
129	Rovnoye (rôv'nô-yĕ) . . . . . Sov. Un.	48·11 N	31·46 E
83	Rowley (rou'lē) Mass. (Boston In.)	42·43 N	70·53 W
74	Roxana (rŏks'ăn-nȧ) Ill. (St. Louis In.)	38·51 N	90·05 W
154	Roxas (rô-xäs) . . . . Phil.	11·30 N	122·47 E
79	Roxboro (rŏks' bŭr-ô) . . . . N. C.	36·22 N	78·58 W
72	Roy (roi) . . . . N. Mex.	35·54 N	104·09 W
74	Roy . . . . Utah (Salt Lake City In.)	41·10 N	112·02 W
94	Royal (I.) . . . . Ba. Is.	25·30 N	76·50 W
116	Royal Can. (roi-ăl) . . . . Ire.	53·28 N	6·45 W
167	Royal Natal Natl. Pk. (roi'ăl) S. Afr. (Natal In.)	28·35 S	28·54 E
65	Royal Oak (roi'ăl ōk) Can. (Seattle In.)	48·30 N	123·24 W
75	Royal Oak . . . . Mich. (Detroit In.)	42·29 N	83·09 W
80	Royalton (roi'ăl-tŭn) . . . . Mich.	42·00 N	86·25 W
122	Royan (rwä-yäN') . . . . Fr.	45·40 N	1·02 W
122	Roye (rwä) . . . . Fr.	49·43 N	2·40 E
84	Royersford (rô' yĕrz-fērd) Pa. (Philadelphia In.)	40·11 N	75·32 W
78	Royston (roiz'tŭn) . . . . Ga.	34·15 N	83·06 W
110	Royton (roi'tŭn) . . . . Eng.	53·34 N	2·07 W
123	Rozay-en-Brie (rô-zā-ĕN-brē') Fr. (Paris In.)	48·41 N	2·57 E
136	Rozhaya R. (rô'zhȧ-yȧ) Sov. Un. (Moskva In.)	55·20 N	37·37 E
121	Rožňava (rôzh'nyȧ-vȧ) . . . . Czech.	48·39 N	20·32 E
133	Rtishchevo ('r-tĭsh'chĕ-vô) Sov. Un.	52·15 N	43·40 E
167	Ruaha (R.) (rwä'hȧ) . . . . Tan.	7·51 S	37·00 E
163	Ruanda-Urundi (rōō-än-dȧ ōō-rōōn'dê) . Afr.	3·00 S	30·15 E
159	Ruapehu (Mtn.) (rōō-ȧ-pā'hōō) N. Z. (In.)	39·15 S	175·37 E
139	Ruâq (R.) . U. A. R. (Palestine In.)	29·48 N	33·59 E
134	Rubtsovak . . . . Sov. Un.	51·31 N	81·17 E
64	Ruby (rōō'bê) . . . . Alaska	64·38 N	155·22 W
68	Ruby (L.) . . . . Nev.	40·11 N	115·20 W
68	Ruby Mts. . . . . Nev.	40·11 N	115·36 W
67	Ruby R. . . . . Mont.	45·06 N	112·10 W
95	Rucilla, Loma (Hill) (lô'mä-rōō-sē'l-yä) . Dom. Rep.	19·05 N	70·55 W
144	Rūd-E-Kar (R.) . . . . Iran	33·15 N	47·31 E
118	Rudkøbing (rōōdh'kûb-ĭng) . . Den.	54·56 N	10·44 E
111	Rüdnitz (rüd'nētz) Ger. (Berlin In.)	52·44 N	13·38 E
142	Rudok (rōō'dôk) . . . . China	33·42 N	79·56 E
165	Rudolf, L. (rōō'dŏlf) . . . Ken.-Eth.	3·43 N	35·49 E
117	Rudolstadt (rōō'dôl-shtät) . . . Ger.	50·46 N	13·30 E
165	Rufa'a (rōō-fä'ä) . . . . Sud.	14·52 N	33·30 E
122	Ruffec (rü-fĕk') . . . . Fr.	46·03 N	0·11 E
167	Rufiji (R.) (rōō-fē'jê) . . . . Tan.	8·29 S	37·39 E
164	Rufisque (rü-fēsk') . . . . Senegal	14·41 N	17·13 W
110	Rugby (rŭg'bê) . . . . Eng.	52·22 N	1·15 W
70	Rugby . . . . N. D.	48·22 N	100·00 W
110	Rugeley (rōōj'lē) . . . . Eng.	52·46 N	1·56 W
120	Rügen (Pen.) (rü'ghĕn) . . . . . . Ger.	54·28 N	13·47 E
119	Ruhnu-Saar (I.) (rōōnōō-sâ'âr) Sov. Un.	57·46 N	23·15 E
120	Ruhr R. (rōōr) . . . . Ger.	51·18 N	8·17 E
90	Ruiz (rōōē'z) . . . . Mex.	21·55 N	105·09 W
98	Ruiz, Nevado del (Pk.) (nĕ-vä'dô-dĕl-rōōē'z) . Col. (In.)	4·52 N	75·20 W
119	Rūjiena (rōō'yĭ-ă-nȧ) . . . . Sov. Un.	57·54 N	25·19 E
166	Rukwa (L.) (rōōk-wä') . . . . . . Tan.	8·15 S	33·14 E
71	Rum (R.) (rŭm) . . . . Minn.	45·52 N	93·45 W
127	Ruma (rōō'mȧ) . . . . Yugo.	45·00 N	19·53 E
165	Rumbek (rŭm'bĕk) . . . . Sud.	6·52 N	29·43 E
95	Rum Cay (I.) . . . . Ba. Is.	23·40 N	74·50 W
82	Rumford (rŭm'fērd) . . . . Maine	44·32 N	70·35 W
139	Rummānah U. A. R. (Palestine In.)	31·01 N	32·39 E
110	Runcorn (rŭŋ'kôrn) . . . . Eng.	53·20 N	2·44 W
139	Rupat, Palau (I.) (rōō'pät) Indon. (Singapore In.)	1·55 N	101·35 E
139	Rupat, Selat (Str.) Indon. (Singapore In.)	1·55 N	101·17 E
67	Rupert (rōō'pērt) . . . . Idaho	42·36 N	113·41 W
87	Rupert (R.) . . . . Can.	76·27 N	77·47 W
127	Ruse (Russe) (rōō'sĕ) (rōō'sĕ) Bul.	43·50 N	25·59 E
71	Rush City . . . . Minn.	45·40 N	92·59 W
65	Rushton (rŭsh'tŭn) Wash. (Seattle In.)	47·18 N	122·30 W
73	Rushville (rŭsh'vĭl) . . . . Ill.	40·08 N	90·34 W
80	Rushville . . . . Ind.	39·35 N	85·30 W
70	Rushville . . . . Nebr.	42·43 N	102·27 W
77	Rusk (rŭsk) . . . . Tex.	31·49 N	95·09 W
65	Ruskin (rŭs'kĭn) Can. (Vancouver In.)	49·10 N	122·25 W
111	Russ (R.) . . . . Aus. (Wien In.)	48·12 N	16·55 E
99	Russas (rōō's-säs) . . . . Braz.	4·48 S	37·50 W
	Russe, see Ruse		
65	Russell . . Calif. (San Francisco In.)	37·39 N	122·08 W
86	Russell (rŭs'ĕl) . . . . Can.	50·47 N	101·20 W
85	Russell . . . . Can. (Ottawa In.)	45·15 N	75·22 W
72	Russell . . . . Kans.	38·51 N	98·51 W
80	Russell . . . . Ky.	38·30 N	82·45 W
159	Russell . . . . N. Z. (In.)	35·38 S	174·13 E
159	Russell Is . . . . Sol. Is.	9·16 S	158·30 E
78	Russellville (rŭs'ĕl-vĭl) . . . . Ala.	34·29 N	87·44 W
73	Russellville . . . . Ark.	35·16 N	93·08 W
78	Russelville . . . . Ky.	36·48 N	86·51 W
130	Russian S. F. S. R. . . . . . . Sov. Un.	61·00 N	60·00 E
68	Russian (R.) (rŭsh'ăn) . . . . . . Calif.	38·59 N	123·10 W
168	Rustenburg (rŭs'tĕn-bûrg) . S. Afr. (Johannesburg & Pretoria In.)	25·40 S	26·15 E
77	Ruston (rŭs'tŭn) . . . . La.	32·32 N	92·39 W
129	Rutchenkovo (rōō-chĕn'kô-vô) Sov. Un.	47·54 N	37·36 E
124	Rute (rōō'tä) . . . . Sp.	37·20 N	4·34 W
68	Ruth (rōōth) . . . . Nev.	39·17 N	115·00 W
121	Ruthenia (Reg.) . . . . Sov. Un.	48·25 N	23·00 E
79	Rutherfordton (rŭdh'ēr-fērd-tŭn) N. C.	35·23 N	81·58 W
81	Rutland (rŭt'lănd) . . . . Vt.	43·35 N	72·55 W
110	Rutland (Co.) . . . . Eng.	52·40 N	0·37 W
166	Rutshuru (rōōt-shōō'rōō) . . Con. L.	1·13 S	29·15 E
126	Ruvo (rōō'vô) . . . . It.	41·07 N	16·32 E
163	Ruwenzori Ra. (rōō-wĕn-zō'rê) Afr.	0·53 N	30·00 E
128	Ruza (rōō'zȧ) . . . . Sov. Un.	55·42 N	36·12 E
121	Ruzhany (rōō-zhän'ĭ) . . . . Sov. Un.	52·49 N	24·54 E
136	Ryabovo (ryä'bô-vô) Sov. Un. (Leningrad In.)	59·24 N	31·08 E
128	Ryazan' (ryä-zän'') . . . . . . Sov. Un.	54·37 N	39·43 E
128	Ryazan' (Oblast) . . . . Sov. Un.	54·10 N	39·37 E
128	Ryazhsk (ryäzh'sk') . . . . . Sov. Un.	53·43 N	40·04 E
132	Rybachiy, P-Ov. (Pen.) . . Sov. Un.	69·50 N	33·20 E
136	Rybatskoye (rĭ-bät'skô-yĕ) Sov. Un. (Leningrad In.)	59·50 N	30·31 E

ăt; finăl; rāte; senâte; ärm; åsk; sofȧ; fâre; ch-choose; dh-as th in other; bē; ēvent; bĕt; recĕnt; cratēr; g-go; gh-guttural g; bĭt; ĭ-short neutral; rīde; K-guttural k as ch in German ich;

260 St. Gotthard–Salamanca PRONOUNCING INDEX

Page	Name Pronunciation Region	Lat. °′	Long. °′
120	St. Gotthard Tun. (sånt gôthàrd) (săN gô-tàr') Switz.	46·38 N	8·55 E
83	St. Gregory, Mt. (sånt grĕg'ẽr-ê) Can.	49·29 N	58·14 W
168	St. Helena (sānt hĕ-lē'nȧ) S. Afr. (Johannesburg & Pretoria In.)	28·01 S	26·47 E
163	St. Helena (I.) Atl. O.	16·01 S	5·16 W
166	St. Helena B. S. Afr.	32·25 S	17·15 E
110	St. Helens (sånt hĕl'ĕnz) Eng.	53·27 N	2·44 W
65	St. Helens (hĕl'ĕnz) Ore. (Portland In.)	45·52 N	122·49 W
66	St. Helens, Mt. Wash.	46·13 N	122·10 W
122	St. Hélier (hyĕl'yĕr) Chan. Is.	49·12 N	2·06 W
85	St. Henri (săN' hĕn'rē) Can. (Quebec In.)	46·41 N	71·04 W
85	St. Hermas (hĕr'măs) Can. (Montreal In.)	45·37 N	74·11 W
81	St. Hyacinthe (săN' tē-ä-săNt') (sånt hī'ȧ-sĭnth) Can.	45·35 N	72·55 W
71	St. Ignace (sånt ĭg'nȧs) Mich.	45·51 N	84·39 W
71	St. Ignace (I.) (săN' ĭg'nȧs) Can.	48·47 N	88·14 W
82	St. Irenee (săN' tē-rȧ-nā') Can.	47·34 N	70·15 W
85	St. Isidore (saN' tē-zē-dōr') (sånt ĭz'ĭ-dôr) Can. (Montreal In.)	45·18 N	73·41 W
85	St. Isidore-de-Prescott (săN' ĭz'ĭ-dôr-prĕs-kŏt) Can. (Ottawa In.)	45·23 N	74·54 W
85	St. Isidore-Dorchester (dŏr-chĕs'tẽr) Can. (Quebec In.)	46·35 N	71·05 W
74	St. Jacob (jā-kŏb) Ill. (St. Louis In.)	38·43 N	89·46 W
85	St. Jacques-le-Mineur (sĕN zhäk-lĕ-mē-nûr) Can. (Montreal In.)	45·16 N	73·25 W
71	St. James (sånt jāmz') Minn.	43·58 N	94·37 W
73	St. James Mo.	37·59 N	91·37 W
85	St. Janvier (săN' zhän-vyā') Can. (Montreal In.)	45·43 N	73·56 W
81	St. Jean (săN' zhäN') Can.	45·20 N	73·15 W
82	St. Jean Can.	48·51 N	67·07 W
85	St. Jean Can. (Quebec In.)	46·55 N	70·54 W
85	St. Jean Chrysostome (krĭ-zōs-tōm') Can. (Quebec In.)	46·43 N	71·12 W
122	St. Jean-d'Angely (däN-zhä-lē') Fr.	45·56 N	0·33 W
122	St. Jean de Luz (dē lüz') Fr.	43·23 N	1·40 W
85	St. Jerome (sånt jĕ-rōm') (săN zhā-rōm') Can. (Montreal In.)	45·47 N	74·00 W
85	St. Joachim (sånt jō'ȧ-kĭm) Can. (Quebec In.)	47·04 N	70·51 W
82	St. John Can.	45·19 N	66·04 W
75	St. John (sånt jŏn) Ind. (Chicago In.)	41·27 N	87·29 W
72	St. John Kans.	37·59 N	98·44 W
70	St. John N. D.	48·57 N	99·42 W
82	St. John (R.) Can.	46·39 N	67·40 W
83	St. John, C. Can.	49·59 N	55·20 W
89	St. John (I.) Vir. Is. (U. S. A.) (Puerto Rico In.)	18·16 N	64·48 W
82	St. John, L. Can.	48·45 N	71·40 W
69	St. Johns (jŏnz) Ariz.	34·30 N	109·25 W
83	St. John's (jŏns) Can.	47·34 N	52·40 W
80	St. Johns Mich.	43·05 N	84·35 W
93	St. Johns W. I. F. (Le. & Wind. Is. In.)	17·07 N	61·50 W
79	St. Johns (R.) Fla.	29·54 N	81·32 W
81	St. Johnsbury (jŏnz'bĕr-ê) Vt.	44·25 N	72·00 W
82	St. Joseph (jō'zhûf) Can.	46·17 N	70·52 W
80	St. Joseph Mich.	42·05 N	86·30 W
73	St. Joseph (sånt jô-sĕf) Mo.	39·44 N	94·49 W
93	St. Joseph W. I. F. (Le. & Wind. Is. In.)	15·25 N	61·26 W
80	St. Joseph (I.) Can.	46·15 N	83·55 W
87	St. Joseph (L.) (jō'zhûf) Can.	51·31 N	90·40 W
78	St. Joseph, B. (jō'zhûf) Fla.	29·48 N	85·26 W
80	St. Joseph (R.) (sånt jô'sĕf) Mich.	41·45 N	85·50 W
87	St. Joseph d' Alma Can.	48·29 N	71·42 W
85	St. Joseph du Lac (sĕN zhō-zĕf' dü läk) Can. (Montreal In.)	45·32 N	74·00 W
77	St. Joseph I. (sånt jô-sĕf) Tex.	27·58 N	96·50 W
122	St. Junien (săN'zhü-nyăN') Fr.	45·53 N	0·54 E
85	Ste. Justine (sånt jŭs-tēn') Can. (Montreal In.)	45·22 N	74·22 W
116	St. Kilda (I.) (kĭl'dȧ) Scot.	57·10 N	8·32 W
	St. Kitts I., see St. Christopher I.		
85	St. Lambert (săN' läN-bĕr') (sånt lăm'bẽrt) Can. (Montreal In.)	45·29 N	73·29 W
85	St. Lambert Can. (Quebec In.)	46·35 N	71·12 W
85	St. Laurent (săN' lō-rän) Can. (Montreal In.)	45·31 N	73·41 W
85	St. Laurent Can. (Quebec In.)	46·52 N	71·00 W
99	St. Laurent Fr. Gu.	5·27 N	53·56 W
83	St. Lawrence (sånt lô'rĕns) Can.	46·54 N	55·23 W
64	St. Lawrence (I.) (sånt lô'rĕns) Alaska	63·10 N	172·12 W
87	St. Lawrence Is. Natl. Park Can.	44·30 N	75·38 W
87	St. Lawrence R. (sånt lô'rĕns) Can.-U. S. A.	48·24 N	69·03 W
85	St. Lazare (săN' lȧ-zȧr') Can. (Montreal In.)	45·24 N	74·08 W
85	St. Lazare Can. (Quebec In.)	46·39 N	70·48 W
123	St. Léger-en-Yvelines (săN-lā-zhĕ'ĕN-nēv-lēn') Fr. (Paris In.)	48·43 N	1·45 E
82	St. Leonard (sånt lĕn'ȧrd) Can.	47·09 N	67·53 W
122	St. Léonard-de-Noblat (săN' lā-ô-när'dē-nô-blȧ') Fr.	45·51 N	1·30 E
85	St. Lin (săN' lăN') Can. (Montreal In.)	45·51 N	73·46 W
122	Saint-Lô (săN'lō') Fr.	49·08 N	1·07 W
85	St. Louis (săN' lōō-ē') Can. (Montreal In.)	45·13 N	74·00 W
80	St. Louis (sånt lōō'ĭs) Mich.	43·25 N	84·35 W
74	St. Louis (sånt lōō'ĭs) (lōō'ē) Mo. (St. Louis In.)	38·39 N	90·15 W
164	St. Louis Senegal	16·08 N	16·29 W
85	St. Louis, Lac (L.) (săN' lōō-ē') Can. (Montreal In.)	45·24 N	73·51 W
71	St. Louis (R.) (sånt lōō'ĭs) Minn.	46·57 N	92·58 W
74	St. Louis Park Minn. (Minneapolis, St. Paul In.)	44·56 N	93·21 W
93	St. Lucia Chan. (lū'shĭ-ȧ) N. A. (Le. & Wind. Is. In.)	14·15 N	61·00 W
93	St. Lucia I. W. I. F. (Le. & Wind. Is. In.)	13·54 N	60·40 W
79	St. Lucie Can. (lū'sê) Fla. (In.)	26·57 N	80·25 W
116	St. Magnus B. (măg'nŭs) Scot.	60·25 N	2·09 W
122	St. Maixent (săN' mĕk-săN') Fr.	46·25 N	0·12 W
122	St. Malo (săN' mȧ-lô') Fr.	48·40 N	2·02 W
122	St. Malo, Golfe de (G.) (gôlf-dĕ-săN-mȧ-lō') Fr.	48·50 N	2·49 W
95	St. Marc (săN' mȧrk') Hai.	19·10 N	72·40 W
95	St.-Marc, Canal de (Chan.) Hai.	19·05 N	73·15 W
123	St. Marcellin (mär-sĕ-lăN') Fr.	45·08 N	5·15 E
82	Ste. Marie (săNt' mȧ-rē') Can.	46·27 N	71·03 W
167	Ste. Marie Malagasy	16·58 S	50·15 E
167	Ste. Marie, Cap (C.) Malagasy	25·31 S	45·00 E
123	Ste. Marie aux Mines (săN'tĕ-mȧ-rē'ō-mēn') Fr.	48·14 N	7·08 E
66	St. Maries (sånt mā'rēs) Idaho	47·18 N	116·34 W
82	St. Margarets (sånt mär'gȧ-rĕts) Can.	44·25 N	63·35 W
85	Ste. Martine Can. (Montreal In.)	45·14 N	73·37 W
93	St. Martin I. (mär'tĭn) N. A. (Le. & Wind. Is. In.)	18·06 N	62·54 W
82	St. Martins (mär'tĭnz) Can.	45·24 N	65·32 W
77	St. Martinville (mär'tĭn-vĭl) La.	30·08 N	91·50 W
82	St. Mary B. (mā'rê) Can.	44·22 N	66·09 W
160	St. Marys (mā'rêz) Austl.	41·40 S	148·10 E
80	St. Marys Can.	43·15 N	81·10 W
79	St. Marys Ga.	30·43 N	81·35 W
73	St. Mary's Kans.	39·12 N	96·03 W
80	St. Marys Ohio	40·30 N	84·25 W
81	St. Marys Pa.	41·25 N	78·30 W
80	St. Marys (mā'rêz) W. Va.	39·20 N	81·15 W
79	St. Marys (R.) Ga.-Fla.	30·37 N	82·05 W
83	St. Marys B. Can.	46·52 N	53·53 W
83	St. Marys Is. Can.	50·19 N	59·17 W
74	St. Marys R. Can.-U. S. (Sault Ste. Marie In.)	46·27 N	84·33 W
79	St. Mathew (măth'ū) S. C.	33·40 N	80·46 W
85	St. Mathieu (sĕN mȧt-yû) Can. (Montreal In.)	45·19 N	73·32 W
64	St. Matthew (I.) Alaska	60·25 N	172·10 W
75	St. Matthews (măth'ūz) Ky. (Louisville In.)	38·15 N	85·39 W
123	St. Maur-des-Fossés Fr. (Paris In.)	48·48 N	2·29 E
82	St. Maurice (R.) (săN' mō-rēs') (sånt mô'rĭs) Can.	47·20 N	72·55 W
64	St. Michael (sånt mī'kĕl) Alaska	63·22 N	162·20 W
85	St. Michel (săN' mē-shĕl') Can. (Montreal In.)	45·14 N	73·34 W
85	St. Michel Can. (Quebec In.)	46·52 N	70·54 W
85	St. Michel, Bras (R.) Can. (Quebec In.)	46·48 N	70·51 W
95	St. Michel-de-l'Atalaye Hai.	19·25 N	72·20 W
123	St. Mihiel (săN' mē-yĕl') Fr.	48·53 N	5·30 E
122	St. Mitre (săN mēt-rĕ) Fr. (Marseille In.)	43·27 N	5·02 E
120	St. Moritz (sånt mō'rĭts) (zäŋkt mō'rĕts) Switz.	46·31 N	9·50 E
122	St. Nazaire-Trignac (săN'nȧ-zȧr'trēn-yäK) Fr.	47·18 N	2·13 W
85	St. Nérée (nā-rā') Can. (Quebec In.)	46·43 N	70·43 W
85	St. Nicolas (ne-kô-lȧ') Can. (Quebec In.)	46·42 N	71·23 W
95	St. Nicolas, Cap (C.) Hai.	19·45 N	73·35 W
85	St. Norbert (sånt nôr'bẽrt) Can. (Winnipeg In.)	49·46 N	97·09 W
122	St. Omer (săN'tô-mâr') Fr.	50·44 N	2·16 E
82	St. Pascal Can.	47·30 N	69·49 W
86	St. Paul (sånt pôl') Can.	53·58 N	111·30 W
74	St. Paul Minn. (Minneapolis, St. Paul In.)	44·57 N	93·05 W
70	St. Paul Nebr.	41·13 N	98·28 W
64	St. Paul (I.) Alaska	57·10 N	170·20 W
83	St. Paul (I.) Can.	47·14 N	60·08 W
47	St. Paul I. Ind. O.	38·43 S	77·31 E
74	St. Paul Park (pärk) Minn. (Minneapolis, St. Paul In.)	44·51 N	93·00 W
79	St. Pauls (pôls) N. C.	34·47 N	78·57 W
71	St. Peter (pē tẽr) Minn.	44·20 N	93·56 W
82	St. Peter, L. (pē'tẽr) Can.	46·07 N	72·42 W
83	St. Peters Can.	45·43 N	60·50 W
79	St. Petersburg (pē'tẽrz-bûrg) Fla. (In.)	27·47 N	82·38 W
85	Ste. Pétronille (sĕNt pĕt-rō-nēl') Can. (Quebec In.)	46·51 N	71·08 W
85	St. Philémon (sĕN fēl-mōN') Can. (Quebec In.)	46·41 N	70·28 W
85	Ste. Philomene (săNt fē-lô-mân') Can. (Montreal In.)	45·19 N	73·45 W
85	St. Philippe (săN' fē-lēp') Can. (Montreal In.)	45·20 N	73·28 W
85	St. Philippe Can. (Montreal In.)	45·38 N	74·25 W
85	St. Pierre (săN' pyâr') Can. (Quebec In.)	46·53 N	71·04 W
85	St. Pierre Can. (Quebec In.)	46·55 N	70·37 W
122	St. Pierre (sånt pyâr') (săN' pyâr') Chan. Is.	49·27 N	2·35 W
93	St. Pierre Mart. (Le. & Wind. Is. In.)	14·45 N	61·12 W
83	St. Pierre (I.) Can.	46·46 N	56·14 W
85	St. Placide (plăs'ĭd) Can. (Montreal In.)	45·32 N	74·11 W
122	St. Pol-de-Léon (săN-pô'dĕ-lā-ôN') Fr.	48·41 N	4·00 W
120	St. Pölten (zäŋkt-pûl'tĕn) Aus.	48·12 N	15·38 E
122	St. Quentin (săN'käN-tăN') Fr.	49·52 N	3·16 E
85	St. Raphaél (rä-fȧ-él') Can. (Quebec In.)	46·48 N	70·46 W
82	St. Raymond (săN' rā-môN') (sånt rā'mŭnd) Can.	46·50 N	71·51 W
85	St. Rédempteur (săN rā-däNp-tûr') Can. (Montreal In.)	45·26 N	74·23 W
85	St. Rédempteur Can. (Quebec In.)	46·42 N	71·18 W
85	St. Rémi (sĕN rĕ-mē') Can. (Montreal In.)	45·15 N	73·36 W
85	St. Romuald (săN' rô-mü-äl') Can. (Quebec In.)	46·45 N	71·14 W
84	St. Rosalie (sånt rōz'ȧ-lē) La. (New Orleans In.)	29·40 N	89·58 W
85	Ste. Rose (săNt rôz') Can. (Montreal In.)	45·37 N	73·47 W
93	Ste. Rose Guad. (Le. & Wind. Is. In.)	16·19 N	61·45 W
122	Saintes Fr.	45·44 N	0·41 W
85	Ste. Scholastique (skô-lȧs-tēk') Can. (Montreal In.)	45·39 N	74·05 W
122	St. Servan-sur-Mer (sĕr-väN') Fr.	48·37 N	1·59 W
82	St. Simeon Can.	47·51 N	69·55 W
85	St. Stanislas-de Kostka (sĕN stä-nēs-läz' de kōst'kȧ) Can. (Montreal In.)	45·11 N	74·08 W
82	St. Stephen (stē'vĕn) Can.	45·12 N	65·17 W
85	St. Sulpice Can. (Montreal In.)	45·50 N	73·21 W
85	St. Therese de Blainville (tĕ-rĕz' dĕ blĕN-vēl') Can. (Monteral In.)	45·38 N	73·51 W
80	St. Thomas (tŏm'ȧs) Can.	42·45 N	81·15 W
	St. Thomas, see Charlotte Amalie		
89	St. Thomas (I.) Vir. Is. (U. S. A.) (St. Thomas In.)	18·22 N	64·57 W
89	St. Thomas Hbr. (tŏm'ȧs) Vir. Is. (U. S. A.) (St. Thomas In.)	18·19 N	64·56 W
85	St. Timothee (tē-mô-tā') Can. (Montreal In.)	45·17 N	74·03 W
123	St. Tropez (trô-pĕ') Fr.	43·15 N	6·42 E
85	St. Urbain Can. (Montreal In.)	45·14 N	73·44 W
85	St. Valentin (väl-ĕn-tĭn) Can. (Montreal In.)	45·07 N	73·19 W
122	St. Valéry (vȧ-lā-rē') Fr.	50·10 N	1·39 E
85	St. Vallier (väl-yā') Can. (Quebec In.)	46·54 N	70·49 W
120	St. Veit (zäŋKt vĭt') Aus.	46·46 N	14·20 E
82	St. Victor (vĭk'tẽr) Can.	46·09 N	70·56 W
160	St. Vincent, G. (vĭn'sĕnt) Austl.	34·55 S	138·00 E
85	St. Vincent-de-Paul (săN' văN-săN' dē pôl') Can. (Montreal In.)	45·37 N	73·39 W
93	St. Vincent I. W. I. F. (Le. & Wind. Is. In.)	13·14 N	60·50 W
93	St. Vincent Pass. N. A. (Le. & Wind. Is. In.)	13·35 N	61·10 W
86	St. Walburg Can.	53·40 N	109·10 W
69	St. Xavier Ind. Res. (x-ā'vĭ ẽr) Ariz.	32·07 N	111·12 W
122	St. Yrieix (ē-rē-ĕ) Fr.	45·30 N	1·08 E
153	Saitama (Pref.) (sī'tä-mä) Jap. (Tōkyō In.)	35·52 N	139·40 E
136	Saitbaba (sá-ĕt'bá-bȧ) Sov. Un. (Urals In.)	54·06 N	56·42 E
98	Sajama, Nevada (Pk.) (nĕ-vä'dä-sä-hä'mä) Bol.	18·13 S	68·53 W
153	Sakai (sä'kä-ê) Jap. (Ōsaka In.)	34·34 N	135·28 E
144	Sakākah Sau. Ar.	29·58 N	40·03 E
166	Sakania (sȧ-kä'nĭ-ȧ) Con. L.	12·41 S	28·39 E
133	Sakarya (R.) (sȧ-kär'yȧ) Tur.	40·10 N	31·00 E
152	Sakata (sä'kä-tä) Jap.	38·56 N	139·57 E
152	Sakchu (säk'chōō) Kor.	40·29 N	125·09 E
135	Sakhalin (I.) (sȧ-kȧ-lēn') Sov. Un.	51·52 N	144·15 E
119	Šakiai (shä'kĭ-ī) Sov. Un.	54·59 N	23·05 E
151	Sakishima-Gunto (Is.) (sä'kê-shē'ma gōōn'tō') China	24·25 N	125·00 E
133	Sakmara (R.) Sov. Un.	52·00 N	56·10 E
84	Sakomet R. (sȧ-kō'mĕt) R. I. (Providence In.)	41·32 N	71·11 W
165	Sak'ot'ā Eth.	12·47 N	38·59 E
94	Sal, Cay (I.) (kē săl) Ba. Is.	23·45 N	80·25 W
133	Sal (R.) (sȧl) Sov. Un.	47·20 N	42·10 E
118	Sala (sô'lä) Swe.	59·56 N	16·34 E
126	Sala Consilina (sä'lä kôn-sê-lē'nä) It.	40·24 N	15·38 E
68	Salada, Laguna (L.) (lä-gōō'nä-sä-lä'dä) Mex.	32·34 N	115·45 W
101	Saladillo (sä-lä-dēl'yō) Arg. (Buenos Aires In.)	35·38 S	59·48 W
92	Salado (sä-lä'dhō) Hond.	15·44 N	87·03 W
100	Salado (sä-lä'dō) (R.) Arg.	26·05 S	63·35 W
101	Salado (R.) Arg. (Buenos Aires In.)	35·53 S	58·12 W
91	Salado (R.) (sä-lä'dō) Mex.	18·30 N	97·29 W
76	Salado, Rio (R.) (rē'ō) Mex.	26·55 N	99·36 W
74	Salado Cr. Tex. (San Antonio In.)	29·23 N	98·25 W
76	Salado de los Nadadores Rio (R.) (dĕ-lōs-nä-dä-dō'rĕs) Mex.	27·26 N	101·35 W
154	Salajar (I.) Indon.	6·15 S	121·15 E
92	Salamá (sä-lä'mä) Guat.	15·06 N	90·19 W
92	Salamá (sä-lä-mä') Hond.	14·43 N	86·30 W
101	Salamanca (sä-lä-mä'n-kä) Chile (Santiago In.)	31·48 S	70·57 W
90	Salamanca Mex.	20·36 N	101·10 W
81	Salamanca (săl-ȧ-măŋ'kȧ) N. Y.	42·10 N	78·45 W

ăt; finȧl; rāte; senâte; ärm; ȧsk; sofȧ; fâre; ch-choose; dh-as th in other; bē; ēvent; bĕt; recĕnt; cratẽr; g-go; gh-guttural g; bĭt; ĭ-short neutral; rīde; K-guttural k as ch in German ich;

Page Name Pronunciation Region Lat. °' Long. °'

124 Salamanco (sä-lä-mä'n-kô) . . . . Sp. 40·54 N 5·42 W
155 Salamaua (sä-lä-mä'wä) N. Gui. Ter. 6·50 S 146·55 E
98 Salamina (sä-lä-mē'-nä) . Col. (In.) 5·25 N 75·29 W
127 Salamis (săl'á-mĭs) . . . . Grc. 37·58 N 23·30 E
98 Salaverry (sä-lä-vä'rē) . . . . Peru 8·16 S 78·54 W
155 Salawati (I.) (sä-lä-wä'tē) Neth. N. Gui. 1·22 S 130·15 E
157 Sala-Y-Gomez (I.) (sä'lä-ē-gō'māz) . Chile 26·50 S 105·50 W
95 Salcedo (säl-sā'dō) . . . . Dom. Rep. 19·25 N 70·30 W
98 Saldaña (R.) (säl-dá'n-yä) Col. (In.) 3·42 N 75·16 W
166 Saldanha . . . . S. Afr. 32·55 S 18·05 E
119 Saldus (säl'dŏŏs) . . . . Sov. Un. 56·39 N 22·30 E
160 Sale (sāl) . . . . Austl. 38·10 S 147·07 E
110 Sale . . . . Eng. 53·24 N 2·20 W
164 Salé (sà-lā') . . . . Mor. 34·09 N 6·42 W
85 Sale, Rivière (R.) (säl'rē-vyâr') Can. (Winnipeg In.) 49·44 N 97·11 W
132 Salekhard (sŭ-lyĭ-kärt) . . . Sov. Un. 66·35 N 66·50 E
80 Salem (sā'lĕm) . . . . Ill. 38·40 N 89·00 W
143 Salem . . . . India 11·39 N 78·11 E
80 Salem . . . . Ind. 38·35 N 86·00 W
83 Salem . . . . Mass. (Boston In.) 42·31 N 70·54 W
73 Salem . . . . Mo. 37·36 N 91·33 W
83 Salem . . . . N. H. (Boston In.) 42·46 N 71·16 W
81 Salem . . . . N. J. 39·35 N 75·30 W
80 Salem . . . . Ohio 40·55 N 80·50 W
66 Salem . . . . Ore. 44·55 N 123·03 W
70 Salem . . . . S. D. 43·43 N 97·23 W
167 Salem . . . . S. Afr. (Natal In.) 33·29 S 26·30 E
79 Salem . . . . Va. 37·16 N 80·05 W
80 Salem . . . . W. Va. 39·15 N 80·35 W
126 Salemi (sä-lå'mē) . . . . It. 37·48 N 38·50 E
125 Salerno (sä-lĕr'nô) It. (Napoli In.) 40·27 N 14·46 E
126 Salerno, Golfo di (G.) (gôl-fô-dē) It. 40·30 N 14·40 E
110 Salford (săl'fērd) . . . . Eng. 53·26 N 2·19 W
129 Salgir (R.) (sàl'gēr) . . . . . Sov. Un. 45·25 N 34·22 E
121 Salgōtarjan (shôl'gô-tôr-yăn) Hung. 48·06 N 19·50 E
72 Salida (sà-lī'dà) . . . . Colo. 38·31 N 106·01 W
122 Salies (sà-lēs') . . . . Fr. 43·27 N 0·58 W
73 Salina (sȧ-lī'nȧ) . . . . Kans. 38·50 N 97·37 W
69 Salina . . . . Utah 39·00 N 111·55 W
126 Salina (I.) (sä-lē'nä) . . . . It. 38·35 N 14·48 E
95 Salina Pt. . . . . Ba. Is. 22·10 N 74·20 W
91 Salina Cruz (sä-lē'nä krōōz') . Mex. 16·10 N 95·12 W
68 Salinas (sȧ-lē'nȧs) . . . . Calif. 36·41 N 121·40 W
88 Salinas . . . . Mex. 22·38 N 101·42 W
89 Salinas . . . P. R. (Puerto Rico In.) 17·58 N 66·16 W
68 Salinas (R.) . . . . Calif. 36·33 N 121·29 W
91 Salinas (R.) (sä-lē'näs) . . . . . Mex. 16·15 N 90·31 W
92 Salinas, Bahia de (B.) (bä-ē'ä-dě-sä-lē'näs) . Nic.-C. R. 11·05 N 85·55 W
125 Salinas, Cape (sä-lĕnås) . . . . . . Sp. 39·14 N 1·02 E
76 Salinas Victoria (sä-lē'näs vêk-tō'rē-ä) . Mex. 25·59 N 100·19 W
73 Saline (R.) (sȧ-lēn') . . . . Ark. 34·06 N 92·30 W
72 Saline (R.) . . . . Kans. 39·05 N 99·43 W
123 Salins-les-Bains (sà-lăɴ'-lā-băɴ') Fr. 46·55 N 5·54 E
166 Salisbury . . . . . Fed. of Rh. & Nya. 17·49 S 30·52 E
116 Salisbury (sôlz'bē-rē) . . . . Eng. 50·35 N 1·51 W
82 Salisbury . . . . Can. 46·03 N 65·05 W
81 Salisbury . . . . Md. 38·20 N 75·40 W
73 Salisbury . . . . Mo. 39·24 N 92·47 W
79 Salisbury . . . . N. C. 35·40 N 80·29 W
87 Salisbury (I.) . . . . Can. 63·36 N 76·20 W
116 Salisbury Plain . . . . Eng. 51·15 N 1·52 W
164 Sal I. (säal) . . . . C. V. Is. (In.) 16·45 N 22·39 W
79 Salkehatchie (R.) (sô-kē-hăch'ē) S. C. 33·09 N 81·10 W
73 Sallisaw (săl'ĭ-sô) . . . . Okla. 35·27 N 94·48 W
67 Salmon (săm'ŭn) . . . . Idaho 45·11 N 113·54 W
66 Salmon Falls R. . . . . Idaho 42·22 N 114·53 W
158 Salmon Gums (gŭmz) . . . . . . Austl. 33·00 S 122·00 E
82 Salmon (R.) . . . . Can. 46·19 N 65·36 W
81 Salmon (R.) . . . . N. Y. 44·35 N 74·15 W
65 Salmon (R.) . Wash. (Portland In.) 45·44 N 122·36 W
66 Salmon R. . . . . Idaho 45·30 N 115·45 W
66 Salmon R., Middle Fork . . . . Idaho 44·54 N 114·50 W
66 Salmon R., South Fork . . . . . Idaho 44·51 N 115·47 W
66 Salmon River Mts. . . . . Idaho 44·15 N 115·44 W
123 Salon-de-Provence (sà-lôɴ-dē-prô-văɴs') . Fr. 43·48 N 5·09 E
121 Salonta (sä-lôn'tä) . . . . Rom. 46·46 N 21·38 E
133 Sal'sk (sälsk) . . . . Sov. Un. 46·30 N 41·20 E
69 Salt, (R.) (sôlt) . . . . Ariz. 33·28 N 111·35 W
73 Salt (R.) . . . . Mo. 39·54 N 92·11 W
100 Salta (säl'tä) . . . . Arg. 24·50 S 65·16 W
100 Salta (Prov.) . . . . Arg. 25·15 S 65·00 W
74 Saltair (sôlt'âr) Utah (Salt Lake City In.) 40·46 N 112·09 W
95 Salt Cay (I.) . . . . Ba. Is. 21·20 N 71·15 W
75 Salt Cr. (sôlt) . . . Ill. (Chicago In.) 42·01 N 88·01 W
76 Saltillo (säl-tēl'yō) . . . . Mex. 25·24 N 100·59 W
74 Salt Lake City (sôlt läk sĭ'tĭ) Utah (Salt Lake City In.) 40·45 N 111·52 W
101 Salto (säl'tō) Arg. (Buenos Aires In.) 34·17 S 60·15 W
100 Salto . . . . Ur. 31·18 S 57·45 W
101 Salto, Serra do (Mtn.) (sĕ'r-rä-dô) Braz. (Rio de Janeiro In.) 20·26 S 43·28 W
90 Salto (R.) . . . . Mex. 22·16 N 99·18 W
99 Salto Grande (grän'dä) . . . . . Braz. 22·57 S 49·58 W
68 Salton Sea (sôlt'ŭn) . . . . Calif. 33·28 N 115·43 W
164 Saltpond . . . . Ghana 5·16 N 1·07 W
69 Salt River Ind. Res. (sôlt rĭv'ẽr) Ariz. 33·40 N 112·01 W
95 Saltrou (sål-trōō') . . . . Hai. 18·15 N 72·00 W
118 Saltsjöbaden (sält'shû-bäd'ĕn) Swe. 59·15 N 18·20 E
79 Saltville (sôlt'vĭl) . . . . Va. 36·50 N 81·45 W
136 Saltykovka (sál-tē'kôf-kȧ) Sov. Un. (Moskva In.) 55·45 N 37·56 E
88 Salud, Mt. (sä-lōō'th) Pan. (Panama Canal In.) 9·14 N 79·42 W
79 Saluda (sȧ-lōō'dȧ) . . . . S. C. 34·02 N 81·46 W
79 Saluda (R.) . . . . S. C. 34·07 N 81·48 W
126 Saluzzo (sä-lōōt'sō) . . . . It. 44·39 N 7·31 E
99 Salvador (Bahia) (säl-vä-dōr') (bä-ē'ä) . Braz. 12·59 S 38·27 W
77 Salvador L. . . . . La. 29·45 N 90·20 W
94 Salvador Pt. . . . . Ba. Is. 24·30 N 77·45 W
90 Salvatierra (säl-vä-tyĕr'rä) . . Mex. 20·13 N 100·52 W
146 Salween R. (săl-wēn') . . . . Bur. 26·46 N 98·19 E
133 Sal'yany . . . . Sov. Un. 39·40 N 49·10 E
120 Salzburg (sälts'bŏŏrgh) . . . . . . Aus. 47·48 N 13·04 E
120 Salzburg (State) . . . . Aus. 47·30 N 13·18 E
120 Salzwedel (sälts-vā'dĕl) . . . . . . Ger. 52·51 N 11·10 E
168 Samālūt (sä-mä-lōōt') U. A. R. (Nile In.) 28·17 N 30·43 E
95 Samaná (sä-mä-nä') . . . Dom. Rep. 19·15 N 69·25 W
95 Samana, Cabo (C.) (kà'bô) Dom. Rep. 19·20 N 69·00 W
95 Samana or Atwood Cay (I.) Ba. Is. 23·05 N 73·45 W
155 Samar (I.) (sä'mär) . . . . Phil. 11·30 N 126·07 E
133 Samara (R.) . . . . Sov. Un. 52·50 N 50·35 E
129 Samara (R.) (sà-mà'rà) . . Sov. Un. 48·47 N 35·30 E
155 Samarai (sä-mä-rä'ê) . . . . Pap. Ter. 10·45 S 150·49 E
134 Samarkand (sà-màr-känt') Sov. Un. 39·42 N 67·00 E
142 Sambalpur (sŭm'bŭl-pŏŏr) . . India 21·38 N 83·59 E
142 Sāmbhar (R.) . . . . India 27·00 N 74·58 E
121 Sambor (säm'bôr) . . . . Sov. Un. 49·31 N 23·12 E
101 Samborombón, Bahia (B.) (bä-ē'ä-säm-bô-rôm-bô'n) Arg. (Buenos Aires In.) 35·57 S 57·05 W
101 Samborombón (R.) Arg. (Buenos Aires In.) 35·20 S 57·52 W
117 Sambre (R.) (säɴ'br') . . . . Bel. 50·20 N 4·15 E
65 Sammamish, L. (sȧ-măm'ĭsh) Wash. (Seattle In.) 47·35 N 122·02 W
65 Sammamish (R.) Wash. (Seattle In.) 47·43 N 122·08 W
156 Samoa Is. (sä-mō'ȧ) . . . . . . Oceania 14·30 S 172·00 W
127 Samokov (sä'mô-kôf) . . . . Bul. 42·20 N 23·33 E
125 Samora Correia (sä-mô'rä-kôr-rĕ'yä) Port. (Lisboa In.) 38·55 N 8·52 W
134 Samorovo (sà-mà-rô'vô) . Sov. Un. 60·47 N 69·13 E
127 Sámos (I.) (să'mŏs) . . . . Grc. 37·53 N 26·35 E
127 Samothráki (I.) . . . . Grc. 40·23 N 25·10 E
155 Sampaloc Pt. (säm-pä'lōk) Phil. (Manila In.) 14·43 N 119·56 E
118 Samsö (I.) (säm'sû) . . . . Den. 55·49 N 10·47 E
78 Samson (săm'sŭn) . . . . Ala. 31·06 N 86·02 W
152 Samsu (säm'sōō') . . . . Kor. 41·12 N 128·00 E
133 Samsun (sàm'sōōn') . . . . Tur. 41·20 N 36·05 E
133 Samtredia (sàm'trĕ-dē) . . Sov. Un. 42·18 N 42·25 E
65 Samuel (I.) (săm'ū-ĕl) Can. (Vancouver In.) 48·50 N 123·10 W
133 Samur (R.) (sà-mōōr') . . . Sov. Un. 41·40 N 47·20 E
164 San (săn) . . . . Mali 13·37 N 4·45 W
144 San'a (sän'ä) . . . . Yemen 15·45 N 44·00 E
164 Sanaga R. (sä-nä'gä) . . . . Cam. 4·33 N 11·50 E
96 San Ambroisio, Isla de (I.) (ē's-lä-dĕ-sän äm-brō'zē-ō) Chile 26·40 S 80·00 W
155 Sanana (I.) . . . . Indon. 2·15 S 126·38 E
144 Sanandaj . . . . Iran 36·44 N 46·43 E
68 San Andreas (săn ăn'drē-ăs) . Calif. 38·10 N 120·42 W
65 San Andreas (L.) Calif. (San Francisco In.) 37·36 N 122·26 W
98 San Andrés (sän-än-drĕ's) Col. (In.) 6·57 N 75·41 W
91 San Andrés (sän än-dräs') Mex. (Mexico In.) 19·15 N 99·10 W
91 San Andres, Laguna de (L.) . Mex. 22·40 N 97·50 W
62 San Andres, Mts. (săn ăn'drē-ăs) U. S. 33·00 N 106·40 W
San Andrés, see Petén, Laguna de
101 San Andrés de Giles (sän-än-drĕ's-dĕ-gē'lĕs) Arg. (Buenos Aires In.) 34·26 S 59·28 W
93 San Andres I. . . . . Col. 12·32 N 81·34 W
69 San Andres Mts. . . . . N. Mex. 23·45 N 106·40 W
91 San Andrés Tuxtla (sän-än-drā's-tōōs'tlä) . Mex. 18·27 N 95·12 W
76 San Angelo (săn ăn'jĕ-lō) . . . Tex. 31·28 N 100·22 W
126 San Antioco, I. di (ē'sō-lä-dē-sän-än-tyŏ'kô) . It. 39·00 N 8·25 E
101 San Antonio (sän-än-tō'nyō) Chile (Santiago In.) 33·34 S 71·36 W
98 San Antonio . . . . Col. (In.) 2·57 N 75·06 W
98 San Antonio . . . . Col. (In.) 3·55 N 75·38 W
155 San Antonio . . . . Phil. (Manila In.) 14·57 N 120·05 E
74 San Antonio (săn ăn-tō'nē-ô) Tex. (San Antonio In.) 29·25 N 98·30 W
68 San Antonio (R.) . . . . Calif. 36·00 N 121·13 W
94 San Antonio, Cabo (C.) (kä'bô-sän-än-tô'nyô) . Cuba 21·55 N 84·55 W
125 San Antonio Abad (sän än-tō'nyô ä-bädh') . Sp. 38·59 N 1·17 E
77 San Antonio B. . . . . Tex. 28·20 N 97·08 W
101 San Antonio de Areco (dā ä-rä'kō) Arg. (Buenos Aires In.) 34·16 S 59·30 W
95 San Antonio de las Vegas (sän än-tō'nyō-dĕ-läs-vĕ'gäs) Cuba (La Habana In.) 22·07 N 82·16 W
95 San Antonio de los Baños (dā lōs bän'yōs) Cuba (La Habana In.) 22·08 N 82·30 W
100 San Antonio de los Cobres (dā lōs kō'brās) . Arg. 24·15 S 66·29 W
101 San Antônio de Pádua (dĕ-pä'dwä) Braz. (Rio de Janeiro In.) 21·32 S 42·09 W
99 San Antonio de Tamanaco (sän-än-tô-nyō-dĕ-tä-mä-nà'kô) Ven. (In.) 9·42 N 66·03 W
100 San Antonio Oeste (sän-än-tō'nyô ô-ĕs'tā) . Arg. 40·49 S 64·56 W
74 San Antonio Pk. (săn ăn-tō'nĭ-ô) Calif. (Los Angeles In.) 34·17 N 117·39 W
76 San Antonio R. . . . . Tex. 29·00 N 97·58 W
92 Sanarate (sä-nä-rä'tĕ) . . . . . . Guat. 14·47 N 90·12 W
77 San Augustine (săn ô'gŭs-tēn) Tex. 31·33 N 94·08 W
76 San Bartolo . . . . Mex. 24·43 N 103·12 W
91 San Bartolo (sän bär-tō'lô) Mex. (Mexico In.) 19·36 N 99·43 W
126 San Bartolomeo (bär-tô-lô-mā'ô) It. 41·25 N 15·04 E
126 San Benedetto del Tronto (bā'nâ-dĕt'tô dĕl trōn'tô) . It. 42·58 N 13·54 E
77 San Benito (săn bĕ-nē'tô) . . . . Tex. 26·07 N 97·37 W
68 San Benito (R.) . . . . Calif. 36·40 N 121·20 W
74 San Bernardino (bûr-när-dē'nô) Calif. (Los Angeles In.) 34·07 N 117·19 W
68 San Bernardino Mts. . . . . Calif. 34·05 N 116·23 W
101 San Bernardo (sän bĕr-när'dô) Chile (Santiago In.) 33·35 S 70·42 W
90 San Blas (sän bläs') . . . . Mex. 21·33 N 105·19 W
78 San Blas, C. . . . . Fla. 29·38 N 85·38 W
93 San Blas, Cord. de (Mts.) (kôr-dĕl-yĕ'rä-dĕ) . Pan. 9·17 N 78·20 W
93 San Blas, Golfo de (G.) . . . . . . Pan. 9·33 N 78·42 W
65 San Bruno (săn brū-nô) Calif. (San Francisco In.) 37·38 N 122·25 W
76 San Buenaventura (bwā'nà-vĕn-tōō'rà) . Mex. 27·07 N 101·30 W
65 San Carlos (săn kär'lōs) Calif. (San Francisco In.) 37·30 N 122·15 W
100 San Carlos (sän-kà'r-lŏs) . . . . Chile 36·23 S 71·58 W
98 San Carlos . . . . Col. (In.) 6·11 N 74·58 W
91 San Carlos (sän kär'lōs) . . . . . Mex. 17·49 N 92·33 W
76 San Carlos . . . . Mex. 24·36 N 98·52 W
93 San Carlos (sän-kà'r-lôs) . . . . . Nic. 11·08 N 84·48 W
155 San Carlos . . . . . Phil. (Manila In.) 15·56 N 120·20 E
98 San Carlos . . . . Ven. 9·36 N 68·35 W
100 San Carlos de Bariloche (sän-kà'r lŏs-dĕ-bä-rē-lô'chĕ) Arg. 41·15 S 71·26 W
69 San Carlos Ind. Res. (săn kär'lōs) Ariz. 33·27 N 110·15 W
69 San Carlos Res. . . . . Ariz. 33·05 N 110·29 W
93 San Carlos R. . . . . C. R. 10·36 N 84·18 W
99 San Casimiro (kä-sē-mē'rô) Ven. (In.) 10·01 N 67·02 W
126 San Cataldo (kä-täl'dō) . . . . It. 37·30 N 13·59 E
95 Sanchez (sän'chĕz) . . . . . Dom. Rep. 19·15 N 69·40 W
90 Sanchez, Río de los (R.) (rē'ō-dĕ-lôs) . Mex. 20·31 N 102·29 W
90 Sánchez Román (Tlaltenango) (rô-mà'n) (tlä'l-tĕ-nän-gô) . Mex. 21·48 N 103·20 W
124 San Clemente (sän klâ-mĕn'tā) Sp. 39·25 N 2·24 W
68 San Clemente (I.) . . . . Calif. 33·02 N 118·36 W
95 San Cristobal (krēs-tō'bäl) Dom. Rep. 18·25 N 70·05 W
92 San Cristóbal . . . . Guat. 15·22 N 90·26 W
98 San Cristóbal . . . . Ven. 7·43 N 72·15 W
98 San Cristobal (I.) . . . . Ec. 1·05 S 89·15 W
159 San Cristobal (I.) . . . . Sol. Is. 10·47 S 162·17 E
126 San Croce, C. (krô'chā) . . . . It. 37·15 N 15·18 E
94 Sancti Spíritus (säŋk'tê spē'rē-tōōs) . Cuba 21·55 N 79·25 W
122 Sancy, Puy de (Pk.) (pwē-dĕ-säɴ-sē') . Fr. 45·30 N 2·53 E
65 Sand (I.) (sănd) Ore. (Portland In.) 46·16 N 124·01 W
71 Sand (I.) . . . . Wis. 46·03 N 91·09 W
153 Sanda (sän'dä) . . . Jap. (Ōsaka In.) 34·53 N 135·14 E
154 Sandakan (sän-dä'kän) . . . N. Bor. 5·51 N 118·03 E
116 Sanday (I.) (sănd'ā) . . . . Scot. 59·17 N 2·25 W
110 Sandbach (sănd'băch) . . . . Scot. 53·08 N 2·22 W
118 Sandefjord (sän'dĕ-fyôr') . . . . Nor. 59·09 N 10·14 E
65 San de Fuca (de-fōō-cä) Wash. (Seattle In.) 48·14 N 122·44 W
76 Sanderson (săn'dĕr-sŭn) . . . . . Tex. 30·09 N 102·24 W
78 Sandersville (săn'dērz-vĭl) . . . . . Ga. 32·57 N 82·50 W
167 Sandflats (sănd-flăts) S. Afr. (Natal In.) 33·26 S 25·57 E
118 Sandhammar, C. (sänt'häm-mȧr) Swe. 55·24 N 14·37 E
70 Sand Hills (Reg.) (sănd) . . . . Nebr. 41·57 N 101·29 W
84 Sand Hook (sănd hŏŏk) N. J. (New York In.) 40·29 N 74·05 W
110 Sandhurst (sănd'hûrst) Eng. (London In.) 51·20 N 0·48 W
68 San Diego (săn dē-á'gô) Calif. (San Diego In.) 32·43 N 117·10 W
76 San Diego . . . . Tex. 27·47 N 98·13 W
68 San Diego (R.) . . . . Calif. 32·53 N 116·57 W
90 San Diego de la Unión (sän dĕ-á'gô dà lä ōō-nyōn') Mex. 21·27 N 100·52 W
77 Sandies Cr. (sănd'ēz) . . . . Tex. 29·13 N 97·34 W
74 San Dimas (săn dĕ'màs) Calif. (Los Angeles In.) 34·07 N 117·49 W
90 San Dimas (dê-mäs') . . . . Mex. 24·08 N 105·57 W
118 Sandnes (sänd'nĕs) . . . . Nor. 58·52 N 5·44 E
166 Sandoa (sän-dō'á) . . . . Con. L. 9·39 S 23·00 E
121 Sandomierz (sän-dô'myĕzh) . . . Pol. 50·39 N 21·45 E
126 San Donà di Piave (sän dô-nà' dê pyä'vĕ) . It. 45·38 N 12·34 E
146 Sandoway (sän-dô-wī') . . . . Bur. 18·24 N 94·28 E
66 Sandpoint (sănd point) . . . . . Idaho 48·17 N 116·34 W
161 Sandringham (săn'drĭng-ăm) Austl. (Melbourne In.) 37·57 S 145·01 E
126 Sandrio (sä'n-dryô) . . . . It. 46·11 N 9·53 E
73 Sand Springs (sănd sprĭnz) . . Okla. 36·08 N 96·06 W

ng-sing; ŋ-baŋk; ɴ-nasalized n; nŏd; cŏmmit; ōld; ôbey; ôrder; fōōd; fŏŏt; ou-out; s-soft; sh-dish; th-thin; pūre; ûnite; ûrn; stŭd; circŭs; ü-as "y" in study; '-indeterminate vowel.

262 Sandstone–San Miguel PRONOUNCING INDEX

Page	Name Pronunciation Region	Lat. °′	Long. °′
158	Sandstone (sănd′stōn) ...... Austl.	28·00 s	119·25 e
71	Sandstone .... Minn.	46·08 n	92·53 w
84	Sandusky (săn-dŭs′kē) Ala. (Birmingham In.)	33·32 n	86·50 w
80	Sandusky .... Mich.	43·25 n	82·50 w
80	Sandusky .... Ohio	41·25 n	82·45 w
80	Sandusky (R.) .... Ohio	41·10 n	83·20 w
80	Sandwich (sănd′wĭch) .... Ill.	42·35 n	88·35 w
65	Sandy (sănd′ē) . Ore. (Portland In.)	45·24 n	122·16 w
74	Sandy . . Utah (Salt Lake City In.)	40·36 n	111·53 w
83	Sandy (I.) .... Can.	51·13 n	58·10 w
65	Sandy (R.) .... Ore. (Portland In.)	45·28 n	122·17 w
160	Sandy C .... Austl.	24·25 s	153·10 e
67	Sandy Cr .... Mont.	48·20 n	110·08 w
67	Sandy Cr .... Wyo.	42·08 n	109·35 w
84	Sandy Hook (ho͝ok) Conn. (New York In.)	41·25 n	73·17 w
85	Sandy L .... Can. (Edmonton In.)	53·46 n	113·58 w
77	Sandy Point .... Tex. (In.)	29·22 n	95·27 w
65	Sandy Pt . . Wash. (Vancouver In.)	48·48 n	122·42 w
84	Sandy Springs (sprinz) Ga. (Atlanta In.)	33·55 n	84·23 w
101	San Enrique (săn-ĕn-rē′kĕ) Arg. (Buenos Aires In.)	35·47 s	60·22 w
100	San Estanislao (ĕs-tä-nēs-lä′ô) Par.	24·38 s	56·20 w
92	San Esteban (ĕs-tĕ′băn) .... Hond.	15·13 n	85·53 w
155	San Fabian (fä-byä′n) Phil. (Manila In.)	16·14 n	120·28 e
101	San Felipe (fâ-lē′pâ) Chile (Santiago In.)	32·45 s	70·43 w
90	San Felipe (fĕ-lē′pĕ) .... Mex.	21·29 n	101·13 w
90	San Felipe .... Mex.	22·21 n	105·26 w
98	San Felipe (fĕ-lē′pĕ) .... Ven.	10·13 n	68·45 w
	San Felipe, see Jalapa de Diaz		
68	San Felipe, Cr. (săn fê-lēp′â) Calif.	33·10 n	116·03 w
94	San Felipe, Cayos de (Is.) (kä′yōs-dĕ-sän-fĕ-lē′pĕ) . Cuba	22·00 n	83·30 w
125	San Felíu de Guixols (sän fâ-lē′o͞o dâ gē-hôls) . Sp.	41·45 n	3·01 e
96	San Felix, Isla de (I.) (ē′s-lä-dĕ-sän fâ-lēks′) . Chile	26·20 s	80·10 w
124	San Fernanda (fĕr-nä′n-dä) .... Sp.	36·28 n	6·13 w
100	San Fernando (fĕr-nà′n-dô) Arg. (In.)	34·11 s	58·34 w
74	San Fernando (fĕr-năn′dô) Calif. (Los Angeles In.)	34·17 n	118·27 w
101	San Fernando . Chile (Santiago In.)	36·36 s	70·58 w
76	San Fernando (fĕr-nän′dô) . . Mex.	24·52 n	98·10 w
155	San Fernando (sän fĕr-nä′n-dô) Phil. (Manila In.)	16·38 n	120·19 e
98	San Fernando de Apure (sän-fĕr-nä′n-dō-dĕ-ä-po͞o′rä) Ven.	7·46 n	67·29 w
98	San Fernando de Atabapo (dĕ-ä-tä-bà′pô) . Ven.	3·58 n	67·41 w
125	San Fernando de Henares (dĕ-ä-nä′räs) . Sp. (Madrid In.)	40·23 n	3·31 w
76	San Fernando R. (săn fĕr-năn′dô) . Mex.	25·07 n	98·25 w
118	Sånfjället (Mtn.) .... Swe.	62·19 n	13·30 e
85	Sanford (săn′fẽrd) Can. (Winnipeg In.)	49·41 n	97·27 w
79	Sanford (săn′fôrd) ...... Fla. (In.)	28·46 n	80·18 w
82	Sanford (săn′fẽrd) .... Maine	43·26 n	70·47 w
79	Sanford .... N. C.	35·26 n	79·10 w
100	San Francisco (săn frăn-sĭs′kô) Arg.	31·23 s	62·09 w
65	San Francisco Calif. (San Francisco In.)	37·45 n	122·26 w
92	San Francisco .... Sal.	13·48 n	88·11 w
	San Francisco, see Ixhuatán		
69	San Francisco (R.) ...... N. Mex.	33·35 n	108·55 w
65	San Francisco B. (săn frăn-sĭs′kô) Calif. (San Francisco In.)	37·45 n	122·21 w
88	San Francisco del Oro (dĕl ō′rō) Mex.	27·00 n	106·37 w
90	San Francisco del Rincón (dĕl rēn-kōn′) . Mex.	21·01 n	101·51 w
99	San Francisco de Macaira (dĕ-mä-kī′rä) . Ven. (In.)	9·58 n	66·17 w
95	San Francisco de Macoris (dā-mä-kō′rēs) . Dom. Rep.	19·20 n	70·15 w
95	San Francisco de Paula (dā pou′là) . CubaLa Habana In.)	23·04 n	82·18 w
62	San Francisco Mts .... U. S.	35·30 n	112·35 w
74	San Gabriel (săn gä-brē-ĕl′) (gā′brē-ĕl) Calif. (Los Angeles In.)	34·06 n	118·06 w
90	San Gabriel Chilac (sän-gä-brē-ĕl-chē-läk′) . Mex.	18·19 n	97·22 w
74	San Gabriel Mts. Calif. (Los Angeles In.)	34·17 n	118·03 w
74	San Gabriel Res. Calif. (Los Angeles In.)	34·14 n	117·48 w
74	San Gabriel R. Calif. (Los Angeles In.)	33·47 n	118·06 w
73	Sangamon (R.) (săn′gá-mŭn) . . Ill.	40·08 n	90·08 w
165	Sanga R. (säŋ-gä) .... Afr.	3·41 n	16·12 e
68	Sanger (săng′ẽr) .... Calif.	36·42 n	119·33 w
120	Sangerhausen (säng′ĕr-hou-zĕn) Ger.	51·28 n	11·17 e
155	Sangihe (I.) (säŋ′gē-ē) ..... Indon.	3·30 n	125·30 e
98	San Gil (sän-ĸē′l) .... Col.	6·32 n	73·13 w
126	San Giovanni in Fiore (sän jô-văn′nē ēn fyō′rä) . It.	39·15 n	16·40 e
125	San Giuseppe Vesuviano (sän-zhĕo͞o-sĕ′p-pĕ-vĕ-so͞o-vyä′nô) It. (Napoli In.)	40·36 n	14·31 e
152	Sangju (säng′jo͞o′) .... Kor.	36·20 n	128·07 e
124	Sangonera (R.) (säŋ-gō-nä′rä) . Sp.	37·43 n	1·58 w
74	San Gorgonio Mt. (săn gôr-gō′nĭ-ō) Calif. (Los Angeles In.)	34·06 n	116·50 w
62	Sangre De Cristo, Mts. (săng′ẽr-de-krēs-tō) . U. S.	37·45 n	105·50 w
65	San Gregoria (săn grĕ-gôr′ä) Calif. (San Francisco In.)	37·20 n	122·23 w
126	Sangro (R.) (säŋ′grô) .... It.	41·38 n	13·56 e
124	Sangüesa (sän-gwĕ′sä) .... Sp.	42·36 n	1·15 w
148	Sanho (săn′hô) .... China	39·59 n	117·06 e
79	Sanibel I. (săn′ĭ-bĕl) .... Fla. (In.)	26·26 n	82·15 w
	San Ildefonso, see Villa Alta		
155	San Ildefonso, C. (sän-êl-dĕ-fōn-sô) Phil. (Manila In.)	16·03 n	122·10 e
124	San Ildefonso o la Granja (ō lä grän′khä) . Sp.	40·54 n	4·02 w
100	San Isidro (ē-sē′drô) .... Arg. (In.)	34·13 s	58·31 w
93	San Isidro .... C. R.	9·24 n	83·43 w
74	San Jacinto (săn jȧ-sĭn′tô) Calif. (Los Angeles In.)	33·47 n	116·57 w
155	San Jacinto (sän hä-sēn′tô) Phil. (Manila In.)	12·33 n	123·43 e
77	San Jacinto (R.), West Fork . Tex.	30·35 n	95·37 w
74	San Jacinto R. (săn jȧ-sĭn′tô) Calif. (Los Angeles In.)	33·44 n	117·14 w
77	San Jacinto R .... Tex.	30·25 n	95·05 w
101	San Javier (sän-hà-vē-ĕr) Chile (Santiago In.)	35·35 s	71·43 w
91	San Jerónima (hĕ-rô′nē-mä) Mex. (Mexico In.)	19·31 n	98·46 w
90	San Jerónimo de Juárez (hâ-rō′nê-mô dâ hwä′räz) . Mex.	17·08 n	100·30 w
99	San Joaquin (hô-ä-kē′n) Ven. (In.)	10·16 n	67·47 w
68	San Joaquin (R.) (săn hwä-kēn′) Calif.	37·10 n	120·51 w
68	San Joaquin Valley .... Calif.	36·45 n	120·30 w
100	San Jorge, Golfo (G.) (gôl-fô-sän-ĸô′r-ĸĕ) . Arg.	46·15 s	66·45 w
99	San José (sän hô-sā′) .... Bol.	17·54 s	60·42 w
65	San Jose (săn hô-zā′) Calif. (San Francisco In.)	37·20 n	121·54 w
93	San Jose (sän hô-sā′) .... C. R.	9·57 n	84·05 w
92	San José .... Guat.	13·56 n	90·49 w
155	San Jose ...... Phil. (Manila In.)	12·22 n	121·04 e
155	San Jose (sän-ĸô-sĕ′) Phil. (Manila In.)	13·52 n	121·07 e
155	San José .... Phil. (Manila In.)	14·49 n	120·47 e
155	San Jose .... Phil. (Manila In.)	15·49 n	120·57 e
101	San José (hô-sĕ′) Ur. (Buenos Aires In.)	34·20 s	56·43 w
101	San José (Dept.) Ur. (Buenos Aires In.)	34·17 s	56·23 w
88	San Jose (I.) (ĸô-sĕ′) .... Mex.	25·00 n	110·35 w
69	San Jose (R.) (săn hô-zā′) N. Mex.	35·15 n	108·10 w
93	San Jose, Isla de (I.) (ē′s-lä-dĕ-sän hô-sā′) . Pan.	8·17 n	79·20 w
101	San José (R.) (sän-hô-sĕ′) Ur. (Buenos Aires In.)	34·05 s	56·47 w
100	San José de Feliciano (dâ lē ĕs-kē′nȧ) . Arg.	30·26 s	58·44 w
99	San José de Gauribe (sän-hô-sĕ′dĕ-gào͞o-rē′bĕ) Ven. (In.)	9·51 n	65·49 w
95	San Jose de las Lajas (sän-ĸô-sĕ′dĕ-läs-lä′käs) Cuba (La Habana In.)	22·13 n	82·10 w
90	San José Iturbide (ē-to͞or-bē′dĕ) Mex.	21·00 n	100·24 w
100	San Juan (hwän′) .... Arg.	31·36 s	68·29 w
98	San Juan (hōōá′n) ...... Col. (In.)	3·23 n	73·48 w
95	San Juan (sän hwän′) . . Dom. Rep.	18·50 n	71·15 w
155	San Juan (sän-ĸo͞oá′n) Phil. (Manila In.)	14·30 n	121·14 e
155	San Juan ...... Phil. (Manila In.)	16·41 n	120·20 e
89	San Juan (sän hwän′) P. R. (Puerto Rico In.)	18·30 n	66·10 w
	San Juan, see Guichicovi		
	San Juan, see Mazatlán		
100	San Juan (Prov.) .... Arg.	31·00 s	69·30 w
89	San Juan, Cabezas de (C.) P. R. (Puerto Rico In.)	18·29 n	65·30 w
94	San Juan, Pico (Pk.) (pē′kô-sän-ko͞oá′n) . Cuba	21·55 n	80·00 w
91	San Juan (R.) (sän-ho͞o-än′) . Mex.	18·10 n	95·23 w
76	San Juan, Rio (R.) (rē′ō-sän hwän) . Mex.	25·35 n	99·15 w
69	San Juan (R.) .... Utah	37·10 n	110·30 w
100	San Juan Bautista (sän hwän′ bou-tēs′tä) . Par.	26·48 s	57·09 w
90	San Juan Capistrano (sän-ho͞o-än′ kä-pēs-trä′nô) Mex.	22·41 n	104·07 w
68	San Juan Cr. (săn hwän′) ... Calif.	35·24 n	120·12 w
76	San Juan de Guadalupe (sän hwan dâ gwä-dhä-lo͞o′pä) Mex.	24·37 n	102·43 w
93	San Juan del Norte (Greytown) (dĕl nôr-tâ) (grā′toun) . Nic.	10·55 n	83·44 w
93	San Juan del Norte Bahia de (B.) (bä-ē′ä-dĕ-sän hwän dĕl nôr′tâ) Nic.	11·12 n	83·40 w
90	San Juan de los Lagos (sän-ho͞o-än′dâ los lä′gôs) . Mex.	21·15 n	102·18 w
90	San Juan de los Lagos (R.) (dâ lōs lä′gôs) . Mex.	21·13 n	102·12 w
99	San Juan de los Morros (dĕ-lôs-mô′r-rôs) . Ven. (In.)	9·54 n	67·22 w
90	San Juan del Rio (dĕl rē′ō) .. Mex.	20·21 n	99·59 w
76	San Juan del Rio (sän hwän del rē′ô) . Mex.	24·47 n	104·29 w
92	San Juan del Sur (dĕl so͞or) ... Nic.	11·15 n	85·53 w
76	San Juan de Sabinas (dĕ-sä-bē′näs) . Mex.	27·56 n	101·23 w
91	San Juan Evangelista (sän-ho͞o-ä′n-ā-vaŋ-kå-lĕs′ta′) Mex.	17·57 n	95·08 w
74	San Juan Hot Springs (săn hwän′) . Calif. (Los Angeles In.)	33·37 n	117·28 w
65	San Juan I .... Wash. (Seattle In.)	48·28 n	123·08 w
65	San Juan Is. (săn hwän) Can. (Vancouver In.)	48·49 n	123·14 w
91	San Juan Ixtenco (ēx-tĕ′n-kô) Mex.	19·14 n	97·52 w
94	San Juan Martinez (sän ko͞o ä′n-mär-tē′nĕz) . Cuba	22·15 n	83·50 w
69	San Juan Mts. (san hwän′) . . Colo.	37·50 n	107·30 w
93	San Juan R .... Nic.	10·58 n	84·18 w
100	San Julián (sän ho͞o-lyȧ′n) ... Arg.	49·17 s	68·02 w
100	San Justo (ho͞os′tô) ..... Arg. (In.)	34·25 s	58·33 w
164	Sankarani R. (săn′kä-rä′nê) Mali-Gui.	11·15 n	8·01 w
120	Sankt Gallen .... Switz.	47·25 n	9·22 e
166	Sankuru (R.) (săn-ko͞o′ro͞o) Con. L.	4·12 s	22·08 e
88	San Lazaro, C. (sän-là′zä-rō) Mex.	24·58 n	113·30 w
65	San Leandro (săn lê-ăn′drô) Calif. (San Francisco In.)	37·43 n	122·10 w
101	San Lorenzo (sän lô-rĕn′zô) Arg. (Buenos Aires In.)	32·46 s	60·44 w
65	San Lorenzo (săn lô-rĕn′zô) Calif. (San Francisco In.)	37·41 n	122·08 w
92	San Lorenzo (sän lô-rĕn′zô) . Hond.	13·24 n	87·24 w
125	San Lorenzo de El Escorial (sän lô-rĕn′tho dĕl ĕs-kō-rê-äl′) Sp. (Madrid In.)	40·36 n	4·09 w
124	Sanlúcar (sän-lo͞o′kär) .... Sp.	36·46 n	6·21 w
98	San Lucas (lo͞o′kás) .... Bol.	20·12 s	65·06 w
	San Lucas, see Ojitlán		
88	San Lucas, C .... Mex.	22·45 n	109·45 w
100	San Luis (lo͞o-ēs′) .... Arg.	33·16 s	66·15 w
98	San Luis (lo͞oē′s) .... Col. (In.)	6·03 n	74·57 w
95	San Luis .... Cuba	20·15 n	75·50 w
92	San Luis .... Guat.	14·38 n	89·42 w
100	San Luis (Prov.) .... Arg.	32·45 s	66·00 w
88	San Luis (State) .... Mex.	22·45 n	101·45 w
90	San Luis de la Paz (dâ lä päz′) Mex.	21·17 n	100·32 w
76	San Luis del Cordero (dĕl kōr-dā′rô) . Mex.	25·25 n	104·20 w
68	San Luis Obispo (ô-bĭs′pō) . . Calif.	35·18 n	120·40 w
68	San Luis Obispo, B .... Calif.	35·07 n	121·05 w
90	San Luis Potosi (pō-tô-sē′) . . Mex.	22·08 n	100·58 w
68	San Luis Rey (R.) (rā′ē) .... Calif.	133·22 n	117·06 w
69	San Manuel (sän măn′ū-ĕl) . . Ariz.	32·30 n	110·45 w
69	San Marcial (săn mȧr-shäl′) N. Mex.	33·40 n	107·00 w
126	San Marco (sän mär′kô) .... It.	41·53 n	15·50 e
92	San Marcos (mär′kôs) ...... Guat.	14·57 n	91·49 w
90	San Marcos .... Mex.	16·46 n	99·23 w
76	San Marcos (săn mär′kôs) ... Tex.	29·53 n	97·56 w
92	San Marcos de Colón (sän-mȧ′r-kōs-dĕ-kô-lô′n) . Hond.	13·17 n	86·50 w
76	San Marcos R .... Tex.	30·08 n	98·15 w
92	San Maria (Vol.) (sän-mä-rē′ä) Guat.	14·45 n	91·33 w
127	San Maria di Léuca, C. (dĕ-lĕ′o͞o-kä) . It.	39·47 n	18·20 e
155	San Mariano (sän mä-rê-ä′nô) Phil. (Manila In.)	17·00 n	121·58 e
74	San Marino (săn mĕr-ē′nô) Calif. (Los Angeles In.)	34·07 n	118·06 w
126	San Marino (sän mä-rē′nō) ... Eur.	43·52 n	12·38 e
126	San Marino .... San Marino	44·55 n	12·26 e
98	San Martín (sän mär-tē′n) Col. (In.)	3·42 n	73·44 w
91	San Martín (mär-tē′n) ...... Mex.	18·36 n	95·11 w
100	San Martín (L.) .... Arg.-Chile	48·15 s	72·30 w
90	San Martin Chalchicuautla (sän mär-tē′n chäl-chē-kwä-o͞o′tlä) . Mex.	21·22 n	98·39 w
125	San Martin de la Vega (sän mär ten′ dâ lä vā′gä) Sp. (Madrid In.)	40·12 n	3·34 w
90	San Martín Hidalgo (sän mär-tē′n-ē-däl′gô) . Mex.	20·27 n	103·55 w
65	San Mateo (săn mä-tā′ô) Calif. (San Francisco In.)	37·34 n	122·20 w
91	San Mateo (Etlatongo) (sän-mä-tĕ′ô) (ĕ-tlä-tô′n-gō) Mex.	16·59 n	97·04 w
125	San Mateo (sän mä-tā′ō) ...... Sp.	40·26 n	0·09 e
99	San Mateo (sän mä-tĕ′ô) Ven. (In.)	9·45 n	64·34 w
100	San Matías, Golfo (G.) (sän mä-tē′äs) . Arg	41·30 s	63·45 w
151	Sanmen Wan (B.) .... China	29·00 n	122·15 e
100	San Miguel (sän mē-gĕ′l) Arg. (In.)	34·17 s	58·43 w
91	San Miguel (sän mê-gäl′) .... Mex.	18·18 n	97·09 w
93	San Miguel .... Pan.	8·26 n	78·55 w
155	San Miguel (sän mē-gĕ′l) Phil. (Manila In.)	15·09 n	120·56 e
92	San Miguel (sän mê-gäl′) ..... Sal.	13·28 n	88·11 w
99	San Miguel (sän mē-gĕ′l) Ven. (In.)	9·56 n	64·58 w
	San Miguel, see Sola de Vega		
	San Miguel, see Talea de Castro		
93	San Miguel, Bahia (B.) (bä-ē′ä-sän mê-gäl′) . Pan.	8·17 n	78·26 w
68	San Miguel (I.) .... Calif.	34·03 n	120·23 w
98	San Miguel (R.) (sän-mē-gĕl′) Bol.	13·34 s	63·58 w
69	San Miguel (R.) (săn mê-gĕl′) Colo.	38·15 n	108·40 w
91	San Miguel (R.) (sän mê-gäl′) Mex.	15·27 n	92·00 w
92	San Miguel (Vol.) .... Sal.	13·27 n	88·17 w
155	San Miguel B . . Phil. (Manila In.)	13·55 n	123·12 e
90	San Miguel de Allende (dâ ä-lyĕn′dâ) . Mex.	20·54 n	100·44 w

ăt; finăl; rāte; senâte; ärm; ásk; sofȧ; fâre; ch-choose; dh-as th in other; bē; ēvent; bĕt; recĕnt; cratẽr; g-go; gh-guttural g; bĭt; ĭ-short neutral; rīde; ĸ-guttural k as ch in German ich;

PRONOUNCING INDEX San Miguel–Santiago 263

Page	Name Pronunciation Region	Lat. °'	Long. °'
90	San Miguel el Alto (ĕl äl'tō) . Mex.	21·03 N	102·26 W
168	Sanmur, Wadi (Val.) U. A. R. (Nile In.)	28·48 N	31·12 E
155	San Narcisco . . . Phil. (Manila In.)	15·01 N	120·05 E
155	San Narciso (sän när-sē'sô) Phil. (Manila In.)	13·34 N	123·33 E
101	San Nicolás (sän nē-kô-lä's) Arg. (Buenos Aires In.)	33·20 S	60·14 W
155	San Nicolas (nê-kô-läs') Phil. (Manila In.)	16·05 N	120·45 E
68	San Nicolas (I.) (săn nĭ'kô-lȧ) Calif.	33·14 N	119·10 W
90	San Nicolás (R.) . Mex.	19·40 N	105·08 W
121	Sanok (sä'nôk) . Pol.	49·31 N	22·13 E
65	San Pablo (săn păb'lô) Calif. (San Francisco In.)	37·58 N	122·21 W
155	San Pablo (sän-pä-blô) Phil. (Manila In.)	14·05 N	121·20 E
155	San Pablo . . . Phil. (Manila In.)	17·29 N	121·49 E
99	San Pablo (sän-pȧ'blô) . Ven. (In.)	9·46 N	65·04 W
65	San Pablo B. (săn păb'lô) Calif (San Francisco In.)	38·04 N	122·25 W
65	San Pablo Re.s Calif. (San Francisco In.)	37·55 N	122·12 W
93	San Pablo R. (sän päb'lô) . Pan.	8·12 N	81·12 W
155	San Pascual (päs-kwäl') Phil. (Manila In.)	13·08 N	122·59 E
100	San Pedro (sän pā'drô) . Arg.	24·15 S	64·51 W
101	San Pedro . Arg. (Buenos Aires In.)	33·41 S	59·42 W
74	San Pedro (săn pē'drô) Calif. (Los Angeles In.)	33·44 N	118·17 W
101	San Pedro (sän pĕ'drô) Chile (Santiago In.)	33·54 S	71·27 W
91	San Pedro (sän pā'drô) . Mex.	18·38 N	92·25 W
100	San Pedro (sän-pĕ'drô) . Par.	24·13 S	57·00 W
92	San Pedro (sän pā'drô) . Sal.	13·49 N	88·58 W
	San Pedro, see Amusgos		
	San Pedro, see Pochutla		
69	San Pedro (R.) . Ariz.	32·48 N	110·37 W
94	San Pedro (R.) (sän-pĕ'drô) . Cuba	21·05 N	78·15 W
91	San Pedro, Rio de (R.) (rē'ō-dĕ-sän-pĕ'drô) . Mex.	18·23 N	92·13 W
90	San Pedro, Río de (R.) . Mex.	21·51 N	102·24 W
90	San Pedro (R.) (sän pā'drô) . Mex.	22·08 N	104·59 W
74	San Pedro B. (săn pē'drô) Calif. (Los Angeles In.)	33·42 N	118·12 W
76	San Pedro de las Colonias (dĕ-läs-kô-lô'nyäs) . Mex.	25·47 N	102·58 W
95	San Pedro de Macorís (sän-pĕ'drō-dä mä-kô-rēs') Dom. Rep.	18·30 N	69·30 W
90	San Pedro Lagunillas (sän pā'drô lä-gōō-nēl'yäs) . Mex.	21·12 N	104·47 W
92	San Pedro R. (sän pā'drô) Guat. (Yucatan In.)	17·11 N	90·23 W
76	San Pedro R. . Mex.	27·56 N	105·50 W
92	San Pedro Sula (sän pā'drô sōō'lä) Hond.	15·29 N	88·01 W
	San Pedro y San Pablo, see Teposcolula		
126	San Pietro, I. di (ē'sō-lä-dē-sän pyā'trô) . It.	39·09 N	8·15 E
65	San Quentin (săn kwĕn-tēn') Calif. (San Francisco In.)	37·57 N	122·29 W
155	San Quintin (sän kēn-tēn') Phil. (Manila In.)	15·59 N	120·47 E
100	San Rafael (sän rä-fä-ĕl') . Arg.	34 30 S	68·13 W
65	San Rafael (săn rȧ-fĕl) Calif. (San Francisco In.)	37·58 N	122·31 W
98	San Rafael (sän-rä-fä-ĕ'l) Col. (In.)	6·18 N	75·02 W
69	San Rafael (R.) (săn rȧ-fĕl') Utah	39·05 N	110·50 W
95	San Rafael, Cabo (C.) (kȧ'bô) Dom. Rep.	19·00 N	68·50 W
65	San Ramon (săn rä-mōn') Calif. (San Francisco In.)	37·47 N	122·59 W
93	San Ramōn . C. R.	10·07 N	84·30 W
126	San Remo (sän rā'mô) . It.	43·48 N	7·46 E
121	San R . Pol.	50·33 N	22·12 E
89	San Roman, C. (sän-rô-mä'n) Ven.	12·00 N	69·45 W
98	San Roque (sän-rô'kĕ) . Col. (In.)	6·29 N	75·00 W
124	San Roque . Sp.	36·13 N	5·23 W
76	San Saba (săn sä'bȧ) . Tex.	31·12 N	98·43 W
76	San Saba R. . Tex.	30·58 N	99·12 W
92	San Salvador (sän säl-vä-dōr') . Sal.	13·45 N	89·11 W
98	San Salvador (I.) . Ec.	0·14 S	90·50 W
95	San Salvador (Watling) (I.) (săn săl'vȧ-dôr) . Ba. Is.	24·05 N	74·30 W
101	San Salvador (R.) (sän-säl-vä-dô'r) Ur. (Buenos Aires In.)	33·42 S	58·04 W
164	Sansanné-Mango (sän-sȧ-nā' mäN'gô) . Togo	10·31 N	0·23 E
164	San Sebastian (sän sȧ-bäs-tyän') Can. Is.	28·09 N	17·11 W
124	San Sebastian . Sp.	43·19 N	1·59 W
99	San Sebastián (sän-sĕ-bäs-tyà'n) Ven. (In.)	9·58 N	67·11 W
125	San Sebastián de los Reyes (sän sä-bäs-tyän'dä lōs rā'yĕs) Sp. (Madrid In.)	40·33 N	3·38 W
126	San Severo (sän sĕ-vâ'rō) . It.	41·43 N	15·24 E
150	San She (Mtn.) . China	33·00 N	103·50 E
147	San Shui . China	23·14 N	112·51 E
69	San Simon Cr. (sän sī-mōn') Ariz.	32·45 N	109·30 W
74	Santa Ana (săn'tȧ ăn'ȧ) Calif. (Los Angeles In.)	33·45 N	117·52 W
90	Santa Ana (sän'tä ä'nä) . Mex.	19·18 N	98·10 W
92	Santa Ana . Sal.	14·02 N	89·35 W
74	Santa Ana Mts. Calif. (Los Angeles In.)	33·44 N	117·36 W
74	Santa Ana R. Calif. (Los Angeles In.)	33·41 N	117·57 W
76	Santa Anna . Tex.	31·44 N	99·18 W
100	Santa Anna, Cochilha de (Mts.) (kô-chē'lä dē sän-tä-nä) . Braz.	30·30 S	56·30 W
101	Santa Bárbara (sän-tä-bà'r-bä-rä) Braz. (Rio de Janeiro In.)	19·57 S	43·25 W
68	Santa Barbara (săn'tȧ bär'bȧ-rȧ) Calif.	34·26 N	119·43 W
92	Santa Barbara (sän'tä bär'bä-rȧ) Hond.	14·52 N	88·20 W
76	Santa Barbara . Mex.	26·48 N	105·50 W
68	Santa Barbara (I.) . Calif.	33·30 N	113·01 W
68	Santa Barbara (Is.) . Calif.	33·45 N	119·46 W
68	Santa Barbara Chan. . Calif.	34·15 N	120·00 W
101	Santa Branca (sän-tä-brä'N-kä) Braz. (Rio de Janeiro In.)	23·25 S	45·52 W
68	Santa Catalina (I.) . Calif.	33·29 N	118·37 W
93	Santa Catalina, Cerro de (Mt.) (sĕ'r-rô-dĕ-sän-tä-kä-tä-lē'nä) Pan.	8·39 N	81·36 W
68	Santa Catalina, G. of (săn'tȧ kă-tȧ-lē'nȧ) . Calif.	33·00 N	117·58 W
76	Santa Catarina (sän'tä kä-tä-rē'nä) Mex.	25·41 N	100·27 W
	Sta. Catarina, see Loxicha		
	Sta. Catarina, see Yosonotú		
100	Santa Catarina (State) (sän-tä-kä-tä-rē'nȧ) . Braz.	27·15 S	50·30 W
90	Santa Catarina (R.) . Mex.	16·31 N	98·39 W
65	Santa Clara (săn'tȧ klâr'ȧ) Calif. (San Francisco In.)	37·21 N	121·56 W
94	Santa Clara (sän'tä klä'rä) . Cuba	22·25 N	80·00 W
76	Santa Clara . Mex.	24·29 N	103·22 W
100	Santa Clara . Ur.	32·46 S	54·51 W
68	Santa Clara (R.) (săn'tȧ klă'rȧ) Calif.	34·22 N	118·53 W
92	Santa Clara, (Vol.) . Nic.	12·44 N	87·00 W
94	Santa Clara, Bahía de (B.) (bä-ē'ä-dĕ-sän-tä-klä-rä) . Cuba	23·05 N	80·50 W
88	Santa Clara, Sierra, (Mts.) (sē-ĕ'r-rä-sän'tä klä'rà) . Mex.	27·30 N	113·50 W
98	Santa Cruz (sän'tä krōōz') . Bol.	17·45 S	63·03 W
100	Santa Cruz (sän-tä-krōō's) . Braz.	29·43 S	52·15 W
100	Santa Cruz . Braz. (In.)	22·55 S	43·41 W
68	Santa Cruz (săn'tȧ krōōz') . Calif.	36·59 N	122·02 W
101	Santa Cruz . Chile (Santiago In.)	34·38 S	71·21 W
92	Santa Cruz . C. R.	10·16 N	85·37 W
76	Santa Cruz . Mex.	25·50 N	105·25 W
155	Santa Cruz . Phil. (Manila In.)	13·28 N	122·02 E
155	Santa Cruz . Phil. (Manila In.)	14·17 N	121·25 E
155	Santa Cruz . Phil. (Manila In.)	15·46 N	119·53 E
155	Santa Cruz . Phil. (Manila In.)	17·06 N	120·27 E
100	Santa Cruz (Prov.) . Arg.	48·00 S	70·00 W
68	Santa Cruz (I.) (săn'tȧ krōōz') Calif.	34·05 N	119·55 W
98	Santa Cruz (I.) (sän-tä-krōō'z) . Ec.	0·38 S	90·20 W
69	Santa Cruz (R.) (săn'tȧ krōōz') Ariz.	32·30 N	111·30 W
100	Santa Cruz (R.) (sän'tä krōōz') Arg.	50·05 S	66·30 W
92	Santa Cruz Barillas (sän-tä-krōō'z-bä-rē'l-yäs) Guat.	15·47 N	91·22 W
	Santa Cruz Chico, see Pedro Antonio Santos		
94	Santa Cruz del Sur (sän-tä-krōō's-dĕl-sōō'r) . Cuba	20·45 N	78·00 W
164	Santa Cruz de Tenerife (sän'tä krōōz dā tā-nå-rē'fā) Can. Is.	28·07 N	15·27 W
159	Santa Cruz Is. . Sol. Is.	10·58 S	166·47 E
65	Santa Cruz Mts. (săn'tȧ krōōz') Calif. (San Francisco In.)	37·30 N	122·19 W
95	Santa Domingo, Cay (I.) . Ba. Is.	21·50 N	75·45 W
126	Sant'Eufemia, Golfo di (G.) (gôl-fô-dē-sän-tĕ'ōō-fĕ'myä) . It.	38·53 N	15·53 E
124	Santa Eugenia de Ribeira (sän-tä-ĕōō-hĕ'nyä-dĕ-rē-bĕ'y-rä) Sp.	42·34 N	8·55 W
125	Santa Eulalia del Rio (sän'tä ā-ōō-lä'lē-ä dĕl rē'ô) . Sp.	38·58 N	1·29 E
100	Santa Fe (sän'tä fā') . Arg.	31·33 S	60·45 W
94	Santa Fe (sän-tä-fĕ') . Cuba	21·45 N	82·40 W
69	Santa Fe (săn'tȧ fā') . N. Mex.	35·10 N	106·00 W
124	Santafé (sän'tä-fā') . Sp.	37·12 N	3·43 W
100	Santa Fe (Prov.) (sän'tä fā') . Arg.	32·00 S	61·15 W
99	Santa Filomena (sän-tä-fē-lô-mĕ'nä) . Braz.	9·09 S	44·45 W
88	Santa Genoveva, (Mtn.) (sän-tä-hĕ-nō-vĕ'vä) . Mex.	23·30 N	110·00 W
151	Sant'ai . China	31·02 N	105·02 E
99	Santa Inés (sän'tä ē-nĕ's) Ven. (In.)	9·54 N	64·21 W
100	Santa Inés (I.) (sän'tä ê-näs') Chile	53·45 S	74·15 W
164	Santa Isabel (ê-sä-bĕl') . Sp. Gui.	3·43 N	8·42 E
159	Santa Isabel, (I.) . Sol. Is.	7·57 S	159·28 E
94	Santa Lucia (sän'tä lōō-sē'ä) . Cuba	21·50 N	77·30 W
101	Santa Lucia (sän-tä-lōō-sē'ä) Ur. (Buenos Aires In.)	34·27 S	56·23 W
99	Santa Lucia . Ven. (In.)	10·18 N	66·40 W
101	Santa Lucia (R.) (sän-tä-lōō-sē'ä) Ur. (Buenos Aires In.)	34·19 S	56·13 W
94	Santa Lucia B. (sän'tä lōō-sē'ä) Cuba	22·55 N	84·20 W
88	Santa Magarita (I.) (sän'tä mär-gä-rē'tä) . Mex.	24·15 N	112·00 W
100	Santa Maria (sän'tä mä-rē'ä) Braz.	29·40 S	28·45 W
68	Santa Maria (săn-tȧ mȧ-rē'ȧ) Calif.	34·57 N	120·28 W
126	Santa Maria (sän-tä mä-rē'ä) . It.	41·05 N	14·15 E
155	Santa Maria (sän-tä-mä-rē'ä) Phil. (Manila In.)	14·48 N	120·57 E
	Santa Maria, see Huazolotitlán		
90	Santa Maria (R.) (sän'tȧ mä-rē'ä) . Mex.	21·33 N	100·17 W
95	Santa Maria, C . Ba. Is.	23·45 N	75·30 W
124	Santa Maria, Cabo de (C.) (kȧ'bō-dĕ-sän-tä-mä-rē'ä) . Port.	36·58 N	7·54 W
94	Santa Maria, Cayo (I.) (kä'yō-săn'tȧ mȧ-rē'ȧ) . Cuba	22·40 N	79·00 W
90	Santa María del Oro (sän'tä-mä-rē'ä-dĕl-ô-rô) . Mex.	21·21 N	104·35 W
90	Santa Maria de los Angeles (dĕ-lôs-ä'n-hĕ-lĕs) . Mex.	22·10 N	103·34 W
90	Santa María del Rio (sän'tä mä-rē'ä dĕl rē'ō) . Mex.	21·46 N	100·43 W
90	Santa Maria de Ocotán (sän'tä-mä-rē'ä-dĕ-ô-kô-tä'n) Mex.	22·56 N	104·30 W
164	Santa Maria I. (sän-tä-mä-rē'ä) Azores (In.)	37·09 N	26·02 W
101	Santa Maria Madalena (sän-tä-mȧ-rē'ä-mȧ-dȧ-lĕ-nä) Braz. (Rio de Janeiro In.)	22·00 S	42·00 W
98	Santa Marta (sän'tä mär'tä) . Col.	11·15 N	74·13 W
74	Santa Monica (săn'tȧ mŏn'ĭ-kȧ) Calif. (Los Angeles In.)	34·01 N	118·29 W
74	Santa Monica Mts. Calif. (Los Angeles In.)	34·08 N	118·38 W
100	Santana (R.) (sän-tä'nä) Braz. (In.)	22·33 S	43·37 W
98	Santander (sän-tän-dĕr') Col. (In.)	3·00 N	76·25 W
124	Santander (sän-tän-dâr') . Sp.	43·27 N	3·50 W
125	Sant'Angelo Romano (sän-tä'n-gzhĕ-lô-rô-mä'nô) It. (Roma In.)	42·02 N	12·45 E
125	Sant' Antimo . It. (Napoli In.)	40·40 N	14·11 E
125	Santañy (sän-tän'yē) . Sp.	39·21 N	3·08 E
68	Santa Paula (săn'tȧ pô'lȧ) . Calif.	34·24 N	119·05 W
99	Santarém (sän-tä-rĕN') . Braz.	2·28 S	54·37 W
124	Santarém . Port.	39·18 N	8·48 W
94	Santaren Chan. (sän-tȧ-rĕn') Ba. Is.	24·15 N	79·30 W
69	Santa Rita (săn'tȧ rē'tȧ) . N. Mex.	32·45 N	108·05 W
101	Santa Rita do Passo Quatro (sän-tä-rē'tȧ-dô-pä'sô-kwȧ'trô) Braz. (Rio de Janeiro In.)	21·43 S	47·27 W
101	Santa Rita do Sapucai (sä-pōō-kȧ'ē) Braz. (Rio de Janeiro In.)	22·15 S	45·41 W
100	Santa Rosa (sän-tä-rô-sä) . Arg.	36·45 S	64·10 W
68	Santa Rosa (săn'tȧ rō'zȧ) . Calif.	38·27 N	122·42 W
98	Santa Rosa (sän-tä-rô-sä) Col. (In.)	6·38 N	75·26 W
98	Santa Rosa . Ec.	3·29 S	78·55 W
92	Santa Rosa (sän'tä rō'sȧ) . Guat.	14·21 N	90·16 W
92	Santa Rosa . Hond.	14·45 N	88·51 W
72	Santa Rosa (săn'tȧ rō'sȧ) N. Mex.	34·55 N	104·41 W
155	Santa Rosa (sän'tä rō'sä) Phil. (Manila In.)	14·18 N	121·07 E
99	Santa Rosa (sän-tä-rô-sä) Ven. (In.)	9·37 N	64·10 W
98	Santa Rosa de Cabal (sän-tä-rô-sä-dĕ-kä-bä'l) Col. (In.)	4·53 N	75·38 W
101	Santa Rosa de Viterbo (sän-tä-rô-sä-dĕ-vē-tĕr'-bô) Braz. (Rio de Janeiro In.)	21·30 S	47·21 W
68	Santa Rosa Ind. Res. (săn'tȧ rō'zȧ') . Calif.	33·28 N	116·50 W
88	Santa Rosalía (sän'tä rô-zä'lē-ȧ) Mex.	27·13 N	112·15 W
	Santa Rosalia, see Ciudad Camargo		
66	Santa Rosa Mts. (săn'tȧ rō'zȧ) Nev.	41·33 N	117·50 W
74	Santa Susana (săn'tȧ sōō-ză'nȧ) Calif. (Los Angeles In.)	34·16 N	118·42 W
	Santa Tecla, see Nueva San Salvador		
101	Santa Teresa (sän-tä-tĕ-rĕ'sä) Arg. (Buenos Aires In.)	33·27 S	60·47 W
99	Santa Teresa . Ven. (In.)	10·14 N	66·40 W
100	Santa Vitória do Palmar (sän-tä-vē-tô'ryä-dô-päl-mȧr) Braz.	33·30 S	53·16 W
68	Santa Ynez (R.) (săn'tȧ ē-nĕz') Calif.	34·40 N	120·20 W
68	Santa Ysabel Ind. Res. (săn-tȧ ĭ-zȧ-bĕl') . Calif.	33·05 N	116·46 W
68	Santee (săn-tē') Calif. (San Diego In.)	32·50 N	116·58 W
79	Santee (R.) . S. C.	33·27 N	80·02 W
100	Santiago (sän-tyȧ'gô) . Braz.	29·05 S	54·46 W
101	Santiago (sän-tē-ȧ'gô) Chile (Santiago In.)	33·26 S	70·40 W
93	Santiago . Pan.	8·07 N	80·58 W
155	Santiago (sän-tyä'gô) Phil. (Manila In.)	16·42 N	121·33 E
124	Santiago . Sp.	42·52 N	8·32 W
	Santiago, see Tejupan		
	Santiago, see Zacatepec		
101	Santiago (Prov.) (sän-tyä'gō) Chile (Santiago In.)	33·28 S	70·55 W
90	Santiago, Rio Grande de (R.) (rē'ō-grä'n-dĕ-dĕ-sän-tyä'gô) Mex.	21·15 N	104·05 W
155	Santiago (I.) . Phil. (Manila In.)	16·29 N	120·03 E
95	Santiago de los Cabelleros (sän-tyä'gô-dä lōs kä-bä-yä'rōs) Dom. Rep.	19·30 N	70·45 W
95	Santiago de Cuba (sän-tyȧ'gô-dā kōō'bȧ) . Cuba	20·00 N	75·50 W
95	Santiago de las Vegas (sän-tyȧ'gô-dĕ-läs-vĕ'gäs) Cuba (La Habana In.)	22·13 N	82·23 W
100	Santiago del Estero (sän-tē-ȧ'gō-dĕl ĕs-tä'rô) . Arg.	27·50 S	64·14 W

ng-sing; ŋ-baŋk; N-nasalized n; nŏd; cŏmmit; ōld; ôbey; ôrder; fōōd; fŏŏt; ou-out; s-soft; sh-dish; th-thin; pūre; ûnite; ûrn; stŭd; circŭs; ü-as "y" in study; '-indeterminate vowel.

264 Santiago–Savannah PRONOUNCING INDEX

Page	Name Pronunciation Region	Lat. °′	Long. °′
100	Santiago del Estero (Prov.) (sän-tē-ä'gō-dĕl ĕs-tā'rō). Arg.	27·15 s	63·30 w
76	Santiago Mts. (sän-tê-ä'gō) Tex.	30·00 n	103·30 w
74	Santiago Res. Calif. (Los Angeles In.)	33·47 n	117·42 w
95	Santiago Rodriguez (sän-tyä'gô-rô-drē'gĕz) Dom. Rep.	19·30 n	71·25 w
91	Santiago Tuxtla (sän-tyä'gô-tōō'x-tlä). Mex.	18·28 n	95·18 w
76	Santiaguillo, Laguna de (L.) (lä-ōō'nä-dĕ-sän-tê-ä-gēl'yō) Mex.	24·51 n	104·43 w
66	Santiam R. (săn'tyăm) Ore.	44·42 n	122·26 w
124	Santisteban del Puerto (sän'tê stä-bän'dĕl pwĕr'tō). Sp.	38·15 n	3·12 w
148	Santo (sän'tō) China	32·49 n	119·39 e
99	Santo Amaro (sän'tōō ä-mä'rōō) Braz.	12·32 s	38·33 w
101	Santo Amaro de Campos (sän-tô-ä-mä'rô-dĕ-käm'pôs) Braz. (Rio de Janeiro In.)	22·01 s	41·05 w
101	Santo André (sän-tô-än-drĕ') Braz. (Rio de Janeiro In.)	23·40 s	46·31 w
100	Santo Angelo (sän-tô-ä'n-zhĕ-lô) Braz.	28·16 s	53·59 w
164	Santo Antào I. (sän-tô-än-tä-ô) C. V. Is. (In.)	17·20 n	26·05 w
166	Santo Antonio (sän'tōō än-tō'nê-ōō). Ang.	6·10 s	12·25 e
101	Santo Antônio do Monte (sän-tô-än-tô'nyô-dô-môn'tĕ) Braz. (Rio de Janeiro In.)	20·06 s	45·18 w
94	Santo Domingo (sän'tô-dōmĭn'gô) Cuba	22·35 n	80·20 w
92	Santo Domingo (sän-tô-dô-mê'n-gō). Nic.	12·15 n	84·56 w
155	Santo Domingo. Phil. (Manila In.)	17·39 n	120·24 e
95	Santo Domingo (sän'tô dô-mĭn'gô) Dom. Rep.	18·30 n	69·55 w
	Santo Domingo, see Zanatepec		
124	Santo Domingo de la Calzada (dä lä käl-thä'dä). Sp.	42·27 n	2·55 w
124	Santoña (sän-tō'nyä) Sp.	43·25 n	3·27 w
101	Santos (sän'tozh) Braz. (Rio de Janeiro In.)	23·58 s	46·20 w
101	Santos Dumont (sän'tôs-dōō-mô'nt) Braz. (Rio de Janeiro In.)	21·28 s	43·33 w
155	Santo Thomas (sän-tô-tô-mä's) Phil. (Manila In.)	14·07 n	121·09 e
155	Santo Tomas (Mtn.) Phil. (Manila In.)	16·23 n	120·32 e
100	Santo Tomé (sän-tô-tô-mĕ'). Arg.	28·32 s	56·04 w
153	Sanuki (sä'nōō-kê) Jap. (Tōkyō In.)	35·16 n	139·53 e
101	San Urbano (sän-ōōr-bä'nô) Arg. (Buenos Aires In.)	33·39 s	61·28 w
100	San Valentin, M. (Mtn.) (sän-vä-lĕn-tē'n). Chile	46·41 s	73·30 w
122	Sanvic (säN-vēk') Fr.	49·34 n	0·08 e
101	San Vicente (sän-vē-sĕn'tĕ) Arg. (Buenos Aires In.)	35·00 s	58·26 w
101	San Vicente. Chile (Santiago In.)	34·25 s	71·06 w
92	San Vicente (sän vē-sĕn'tä) Sal.	13·41 n	88·43 w
124	San Vicente de Alcántara (sän vē-thĕn'tä dä äl-kän'tä-rä) Sp.	39·24 n	7·08 w
126	San Vito (sän vē'tô) It.	45·53 n	12·52 e
151	Sanya China	18·10 n	109·32 e
166	Sanyati (R.) (sän-yä'tê) Fed. of Rh. & Nya.	17·08 s	29·11 e
149	Sanyüanli. China (Canton In.)	23·11 n	113·16 e
68	San Ysidro (sän ysĭ-drō') Calif. (San Diego In.)	32·33 n	117·02 w
101	São Bernardo do Campo (souN-bĕr-nár'dô-dô-kä'm-pô) Braz. (Rio de Janeiro In.)	23·44 s	46·33 w
100	São Borja (souN-bôr-zhä) Braz.	28·44 s	55·59 w
101	São Carlos (souN kär'lōzh) Braz. (Rio de Janeiro In.)	22·02 s	47·54 w
99	São Cristovão (souN-krĕs-tō-vouN) Braz.	11·04 s	37·11 w
101	São Fidélis (souN-fē-dĕ'lēs) Braz. (Rio de Janeiro In.)	21·41 s	41·45 w
99	São Francisco (souN frăN-sĕsh'kōō) Braz.	15·59 s	44·42 w
99	São Francisco, Rio (R.) (rē'ō-sän-frän-sĕ's-kō). Braz.	8·56 s	40·20 w
100	São Francisco do Sul (souN frăN-sĕsh'kōō-dô-sōō'l) Braz.	26·15 s	48·42 w
100	São Gabriel (souN'gä-brê-ĕl') Braz.	30·28 s	54·11 w
101	São Geraldo (souN-zhĕ-rä'l-dô) Braz. (Rio de Janeiro In.)	21·01 s	42·49 w
100	São Gonçalo (souN'gōŋ-sä'lōō) Braz. (In.)	22·55 s	43·04 w
101	São Gonçalo do Sapucaí (souN-gôn-sä'lô-dô-sä-pōō-kī') Braz. (Rio de Janeiro In.)	21·55 s	45·34 w
101	São João da Barra (souN-zhôuN-dä-bä'rä) Braz. (Rio de Janeiro In.)	21·40 s	41·03 w
101	São João da Boa Vista (souN-zhôuN-dä-bôä-vē's-tä) Braz. (Rio de Janeiro In.)	21·58 s	46·45 w
101	São João del Rei (souN zhô-ouN'dĕl-rā) Braz. (Rio de Janeiro In.)	21·08 s	44·14 w
100	São João de Meriti (souN-zhôuN-dĕ-mĕ-rē-tê) Braz. (In.)	22·47 s	43·22 w
99	São João do Araguaia (souN zhô-ouN'dô-ä-rä-gwä'yä) Braz.	5·29 s	48·44 w
125	São João dos Lampas (souN' zhô-ouN' dōzh län-päzh') Port. (Lisboa In.)	38·52 n	9·24 w
101	São João Nepomuceno (souN-zhôuN-nĕ-pô-mōō-sĕ-nō) Braz. (Rio de Janeiro In.)	21·33 s	43·00 w
164	São Jorge I. (souN zhôr' zhĕ) Azores (In.)	38·28 n	27·34 w
101	São José do Rio Pardo (souN-zhô-sĕ'dô-rē'ō-pá'r-dō) Braz. (Rio de Janeiro In.)	21·36 s	46·50 w
99	São José do Rio Prêto (souN zhô-zĕ'dô-rē'ō-prĕ-tō) Braz.	20·57 s	49·12 w
101	São José dos Campos (souN zhô-zā'dōzh käN pōzh') Braz. (Rio de Janeiro In.)	23·12 s	45·53 w
100	São Leopoldo (souN-lĕ-ô-pôl'dō) Braz.	29·46 s	51·09 w
99	São Luis (Maranhão) (souN-lōōē's-mä-rän-youN'). Braz.	2·31 s	43·14 w
101	São Luis do Paraitinga (souN-lōōē's-dô-pä-rä-ē-tē'n-gä) Braz. (Rio de Janeiro In.)	23·15 s	44·18 w
99	São Mateus (souN mä-tā'ōōzh) Braz.	18·44 s	39·45 w
101	São Miguel Arcanjo (souN-mē-gĕ'l-är-kän-zhō) Braz. (Rio de Janeiro In.)	23·54 s	47·59 w
164	São Miguel I. Azores (In.)	37·59 n	26·38 w
95	Saona (I.) (sä-ō'nä) Dom. Rep.	18·10 n	68·55 w
122	Saône (R.) (sōn) Fr.	46·27 n	4·58 e
164	São Nicolau (souN' nê-kô-louN') C. V. Is. (In.)	16·19 n	25·19 w
101	São Paulo (souN' pou'lōō) Braz. (Rio de Janeiro In.)	23·34 s	46·38 w
99	São Paulo (State) (souN pou'lōō) Braz.	21·45 s	50·47 w
98	São Paulo de Olivença (souN'pou'lōōdä ô-lê-vĕn'sȧ) Braz.	3·32 s	68·46 w
101	São Pedro (souN-pĕ'drô) Braz. (Rio de Janeiro In.)	22·34 s	47·54 w
101	São Pedro de Aldeia (souN-pĕ'drô-dĕ-äl-dĕ'yä) Braz. (Rio de Janeiro In.)	22·50 s	42·04 w
99	São Raimundo Nonato (souN' rī-mōō'n-do nô-nä'tōō) Braz.	9·09 s	42·32 w
101	São Roque (souN' rō'kĕ) Braz. (Rio de Janeiro In.)	23·32 s	47·08 w
99	São Roque, Cabo de (C) (kä'bo-dĕ-souN' rō'kĕ). Braz.	5·06 s	35·11 w
101	São Sebastião (souN sȧ-bäs-tê-ouN') Braz. (Rio de Janeiro In.)	23·48 s	45·25 w
101	São Sebastião, Ilha de (I.) (ēl'yȧ dä souN' sȧ-bäs-tê-ouN') Braz. (Rio de Janeiro In.)	23·52 s	45·22 w
101	São Sebastião do Paraíso (souN-sĕ-bäs-tē-ouN-dô-pä-rä-ē'sō). Braz. (Rio de Janeiro In.)	20·54 s	46·58 w
101	São Simão (souN-sē-mouN) Braz. (Rio de Janeiro In.)	21·30 s	47·33 w
164	São Tiago I. (souN tê-ä'gōō) C. V. Is. (In.)	15·09 n	24·45 w
164	São Tomé (souN tô-mā') Afr.	0·16 n	6·44 e
101	São Tomé, Cabo de (C.) (kä'bō-dĕ-souN-tô-mĕ') Braz. (Rio de Janeiro In.)	22·00 s	40·00 w
164	São Tomé, Ilhade (I.) (ē'lä-dĕ) Afr.	0·41 n	6·01 e
114	Saoura, Oued (R.) Alg.	29·39 n	1·42 w
124	São Vinente, Cabo de (C.) (kä'bō-dĕ-sän-vē-sĕ'n-tĕ). Port.	37·03 n	9·31 w
101	São Vicente (souN ve-se'n-tĕ) Braz. (Rio de Janeiro In.)	23·57 s	46·25 w
164	Sao Vincente I. (souN vē-sĕn'tä) C. V. Is. (In.)	16·51 n	24·35 w
164	Sapele (sä-pā'lā) Nig.	5·57 n	5·22 e
128	Sapozhok (sä-pô-zhôk') Sov. Un.	53·58 n	40·44 e
152	Sapporo (säp-pô'rô) Jap.	43·02 n	141·29 e
136	Sapronovo (säp-rô'nô-vô) Sov. Un. (Moskva In.)	55·13 n	38·25 e
101	Sapucaí (R.) (sä-pōō-kä-ē') Braz. (Rio de Janeiro In.)	21·07 s	45·53 w
101	Sapucaia (sä-pōō-kä'yä) Braz. (Rio de Janeiro In.)	22·01 s	42·54 w
101	Sapucaí Mirim (R.) (sä-pōō-kä-ē'mē-rêN) Braz. (Rio de Janeiro In.)	21·06 s	47·03 w
73	Sapulpa (sȧ-pŭl'pȧ) Okla.	36·01 n	96·05 w
101	Saquarema (sä-kwä-rĕ-mä) Braz. (Rio de Janeiro In.)	22·56 s	42·32 w
65	Sara (sä'rä). Wash. (Portland In.)	45·45 n	122·42 w
127	Sara, Bahr (R.) (bär) Chad-Cen. Afr. Rep.	8·19 n	17·44 e
127	Sarajevo (sȧ-rȧ-yĕv'ô) (sä-rä'ya-vô). Yugo.	43·15 n	18·26 e
136	Sarana (sá-rä'ná) Sov. Un. (Urals In.)	56·31 n	57·44 e
• 81	Saranac Lake N. Y.	44·20 n	74·05 w
81	Saranac L. (săr'á-năk) N. Y.	44·15 n	74·20 w
100	Sarandi (sä-rän'dē) Arg. (In.)	34·26 s	58·21 w
101	Sarandi Grande (sä-rän'dē-grän'dĕ) Ur. (Buenos Aires In.)	33·42 s	56·21 w
142	Sarangpur India	23·39 n	76·32 e
132	Saransk (sá-ränsk') Sov. Un.	54·10 n	45·10 e
136	Sarany (sá-rä'nĭ) Sov. Un. (Urals In.)	58·33 n	58·48 e
132	Sarapul (sä-rä'pōōl') Sov. Un.	56·28 n	53·50 e
79	Sarasota (săr-ȧ-sōtȧ) Fla. (In.)	27·27 n	82·30 w
77	Saratoga (săr-ȧ-tō'gȧ) Tex.	30·17 n	94·31 w
65	Saratoga Wash. (Seattle In.)	48·04 n	122·29 w
65	Saratoga Pass. Wash. (Seattle In.)	48·09 n	122·33 w
81	Saratoga Springs (sprĭngz) N. Y.	43·05 n	74·50 w
133	Saratov (sȧ rä'tôf) Sov. Un.	51·50 n	45·00 e
151	Saravane Laos	15·48 n	106·40 e
154	Sarawak (sä-rä'wäk) Asia	2·30 n	112·45 e
121	Sárbogárd (shär'bô-gärd) Hung.	46·53 n	18·38 e
85	Sarcee Ind. Res. (sär'sē) Can. (Calgary In.)	50·58 n	114·23 w
164	Sardalas Libya	25·59 n	10·33 e
126	Sardinia (I.) (sär-dĭn'ĭȧ) It.	40·08 n	9·05 e
78	Sardis (sär'dĭs) Miss.	34·26 n	89·55 w
70	Sargent (sär'jĕnt) Nebr.	41·40 n	99·38 w
133	Sarikamis Tur.	40·30 n	42·40 e
125	Sariñena (sä-rēn-yĕ'nä) Sp.	41·46 n	0·11 w
150	Sariwŏn (sä'rê-wŭn') Korea	38·40 n	125·45 e
122	Sark (I.) (särk) Chan. Is.	49·28 n	2·22 w
127	Şarkoy (shär'kû-ê) Tur.	40·39 n	27·07 e
122	Sarlat (sär-lä') Fr.	44·52 n	1·13 e
100	Sarmiento, Monte (Mt.) (mô'n-tē-sär-myĕn'tō). Chile	54·28 s	70·40 w
80	Sarnia (sär'nê-ȧ) Can.	43·00 n	82·25 w
125	Sarno (sä'r-nô) It. (Napoli In.)	40·35 n	14·38 e
121	Sarny (sär'nê) Sov. Un.	51·17 n	26·39 e
127	Saronikós Kólpos (G.) Grc.	37·51 n	23·30 e
127	Saros Körfezi (G.) (sä'rôs) Tur.	40·30 n	26·20 e
121	Sárospatak (shä'rôsh-pô'tôk) Hung.	48·19 n	21·35 e
127	Šar Planina (Mts.) (shär plä'nê-na). Yugo.	42·07 n	21·54 e
118	Sarpsborg (särps'bôrg) Nor.	59·17 n	11·07 e
123	Sarrebourg (sär-bōōr') Fr.	48·44 n	7·02 e
123	Sarreguemines (sär-gē-mēn') Fr.	49·06 n	7·05 e
124	Sarria (sär'ê-ä) Sp.	42·14 n	7·17 w
92	Sarstun R. (särs-tōō'n) Guat.	15·50 n	89·26 w
126	Sartène (sär-tĕn') Fr.	41·36 n	8·59 e
122	Sarthe (R.) (särt) Fr.	47·44 n	0·32 w
	Sartor, see Store Sotra		
120	Sárvár (shär'vär) Hung.	47·14 n	16·55 e
133	Sarych, Mys (C.) (mĭs sä-rēch') Sov. Un.	44·25 n	33·00 e
134	Sary Ishikotrau, Peski (des.) (sä'rê ē' shĕk-ō'trou). Sov. Un.	46·12 n	75·30 e
134	Sarysu (R.) (sä'rê-sōō) Sov. Un.	47·47 n	69·14 e
142	Sasaram (sŭs-ŭ-räm') India	25·00 n	84·00 e
153	Sasayama (sä'sä-yä'mä) Jap.	35·05 n	135·14 e
153	Sasebo (sä'sä-bô) Jap.	33·12 n	129·43 e
	Saseno, see Sazan		
120	Sašice Czech.	49·14 n	13·31 e
86	Saskatchewan (Prov.) Can.	54·46 n	107·40 w
86	Saskatchewan (R.) (săs-kăch'ê-wän). Can.	53·30 n	103·41 w
86	Saskatoon (săs-kȧ-tōōn') Can.	52·11 n	106·42 w
119	Saslauka (sȧs-lä'û-kä) Sov. Un.	57·22 n	22·34 e
132	Sasovo (säs'ô-vô) Sov. Un.	54·20 n	42·00 e
74	Saspamco (săs-păm'cō) Tex. (San Antonio In.)	29·13 n	98·18 w
164	Sassandra R. (sȧs-sän'drȧ) Ivory Coast	6·23 n	6·52 w
126	Sassari (säs'sä-rê) It.	40·44 n	8·33 e
120	Sassnitz (säs'nēts) Ger.	54·31 n	13·37 e
164	Satadougou (sä-tá-dōō-gōō') Mali	12·31 n	11·26 w
118	Säter (sĕ'tĕr) Swe.	60·21 n	15·50 e
79	Satilla (R.) (sá-tĭl'ȧ) Ga.	31·15 n	82·13 w
136	Satka (sät'kȧ) Sov. Un. (Urals In.)	55·03 n	59·02 e
121	Sátoraljaujhely (shä'tô-rô-lyô-ōō'yĕl'). Hung.	48·24 n	21·40 e
121	Satu-Mare (sȧ'tōō-mȧ'rĕ) Rom.	47·50 n	22·53 e
65	Saturna (sȧ-tûr'nȧ) Can. (Vancouver In.)	48·48 n	123·12 w
65	Saturna (I.). Can. (Vancouver In.)	48·47 n	123·03 w
118	Saude (sou'dĕ) Nor.	59·40 n	6·21 e
112	Saudhárkrokur Ice.	65·41 n	19·38 w
138	Saudi Arabia (sȧ-ōō'dĭ ȧ-rä'bĭ-ȧ) Asia	22·40 n	46·00 e
111	Sauerlach (zou'ĕr-läk) Ger. (München In.)	47·58 n	11·39 e
80	Saugatuck (sô'gȧ-tŭk) Mich.	42·40 n	86·10 w
80	Saugeen Pen. (sô'gēn) Can.	44·55 n	81·20 w
80	Saugeer (R.) (sô'gēr) Can.	44·20 n	81·20 w
81	Saugerties (sô'gēr-tēz) N. Y.	42·05 n	73·55 w
142	Saugor (sô-gŭr') (sô-gōr') India	23·55 n	78·45 e
83	Saugus (sô'gŭs) Mass. (Boston In.)	42·28 n	71·01 w
71	Sauk (R.) (sôk) Minn.	45·30 n	94·45 w
71	Sauk Center Minn.	45·43 n	94·58 w
71	Sauk City Wis.	43·16 n	89·45 w
71	Sauk Rapids (răp'ĭd) Minn.	45·35 n	94·08 w
	Saulai, see Shyaulyay		
82	Sault-au-Mouton Can.	48·34 n	69·20 w
74	Sault Ste. Marie (sōō sānt mȧ-rē') Mich. (Sault Ste. Marie In.)	46·29 n	84·21 w
95	Saumatre, Etang (L.) Hai.	18·40 n	72·10 w
159	Saunders, C. (sôrn'dĕrs) N. Z. (In.)	45·55 s	170·50 e
85	Saunders L. (săn'dĕrs) Can. (Edmonton In.)	53·18 n	113·25 w
65	Sausalito (sô-sȧ-lē'tô) Calif. (San Francisco In.)	37·51 n	122·29 w
122	Sausset-les-Pins (sō-sĕ'lā-păN') Fr. (Marseille In.)	43·20 n	5·08 e
65	Sauvie I. (sô'vē) Ore. (Portland In.)	45·43 n	123·49 w
127	Sava (R.) (sä'vä) Yugo.	44·50 n	19·07 e
84	Savage (să'vĕj) Md. (Baltimore In.)	39·07 n	76·49 w
74	Savage Minn. (Minneapolis, St. Paul In.)	44·47 n	93·20 w
133	Savalan (Mtn.) Iran	38·20 n	48·00 e
164	Savalou Dahomey	7·58 n	2·00 e
71	Savanna (sȧ-văn'ȧ) Ill.	42·05 n	90·09 w
79	Savannah (sȧ-văn'ȧ) Ga.	32·04 n	81·07 w
73	Savannah Mo.	39·58 n	94·49 w
78	Savannah Tenn.	35·13 n	88·14 w
79	Savannah (R.) Ga.-S. C.	33·11 n	81·51 w

ăt; finăl; rāte; senāte; ärm; åsk; sofȧ; fâre; ch-choose; dh-as th in other; bē; ēvent; bĕt; recĕnt; cratēr; g-go; gh-guttural g; bĭt; ĭ-short neutral; rīde; K-guttural k as ch in German ich;

PRONOUNCING INDEX Savanna–Sepik 265

Page Name Pronunciation Region Lat. °' Long. °'

94 Savanna la Mar (sȧ-văn'ȧ lȧ mär') Jam. 18·10 N 78·10 W
120 Sávava R. Czech. 49·36 N 15·24 E
164 Savé (sȧ-vā') Dahomey 8·09 N 2·30 E
122 Save (R.) Fr. 43·32 N 0·50 E
166 Save, Rio (R.) (rē'ō-sä'vĕ) Moz. 21·28 S 34·14 E
123 Saverne (sȧ-vĕrn') Fr. 48·40 N 7·22 E
126 Savigliano (sä-vēl-yä'nô) It. 44·38 N 7·42 E
126 Savona (sä-vō'nä) It. 44·19 N 8·28 E
119 Savonlinna (sȧ'vôn-lēn'nȧ) Fin. 61·53 N 28·49 E
129 Savran' (säv-rän') Sov. Un. 48·07 N 30·09 E
154 Savu Sea (sä'vōō) Indon. 9·15 S 122·15 E
154 Sawahlunto Indon. 0·37 S 100·50 E
154 Sawankhalok Thai. 17·16 N 99·48 E
165 Sawda, Jabal as (Mts.) Libya 28·14 N 13·46 E
114 Sawfjjin, Wadi (R.) Libya 31·18 N 13·16 E
168 Sawhāj U. A. R. (Nile In.) 26·34 N 31·40 E
165 Sawknah Libya 29·04 N 15·53 E
154 Sawu (I.) Indon. 10·15 S 122·00 E
65 Sawyer (L.) (sô'yẽr) Wash. (Seattle In.) 47·20 N 122·02 W
164 Say (sä'ē) Niger 13·09 N 2·16 E
134 Sayan Khrebet (Mts.) (sŭ-yän') Sov. Un. 51·30 N 90·00 E
139 Sayda (Sidon) (sä'ē-dä) (sī'dŏn) Leb. (Palestine In.) 33·34 N 35·23 E
74 Sayers (sā'ẽrs) Tex. (San Antonio In.) 29·22 N 98·18 W
144 Sayhūt Aden 15·23 N 51·28 E
72 Sayre (sā'ẽr) Okla. 35·19 N 99·40 W
81 Sayre Pa. 41·55 N 76·30 W
84 Sayreton (sā'ẽr-tŭn) Ala. (Birmingham In.) 33·34 N 86·51 W
84 Sayreville (sâr'vĭl) N. J. (New York In.) 40·28 N 74·21 W
146 Sayr Usa Mong. 44·51 N 107·00 E
144 Saytum Aden 16·00 N 48·59 E
91 Sayula (sä-yōō'lä) Mex. 17·51 N 94·56 W
90 Sayula Mex. 19·50 N 101·33 W
90 Sayula, Luguna de (L.) (lä-gōō'nä-dĕ) Mex. 20·00 N 103·33 W
81 Sayville (sā'vĭl) N. Y. 40·45 N 73·10 W
127 Sazan (Saseno) (I.) Alb. 40·30 N 19·17 E
136 Sazhino (sáz-hē'nô) Sov. Un. (Urals In.) 56·20 N 58·15 E
118 Scäffle Swe. 59·10 N 12·55 E
138 Scandinavian Pen. Eur. 62·00 N 14·00 E
74 Scanlon (skăn'lôn) Minn. (Duluth In.) 46·27 N 92·26 W
65 Scappoose (skă-pōōs') Ore. (Portland In.) 45·46 N 122·53 W
65 Scappoose (R.) Ore. (Portland In.) 45·47 N 122·57 W
85 Scarborough (skär'bẽr-ô) Can. (Toronto In.) 43·45 N 79·12 W
116 Scarborough (skär'bŭr-ô) Eng. 54·16 N 0·19 W
85 Scarborough Junction Can. (Toronto In.) 43·43 N 79·15 W
84 Scarsdale (skärz'dāl) N. Y. (New York In.) 41·01 N 73·47 W
165 Sceui Ghimira Eth. 7·13 N 35·49 E
111 Schaerbeek (skär'bāk) Bel. (Bruxelles In.) 50·53 N 4·23 E
120 Schaffhausen (shäf'hou-zĕn) Switz. 47·43 N 8·38 E
87 Schefferville Can. 54·52 N 67·01 W
117 Schelde, R. Bel. 51·04 N 3·55 E
81 Schenectady (skĕ-nĕk'tȧ-dĕ) N. Y. 42·50 N 73·55 W
111 Scheveningen Neth. (Amsterdam In.) 52·06 N 4·15 E
111 Schiedam Neth. (Amsterdam In.) 51·55 N 4·23 E
123 Schiltigheim (shēl'tegh-hīm) Fr. 48·48 N 7·47 E
126 Schio (skē'ô) It. 45·43 N 11·23 E
120 Schleswig (shlĕs'vēgh) Ger. 54·32 N 9·32 E
120 Schleswig-Holstein (State) (shlĕs'vēgh-hōl'shtīn) Ger. 54·40 N 9·10 E
120 Schmalkalden (shmäl'käl-dĕn) Ger. 50·41 N 10·25 E
75 Schneider (schnīd'ẽr) Ind. (Chicago In.) 41·12 N 87·26 W
71 Schofield (skō'fēld) Wis. 44·52 N 89·37 W
120 Schönebeck (shû'nĕ-bergh) Ger. 52·01 N 11·44 E
111 Schoonhoven Neth. (Amsterdam In.) 51·56 N 4·51 E
155 Schouten (I.) (skou'tĕn) Neth. N. Gui. 0·45 S 136·40 E
120 Schramberg (shräm'bĕrgh) Ger. 48·14 N 8·24 E
81 Schroon (L.) (skrōōn) N. Y. 43·50 N 73·50 W
111 Schultzendorf (shōōl'tzĕn-dōrf) Ger. (Berlin In.) 52·21 N 13·35 E
70 Schuyler (skī'ler) Nebr. 41·28 N 97·05 W
81 Schuylkill (skōōl'kĭl) Pa. 40·35 N 76·10 W
120 Schwabach (shvä'bäk) Ger. 49·19 N 11·02 E
120 Schwäbische Alb (Mts.) (shvă'bē-shĕ älb) Ger. 48·11 N 9·09 E
120 Schwäbisch Gmünd (shvă'bēsh gmünd) Ger. 48·47 N 9·49 E
120 Schwäbisch Hall (häl) Ger. 49·08 N 9·44 E
120 Schwandorf (shvän'dôrf) Ger. 49·19 N 12·08 E
154 Schwaner Mts. (skvän'ẽr) Indon. 1·38 S 111·08 E
120 Schwarzwald (For.) (shvärts' väld) Ger. 47·54 N 7·57 E
120 Schwaz Aus. 47·20 N 11·45 E
111 Schwechat (shvĕk'ät) Aus. (Wien In.) 48·09 N 16·29 E
120 Schwedt (shvĕt) Ger. 53·04 N 14·17 E
120 Schweinfurt (shvīn'fōōrt) Ger. 50·03 N 10·14 E
123 Schwelm (shvĕlm) Ger. (Ruhr In.) 51·17 N 7·18 E
120 Schwenningen (shvĕn'ĭng-ĕn) Ger. 48·04 N 8·33 E
120 Schwerin (shvĕ-rēn') Ger. 53·36 N 11·25 E
120 Schweriner See (L.) (shvĕ'rē-nĕr zä) Ger. 53·40 N 11·06 E
123 Schwerte (shvĕr'tĕ) Ger. (Ruhr In.) 51·26 N 7·34 E
111 Schwielow L. (shvē'lōv) Ger. (Berlin In.) 52·20 N 12·52 E
120 Schwyz (shvēts) Switz. 47·01 N 8·38 E
126 Sciacca (shē-äk'kä) It. 37·30 N 13·09 E
116 Scilly (Is.) (sĭl'ē) Eng. 49·56 N 6·50 W
80 Scioto (R.) (sī-ō'tō) Ohio 39·10 N 82·55 W
83 Scituate (sĭt'ū-āt) Mass. (Boston In.) 42·12 N 70·45 W
67 Scobey (skō'bē) Mont. 48·48 N 105·29 W
65 Scoggin (skō'gĭn) Ore. (Portland In.) 45·28 N 123·14 W
85 Scotch R. (skŏch) Can. (Ottawa In.) 45·21 N 74·56 W
66 Scotia (skō'shȧ) Calif. 40·29 N 124·06 W
116 Scotland (skŏt'lȧnd) U. K. 57·05 N 5·10 W
70 Scotland S. D. 43·08 N 97·43 W
79 Scotland Neck (nĕk) N. C. 36·06 N 77·25 W
81 Scotstown (skŏts'toun) Can. 45·35 N 71·15 W
86 Scott, C. (skŏt) Can. 50·48 N 129·34 W
66 Scott, Mt. Ore. 42·55 N 122·00 W
65 Scott, Mt. Ore. (Portland In.) 45·27 N 122·33 W
74 Scott Air Force Base Ill. (St. Louis In.) 38·33 N 89·52 W
72 Scott City Kans. 38·28 N 100·54 W
84 Scottdale (skŏt' dāl Ga. (Atlanta In.) 33·47 N 84·16 W
47 Scott Is. Ant. 67·24 S 179·55 W
47 Scott Ra. Ant. 68·00 S 55·00 E
70 Scottsbluff (skŏts'blŭf) Nebr. 41·52 N 103·40 W
70 Scotts Bluff Natl. Mon. Nebr. 41·45 N 103·47 W
78 Scottsboro (skŏts'bŭro) Ala. 34·40 N 86·03 W
80 Scottsburg (skŏts' bûrg) Ind. 38·40 N 85·50 W
167 Scottsburg (scŏts'bẽrg) S. Afr. (Natal In.) 30·18 S 30·42 E
160 Scottsdale (skŏts'dāl) Austl. 41·12 S 147·37 E
78 Scottsville (skŏts'vĭl) Ky. 36·45 N 86·10 W
80 Scottville Mich. 44·00 N 86·20 W
81 Scranton (skrăn'tŭn) Pa. 41·45 N 75·45 W
81 Scugog (L.) (skŭ'gôg) Can. 44·05 N 78·55 W
110 Scunthorpe (skŭn'thôrp) Eng. 53·36 N 0·38 W
Scutari, see Shkodër
127 Scutari (R.) (skōō'tä-rē) Alb. 42·14 N 19·33 E
79 Sea, Is. (sē) Ga.-S. C. 31·21 N 81·05 W
65 Seabeck (sē'bĕck) Wash. (Seattle In.) 47·38 N 122·50 W
65 Seabold (sē'bōld) Wash. (Seattle In.) 47·42 N 122·33 W
84 Sea Bright (sē brīt) N. J. (New York In.) 40·22 N 73·58 W
77 Seabrook (sē'brŏŏk) Tex. (In.) 29·34 N 95·01 W
81 Seaford (sē'fẽrd) Del. 38·35 N 75·40 W
72 Seagraves (sē'grāvs) Tex. 32·51 N 102·38 W
86 Seal (R.) Can. 59·08 N 96·37 W
74 Seal Beach Calif. (Los Angeles In.) 33·44 N 118·06 W
95 Seal Cays (Is.) Ba. Is. 21·10 N 71·45 W
95 Seal Cays (Is.) Ba. Is. 22·40 N 75·55 W
166 Seal I. (sēl) S. Afr. (Cape Town In.) 34·07 S 18·36 E
77 Sealy (sē'lē) Tex. 29·46 N 96·10 W
166 Sea Point (sē point) S. Afr. (Cape Town In.) 33·55 S 18·23 E
73 Searcy (sûr'sē) Ark. 35·13 N 91·43 W
68 Searles (L.) (sûrl's) Calif. 35·44 N 117·22 W
82 Searsport (sērz'pōrt) Maine 44·28 N 68·55 W
66 Seaside (sē'sīd) Ore. 45·59 N 123·55 W
65 Seattle (sē-ăt''l) Wash. (Seattle In.) 47·36 N 122·20 W
92 Sebaco (sĕ-bä'kô) Nic. 12·50 N 86·03 W
82 Sebago (sē-bā'gō) Maine 43·52 N 70·20 W
88 Sebastion Vizcaino, Bahia (B.) (bä-ē'ä-sĕ-bäs-tyô'n-vēs-kä-ē'nô) Mex. 28·45 N 115·15 W
68 Sebastopol (sē-bȧs'tō-pōl) Calif. 38·27 N 122·50 W
154 Sebatik (I.) Indon. 3·52 N 118·14 E
127 Sebes Rom. 45·58 N 23·34 E
80 Sebewaing (se'bē-wăng) Mich. 43·45 N 83·25 W
128 Sebezh (syĕ'bĕzh) Sov. Un. 56·16 N 28·29 E
133 Sebinkarahisar Tur. 40·15 N 38·10 E
124 Sebkha bou Areg (Marsh) Mor. 35·09 N 3·02 W
125 Sebkhan d'Oran (L.) Alg. 35·28 N 0·28 W
120 Sebnitz (zĕb'nēts) Ger. 51·01 N 14·16 E
125 Seborbe (sĕ-bôr-dĕ) Sp. 39·50 N 0·30 W
114 Sebou, Oued R. Mor. 34·23 N 5·18 W
80 Sebree (sē-brē') Ky. 37·35 N 87·30 W
79 Sebring (sē'brĭng) Fla. (In.) 27·30 N 81·26 W
80 Sebring Ohio 40·55 N 81·05 W
126 Secchia (R.) (sĕ'kyä) It. 44·25 N 10·25 E
91 Seco (R.) (sĕ'kô) Mex. 18·11 N 93·18 W
165 Second Cataract Sud. 21·52 N 31·18 E
73 Sedalia (sē-dā'lē-ȧ) Mo. 38·42 N 93·12 W
122 Sedan (sē-dän') Fr. 49·49 N 4·55 E
73 Sedan (sē-dăn') Kans. 37·07 N 96·08 W
110 Sedgley (sĕdj'lĭ) Eng. 52·32 N 2·07 W
139 Sedom Isr. (Palestine In.) 31·04 N 35·24 E
65 Sedro Woolley (sē'drô-wŏŏl'ē) Wash. (Seattle In.) 48·30 N 122·14 W
119 Šeduva (shĕ'dŏŏ-vȧ) Sov. Un. 55·46 N 23·45 E
111 Seestall (zā'shtäl) Ger. (München In.) 47·58 N 10·52 E
114 Sefrou (sē-frōō') Mor. 33·49 N 4·46 W
132 Seg (L.) (syĕgh) Sov. Un. 64·00 N 33·30 E
139 Segamat (sā'gȧ-mȧt) Mala. (Singapore In.) 2·30 N 102·49 E
164 Ségou (sā-gōō') Mali 13·24 N 6·20 W
98 Segovia (sĕ-gō'vēä) Col. (In.) 7·08 N 74·42 W
124 Segovia (sā-gō'vē-ä) Sp. 40·58 N 4·05 W
Segovia, see Coco
125 Segre (R.) (sā'grä) Sp. 41·54 N 1·10 E
64 Seguam (I.) (sē'gwäm) Alaska 52·16 N 172·10 W
64 Seguam P. Alaska 52·20 N 173·00 W
164 Séguela (sā-gā-lä') Ivory Coast 8·03 N 7·05 W
76 Seguin (sĕ-gēn') Tex. 29·35 N 97·58 W
64 Segula (I.) (sē-gū'lȧ) Alaska 52·08 N 178·35 E
125 Segura (R.) (sā-gōō'rä) Sp. 38·07 N 0·33 W
124 Segura, Sierra de (Mts.) (sē-ĕ'r-rä-dĕ) Sp. 38·05 N 2·45 W
124 Segura (R.) Sp. 38·24 N 2·12 W
142 Sehwān W. Pak. 26·33 N 67·51 E
95 Seibo (sĕ'y-bō) Dom. Rep. 18·45 N 69·05 W
119 Seinäjoki (sâ'ē-nĕ-yô'kē) Fin. 62·47 N 22·50 E
122 Seine, Baie de la (B.) (bī dĕ lä sân) Fr. 49·37 N 0·53 W
71 Seine (R.) (sân) Can. 49·04 N 91·00 W
122 Seine, Rivière (R.) (rēv-yâr') Fr. 49·21 N 1·17 E
85 Seine R. (sân) Can. (Winnipeg In.) 49·48 N 97·04 W
100 Seio do Venus (Mtn.) (sĕ-yô-dô-vĕ'nōōs) Braz. (In.) 22·28 S 43·12 W
125 Seixal (sâ-ê-shäl') Port. (Lisboa In.) 38·38 N 9·06 W
164 Sekondi (sĕ-kôn'dē) Ghana 4·59 N 1·45 W
139 Selangor (State) (sâ-län'gôr) Mala. (Singapore In.) 2·53 N 101·29 E
127 Selanovci (sĕl'á-nôf-tsĭ) Bul. 43·42 N 24·05 E
155 Selaru (I.) Indon. 8·30 S 130·30 E
154 Selatan, Tandjung (C.) (sâ-lä'tän) Indon. 4·09 S 114·40 E
64 Selawik (sē-lȧ-wĭk) Alaska 66·30 N 160·09 W
118 Selbu (L.) (sĕl'bōō) Nor. 63·18 N 11·55 E
110 Selby (sĕl'bē) Eng. 53·47 N 1·03 W
64 Seldovia (sĕl-dō'vē-ȧ) Alaska 59·26 N 151·42 W
135 Selemdzha (R.) (sâ-lĕmt-zhä') Sov. Un. 52·28 N 131·50 E
135 Selenga (R.) (sĕ lĕŋ gä') Sov. Un. 51·00 N 106·40 E
146 Selenge Gol (R.) Mong. 49·04 N 102·23 E
135 Selennyakh (R.) (sĕl-yĭn-yäk) Sov. Un. 67·42 N 141·45 E
123 Sélestat (sĕ-lē-stä') Fr. 48·16 N 7·27 E
164 Selibaby (sâ-lē-bȧ-bē') Mauritania 15·21 N 12·11 W
128 Seliger (L.) (sĕl'lē-gĕr) Sov. Un. 57·14 N 33·18 E
142 Seling Tsho (L.) China 31·55 N 89·00 E
142 Selipuk Gömpa China 31·37 N 82·42 E
128 Selizharovo (sâ'lē-zhä'rô-vô) Sov. Un. 56·51 N 33·28 E
86 Selkirk (sĕl'kûrk) Can. 50·13 N 97·07 W
86 Selkirk Mts. Can. 50·14 N 116·42 W
65 Selleck (sĕl'ĕck) Wash. (Seattle In.) 47·22 N 121·52 W
75 Sellersburg (sĕl'ĕrs-bûrg) Ind. (Louisville In.) 38·25 N 85·45 W
135 Sellya Khskaya, Guba (B.) (sĕl-yäk'skȧ-yȧ) Sov. Un. 72·30 N 136·00 E
78 Selma (sĕl'mȧ) Ala. 32·25 N 87·00 W
68 Selma Calif. 36·34 N 119·37 W
79 Selma N. C. 35·33 N 78·16 W
74 Selma Tex. (San Antonio In.) 29·33 N 98·19 W
111 Selsingen (zĕl'zĕn-gĕn) Ger. (Hamburg In.) 53·22 N 9·13 E
166 Selukwe (sē-lŭk'wē) Fed. of Rh. & Nya. 19·34 S 30·03 E
66 Selway R. (sĕl'wȧ) Idaho 46·07 N 115·12 W
86 Selwyn (L.) (sĕl'wĭn) Can. 59·41 N 104·30 W
127 Seman (R.) Alb. 40·48 N 19·53 E
154 Semarang (sĕ-mä'räng) Indon. 7·03 S 110·27 E
154 Semarinda Indon. 0·30 S 117·10 E
Semendria, see Smederevo
129 Semënovka (sĕ-myôn'ôf-kȧ) Sov. Un. 52·10 N 32·34 E
65 Semiahmoo Ind. Res. Can. (Vancouver In.) 49·01 N 122·43 W
65 Semiahmoo Spit (sĕm'ĭ-ȧ-mōō) Wash. (Vancouver In.) 48·59 N 122·52 W
64 Semichi Is. (sē mē'chī) Alaska 52·40 N 174·50 E
67 Seminoe Res. (sĕm'ĭ nô) Wyo. 42·08 N 107·10 W
73 Seminole (sĕm'ĭ-nōl) Okla. 35·13 N 96·41 W
79 Seminole Ind. Res. Fla. (In.) 26·19 N 81·11 W
79 Seminole Ind. Res. Fla. (In.) 27·05 N 81·25 W
134 Semipalatinsk (sĕ'mē-pȧ-lȧ-tyēnsk') Sov. Un. 50·28 N 80·29 E
64 Semisopochnoi (I.) (sĕ-mē-sȧ-pôsh' noi) Alaska 51·45 N 179·25 E
134 Semiyarskoye (sĕ'mē-yär'skô-yĕ) Sov. Un. 51·03 N 78·28 E
165 Semliki R. (sĕm'lē-kē) Con. L.-Ug. 0·45 N 29·36 E
Semlin, see Zemun
120 Semmering P. (sĕm'ĕr-ĭng) Aus. 47·39 N 15·50 E
133 Semnān Iran 35·30 N 53·30 E
99 Senador Pompeu (sĕ-nä-dōr-pôm-pĕ'ōō) Braz. 5·34 S 39·18 W
78 Senatobia (sĕ-nȧ-tō'bē-ȧ) Miss. 34·36 N 89·56 W
152 Sendai (sĕn-dī') Jap. 38·18 N 141·02 E
168 Sendelingsfontein S. Afr. (Johannesburg & Pretoria In.) 26·57 S 26·17 E
73 Seneca (sĕn'ĕ-kȧ) Kans. 39·49 N 96·03 W
78 Seneca S. C. 34·40 N 82·58 W
81 Seneca (L.) N. Y. 42·30 N 76·55 W
81 Seneca Falls N. Y. 42·55 N 76·55 W
163 Sénégal (sĕn-ĕ-gôl') Afr. 14·53 N 14·58 W
164 Senegal R. Senegal-Mauritania 16·45 N 14·37 W
168 Senekal (sĕn'ĕ-kȧl) S. Afr. (Johannesburg & Pretoria In.) 28·20 S 27·37 E
120 Senftenberg (zĕnf'tĕn-bĕrgh) Ger. 51·32 N 14·00 E
99 Senhor do Bonfim (sĕn-yôr dô bôN-fē'N) Braz. 5·21 S 40·09 W
126 Senigallia (sâ-nē-gäl'lyä) It. 43·42 N 13·16 E
126 Senj (sĕnj') Yugo. 44·58 N 14·55 E
112 Senja (I.) (sĕnyä) Nor. 69·28 N 16·10 E
123 Senlis (säN-lēs') Fr. (Paris In.) 49·13 N 2·35 E
165 Sennar (sĕn-när') Sud. 13·34 N 33·32 E
165 Sennar Dam Sud. 13·38 N 33·38 E
87 Senneterre Can. 48·20 N 77·22 W
128 Senno (syĕ'nô) Sov. Un. 54·48 N 29·43 E
122 Sens (säNs) Fr. 48·05 N 3·18 E
92 Sensuntepeque (sĕn-sōōn-tȧ-pä'kȧ) Sal. 13·53 N 88·34 W
127 Senta (sĕn'tä) Yugo. 45·54 N 20·05 E
153 Senzaki (sĕn'zä-kē) Jap. 34·22 N 131·09 E
Seoul, see Sŏul
139 Sepang Mala. (Singapore In.) 2·43 N 101·45 E
100 Sepetiba, Baia de (B.) (bäē'ȧ dĕ sȧ-pȧ-tē'bȧ) Braz. (In.) 23·01 S 43·42 W
155 Sepik (R.) (sĕp-ēk') N. Gui. Ter. 4·07 S 142·40 E

ng-sing; ŋ-baŋk; N-nasalized n; nŏd; cŏmmit; ōld; ôbey; ôrder; fōōd; fŏŏt; ou-out; s-soft; sh-dish; th-thin; pūre; ûnite; ûrn; stŭd; circŭs; ü-as "y" in study; '-indeterminate vowel.

266 Septemes-les-Vallons–Shibeli PRONOUNCING INDEX

Page	Name Pronunciation Region	Lat. °′	Long. °′
122	Septèmes-les-Vallons (sĕ-tàm′la-vä-ôɴ′) Fr. (Marseille In.)	43·25 N	5·23 E
95	Septentrional, Cordillera (Mts.) (kôr-dēl-yĕ′rä sĕp-tĕn-tryô-nä′l) Dom. Rep.	19·50 N	71·15 W
123	Septeuil (sĕ-tû′)....Fr. (Paris In.)	48·53 N	1·40 E
82	Sept-Iles..................Can.	50·11 N	66·21 W
78	Sequatchie (R.) (sē-kwăch′ē) Tenn.	35·33 N	85·14 W
65	Sequim (sē′kwĭm) Wash. (Seattle In.)	48·05 N	123·07 W
65	Sequim B.....Wash. (Seattle In.)	48·04 N	122·58 W
68	Sequoia Natl. Park (sē-kwoi′ȧ) Calif.	36·34 N	118·37 W
117	Seraing (sē-răɴ′)............Bel.	50·38 N	5·28 E
155	Seram (I.)................Indon.	2·45 S	129·30 E
142	Sèrampore...India (Calcutta In.)	22·44 N	88·21 E
154	Serang (sȧ-räng′)..........Indon.	6·13 S	106·10 E
139	Seranggung.Indon. (Singapore In.)	0·49 N	104·11 E
	Serbia (Reg.), see Srbija		
133	Serdobsk (sĕr-dôpsk′)....Sov. Un.	52·30 N	44·20 E
129	Seredina-Buda (sĕ-rȧ-dē′nȧ-bōō′dȧ).Sov. Un.	52·11 N	34·03 E
139	Seremban (sĕr-ĕm-băn′) Mala. (Singapore In.)	2·44 N	101·57 E
166	Serenje (sē-rĕn′yē) Fed. of Rh. & Nya.	13·12 S	30·49 E
168	Serenli (sȧ-rĕn′lē) Som. (Horn of Afr. In.)	2·28 N	42·15 E
	Seres, see Sérrai		
121	Seret.....................Czech.	48·17 N	17·43 E
121	Seret......................Rom.	47·58 N	26·01 E
121	Seret R. (sĕr′ĕt).........Sov. Un.	49·45 N	25·30 E
134	Sergeya Kirova (I.) (sĕr-gyē′yȧ kē′rô-vȧ).Sov. Un.	77·30 N	86·10 E
99	Sergipe (State) (sĕr-zhē′pĕ).Braz.	10·27 S	37·04 W
132	Sergiyevsk.............Sov. Un.	53·58 N	51·00 E
127	Sérifos....................Grc.	37·10 N	24·32 E
127	Sérifos (I.)...............Grc.	37·42 N	24·17 E
101	Serodino (sĕ-rô-dē′nō) Arg. (Buenos Aires In.)	32·36 S	60·56 W
100	Seropédica (sĕ-rô-pĕ′dē-kä) Braz. (In.)	22·44 S	43·43 W
136	Serov (syĕ-rôf′) Sov. Un. (Urals In.)	59·36 N	60·30 E
166	Serowe (sĕ-rō′wĕ)..........Bech.	22·18 S	26·39 E
124	Serpa (sĕr-pȧ).............Port.	37·56 N	7·38 W
128	Serpukhov (syĕr′pōō-ĸôf) Sov. Un.	54·53 N	37·27 E
127	Sérrai (Seres) (sĕr′rĕ) (sĕr′ĕs).Grc.	41·06 N	23·36 E
76	Serranias Del Burro (sĕr-rä-nē′äs dĕl bōō′r-rô).Mex.	29·39 N	102·07 W
99	Serrinha (sĕr-rēn′yȧ)........Braz.	11·43 S	38·49 W
124	Serta (sĕr′tȧ)...............Port.	39·48 N	8·01 W
99	Sertânia (sĕr-tä′nyȧ).......Braz.	8·28 S	37·13 W
101	Sertãozinho (sĕr-touɴ-zē′n-yō) Braz. (Rio de Janeiro In.)	21·10 S	47·58 W
139	Serting (R.).Mala. (Singapore In.)	3·01 N	102·32 E
100	Seruí (sĕ-rōō-ē′).......Braz. (In.)	22·40 S	43·08 W
126	Sesia (R.) (sâz′yä)............It.	45·33 N	8·25 E
125	Sesimbra (sĕ-sē′m-brä) Port. (Lisboa In.)	38·27 N	9·06 W
167	Sesmyl (R.)...............S. Afr. (Johannesburg & Pretoria In.)	25·51 S	28·06 E
126	Sestri Levante (sĕs′trē lâ-vän′tâ) It.	44·15 N	9·24 E
136	Sestroretsk (sĕs-trô′rĕtsk) Sov. Un. (Leningrad In.)	60·06 N	29·58 E
136	Sestroretskiy Razliv, Ozero (L.) (ô′zĕ-rō sĕs-trô′ rĕts-kĭ räz′lĭf) Sov. Un. (Leningrad In.)	60·05 N	30·07 E
153	Seta (sĕ′tä)......Jap. (Ōsaka In.)	34·58 N	135·56 E
122	Sète (Cette) (sĕt)...........Fr.	43·24 N	3·42 E
99	Sete Lagoas (sĕ-tĕ lä-gō′äs)..Braz.	19·23 S	43·58 W
164	Setif (sā-tēf′)..............Alg.	36·18 N	5·21 E
153	Seto (sĕ′tō).................Jap.	35·11 N	137·07 E
153	Seto-Naikai (Sea) (sĕ′tô nī′kī).Jap.	33·50 N	132·25 E
164	Settat (sĕt-ät′) (sē-tȧ′)......Mor.	33·02 N	7·30 W
166	Setté-Cama (sĕ-tē-kä-mä′).Gabon	2·29 S	9·40 E
94	Settlement Pt. (sĕt′l-mĕnt).Ba. Is.	26·40 N	79·00 W
168	Settlers (sĕt′lērs)..........S. Afr. (Johannesburg & Pretoria In.)	24·57 S	28·33 E
125	Setúbal (sâ-tōō′bäl) Port. (Lisboa In.)	30·32 N	8·54 W
124	Setúbal, B. de (bä-ē′ȧ)......Port.	38·27 N	9·08 W
87	Seul, Lac (L.) (läk sûl).......Can.	50·28 N	91·26 W
118	Sevalen (L.) (sĕ′vä-lĕn).......Nor.	62·19 N	10·15 E
133	Sevan (L.) (syĭ-vän′)....Sov. Un.	40·10 N	45·20 E
129	Sevastopol′ (Akhiar) (syĕ-väs-tô′pôl″) (äĸ′yär) Sov. Un.	44·34 N	33·34 E
	Seven Is., see Shichitō		
110	Sevenoaks (sĕ-vĕn-ōks′) Eng. (London In.)	51·16 N	0·12 E
136	Severka R. (sȧ′vĕr-kȧ) Sov. Un. (Moskva In.)	55·11 N	38·41 E
87	Severn (R.) (sĕv′ērn)........Can.	55·21 N	88·42 W
116	Severn (R.)..................Eng.	51·42 N	2·25 W
84	Severna Park (sĕv′ērn-ȧ) Md. (Baltimore In.)	39·04 N	76·33 W
132	Severnaya Dvina (Northern Dvina) (R.).Sov. Un.	63·00 N	42·40 E
130	Severnaya Zemlya (Northern Land) (Is.) (sĕ-vyĭr-nī′u zĭ-m′lyä′).Sov. Un.	79·33 N	101·15 E
136	Severoural′sk (sĕ-vyĭ-rŭ-ōō-rälsk′) Sov. Un. (Urals In.)	60·08 N	59·53 E
69	Sevier (L.) (sē-vēr′).........Utah	38·55 N	113·10 W
69	Sevier R.....................Utah	39·25 N	112·20 W
69	Sevier R., East Fork........Utah	37·45 N	112·10 W
98	Sevilla (sĕ-vē′l-yä)......Col. (In.)	4·16 N	75·56 W
124	Sevilla (sā-vēl′yä)............Sp.	37·29 N	5·58 W
75	Seville (sĕ′vĭl) Ohio (Cleveland In.)	41·01 N	81·54 W
127	Sevlievo (sĕv′lyĕ-vô).........Bul.	41·02 N	25·05 E
122	Sèvre Nantaise (R.) (sâ′vrĕ näɴ-tàz′)....Fr.	47·00 N	1·02 W
122	Sèvre Niortaise (R.) (sâ′vr′ nyôr-tâz′).Fr.	46·23 N	1·05 W
128	Sevsk (syĕfsk)..........Sov. Un.	52·08 N	34·28 E
64	Seward (sū′ărd)...........Alaska	60·18 N	149·28 W
73	Seward....................Nebr.	40·55 N	97·06 W
64	Seward Pen.............Alaska	65·40 N	164·00 W
100	Sewell (sĕ′ōō-ĕl)............Chile	34·01 S	70·18 W
75	Sewickley (sē-wĭk′lē) Pa. (Pittsburg In.)	40·33 N	80·11 W
91	Seybaplaya (sā-ē-bä-plä′yä)..Mex.	19·38 N	90·40 W
47	Seychelles (Is.) (sā-shĕl′).....Afr.	5·20 S	55·10 E
112	Seydhisfjördhur (sā′dēs-fyûr-dŏŏr).Ice.	65·21 N	14·08 W
92	Seyé (sĕ-yĕ′)..Mex. (Yucatan In.)	20·51 N	89·22 W
115	Seyhan (R.)..................Tur.	37·28 N	35·40 E
129	Seym (R.) (sĕym).......Sov. Un.	51·23 N	33·22 E
80	Seymour (sē′mōr)...........Ind.	38·55 N	85·55 W
71	Seymour...................Iowa	40·41 N	93·03 W
72	Seymour....................Tex.	33·35 N	99·16 W
167	Seymour (sē′môr) S. Afr. (Natal In.)	32·33 S	26·48 E
126	Sezze (sĕt′sȧ)................It.	41·32 N	13·03 E
127	Sfântul-Gheorghe..........Rom.	45·53 N	25·49 E
164	Sfax (sfäks)..................Tun.	34·51 N	10·45 E
111	s′Gravenhage (The Hague) (′s ĸrä′vĕn-hä′ĸĕ) (hāg) Neth. (Amsterdam In.)	52·05 N	4·16 E
147	Sha (R.) (shä)............China	33·33 N	114·30 E
148	Sha (R.)..................China	34·47 N	118·27 E
148	Sha (R.)..................China	39·26 N	122·08 E
166	Shabani......Fed. of Rh. & Nya.	20·15 S	30·28 E
136	Shablykino (sháb-lē′kĭ-nô) Sov. Un. (Moskva In.)	56·22 N	38·37 E
149	Shaching.....China (Canton In.)	22·44 N	113·48 E
47	Shackleton Shelf Ice (shăk″l-tŭn) Ant.	65·00 S	100·00 E
84	Shades Cr. (shādz) Ala. (Birmingham In.)	33·20 N	86·55 W
84	Shades Mtn. Ala. (Birmingham In.)	33·22 N	86·51 W
144	Shagrā (shăg′rä).........Sau. Ar.	25·13 N	45·15 E
144	Shahdād....................Iran	30·45 N	57·45 E
142	Shah Fuladi (Mt.)..........Afg.	39·33 N	67·38 E
165	Shahhāt...................Libya	32·49 N	21·46 E
142	Shāhjahānpur (shä-jŭ-hän′pōōr) India	27·58 N	79·58 E
150	Shaho (shä-hō′) China (Peking In.)	40·08 N	116·16 E
144	Shahrezā (shä-rā′zä).........Iran	31·47 N	51·47 E
133	Shahsavār...................Iran	36·40 N	51·00 E
75	Shaker Hts. (shā′kēr) Ohio (Cleveland In.)	41·28 N	81·34 W
129	Shakhty (shäĸ′tē).......Sov. Un.	47·41 N	40·11 E
74	Shakopee (shăk′ô-pe) Minn. (Minneapolis, St. Paul In.)	44·48 N	93·31 W
165	Shala L. (shä′lȧ)...........Eth.	7·34 N	39·00 E
144	Sham, Jabal ash (Mtn.) Mus. & Om.	23·01 N	57·45 E
165	Shambe (shăm′bȧ)..........Sud.	7·08 N	30·46 E
144	Shammar, Jabal (Mts.) (jĕb′ĕl shŭm′ár).Sau. Ar.	27·13 N	40·16 E
81	Shamokin (shȧ-mō′kĭn).......Pa.	40·45 N	76·30 W
72	Shamrock (shăm′rŏk).........Tex.	35·14 N	100·12 W
166	Shamva (shăm′vȧ) Fed. of Rh. & Nya.	17·18 S	31·35 E
75	Shandon (shăn-dŭn) Ohio (Cincinnati In.)	39·20 N	84·13 W
148	Shangch′eng (shăng′chĕng).China	31·47 N	115·22 E
148	Shangchialin (shăng′jĭä′lin).China	38·20 N	116·05 E
148	Shangch′iu (shăng′chĭō).....China	34·24 N	115·39 E
149	Shanghai (shăng′hī′) China (Shanghai In.)	31·14 N	121·27 E
149	Shanghaihsien China (Shanghai In.)	31·02 N	121·24 E
148	Shanghai Shih (Prov.).....China	31·30 N	121·45 E
148	Shangho (shăng′hŏ).......China	37·18 N	117·10 E
151	Shangjao..................China	28·25 N	117·58 E
148	Shangts′ai (shăng′zhī′).......China	33·16 N	114·16 E
150	Shangtu....................China	41·38 N	113·22 E
147	Shanhsi (Shansi) (Prov.)...China	37·31 N	111·30 E
148	Shanhsien (shän′hsyĕn′)....China	34·47 N	116·04 E
84	Shannon (shăn′ăn) Ala. (Birmingham In.)	33·23 N	86·52 W
116	Shannon R. (shăn′ŏn)........Ire.	52·30 N	9·58 W
146	Shanshan (shän′shän′)......China	42·51 N	89·53 E
	Shansi, see Shanhsi		
135	Shantar (I.) (shän′tär)...Sov. Un.	55·13 N	138·42 E
	Shant′ou, see Swatow		
147	Shantung (Prov.)...........China	36·08 N	117·09 E
151	Shantung Pantao (Pen.)....China	37·00 N	120·10 E
151	Shantung Pt. (shän′tōōng′).China	37·28 N	122·40 E
151	Shaohsing..................China	30·00 N	120·40 E
148	Shaopo (shou′pō′)..........China	32·33 N	119·30 E
148	Shaopo Hu (L.) (shou′pŏ′ hōō) China	32·07 N	119·13 E
136	Shapki (shăp′kĭ) Sov. Un. (Leningrad In.)	59·36 N	31·11 E
165	Shari R. (shä-rē′)..........Chad	11·02 N	15·46 E
158	Shark B. (shärk)..........Austl.	25·30 S	113·00 E
83	Sharon (shăr′ŏn) Mass. (Boston In.)	42·07 N	71·11 W
80	Sharon......................Pa.	41·15 N	80·30 W
72	Sharon Springs.............Kan.	38·51 N	101·45 W
75	Sharonville (shăr′ŏn vĭl) Ohio (Cincinnati In.)	39·16 N	84·24 W
75	Sharpsburg (shärps′bûrg) Pa. (Pittsburgh In.)	40·30 N	79·54 W
144	Sharr, Jabal (Mtn.)......Sau. Ar.	28·00 N	36·07 E
151	Shashih....................China	30·20 N	112·18 E
66	Shasta, Mt.................Calif.	41·35 N	122·12 W
66	Shasta L. (shăs′tȧ).........Calif.	40·51 N	122·32 W
132	Shatsk (shàtsk)..........Sov. Un.	54·00 N	41·40 E
72	Shattuck (shăt′ŭk)..........Okla.	36·16 N	99·53 W
86	Shaunavon..................Can.	49·37 N	108·29 W
78	Shaw (shô).................Miss.	33·36 N	90·44 W
71	Shawano (shȧ-wô′nô)........Wis.	44·41 N	88·13 W
82	Shawinigan Falls...........Can.	46·32 N	72·46 W
74	Shawnee (shô-nē′) Mo. (Kansas City In.)	39·01 N	94·43 W
73	Shawnee...................Okla.	35·20 N	96·54 W
80	Shawneetown (shô′nē-toun)....Ill.	37·40 N	88·05 W
151	Shayang...................China	31·00 N	112·38 E
121	Shchara (R.) (sh-chä′rä).Sov. Un.	53·17 N	25·12 E
136	Shchëlkovo (shchĕl′kô-vô) Sov. Un. (Moskva In.)	55·55 N	38·00 E
129	Shchëtovo (shchĕ′tô-vô)..Sov. Un.	48·11 N	39·13 E
129	Shchigry (shchē′grê).....Sov. Un.	51·52 N	36·54 E
129	Shchors (shchôrs).......Sov. Un.	51·38 N	31·58 E
136	Shchuch′ye Ozero (shchōōch′yĕ ô′zĕ-rō) Sov. Un. (Urals In.)	56·31 N	56·35 E
142	Sheakhala....India (Calcutta In.)	22·47 N	88·10 E
168	Shebeli R. (shā′bå-lē) Eth. (Horn of Afr. In.)	6·07 N	43·10 E
71	Sheboygan (shē-boi′găn).....Wis.	43·45 N	87·44 W
71	Sheboygan Falls............Wis.	43·43 N	87·51 W
164	Shebshi Mts..........Nig.-Cam.	8·22 N	12·14 E
82	Shediac (shĕ′dē-ăk).........Can.	46·16 N	64·33 W
116	Sheelin (L.) (shē′lĭn)..........Ire.	53·46 N	7·34 W
110	Sheerness (shēr′nĕs) Eng. (London In.)	51·26 N	0·46 E
78	Sheffield (shĕf′fēld)..........Ala.	35·42 N	87·42 W
85	Sheffield......Can. (Toronto In.)	43·20 N	80·13 W
110	Sheffield...................Eng.	53·23 N	1·28 W
75	Sheffield.....Ohio (Cleveland In.)	41·26 N	82·05 W
75	Sheffield Lake Ohio (Cleveland In.)	41·30 N	82·03 W
148	Shehsien (shĕ′hsyĕn′)......China	36·34 N	113·42 E
116	Shehy, Mts..................Ire.	51·46 N	9·35 W
132	Sheksna (R.) (shĕks′nȧ)..Sov. Un.	59·50 N	38·40 E
135	Shelagskiy, Mys (C.) (shĭ-läg′skē) Sov. Un.	70·08 N	170·52 E
73	Shelbina (shĕl-bī′nȧ)........Ark.	39·41 N	92·03 W
82	Shelbourne (shĕl′bŭrn.......Can.	43·46 N	65·20 W
80	Shelburn (shĕl′bŭrn).........Ind.	39·10 N	87·30 W
81	Shelburne..................Can.	44·05 N	80·05 W
75	Shelby (shĕl′bē) Ind. (Chicago In.)	41·12 N	87·21 W
80	Shelby.....................Mich.	43·35 N	86·20 W
78	Shelby.....................Miss.	33·56 N	90·44 W
79	Shelby......................N. C.	35·16 N	81·35 W
80	Shelby......................Ohio	40·50 N	82·40 W
80	Shelbyville (shĕl′bē-vĭl).......Ill.	39·20 N	88·45 W
80	Shelbyville..................Ind.	39·30 N	85·45 W
80	Shelbyville..................Ky.	38·10 N	85·15 W
78	Shelbyville.................Tenn.	35·30 N	86·28 W
71	Sheldon (shĕl′dŭn)..........Iowa	43·10 N	95·50 W
77	Sheldon..............Tex. (In.)	29·52 N	95·07 W
135	Shelekhova, Zaliv (B.)...Sov. Un.	60·00 N	156·00 E
64	Shelikof Str. (shĕ′lē-kôf)...Alaska	57·56 N	154·20 W
84	Shell Beach (bēch) La. (New Orleans In.)	29·52 N	89·41 W
67	Shelley (shĕl′lē)...........Idaho	43·24 N	112·06 W
84	Shell I. (shĕl) La. (New Orleans In.)	29·17 N	89·42 W
71	Shellrock (R.) (shĕl′rŏk).....Iowa	43·25 N	93·19 W
128	Shelon′ (R.) (shä′lôn)....Sov. Un.	57·50 N	29·40 E
81	Shelton (shĕl′tŭn).........Conn.	41·15 N	73·05 W
72	Shelton.....................Nebr.	40·46 N	98·41 W
66	Shelton....................Wash.	47·14 N	123·05 W
136	Shemakha (shĕ-mȧ-kä′) Sov. Un. (Urals In.)	56·16 N	59·19 E
133	Shemakha................Sov. Un.	40·35 N	48·40 E
73	Shenandoah (shĕn-ăn-dō′ȧ)..Iowa	40·46 N	95·23 W
81	Shenandoah..................Pa.	40·50 N	76·15 W
81	Shenandoah..................Va.	38·30 N	78·30 W
81	Shenandoah Natl. Park......Va.	38·35 N	78·25 W
81	Shenandoah (R.).............Va.	38·55 N	78·05 W
148	Shenchiu (shenchĭō)........China	33·11 N	115·06 E
165	Shendi (shĕn′dē)............Sud.	16·44 N	33·29 E
148	Shengfang (shengfăng)......China	39·05 N	116·40 E
146	Shenhsi (Shensi) (Prov.) (shĕn′sē′).China	35·04 N	108·45 E
148	Shenhsien (shen′sĭän)......China	38·02 N	115·33 E
132	Shenkursk (shĕn-kōōrsk′).Sov. Un.	62·10 N	43·08 E
150	Shenmu....................China	38·55 N	110·35 E
	Shensi, see Shenhsi		
148	Shentse (shen′zhŏ)..........China	38·12 N	115·12 E
150	Shenyang (Mukden) (shĕn′yăng′) (mōōk′dĕn).China	41·45 N	123·22 E
142	Sheopur....................India	25·37 N	78·10 E
85	Shepard (shĕ′pård) Can. (Calgary In.)	50·57 N	113·54 W
129	Shepetovka (shĕ-pĕ-tôf′kȧ) Sov. Un.	50·10 N	27·01 E
83	Sherborn (shûr′bŭrn) Mass. (Boston In.)	42·15 N	71·22 W
81	Sherbrooke (shûr′brŏŏk).....Can.	45·25 N	72·00 W
110	Sherburn (shûr′bŭrn)........Eng.	53·47 N	1·15 W
121	Shereshevo (shĕ-rĕ-shĕ-vô) Sov. Un.	52·31 N	24·08 E
73	Sheridan (shĕr′ĭ-dăn)........Ark.	34·19 N	92·21 W
66	Sheridan....................Ore.	45·06 N	123·22 W
67	Sheridan...................Wyo.	44·48 N	106·56 W
73	Sherman (shĕr′măn)..........Tex.	33·39 N	96·37 W
136	Sherna R. (shĕr′nȧ) Sov. Un. (Moskva In.)	56·08 N	38·45 E
86	Sherridon...................Can.	55·08 N	101·00 W
111	′s Hertogenbosch (sĕr-tō′ghĕn-bôs) Neth. (Amsterdam In.)	51·41 N	5·19 E
65	Sherwood (shûr′wŏŏd) Ore. (Portland In.)	45·21 N	122·50 W
110	Sherwood For...............Eng.	53·11 N	1·07 W
116	Shetland (Is.) (shĕt′lănd)....Scot.	60·35 N	2·10 W
139	Sheva R.......Isr. (Palestine In.)	31·15 N	34·38 E
70	Sheyenne (R.) (shī-ĕn′).....N. D.	46·42 N	97·52 W
80	Shiawassee (R.) (shī-ȧ-wôs′ē) Mich.	43·15 N	84·05 W
144	Shibām (shē′bäm)........Sau. Ar.	16·02 N	48·40 E
168	Shibeli R.Som. (Horn of Afr. In.)	1·38 N	43·50 E

ăt; finăl; rāte; senāte; ärm; àsk; sofȧ; fâre; ch-choose; dh-as th in other; bē; ēvent; bĕt; recĕnt; cratẽr; g-go; gh-guttural g; bĭt; ĭ-short neutral; rīde; ĸ-guttural k as ch in German ich;

PRONOUNCING INDEX

Shibin al Kawn–Singunyane 267

Page	Name Pronunciation Region	Lat. °′	Long. °′
168	Shibīn al Kawn (shē-bēn'ĕl kōm') U. A. R. (Nile In.)	30·31 N	31·01 E
168	Shībīn al Qanāţir (kȧ-nä'tēr) U. A. R. (Nile In.)	30·18 N	31·21 E
153	Shichitō (Seven Is.) (shē'chē-tō) Jap.	34·18 N	139·28 E
67	Shields R. (shēldz) Mont.	45·54 N	110·40 W
110	Shifnal (shĭf'năl) Eng.	52·40 N	2·22 W
148	Shih (R.) (shē hŏ) China	32·09 N	114·11 E
148	Shihchiangchen (shē'kĭäng'zhen) China	32·16 N	120·59 E
149	Shihch'iao China (Canton In.)	22·56 N	113·22 E
148	Shihchiu Hu (L.) (shē'jĭō'hōō) China	31·29 N	119·07 E
	Shihkiachwang, see Shihmen		
151	Shihlung China	23·05 N	113·58 E
148	Shihmen (Shihkiachwang) (shē mēn) (shē'jĭä'zhōōäng) China	38·04 N	114·31 E
148	Shihohienfou China	31·27 N	117·51 E
144	Shihr Aden	14·45 N	49·32 E
149	Shiht'ou China (Canton In.)	23·01 N	113·23 E
148	Shihts'un (shē'chōōen) China	33·47 N	117·18 E
148	Shihtzu Shan (Mts.) (shē'jē shän) China	37·17 N	121·38 E
149	Shihwan China (Canton In.)	23·01 N	113·04 E
151	Shihwanta Shan (Mtns.) China	22·10 N	107·30 E
150	Shihwei Pk China	47·11 N	119·59 E
142	Shikarpur W. Pak.	27·51 N	68·52 E
153	Shiki (shē'kē) Jap. (Tōkyō In.)	35·50 N	139·35 E
153	Shikoku (I.) (shē'kō'kōō) Jap.	33·43 N	133·33 E
135	Shilka (R.) (shĭl'kȧ) Sov. Un.	53·00 N	118·45 E
142	Shilla (Mt.) India	37·18 N	78·17 E
142	Shillong (shēl-lông') India	25·39 N	91·58 E
74	Shiloh (shī'lō) Ill. (St. Louis In.)	38·34 N	89·54 W
153	Shimabara (shē'mä-bä'rä) Jap.	32·46 N	130·22 E
153	Shimada (shē'mä-dä) Jap.	34·49 N	138·13 E
153	Shimizu (shē'mē-zōō) Jap.	35·00 N	138·29 E
153	Shimminato (shēm'mē'nä-tô) Jap.	36·47 N	137·05 E
153	Shimoda (shē'mô-dä) Jap.	34·41 N	138·58 E
143	Shimoga India	13·59 N	75·38 E
153	Shimonoseki (shē'mô-nō-sĕ'kē) (shē-mô-nō'sĕ-kĭ) Jap.	33·58 N	130·55 E
153	Shimo-Saga (shē'mô sä'gä) Jap. (Ōsaka In.)	35·01 N	135·41 E
116	Shin, Loch (L.) (lŏk shĭn) Scot.	58·08 N	4·20 W
153	Shinagawa-Wan (B.) (shē'nä-gä'wä wän) Jap. (Tōkyō In.)	35·37 N	139·49 E
153	Shinano-Gawa (Strm.) (shē-nä'nô gä'wä) Jap.	36·43 N	138·22 E
65	Shine (shīn) Wash. (Seattle In.)	47·52 N	122·40 W
153	Shingū (shĭn'gōō) Jap.	33·43 N	135·59 E
153	Shinji (L.) (shĭn'jē) Jap.	35·23 N	133·05 E
155	Shinko R. (shĭn'kō) Cen. Afr. Rep.	6·37 N	24·31 E
166	Shinyanga (shĭn-yäŋ'gä) Tan.	3·35 S	33·07 E
152	Shiono Misaki (C.) (shē-ô'nô mē'sä-kē) Jap.	33·20 N	136·10 E
94	Ship Channel Cay (I.) (shĭp chă-nĕl kē) Ba. Is.	24·50 N	76·50 W
110	Shipley (shĭp'lē) Eng.	53·50 N	1·47 W
82	Shippegan Can.	47·44 N	64·45 W
82	Shippegan (I.) Can.	47·50 N	64·38 W
81	Shippenburg (shĭp'ĕn bûrg) Pa.	40·00 N	77·30 W
82	Shipshaw (R.) (shĭp'shô) Can.	48·50 N	71·03 W
139	Shiqma (R.) Isr. (Palestine In.)	31·31 N	34·40 E
153	Shirane-san (Mtn.) (shē'rä'nā-sän') Jap.	35·44 N	138·14 E
152	Shira Saki (C.) (shē'rä sä'kē) Jap.	41·25 N	142·10 E
166	Shirati (shē-rä'tē) Tan.	1·15 S	34·02 E
144	Shiraz (shē-räz') Iran	29·32 N	52·27 E
166	Shire (R.) (shē'rȧ) Fed. of Rh. & Nya.	15·10 S	34·58 E
129	Shirokoye (shē'rô-kô-yĕ) Sov. Un.	47·40 N	33·18 E
142	Shirpuri India	25·31 N	77·46 E
64	Shishaldin Vol. (shī-shăl'dĭn) Alaska	54·48 N	164·00 W
75	Shively (shīv'lē) Ky. (Louisville In.)	38·11 N	85·47 W
139	Shivta Isr. (Palestine In.)	30·53 N	34·38 E
69	Shivwits (Shebit) Ind. Res. (shĭv'wĭts) (shē'bĭt) Utah	37·10 N	113·50 W
69	Shivwits Plat Ariz.	36·13 N	113·42 W
83	Shirley (shûr'lē) Mass. (Boston In.)	42·33 N	71·39 W
153	Shizuki (shē'zōō-kē) Jap.	34·29 N	134·51 E
153	Shizuoka (shē'zōō'ōkȧ) Jap.	34·58 N	138·24 E
128	Shklov (shklôf) Sov. Un.	54·11 N	30·23 E
127	Shkodër (Scutari) (shkô'dûr) (skōō'tȧrē) Alb.	42·04 N	19·30 E
152	Shkotovo (shkô'tô-vô) Sov. Un.	43·15 N	132·21 E
73	Shoal Cr. (shōl) Ill.	38·37 N	89·25 W
80	Shoals (shōlz) Ind.	38·40 N	86·45 W
142	Shoapur India	25·53 N	76·45 E
153	Shodo (I.) (shō'dō) Jap.	34·27 N	134·27 E
143	Sholāpur (shō'lä-pōōr) India	17·42 N	75·51 E
139	Shoniron Jordan (Palestine In.)	32·18 N	35·14 E
75	Shorewood (shōr'wŏŏd) Wis. (Milwaukee In.)	43·05 N	77·54 W
67	Shoshone (shô-shōn'ē) Idaho	42·56 N	114·24 W
67	Shoshone L Wyo.	44·17 N	110·50 W
67	Shoshone R Wyo.	44·20 N	109·28 W
129	Shostka (shôst'kȧ) Sov. Un.	51·51 N	33·31 E
148	Sh'ouchang (shō'zhäng) China	35·59 N	115·52 E
148	Shouhsien China	32·36 N	116·45 E
148	Shoukuang (shō'gōōäng) China	36·53 N	118·45 E
129	Shpola (shpô'lȧ) Sov. Un.	49·01 N	31·36 E
77	Shreveport (shrēv'pôrt) La.	32·30 N	93·46 W
110	Shrewsbury (shrōōz'bēr-ĭ) Eng.	52·43 N	2·44 W
83	Shrewsbury Mass. (Boston In.)	42·18 N	71·43 W
110	Shropshire (Co.) (shrŏp'shēr) Eng.	52·36 N	2·45 W
94	Shroud Cay (I.) (shroud) Ba. Is.	24·20 N	76·40 W
150	Shuangch'eng China	45·18 N	126·18 E
148	Shuangho (shōōäng hŏ) China	31·33 N	116·48 E
148	Shuanglunho (shōōäng'lōōĕn'hŏ) China	31·50 N	115·07 E
150	Shuangyang China	43·28 N	125·45 E
71	Shullsburg (shŭlz'bûrg) Wis.	42·35 N	90·16 W
148	Shulyehehen (shōōlĭĕhŭhĕn) China	36·08 N	114·07 E
64	Shumagin (Is.) (shōō'mȧ-gēn) Alaska	55·22 N	159·20 W
151	Shunan (shōō'nän') China	29·38 N	119·00 E
64	Shungnak (shŭng'nȧk) Alaska	66·55 N	157·20 W
150	Shuni (shōōn'yĭ') China (Peking In.)	40·09 N	116·38 E
146	Shunning (shŭ'nĭng') China	24·34 N	99·49 E
149	Shunte China (Canton In.)	22·50 N	113·15 E
136	Shunut, 'Gora (Mt.) (gȧ-rä shōō'nōōt) Sov. Un. (Urals In.)	56·33 N	59·45 E
144	Shuqrah Aden	13·32 N	46·02 E
144	Shūrāb (R.) (shōō räb) Iran	31·02 N	55·43 E
152	Shuri (shōō'rē) Jap.	26·10 N	127·48 E
133	Shur R. (shōōr) Iran	35·40 N	50·10 E
144	Shūstar (shōōsh'tŭr) Iran	31·50 N	48·46 E
128	Shuya (shōō'yȧ) Sov. Un.	56·52 N	41·23 E
148	Shuyang (shōō yäng) China	34·09 N	118·47 E
145	Shweba Bur.	22·23 N	96·13 E
	Shyaulyay, see Šiauliai		
152	Siakin (L.) (sĭä'jĭn) China	42·25 N	132·45 E
139	Siak Ketjil (R.) Indon. (Singapore In.)	1·01 N	101·45 E
139	Siak Sri Indrapura (sē-äks'rĭ ēn'drȧ-pōō'rä) Indon. (Singapore In.)	0·48 N	102·05 E
142	Sialkot (sē-äl'kōt) W. Pak.	32·39 N	74·30 E
	Siam, see Thailand		
154	Siam, G. of (sī-ăm') Thai.	11·37 N	100·46 E
150	Sian (Hsian) (syän') China	34·20 N	109·00 E
148	Siaowu Shan (Mts.) (sĭou'wōō shän) China	39·48 N	114·52 E
127	Siátista (syä'tĭs-ta) Grc.	40·15 N	21·32 E
155	Siau (I.) Indon.	2·40 N	126·00 E
119	Šiauliai (Shyaulyay) (shē-ou'lē-ī) Sov. Un.	55·57 N	23·19 E
136	Sibay (sē'bȧy) Sov. Un. (Urals In.)	52·41 N	58·40 E
126	Šibenik (shē-bā'nēk) Yugo.	43·44 N	15·55 E
138	Siberia (Reg.) Asia	57·00 N	97·00 E
154	Siberut (I.) (sē'bȧ-rōōt) Indon.	1·22 S	99·45 E
142	Sibi W. Pak.	29·41 N	67·52 E
166	Sibiti (sē-bē-tē') Con. B.	3·35 S	13·10 E
127	Sibiu (sē-bĭ-ōō') Rom.	45·47 N	24·09 E
70	Sibley (sĭb'lē) Iowa	43·24 N	95·33 W
154	Sibolga (sē-bō'gä) Indon.	1·45 N	98·45 E
145	Sibsagar (sēb-sŭ'gŭr) India	26·47 N	94·45 E
154	Sibuti Phil.	4·40 N	119·30 E
155	Sibuyan (I.) (sē-bōō-yän') Phil. (Manila In.)	12·19 N	122·25 E
154	Sibuyan Sea Phil.	12·43 N	122·38 E
154	Sicapoo (Mtn.) (sē-kȧ-pōō') Phil.	18·05 N	121·03 E
113	Sicily (I.) (sĭs'ĭ-lē) It.	37·38 N	13·30 E
92	Sico R. (sē'kô) Hond.	15·32 N	85·42 W
98	Sicuaní (sē-kwä'nē) Peru	14·12 S	71·12 W
165	Sidamo (Prov.) (sē-dä'mô) Eth.	5·08 N	37·45 E
126	Siderno Marina (sē-dĕr'nô mä-rē'nä) It.	38·18 N	16·19 E
126	Sídheros, Akr. (C.) Grc. (Inset)	35·19 N	26·20 E
127	Sidhiró Kastron Grc.	41·13 N	23·27 E
125	Sidi-Aïsa Alg.	35·53 N	3·44 E
165	Sīdī Barrānī U. A. R.	31·41 N	26·09 E
164	Sidi-bel Abbès (sē'dē-bĕl ȧ-bĕs') Alg.	35·15 N	0·43 W
164	Sidi Ifni (ēf'nē) Ifni	29·22 N	10·15 W
47	Sidley, Mt. (sĭd'lē) Ant.	77·25 S	129·00 W
67	Sidney (sĭd'nē) Mont.	47·43 N	104·07 W
70	Sidney Nebr.	41·10 N	103·00 W
80	Sidney Ohio	40·20 N	84·10 W
78	Sidney Lanier, L. (lăn'yēr) Ga.	34·27 N	83·56 W
	Sidon, see Sayda		
121	Siedlce (syĕd'l-tsĕ) Pol.	52·09 N	22·20 E
123	Siegburg (zĕg'bōōrgh) Ger. (Ruhr In.)	50·48 N	7·13 E
123	Siegen (zē'ghĕn) Ger. (Ruhr In.)	50·52 N	8·01 E
111	Sieghartskirchen Aus. (Wien In.)	48·16 N	16·00 E
120	Sieg R. (zēg) Ger.	50·51 N	7·53 E
121	Siemiatycze (syĕm'yȧ'tē-chĕ) Pol.	52·26 N	22·52 E
154	Siem Reap (syĕm'rä'äp) Camb.	13·32 N	103·54 E
126	Siena (sē-ĕn'ä) It.	43·19 N	11·21 E
121	Sieradz (syĕ'rädz) Pol.	51·35 N	18·45 E
124	Siero (syä'rō) Sp.	43·24 N	5·39 W
121	Sierpc (syĕrpts) Pol.	52·51 N	19·42 E
76	Sierra Blanca (sē-ĕ'rȧ blaŋ-kȧ) Tex.	31·10 N	105·20 W
69	Sierra Blanca Pk. (blăn'kȧ) N. Mex.	33·25 N	105·50 W
163	Sierra Leone (sē-ĕr'rä lā-ō'nȧ) Afr.	8·48 N	12·30 W
74	Sierra Madre (mă'drē) Calif. (Los Angeles In.)	34·10 N	118·03 W
76	Sierra Mojada (sē-ĕ'r-rä-mô-ĸä'dä) Mex.	27·22 N	103·42 W
127	Sífnos (I.) Grc.	36·58 N	24·30 E
118	Sigdal (sēgh'däl) Nor.	60·01 N	9·35 E
122	Sigean (sē-zhōɴ') Fr.	43·02 N	2·56 E
71	Sigeurney (sē-gûr-nĭ) Iowa	41·16 N	92·10 W
121	Sighet (sē-gāt') Rom.	47·57 N	23·55 E
121	Sighisoara (sē-gē-shwä'rȧ) Rom.	46·11 N	24·48 E
112	Siglufjördhur Ice.	66·06 N	18·45 W
133	Signakhi Sov. Un.	41·45 N	45·50 E
74	Signal Hill (sĭg'nȧl hĭl) Calif. (Los Angeles In.)	33·48 N	118·11 W
98	Sigsig (sēg-sēg') Ec.	3·05 S	78·44 W
118	Sigtuna (sēgh-tōō'nȧ) Swe.	59·40 N	17·39 E
94	Siguanea, Ensenada de la (B.) (ĕn-sĕ-nä-dä-dĕ-lä-sē-gwä-nā'ä) Cuba	21·45 N	83·15 W
92	Siguatepeque (sē-gwä'tĕ-pĕ-kĕ) Hond.	14·33 N	87·51 W
124	Sigüenza (sē-gwĕ'n-zä) Sp.	41·03 N	2·38 W
164	Siguiri (sē-gē-rē') Gui.	11·30 N	9·04 W
133	Siirt (sĭ-ērt') Tur.	38·00 N	42·00 E
164	Sikasso (sē-käs'sō) Mali	11·15 N	5·43 W
73	Sikeston (sīks'tŭn) Mo.	36·50 N	89·35 W
135	Sikhote Alin', Khrebet (Mts.) (se-ĸô'ta a-lēn') Sov. Un.	45·00 N	135·45 E
127	Sikinos (I.) (sĭ'kĭ-nōs) Grc.	36·45 N	24·55 E
142	Sikkim Asia	27·42 N	88·25 E
121	Siklós (sĭ'klōsh) Hung.	45·51 N	18·18 E
124	Sil (R.) (sē'l) Sp.	42·20 N	7·13 W
155	Silang (sē-läng') Phil. (Manila In.)	14·14 N	120·58 E
90	Silao (sē-lä'ō) Mex.	20·56 N	101·25 W
142	Silchar (sĭl-chär') India	24·52 N	92·50 E
168	Silent Valley (sī'lĕnt vă'lē) S. Afr. (Johannesburg & Pretoria In.)	24·32 S	26·40 E
79	Siler City (sī'lēr) N. C.	35·45 N	79·29 W
121	Silesia (Reg.) (sĭ-lē'shȧ) Pol.	50·58 N	16·53 E
133	Silifke Tur.	36·20 N	34·00 E
115	Silistra (sē-lēs'trȧ) Bul.	44·01 N	27·13 E
118	Siljan (sēl'yän) Swe.	60·48 N	14·28 E
118	Silkeborg (sĭl'kĕ-bôr') Den.	56·10 N	9·33 E
85	Sillery (sĭl'-re') Can. (Quebec In.)	46·46 N	71·15 W
73	Siloam Springs (sĭ-lōm) Ark.	36·10 N	94·32 W
90	Silocayoápan (sē-lō-kä-yô-ä'pän) Mex.	17·29 N	98·09 W
77	Silsbee (sĭlz' bē) Tex.	30·19 N	94·09 W
119	Šilutė (shĭ-lōō'tā) Sov. Un.	55·23 N	21·26 E
101	Silva Jardim (sē'l-vä-zhär-dēɴ) Braz. (Rio de Janeiro In.)	22·40 S	42·24 W
65	Silvana (sĭl-văn'ȧ) Wash. (Seattle In.)	48·12 N	122·16 W
99	Silvânia (sēl-vä'nyä) Braz.	16·43 S	48·33 W
166	Silva Porto (sĭl'vȧ pôr'tōō) Ang.	12·20 S	17·05 E
73	Silver (L.) Mo.	39·38 N	93·12 W
74	Silverado (sĭl-vēr-ä'dō) Calif. (Los Angeles In.)	33·45 N	117·40 W
95	Silver Bk Ba. Is.	20·40 N	69·40 W
95	Silver Bank Passage (Str.) Ba. Is.	20·40 N	70·20 W
71	Silver Bay Minn.	47·24 N	91.07 W
69	Silver City (sĭl'vēr sĭ'tĭ) N. Mex.	32·45 N	108·20 W
93	Silver City Pan.	9·20 N	79·54 W
81	Silver Creek (crēk) N. Y.	42·35 N	79·10 W
69	Silver Cr Ariz.	34·30 N	110·05 W
75	Silver Cr Ind. (Louisville In.)	38·20 N	85·45 W
75	Silver Cr., Muddy Fk. Ind. (Louisville In.)	38·26 N	85·52 W
65	Silverdale (sĭl'vēr-dāl) Wash. (Seattle In.)	49·39 N	122·42 W
75	Silver Lake (lāk) Wis. (Milwaukee In.)	42·33 N	88·10 W
75	Silver L Wis. (Milwaukee In.)	42·35 N	88·08 W
81	Silver Spring (sprĭng) Md.	39·00 N	77·00 W
65	Silver Star Mtn. Wash. (Portland In.)	45·45 N	122·15 W
69	Silverton (sĭl'vēr-tŭn) Colo.	37·50 N	107·40 W
75	Silverton Ohio (Cincinnati In.)	39·12 N	84·24 W
66	Silverton Ore.	45·02 N	122·46 W
167	Silverton S. Afr. (Johannesburg & Pretoria In.)	25·45 S	28·13 E
124	Silves (sēl'vĕzh) Port.	37·15 N	8·24 W
66	Silvies R. (sĭl'vēz) Ore.	43·44 N	119·15 W
168	Silwá (Baḥrī) U. A. R. (Nile In.)	24·43 N	32·58 E
136	Sim (sĭm) Sov. Un. (Urals In.)	55·00 N	57·42 E
80	Simcoe (sĭm'kō) Can.	42·50 N	80·20 W
81	Simcoe (L.) Can.	44·30 N	79·20 W
154	Simeuloee (I.) Indon.	2·27 N	95·30 E
129	Simferopol' (Akmechet) (sēm-fĕ-rô'pôl') (ȧk-mĕch'ĕt) Sov. Un.	44·58 N	34·04 E
115	Simi (I.) Grc.	36·27 N	27·41 E
65	Similk Beach (sē'mĭlk) Wash. (Seattle In.)	48·27 N	122·35 W
142	Simla (sĭm'lȧ) India	31·09 N	77·15 E
121	Simleul-Silvaniei (shēm-lā'ōōl-sēl-vä'nyĕ-ē) Rom.	47·14 N	22·46 E
94	Simms Pt Ba. Is.	25·00 N	77·40 W
91	Simojovel (sē-mō-hō-vĕl') Mex.	17·12 N	92·43 W
119	Simola (sē'mô-lȧ) Fin.	60·55 N	28·06 E
101	Simonésia (sē-mô-nĕ'syä) Braz. (Rio de Janeiro In.)	20·04 S	41·53 W
166	Simonstad (sī-mŏn-shtät') S. Afr. (Cape Town In.)	34·11 S	18·25 E
120	Simplon P. (sĭm'plŏn) (săɴ-plôɴ') Switz.	46·13 N	7·53 E
120	Simplon Tun It.-Switz.	46·16 N	8·20 E
71	Simpson (I.) Can.	48·43 N	87·44 W
158	Simpson Des. (sĭmp-sŭn) Austl.	24·40 S	136·40 E
86	Simpson Pen Can.	68·58 N	89·20 W
118	Simrishamn (sēm'rēs-häm'n) Swe.	55·35 N	14·19 E
136	Sim R Sov. Un. (Urals In.)	55·00 N	57·42 E
77	Sims Bay, (sĭmz bī-yōō') Tex. (In.)	29·37 N	95·23 W
135	Simushir (I.) (se-mōō'shēr) Sov. Un.	47·15 N	150·47 E
127	Sinaia (sĭ-nä'yȧ) Rom.	45·20 N	25·30 E
165	Sinai Pen. (sī'nī) U. A. R.	29·24 N	33·29 E
155	Sinait (sē-nä'ēt) Phil. (Manila In.)	15·54 N	120·28 E
88	Sinaloa (State) (sē-nä-lō-ä) Mex.	25·15 N	107·45 W
152	Sinanju (sĭ'nän-jōō') Kor.	39·39 N	125·41 E
133	Sinap Tur.	42·00 N	35·05 E
98	Sincé (sēn'sā) Col.	9·15 N	75·14 W
98	Sincelejo (sēn-sȧ-lā'hō) Col.	9·12 N	75·30 W
65	Sinclair Inlet (sĭn-klâr') Wash. (Seattle In.)	47·31 N	122·41 W
119	Sindi (sēn'dē) Sov. Un.	58·20 N	24·40 E
129	Sinel'nikovo (sē'nyĕl-nē'kô'vô) Sov. Un.	49·19 N	35·33 E
124	Sines (sē'nāzh) Port.	37·57 N	8·50 W
165	Singa (sĭŋ'gȧ) Sud.	13·09 N	33·52 E
139	Singapore (sĭn'gȧ-pōr') Singapore I. (Singapore In.)	1·18 N	103·52 E
139	Singapore I. Asia (Singapore In.)	1·22 N	103·45 E
139	Singapore Str. Indon. (Singapore In.)	1·14 N	104·20 E
154	Singaradjac (sĭŋ'gȧ-rä'jä) Indon.	8·15 S	115·03 E
127	Singitikós Kólpos (G.) Grc.	40·15 N	24·00 E
146	Singu (sĭn'gŭ) Bur.	22·37 N	96·04 E
167	Singunyane (R.) Bas. (Natal In.)	29·35 S	28·08 E

ng-sing; ŋ-baŋk; ɴ-nasalized n; nŏd; cŏmmit; ōld; ôbey; ôrder; fōōd; fŏŏt; ou-out; s-soft; sh-dish; th-thin; pūre; ůnite; ûrn; stŭd; circŭs; ü-as "y" in study; '-indeterminate vowel.

268 Siniye–Solomon PRONOUNCING INDEX

Page	Name Pronunciation Region	Lat. °'	Long. °'
129	Siniye Lipyagi (sĕn'ê-ĕ lĕp'yä-gê) Sov. Un.	51·24 N	38·29 E
126	Sinj (sēn') Yugo.	43·42 N	16·39 E
146	Sinkiang Uighur (Aut. Reg.) China	40·15 N	82·15 E
136	Sin'kovo (sĭn-kô'vô) Sov. Un. (Moskva In.)	56·23 N	37·19 E
99	Sinnamary Fr. Gu.	5·15 N	57·52 W
126	Sinni (R.) (sēn'nē) It.	40·05 N	16·15 E
168	Sinnūris U. A. R. (Nile In.)	29·25 N	30·52 E
100	Sino, Pedra do (Mtn.) (pĕ'drä-dô-sē'nô) Braz. (In.)	22·27 S	43·02 W
166	Sinoia (sĭ-noi'ȧ) Fed. of Rh. & Nya.	17·17 S	30·09 E
111	Sint Niklaas Bel. (Bruxelles In.)	51·10 N	4·07 E
77	Sinton (sĭn'tŭn) Tex.	28·03 N	97·30 W
125	Sintra (sēn'trȧ) Port. (Lisboa In.)	38·48 N	9·23 W
111	Sint Truiden Bel. (Bruxelles In.)	50·49 N	5·14 E
152	Sinŭiju (sĭ'nŏŏĭ-jōō) Kor.	40·04 N	124·33 E
136	Sinyavino (sĭn-yä'vĭ-nô) Sov. Un. (Leningrad In.)	59·50 N	31·07 E
128	Sinyaya (R.) (sēn'yȧ-yȧ) Sov. Un.	56·40 N	28·20 E
129	Sinyukha (R.) (sē'nyōō-ĸȧ) Sov. Un.	48·34 N	30·49 E
120	Sion (sē'ôN') Switz.	46·15 N	7·17 E
70	Sioux City (sōō) Iowa	42·30 N	96·25 W
70	Sioux Falls (fôlz) S. D.	43·33 N	96·43 W
87	Sioux Lookout Can.	50·11 N	91·42 W
98	Sipí (sē-pê') Col. (In.)	4·39 N	76·38 W
86	Sipiwesk Can.	55·36 N	97·24 W
78	Sipsey (R.) (sĭp'sê) Ala.	33·26 N	87·42 W
154	Sipura (I.) Indon.	2·15 S	99·33 E
90	Siqueros (sê-kā'rōs) Mex.	23·19 N	106·14 W
93	Siquia, R. (sê-kē'ä) Nic.	12·23 N	84·36 W
113	Siracusa (sē-rä-koo'sä) It.	37·02 N	15·19 E
142	Sirajganj E. Pak.	24·32 N	89·43 E
92	Sirama (sē-rä-mä) Sal.	13·23 N	87·55 W
158	Sir Edward Pellew Group (Is.) (pĕl'ū) Austl.	15·15 S	137·15 E
121	Siretul R. Rom.	46·10 N	27·18 E
144	Sirham, Wadi (R.) Sau. Ar.	31·02 N	37·16 E
127	Síros (Ermoúpolis) Grc.	37·30 N	24·56 E
127	Síros (I.) Grc.	37·23 N	24·55 E
142	Sirsa India	29·39 N	75·02 E
118	Širvintos (shēr'vĭn-tôs) Sov. Un.	55·02 N	24·59 E
91	Sisal (sê-säl') Mex.	21·09 N	90·03 W
126	Siska (sē'sȧk) Yugo.	45·29 N	16·20 E
68	Sisquoc (R.) (sĭs'kwŏk) Calif.	34·47 N	120·13 W
70	Sisseton (sĭs'tŭn) S. D.	45·39 N	97·04 W
144	Sistān, Daryacheh-ye (L.) Iran-Afg.	31·45 N	61·15 E
123	Sisteron (sēst'rôN') Fr.	44·10 N	5·55 E
80	Sisterville (sĭs'tēr-vĭl) W. Va.	39·30 N	81·00 W
126	Sitía (sē'tĭ-ȧ) Grc. (In.)	26·10 N	35·09 E
64	Sitka (sĭt'kȧ) Alaska	57·08 N	135·18 W
64	Sitka Natl. Mon. Alaska	57·20 N	136·10 W
110	Sittingbourne (sĭt-ĭng-bôrn) Eng. (London In.)	51·20 N	0·44 E
133	Sivas (sē'väs) Tur.	39·50 N	36·50 E
129	Sivash (L.) (sē'vȧsh) Sov. Un.	45·55 N	34·42 E
133	Siverek (sē'vĕ-rĕk) Tur.	37·50 N	39·20 E
119	Siverskaya (sē'vĕr-skȧ-yȧ) Sov. Un.	59·17 N	30·03 E
165	Sīwah (Oasis) (sē'wä) U. A. R.	29·33 N	25·11 E
93	Sixaola R. (sē-kä-ō'lä) (sĕk-sȧ-ō'lä) C. R.	9·31 N	83·07 W
165	Sixth Cataract Sud.	16·26 N	32·44 E
118	Sjaelland (I.) (shĕl'lăn') Den.	55·34 N	11·35 E
127	Sjenica (syĕ'nē-tsȧ) Yugo.	43·15 N	20·02 E
129	Skadovsk (skä'dôfsk) Sov. Un.	46·08 N	32·54 E
118	Skagen (skä'ghĕn) Den.	57·43 N	10·32 E
118	Skagen (Pt.) Den.	57·43 N	10·31 E
118	Skagerrak (Str.) (skä-ghĕ-räk') Eur.	57·43 N	8·28 E
65	Skagit B. (skăg'ĭt) Wash. (Seattle In.)	48·20 N	122·32 W
66	Skagit R. Wash.	48·29 N	121·52 W
64	Skagway (skăg-wā) Alaska	59·30 N	135·28 W
118	Skälderviken (B.) Swe.	56·20 N	12·25 E
135	Skalistyy, Golets (Mtn.) Sov. Un.	57·28 N	119·48 E
65	Skamania (skȧ-mā'nĭ-ȧ) Wash. (Portland In.)	45·37 N	122·03 W
65	Skamokawa (skȧ-mā'nĭ-ȧ) Wash. (Portland In.)	46·16 N	123·27 W
118	Skanderborg (skän'ĕr-bôr') Den.	56·04 N	9·55 E
81	Skaneateles (skăn-ĕ-ăt'lĕs) N. Y.	42·55 N	76·25 W
81	Skaneateles (L.) N. Y.	42·50 N	76·20 W
118	Skänninge (shĕn'ĭng-ĕ) Swe.	58·24 N	15·02 E
118	Skanör (skän'ûr) Swe.	55·24 N	12·49 E
127	Skantzoúra (Is.) (skän'tsōō-rä) Grc.	39·03 N	24·05 E
118	Skara (skä'rȧ) Swe.	58·25 N	13·24 E
86	Skeena (R.) Can.	54·31 N	129·21 W
167	Skeerpoort S. Afr. (Johannesburg & Pretoria In.)	25·49 S	27·45 E
167	Skeerpoort (R.) S. Afr. (Johannesburg & Pretoria In.)	25·58 N	27·41 E
99	Skeldon (skĕl'dŭn) Br. Gu.	5·49 N	57·15 W
112	Skellefte (R.) (shĕl'ĕ-ftĕ) Swe.	65·18 N	19·08 E
112	Skellefteå (shĕl'ĕf-tĕ-ô') Swe.	64·47 N	20·48 E
118	Skern (R.) (skĕrn) Den.	55·56 N	8·52 E
116	Skerries (Is.) (skĕr'ēz) Wales	53·30 N	4·59 W
136	Skhodnya R. (skôd'nyȧ) Sov. Un. (Moskva In.)	55·55 N	37·16 E
127	Skíathos (I.) (skē'ȧ-thôs) Grc.	39·15 N	23·25 E
116	Skibbereen (skĭb'ēr-ēn) Ire.	51·32 N	9·25 W
77	Skidmore (skĭd'môr) Tex.	28·16 N	97·40 W
118	Skien (skē'ĕn) Nor.	59·13 N	9·35 E
121	Skierniewice (skyĕr-nyĕ-vēt'sĕ) Pol.	51·58 N	20·13 E
168	Skilpadfontein S. Afr. (Johannesburg & Pretoria In.)	25·02 S	28·50 E
127	Skíros Grc.	38·53 N	24·32 E
127	Skiros (I.) Grc.	38·50 N	24·43 E
118	Skive (skē'vĕ) Den.	56·34 N	8·56 E
112	Skjalfandá (R.) (skyäl'fänd-ô) Ice.	65·24 N	16·40 W
112	Skjerstad (skyĕr-städ) Nor.	67·12 N	15·37 E
126	Škofja Loka (shkôf'yȧ lō'kȧ) Yugo.	46·10 N	14·20 E
75	Skokie (skō'kê) Ill. (Chicago In.)	42·02 N	87·45 W
65	Skokomish Ind. Res. (skŏ-kō'mĭsh) Wash. (Seattle In.)	47·22 N	123·07 W
121	Skole (skô'lĕ) Sov. Un.	49·03 N	23·32 E
127	Skópelos (I.) (skô'pȧ-lôs) Grc.	39·04 N	23·31 E
128	Skopin (skô'pēn) Sov. Un.	53·49 N	39·35 E
127	Skoplje (skôp'lyĕ) Yugo.	42·02 N	21·26 E
118	Skövde (shûv'dĕ) Swe.	58·25 N	13·48 E
135	Skovorodino (skô'vô-rô'dĭ-nô) Sov. Un.	53·53 N	123·56 E
82	Skowhegan (skou-hē'gȧn) Maine	44·45 N	69·27 W
126	Skradin (skrä'dēn) Yugo.	43·49 N	17·58 E
118	Skreia (skrā'ȧ) Nor.	60·40 N	10·55 E
118	Skudeneshavn (skōō'dĕ-nes-houn') Nor.	59·10 N	5·19 E
118	Skulerud (skōō'lĕ-rōōdh) Nor.	59·40 N	11·30 E
69	Skull Valley Ind. Res. (skŭl) Utah	40·25 N	112·50 W
78	Skuna, (R.) (skû'nȧ) Miss.	33·57 N	89·36 W
71	Skunk (R.) (skŭnk) Iowa	41·12 N	92·14 W
119	Skuodas (skwô'dȧs) Sov. Un.	56·16 N	21·32 E
118	Skurup (skû'rōōp) Swe.	55·29 N	13·27 E
129	Skvira (skvē'rȧ) Sov. Un.	49·43 N	29·41 E
100	Skvring, Seno (B.) (sĕ'nô-s-krĕ'ng) Chile	52·35 S	72·30 W
120	Skwierzyna (skvê-ĕr'zhĭ-nȧ) Pol.	52·35 N	15·30 E
116	Skye (I.) (skī) Scot.	57·25 N	6·17 W
65	Skykomish (R.) (skī'kō-mĭsh) Wash. (Seattle In.)	47·50 N	121·55 W
118	Slagese Den.	55·25 N	11·19 E
154	Slamet, Gunung (Mtn.) (slä'mĕt) Indon.	7·15 S	109·15 E
127	Slanic (slŭ'nĕk) Rom.	45·13 N	25·56 E
71	Slate (I.) (slāt) Can.	48·38 N	87·14 W
73	Slater (slāt'ēr) Mo.	39·13 N	93·03 W
127	Slatina (slä'tē-nä) Rom.	44·26 N	24·21 E
72	Slaton (slā'tŭn) Tex.	33·26 N	101·38 W
86	Slave (R.) (slāv) Can.	59·40 N	111·21 W
134	Slavgorod (slȧf'gô-rôt) Sov. Un.	52·58 N	78·43 E
127	Slavonija (Reg.) (slä-vô'nê-yä) Yugo.	45·29 N	17·31 E
126	Slavonska Požega (slä-vôn'skä pô'zhĕ-gä) Yugo.	45·18 N	17·42 E
127	Slavonski Brod (slä-vôn'skê brôd) Yugo.	45·10 N	18·01 E
129	Slavuta (slȧ-vōō'tȧ) Sov. Un.	50·18 N	27·01 E
129	Slavyansk (slȧv'yänsk') Sov. Un.	48·52 N	37·34 E
129	Slavyanskaya (slȧv-yȧn'skȧ-yȧ) Sov. Un.	45·14 N	38·09 E
70	Slayton (slā'tŭn) Minn.	44·00 N	95·44 W
110	Sleaford (slē'fērd) Eng.	53·00 N	0·25 W
71	Sleepy Eye (slēp'ĭ ī) Minn.	44·17 N	94·44 W
77	Slidell (slĭ-dĕl') La.	30·17 N	89·47 W
111	Sliedrecht Neth. (Amsterdam In.)	51·49 N	4·46 E
116	Sligo (slī'gō) Ire.	54·17 N	8·19 W
118	Slite (slē'tĕ) Swe.	57·41 N	18·47 E
127	Sliven (slē'vĕn) Bul.	42·41 N	26·20 E
84	Sloatsburg (slōts'bûrg) N. Y. (New York In.)	41·09 N	74·11 W
119	Slobodka (slô'bôd-kȧ) Sov. Un.	54·34 N	26·12 E
132	Slobodskoy (slô'bôt-skoi) Sov. Un.	58·48 N	50·02 E
119	Sloka (slô'kȧ) Sov. Un.	56·57 N	23·37 E
121	Slonim (swō'nĕm) Sov. Un.	53·05 N	25·19 E
110	Slough (slou) Eng. (London In.)	51·29 N	0·36 W
	Slovakia, see Slovensko		
126	Slovenija (Reg.) (slô-vĕ'nê-yä) Yugo.	45·58 N	14·43 E
121	Slovensko (Slovakia) (Prov.) (slô-vĕn'skô) (slô-vȧk'ĭ-ȧ) Czech.	48·40 N	19·00 E
121	Sluch' (R.) Sov. Un.	50·56 N	26·48 E
126	Sluderno (slōō-dĕr'nô) It.	46·38 N	10·37 E
126	Slunj (slōōn') Yugo.	45·08 N	15·46 E
121	Slupsk (swōōpsk) Pol.	54·28 N	17·02 E
128	Slutsk (slōōtsk) Sov. Un.	53·02 N	27·34 E
116	Slyne Head (slīn) Ire.	53·25 N	10·05 W
73	Smackover (smăk'ô-vēr) Ark.	33·22 N	92·42 W
127	Smederevo (Semendria) (smĕ'dĕ-rĕ-vô) (sĕ-mĕn'drĭ-ȧ) Yugo.	44·39 N	20·54 E
127	Smederevska Palanka (smĕ-dĕ-rĕv'skä pä-län'kä) Yugo.	44·21 N	21·00 E
118	Smedjebacken (smĭ'tyĕ-bä-kĕn) Swe.	60·09 N	15·19 E
129	Smela (smyä'lȧ) Sov. Un.	49·14 N	31·52 E
129	Smeloye (smyä'lô-ĕ) Sov. Un.	50·55 N	33·36 E
81	Smethport (smĕth'pōrt) Pa.	41·50 N	78·25 W
128	Smiltene (smĕl'tĕ-nĕ) Sov. Un.	57·26 N	25·57 E
86	Smith (smĭth) Can.	55·10 N	113·53 W
65	Smith (I.) Wash. (Seattle In.)	48·20 N	122·53 W
72	Smith Center (sĕn'tēr) Kans.	39·45 N	98·46 W
86	Smithers (smĭth'ērs) Can.	54·13 N	127·22 W
79	Smithfield (smĭth'fēld) N. C.	35·30 N	78·21 W
74	Smithfield Tex. (Dallas, Fort Worth In.)	32·52 N	97·12 W
67	Smithfield Utah	41·50 N	111·49 W
80	Smithland (smĭth'lănd) Ky.	37·10 N	88·25 W
77	Smith Point Tex. (In.)	29·32 N	94·45 W
67	Smith R. Mont.	47·00 N	111·20 W
81	Smiths Falls (smĭths) Can.	44·55 N	76·05 W
83	Smith Sd. Can.	48·15 N	53·50 W
160	Smithton (smĭth'tŭn) Austl.	40·55 S	145·12 E
74	Smithton Ill. (St. Louis In.)	38·24 N	89·59 W
77	Smithville (smĭth'vĭl) Tex.	30·00 N	97·08 W
167	Smits (R.) S. Afr. (Natal In.)	31·45 S	26·33 E
166	Smitswinkel Flats S. Afr. (Cape Town In.)	34·16 S	18·25 E
68	Smoke Creek Des. (smōk crēk) Nev.	40·28 N	119·40 W
73	Smoky Hill (R.) (smōk'ĭ hĭl) Kans.	38·40 N	97·32 W
118	Smøla (I.) (smûlä) Nor.	63·16 N	7·40 E
128	Smolensk (smô-lyĕnsk') Sov. Un.	54·46 N	32·03 E
128	Smolensk (Oblast) Sov. Un.	55·00 N	32·18 E
127	Smyadovo Bul.	43·04 N	27·00 E
81	Smyrna (smûr'nȧ) Del.	39·20 N	75·35 W
84	Smyrna Ga. (Atlanta In.)	33·53 N	84·31 W
	Smyrna, see Izmir		
64	Snag (snăg) Can.	62·18 N	140·30 W
71	Snake (R.) (snāk) Minn.	45·58 N	93·20 W
69	Snake Ra. Nev.	39·20 N	114·15 W
67	Snake R., Henrys Fork Idaho	43·52 N	111·55 W
66	Snake R. Wash.	46·33 N	118·18 W
66	Snake River Pln. (rĭv'ēr) Idaho	43·08 N	114·46 W
94	Snap Pt. Ba. Is.	23·45 N	77·30 W
69	Sneffels Pk. (snĕf'ĕlz) Colo.	38·00 N	107·50 W
67	Snelby (snĕl'bē) Mont.	48·26 N	111·50 W
85	Snelgrove (snĕl'grōv) Can. (Toronto In.)	43·44 N	79·50 W
121	Sniardwy L. (snyärt'vĭ) Pol.	53·46 N	21·59 E
118	Snöhetta (Mtn.) (snû-hĕttä) Nor.	62·18 N	9·12 E
65	Snohomish (snô-hō'mĭsh) Wash. (Seattle In.)	47·55 N	122·05 W
65	Snohomish (R.) Wash. (Seattle In.)	47·53 N	122·04 W
65	Snoqualmie (snō qwäl'mē) Wash. (Seattle In.)	47·32 N	121·50 W
66	Snoqualmie R. Wash.	47·32 N	121·53 W
129	Snov (R.) (snôf) Sov. Un.	51·38 N	31·38 E
116	Snowdon, Mt. (snō'dŭn) Wales	53·05 N	4·04 W
81	Snow Hill (hĭl) Md.	38·15 N	75·20 W
159	Snowy Mts. (snō'ē) Austl.	36·17 S	148·30 E
72	Snyder (snī'dēr) Okla.	34·40 N	98·57 W
76	Snyder Tex.	32·48 N	100·53 W
110	Soar (R.) (sōr) Eng.	52·44 N	1·09 W
165	Sobat R. (sō'bȧt) Sud.	9·04 N	32·02 E
128	Sobinka (sô-bĭŋ'kȧ) Sov. Un.	55·59 N	40·02 E
153	Sobo-Zan (Mt.) (sô'bô zän) Jap.	32·47 N	131·27 E
99	Sobral (sô-brä'l) Braz.	3·39 S	40·16 W
121	Sochaczew (sô-ĸä'chĕf) Pol.	52·14 N	20·18 E
146	Soché (Yarkand) (sō'chĕ) (yär-känt') China	38·15 N	77·15 E
133	Sochi (sôch'ĭ) Sov. Un.	43·35 N	39·50 E
157	Society Is. (sô-sī'ĕ-tē) Fr. Polynesia	15·00 S	157·30 W
84	Socola (sô-kō'lȧ) La. (New Orleans In.)	29·32 N	89·46 W
91	Socoltenango (sô-kôl-tĕ-näŋ'gō) Mex.	16·17 N	92·20 W
101	Socorro (sŏ-kô'r-rō) Braz. (Rio de Janeiro In.)	22·35 S	46·32 W
98	Socorro (sô-kôr'rō) Col.	6·23 N	73·19 W
69	Socorro N. Mex.	34·05 N	106·55 W
168	Socotra I. (sô-kō'trȧ) Som. (Horn of Afr. In.)	13·00 N	52·30 E
124	Socuellamos (sō-kōō-āl'yä-mōs) Sp.	39·18 N	2·48 W
68	Soda (L.) (sō'dȧ) Calif.	35·12 N	116·25 W
65	Soda Pk. Wash. (Portland In.)	45·53 N	122·04 W
67	Soda Springs (sprĭngz) Idaho	42·39 N	111·37 W
118	Söderhamn (sû-dĕr-häm''n) Swe.	61·20 N	17·00 E
118	Söderköping Swe.	58·30 N	16·14 E
118	Södertälje (sû-dĕr-tĕl'yĕ) Swe.	59·12 N	17·35 E
150	Sodi Soruksum (Mtn.) China	37·20 N	102·00 E
165	Sodo Eth.	7·03 N	37·46 E
118	Södra Dellen (L.) Swe.	61·45 N	16·30 E
120	Soest (zōst) Ger.	51·35 N	8·05 E
	Sofia, see Sofiya		
127	Sofiya (Sofia) (sô'fê-yȧ) (sô'fê-ȧ) Bul.	42·43 N	23·20 E
129	Sofiyevka (sô-fē'yĕf-kȧ) Sov. Un.	48·03 N	33·53 E
153	Soga (sô'gä) Jap. (Tōkyō In.)	35·35 N	140·08 E
98	Sogamoso (sô-gä-mô'sō) Col.	5·42 N	72·51 W
118	Sogndal (sôghn'dȧl) Nor.	58·20 N	6·17 E
118	Sogndal Nor.	61·14 N	7·04 E
118	Sogne Fd. (sôgn'ĕ fyôrd) Nor.	61·09 N	5·30 E
128	Sogozha (R.) (sô'gô-zhȧ) Sov. Un.	58·35 N	39·08 E
122	Soissons (swä-sôN') Fr.	49·23 N	3·17 E
153	Sōka (sō'kä) Jap. (Tōkyō In.)	35·50 N	139·49 E
121	Sokal (sô'käl') Sov. Un.	50·28 N	24·20 E
133	Soke (sû'kĕ) Tur.	37·40 N	27·10 E
164	Sokodé (sô-kô-dā') Togo	8·56 N	1·08 E
121	Sokolka (sô-kōōl'kȧ) Pol.	53·23 N	23·30 E
164	Sokolo (sô-kô-lō') Mali	14·51 N	6·09 W
164	Sokoto (sō'kô-tō) Nig.	13·03 N	5·14 E
164	Sokoto (Reg.) Nig.	12·29 N	6·34 E
121	Sokotów Podlaski (sô-kô-wōōf' pŭd-lä'skĭ) Pol.	52·24 N	22·15 E
91	Sola de Vega (San Miguel) (sō'lä dā vā'gä) (sän mê-gāl') Mex.	16·31 N	96·58 W
155	Solana (sō-lä'nä) Phil. (Manila In.)	17·40 N	121·41 E
161	Solander, C. Austl. (Sydney In.)	34·03 S	151·16 E
155	Solano (sō-lä'nō) Phil. (Manila In.)	16·31 N	121·11 E
98	Soledad (sŏ-lĕ-dä'd) Col.	10·47 N	75·00 W
90	Soledad Díez Gutierrez (sô-lä-dhädh'dē'äz gōō-tyä'rĕz) Mex.	22·19 N	100·54 W
66	Soleduck R. (sōl'dŭk) Wash.	47·59 N	124·28 W
92	Solentiname, Islas de (Is.) (ē's-läs-dĕ-sô-lĕn-tē-nä'mȧ) Nic.	11·15 N	85·16 W
110	Solihull (sō'lĭ-hŭl) Eng.	52·25 N	1·46 W
136	Solikamsk (sô-lē-kȧmsk') Sov. Un. (Urals In.)	59·38 N	56·48 E
98	Solimões, Rio (R.) (rē'ô-sô-lē-mô'ĕs) Braz.	2·45 S	67·44 W
123	Solingen (zō'lĭng-ĕn) Ger. (Ruhr In.)	51·10 N	7·05 E
118	Sollefteå (sôl-lĕf'tĕ-ô) Swe.	63·06 N	17·17 E
125	Sóller (sō'lyĕr) Sp.	39·45 N	2·40 E
133	Sol'-lletsk Sov. Un.	51·10 N	55·05 E
122	Sologne (Reg.) (sō-lōn'yĕ) Fr.	47·36 N	1·53 E
92	Solola (sō-lō'lä) Guat.	14·45 N	91·12 W
159	Solomon Is. Prot. (sŏ'ô-mŭn) Oceania	8·50 S	157·52 E
156	Solomon Is. Oceania	7·00 S	148·00 E
72	Solomon R. Kans.	39·24 N	98·19 W
72	Solomon R., North Fk. Kans.	39·34 N	99·52 W
72	Solomon R., South Fk. Kans.	39·19 N	99·52 W

ăt; finăl; rāte; senāte; ärm; åsk; sofȧ; fâre; ch-choose; dh-as th in other; bē; ēvent; bĕt; recĕnt; cratēr; g-go; gh-guttural g; bĭt; ĭ-short neutral; rīde; ĸ-guttural k as ch in German ich;

Page	Name Pronunciation Region	Lat. °'	Long. °'
75	Solon (sō'lŭn) Ohio (Cleveland In.)	41·23 N	81·26 W
120	Solothurn (zō'lō-thōōrn) Switz.	47·13 N	7·30 E
132	Solov'etskiy (I.) Sov. Un.	65·10 N	35·40 E
126	Šolta (I.) (shôl'tä) Yugo.	43·20 N	16·15 E
144	Soltānābād Iran	28·06 N	55·24 E
120	Soltau (sōl'tou) Ger.	53·00 N	9·50 E
128	Sol'tsy (sôl'tsē) Sov. Un.	58·04 N	30·13 E
150	Solun (sô-lōōn') China	47·32 N	121·18 E
81	Solvay (sŏl'vā) N. Y.	43·05 N	76·10 W
118	Sölvesborg (sûl'vĕs-bôrg) Swe.	56·04 N	14·35 E
132	Sol'vychegodsk (sôl'vē-chĕ-gôtsk') Sov. Un.	61·18 N	46·58 E
116	Solway Firth (sŏl'wāfûrth') Eng.-Scot.	54·42 N	3·55 W
163	Somalia (sō-mä'lē-ȧ) Afr.	3·28 N	44·47 E
127	Sombor (sôm'bôr) Yugo.	45·45 N	19·10 E
90	Sombrerete (sōm-brå-rā'tå) Mex.	23·38 N	103·37 W
99	Sombrero, Cayo (C.) (kä-yô-sôm-brĕ'rô) Ven. (In.)	10·52 N	68·12 W
78	Somerset (sŭm'ēr-sĕt) Ky.	37·05 N	84·35 W
84	Somerset Mass. (Providence In.)	41·46 N	71·05 W
81	Somerset Pa.	40·00 N	79·05 W
74	Somerset Tex. (San Antonio In.)	29·13 N	98·39 W
67	Somerset-Oos S. Afr. (Natal In.)	32·44 S	25·36 E
82	Somersworth (sŭm'ērz-wûrth) N. H.	43·16 N	70·53 W
68	Somerton (sŭm'ēr-tŭn) Ariz.	32·36 N	114·43 W
83	Somerville (sŭm'ēr-vĭl) Mass. (Boston In.)	42·23 N	71·06 W
84	Somerville N.J. (New York In.)	40·34 N	74·37 W
78	Somerville Tenn.	35·14 N	89·21 W
77	Somerville Tex.	30·21 N	96·31 W
121	Somesul R. (sô-mȧ'shŏŏl) Rom.	47·43 N	23·09 E
125	Somma Vesuviana (sôm'mä vā-zōō-vē-ä'nä) It. (Napoli In.)	40·38 N	14·27 E
122	Somme (R.) (sŏm) Fr.	50·02 N	2·04 E
111	Sommerfeld (zō'mĕr-fĕld) Ger. (Berlin In.)	52·48 N	13·02 E
161	Sommerville Austl. (Melbourne In.)	38·14 S	145·10 E
92	Somoto (sô-mō'tō) Nic.	13·28 N	86·37 W
100	Somuncurá, Meseta de (Plat.) (mĕ-sĕ'tä-dĕ-sô-mōō'n-kōō-rä') Arg.	41·15 S	68·00 W
142	Son (R.) (sōn) India	24·40 N	82·35 E
93	Soná (sō'nä) Pan.	8·00 N	81·19 W
152	Sŏnchŏn (sŭn'shŭn) Kor.	39·49 N	124·56 E
118	Sönderborg (sûn''er-bôrgh) Den.	54·55 N	9·47 E
120	Sondershausen (zôn'dērz-hou'zĕn) Ger.	51·17 N	10·45 E
151	Song Ca (R.) Viet.	19·15 N	105·00 E
166	Songea (sôn-gā'ȧ) Tan.	10·39 S	35·44 E
152	Sŏngjin (sŭng'jĭn') Kor.	40·38 N	129·10 E
154	Songkhla (sông'klä') Thai.	7·09 N	100·34 E
120	Sonneberg (sôn'ē-bĕrgh) Ger.	50·20 N	11·14 E
68	Sonora (sō-nō'rȧ) Calif.	37·58 N	120·22 W
76	Sonora Tex.	30·33 N	100·38 W
88	Sonora (State) Mex.	29·45 N	111·15 W
88	Sonora (R.) Mex.	28·45 N	111·35 W
68	Sonora Pk. Calif.	38·22 N	119·39 W
124	Sonseca (sôn-sā'kä) Sp.	39·41 N	3·56 W
98	Sonsón (sôn-sôn') Col. (In.)	5·42 N	75·28 W
92	Sonsonate (sōn-sō-nä'tå) Sal.	13·46 N	89·43 W
155	Sonsorol Is. (sŏn-sô-rōl') Pac. Is. Trust Ter.	5·03 S	132·33 E
151	Son Tay (sôn tē') Viet.	21·00 N	105·35 E
148	Soochow (Wuhsien) (sōō'jō) (wōō'sĭän) China	31·19 N	120·37 E
65	Sooke Basin (sŏŏk) Can. (Seattle In.)	48·21 N	123·47 W
74	Soo Locks (sōō lŏks) U. S.-Can.	46·30 N	84·30 W
98	Sopetrán (sô-pĕ-trä'n) Col. (In.)	6·30 N	75·44 W
118	Sopot (sô'pôt) Pol.	54·26 N	18·25 E
120	Sopron (shŏp'rôn) Hung.	47·41 N	16·36 E
126	Sora (sô'rä) It.	41·43 N	13·37 E
118	Sör Aurdal (sûr äûr-däl) Nor.	60·54 N	9·24 E
124	Sorbas (sôr'bäs) Sp.	37·05 N	2·07 W
91	Sordo (R.) (sô'r-dō) Mex.	16·39 N	97·33 W
82	Sorel (sô-rĕl') Can.	46·01 N	73·07 W
160	Sorell, C. Austl.	42·10 S	144·50 E
126	Soresina (sō-rȧ-zē'nä) It.	45·17 N	9·51 E
124	Soria (sō'rē-ä) Sp.	41·46 N	2·28 W
101	Soriano (sŏ-rēä'nō) (Dept.) Ur. (Buenos Aires In.)	33·25 S	58·00 W
101	Sorocaba (sô-rô-kä'bȧ) Braz. (Rio de Janeiro In.)	23·29 S	47·27 W
129	Soroki (sŏ-rō'kē) Sov. Un.	48·09 N	28·17 E
155	Sorong (sō-rông') Neth. N. Gui.	1·15 S	131·30 E
128	Sorot' (R.) (sō-rō'tzh) Sov. Un.	57·08 N	29·23 E
165	Soroti (sō-rō'tē) Ug.	1·51 N	33·33 E
112	Söröy (I.) (sûr-ûē) Nor.	70·37 N	20·58 E
124	Sorraia (R.) (sôr-rī'ȧ) Port.	38·55 N	8·42 W
125	Sorrento (sôr-rĕn'tō) It. (Napoli In.)	40·23 N	14·23 E
155	Sorsogon (sôr-sōgōn') Phil.	12·51 N	124·02 E
119	Sortavala (sôr'tä-vä-lä) Sov. Un.	61·43 N	30·40 E
150	Sŏsan (sŭ'sän) Korea	36·40 N	126·25 E
129	Sosna (R.) (sôs'nä) Sov. Un.	50·33 N	38·15 E
129	Sosnitsa (sôs-nē'tså) Sov. Un.	51·30 N	32·29 E
134	Sosnogorsk Sov. Un.	63·13 N	54·09 E
121	Sosnowiec (sôs-nô'vyĕts) Pol.	50·17 N	19·10 E
152	Sosunova, Mys (Pt.) (mĭs sô'sŏŏ-nôf'ȧ) Sov. Un.	46·28 N	138·06 E
136	Sos'va R. (sôs'vȧ) Sov. Un. (Urals In.)	59·55 N	60·40 E
132	Sos'va (R.) (sôs'vȧ) Sov. Un.	63·10 N	63·30 E
90	Sota la Marina (sô-tä-lä-mä-rē'nä) Mex.	22·45 N	98·11 W
91	Soteapan (sō-tå-ä'pän) Mex.	18·14 N	94·51 W
90	Soto la Marina, Rio (R.) (rē'ō-sō'tō lä mä-rē'nä) Mex.	23·55 N	98·30 W
92	Sotuta (sô-tōō'tä) Mex. (Yucatan In.)	20·35 N	89·00 W
99	Soublette (sŏ-ōō-blĕ'tĕ) Ven. (In.)	9·55 N	66·06 W
126	Soúdhas, Kólpos (G.) Grc. (Inset)	35·33 N	24·22 E
115	Soueida Syr.	32·41 N	36·41 E
127	Souflion Grc.	41·12 N	26·17 E
93	Soufrière (sōō-frê-âr') W. I. F. (Le. & Wind. Is. In.)	13·50 N	61·03 W
93	Soufrière (Vol.) Guad. (Le. & Wind. Is. In.)	16·02 N	61·41 W
93	Soufrière Vol. W. I. F. (Le. & Wind. Is. In.)	16·43 N	62·10 W
113	Souk-Ahras (sōōk-ä-räs') Alg.	36·18 N	8·19 E
152	Sŏul (Seoul) Kor.	37·35 N	127·03 E
167	Sources, Mt. aux (môn'tō sōōrs') Bas. (Natal In.)	28·47 S	29·04 E
124	Soure (sōr-ĕ) Port.	40·04 N	8·37 W
83	Souris (sōō-rē') Can.	46·20 N	62·17 W
86	Souris Can.	49·32 N	100·23 W
86	Souris (R.) Can.	48·46 N	101·32 W
77	Sourlake (sour'lāk) Tex.	30·09 N	94·24 W
164	Sousse (sōōs) Tun.	36·00 N	10·39 E
122	Soustons (sōōs-tôn') Fr.	43·46 N	1·22 W
79	South (R.) N. C.	34·49 N	78·33 W
167	South Africa Afr. (Natal In.)	31·50 S	28·05 E
84	South Amboy (south'ăm'boi) N. J. (New York In.)	40·28 N	74·17 W
6	South America		
116	Southampton (south-ămp'tŭn) Eng.	50·54 N	1·30 W
87	Southampton I. Can.	64·38 N	84·00 W
154	South Andaman I. (ăn-dȧ-măn') India	11·57 N	93·24 E
158	South Australia (State) (ôs-trā'lĭ-ȧ) Austl.	29·45 S	132·00 E
95	South B. Ba. Is.	20·55 N	73·35 W
80	South Bend (bĕnd) Ind.	41·40 N	86·20 W
66	South Bend (bĕnd) Wash.	46·39 N	123·48 W
94	South Bight (B.) Ba. Is.	24·20 N	77·35 W
94	South Bimini (I.) (bē'mē-nē) Ba. Is.	25·40 N	79·20 W
83	Southboro (south'bŭr-ô) Mass. (Boston In.)	42·18 N	71·33 W
79	South Boston (bôs'tŭn) Va.	36·41 N	78·55 W
81	Southbridge (south'brĭj) Mass.	42·05 N	72·00 W
95	South Caicos (I.) (kī'kōs) Ba. Is.	21·30 N	71·35 W
155	South C. Pap. Ter.	10·40 S	149·00 E
159	South C. N. Z. (In.)	47·17 S	167·12 E
63	South Carolina (State) (kăr-ô-lī'nȧ) U. S.	34·15 N	81·10 W
110	South Cave (cāv) Eng.	53·45 N	0·35 W
80	South Charleston (south chärlz'tŭn) W. Va.	38·20 N	81·40 W
154	South China Sea (chī'nȧ) Asia	15·23 N	114·12 E
161	South Cr. Austl. (Sydney In.)	33·43 S	167·00 E
62	South Dakota (State) (dȧ-kō'tȧ) U. S.	44·20 N	101·55 W
116	South Downs (dounz) Eng.	50·55 N	1·13 W
159	Southeast, C. Austl.	43·47 S	146·03 E
110	Southend-on-Sea (south-ĕnd') Eng. (London In.)	51·33 N	0·41 E
159	Southern Alps (Mts.) (sŭ-thûrn ălps) N. Z. (In.)	44·08 S	169·18 E
158	Southern Cross Austl.	31·13 S	119·30 E
86	Southern Indian (L.) (sŭth'ērn ĭn'dĭ-ăn) Can.	57·20 N	99·29 W
79	Southern Pines (sŭth'ērn pīnz) N. C.	35·10 N	79·23 W
166	Southern Rhodesia (Ter.) (rô-dē'zhĭ-ȧ) Fed. of Rh. & Nya.	17·50 S	29·30 E
116	Southern Uplands (ŭp'lăndz) Scot.	55·15 N	4·28 W
69	Southern Ute Ind. Res. (ūt) Colo.	37·05 N	108·23 W
75	South Euclid (ū'klĭd) Ohio (Cleveland In.)	41·30 N	81·34 W
80	South Fox (I.) (fŏks) Mich.	45·25 N	85·55 W
74	South Gate (gāt) Calif. (Los Angeles In.)	33·57 N	118·13 W
96	South Georgia (I.) (jôr'jȧ) Atl. O.	54·00 S	37·00 W
80	South Haven (hāv''n) Mich.	42·25 N	86·15 W
81	Southington (sŭdh'ĭng-tŭn) Conn.	41·35 N	72·55 W
159	South I. N. Z. (In.)	43·15 S	167·00 E
70	South Loup (R.) (lōōp) Nebr.	41·21 N	100·08 W
83	South Merrimack (mĕr'ĭ-măk) N. H. (Boston In.)	42·47 N	71·36 W
75	South Milwaukee (mĭl-wô'kē) Wis. (Milwaukee In.)	42·55 N	87·52 W
94	South Negril Pt. (nȧ-grēl') Jam.	18·15 N	78·25 W
84	South Norfolk (nôr'fŏk) Va. (Norfolk In.)	36·48 N	76·16 W
74	South Ogden (ŏg'dĕn) Utah (Salt Lake City In.)	41·12 N	111·58 W
82	South Paris (păr'ĭs) Maine	44·13 N	70·32 W
75	South Park (pärk) Ky. (Louisville In.)	38·06 N	85·43 W
74	South Pasadena (păs-ȧ-dē'nȧ) Calif. (Los Angeles In.)	34·06 N	118·08 W
72	South Pease (R.) (pēz) Tex.	33·54 N	100·45 W
65	South Pender (I.) (pĕn'dēr) Can. (Vancouver In.)	48·45 N	123·09 W
78	South Pittsburg (pĭts'bûrg) Tenn.	35·00 N	85·42 W
62	South Platte (R.) (plăt) U. S.	40·40 N	102·40 W
80	South Pt. Mich.	44·50 N	83·20 W
93	South Pt. W. I. F. (Le. & Wind. Is. In.)	13·00 N	59·43 W
47	South Polar Plat. Ant.	87·00 S	2·00 W
160	Southport (south'pōrt) Austl.	27·57 S	153·27 E
79	Southport N. C.	35·55 N	78·02 W
110	Southport (south'pôrt) Eng.	53·38 N	3·00 W
75	Southport Ind. (Indianapolis In.)	39·40 N	86·07 W
82	South Portland (pōrt-lănd) Maine	43·37 N	70·15 W
65	South Prairie (prā'rĭ) Wash. (Seattle In.)	47·08 N	122·06 W
74	South Range (rānj) Wis. (Duluth In.)	46·37 N	91·59 W
84	South River (rĭv'ēr) N. J. (New York In.)	40·27 N	74·23 W
84	South R. Ga. (Atlanta In.)	33·40 N	84·15 W
74	South St. Paul Minn. (Minneapolis, St. Paul In.)	44·54 N	93·02 W
74	South Salt Lake (sôlt lāk) Utah (Salt Lake City In.)	40·44 N	111·53 W
96	South Sandwich Is. (sănd'wĭch) Atl. O.	58·00 S	27·00 W
96	South Sandwich Trench S. A.-Ant.	55·00 S	27·00 W
65	South San Francisco (săn frăn-sĭs'kō) Calif. (San Francisco In.)	37·39 N	122·24 W
86	South Saskatchewan (R.) (săs-kăch'ē-wän) Can.	50·29 N	110·25 W
116	South Shields (shēldz) Eng.	55·00 N	1·22 W
116	South Shropshire Hills (shrŏp'shĭr) Eng.	52·30 N	3·02 W
70	South Sioux City (sōō sĭt'ē) Nebr.	42·28 N	96·26 W
159	South Taranaki Bght. (tä-rä-nä'kē) N. Z. (In.)	39·27 S	171·44 E
74	Southton (south'tŭn) Tex. (San Antonio In.)	29·18 N	98·26 W
116	South Uist (I.) (ū'ĭst) Scot.	56·83 N	6·64 W
66	South Umpqua R. (ŭmp'kwȧ) Ore.	43·00 N	122·54 W
154	South Vietnam (vyĕt'nām') Asia	13·19 N	109·51 E
110	Southwell (south'wĕl) Eng.	53·04 N	0·56 W
163	South-West Africa (ăf'rĭ-kȧ) Afr.	19·30 S	16·13 E
65	South Westminster (wĕst'mĭn-stēr) Can. (Vancouver In.)	49·12 N	122·53 W
95	Southwest Pt. Ba. Is.	23·55 N	74·30 W
94	Southwest Pt. Ba. Is.	25·50 N	77·10 W
94	Southwest Pt. Ba. Is.	26·35 N	78·35 W
119	Sovetsk (Tilsit) (sô-vyĕtsk') Sov. Un.	55·04 N	21·54 E
135	Sovetskaya Gavan' (sŭ-vyĕt'skī-u gä'vŭn') Sov. Un.	48·59 N	140·14 E
138	Soviet Union (sō-vĭ-ĕt') Eur.-Asia	60·30 N	64·00 E
110	Sow (R.) (sou) Eng.	52·45 N	2·12 W
152	Sōya Kaikyō (Str.) (sō'yȧ kī'kyō) Jap.-Sov. Un.	45·45 N	141·38 E
152	Sōya Misaki (C.) (sō'yȧ mē'sä-kē) Jap.	45·35 N	141·25 E
128	Sozh (R.) (sôzh) Sov. Un.	52·17 N	31·00 E
127	Sozopol (sôz'ô-pôl') Bul.	42·18 N	27·50 E
117	Spa (spä) Bel.	50·30 N	5·50 E
74	Spadra (spăd'rȧ) Calif. (Los Angeles In.)	34·03 N	117·48 W
102	Spain (spān) Eur.	40·15 N	4·30 W
70	Spalding (spôl'dĭng) Nebr.	41·43 N	98·23 W
65	Spanaway (spăn'ȧ-wā) Wash. (Seattle In.)	47·06 N	122·26 W
81	Spangler (spăng'lēr) Pa.	40·40 N	78·50 W
69	Spanish Fork (spăn'ĭsh fôrk) Utah	40·10 N	111·40 W
163	Spanish Sahara (sȧ hä'rȧ) Afr.	23·05 N	15·33 W
94	Spanish Town Jam.	18·00 N	76·55 W
68	Sparks (spärks) Nev.	39·34 N	119·45 W
84	Sparrows Point (spăr'ōz) Md. (Baltimore In.)	39·13 N	76·29 W
78	Sparta (spär'tȧ) Ga.	33·16 N	82·59 W
73	Sparta Ill.	38·07 N	89·42 W
80	Sparta Mich.	43·10 N	85·45 W
78	Sparta Tenn.	35·54 N	85·26 W
71	Sparta Wis.	43·56 N	90·50 W
	Sparta, see Spárti		
84	Sparta Mts. N. J. (New York In.)	41·00 N	74·38 W
79	Spartanburg (spär'tăn-bûrg) S. C.	34·57 N	82·13 W
124	Spartel (C.) (spär-tĕl') Mor.	35·48 N	5·50 W
127	Spárti (Sparta) Grc.	37·07 N	22·28 E
126	Spartivento (spär-tē-vĕn'tô) It.	37·55 N	16·09 E
126	Spartivento, C. It.	38·54 N	8·52 E
128	Spas-Demensk (spȧs dyĕ-mĕnsk') Sov. Un.	54·24 N	34·02 E
128	Spas-Klepiki (spȧs klĕp'ē-kē) Sov. Un.	55·09 N	40·11 E
135	Spassk-Dal'niy (spŭsk'däl'nyē) Sov. Un.	44·30 N	133·00 E
128	Spassk-Ryazanskiy (ryä-zän'skĭ) Sov. Un.	54·24 N	40·21 E
126	Spátha, Akr. (C.) Grc. (Inset)	35·42 N	23·45 E
84	Spaulding (spôl'dĭng) Ala. (Birmingham In.)	33·27 N	86·50 W
83	Spear, C. (spēr) Can.	47·28 N	52·30 W
70	Spearfish (spēr'fĭsh) S. D.	44·28 N	103·52 W
75	Speed (spēd) Ind. (Louisville In.)	38·25 N	85·45 W
75	Speedway (spēd'wā) Ind. (Indianapolis In.)	39·47 N	86·14 W
111	Speicher L. (shpī'kĕr) Ger. (München In.)	48·12 N	11·47 E
80	Spencer (spĕn'sēr) Ind.	39·15 N	86·45 W
71	Spencer Iowa	43 09 N	95·08 W
79	Spencer N. C.	35·43 N	80·25 W
80	Spencer W. Va.	38·55 N	81·20 W
160	Spencer G. (spĕn'sēr) Austl.	34·20 S	136·55 E
111	Sperenberg (shpĕ'rĕn-bĕrgh) Ger. (Berlin In.)	52·09 N	13·22 E
127	Sperkhiós (R.) Grc.	38·54 N	22·02 E
116	Sperrin Mts. (spĕr'ĭn) N. Ire.	54·55 N	6·45 E
120	Spessart (Mts.) (shpĕ'särt) Ger.	50·07 N	9·32 E
116	Spey (L.) (spā) Scot.	57·25 N	3·29 W
120	Speyer (shpī'ĕr) Ger.	49·18 N	8·26 E
168	Sphinx (Pyramid) (sfĭnks) U. A. R. (Nile In.)	29·57 N	31·08 E
111	Spijkenisse Neth. (Amsterdam In.)	51·51 N	4·18 E
126	Spinazzola (spē-nät'zô-lä) It.	40·58 N	16·05 E
66	Spirit Lake (spĭr'ĭt) Idaho	47·58 N	116·51 W
71	Spirit Lake (lāk) Iowa	43·25 N	95·08 W
86	Spirit River Can.	55·50 N	118·50 W
121	Spišská Nová Ves (spēsh'skä nō'vä vĕs) Czech.	48·56 N	20·35 E
120	Spittal (shpē-täl') Aus.	46·48 N	13·28 E
	Spitzbergen (Is.), see Svalbard		
126	Split (splēt) Yugo.	43·30 N	16·28 E
66	Spokane (spō-kăn') Wash.	47·39 N	117·25 W
66	Spokane R. Wash.	47·47 N	118·00 W
126	Spoleto (spô-lā'tō) It.	42·44 N	12·44 E
73	Spoon (R.) (spōōn) Ill.	40·36 N	90·22 W
71	Spooner (spōōn'ēr) Wis.	45·50 N	91·53 W

ng-sing; ŋ-baŋk; N-nasalized n; nŏd; cŏmmit; ōld; ôbey; ôrder; fōōd; fŏŏt; ou-out; s-soft; sh-dish; th-thin; pūre; ûnite; ûrn; stŭd; circŭs; ü-as "y" in study; '-indeterminate vowel.

Page	Name Pronunciation Region	Lat. °'	Long. °'
127	Sporádhes (Is.) Grc.	38·55 N	24·05 E
84	Spotswood (spŏtz'wood) N. J. (New York In.)	40·23 N	74·22 W
66	Sprague R. (sprāg) Ore.	42·30 N	121·42 W
154	Spratly (I.) (sprăt'lē) China	8·38 N	11·54 E
79	Spray (sprā) N. C.	36·30 N	79·44 W
120	Spree R. (shprā) Ger.	51·53 N	14·08 E
120	Spremberg (shprĕm'bĕrgh) Ger.	51·35 N	14·23 E
73	Spring (R.) Ark.	36·25 N	91·35 W
166	Springbok (spring'bŏk) S. Afr.	29·35 S	17·55 E
68	Spring, Cr. (spring) Nev.	40·18 N	117·45 W
77	Spring Cr Tex.	30·03 N	95·43 W
76	Spring Cr Tex.	31·08 N	100·50 W
73	Springdale (spring'dāl) Ark.	36·10 N	94·07 W
84	Springdale . Conn. (New York In.)	41·05 N	73·31 W
75	Springdale . . . Pa. (Pittsburgh In.)	40·33 N	79·46 W
72	Springer (spring'ēr) N. Mex.	36·21 N	104·37 W
72	Springfield (spring'fēld) Colo.	37·24 N	102·40 W
71	Springfield Minn.	44·14 N	94·59 W
66	Springfield Ore.	44·01 N	123·02 W
73	Springfield Ill.	39·46 N	89·37 W
80	Springfield Ky.	37·35 N	85·10 W
81	Springfield Mass.	42·05 N	72·35 W
73	Springfield Mo.	37·13 N	93·17 W
80	Springfield Ohio	39·55 N	83·50 W
78	Springfield Tenn.	36·30 N	86·53 W
81	Springfield Vt.	43·20 N	72·35 W
166	Springfontein (spring'fŏn-tīn) S. Afr.	30·16 S	25·45 E
82	Springhill (spring-hĭl') Can.	45·39 N	64·04 W
68	Spring Mts. Nev.	36·18 N	115·49 W
167	Springs (springs) S. Afr. (Johannesburg & Pretoria In.)	26·16 S	28·27 E
85	Springstein (spring'stīn) Can. (Winnipeg In.)	49·49 N	97·29 W
84	Springton Res. (spring-tŭn) Pa. (Philadelphia In.)	39·57 N	75·26 W
161	Springvale Austl. (Melbourne In.)	37·57 S	145·09 E
68	Spring Valley Calif. (San Diego In.)	32·46 N	117·01 W
80	Springvalley (spring-văl'ĭ) Ill.	41·20 N	89·15 W
71	Spring Valley Minn.	43·41 N	92·26 W
84	Spring Valley N. Y. (New York In.)	41·07 N	74·03 W
69	Springville (spring-vĭl) Utah	40·10 N	111·40 W
161	Springwood . . . Austl. (Sydney In.)	33·42 S	150·34 E
85	Spruce Grove (sprōōs grōv) Can. (Edmonton In.)	53·33 N	113·55 W
72	Spur (spûr) Tex.	33·29 N	100·51 W
81	Squam (L.) (skwôm) N. H.	43·45 N	71·30 W
126	Squillace, Gulfo di (G.) (gōō'l-fô-dē skwēl-lä'chā) It.	38·44 N	16·47 E
127	Srbija (Serbia) (Reg.) (sr bē-yä) (sĕr'bē-ä) Yugo.	44·05 N	20·35 E
127	Srbobran (s'r'bô-brän') Yugo.	45·32 N	19·50 E
135	Sredne-Kolymsk (s'rĕd'nyĕ kô-lēmsk') Sov. Un.	67·49 N	154·55 E
136	Sredne Rogartka (s'red'ná-ya) (rô gär'tkä) Sov. Un. (Leningrad In.)	59·49 N	30·20 E
136	Sredniy Ik (R.) (srĕd'nĭ ĭk) Sov. Un. (Urals In.)	55·46 N	58·50 E
136	Sredniy Ural (Mts.) (ōō'rál) Sov. Un. (Urals In.)	57·47 N	59·00 E
121	Śrem (shrĕm) Pol.	52·06 N	17·01 E
127	Sremska Karlovci (srĕm'skē kär'lov-tsē) Yugo.	45·10 N	19·57 E
127	Sremska Mitrovica (srĕm'ská mē'trô-vē-tsä') Yugo.	44·59 N	19·39 E
135	Sretensk (s'rĕ'tĕnsk) Sov. Un.	52·13 N	117·39 E
142	Srinagar (srē-nŭg'ŭr) India	34·11 N	74·49 E
121	Sroda (shrô'dá) Pol.	52·14 N	17·17 E
146	Ssuch'uan (Szechwan) (Prov.) China	31·30 N	102·52 E
151	Ssuen China	24·50 N	108·18 E
148	Ssuhsien (sü'siän) China	33·29 N	116·57 E
146	Ssumao China	22·56 N	101·07 E
146	Ssŭnan China	27·50 N	108·30 E
150	Ssup'ing China	43·05 N	124·24 E
148	Ssushui (sĕ'sōōĭ) China	35·40 N	117·17 E
149	Ssut'uan China (Shanghai In.)	30·57 N	121·43 E
111	Stabroek Bel. (Bruxelles In.)	51·20 N	4·21 E
111	Stade (shtä'dĕ) Ger. (Hamburg In.)	53·36 N	9·28 E
112	Stadhur Ice.	65·08 N	20·56 W
118	Städjan (stĕd'yän) Swe.	61·53 N	12·50 E
110	Stafford (stăf'fērd) Eng.	52·48 N	2·06 W
72	Stafford Kans.	37·58 N	78·37 W
110	Stafford (Co.) Eng.	52·45 N	2·00 W
111	Stahnsdorf (shtäns'dôrf) Ger. (Berlin In.)	52·22 N	13·10 E
	Stalin, see Varna		
127	Stalin (Musala) Pk Bul.	42·05 N	23·34 E
146	Stalina, Pik (Pk.) Sov. Un.	39·46 N	71·23 E
	Stalinabad, see Dyushambe		
	Stalingrad, see Volgograd		
133	Stalingrad (L.) (stá'lēn-grát) Sov. Un.	51·10 N	45·10 E
	Stalino, see Donetsk		
129	Stalino (Oblast) (stá'lĭ-nô) (ôb'lást) Sov. Un.	47·54 N	37·13 E
134	Stalino, Pik (Mtn.) Sov. Un.	39·00 N	72·15 E
128	Stalinogorsk (stä'lyin-ŭ-gôrsk') Sov. Un.	54·06 N	38·08 E
	Stalinsk, see Novokuznetsk		
110	Stalybridge (stā'lē-brĭj) Eng.	53·29 N	2·03 W
71	Stambaugh (stăm'bô) Mich.	46·03 N	88·38 W
84	Stamford (stăm'fērd) Conn. (New York In.)	41·03 N	73·32 W
110	Stamford Eng.	52·39 N	0·28 W
72	Stamford Tex.	32·57 N	99·48 W
111	Stammersdorf (shtäm'ĕrs-dôrf) Aus. (Wien In.)	48·19 N	16·25 E
73	Stamps (stămps) Ark.	33·22 N	93·31 W
73	Stanberry (stan'bĕr-ē) Mo.	40·12 N	94·34 W
168	Standerton (stăn'dēr-tŭn) S. Afr. (Johannesburg & Prestoria In.)	26·57 S	29·17 E
70	Standing Rock Ind. Res. (stănd'ĭng rŏk) N. D.	47·07 N	101·05 W
110	Standish (stăn'dĭsh) Eng.	53·36 N	2·39 W
78	Stanford (stăn'fērd) Ky.	37·29 N	84·40 W
167	Stanger (stăŋ-ger) S. Afr. (Natal In.)	29·22 S	31·18 E
118	Stangvik Fd. (stang'vêk fyôrd) Nor.	62·54 N	8·55 E
94	Staniard Creek Ba. Is.	24·50 N	77·55 W
68	Stanislaus (R.) (stăn'ĭs-lô) Calif.	38·10 N	120·16 W
121	Stanislav (stá-nê-släf') Sov. Un.	48·53 N	24·46 E
82	Stanley (stăn'lē) Can.	46·19 N	66·45 W
70	Stanley N. D.	48·20 N	102·25 W
71	Stanley Wis.	44·56 N	90·56 W
165	Stanley Falls Con. L.	0·12 N	25·34 E
166	Stanley Pool (L.) Con. L.	4·15 S	16·00 E
142	Stanley Res. (stăn'lē) India	12·07 N	77·27 E
165	Stanleyville (stan'lē-vĭl) Con.L.	0·32 N	25·14 E
92	Stann Creek (stăn krēk) Br. Hond. (Yucatan In.)	17·01 N	88·14 W
135	Stanovoy Khrebet (Mts.) (stŭn-á-voi') Sov. Un.	56·12 N	127·12 E
74	Stanton (stăn'tŭn) Calif. (Los Angeles In.)	33·48 N	118·00 W
70	Stanton Nebr.	41·57 N	97·15 W
76	Stanton Tex.	32·08 N	101·46 W
65	Stanwood (stăn'wood) Wash. (Seattle In.)	48·14 N	122·23 W
71	Staples (stā'p'lz) Minn.	46·21 N	94·48 W
127	Stara Planina (Balkan Mts.) Bul.	42·50 N	24·45 E
136	Staraya Kupavna (stä'rá-yá kû-päf'ná) Sov. Un. (Moskva In.)	55·48 N	38·10 E
128	Staraya Russa (stä'rá-yá rōōsȧ) Sov. Un.	57·58 N	31·21 E
127	Stara Zagora (zä'gô-rá) Bul.	42·26 N	25·37 E
85	Starbuck (stär'bŭk) Can. (Winnipeg In.)	49·46 N	97·38 W
120	Stargard Szczecinski (shtär'gärt shchĕ-chyn'skē) Pol.	53·19 N	15·03 E
128	Staritsa (stä'rê-tsá) Sov. Un.	56·29 N	34·58 E
79	Starke (stärk) Fla.	29·55 N	82·07 W
72	Starkville (stärk'vĭl) Colo.	37·06 N	104·34 W
78	Starkville Miss.	33·27 N	88·47 W
111	Starnberg (shtärn-bĕrgh) Ger. (München In.)	47·59 N	11·20 E
129	Starobel'sk (stä-rô-byĕlsk') Sov. Un.	49·19 N	38·57 E
128	Starodub (stä-rô-drōōp') Sov. Un.	52·25 N	32·49 E
121	Starogard Gdenski (stä'rō-gärd gdĕn'skē) Pol.	53·58 N	18·33 E
129	Staro-Konstantinov (stä'rô kôn-stán-tē'nôf) Sov. Un.	49·45 N	27·12 E
129	Staro-Minskaya (stä'rô mĭn'ská-yá) Sov. Un.	46·19 N	38·51 E
129	Staro-Shcherbinovskaya Sov. Un.	46·38 N	38·38 E
136	Staro-Subkhangulovo (stăro-sōōb-kan-gōō'lōvō) Sov. Un. (Urals In.)	53·08 N	57·24 E
136	Staroutkinsk (stá-rô-ōōt'kĭnsk) Sov. Un. (Urals In.)	57·14 N	59·21 E
129	Staroverovka Sov. Un.	49·31 N	35·48 E
116	Start Pt. (stärt) Eng.	50·14 N	3·34 W
121	Stary Sącz (stä-rē sônch') Pol.	49·32 N	20·36 E
129	Staryy Oskol (stä'rē ôs-kôl') Sov. Un.	51·18 N	37·51 E
120	Stassfurt (shtäs'fōōrt) Ger.	51·52 N	11·35 E
121	Staszów (stä'shōōf) Pol.	50·32 N	21·13 E
81	State College (stāt kŏl'ĕj) Pa.	40·50 N	77·55 W
74	State Line (līn) Minn. (Duluth In.)	46·36 N	92·18 W
84	Staten I. (stăt'ĕn) N. Y. (New York In.)	40·35 N	74·10 W
79	Statesboro (stāts'bŭr-ō) Ga.	32·26 N	81·47 W
79	Statesville (stāts'vĭl) N. C.	35·45 N	80·54 W
74	Staunton (stôn'tŭn) Ill. (St. Louis In.)	39·01 N	89·47 W
81	Staunton Va.	38·10 N	79·05 W
118	Stavanger (stä'väng'ēr) Nor.	58·59 N	5·44 E
65	Stave (R.) (stāv) Can. (Vancouver In.)	49·12 N	122·24 W
110	Staveley (stāv'lē) Eng.	53·17 N	1·21 W
111	Stavenisse . Neth.(Amsterdam In.)	51·35 N	3·59 E
132	Stavropol' (stäv'rô-pôl') Sov. Un.	53·30 N	49·10 E
133	Stavropol' Sov. Un.	45·05 N	41·50 E
120	Stawno (swav'nō) Pol.	54·21 N	16·38 E
72	Steamboat Springs (stēm'bōt') Colo.	40·30 N	106·48 W
129	Steblëv (styĕp'lyôf) Sov. Un.	49·23 N	31·03 E
71	Steel (R.) (stēl) Can.	49·08 N	86·55 W
81	Steelton (stēl'tŭn) Pa.	40·15 N	76·45 W
111	Steenbergen Neth. (Amsterdam In.)	51·35 N	4·18 E
66	Steens Mts. (stēnz) Ore.	42·15 N	118·52 W
158	Steep Pt. (stēp) Austl.	26·15 S	112·05 E
165	Stefanie L. (stĕf-á-nē') Eth.	4·46 N	37·31 E
75	Steger (stē'gēr) Ill. (Chicago In.)	41·28 N	87·38 W
120	Steiermark (Styria) (state) (shti'ēr-märk) Aus.	47·22 N	14·40 E
86	Steinbach Can.	49·28 N	96·52 W
112	Steinkjer (stēĭn-kyĕr) Nor.	64·00 N	11·19 E
65	Stella (stĕl'á) Wash. (Portland In.)	46·11 N	123·12 W
83	Stellarton (stĕl'ár-tŭn) Can.	45·34 N	62·41 W
120	Stendal (shtĕn'däl) Ger.	52·37 N	11·51 E
133	Stepanakert (styĕ'pän-á-kĕrt) Sov. Un.	39·50 N	46·40 E
160	Stephens, Port (stē'fĕns) Austl.	32·43 S	152·55 E
83	Stephenville (stē'vĕn-vĭl) Can.	48·31 N	58·38 W
84	Stepney Depot (stĕp-nē) Conn. (New York In.)	41·17 N	73·15 W
134	Stepnyak (styĭp-nyäk') Sov. Un.	52·37 N	70·43 E
123	Sterkrade (shtĕr'krädĕ) Ger. (Ruhr In.)	51·31 N	6·51 E
167	Sterkstroom S. Afr. (Natal In.)	31·33 S	26·36 E
72	Sterling (stûr'lĭng) Colo.	40·38 N	103·14 W
71	Sterling Ill.	41·48 N	89·42 W
72	Sterling Kans.	38·11 N	98·11 W
83	Sterling Mass. (Boston In.)	42·26 N	71·41 W
76	Sterling Tex.	31·53 N	100·58 W
136	Sterlitamak (styĕr'lē-ta-mȧk') Sov. Un. (Urals In.)	53·38 N	55·56 E
121	Sternberk (shtĕrn'bĕrk) Czech.	49·44 N	17·18 E
	Stettin, see Szczec'in		
120	Stettiner Haff (L.) (shtĕ'tē-nēr häf) Ger.	53·47 N	14·02 E
86	Stettler Can.	52·19 N	112·50 W
80	Steubenville (stū'bĕn-vĭl) Ohio	40·20 N	80·40 W
65	Stevens (L.) (stē'vĕnz) Wash. (Seattle In.)	47·59 N	122·06 W
71	Stevens Point Wis.	44·30 N	89·35 W
67	Stevensville (stē'vĕnz-vĭl) Mont.	46·31 N	114·03 W
65	Steveston (stēvz'tŭn) Can. (Vancouver In.)	49·08 N	123·11 W
86	Steward (stū'ărd) Can.	56·04 N	129·59 W
86	Stewart (R.) (stū'ērt) Can.	63·27 N	138·48 W
159	Stewart I. N. Z. (In.)	46·50 S	168·06 E
82	Stewiacke (stū'wē-ăk) Can.	45·08 N	63·22 W
168	Steynsrus (stīns'rōōs) S. Afr. (Johannesburg & Pretoria In.)	27·58 S	27·33 E
120	Steyr (shtīr) Aus.	48·03 N	14·24 E
86	Stikine (R.) (stĭ-kēn') Can.	58·17 N	103·10 W
86	Stikine Mts. Can.	59·24 N	129·12 W
65	Stillaguamish (R.) Wash. (Seattle In.)	48·11 N	122·18 W
65	Stillaguamish (R.), South Fk. (stĭl-á-gwä'mĭsh) Wash. (Seattle In.)	48·05 N	121·59 W
74	Stillwater (stĭl'wô-tēr) Minn. (Minneapolis, St. Paul In.)	45·04 N	92·48 W
67	Stillwater Mont.	45·23 N	109·45 W
73	Stillwater Okla.	36·06 N	97·03 W
68	Stillwater Ra. Nev.	39·43 N	118·11 W
66	Stillwater R. Mont.	48·47 N	114·40 W
127	Štip (shtĭp) Yugo.	41·43 N	22·07 E
116	Stirling (stûr'lĭng) Scot.	56·05 N	3·59 W
85	Stittsville (stĭts'vĭl) Can. (Ottawa In.)	45·15 N	75·54 W
118	Stjördalshalsen (styûr-däls-hälsĕn) Nor.	63·26 N	11·00 E
71	Stockbridge Munsee Ind. Res. (stŏk'brĭdj mŭn-sē) Wis.	44·49 N	89·00 W
111	Stockerau (shtô'kĕ-rou) Aus. (Wien In.)	48·24 N	16·13 E
82	Stockholm (stŏk'hōlm) Maine	47·05 N	68·08 W
118	Stockholm (stôk'hôlm') Swe.	59·23 N	18·00 E
110	Stockport (stŏk'pôrt) Eng.	53·24 N	2·09 W
68	Stockton (stŏk'tŭn) Calif.	37·56 N	121·16 W
116	Stockton Eng.	54·35 N	1·25 W
72	Stockton Kans.	39·26 N	99·16 W
71	Stockton (I.) Wis.	46·56 N	90·25 W
76	Stockton Plat Tex.	30·34 N	102·35 W
118	Stöde (stû'dĕ) Swe.	62·26 N	16·35 E
110	Stoke-on-Trent (stōk-ŏn-trĕnt) Eng.	53·01 N	2·12 W
121	Stokhod (R.) (stō-kōd) Sov. Un.	51·24 N	25·20 E
127	Stolac (stō'làts) Yugo.	43·03 N	17·59 E
135	Stolbovoy (Is.) (stôl-bô-voi') Sov. Un.	73·43 N	133·05 E
121	Stolin (stô'lēn) Sov. Un.	51·54 N	26·52 E
123	Stommeln (shtō'mĕln) Ger. (Ruhr In.)	51·01 N	6·46 E
118	Stömstad Swe.	58·58 N	11·09 E
110	Stone Eng.	52·54 N	2·09 W
85	Stoneham (stōn'ăm) Can. (Quebec In.)	46·59 N	71·22 W
83	Stoneham Mass. (Boston In.)	42·30 N	71·05 W
116	Stonehaven (stōn'hā-v'n) Scot.	56·57 N	2·09 W
84	Stone Mountain (stōn) Ga. (Atlanta In.)	33·49 N	84·10 W
85	Stonewall (stōn'wôl) Can. (Winnipeg In.)	50·08 N	97·19 W
78	Stonewall Miss.	32·08 N	88·44 W
85	Stoney Creek (stō'nē) Can. (Toronto In.)	43·13 N	79·45 W
85	Stoney Ind. Res. Can (Calgary In.)	51·10 N	114·45 W
81	Stonington (stōn'ĭng-tŭn) Conn.	41·20 N	71·55 W
68	Stony Cr. (stō'nē) Calif.	39·28 N	122·35 W
85	Stony Mountain Can. (Winnipeg In.)	50·05 N	97·13 W
85	Stony Plain (stō'nē plān) Can. (Edmonton In.)	53·23 N	114·00 W
84	Stony Point N. Y. (New York In.)	41·13 N	73·58 W
118	Storaa (R.) Den.	56·22 N	8·35 E
132	Stora Lule (R.) (stōō'rá lōō'lĕ) Swe.	67·00 N	19·30 E
118	Stord (I.) (stôrd) Nor.	59·54 N	5·15 E
118	Store Baelt (Str.) Den.	55·25 N	10·50 E
112	Stören (stûrĕn) Nor.	62·58 N	10·21 E
118	Store Sotra (Sartor) (stô-rĕ-sô'-trá) (sär'tôr) Nor.	60·24 N	4·35 E
118	Stor Fd. (stôr fyôrd) Nor.	62·17 N	6·19 E
167	Stormberg (Mts.) (stôrm'bûrg) S. Afr. (Natal In.)	31·28 S	26·35 E
71	Storm Lake Iowa	42·39 N	95·12 W
89	Stormy Pt. (stôrm'ē) Vir. Is. (U. S. A.) (St. Thomas In.)	18·22 N	65·01 W
116	Stornoway (stôr'nô-wā) Scot.	58·13 N	6·21 W
121	Storozhinets (stô-rô'zhĕn-yĕts) Sov. Un.	48·10 N	25·44 E
118	Storsjö (stôr'shû) Swe.	62·49 N	13·08 E
118	Storsjöen (L.) (stôr-syûĕn) Nor.	61·32 N	11·30 E
118	Storsjön (L.) Swe.	63·06 N	14·00 E
118	Storvik (stôr'vēk) Swe.	60·37 N	16·31 E
83	Stoughton (stō'tŭn) Mass. (Boston In.)	42·07 N	71·06 W
71	Stoughton Wis.	42·54 N	89·15 W
117	Stour (R.) (stour) Eng.	52·09 N	0·29 E

ăt; finăl; rāte; senâte; ärm; ȧsk; sofȧ; fâre; ch-choose; dh-as th in other; bē; ēvent; bĕt; recĕnt; cratẽr; g-go; gh-guttural g; bĭt; ĭ-short neutral; rīde; K-guttural k as ch in German ich;

PRONOUNCING INDEX Stourbridge–Sutherland 271

Page	Name Pronunciation Region	Lat. °′	Long. °′
110	Stourbridge (stour'brĭj)......Eng.	52·27 N	2·08 W
83	Stow (stō).....Mass. (Boston In.)	42·56 N	71·31 W
75	Stow........Ohio (Cleveland In.)	41·09 N	81·26 W
168	Straatsdrif..............S. Afr. (Johannesburg & Pretoria In.)	25·19 S	26·22 E
116	Strabane (stră-băn')......N. Ire.	54·52 N	6·60 W
159	Stradbroke Is. (străd'brōk) . Austl.	27·45 S	154·18 E
123	Straelen (shtră'lĕn) Ger. (Ruhr In.)	51·26 N	6·16 E
159	Strahan (strā'ăn)..........Austl.	42·08 S	145·28 E
120	Strakonice (strä'kô-nyê-tsĕ) Czech.	49·18 N	13·52 E
127	Straldzha (sträl'dzhȧ)........Bul.	42·37 N	26·44 E
120	Stralsund (shräl'sŏŏnt).......Ger.	54·18 N	13·04 E
118	Strand (stränd)............Nor.	59·05 N	5·59 E
116	Strangford, Lough (B.) (lŏk străng'fērd) . Ire.	54·30 N	5·34 W
118	Strängnas (strĕng'nĕs).......Swe.	59·23 N	16·59 E
116	Stranraer (străn-rär').......Scot.	54·55 N	5·05 W
123	Strasbourg (stràs-bōōr').......Fr.	48·36 N	7·49 E
80	Stratford (străt'fērd)........Can.	43·20 N	81·05 W
81	Stratford................Conn.	41·10 N	73·05 W
116	Stratford.................Eng.	52·13 N	1·41 W
71	Stratford.................Wis.	44·16 N	90·02 W
120	Straubing (strou'bĭng)........Ger.	48·52 N	12·36 E
120	Strausberg (strous'bĕrgh)....Ger.	52·35 N	13·50 E
69	Strawberry (R.)...........Utah	40·05 N	110·55 W
66	Strawberry Mts. (strô'bĕr'ĭ) . Ore.	44·19 N	119·20 W
76	Strawn (strôn)..............Tex.	32·38 N	98·28 W
80	Streator (strē'tēr)...........Ill.	41·05 N	88·50 W
70	Streeter..................N. D.	46·40 N	99·22 W
85	Streetsville (strētz'vĭl) Can. (Toronto In.)	43·34 N	79·43 W
127	Strehaia (strĕ-kä'yȧ).......Rom.	44·37 N	23·13 E
136	Strel'na (strĕl'nȧ) Sov. Un. (Leningrad In.)	59·52 N	30·01 E
110	Stretford (strĕt'fērd)........Eng.	53·25 N	2·19 W
155	Strickland (R.) (strĭk'lănd) Pap. Ter.	6·15 S	142·00 E
111	Strijen....Neth. (Amsterdam In.)	51·44 N	4·32 E
127	Strimonikós Kólpos (G.)......Grc.	40·40 N	23·55 E
126	Strómboli (Vol.) (strôm'bô-lē) . . It.	38·46 N	15·16 E
136	Stromyn (strô'mĭn) Sov. Un. (Moskva In.)	56·02 N	38·29 E
78	Strong (R.) (strông)........Miss.	32·03 N	89·42 W
75	Strongsville (strôngz'vĭl) Ohio (Cleveland In.)	41·19 N	81·50 W
116	Stronsay (I.) (strŏn'sā)......Scot.	59·09 N	2·35 W
81	Stroudsburg (stroudz'bûrg)....Pa.	41·00 N	75·15 W
118	Struer....................Den.	56·29 N	8·34 E
128	Strugi Krasnyye (strōō'gĭ krä's-ny'yĕ) . Sov. Un.	58·14 N	29·10 E
127	Struma (R.) (strōō'mȧ)......Bul.	41·55 N	23·05 E
127	Strumica (strōō'mĭ-tsȧ).....Yugo.	41·26 N	22·38 E
80	Struthers (strŭdh'ērz)........Ohio	41·00 N	80·35 W
111	Struvenhütten (shtrōō'vĕn-hü-tĕn) Ger. (Hamburg In.)	53·52 N	10·04 E
168	Strydpoortberg (Mts.).....S. Afr. (Johannesburg & Pretoria In.)	24·08 S	29·18 E
121	Stryy (strē')............Sov. Un.	49·16 N	23·51 E
121	Strzelce Opolskie (stzhĕl'tsĕ o-pŏl'skyĕ) . Pol.	50·31 N	18·20 E
121	Strzelin (stzhĕ-lĭn)...........Pol.	50·48 N	17·06 E
121	Strzelno (stzhäl'nô)..........Pol.	52·37 N	18·10 E
79	Stuart (stū'ērt)........Fla. (In.)	27·10 N	80·14 W
71	Stuart....................Iowa	41·31 N	94·20 W
64	Stuart (I.)...............Alaska	63·25 N	162·45 W
65	Stuart (I.) . Wash. (Vancouver In.)	48·42 N	123·10 W
158	Stuart Ra................Austl.	29·00 S	134·30 E
154	Stung Treng (stŏŏng'trĕng') Camb.	13·36 N	106·00 E
111	Stupava.......Czech. (Wien In.)	48·17 N	17·02 E
121	Stupsk (swŏŏpsk)............Pol.	54·28 N	17·02 E
71	Sturgeon (R.).............Mich.	46·43 N	88·43 W
71	Sturgeon Bay..............Wis.	44·50 N	87·22 W
87	Sturgeon Falls.............Can.	46·19 N	79·49 W
85	Sturgeon R. (stûr'jŭn) Can. (Edmonton In.)	53·41 N	113·46 W
80	Sturgis....................Ky.	37·35 N	88·00 W
80	Sturgis (stûr'jĭs)..........Mich.	41·45 N	85·25 W
70	Sturgis....................S. D.	44·25 N	103·31 W
158	Sturt Cr..................Austl.	19·40 S	127·40 E
75	Sturtevant (stŭr'tē-vănt) Wis. (Milwaukee In.)	42·42 N	87·54 W
167	Stutterheim (stŭrt'ēr-hĭm) S. Afr. (Natal In.)	32·34 S	27·27 E
73	Stuttgart (stŭt'gärt).........Ark.	34·30 N	91·33 W
120	Stuttgart (shtŏŏt'gärt).......Ger.	48·48 N	9·15 E
112	Stykkisholmur.............Ice.	65·00 N	21·48 W
121	Styr' R. (stêr)..........Sov. Un.	51·44 N	26·07 E
	Styria, see Steiermark		
165	Suakin (swä'kĕn)...........Sud.	19·02 N	37·19 E
151	Suao (sōō'ou)..............China	24·35 N	121·45 E
142	Subarnarakha (R.)..........India	22·38 N	86·26 E
119	Subata (sŏŏ'bȧ-tȧ)......Sov. Un.	56·02 N	25·54 E
155	Subic (sōō'bĭk) . Phil. (Manila In.)	14·52 N	120·15 E
155	Subic B........Phil. (Manila In.)	14·41 N	120·11 E
127	Subotica (sōō'bô'tē-tsȧ).....Yugo.	46·06 N	19·41 E
84	Succasunna (sŭk'kȧ-sŭn'nȧ) N. J. (New York In.)	40·52 N	74·37 W
121	Suceava (sōō-chȧ-ä'vȧ).....Rom.	47·39 N	26·17 E
121	Suceava R................Rom.	47·45 N	26·10 E
121	Sucha (sōō'kȧ)..............Pol.	49·44 N	19·40 E
135	Suchan (sōō-chän')......Sov. Un.	43·15 N	133·19 E
91	Suchiapa (sōō-chê-ä'pä).....Mex.	16·38 N	93·08 W
91	Suchiapa (R.)..............Mex.	16·27 N	93·26 W
148	Such'ien (sü'chĭăn)..........China	33·57 N	118·17 E
92	Suchitoto (sōō-chê-tō'tō).....Sal.	13·58 N	89·03 W
	Süchow, see Hsüchou		
	Süchow, see Ipin		
65	Sucia Is. (sōō'sē-ȧ) Wash. (Vancouver In.)	48·46 N	122·54 W
98	Sucio (R.) (sōō'syô).....Col. (In.)	6·55 N	76·15 W
116	Suck (sŭk)..................Ire.	53·34 N	8·16 W
98	Sucre (sōō'krā)..............Bol.	19·06 S	65·16 W
99	Sucre (State) (sōō'krĕ) . . Ven. (In.)	10·18 N	64·12 W
99	Suçuapara (sōō-sŏŏȧ-pȧ'rä) . . Braz.	16·57 S	48·47 W
95	Sud, Canal du (Chan.).......Hai.	18·40 N	73·15 W
85	Sud, Rivière du (rē-vyâr'dü süd') Can. (Quebec In.)	46·56 N	70·35 W
136	Suda (sŏŏ'dȧ) . . Sov. Un. (Urals In.)	56·58 N	56·45 E
128	Suda (R.) (sŏŏ'dȧ)........Sov. Un.	59·24 N	36·40 E
144	Sudair (sŭ-dä'ēr)........Sau. Ar.	25·48 N	46·28 E
163	Sudan......................Afr.	14·00 N	28·00 E
163	Sudan (Reg.) (sōō-dän')......Afr.	16·48 N	3·11 E
87	Sudbury (sŭd'bĕr-ê)..........Can.	46·28 N	81·00 W
83	Sudbury......Mass. (Boston In.)	42·23 N	71·25 W
120	Sudetes (Mts.)............Czech.	50·41 N	15·37 E
128	Sudogda (sŏŏ'dôk-dȧ)....Sov. Un.	55·57 N	40·29 E
128	Sudost' (R.) (sōō-dôst') . . Sov. Un.	52·43 N	33·13 E
139	Sudr (R.) . U. A. R. (Palestine In.)	29·46 N	32·57 E
129	Sudzha (sŏŏd'zhȧ)........Sov. Un.	51·14 N	35·11 E
125	Sueca (swā'kä)..............Sp.	39·12 N	0·18 W
	Suez, see As Suways		
	Suez Canal, see Qana el Suweis		
168	Suez, G. of (sōō-ĕz') U. A. R. (Suez In.)	29·53 N	32·33 E
84	Suffern (sŭf'fērn) N. Y. (New York In.)	41·07 N	74·09 W
84	Suffolk (sŭf'ŭk) . . Va. (Norfolk In.)	36·43 N	76·35 W
146	Sufu (Kashgar)............China	39·29 N	76·00 E
134	Sufu....................Sov. Un.	39·47 N	76·17 E
80	Sugar (Cr.)................Ind.	39·55 N	87·10 W
72	Sugar City.................Colo.	38·12 N	103·42 W
74	Sugar Creek Mo. (Kansas City In.)	39·07 N	94·27 W
73	Sugar Cr. (shŏŏg'ēr)..........Ill.	40·14 N	89·28 W
74	Sugar I. Mich. (Sault Ste. Marie In.)	46·31 N	84·12 W
77	Sugarland Jct. (shŏŏg'ēr-lănd) Tex. (In.)	29·29 N	95·31 W
160	Sugarloaf Pt. (sŏŏgēr'lōf) . . . Austl.	32·19 S	153·04 E
120	Suhl (zōōl).................Ger.	50·37 N	10·41 E
148	Suhsien (sōō'sĭän).........China	33·37 N	117·51 E
151	Suichuan (Mtn.)...........China	26·25 N	114·10 E
148	Suichung (sōōĭ'jŏŏng)......China	40·22 N	120·20 E
135	Suifenho (swā'fŭn'hŭ')...Sov. Un.	44·47 N	131·13 E
150	Suihua (Peilintzu).........China	41·38 N	126·42 E
146	Suilai (sōō'ē-lī')..........China	44·30 N	86·00 E
148	Suining (sōō'ê-nĭng')........China	33·54 N	117·57 E
101	Suipacha (swê-pä'chȧ) Arg. (Buenos Aires In.)	34·45 S	59·43 W
148	Suip'ing (sōō'ê-pĭng).......China	33·09 N	113·58 E
116	Suir R. (sūr)................Ire.	52·20 N	7·32 W
65	Suisun B. (sōō-ê-sōōn') Calif. (San Francisco In.)	38·07 N	122·02 W
153	Suita (sŏŏ'ē-tȧ) . . Jap. (Ōsaka In.)	34·45 N	135·32 E
150	Suite.....................China	37·32 N	110·12 E
146	Suiyuan (Prov.) (sōō'ê-yän') China	41·31 N	107·04 E
154	Sukabumi...............Indon.	6·52 S	106·56 E
154	Sukadana...............Indon.	1·15 S	110·30 E
153	Sukagawa (sōō'kä-gä'wä).....Jap.	37·08 N	140·07 E
128	Sukhinichi (sōō'kē'nē-chē) Sov. Un.	54·07 N	35·18 E
132	Sukhona (R.) (sŏŏ-kô'nȧ) Sov. Un.	59·30 N	42·20 E
136	Sukhoy Log (sōō'kôy lôg) Sov. Un. (Urals In.)	56·55 N	62·03 E
133	Sukhumi (sŏŏ-kŏŏm')....Sov. Un.	43·00 N	41·00 E
142	Sukkur (sŭk'ŭr)........W. Pak.	27·49 N	68·50 E
136	Suksun (sŏŏk'sŏŏn) Sov. Un. (Urals In.)	57·08 N	57·22 E
153	Sukumo (sōō'kŏŏ-mô)........Jap.	32·58 N	132·45 E
153	Sukurai (sōō'kŏŏ-rĭ) Jap. (Ōsaka In.)	34·31 N	135·51 E
155	Sula (I.)..................Indon.	2·20 S	125·20 E
129	Sula (R.) (sōō-lȧ').......Sov. Un.	50·36 N	33·13 E
92	Sulaco R. (sōō-lä'kō).......Hond.	14·55 N	87·31 W
142	Sulaiman Ra. (sōō-lä-ê-män') W. Pak.	34·22 N	69·10 E
133	Sulak (R.) (sōō-lȧk')......Sov. Un.	43·30 N	47·00 E
154	Sulawesi (Prov.)...........Indon.	1·30 S	120·22 E
144	Sulaymānīyah...............Iraq	35·47 N	45·23 E
118	Suldals Vand (L.) (sŭl-däls vän) Nor.	59·35 N	6·59 E
136	Suleya (sŏŏ-lĕ'yȧ) Sov. Un. (Urals In.)	55·12 N	58·52 E
111	Sulfeld (zōōl'fĕld) Ger. (Hamburg In.)	53·48 N	10·13 E
129	Sulina (sōō-lē'nȧ)..........Rom.	45·08 N	29·38 E
112	Sulitjema (Mtn.) (sōō-lê-tyĕl'mȧ) Nor.-Swe.	67·03 N	16·09 E
98	Sullana (sōō-lyä'nä)........Peru	4·57 N	80·47 W
78	Sulligent (sŭl'ĭ-jĕnt)........Ala.	33·52 N	88·06 W
80	Sullivan (sŭl'ĭ-văn)..........Ill.	41·35 N	88·35 W
80	Sullivan...................Ind.	39·05 N	87·20 W
73	Sullivan...................Mo.	38·13 N	91·09 W
126	Sulmona (sōōl-mō'nä)........It.	42·02 N	13·58 E
146	Sulo.....................China	41·29 N	80·15 E
146	Sulo Ho (R.)..............China	40·53 N	94·55 E
73	Sulphur (sŭl'fŭr)...........Okla.	34·31 N	96·58 W
73	Sulphur (R.)...............Tex.	33·26 N	95·06 W
73	Sulphur Springs (sprĭngz)....Tex.	33·09 N	95·36 W
65	Sultan (sŭl'tăn) Wash. (Seattle In.)	47·52 N	121·49 W
65	Sultan (R.) . . . Wash. (Seattle In.)	47·55 N	121·49 W
90	Sultepec (sōōl-tȧ-pĕk')......Mex.	18·50 N	99·51 W
154	Sulu Arch. (sōō'lōō)........Phil.	5·52 N	122·00 E
115	Suluntah..................Libya	32·39 N	21·49 E
115	Sulūq.....................Libya	31·41 N	20·23 E
154	Sulu Sea...................Phil.	8·25 N	119·00 E
153	Suma (sōō'mä) . . . Jap. (Ōsaka In.)	34·39 N	135·08 E
65	Sumas (sōō'mȧs) Wash. (Vancouver In.)	49·00 N	122·16 W
139	Sumatera Tenga (Prov.) Indon. (Singapore In.)	0·56 N	101·25 E
154	Sumatra (I.) (sŏŏ-mä'trȧ) . . Indon.	2·06 N	99·40 E
154	Sumba (I.) (sŭm'bȧ).......Indon.	9·52 S	119·00 E
154	Sumbawa (I.) (sŏŏm-bä'wä) Indon.	9·00 S	118·18 E
154	Sumbawa-Besar...........Indon.	8·32 S	117·20 E
121	Sümeg (shü'mĕg)..........Hung.	46·59 N	17·19 E
153	Sumida (R.) (sōō'mê-dä).....Jap.	36·01 N	139·24 E
101	Sumidouro (sōō-mê-dō'rōō) Braz. (Rio de Janeiro In.)	22·04 S	42·41 W
153	Sumiyoshi (sōō'mê-yō'shê) Jap. (Ōsaka In.)	34·43 N	135·16 E
66	Summer L. (sŭm'ēr).........Ore.	42·50 N	120·35 W
82	Summerside (sŭm'ēr-sīd).....Can.	46·25 N	63·47 W
79	Summerton (sŭm'ēr-tŭn)....S. C.	33·37 N	80·22 W
79	Summerville (sŭm'ēr-vĭl)....S. C.	33·00 N	80·10 W
75	Summit (sŭm'mĭt) Ill. (Chicago In.)	41·47 N	87·48 W
84	Summit....N. J. (New York In.)	40·43 N	74·21 W
66	Summit Lake Ind. Res......Nev.	41·35 N	119·30 W
69	Summit Pk.................Colo.	37·20 N	106·40 W
65	Sumner (sŭm'nĕr) Wash. (Seattle In.)	47·12 N	122·14 W
120	Šumperk (shŏŏm'pĕrk).....Czech.	49·57 N	17·02 E
78	Sumrall (sŭm'rôl)..........Miss.	31·25 N	89·34 W
79	Sumter (sŭm'tēr)..........S. C.	33·55 N	80·21 W
129	Sumy (sōō'mĭ)..........Sov. Un.	50·54 N	34·47 E
129	Sumy (Oblast)..........Sov. Un.	51·02 N	34·05 E
81	Sunbury (sŭn'bĕr-ê)..........Pa.	40·50 N	76·45 W
118	Sundals Fd. (sŏŏn'dȧls)......Nor.	62·50 N	7·55 E
67	Sundance (sŭn'dăns)........Wyo.	44·24 N	104·27 W
154	Sunda Selat (Str.).........Indon.	5·45 S	106·15 E
154	Sunda Trench (sŏŏn'dȧ) . . . Indon.	9·45 S	107·30 E
167	Sundays (R.) (sŭn'dās) S. Afr. (Natal In.)	33·17 S	25·14 E
158	Sunday Str. (sŭn'dā).......Austl.	15·50 S	122·45 E
118	Sundbyberg (sŏŏn'bü-bĕrgh) . Swe.	59·24 N	17·56 E
116	Sunderland (sŭn'dĕr-lănd) . . . Eng.	54·55 N	1·25 W
154	Sundra Is..................Indon.	9·00 S	108·40 E
118	Sundsvall (sŏŏnds'väl)........Swe.	62·24 N	19·19 E
78	Sunflower, (R.) (sŭn-flou'ēr) . Miss.	32·57 N	90·40 W
150	Sungari Res. (sŏŏn'gȧ-rē) . . . China	42·55 N	127·50 E
	Sungari, see Sung Hua (R.)		
149	Sungchiang . . China (Shanghai In.)	31·01 N	121·14 E
147	Sung Hua (R.) (Sungari) (sŏŏn'gȧ-rē) China	46·09 N	127·53 E
150	Sungtzu (Mtn.)............China	39·40 N	114·50 E
133	Sungurlu (sŏŏn'gŏŏr-lŏŏ')....Tur.	40·08 N	34·20 E
142	Sun Kosi (R.).............Nepal	27·13 N	85·52 E
74	Sunland (sŭn-lănd) Calif. (Los Angeles In.)	34·16 N	118·18 W
118	Sunne (sŏŏn'ĕ)...............Swe.	59·51 N	13·07 E
110	Sunninghill (sŭnĭng'hĭl) Eng. (London In.)	51·23 N	0·40 W
65	Sunnydale (sŭn-nê-dāl) Calif. (San Francisco In.)	37·23 N	122·02 W
74	Sunnymead (sŭn'ĭ-mēd) Calif. (Los Angeles In.)	33·56 N	117·15 W
69	Sunnyside (sŭn'ĭ-sīd)........Utah	39·35 N	110·20 W
66	Sunnyside.................Wash.	46·19 N	120·00 W
65	Sunol (sōō'nŭl) Calif. (San Francisco In.)	37·36 N	122·53 W
67	Sun R. (sŭn)..............Mont.	47·34 N	111·53 W
74	Sunset (sŭn-sĕt) Utah (Salt Lake City In.)	41·08 N	112·02 W
69	Sunset Crater Natl. Mon. (krā'tēr) . Ariz.	35·20 N	111·30 W
161	Sunshine . . Austl. (Melbourne In.)	37·47 S	144·50 E
135	Suntar (sŏŏn-tär')......Sov. Un.	62·14 N	117·49 E
119	Suoyärvi (sōō'ô-yĕr'vē) . . Sov. Un.	62·14 N	32·24 E
69	Superior (su-pē'rĭ-ēr)........Ariz.	33·15 N	111·10 W
72	Superior..................Nebr.	40·04 N	98·05 W
74	Superior......Wis. (Duluth In.)	46·44 N	92·06 W
67	Superior..................Wyo.	41·45 N	108·57 W
91	Superior, Laguna (L.) (lä-gōō'nȧ sōō-pä-rē-ôr') . Mex.	16·20 N	94·55 W
63	Superior, L............U. S.-Can.	47·38 N	89·20 W
74	Superior Village . Wis. (Duluth In.)	46·38 N	92·07 W
152	Sup'ung Res. (sōō'pŏŏng) Kor.-China	40·35 N	126·00 E
65	Suquamish (sōō-gwä'mĭsh) Wash. (Seattle In.)	47·44 N	122·34 W
139	Sūr (Tyre) (sōōr) (tīr) Leb. (Palestine In.)	33·16 N	35·13 E
144	Sūr..........Muscat and Oman	22·23 N	59·28 E
154	Surabaja................Indon.	7·23 S	112·45 E
168	Surad Ad (Mt.) (sōō'răd-ăd) Som. (Horn of Afr. In.)	10·40 N	47·23 E
154	Surakarta...............Indon.	7·35 S	110·45 E
121	Šurany (shōō'rȧ-nū')......Czech.	48·05 N	18·11 E
160	Surat (sū-răt).............Austl.	27·18 S	149·00 E
142	Surat (sōō'rŭt)............India	21·08 N	73·22 E
154	Surat Thani................Thai.	8·59 N	99·14 E
128	Surazh (sōō-räzh')......Sov. Un.	53·02 N	32·27 E
128	Surazh..................Sov. Un.	55·24 N	30·46 E
122	Surgères (sür-zhâr')...........Fr.	46·06 N	0·51 W
134	Surgut (sōōr-gōōt')......Sov. Un.	61·18 N	73·38 E
99	Surinam (Neth. Guiana) (sōō-rē-näm') (gē-än'ȧ) . S. A.	3·45 N	56·30 W
99	Suriname (R.).............Sur.	4·15 N	55·38 W
119	Sur-Sari (I.) (sōōr-sä'rĭ) . Sov. Un.	60·04 N	26·55 E
153	Suruga-Wan (B.) (sōō'rōō-gȧ wän) . Jap.	34·52 N	138·36 E
165	Surt......................Libya	31·14 N	16·37 E
115	Surt, Khalij (G.)............Afr.	31·30 N	18·28 E
126	Susa (sōō'sä)................It.	45·01 N	7·09 E
153	Susa......................Jap.	34·40 N	131·39 E
126	Sušac (sōō'shäts)..........Yugo.	44·31 N	14·15 E
126	Sušak (sōō'shäk)...........Yugo.	45·20 N	14·24 E
126	Sušak (I.)................Yugo.	42·45 N	16·30 E
153	Susaki (sōō'sä-kē)...........Jap.	33·23 N	133·16 E
64	Susitna (sōō-sĭt'nȧ).......Alaska	61·28 N	150·28 W
64	Susitna (R.)..............Alaska	62·00 N	150·28 W
81	Susquehanna (sŭs'kwê-hăn'ȧ) . Pa.	41·55 N	75·35 W
81	Susquehanna (R.)...........Pa.	39·50 N	76·20 W
75	Sussex....Wis. (Milwaukee In.)	43·08 N	88·12 W
82	Sussex (sŭs'ĕks)..........Can.	45·42 N	65·32 W
84	Sussex.....N. J. (New York In.)	41·12 N	74·36 W
151	Susung (sōō'sŏŏng').......China	30·18 N	116·08 E
161	Sutherland (sŭdh' ēr-lănd) Austl. (Sydney In.)	34·02 S	151·04 E
166	Sutherland (sŭ'thēr-lănd) . . S. Afr.	32·25 S	20·40 E

ng-sing; ŋ-baŋk: ɴ-nasalized n; nŏd; cŏmmit; ōld; ôbey; ôrder; fōōd; fŏŏt; ou-out; s-soft; sh-dish; th-thin; pūre; ûnite; ûrn; stŭd; circŭs; ü-as "y" in study; '-indeterminate vowel.

272 Sutlej–Talasea PRONOUNCING INDEX

Page Name Pronunciation Region Lat. °′ Long. °′

142 Sutlej (R.) (sŭt′lĕj)....Pak.-India 29·53 N 72·25 E
110 Sutton (sut′'n).Eng. (London In.) 51·21 N 0·12 W
83 Sutton........Mass. (Boston In) 42·09 N 71·46 W
110 Sutton Coldfield (kōld′fēld)..Eng. 52·34 N 1·49 W
110 Sutton-in-Ashfield (ĭn-ăsh′fēld) Eng. 53·07 N 1·15 W
153 Suwa (sōō′wä)..............Jap. 36·03 N 138·08 E
121 Suwatki (sōō-vou′kê)........Pol. 54·05 N 22·58 E
78 Suwannee (R.) (sōō-wô′nê) Fla.-Ga. 29·42 N 83·00 W
128 Suzdal' (sōōz′dȧl).......Sov. Un. 56·26 N 40·29 E
152 Suzu Misaki (C.) (sōō′zōō mê′sä-kê).Jap. 37·30 N 137·35 E
130 Svalbard (Spitzbergen) (Is.) (sväl′bärt) (spĭts′bûr-gĕn).Eur. 77·00 N 20·00 E
118 Svaneke (svä′nĕ-kĕ).........Den. 55·08 N 15·07 E
129 Svatovo (svä′tô-vô).....Sov. Un. 49·23 N 38·10 E
118 Svedala (svĕ′dä-lä)..........Swe. 55·29 N 13·11 E
118 Sveg......................Swe. 62·03 N 14·22 E
118 Svelvik (svĕl′vĕk)...........Nor. 59·37 N 10·18 E
118 Svendborg (svĕn-bôrgh).....Den. 55·05 N 10·35 E
65 Svensen (svĕn′sĕn) Ore. (Portland In.) 46·10 N 123·39 W
136 Sverdlovsk (svĕrd-lôfsk′) Sov. Un. (Urals In.) 56·48 N 60·37 E
152 Svetlaya (svyĕt′lȧ-yȧ)...Sov. Un. 46·09 N 137·53 E
127 Svilajnac (svê′lȧ-ê-nȧts)....Yugo. 44·12 N 21·14 E
127 Svilengrad (svĕl′ĕn-grȧt).....Bul. 41·44 N 26·11 E
128 Svir' (R.)..............Sov. Un. 60·55 N 33·40 E
119 Svir Kanal (can.) (kȧ-näl′) Sov. Un. 60·10 N 32·40 E
127 Svishtov (svēsh′tôf).........Bul. 43·36 N 25·21 E
128 Svisloch' (svēs′lŏk)......Sov. Un. 53·38 N 28·10 E
120 Svitavy..................Czech. 49·46 N 16·28 E
121 Svitsa (R.) (svĭ-tsȧ).....Sov. Un. 49·09 N 24·10 E
135 Svobodnyy (svô-bôd′nĭ)..Sov. Un. 51·28 N 128·28 E
112 Svolvaer (svôl′vĕr)..........Nor. 68·15 N 14·29 E
135 Svyatoy Nos, Mys (C.) (svyŭ′toi nôs).Sov. Un. 72·18 N 139·28 E
119 Svyentsyany (shvyĕn′tsyȧ-nĭ) Sov. Un. 55·09 N 26·09 E
110 Swadlincote (swŏd′lĭn-kôt)...Eng. 52·46 N 1·33 W
159 Swain Rfs. (swān)........Austl. 22·12 S 152·08 E
79 Swainsboro (swānz′bŭr-ô).....Ga. 32·37 N 82·21 W
166 Swakopmund (svä′kôp-mōōnt) (swȧ′kôp-mōōnd).S. W. Afr. 22·40 S 14·30 E
116 Swale (R.) (swāl)...........Eng. 54·12 N 1·30 W
110 Swallowfield (swŏl′ô-fēld) Eng. (London In.) 51·21 N 0·58 W
83 Swampscott (swŏmp′skŏt) Mass. (Boston In.) 42·28 N 70·55 W
161 Swan, I. (swŏn) Austl. (Melbourne In.) 38·15 S 144·41 E
158 Swan (R.)................Austl. 31·30 S 126·30 E
160 Swan Hill................Austl. 35·20 S 143·30 E
86 Swan Hills (hĭlz)...........Can. 54·50 N 118·10 W
158 Swanland (Reg.) (swŏn′lănd) Austl. 31·45 S 119·15 E
86 Swan River (swŏn rĭv′ēr)....Can. 52·01 N 101·29 W
67 Swan R.................Mont. 47·40 N 113·45 W
85 Swansea (swän′sē) Can. (Toronto In.) 43·38 N 79·28 W
116 Swansea.................Wales 51·37 N 3·59 W
74 Swansea (swŏn′sē) Ill. (St. Louis In.) 38·32 N 89·59 W
84 Swansea...Mass. (Providence In.) 41·45 N 71·09 W
116 Swansea B...............Wales 51·25 N 4·12 W
72 Swanson Res. (swŏn′sŭn)...Nebr. 40·13 N 101·30 W
166 Swartkop (Mtn.) S. Afr. (Cape Town In.) 34·13 S 18·27 E
167 Swartspruit S. Afr. (Johannesburg & Pretoria In.) 25·44 S 28·01 E
151 Swatow (Shant'ou) (swä′tō′).China 23·20 N 116.40 E
166 Swaziland (Swä′zē-lănd).....Afr. 26·45 S 31·30 E
102 Sweden (swē′dĕn)...........Eur. 60·10 N 14·10 E
84 Swedesboro (swēdz′bē-rô) N. J. (Philadelphia In.) 39·45 N 75·22 W
78 Sweetwater (swēt′wô-tēr)...Tenn. 35·36 N 84·29 W
76 Sweetwater................Tex. 32·28 N 100·25 W
70 Sweetwater (L.)..........N. D. 48·15 N 98·35 W
168 Sweetwater (can.) U. A. R. (Suez In.) 30·14 N 32·25 E
68 Sweetwater Res. Calif. (San Diego In.) 32·42 N 116·54 W
67 Sweetwater R............Wyo. 42·19 N 108·35 W
120 Świdnica (shvĭd-nē′tsȧ)......Pol. 50·50 N 16·30 E
120 Swidwin (shvĭd′vĭn).........Pol. 53·46 N 15·48 E
120 Swiebodziec (shvyĕɴ-bo′ jĕts).Pol. 52·16 N 15·36 E
120 Swiebodzin(shvyăɴ-bôd′jĕn)..Pol. 50·51 N 16·17 E
120 Swiecie (shvyăɴ′tsyĕ)........Pol. 53·23 N 18·26 E
121 Swietokrzyskie Góry (Mts.) (shvyĕɴ-tō-kzhĭ′skyĕ gōō′rĭ) Pol. 50·57 N 21·02 E
110 Swift (R.)................Eng. 52·26 N 1·08 W
82 Swift (R.) (swĭft)..........Maine 44·42 N 70·40 W
86 Swift Current (swĭft kûr′ĕnt).Can. 50·20 N 107·59 W
116 Swilly, Lough (B.) (lŏk swĭ-lē) Ire. 54·84 N 8·04 W
116 Swindon (swĭn′dŭn).........Eng. 51·35 N 1·55 W
65 Swinomish Ind. Res. (swĭ-nō′mĭsh) Wash. (Seattle In.) 48·25 N 122·27 W
120 Swinoujscie (slvĭ-nĭ-ô-wēsh′chyĕ).Pol. 53·56 N 14·14 E
110 Swinton (swĭn′tŭn)..........Eng. 53·30 N 1·19 W
75 Swissvale (swĭs′vāl) Pa. (Pittsburgh In.) 40·25 N 79·53 W
102 Switzerland (swĭt′zēr-lănd)...Eur. 46·30 N 7·43 E
128 Syas' (R.) (syäs).......Sov. Un. 59·28 N 33·24 E
71 Sycamore (sĭk′ȧ-mōr).........Ill. 42·00 N 88·42 W
128 Sychëvka (sē-chôf′kȧ)....Sov. Un. 55·52 N 34·18 E
161 Sydney (sĭd′nê) Austl. (Sydney In.) 33·55 S 151·17 E
83 Sydney...................Can. 46·08 N 60·11 W
Syene, see Aswān
83 Sydney Mines.............Can. 46·15 N 60·15 W
132 Syktyvkar (sük-tüf′kär)..Sov.Un. 61·35 N 50·40 E
78 Sylacauga (sĭl-ȧ-kô′gȧ).......Ala. 33·10 N 86·15 W
118 Sylfjällen (sül′fyĕl-ĕn).......Swe. 63·00 N 12·10 E
118 Sylling (sül′lĭng)............Nor. 59·52 N 10·12 E
120 Sylt I. (sĭlt)...............Ger. 54·55 N 8·30 E
79 Sylvania (sĭl-vā′nĭ-ȧ).........Ga. 32·44 N 81·40 W
78 Sylvester (sĭl-vĕs′tēr)........Ga. 31·32 N 83·50 W
81 Syracuse.................N. Y. 43·05 N 76·10 W
72 Syracuse (sĭr′ȧ-kūs)........Kans. 37·59 N 101·44 W
74 Syracuse Utah (Salt Lake City In.) 41·06 N 112·04 W
115 Syra I....................Grc. 37·19 N 25·10 E
103 Syr-Dar'ya (R.).........Sov. Un. 44·15 N 65·45 E
165 Syria (sĭr′ĭ-ȧ)...............Asia 35·00 N 37·15 E
144 Syrian Des. (sĭr′ĭ-ăn)........Asia 32·03 N 39·30 E
136 Sysert' (sĕ′sĕrt) Sov. Un. (Urals In.) 56·30 N 60·48 E
132 Syso'la (R.)............Sov. Un. 60·50 N 50·40 E
133 Syzran' (sĕz-rän′′)........Sov. Un. 53·00 N 46·30 E
121 Szabadszallas (sô′bôd-sä′lăsh) Hung. 46·52 N 19·15 E
120 Szamotuty (shȧ-mô-tōō′wê)...Pol. 52·36 N 16·34 E
121 Szarvas (sôr′vôsh)..........Hung. 46·51 N 20·36 E
121 Szczebrzeszyn (shchĕ-bzhā′shĕn) Pol. 50·41 N 22·58 E
120 Szczecin (Stettin) (shchĕ′tsĭn) (shtĕ-tēn′).Pol. 53·25 N 14·35 E
120 Szczecinek (shchĕ′tsĭ-nĕk)....Pol. 53·42 N 16·42 E
121 Szczuczyn (shchōō′chĕn).....Pol. 53·32 N 22·17 E
121 Szczytno (shchĭt′nô).........Pol. 53·33 N 21 00 E
Szechwan, see Ssuchuan
121 Szeged (sĕ′gĕd)............Hung. 46·15 N 20·12 E
121 Székesfehérvar (sā′kĕsh-fĕ′hār-vär).Hung. 47·12 N 18·26 E
121 Szekszard (sĕk′särd).......Hung. 46·19 N 18·42 E
146 Szengen..................China 23·39 N 107·45 E
121 Szentendre (sĕnt′ĕn-drĕ)....Hung. 47·40 N 19·07 E
121 Szentes (sĕn′tĕsh).........Hung. 46·38 N 20·18 E
121 Szigetvar (sĕ′gĕt-vär)......Hung. 46·05 N 17·50 E
121 Szolnok (sôl′nôk)..........Hung. 47·11 N 20·12 E
120 Szombathely (sôm′bôt-hĕl′).Hung. 47·13 N 16·35 E
120 Szprotawa..................Pol. 51·34 N 15·29 E
121 Sztalinváros..............Hung. 46·57 N 18·55 E
121 Szydlowiec (shid-wô′vyets)...Pol. 51·13 N 20·53 E
155 Taal (L.) (tä-äl′) Phil. (Manila In.) 13·58 N 121·06 E
155 Tabaco (tä-bä′kō) Phil. (Manila In.) 13·27 N 123·40 E
167 Tabankulu (tä-băn-kōō′la) S. Afr. (Natal In.) 30·56 S 29·19 E
93 Tabasara, Serrania de (Ra.) (sĕr-rä-nē′ä dā tä-bä-sä′rä).Pan. 8·29 N 81·22 W
90 Tabasco (tä-bäs′kô)........Mex. 21·47 N 103·04 W
86 Taber....................Can. 49·47 N 112·20 W
155 Tablas (I.) (tä′bläs) Phil. (Manila In.) 12·26 N 112·15 E
155 Tablas Str.....Phil. (Manila In.) 12·17 N 121·41 E
166 Table B. (tā′b'l) S. Afr. (Cape Town In.) 33·41 S 18·27 E
166 Table Mt.S. Afr. (Cape Town In.) 33·58 S 18·26 E
Tabletop, see Jacques Cartier, Mt.
88 Taboga (I.) (tä-bō′gä) Pan. (Panama Canal In.) 8·48 N 79·35 W
88 Taboguilla (I.) (tä-bō-gē′l-yä) Pan. (Panama Canal In.) 8·48 N 79·31 W
99 Taboleiro (Plat.) (tä-bô-lā′rô) Braz. 9·34 S 39·22 W
120 Tábor (tä′bôr)............Czech. 49·25 N 14·40 E
166 Tabora (tä-bō′rä)...........Tan. 5·07 S 32·47 E
164 Tabou (tȧ-bōō′)......Ivory Coast 4·30 N 7·25 W
144 Tabrīz (tȧ-brēz′)...........Iran 38·00 N 46·13 E
90 Tacámbaro (R.) (tä-käm′bä-rō) Mex. 18·55 N 101·25 W
90 Tacambaro de Codallos (dä kô-däl′yōs).Mex. 19·12 N 101·28 W
92 Tacaná (Vol.) (tä-kä-nä′) Mex.-Guat. 15·09 N 92·07 W
99 Tacarigua, Laguna de la (L.) (lä-gōō′nä-dĕ-lä-tä-kä-rē′gwä) Ven. (In.) 10·18 N 65·43 W
93 Tacarouna, Cerro (Mt.) (sĕ′r-rô-tä-kä-rô-ōō′nä).Pan. 8·07 N 77·18 W
149 Tach'ang....China (Shanghai In.) 31·18 N 121·25 E
148 Tach'angshan Tao (I.) (dȧ′chäng′shän dou).China 39·21 N 122·31 E
146 T'ach'eng (Chuguchak) (tä′chĕng′).China 46·50 N 83·24 E
148 Tach'iao (dȧ′chĭou)........China 32·23 N 119·41 E
148 Tach'in Tao (I.) (dä′chĭn dou) China 38·18 N 120·50 E
155 Tacloban (tä-klō′bän).......Phil. 11·06 N 124·58 E
98 Tacna (täk′nä).............Peru 18·34 S 70·16 W
65 Tacoma (tȧ-kō′mȧ) Wash. (Seattle In.) 47·14 N 122·27 W
81 Taconic Ra. (tȧ-kŏn′ĭk).....N. Y. 41·55 N 73·40 W
91 Tacotalpa (tä-kô-täl′pä).....Mex. 17·37 N 92·51 W
91 Tacotalpa (R.)..............Mex. 17·24 N 92·38 W
100 Tacuarembó (tä-kwä-rĕm′bô)..Ur. 31·44 S 55·56 W
164 Tademaït, Plat. du (tä-dê-mä′ēt) Alg. 28·00 N 2·15 E
168 Tadjoura (tȧd-zhōō′rȧ) Fr. Som. (Horn of Afr. In.) 11·48 N 42·54 E
110 Tadley (tăd′lê).Eng. (London In.) 51·19 N 1·08 W
98 Tadó (tä-dō′)..........Col. (In.) 5·15 N 76·30 W
153 Tadotsu (tä′dô-tsōō).........Jap. 34·14 N 133·43 E
82 Tadoussac (tȧ-dōō-sȧk′).....Can. 48·09 N 69·44 W
130 Tadzhik (S. S. R.) (tȧt′zhĕk) Sov. Un. 39·22 N 69·30 E
152 Taebaek Sanmaek (Mts.) (tī-bĭk′ sän-mīk′).Kor. 37·20 N 128·50 E
152 Taedong R. (tĭ-dŏng)........Kor. 38·38 N 124·32 E
152 Taegu (tī′gōō′)............Kor. 35·49 N 128·41 E
124 Tafalla (tä-fäl′yä)...........Sp. 42·30 N 1·42 W
149 Tafan........China (Canton In.) 23·27 N 113·06 E
114 Tafilelt (Oasis) (tä-fē′lĕlt)...Mor. 31·49 N 4·44 W
125 Tafna (R.) (täf′nä)..........Alg. 35·28 N 1·00 W
68 Taft (tȧft)................Calif. 35·09 N 119·27 W
129 Taganrog (tȧ-gȧn-rôk′)..Sov. Un. 47·13 N 38·44 E
129 Taganrogskiy Zaliv (B.) (tȧ-gȧn-rôk′skĭ zȧ′lĭf).Sov. Un. 46·55 N 38·17 E
126 Tagliamento (R.) (täl-yä-mĕn′tō) It. 46·11 N 12·53 E
159 Tagula (I.) (tä′gōō-lȧ)......Austl. 11·45 S 153·46 E
Tagus, see Tajo, Río
154 Tahan, Gunong (Pk.)......Mala. 4·33 N 101·52 E
164 Tahat, Mt. (tä-hät′).........Alg. 23·22 N 5·21 E
148 Taheishan Tao (I.) (dȧ′hā′shän dou).China 37·57 N 120·37 E
157 Tahiti (I.) (tä-hē′tē) (tä′ē-tē′) Fr. Polynesia 17·30 S 149·30 W
119 Tahkuna Nina (tȧh-kōō′nȧ nē′nȧ) Sov. Un. 59·08 N 22·03 E
73 Tahlequah (tă-lĕ-kwä′).....Okla. 35·54 N 94·58 W
68 Tahoe (L.) (tä′hō)....Calif.-Nev. 39·09 N 120·18 W
164 Tahoua (tä′ōō-ä)...........Niger 14·52 N 5·16 E
151 Tahsien...................China 31·12 N 107·30 E
148 Tahsien Shan (Mts.) (dä′sĭän shän).China 36·28 N 117·42 E
150 Tahsing.......China (Peking In.) 39·44 N 116·19 E
150 Tahsinganling Shanmo (Greater Khingan Mts.).China 46·30 N 120·00 E
168 Ţahţā (tä′tä)..U. A. R. (Nile In.) 26·48 N 31·29 E
65 Tahuya (tȧ-hū-yā′) Wash. (Seattle In.) 47·23 N 123·03 W
65 Tahuya (R.)..Wash. (Seattle In.) 47·28 N 122·55 W
148 T'aian (tī′ăn′).............China 36·13 N 117·08 E
148 Taich'iao (dăĭ′chĭou)......China 31·43 N 120·40 E
151 T'aichung (tī′chōōng)......China 24·10 N 120·42 E
148 T'aierhchuang (tī′ē′jōōăng).China 34·34 N 117·44 E
148 Taifou (dăĭ′fōō)...........China 31·22 N 119·29 E
Taigones, see Taygonos
150 T'aihang Shan (Mts.) (tī′häng′ shän′).China 35·45 N 112·00 E
151 T'aiho (tăĭ′hŭ)............China 33·10 N 115·38 E
148 Taihsien (tăĭ′sĭän)........China 32·31 N 119·54 E
148 T'aihsing (tăĭ′sĭng)........China 32·12 N 119·58 E
148 T'ai Hu (L.) (tăĭ′hōō)......China 31·13 N 120·00 E
150 Taiku.....................China 37·25 N 112·35 E
146 Tailagein Khara (Reg.) (tī′lä-gän′ kä′rä).Mong. 43·39 N 105·54 E
150 T'ailai....................China 46·20 N 123·10 E
160 Tailem Bend (tā-lĕm)......Austl. 35·15 S 139·30 E
Taimyr, see Taymyr
151 T'ainan (tī′nan′)...........China 23·08 N 120·18 E
115 Tainaron, Akra (C.).........Grc. 36·20 N 21·20 E
151 Taining (tī′nĭng′)..........China 26·58 N 117·15 E
150 T'aipai Shan (Mtn.)........China 33·42 N 107·25 E
151 T'aipei (tī′pâ′)............China 25·02 N 121·38 E
154 Taiping....................Mala. 4·56 N 100·39 E
152 Taira (tī′rä)...............Jap. 37·03 N 140·57 E
153 Taisha (tī′shä).............Jap. 35·23 N 132·40 E
151 T'aishan...................China 22·15 N 112·50 E
148 T'ai Shan (Mtn.) (tăĭ′ shän) China 36·16 N 117·05 E
Taishet, see Tayshet
100 Taitao, Peninsula de (pĕ-nē′ng-ōō-lä-dĕ-tä-ē-tä′ō) Chile 46·20 S 77·15 W
149 T'aits'ang (tī′tsäng′) China (Shanghai In.) 31·26 N 121·06 E
151 T'aitung (tī′tōōng′)........China 22·45 N 121·02 E
150 Taiwan (Formosa) (I.) (tī-wän) (fŏr-mō′sȧ).China 23·30 N 122·20 E
150 T'aiyüan (tī′yü-än′)........China 37·32 N 112·38 E
151 Taiyün (Mtn.) (tī′yü-än′)..China 25·40 N 118·08 E
101 Tajano de Morais (tĕ-zhä′nô-dĕ-mô-rä′ēs) Braz. (Rio de Janeiro In.) 22·05 S 42·04 W
124 Tajo, Río (Tagus) (R.) (rē′ō-tä′hō) (tā′gŭs).Sp. 39·43 N 5·52 W
92 Tajumulco (Vol.) (tä-hōō-mōōl′kô) Guat. 15·03 N 91·53 W
124 Tajuña (R.) (tä-ᴋōō′n-yä).....Sp. 40·23 N 2·36 W
114 Tājūrā....................Libya 32·56 N 13·24 W
153 Taka (I.) (tä′kä)...........Jap. 30·47 N 130·23 E
153 Takada (tä′kȧ-dȧ)...........Jap. 37·08 N 138·30 E
153 Takahashi (tä′kä′hä-shĭ′)....Jap. 34·47 N 133·35 E
153 Takamatsu (tä′kä′mä-tsōō′)..Jap. 34·20 N 134·02 E
153 Takamori (tä′kä′mô-rē′)......Jap. 32·50 N 131·08 E
149 Takang.......China (Canton In.) 22·48 N 113·24 E
153 Takaoka (tä′kä′ô-kä′).......Jap. 36·45 N 136·59 E
153 Takarazuka (tä′kä-rä-zōō′kä) Jap. (Ōsaka In.) 34·48 N 135·22 E
153 Takasaki (tä′kät′sōō-kē′).....Jap. 36·20 N 139·00 E
153 Takatsu (Mizonokuchi) (tä-kät′sōō) (mê′zō-nô-kōō′chê) Jap. (Tōkyō In.) 35·36 N 139·37 E
153 Takatsuki (tä′kät′sōō-kē′) Jap. (Ōsaka In.) 34·51 N 135·38 E
167 Takaungu (tä′kä′ōōŋ-gōō′)...Ken. 3·41 S 39·48 E
153 Takayama (tä′kä′yä′mä)......Jap. 36·11 N 137·16 E
153 Takefu (tä′kĕ-fōō)..........Jap. 35·57 N 136·09 E
165 Takkaze R. (täk′ȧ-zȧ).......Eth. 13·38 N 38·00 E
86 Takla (L.) (tă′klȧ)..........Can. 55·33 N 125·22 W
146 Takla Makan (Des.) (mä-kän′) China 39·22 N 82·34 E
164 Takoradi (tä-kô-rä′dê).....Ghana 4·52 N 2·02 W
148 Taku.....................China 39·00 N 117·42 E
148 Taku (R.) (dä′gōō).........China 37·07 N 120·14 E
90 Tala (tä′lä)...............Mex. 20·39 N 103·42 W
101 Talagante (tä-lä-gá′n-tĕ) Chile (Santiago In.) 33·39 S 70·54 W
150 Tal'ai....................China 45·25 N 124·22 E
154 Talakmau, Gunung (Mtn.).Indon. 0·12 N 100·05 E
165 Tala Mt..................Eth. 11·00 N 38·41 E
92 Talanga (tä-lä′n-gä).......Hond. 14·21 N 87·09 W
98 Talara (tä-lä′rä)...........Peru 4·32 N 81·17 W
155 Talaud, Pulau-Pulau (Is.) (tä-lout′).Indon. 4·17 N 127·30 E
155 Talasea (tä-lä-sä′ä)...N. Gui. Ter. 5·20 S 150·00 E

ăt; finăl; rāte; senâte; ärm; åsk; sofȧ; fâre; ch-choose; dh-as th in other; bē; êvent; bĕt; recĕnt; cratēr; g-go; gh-guttural g; bĭt; ĭ-short neutral; rīde; ᴋ-guttural k as ch in German ich;

PRONOUNCING INDEX Talavera–Taunton 273

Page	Name Pronunciation Region	Lat. °'	Long. °'
124	Talavera de la Reina (tä-lä-vä'rä dā lä rå-ē'nä). Sp.	39·58 N	4·51 W
74	Talbert (tôl'bûrt) Calif. (Los Angeles In.)	33·42 N	117·57 W
101	Talca (täl'kä). Chile (Santiago In.)	35·25 S	71·39 W
101	Talca (Prov.). Chile (Santiago In.)	35·23 S	71·15 W
101	Talca, Punta (Pt.) (pōō'n-tä-täl'kä) Chile (Santiago In.)	33·25 S	71·42 W
100	Talcahuano (täl-kä-wä'nō) .. Chile	36·41 S	73·05 W
128	Taldom (tål-dôm) ...... Sov. Un.	56·44 N	37·33 E
134	Taldy-Kurgan (tål'dĭ-kŏŏr-gän') Sov. Un.	45·03 N	77·18 E
91	Talea de Castro (San Miguel) (tä'lå-ä dā käs'trō). Mex.	17·22 N	96·14 W
122	Talence (tå-lôns) ...... Fr.	44·48 N	0·38 W
146	Tali (tä'lē) ...... China	26·00 N	100·08 E
155	Taliabu (tä-lē-ä'bōō) ...... Indon.	1·30 S	125·00 E
148	Talichi (dä'lē'jē) ...... China	33·47 N	117·47 E
148	Talien (Dairen) (dä'lĭän) ... China	38·54 N	121·35 E
148	Talien Wan (B.) (wän) ..... China	38·55 N	121·50 E
155	Talim (I.) (tä-lēm') Phil. (Manila In.)	14·21 N	121·14 E
155	Talisay (tä-lē'sī). Phil. (Manila In.)	14·08 N	122·56 E
64	Talkeetna (tål-kēt'nå) ..... Alaska	62·18 N	150·02 W
133	Talkheh Rūd (R.) ...... Iran	38·00 N	46·50 E
78	Talladega (tăl-å-dē'gå) ...... Ala.	33·25 N	86·06 W
78	Tallahassee (tăl-å-hăs'ē) ...... Fla.	30·25 N	84·17 W
78	Tallahatchie (R.) (tal-å hăch'ē) Miss.	34·21 N	90·03 W
78	Tallapoosa (tăl-å-pōō'så) ..... Ga.	33·44 N	85·15 W
78	Tallapoosa (R.) ...... Ala.	32·22 N	86·08 W
78	Tallassee (tăl'å-sē) ...... Ala.	32·30 N	85·54 W
119	Tallinn (Reval) (tál'lĕn) (rä'väl) Sov. Un.	59·26 N	24·44 E
75	Tallmadge (tăl'mĭj) Ohio (Cleveland In.)	41·06 N	81·26 W
77	Tallulah (tă-lōō'lå) ...... La.	32·25 N	91·13 W
93	Talmanca, Cord. de (Mts.) (kôr-dēl-yĕ'rä-dĕ-tāl-mä'n-kä) C. R.	9·37 N	83·55 W
129	Tal'noye (tál'nô-yĕ) ..... Sov. Un.	48·52 N	30·43 E
165	Talōdi (tä-lō'dē) ...... Sud.	10·41 N	30·21 E
143	Taloje Budrukh India (Bombay In.)	19·05 N	73·05 E
90	Talpa de Allende (täl'pä dā äl-yĕn'då). Mex.	20·25 N	104·48 W
119	Talsi (tal'sĭ) ...... Sov. Un.	57·16 N	22·35 E
100	Taltal (täl-täl') ...... Chile	25·26 S	70·32 W
129	Taly (täl'ĭ) ...... Sov. Un.	49·51 N	40·07 E
71	Tama (tā'mä) ...... Iowa	41·57 N	92·36 W
153	Tama (R.) ...... Jap. (Tōkyō In.)	35·38 N	139·35 E
164	Tamale (tä-mä'lå) ...... Ghana	9·16 N	00·53 W
129	Taman' (tå-män'') ...... Sov. Un.	45·13 N	36·46 E
98	Tamaná, Cerro (Mtn.) (sĕ'r-rô-tä-mä-nä'). Col. (In.)	5·06 N	76·10 W
99	Tamanaco (tä-mä-nä'kō) (R.) Ven. (In.)	9·32 N	66·00 W
164	Tamanr'aset R. (tä-män-räs'sĕt) Alg.	22·15 N	2·51 E
	Tamanrasset, see Fort Laperrine		
81	Tamaqua (tå-mô'kwå) ...... Pa.	40·45 N	75·50 W
116	Tamar (R.) (tā'mär) ...... Eng.	50·35 N	4·15 W
125	Tamarite (tä-mä-rē'tä) ...... Sp.	41·52 N	0·24 E
167	Tamatave (tä-må-täv') .. Malagasy	18·14 S	49·25 E
90	Tamaulipas (State) (tä-mä-ōō-lē'päs'). Mex.	23·45 N	98·30 W
90	Tamazula de Gordiano (tä-mä-zōō'lä dā gôr-dē-ä'nō) Mex.	19·44 N	103·09 W
91	Tamazulapan del Progreso (tä-mä-zōō-lä'päm-dĕl-prô-grĕ-sō). Mex.	17·41 N	97·34 W
90	Tamazunchale (tä-mä-zōōn-chä'lå) Mex.	21·16 N	98·46 W
164	Tambacounda (täm-bä-kōōn'dä) Senegal	13·45 N	13·52 W
99	Tambador, Serra do (Mts.) (sĕ'r-rä-dô-tâm'bä-dōr). Braz.	10·33 S	41·16 W
153	Tambaichi (täm'bĭ'chē) Jap. (Ōsaka In.)	34·36 N	135·50 E
154	Tambelan, Pulau-Pulau (Is.) (täm-bå-län'). Indon.	0·38 N	107·38 E
160	Tambo (tăm'bō) ...... Austl.	24·50 S	146·15 E
133	Tambov (tám-bôf') ...... Sov. Un.	52·45 N	41·10 E
128	Tambov (Oblast) ...... Sov. Un.	52·50 N	40·42 E
124	Tambre (R.) (täm'brā) ...... Sp.	42·59 N	8·33 W
165	Tambura (täm-bōō'rä) ...... Sud.	5·34 N	27·30 E
110	Tame (R.) (tām) ...... Eng.	52·41 N	1·42 W
124	Tamega (R.) (tå-mā'gå) ..... Port.	41·30 N	7·45 W
90	Tamesí (R.) (tä-mĕ-sē') ..... Mex.	22·36 N	98·32 W
164	Tamgak, Monts (Mt.) (tam-gäk') Niger	19·06 N	8·31 E
114	Tamgrout (täm-grōōt') ...... Mor.	30·12 N	5·46 W
164	Tamgue, M. du (Mt.) ...... Gui.	12·13 N	12·28 W
91	Tamiahua (tä-myä-wä) ...... Mex.	21·17 N	97·26 W
91	Tamiahua, Laguna (L.) (lä-gōō'nä-tä-myä-wä). Mex.	21·38 N	97·33 W
79	Tamiami, can. (tă-mī-ăm'ĭ) Fla. (In.)	25·52 N	80·08 W
148	Taming (dä'mĭng) ...... China	36·15 N	115·09 E
119	Tammela (tám'ĕ-lå) ...... Fin.	60·49 N	23·45 E
	Tammisaari, see Ekenäs		
79	Tampa (tăm'på) ...... Fla. (In.)	27·57 N	82·25 W
79	Tampa B. ...... Fla. (In.)	27·35 N	82·38 W
112	Tampere (tám'pĕ-rĕ) ...... Fin.	61·21 N	23·39 E
91	Tampico (täm-pē'kō) ...... Mex.	22·14 N	97·51 W
91	Tampico Alto (täm-pē'kō äl'tō) Mex.	22·07 N	97·48 W
139	Tampin.... Mala. (Singapore In.)	2·28 N	102·15 E
155	Tamrau (Mtn.) .... Neth. N. Gui.	0·45 S	132·26 E
90	Tamuín (tä-mōō-ē'n) ...... Mex.	22·04 N	98·47 W
160	Tamworth (tăm'wûrth) ..... Austl.	31·01 S	151·00 E
110	Tamworth ...... Eng.	52·58 N	1·41 W
167	Tana (R.) (tä'nä) ...... Ken.	0·22 S	39·33 E
159	Tana (I.) ...... New Hebr.	19·32 S	169·27 E
112	Tana (R.) ...... Nor.-Fin.	69·20 N	24·54 E
153	Tanabe (tä-nä'bā) ...... Jap.	33·45 N	135·21 E
153	Tanabe ...... Jap. (Ōsaka In.)	34·49 N	135·46 E
64	Tanacross (tă'nå-crōs) ..... Alaska	63·20 N	143·30 W
64	Tanaga (I.) (tä-nä'gä) ..... Alaska	51·28 N	178·10 W
154	Tanahbala (I.) (tå-nä-bä'lä) Indon.	0·30 S	98·22 E
154	Tanahmasa (I.) (tå-nä-mä'sä) Indon.	0·03 S	97·30 E
165	Tana L. ...... Eth.	12·09 N	36·41 E
158	Tanami (tå-nä'mē) ...... Austl.	19·45 S	129·50 E
64	Tanana (tă'nå-nô) ...... Alaska	65·18 N	152·20 W
64	Tanana (R.) ...... Alaska	64·26 N	148·40 W
167	Tananarive (tå-nä-nä-rēv') Malagasy	18·51 S	47·40 E
126	Tanaro (R.) (tä-nä'rô) ...... It.	44·45 N	8·02 E
155	Tanauan (tä-nä'wän) Phil. (Manila In.)	14·04 N	121·10 E
148	T'anch'eng (tän'chĕng) ..... China	34·37 N	118·22 E
152	Tanchŏn (tän'chŭn) ...... Kor.	40·29 N	128·50 E
90	Tancítaro (tän-sē'tä-rō) ..... Mex.	19·16 N	102·24 W
90	Tancítaro, Cerro de (sĕ'r-rô-dĕ) Mex.	19·24 N	102·19 W
91	Tancoco (tän-kō'kō) ...... Mex.	21·16 N	99·45 W
100	Tandil (tän-dēl') ...... Arg.	36·16 S	59·01 W
100	Tandil, Sierra del (Mts.) ..... Arg.	38·40 S	59·40 W
154	Tandjungbalai (tän'jông-bä'lå') Indon.	2·52 N	99·43 E
139	Tandjungbalai Indon. (Singapore In.)	1·00 N	103·26 E
139	Tandjung Berakit (C.) Indon. (Singapore In.)	1·16 N	104·44 E
154	Tandjungpandan ...... Indon.	2·47 S	107·51 E
139	Tandjungpinang (tän'jŏng-pē'näng) Indon. (Singapore In.)	0·55 N	104·29 E
153	Tanega (I.) (tä'nå-gä') ...... Jap.	30·36 N	131·11 E
164	Tanezrouft (Reg.) (tä'nĕz-rōōft) Alg.	24·17 N	0·30 W
148	T'ang (R.) (täng) ...... China	33·38 N	117·29 E
167	Tanga (tăŋ'gå) ...... Tan.	5·07 S	39·06 E
90	Tangancícuaro (täŋ-gän-sē'kwä rô). Mex.	19·52 N	102·13 W
163	Tanganyika (tăŋ-găn-yē'kå) .. Afr.	6·48 S	33·58 E
166	Tanganyika, L. ...... Tan.	6·00 S	30·15 E
148	T'angchiacha (täng'jēä'jä) .. China	32·06 N	120·48 E
149	Tangchiaochen China (Shanghai In.)	31·13 N	121·30 E
164	Tanger (tăn-jēr') ...... Mor.	35·52 N	5·55 W
120	Tangermünde (täŋ'ĕr-mün'de) Ger.	52·33 N	11·58 E
150	Tangho ...... China	32·40 N	112·50 E
148	T'anghsien (täng'sĭän) ...... China	38·09 N	115·00 E
77	Tangipahoa R. (tăn'jē-på-hō'å) La.	30·48 N	90·28 W
148	T'angku (täŋ'kōō') ...... China	39·04 N	117·41 E
142	Tangra Tsho (L.) ...... China	30·38 N	85·40 E
148	Tangt'u (däng'tōō) ...... China	31·35 N	118·28 E
148	Tangshan (täng'shän') ...... China	34·27 N	116·27 E
148	T'angshan ...... China	39·38 N	118·11 E
155	Tanimbar, Pulau-Pulau (Is.) Indon.	8·00 S	132·00 E
139	Tanjong (C.). Mala. (Singapore In.)	1·53 N	102·29 E
139	Tanjong Piai (I.) Mala. (Singapore In.)	1·16 N	103·11 E
139	Tanjong Ramunia (C.) Mala. (Singapore In.)	1·27 N	104·44 E
143	Tanjore (tăn-jôr') ...... India	10·51 N	79·11 E
131	Tannu-Ola (Mts.) ...... Sov. Un.	51·00 N	94·00 E
155	Tañong (tän-yōn') Phil. (Manila In.)	14·46 N	120·52 E
149	T'anpu ...... China (Canton In.)	23·20 N	113·06 E
91	Tanquijo, Arrecife (Reef) (är-rĕ-sē'fĕ-tän-kē'kō). Mex.	21·07 N	97·16 W
168	Ṭanṭā (tän'tä). U. A. R. (Nile In.)	30·50 N	31·00 E
90	Tantoyuca (tän-tō-yōō'kä) .. Mex.	21·22 N	98·13 W
148	Tanyang (dän'yäng) ...... China	32·01 N	119·32 E
152	Tanyang ...... Kor.	36·53 N	128·20 E
152	Taoan (tä'ō-än') ...... China	45·41 N	123·00 E
148	T'aoch'ichen (tou'chē'jĕn) .. China	31·33 N	117·01 E
150	Taoerh (R.) ...... China	45·40 N	122·00 E
150	Táo Ho' (R.) (tä'ō hō') ..... China	35·30 N	103·40 E
148	Tao Hu (L.) (tou'hōō) ...... China	31·37 N	119·29 E
148	T'aok'ou (tou'kō) ...... China	35·34 N	114·32 E
150	T'aonan (tä'ō-nän') ...... China	45·15 N	122·45 E
126	Taormina (tä-ôr-mē'nä) ...... It.	37·53 N	15·18 E
69	Taos (tä'ôs) ...... N. Mex.	36·25 N	105·35 W
164	Taoudenni (tä'ōō-dĕ-nē') .... Mali	22·57 N	3·37 W
164	Taoudenni (Oasis) ...... Mali	23·00 N	3·48 W
164	Taoulo (tä'ōō-lō) ...... Lib.	6·30 N	8·49 W
164	Taourirt (tä-ōō-rērt') ...... Alg.	27·08 N	0·06 E
151	Taoyüan (tä'ō-yü-än') ...... China	29·00 N	111·15 E
119	Tapa (tá'pà) ...... Sov. Un.	59·16 N	25·56 E
92	Tapachula ...... Guat.	14·55 N	92·20 W
150	Tapa Shan (Mts.) ...... China	32·25 N	108·20 E
99	Tapajós (R.) (tä-pä-zhô's) .. Braz.	3·27 S	55·33 W
101	Tapalqué (tä-päl-kĕ') Arg. (Buenos Aires In.)	36·22 S	60·05 W
91	Tapanatepec (tä-pä-nä-tĕ-pĕk) Mex.	16·22 N	94·19 W
166	Tapepo (Mtn.) ...... Tan.	7·57 S	31·28 E
151	Tapieh Shan (Mts.) ...... China	31·40 N	114·50 E
148	Tapingi (dä'pĭng'yē) ...... China	35·30 N	117·38 E
152	Tappi Saki (C.) (täp'pē sä'kē) Jap.	41·05 N	139·40 E
65	Tapps (L.) (tăpz) Wash. (Seattle In.)	47·20 N	122·12 W
142	Tāpti (R.) (täp'tē) ...... India	21·38 N	74·10 E
149	Tapuhsü .... China (Canton In.)	23·17 N	113·34 E
99	Taquara, Serra de (Mts.) (sĕ'r-rä-dĕ-tä-kwä'rä). Braz.	15·28 S	54·33 W
99	Taquari (R.) (tä-kwä'rĭ) .... Braz.	18·35 S	56·50 W
79	Tar (R.) (tär) ...... N. C.	35·58 N	78·06 W
134	Tara (tä'rà) ...... Sov. Un.	56·58 N	74·13 E
155	Tara (I.) (tä'rä). Phil. (Manila In.)	12·18 N	120·28 E
134	Tara (R.) (tä'rà) ...... Sov. Un.	56·32 N	76·13 E
139	T'arābulus (Tripoli) (tå-rä'bōō-lōōs) Leb. (Palestine In.)	34·25 N	35·50 E
165	Tarābulus (Tripoli) ...... Libya	32·50 N	13·13 E
165	Tarābulus (Tripolitania) (Prov.) Libya	31·00 N	12·26 E
154	Tarakan (Bunju) ...... Indon.	3·17 N	118·04 E
124	Tarancón (tä-rän-kōn') ...... Sp.	40·01 N	3·00 W
126	Taranto (tä'rän-tô) ...... It.	40·30 N	17·15 E
126	Taranto, Golfo di (G.) (gôl-fô-dē tä'rän-tô). It.	40·03 N	17·10 E
98	Tarapoto (tä-rä-pô'tō) ...... Peru	6·29 S	76·26 W
122	Tarare (tå-rär') ...... Fr.	45·55 N	4·23 E
122	Tarascon (tå-rås-kôn') ...... Fr.	42·53 N	1·35 E
122	Tarascon-sur-Rhône (tå-rås-kôn-sür-rōn'). Fr.	43·47 N	4·41 E
129	Tarashcha (tä'råsh-chå). Sov. Un.	49·34 N	30·52 E
98	Tarata (tä-rä'tä) ...... Bol.	17·43 S	66·00 W
126	Taravo (R.) ...... Fr.	41·54 N	8·58 E
124	Tarazona (tä-rä-thō'nä) ...... Sp.	41·54 N	1·45 W
124	Tarazona de la Mancha (tä-rä-zō'nä-dĕ-lä-mä'n-chä). Sp.	39·13 N	1·50 W
116	Tarbat Ness (Hd.) (tár'bát). Scot.	57·51 N	3·50 W
122	Tarbes (tàrb) ...... Fr.	43·04 N	0·05 E
79	Tarboro (tär'bŭr-ô) ...... N. C.	35·53 N	77·34 W
165	Tarbū ...... Libya	26·07 N	15·49 E
160	Taree (tă-rē') ...... Austl.	31·52 S	152·21 E
139	Tareifiya (R.) U. A. R. (Palestine In.)	29·34 N	33·41 E
75	Tarentum (tå-rĕn'tŭm) Pa. (Pittsburgh In.)	40·36 N	79·44 W
168	Tarfa, Wadi el (Val.) U. A. R. (Nile In.)	28·14 N	31·00 E
164	Tarhmanant (Well) (tär-mä-nänt'). Mali	24·32 N	4·58 W
124	Tarifa (tä-rē'fä) ...... Sp.	36·02 N	5·35 W
98	Tarija (tär-rē'hä) ...... Bol.	21·42 S	64·52 W
144	Tarim (tá-rĭm') ...... Sau. Ar.	16·13 N	49·08 E
146	Tarim (R.) (tå-rĭm') ...... China	40·45 N	85·39 E
146	Tarim Basin (tå-rĭm') ...... China	39·52 N	82·34 E
167	Tarka (R.) (tä'kå) S. Afr. (Natal In.)	32·15 S	26·00 E
167	Tarkastad .... S. Afr. (Natal In.)	32·01 S	26·18 E
129	Tarkhankut, Mys (C.) (mĭs tár-kän'kŏŏt). Sov. Un.	45·18 N	32·08 E
73	Tarkio (tär'kĭ-ō) ...... Mo.	40·27 N	95·22 W
164	Tarkwa (tärk'wä) ...... Ghana	5·16 N	2·03 W
155	Tarlac (tär'läk) Phil. (Manila In.)	15·29 N	120·36 E
167	Tarlton (tärl'tŭn) ...... S. Afr. (Johannesburg & Pretoria In.)	26·05 S	27·38 E
98	Tarma (tär'mä) ...... Peru	11·26 S	75·40 W
122	Tarn (R.) (tärn) ...... Fr.	44·03 N	2·41 E
121	Târnava Mica R. (tĕr-nä'vå mē'kŏ). Rom.	46·17 N	24·20 E
121	Tarnów (tär'nŏŏf) ...... Pol.	50·02 N	21·00 E
126	Taro (R.) (tä'rō) ...... It.	44·41 N	10·03 E
164	Taroudant (tå-rōō-dänt') .... Mor.	30·39 N	8·52 W
79	Tarpon Springs (tär'pŏn) Fla. (In.)	28·07 N	82·44 W
110	Tarporley (tär'pēr-lē) ...... Eng.	53·09 N	2·40 W
95	Tarpum B. (tär'pŭm) .... Ba. Is.	25·05 N	76·20 W
126	Tarquinia (Corneto) (tär-kwē'nē-ä) (kôr-nä'tô). It.	42·16 N	11·46 E
125	Tarragona (tär-rä-gō'nä) ...... Sp.	41·05 N	1·15 E
84	Tarrant (tăr'ănt) Ala. (Birmingham In.)	33·35 N	86·46 W
125	Tarrasa (tär-rä'sä) ...... Sp.	41·34 N	2·01 E
125	Tárrega (tä'rå-gä) ...... Sp.	41·40 N	1·09 E
125	Tarrejón de Ardoz (tär-rĕ-kô'n-dĕ-är-dôz) Sp. (Madrid In.)	40·28 N	3·29 W
84	Tarrytown (tăr'ĭ-toun) N. Y. (New York In.)	41·04 N	73·52 W
133	Tarsus (tàr'sŏŏs) (tär'sŭs) .... Tur.	37·00 N	34·50 E
100	Tartagal (tär-tä-gä'l) ...... Arg.	23·31 S	63·47 W
115	Tartous (tàr-tōōs') ...... U. A. R.	34·54 N	35·59 E
128	Tartu (Dorpat) (tär'tōō) (dôr'pät) Sov. Un.	58·23 N	26·44 E
153	Tarumi (tä'rōō-mē) Jap. (Ōsaka In.)	34·38 N	135·04 E
128	Tarusa (tä-rōōs'å) ...... Sov. Un.	54·43 N	37·11 E
74	Tarzana (tär-ză'å) Calif. (Los Angeles In.)	34·10 N	118·32 W
148	Tashanchen (dä'shän'jĕn). China	34·17 N	119·17 E
103	Tashauz (tŭ-shŭ-ōōs') ... Sov. Un.	41·50 N	59·45 E
142	Tashi-Chho Dzong ...... Bhu.	27·33 N	89·42 E
134	Tashkent (tåsh'kĕnt) .... Sov. Un.	41·23 N	69·04 E
159	Tasman B. (tăz'măn). N. Z. (In.)	39·11 S	173·22 E
159	Tasmania (I.) (tăz-mā'nĭ-å) Austl.	41·28 S	142·30 E
160	Tasman Pen. ...... Austl.	43·00 S	148·30 E
156	Tasman Sea ...... Oceania	29·30 S	155·00 E
90	Tasquillo (täs-kē'lyō) ...... Mex.	20·34 N	99·21 W
164	Tassili-n-Ajjer (Plat.) (tås'ē-lē ä'jĕr). Alg.	25·40 N	6·57 E
132	Tatar (A. S. S. R.) (tå-tär') Sov. Un.	55·30 N	51·00 E
134	Tatarsk (tå-tärsk') ...... Sov. Un.	55·15 N	75·00 E
135	Tatar Str. ...... Sov. Un.	51·00 N	141·45 E
65	Tater Hill (Mtn.) (tāt'ĕr hĭl) Ore. (Portland In.)	45·47 N	123·02 W
153	Tateyama (tä'tē-yä'mä) ...... Jap.	35·04 N	139·52 E
166	Tati (tä'tē) ...... Bech.	21·18 S	27·43 E
151	Tattien Ting (Mtn.) ...... China	22·25 N	111·20 E
151	Tatu Ho (R.) ...... China	29·20 N	103·30 E
101	Tatuí (tä-tōō-ē') Braz. (Rio de Janeiro In.)	23·21 S	47·49 W
150	Tat'ung (tä'tōōng') ...... China	40·00 N	113·30 E
101	Taubaté (tou-bä-tā') Braz. (Rio de Janeiro In.)	23·03 S	45·32 W
120	Tauern Tun. ...... Aus.	47·12 N	13·17 E
165	Taufikia (tou-fēk'yå) ...... Sud.	9·30 N	31·47 E
166	Taungs (tä'ōōngs) ...... S. Afr.	27·25 S	29·45 E
84	Taunton (tän'tŭn) Mass. (Providence In.)	41·54 N	71·03 W

ng-sing; ŋ-baŋ; ɴ-nasalized n; nŏd; cŏmmit; ōld; ôbey; ôrder; fōōd; fŏŏt; ou-out; s-soft; sh-dish; th-thin; pūre; ûnite; ûrn; stŭd; circŭs; ü-as "y" in study; '-indeterminate vowel.

274 Taunton–Tetyushi PRONOUNCING INDEX

Page	Name Pronunciation Region	Lat. °′	Long. °′
84	Taunton R. . R. I. (Providence In.)	41·50 N	71·02 W
117	Taunus (Mts.) (tou'nōōz) . . . . Ger.	50·15 N	8·33 E
159	Taupo, L. (tä'ōō-pō) . . . N. Z. (In.)	38·38 S	175·27 E
119	Taurage (tou'rá-gā) . . . . . Sov. Un.	55·15 N	22·18 E
	Taurus Mts., see Toros Dağlari		
124	Tauste (tä-ōōs'tå) . . . . Sp.	41·55 N	1·15 W
134	Tavda (tàv-dá') . . . . Sov. Un.	58·00 N	64·44 E
132	Tavda (R.) . . . . Sov. Un.	59·20 N	63·28 E
123	Taverny (tà-vēr-nē') Fr. (Paris In.)	49·02 N	2·13 E
91	Taviche (tä-vē'chĕ) . . . . Mex.	16·43 N	96·35 W
124	Tavira (tä-vē'rà) . . . . Port.	37·09 N	7·42 W
154	Tavoy . . . . Bur.	14·04 N	98·19 E
133	Tavşanli (tàv'shän-lĭ) . . . . Tur.	39·30 N	29·30 E
153	Tawaramoto (tä'wä-rä-mô-tô) Jap. (Ōsaka In.)	34·33 N	135·48 E
80	Tawas City . . . . Mich.	44·15 N	83·30 W
80	Tawas Pt. (tô'wås) . . . . Mich.	44·15 N	83·25 W
148	Tawen (R.) (dä'wĕn) . . . . China	35·58 N	116·53 E
154	Tawitawi Group (Is.) (tä'wē-tä'wē) . Phil.	4·52 N	120·35 E
90	Taxco de Alarcón (täs'kō dĕ ä-lär-kô'n) . . Mex.	18·34 N	99·37 W
116	Tay, Firth of (fûrth ŏv tā) . . Scot.	56·26 N	2·45 W
116	Tay (L.) . . . . Scot.	56·25 N	5·07 W
116	Tay (R.) . . . . Scot.	56·35 N	3·37 W
155	Tayabas B. (tä-yä'bäs) Phil. (Manila In.)	13·44 N	121·40 E
134	Tayga (tī'gä) . . . . Sov. Un.	56·12 N	85·47 E
135	Taygonos, Mys (Taigonos) (C.) Sov. Un.	60·37 N	160·17 E
77	Taylor (tā'lẽr) . . . . Tex.	30·35 N	97·25 W
69	Taylor, Mt. . . . . N. Mex.	35·20 N	107·40 W
80	Taylorville (tā'lẽr-vĭl) . . . . Ill.	39·30 N	89·20 W
144	Taymā . . . . Sau. Ar.	27·45 N	38·55 E
135	Taymyr (Taimyr) (L.) (tī-mĭr') Sov. Un.	74·13 N	100·45 E
134	Taymyr, P-Ov (Taimyr) (Pen.) Sov. Un.	75·15 N	95·00 E
134	Tayshet (Taishet) (tī-shĕt') Sov. Un.	56·09 N	97·49 E
154	Taytay (tī-tī) . . . . Phil.	10·37 N	119·10 E
151	Tayü . . . . China	25·20 N	114·20 E
155	Tayung (tä-yōōng') Phil. (Manila In.)	16·01 N	120·45 E
134	Taz (B.) (táz) . . . . Sov. Un.	67·15 N	80·45 E
164	Taza (tä'zä) . . . . Mor.	34·08 N	4·00 W
134	Tazotskoye . . . . Sov. Un.	66·58 N	78·28 E
133	Tbilisi ('tbĭl-yē'sē) . . . . Sov. Un.	41·40 N	44·45 E
166	Tchibanga (chē-bäŋ'gä) . . . Gabon	2·48 S	10·50 E
121	Tczew (t'chĕf') . . . . Pol.	54·06 N	18·48 E
92	Teabo (tĕ-ä'bŏ) Mex. (Yucatan In.)	20·25 N	89·14 W
77	Teague (tēg) . . . . Tex.	31·39 N	96·16 W
91	Teapa (tā-ä'pä) . . . . Mex.	17·35 N	92·56 W
164	Tébessa (tā'bĕs'ä) . . . . Alg.	35·27 N	8·13 E
139	Tebingtinggi, Palau (I.) (teb'ĭng-tĭng'gä) Indon. (Singapore In.	0·54 N	102·39 E
90	Tecalitlán (tā-kä-lē-tlän') . . . Mex.	19·28 N	103·17 W
90	Tecoanapa (tāk-wä-nä-pä') . . Mex.	16·33 N	98·46 W
92	Tecoh (tĕ-kô) . Mex. (Yucatan In.)	20·46 N	89·27 W
90	Tecolotlán (tā-kô-lô-tlän') . . . Mex.	20·13 N	103·57 W
91	Tecolutla (tā-kô-lōō'tlä) . . . . Mex.	20·33 N	97·00 W
91	Tecolutla (R.) . . . . Mex.	20·16 N	97·14 W
90	Tecomán (tā-kô-män') . . . . . . Mex.	18·53 N	103·53 W
91	Tecómitl (tĕ-kŏ'mētl) Mex. (Mexico In.)	19·13 N	98·59 W
90	Tecozautla (tā'kô-zä-ōō'tlä) . Mex.	20·33 N	99·38 W
90	Tecpan de Galeana (tĕk-pän' dā gä-lā-ä'nä) . Mex.	17·13 N	100·41 W
91	Tecpatán (tĕk-pä-tá'n) . . . . . . Mex.	17·08 N	93·18 W
90	Tecuala (tĕ-kwä-lä) . . . . Mex.	22·24 N	105·29 W
121	Tecuci (ta-kōōch') . . . . Rom.	45·51 N	27·30 E
75	Tecumseh (tē-kŭm'sē) Can. (Detroit In.)	42·19 N	82·53 W
80	Tecumseh . . . . Mich.	42·00 N	84·00 W
76	Tecumseh . . . . Nebr.	40·21 N	96·09 W
73	Tecumseh . . . . Okla.	35·18 N	96·55 W
116	Tees (R.) (tēz) . . . . Eng.	54·40 N	2·10 W
98	Tefé (tĕf-ā') . . . . Braz.	3·27 S	64·43 W
153	Teganuna (L.) (tā'gä-nōō'nä) Jap. (Tōkyō In.)	35·50 N	140·02 E
92	Tegucigalpa (tå-gōō-sē-gäl'pä) Hond.	14·08 N	87·15 W
68	Tehachapi Mts. (tĕ-hă-shā'pĭ) Calif.	34·50 N	118·55 W
144	Tehrān (tĕ-hrän') . . . . Iran	35·45 N	51·30 E
148	Tehsien (dŭ'sĭän) . . . . China	37·28 N	116·17 E
151	Tehua . . . . China	25·30 N	118·15 E
91	Tehuacan (tā-wä-kän') . . . . . . Mex.	18·27 N	97·23 W
91	Tehuantepec (Sto. Domingo) (tå-wän-tå-pĕk') (sän-tô dô-mē'n-gô) . Mex.	16·20 N	95·14 W
88	Tehuantepec, Golfo de (G.) (gôl-fô dĕ) . Mex.	15·45 N	95·00 W
91	Tehuantepec, Istmo de (Isth.) (ē'st-mô dĕ) . Mex.	17·55 N	94·35 W
91	Tehuantepec (R.) . . . . Mex.	16·30 N	95·23 W
90	Tehuehuetla Arroyo (R.) (tĕ-wĕ-wĕ'tlä är-rô-yô) . Mex.	17·54 N	100·26 W
90	Tehuitzingo (tā-wē-tzĭŋ'gō) . . Mex.	18·21 N	98·16 W
124	Tejeda, Sierra de. (Mts.) (sē-ĕ'r-rä dĕ tĕ-kĕ'dä) . Sp.	36·55 N	5·57 W
124	Tejo, Rio (R.) (rē-ōtä'hōō) . . Port.	39·23 N	8·01 W
91	Tejúpan (Santiago) (tĕ-kōō-pä'n) (sän-tyä'gô) . Mex.	17·39 N	97·34 W
90	Tejúpan, Punta (Pt.) (pōō'n-tä) Mex.	18·19 N	103·30 W
90	Tejupilco de Hidalgo (tå-hōō-pēl'kô dä ē-dhäl'gō) Mex.	18·52 N	100·07 W
70	Tekamah (tē-kā'mà) . . . . Nebr.	41·46 N	96·13 W
92	Tekax de Alvaro Obregon (tĕ-kä'x dĕ à'l-vä-rô-brĕ-gô'n) Mex. (Yucatan In.)	20·12 N	89·11 W
127	Tekirdağ (Rodosto) (tĕ-kēr'dägh') Tur.	41·00 N	27·28 E
92	Tekit (tĕ-kē't) . Mex. (Yucatan In.)	20·35 N	89·18 W
66	Tekoa (tē-kō'á) . . . . Wash.	47·15 N	117·03 W
92	Tela (tā'lä) . . . . Hond.	15·45 N	87·25 W
92	Tela, Bahia de (B.) (bä-ē'ä dĕ) Hond.	15·53 N	87·29 W
139	Telapa Burok, Gunong (Mt.) Mala. (Singapore In.)	2·51 N	102·04 E
133	Telavi . . . . Sov. Un.	42·00 N	45·20 E
139	Tel Aviv-Jaffa (tĕl-ä-vēv'jä'fá) Isr. (Palestine In.)	32·03 N	34·46 E
86	Telegraph Creek (tĕl'ē-gràf) . . Can.	57·59 N	131·22 W
129	Teleneshty (tyĕ-le-nĕsht'ĭ) . Sov. Un.	47·31 N	28·22 E
68	Telescope Pk. (tĕl'ē skōp) . . . Calif.	36·12 N	117·05 W
99	Teles Pirez (R.) (tĕ-lĕs pē'rĕz) Braz.	8·28 S	57·07 W
139	Telesung . . . Indon. (Singapore In.)	1·07 N	102·53 E
92	Telica (Vol.) (tå-lē'kä) . . . . Nic.	12·38 N	86·52 W
146	Telii Nuur (L.) . . . . China	45·49 N	86·08 E
80	Tell City (tĕl) . . . . Ind.	38·00 N	86·45 W
64	Teller (tĕl'ẽr) . . . . Alaska	65·17 N	166·28 W
98	Tello (tĕ'l-yô) . . . . Col. (In.)	3·05 N	75·08 W
69	Telluride (tĕl'ū-rīd) . . . . Colo.	37·55 N	107·50 W
139	Telok Datok Mala. (Singapore In.)	2·51 N	101·33 E
90	Teloloapan (tā'lô-lô-ä'pän) . . . Mex.	18·19 N	99 54 W
132	Tel'pos-Iz, Gora (Mtn.) (tyĕl'pôs-ēz') . Sov. Un.	63·50 N	59·20 E
139	Tel Sharuhea . . Isr. (Palestine In.)	31·16 N	34·29 E
119	Telšiai (tĕl'-shä'ē) . . . . . . Sov. Un.	55·59 N	22·17 E
111	Teltow (tĕl'tō) . . . Ger. (Berlin In.)	52·24 N	13·12 E
154	Telukbetung . . . . Indon.	5·30 S	105·04 E
139	Telukletjak Indon. (Singapore In.)	1·53 N	101·45 E
90	Temascalcingo (tā'mäs-käl-sĭŋ'gō) . Mex.	19·55 N	100·00 W
90	Temascaltepec (tā'mäs-käl-tå pĕk) . Mex.	19·00 N	100·03 W
92	Temax (tĕ'mäx) Mex. (Yucatan In.)	21·10 N	88·51 W
133	Temir (tyĕ'mĕr) . . . . Sov. Un.	49·10 N	57·15 E
134	Temir-Tau . . . . Sov. Un.	50·08 N	73·13 E
82	Temiscouata (L.) (tĕ'mĭs-kōō-ä'tä) . Can.	47·46 N	69·10 W
91	Temoaya (tĕ-mô-ä-yä) Mex. (Mexico In.)	19·28 N	99·36 W
100	Temperley (tĕ'm-pĕr-lā) . Arg. (In.)	34·32 S	58·24 W
126	Tempio Pausania (tĕm'pē-ō pou-sä'nē-ä) . Sard.	40·55 N	9·05 E
77	Temple (tĕm'p'l) . . . . Tex.	31·06 N	97·20 W
74	Temple City Calif. (Los Angeles In.)	34·07 N	118·02 W
85	Templeton (tĕm'p'l-tŭn) Can. (Ottawa In.)	45·29 N	75·37 W
120	Templin (tĕm-plēn') . . . . Ger.	53·08 N	13·30 E
90	Tempoal (R.) (tĕm-pô-ä'l) . . . Mex.	21·38 N	98·23 W
129	Temryuk (tyĕm-ryōōk') . Sov. Un.	45·17 N	37·21 E
100	Temuco (tå-mōō'kō) . . . . Chile	38·46 S	72·38 W
136	Temyasovo (tĕm-yä'sô-vô) Sov. Un. (Urals In.)	53·00 N	58·06 E
92	Tenabó (tĕ-nä-bŏ') Mex. (Yucatan In.)	20·05 N	90·11 W
90	Tenamaxtlán (tā'nä-mäs-tlän') Mex.	20·13 N	104·06 W
90	Tenancingo (tå-nän-sēŋ'gō) . . Mex.	18·54 N	99·36 W
91	Tenango (tå-näŋ'gō) Mex. (Mexico In.)	19·09 N	98·51 W
154	Tenasserim (tĕn-ăs'ēr-ĭm) . . . . Bur.	12·09 N	99·01 E
129	Tenderovskaya Kosa (C.) (tĕn-dĕ-rôf'skå-yå kô-sä') Sov. Un.	46·12 N	31·17 E
	Tenedos, see Bozcaada		
164	Ténéré . (Reg.) . . . . Niger	18·45 N	11·16 E
164	Tenerife I. (tå-nå-rē'få) (tĕn-ēr-ĭf') . Can. Is.	28·41 N	17·02 W
113	Ténés (tā-nĕs') . . . . Alg.	36·28 N	1·22 E
148	T'enghsien (tĕng'hsē-ĕn') . . . China	35·07 N	117·08 E
134	Tengiz (L.) (tyĭn-gēs') . . . Sov. Un.	50·45 N	68·39 E
146	Tengri Khan (tĕŋ'grē кän') . China	42·10 N	80·20 E
153	Tenjin (tĕn'jĕn) . . Jap. (Ōsaka In.)	34·54 N	135·04 E
166	Tenke (tĕŋ'kä) . . . . Con. L.	10·36 S	26·12 E
73	Tenkiller Ferry Res. (tĕn-kĭl'ẽr) Okla.	35·42 N	94·47 W
164	Tenkodogo (tĕŋ-kô-dō'gō) Upper Volta	11·42 N	0·30 W
65	Tenmile (R.) (tĕn mīl) Wash. (Vancouver In.)	48·52 N	122·32 W
158	Tennant Creek (tĕn'ănt) . . . Austl.	19·45 S	134·00 E
63	Tennessee (State) (tĕn-ĕ-sē') . U. S.	35·50 N	88·00 W
63	Tennessee (L.) . . . . U. S.	35·35 N	88·20 W
78	Tennessee (R.) . . . . U. S.	35·10 N	88·20 W
78	Tennille (tĕn'ĭl) . . . . Ga.	32·55 N	86·50 W
101	Teno (tĕ'nô) (R.) Chile (Santiago In.)	34·55 S	71·00 W
160	Tenora (tĕn-ōrà) . . . . Austl.	34·23 S	147·33 E
91	Tenosique (tā-nô-sē'kå) . . . . . Mex.	17·27 N	91·25 W
153	Tenryū-Gawa (Strm.) (tĕn'ryōō'gä'wä) . Jap.	35·16 N	137·54 E
77	Tensas R. (tĕn'sô) . . . . La.	31·54 N	91·30 W
78	Tensaw (R.) (tĕn'sô) . . . . Ala.	30·45 N	87·52 W
160	Tenterfield (tĕn'tẽr-fēld) . . . . Austl.	29·00 S	52·06 E
79	Ten Thousand, Is. (tĕn thou'zănd) . Fla (In.)	25·45 N	81·35 W
90	Teocaltiche (tā'ô-käl-tē'chā) . Mex.	21·27 N	102·38 W
91	Teocelo (tā-ô-sā'lō) . . . . Mex.	19·22 N	96·57 W
90	Teocuitatlán de Corona (tā'ô-kwē'tä-tlän' dä kô-rō'nä) Mex.	20·06 N	103·22 W
99	Teófilo Otoni (tĕ-ô'fē-lō-tô'nē) Braz.	17·49 S	41·18 W
90	Teoloyucan (tā'ô-lô-yōō'kän) . Mex.	19·43 N	99·12 W
91	Teopisca (tā-ô-pēs'kä) . . . . . . Mex.	16·30 N	92·33 W
91	Teotihuacán (tĕ-ô-tē-wä-kà'n) Mex. (Mexico In.)	19·40 N	98·52 W
91	Teotitlán del Camino (tā-ô-tē-tlän' dĕl kä-mē'nō) . Mex.	18·07 N	97·04 W
90	Tepalcatepec (tā'päl-kä-tå'pĕk) Mex.	19·11 N	102·51 W
90	Tepalcatepec (R.) . . . . Mex.	18·54 N	102·25 W
90	Tepalcingo (tā-päl-sēŋ'gô) . . . Mex.	18·34 N	98·49 W
90	Tepatitlan de Morelos (tā-pä-tê-tlän' dā mô-rā'los) Mex.	20·15 N	102·47 W
91	Tepeaca (tā-på-ä'kä) . . . . Mex.	18·57 N	97·54 W
90	Tepecoacuilco de Trujano (tā'på-kô-ä-kwēl'kō dā trōō-hä'nō) . Mex.	19·15 N	99·29 W
90	Tepeji del Rio (tā-på-кe' dĕl rē'ō) Mex.	19·55 N	99·22 W
91	Tepelmeme (tā'pĕl-mā'må) . . Mex.	17·51 N	97·23 W
91	Tepetlaoxtoc (tā'på-tlä'ôs-tōk') Mex. (Mexico In.)	19·34 N	98·49 W
90	Tepezala (tā-på-zä-lä') . . . . . . Mex.	22·12 N	102·12 W
90	Tepic (tā-pēk') . . . . Mex.	21·32 N	104·53 W
148	Tep'ing (dŭ'pĭng) . . . . China	37·28 N	116·57 E
136	Tëplaya Gora (tyôp'lá-yá gô-rá) Sov. Un. (Urals In.)	58·32 N	59·08 E
120	Teplice Sanov (tĕp'lĭ-tsĕ shä'nôf) Czech.	50·39 N	13·50 E
91	Teposcolula (San Pedro y San Pablo) (tā-pôs-kô-lōō'lä) (sän pä'drō ē sän pä'blō) . Mex.	17·33 N	97·29 W
98	Tequendama, Salto de (Falls) (sä'l-tô dĕ tĕ-kĕn-dä'mä) Col. (In.)	4·34 N	74·18 W
90	Tequila (tå-kē'lä) . . . . Mex.	20·53 N	103·48 W
91	Tequisistlán (R.) (tĕ-kē-sēs-tlå'n) Mex.	16·20 N	95·40 W
90	Tequisquiapan (tå-kēs-kē-ä'pän) . Mex.	20·33 N	99·57 W
125	Ter (R.) (tĕr) . . . . Sp.	42·04 N	2·52 E
124	Tera (R.) (tā'rä) . . . . Sp.	42·05 N	6·24 W
126	Teramo (tĕ'rä-mô) . . . . It.	42·40 N	13·41 E
123	Terborg (tĕr'bōrg) Neth. (Ruhr In.)	51·55 N	6·23 E
133	Tercan (tĕr'jän) . . . . Tur.	39·40 N	40·12 E
164	Terceira I. (tĕr-sā'rä) Azores (In.)	38·49 N	26·36 W
121	Terebovlya (tĕ-rĕ'bôv-lyä) Sov. Un.	49·18 N	25·43 E
133	Terek (R.) . . . . Sov. Un.	43·30 N	45·10 E
136	Terenkul' (tĕ-rĕn'kōōl) Sov. Un. (Urals In.)	55·38 N	62·18 E
99	Teresina (tĕr-å-sē'nà) . . . . . . Braz.	5·04 S	42·42 W
100	Teresópolis (tĕr-ā-sô'pō-lēzh) Braz. (In.)	22·25 S	42·59 W
132	Teriberka (tyĕr-ē-byôr'kå) Sov. Un.	69·00 N	35·15 E
133	Terme (tĕr'mĕ) . . . . Tur.	41·05 N	42·00 E
142	Termez (tyĕr'mĕz) . . . . . . Sov. Un.	37·19 N	67·20 E
126	Termini (tĕr'mē-nē) . . . . It.	37·58 N	13·39 E
91	Términos, Laguna de (L.) (lä-gōō'nä dĕ ĕ'r-mē-nôs) . . Mex.	18·37 N	91·32 W
126	Termoli (tĕr'mô-lē) . . . . It.	42·00 N	15·01 E
110	Tern (R.) (tûrn) . . . . Eng.	52·49 N	2·31 W
155	Ternate (tĕr-nä'tä) . . . . Indon.	0·52 N	127·25 E
126	Terni (tĕr'nē) . . . . It.	42·38 N	12·41 E
121	Ternopol' (tĕr-nō-pōl') . . . Sov. Un.	49·32 N	25·36 E
152	Terpeniya, Zaliv (B.) (zä'lĭf tĕr-pă'nĭ-yå) . Sov. Un.	49·10 N	143·05 E
135	Terpeniya, Mys (C.) . . . . Sov. Un.	48·44 N	144·42 E
86	Terrace (tĕr'ĭs) . . . . Can.	54·36 N	128·38 W
126	Terracina (tĕr-rä-chē'nä) . . . . . . It.	41·18 N	13·14 E
83	Terra Nova Natl. Park . . . . . Can.	48·37 N	54·15 W
85	Terrebonne (tĕr-bŏn') Can. (Montreal In.)	45·42 N	73·38 W
77	Terrebonne B . . . . La.	28·55 N	90·30 W
80	Terre Haute (tĕr-ē hōt') . . . . . Ind.	39·25 N	87·25 W
77	Terrell (tĕr'ĕl) . . . . Tex.	32·44 N	96·15 W
65	Terrell . . . . Wash. (Vancouver In.)	48·53 N	122·44 W
74	Terrell Hills (tĕr'ĕl hĭlz) Tex. (San Antonio In.)	29·28 N	98·27 W
117	Terschelling (I.) (tĕr-sкĕl'ĭng) Neth.	53·25 N	5·12 E
124	Teruel (tå-rōō-ĕl') . . . . Sp.	40·20 N	1·05 W
127	Tešanj (tĕ'shän') . . . . Yugo.	44·36 N	17·59 E
111	Teschendorf (tĕ'shĕn-dōrf) Ger. (Berlin In.)	52·51 N	13·10 E
91	Tesecheacan (tĕ-sĕ-chĕ-ä-kà'n) Mex.	18·10 N	95·41 W
64	Teshekpuk (L.) (tē-shĕk'pŭk) Alaska	70·18 N	152·36 W
152	Teshio Dake (Mt.) (tĕsh'ē-ō-dä'kä) . Jap.	44·00 N	142·50 E
152	Teshio Gawa (R.) (tĕsh'ē-ō gä'wä) . Jap.	44·35 N	114·55 E
86	Teslin (L.) (tĕs-lĭn) . . . . Can.	60·12 N	132·08 W
86	Teslin (R.) . . . . Can.	61·18 N	134·14 W
146	Tesiin Gol (R.) . . . . Mong.	50·14 N	94·30 E
164	Tessaoua (tĕs-sä'ōō-ä) . . . . . . Niger	13·53 N	7·53 E
111	Tessenderlo . . . Bel. (Bruxelles In.)	51·04 N	5·08 E
116	Test (R.) (tĕst) . . . . Eng.	51·10 N	2·20 W
126	Testa del Gargano (Pt.) (täs'tä dĕl gär-gä'nō) . It.	41·48 N	16·13 E
166	Tete (tā'tĕ) . . . . Moz.	15·13 S	33·40 E
129	Teterev (R.) (tyĕ'tyĕ-rĕf) Sov. Un.	50·35 N	29·18 E
120	Teterow (tā'tĕ-rō) . . . . Ger.	53·46 N	12·33 E
127	Teteven (tĕt'ĕ-ven') . . . . Bul.	42·57 N	24·15 E
67	Teton R. (tē'tŏn) . . . . Mont.	47·54 N	111·37 W
127	Tetovo (tā'tô-vô) . . . . Yugo.	42·01 N	21·00 E
110	Tettenhall (tĕt'ĕn-hôl) . . . . . . Eng.	52·36 N	2·10 W
164	Tetuán (tå-twän') . . . . Mor.	35·42 N	5·34 W
152	Tetyukhe-Pristan (tĕt-yōō'кĕ prĭ-stän') . Sov. Un.	44·21 N	135·44 E
132	Tetyushi (tyĕt-yōō'shĭ) . . Sov. Un.	54·58 N	48·40 E

ăt; finăl; rāte; senāte; ärm; åsk: sofá; fâre; ch-choose; dh-as th in other; bē; ēvent; bĕt; recĕnt; cratẽr; g-go; gh-guttural g; bĭt; ĭ-short neutral; rīde; к-guttural k as ch in German ich;

PRONOUNCING INDEX Teupitz–Tirunelveli 275

Page	Name Pronunciation Region	Lat. °′	Long. °′
111	Teupitz (toi'pĕtz). Ger. (Berlin In.)	52·08 N	13·37 E
126	Tevere (Tiber) (R.) (tā'vā-rā) (tī'bēr). It.	42·30 N	12·14 E
83	Tewksbury (tūks'bĕr-ĭ) Mass. (Boston In.)	42·37 N	71·14 W
73	Texarkana (tĕk-sär-kăn'ȧ) Ark.	33·26 N	94·02 W
73	Texarkana Tex.	33·26 N	94·04 W
73	Texarkana Dam Tex.	33·18 N	94·09 W
84	Texas (tĕk'sȧs) Md. (Baltimore In.)	39·28 N	76·40 W
62	Texas (State) U. S.	31·00 N	101·00 W
77	Texas City Tex. (In.)	29·23 N	94·54 W
90	Texcaltitlán (tās-käl'tē-tlän') Mex.	18·54 N	99·51 W
117	Texel (I.) (tĕk'sĕl) Neth.	53·10 N	4·45 E
91	Texcoco (tās-kō'kō) Mex. (Mexico In.)	19·31 N	98·53 W
90	Texcoco, Lago de (L.) (lä'gô-dĕ) Mex.	19·28 N	98·59 W
91	Texistepec (tĕk-sēs-tā-pĕk') Mex.	17·51 N	94·46 W
91	Texmelucan (tās-mâ-lōō'kän) Mex. (Mexico In.)	19·17 N	98·26 W
73	Texoma, L. (tĕk'ō-mă) Okla.	34·03 N	96·28 W
167	Teyateyaneng Bas. (Natal In.)	29·11 S	27·43 E
128	Teykovo (tĕy-kô-vô) Sov. Un.	56·52 N	40·34 E
91	Teziutlán (tā-zē-ōō-tlän') Mex.	19·48 N	97·21 W
90	Tezontepec (tā-zōn-tā-pĕk') Mex.	19·52 N	98·48 W
90	Tezontepec de Aldama (dā äl-dä'mä). Mex.	20·19 N	99·19 W
142	Tezpur India	26·42 N	92·52 E
86	Tha-anne (R.) Can.	60·50 N	96·56 W
167	Thaba Putsua (Mtn.) Bas. (Natal In.)	29·44 S	27·58 E
168	Thabazimbi S. Afr. (Johannesburg & Pretoria In.)	24·36 S	27·22 E
138	Thailand (Siam) Asia	16·30 N	101·00 E
154	Thale Luang (L.) Thai.	7·51 N	99·39 E
110	Thame (tām) Eng. (London In.)	51·43 N	0·59 W
80	Thames (R.) (tĕmz) Can.	42·40 N	81·45 W
117	Thames, R. Eng.	51·26 N	0·54 E
115	Thamit R. Libya	30·39 N	16·23 E
143	Thāna (thä'nŭ) India (Bombay In.)	19·13 N	72·58 E
143	Thāna Cr. India (Bombay In.)	19·03 N	72·58 E
146	Thang Ha Ri (Mts.) China	33·15 N	89·07 E
151	Thanh-Hoa (tän'hō'ä) Viet.	19·46 N	105·42 E
123	Thann (tän) Fr.	47·49 N	7·05 E
123	Thaon-les-Vosges (tä-ŏn-lā-vōzh') Fr.	48·16 N	6·24 E
160	Thargomindah (thär'gō-mĭn'dȧ) Austl.	27·58 S	143·57 E
127	Thásos (I.) (thă'sôs) Grc.	40·41 N	24·53 E
89	Thatch Cay (I.) (thăch) Vir. Is. (U. S. A.) (St. Thomas In.)	18·22 N	64·53 W
120	Thaya R. (tä'yȧ) Aus.-Czech.	48·48 N	15·40 E
73	Thayer (thâ'ēr) Mo.	36·30 N	91·34 W
	Thebes, see Thivai		
168	Thebes (Ruins) (thēbz) U. A. R. (Nile In.)	25·47 N	32·39 E
65	The Brothers (Mtn.) (brŭth'ērs) Wash. (Seattle In.)	47·39 N	123·08 W
66	The Dalles (dălz) Ore.	45·36 N	121·10 W
155	The Father, (Mtn.) N. Gui. Ter.	5·10 S	151·55 E
	The Hague, see s'Gravenhage		
142	Thelum W. Pak.	32·59 N	73·43 E
161	The Oaks Austl. (Sydney In.)	34·04 S	150·36 E
160	Theodore (thēō'dôr) Austl.	24·51 S	150·09 E
69	Theodore Roosevelt Dam (thē-ô-dōr' rōō-sȧ-vĕlt). Ariz.	33·46 N	111·25 W
70	Theodore Roosevelt Natl. Mem. Park N. D.	47·20 N	103·42 W
86	The Pas (pä) Can.	53·48 N	101·17 W
67	Thermopolis (thēr-mŏp'ō-lĭs) Wyo.	43·38 N	108·11 W
160	The Round Mtn. Austl.	30·17 S	152·19 E
127	Thessalía (Reg.) Grc.	39·50 N	22·09 E
87	Thessalon Can.	46·11 N	83·37 W
127	Thessaloníki (thĕs-sȧ-lô-nē'kē) Grc.	40·38 N	22·59 E
82	Thetford Mines (thĕt'fērd mīns) Can.	46·05 N	71·20 W
167	The Twins (Mtn.) (twĭnz) S. Afr. (Natal In.)	30·09 S	28·29 E
168	Theunissen S. Afr. (Johannesburg & Pretoria In.)	28·25 S	26·44 E
77	Thibodaux (tē-bô-dō') La.	29·48 N	90·48 W
86	Thickwood Hills (thĭk'wŏŏd). Can.	53·28 N	108·30 W
70	Thief (L.) (thēf) Minn.	48·32 N	95·46 W
70	Thief (R.) Minn.	48·18 N	96·07 W
70	Thief River Falls (thēf rĭv'ēr fôlz). Minn.	48·07 N	96·11 W
84	Thiells (thēlz) N. Y. (New York In.)	41·12 N	74·01 W
122	Thiers (tyâr) Fr.	45·51 N	3·32 E
164	Thiès (tē-ĕs') Senegal	14·43 N	16·56 W
112	Thingvallavatn (L.) Ice.	64·12 N	20·22 W
123	Thionville (tyôn-vēl') Fr.	49·23 N	6·31 E
165	Third Cataract Sud.	19·53 N	30·11 E
118	Thisted (tēs'tĕdh) Den.	56·57 N	8·38 E
112	Thistil Fd. (tēs'tĕl) Ice.	66·29 N	14·59 W
160	Thistle (I.) (thĭs''l) Austl.	34·55 S	136·11 E
127	Thivai (Thebes) Grc.	38·20 N	23·18 E
112	Thjórsá (R.) (tyûr'sȧ) Ice.	64·23 N	19·18 W
111	Tholen Neth. (Amsterdam In.)	51·32 N	4·11 E
72	Thomas (tŏm'ăs) Okla.	35·44 N	98·43 W
81	Thomas W. Va.	39·15 N	79·30 W
78	Thomaston (tŏm'ăs-tŭn) Ga.	32·51 N	84·17 W
78	Thomasville (tŏm'ăs-vĭl) Ala.	31·55 N	87·43 W
79	Thomasville N. C.	35·52 N	80·05 W
86	Thompson (tŏmp'sŭn) Can.	55·48 N	97·59 W
73	Thompson (R.) Mo.	40·32 N	93·49 W
66	Thompson Falls Mont.	47·35 N	115·20 W
75	Thompsonville (tomp'sŭn-vĭl) Wis. (Milwaukee In.)	42·47 N	87·57 W
79	Thomson (tŏm'sŭn) Ga.	33·28 N	82·29 W
159	Thomson (R.) (tŏm-sŏn) Austl.	29·30 S	143·07 E
120	Thonon (tô-nôN') Fr.	46·23 N	6·25 E
123	Thonon-les-Bains (tô-nôN'lā-băN') Switz.	46·22 N	6·27 E
112	Thórisvatn (L.) Ice.	64·02 N	119·09 W
110	Thorne (thôrn) Eng.	53·37 N	0·58 W
85	Thornhill (thôrn-hĭl) Can. (Toronto In.)	43·49 N	79·25 W
80	Thorntown (thôrn'tŭn) Ind.	40·05 N	86·35 W
85	Thorold (thō'rōld) Can. (Toronto In.)	43·13 N	79·12 W
112	Thorshavn (tôrs-houn') Den.	62·00 N	6·55 W
122	Thouars (tōō-är') Fr.	47·00 N	0·17 W
81	Thousand Is. (thou'zănd) N. Y.-Can.	44·15 N	76·10 W
127	Thrace (Reg.) (thrās) Grc.-Tur.	41·20 N	26·07 E
110	Thrapston (thrăp'stŭn) Eng.	52·23 N	0·32 W
67	Three Forks (thrē fôrks) Mont.	45·56 N	111·35 W
80	Three Oaks (thrē ōks) Mich.	41·50 N	86·40 W
164	Three Points, C. Ghana	4·27 N	2·29 W
80	Three Rivers Mich.	42·00 N	83·40 W
120	Thun (tōōn) Switz.	46·46 N	7·34 E
71	Thunder B. (thŭn'dēr) Can.	48·29 N	88·52 W
120	Thunner See (L.) Switz.	46·40 N	7·30 E
76	Thurber (thûr'bēr) Tex.	32·30 N	98·23 W
120	Thüringen (Thuringia) (Reg.) (tü'rĭng-ĕn). Ger.	51·07 N	10·45 E
116	Thurles (thûrlz) Ire.	52·44 N	7·45 W
110	Thurrock (thŭ'rŏk) Eng. (London In.)	51·28 N	0·19 E
159	Thursday (I.) (thûrz-dā) Austl.	10·17 S	142·23 E
85	Thurso (thŭr'sô) Can. (Ottawa In.)	45·36 N	75·15 W
116	Thurso Scot.	58·35 N	3·40 W
47	Thurston Pen. (thûrs'tŭn) Ant.	71·20 S	98·00 W
166	Thysville (tēs-vēl') Con. L.	5·08 S	14·58 E
155	Tiaong (tē-ä-ông') Phil. (Manila In.)	13·56 N	121·20 E
164	Tiaret (tyä-rĕ') Alg.	35·28 N	1·15 E
100	Tibagi (tē-bȧ-zhē) Braz.	24·40 S	50·35 W
165	Tibasti, Sarir (Des.) Chad	23·08 N	15·57 E
	Tiber (R.), see Tévere		
139	Tiberias (tī-bē'rĭ-ăs) Isr. (Palestine In.)	32·48 N	35·32 E
165	Tibesti Massif (Mts.) Chad	20·43 N	17·16 E
146	Tibet Aut. Reg. (tĭ-bĕt') China	31·15 N	84·48 E
146	Tibet, Plat. of China	32·22 N	83·30 E
139	Tibnīn Leb. (Palestine In.)	33·12 N	35·23 E
65	Tiburon (tē-bōō-rōn') Calif. (San Francisco In.)	37·53 N	122·27 W
95	Tiburon Hai.	18·35 N	74·25 W
88	Tiburón (I.) Mex.	28·45 N	113·10 W
93	Tiburon, Cabo (C.) (kȧ'bô) Pan.	8·42 N	77·19 W
65	Tiburon I. Calif. (San Francisco In.)	37·52 N	122·26 W
155	Ticaco Pass (tē-kä-kô) Phil. (Manila In.)	12·38 N	123·50 E
155	Ticao (I.) (tē-kä'ō) Phil. (Manila In.)	12·40 N	123·30 E
110	Tickhill (tĭk'ĭl) Eng.	53·26 N	1·06 W
81	Ticonderaga (tī-kŏn-dēr-ō'gȧ) N. Y.	43·50 N	73·30 W
92	Ticul (tē-kōō'l) Mex. (Yucatan In.)	20·22 N	89·32 W
118	Tidaholm (tē'dȧ-hōlm) Swe.	58·11 N	13·53 E
110	Tideswell (tīdz'wĕl) Eng.	53·17 N	1·47 W
164	Tidikelt (Reg.) (tē-dē-kĕlt') Alg.	25·53 N	2·11 E
164	Tidjikdja (tē-jĭk'jä) Mauritania	18·37 N	11·30 W
150	Tiehling (tyȧ'lĭng) China	42·18 N	123·58 E
125	Tielmes (tyȧl-màs') Sp. (Madrid In.)	40·15 N	3·20 W
151	Tien Ch'ih (L.) (tyĕn) China	24·58 N	103·18 E
	Tienching see Tientsin		
111	Tienen Bel. (Bruxelles In.)	50·49 N	4·58 E
148	Tienerhwan (dĭän'ĕ'hōōän) China	31·39 N	114·08 E
148	Tienfou (dĭän'fōō) China	31·53 N	117·28 E
148	T'ienma Shan (Mts.) (tiän'mä shän). China	36·02 N	117·57 E
151	Tienmen (tyĕn'mĕn') China	30·40 N	113·10 E
151	Tienpai China	21·30 N	111·20 E
151	T'ienpao China	23·18 N	106·40 E
	Tien-Shan (Mts.), see Tyan' Shan'		
148	Tienshan Hu (L.) (dĭän'shän'hōō) China	31·08 N	120·30 E
150	T'ienshui China	34·25 N	105·40 E
150	T'ientsaokang China	45·58 N	126·00 E
148	Tientsin (Tienching) (tyĕn'tsĕn') China	39·08 N	117·14 E
151	T'ientung China	23·32 N	107·10 E
118	Tierp (tyĕrp) Swe.	60·21 N	17·28 E
167	Tierpoort S. Afr. (Johannesburg & Pretoria In.)	25·53 S	28·26 E
91	Tierra Blanca (tyĕ'r-rä-blä'n-kä) Mex.	18·28 N	96·19 W
100	Tierra del Fuego (Reg.) (tyĕr'rä dĕl fwā'gō). Chile-Arg.	53·50 S	68·45 W
124	Tiétar (R.) (tē-ā'tär) Sp.	39·56 N	5·44 W
101	Tietê (tyā-tā') Braz. (Rio de Janeiro In.)	23·08 S	47·42 W
99	Tieté (R.) Braz.	20·46 S	50·46 W
80	Tiffin (tĭf'ĭn) Ohio	41·10 N	83·15 W
78	Tifton (tĭf'tŭn) Ga.	31·25 N	83·34 W
65	Tigard (tī'gärd) Ore. (Portland In.)	45·25 N	122·46 W
82	Tignish (tĭg'nĭsh) Can.	46·56 N	64·03 W
136	Tigoda R. (tē'gô-dȧ) Sov. Un. (Leningrad In.)	59·29 N	31·15 E
100	Tigre (tē'grĕ) Arg. (In.)	34·09 S	58·35 W
98	Tigre (R.) Peru	2·20 S	75·41 W
166	Tigres, Peninsula dos (Pen.) (pĕ-nē'ŋ-sōō-lä-dôs-tē'grĕs). Ang.	16·30 S	11·45 E
144	Tigris, R. Asia	34·30 N	44·00 E
139	Tīh, Gebel el (Mts.) U. A. R. (Palestine In.)	29·24 N	33·42 E
146	Tihua (Urumchi) (ōō-rōōm'chē) China	43·49 N	87·43 E
91	Tihuatlán (tē-wä-tlän') Mex.	20·43 N	97·34 W
68	Tijuana (tē-hwä'nä) Mex. (San Diego In.)	32·32 N	117·02 W
100	Tijuca, Pico da (Mtn.) (pē'kō-dä-tē-zhōō'kȧ). Braz. (In.)	22·56 S	43·17 W
92	Tikal (Ruins) (tē-käl') Guat. (Yucatan In.)	17·16 N	89·49 W
133	Tikhoretsk (tē kôr-yĕtsk') Sov. Un.	45·55 N	40·05 E
128	Tikhvin (tēk-vēn') Sov. Un.	59·36 N	33·38 E
144	Tikrīt Iraq	34·36 N	43·31 E
135	Tiksi (tēk-sē') Sov. Un.	71·42 N	128·32 E
111	Tilburg (tĭl'bûrg) Neth. (Amsterdam In.)	51·33 N	5·05 E
164	Tilemsi, Vallée du (Valley) Mali	18·09 N	0·02 W
135	Tilichiki (tyĭ-le-chĭ-kē) Sov. Un.	60·49 N	166·14 E
129	Tiligul (R.) (tē'lĭ-gûl) Sov. Un.	47·25 N	30·27 E
164	Tillabéri (tē-yȧ-bā-rē') Niger	14·14 N	1·30 E
66	Tillamook (tĭl'ȧ-mŏŏk) Ore.	45·27 N	123·50 W
66	Tillamook B. Ore.	45·32 N	124·26 W
118	Tillberga (tĕl-bĕr'ghȧ) Swe.	59·40 N	16·34 E
80	Tillsonburg (tĭl'sŭn-bûrg) Can.	42·50 N	80·50 W
	Tilsit, see Sovetsk		
129	Tim (tēm) Sov. Un.	51·39 N	37·07 E
159	Timaru (tĭm'ȧ-rōō) N. Z. (In.)	44·26 S	171·17 E
129	Timashevskaya (tĕmă-shĕfś-kă'yă). Sov. Un.	45·47 N	38·57 E
77	Timbalier B. (tĭm'bȧ-lēr) La.	28·55 N	90·14 W
65	Timber (tĭm'bēr) Ore. (Portland In.)	45·43 N	123·17 W
164	Timbo (tĭm'bō) Gui.	10·41 N	11·51 W
	Timbuktu, see Tombouctou		
118	Time (tē'mĕ) Nor.	58·45 N	5·39 E
164	Timimoun (tē-mē-mōōn') Alg.	29·14 N	0·22 E
164	Timiris, Cap (C.) Mauritania	19·37 N	17·38 W
127	Timiș (R.) Rom.	45·28 N	21·06 E
87	Timiskaming (L.) Can.	47·27 N	81·00 W
87	Timiskaming Station (tē-mĭs'kȧ-mĭng). Can.	46·41 N	79·01 W
87	Timmins (tĭm'ĭnz) Can.	48·25 N	81·22 W
164	Timmissao (tē-mē-sä'ō) Alg.	22·03 N	2·56 E
79	Timmonsville (tĭm'ŭnz-vĭl) S. C.	34·09 N	79·55 W
155	Timor (I.) (tē-mōr') Indon.	10·08 S	125·00 E
156	Timor Sea Oceania	12·40 S	95·00 E
127	Timoșoara Rom.	45·44 N	21·21 E
69	Timpanogos Cave Natl. Mon. (tĭ-măn'ō-gōz). Utah	40·25 N	111·45 W
77	Timpson (tĭmp'sŭn) Tex.	31·55 N	94·24 W
135	Timpton (R.) (tĕmp'tŏn). Sov. Un.	57·15 N	126·35 E
168	Timsāh (L.) (tĭm'sä) U. A. R. (Suez In.)	30·34 N	32·22 E
95	Tina, Monte (Mtn.) (mô'n-tĕ-tē'nȧ). Dom. Rep.	18·50 N	70·40 W
167	Tina (R.) (tē'nă) S. Afr. (Natal In.)	30·50 S	28·44 E
99	Tinaguillo (tē-nä-gē'l-yō) Ven. (In.)	9·55 N	68·18 W
164	Tindouf (tēn-dōōf') Alg.	27·43 N	7·44 W
139	Tinggi, Palau (I.) Mala. (Singapore In.)	2·16 N	104·16 E
148	T'ingho (dĭng'hŭ) China	37·45 N	118·29 E
148	Tinghsien (dĭng'siän) China	38·30 N	115·00 E
148	Tinghsing (dĭng'sĭng) China	39·18 N	115·50 E
149	Tinglin China (Shanghai In.)	30·53 N	121·18 E
98	Tingo María (tē'ngō-mä-rē'ä). Peru	9·15 S	76·04 W
118	Tingsryd (tĭngs'rüd) Swe.	56·32 N	14·58 E
148	Tingtzu Wan (B.) (dĭng'tze wän) China	36·33 N	121·06 E
90	Tinguindio Paracho (tēn-kē'n-dyō-pärä-chô). Mex.	19·38 N	102·02 W
101	Tinguiririca (R.) (tē'n-gē-rē-rē'kä) Chile (Santiago In.)	36·48 S	70·45 W
148	Tingyüan (tĭng'yü-än') China	32·32 N	117·40 E
75	Tinley Park (tĭn'lē) Ill. (Chicago In.)	41·34 N	87·47 W
118	Tinnosset (tĕn'nôs'sĕt) Nor.	49·44 N	9·00 E
118	Tinnsjö (tĭnnsyû) Nor.	59·55 N	8·49 E
100	Tinogasta (tē-nô-gäs'tä) Arg.	28·07 S	67·30 W
127	Tínos (I.) Grc.	37·45 N	25·12 E
145	Tinsukia (tin-sōō'kĭ-ȧ) India	27·18 N	95·29 E
69	Tintic (tĭn'tĭk) Utah	39·55 N	112·15 W
165	Tin Toumma Steppe (Plat.) (tĭn tōōm'ȧ). Niger	16·16 N	13·06 E
139	Tioman (I.) Mala. (Singapore In.)	2·25 N	104·30 E
92	Tipitapa (tē-pê-tä'pä) Nic.	12·14 N	86·05 W
92	Tipitapa R. Nic.	12·13 N	85·57 W
78	Tippah Cr., (R.) (tĭp'pȧ) Miss.	34·43 N	88·15 W
80	Tippecanoe (R.) (tĭp-ē-kȧ-nōō') Ind.	40·55 N	86·45 W
166	Tipperary (tĭ-pē-râ'rē) Ire.	52·28 N	8·13 W
73	Tippo Bay. (tĭp'ō bīōō') Miss.	33·35 N	90·06 W
110	Tipton (tĭp'tŭn) Eng.	52·32 N	2·04 W
80	Tipton Ind.	40·15 N	86·00 W
71	Tipton Iowa	41·46 N	91·10 W
127	Tiranë (tē-rä'nä) Alb.	41·18 N	19·50 E
126	Tirano (tē-rä'nō) It.	46·12 N	10·09 E
129	Tiraspol' (tē-räs'pôl') Sov. Un.	46·52 N	29·38 E
168	Tir'at el'Abbāsīya R. U. A. R. (Suez In.)	32·45 N	32·15 E
133	Tire (tē'rĕ) Tur.	38·05 N	27·48 E
116	Tiree (I.) (tī-rē') Scot.	56·34 N	6·30 W
127	Tîrgoviște Rom.	44·54 N	25·29 E
121	Tîrgu-Mures Rom.	46·33 N	24·35 E
121	Tîrgu Neamt Rom.	47·14 N	26·23 E
121	Tîrgu-Ocna Rom.	46·18 N	26·38 E
121	Tîrgu Săcuesc Rom.	46·04 N	26·06 E
142	Tirich Mir (Mt.) Afg.	41·06 N	71·48 E
136	Tirlyanskiy (tĭr-lyän'skĭ) Sov. Un. (Urals In.)	54·13 N	58·37 E
121	Tîrnava Sinmartin Rom.	46·19 N	24·18 E
127	Tîrnavos Grc.	39·50 N	22·14 E
120	Tirol (State) (tē-rōl') Aus.	47·13 N	11·10 E
126	Tirso (R.) (tēr'sō) It.	40·15 N	9·03 E
143	Tiruchchirāppalli (tĭr'ōō-chĭ-rä'pȧ-lĭ). India	10·49 N	78·48 E
143	Tirunelveli India	8·48 N	77·49 E

ng-sing; ŋ-baŋk; N-nasalized n; nŏd; cŏmmit; ōld; ôbey; ôrder; fōōd; fŏŏt; ou-out; s-soft; sh-dish; th-thin; pūre; ûnite; ûrn; stŭd; circŭs; ü-a "y" in study; '-indeterminate vowel.

Page	Name	Pronunciation	Region	Lat. °′	Long. °′
143	Tiruppūr		India	11·11 N	77·08 E
86	Tisdale	(tĭz'dāl)	Can.	52·55 N	103·56 W
142	Tista (R.)		India	26·03 N	88·52 E
127	Tisza (R.)	(tē'sä)	Yugo.	45·50 N	20·13 E
121	Tisza R.	(tē'sä)	Hung.	46·30 N	20·08 E
142	Titagarh		India (Calcutta In.)	22·44 N	88·23 E
98	Titicaca, Lago (L.)	(lä'gô-tē-tē-kä'kä)	Bol.-Peru	16·12 S	70·33 W
98	Titiribí	(tē-tē-rē-bē')	Col. (In.)	6·05 N	75·47 W
127	Titograd		Yugo.	42·25 N	20·42 E
127	Titovo Užice	(tê'tô-vô ōō'zhê-tsě)	Yugo.	43·51 N	19·53 E
127	Titov Veles	(tê'tôv vě'lěs)	Yugo.	41·42 N	21·50 E
79	Titusville	(tī'tŭs-vĭl)	Fla. (In.)	28·37 N	80·44 W
81	Titusville		Pa.	40·40 N	79·40 W
123	Titz	(tětz)	Ger. (Ruhr In.)	51·00 N	6·26 E
84	Tiverton	(tĭv'ẽr-tŭn)	R. I. (Providence In.)	41·38 N	71·11 W
125	Tívoli	(tē'vô-lê)	It. (Roma In.)	41·58 N	12·48 E
92	Tixkokob	(tēx-kō-kō'b)	Mex. (Yucatan In.)	21·01 N	89·23 W
90	Tixtla de Guerrero	(tē'x-tlä-dě-gěr-rě'rô)	Mex.	17·36 N	99·24 W
154	Tizard Bk. and Rf.	(tĭz'ard)	China	10·51 N	113·20 E
92	Tizimín	(tē-zē-mē'n)	Mex. (Yucatan In.)	21·08 N	88·10 W
164	Tizi-Ouzou	(tē'zē-ōō-zōō')	Alg.	36·44 N	4·04 E
99	Tiznados (R.)	(têz-nä'dôs)	Ven. (In.)	9·53 N	67·49 W
164	Tiznit	(têz-nēt)	Mor.	29·52 N	9·39 W
154	Tjirebon		Indon.	6·50 S	108·33 E
91	Tlacolula de Matamoros	(tlä-kô-lōō'lä dā mätä-mō'rôs)	Mex.	16·56 N	96·29 W
91	Tlacotálpan	(tlä-kô-täl'pän)	Mex.	18·39 N	95·40 W
90	Tlacotepec	(tlä-kô-tå-pě'k)	Mex.	17·46 N	99·57 W
91	Tlacotepec		Mex.	18·41 N	97·40 W
90	Tlacotepec		Mex.	19·11 N	99·41 W
91	Tláhuac	(tlä-wäk')	Mex. (Mexico In.)	19·16 N	99·00 W
90	Tlajomulca de Zúñiga	(tlä-hô-mōō'l-kä-dě-zōō'n-yē-gä)	Mex.	20·30 N	103·27 W
90	Tlalchapa	(tläl-chä'pä)	Mex.	18·26 N	100·29 W
91	Tlalixcoyan	(tlä-lēs'kô-yän')	Mex.	18·53 N	96·04 W
91	Tlalmanalco	(tläl-mä-nä'l-kô)	Mex. (Mexico In.)	19·12 N	98·48 W
91	Tlalnepantia	(tläl-ně-pä'n-tyä)	Mex. (Mexico In.)	19·32 N	99·13 W
91	Tlalnepantla	(tläl-nå-pän'tlä)	Mex. (Mexico In.)	18·59 N	99·01 W
91	Tlalpan	(tläl-pä'n)	Mex. (Mexico In.)	19·17 N	99·10 W
90	Tlalpujahua	(tläl-pōō-kä'wä)	Mex.	19·50 N	100·10 W
	Tlaltenango, see Sanchez Román				
90	Tlapa	(tlä'pä)	Mex.	17·30 N	98·09 W
90	Tlapa	(tlä'pä)	Mex.	17·30 N	98·09 W
91	Tlapacoyan	(tlä-pä-kô-yä'n)	Mex.	19·57 N	97·11 W
90	Tlapaneco (R.)	(tlä-pä-ně'kô)	Mex.	17·59 N	98·44 W
90	Tlapehuala	(tlä-på-wä'lä)	Mex.	18·17 N	100·30 W
90	Tlaquepaque	(tlä-kě-pä'kě)	Mex.	20·39 N	103·17 W
90	Tlatlaya	(tlä-tlä'yä)	Mex.	18·36 N	100·14 W
90	Tlaxcala	(tläs-kä'lä)	Mex.	19·16 N	98·14 W
90	Tlaxco	(tläs'kō)	Mex.	19·37 N	98·06 W
91	Tlaxiaco Sta. Maria Asunción	(tläk-sē-ä'kō sän'tä mä-rē'ä ä-sōōn-syōn')	Mex.	17·16 N	95·41 W
91	Tlayacapan	(tlä-yä-kä-pä'n)	Mex. (Mexico In.)	18·57 N	99·00 W
164	Tlemçen	(tlěm-sěn')	Alg.	34·53 N	1·21 W
121	Tlumach	(t'lû-mäch')	Sov. Un.	48·47 N	25·00 E
95	Toa (R.)	(tō'ä)	Cuba	20·25 N	74·35 W
67	Toano Ra. (Mts.)	(tō-à-nō')	Nev.	40·45 N	114·11 W
95	Toar, Cuchillas de (Mtn.)	(kōō-chē'l-lyäs-dě-tō-ä'r)	Cuba	18·20 N	74·50 W
153	Toba	(tō'bä)	Jap.	34·27 N	136·51 E
89	Tobago (I.)	(tô-bā'gō)	W. I. F.	11·15 N	60·30 W
124	Tobarra	(tô-bär'rä)	Sp.	38·37 N	1·42 W
134	Tobol (R.)	(tô-bôl')	Sov. Un.	56·02 N	65·30 E
134	Tobol'sk	(tô-bôlsk')	Sov. Un.	58·09 N	68·28 E
	Tobruk, see Tubruq				
98	Tocaima	(tô-kä'y-mä)	Col. (In.)	4·28 N	74·38 W
99	Tocantinópoliç	(tô-kän-tē-nō'pō-lēs)	Braz.	6·27 S	47·18 W
99	Tocantins (R.)	(tō-kän-tēNS')	Braz.	3·28 S	49·22 W
78	Toccoa	(tŏk'ō-à)	Ga.	34·35 N	83·20 W
78	Toccoa (R.)		Ga.	34·53 N	84·24 W
153	Tochigi	(tō'chē-gĭ)	Jap.	36·25 N	139·45 E
148	T'ochi Tao (I.)	(tōōŭ'jē dou)	China	38·11 N	120·45 E
92	Tocoa	(tō-kō'ä)	Hond.	15·37 N	86·01 W
100	Tocopilla	(tō-kô-pēl'yä)	Chile	22·03 S	70·08 W
99	Tocuyo de la Costa	(tô-kōō'yō-dě-lä-kôs'tä)	Ven. (In.)	11·03 N	68·24 W
110	Todmorden	(tŏd'môr-děn)	Eng.	53·43 N	2·05 W
118	Töfsingdalens (Natl. Park)		Swe.	62·09 N	13·05 E
153	Tōgane	(tō'gä-nä)	Jap.	35·29 N	140·16 E
163	Togo	(tō'gō)	Afr.	8·00 N	0·52 E
136	Toguzak R.	(tô'gōō-zák)	Sov. Un. (Urals In.)	53·40 N	61·42 E
79	Tohopekaliga (L.)	(tō'hō-pē'kà-lī'gà)	Fla. (In.)	28·16 N	81·09 W
148	To'Hu (L.)	(tōōŭ'hōō)	China	33·07 N	117·25 E
119	Toijala	(toi'yà-là)	Fin.	61·11 N	21·46 E
153	Toi-Misaki (C.)	(toi mē'sä-kē)	Jap.	31·20 N	131·20 E
68	Toiyabe Ra.	(toi'yă-bē)	Nev.	38·59 N	117·22 W
152	Tokachi Gawa (R.)	(tō-kä'chē gä'wä)	Jap.	43·10 N	142·30 E
121	Tokaj	(tô'kô-ê)	Hung.	48·06 N	21·24 E
165	Tokar	(tō'kär)	Sud.	18·28 N	37·46 E
152	Tokara Guntō (Is.)	(tō-kä'rä gōōn'tō')	Jap.	29·45 N	129·15 E
152	Tokara Kaikyo (Str.)	(tô'kä-rä kī'kyō)	Jap.	30·20 N	129·50 E
133	Tokat	(tô-kät')	Tur.	40·20 N	36·30 E
156	Tokelau Is.	(tō-kê-lä'ōō)	N. Z.	8·00 S	176·00 W
134	Tokmak	(tôk'mäk)	Sov. Un.	42·44 N	75·41 E
153	Tokorozawa	(tô'kô-rô-zä'wä)	Jap. (Tōkyō In.)	35·47 N	139·29 E
152	Tokuno (I.)	(tô-kōō'nō)	Jap.	27·42 N	129·25 E
153	Tokushima	(tō'kōō'shē-mä)	Jap.	34·06 N	134·31 E
153	Tokuyama	(tō'kōō'yä-mä)	Jap.	34·04 N	131 49 E
153	Tōkyō	(tō'kē-ō)	Jap. (Tōkyō In.)	35·41 N	139·44 E
153	Tōkyō (Pref.)		Jap. (Tōkyō In.)	35·42 N	139·40 E
153	Tōkyō-Wan (B.)	(tō'kyō wän)	Jap. (Tōkyō In.)	35·32 N	139·56 E
127	Tolbukhin		Bul.	43·33 N	27·52 E
90	Tolcayuca	(tôl-kä-yōō'kä)	Mex.	19·55 N	98·54 W
71	Toledo	(tô-lē'dō)	Iowa	41·59 N	92·35 W
80	Toledo		Ohio	41·40 N	83·35 W
66	Toledo		Ore.	44·37 N	123·58 W
124	Toledo	(tô-lě'dô)	Sp.	39·53 N	4·02 W
124	Toledo, Montes de (Mts.)	(mô'n-těs-dě-tô-lě'dô)	Sp.	39·33 N	4·40 W
98	Tolima (Dept.)	(tô-lē'mä)	Col. (In.)	4·07 N	75·20 W
98	Tolima, Nevado del (Pk.)	(ně-vä-dô-děl-tô-lē'mä)	Col. (In.)	4·40 N	75·20 W
90	Tolimán	(tô-lê-män')	Mex.	20·54 N	99·54 W
110	Tollesbury	(tōl'z-bẽrĭ)	Eng. (London In.)	51·46 N	0·49 E
126	Tolmezzo	(tôl-mět'sô)	It.	46·25 N	13·03 E
126	Tolmin	(tôl'mên)	Yugo.	46·12 N	13·45 E
121	Tolna	(tôl'nô)	Hung.	46·25 N	18·47 E
154	Tolo, Teluk (B.)	(tō'lō)	Indon.	2·00 S	122·06 E
124	Tolosa	(tô-lō'sä)	Sp.	43·10 N	2·05 W
65	Tolt (R.)	(tōlt)	Wash. (Seattle In.)	47·13 N	121·49 W
80	Toluca	(tô-lōō'kà)	Ill.	41·00 N	89·10 W
91	Toluca	(tô-lōō'kä)	Mex. (Mexico In.)	19·17 N	99·40 W
91	Toluca, Nevado de (Zinántecatl) Mtn.	(ně-vä-dô-dě-tô-lōō'kä) (zē-nä'n-tě-kä'tl)	Mex. (Mexico In.)	19·09 N	99·42 W
150	Tolun		China	42·12 N	116·15 E
134	Tom' (R.)		Sov. Un.	55·33 N	85·00 E
71	Tomah	(tō'mà)	Wis.	43·58 N	90·31 W
71	Tomahawk	(tŏm'à-hôk)	Wis.	45·27 N	89·44 W
129	Tomakovka	(tô-mä'kôf-kà)	Sov. Un.	47·49 N	34·43 E
124	Tomar	(tō-mär')	Port.	39·36 N	8·26 W
121	Tomaszow Lubelski	(tô-mä'shōōf lōō-běl'skĭ)	Pol.	50·20 N	23·27 E
121	Tomaszów Mazowiecki	(tô-mä'shōōf mä-zô'vyět-skĭ)	Pol.	51·33 N	20·00 E
90	Tomatlán	(tô-mä-tlä'n)	Mex.	19·54 N	105·14 W
90	Tomatlán (R.)		Mex.	19·56 N	105·14 W
99	Tombador, Serra do (Mts.)	(sěr'rà dōō tōm-bä-dôr')	Braz.	11·31 S	57·33 W
78	Tombigbee (R.)	(tŏm-bĭg'bê)	Ala.	31·45 N	88·02 W
101	Tombos	(tô'm-bōs)	Braz. (Rio de Janeiro In.)	20·53 S	42·00 W
164	Tombouctou (Timbuktu)	(tôm-bōōk-tōō')	Mali	16·52 N	2·53 W
69	Tombstone	(tōōm'stōn)	Ariz.	31·40 N	110·00 W
118	Tomelilla	(tô'mě-lēl-lä)	Swe.	55·34 N	13·55 E
124	Tomelloso	(tō-mäl-lyō'sō)	Sp.	39·09 N	3·02 W
154	Tomini, Teluk (B.)	(tô-mē'nê)	Indon.	0·10 N	121·00 E
135	Tommot	(tŏm-mŏt')	Sov. Un.	59·13 N	126·22 E
134	Tomsk	(tŏmsk)	Sov. Un.	56·29 N	84·57 E
91	Tonalá	(tō-nä-lä')	Mex.	16·05 N	93·45 W
90	Tonala		Mex.	20·38 N	103·14 W
91	Tonalá (R.)		Mex.	18·05 N	94·08 W
75	Tonawanda	(tŏn-à-wŏn'dà)	N. Y. (Buffalo In.)	43·01 N	78·53 W
75	Tonawanda Cr.		N. Y. (Buffalo In.)	43·05 N	78·43 W
110	Tonbridge	(tŭn-brij)	Eng. (London In.)	51·11 N	0·17 E
153	Tonda	(tôn'dä)	Jap. (Ōsaka In.)	34·51 N	135·38 E
153	Tondabayashi	(tôn'dä-bä'yä-shê)	Jap. (Ōsaka In.)	34·29 N	135·36 E
155	Tondano	(tôn-dä'nō)	Indon.	1·15 N	124·50 E
118	Tönder	(tûn'nẽr)	Den.	54·47 N	8·49 E
91	Tondlá		Mex.	16·04 N	93·57 W
153	Tone (R.)	(tō'nê)	Jap. (Tōkyō In.)	35·55 N	139·57 E
153	Tone-Gawa (Strm.)	(tō'nê gä'wa)	Jap.	36·12 N	139·19 E
156	Tonga Is.	(tŏŋ'gà)	Oceania	18·50 S	175·20 W
100	Tongoy	(tōn-goi')	Chile	30·16 S	71·29 W
	Tongue of Arabat, see Arabatskaya Strelka (Spit)				
94	Tongue of the Ocean (Chan.)	(tŭng ŏv thē ōshŭn)	Ba. Is.	24·05 N	77·20 W
67	Tongue R.	(tŭng)	Mont.	45·08 N	106·40 W
67	Tongue River Ind. Res.		Mont.	45·32 N	106·43 W
165	Tonj R.	(tônj)	Sud.	6·18 N	28·33 E
142	Tonk	(tŏŋk)	India	26·13 N	75·45 E
73	Tonkawa	(tŏŋ'kà-wô)	Okla.	36·42 N	97·19 W
151	Tonkin, Gulf of	(tôn-kăn')	Viet.	20·30 N	108·10 E
154	Tonle Sap (L.)	(tôn'lā säp')	Camb.	13·03 N	102·49 E
122	Tonneins	(tô-năN')	Fr.	44·24 N	0·18 E
120	Tönning	(tû'něng)	Ger.	54·20 N	8·55 E
68	Tonopah	(tō-nô-pä')	Nev.	38·04 N	117·15 W
118	Tönsberg	(tûns'běrgh)	Nor.	59·19 N	10·25 E
91	Tonto (R.)	(tōn'tō)	Mex.	18·15 N	96·13 W
69	Tonto Cr.		Ariz.	34·05 N	111·15 W
69	Tonto Natl. Mon.	(tōn'tō)	Ariz.	33·33 N	111·08 W
74	Tooele	(tōō-ĕl'ê)	Utah (Salt Lake City In.)	40·33 N	112·17 W
151	Toohsien		China	25·30 N	111·32 E
160	Toowoomba	(tōō wōōm'bà)	Austl.	27·32 S	152·10 E
74	Topanga	(tō'păn-gà)	Calif. (Los Angeles In.)	34·05 N	118·36 W
73	Topeka	(tô-pē'kà)	Kans.	39·02 N	95·41 W
91	Topilejo	(tô-pē-lě'hô)	Mex. (Mexico In.)	19·12 N	99·09 W
121	Topol'čany	(tô-pôl'chä-nü)	Czech.	48·38 N	18·10 E
88	Topolobampo	(tō-pō-lô-bä'm-pô)	Mex.	25·45 N	109·00 W
127	Topolovgrad		Bul.	42·05 N	26·19 E
66	Toppenish	(tôp'ĕn-ĭsh)	Wash.	46·22 N	120·00 W
83	Torbay	(tôr-bā')	Can.	47·41 N	52·38 W
160	Torbreck, Mt.	(tôr-brěk)	Austl.	37·05 S	146·55 E
80	Torch (L.)	(tôrch)	Mich.	45·00 N	85·30 W
118	Töreboda	(tû'rě-bō'dä)	Swe.	58·44 N	14·04 E
117	Torhout		Bel.	51·01 N	3·04 E
98	Toribío	(tô-rē-bē'ô)	Col. (In.)	2·58 N	76·14 W
153	Toride	(tô'rê-dā)	Jap. (Tōkyō In.)	35·54 N	140·04 E
126	Torino (Turin)	(tô-rē'no) (tū'rĭn)	It.	45·05 N	7·44 E
112	Torino (R.)	(tôr'nĭ-ô)	Fin.-Swe.	67·00 N	23·50 E
124	Tormes (R.)	(tōr'mās)	Sp.	41·12 N	6·15 W
112	Torne (R.)	(tôr'ně)	Swe.	67·29 N	21·44 E
112	Torne Träsk (L.)	(tôr'ně trěsk)	Swe.	68·10 N	20·36 E
87	Torngat Mts.		Can.	59·18 N	64·35 W
112	Tornio	(tôr'nĭ-ô)	Fin.	65·55 N	24·09 E
82	Toro, Lac (L.)		Can.	46·53 N	73·46 W
127	Toronaíos Kólpos (G.)		Grc.	40·10 N	23·35 E
85	Toronto	(tô-rŏn'tō)	Can. (Toronto In.)	43·40 N	79·23 W
80	Toronto		Ohio	40·30 N	80·35 W
76	Toronto, L.	(lä'gô-tô-rô'n-tō)	Mex.	27·35 N	105·37 W
128	Toropets	(tô'rô-pyěts)	Sov. Un.	56·31 N	31·37 E
133	Toros Dağlari (Taurus Mts.)	(tô'rŭs)	Tur.	37·00 N	32·40 E
125	Torote (R.)	(tô-rō'tä)	Sp. (Madrid In.)	40·36 N	3·24 W
118	Torp	(tôrp)	Swe.	62·30 N	16·04 E
	Torpen, see Åmot				
116	Torquay	(tôr-kē')	Eng.	50·30 N	3·26 W
98	Torra, Cerro (Mtn.)	(sě'r-rō-tō'r-rä)	Col. (In.)	4·41 N	76·22 W
74	Torrance	(tŏr'rănc)	Calif. (Los Angeles In.)	33·50 N	118·20 W
125	Torre Annunziata	(tôr'rä ä-nōōn-tsê-ä'tä)	It. (Napoli In.)	40·31 N	14·27 E
124	Torre de Cerredo (Mtn.)	(tôr'rā dā thā-rā'dhō)	Sp.	43·10 N	4·47 W
125	Torre del Greco	(tôr'rā děl grā'kô)	It. (Napoli In.)	40·32 N	14·23 E
124	Torrejoncillo	(tôr'rā-hōn-thē'lyō)	Sp.	39·54 N	6·26 W
124	Torrelavega	(tôr-rā'lä-vā'gä)	Sp.	43·22 N	4·02 W
126	Torre Maggiore	(tôr'rā mäd-jō'rā)	It.	40·41 N	15·18 E
160	Torrens, L.	(tŏr-ĕns)	Austl.	30·07 S	137·40 E
125	Torrente	(tôr-rěn'tä)	Sp.	39·25 N	0·28 W
76	Torreon	(tôr-rå-ōn')	Mex.	25·32 N	103·26 W
125	Torre-Pacheco	(tôr-rě-pä-chě'kô)	Sp.	37·44 N	0·58 W
159	Torres Is.	(tôr'rěs) (tŏr'ěz)	New Hebr.	13·18 S	165·59 E
68	Torres Martinez Ind. Res.	(tôr'ěz mär-tē'něz)	Calif.	33·33 N	116·21 W
124	Tôrres Novas	(tôr'rězh nō'väzh)	Port.	39·28 N	8·37 W
155	Torres Str.	(tôr'rěs)	Austl.	10·30 S	141·30 E
124	Tôrres Vedras	(tôr'rězh vă'drázh)	Port.	39·08 N	9·18 W
125	Torrevieja	(tôr-rā-vyā'hä)	Sp.	37·58 N	0·40 W
155	Torrijos	(tôr-rē'hōs)	Phil. (Manila In.)	13·19 N	122·06 E
81	Torrington	(tŏr'ĭng-tŭn)	Conn.	41·50 N	73·10 W
70	Torrington		Wyo.	42·04 N	104·11 W
124	Torro	(tô'r-rō)	Sp.	41·27 N	5·23 W
118	Torsby	(tôrs'bü)	Swe.	60·07 N	12·56 E
118	Torshälla	(tôrs'hěl-ä)	Swe.	59·26 N	16·21 E
89	Tortola (I.)	(tôr-tō'lä)	Vir. Is. (Br.) (Puerto Rico In.)	18·34 N	64·40 W
126	Tortona	(tôr-tō'nä)	It.	44·52 N	8·52 W
125	Tortosa	(tôr-tō'sä)	Sp.	40·59 N	0·33 E
125	Tortosa, Cabo de (C.)	(kä'bô-dě-tôr-tō-sä)	Sp.	40·42 N	0·55 E
95	Tortue, Canal de la (Chan.)	(tôr-tü')	Hai.	20·05 N	73·20 W
95	Tortue, Ile de la (I.)		Hai.	20·10 N	73·00 W
99	Tortuga, Isla la (I.)	(ê's-lä-lä-tôr-tōō'gä)	Ven. (In.)	10·55 N	65·18 W
121	Toruń	(tō'rōōn')	Pol.	53·01 N	18·37 E
128	Tōrva	(t'r'vä)	Sov. Un.	58·02 N	25·56 E
116	Tory (I.)	(tō'rê)	Ire.	54·77 N	8·08 W
128	Torzhok	(tôr'zhôk)	Sov. Un.	57·03 N	34·53 E
153	Tosa-Wan (B.)	(tô'sä wän)	Jap.	33·14 N	133·39 E
126	Toscana (Reg.)	(tôs-kä'nä)	It.	43·23 N	11·08 E
136	Tosna R.		Sov. Un. (Leningrad In.)	59·38 N	30·52 E
136	Tosno	(tôs'nô)	Sov. Un. (Leningrad In.)	59·32 N	30·52 E
100	Tostado	(tôs-tä'dô)	Arg.	29·10 S	61·43 W
133	Tosya	(tôz'yä)	Tur.	41·00 N	34·00 E
124	Totana	(tô-tä-nä)	Sp.	37·45 N	1·28 W
132	Tot'ma	(tôt'mä)	Sov. Un.	60·00 N	42·20 E
92	Totonicapán	(tō-tō-nē-kä'pän)	Guat.	14·55 N	91·20 W
101	Totoras	(tô-tô'räs)	Arg. (Buenos Aires In.)	32·33 S	61·13 W
153	Totsuka	(tōt'sōō-kä)	Jap.	35·24 N	139·32 E
110	Tottenham	(tŏt'ĕn-ăm)	Eng. (London In.)	51·35 N	0·06 W
153	Tottori	(tō'tô-rê)	Jap.	35·30 N	134·15 E
164	Touat (Oases)	(tōō'ät)	Alg.	27·22 N	00·38 W
164	Toubkal Pk.		Mor.	31·15 N	7·46 W
164	Touggourt	(tōō-gōōrt') (tōō-gōōr')	Alg.	33·09 N	6·07 E
114	Touil R.	(tōō-ēl')	Alg.	34·42 N	2·16 E
123	Toul	(tōōl)	Fr.	48·39 N	5·51 E
82	Toulnustouc, Riviere (R.)		Can.	50·30 N	67·55 W
123	Toulon	(tōō-lôN')	Fr.	43·09 N	5·54 E

ăt; finăl; rāte; senâte; ärm; åsk; sofà; fâre; ch-choose; dh-as th in other; bē; êvent; bět; recěnt; cratẽr; g-go; gh-guttural g; bĭt; ĭ-short neutral; rīde; K-guttural k as ch in German ich;

PRONOUNCING INDEX Toulouse–Tuktoyaktuk 277

Page	Name Pronunciation Region	Lat. °′	Long. °′
122	Toulouse (tōō-lōōz') . . . Fr.	43·37 N	1·27 E
154	Toungoo (tŏ-ōōŋ-gōō') . . . Bur.	19·00 N	96·29 E
151	Tourane (tōō-rän') . . . Viet.	16·08 N	108·22 E
122	Tourcoing (tōōr-kwăN') . . . Fr.	50·44 N	3·06 E
123	Tournan-en-Brie (tōōr-näN-ĕN-brē') Fr. (Paris In.)	48·45 N	2·47 E
122	Tours (tōōr) . . . Fr.	47·23 N	0·39 E
165	Toussidé, Pic (Pk.) (tōō-sē-dā') Chad	21·10 N	16·30 E
118	Tovdalselv (R.) (tôv-däls-ĕlv) Nor.	58·23 N	8·16 E
81	Towanda (tô-wän'dȧ) . . . Pa.	41·45 N	76·30 W
70	Towner (tou'nēr) . . . N. D.	48·21 N	100·24 W
83	Townsend (toun'zĕnd) Mass. (Boston In.)	42·41 N	71·42 W
67	Townsend . . . Mont.	46·19 N	111·35 W
65	Townsend, Mt. Wash. (Seattle In.)	47·52 N	123·03 W
159	Townsville (tounz'vĭl) . . . Austl.	19·18 S	146·50 E
84	Towson (tou'sŭn) Md. (Baltimore In.)	39·24 N	76·36 W
154	Towuti, Danau (L.) (tô-wōō'tê) Indon.	3·00 S	121·45 E
76	Toyah (tô'yȧ) . . . Tex.	31·19 N	103·46 W
153	Toyama (tō'yä-mä) . . . Jap.	36·42 N	137·14 E
153	Toyama-Wan (B.) . . . Jap.	36·58 N	137·16 E
153	Toyohashi (tō'yô-hä'shê) . . . Jap.	34·44 N	137·21 E
153	Toyonaka (tō'yô-nä'kä) Jap. (Ōsaka In.)	34·47 N	135·28 E
114	Tozeur (tô-zûr') . . . Tun.	33·59 N	8·11 E
124	Trabancos (R.) (trä-bäŋ'kōs) . . Sp.	41·15 N	5·13 W
133	Trabzon (tráb'zôn) . . . Tur.	41·00 N	39·45 E
68	Tracy (trā'sē) . . . Calif.	37·45 N	121·27 W
70	Tracy . . . Minn.	44·13 N	95·37 W
78	Tracy City . . . Tenn.	35·15 N	85·44 W
124	Trafalgar, Cabo de (C.) (kä'bô-dĕ-trä-fäl-gä'r) . Sp.	36·10 N	6·02 W
167	Trafonomby (Mtn.) . . . Malagasy	24·32 S	46·35 E
86	Trail (trāl) . . . Can.	49·04 N	117·56 W
111	Traisen (R.) . . . Aus. (Wien In.)	48·15 N	15·55 E
111	Traiskirchen . . . Aus. (Wien In.)	48·01 N	16·18 E
119	Trakai (trá-kāy) . . . Sov. Un.	54·38 N	24·59 E
116	Tralee (trȧ-lē') . . . Ire.	52·16 N	9·20 W
118	Trälleborg (trĕl'ĕ-bôrg) . . . Swe.	55·24 N	13·07 E
118	Tranas (trän'ôs) . . . Swe.	58·03 N	14·56 E
142	Tranbonsha (Mt.) . . . China	35·27 N	86·25 E
124	Trancoso (träŋ-kō'sōō) . . . Port.	40·46 N	7·23 W
155	Trangan (I.) (träŋ'gän) . . . Indon.	6·52 S	133·30 E
126	Trani (trä'nē) . . . It.	41·15 N	16·25 E
103	Transcaucasia (Reg.) . . . Sov. Un.	41·17 N	44·30 E
85	Transcona (trăns-kō'nȧ) Can. (Winnipeg In.)	49·54 N	97·00 W
146	Trans Himalaya Mts. (trăns'hĭ-mä'lȧ-yȧ) . China	31·15 N	81·56 E
166	Transvaal (Prov.) (trăns-väl') S. Afr.	24·21 S	28·18 E
121	Transylvania (Reg.) (trăn-sĭl-vā'nĭ-ȧ) . Rom.	46·30 N	22·35 E
	Transylvanian Alps (Mts.), see Carpatii Meridionali		
126	Trapani (trä'pä-nê) . . . It.	38·02 N	14·34 E
123	Trappes (tráp) . . . Fr. (Paris In.)	48·47 N	2·01 E
160	Traralgon (trȧ'răl-gŏn) . . . Austl.	38·15 S	146·33 E
126	Trasimeno, Lago (L.) (lä'gō trä-sê-mā'nō) . It.	43·00 N	12·12 E
124	Tras os Montes (Mts.) (träzh'ōzh môn'tāzh) . Port.	41·33 N	7·13 W
124	Trasparga (träs-pär-gä) . . . Sp.	43·13 N	7·50 W
120	Traun R. (troun) . . . Aus.	48·10 N	14·15 E
120	Traunstein (troun'stīn) . . . Ger.	47·52 N	12·38 E
70	Traverse, L. (trăv'ērs) Minn.-S. D.	45·46 N	96·53 W
80	Traverse City . . . Mich.	44·45 N	85·40 W
126	Travnik (träv'nēk) . . . Yugo.	44·13 N	17·43 E
65	Treasure I. (trĕzh'ēr) Calif. (San Francisco In.)	37·49 N	122·22 W
111	Trebbin (trĕ'bēn) . Ger. (Berlin In.)	52·13 N	13·13 E
120	Třebič (t'rzhĕ'bēch) . . . Czech.	49·13 N	15·53 E
127	Trebinje (trä'bēn-yĕ) . . . Yugo.	42·43 N	18·21 E
121	Trebisow (trĕ'bê-shôf) . . . Czech.	48·36 N	21·32 E
120	Třeboň (t'rzhĕ'bōn') . . . Czech.	49·00 N	14·48 E
159	Tregrosse Is. (trê-grōs') . . . Austl.	18·08 S	150·53 E
100	Treinta y Tres (trā-ēn'tä ē trās') Ur.	33·14 S	54·17 W
122	Trélazé (trā-lȧ-zā') . . . Fr.	47·27 N	0·32 W
100	Trelew (trē'lū) . . . Arg.	43·15 S	65·25 W
116	Tremadoc B. (trē-mă'dŏk) . . Wales	52·43 N	4·27 W
126	Tremiti, Isole di (Is.) (ê'sō-lĕ dē trä-mē'tē) . It.	42·07 N	16·33 E
121	Trenčín (trĕn'chēn) . . . Czech.	48·52 N	18·02 E
154	Trengganu (State) (trĕng-gä'nōō) . Mala.	4·53 N	102·26 E
100	Trenque Lauquén (trĕn'kĕ-lä'ōō-kĕ'n) . Arg.	35·50 S	62·44 W
81	Trent (R.) (trĕnt) . . . Can.	44·15 N	77·55 W
116	Trent (R.) . . . Eng.	53·05 N	1·00 W
110	Trent and Mersey Can. (trĕnt) (mûr'zē) . Eng.	53·11 N	2·24 W
126	Trentino (Reg.) (trĕn-tē'nô) . . . It.	46·16 N	10·47 E
126	Trento (trĕn'tô) . . . It.	46·04 N	11·07 E
81	Trenton (trĕn'tŭn) . . . Can.	44·05 N	77·35 W
83	Trenton . . . Can.	45·39 N	62·40 W
75	Trenton . . . Mich. (Detroit In.)	42·08 N	83·12 W
73	Trenton . . . Mo.	40·05 N	93·36 W
84	Trenton . . . N. J. (New York In.)	40·13 N	74·46 W
78	Trenton . . . Tenn.	35·57 N	88·55 W
83	Trepassey (trê-păs'ē) . . . Can.	46·47 N	53·20 W
83	Trepassey B. . . . Can.	46·35 N	53·25 W
100	Tres Arroyos (träs'är-rō'yōs) . Arg.	38·18 S	60·16 W
101	Três Coraçoes (trĕ's kō-rä-zō'ĕs) Braz. (Rio de Janeiro In.)	21·41 S	45·14 W
91	Tres Cumbres (trĕ's kōō'm-brĕs) Mex. (Mexico In.)	19·03 N	99·14 W
99	Três Lagoas (trĕ's lä-gô'äs) . . Braz.	20·48 S	51·42 W

Page	Name Pronunciation Region	Lat. °′	Long. °′
98	Tres Morros, Alto de (Mtn.) (ä'l-tō dĕ trĕ's mô'r-rōs) Col. (In.)	7·08 N	76·10 W
101	Três Pontas (trĕ's pô'n-täs) Braz. (Rio de Janeiro In.)	21·22 S	45·30 W
101	Três Rios (trĕ's rê'ōs) Braz. (Rio de Janeiro In.)	22·07 S	43·13 W
111	Treuenbrietzen (troi'ĕn-brē-tzĕn) Ger. (Berlin In.)	52·06 N	12·52 E
126	Treviglio (trā-vē'lyô) . . . It.	45·30 N	9·34 E
126	Treviso (trĕ-vê'sō) . . . It.	45·39 N	12·15 E
146	Triangle, The (Reg.) . . . Asia	26·00 N	98·00 E
168	Trichardt (trĭ-kärt') . . . S. Afr. (Johannesburg & Pretoria In.)	26·32 S	29·16 E
126	Trieste (Trst) (trē-ĕs'tā) . . . It.	45·39 N	13·48 E
126	Trieste, G. of . . . It.	45·38 N	13·40 E
124	Trigueros (trē-gā'rōs) . . . Sp.	37·23 N	6·50 W
142	Trigu Tsho (L.) . . . China	28·47 N	91·37 E
127	Trikkala . . . Grc.	39·33 N	21·49 E
75	Trim Cr. (trĭm) . Ill. (Chicago In.)	41·19 N	87·39 W
143	Trincomalee (trĭŋ-kô-mȧ-lē') Ceylon	8·39 N	81·12 E
110	Tring (trĭng) . . . Eng. (London In.)	51·46 N	0·40 W
98	Trinidad (trē-nê-dhädh') . . . Bol.	14·48 S	64·43 W
72	Trinidad (trĭn'ĭ-dăd) . . . Colo.	37·11 N	104·31 W
94	Trinidad (trē-nê-dhädh') . . . Cuba	21·50 N	80·00 W
101	Trinidad . . . Ur. (Buenos Aires In.)	33·29 S	56·55 W
94	Trinidad, Sierra de (Mts.) (sē-ĕ'r-rä dĕ trê-nê-dä'd) . Cuba	21·50 N	79·55 W
99	Trinidad (I.) (trĭn'ĭ-dăd) . W. I. F.	10·30 N	60·30 W
96	Trinidade, Ilha de (I.) (ê'lä dĕ trê-nē-dä-dĕ) . Braz.	21·00 S	32·00 W
88	Trinidad R. Pan. (Panama Canal In.)	8·55 N	80·01 W
91	Trinitaria (trē-nē-tä'ryä) . . . Mex.	16·09 N	92·04 W
93	Trinité Mart. (Le. & Wind. Is. In.)	14·47 N	61·00 W
83	Trinity (trĭn'ĭ-tê) . . . Can.	48·22 N	53·24 W
77	Trinity . . . Tex.	30·52 N	95·27 W
64	Trinity (Is.) . . . Alaska	56·25 N	153·15 W
72	Trinity (R.), West Fk. . . . Tex.	33·22 N	98·26 W
73	Trinity (R.), East Fk. . . . Tex.	33·24 N	96·42 W
83	Trinity B. . . . Can.	47·55 N	53·30 W
66	Trinity R. . . . Calif.	40·50 N	123·20 W
77	Trinity R. . . . Tex.	30·50 N	95·09 W
126	Trino (trē'nô) . . . It.	45·11 N	8·16 E
78	Trion (trī'ŏn) . . . Ga.	34·32 N	85·18 W
	Tripoli, see T'arābulus		
	Tripoli, see Tarābulus		
127	Tripolis (trĭ'pô-lĭs) . . . Grc.	37·32 N	22·32 E
	Tripolitania, see Tarābulus		
70	Tripp (trĭp) . . . S. D.	43·13 N	97·58 W
142	Tripura (Mts.) . . . W. Pak.	28·38 N	91·37 E
47	Tristan da Cunha Is. (trēs-tän'dä kōōn'yȧ) . Atl. O.	35·30 S	12·15 W
99	Triste, Golfo (G.) (gôl-fô trē's-tĕ) Ven. (In.)	10·40 N	68·05 W
84	Triticus Res. (trī tĭ-cŭs) N. Y. (New York In.)	41·20 N	73·36 W
84	Triumph (trī'ŭmf) La. (New Orleans In.)	29·21 N	89·29 W
143	Trivandrum (trê-vŭn'drŭm) . India	8·34 N	76·58 E
127	Trn (t'rn) . . . Bul.	42·49 N	22·39 E
121	Trnava (t'r'nȧ-vȧ) . . . Czech.	48·22 N	17·34 E
155	Trobriand Is. (trō-brê-ănd') Pap. Ter.	8·25 S	151·45 E
126	Trogir (trô'gēr) . . . Yugo.	43·32 N	16·17 E
82	Trois Pistoles (trwä' pēs-tôl') . Can.	48.07 N	69·10 W
82	Trois-Rivières (rê-vyâr') . . . Can.	46·21 N	72·35 W
136	Troitsk (trô'ētsk) Sov. Un. (Urals In.)	54·06 N	61·34 E
134	Troitsko-Pechorsk (trô'ĭtsk-ô-pyĕ-chôrsk') . Sov. Un.	62·18 N	56·07 E
129	Troitskoye . . . Sov. Un.	47·39 N	30·16 E
118	Trollhättan (trôl'hĕt-ĕn) . . . Swe.	58·17 N	12·17 E
118	Trollheim (Mts.) (trôll-hĕĭm) . Nor.	62·48 N	9·05 E
112	Tromsö (trôm'sŭ) . . . Nor.	69·38 N	19·12 E
68	Trona (trō'nȧ) . . . Calif.	35·49 N	117·20 W
100	Tronador, Cerro (Mtn.) (sĕ'r-rô trō-nä'dôr) . Arg.	41·17 S	71·56 W
90	Troncoso (trôn-kō'sō) . . . Mex.	22·43 N	102·22 W
118	Trondheim (Nidaros) (trôn'hăm) (nē'dhä-rôs) . Nor.	63·25 N	11·35 E
139	Troodos, Mt. Cyprus (Palestine In.)	34·56 N	32·52 E
118	Trosa (trô'sä) . . . Swe.	58·54 N	17·25 E
87	Trout (L.) . . . Can.	51·16 N	92·46 W
66	Trout Cr. . . . Ore.	42·18 N	118·31 W
65	Troutdale (trout'dāl) Ore. (Portland In.)	45·32 N	122·23 W
122	Trouville-sur-Mer (trōō-vēl'sür-mâr') . Fr.	49·23 N	0·05 E
78	Troy (troi) . . . Ala.	31·47 N	85·46 W
74	Troy . . . Ill. (St. Louis In.)	38·44 N	89·53 W
73	Troy . . . Kans.	39·46 N	95·07 W
73	Troy . . . Mo.	38·56 N	90·57 W
66	Troy . . . Mont.	48·28 N	115·56 W
81	Troy . . . N. Y.	42·45 N	73·45 W
79	Troy . . . N. C.	35·21 N	79·58 W
80	Troy . . . Ohio	40·00 N	84·10 W
127	Troy (Ruins) . . . Tur.	39·59 N	26·14 E
122	Troyes (trwä) . . . Fr.	48·18 N	4·03 E
	Trst, see Trieste		
127	Trstenik (t'r'stĕ-nêk) . . . Yugo.	43·36 N	20·00 E
128	Trubchëvsk (trōōp'chĕfsk) Sov. Un.	52·36 N	32·46 E
138	Trucial Coast (trōō'shăl) . . . Asia	23·30 N	53·00 E
68	Truckee (trŭk'ē) . . . Calif.	39·20 N	120·12 W
68	Truckee (R.) . . . Calif.-Nev.	39·25 N	120·07 W
161	Truganina . Austl. (Melbourne In.)	37·49 S	144·44 E
98	Trujillo (trōō-kĕ'l-yō) . . Col. (In.)	4·10 N	76·20 W
92	Trujillo (trōō-ĸēl'yō) . . . Hond.	15·55 N	85·58 W
98	Trujillo . . . Peru	8·08 S	79·00 W
124	Trujillo (trōō-ĸē'l-yō) . . . Sp.	39·27 N	5·50 W
98	Trujillo . . . Ven.	9·15 N	70·28 W
90	Trujillo (R.) . . . Mex.	23·12 N	103·10 W

Page	Name Pronunciation Region	Lat. °′	Long. °′
95	Trujin, L. (trōō-ĸēn') . . Dom. Rep.	17·45 N	71·25 W
73	Trumann (trōō'măn) . . . Ark.	35·41 N	90·31 W
82	Truro (trōō'rō) . . . Can.	45·22 N	63·20 W
116	Truro . . . Eng.	50·17 N	5·05 W
84	Trussville (trŭs'vĭl) Ala. (Birmingham In.)	33·37 N	86·37 W
69	Truth or Consequences (trōōth ŏr kŏn'sê-kwĕn-sĭs) N. Mex.	33·10 N	107·20 W
120	Trutnov (trōōt'nôf) . . . Czech.	50·36 N	15·36 E
120	Trzcianka (tchyän'kȧ) . . . Pol.	53·02 N	16·27 E
120	Trzebiatowo (tchĕ-byȧ'tōō-vô) . Pol.	54·03 N	15·16 E
146	Tsaidam Swp. (tsī'däm) . . . China	37·19 N	94·08 E
150	Ts'aiyü . . . China (Peking In.)	39·39 N	116·36 E
79	Tsala Apopka (R.) (tsȧ'lȧ ă-pŏp'kȧ) . Fla.	28·57 N	82·11 W
148	Ts'anghsien (chäng'sĭän) . . . China	38·21 N	116·53 E
149	Ts'angmen . . . China (Canton In.)	22·42 N	113·09 E
	Tsangwu, see Wuchou		
148	Tsaochuang (jou'jōōäng) . . . China	34·51 N	117·34 E
148	Ts'aohsien (tsou'sĭän) . . . China	34·48 N	115·33 E
146	Tsasata Bogda Uula (Mt.) . Mong.	46·44 N	92·34 E
65	Tsawwassen Ind. Res. Can. (Vancouver In.)	49·03 N	123·11 W
134	Tselinograd (tsĕ'lĕ-nô-grȧ'd) Sov. Un.	51·10 N	71·43 E
149	Tsengch'en . . . China (Canton In.)	23·18 N	113·49 E
136	Tsentral'nyy-Kospashskiy (tsĕn-träl'nyĭ-kôs-pash'skĭ) Sov. Un. (Urals In.)	59·03 N	57·48 E
142	Tsethang . . . China	29·20 N	91·49 E
166	Tshela (tshā'lȧ) . . . Con. L.	4·50 S	13·05 E
166	Tshikapa (tshê-kä'pä) . . . Con. L.	6·29 S	20·53 E
166	Tshilongo (tshê-lôŋ'gō) . . . Con. L.	10·28 S	26·09 E
166	Tshuapa (R.) . . . Con. L.	0·25 S	22·07 E
167	Tsiandro (tsē-än-drō') . . Malagasy	18·46 S	44·58 E
133	Tsimlyanskiy (Res.) (tsym-lyȧ'ns-kēē) . Sov. Un.	47·50 N	43·40 E
139	Tsin (R.) . . . Isr. (Palestine In.)	30·52 N	35·05 E
148	Tsinan (Chinan) (je'nän) . . . China	36·40 N	117·01 E
	Tsinghai (Prov.), see Chinghai		
148	Tsingtao (Ch'ingtao) (tsĭng'dou) China	36·05 N	102·10 E
167	Tsiribihina (R.) (tsē'rê-bē-hê-nä') Malagasy	19·45 S	43·30 E
167	Tsitsa (R.) (tsê'tsȧ) S. Afr. (Natal In.)	31·28 S	28·53 E
	Tsitsihar, see Ch'ich'ihaerh		
167	Tsolo (tsō'lō) . . S. Afr. (Natal In.)	31·19 S	28·47 E
167	Tsomo . . . S. Afr. (Natal In.)	32·03 S	27·49 E
167	Tsomo (R.) . . . S. Afr. (Natal In.)	31·53 S	27·48 E
153	Tsu (tsōō) . . . Jap.	34·42 N	136·31 E
153	Tsuchiura (tsōō'chê-ōō-rä) . . . Jap.	36·04 N	140·09 E
153	Tsuda (tsōō'dä) . . Jap. (Ōsaka In.)	34·48 N	135·43 E
152	Tsugaru Kaikyō (str.) (tsōō'gä-rōō kī'kyō) . Jap.	41·25 N	140·20 E
166	Tsumeb (tsōō'mĕb) . . . S. W. Afr.	19·10 S	17·45 E
153	Tsunashima (tsōō'nä-shê'mä) Jap. (Tōkyō In.)	35·32 N	139·37 E
151	Ts'unghua . . . China	23·30 N	113·40 E
148	Tsunhua (zhōōn'hooȧ) . . . China	40·12 N	117·55 E
153	Tsuruga (tsōō'rōō-gä) . . . Jap.	35·39 N	136·04 E
153	Tsurugi-san (Mtn.) (tsōō'rōō-gê sän) . Jap.	33·52 N	134·07 E
152	Tsuruoka (tsōō'rōō-ō'kä) . . . Jap.	38·43 N	139·51 E
153	Tsurusaki (tsōō'rōō-sä'kê) . . . Jap.	33·15 N	131·42 E
153	Tsu Shima (I.) (tsōō shê'mä) . Jap.	34·28 N	129·30 E
153	Tsushima Kaikyō (Str.) (tsōō'shê-mä kī'kyō) . Asia	33·52 N	129·30 E
153	Tsuwano (tsōō'wä-nô') . . . Jap.	34·28 N	131·47 E
153	Tsuyama (tsōō'yä-mä') . . . Jap.	35·05 N	134·00 E
124	Tua (R.) (tōō'ä) . . . Port.	41·23 N	7·18 W
65	Tualatin (R.) (tōō'ȧ-lă-tĭn) Ore. (Portland In.)	45·25 N	122·54 W
157	Tuamotu, Arch. (tōō-ä-mō'tōō) Fr. Polynesia	19·00 S	141·20 W
155	Tuao (tōō-ä'ō) Phil. (Manila In.)	17·44 N	121·26 E
133	Tuapse (tōō'áp-sĕ) . . . Sov. Un.	44·00 N	39·10 E
164	Tuareg (Reg.) . . . Alg.	21·26 N	2·51 E
144	Tuayq, Jabal (Mts.) . . . Sau. Ar.	20·45 N	46·30 E
100	Tubarão (tōō-bä-rouN') . . . Braz.	28·23 S	48·56 W
120	Tübingen (tü'bĭng-ĕn) . . . Ger.	48·33 N	9·05 E
136	Tubinskiy (tû bĭn'skĭ) Sov. Un. (Urals In.)	52·53 N	58·15 E
165	Tubruq (Tobruk) . . . Libya	32·03 N	24·04 E
99	Tucacas (tōō-kä'käs) . . . Ven. (In.)	10·48 N	68·20 W
84	Tucker (tŭk'ēr) Ga (Atlanta In.)	33·51 N	84·13 W
69	Tucson (tōō-sŏn') . . . Ariz.	32·15 N	111·00 W
100	Tucumán (tōō-kōō-män') . . . Arg.	26·52 S	65·08 W
100	Tucumán (Prov.) . . . Arg.	26·30 S	65·30 W
72	Tucumcari (tōō'kŭm-kâr-ê) N. Mex.	35·11 N	103·43 W
98	Tucupita (tōō-kōō-pê'tä) . . . Ven.	9·00 N	62·09 W
99	Tucuruí (tōō-kōō-tōō-ē') . . . Braz.	3·34 S	49·44 W
124	Tudela (tōō-dhā'lä) . . . Sp.	42·03 N	1·37 W
78	Tugaloo (R.) (tŭg'ȧ-lōō) . Ga.-S. C.	34·35 N	83·05 W
167	Tugela (R.) (tōō-gel'ȧ) S. Afr. (Natal In.)	28·50 S	30·52 E
167	Tugela Ferry . S. Afr. (Natal In.)	29·16 S	30·24 E
80	Tug Fork (R.) (tŭg) . . . W. Va.	37·50 N	82·30 W
155	Tuguegarao (tōō-gä-gä-rä'ō) Phil. (Manila In.)	17·37 N	121·44 E
148	T'uhsieh (R.) (tōō'hăĭ) . . . China	37·05 N	116·56 E
168	Tuinplaas . . . S. Afr. (Johannesburg & Pretoria In.)	24·54 S	28·46 E
74	Tujunga (tōō-jŭŋ'gȧ) Calif. (Los Angeles In.)	34·15 N	118·16 W
136	Tukan (tōō'kän) Sov. Un. (Urals In.)	53·52 N	57·25 E
155	Tukengbesi, Palau-Palau (Is.) Indon.	6·00 S	124·15 E
165	Tukrah . . . Libya	32·34 N	20·47 E
86	Tuktoyaktuk (tōōk-tō-yăk'tōōk) Can.	69·32 N	132·37 W

278 Tukum–Ugurchin PRONOUNCING INDEX

Page	Name Pronunciation	Region	Lat. °′	Long. °′
132	Tukum (to͝o'ko͝om)	Sov. Un.	57·00 N	22·50 E
119	Tukums (to͝o'ko͝oms)	Sov. Un.	56·57 N	23·09 E
166	Tukuyu (to͞o-ko͞o'yȧ)	Tan.	9·13 S	33·43 E
65	Tukwila (tŭk'wĭ-lȧ)	Wash. (Seattle In.)	47·28 N	122·16 W
90	Tula (to͞o'lä)	Mex.	20·04 N	99·22 W
128	Tula (to͞o'lȧ)	Sov. Un.	54·12 N	37·37 E
128	Tula (Oblast)	Sov. Un.	53·45 N	37·19 E
90	Tula (R.) (to͞o'lä)	Mex.	20·40 N	99·27 W
159	Tulagi (I.) (to͞o-lä'gē)	Sol. Is.	9·15 S	160·17 E
65	Tulalip (tū-lă'lĭp)	Wash. (Seattle In.)	48·04 N	122·18 W
65	Tulalip Ind. Res.	Wash. (Seattle In.)	48·06 N	122·16 W
90	Tulancingo (to͞o-län-sĭŋ'gō)	Mex.	20·04 N	98·24 W
68	Tulare (to͞o-lä'râ) (tûl-âr')	Calif.	36·12 N	119·22 W
68	Tulare Basin	Calif.	35·57 N	120·18 W
69	Tularosa (to͞o-lȧ-rō'zȧ)	N. Mex.	33·05 N	106·05 W
98	Tulcán (to͞ol-kän')	Ec.	0·44 N	77·52 W
129	Tulcea (to͝ol'chȧ)	Rom.	45·10 N	28·47 E
129	Tul'chin (to͝ol'chĕn)	Sov. Un.	48·42 N	28·53 E
90	Tulcingo (to͞ol-sĭŋ'gō)	Mex.	18·03 N	98·27 W
68	Tule (R.) (to͞o'lâ)	Calif.	36·08 N	118·50 W
167	Tuléar (to͞o-lā-är')	Malagasy	20·16 S	43·44 E
68	Tule River Ind. Res. (to͞o'lâ)	Calif.	36·05 N	118·35 W
166	Tuli (to͞o'lê)	Fed. of Rh. & Nya.	20·58 S	29·12 E
72	Tulia (to͞o'lĭ-ȧ)	Tex.	34·32 N	101·46 W
91	Tulijá (R.) (to͞o-lē-ĸȧ')	Mex.	17·28 N	92·11 W
64	Tulik Vol. (to͝o'lĭk)	Alaska	53·28 N	168·10 W
139	Tūl Karm (to͞ol kärm)	Jordan (Palestine In.)	32·19 N	35·02 E
78	Tullahoma (tŭl-ȧ-hō'mȧ)	Tenn.	35·21 N	86·12 W
116	Tullamore (tŭl-ȧ-mōr')	Ire.	53·15 N	7·29 W
122	Tulle (tül)	Fr.	45·15 N	1·45 E
111	Tulln (to͝oln)	Aus. (Wien In.)	48·21 N	16·04 E
111	Tullner Feld (Reg.)	Aus. (Wien In.)	48·20 N	15·59 E
165	Tulmaythah	Libya	32·44 N	21·08 E
91	Tulpetlac (to͞ol-pâ-tlăk')	Mex. (Mexico In.)	19·33 N	99·04 W
73	Tulsa (tŭl'sȧ)	Okla.	36·08 N	95·58 W
98	Tuluá (to͞o-lo͞o-ȧ')	Col. (In.)	4·06 N	76·12 W
146	T'ulufan (Turfan) (to͞o'lo͞o-fän') (to͞or-făn')	China	43·06 N	88·41 E
92	Tulum (to͞o-lo͝o'm)	Mex. (Yucatan In.)	20·17 N	87·26 W
134	Tulun (to͝o-lo͞on')	Sov. Un.	54·29 N	100·43 E
69	Tumacacori Natl. Mon. (to͞o-mä-kä'kô-rē)	Ariz.	31·36 N	110·20 W
98	Tumaco (to͞o-mä'kô)	Col.	1·41 N	78·44 W
92	Tuma R. (to͞o'mä)	Nic.	13·07 N	85·32 W
166	Tumba (L.) (to͝om'bă)	Con. L.	1·03 S	18·28 E
98	Tumbes (to͞o'm-bĕs)	Peru	3·39 S	80·27 W
90	Tumbiscatío (to͞om-bê-skȧ-tē'ō)	Mex.	18·32 N	102·23 W
65	Tumbo (I.)	Can. (Vancouver In.)	48·49 N	123·04 W
150	T'umen (to͞o'mĕn)	China	43·00 N	129·50 E
152	Tumen (R.)	China	42·08 N	128·40 E
99	Tumeremo (to͞o-mâ-rā'mō)	Ven.	7·15 N	61·28 W
99	Tumuc-Humac Mts. (to͞o-mo͝ok'o͞o-mäk')	S. A.	2·15 N	54·50 W
94	Tunas de Zaza (to͞o'näs dā zä'zä)	Cuba	21·40 N	79·35 W
116	Tunbridge Wells (tŭn'brĭj welz')	Eng.	51·05 N	0·09 E
134	Tundra (Reg.)	Sov. Un.	70·45 N	84·00 E
147	Tung (R.)	China	24·13 N	115·08 E
148	Tunga (do͞ong'ä)	China	36·11 N	116·16 E
142	Tungabhadra Res.	India	15·26 N	75·57 E
151	T'ungan (to͞on'gän')	China	24·48 N	118·02 E
148	T'ungch'engi (to͞ong'chĕng'yē)	China	36·21 N	116·14 E
147	T'ungchiang	China	47·38 N	132·54 E
148	Tungeh'angshou (to͞ong'chăng'shō)	China	38·21 N	114·41 E
148	Tunghai (do͞ong'hăĭ)	China	34·35 N	119·05 E
150	T'ungho	China	45·58 N	128·40 E
151	Tunghsiang	China	28·18 N	116·38 E
150	Tunghsien	China (Peking In.)	39·55 N	116·40 E
148	Tung Hu (L.) (to͞ong' ho͞o')	China	32·22 N	116·32 E
151	Tungjen (to͝ong'jĕn')	China	27·45 N	109·12 E
149	Tungkuan	China (Canton In.)	23·03 N	113·14 E
150	T'ung-Kuan	China	34·48 N	110·25 E
148	Tungkuang (do͞ong'go͞oäng)	China	37·54 N	116·33 E
151	T'ungku Chiao (Pt.)	China	19·40 N	111·15 E
150	Tungliao (Payintala)	China	43·30 N	122·15 E
148	Tungming (to͝ong'mĭng')	China	35·16 N	115·06 E
148	Tungpa (to͞ong'bä)	China	31·40 N	119·02 E
148	Tungpa	China	35·56 N	116·19 E
150	T'ungpei (to͞ong'pâ)	China	48·00 N	126·48 E
148	Tungping (to͞ong'pĭng)	China	35·50 N	116·24 E
148	Tungp'ing Hu (L.) (ho͞o)	China	36·06 N	116·24 E
148	Tungt'antien (do͞ong'tän'dĭăn)	China	35·26 N	116·54 E
151	Tungt'ing Hŭ (L.) (to͞ong'tēng' ho͞o)	China	29·10 N	112·30 E
148	Tungwen (R.) (do͞ong'wĕn)	China	36·24 N	119·00 E
150	Tunhua	China	48·18 N	128·10 E
143	Tuni	India	17·29 N	82·38 E
78	Tunica (tū'nĭ-kȧ)	Miss.	34·41 N	90·23 W
164	Tunis (tū'nĭs)	Tun.	36·59 N	10·06 E
113	Tunis, Golfe de (G.)	Tun.	37·06 N	10·43 E
163	Tunisia (tû-nĭzh'ê-ȧ)	Afr.	35·00 N	10·11 E
98	Tunja (to͞o'n-hȧ)	Col.	5·32 N	73·19 W
81	Tunkhannock (tŭnk-hăn'ŭk)	Pa.	41·35 N	75·55 W
65	Tunnel (R.) (tŭn'ĕl)	Wash. (Seattle In.)	47·48 N	123·04 W
68	Tuolumne (R.) (twô-lŭm'nê)	Calif.	37·35 N	120·37 W
135	Tuostakh (R.)	Sov. Un.	67·09 N	137·30 E
99	Tupã (to͞o-pȧ)	Braz.	21·47 S	50·33 W
78	Tupelo (tū'pê-lō)	Miss.	34·14 N	88·43 W
99	Tupinambaranas, Ilha (I.) (ē'lä-to͞o-pē-näɴ-bă-ră'năs)	Braz.	3·04 S	58·09 W
98	Tupiza (to͞o-pē'zä)	Bol.	21·26 S	65·43 W
81	Tupper Lake (tŭp'ẽr)	N. Y.	44·15 N	74·25 W
98	Tuquerres (to͞o-kĕ'r-rĕs)	Col.	1·12 N	77·44 W
134	Tura (to͝or'ȧ)	Sov. Un.	64·08 N	99·58 E
103	Tura (R.)	Sov. Un.	57·15 N	64·23 E
144	Turayf	Sau. Ar.	31·32 N	38·30 E
90	Turbio (R.) (to͞or-byô)	Mex.	20·28 N	101·40 W
98	Turbo (to͞o'bō)	Col.	8·02 N	76·43 W
121	Turciansky Sväty Martin (to͞or'chyȧn-skû'svă'tû' mär'tyĕn)	Czech.	49·02 N	18·48 E
121	Turda (to͝or'dȧ)	Rom.	46·35 N	23·47 E
	Turfan, see T'ulufan			
146	Turfan Depression	China	42·16 N	90·00 E
167	Turffontein	S. Afr. (Johannesburg & Pretoria In.)	26·15 S	28·03 E
134	Turgay (to͞or'gī)	Sov. Un.	49·42 N	63·39 E
103	Turgayka (R.) (to͞or-gī'kă)	Sov. Un.	49·44 N	66·15 E
127	Turgovishte	Bul.	43·14 N	26·36 E
133	Turgutlu	Tur.	38·30 N	27·20 E
119	Türi (tü'rĭ)	Sov. Un.	58·49 N	25·29 E
124	Turia (R.) (to͞o'ryä)	Sp.	40·12 N	1·18 W
90	Turicato (to͞o-rê-kä'tō)	Mex.	19·03 N	101·24 W
94	Turiguano (I.) (to͞o-rê-gwä'nō)	Cuba	22·20 N	78·35 W
	Turin, see Torino			
121	Turka (to͝or'kȧ)	Sov. Un.	49·10 N	23·02 E
134	Turkestan (tûr-kĕ-stăn') (to͝or-kĕ-stan')	Sov. Un.	42·40 N	65·00 E
130	Turkestan (Reg.)	Sov. Un.	43·27 N	62·14 E
138	Turkey	Eur.-Asia	38·45 N	32·00 E
71	Turkey (R.) (tûrk'ê)	Iowa	43·20 N	92·16 W
130	Turkmen (S. S. R.) (to͞ork-mĕn')	Sov. Un.	40·46 N	56·01 E
95	Turks I. Pass	W. I. F.	21·15 N	71·25 W
95	Turks Is. (tûrks)	W. I. F.	21·25 N	71·10 W
119	Turku (Åbo) (to͝or'ko͝o) (ô'bô)	Fin.	60·28 N	22·12 E
68	Turlock (tûr'lŏk)	Calif.	37·30 N	120·51 W
92	Turneffe I. (tûr-nĕf'fê)	Br. Hond. (Yucatan In.)	17·25 N	87·43 W
74	Turner (tûr'nẽr)	Mo. (Kansas City In.)	39·05 N	94·42 W
94	Turner Sd	Ba. Is.	24·20 N	78·05 W
111	Turnhout (tŭrn-hout')	Bel. (Bruxelles In.)	51·19 N	4·58 E
120	Turnov (to͝or'nôf)	Czech.	50·36 N	15·12 E
127	Turnovo	Bul.	43·06 N	25·38 E
127	Turnu Măgurele (to͝or'no͝o mŭ-go͞o-rĕ'ly')	Rom.	43·54 N	24·49 E
127	Turnu-Severin (sĕ-vĕ-rēn')	Rom.	44·37 N	22·38 E
94	Turquino, Pico de (Pk.) (pē'kō dā to͞or-kē'nō)	Cuba	20·00 N	76·50 W
93	Turrialba (to͞or-ryä'l-bä)	C. R.	9·54 N	83·41 W
127	Turski Trstenik	Bul.	43·26 N	24·50 E
103	Turtkul' (to͝ort-ko͝ol')	Sov. Un.	41·28 N	61·02 E
77	Turtle B. (tûr't'l)	Tex. (In.)	29·48 N	94·38 W
70	Turtle Cr	S. D.	44·40 N	98·53 W
70	Turtle Mountain Ind. Res.	N. D.	48·45 N	99·57 W
70	Turtle Mts	N. D.	48·57 N	100·11 W
134	Turukhansk (to͞o-ro͞o-ĸänsk')	Sov. Un.	66·03 N	88·39 E
121	Turya R. (to͞or'yȧ)	Sov. Un.	51·18 N	24·55 E
78	Tuscaloosa (tŭs-kȧ-lo͞o'sȧ)	Ala.	33·10 N	87·35 W
66	Tuscarora (tŭs-kȧ-rō'rȧ)	Nev.	41·18 N	116·15 W
75	Tuscarora Ind. Res.	N. Y. (Buffalo In.)	43·10 N	78·51 W
80	Tuscola (tŭs-kō'lȧ)	Ill.	39·50 N	88·20 W
78	Tuscumbia (tŭs-kŭm'bĭ-ȧ)	Ala.	35·41 N	87·42 W
151	Tushan (do͞o'shän)	China	25·50 N	107·42 E
148	Tushan	China	31·38 N	116·16 E
136	Tushino (to͞o'shĭ-nô)	Sov. Un. (Moskva In.)	55·51 N	37·22 E
78	Tuskegee (tŭs-kē'gê)	Ala.	32·25 N	85·40 W
148	T'ussuk'ou (to͞o'sĕ'kō)	China	36·19 N	117·37 E
74	Tustin (tŭs'tĭn)	Calif. (Los Angeles In.)	33·44 N	117·49 W
128	Tutayev (to͞o-tȧ-yĕf')	Sov. Un.	57·53 N	39·34 E
110	Tutbury (tŭt'bẽr-ê)	Eng.	52·52 N	1·51 W
143	Tuticorin (to͞o-tê-kô-rĭn')	India	8·51 N	78·09 E
91	Tutitlan (to͞o-tē-tlä'n)	Mex. (Mexico In.)	19·38 N	99·10 W
99	Tutóia (to͞o-tō'yȧ)	Braz.	2·42 S	42·21 W
127	Tutrakan	Bul.	44·02 N	26·36 E
120	Tuttlingen (to͝ot'lĭng-ĕn)	Ger.	47·58 N	8·50 E
78	Tutwiler (tŭt'wĭ-lẽr)	Miss.	34·01 N	90·25 W
134	Tuva Aut. Oblast	Sov. Un.	51·15 N	90·45 E
85	Tuxedo (tŭk-sē'dō)	Can. (Winnipeg In.)	49·51 N	97·13 W
84	Tuxedo Park (tŭk-sē'dō pärk)	N. Y. (New York In.)	41·11 N	74·11 W
110	Tuxford (tŭks'fẽrd)	Eng.	53·14 N	0·54 W
90	Tuxpan (to͞os'pän)	Mex.	19·34 N	103·22 W
91	Túxpan	Mex.	20·57 N	97·26 W
91	Túxpan (R.) (to͞os'pän)	Mex.	20·55 N	97·52 W
91	Túxpan, Arrecife (Rf.) (är-rĕ-sê'fĕ-to͞o'x-pä'n)	Mex.	21·01 N	97·12 W
91	Tuxtepec (to͝os-tâ-pĕk')	Mex.	18·06 N	96·09 W
91	Tuxtla Gutiérrez (to͝os'tlä go͞o-tyâr'rĕs)	Mex.	16·44 N	93·08 W
112	Tuy	Port.	42·07 N	8·49 W
99	Tuy (to͞o'ê) (R.)	Ven. (In.)	10·15 N	66·03 W
93	Tuyra R. (to͞o-ē'rȧ)	Pan.	7·55 N	77·37 W
151	Tuyün (to͞o'yün')	China	26·18 N	107·40 E
133	Tuz Gölü (L.)	Tur.	39·00 N	33·30 E
127	Tuzla (to͝oz'lȧ)	Yugo.	44·33 N	18·46 E
118	Tvedestrand (tvĭ'dhĕ-stränd)	Nor.	58·39 N	8·54 E
118	Tveitsund (tvât'so͝ond)	Nor.	59·03 N	8·29 E
	Tver, see Kalinin			
128	Tvertsa (L.) (tvĕr'tsȧ)	Sov. Un.	56·58 N	35·22 E
116	Tweed (R.) (twēd)	Scot.	55·32 N	2·35 W
168	Tweeling (twē'lĭng)	S. Afr. (Johannesburg & Pretoria In.)	27·34 S	28·31 E
75	Twelvemile Cr. (twĕlv'mīl)	N. Y. (Buffalo In.)	43·13 N	78·58 W
85	Twenty Mile Cr. (twĕn'tĭ mīl)	Can. (Toronto In.)	43·09 N	79·49 W
110	Twickenham (twĭk''n-ăm)	Eng. (London In.)	51·26 N	0·20 W
83	Twillingate (twĭl'ĭn-gāt)	Can.	49·41 N	54·49 W
67	Twin Bridges (twĭn brĭ-jėz)	Mont.	45·34 N	112·17 W
67	Twin Falls (fôls)	Idaho	42·33 N	114·29 W
75	Twinsburg (twĭnz'bŭrg)	Ohio (Cleveland In.)	41·19 N	81·26 W
72	Two Butte Cr. (to͞o būt)	Colo.	37·39 N	102·45 W
71	Two Harbors	Minn.	47·00 N	91·42 W
73	Two Prairie Bay. (prā'rĭ bī o͞o')	Ark.	34·48 N	92·07 W
71	Two Rivers (rĭv'ẽrz)	Wis.	44·09 N	87·36 W
161	Tyabb	Austl. (Melbourne In.)	38·16 S	145·11 E
121	Tyachev (tyä'chĕf)	Sov. Un.	48·01 N	23·42 E
146	Tyan' Shan' (Tien-Shan) (Mts.)	Sov. Un.-China	42·00 N	78·46 E
129	Tyasmin (R.) (tyȧs-mĭn')	Sov. Un.	49·14 N	32·23 E
167	Tylden (tĭl-dĕn)	S. Afr. (Natal In.)	32·08 S	27·06 E
110	Tyldesley (tĭldz'lê)	Eng.	53·32 N	2·28 W
70	Tyler (tī'lẽr)	Minn.	44·18 N	96·08 W
77	Tyler	Tex.	32·21 N	95·19 W
78	Tylertown (tī'lẽr-toun)	Miss.	31·08 N	90·06 W
70	Tyndall (tĭn'dȧl)	S. D.	42·58 N	97·52 W
135	Tyndinskiy	Sov. Un.	55·22 N	124·45 E
116	Tyne (R.) (tīn)	Eng.	54·59 N	1·56 W
116	Tynemouth (tīn'mŭth)	Eng.	55·04 N	1·39 W
118	Tynest (tün'sĕt)	Nor.	62·17 N	10·45 E
83	Tyngsboro (tĭnj-bûr'ô)	Mass. (Boston In.)	42·40 N	71·27 W
	Tyre, see Sūr			
118	Tyri Fd. (tü'rê)	Nor.	60·03 N	10·25 E
69	Tyrone (tī'rōn)	N. Mex.	32·40 N	108·20 W
81	Tyrone	Pa.	40·40 N	78·15 W
160	Tyrrel (L.) (tĭr'ĕl)	Austl.	35·12 S	143·00 E
113	Tyrrhenian Sea (tĭr-rē'nĭ-ȧn)	It.	40·10 N	12·15 E
119	Tyrvää (tür'vâ)	Fin.	61·19 N	22·51 E
133	Tyub-Karagan, Mys (C.)	Sov. Un.	44·30 N	50·10 E
134	Tyukalinsk (tyo͝o-kȧ-lĭnsk')	Sov. Un.	56·03 N	71·43 E
135	Tyukyan (R.) (tyo͝ok'yȧn)	Sov. Un.	65·42 N	116·09 E
133	Tyuleniy (I.)	Sov. Un.	44·30 N	48·00 E
134	Tyumen' (tyo͞o-mĕn')	Sov. Un.	57·02 N	65·28 E
134	Tyura-Tam	Sov. Un.	46·00 N	63·15 E
92	Tzucacab (tzo͞o-kä-kä'b)	Mex. (Yucatan In.)	20·06 N	89·03 W
148	Tz'uhsien (tsĕ'sĭän)	China	36·22 N	114·23 E
151	Tzu Shui (R.) (tso͞o)	China	26·50 N	111·00 E
148	Tzuya (R.) (zhĕ'yä)	China	38·38 N	116·31 E
148	Tzuyang (tsĕ'yäng)	China	35·35 N	116·50 E
114	Uarc, Ras (C.)	Mor.	35·31 N	2·45 W
98	Uaupés (wä-o͞o'pās)	Braz.	0·02 S	67·03 W
101	Ubá (o͝o-bȧ')	Braz. (Rio de Janeiro In.)	21·08 S	42·55 W
163	Ubangi R. (o͞o-bäŋ'gê)	Afr.	0·45 N	17·28 E
101	Ubatuba (o͞o-bâ-to͞o'bȧ)	Braz. (Rio de Janeiro In.)	23·25 S	45·06 W
153	Ube (o͞o'bā)	Jap.	33·57 N	131·18 E
124	Ubeda (o͞o'bâ-dä)	Sp.	38·01 N	3·23 W
99	Uberaba (o͞o-bâ-rä'bȧ)	Braz.	19·47 S	47·47 W
99	Uberlândia (o͞o-bĕr-lȧ'n-dyä)	Braz.	18·54 S	48·11 W
166	Ubombo (o͞o-bôm'bô)	S. Afr.	27·33 S	32·13 E
129	Ubort' (R.) (o͞o-bôrt')	Sov. Un.	51·18 N	27·43 E
124	Ubrique (o͞o-brē'kâ)	Sp.	36·43 N	5·36 W
146	Ubsa Nuur (L.)	Mong.	50·29 N	93·32 E
98	Ucayali (R.) (o͞o'kä-yä'lē)	Peru	8·58 S	74·13 W
111	Uccle (ü'kl')	Bel. (Bruxelles In.)	50·48 N	4·17 E
136	Uchaly (û-chä'lĭ)	Sov. Un. (Urals In.)	54·22 N	59·28 E
134	Uch-Aral (o͝och'ȧ-ral')	Sov. Un.	46·14 N	80·58 E
153	Uchiko (o͞o'chê-kō)	Jap.	33·30 N	132·39 E
153	Uchinoura (o͞o'chê-nô-o͞o'rȧ)	Jap.	31·16 N	131·03 E
136	Uchinskoye Vodokhranilishche L. (o͞och-ēn'skô-yĕ vô-dô-ĸrȧ-nĭ'li-shchĕ)	Sov. Un. (Moskva In.)	56·08 N	37·44 E
152	Uchiura-Wan (B.) (o͞o'chê-o͞o'rä wän)	Jap.	42·20 N	140·44 E
142	Uch-Korgon	Sov. Un.	37·22 N	68·41 E
	Uch Turfan, see Wushih			
135	Uchur (R.) (o͝o-cho͝or')	Sov. Un.	58·27 N	131·34 E
135	Uda (R.) (o͝o'dȧ)	Sov. Un.	52·28 N	110·51 E
135	Uda (R.)	Sov. Un.	53·54 N	131·29 E
142	Udaipur (o͝o-dŭ'ê-po͞or)	India	24·41 N	73·41 E
129	Uday (R.) (o͝o-dī')	Sov. Un.	50·45 N	32·13 E
118	Uddevalla (o͞od'dĕ-väl-ȧ)	Swe.	58·21 N	11·55 E
126	Udine (o͞o'dê-nâ)	It.	46·05 N	13·14 E
134	Udmurt (A. S. S. R.)	Sov. Un.	52·30 N	52·17 E
154	Udon Thani	Thai.	17·31 N	102·51 E
135	Udskaya Guba (B.)	Sov. Un.	55·00 N	136·30 E
165	Ueb Gestro R. (wĕb gĕs'tro)	Eth.	6·25 N	41·21 E
120	Ueckermünde (ü'kĕr-mün-dĕ)	Ger.	53·43 N	14·01 E
153	Ueda (wā'dä)	Jap.	36·26 N	138·16 E
135	Uelen (wĕ-lĕn')	Sov. Un.	66·23 N	179·58 E
165	Uele R. (wā'lâ)	Con. L.	3·34 N	23·23 E
136	Ufa (o͝o'fá)	Sov. Un. (Urals In.)	54·45 N	55·57 E
132	Ufa (R.)	Sov. Un.	56·00 N	57·05 E
166	Ugab (R.) (o͞o'gäb)	S. W. Afr.	21·10 S	14·00 E
166	Ugalla (R.) (o͞o-gä'lä)	Tan.	6·09 S	32·30 E
163	Uganda (o͞o-gän'dä) (û-găn'dȧ)	Afr.	2·00 N	32·28 E
64	Ugashik L. (o͞o'gȧ-shêk)	Alaska	57·36 N	157·10 W
167	Ugie (o͝o'jē)	S. Afr. (Natal In.)	31·13 S	28·14 E
135	Uglegorsk (o͞o-glĕ-gôrsk)	Sov. Un.	49·00 N	142·31 E
136	Ugleural'sk (o͝og-lĕ-o͝o-rálsk')	Sov. Un. (Urals In.)	58·58 N	57·35 E
128	Uglich (o͞og-lêch')	Sov. Un.	57·33 N	38·19 E
136	Uglitskiy (o͝og-lĭt'skĭ)	Sov. Un. (Urals In.)	53·50 N	60·18 E
128	Uglovka (o͞og-lôf'kȧ)	Sov. Un.	58·14 N	33·24 E
128	Ugra (R.) (o͞og'rȧ)	Sov. Un.	54·43 N	34·20 E
127	Ugŭrchin	Bul.	43·06 N	24·23 E

ăt; finăl; rāte; senâte; ärm; ȧsk; sofȧ; fâre; ch-choose; dh-as th in other; bē; êvent; bĕt; recĕnt; cratẽr; g-go; gh-guttural g; bĭt; ĭ-short neutral; rīde: ĸ-guttural k as ch in German ich;

PRONOUNCING INDEX

Uherske Hradiste–Utuado 279

Page	Name Pronunciation Region	Lat. °'	Long. °'
121	Uherske Hradiště (ōō-hĕr'skyĕ hrä-dêsh'tyĕ) Czech.	49·01 N	17·28 E
80	Uhrichsville (ū'rĭks-vĭl) Ohio	40·25 N	81·20 W
152	Uiju (ōō'ējōō) Kor.	40·09 N	124·33 E
133	Uil (R.) (ōō-ēl') Sov. Un.	49·30 N	55·10 E
69	Uinkaret Plat. (û-ĭn'kâr-ĕt) Ariz.	36·43 N	113·15 W
136	Uinskoye (ōō-ĭn'skô-yĕ) Sov. Un. (Urals In.)	56·53 N	56·25 E
69	Uinta (R.) (û-ĭn'tȧ) Utah	40·25 N	109·55 W
74	Uintah (û-ĭn'tȧ) Utah (Salt Lake City In.)	41·09 N	111·56 W
69	Uintah and Ouray Ind. Res. Utah	39·55 N	109·20 W
167	Uitenhage S. Afr. (Natal In.)	33·46 S	25·26 E
111	Uithorn Neth. (Amsterdam In.)	52·13 N	4·49 E
153	Uji (ōō'jē) Jap. (Ōsaka In.)	34·53 N	135·49 E
166	Ujiji (ōō-jē'jē) Tan.	4·57 S	29·43 E
153	Uji-Yamada (ōō'jē yä'mä-dä) Jap.	34·30 N	136·43 E
142	Ujjain (ōō-jŭēn) India	23·13 N	75·49 E
68	Ukiah (ū-kī'ȧ) Calif.	35·09 N	122·12 W
134	Ukhta Sov. Un.	63·08 N	53·42 E
132	Ukhta (ōōk'tȧ) Sov. Un.	65·22 N	31·30 E
119	Ukmergė (ōōk'mĕr-ghȧ) Sov. Un.	55·16 N	24·45 E
130	Ukrainian (S. S. R.) (ū'krān) Sov. Un.	49·15 N	30·15 E
153	Uku (I.) (ōōk'ōō) Jap.	33·18 N	129·02 E
146	Ulaan Baatar Mong.	47·56 N	107·00 E
146	Ulaan Goom Mong.	50·23 N	92·14 E
135	Ulan Ude (ōō'lån ōō'dȧ) Sov. Un.	51·59 N	107·41 E
152	Ulchin (ōōl'chĕn') Kor.	36·57 N	129·26 E
127	Ulčinj (Dulcigno) (ōōl'tsēn') Yugo.	41·56 N	19·15 E
143	Ulhās (R.) India (Bombay In.)	19·13 N	73·03 E
166	Ulindi (R.) (ōō-lĭn'dē) Con. L.	1·47 S	26·29 E
128	Ulla (ōōl'ȧ) Sov. Un.	55·14 N	29·15 E
128	Ulla (R.) Sov. Un.	54·58 N	29·03 E
124	Ulla (R.) (ōō'lä) Sp.	42·45 N	8·33 W
152	Ullŭng (I.) (ōōl'lōōng') Kor.	37·29 N	130·50 E
120	Ulm (ōōlm) Ger.	48·24 N	9·59 E
47	Ulmer, Mt. (ŭl'mûr') Ant.	77·30 S	86·00 W
118	Ulricehamn (ōōl-rē'sĕ-häm) Swe.	57·49 N	13·23 E
152	Ulsan (ōōl'sän') Kor.	35·35 N	129·22 E
116	Ulster (Reg.) (ŭl'stēr) Ire.-N. Ire.	54·41 N	7·10 W
92	Ulua R. (ōō-lōō'ȧ) Hond.	15·49 N	87·45 W
133	Ulukisla (ōō-lōō-kēsh'lȧ) Tur.	36·40 N	34·30 E
152	Ulunga (ōō-lōōn'gȧ) Sov. Un.	46·16 N	136·29 E
136	Ulu-Telyak (ōō lōō'tĕlyăk) Sov. Un. (Urals In.)	54·54 N	57·01 E
160	Ulverstone (ŭl'vĕr-stŭn) Austl.	41·20 S	146·22 E
118	Ulvik (ōōl'vĕk) Nor.	60·35 N	6·53 E
136	Ul'yanovka (ōō-lyä'nôf-kȧ) Sov. Un. (Leningrad In.)	59·38 N	30·47 E
132	Ul'yanovsk (ōō-lyä'nôfsk) Sov. Un.	54·20 N	53·05 E
72	Ulysses (ū-lĭs'ēz) Kans.	37·34 N	101·25 W
120	Ülzen (ült'sĕn) Ger.	52·58 N	10·34 E
91	Umán (ōō-män') Mex.	20·52 N	89·44 W
129	Uman' (ōō-män') Sov. Un.	48·44 N	30·13 E
66	Umatilla Ind. Res. (ū-mȧ-tĭl'ȧ) Ore.	45·38 N	118·35 W
82	Umbagog (L.) (ŭm-bā'gôg) Maine	44·44 N	71·20 W
143	Umberpādā India (Bombay In.)	19·28 N	73·04 E
126	Umbria (Reg.) (ŭm'brĭ-ȧ) It.	42·53 N	12·22 E
112	Ume (R.) (ōō'mĕ) Swe.	64·57 N	18·51 E
112	Umeå (ōō'mĕ-ô) Swe.	63·48 N	20·29 E
167	Umgeni (R.) (ōōm-gä'nē) S. Afr. (Natal In.)	29·38 S	30·53 E
167	Umhlatuzi (R.) (ōōm'hlȧ-tōō'zĭ) S. Afr. (Natal In.)	28·47 S	31·17 E
64	Umiat (ōō'mĭ-ăt) Alaska	69·20 N	152·28 W
167	Umkomaas (ōōm-kō'mäs) S. Afr. (Natal In.)	30·12 S	30·48 E
167	Umkomaas (R.) S. Afr. (Natal In.)	30·10 S	30·30 E
167	Umlaas (R.) S. Afr. (Natal In.)	29·52 S	30·42 E
64	Umnak (I.) (ōōm'nȧk) Alaska	53·10 N	169·08 W
64	Umnak P. Alaska	53·10 N	168·04 W
66	Umpqua R. (ŭmp'kwȧ) Ore.	43·42 N	123·50 W
166	Umtali (ōōm-tä'lē) Fed. of Rh. & Nya.	18·49 S	32·39 E
167	Umtamvuna (R.) (ōōm-täm-vōō'nȧ) S. Afr. (Natal In.)	30·43 S	29·53 E
167	Umtata (ōōm-tä'tȧ) S. Afr. (Natal In.)	31·36 S	28·47 E
167	Umtata (R.) S. Afr. (Natal In.)	31·48 S	29·03 E
167	Umtentweni S. Afr. (Natal In.)	30·41 S	30·29 E
167	Umvoti (R.) (ōōm-vō'tĭ) S. Afr. (Natal In.)	29·18 S	30·52 E
167	Umzimkulu (ōōm-zēm-kōō'lōō) S. Afr. (Natal In.)	30·12 S	29·53 E
167	Umzimkulu (R.) S. Afr. (Natal In.)	30·12 S	29·57 E
167	Umzimvubu (R.) (ōōm-zēm-vōō'bōō) S. Afr. (Natal In.)	31·22 S	29·20 E
167	Umzinto (ōōm-zĭn'tō) S. Afr. (Natal In.)	30·19 S	30·41 E
126	Una (R.) (ōō'nȧ) Yugo.	44·38 N	16·10 E
64	Unalakleet (ū-nȧ-lăk'lēt) Alaska	63·50 N	160·42 W
64	Unalaska (ū-nȧ-lăs'kȧ) Alaska	53·30 N	166·20 W
99	Unare (R.) Ven. (In.)	9·45 N	65·12 W
99	Unare, Laguna de (L.) (lä-gōō'nä-de-ōō-nä'rĕ) Ven. (In.)	10·07 N	65·23 W
144	Unayzah Sau. Ar.	25·50 N	44·02 E
85	Uncas (ŭŋ'kȧs) Can. (Edmonton In.)	53·30 N	113·02 W
98	Uncía (ōōn'sē-ä) Bol.	18·28 S	66·32 W
69	Uncompahgre (R.) Colo.	38·20 N	107·45 W
69	Uncompahgre Pk. (ŭn-kŭm-pä'grē) Colo.	38·00 N	107·30 W
69	Uncompahgre Plat. Colo.	38·40 N	108·40 W
167	Underberg (ŭn'dēr-bûrg) S. Afr. (Natal In.)	29·51 S	29·32 E
165	Undo Eth.	6·37 N	38·29 E
128	Unecha (ōō-nĕ'chȧ) Sov. Un.	32·51 N	32·44 E
80	Ungava B. (ŭŋ-gā'vȧ) Can.	59·46 N	67·18 W
87	Ungava Pen. Can.	60·38 N	74·00 W
100	União da Vitória (ōō-nê-ouN' dä vē-tô'ryä) Braz.	26·17 S	51·13 W
126	Unije (I.) (ōō'nē-yĕ) Yugo.	44·39 N	14·10 E
64	Unimak (I.) (ōō-nē-mȧk') Alaska	54·30 N	163·35 W
64	Unimak P. Alaska	54·22 N	165·22 W
78	Union (ūn'yŭn) Miss.	32·35 N	89·07 W
73	Union Mo.	38·28 N	90·59 W
79	Union N. C.	34·42 N	81·40 W
66	Union Ore.	45·13 N	117·52 W
80	Union City Ind.	40·10 N	85·00 W
80	Union City Mich.	42·00 N	85·10 W
81	Union City Pa.	41·50 N	79·50 W
78	Union City Tenn.	36·25 N	89·04 W
94	Union de Reves (ōō-nyô'n-dĕ-rĕ-vĕ's) Cuba	22·45 N	81·30 W
90	Union de San Antonio (sän än-tō'nyō) Mex.	21·07 N	101·56 W
90	Union de Tula (tōō'lä) Mex.	19·57 N	104·14 W
75	Union Grove (ūn'yŭn grōv) Wis. (Milwaukee In.)	42·41 N	88·03 W
91	Unión Hidalgo (ē-dä'l-gō) Mex.	16·29 N	94·51 W
75	Union Hill Ill. (Chicago In.)	41·06 N	88·09 W
78	Union Point Ga.	33·37 N	83·08 W
78	Union Springs (sprĭngz) Ala.	32·08 N	85·43 W
78	Uniontown (ūn'yŭn-toun) Ala.	32·26 N	87·30 W
75	Uniontown Ohio (Cleveland In.)	40·58 N	81·25 W
81	Uniontown Pa.	39·55 N	79·45 W
85	Unionville (ūn'yŭn-vĭl) Can. (Toronto In.)	43·52 N	79·19 W
73	Unionville Mo.	40·28 N	92·58 W
155	Unisan (ōō-nē'sän) Phil. (Manila In.)	13·50 N	121·59 E
62	Unitas, Mts. (ū-nĭ'tăs) U. S.	40·35 N	111·00 W
163	United Arab Republic (Egypt) (ē'jĭpt) Afr.	26·58 N	27·01 E
69	United Pueblo Ind. Res. (u-nīt'ĕd pōō-ĕb'lō) (pwā'blō) N. Mex.	35·30 N	107·00 W
49	United States N. A.	38·00 N	110·00 W
75	Unity (ū'nĭ-tĭ) Pa. (Pittsburgh In.)	40·49 N	79·46 W
80	Universal (ū-nĭ-vûr'sȧl) Ind.	39·35 N	87·30 W
124	Universales, Montes (Mts.) (mōn'tȧs ōō-nē-vĕr-sä'lås) Sp.	40·21 N	1·43 W
74	University City (ū'nĭ-vûr'sĭ-tĭ) Mo. (St. Louis In.)	38·40 N	90·19 W
74	University Park Tex. (Dallas, Fort Worth In.)	32·51 N	96·48 W
123	Unna (ōō'nä) Ger. (Ruhr In.)	51·32 N	7·41 E
116	Unst (I.) (ōōnst) Scot.	60·50 N	1·24 W
111	Unterhaching (ōōn'tĕr-hä-kĕng) Ger. (München In.)	48·03 N	11·38 E
133	Unye (ün'yĕ) Tur.	41·00 N	37·10 E
132	Unzha (R.) (ōōn'zhȧ) Sov. Un.	57·45 N	44·10 E
165	Uorra Ilu (vō'rä) Eth.	10·39 N	39·21 E
128	Upa (R.) (ōō'pȧ) Sov. Un.	53·54 N	36·48 E
163	Upanda, Sierra do (Mts.) (sĕ-ĕ'r-rä-dō-ōō-pä'n-dä) Ang.	13·15 S	14·15 E
98	Upata (ōō-pä'tä) Ven.	7·58 N	62·27 W
166	Upington (ŭp'ĭng-tŭn) S. Afr.	28·25 S	21·15 E
74	Upland (ŭp'lănd) Calif. (Los Angeles In.)	34·06 N	117·38 W
157	Upolu Pt. (ōō-pō'lōō) Hawaii (In.)	20·15 N	155·48 W
86	Upper Arrow (L.) Can.	50·28 N	117·29 W
84	Upper Darby (där'bĭ) Pa. (Philadelphia In.)	39·58 N	75·16 W
70	Upper de Lacs (R.) (dĕ läk) N. D.	48·58 N	101·55 W
84	Upper Falls (fôlz) Md. (Baltimore In.)	39·26 N	76·24 W
154	Upper Kapuas Mts. Sar.	1·45 N	112·06 E
167	Upper Kubusi (kōō-bōō'sĭ) S. Afr. (Natal In.)	32·37 S	27·31 E
66	Upper L. (ŭp'ēr) Nev.	41·42 N	119·59 W
65	Upper Mill (mĭl) Wash. (Seattle In.)	47·11 N	121·55 W
71	Upper Red L. (rĕd) Minn.	48·14 N	94·53 W
80	Upper Sandusky (săn-dŭs'kē) Ohio	40·50 N	83·20 W
65	Upper San Leandro Res. (ŭp'ēr săn lē-ăn'drō) Calif. (San Francisco In.)	37·47 N	122·04 W
163	Upper Volta (vôl'tȧ) Afr.	11·46 N	3·18 E
110	Uppingham (ŭp'ĭng-ăm) Eng.	52·35 N	0·43 W
118	Uppsala (ōōp'sȧ-lä) Swe.	59·53 N	17·39 E
83	Uptown (ŭp'toun) Mass. (Boston In.)	42·10 N	71·36 W
153	Uraga (ōō'rȧ-gȧ') Jap. (Tōkyō In.)	35·15 N	139·43 E
153	Uraga-Kaikyō (Str.) (ōō'rä-gä kī'kyō) Jap. (Tōkyō In.)	35·11 N	139·44 E
133	Ural (R.) (ōō-räl') (ū-rôl) Sov. Un.	49·50 N	51·30 E
130	Urals (Mts.) Sov. Un.	56·28 N	58·13 E
133	Ural'sk (ōō-rȧlsk') Sov. Un.	51·15 N	51·10 E
143	Uran (ōō-rän') India (Bombay In.)	18·53 N	72·56 E
86	Uranium City Can.	59·34 N	108·59 W
153	Urawa (ōō'rä-wä') Jap. (Tōkyō In.)	35·52 N	139·39 E
153	Urayasu (ōō'rä-yä'sōō) Jap. (Tōkyō In.)	35·40 N	139·54 W
129	Urazovo (ōō-rȧ'zō-vō) Sov. Un.	50·08 N	38·03 E
80	Urbana (ûr-băn'ȧ) Ill.	40·10 N	88·15 W
80	Urbana Ohio	40·05 N	83·50 W
126	Urbino (ōōr-bē'nō) It.	43·43 N	12·37 E
133	Urda (ōōr'dȧ) Sov. Un.	48·50 N	47·30 E
155	Urdaneta (ōōr-dä-nä'tä) Phil. (Manila In.)	15·59 N	120·34 E
101	Urdinarrain (ōōr-dē-nȧr-rȧē'n) Arg. (Buenos Aires In.)	32·43 S	58·53 W
134	Urdzhar (ōōrd-zhär') Sov. Un.	47·28 N	82·00 E
133	Urfa (ōōr'fȧ) Tur.	37·20 N	38·45 E
103	Urgench (ōōr-gĕnch') Sov. Un.	41·32 N	60·33 E
136	Uritsk (ōō'rĭtsk) Sov. Un. (Leningrad In.)	59·50 N	30·11 E
127	Urla (ōōr'lȧ) Tur.	38·20 N	26·44 E
136	Urman (ōōr'mán) Sov. Un. (Urals In.)	54·53 N	56·52 E
152	Urmi (R.) (ōōr'mē) Sov. Un.	48·50 N	134·00 E
98	Urrao (ōōr-rá'ô) Col. (In.)	6·19 N	76·11 W
128	Urshel'skiy (ōōr-shĕl'skēē) Sov. Un.	55·50 N	40·11 E
98	Urubamba (R.) (ōō-rōō-bäm'bä) Peru	11·48 S	72·34 W
100	Uruguaiana (ōō-rōō-gwī-ä'nȧ) Braz.	29·45 S	57·00 W
96	Uruguay (ōō-rōō-gwī') (ū'rōō-gwā) S. A.	32·45 S	56·00 W
100	Uruguay, Rio (R.) (rē'ō-ōō-rōō-gwī) Braz.	27·05 S	55·15 W
	Urumchi, see Tihua		
146	Urungu R. (ōō-rōōŋ'gōō') China	46·31 N	87·44 E
135	Urup (I.) (ōō'rōōp') Sov. Un.	46·08 N	151·00 E
133	Uryupinsk (ōōr'yōō-pēn-sk') Sov. Un.	50·50 N	42·00 E
142	Urzan W. Pak.	33·03 N	70·39 E
127	Urziceni (ōō-zē-chĕn'') Rom.	44·45 N	26·42 E
132	Usa (R.) (ōō'sȧ) Sov. Un.	66·00 N	58·20 E
133	Uşak (ōō'shȧk) Tur.	39·50 N	29·15 E
166	Usakos (ōō-sä'kōs) S. W. Afr.	22·00 S	15·40 E
136	Ushaki (ōō'shá-kĭ) Sov. Un. (Leningrad In.)	59·28 N	31·00 E
136	Ushakovskoye (ōō-shá-kôv'skô-yĕ) Sov. Un. (Urals In.)	56·18 N	62·23 E
153	Ushiku (ōō'shē-kōō) Jap. (Tōkyō In.)	35·24 N	140·09 E
153	Ushimado (ōō'shē-mä'dō) Jap.	34·37 N	134·09 E
100	Ushuaia (ōō-shōō-ī'ä) Arg.	54·46 S	68·24 W
133	Üsküdar Tur.	40·55 N	29·00 E
128	Usman' (ōōs-män') Sov. Un.	52·03 N	39·40 E
136	Usol'ye (ōō-sô'lyĕ) Sov. Un. (Urals In.)	59·24 N	56·40 E
134	Usol'ye-Sibirskoye (ōō-sô'lyĕsĭ' bĕr'skô-yĕ) Sov. Un.	52·44 N	103·46 E
100	Uspallata P. (ōōs-pä-lyä'tä) Arg.-Chile	32·47 S	70·08 W
91	Uspanapa (R.) (ōōs-pä-nä'pä) Mex.	17·43 N	94·14 W
122	Ussel (üs'ĕl) Fr.	45·33 N	2·17 E
147	Ussuri (R.) (ōō-sōō'rē) China	46·30 N	133·56 E
135	Ussuriysk Sov. Un.	43·48 N	132·09 E
135	Ust'-Bol'sheretsk Sov. Un.	52·41 N	157·00 E
126	Ustica, I. di (ē'sō-lä-dē-ōōs'tē-kä) It.	38·43 N	12·11 E
120	Usti nad Labem (Aussig) (ōōs'tê) Czech.	50·39 N	14·02 E
129	Ustinovka (ōōs-tē'nôf-kä) Sov. Un.	47·59 N	32·31 E
136	Ust'-Izhora (ōōst-ēz'hô-rȧ) Sov. Un. (Leningrad In.)	59·49 N	30·35 E
120	Ustka (ōōst'kȧ) Pol.	54·34 N	16·52 E
135	Ust'-Kamchatsk Sov. Un.	56·13 N	162·18 E
136	Ust'-Katav (ōōst kȧ'tȧf) Sov. Un. (Urals In.)	54·55 N	58·12 E
134	Ust-Kemenogorsk Sov. Un.	49·58 N	80·43 E
136	Ust'-Kishert' (ōōst kē'shĕrt) Sov. Un. (Urals In.)	57·21 N	57·13 E
132	Ust'-Kulom (kōō'lŭn) Sov. Un.	61·38 N	54·00 E
135	Ust'-Maya (mä'yȧ) Sov. Un.	60·33 N	134·43 E
135	Ust'-Olene Sov. Un.	72·52 N	120·15 E
135	Ust-Ordynskiy (ōōst-ôr-dyĕnsk'ĭ) Sov. Un.	52·47 N	104·39 E
135	Ust' Penzhino Sov. Un.	62·43 N	170·18 E
134	Ust' Port (ōōst'pôrt') Sov. Un.	69·20 N	83·41 E
132	Ust'-Tsil'ma (tsĭl'mȧ) Sov. Un.	65·25 N	52·10 E
135	Ust'-Tyrma (tor'mȧ) Sov. Un.	50·27 N	131·17 E
136	Ust'Uls (ōōls) Sov. Un. (Urals In.)	60·35 N	58·32 E
130	Ust'-Urt, Plato (Plat.) (ōōrt) Sov. Un.	44·03 N	54·58 E
128	Ustyuzhna (yōōzh'nȧ) Sov. Un.	58·49 N	36·19 E
153	Usuki (ōō'sōō-kē') Jap.	33·06 N	131·47 E
92	Usulutan (ōō-sōō-lä-tän') Sal.	13·22 N	88·25 W
91	Usumacinta (R.) (ōō'sōō-mä-sēn'tō) Mex.	18·24 N	92·30 W
166	Usumbura (ōō-sōōm-bōō'rä) Ruanda Urundi	3·19 S	29·28 E
136	Us'va (ōōs'vȧ) Sov. Un. (Urals In.)	58·41 N	57·38 E
62	Utah (State) (ū'tô) U. S.	39·25 N	112·40 W
69	Utah (L.) Utah	40·10 N	111·55 W
143	Utan India (Bombay In.)	19·27 N	72·43 E
69	Ute Mtn. Ind. Res. N. Mex.	36·57 N	108·34 W
119	Utena (ōō'tā-nä) Sov. Un.	55·32 N	25·40 E
167	Utete (ōō-tā'tȧ) Tan.	8·05 S	38·47 E
75	Utica (ū'tĭ-kȧ) Ind. (Louisville In.)	38·20 N	85·39 W
81	Utica N. Y.	43·05 N	75·10 W
124	Utiel (ōō-tyāl') Sp.	39·34 N	1·13 W
75	Utika (ū'tĭ-kȧ) Mich. (Detroit In.)	42·37 N	83·02 W
92	Utila I. (ōō-tē'lä) Hond.	16·07 N	87·05 W
153	Uto (ōō'tō') Jap.	32·43 N	130·39 E
111	Utrecht (ū'trĕkt) (ü'trĕkt) Neth. (Amsterdam In.)	52·05 N	5·06 E
124	Utrera (ōō-trā'rä) Sp.	37·12 N	5·48 W
118	Utsira (I.) (ŭtsĭrä) Nor.	59·21 N	4·50 E
153	Utsunomiya (ōōt'sōō-nō'mē-yȧ') Jap.	36·35 N	139·52 E
154	Uttaradit Thai.	17·47 N	100·10 E
142	Uttar Pradesh (State) (ōōt-tär-prä-dĕsh) India	34·19 N	78·40 E
110	Uttoxeter (ŭt-tŏk'sē-tēr) Eng.	52·54 N	1·52 W
89	Utuado (ōō-tōō-ä'dhō) P. R. (Puerto Rico In.)	18·16 N	66·40 W

ng-sing; ŋ-bank; N-nasalized n; nŏd; cŏmmit; ōld; ôbey; ôrder; fōōd; fŏŏt; ou-out; s-soft; sh-dish; th-thin; pūre; ûnite; ûrn; stŭd; circŭs; ü-as "y" in study; '-indeterminate vowel.

280 Uusikaupunki–Ventnor PRONOUNCING INDEX

Page	Name Pronunciation Region	Lat. °′	Long. °′
119	Uusikaupunki (Nystad) (ōō'sĭ-kou'pōōn-kĭ) (nü'stādh) Fin.	60·48 N	21·24 E
76	Uvalde (ū-văl'dē) Tex.	29·14 N	99·47 W
136	Uvel'skiy (ōō-vyĕl'skĭ) Sov. Un. (Urals In.)	54·27 N	60·22 E
166	Uvira (ōō-vē'rä) Con. L.	3·28 S	29·03 E
128	Uvod' (R.) (ōō-vôd') Sov. Un.	56·52 N	41·03 E
167	Uvongo S. Afr. (Natal In.)	30·49 S	30·23 E
153	Uwajima (ōō-wä'jē-mä) Jap.	33·12 N	132·35 E
83	Uxbridge (ŭks'brĭj) Mass. (Boston In.)	42·05 N	71·38 W
92	Uxmal (Ruins) (ōō'x-mä'l) Mex. (Yucatan In.)	20·22 N	89·44 W
136	Uy R. (ōōy) Sov. Un. (Urals In.)	54·05 N	62·11 E
136	Uyskoye (ûy'skô-yĕ) Sov. Un. (Urals In.)	54·22 N	60·01 E
98	Uyuni (ōō-yōō'nē) Bol.	20·28 S	66·45 W
98	Uyuni, Salar de (Salt Flat) (sä-lär-dĕ) Bol.	20·58 S	67·09 W
130	Uzbek S. S. R. (ōōz-bĕk') Sov. Un.	42·42 N	60·00 E
133	Uzen, Bol'shoy (R.) Sov. Un.	49·50 N	49·35 E
129	Uzh (R.) (ōōzh) Sov. Un.	51·07 N	29·05 E
121	Uzhgorod (ōōzh'gô-rôt) Sov. Un.	48·38 N	22·18 E
127	Uzunköpru (ōō'zōōn'kû-prü) Tur.	41·17 N	26·42 E
166	Vaal (R.) (väl) S. Afr.	28·15 S	24·30 E
168	Vaaldam (L.) S. Afr. (Johannesburg & Pretoria In.)	26·58 S	28·37 E
168	Vaalplaas S. Afr. (Johannesburg & Pretoria In.)	25·39 S	28·56 E
168	Vaalwater S. Afr. (Johannesburg & Pretoria In.)	24·17 S	28·08 E
119	Vaasa (vä'sȧ) Fin.	63·06 N	21·39 E
121	Vac (väts) Hung.	47·46 N	19·10 E
95	Vache, Ile À (I.) (väsh) Hai.	18·05 N	73·40 W
112	Vadso (vädh'sû) Nor.	70·08 N	29·52 E
118	Vadstena (väd'stĭ'nȧ) Swe.	58·27 N	14·53 E
120	Vaduz (vä'dōōts) Liech.	47·10 N	9·32 E
132	Vaga (R.) (va'gȧ) Sov. Un.	61·55 N	42·30 E
118	Vågsöy (I.) Nor.	61·58 N	4·44 E
121	Vah R. (väĸ) Czech.	48·07 N	17·52 E
142	Vaigai (R.) India	10·20 N	78·13 E
134	Vakh (R.) (väĸ) Sov. Un.	61·30 N	81·33 E
127	Valachia (Reg.) Rom.	44·45 N	24·17 E
85	Valcartier-Village (väl-kärt-yĕ' vē-läzh') Can. (Quebec In.)	46·56 N	71·28 W
128	Valdai Hills (vål-dī' gô'rĭ) Sov. Un.	57·50 N	32·35 E
128	Valday (Valdai) (vål-dī') Sov. Un.	57·58 N	33·13 E
125	Valdemorillo (väl-dȧ-mô-rēl'yō) Sp. (Madrid In.)	40·30 N	4·04 W
124	Valdepeñas (väl-dȧ-pän'yäs) Sp.	38·46 N	3·22 W
124	Valderaduey (R.) (väl-dĕ-rä-dwĕ'y) Sp.	41·39 N	5·35 W
100	Valdés, Pen. (väl-dĕ's) Arg.	42·15 S	63·15 W
64	Valdez (văl'dĕz) Alaska	61·10 N	146·18 W
125	Valdilecha (väl-dē-lā'chä) Sp. (Madrid In.)	40·17 N	3·19 W
100	Valdiva (väl-dē'vä) Chile	39·47 S	73·13 W
98	Valdivia (väl-dē'vēä) Col. (In.)	7·10 N	75·26 W
87	Val d' Or Can.	48·03 N	77·50 W
78	Valdosta (văl-dŏs'tȧ) Ga.	30·50 N	83·18 W
124	Valdovino (väl-dô-vē'nō) Sp.	43·36 N	8·05 W
66	Vale (vāl) Ore.	43·59 N	117·14 W
99	Valença (vä-lĕN'sȧ) Braz.	13·43 S	38·58 W
122	Valence-sur-Rhône (vȧ-lĕNs-sür-rōn') Fr.	44·56 N	4·54 E
124	Valencia (vä-lĕ'n-syä) Port.	42·03 N	8·36 W
125	Valencia (vä-lĕn'thē-ä) Sp.	39·26 N	0·23 W
124	Valencia Sp.	39·34 N	7·13 W
99	Valencia (vä-lĕn'syä) Ven. (In.)	10·11 N	68·00 W
125	Valencia (Reg.) (vä-lĕn'thē-ä) Sp.	39·08 N	0·43 W
116	Valencia (I.) (vȧ-lĕn'shȧ) Ire.	51·55 N	10·26 W
99	Valencia, Lago de (L.) Ven. (In.)	10·11 N	67·45 W
122	Valenciennes (vȧ-län-syĕn') Fr.	50·24 N	3·36 E
70	Valentine (vȧ lăN-tē-nyē') Nebr.	42·52 N	100·34 W
98	Valera (vä-lĕ'rä) Ven.	9·12 N	70·45 W
136	Valerianovsk (vȧ-lĕ-rĭ-ä'nôvsk) Sov. Un. (Urals In.)	58·47 N	59·34 E
128	Valga (väl'gȧ) Sov. Un.	57·47 N	26·03 E
167	Valhalla (văl-hăl-ȧ) S. Afr. (Johannesburg & Pretoria In.)	25·49 S	28·09 E
67	Valier (vă-lēr') Mont.	48·17 N	112·14 W
127	Valjevo (väl'yȧ-vô) Yugo.	44·17 N	19·57 E
129	Valki (väl'kē) Sov. Un.	49·49 N	35·40 E
92	Valladolid (väl-yä-dhô-lēdh') Mex. (Yucatan In.)	20·39 N	88·13 W
124	Valladolid (väl-yä-dhô-lēdh') Sp.	41·41 N	4·41 W
125	Vall de Uxo' (väl-dĕ-ōō-ō') Sp.	39·50 N	0·15 W
98	Valle (Dept.) (vä'l-yĕ) Col. (In.)	4·03 N	76·13 W
68	Valle, Arroyo del (ä-rō'yō dĕl väl'yȧ) Calif.	37·36 N	121·43 W
125	Vallecas (väl-yā'käs) Sp. (Madrid In.)	40·23 N	3·37 W
76	Valle de Allende (väl'yä dā äl-yĕn'dȧ) Mex.	26·55 N	105·25 W
90	Valle de Bravo (brä'vô) Mex.	19·12 N	100·07 W
99	Valle de Guanape (vä'l-yĕ-dĕ-gwä-nä'pĕ) Ven. (In.)	9·54 N	65·41 W
98	Valle de la Pascua (lä-pä's-kōōä) Ven.	9·12 N	65·08 W
90	Valle de Santiago (sän-tē-ä'gô) Mex.	20·23 N	101·11 W
98	Valledupar (dōō-pär') Col.	10·13 N	73·39 W
98	Valle Grande (grän'dä) Bol.	18·27 S	64·03 W
65	Vallejo (vä-yā'hō) (vă-lā'hō) Calif. (San Francisco In.)	38·06 N	122·15 W
90	Vallejo, Sierra de (Mts.) (sē-ĕ'r-rä-dĕ-väl-yĕ'ĸô) Mex.	21·00 N	105·10 W
100	Vallenar (väl-yȧ-när') Chile	28·39 S	70·52 W
125	Vallerano (R.) (vä-lĕ-rä'nô) It. (Roma In.)	41·46 N	12·29 E
114	Valletta (väl-lĕt'ä) Malta	35·50 N	14·29 E
74	Valle Vista (văl'yä vĭs'tȧ) Calif. (Los Angeles In.)	33·45 N	116·53 W
70	Valley City N. D.	46·55 N	97·59 W
75	Valley City (văl'ĭ) Ohio (Cleveland In.)	41·14 N	81·56 W
73	Valley Falls Kans.	39·21 N	95·26 W
84	Valley Falls (fôls) R. I. (Providence In.)	41·55 N	71·23 W
85	Valleyfield (văl'ē-fēld) Can. (Montreal In.)	45·16 N	74·09 W
74	Valley Park (văl'ē pärk) Mo. (St. Louis In.)	38·33 N	90·30 W
84	Valley Stream (văl'ĭ strēm) N. Y. (New York In.)	40·39 N	73·42 W
126	Valli di Comácchio (L.) (vä'lē-dē-kô-mä'chyô) It.	44·38 S	12·15 E
95	Vallière (väl-yâr') Hai.	19·30 N	71·55 W
101	Vallimanca (R.) (väl-yē-mä'n-kä) Arg. (Buenos Aires In.)	36·21 S	60·55 W
125	Valls (väls) Sp.	41·15 N	1·15 E
86	Val Marie Can.	49·10 N	107·59 W
119	Valmiera (vål'myĕ-rȧ) Sov. Un.	57·34 N	25·54 E
122	Valognes (vȧ-lôn'y') Fr.	49·32 N	1·30 W
	Valona, see Vlonë		
101	Valparaíso (väl'pä-rä-ē'sô) Chile (Santiago In.)	33·02 S	71·32 W
80	Valparaiso (văl-pȧ-rā'zō) Ind.	41·25 N	87·05 W
90	Valparaiso Mex.	22·49 N	103·33 W
101	Valpariso (Prov.) Chile (Santiago In.)	32·58 S	71·23 W
122	Valréas (vål-rȧ-ä') Fr.	45·25 N	4·56 E
	Valsbaai, see False B.		
155	Valsch, Kap (C.) (välsh) Neth. N. Gui.	8·30 S	137·15 E
168	Valsch R. S. Afr. (Johannesburg & Pretoria In.)	27·32 S	26·51 E
136	Valuyevo (vȧ-lōō'yĕ-vô) Sov. Un. (Moskva In.)	55·34 N	37·21 E
129	Valuyki (vȧ-lōō-ē'kē) Sov. Un.	50·14 N	38·04 E
74	Val Verde (văl vûr'dē) Calif. (Los Angeles In.)	33·51 N	117·15 W
95	Valverde (väl-vĕ'r-dĕ) Dom. Rep.	19·35 N	71·10 W
124	Valverde del Camino (väl-vĕr-dĕ-dĕl-kä-mē'nō) Sp.	37·34 N	6·44 W
142	Vambanād (R.) India	10·00 N	76·03 E
133	Van (vän) Tur.	38·04 N	43·10 E
73	Van Buren (văn bū'rĕn) Ark.	35·26 N	94·20 W
82	Van Buren Maine	47·09 N	67·58 W
80	Vanceburg (văns'bûrg) Ky.	38·35 N	83·20 W
65	Vancouver (văn-kōō'vĕr) Can. (Vancouver In.)	49·16 N	123·06 W
65	Vancouver Wash. (Portland In.)	45·37 N	122·40 W
86	Vancouver I. Can.	49·47 N	128·23 W
80	Vandalia (văn-dā'lĭ-ȧ) Ill.	39·00 N	89·00 W
73	Vandalia Mo.	39·19 N	91·30 W
168	Vanderbijlpark S. Afr. (Johannesburg & Pretoria In.)	26·43 S	27·50 E
86	Vanderhoof Can.	53·59 N	124·10 W
	Van Diemen, see Ōsumi Kaikyō		
158	Van Diemen, C. (văndē'mĕn) Austl.	11·05 S	130·15 E
158	Van Diemen G. Austl.	11·50 S	131·30 E
75	Van Dyke (văn dīk) Mich. (Detroit In.)	42·27 N	83·01 W
90	Vanegas (vä-nĕ'gäs) Mex.	23·54 N	100·54 W
118	Vänern (L.) Swe.	58·52 N	13·17 E
118	Vänersborg (vĕ'nĕrs-bôr') Swe.	58·24 N	12·15 E
167	Vanga (väŋ'gä) Ken.	4·38 S	39·10 E
143	Vangani India (Bombay In.)	19·07 N	73·15 E
133	Van Gölü (L.) Tur.	38·45 N	43·00 E
80	Van Lear (văn lēr') Ky.	37·45 N	82·50 W
122	Vannes (vȧn) Fr.	47·42 N	2·46 W
74	Van Nuys (văn nīz') Calif. (Los Angeles In.)	34·11 N	118·27 W
119	Vantaan (R.) Fin.	60·25 N	24·43 E
80	Van Wert (văn wûrt') Ohio	40·50 N	84·35 W
118	Vara (vä'rä) Swe.	58·17 N	12·55 E
128	Varakļāni Sov. Un.	56·38 N	26·46 E
126	Varallo (vä-räl'lô) It.	45·44 N	8·14 E
142	Vārānasi (Banaras) India	25·25 N	83·00 E
112	Varanger Fd. (vä-räng'gĕr) Nor.	70·05 N	30·53 E
126	Varano, Lago di (L.) (lä'gō-dē-vä-rä'nô) It.	41·52 N	15·55 E
126	Varaždin (vä'räzh'dēn) Yugo.	46·17 N	16·20 E
126	Varazze (vä-rät'sā) It.	44·23 N	8·34 E
118	Varberg (vär'bĕrg) Swe.	57·06 N	12·16 E
127	Vardar (R.) (vär'där) Yugo.	41·40 N	21·50 E
118	Varde (vär'dĕ) Den.	55·39 N	8·28 E
154	Varella, C. Viet.	12·58 N	109·50 E
119	Varèna (vä-rā'nȧ) Sov. Un.	54·16 N	24·35 E
85	Varennes (vȧ-rĕn') Can. (Montreal In.)	45·41 N	73·27 W
112	Vardō (vård'û) Nor.	70·23 N	30·43 E
127	Varěs (vä'rĕsh) Yugo.	44·10 N	18·20 E
126	Varese (vä-rä'sȧ) It.	45·45 N	8·49 E
101	Varginha (vär-zhē'n-yä) Braz. (Rio de Janeiro In.)	21·33 S	45·25 W
119	Varkaus (vär'kous) Fin.	62·19 N	27·51 E
136	Varlamovo (vár-lá'mô-vô) Sov. Un. (Urals In.)	54·37 N	60·41 E
127	Varna (Stalin) (vär'nȧ) (stä'lĭn) Bul.	43·14 N	27·58 E
136	Varna Sov. Un. (Urals In.)	53·22 N	60·59 E
118	Värnamo (vĕr'nȧ-mô) Swe.	57·11 N	13·45 E
120	Varnsdorf (värns'dôrf) Czech.	50·54 N	14·36 E
79	Varnville (värn'vĭl) S. C.	32·49 N	81·05 W
85	Vars (värz) Can. (Ottawa In.)	45·21 N	75·21 W
129	Varvaropolye (vár'vár'ô-pô-lyĕ) Sov. Un.	48·38 N	38·37 E
124	Vascongadas (Reg.) (väs-kôn-gä'däs) Sp.	42·35 N	2·46 W
132	Vashka (R.) Sov. Un.	63·20 N	47·50 E
65	Vashon (văsh'ŭn) Wash. (Seattle In.)	47·27 N	122·28 W
65	Vashon Heights (hīts) Wash. (Seattle In.)	47·30 N	122·28 W
65	Vashon I. Wash. (Seattle In.)	47·27 N	122·27 W
129	Vasil'kov (vȧ-sēl'-kôf') Sov. Un.	50·10 N	30·22 E
121	Vaslui (vȧs-lōō'ē) Rom.	46·39 N	27·49 E
80	Vassar (văs'ēr) Mich.	43·25 N	83·35 W
100	Vassouras (väs-sō'räzh) Braz. (In.)	22·25 S	43·40 W
118	Västanfors (vĕst'ån-fôrs) Swe.	59·59 N	15·49 E
118	Västerås (vĕs'tĕr-ôs) Swe.	59·39 N	16·30 E
118	Väster-dalälven Swe.	61·06 N	13·10 E
118	Västervik (vĕs'tĕr-vēk) Swe.	57·45 N	16·35 E
126	Vasto (väs'tô) It.	42·06 N	12·42 E
134	Vasyugan (R.) (vås-yōō-gån') Sov. Un.	58·52 N	77·30 E
125	Vatican City (Cittádel Vaticano) (văt'ĭ-kăn sĭt'ē) (chē-tá'del vä-tē-kä'nô) It. (Roma In.)	41·54 N	12·22 E
126	Vaticano, C. (vä-tē-kä'nô) It.	38·38 N	15·52 E
112	Vatnajökull (Gl.) (vät'nȧ-yû-kōōl) Ice.	64·34 N	16·41 W
121	Vatra Dornei (vät'rȧ dôr'nā') Rom.	47·22 N	25·20 E
118	Vättern (L.) Swe.	58·15 N	14·24 E
85	Vaudreuil (vô-drû'y') Can. (Montreal In.)	45·24 N	74·02 W
65	Vaugh (vôn) Wash. (Seattle In.)	47·21 N	122·47 W
72	Vaughn N. Mex.	34·37 N	105·13 W
98	Vaupés (R.) (vä'ōō-pĕ's) Col.	1·18 N	71·14 W
118	Vaxholm (väks'hôlm) Swe.	59·26 N	18·19 E
118	Växjo (vĕks'shû) Swe.	56·53 N	14·46 E
132	Vaygach (I.) (vī-gäch') Sov. Un.	70·00 N	59·00 E
99	Veadeiros, Chapadas dos (Mts.) (shä-pä'däs-dôs-vĕ-ȧ-dā'rōs) Braz.	15·20 S	48·43 W
118	Veblungsnares (vib'lōōngs-nĕs) Nor.	62·33 N	7·46 E
127	Vedea (R.) (vȧ'dyȧ) Rom.	44·25 N	24·45 E
101	Vedia (vĕ'dyä) Arg. (Buenos Aires In.)	34·29 S	61·30 W
80	Veedersburg (vē'dĕrz-bûrg) Ind.	40·05 N	87·15 W
91	Vega de Alatorre (vā'gä dā ä-lä-tōr'rā) Mex.	20·02 N	96·39 W
95	Vega Real (Mts.) (vĕ'gä-rĕ-ä'l) Dom. Rep.	19·30 N	71·05 W
112	Vegen (I.) (vĕ'ghĕn) Nor.	65·38 N	10·51 E
86	Vegreville Can.	53·26 N	112·27 W
143	Vehār L. India (Bombay In.)	19·11 N	72·50 E
101	Veinticinco de Mayo (vā-ēn'tē-sēn'kō dā mä'yō) Arg. (Buenos Aires In.)	35·26 S	60·09 W
124	Vejer (vā-kĕr') Sp.	36·15 N	5·58 W
118	Vejle (vī'lĕ) Den.	55·41 N	9·29 E
123	Velbert (fĕl'bĕrt) Ger. (Ruhr In.)	51·20 N	7·03 E
126	Velebit (Mts.) (vā'lĕ-bēt) Yugo.	44·25 N	15·23 E
123	Velen (fĕ'lĕn) Ger. (Ruhr In.)	51·54 N	7.00 E
124	Vélez-Málaga (vā'lāth-mä'lä-gä) Sp.	36·48 N	4·05 W
124	Vélez Rubio (rōō'bē-ô) Sp.	37·38 N	2·05 W
126	Velika Kapela (Mts.) (vĕ'lĕ-kä kä-pĕ'lä) Yugo.	45·03 N	15·20 E
127	Velika Morava (R.) (mô'rä-vä) Yugo.	44·20 N	21·10 E
128	Velikaya (R.) (vȧ-lē'kȧ-yȧ) Sov. Un.	57·25 N	28·07 E
121	Velikiy Bychkov (vĕ-lē'kē bōōch-kôf') Sov. Un.	47·59 N	24·01 E
128	Velikiye Luki (vyē-lē'-kyē lōō'ke) Sov. Un.	56·19 N	30·32 E
132	Velikiy Ustyug (vȧ-lē'kĭ ōōs-tyōōg') Sov. Un.	60·45 N	46·38 E
128	Velikoye (vȧ-lē'kô-yĕ) Sov. Un.	57·21 N	39·45 E
128	Velikoye (L.) Sov. Un.	57·00 N	36·53 E
128	Velizh (vĕ'lēzh) Sov. Un.	55·37 N	31·11 E
120	Velke Meziříčí (vĕl'kä mĕzh''r-zhĭ-chĭ) Czech.	49·21 N	16·01 E
159	Vella (I.) (väl'yä) Sol. Is.	8·00 S	156·42 E
125	Velletri (vĕl-lā'trē) It. (Roma In.)	41·42 N	12·48 E
143	Vellore (vĕl-lōr') India	12·57 N	79·09 E
136	Vels (vĕls) Sov. Un. (Urals In.)	60·35 N	58·47 E
132	Vel'sk (vĕlsk) Sov. Un.	61·00 N	42·18 E
111	Velten (fel'tĕn) Ger. (Berlin In.)	52·41 N	13·11 E
136	Velya R. (vĕl'yȧ) Sov. Un. (Moskva In.)	56·23 N	37·54 E
98	Venadillo (vĕ-nä-dē'l-yō) Col. (In.)	4·43 N	74·55 W
90	Venado (vȧ-nä'dō) Mex.	22·54 N	101·07 W
100	Venado Tuerto (vĕ-nä'dô-tōōĕ'r-tô) Arg.	33·28 S	61·47 W
122	Vendée, Collines de (hills) (kō-lēn' dĕ väN-dā') Fr.	46·44 N	0·17 W
122	Vendôme (väN-dōm') Fr.	47·46 N	1·05 E
126	Veneto (Reg.) (vĕ-nĕ'tô) It.	45·58 N	11·24 E
128	Venëv (vĕn-ĕf') Sov. Un.	54·19 N	38·14 E
126	Venezia (Venice) (vå-nāt'sē-ä) It.	45·25 N	12·18 E
126	Venezia, Golfo di (G.) (gôl-fô-dē-vå-nāt'sē-ä) It.	45·23 N	13·00 E
96	Venezuela (vĕn-ē-zwē'lȧ) S. A.	8·00 N	65·00 W
98	Venezuela, Golfo de (G.) (gôl-fô-dĕ) Ven.	11·34 N	71·02 W
64	Veniaminof, Mt. Alaska	56·12 N	159·20 W
74	Venice (vĕn'ĭs) Calif. (Los Angeles In.)	33·59 N	118·28 W
74	Venice Ill. (St. Louis In.)	38·40 N	90·10 W
84	Venice La. (New Orleans In.)	29·17 N	89·22 W
	Venice, see Venezia		
123	Venlo Neth. (Ruhr In.)	51·22 N	6·11 E
119	Venta (R.) (vĕn'tä) Sov. Un.	57·05 N	21·45 E
100	Ventana, Sierra de la (Mts.) (sē-ĕ'r-rä-dĕ-lä-vĕn-tä'nä) Arg.	38·00 S	63·00 W
168	Ventersburg (vĕn-tērs'bûrg) S. Afr. (Johannesburg & Pretoria In.)	28·06 S	27·10 E
168	Ventersdorp (vĕn-tērs'dôrp) S. Afr. (Johannesburg & Pretoria In.)	26·20 S	26·48 E
126	Ventimiglia (vĕn-tē-mēl'yä) It.	43·46 N	7·37 E
81	Ventnor (vĕnt'nēr) N. J.	39·20 N	74·25 W

ăr; finăl; rāte; senâte; ärm; åsk; sofȧ; fâre; ch-choose; dh-as th in other; bē; ēvent; bĕt; recĕnt; cratēr; g-go; gh-guttural g; bĭt; ĭ-short neutral; rīde; ĸ-guttural k as ch in German ich;

PRONOUNCING INDEX Ventspils–Villa Maria 281

Page	Name Pronunciation	Region	Lat. °′	Long. °′
119	Ventspils (věnt'spěls)	Sov. Un.	57·24 N	21·41 E
98	Ventuari (R.) (věn-tōōä'rē)	Ven.	4·47 N	65·56 W
68	Ventura (věn-tōō'rá)	Calif.	34·18 N	119·18 W
136	Venukovsky (vě-nōō'kôv-skĭ)	Sov. Un. (Moskva In.)	55·10 N	37·26 E
90	Venustiano Carranza (vě-nōōs-tyä'nō-kär-rä'n-zä)	Mex.	19·44 N	103·48 W
91	Venustiano Carranzo (kär-rä'n-zō)	Mex.	16·21 N	92·36 W
100	Vera (vě-rä)	Arg.	29·22 S	60·09 W
124	Vera (vä'rä)	Sp.	37·18 N	1·53 W
88	Vera Cruz (State) (vä-rä-krōōz')	Mex.	20·30 N	97·15 W
91	Veracruz Llave (l-yä'vě)	Mex.	19·13 N	96·07 W
142	Verāval (věr'ŭ-väl)	India	20·59 N	70·49 E
126	Vercelli (věr-chěl'lē)	It.	45·18 N	8·27 E
85	Verchères (věr-shâr')	Can. (Montreal In.)	45·46 N	73·21 W
69	Verde (R.) (vûrd)	Ariz.	34·04 N	111·40 W
95	Verde, Cap (C.)	Ba. Is.	22·50 N	75·00 W
95	Verde, Cay (I.)	Ba. Is.	22·00 N	75·05 W
91	Verde (R.)	Mex.	16·05 N	97·44 W
90	Verde (R.)	Mex.	20·50 N	103·00 W
90	Verde (R.)	Mex.	21·48 N	99·50 W
155	Verde (I.) (věr'då)	Phil. (Manila In.)	13·34 N	121·11 E
155	Verde Island Pass. (věr'dē)	Phil. (Manila In.)	13·36 N	120·39 E
74	Verdemont (vûr'dê-mŏnt)	Calif. (Los Angeles In.)	34·12 N	117·22 W
120	Verden (fĕr'dĕn)	Ger.	52·55 N	9·15 E
73	Verdigris (R.) (vûr'dê-grēs)	Okla.	36·50 N	95·29 W
85	Verdun (věr'dŭn')	Can. (Montreal In.)	45·27 N	73·34 W
122	Verdun-sur-Meuse (vâr-dûn'sür-mûz')	Fr.	49·09 N	5·21 E
168	Vereeniging (vě-rä'nĭ-gĭng)	S. Afr. (Johannesburg & Pretoria In.)	26·40 S	27·56 E
168	Verena (věr-ên á)	S. Afr. (Johannesburg & Pretoria In.)	25·30 S	29·02 E
128	Vereya (vě-rä'yå)	Sov. Un.	55·21 N	36·08 E
124	Vergara (věr-gä'rä)	Sp.	43·08 N	2·23 W
124	Verin (vå-rēn')	Sp.	41·56 N	7·26 W
136	Verkhne Chusovskiye Gorodki (vyěrk'nyě chōō-sôv'skĭ-ye gå-rôd'ki)	Sov. Un. (Urals In.)	58·13 N	75·06 E
135	Verkhne-Kamchatsk (vyěrk'nyě kám-chatsk')	Sov. Un.	54·42 N	158·41 E
136	Verkhne Neyvinskiy (nā-vĭn'skĭ)	Sov. Un. (Urals In.)	57·17 N	60·10 E
136	Verkhne Ural'sk (ŏŏ-ralsk')	Sov. Un. (Urals In.)	53·53 N	59·15 E
129	Verkhneye (vyěrk'ně-yě)	Sov. Un.	48·53 N	38·29 E
136	Verkhniy Avzyan (vyěrk'nyě áv-zyán')	Sov. Un. (Urals In.)	53·32 N	57·30 E
136	Verkhniye Kigi (vyěrk'nĭ-yě kĭ'gĭ)	Sov. Un. (Urals In.)	55·23 N	58·37 E
136	Verkhniy Ufaley (ŏŏ-fá'lā)	Sov. Un. (Urals In.)	56·04 N	60·15 E
121	Verkhniy Yasenov (vyě'rk-nēē yä'syě-ŋěf)	Sov. Un.	48·17 N	24·21 E
136	Verkhnyaya Pyshma (vyěrk'nyä-yä pōōsh'má)	Sov. Un. (Urals In.)	56·57 N	60·37 E
136	Verkhnyaya Salda (säl'dá)	Sov. Un. (Urals In.)	58·03 N	60·33 E
134	Verkhnyaya Tunguska (Angara) (R.) (tōōn-gŏŏs'kå)	Sov. Un.	58·13 N	97·00 E
136	Verkhnyaya Tura (tōō'rá)	Sov. Un. Urals. In.)	58·22 N	59·51 E
136	Verkhnyaya Yayva (yäy'vá)	Sov. Un. (Urals In.)	59·28 N	59·38 E
136	Verkhotur'ye (vyěr-kô-tōōr'yě)	Sov. Un. (Urals In.)	58·52 N	60·47 E
135	Verkhoyansk (vyěr-kô-yänsk')	Sov. Un.	67·43 N	133·33 E
135	Verkhoyanskiy Khrebet (Mts.) (vyěr-kô-yänsk')	Sov. Un.	67·45 N	128·00 E
86	Vermilion (věr-mĭl'yŭn)	Can.	53·19 N	110·53 W
82	Vermilion (R.)	Can.	47·30 N	73·15 W
80	Vermilion (R.)	Ill.	41·05 N	89·00 W
71	Vermilion (L.)	Minn.	47·49 N	92·35 W
70	Vermillion	S. D.	42·46 N	96·56 W
71	Vermillion (R.)	Minn.	48·09 N	92·31 W
70	Vermillion (R.)	S. D.	43·54 N	97·14 W
77	Vermillion B.	La.	29·47 N	92·00 W
71	Vermillion Ra.	Minn.	47·55 N	91·59 W
63	Vermont (State) (vēr-mŏnt')	U. S.	43·50 N	72·50 W
67	Vernal (vûr'nál)	Utah	40·29 N	109·40 W
166	Verneuk Pan (L.) (věr-nŭk')	S. Afr.	30·10 S	21·46 E
74	Vernon (vŭr'nŭn)	Calif. (Los Angeles In.)	34·01 N	118·12 W
86	Vernon (věr-nôn')	Can.	50·18 N	119·15 W
85	Vernon	Can. (Ottawa In.)	45·10 N	75·27 W
80	Vernon (vûr'nŭn)	Ind.	39·00 N	85·40 W
84	Vernon	N. J. (New York In.)	41·12 N	74·29 W
72	Vernon	Tex.	34·09 N	99·16 W
79	Vero Beach (vē'rō)	Fla. (In.)	27·36 N	80·25 W
127	Véroia	Grc.	40·30 N	22·13 E
126	Verona (vä-rō'nä)	It.	45·28 N	11·02 E
65	Veronica (vě-rŏn'ĭ-ká)	Ore. (Portland In.)	45·52 N	123·12 W
123	Versailles (věr-sī'y')	Fr. (Paris In.)	48·48 N	2·07 E
80	Versailles (věr-sālz')	Ky.	38·05 N	84·45 W
73	Versailles	Mo.	38·27 N	92·52 W
82	Verte, B. (vûrt)	Can.	46·03 N	63·57 W
164	Vert, Cap (C.)	Senegal	14·52 N	17·49 W
167	Verulam (vě-rōō-lăm)	S. Afr. (Natal In.)	29·39 S	31·08 E
117	Verviers (věr-vyā')	Bel.	50·35 N	5·57 E
129	Vesëloye (vě-syô'lô-yě)	Sov. Un.	46·59 N	34·56 E
119	Vesijärvi (L.)	Fin.	61·09 N	25·10 E
123	Vesoul (vē-sōōl')	Fr.	47·38 N	6·11 E
112	Vester Aalen (Is.) (věs'tēr ô'lěn)	Nor.	68·54 N	14·03 E
112	Vestfjord	Nor.	67·33 N	12·59 E
112	Vestmannaeyjar (věst'män-ä-ā'yär)	Ice.	63·12 N	20·17 W
125	Vesuvia (Mtn.) (vě-sōō'vyä)	It. (Napoli In.)	40·35 N	14·26 E
128	Ves'yegonsk (vě-syě-gônsk')	Sov. Un.	58·42 N	37·09 E
121	Veszprem (věs'prām)	Hung.	47·05 N	17·53 E
121	Vesztö (věs'tû)	Hung.	46·55 N	21·18 E
128	Vetka (vyět'kå)	Sov. Un.	52·36 N	31·05 E
118	Vetlanda (vět-län'dä)	Swe.	57·26 N	15·05 E
132	Vetluga (vyět-lōō'gå)	Sov. Un.	57·50 N	45·42 E
132	Vetluga (R.)	Sov. Un.	56·50 N	45·50 E
127	Vetovo (vä'tô-vô)	Bul.	43·42 N	26·18 E
127	Vetren (vět'rěn')	Bul.	42·16 N	24·04 E
168	Vet R. (vět)	S. Afr. (Johannesburg & Pretoria In.)	28·25 S	26·37 E
80	Vevay (vē'vā)	Ind.	38·45 N	85·05 W
123	Veynes (vān'')	Fr.	44·31 N	5·47 E
122	Vézère (R.) (vā-zer')	Fr.	45·01 N	1·00 E
98	Viacha (vēä'chå)	Bol.	16·43 S	68·16 W
126	Viadana (vê-ä-dä'nä)	It.	44·55 N	10·30 E
73	Vian (vī'ăn)	Okla.	35·30 N	95·00 W
99	Viana (vē-ä'nä)	Braz.	3·09 S	44·44 W
124	Viana del Bollo (vê-ä'nä děl bôl'yô)	Sp.	42·10 N	7·07 W
124	Viana do Alentejo (vê-ä'ná dŏŏ ä-lĕn-tā'hŏŏ)	Port.	38·20 N	8·02 W
124	Viana do Castélo (dŏŏ käs-tā'lŏŏ)	Port.	41·41 N	8·45 W
124	Viar (R.) (vê-ä'rä)	Sp.	38·15 N	6·08 W
126	Viareggio (vē-ä-rěd'jô)	It.	43·52 N	10·14 E
118	Viborg (vē'bôr)	Den.	56·27 N	9·22 E
126	Vibo Valentia (vē'bô-vä-lě'n-tyä)	It.	38·47 N	16·06 E
125	Vicálvero (vē-kä'l-vě-rō)	Sp. (Madrid In.)	40·25 N	3·37 W
100	Vicente López (vē-sě'n-tě-lŏ'pěz)	Arg. (In.)	34·15 S	58·29 W
126	Vicenza (vê-chěnt'sä)	It.	45·33 N	11·33 E
125	Vich (vēch)	Sp.	41·55 N	2·14 E
128	Vichuga (vē-chōō'gä)	Sov. Un.	57·13 N	41·58 E
122	Vichy (vê-shē')	Fr.	46·06 N	3·28 E
80	Vicksburg (vĭks'bûrg)	Mich.	42·10 N	85·30 W
78	Vicksburg	Miss.	32·20 N	90·50 W
101	Viçosa (vē-sô'sä)	Braz. (Rio de Janeiro In.)	23·46 S	42·51 W
101	Victoria (vēk-tō'rēä)	Arg. (Buenos Aires In.)	32·36 S	60·09 W
65	Victoria (vĭk-tō'rĭ-á)	Can. (Seattle In.)	48·26 N	123·23 W
100	Victoria (vēk-tô-rêä)	Chile	38·15 S	72·16 W
151	Victoria (vĭk-tō'rĭ-á)	Hong Kong	22·10 N	114·18 E
98	Victoria (vēk-tô'rēä)	Col. (In.)	5·19 N	74·54 W
164	Victoria (vĭk-tō'rĭ-á)	Nig.	4·06 N	9·13 E
155	Victoria (vēk-tô-ryä)	Phil. (Manila In.)	15·34 N	120·41 E
77	Victoria (vĭk-tō'rĭ-á)	Tex.	28·48 N	97·00 W
79	Victoria	Va.	36·57 N	78·13 W
159	Victoria (State)	Austl.	36·46 S	143·15 E
158	Victoria (R.)	Austl.	17·25 S	130·50 E
146	Victoria, Mt.	Bur.	21·26 N	93·59 E
166	Victoria (L.)	Tan.	2·00 S	32·16 E
90	Victoria de Durango (vēk-tō'ryä-dě-dōō-rä'n-gô)	Mex.	24·02 N	104·42 W
94	Victoria de las Tunas (vēk-tō'rē-ä dā läs tōō'näs)	Cuba	20·55 N	77·05 W
166	Victoria Falls	Fed. of Rh. & Nya.	18·15 S	25·35 E
86	Victoria I.	Can.	70·13 N	107·45 W
47	Victoria Land	Ant.	75·00 S	160·00 E
92	Victoria Pk. (vêk-tōrĭ'á)	Br. Hond. (Yucatan In.)	16·47 N	88·40 W
158	Victoria River Downs (vĭc-tōr'ĭá)	Austl.	16·30 S	131·10 E
86	Victoria Str. (vĭk-tō'rĭ-á)	Can.	69·10 N	100·58 E
82	Victoriaville (vĭk-tō'rĭ-á-vĭl)	Can.	46·04 N	71·59 W
166	Victoria West (wěst)	S. Afr.	31·25 S	23·10 E
79	Vidalia (vĭ-dā'lĭ-á)	Ga.	32·10 N	82·26 W
77	Vidalia	La.	31·33 N	91·28 W
127	Vidin (vĭ'děn)	Bul.	44·00 N	22·53 E
128	Vidzy (vē'dzĭ)	Sov. Un.	55·23 N	26·46 E
100	Viedma (vyād'mä)	Arg.	40·55 S	63·03 W
100	Viedma (L.)	Arg.	49·40 S	72·35 W
92	Viejo R. (vyā'hō)	Nic.	12·45 N	86·19 W
78	Vienna (vē-ěn'á)	Ga.	32·03 N	83·50 W
73	Vienna	Ill.	37·24 N	88·50 W
	Vienna, see Wien			
122	Vienne (vyěn')	Fr.	45·31 N	4·54 E
122	Vienne (R.)	Fr.	47·06 N	0·20 E
154	Vientiane (vyän'tyän')	Laos	18·07 N	102·33 E
89	Vieques (vyā'kås)	P. R. (Puerto Rico In.)	18·09 N	65·27 W
89	Vieques (I.) (vyā'kås)	P. R. (Puerto Rico In.)	18·05 N	65·28 W
168	Vierfontien (vēr'fôn-tān)	S. Afr. (Johannesburg & Pretoria In.)	27·06 S	26·45 E
123	Viersen (fēr'zěn)	Ger. (Ruhr In.)	51·15 N	6·24 E
120	Vierwaldstätter See (L.)	Switz.	46·54 N	8·36 E
122	Vierzon (vyâr-zôn')	Fr.	47·14 N	2·04 E
76	Viesca (vê-ās'kä)	Mex.	25·21 N	102·47 W
76	Viesca, Laguna de (L.) (lä-ōō'nä-dě)	Mex.	25·30 N	102·40 W
126	Vieste (vyěs'tå)	It.	41·52 N	16·10 E
139	Vietnam (vyět'näm')	Asia	18·00 N	106·20 E
155	Vigan (vēgän)	Phil. (Manila In.)	17·36 N	120·22 E
126	Vigevano (vē-jå-vä'nô)	It.	45·18 N	8·52 E
123	Vigny (vên-y'ē')	Fr. (Paris In.)	49·05 N	1·54 E
124	Vigo (vē'gō)	Sp.	42·18 N	8·42 W
119	Vihti (vē'tĭ)	Fin.	60·27 N	24·18 E
	Viipuri, see Vyborg			
127	Vijosë (R.)	Alb.	40·15 N	20·30 E
112	Vik	Ice.	63·22 N	18·58 W
118	Vik (vĭk)	Nor.	61·06 N	6·35 E
159	Vila	New Hebr.	18·00 S	168·30 E
166	Vila de João Belo (vě'lä-dě-zho'un-bě'lô)	Moz.	25·00 S	33·45 E
124	Vila de Rei (vē'lá dā rā'ĭ)	Port.	39·42 N	8·03 W
124	Vila do Conde (vē'lá dŏŏ kôn'dě)	Port.	41·21 N	8·44 W
124	Vila Franca de Xira (fräŋ'ká dā shē'rá)	Port.	38·58 N	8·59 W
166	Vila Henrique De Carvalho (vě'lä-ěn-rě'kě-dě-kär-vä'lô)	Ang.	9·25 S	20·30 E
122	Vilaine (R.) (vē-lán')	Fr.	47·34 N	0·20 W
166	Vila Luso (vě'lä-lōō'sô)	Ang.	11·45 S	19·55 E
166	Vila Marechal Carmona (mä-rě-zhäl-kär-mô-nä)	Ang.	7·30 S	15·05 E
166	Vilanculos (vê-län-kōō'lôs)	Moz.	22·03 S	35·13 E
128	Vilāni (vē'lå-nĭ)	Sov. Un.	56·31 N	27·00 E
124	Vila Nova de Fozcoa (nō'vá dā fôz-kō'á)	Port.	41·08 N	7·11 W
124	Vila Nova de Gaia (vě'lä nō'vá dā gä'yä)	Port.	41·08 N	8·40 W
124	Vila Nova de Milfontes (nō'vá dā měl-fôn'tāzh)	Port.	37·44 N	8·48 W
124	Vila Real (rā-äl')	Port.	41·18 N	7·48 W
124	Vila Real de Santo Antonio (vê'lä-rě-ä'l-dě-sän-tô-än-tô'nyô)	Port.	37·14 N	7·25 W
166	Vila Rocadas (rô-kä'dās)	Ang.	16·50 S	15·05 E
124	Vila Vicosa (vê-sō'zá)	Port.	38·47 N	7·24 W
128	Vileyka (vē-lā'ē-kå)	Sov. Un.	54·19 N	26·58 E
112	Vilhelmina	Swe.	64·37 N	16·30 E
119	Viljandi (vēl'yän-dē)	Sov. Un.	58·24 N	25·34 E
168	Viljoenskroon	S. Afr. (Johannesburg & Pretoria In.)	27·13 S	26·58 E
119	Vilkaviškis (vēl-kå-vēsh'kēs)	Sov. Un.	54·40 N	23·08 E
134	Vil'kitskogo (I.) (vyl-kēts-kōgō)	Sov. Un.	73·25 N	76·00 E
133	Vilkovo (vĭl-kō-vō)	Sov. Un.	45·24 N	29·36 E
76	Villa Acuña (vêl'yä-kōō'n-yä)	Mex.	29·20 N	100·56 W
76	Villa Ahumada (ä-ōō-mä'dä)	Mex.	30·43 N	106·30 W
91	Villa Alta (San Ildefonso) (äl'tä) (sän ēl-dâ-fōn'sō)	Mex.	17·20 N	96·08 W
100	Villa Angela (vě'l-yä á'n-ĸě-lä)	Arg.	27·31 S	60·42 W
124	Villaba (vēl-yä'bä)	Sp.	43·18 N	7·43 W
100	Villa Ballester (vě'l-yä-bäl-yěs-těr)	Arg. (In.)	34·18 S	58·33 W
98	Villa Bella (bě'l-yä)	Bol.	10·25 S	65·22 W
164	Villa Bens (běns)	Mor.	27·54 N	12·41 W
124	Villablino (vêl-yä-blě'nô)	Sp.	42·58 N	6·18 W
124	Villacañas (vêl-yä-kän'yäs)	Sp.	39·39 N	3·20 W
124	Villacarrillo (vêl-yä-kä-rēl'yô)	Sp.	38·09 N	3·07 W
120	Villach (fē'läĸ)	Aus.	46·38 N	13·50 E
126	Villacidro (vē-lä-chē'drô)	It.	39·28 N	8·41 E
164	Villa Cisneros (vēl'yä thēs-nā'rôs)	Sp. Sah.	23·45 N	16·04 W
101	Villa Constitución (kōn-stê-tōō-syōn')	Arg. (Buenos Aires In.)	33·15 S	60·19 W
76	Villa Coronado (kō-rō-nä'dhō)	Mex.	26·45 N	105·10 W
91	Villa Cuauhtémoc (vêl'yä-kōō-äōō-tě'môk)	Mex.	22·11 N	97·50 W
76	Villa de Allende (vēl'yä dā äl-yěn'dā)	Mex.	25·18 N	100·01 W
90	Villa de Alvarez (vêl'yä-dě-ä'l-vä-rěz)	Mex.	19·17 N	103·44 W
99	Villa de Cura (dě-kōō'rä)	Ven. (In.)	10·03 N	67·29 W
90	Villa de Guadalupe (dě-gwä-dhä-lōō'på)	Mex.	23·22 N	100·44 W
90	Villa de Reyes (dā rā'yěs)	Mex.	21·45 N	100·55 W
100	Villa Dolores (vēl'yä dô-lō'räs)	Arg.	31·50 S	65·05 W
90	Villa Escalante (vêl'yä-ěs-kä-lán'tě)	Mex.	19·24 N	101·36 W
125	Villafamés (vēl'yä-fä-mās')	Sp.	40·07 N	0·05 W
91	Villa Flores (vêl'yä-flō'räs)	Mex.	16·13 N	93·17 W
126	Villafranca (vēl-lä-fräŋ'kä)	It.	45·22 N	10·53 E
124	Villafranca del Bierzo (vēl-yä-fräŋ'kä děl byěr'thō)	Sp.	42·37 N	6·49 W
124	Villafranca de los Barros (vēl-yä-fräŋ'kä dā lōs bär'rōs)	Sp.	38·34 N	6·22 W
125	Villafranca del Panadés (vēl-yä frän'kä děl pä-nä-dās')	Sp.	41·20 N	1·40 E
90	Villa García (gär-sē'ä)	Mex.	22·07 N	101·55 W
124	Villagarcia (vēl'yä-gär-thē'ä)	Sp.	42·38 N	8·43 W
168	Villaggio Duca degli Abruzzi	Som. (Horn of Afr. In.)	2·40 N	45·20 E
76	Villagran (vēl-yä-grän')	Mex.	24·28 N	99·30 W
80	Villa Grove (vĭl'á grōv')	Ill.	39·55 N	88·15 W
100	Villaguay (vě'l-yä-gwī)	Arg.	31·47 S	58·53 W
100	Villa Hayes (vēl'yä äyås) (hāz)	Par.	25·07 S	57·31 W
91	Villahermosa (vēl'yä-ěr-mō'sä)	Mex.	17·59 N	92·56 W
90	Villa Hidalgo (vēl'yäē-däl'gō)	Mex.	21·39 N	102·41 W
125	Villajoyosa (vēl'yä-hô-yō'sä)	Sp.	38·30 N	0·14 W
76	Villaldama (vēl-yäl-dä'mä)	Mex.	26·30 N	100·26 W
76	Villa Lopez (vēl'yä lō'pěz)	Mex.	27·00 N	105·02 W
124	Villalpando (vēl-yäl-pän'dō)	Sp.	41·54 N	5·24 W
100	Villa Maria (vě'l-yä-mä-rē'ä)	Arg.	32·17 S	63·08 W

ng-sing; ŋ-baŋk; ɴ-nasalized n; nŏd; cŏmmit; ōld; ôbey; ôrder; fōōd; fŏŏt; ou-out; s-soft; sh-dish; th-thin; pūre; ûnite; ûrn; stŭd; circŭs; ü-as "y" in study; '-indeterminate vowel.

282 Villamatin–Wagoner PRONOUNCING INDEX

Page	Name Pronunciation Region	Lat. °′	Long. °′
124	Villamatín (vēl-yä-mä-tē'n) Sp.	36·50 N	5·38 W
100	Villa Mercedes (mĕr-sä'dås) Arg.	33·38 S	65·16 W
98	Villa Montes (vē'l-yä-mô'n-tĕs) Bol.	21·13 S	63·26 W
90	Villa Morelos (mô-rĕ'lōs) Mex.	20·01 N	101·24 W
98	Villanueva (vē'l-yä-nōō'ĕ'vä) Col.	10·44 N	73·08 W
92	Villanueva (vēl'yä-nwä'vä) Hond.	15·19 N	88·02 W
90	Villanueva (vēl'yä-nōō'ĕ'vä) Mex.	22·25 N	102·53 W
124	Villanueva de Córdoba (vêl-yä-nwĕ'vä-dā kôr'dô-bä) Sp.	38·18 N	4·38 W
124	Villanueva de la Serena (lä sā-rā'nä) Sp.	38·59 N	5·56 W
125	Villanueva y Geltrú (ē'kĕl-trōō') Sp.	41·13 N	1·44 E
91	Villa Obregón (vē'l-yä-ô-brĕ-gô'n) Mex. (Mexico In.)	19·21 N	99·11 W
76	Villa Ocampo (ô-käm'pō) Mex.	26·26 N	105·30 W
90	Villa Pedro Montoya (vêl'yä-pĕ'drô-môn-tô'yà) Mex.	21·38 N	99·51 W
123	Villard-Bonnot (vēl-yär'bôn-nō') Fr.	45·15 N	5·53 E
125	Villarreal (vêl-yär-rĕ-äl) Sp.	39·55 N	0·07 W
100	Villarrica (vēl-yä-rē'kä) Par.	25·55 S	56·23 W
124	Villarrobledo (vēl-yär-rô-blā'dhō) Sp.	39·15 N	2·37 W
124	Villa Sanjurjo (vêl-yä-sän-ĸōō'r-ĸô) Sp.	35·15 N	3·55 W
90	Villa Union (vēl'yä-ōō-nyōn') Mex.	23·10 N	106·14 W
98	Villavicencio (vē'l-yä-vē-sĕ'n-syō) Col. (In.)	4·09 N	73·38 W
125	Villaviciosa de Odón (vēl'yä-vê-thê-ō'sä dä ō-dōn') Sp. (Madrid In.)	40·22 N	3·54 W
98	Villavieja (vē'l-yä-vē-ĕ'ĸà) Col. (In.)	3·13 N	75·13 W
100	Villazón (vē'l-yä-zô'n) Bol.	22·02 S	65·42 W
122	Villefranche-de-Lauragais (vēl-fräɴsh'dĕ-lô-rä-gā') Fr.	43·25 N	1·41 E
122	Villefranche-de-Rouergue (dē-rōō-ĕrg') Fr.	44·21 N	2·02 E
122	Villefranche sur-Saône (sür-sä-ōn') Fr.	45·59 N	4·43 E
123	Villejuif (vēl'zhüst') Fr. (Paris In.)	48·48 N	2·22 E
87	Ville Marie Can.	47·18 N	79·22 W
125	Villena (vē-lyä'nä) Sp.	38·37 N	0·52 W
85	Villeneuve (vēl'nûv') Can. (Edmonton In.)	53·40 N	113·49 W
123	Villeneuve-St. Georges (säɴ-zhôrzh') Fr. (Paris In.)	48·43 N	2·27 E
122	Villeneuve-sur-Lot (sür-lō') Fr.	44·25 N	0·41 E
77	Ville Platte (vēl plåt') La.	30·41 N	92·17 W
122	Villers Cotterêts (vē-ār'kô-trā') Fr. (Paris In.)	49·15 N	3·05 E
123	Villerupt (vēl'rüp') Fr.	49·28 N	6·16 E
98	Villeta (vē'l-yĕ'tä) Col. (In.)	5·02 N	74·29 W
122	Villeurbanne (vēl-ûr-bän') Fr.	45·43 N	4·55 E
168	Villiers (vĭl'ĭ-ērs) S. Afr. (Johannesburg & Pretoria In.)	27·03 S	28·38 E
120	Villingen (fĭl'ĭng-ĕn) Ger.	48·04 N	8·28 E
71	Villisca (vĭ-lĭs'ká) Iowa	40·56 N	94·56 W
143	Villupuram India	11·59 N	79·33 E
119	Vilnius (Wilno) (vĭl'nē-ōōs) Sov. Un.	54·40 N	25·26 E
119	Vilppula (vĭl'pŭ-là) Fin.	62·01 N	24·24 E
111	Vilvoorde Bel. (Bruxelles In.)	50·56 N	4·25 E
135	Vilyuy (R.) (vēl'yà) Sov. Un.	65·22 N	108·45 E
135	Vilyuysk (vē-lyōō'ĭsk') Sov. Un.	63·41 N	121·47 E
135	Vilyuyskiye Gory (Mts.) (vē-lyōōs-kē-yĕ) Sov. Un.	67·45 N	109·45 E
118	Vimmerby (vĭm'ĕr-bü) Swe.	57·41 N	15·51 E
120	Vimperk (vĭm-pĕrk') Czech.	49·04 N	13·41 E
101	Viña del Mar (vē'nyä dĕl mär') Chile (Santiago In.)	33·00 S	71·33 W
82	Vinalhaven (vī-nål-hā'vĕn) Maine	44·03 N	68·49 W
125	Vinaroz (vē-nä'rōth) Sp.	40·29 N	0·27 E
123	Vincennes (văn-sĕn') Fr. (Paris In.)	48·51 N	2·27 E
80	Vincennes (vĭn-zĕnz') Ind.	38·40 N	87·30 W
78	Vincent (vĭn'sĕnt) Ala.	33·21 N	86·25 W
112	Vindelälven (R.) Swe.	65·02 N	18·30 E
112	Vindeln (vĭn'dĕln) Swe.	64·10 N	19·52 E
142	Vindhya Ra. (vĭnd'yä) India	22·30 N	75·50 E
81	Vineland (vīn'lǎnd) N. J.	39·30 N	75·00 W
151	Vinh (vên'y') Viet.	18·38 N	105·42 E
124	Vinhais (vēn-yä'ēzh) Port.	41·51 N	7·00 W
154	Vinh Long (lŏng') Viet.	10·16 N	106·06 E
84	Vinings (vī'nĭngz) Ga. (Atlanta In.)	33·52 N	84·28 W
73	Vinita (vĭ-nē'tá) Okla.	36·38 N	95·09 W
127	Vinkovci (vēn'kôv-tsē) Yugo.	45·17 N	18·47 E
129	Vinnitsa (vē'nêt-sà) Sov. Un.	49·13 N	28·31 E
129	Vinnitsa (Oblast) Sov. Un.	48·45 N	28·01 E
136	Vinogradovo (vĭ-nô-grä'do-vô) Sov. Un. (Moskva In.)	55·25 N	38·33 E
71	Vinton (vĭn'tŭn) Iowa	42·08 N	92·01 W
77	Vinton La.	30·12 N	93·35 W
143	Vinukonda India	16·05 N	79·48 E
84	Violet (vī'ō-lĕt) La. (New Orleans In.)	29·54 N	89·54 W
151	Virac (vē-räk') Phil.	13·38 N	124·20 E
119	Virbalis (vĕr'bä-lēs) Sov. Un.	54·38 N	22·55 E
86	Virden (vûr'dĕn) Can.	49·48 N	101·00 W
73	Virden Ill.	39·28 N	89·46 W
69	Virgin (R.) Ariz.-Nev.-Utah	36·51 N	113·50 W
71	Virginia (vēr-jĭn'yá) Minn.	47·32 N	92·36 W
168	Virginia S. Afr. (Johannesburg & Pretoria In.)	28·07 S	26·54 E
63	Virginia (State) U. S.	37·00 N	80·45 W
84	Virginia Beach Va. (Norfolk In.)	36·50 N	75·58 W
68	Virginia City Nev.	39·18 N	119·40 W
89	Virgin Is. (vûr'jĭn) N. A.	18·15 N	64·00 W
119	Virmo (vĭr'mô) Fin.	60·41 N	21·58 E
71	Viroqua (vĭ-rō'kwá) Wis.	43·33 N	90·54 W
126	Virovitica (vê-rô-vē'tē-tsà) Yugo.	45·50 N	17·24 E
127	Virpazar (vêr'pä-zär') Yugo.	42·16 N	19·06 E
119	Virrat (vĭr'ät) Fin.	62·15 N	23·45 E
118	Virserum (vĭr'sĕ-rōōm) Swe.	57·22 N	15·35 E
126	Vis (vês) Yugo.	43·03 N	16·11 E
126	Vis (I.) Yugo.	43·00 N	16·10 E
126	Visa, Mt. (Mtn.) (vē'sä) It.	45·42 N	7·08 E
143	Visākhapatnan (vĭ-zä'ká-pŭt'nän) India	17·48 N	83·21 E
68	Visalia (vĭ-sā'lĭ-á) Calif.	36·20 N	119·18 W
118	Visby (vĭs'bü) Swe.	57·39 N	18·19 E
49	Viscount Mellville Sound (vī'kount') Can.	74·80 N	110·00 W
127	Višegrad (vē'shĕ-gräd) Yugo.	43·45 N	19·19 E
136	Vishera R. (vĭ'shĕ-rà) Sov. Un. (Urals In.)	60·40 N	58·46 E
166	Vishoek S. Afr. (Cape Town In.)	34·13 S	18·26 E
136	Visim (vē'sĭm) Sov. Un. (Urals In.)	57·38 N	59·32 E
118	Viskan (R.) Swe.	57·20 N	12·25 E
128	Viški (vēs'kĭ) Sov. Un.	56·02 N	26·47 E
127	Visoko (vē'sô-kô) Yugo.	43·59 N	18·10 E
127	Vistonís (L.) (vês'tô-nĭs) Grc.	40·58 N	25·12 E
	Vistula, see Wisla		
127	Vitanovac (vē'tä'nô-vàts) Yugo.	43·44 N	20·50 E
128	Vitebsk (vē'tyĕpsk) Sov. Un.	55·12 N	30·16 E
128	Vitebsk (Oblast) Sov. Un.	55·05 N	29·18 E
126	Viterbo (vê-tĕr'bō) It.	42·24 N	12·08 E
135	Vitim (vē'têm) Sov. Un.	59·22 N	112·43 E
135	Vitim (R.) (vē'têm) Sov. Un.	56·12 N	115·30 E
136	Vitino (vē'tĭ-nô) Sov. Un. (Leningrad In.)	59·40 N	29·51 E
99	Vitória (vē-tō'rē-ä) Braz.	20·09 S	40·17 W
124	Vitoria (vē-tô-ryä) Sp.	42·43 N	2·43 W
99	Vitória da Conquista (-dä-kōn-kwē's-tä) Braz.	14·51 S	40·44 W
122	Vitré (vē-trā') Fr.	48·09 N	1·15 W
122	Vitrolles (vē-trōl') Fr. (Marseille In.)	43·27 N	5·15 E
122	Vitry-le-François (vē-trē'lĕ-fräɴ-swå') Fr.	48·44 N	4·34 E
113	Vittoria (vê-tô'rē-ō) It.	37·01 N	14·31 E
126	Vittorio (vē-tô'rē-ô) It.	45·59 N	12·17 E
155	Vitu Is. (vē'tōō) N. Gui. Ter.	4·45 S	149·50 E
124	Vivero (vē-vā'rō) Sp.	43·39 N	7·37 W
77	Vivian (vĭv'ĭ-ån) La.	32·51 N	93·59 W
127	Vize (vē'zĕ) Tur.	41·34 N	27·46 E
143	Vizianagram (vē-zē-å-nŭ'gråm') India	18·10 N	83·29 E
111	Vlaardingen (vlär'dĭng-ĕn) Neth. (Amsterdam In.)	51·54 N	4·20 E
128	Vladimir (vlå-dyē'mēr) Sov. Un.	56·08 N	40·24 E
128	Vladimir (Oblast) (vlä-dyē'mēr) Sov. Un.	56·08 N	39·53 E
152	Vladimiro-Aleksandrovskoye (vlå-dyē'mē-rô å-lĕk-sän'drôf-skô-yĕ) Sov. Un.	42·50 N	133·00 E
121	Vladimir-Volynskiy (vlå-dyē'mēr vô-lēn'skĭ) Sov. Un.	50·50 N	24·20 E
135	Vladivostok (vlå-dê-vôs-tôk') Sov. Un.	43·06 N	131·47 E
127	Vlasenica (vlä'sĕ-nêt'sä) Yugo.	44·11 N	18·58 E
127	Vlasotinci (vlä'sô-tēn-tsĕ) Yugo.	42·58 N	22·08 E
117	Vlieland (I.) (vlē'länt) Neth.	53·19 N	4·55 E
117	Vlissingen (vlĭs'sĭng-ĕn) Neth.	51·30 N	3·34 E
127	Vlonë (Valona) (vlō'nä) Alb.	40·28 N	19·31 E
120	Vltana R. Czech.	49·24 N	14·18 E
132	Vodl (L.) (vôd''l) Sov. Un.	62·20 N	37·20 E
167	Vogel (R.) (vō'gĕl) S. Afr. (Natal In.)	32·52 S	25·12 E
155	Vogelkop Pen. (fō'gĕl-kôp) Neth. N. Gui.	1·25 S	133·15 E
126	Voghera (vô-gā'rä) It.	44·58 N	9·02 E
167	Vohémar (vô-ā-mär') Malagasy	13·35 S	50·05 E
65	Voight (R.) Wash. (Seattle In.)	47·03 N	122·08 W
123	Voiron (vwå-rôɴ') Fr.	45·23 N	5·48 E
127	Voiviïs (L.) Grc.	39·34 N	22·50 E
129	Volchansk (vôl-chänsk') Sov. Un.	50·18 N	36·56 E
129	Volch'ya (R.) (vôl-chyä') Sov. Un.	49·42 N	34·39 E
133	Volga (R.) (vôl'gä) Sov. Un.	47·30 N	46·20 E
133	Volga, Mouths of the Sov. Un.	46·00 N	49·10 E
113	Volgograd (Stalingrad) (vôl'gō-grä't) (stá'lên-grat) Sov. Un.	48·40 N	42·20 E
128	Volkhov (vôl'kôf) Sov. Un.	59·54 N	32·21 E
128	Volkhov (R.) Sov. Un.	58·45 N	31·40 E
121	Volkovysk (vôl-kô-vêsk') Sov. Un.	53·11 N	24·29 E
85	Volmer (vŏl'mĕr) Can. (Edmonton In.)	53·43 N	113·40 W
136	Volodarskiy (vô-lô-där'skĭ) Sov. Un. (Leningrad In.)	59·49 N	30·06 E
128	Vologda (vô'lôg-dà) Sov. Un.	59·12 N	39·52 E
128	Vologda (Oblast) Sov. Un.	59·00 N	37·26 E
129	Volokonovka (vô-lô-kô'nôf-kà) Sov. Un.	50·28 N	37·52 E
128	Volokolamsk (vô-lô-kôlámsk) Sov. Un.	56·02 N	35·58 E
127	Vólos (vô'lôs) Grc.	39·23 N	22·56 E
128	Volozhin (vô'lô-shēn) Sov. Un.	54·04 N	26·38 E
133	Vol'sk (vôl'sk) Sov. Un.	52·10 N	47·00 E
164	Volta R. (vôl'tà) Ghana	8·15 N	0·57 W
101	Volta Redonda (vōl'tä-rē-dôn'dä) Braz. (Rio de Janeiro In.)	22·32 S	44·05 W
126	Volterra (vōl-tĕr'rä) It.	43·22 N	10·51 E
126	Voltri (vōl'trē) It.	44·25 N	8·45 E
126	Volturno (R.) (vôl-tōōr'nô) It.	41·12 N	14·20 E
128	Volzhskoye (L.) (vôl'sh-skô-yĕ) Sov. Un.	56·43 N	36·18 E
74	Von Ormy (vŏn ôr'mê) Tex. (San Antonio In.)	29·18 N	98·36 W
128	Vōōpsu (vōōp'-sōō) Sov. Un.	58·06 N	27·30 E
111	Voorberg Neth. (Amsterdam In.)	52·04 N	4·21 E
167	Voortrekkerhoogte S. Afr. (Johannesburg & Pretoria In.)	25·48 S	28·10 E
168	Voortrekkerspos (vôr'trĕ-kĕrs-pŏs) S. Afr. (Johannesburg & Pretoria In.)	24·12 S	27·00 E
128	Vop' (R.) (vôp) Sov. Un.	55·20 N	32·40 E
112	Vopnafjördhur Ice.	65·43 N	14·58 W
120	Vorarlberg (Prov.) Aus.	47·20 N	9·55 E
118	Vordingborg (vôr'dĭng-bôr) Den.	55·10 N	11·55 E
127	Vorïai (Is.) Grc.	39·12 N	24·03 E
127	Vorios Evvïkós Kólpos (G.) Grc.	38·48 N	23·02 E
132	Vorkuta (vôr-kōō'tá) Sov. Un.	67·28 N	63·40 E
119	Vormsi (I.) (vôrm'sĭ) Sov. Un.	59·06 N	23·05 E
133	Vorona (R.) (vô-rō'nä) Sov. Un.	51·50 N	42·00 E
132	Voron'ya (R.) (vô-rô'nyà) Sov. Un.	68·20 N	35·20 E
129	Voronezh (vô-rô'nyĕzh) Sov. Un.	51·39 N	39·11 E
129	Voronezh (Oblast) Sov. Un.	51·10 N	39·13 E
128	Voronezh (R.) Sov. Un.	52·17 N	39·32 E
121	Voronovo (vô'rô-nô-vô) Sov. Un.	54·13 N	25·23 E
136	Vorontsovka (vô-rônt'sôv-kà) Sov. Un. (Urals In.)	59·40 N	60·14 E
128	Võrts-Järv (L.) (vôrts yärv) Sov. Un.	58·15 N	26·12 E
128	Võru (vô'rû) Sov. Un.	57·50 N	26·58 E
136	Vorya R. (vôr'yà) Sov. Un. (Moskva In.)	55·55 N	38·15 E
123	Vosges (Mts.) (vōzh) Fr.	48·09 N	6·57 E
136	Voskresensk (vôs-krĕ-sĕnsk') Sov. Un. (Moskva In.)	55·20 N	38·42 E
118	Voss (vôs) Nor.	60·40 N	6·24 E
132	Votkinsk (vôt-kēnsk') Sov. Un.	57·00 N	54·00 E
124	Vouga (R.) (vō'gå) Port.	40·43 N	7·51 W
122	Vouziers (vōō-zyā') Fr.	49·25 N	4·40 E
118	Voxna älv (R.) Swe.	61·30 N	15·24 E
132	Vozhe (L.) (vôzh'yĕ) Sov. Un.	60·40 N	39·00 E
129	Voznesensk (vôz-nyĕ-sĕnsk') Sov. Un.	47·34 N	31·22 E
130	Vrangelya (Wrangel) (I.) Sov. Un.	71·25 N	173·38 E
127	Vranje (vrän'yĕ) Yugo.	42·33 N	21·55 E
127	Vratsa (vrät'tsà) Bul.	43·12 N	23·31 E
127	Vrbas (v'r'bäs) Yugo.	45·34 N	19·43 E
126	Vrbas (R.) Yugo.	44·25 N	17·17 E
120	Vrchlabi (v'r'chlà-bē) Czech.	50·32 N	15·51 E
168	Vrede (vrĭ'dĕ) (vrēd) S. Afr. (Johannesburg & Pretoria In.)	27·25 S	29·11 E
168	Vredefort (vrĭ'dĕ-fôrt) (vrĕd'fôrt) S. Afr. (Johannesburg & Pretoria In.)	27·00 S	27·21 E
111	Vreeswijk Neth. (Amsterdam In.)	52·00 N	5·06 E
127	Vršac (v'r'shàts) Yugo.	45·08 N	21·18 E
121	Vrutky (vrōōt'kē) Czech.	49·09 N	18·55 E
166	Vryburg (vrī'bûrg) S. Afr.	26·55 S	29·45 E
166	Vryheid (vrī'hīt) S. Afr.	27·43 S	30·58 E
121	Vsetín (fsĕt'yēn) Czech.	49·21 N	18·01 E
136	Vsevolozhskiy (vsyĕ'vôlô'zh-skēē) Sov. Un. (Leningrad In.)	60·01 N	30·41 E
94	Vuelta Abajo (Mts.) (vwĕl'tä ä-bä'hō) Cuba	22·20 N	83·45 W
111	Vught Neth. (Amsterdam In.)	51·38 N	5·18 E
127	Vukovar (vōō'kô-vär) Yugo.	45·20 N	19·00 E
80	Vulcan (vŭl'kǎn) Mich.	45·45 N	87·50 W
126	Vulcano (I.) (vōōl-kä'nô) It.	38·23 N	15·00 E
127	Vŭlchedrŭm Bul.	43·43 N	23·29 E
119	Vyartsilya (vyår-tsē'lyà) Sov. Un.	62·10 N	30·40 E
132	Vyatka (R.) (vyát'kà) Sov. Un.	58·25 N	51·25 E
152	Vyazemskiy (vyà-zĕm'skĭ) Sov. Un.	47·29 N	134·39 E
128	Vyaz'ma (vyàz'mà) Sov. Un.	55·12 N	34·17 E
132	Vyazniki (vyáz'nē-kē) Sov. Un.	56·10 N	42·10 E
119	Vyborg (Viipuri) (vwē'bôrk) Sov. Un.	60·43 N	28·46 E
132	Vychegda (R.) (vē'chĕg-dá) Sov. Un.	61·40 N	48·00 E
132	Vyg (L.) Sov. Un.	63·40 N	35·00 E
132	Vym (R.) (vwēm) Sov. Un.	63·15 N	51·20 E
136	Vyritsa (vē'rĭ-tsà) Sov. Un. (Leningrad In.)	59·24 N	30·20 E
128	Vyshnevolotskoye (L.) (vŭy'sh-ŋē'vôlôt's-kô'yĕ) Sov. Un.	57·30 N	34·27 E
128	Vyshniy Volochëk (vêsh'nyĭ vôl-ô-chĕk') Sov. Un.	57·34 N	34·35 E
120	Výškov (vêsh'kôf) Czech.	49·17 N	16·58 E
120	Vysoké Myto (vē'sô-kā mû'tô) Czech.	49·58 N	16·07 E
128	Vysokovsk (vĭ-sô'kôfsk) Sov. Un.	56·16 N	36·32 E
132	Vytegra (vû'tĕg-rà) Sov. Un.	61·00 N	36·20 E
132	Vyur Sov. Un.	57·55 N	27·00 E
117	Waal (L.) (väl) Neth.	51·46 N	5·00 E
111	Waalwijk Neth. (Amsterdam In.)	51·41 N	5·05 E
87	Wabana (wä bä-nä) Can. (Newfoundland In.)	47·32 N	52·29 W
80	Wabash (wô'bǎsh) Ind.	40·45 N	85·50 W
80	Wabash (R.) Ill.-Ind.	38·00 N	88·00 W
71	Wabasha (wä'bá-shô) Minn.	44·24 N	92·04 W
121	Wabrzeźno (vôɴ-bzĕzh'nô) Pol.	53·17 N	18·59 E
79	Waccamaw (R.) (wǎk'á-mô) S. C.	33·47 N	78·55 W
78	Waccasassa B. (wǎ-kà-sǎ'sá) Fla.	29·02 N	83·10 W
111	Wachow (vä'kōv) Ger. (Berlin In.)	52·32 N	12·46 E
77	Waco (wā'kō) Tex.	31·35 N	97·06 W
153	Wadayama (wä'dä'yä-mä) Jap.	35·19 N	134·49 E
117	Waddenzee (Sea) Neth.	53·00 N	4·50 E
86	Waddington, Mt. (wŏd'dĭng-tǔn) Can.	51·30 N	125·23 W
165	Wadelai (wä-dĕ-lä'ê) Ug.	2·45 N	31·34 E
71	Wadena (wŏ-dē'ná) Minn.	46·26 N	95·09 W
79	Wadesboro (wādz'bŭr-ô) N. C.	34·57 N	80·05 W
165	Wādi Halfa (wä'dê häl'fä) Sud.	21·58 N	31·23 E
139	Wādī Musa Jordan (Palestine In.)	30·19 N	35·29 E
79	Wadley (wŏd'lē) Ga.	32·54 N	82·25 W
165	Wad Medani (wäd mē-dä'nē) Sud.	14·27 N	33·31 E
121	Wadowice (vá-dô'vēt-sĕ) Pol.	49·53 N	19·31 E
87	Wager B. (wā'jēr) Can.	65·48 N	88·19 W
160	Wagga Wagga (wôg'á wôg'á) Austl.	35·10 S	147·30 E
73	Wagoner (wǎg'ǔn-ēr) Okla.	35·58 N	95·22 W

ăt; finǎl; rāte; senâte; ärm; åsk; sofá; fâre; ch-choose; dh-as th in other; bē: êvent; bĕt; recĕnt; cratēr; g-go; gh-guttural g; bĭt; ĭ-short neutral; rīde; ĸ-guttural k as ch in German ich;

PRONOUNCING INDEX
Wagon Mound–Waycross 283

Page	Name Pronunciation Region	Lat. °'	Long. °'
72	Wagon Mound (wăg'ŭn mound) N. Mex.	35·59 N	104·45 W
121	Wagrowiec (vôŋ-grô'vyĕts) . . . Pol.	52·47 N	17·14 E
70	Wahoo (wä-hōō') . . . . Nebr.	41·14 N	96·39 W
70	Wahpeton (wô'pē-tŭn) . . . . . N. D.	46·17 N	96·38 W
157	Waialua (wä'ê-ä-lōō'ä) Hawaii (In.)	21·33 N	158·08 W
157	Waianae (wä'ê-à-nä'ā) Hawaii (In.)	21·25 N	158·11 W
120	Waidhofen (vīd'hôf-ĕn) . . . . . . Aus.	47·58 N	14·46 E
155	Waigeo (I.) (wä-ê-gā'ô) Neth. N. Gui.	0·07 N	131·00 E
149	Waikang (wăi'käng) China (Shanghai In.)	31·23 N	121·11 E
159	Waikato (R.) (wä'ê-kä'to) N. Z. (In.)	38·00 S	175·47 E
160	Waikerie (wā'kēr-ē) . . . . Austl.	34·15 S	140·00 E
157	Wailuku (wä'ê-lōō'kōō) Hawaii (In.)	20·55 N	156·30 W
157	Waimanalo (wä-ê-mä'nä-lô) Hawaii (In.)	21·19 N	157·53 W
157	Waimea (wä-ê-mā'ä) . Hawaii (In.)	20·01 N	155·40 W
157	Waimea . . . . Hawaii (In.)	21·56 N	159·38 W
142	Wainganga (R.) (wä-ēn-gŭŋ'gä) India	20·24 N	79·41 E
154	Waingapu . . . . Indon.	9·32 S	120·00 E
64	Wainwright (wān-rīt) . . . . . . Alaska	74·40 N	159·00 W
86	Wainwright . . . . Can.	52·53 N	110·40 W
157	Waipahu (wä'ê-pä'hōō) Hawaii (In.)	21·20 N	158·02 W
74	Waiska R. (wȧ-ĭz-kȧ) Mich. (Sault Ste. Marie In.)	46·20 N	84·38 W
66	Waitsburg (wāts'bûrg) . . . . . Wash.	46·17 N	118·08 W
153	Wajima (wä'jê-mà) . . . . Jap.	37·23 N	136·56 E
153	Wakamatsu (wä-kä'mät-sōō) . Jap.	33·54 N	130·44 E
153	Wakamatsu . . . . Jap.	37·27 N	139·51 E
153	Wakasa-Wan (B.) (wä'kä-sä wän) Jap.	35·43 N	135·39 E
159	Wakatipu (R.) (wä-kä-tē'pōō) N. Z. (In.)	44·24 S	169·00 E
153	Wakayama (wä-kä'yä-mä) . . . Jap.	34·14 N	135 11 E
156	Wake (I.) (wāk) . . . . Oceania	15·30 N	165·00 E
72	Wakeeney (wô-kē'nê) . . . . . . Kans.	39·01 N	99·53 W
85	Wakefield (wāk-fēld) Can. (Ottawa In.)	45·39 N	75·55 W
110	Wakefield . . . . Eng.	53·41 N	1·25 W
83	Wakefield . . . . . Mass. (Boston In.)	42·31 N	71·05 W
71	Wakefield . . . . Mich.	46·28 N	89·55 W
70	Wakefield . . . . Nebr.	42·15 N	96·52 W
84	Wakefield . . R. I. (Providence In.)	41·26 N	71·30 W
79	Wake Forest (wāk fŏr'ĕst) . . N. C.	35·58 N	78·31 W
153	Waki (wä'kê) . . . . Jap.	34·05 N	134·10 E
152	Wakkanai (wä'kä-nä'ê) . . . . . Jap.	45·19 N	141·43 E
166	Wakkerstroom (văk'ēr-strōm) (wăk'ēr-strōōm) . S. Afr.	27·19 S	30·04 E
120	Walbrzych (väl'bzhûk) . . . . Pol.	50·46 N	16·16 E
82	Waldoboro (wôl'dô-bŭr-ô) . . Maine	44·06 N	69·22 W
66	Waldo L. (wôl'dō) . . . . Ore.	43·46 N	122·10 W
74	Waldron (wôl'drŭn) Mo. (Kansas City In.)	39·14 N	94·47 W
65	Waldron (I.) Wash. (Vancouver In.)	48·42 N	123·02 W
64	Wales (wālz) . . . . Alaska	65·35 N	168·14 W
116	Wales . . . . U. K.	52·12 N	3·40 W
120	Wałez (välch) . . . . Pol.	53·16 N	16·30 E
160	Walgett (wôl'gĕt) . . . . Austl.	30·00 S	148·10 E
47	Walgreen Coast (wôl'grēn) . . . Ant.	73·00 S	110·00 W
78	Walhalla (wŏl-hăl'ȧ) . . . . S. C.	34·45 N	83·04 W
71	Walker (wôk'ēr) . . . . Minn.	47·06 N	94·37 W
68	Walker (R.) . . . . Nev.	39·07 N	119·10 W
65	Walker, Mt . . . Wash. (Seattle In.)	47·47 N	122·54 W
68	Walker L . . . . Nev.	38·46 N	118·30 W
68	Walker River Ind. Res . . . . . . Nev.	39·06 N	118·20 W
67	Walkerville (wôk'ēr-vĭl) . . . . Mont.	46·20 N	112·32 W
66	Wallace (wŏl'ås) . . . . Idaho	47·27 N	115·55 W
161	Wallacia . . . . . . Austl. (Sydney In.)	33·52 S	150·40 E
66	Wallapa B (wŏl ȧ pä) . . . . . Wash.	46·39 N	124·30 W
160	Wallaroo (wŏl-ȧ-rōō) . . . . . . Austl.	33·52 S	137·45 E
110	Wallasey (wŏl'ȧ-sê) . . . . Eng.	53·25 N	3·03 W
66	Walla Walla (wŏl'ȧ wŏl'ȧ) . . Wash.	46·03 N	118·20 W
75	Walled Lake (wôl'd lāk) Mich. (Detroit In.)	42·32 N	83·29 W
165	Wallel, Tulu (Mt.) . . . . Eth.	9·00 N	34·52 E
110	Wallingford (wŏl'ĭng-fērd) Eng. (London In.)	51·34 N	1·08 W
81	Wallingford . . . . Vt.	43·30 N	72·55 W
156	Wallis Is . . . . Oceania	13·00 S	183·50 E
77	Wallisville (wŏl'ĭs-vĭl) . . . Tex. (In.)	29·50 N	94·44 W
66	Wallowa (wôl'ô-wȧ) . . . . Ore.	45·34 N	117·32 W
66	Wallowa Mts . . . . Ore.	45·10 N	117·22 W
66	Wallowa R . . . . Ore.	45·28 N	117·28 W
110	Wallsall (wôl-sôl) . . . . Eng.	52·35 N	1·58 W
116	Walney (wôl'nê) . . . . Eng.	54·04 N	3·13 W
74	Walnut (wôl'nŭt) Calif. (Los Angeles In.)	34·00 N	117·51 W
73	Walnut (R.) . . . . Kans.	37·28 N	97·06 W
69	Walnut Canyon Natl. Mon . . Ariz.	35·10 N	111·30 W
65	Walnut Creek Calif. (San Francisco In.)	37·54 N	122·04 W
74	Walnut Cr. Tex. (Dallas, Fort Worth In.)	32·37 N	97·03 W
73	Walnut Ridge (rĭj) . . . . Ark.	36·04 N	90·56 W
83	Walpole (wôl'pōl) Mass. (Boston In.)	42·09 N	71·15 W
81	Walpole . . . . N. H.	43·05 N	72·25 W
72	Walsenburg (wôl'sĕn-bûrg) . . Colo.	37·38 N	104·46 W
72	Walters (wôl'tērz) . . . . Okla.	34·21 N	98·19 W
83	Waltham (wôl'thăm) Mass. (Boston In.)	42·22 N	71·14 W
110	Walthamstow (wôl'tăm-stō) Eng. (London In.)	51·34 N	0·01 W
81	Walton (wôl'tŭn) . . . . N. Y.	42·10 N	75·05 W
110	Walton-le-Dale (lē-dāl') . . . . Eng.	53·44 N	2·40 W
166	Walvis Bay (wôl'vĭs) . . . . . . S. Afr.	22·50 S	14·30 E
71	Walworth (wôl'wŭrth) . . . . . . Wis.	42·33 N	88·39 W
165	Wamba (wäm'bä) . . . . Con. L.	2·15 N	28·05 E
166	Wamba (R.) . . . . Con. L.	6·45 S	17·51 E
73	Wamego (wŏ-mē'gō) . . . . Kans.	39·13 N	96·17 W
167	Wami (R.) (wä'mē) . . . . Tan.	6·31 S	37·17 E
84	Wanaque (wŏn'ȧ-kū) N. J. (New York In.)	41·03 N	74·16 W
84	Wanaque Res. N. J. (New York In.)	41·06 N	74·20 W
148	Wanchih (wän'chĭ') . . . . China	31·11 N	118·31 E
111	Wandsbek (vänds'bĕk) Ger. (Hamburg In.)	53·34 N	10·07 E
110	Wandsworth (wôndz'wûrth) . Eng.	51·26 N	0·12 W
159	Wanganui (wôŋ'gȧ-nōō'ê) N. Z. (In.)	39·53 S	175·01 E
160	Wangaratta (wŏŋ'gȧ-răt'ȧ) . . Austl.	36·23 S	146·18 E
152	Wangching (wäng'chĕng) . . . . China	43·14 N	129·33 E
148	Wangch'ingt'o (wäng'chĭng'tōōŭ) . China	39·14 N	116·56 E
120	Wangeroog I. (vän'gĕ-rōg) . . . Ger.	53·49 N	7·57 E
151	Wanhsien (wän'hsyĕn') . . . . . China	30·48 N	108·22 E
148	Wanhsien (wän'sĭän) . . . . China	38·51 N	115·10 E
166	Wankie (wăŋ'kê) Fed. of Rh. & Nya.	18·27 S	26·30 E
110	Wantage (wŏn'tăj) Eng. (London In.)	51·33 N	1·26 W
151	Wantsai . . . . China	28·05 N	114·25 E
160	Waodoan (wŏd'ŏn) . . . . Austl.	26·12 S	149·52 E
80	Wapakoneta (wä'pȧ-kô-nĕt'ȧ) Ohio	40·35 N	84·10 W
71	Wapello (wŏ-pĕl'ō) . . . . Iowa	41·10 N	91·11 W
73	Wappapello Res. (wă'pȧ-pĕl-lō) Mo.	37·07 N	90·10 W
81	Wappingers Falls (wŏp'ĭn-jērz) N. Y.	41·35 N	73·55 W
71	Wapsipinicon (R.) (wŏp'sĭ-pĭn'ĭ-kŏn) . Iowa	42·16 N	91·35 W
153	Warabi (wä'rä-bê) Jap. (Tōkyō In.)	35·50 N	139·41 E
143	Warangal (wŭ'răŋ-gȧl) . . . . . . India	18·03 N	17·39 E
158	Warburton, The (R.) (wŏr'bûr-tŭn) . Austl.	27·30 S	138·45 E
139	Wardan (R.) U. A. R. (Egypt) (Palestine In.)	29·29 N	32·52 E
168	Warden (wôr'dĕn) . . . . S. Afr. (Johannesburg & Pretoria In.)	27·52 S	28·59 E
142	Wardha (wŭr'dä) . . . . India	20·46 N	78·42 E
75	Wardsworth (wôrdz'wûrth) Ohio (Cleveland In.)	41·01 N	81·44 W
80	War Eagle (wôr ē'g'l) . . . . . W. Va.	37·30 N	81·50 W
120	Waren (vä'rĕn) . . . . Ger.	53·32 N	12·43 E
123	Warendorf (vä'rĕn-dōrf) Ger. (Ruhr In.)	51·57 N	7·59 E
166	Warmbad (värm'bäd) (wôrm'băd) S. W. Afr.	28·25 S	18·45 E
168	Warmbad . . . . S. Afr. (Johannesburg & Pretoria In.)	24·52 S	28·18 E
65	Warm Beach (wôrm) Wash. (Seattle In.)	48·10 N	122·22 W
66	Warm Springs Ind. Res. (wôrm sprĭngz) . Ore.	44·55 N	121·30 W
66	Warm Springs Res . . . . Ore.	43·42 N	118·40 W
118	Warnemünde (vär'nĕ-mün-dĕ) Ger.	54·11 N	12·04 E
66	Warner Ra. (Mts.) (wôrn'ēr) Calif.-Ore.	41·30 N	120·17 W
120	Warnow R. (vär'nō) . . . . Ger.	53·51 N	11·55 E
160	Warracknabeal . . . . Austl.	36·20 S	142·28 E
161	Warragamba (R.) Austl. (Sydney In.)	33·55 S	150·32 E
159	Warrego (R.) (wôr'ê-gô) . . . . Austl.	27·13 S	145·58 E
73	Warren (wŏr'ĕn) . . . . Ark.	33·37 N	92·03 W
80	Warren . . . . Ind.	40·40 N	85·25 W
75	Warren . . . . Mich. (Detroit In.)	42·33 N	83·03 W
70	Warren . . . . Minn.	48·11 N	96·44 W
80	Warren . . . . Ohio	41·15 N	80·50 W
65	Warren . . . . Ore. (Portland In.)	45·49 N	122·51 W
81	Warren . . . . Pa.	41·50 N	79·10 W
84	Warren . . . . R. I. (Providence In.)	41·44 N	71·14 W
75	Warrendale (wŏr'ĕn-dāl) Pa. (Pittsburgh In.)	40·39 N	80·04 W
73	Warrensburg (wŏr'ĕnz-bûrg) . . Mo.	38·45 N	93·42 W
85	Warrenton (wŏr'ĕn-tŭn) Can. (Winnipeg In.)	50·08 N	97·32 W
79	Warrenton . . . . Ga.	33·26 N	82·37 W
65	Warrenton . . . . Ore. (Portland In.)	46·10 N	123·56 W
81	Warrenton . . . . Va.	38·45 N	77·50 W
164	Warri (wär'ê) . . . . Nig.	5·33 N	5·43 E
110	Warrington . . . . Eng.	53·22 N	2·30 W
78	Warrington (wŏr'ĭng-tŭn) . . . . Fla.	30·21 N	87·15 W
160	Warrnambool (wôr'nȧm-bōōl) Austl.	36·20 S	142·28 E
71	Warroad (wôr'rōd) . . . . Minn.	48·55 N	95·20 W
159	Warrumbungle Ra. (wôr'ŭm-bŭŋ-g'l) . Austl.	31·18 S	150·00 E
73	Warsaw (wôr'sô) . . . . Ill.	40·21 N	91·26 W
80	Warsaw . . . . Ind.	41·15 N	85·50 W
81	Warsaw . . . . N. Y.	42·45 N	78·10 W
79	Warsaw . . . . N. C.	35·00 N	78·07 W
	Warsaw, see Warszawa		
110	Warsop (wôr'sŭp) . . . . Eng.	53·13 N	1·05 W
121	Warszawa (Warsaw) (vȧr-shä'vȧ) Pol.	52·15 N	21·05 E
120	Warta R. (vär'tȧ) . . . . Pol.	52·35 N	15·07 E
167	Wartburg . . . . . S. Afr. (Natal In.)	29·26 S	30·39 E
160	Warwick (wŏr'ĭk) . . . . Austl.	28·05 S	152·10 E
82	Warwick . . . . Can.	45·58 N	71·57 W
116	Warwick . . . . Eng.	52·19 N	1·46 W
84	Warwick . . N. Y. (New York In.)	41·15 N	74·22 W
84	Warwick . . . R. I. (Providence In.)	41·42 N	71·27 W
110	Warwick (Co.) . . . . Eng.	52·22 N	1·34 W
74	Wasatch Mts. (wô'săch) Utah (Salt Lake City In.)	40·45 N	111·46 W
69	Wasatch Plat . . . . Utah	38·55 N	111·40 W
62	Wasatch Ra . . . . U. S.	39·10 N	111·30 W
167	Wasbank . . . . . . S. Afr. (Natal In.)	28·27 S	30·09 E
167	Waschbank Pk. (Mtn.) (vȧsh'bȧnk) . S. Afr. (Natal In.)	31·17 S	27·26 E
66	Wasco (wăs'kō) . . . . Ore.	45·36 N	120·42 W
71	Waseca (wô-sē'kȧ) . . . . Minn.	44·04 N	93·31 W
117	Wash, The (Est.) (wŏsh) . . . . Eng.	53·00 N	0·20 E
82	Washburn (wŏsh'bŭrn) . . . . . Maine	46·46 N	68·10 W
71	Washburn . . . . Wis.	46·41 N	90·55 W
67	Washburn, Mt . . . . Wyo.	44·55 N	110·10 W
81	Washington (wŏsh'ĭng-tŭn) . . D. C.	38·50 N	77·00 W
78	Washington . . . . Ga.	33·43 N	82·46 W
80	Washington . . . . Ind.	38·40 N	87·10 W
71	Washington . . . . Iowa	41·17 N	91·42 W
73	Washington . . . . Kans.	39·48 N	97·04 W
73	Washington . . . . Mo.	38·33 N	91·00 W
79	Washington . . . . N. C.	35·32 N	77·01 W
75	Washington . . Pa. (Pittsburgh In.)	40·10 N	80·14 W
62	Washington (State) . . . . U. S.	47·30 N	121·10 W
81	Washington, Mt . . . . N. H.	44·15 N	71·15 W
65	Washington, L. Wash. (Seattle In.)	47·34 N	122·12 W
71	Washington (I.) . . . . Wis.	45·18 N	86·42 W
80	Washington Court House . . . . Ohio	39·30 N	83·25 W
74	Washington Park Ill. (St. Louis In.)	38·38 N	90·06 W
72	Washita (R.) (wŏsh'ĭ-tô) . . . . Okla.	35·33 N	99·16 W
65	Washougal (wŏ-shōō'gȧl) Wash. (Portland In.)	45·35 N	122·21 W
65	Washougal (R.) Wash. (Portland In.)	45·38 N	122·17 W
121	Wasilkow (vȧ-sēl'kōōf) . . . . Pol.	53·12 N	23·13 E
123	Wassenberg (vä'sĕn-bĕrgh) Ger. (Ruhr In.)	51·06 N	6·07 E
68	Wassuk Ra. (wȧs'sŭk) . . . . Nev.	38·58 N	119·00 W
74	Watauga (wȧ tō gä') Tex. (Dallas, Fort Worth In.)	32·51 N	97·16 W
89	Water (I.) (wô'tēr) Vir. Is. (U. S. A.) (St. Thomas In.)	18·20 N	64·57 W
168	Waterberg (Mts.) (wôrtēr'bûrg) . S. Afr. (Johannesburg & Pretoria In.)	24·25 S	27·53 E
79	Waterboro (wô'tēr-bŭr-ô) . . . . S. C.	32·50 N	80·40 W
81	Waterbury (wô'tēr-bĕr-ê) . . . Conn.	41·30 N	73·00 W
82	Waterbury . . . . Vt.	44·20 N	72·44 W
95	Water Cay (I.) . . . . Ba. Is.	22·55 N	75·50 W
85	Waterdown (wô'tēr-doun) Can. (Toronto In.)	43·20 N	79·54 W
79	Wateree (R.) (wô'tēr-ē) . . . . . S. C.	34·40 N	80·48 W
116	Waterford (wô'tēr-fērd) . . . . . . Ire.	52·20 N	7·03 W
75	Waterford . . Wis. (Milwaukee In.)	42·46 N	88·13 W
167	Waterkloof . . . . S. Afr. (Johannesburg & Pretoria In.)	25·48 S	28·15 E
111	Waterloo . . . . . Bel. (Bruxelles In.)	50·44 N	4·24 E
80	Waterloo (wô-tēr-lōō') . . . . Can.	43·30 N	80·40 W
81	Waterloo . . . . Can.	45·25 N	72·30 W
73	Waterloo . . . . Ill.	38·19 N	90·08 W
71	Waterloo . . . . Iowa	42·30 N	92·22 W
81	Waterloo . . . . N. Y.	42·55 N	76·50 W
67	Waterton-Glacier Intl. Peace Park (wô'ter-tŭn-glā'shûr) Mont.-Can.	48·55 N	114·10 W
83	Watertown (wô'tēr-toun) Mass. (Boston In.)	42·22 N	71·11 W
81	Watertown . . . . N. Y.	44·00 N	75·55 W
70	Watertown . . . . S. D.	44·53 N	97·07 W
71	Watertown . . . . Wis.	43·13 N	88·40 W
78	Water Valley (văl'ê) . . . . Miss.	34·08 N	89·38 W
82	Waterville (wô'tēr-vĭl) . . . . . Maine	44·34 N	69·37 W
71	Waterville . . . . Minn.	44·10 N	93·35 W
66	Waterville . . . . Wash.	47·38 N	120·04 W
81	Watervliet (wô'tēr-vlēt') . . . . . N. Y.	42·45 N	73·45 W
110	Watford (wŏt'fōrd) Eng. (London In.)	51·38 N	0·24 W
	Watling I., see San Salvador I.		
110	Watlington (wŏt'lĭng-tŭn) Eng. (London In.)	51·37 N	1·01 W
72	Watonga (wŏ-tôŋ'gȧ) . . . . Okla.	35·50 N	98·26 W
86	Watrous . . . . Can.	51·40 N	105·32 W
165	Watsa (wät'sä) . . . . Con. L.	3·02 N	29·30 E
80	Watseka (wŏt-sē'kȧ) . . . . Ill.	40·45 N	87·45 W
75	Watson (wŏt'sŭn) Ind. (Louisville In.)	38·21 N	85·42 W
86	Watson Lake . . . . Can.	60·18 N	128·50 W
68	Watsonville (wŏt'sŭn-vĭl) . . . Calif.	36·55 N	121·46 W
123	Wattenscheid (vä'tĕn-shīd) Ger. (Ruhr In.)	51·30 N	7·07 E
74	Watts (wŏts) Calif. (Los Angeles In.)	33·56 N	118·15 W
78	Watts Bar (R.) (bär) . . . . Tenn.	35·45 N	84·49 W
165	Wau (wä'ōō) . . . . Sud.	7·41 N	28·00 E
165	Wāu al Kebir . . . . Libya	25·23 N	16·52 E
70	Waubay (wô'bā) . . . . S. D.	45·19 N	97·18 W
79	Wauchula (wô-chōō'lȧ) . . Fla. (In.)	27·32 N	81·48 W
75	Wauconda (wô-kŏn'dȧ) Ill. (Chicago In.)	42·15 N	88·08 W
75	Waukegan (wŏ-kē'gȧn) Ill. (Chicago In.)	42·22 N	87·51 W
75	Waukesha (wô'kê-shô) Wis. (Milwaukee In.)	43·01 N	88·13 W
71	Waukon (wô kŏn) . . . . Iowa	43·15 N	91·30 W
65	Wauna (wô-nȧ) . Ore. (Portland In.)	46·09 N	123·25 W
71	Waupaca (wô-păk'ȧ) . . . . Wis.	44·22 N	89·06 W
71	Waupun (wô-pŭn') . . . . Wis.	43·37 N	88·45 W
72	Waurika (wô-rē'kȧ) . . . . Okla.	34·09 N	97·59 W
71	Wausau (wô'sô) . . . . Wis.	44·58 N	89·40 W
71	Wausaukee (wô-sô'kê) . . . . Wis.	45·22 N	87·58 W
80	Wauseon (wô'sê-ŏn) . . . . Ohio	41·30 N	84·10 W
71	Wautoma (wô-tō'mȧ) . . . . Wis.	44·04 N	89·11 W
75	Wauwatosa (wô-wȧ-tō'sȧ) Wis. (Milwaukee In.)	43·03 N	88·00 W
117	Waveney (R.) (wāv'nê) . . . . . Eng.	52·27 N	1·17 E
167	Waverley . . . . . . S. Afr. (Natal In.)	31·54 S	26·29 E
71	Waverly (wā'vēr-lê) . . . . Iowa	42·43 N	92·29 W
78	Waverly . . . . Tenn.	36·04 N	87·46 W
80	Wawasee (L.) (wô-wô-sē') . . . . Ind.	41·25 N	85·45 W
77	Waxahachie (wăk-sȧ-hăch'ê) . . Tex.	32·23 N	96·50 W
79	Waycross (wā'krôs) . . . . Ga.	31·11 N	82·24 W

ng-sing; ŋ-baŋk; N-nasalized n; nŏd; cŏmmit; ōld; ôbey; ôrder; fōōd; fŏŏt; ou-out; s-soft; sh-dish; th-thin; pūre; ûnite; ûrn; stŭd; circŭs; ü-as "y" in study; '-indeterminate vowel.

284 Wayland–Wheelwright PRONOUNCING INDEX

Page	Name Pronunciation Region	Lat. °′	Long. °′
78	Wayland (wā'lănd) Ky.	37·25 N	82·47 W
83	Wayland Mass. (Boston In.)	42·23 N	71·22 W
75	Wayne Mich. (Detroit In.)	42·17 N	83·23 W
70	Wayne (wān) Nebr.	42·13 N	97·03 W
84	Wayne Pa. (Philadelphia In.)	40·03 N	75·22 W
79	Waynesboro (wānz'bŭr-ō) Ga.	33·05 N	82·02 W
81	Waynesboro Pa.	39·45 N	77·35 W
81	Waynesboro Va.	38·05 N	78·50 W
81	Waynesburg (wānz'bûrg) Pa.	39·55 N	80·10 W
78	Waynesville (wānz'vĭl) N. C.	35·28 N	82·58 W
72	Waynoka (wā-nō'kȧ) Okla.	36·34 N	98·52 W
74	Wayzata (wā-zä-tȧ) Minn. (Minneapolis, St. Paul In.)	44·58 N	93·31 W
142	Wazīrbad W. Pak.	32·39 N	74·11 E
116	Weald, The (Reg.) (wēld) Eng.	50·58 N	0·15 W
72	Weatherford (wĕ-dhĕr-fērd) Okla.	35·32 N	98·41 W
77	Weatherford Tex.	32·45 N	97·46 W
110	Weaver (R.) (wē'vēr) Eng.	53·09 N	2·31 W
66	Weaverville (wē'vēr-vĭl) Calif.	40·44 N	122·55 W
73	Webb City (wĕb) Mo.	37·10 N	94·26 W
74	Weber R. (wĕb'ēr) Utah (Salt Lake City In.)	41·13 N	112·07 W
83	Webster (wĕb'stēr) Mass. (Boston In.)	42·04 N	71·52 W
70	Webster S. D.	45·19 N	97·30 W
77	Webster Tex. (In.)	29·32 N	95·07 W
71	Webster City Iowa	42·28 N	93·49 W
74	Webster Groves (grōvz) Mo. (St. Louis In.)	38·36 N	90·22 W
81	Webster Springs (sprĭngz) W. Va.	38·30 N	80·20 W
47	Weddell Sea (wĕd'ĕl) Ant.	73·00 S	45·00 W
111	Wedel (vā'dĕl) Ger. (Hamburg In.)	53·35 N	9·42 E
82	Wedgeport (wĕj'pōrt) Can.	43·46 N	65·58 W
110	Wednesbury (wĕd''nz-bŭr-ē) Eng.	52·33 N	2·01 W
110	Wednesfield (wĕd''nz-fēld) Eng.	52·36 N	2·04 W
66	Weed (wēd) Calif.	41·35 N	122·21 W
85	Weed Cr. Can. (Edmonton In.)	53·18 N	114·01 W
167	Weenen (vā'nĕn) S. Afr. (Natal In.)	28·52 S	30·05 E
117	Weert Neth.	51·16 N	5·39 E
111	Weesp Neth. (Amsterdam In.)	52·18 N	5·01 E
87	Weggs, C. Can.	62·14 N	73·43 W
121	Wegorzewo (vôŋ-gô'zhĕ-vô) Pol.	54·14 N	21·46 E
121	Wegrow (vôŋ'grōōf) Pol.	52·23 N	22·02 E
121	Wehlau (vā'lou) Sov. Un.	54·37 N	21·17 E
148	Wei (R.) (wā) China	35·47 N	114·27 E
150	Weich'ang (wā'chăng') China	41·50 N	118·00 E
148	Weihaiwei Shih (wa'hăi'wā) China	37·30 N	122·05 E
148	Wei Ho (R.) China	34·00 N	108·10 E
146	Weihsi (wā'hsē') China	27·27 N	99·30 E
148	Weihsien (wā'hsyĕn') China	36·43 N	119·08 E
148	Weihsien China	36·59 N	115·17 E
120	Weilheim (vīl'hīm') Ger.	47·50 N	11·06 E
120	Weimar (vī'mȧr) Ger.	50·59 N	11·20 E
150	Weinan China	34·32 N	109·40 E
80	Weirton (wēr'tŭn) W. Va.	40·25 N	80·35 W
66	Weiser (wē'zēr) Idaho	44·15 N	116·58 W
66	Weiser R. Idaho	44·26 N	116·40 W
148	Weishih (wā'shē) China	34·23 N	114·12 E
120	Weissenburg (vī'sĕn-bōōrgh) Ger.	49·04 N	11·20 E
120	Weissenfels (vī'sĕn-fĕlz) Ger.	51·13 N	11·58 E
121	Wejherowo (vä-hĕ-rō'vô) Pol.	54·36 N	18·15 E
79	Welch (wĕlch) W. Va.	37·24 N	81·28 W
79	Weldon (wĕl'dŭn) N. C.	36·24 N	77·36 W
73	Weldon (R.) Mo.	40·22 N	93·39 W
73	Weleetka (wē-lēt'kȧ) Okla.	35·19 N	96·08 W
160	Welford (wĕl'fērd) Austl.	25·08 S	144·43 E
168	Welkom (wĕl'kŏm) S. Afr. (Johannesburg & Pretoria In.)	27·57 S	26·45 E
75	Welland (wĕl'ănd) Can. (Buffalo In.)	42·59 N	79·13 W
116	Welland (R.) Eng.	52·38 N	0·40 W
83	Wellesley (wĕlz'lē) Mass. (Boston In.)	42·18 N	71·17 W
158	Wellesley Is. Austl.	16·15 S	139·25 E
160	Wellington (wĕl'lĭng-tŭn) Austl.	32·38 S	148·37 E
110	Wellington Eng.	52·42 N	2·30 W
73	Wellington Kans.	37·16 N	97·24 W
159	Wellington N. Z. (In.)	41·15 S	174·45 E
80	Wellington Ohio	41·10 N	82·10 W
72	Wellington Tex.	34·51 N	100·12 W
100	Wellington (I.) (ōōĕ'lĕng-tōn) Chile	49·30 S	76·30 W
158	Wells (wĕlz) Austl.	26·35 S	123·40 E
86	Wells Can.	54·11 N	121·40 W
80	Wells Mich.	45·50 N	87·00 W
71	Wells Minn.	43·44 N	93·43 W
66	Wells Nev.	41·07 N	115·04 W
81	Wellsboro (wĕlz'bŭ-rō) Pa.	41·45 N	77·15 W
80	Wellsburg (wĕlz'bûrg) W. Va.	40·10 N	80·40 W
74	Wellston (wĕlz'tŭn) Mo. (St. Louis In.)	38·41 N	90·18 W
80	Wellston Ohio	39·05 N	82·30 W
73	Wellsville (wĕlz'vĭl) Mo.	39·04 N	91·33 W
81	Wellsville N. Y.	42·10 N	78·00 W
80	Wellsville Ohio	40·35 N	80·40 W
67	Wellsville Utah	41·38 N	111·57 W
120	Wels (vĕls) Aus.	48·10 N	14·01 E
116	Welshpool (wĕlsh'pōōl) Wales	52·44 N	3·10 W
168	Welverdiend (vĕl-vēr-dēnd') S. Afr. (Johannesburg & Pretoria In.)	26·23 S	27·16 E
110	Welwyn Garden City (wĕl'ĭn) Eng. (London In.)	51·46 N	0·17 W
110	Wem (wĕm) Eng.	52·51 N	2·44 W
148	Wenan Wa (Swp.) (wĕn'ăn' wä) China	38·56 N	116·29 E
66	Wenatchee (wē-năch'ē) Wash.	47·24 N	120·18 W
66	Wenatchee Mts. Wash.	47·28 N	121·10 W
151	Wench'ang China	19·32 N	110·42 E
151	Wenchow (Yungchia) (wĕn'chō') China	28·00 N	120·40 E
150	Wenchüan (Halunrshan) China	47·10 N	120·00 E
67	Wendorer Utah	40·47 N	114·01 W
85	Wendover (wĕn-dōv'ēr) Can. (Ottawa In.)	45·34 N	75·07 W
110	Wendover Eng. (London In.)	51·44 N	0·45 W
83	Wenham (wĕn'ăm) Mass. (Boston In.)	42·36 N	70·53 W
84	Wenonah (wĕn'ō-nȧ) N. J. (Philadelphia In.)	39·48 N	75·08 W
151	Wenshan China	23·20 N	104·15 E
148	Wenshang (wĕn'shăng) China	35·43 N	116·31 E
148	Wenshussu (wĕn'shōō'sĕ) China	31·55 N	114·47 E
146	Wensu (Aksu) (wĕn'sōō') (äk'sōō') China	41·45 N	79·54 E
117	Wensum (R.) (wĕn'sŭm) Eng.	52·45 N	1·08 E
110	Went (R.) (wĕnt) Eng.	53·38 N	1·08 W
148	Wenteng (wĕn'tĕng') China	37·14 N	122·03 E
160	Wentworth (wĕnt'wûrth) Austl.	34·03 S	141·53 E
166	Wepener (wē'pĕn-ēr) (vā'pĕn-ēr) S. Afr.	29·43 S	27·04 E
111	Werder (vĕr'dĕr) Ger. (Berlin In.)	52·23 N	12·56 E
123	Werl (vĕrl) Ger. (Ruhr In.)	51·33 N	7·55 E
123	Werne (vĕr'nĕ) Ger. (Ruhr In.)	51·39 N	7·38 E
111	Werneuchen (vĕr'hoi-kĕn) Ger. (Berlin In.)	52·38 N	13·44 E
120	Werra R. (vĕr'ä) Ger.	51·16 N	9·54 E
161	Werribee Austl. (Melbourne In.)	37·54 S	144·40 E
161	Werribee (R.) Austl. (Melbourne In.)	37·40 S	144·37 E
120	Wertach R. (vĕr'täk) Ger.	48·12 N	10·40 E
123	Weseke (vĕ'zĕ-kĕ) Ger. (Ruhr In.)	51·54 N	6·51 E
123	Wesel (vā'zĕl) Ger. (Ruhr In.)	51·39 N	6·37 E
120	Weser R. (vā'zĕr) Ger.	53·08 N	8·35 E
76	Weslaco (wĕs-lä'kō) Tex.	26·10 N	97·59 W
83	Wesleyville (wĕs'lē-vĭl) Can.	49·09 N	53·33 W
158	Wessel (Is.) (wĕs'ĕl) Austl.	11·45 S	136·25 E
168	Wesselsbron (wĕs'ĕl-brŏn) S. Afr. (Johannesburg & Pretoria In.)	27·51 S	26·22 E
70	Wessington Springs (wĕs'ĭng-tŭn) S. D.	44·06 N	98·35 W
88	West, Mt C. Z. (Panama Canal In.)	9·10 N	79·52 W
75	West Allis (wĕst-ăl'ĭs) Wis. (Milwaukee In.)	43·01 N	88·01 W
74	West Alton (ôl'tŭn) Mo. (St. Louis In.)	38·52 N	90·13 W
77	West B. Tex. (In.)	29·11 N	95·03 W
71	West Bend (wĕst bĕnd) Wis.	43·25 N	88·13 W
142	West Bengal (State) (bĕn-gôl') India	28·00 N	87·42 E
111	West Berlin (bĕr-lēn') Ger. (Berlin In.)	52·31 N	13·20 E
78	West Blocton (blŏk'tŭn) Ala.	33·05 N	87·05 W
83	Westboro (wĕst'bŭr-ō) Mass. (Boston In.)	42·17 N	71·37 W
83	West Boylston (boil'stŭn) Mass. (Boston In.)	42·22 N	71·46 W
80	West Branch (wĕst brȧnch) Mich.	44·15 N	84·10 W
110	West Bridgford (brĭj'fērd) Eng.	52·55 N	1·08 W
110	West Bromwich (wĕst brŭm'ĭj) Eng.	52·32 N	1·59 W
82	Westbrook (wĕst'brōōk) Maine	43·41 N	70·23 W
71	Westby (wĕst'bē) Wis.	43·40 N	90·52 W
95	West Caicos (I.) (käē'kōs) Ba. Is.	21·40 N	72·30 W
158	West Cape Howe (C.) Austl.	35·15 S	117·30 E
75	West Chester (chĕs'tēr) Ohio (Cincinnati In.)	39·20 N	84·24 W
84	West Chester Pa. (Philadelphia In.)	39·57 N	75·36 W
75	West Chicago (chĭ-kä'gō) Ill. (Chicago In.)	41·53 N	88·12 W
79	West Columbia (cŏl'ŭm-bē-ȧ) S. C.	33·58 N	81·05 W
77	West Columbia Tex.	29·08 N	95·39 W
77	West Cote Blanche B. (kōt blănch) La.	29·30 N	92·17 W
74	West Covina (wĕst kô-vē'nȧ) Calif. (Los Angeles In.)	34·04 N	117·55 W
71	West Des Moines (dē moin') Iowa	41·35 N	93·42 W
71	West Des Moines (R.) Iowa	42·52 N	94·32 W
94	West End Ba. Is.	26·40 N	78·55 W
110	Westerham (wĕ'stēr'ŭm) Eng. (London In.)	51·15 N	0·05 E
111	Westerhorn (vĕs'tĕr-hōrn) Ger. (Hamburg In.)	53·52 N	9·41 E
111	Westerlo Bel. (Bruxelles In.)	51·05 N	4·57 E
81	Westerly (wĕs'tēr-lē) Conn.	41·25 N	71·50 W
120	Western Alps (Mts.) Switz.-Fr.	46·19 N	7·03 E
158	Western Australia (State) (ôs-trā'lĭ-ȧ) Austl.	24·15 S	121·30 E
	Western Dvina, see Zapadnaya Dvina		
116	Western Downs Eng.	50·50 N	2·25 W
143	Western Ghats (Mts.) India	22·09 N	74·15 E
81	Western Port (wĕs'tērn pōrt) Md.	39·30 N	79·00 W
164	Western Region (Div.) Nig.	8·54 N	3·30 E
66	Western Shoshone Ind. Res. (wĕst'ērn shō-shōn'ē) Idaho	42·02 N	115·49 W
130	Western Siberian Lowland Sov. Un.	63·37 N	72·45 E
80	Westerville (wĕs'tēr-vĭl) Ohio	40·10 N	83·00 W
120	Westerwald (For.) (vĕs'tĕr-väld) Ger.	50·35 N	7·45 E
84	Westfield (wĕst'fēld) Ala. (Birmingham In.)	33·29 N	86·57 W
81	Westfield Mass.	42·05 N	72·45 W
84	Westfield N. J. (New York In.)	40·39 N	74·21 W
81	Westfield (wĕst'fēld) N. Y.	42·20 N	79·40 W
83	Westford (wĕst'fērd) Mass. (Boston In.)	42·35 N	71·26 W
80	West Frankfort (frăŋk'fŭrt) Ill.	37·55 N	88·55 W
110	West Ham Eng. (London In.)	51·30 N	0·00
81	West Hartford (härt'fērd) Conn.	41·45 N	72·45 W
116	West Hartlepool (här't'l-pōōl) Eng.	54·40 N	1·12 W
73	West Helena (hĕl'ĕn-ȧ) Ark.	34·32 N	90·39 W
85	West Hill Can. (Toronto In.)	43·46 N	79·09 W
89	West Indies (Reg.) (ĭn'dēz) N. A.	19·00 N	78·30 W
74	West Jordan (jôr'dăn) Utah (Salt Lake City In.)	40·37 N	111·56 W
110	West Kirby (kûr'bē) Eng.	53·22 N	3·11 W
80	West Lafayette (lă-fā-yĕt') Ind.	40·25 N	86·55 W
75	Westlake Ohio (Cleveland In.)	41·27 N	81·55 W
168	Westleigh (wĕst-lē) S. Afr. (Johannesburg & Pretoria In.)	27·39 S	27·18 E
71	West Liberty (wĕst lĭb'ēr-tĭ) Iowa	41·34 N	91·15 W
65	West Linn (lĭn) Ore. (Portland In.)	45·22 N	122·37 W
74	Westminster (wĕst'mĭn-stēr) Calif. (Los Angeles In.)	33·45 N	117·59 W
81	Westminster Md.	39·40 N	76·55 W
78	Westminster S. C.	34·38 N	83·10 W
85	Westmount (wĕst'mount) Can. (Montreal In.)	45·29 N	73·36 W
83	West Newbury (nū'bĕr-ē) Mass. (Boston In.)	42·47 N	70·57 W
75	West Newton (nū'tŭn) Pa. (Pittsburgh In.)	40·12 N	79·45 W
84	West New York (nû yŏrk) N. J. (New York In.)	40·47 N	74·01 W
73	West Nishnabotna (R.) (nĭsh-nȧ-bŏt'nȧ) Iowa	40·56 N	95·37 W
84	West Norfolk (nôr'fŏk) Va. (Norfolk In.)	36·52 N	76·20 W
85	Weston (wĕs'tŭn) Can. (Toronto In.)	43·40 N	79·30 W
83	Weston Mass. (Boston In.)	42·22 N	71·18 W
80	Weston W. Va.	39·00 N	80·30 W
168	Westonaria S. Afr. (Johannesburg & Pretoria In.)	26·19 S	27·38 E
116	Weston-super-Mare (wĕs'tŭn sū'pēr-mā'rē) Eng.	51·23 N	3·00 W
84	West Orange (wĕst ŏr'ĕnj) N. J. (New York In.)	40·46 N	74·14 W
79	West Palm Beach (päm bēch) Fla. (In.)	26·44 N	80·04 W
78	West Pensacola (pĕn-sȧ-kō'lȧ) Fla.	30·24 N	87·18 W
65	West Pittsburg (pĭts'bûrg) Calif. (San Francisco In.)	38·02 N	121·56 W
73	Westplains (wĕst-plānz') Mo.	36·42 N	91·51 W
78	West Point Ga.	32·52 N	85·10 W
78	West Point Miss.	33·36 N	88·39 W
70	Westpoint Nebr.	41·50 N	96·00 W
84	West Point N. Y. (New York In.)	41·23 N	73·58 W
74	West Point Utah (Salt Lake City In.)	41·07 N	112·05 W
81	West Point Va.	37·35 N	76·50 W
82	West Pt. (wĕst' point) Can.	49·53 N	64·35 W
84	Westport (wĕst'pōrt) Conn. (New York In.)	41·07 N	73·22 W
116	Westport Ire.	53·44 N	9·36 W
65	Westport (wĕst'pōrt) Ore. (Portland In.)	46·08 N	123·22 W
116	Westray (I.) (wĕs'trā) Scot.	59·19 N	3·05 W
110	West Riding (Co.) (rīd'ĭng) Eng.	53·37 N	1·30 W
74	West Riverside (wĕst rĭv'ēr-sīd) Calif. (Los Angeles In.)	33·59 N	117·24 W
74	West St. Paul (sȧnt pôl') Minn. (Minneapolis, St. Paul In.)	44·55 N	93·05 W
95	West Sand Spit (I.) Ba. Is.	21·25 N	72·10 W
117	West Schelde (R.) Neth.	51·25 N	3·30 E
69	West Tavaputs Plat. (wĕst tăv'ȧ-pōōts) Utah	39·45 N	110·35 W
80	West Terre Haute (tĕr-ē hōt') Ind.	39·30 N	87·30 W
71	West Union (ūn'yŭn) Iowa	42·58 N	91·48 W
75	Westview (wĕst'vū) Ohio (Cleveland In.)	41·21 N	81·54 W
75	West View Pa. (Pittsburgh In.)	40·31 N	80·02 W
83	Westville (wĕst'vĭl) Can.	45·35 N	62·45 W
80	Westville Ill.	40·00 N	87·40 W
63	West Virginia (State) (wĕst vēr-jĭn'ĭ-ȧ) U. S.	39·00 N	80·50 W
68	West Walker (R.) (wôk'ēr) Calif.	38·25 N	119·25 W
84	West Warwick (wŏr'ĭk) R. I. (Providence In.)	41·42 N	71·31 W
84	Westwego (wĕst-wē'gō) La. (New Orleans In.)	29·55 N	90·09 W
68	Westwood (wĕst'wōōd) Calif.	40·18 N	121·00 W
83	Westwood Mass. (Boston In.)	42·13 N	71·14 W
74	Westwood Mo. (Kansas City In.)	39·03 N	94·37 W
84	Westwood N. J. (New York In.)	40·59 N	74·02 W
155	Wetar (I.) (wĕt'ăr) Indon.	7·34 S	126·00 E
86	Wetaskiwin (wĕ-tăs'kē-wŏn) Can.	53·01 N	113·24 W
74	Wetmore (wĕt'mōr) Tex. (San Antonio In.)	29·34 N	98·25 W
123	Wetten (vĕ'tĕn) Ger. (Ruhr In.)	51·23 N	7·23 E
78	Wetumpka (wē-tŭmp'kȧ) Ala.	32·33 N	86·12 W
123	Wetzlar (vĕts'lär) Ger.	50·35 N	8·30 E
155	Wewak (wā-wäk') N. Gui. Ter.	3·19 S	143·30 E
73	Wewoka (wē-wō'kȧ) Okla.	35·09 N	96·30 W
116	Wexford (wĕks'fērd) Ire.	52·20 N	6·30 W
110	Weybridge (wā'brĭj) Eng. (London In.)	51·20 N	0·26 W
86	Weyburn Can.	49·31 N	103·50 W
116	Weymouth (wā'mŭth) Eng.	50·37 N	2·34 W
83	Weymouth Mass. (Boston In.)	42·44 N	70·57 W
75	Weymouth Ohio (Cleveland In.)	41·11 N	81·48 W
94	Whale Cay (I.) Ba. Is.	24·50 N	77·45 W
94	Whale Cay Chans Ba. Is.	26·45 N	77·10 W
116	Wharfe (R.) (hwôr'fē) Eng.	54·01 N	1·53 W
84	Wharton (hwôr'tŭn) N. J. (New York In.)	40·54 N	74·35 W
77	Wharton Tex.	29·19 N	96·06 W
71	What Cheer (hwŏt chēr) Iowa	41·23 N	92·24 W
65	Whatcom, L. (hwät'kŭm) Wash. (Portland In.)	48·44 N	123·34 W
75	Wheatland (hwēt'lănd) Wis. (Milwaukee In.)	42·36 N	88·12 W
67	Wheatland Wyo.	42·04 N	104·52 W
75	Wheaton (hwē'tŭn) Ill. (Chicago In.)	41·52 N	88·06 W
81	Wheaton Md.	39·05 N	77·05 W
70	Wheaton Minn.	45·48 N	96·29 W
66	Wheeler Pk. (hwē'lēr) Nev.	38·58 N	114·15 W
75	Wheeling (hwēl'ĭng) Ill. (Chicago In.)	42·08 N	87·54 W
80	Wheeling W. Va.	40·05 N	80·45 W
101	Wheelwright (ōōē'l-rē'gt) Arg. (Buenos Aires In.)	33·46 S	61·14 W

ăt; finăl; rāte; senâte; ärm; åsk; sofȧ; fâre; ch-choose; dh-as th in other; bē; ēvent; bĕt; recĕnt; cratēr; g-go; gh-guttural g; bĭt; ĭ-short neutral; rīde; K-guttural k as ch in German ich;

PRONOUNCING INDEX Whidbey–Winton 285

Page	Name Pronunciation Region	Lat. °′	Long. °′
65	Whidbey I. (hwĭd'bē) Wash. (Seattle In.)	48·13 N	122·50 W
84	Whippany (hwĭp'á-nē) N. J. (New York In.)	40·49 N	74·25 W
78	Whistler (hwĭs'lẽr) Ala.	30·46 N	88·07 W
81	Whitby (hwĭt'bē) Can.	43·50 N	79·00 W
110	Whitchurch (hwĭt'chûrch) Eng.	52·58 N	79·00 W
73	White (R.) Ark.	34·32 N	91·11 W
68	White, Mt. Calif.	37·38 N	118·13 W
81	White (L.) Can.	45·15 N	76·35 W
71	White (L.) Can.	48·47 N	85·50 W
71	White (R.) Can.	48·34 N	85·46 W
69	White (R.) Colo.	40·10 N	108·55 W
80	White (R.) Ind.	39·15 N	86·45 W
70	White (R.) S. D.	43·41 N	99·48 W
70	White (R.), South Fork S. D.	43·13 N	101·04 W
72	White (R.) Tex.	36·25 N	102·20 W
81	White (R.) Vt.	43·45 N	72·35 W
83	White B. Can.	50·07 N	56·24 W
83	White Bear B. Can.	47·28 N	57·55 W
74	White Bear Lake Minn. (Minneapolis, St. Paul In.)	45·05 N	93·01 W
74	White Bear L. Minn. (Minneapolis, St. Paul In.)	45·04 N	92·58 W
77	White Castle La.	30·10 N	91·09 W
80	White Cloud Mich.	43·35 N	85·45 W
86	White Court Can.	54·09 N	115·34 W
70	White Earth (R.) N. D.	48·30 N	102·44 W
70	White Earth Ind. Res. Minn.	47·18 N	95·42 W
71	Whiteface (R.) (whīt'fās) Minn.	47·12 N	92·13 W
81	Whitefield (hwīt'fēld) N. H.	44·20 N	71·35 W
67	Whitefish (hwīt'fĭsh) Mont.	48·24 N	114·25 W
71	Whitefish (B.) Mich.	46·36 N	84·50 W
71	Whitefish (R.) Mich.	46·12 N	86·56 W
75	Whitefish Bay Wis. (Milwaukee In.)	43·07 N	77·54 W
73	White Hall Ill.	39·26 N	90·23 W
80	Whitehall (hwīt'hôl) Mich.	43·20 N	86·20 W
81	Whitehall N. Y.	43·30 N	73·25 W
116	Whitehaven (hwīt'hā-vĕn) Eng.	54·35 N	3·30 W
65	Whitehorn, Pt. (hwīt'hôrn) Wash. (Vancouver In.)	48·54 N	122·48 W
86	Whitehorse (whīt'hôrs) Can.	60·39 N	135·01 W
84	White House N. J. (New York In.)	40·37 N	74·46 W
77	White L. La.	29·40 N	92·35 W
82	White Mts. Maine	44·22 N	71·15 W
81	White Mts. N. H.	42·20 N	71·05 W
70	Whitemouth (L.) (hwīt'mŭth) Can.	49·18 N	95·50 W
	White Nile, see El Abyad, Bahr		
71	White Otter (L.) Can.	49·15 N	91·48 W
86	White P. Alaska-Can.	59·35 N	135·03 W
84	White Plains N. Y. (New York In.)	41·02 N	73·47 W
80	White R., East Fork Ind.	38·45 N	86·20 W
66	White R. Wash.	47·07 N	121·48 W
69	White River Plat. Colo.	39·45 N	107·50 W
65	White Rock Can. (Vancouver In.)	49·01 N	122·49 W
74	Whiterock Res. (hwīt'rŏk) Tex. (Dallas, Fort Worth In.)	32·51 N	96·40 W
168	Whites (wīts) S. Afr. (Johannesburg & Pretoria In.)	28·02 S	27·00 E
69	White Sands Natl. Mon. N. Mex.	32·50 N	106·20 W
132	White Sea Sov. Un.	66·00 N	40·00 E
74	White Settlement Tex. (Dallas, Fort Worth In.)	32·45 N	97·28 W
67	White Sulphur Springs Mont.	46·32 N	110·49 W
167	White Umfolosi (R.) (ŭm-fô-lō'zē) S. Afr. (Natal In.)	28·12 S	30·55 E
79	Whiteville (hwīt'vĭl) N. C.	34·18 N	78·45 W
71	Whitewater (whīt-wôt'ẽr) Wis.	42·49 N	88·40 W
70	Whitewater (L.) Can.	49·14 N	100·39 W
79	Whitewater B. Fla. (In.)	25·16 N	80·21 W
67	Whitewater Cr. Mont.	48·50 N	107·50 W
75	Whitewater R. Ind. (Cincinnati In.)	39·19 N	84·55 W
78	Whitewell (hwĭt'wĕl) Tenn.	35·11 N	85·31 W
73	Whitewright (hwīt'rīt) Tex.	33·33 N	96·25 W
116	Whitham (R.) (wĭth'ŭm) Eng.	53·08 N	0·15 W
75	Whiting (hwīt'ĭng) Ind. (Chicago In.)	41·41 N	87·30 W
83	Whitinsville (hwīt'ĕns-vĭl) Mass. (Boston In.)	42·06 N	71·40 W
83	Whitman (hwĭt'măn) Mass. (Boston In.)	42·05 N	70·57 W
66	Whitman Natl. Mon. Ore.	45·58 N	118·10 W
79	Whitmire (hwĭt'mīr) S. C.	34·30 N	81·40 W
68	Whitney, Mt. Calif.	36·34 N	118·18 W
77	Whitney L. (hwĭt'nē) Tex.	32·02 N	97·36 W
110	Whitstable (wĭt'stăb'l) Eng. (London In.)	51·22 N	1·03 E
159	Whitsunday (I.) (hwĭt's'n-dā) Austl.	20·16 S	149·00 E
74	Whittier (hwĭt'ĭ-ẽr) Calif. (Los Angeles In.)	33·58 N	118·02 W
167	Whittlesea (wĭt'l'sē) S. Afr. (Natal In.)	32·11 S	26·51 E
110	Whitworth (hwĭt'wŭrth) Eng.	53·40 N	2·10 W
160	Whyalla (hwī-ăl'à) Austl.	33·00 S	137·32 E
80	Wiarton (wī'ăr-tŭn) Can.	44·45 N	80·45 W
73	Wichita (wĭch'ĭ-tô) Kans.	37·42 N	97·21 W
72	Wichita (R.) Tex.	33·50 N	99·38 W
72	Wichita Falls (fôls) Tex.	33·54 N	98·29 W
72	Wichita Mts. Okla.	34·48 N	98·43 W
116	Wick (wĭk) Scot.	58·25 N	3·05 W
84	Wickatunk (wĭk'á-tŭnk) N. J. (New York In.)	40·21 N	74·15 W
84	Wickford (wĭk'fẽrd) R. I. (Providence In.)	41·34 N	71·26 W
75	Wickliffe (wĭk'klĭf) Ohio (Cleveland In.)	41·37 N	81·29 W
	Wicklow, see Cill Mantainn		
116	Wicklow Mts. (wĭk'lō) Ire.	52·49 N	6·20 W
65	Wickup Mtn. (wĭk'ŭp) Ore. (Portland In.)	46·06 N	123·35 W
81	Wiconisco (wĭ-kŏn'ĭs-kō) Pa.	40·35 N	76·45 W
80	Widen (wī'dĕn) W. Va.	38·25 N	80·55 W
110	Widnes (wĭd'nĕs) Eng.	53·21 N	2·44 W
120	Wieden (vē'dĕn) Ger.	49·41 N	12·09 E
121	Wieliczka (vyĕ-lēch'kà) Pol.	49·58 N	20·06 E
121	Wieluń (vyĕ'lōōn') Pol.	51·13 N	18·33 E
111	Wien (Vienna) (vēn) (vē-ĕn'ä) Aus. (Wien In.)	48·13 N	16·22 E
111	Wien (State) Aus. (Wien In.)	48·11 N	16·23 E
120	Wiener Neustadt (vē'nẽr noi'shtät) Aus.	47·48 N	16·15 E
111	Wiener Wald (For.) Aus. (Wien In.)	48·09 N	16·05 E
121	Wieprz, R. (vyĕpzh) Pol.	51·25 N	22·45 E
77	Wiergate (wẽr'gāt) Tex.	31·00 N	93·42 W
120	Wiesbaden (vēs'bä-dĕn) Ger.	50·05 N	8·15 E
110	Wigan (wĭg'ăn) Eng.	53·33 N	2·37 W
78	Wiggins (wĭg'ĭnz) Miss.	30·51 N	89·05 W
116	Wight, Isle of (I.) (wīt) Eng.	50·44 N	1·17 W
73	Wilber (wĭl'bẽr) Nebr.	40·29 N	96·57 W
73	Wilburton (wĭl'bẽr-tŭn) Okla.	34·54 N	95·18 W
160	Wilcannia (wĭl-căn-ĭà) Austl.	31·30 S	143·30 E
111	Wildau (vēl'dou) Ger. (Berlin In.)	52·20 N	13·39 E
111	Wildberg (vēl'bĕrgh) Ger. (Berlin In.)	52·52 N	12·39 E
74	Wildomar (wĭl'dô-mär) Calif. (Los Angeles In.)	33·35 N	117·17 W
70	Wild Rice (R.) Minn.	47·10 N	96·40 W
70	Wild Rice (R.) N. D.	46·10 N	97·12 W
74	Wild Rice L. Minn. (Duluth In.)	46·54 N	92·10 W
120	Wild Spitze Pk. Aus.	46·49 N	10·50 E
81	Wildwood (wīld'wŏŏd) N. J.	39·00 N	74·50 W
72	Wiley (wī'lē) Colo.	38·08 N	102·41 W
168	Wilge R. (wĭl'jē) S. Afr. (Johannesburg & Pretoria In.)	25·38 S	29·09 E
168	Wilge R. S. Afr. (Johannesburg & Pretoria In.)	27·27 S	28·46 E
155	Wilhelm, Mt. N. Gui. Ter.	5·58 S	144·58 E
99	Wilhelmina Gebergte (Mts.) Sur.	4·30 N	57·00 W
155	Wilhelmina-Top (Pk.) (vēl-hĕl-mē'nà) Neth. N. Gui.	3·55 S	138·26 E
120	Wilhelmshaven (vēl-hĕlms-hä'fĕn) Ger.	53·30 N	8·10 E
111	Wilhemina, Kanal (can.) Neth. (Amsterdam In.)	51·37 N	4·55 E
81	Wilkes-Barre (wĭlks'băr-ē) Pa.	41·15 N	75·50 W
47	Wilkes Land Ant.	71·00 S	126·00 E
65	Wilkeson (wĭl-kē'sŭn) Wash. (Seattle In.)	47·06 N	122·03 W
86	Wilkie (wĭlk'ē) Can.	52·29 N	108·50 W
75	Wilkinsburg (wĭl'kĭnz-bûrg) Pa. (Pittsburgh In.)	40·26 N	79·53 W
66	Willamette R. Ore.	44·15 N	123·13 W
80	Willard (wĭl'ărd) Ohio	41·00 N	82·50 W
74	Willard Utah (Salt Lake City In.)	41·24 N	112·02 W
69	Willcox (wĭl'kŏks) Ariz.	32·15 N	109·50 W
98	Willemstad Curaçao	12·12 N	68·58 W
110	Willenhall (wĭl'ĕn-hôl) Eng.	52·35 N	2·03 W
110	Willesden (wĭlz'dĕn) Eng. (London In.)	51·31 N	0·17 W
158	William Creek (wĭl'yăm) Austl.	28·45 S	136·20 E
69	Williams (wĭl'yămz) Ariz.	35·15 N	112·15 W
94	Williams (I.) Ba. Is.	25·30 N	78·30 W
78	Williamsburg (wĭl'yămz-bûrg) Ky.	36·42 N	84·09 W
75	Williamsburg Ohio (Cincinnati In.)	39·04 N	84·02 W
79	Williamsburg Va.	37·15 N	76·41 W
80	Williamson (wĭl'yăm-sŭn) W. Va.	37·40 N	82·15 W
81	Williamsport (wĭl'yămz-pōrt) Md.	39·35 N	77·45 W
81	Williamsport Pa.	41·15 N	77·05 W
79	Williamston (wĭl'yămz-tŭn) N. C.	35·50 N	77·04 W
79	Williamston S. C.	34·36 N	82·30 W
80	Williamstown (wĭl'yămz-toun) W. Va.	39·20 N	81·30 W
75	Williamsville (wĭl'yăm-vĭl) N. Y. (Buffalo In.)	42·58 N	78·46 W
81	Willimantic (wĭl-ĭ-măn'tĭk) Conn.	41·40 N	72·10 W
77	Willis (wĭl'ĭs) Tex.	30·24 N	95·29 W
159	Willis Is. Austl.	16·15 S	150·30 E
70	Williston (wĭl'ĭs-tŭn) N. D.	48·08 N	103·38 W
75	Willoughby (wĭl'ô-bē) Ohio (Cleveland In.)	41·39 N	81·25 W
67	Willow Cr. (wĭl'ō) Mont.	48·45 N	111·34 W
66	Willow Cr. Ore.	44·21 N	117·34 W
85	Willowdale (wĭl'ô-dāl) Can. (Toronto In.)	43·47 N	79·25 W
84	Willow Grove Pa. (Philadelphia In.)	40·07 N	75·07 W
74	Willowick (wĭl'ô-wĭk) Calif. (Los Angeles In.)	33·45 N	117·55 W
75	Willowick Ohio (Cleveland In.)	41·39 N	81·28 W
166	Willowmore (wĭl'ô-môr) S. Afr.	33·15 S	23·37 E
75	Willow Run (wĭl'ô rŭn) Mich. (Detroit In.)	42·16 N	83·34 W
68	Willows (wĭl'ōz) Calif.	39·32 N	122·11 W
73	Willow Springs (sprĭngz) Mo.	36·59 N	91·56 W
167	Willowvale (wĭ-lô'vāl) S. Afr. (Natal In.)	32·17 S	28·32 E
77	Wills Point (wĭlz point) Tex.	32·42 N	96·02 W
71	Wilmar (wĭl'mär) Minn.	45·07 N	95·05 W
74	Wilmer (wĭl'mẽr) Tex. (Dallas, Fort Worth In.)	32·35 N	96·40 W
75	Wilmette (wĭl-mĕt') Ill. (Chicago In.)	42·04 N	87·42 W
74	Wilmington (wĭl'mĭng-tŭn) Calif. (Los Angeles In.)	33·46 N	118·16 W
84	Wilmington Del. (Philadelphia In.)	39·45 N	75·33 W
75	Wilmington Ill. (Chicago In.)	41·19 N	88·09 W
83	Wilmington Mass. (Boston In.)	42·34 N	71·10 W
79	Wilmington N. C.	34·12 N	77·56 W
80	Wilmington Ohio	39·20 N	83·50 W
80	Wilmore (wĭl'mōr) Ky.	37·50 N	84·35 W
110	Wilmslow (wĭlmz' lō) Eng.	53·19 N	2·14 W
	Wilno, see Vilnius		
73	Wilson (wĭl'sŭn) Ark.	35·35 N	90·02 W
79	Wilson N. C.	35·42 N	77·55 W
73	Wilson Okla.	34·09 N	97·27 W
78	Wilson, L. Ala.	34·45 N	86·58 W
78	Wilson (R.) Ala.	34·53 N	87·28 W
161	Wilson, Pt. Austl. (Melbourne In)	38·05 S	144·31 E
74	Wilson, Mt. Calif. (Los Angeles In.)	34·15 N	118·06 W
71	Wilson (I.) Can.	48·48 N	87·23 W
67	Wilson Pk. Utah	40·46 N	110·27 W
160	Wilson's Prom. (wĭl'sŭnz) Austl.	39·05 S	146·50 E
74	Wilsonville (wĭl'sŭn-vĭl) Ill. (St. Louis In.)	39·04 N	89·52 W
111	Wilstedt (vēl'shtĕt) Ger. (Hamburg In.)	53·45 N	10·04 E
111	Wilster (vēl'stẽr) Ger. (Hamburg In.)	53·55 N	9·23 E
84	Wilton (wĭl'tŭn) Conn. (New York In.)	41·11 N	73·25 W
70	Wilton N. D.	47·09 N	100·47 W
158	Wiluna (wĭ-lōō'nà) Austl.	26·35 S	120·25 E
80	Winamac (wĭn'à măk) Ind.	41·05 N	86·40 W
169	Winburg (wĭm-bûrg) S. Afr. (Johannesburg & Pretoria In.)	28·31 S	27·02 E
74	Winchester (wĭn'chĕs-tẽr) Calif. (Los Angeles In.)	33·41 N	117·06 W
116	Winchester Eng.	3·03 N	1·20 W
66	Winchester Idaho	46·14 N	116·39 W
80	Winchester Ind.	40·10 N	84·50 W
80	Winchester Ky.	38·00 N	84·15 W
83	Winchester Mass. (Boston In.)	42·28 N	71·09 W
81	Winchester N. H.	42·45 N	72·25 W
78	Winchester Tenn.	35·11 N	86·06 W
81	Winchester Va.	39·40 N	78·10 W
81	Windber (wĭnd'bẽr) Pa.	40·15 N	78·45 W
70	Wind Cave Natl. Park S. D.	43·36 N	103·53 W
78	Winder (wīn'dẽr) Ga.	33·58 N	83·43 W
116	Windermere (wĭn'dẽr-mẽr) Eng.	54·25 N	2·59 W
81	Windham (wĭnd'ăm) Conn.	41·45 N	72·05 W
83	Windham N. H. (Boston In.)	42·49 N	71·21 W
166	Windhoek (vĭnt'hŏŏk) S. W. Afr.	22·05 S	17·10 E
75	Wind L. Wis. (Milwaukee In.)	42·49 N	88·06 W
76	Wind Mtn. N. Mex.	32·02 N	105·30 W
71	Windom (wĭn'dŭm) Minn.	43·50 N	95·04 W
160	Windora (wĭn-dō'rà) Austl.	25·15 S	142·50 E
67	Wind R. Wyo.	43·17 N	109·02 W
67	Wind River Ind Res. Wyo.	43·07 N	109·08 W
67	Wind River Ra. Wyo.	43·19 N	109·47 W
161	Windsor (wĭn'zẽr) Austl. (Sydney In.)	33·37 S	150·49 E
75	Windsor Can. (Detroit In.)	42·19 N	83·00 W
82	Windsor Can.	44·59 N	64·07 W
83	Windsor Can.	49·00 N	55·39 W
72	Windsor Colo.	40·27 N	104·51 W
110	Windsor Eng. (London In.)	51·27 N	0·37 W
73	Windsor Mo.	38·32 N	93·31 W
82	Windsor N. H.	43·29 N	72·23 W
79	Windsor N. C.	35·58 N	76·57 W
89	Windward Is. (wĭnd'wẽrd) N. A.	12·45 N	61·40 W
95	Windward Pass N. A.	19·30 N	74·20 W
73	Winfield (wĭn'fēld) Kans.	37·14 N	97·00 W
87	Wingham (wĭn'gàm) Can.	43·48 N	81·23 W
67	Winifred (wĭn ĭ frĕd) Mont.	47·35 N	109·20 W
76	Wink (wĭŋk) Tex.	31·48 N	103·06 W
164	Winneba (wĭn'ē-bà) Ghana	5·29 N	0·43 W
71	Winnebago (wĭn'ē-bā'gō) Minn.	43·45 N	94·08 W
71	Winnebago, L. Wis.	44·09 N	88·10 W
70	Winnebago Ind. Res. Nebr.	42·15 N	96·06 W
66	Winnemucca (wĭn-ē-mŭk'à) Nev.	40·59 N	117·43 W
68	Winnemucca (L.) Nev.	40·06 N	119·07 W
70	Winner (wĭn'ẽr) S. D.	43·22 N	99·50 W
75	Winnetka (wĭ-nĕt'kà) Ill. (Chicago In.)	42·07 N	87·44 W
67	Winnett (wĭn'ĕt) Mont.	47·01 N	108·20 W
77	Winnfield (wĭn'fēld) La.	31·56 N	92·39 W
71	Winnibigoshish (L.) (wĭn'ĭ-bĭ-gō'shĭsh) Minn.	47·30 N	93·45 W
85	Winnipeg (wĭn'ĭ-pĕg) Can. (Winnipeg In.)	49·55 N	97·09 W
86	Winnipeg, L. Can.	53·29 N	98·41 W
86	Winnipeg (R.) Can.	50·30 N	95·34 W
86	Winnipegosis (wĭn'ĭ-pē-gō'sĭs) Can.	51·40 N	100·01 W
86	Winnipegosis (L.) Can.	52·19 N	101·40 W
81	Winnipesaukee (L.) (wĭn'ē-pē-sô'kē) N. H.	43·40 N	71·20 W
77	Winnsboro (wĭnz'bŭr-ô) La.	32·09 N	91·42 W
79	Winnsboro S. C.	34·29 N	81·05 W
73	Winnsboro Tex.	32·56 N	95·15 W
85	Winona (wĭ-nō'nà) Can. (Toronto In.)	43·13 N	79·39 W
71	Winona Minn.	44·03 N	91·40 W
78	Winona Miss.	33·29 N	89·43 W
81	Winooski (wĭ-nōōs'kē) Vt.	44·30 N	73·10 W
111	Winsen (Luhe) (vēn'zĕn)(lōō'hĕ) Ger. (Hamburg In.)	53·22 N	10·13 E
110	Winsford (wĭnz'fẽrd) Eng.	53·11 N	2·30 W
69	Winslow (wĭnz'lō) Ariz.	35·00 N	110·45 W
65	Winslow Wash. (Seattle In.)	47·38 N	122·31 W
81	Winsted (wĭn'stĕd) Conn.	41·55 N	73·05 W
110	Winster (wĭn'stẽr) Eng.	53·08 N	1·38 W
79	Winston-Salem (wĭn stŭn-sā'lĕm) N. C.	36·05 N	80·15 W
167	Winterberg (Mts.) S. Afr. (Natal In.)	32·18 S	26·25 E
79	Winter Garden (wĭn'tẽr gär'd'n) Fla. (In.)	28·32 N	81·35 W
79	Winter Haven (hā'vĕn) Fla. (In.)	28·01 N	81·38 W
79	Winter Park (pärk) Fla. (In.)	28·35 N	81·21 W
76	Winters (wĭn'tẽrz) Tex.	31·59 N	99·58 W
71	Winterset (wĭn'tẽr-sĕt) Iowa	41·19 N	94·03 W
123	Winterswijk Neth. (Ruhr In.)	51·58 N	6·44 E
120	Winterthur (vĭn'tẽr-tōōr) Switz.	47·30 N	8·32 E
167	Winterton (wĭn-tẽr-tŏn) S. Afr. (Natal In.)	28·51 S	29·33 E
82	Winthrop (wĭn'thrŭp) Maine	44·19 N	70·00 W
83	Winthrop Mass. (Boston In.)	42·23 N	70·59 W
71	Winthrop Minn.	44·31 N	94·20 W
159	Winton (wĭn-tŭn) Austl.	22·17 S	143·08 E

ng-sing; ŋ-baŋk; N-nasalized n; nŏd; cŏmmit; ōld; ôbey; ôrder; fōōd; fŏŏt; ou-out; s-soft; sh-dish; th-thin; pūre; ûnite; ûrn; stŭd: circŭs; ü-as "y" in study; '-indeterminate vowel.

286 Wipperfurth–Yanbu PRONOUNCING INDEX

Page	Name Pronunciation Region	Lat. °′	Long. °′
123	Wipperfürth (vē'pĕr-fürt) Ger. (Ruhr In.)	51·07 N	7·23 E
110	Wirksworth (wûrks'wûrth) Eng.	53·05 N	1·35 W
63	Wisconsin (State) (wĭs-kŏn'sĭn) U. S.	44·30 N	91·00 W
71	Wisconsin (R.) Wis.	43·14 N	90·34 W
71	Wisconsin Dells Wis.	43·38 N	89·46 W
71	Wisconsin Rapids Wis.	44·24 N	89·50 W
70	Wishek (wĭsh'ĕk) N. D.	46·15 N	99·34 W
121	Wisla (Vistula) R. (vês'wȧ) (vĭs'tû-lȧ) Pol.	52·48 N	19·02 E
121	Wisloka R. (vês-wô'kȧ) Pol.	49·55 N	21·26 E
99	Wismar (wĭs'mȧr) Br. Gu.	5·58 N	58·15 W
120	Wismar (vĭs'mär) Ger.	53·53 N	11·28 E
70	Wisner (wĭz'nĕr) Nebr.	42·00 N	96·55 W
123	Wissembourg (vê-säN-bo͞or') Fr.	49·03 N	7·58 E
166	Wissmann Pool (L.) Con. L.	3·18 S	17·28 E
73	Wister Res. (vĭs'tẽr) Okla.	35·02 N	94·52 W
168	Witbank (wĭt-băŋk) S. Afr. (Johannesburg & Pretoria In.)	25·53 S	29·14 E
110	Witham (wĭdh'ăm) Eng. (London In.)	51·48 N	0·37 E
110	Witham (R.) Eng.	53·11 N	0·20 W
75	Withamsville (wĭdh'ămz-vĭl) Ohio (Cincinnati In.)	39·04 N	84·16 W
79	Withlacoochee (R.) (wĭth-lȧ-ko͞o'chê) Fla. (In.)	28·58 N	82·30 W
78	Withlacoochee (R.) Ga.	31·15 N	83·30 W
74	Withrow (wĭdh'rō) Minn. (Minneapolis, St. Paul In.)	45·08 N	92·54 W
110	Witney (wĭt'nê) Eng. (London In.)	51·45 N	1·30 W
168	Witsieshoek (wĭt'sêz-ho͝ok) S. Afr. (Johannesburg & Pretoria In.)	28·33 S	28·48 E
80	Witt (vĭt) Ill.	39·10 N	89·15 W
123	Witten (vē'tĕn) Ger. (Ruhr In.)	51·26 N	7·19 E
120	Wittenberg (vē'tĕn-bĕrgh) Ger.	51·53 N	12·40 E
120	Wittenberge (vĭt-ĕn-bĕr'gẽ) Ger.	52·59 N	11·45 E
120	Wittlich (vĭt'lĭk) Ger.	49·58 N	6·54 E
167	Witu (wē'to͞o) Ken.	2·18 S	40·28 E
167	Witwatersberg (Mts.) (wĭt-wôr-tẽrz-bûrg) S. Afr. (Johannesburg & Pretoria In.)	25·58 S	27·43 E
168	Witwatersrand (Ridge) (wĭt-wôr'tẽrs-rănd) S. Afr. (Johannesburg & Pretoria In.)	25·55 S	26·27 E
121	Wkra R. (f'krȧ) Pol.	52·40 N	20·35 E
121	Włocławek (vwô-tswä'vĕk) Pol.	52·38 N	19·08 E
121	Włodawa (vwô-dä'vä) Pol.	51·33 N	23·33 E
121	Wloszczowa (vwôsh-chô'vă) Pol.	50·51 N	19·58 E
83	Woburn (wo͞o'bŭrn) (wō'bŭrn) Mass. (Boston In.)	42·29 N	71·10 W
111	Woerden Neth. (Amsterdam In.)	52·05 N	4·52 E
110	Woking (wô'kĭng) Eng. (London In.)	51·18 N	0·33 W
110	Wokingham (wô'kĭng-hăm) Eng. (London In.)	51·23 N	0·50 W
74	Wolcott (wōl'kŏt) Kans. (Kansas City In.)	39·12 N	94·47 W
81	Wolf (I.) (wo͝olf) Can.	44·10 N	76·25 W
78	Wolf (R.) Miss.	30·45 N	89·36 W
71	Wolf (R.) Wis.	45·14 N	88·45 W
120	Wolfenbüttel (vôl'fĕn-büt-ĕl) Ger.	52·10 N	10·32 E
75	Wolf L. Ill. (Chicago In.)	41·39 N	87·33 W
67	Wolf Point (wo͝olf point) Mont.	48·07 N	105·40 W
111	Wolfratshausen (vōlf'räts-hou-zĕn) Ger. (München In.)	47·55 N	11·25 E
120	Wolfsburg (vōlfs'bo͝orgh) Ger.	52·30 N	10·37 E
82	Wolfville (wo͝olf'vĭl) Can.	45·06 N	64·02 W
120	Wolgast (vôl'gäst) Ger.	54·04 N	13·46 E
167	Wolhuterskop S. Afr. (Johannesburg & Pretoria In.)	25·41 S	27·40 E
111	Wolkersdorf Aus. (Wien In.)	48·24 N	16·31 E
86	Wollaston (L.) (wo͝ol'ȧs-tŭn) Can.	58·03 N	105·00 W
86	Wollaston Pen Can.	69·55 N	115·13 W
160	Wollongong (wo͝ol'ŭn-gŏng) Austl.	34·26 S	151·05 E
121	Wołomin (vô-wō'mên) Pol.	52·19 N	21·17 E
110	Wolstanton (wo͝ol-stăn'tŭn) Eng.	53·02 N	2·13 W
111	Woltersdorf (vōl'tĕrs-dōrf) Ger. (Berlin In.)	52·07 N	13·13 E
110	Wolverhampton (wo͝ol'vẽr-hămp-tŭn) Eng.	52·35 N	2·07 W
168	Wolwehoek S. Afr. (Johannesburg & Pretoria In.)	26·55 S	27·50 E
152	Wōnsan (wŭn'sän') Kor.	39·08 N	127·24 E
160	Wonthaggi (wônt-hăg'ê) Austl.	38·40 S	145·41 E
70	Wood (wo͝od) S. D.	43·26 N	100·25 W
70	Woodbine (wo͝od'bīn) Iowa	41·44 N	95·42 W
85	Woodbridge (wo͝od'brĭj') Can. (Toronto In.)	43·47 N	79·36 W
84	Woodbridge N. J. (New York In.)	40·33 N	74·18 W
86	Wood Buffalo Natl. Park Can.	59·50 N	118·53 W
74	Woodburn (wo͝od'bûrn) Ill. (St. Louis In.)	39·03 N	90·01 W
66	Woodburn Ore.	45·10 N	122·51 W
84	Woodbury (wo͝od'bĕr-ê) N. J. (Philadelphia In.)	39·50 N	75·14 W
74	Woodcrest (wo͝od'krĕst) Calif. (Los Angeles In.)	33·53 N	117·18 W
65	Woodinville (wo͝od'ĭn-vĭl) Wash. (Seattle In.)	47·46 N	122·09 W
68	Woodland (wo͝od'lănd) Calif.	38·41 N	121·47 W
65	Woodland Wash. (Portland In.)	45·54 N	122·45 W
74	Woodland Hills Calif. (Los Angeles In.)	34·10 N	118·36 W
155	Woodlark (I.) (wo͝od'lärk) Pap. Ter.	9·07 S	152·00 E
75	Woodlawn Beach (wo͝od'lôn bēch) N. Y. (Buffalo In.)	42·48 N	78·51 W
74	Wood River Ill. (St. Louis In.)	38·52 N	90·06 W
158	Woodroffe, Mt. (wo͝od'rŭf) Austl.	26·05 S	132·00 E
79	Woodruff (wo͝od'rŭf) S. C.	34·43 N	82·03 W
75	Woodruff Place Ind. (Indianapolis In.)	39·47 N	86·07 W
158	Woods (L.) (wo͝odz) Austl.	18·00 S	133·18 E
63	Woods, L. of the Can.-Minn.	49·25 N	93·25 W
74	Woods Cross (krôs) Utah (Salt Lake City In.)	40·53 N	111·54 W
80	Woodsfield (wo͝odz-fēld) Ohio	39·45 N	81·10 W
160	Woodside (wo͝od'sīd) Austl.	38·40 S	46·48 E
65	Woodson (wo͝odsŭn) Ore. (Portland In.)	46·07 N	123·20 W
80	Woodstock (wo͝od'stŏk) Can.	43·10 N	80·50 W
82	Woodstock Can.	46·09 N	67·36 W
110	Woodstock Eng. (London In.)	51·49 N	1·22 W
71	Woodstock Ill.	42·20 N	88·29 W
81	Woodstock Va.	38·55 N	78·25 W
81	Woodsville (wo͝odz'vĭl) N. H.	44·10 N	72·00 W
78	Woodville (wo͝od'vĭl) Miss.	31·06 N	91·11 W
77	Woodville Tex.	30·48 N	94·25 W
72	Woodward (wo͝od'wôrd) Okla.	36·25 N	99·24 W
110	Woolwich (wo͝ol'ĭj) Eng. (London In.)	51·28 N	0·05 E
160	Woomera (wo͞om'ẽrȧ) Austl.	31·06 S	136·35 E
84	Woonsocket (wo͞on-sŏk'ĕt) R. I. (Providence In.)	42·00 N	71·30 W
70	Woonsocket S. D.	44·03 N	98·17 W
80	Wooster (wo͝os'tẽr) Ohio	40·50 N	81·55 W
116	Worcester (wo͝o-stẽr) Eng.	52·09 N	2·14 W
166	Worcester (wo͞os'tẽr) S. Afr.	33·35 S	19·31 E
110	Worcester (Co.) (wo͝o'stẽr) Eng.	52·24 N	2·15 W
83	Worchester (wôr'chĕs-tẽr) Mass. (Boston In.)	42·16 N	71·49 W
74	Worden (wôr'dĕn) Ill. (St. Louis In.)	38·56 N	89·50 W
116	Workington (wûr'kĭng-tŭn) Eng.	54·40 N	3·30 W
110	Worksop (wûrk'sŏp) (wûr'sŭp) Eng.	53·18 N	1·07 W
67	Worland (wûr'lănd) Wyo.	44·02 N	107·56 W
120	Worms (vōrms) Ger.	49·37 N	8·22 E
161	Worona Res. Austl. (Sydney In.)	34·12 S	150·55 E
75	Worth (wûrth) Ill. (Chicago In.)	41·42 N	87·47 W
74	Worth L. Tex. (Dallas, Fort Worth In.)	32·48 N	97·32 W
77	Wortham (wûr'dhăm) Tex.	31·46 N	96·22 W
116	Worthing (wûr'dhĭng) Eng.	50·48 N	0·29 W
80	Worthington (wûr'dhĭng-tŭn) Ind.	39·05 N	87·00 W
70	Worthington Minn.	43·38 N	95·36 W
155	Wowoni (I.) (wō-wō'nê) Indon.	4·05 S	123·45 E
110	Wragby (răg'bê) Eng.	53·17 N	0·19 W
64	Wrangell (răn'gĕl) Alaska	56·28 N	132·25 W
64	Wrangell, Mt Alaska	61·58 N	143·50 W
64	Wrangell Mts Alaska-Can.	62·28 N	142·40 W
116	Wrath, C. (răth) Scot.	58·34 N	5·01 W
72	Wray (rā) Colo.	40·06 N	102·14 W
101	Wreak (R.) (rēk) Eng.	52·45 N	0·59 W
159	Wreck Rfs. (rĕk) Austl.	22·00 S	155·52 E
110	Wrekin, The (Mt.) (rĕk'ĭn) Eng.	52·40 N	2·33 W
79	Wrens (rĕnz) Ga.	33·15 N	82·25 W
83	Wrentham (rĕn'thăm) Mass. (Boston In.)	42·04 N	71·20 W
110	Wrexham (rĕk'săm) Wales	53·03 N	3·00 W
75	Wrights Corners (rītz kôr'nẽrz) N. Y. (Buffalo In.)	43·14 N	78·42 W
79	Wrightsville (rīts'vĭl) Ga.	32·44 N	82·44 W
121	Wrocław (Breslau) (vrô'tsläv) (brĕs'lou) Pol.	51·07 N	17·10 E
110	Wrotham (ro͞ot'ŭm) Eng. (London In.)	51·18 N	0·19 E
121	Września (vzhāsh'nyȧ) Pol.	52·19 N	17·33 E
151	Wuch'ang (wo͞o'chäng') China	30·32 N	114·25 E
150	Wuch'ang China	44·59 N	127·00 E
148	Wuchi (wo͞o'jē) China	38·12 N	114·57 E
148	Wuchiang (wo͞o'jĭäng) China	31·10 N	120·38 E
148	Wuch'iao (wo͞o'chĭou) China	37·37 N	116·29 E
148	Wuchin (wo͞o'jĭn) China	31·47 N	119·56 E
150	Wuch'ing (wo͞o'chĭng') China (Peking In.)	39·32 N	116·51 E
151	Wu Chin Shan China	18·48 N	109·30 E
151	Wuchou (Tsangwu) (wo͞o'chō') China	23·32 N	111·25 E
151	Wuhan China	30·30 N	114·15 E
148	Wuhsi (wo͞o'sē) China	31·36 N	120·17 E
	Wuhsien, see Soochow		
151	Wuhsing China	30·38 N	120·10 E
148	Wuhu (wo͞o'ho͞o') China	31·22 N	118·22 E
151	Wui Shan (Mts.) China	26·38 N	116·35 E
147	Wukung Shan (Mts.) (wo͞o'ko͝ong'shän') China	26·45 N	115·19 E
152	Wulachieh (wo͞o'lä-ĸē'å) China	44·08 N	126·25 E
	Wulanhata, see Ch'ihfeng		
154	Wu Liang Shan (Mts.) China	23·07 N	100·45 E
148	Wulitien (wo͞o'lē'dĭän) China	32·09 N	114·17 E
111	Wünsdorf (vüns'dōrf) Ger. (Berlin In.)	52·10 N	13·29 E
69	Wupatki Natl. Mon. (wo͞o-păt'kē) Ariz.	35·36 N	111·45 W
151	Wup'ing (wo͞o'pĭng') China	25·05 N	116·01 E
123	Wuppertal (vo͝op'ẽr-täl) Ger. (Ruhr In.)	51·16 N	7·14 E
151	Wu R. (wo͞o') China	27·30 N	108·00 E
111	Würm (R.) Ger.	48·50 N	11·17 E
120	Würm See (L.) (vürm zā) Ger.	47·58 N	11·30 E
123	Würselen (vür'zĕ-lĕn) Ger. (Ruhr In.)	50·49 N	6·09 E
120	Würtzburg (vürts'bo͝orgh) Ger.	49·48 N	9·57 E
120	Wurzen (vo͝ort'sĕn) Ger.	51·22 N	12·45 E
146	Wushih (Uch Turfan) (wo͞o'shĭ) (o͞och' to͝or-fän') China	41·13 N	79·08 E
111	Wustermark (vo͞os'tĕr-märk) Ger. (Berlin In.)	52·33 N	12·57 E
111	Wustrau (vōost'rou) Ger. (Berlin In.)	52·51 N	12·51 E
146	Wusu (Kweitun) (wo͞o'so͞o') (kwā'to͞on') China	44·28 N	84·07 E
149	Wusung (wo͞o'so͞ong) China (Shanghai In.)	31·23 N	121·29 E
111	Wuustwezel Bel. (Bruxelles In.)	51·23 N	4·36 E
148	Wuwei (wo͞o'wā') China	31·19 N	117·53 E
148	Wuyang (wo͞o'yäng) China	33·16 N	113·37 E
148	Wuyuch'ang China	33·18 N	120·15 E
147	Wuyün (wo͞o-yŭn') China	48·51 N	130·06 E
160	Wyalong (wī'ȧ-lông) Austl.	34·00 S	147·20 E
75	Wyandotte (wī'ăn-dŏt) Mich. (Detroit In.)	42·12 N	83·10 W
110	Wye (wī) Eng. (London In.)	51·12 N	0·57 E
110	Wye (R.) Eng.	53·14 N	1·46 W
73	Wymore (wī'mōr) Nebr.	40·09 N	96·41 W
166	Wynberg (wīn'bĕrg) S. Afr. (Cape Town In.)	34·00 S	18·28 E
158	Wyndham (wīnd'ăm) Austl.	15·30 S	128·15 E
73	Wynne (wĭn) Ark.	35 12 N	90·46 W
73	Wynnewood (wĭn'wo͝od) Okla.	34·39 N	97·10 W
73	Wynona (wī-nō'nȧ) Okla.	36·33 N	96·19 W
86	Wynyard (wīn'yẽrd) Can.	51·48 N	104·13 W
75	Wyoming (wī-ō'mĭng) Ohio (Cincinnati In.)	39·14 N	84·28 W
62	Wyoming (State) U. S.	42·50 N	108·30 W
67	Wyoming Ra. Wyo.	42·43 N	110·35 W
110	Wyre Fon. (wīr) Eng.	52·24 N	2·24 W
121	Wysokie Mazowieckie (vê-sô'kyĕ mä-zô-vyĕts'kyĕ) Pol.	52·55 N	22·42 E
121	Wyszków (vêsh'ko͝of) Pol.	52·35 N	21·29 E
79	Wytheville (wĭth'vĭl) Va.	36·55 N	81·06 W
94	Xagua, Banco (Bk.) (bä'n-kō-sä'gwä) Cuba	21·35 N	80·50 W
123	Xanten (ksän'tĕn) Ger. (Ruhr In.)	51·40 N	6·28 E
127	Xanthi Grc.	41·08 N	24·53 E
92	Xcalak (sä-lä'k) Mex. (Yucatan In.)	18·15 N	87·50 W
80	Xenia (zē'nĭ-ȧ) Ohio	39·40 N	83·55 W
90	Xicotencatl (sē-kô-tĕn-kät''l) Mex.	23·00 N	98·58 W
90	Xilitla (sê-lē'tlä) Mex.	21·24 N	98·59 W
99	Xingú (R.) (zhêŋ-go͞o') Braz.	6·20 S	52·34 W
90	Xochihuehuetlán (sô-chē-wĕ-wĕ-tlȧ'n) Mex.	17·53 N	98·29 W
91	Xochimilco (sō-chê-mēl'kô) Mex. (Mexico In.)	19·15 N	99·06 W
151	Yaan China	30·00 N	103·20 E
121	Yablonitskiy Pereval (P.) (yȧb-lô' nĭt-skĭ pĕ-rĕ-väl') Sov. Un.	48·20 N	24·25 E
135	Yablonovyy Khrebet (Mts.) (yȧ-blô-nô-vê') Sov. Un.	51·15 N	111·30 E
65	Yacolt (yă'kôlt) Wash. (Portland In.)	45·52 N	122·24 W
65	Yacolt (Mt.) Wash. (Portland In.)	45·52 N	122·27 W
78	Yacona (R.) (yȧ'cō nă) Miss.	34·13 N	89·30 W
100	Yacuiba (yȧ-ko͞o-ē'bȧ) Arg.	22·02 S	63·44 W
79	Yadkin (R.) (yăd'kĭn) N. C.	36·12 N	80·40 W
153	Yagi (yä'gê) Jap. (Ōsaka In.)	34·31 N	135·48 E
129	Yagotin (yä'gô-tên) Sov. Un.	50·18 N	31·46 E
94	Yaguajay (yä-guä-hä'ê) Cuba	22·20 N	79·20 W
153	Yahagi-Gawa (Strm.) (yä'hä-gê gä'wä) Jap.	35·16 N	137·22 E
153	Yahata (yä'hä-tä) Jap.	33·50 N	131·48 E
149	Yahu China (Canton In.)	23·19 N	113·17 E
90	Yahualica (yä-wä-lē'kä) Mex.	21·08 N	102·53 W
148	Yahungch'iao (yä'ho͞ong'chĭou) China	39·45 N	117·52 E
151	Yaihsien China	18·20 N	109·10 E
91	Yajalón (yä-hä-lōn') Mex.	17·16 N	92·20 W
136	Yakhroma (yäk'rô-má) Sov. Un. (Moskva In.)	56·17 N	37·30 E
136	Yakhroma R. Sov. Un. (Moskva In.)	56·15 N	37·38 E
66	Yakima (yăk'ĭ-mȧ) Wash.	46·35 N	120·30 W
66	Yakima R. (yăk'ĭ-mȧ) Wash.	46·48 N	120·22 W
153	Yaku (I.) (yä'ko͞o) Jap.	30·15 N	130·41 E
135	Yakut A.S.S.R Sov. Un.	65·21 N	117·13 E
64	Yakutat (yȧk'o͝o-tȧt) Alaska	59·32 N	139·35 W
135	Yakutsk (yȧ-ko͝otsk') Sov. Un.	62·13 N	129·49 E
152	Yal (R.) (yäl) China	48·20 N	122·35 E
80	Yale Mich.	43·05 N	82·45 W
73	Yale Okla.	36·07 N	96·42 W
165	Yalinga (yȧ-lĭŋ'gȧ) Cen. Afr. Rep.	6·56 N	23·22 E
78	Yalobusha (R.) (yȧ-lô-bo͝osh'ȧ) Miss.	33·48 N	90·02 W
129	Yalta (Krasnoarmeisk) (yäl'tȧ) (kräs-nô-är-māsk') Sov. Un.	44·29 N	34·12 E
152	Yalu (Amnok) (R.) China-Kor.	41·20 N	126·35 E
146	Yalung Chiang (R.) (yā'lo͝ong') China	32·29 N	98·41 E
134	Yalutorovsk (yä-lo͞o-tô'rôfsk) Sov. Un.	56·42 N	66·32 E
153	Yamada (yä'mȧ-dȧ) Jap.	33·37 N	133·39 E
152	Yamagata (yä-mȧ'gä-tȧ) Jap.	38·12 N	140·24 E
153	Yamaguchi (yä-mȧ'go͞o-chê) Jap.	34·10 N	131·30 E
134	Yamal, P-ov (Pen.) (yä-mäl') Sov. Un.	71·15 N	70·00 E
136	Yamantau, Gora (Mt.) (gȧ-rä' yä' mán-tȧw) Sov. Un. (Urals In.)	54·16 N	58·08 E
95	Yamasá (yä-mä'sä) Dom. Rep.	18·50 N	70·00 W
153	Yamasaki (yä'mȧ'sä-kê) Jap.	35·01 N	134·33 E
153	Yamasaki Jap. (Ōsaka In.)	34·53 N	135·41 E
153	Yamashina (yä'mä-shê'nä) Jap. (Ōsaka In.)	34·59 N	135·50 E
153	Yamashita (yä'mä-shê'tä) Jap. (Ōsaka In.)	34·53 N	135·25 E
153	Yamato-takada (yä'mä-tô tä'kä-dä) Jap. (Ōsaka In.)	34·31 N	135·45 E
98	Yambi, Mesa de (mĕ'sä-dĕ-yȧ'm-bē) Col.	1·55 N	71·45 W
146	Yamdrog Tsho (L.) China	29·11 N	91·26 E
146	Yamethin (yŭ-mē'thĕn) Bur.	20·14 N	96·27 E
65	Yamhill (yäm'hĭl) Ore. (Portland In.)	45·20 N	123·11 W
136	Yamkino (yäm'kĭ-nô) Sov. Un. (Moskva In.)	55·56 N	38·25 E
160	Yamma Yamma (L.) (yäm'ȧ yäm'ȧ) Austl.	26·15 S	141·30 E
67	Yampa R. (yăm'pȧ) Colo.	40·29 N	108·12 W
135	Yamsk (yämsk) Sov. Un.	59·41 N	154·09 E
142	Yamuna (R.) India	26·50 N	79·45 E
135	Yana (R.) (yä'nȧ) Sov. Un.	69·42 N	135·45 E
160	Yanac (yăn'ȧk) Austl.	36·10 S	141·30 E
153	Yanagawa (yä-nä'gä-wä) Jap.	33·11 N	130·24 E
143	Yanam (yŭnŭm') India	16·48 N	82·15 E
144	Yanbu al Bahr Sau. Ar.	23·57 N	38·02 E

ăt; finăl; rāte; senâte; ärm; åsk; sofȧ; fâre; ch-choose; dh-as th in other: bē: êvent; bĕt; recĕnt; cratẽr; g-go; gh-guttural g; bĭt; ĭ-short neutral; rīde; ĸ-guttural k as ch in German ich·

ng-sing; ŋ-baŋk; N-nasalized n; nŏd; cŏmmit; ōld; ȯbey; ôrder; fōōd; fŏŏt; ou-out; s-soft; sh-dish; th-thin; pūre; ûnite; ûrn; stŭd; circŭs; ü-as "y" in study; '-indeterminate vowel.

ăt; fĭnȧl; rāte; senâte; ârm; ȧsk; sofȧ; fâre; ch-choose; dh-as th in other; bē; ĕvent; bĕt; recĕnt; cratēr; g-go; gh-guttural g; bĭt; ĭ-short neutral; rīde; ᴋ-guttural k as ch in German ich;